Hoover's Handbook of American Business 2013

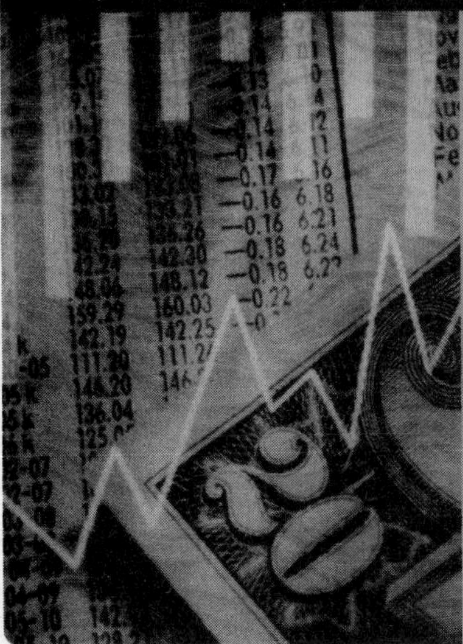

Hoover's Handbook of American Business 2013 is intended to provide readers with accurate and authoritative information about the enterprises covered in it. Hoover's researched all companies and organizations profiled, and in many cases contacted them directly so that companies represented could provide information. The information contained herein is as accurate as we could reasonably make it. In many cases we have relied on third-party material that we believe to be trustworthy, but were unable to independently verify. We do not warrant that the book is absolutely accurate or without error. Readers should not rely on any information contained herein in instances where such reliance might cause financial loss. The publisher, the editors, and their data suppliers specifically disclaim all warranties, including the implied warranties of merchantability and fitness for a specific purpose. This book is sold with the understanding that neither the publisher, the editors, nor any content contributors are engaged in providing investment, financial, accounting, legal, or other professional advice.

The financial data (Historical Financials sections) in this book are from a variety of sources. Morningstar, Inc., provided selected data for the Historical Financials sections of publicly traded companies. For private companies and for historical information on public companies prior to their becoming public, we obtained information directly from the companies or from trade sources deemed to be reliable. Hoover's, Inc., is solely responsible for the presentation of all data.

Many of the names of products and services mentioned in this book are the trademarks or service marks of the companies manufacturing or selling them and are subject to protection under US law. Space has not permitted us to indicate which names are subject to such protection, and readers are advised to consult with the owners of such marks regarding their use. Hoover's is a trademark of Hoover's, Inc.

10 9 8 7 6 5 4 3 2 1

Publishers Cataloging-in-Publication Data

Hoover's Handbook of American Business 2013

Includes indexes.

ISBN: 978-1-59274-645-3

ISSN 1055-7202

1. Business enterprises — Directories. 2. Corporations — Directories.

HF3010 338.7

Hoover's Company Information is also available on the Internet at Hoover's Online (www.mergent/hoovers.com).

U.S. AND WORLD BOOK SALES

Mergent Inc.

580 Kingsley Park Drive
Fort Mill, SC 29715
Phone: 800-342-5647
e-mail: orders@mergent.com
Web: www.mergent.com

Mergent Inc.

ABOUT MERGENT INC.

Mergent, Inc. is a leading provider of business and financial data on global publicly listed companies. Based in the U.S, the company maintains a strong global presence, with offices in New York, Charlotte, San Diego, London, Tokyo and Melbourne.

Founded in 1900, Mergent operates one of the longest continuously collected databases of: descriptive and fundamental information on domestic and international companies; pricing and terms and conditions data on fixed income and equity securities; and corporate action data. In addition, Mergent's Indxis subsidiary develops and licenses equity and fixed income investment products based on its proprietary investment methodologies. Our licensed products have over $9 billion in assets under management and are offered by major investment management firms. The Indxis calculation platform is the chosen technology for some of the world's largest index companies. Its index calculation and pricing distribution protocols are used to administer index rules and distribute real-time pricing data.

Abbreviations

AFL-CIO – American Federation of Labor and Congress of Industrial Organizations
AMA – American Medical Association
AMEX – American Stock Exchange
ARM – adjustable-rate mortgage
ASP – application services provider
ATM – asynchronous transfer mode
ATM – automated teller machine
CAD/CAM – computer-aided design/computer-aided manufacturing
CD-ROM – compact disc – read-only memory
CD-R – CD-recordable
CEO – chief executive officer
CFO – chief financial officer
CMOS – complementary metal oxide silicon
COO – chief operating officer
DAT – digital audiotape
DOD – Department of Defense
DOE – Department of Energy
DOS – disk operating system
DOT – Department of Transportation
DRAM – dynamic random-access memory
DSL – digital subscriber line
DVD – digital versatile disc/digital video disc
DVD-R – DVD-recordable
EPA – Environmental Protection Agency
EPROM – erasable programmable read-only memory
EPS – earnings per share
ESOP – employee stock ownership plan
EU – European Union
EVP – executive vice president
FCC – Federal Communications Commission
FDA – Food and Drug Administration
FDIC – Federal Deposit Insurance Corporation
FTC – Federal Trade Commission
FTP – file transfer protocol
GATT – General Agreement on Tariffs and Trade
GDP – gross domestic product
HMO – health maintenance organization
HR – human resources
HTML – hypertext markup language
ICC – Interstate Commerce Commission
IPO – initial public offering
IRS – Internal Revenue Service
ISP – Internet service provider
kWh – kilowatt-hour
LAN – local-area network
LBO – leveraged buyout
LCD – liquid crystal display
LNG – liquefied natural gas
LP – limited partnership
Ltd. – limited
mips – millions of instructions per second
MW – megawatt
NAFTA – North American Free Trade Agreement
NASA – National Aeronautics and Space Administration
NASDAQ – National Association of Securities Dealers Automated Quotations
NATO – North Atlantic Treaty Organization
NYSE – New York Stock Exchange
OCR – optical character recognition
OECD – Organization for Economic Cooperation and Development
OEM – original equipment manufacturer
OPEC – Organization of Petroleum Exporting Countries
OS – operating system
OSHA – Occupational Safety and Health Administration
OTC – over-the-counter
PBX – private branch exchange
PCMCIA – Personal Computer Memory Card International Association
P/E – price to earnings ratio
RAID – redundant array of independent disks
RAM – random-access memory
R&D – research and development
RBOC – regional Bell operating company
RISC – reduced instruction set computer
REIT – real estate investment trust
ROA – return on assets
ROE – return on equity
ROI – return on investment
ROM – read-only memory
S&L – savings and loan
SCSI – Small Computer System Interface
SEC – Securities and Exchange Commission
SEVP – senior executive vice president
SIC – Standard Industrial Classification
SOC – system on a chip
SVP – senior vice president
USB – universal serial bus
VAR – value-added reseller
VAT – value-added tax
VC – venture capitalist
VoIP – Voice over Internet Protocol
VP – vice president
WAN – wide-area network
WWW – World Wide Web

Contents

List of Lists

HOOVER'S RANKINGS

Companies Profiled

Companies Profiled (continued)

Companies Profiled (continued)

Companies Profiled (continued)

About Hoover's Handbook of American Business 2013

In these tough economic times, it pays to have all the facts, whether you're making business, financial, or employment decisions. When you need information about companies, the 21st edition of *Hoover's Handbook of American Business* is the place to turn for answers. Throughout its history, it has stood as one of America's respected sources of business information, packed with the information you need.

We at Hoover's Business Press pledge we will continue our work to add more value to this already valuable resource. So search away for the business information you need to make the important decisions facing you. Leave the fact-finding and digging and the sorting and sifting to the editors at Hoover's.

Hoover's Handbook of American Business is the first of our four-title series of handbooks that covers, literally, the world of business. The series is available as an indexed set, and also includes *Hoover's Handbook of World Business, Hoover's Handbook of Private Companies,* and *Hoover's Handbook of Emerging Companies.* This series brings you information on the biggest, fastest-growing, and most influential enterprises in the world.

HOOVER'S ONLINE FOR BUSINESS NEEDS

In addition to the 2,550 companies featured in our handbooks, comprehensive coverage of more than 40,000 business enterprises is available in electronic format on our website, Hoover's Online (www.hoovers.com). Our goal is to provide one site that offers authoritative, updated intelligence on US and global companies, industries, and the people who shape them. Hoover's has partnered with other prestigious business information and service providers to bring you all the right business information, services, and links in one place.

We welcome the recognition we have received as a provider of high-quality company information — online, electronically, and in print — and continue to look for ways to make our products more available and more useful to you.

We believe that anyone who buys from, sells to, invests in, lends to, competes with, interviews with, or works for a company should know all there is to know about that enterprise. Taken together, this book and the other Hoover's products and resources represent the most complete source of basic corporate information readily available to the general public.

This latest version of *Hoover's Handbook of American Business* contains, as always, profiles of the largest and most influential companies in the United States. Each of the companies profiled here was chosen because of its important role in American business. For more details on how these companies were selected, see the section titled "Using Hoover's Handbooks."

HOW TO USE THIS BOOK

This book has four sections:

1. "Using Hoover's Handbooks" describes the contents of our profiles and explains the ways in which we gather and compile our data.
2. "A List-Lover's Compendium" contains lists of the largest, smallest, best, most, and other superlatives related to companies involved in American business.
3. The company profiles section makes up the largest and most important part of the book — 750 profiles of major US enterprises.
4. Three indexes complete the book. The first sorts companies by industry groups, the second by headquarters location. The third index is a list of all the executives found in the Executives section of each company profile.

Using Hoover's Handbooks

SELECTION OF THE COMPANIES PROFILED

The 750 enterprises profiled in this book include the largest and most influential companies in America. Among them are:

- more than 710 publicly held companies, from 3M to Zions Bancorporation
- more than 30 large private enterprises (such as Cargill and Mars)
- several mutual and cooperative organizations (such as State Farm and Ace Hardware)
- a selection of other enterprises (such as Kaiser Foundation Health Plan, the US Postal Service, and the Tennessee Valley Authority) that we believe are sufficiently large and influential enough to warrant inclusion.

In selecting these companies, our foremost question was "What companies will our readers be most interested in?" Our goal was to answer as many questions as we could in one book — in effect, trying to anticipate your curiosity. This approach resulted in four general selection criteria for including companies in the book:

1. Size. The 500 or so largest American companies, measured by sales and by number of employees, are included in the book. In general, these companies have sales in excess of $2 billion, and they are the ones you will have heard of and the ones you will want to know about. These are the companies at the top of the *FORTUNE*, *Forbes*, and *Business Week* lists. We have made sure to include the top private companies in this number.

2. Growth. We believe that relatively few readers will be going to work for, or investing in, the railroad industry. Therefore, only a few railroads are in the book. On the other hand, we have included a number of technology firms, as well as companies that provide medical products and services — pharmaceutical and biotech companies, health care insurers, and medical device makers.

3. Visibility. Most readers will have heard of the Hilton Worldwide and Harley-Davidson companies. Their service or consumer natures make them household names, even though they are not among the corporate giants in terms of sales and employment.

4. Breadth of coverage. To show the diversity of economic activity, we've included, among others, a professional sports team, one ranch, the Big Four accounting firms, and one of the largest law firms in the US. We feel that these businesses are important enough to enjoy at least "token" representation. While we might not emphasize certain industries, the industry leaders are present.

ORGANIZATION

The profiles are presented in alphabetical order. This alphabetization is generally word by word, which means that Legg Mason precedes Leggett & Platt. You will find the commonly used name of the enterprise at the beginning of the profile; the full, legal name is found in the Locations section. If a company name is also a person's name, like Walt Disney, it will be alphabetized under the first name; if the company name starts with initials, like J. C. Penney or H.J. Heinz, look for it under the combined initials (in the above examples, JC and HJ, respectively). Basic financial data is listed under the heading Historical Financials; also included is the exchange on which the company's stock is traded if it is public, the ticker symbol used by the stock exchange, and the company's fiscal year-end.

The annual financial information contained in the profiles is current through fiscal year-ends occurring as late as May 2010. We have included certain nonfinancial developments, such as officer changes, through September 2010.

OVERVIEW

In the first section of the profile, we have tried to give a thumbnail description of the company and what it does. The description will usually include information on the company's strategy, reputation, and ownership. We recommend that you read this section first.

HISTORY

This extended section, included for almost all companies in the book, reflects our belief that every enterprise is the sum of its history and that you have to know where you came from in order to know where you are going. While some companies have limited historical awareness, we think the vast majority of the enterprises in this book have colorful backgrounds. We have tried to focus on the people who made the enterprises what they are today. We have found these histories to be full of twists and ironies; they make fascinating reading.

EXECUTIVES

Here we list the names of the people who run the company, insofar as space allows. In the case of public companies, we have shown the ages and total compensation of key officers. In some cases the published data is for the previous year although the company has announced promotions or retirements since year-end. Total compensation is the sum of salary, bonus, and the value of any other benefits, such as stock options or deferred compensation.

Although companies are free to structure their management titles any way they please, most modern corporations follow standard practices. The ultimate power in any corporation lies with the shareholders, who elect a board of directors, usually including officers or "insiders" as well as individuals from outside the company. The chief officer, the person on whose desk the buck stops, is usually called the chief executive officer (CEO). Often, he or she is also the chairman of the board.

As corporate management has become more complex, it is common for the CEO to have a "right-hand person" who oversees the day-to-day operations of the company, allowing the CEO plenty of time to focus on strategy and long-term issues. This right-hand person is usually designated the chief operating officer (COO) and is often the president of the company. In other cases one person is both chairman and president.

A multitude of other titles exists, including chief financial officer (CFO), chief administrative officer, and vice chairman. We have always tried to include the CFO, the chief legal officer, and the chief human resources or personnel officer. Our best advice is that officers' pay levels are clear indicators of who the board of directors thinks are the most important members of the management team.

The people named in the Executives section are indexed at the back of the book.

The Executives section also includes the name of the company's auditing (accounting) firm, where available.

LOCATIONS

Here we include the company's full legal name and its headquarters, street address, telephone and fax numbers, and Web site, as available. The back of the book includes an index of companies by headquarters locations.

In some cases we have also included information on the geographic distribution of the company's business, including sales and profit data. Note that these profit numbers, like those in the Products/Operations section below, are usually operating or pretax profits rather than net profits. Operating profits are generally those before financing costs (interest income and payments) and before taxes, which are considered costs attributable to the whole company rather than to one division or part of the world. For this reason the net income figures (in the Historical Financials section) are usually much lower, since they are after interest and taxes. Pretax profits are after interest but before taxes.

Headquarters for companies that are incorporated in Bermuda, but whose operational headquarters are in the US, are listed under their US address.

PRODUCTS/OPERATIONS

This section lists as many of the company's products, services, brand names, divisions, subsidiaries, and joint ventures as we could fit. We have tried to include all its major lines and all familiar brand names. The nature of this section varies by company and the amount of information available. If the company publishes sales and profit information by type of business, we have included it.

COMPETITORS

In this section we have listed companies that compete with the profiled company. This feature is included as a quick way to locate similar companies and compare them. The universe of competitors includes all public companies and all private companies with sales in excess of $500 million. In a few instances we have identified smaller private companies as key competitors.

HISTORICAL FINANCIALS

Here we have tried to present as much data about each enterprise's financial performance as we could compile in the allocated space. The information varies somewhat from industry to industry and is less complete in the case of private companies that do not release data (although we have always tried to provide annual sales and employment). There are a few industries, venture capital and investment banking, for example, for which revenue numbers are unavailable as a rule.

The following information is generally present.

A 5-year table, with relevant annualized compound growth rates, covers:

- Sales — fiscal year sales (year-end assets for most financial companies)
- Net income — fiscal year net income (before accounting changes)
- Net profit margin — fiscal year net income as a percent of sales (as a percent of assets for most financial firms)
- Employees — fiscal year-end or average number of employees
- Stock price — the fiscal year close
- P/E — high and low price/earnings ratio
- Earnings per share — fiscal year earnings per share (EPS)
- Dividends per share — fiscal year dividends per share
- Book value per share — fiscal year-end book value (common shareholders' equity per share)

The information on the number of employees is intended to aid the reader interested in knowing whether a company has a long-term trend of increasing or decreasing employment. As far as we know, we are the only company that publishes this information in print format.

The numbers on the left in each row of the Historical Financials section give the month and the year in which the company's fiscal year actually ends. Thus, a company with a March 31, 2011, year-end is shown as 3/11.

In addition, we have provided in graph form a stock price history for most public companies. The graphs, covering up to five years, show the range of trading between the high and the low price, as well as the closing price for each fiscal year. Generally, for private companies, we have graphed net income, or, if that is unavailable, sales.

Key year-end statistics in this section generally show the financial strength of the enterprise, including:

- Debt ratio (long-term debt as a percent of shareholders' equity)
- Return on equity (net income divided by the average of beginning and ending common shareholders' equity)
- Cash and cash equivalents
- Current ratio (ratio of current assets to current liabilities)
- Total long-term debt (including capital lease obligations)
- Number of shares of common stock outstanding
- Dividend yield (fiscal year dividends per share divided by the fiscal year-end closing stock price)
- Dividend payout (fiscal year dividends divided by fiscal year EPS)
- Market value at fiscal year-end (fiscal year-end closing stock price multiplied by fiscal year-end number of shares outstanding)

Per share data has been adjusted for stock splits. The data for public companies has been provided to us by Morningstar, Inc. Other public company information was compiled by Hoover's, which takes full responsibility for the content of this section.

In the case of private companies that do not publicly disclose financial information, we usually did not have access to such standardized data. We have gathered estimates of sales and other statistics from numerous sources.

Hoover's Handbook of

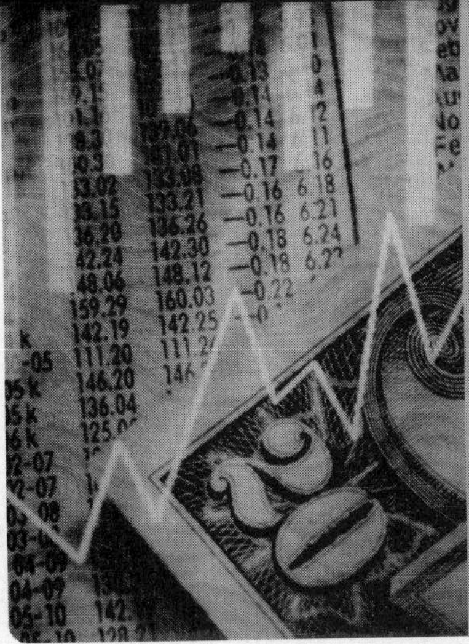

American Business

A List-Lover's Compendium

The 300 Largest Companies by Sales in
Hoover's Handbook of American Business 2013

Rank	Company	Sales ($ thous.)
1	Exxon Mobil Corp.	486,429,000
2	Wal-Mart Stores, Inc.	446,950,000
3	Chevron Corporation	253,706,000
4	ConocoPhillips	251,226,000
5	Phillips 66	200,614,000
6	Apple Inc	156,508,000
7	General Motors Co.	150,276,000
8	General Electric Co	147,300,000
9	Berkshire Hathaway Inc.	143,688,000
10	Fannie Mae	137,451,000
11	Ford Motor Co. (DE)	136,264,000
12	AT&T Inc	126,723,000
13	Valero Energy Corp.	125,987,000
14	McKesson Corp.	122,734,000
15	Hewlett-Packard Co	120,357,000
16	Bank of America Corp.	115,074,000
17	Verizon Communications Inc	110,875,000
18	JPMorgan Chase & Co.	110,838,000
19	Cardinal Health, Inc.	107,552,000
20	CVS Caremark Corporation	107,100,000
21	International Business Machi	106,916,000
22	Citigroup Inc	102,587,000
23	UnitedHealth Group Inc	101,862,000
24	Costco Wholesale Corp	99,137,000
25	Kroger Co.	90,374,000
26	Archer Daniels Midland Co.	89,038,000
27	Freddie Mac	88,262,000
28	Federal Reserve System	88,027,000
29	Wells Fargo & Co.	87,597,000
30	Procter & Gamble Co.	83,680,000
31	AmerisourceBergen Corp.	79,489,596
32	Marathon Petroleum Corp.	78,759,000
33	Philip Morris International	76,346,000
34	Microsoft Corporation	73,723,000
35	Walgreen Co.	71,633,000
36	Home Depot Inc	70,395,000
37	MetLife Inc	70,262,000
38	Target Corp	69,865,000
39	INTL FCStone Inc.	69,249,000
40	Boeing Co.	68,735,000
41	Pfizer Inc	67,425,000
42	Pepsico Inc.	66,504,000
43	Johnson & Johnson	65,030,000
44	American International Group	64,237,000
45	Dell Inc	62,071,000
46	WellPoint Inc	60,710,700
47	Caterpillar Inc.	60,138,000
48	Dow Chemical Co.	59,985,000
49	Bunge Ltd.	58,743,000
50	United Technologies Corp.	58,190,000
51	Comcast Corp	55,842,000
52	Mondelez International Inc	54,365,000
53	Intel Corp	53,999,000
54	United Parcel Service Inc	53,105,000
55	Best Buy Inc	50,705,000
56	Lowe's Companies Inc	50,208,000
57	Prudential Financial, Inc.	49,045,000
58	Amazon.com Inc.	48,077,000
59	Merck & Co., Inc	48,047,000
60	Coca-Cola Co (The)	46,542,000
61	Lockheed Martin Corp.	46,499,000
62	Express Scripts Holdings Co	46,128,300
63	Cisco Systems, Inc.	46,061,000
64	Enterprise Products Partners	44,313,000
65	Safeway Inc.	43,630,200
66	FedEx Corp	42,680,000
67	Sysco Corp.	42,380,939
68	Disney (Walt) Co. (The)	42,278,000
69	Johnson Controls Inc	41,955,000
70	Sears Holdings Corp	41,567,000
71	CHS Inc	40,599,286
72	Federal Reserve Bank Of NY	39,655,000
73	Morgan Stanley	39,310,000
74	Abbott Laboratories	38,851,259
75	Du Pont (E.I.) de Nemours &	38,719,000
76	Google Inc	37,905,000
77	Hess Corp	37,871,000
78	Oracle Corp.	37,121,000
79	United Continental Holdings	37,110,000
80	Humana, Inc.	36,832,000
81	Goldman Sachs Group, Inc.	36,793,000
82	Honeywell International, Inc	36,529,000
83	Ingram Micro Inc.	36,328,701
84	Deere & Co.	36,157,100
85	SUPERVALU INC	36,100,000
86	Delta Air Lines, Inc. (DE)	35,115,000
87	Liberty Mutual Holding Compa	34,671,000
88	World Fuel Services Corp.	34,622,854
89	Plains All American Pipeline	34,275,000
90	Aetna Inc.	33,779,800
91	News Corp	33,706,000
92	Sprint Nextel Corp	33,679,000
93	Tyson Foods, Inc.	33,278,000
94	General Dynamics Corp.	32,677,000
95	Allstate Corp.	32,654,000
96	American Express Co.	32,282,000
97	Tesoro Corporation	30,303,000
98	HCA Holdings Inc	29,682,000
99	3M Co	29,611,000
100	Time Warner Inc	28,974,000
101	Murphy Oil Corp	27,745,549
102	DIRECTV	27,226,000
103	Publix Super Markets, Inc.	27,178,764
104	McDonald's Corp	27,006,000
105	Tech Data Corp.	26,488,124
106	Northrop Grumman Corp	26,412,000
107	Macys Inc	26,405,000
108	Rite Aid Corp.	26,121,222
109	International Paper Co.	26,034,000
110	Avnet Inc	25,707,522
111	Travelers Companies Inc (The	25,446,000
112	Teachers Insurance & Annuity	25,120,000
113	Staples Inc	25,022,192
114	Alcoa, Inc.	24,951,000
115	Raytheon Co.	24,857,000
116	Halliburton Company	24,829,000
117	Emerson Electric Co.	24,412,000
118	Lilly (Eli) & Co.	24,286,500
119	NIKE, Inc	24,128,000
120	Occidental Petroleum Corp	24,119,000
121	AMR Corp. (DE)	23,979,000
122	Altria Group Inc	23,800,000
123	Northwestern Mutual Life Ins.	23,595,000
124	Fluor Corp.	23,381,399
125	TJX Companies, Inc.	23,191,455
126	Goodyear Tire & Rubber Co.	22,767,000
127	Xerox Corp	22,626,000
128	AFLAC Inc.	22,171,000
129	ManpowerGroup	22,006,000
130	Cigna Corp	21,998,000
131	Hartford Financial Services	21,859,000
132	U.S. Bancorp (DE)	21,399,000
133	Arrow Electronics, Inc.	21,390,264
134	Bristol-Myers Squibb Co.	21,244,000
135	Freeport-McMoRan Copper	20,880,000
136	Kimberly-Clark Corp.	20,846,000
137	Nucor Corp.	20,023,564
138	EMC Corp. (MA)	20,007,588
139	United States Steel Corp.	19,884,000
140	Baker Hughes Inc.	19,831,000
141	Time Warner Cable Inc	19,675,000
142	Union Pacific Corp	19,557,000
143	Burlington Northern & Santa F	19,229,000
144	Qualcomm, Inc.	19,121,000
145	Exelon Corp.	18,924,000
146	Kohl's Corp.	18,804,000
147	Whirlpool Corp	18,666,000
148	Kraft Foods Group Inc	18,655,000
149	Capital One Financial Corp	18,525,000
150	Cummins, Inc.	18,048,000
151	Illinois Tool Works, Inc.	17,786,583
152	Southern Co.	17,657,000
153	AbbVie Inc.	17,443,951
154	AES Corp.	17,274,000
155	Penney (J.C.) Co.,Inc. (Hold	17,260,000
156	Jabil Circuit, Inc.	17,151,941
157	Apache Corp.	16,888,000
158	Colgate-Palmolive Co.	16,734,000
159	General Mills, Inc.	16,657,900
160	Paccar Inc.	16,355,200
161	FirstEnergy Corp.	16,258,000
162	TRW Automotive Hldings Corp	16,244,000
163	Medtronic, Inc.	16,184,000
164	Danaher Corp.	16,090,540
165	Eaton Corp plc	16,049,000
166	Computer Sciences Corp.	15,877,000
167	PNC Financial Services Group	15,820,000
168	Bank of New York Mellon Corp	15,804,000
169	Carnival Corp.	15,793,000
170	Southwest Airlines Co	15,658,000
171	Amgen Inc	15,582,000
172	Progressive Corp. (OH)	15,508,100
173	HollyFrontier Corp.	15,439,528
174	CenturyLink, Inc.	15,351,000
175	NextEra Energy Inc	15,341,000
176	Marathon Oil Corp.	15,282,000
177	L-3 Communications Hldings,	15,169,000
178	American Electric Power Co.,	15,116,000

SOURCE: MERGENT INC., DATABASE, AUGUST 2012

The 300 Largest Companies by Sales in **Hoover's Handbook of American Business 2013** (continued)

Rank	Company	Sales ($ thous.)
179	PG&E Corp. (Holding Co.)	14,956,000
180	PPG Industries, Inc.	14,885,000
181	Global Partners LP	14,835,729
182	Dollar General Corp	14,807,188
183	Oneok Inc.	14,805,794
184	National Oilwell Varco Inc	14,658,000
185	The Gap, Inc.	14,549,000
186	Duke Energy Corp	14,529,000
187	Dominion Resources Inc	14,379,000
188	CBS Corp	14,245,000
189	Lear Corp.	14,156,500
190	Loews Corp.	14,127,000
191	Dish Network Corp	14,048,393
192	Anadarko Petroleum Corp	13,967,000
193	Baxter International Inc.	13,893,000
194	Viacom Inc	13,887,000
195	Omnicom Group, Inc.	13,872,500
196	AutoNation, Inc.	13,832,300
197	Thomson Reuters Corp	13,807,000
198	Texas Instruments, Inc.	13,735,000
199	Community Health Systems, In	13,626,168
200	Chubb Corp.	13,585,000
201	Monsanto Co.	13,504,000
202	Waste Management, Inc. (DE)	13,378,000
203	Ally Financial Inc	13,332,000
204	Starbucks Corp.	13,299,500
205	ConAgra Foods, Inc.	13,262,600
206	Kellogg Co	13,198,000
207	Parker Hannifin Corp.	13,145,942
208	Smithfield Foods, Inc.	13,094,300
209	ARAMARK Corp.	13,082,377
210	Dean Foods Co.	13,055,493
211	US Airways Group Inc	13,055,000
212	Navistar International Corp.	12,948,000
213	Consolidated Edison, Inc.	12,938,000
214	West End Indiana Bancshares	12,887,027
215	Edison International	12,760,000
216	PPL Corp	12,737,000
217	Yum! Brands, Inc.	12,626,000
218	Western Digital Corp.	12,478,000
219	Genuine Parts Co.	12,458,877
220	Marriott International, Inc.	12,317,000
221	Coventry Health Care Inc.	12,186,683
222	Health Net, Inc.	11,901,036
223	Icahn Enterprises L P	11,855,000
224	CSX Corp.	11,743,000
225	Thermo Fisher Scientific Inc	11,725,900
226	Whole Foods Market, Inc.	11,698,828
227	eBay Inc.	11,651,654
228	Heinz (H.J.) Co.	11,649,079
229	Chesapeake Energy Corp.	11,635,000
230	Penske Automotive Group Inc	11,556,232
231	Marsh & McLennan Comps	11,526,000
232	Office Depot, Inc.	11,489,533
233	Devon Energy Corp.	11,454,000
234	ONEOK Partners LP	11,322,607
235	Avon Products, Inc.	11,291,600
236	Textron Inc.	11,275,000
237	Praxair, Inc.	11,252,000
238	Entergy Corp. (New)	11,229,073
239	Huntsman Corp	11,221,000
240	Tennessee Valley Authority	11,220,000
241	Norfolk Southern Corp.	11,172,000
242	Mosaic Co (The)	11,107,800
243	Public Service Enterprise Gr	11,079,000
244	Sunoco Logistics Partners L.	10,918,000
245	Jacobs Engineering Group, In	10,893,778
246	Nordstrom, Inc.	10,877,000
247	Automatic Data Processing In	10,665,200
248	Xcel Energy, Inc.	10,654,770
249	Lincoln National Corp.	10,636,000
250	Florida Power & Light Co.	10,613,000
251	Donnelley (R. R.) & Sons Co.	10,611,000
252	SAIC Inc	10,587,000
253	Science Applications Interna	10,587,000
254	Southern California Edison C	10,577,000
255	Consolidated Edison Co. of N	10,484,000
256	Visa Inc	10,421,000
257	Synnex Corp	10,409,840
258	Stanley Black & Decker, Inc.	10,376,400
259	Limited Brands Inc.	10,364,000
260	Newmont Mining Corp. (Holdin	10,358,000
261	Genworth Financial Inc	10,344,000
262	Robinson (C.H.) Worldwide, I	10,336,346
263	Exelon Generation Co LLC	10,308,000
264	Unum Group	10,278,000
265	State Street Corp.	10,207,000
266	Ameriprise Financial Inc	10,192,000
267	EOG Resources, Inc.	10,126,115
268	Fed Reserve Bank of Richm	10,043,000
269	Sempra Energy	10,036,000
270	Carmax Inc.	10,003,599
271	BB&T Corp.	9,998,000
272	Lauder (Estee) Cos., Inc. (T	9,713,600
273	Liberty Interactive Corp	9,616,000
274	Air Products & Chemicals, In	9,611,700
275	Suntrust Banks, Inc.	9,602,000
276	GameStop Corp	9,550,500
277	URS Corp	9,545,000
278	Liberty Global Inc	9,510,800
279	Bed, Bath & Beyond, Inc.	9,499,890
280	VF Corp.	9,459,232
281	Las Vegas Sands Corp	9,410,745
282	Family Dollar Stores, Inc.	9,331,005
283	KBR Inc	9,261,000
284	Rock-Tenn Co.	9,207,600
285	Enbridge Energy Partners, L.	9,109,800
286	BlackRock, Inc.	9,081,000
287	NRG Energy Inc	9,079,000
288	Western Refining Inc	9,071,037
289	CNA Financial Corp.	8,947,000
290	DTE Energy Co.	8,897,000
291	Federal Reserve Bank of San F	8,863,000
292	Tenet Healthcare Corp.	8,854,000
293	Caesars Entertainment Corp	8,834,500
294	Reinsurance Group of America	8,829,538
295	Georgia Power Co.	8,800,000
296	AGCO Corp.	8,773,200
297	Sherwin-Williams Co.	8,765,699
298	Applied Materials, Inc.	8,719,000
299	Principal Financial Group, I	8,709,600
300	Crown Holdings Inc	8,644,000

The 300 Most Profitable Companies in
Hoover's Handbook of American Business 2013

Rank	Company	Net Income ($ thous.)
1	Federal Reserve System	78,538,000
2	Apple Inc	41,733,000
3	Exxon Mobil Corp.	41,060,000
4	Federal Reserve Bank Of NY	35,026,000
5	Chevron Corporation	26,895,000
6	Ford Motor Co. (DE)	20,213,000
7	JPMorgan Chase & Co.	18,976,000
8	American International Group	17,798,000
9	Microsoft Corporation	16,978,000
10	Wells Fargo & Co.	15,869,000
11	International Business Machi	15,855,000
12	Wal-Mart Stores, Inc.	15,699,000
13	General Electric Co	14,151,000
14	Intel Corp	12,942,000
15	ConocoPhillips	12,436,000
16	Citigroup Inc	11,067,000
17	Procter & Gamble Co.	10,756,000
18	Berkshire Hathaway Inc.	10,254,000
19	Pfizer Inc	10,009,000
20	Oracle Corp.	9,981,000
21	Google Inc	9,737,000
22	Johnson & Johnson	9,672,000
23	Federal Reserve Bank of Richm	9,222,000
24	General Motors Co.	9,190,000
25	Philip Morris International	8,591,000
26	Coca-Cola Co (The)	8,572,000
27	Federal Reserve Bank of San F	8,071,000
28	Cisco Systems, Inc.	8,041,000
29	MetLife Inc	6,981,000
30	Occidental Petroleum Corp	6,771,000
31	Federal Reserve Bank Of Atlan	6,498,000
32	Pepsico Inc.	6,443,000
33	Merck & Co., Inc	6,272,000
34	Qualcomm, Inc.	6,109,000
35	Freeport-McMoRan Co & Go	5,747,000
36	Disney (Walt) Co. (The)	5,682,000
37	McDonald's Corp	5,503,100
38	UnitedHealth Group Inc	5,142,000
39	Federal Reserve Bank Of Chica	5,026,000
40	United Technologies Corp.	4,979,000
41	American Express Co.	4,935,000
42	Caterpillar Inc.	4,928,000
43	U.S. Bancorp (DE)	4,872,000
44	Phillips 66	4,775,000
45	Abbott Laboratories	4,728,449
46	Devon Energy Corp.	4,704,000
47	Apache Corp.	4,584,000
48	Goldman Sachs Group, Inc.	4,442,000
49	Lilly (Eli) & Co.	4,347,700
50	3M Co	4,283,000
51	Comcast Corp	4,160,000
52	Morgan Stanley	4,110,000
53	Boeing Co.	4,018,000
54	AT&T Inc	3,944,000
55	Home Depot Inc	3,883,000
56	United Parcel Service Inc	3,804,000
57	Bristol-Myers Squibb Co.	3,709,000
58	Amgen Inc	3,683,000
59	Prudential Financial, Inc.	3,666,000
60	Medtronic, Inc.	3,617,000
61	Mondelez International Inc	3,527,000
62	Dell Inc	3,492,000
63	Du Pont (E.I.) de Nemours &	3,474,000
64	CVS Caremark Corporation	3,461,000
65	AbbVie Inc.	3,433,128
66	Altria Group Inc	3,390,000
67	Union Pacific Corp	3,292,000
68	Burlington Northern & Santa F	3,273,000
69	eBay Inc.	3,229,387
70	Capital One Financial Corp	3,147,000
71	Federal Reserve Bank of Dalla	3,134,000
72	MGM Resorts International	3,114,637
73	PNC Financial Services Group	3,071,000
74	Deere & Co.	3,064,700
75	Marathon Oil Corp.	2,946,000
76	Target Corp	2,929,000
77	Time Warner Inc	2,886,000
78	Halliburton Company	2,839,000
79	Corning, Inc.	2,805,000
80	Gilead Sciences, Inc.	2,803,637
81	Dow Chemical Co.	2,742,000
82	Lockheed Martin Corp.	2,655,000
83	WellPoint Inc	2,646,700
84	DIRECTV	2,609,000
85	Bank of New York Mellon Corp	2,569,000
86	General Dynamics Corp.	2,526,000
87	Exelon Corp.	2,495,000
88	HCA Holdings Inc	2,465,000
89	EMC Corp. (MA)	2,461,337
90	Colgate-Palmolive Co.	2,431,000
91	Verizon Communications Inc	2,404,000
92	Marathon Petroleum Corp.	2,389,000
93	Federal Reserve Bank Of Phila	2,382,000
94	Teachers Insurance & Annuity	2,359,000
95	BlackRock, Inc.	2,337,000
96	Southern Copper Corp	2,336,424
97	Southern Co.	2,268,000
98	Federal Reserve Bank of Cleve	2,246,000
99	Federal Reserve Bank Of Kansa	2,245,000
100	Texas Instruments, Inc.	2,236,000
101	Discover Financial Services	2,226,708
102	Baxter International Inc.	2,224,000
103	NIKE, Inc	2,223,000
104	Danaher Corp.	2,172,264
105	Visa Inc	2,144,000
106	Walgreen Co.	2,127,000
107	Northrop Grumman Corp	2,118,000
108	Valero Energy Corp.	2,090,000
109	Enterprise Products Partners	2,088,300
110	Illinois Tool Works, Inc.	2,071,384
111	Honeywell International, Inc	2,067,000
112	Monsanto Co.	2,045,000
113	FedEx Corp	2,032,000
114	National Oilwell Varco Inc	1,994,000
115	Aetna Inc.	1,985,700
116	Viacom Inc	1,981,000
117	Emerson Electric Co.	1,968,000
118	AFLAC Inc.	1,964,000
119	American Electric Power Co.,	1,946,000
120	Franklin Resources, Inc.	1,931,400
121	Mosaic Co (The)	1,930,200
122	NextEra Energy Inc	1,923,000
123	State Street Corp.	1,920,000
124	Norfolk Southern Corp.	1,916,000
125	Carnival Corp.	1,912,000
126	Federal Reserve Bank Of Bosto	1,909,000
127	MasterCard Inc	1,906,000
128	Raytheon Co.	1,866,000
129	Cummins, Inc.	1,848,000
130	Lowe's Companies Inc	1,839,000
131	Kraft Foods Group Inc	1,839,000
132	CSX Corp.	1,822,000
133	CME Group Inc	1,812,300
134	Ford Motor Credit Company LL	1,795,000
135	Exelon Generation Co LLC	1,771,000
136	Chesapeake Energy Corp.	1,742,000
137	Baker Hughes Inc.	1,739,000
138	Costco Wholesale Corp	1,709,000
139	Duke Energy Corp	1,706,000
140	Hess Corp	1,703,000
141	Chubb Corp.	1,678,000
142	Praxair, Inc.	1,672,000
143	Time Warner Cable Inc	1,665,000
144	Cliffs Natural Resources, In	1,619,100
145	Federal Reserve Bank Of St. L	1,617,000
146	Western Digital Corp.	1,612,000
147	Kimberly-Clark Corp.	1,591,000
148	International Finance Corp.	1,579,000
149	General Mills, Inc.	1,567,300
150	Las Vegas Sands Corp	1,560,123
151	CF Industries Holdings Inc	1,539,200
152	Dish Network Corp	1,515,907
153	Public Service Enterprise Gr	1,503,000
154	TJX Companies, Inc.	1,496,090
155	PPL Corp	1,495,000
156	Publix Super Markets, Inc.	1,491,966
157	Toyota Motor Credit Corp.	1,486,000
158	Bank of America Corp.	1,446,000
159	Travelers Companies Inc (The	1,426,000
160	Humana, Inc.	1,419,000
161	Dominion Resources Inc	1,408,000
162	Sempra Energy	1,407,000
163	Reynolds American Inc	1,406,000
164	McKesson Corp.	1,403,000
165	Automatic Data Processing In	1,388,500
166	Starbucks Corp.	1,383,800
167	Williams Partners L.P.	1,378,000
168	Entergy Corp. (New)	1,367,372
169	CenterPoint Energy, Inc	1,357,000
170	Carlyle Group, L.P. (The)	1,356,900
171	Eaton Corp plc	1,350,000
172	Stryker Corp.	1,345,000
173	International Paper Co.	1,341,000
174	BB&T Corp.	1,332,000
175	Thermo Fisher Scientific Inc	1,329,900
176	Cigna Corp	1,327,000
177	Yum! Brands, Inc.	1,319,000
178	Celgene Corp.	1,318,150

SOURCE: MERGENT INC., DATABASE, AUGUST 2012

The 300 Most Profitable Companies in Hoover's Handbook of American Business 2013 (continued)

Rank	Company	Net Income ($ thous.)
179	CBS Corp	1,305,000
180	Fifth Third Bancorp (Cincinn	1,297,000
181	Xerox Corp	1,295,000
182	Express Scripts Holdings Co	1,275,800
183	CHS Inc	1,260,628
184	Kinder Morgan Energy Partner	1,257,800
185	Macys Inc	1,256,000
186	Simon Property Group, Inc.	1,245,900
187	MetLife Insurance Company of	1,240,000
188	Biogen Idec Inc	1,234,428
189	Kellogg Co	1,231,000
190	Johnson Controls Inc	1,226,000
191	Precision Castparts Corp.	1,224,100
192	Archer Daniels Midland Co.	1,223,000
193	Spectra Energy Corp	1,184,000
194	News Corp	1,179,000
195	Santander Holdings USA Inc.	1,172,642
196	Symantec Corp.	1,172,000
197	Becton, Dickinson & Co.	1,169,927
198	Air Products & Chemicals, In	1,167,300
199	Kohl's Corp.	1,167,000
200	Western Union Co.	1,165,400
201	Georgia Power Co.	1,162,000
202	Federal Reserve Bank of Minne	1,160,000
203	Motorola Solutions Inc.	1,158,000
204	TRW Automotive Holdings Corp	1,157,000
205	Parker Hannifin Corp.	1,155,492
206	Agilent Technologies, Inc.	1,153,000
207	Southern California Edison C	1,144,000
208	Discovery Communications, In	1,132,000
209	Sysco Corp.	1,121,585
210	Lorillard, Inc.	1,116,000
211	PSEG Power LLC	1,098,000
212	PPG Industries, Inc.	1,095,000
213	EOG Resources, Inc.	1,091,123
214	Activision Blizzard, Inc.	1,085,000
215	Ameriprise Financial Inc	1,076,000
216	Cardinal Health, Inc.	1,069,000
217	Florida Power & Light Co.	1,068,000
218	Loews Corp.	1,064,000
219	Consolidated Edison, Inc.	1,062,000
220	Priceline.com, Inc.	1,059,131
221	Yahoo! Inc.	1,048,827
222	Paccar Inc.	1,042,300
223	Coach, Inc.	1,038,910
224	HollyFrontier Corp.	1,023,397
225	HSBC USA, Inc.	1,018,000
226	Progressive Corp. (OH)	1,015,500
227	Facebook, Inc.	1,000,000
228	Marsh & McLennan Companies I	993,000
229	Bed, Bath & Beyond, Inc.	989,537
230	Consolidated Edison Co. of N	989,000
231	SanDisk Corp.	986,990
232	Staples Inc	984,656
233	Forest Laboratories Inc.	979,058
234	Plains All American Pipeline	966,000
235	Diamond Offshore Drilling, I	962,542
236	Waste Management, Inc. (DE)	961,000
237	Peabody Energy Corp	957,700
238	Horton (D.R.) Inc.	956,300
239	L-3 Communications Holdings,	956,000
240	Omnicom Group, Inc.	952,600
241	CA Inc	951,000
242	Bunge Ltd.	942,000
243	Equity Residential	935,197
244	Allergan, Inc	934,500
245	ERP Operating L.P.	934,365
246	AutoZone, Inc.	930,373
247	Broadcom Corp.	927,000
248	Heinz (H.J.) Co.	923,159
249	KeyCorp	920,000
250	Liberty Interactive Corp	912,000
251	Beam Inc	911,400
252	McGraw-Hill Cos., Inc. (The)	911,000
253	Dover Corp	895,243
254	VF Corp.	888,089
255	FirstEnergy Corp.	885,000
256	Cognizant Technology Solutio	883,618
257	Murphy Oil Corp	872,702
258	Schwab (Charles) Corp.	864,000
259	M & T Bank Corp	859,479
260	PG&E Corp. (Holding Co.)	858,000
261	Lauder (Estee) Cos., Inc. (T	856,900
262	Delta Air Lines, Inc. (DE)	854,000
263	Limited Brands Inc.	850,000
264	Hillshire Brands Co	845,000
265	Xcel Energy, Inc.	841,172
266	United Continental Holdings	840,000
267	Pioneer Natural Resources Co	834,489
268	The Gap, Inc.	833,000
269	Adobe Systems, Inc.	832,847
270	ONEOK Partners LP	830,319
271	St. Jude Medical, Inc.	825,793
272	Public Storage	823,842
273	Virginia Electric & Power Co	822,000
274	Starz	812,000
275	Wachovia Preferred Funding Co	795,613
276	Intuit Inc	792,000
277	Allstate Corp.	788,000
278	RiverSource Life Insurance C	779,000
279	Nucor Corp.	778,188
280	Campbell Soup Co.	774,000
281	T Rowe Price Group Inc.	773,200
282	Altera Corp.	770,711
283	American Capital Agency Corp	770,480
284	Mattel Inc	768,508
285	PPL Energy Supply, LLC	768,000
286	Dollar General Corp	766,685
287	Joy Global Inc	762,021
288	Zimmer Holdings, Inc.	760,800
289	KLA-Tencor Corp.	756,015
290	Icahn Enterprises L P	750,000
291	Coca-Cola Enterprises Inc	749,000
292	Alabama Power Co.	747,000
293	Rockwell Automation, Inc.	737,000
294	Rowan Companies Plc	736,841
295	Invesco Ltd	729,700
296	VMWARE, Inc.	723,936
297	AmerisourceBergen Corp.	718,986
298	Vornado Realty L.P.	718,214
299	Principal Financial Group, I	715,000
300	DTE Energy Co.	711,000

The 300 Largest Employers in
Hoover's Handbook of American Business 2013

Rank	Company	Employees
1	Wal-Mart Stores, Inc.	2200000
2	Kelly Services, Inc.	558200
3	Yum! Brands, Inc.	466000
4	International Business Machi	433362
5	McDonald's Corp	420000
6	United Parcel Service Inc	398000
7	Target Corp	365000
8	Kroger Co.	339000
9	Hewlett-Packard Co	331800
10	Home Depot Inc	331000
11	General Electric Co	301000
12	Pepsico Inc.	297000
13	Sears Holdings Corp	293000
14	Bank of America Corp.	282000
15	CVS Caremark Corporation	280000
16	Berkshire Hathaway Inc.	271000
17	Citigroup Inc	266000
18	Wells Fargo & Co.	264200
19	JPMorgan Chase & Co.	260157
20	AT&T Inc	256420
21	ARAMARK Corp.	250000
22	Lowe's Companies Inc	248000
23	Walgreen Co.	240000
24	General Motors Co.	207000
25	United Technologies Corp.	199900
26	Robert Half International In	199300
27	HCA Holdings Inc	199000
28	Verizon Communications Inc	193900
29	Darden Restaurants, Inc. (Un	180000
30	Freescale Semiconductor Ltd	180000
31	Safeway Inc.	178000
32	Costco Wholesale Corp	174000
33	Boeing Co.	171700
34	Macys Inc	171000
35	Johnson Controls Inc	170000
36	TJX Companies, Inc.	168000
37	Best Buy Inc	167000
38	Disney (Walt) Co. (The)	166000
39	Ford Motor Co. (DE)	164000
40	Starbucks Corp.	160000
41	Penney (J.C.) Co.,Inc. (Hold	159000
42	Starwood Hotels & Resorts Wo	154000
43	Publix Super Markets, Inc.	152000
44	FedEx Corp	149000
45	Coca-Cola Co (The)	146200
46	Kohl's Corp.	142000
47	Jabil Circuit, Inc.	141000
48	Xerox Corp	139650
49	Cognizant Technology Solutio	137700
50	Emerson Electric Co.	134900
51	The Gap, Inc.	132000
52	Honeywell International, Inc	132000
53	SUPERVALU INC	130000
54	Weyerhaeuser Co.	128000
55	Procter & Gamble Co.	126000
56	Mondelez International Inc	126000
57	Comcast Corp	126000
58	Caterpillar Inc.	125099
59	Lockheed Martin Corp.	123000
60	Marriott International, Inc.	120000
61	Johnson & Johnson	117900
62	Tyson Foods, Inc.	115000
63	Oracle Corp.	115000
64	Dell Inc	109400
65	Pfizer Inc	103700
66	Western Digital Corp.	103111
67	Intel Corp	100100
68	UnitedHealth Group Inc	99000
69	Computer Sciences Corp.	98000
70	Lear Corp.	97800
71	Limited Brands Inc.	97000
72	General Dynamics Corp.	95100
73	ABM Industries, Inc.	95000
74	Microsoft Corporation	94000
75	Carnival Corp.	91300
76	Abbott Laboratories	91000
77	Dollar General Corp	90000
78	Rite Aid Corp.	90000
79	Abercrombie & Fitch Co.	90000
80	Community Health Systems, In	88000
81	Staples Inc	87782
82	Merck & Co., Inc	86000
83	Bloomin' Brands Inc.	86000
84	3M Co	84198
85	Exxon Mobil Corp.	82100
86	AMR Corp. (DE)	80100
87	Delta Air Lines, Inc. (DE)	78392
88	Philip Morris International	78100
89	Kindred Healthcare Inc	77800
90	Convergys Corp.	77000
91	Apple Inc	76100
92	Eaton Corp plc	73000
93	Goodyear Tire & Rubber Co.	73000
94	Dollar Tree, Inc.	72770
95	Whole Foods Market, Inc.	72700
96	TRW Automotive Holdings Corp	72700
97	Northrop Grumman Corp	72500
98	Dole Food Co., Inc.	71100
99	Brinks Co (The)	71000
100	Raytheon Co.	71000
101	GameStop Corp	71000
102	Omnicom Group, Inc.	70600
103	Du Pont (E.I.) de Nemours &	70000
104	Cracker Barrel Old Country S	70000
105	AutoZone, Inc.	70000
106	Caesars Entertainment Corp	70000
107	Whirlpool Corp	68231
108	Halliburton Company	68000
109	MetLife Inc	67000
110	Deere & Co.	66900
111	Cisco Systems, Inc.	66639
112	Universal Health Services, I	65400
113	Illinois Tool Works, Inc.	65000
114	Jacobs Engineering Group, In	63400
115	U.S. Bancorp (DE)	62529
116	American Express Co.	62500
117	Morgan Stanley	61899
118	International Paper Co.	61500
119	Alcoa, Inc.	61000
120	Chevron Corporation	61000
121	MGM Resorts International	61000
122	L-3 Communications Holdings,	61000
123	Thomson Reuters Corp	60500
124	Icahn Enterprises L P	59559
125	Parker Hannifin Corp.	59300
126	Danaher Corp.	59000
127	Brinker International, Inc.	58068
128	Donnelley (R. R.) & Sons Co.	58000
129	VF Corp.	58000
130	Tenet Healthcare Corp.	57705
131	Baker Hughes Inc.	57700
132	American International Group	57000
133	Automatic Data Processing In	57000
134	Kimberly-Clark Corp.	57000
135	Nordstrom, Inc.	56500
136	Amazon.com Inc.	56200
137	Weight Watchers Internationa	56000
138	Family Dollar Stores, Inc.	55000
139	Ross Stores, Inc.	53900
140	EMC Corp. (MA)	53600
141	Hanesbrands Inc	53300
142	Advance Auto Parts Inc	53000
143	Marsh & McLennan Companies I	52400
144	Regis Corp.	52000
145	PNC Financial Services Group	51891
146	Dow Chemical Co.	51705
147	Prudential Financial, Inc.	50104
148	PETsMART, Inc.	50000
149	Hyatt Hotels Corp	50000
150	Apollo Group, Inc.	49992
151	National Oilwell Varco Inc	49475
152	Barrett Business Services, I	49355
153	CenturyLink, Inc.	49200
154	O'Reilly Automotive, Inc.	49148
155	Bank of New York Mellon Corp	48700
156	Baxter International Inc.	48500
157	Time Warner Cable Inc	48500
158	News Corp	48000
159	Bed, Bath & Beyond, Inc.	48000
160	Sysco Corp.	47800
161	Bob Evans Farms, Inc.	46818
162	Aecom Technology Corp (DE)	46800
163	Brookdale Senior Living Inc	46400
164	Smithfield Foods, Inc.	46050
165	URS Corp	46000
166	Ascena Retail Group Inc	46000
167	Jones Lang LaSalle Inc	45500
168	Southwest Airlines Co	45392
169	Federal-Mogul Corp.	45000
170	Medtronic, Inc.	44944
171	Sanmina Corp	44879
172	Union Pacific Corp	44861
173	Stanley Black & Decker, Inc.	44700
174	Waste Management, Inc. (DE)	44300
175	NIKE, Inc	44000
176	Cummins, Inc.	43900
177	Fluor Corp.	43087
178	United States Steel Corp.	43000

SOURCE: MERGENT INC., DATABASE, AUGUST 2012

The 300 Largest Employers in Hoover's Handbook of American Business 2013 (continued)

Rank	Company	Employees
179	Wendy's Co (The)	42800
180	TeleTech Holdings, Inc.	42300
181	Interpublic Group of Compani	42000
182	Quest Diagnostics, Inc.	42000
183	SAIC Inc	41100
184	Science Applications Interna	41000
185	DaVita HealthCare Partners I	41000
186	Sykes Enterprises, Inc.	41000
187	Vanguard Health Systems, Inc	40900
188	Avon Products, Inc.	40600
189	Health Management Associates	40600
190	Ecolab, Inc.	40200
191	Humana, Inc.	40000
192	Sprint Nextel Corp	40000
193	Las Vegas Sands Corp	40000
194	American Eagle Outfitters, I	39600
195	Pilgrims Pride Corp.	39500
196	Thermo Fisher Scientific Inc	39300
197	Amphenol Corp.	39100
198	Foot Locker, Inc.	39077
199	Burlington Northern & Santa F	39000
200	Office Depot, Inc.	39000
201	Dillard's Inc.	38900
202	Colgate-Palmolive Co.	38600
203	Lauder (Estee) Cos., Inc. (T	38500
204	PPG Industries, Inc.	38400
205	Lilly (Eli) & Co.	38080
206	Huntington Ingalls Industrie	38000
207	McKesson Corp.	37700
208	WellPoint Inc	37700
209	Allstate Corp.	37600
210	Big Lots, Inc.	37400
211	West Corp.	36500
212	Ruby Tuesday, Inc.	36300
213	General Mills, Inc.	35000
214	Texas Instruments, Inc.	34759
215	Burger King Worldwide Inc	34248
216	Molex Inc	34226
217	Dover Corp	34000
218	RadioShack Corp.	34000
219	Time Warner Inc	34000
220	Dish Network Corp	34000
221	Bunge Ltd.	34000
222	CBRE Group Inc	34000
223	Goldman Sachs Group, Inc.	33300
224	Aetna Inc.	33300
225	Command Center, Inc.	33177
226	Fidelity National Informatio	33000
227	Texas Roadhouse Inc	33000
228	Sherwin-Williams Co.	32988
229	Panera Bread Co.	32600
230	Cardinal Health, Inc.	32500
231	Google Inc	32467
232	Heinz (H.J.) Co.	32200
233	Cheesecake Factory Inc. (The	32200
234	Textron Inc.	32000
235	YRC Worldwide Inc	32000
236	BB&T Corp.	31800
237	Freeport-McMoRan Copper & Go	31800
238	Capital One Financial Corp	31542
239	US Airways Group Inc	31500
240	Cigna Corp	31400
241	CSX Corp.	31344
242	Gannett Co Inc	31000
243	Masco Corp.	31000
244	Laboratory Corp. of America	31000
245	ManpowerGroup	31000
246	Chipotle Mexican Grill Inc	30940
247	Expert Global Solutions Inc	30800
248	Kellogg Co	30700
249	Travelers Companies Inc (The	30600
250	Avery Dennison Corp.	30400
251	Norfolk Southern Corp.	30329
252	Archer Daniels Midland Co.	30000
253	Cintas Corp.	30000
254	Barnes & Noble Inc	30000
255	Republic Services, Inc.	30000
256	AbbVie Inc.	30000
257	Genuine Parts Co.	29800
258	ConocoPhillips	29800
259	State Street Corp.	29740
260	Becton, Dickinson & Co.	29555
261	Suntrust Banks, Inc.	29182
262	OfficeMax Inc (DE)	29000
263	Corning, Inc.	28800
264	Select Medical Holdings Corp	28800
265	Pitney Bowes Inc	28700
266	Dick's Sporting Goods, Inc	28400
267	Emeritus Corp.	28100
268	Mattel Inc	28000
269	Avis Budget Group Inc	28000
270	Con-Way Inc	27800
271	Wyndham Worldwide Corp	27800
272	eBay Inc.	27770
273	American Greetings Corp.	27500
274	Ryder System, Inc.	27500
275	Micron Technology Inc.	27400
276	Bon-Ton Stores Inc	27100
277	Bristol-Myers Squibb Co.	27000
278	AES Corp.	27000
279	KBR Inc	27000
280	Williams-Sonoma, Inc.	26900
281	iGate Corp	26889
282	Regions Financial Corp	26813
283	DIRECTV	26800
284	Qualcomm, Inc.	26600
285	Southern Co.	26377
286	Sealed Air Corp.	26300
287	Rock-Tenn Co.	26300
288	Mohawk Industries, Inc.	26200
289	Praxair, Inc.	26184
290	ConAgra Foods, Inc.	26100
291	TRC Companies, Inc.	26000
292	Universal Corp.	26000
293	Visteon Corp.	26000
294	Monsanto Co.	26000
295	Aeropostale Inc	25766
296	PVH Corp	25700
297	Five Star Quality Care Inc	25600
298	Sally Beauty Holdings Inc	25525
299	Harris Teeter Supermarkets,	25300
300	Progressive Corp. (OH)	25007

The 100 Largest Companies by Total Assets in **Hoover's Handbook of American Business 2013**

Rank	Company	Total
1	Fannie Mae	$3,211,484,000
2	Federal Reserve System	$2,918,870,000
3	JPMorgan Chase & Co.	$2,265,792,000
4	Freddie Mac	$2,147,216,000
5	Bank of America Corp.	$2,129,046,000
6	Citigroup Inc	$1,873,878,000
7	Fed Reserve Bank Of NY	$1,630,098,000
8	Wells Fargo & Co.	$1,313,867,000
9	Goldman Sachs Group, Inc.	$923,225,000
10	MetLife Inc	$799,625,000
11	Morgan Stanley	$749,898,000
12	General Electric Co	$717,242,000
13	Prudential Financial, Inc.	$624,521,000
14	American International Grp	$555,773,000
15	Berkshire Hathaway Inc.	$392,647,000
16	Credit Suisse (USA) Inc	$372,187,000
17	Fed Reserve Bank of Richm	$342,753,000
18	U.S. Bancorp (DE)	$340,122,000
19	Exxon Mobil Corp.	$331,052,000
20	Bank of NY Mellon Corp	$325,266,000
21	Hartford Financial Services	$304,064,000
22	Fed Reserve Bank of San F	$293,061,000
23	PNC Fin Services Group	$271,205,000
24	AT&T Inc	$270,344,000
25	West End IN Bancshares	$240,801,918
26	Verizon Comm. Inc	$230,461,000
27	Teachers Ins. & Annuity	$225,932,000
28	Hartford Life Insurance Co	$222,537,000
29	State Street Corp.	$216,827,000
30	Fed Reserve Bank Of Atlan	$212,475,000
31	HSBC USA, Inc.	$210,280,000
32	Chevron Corporation	$209,474,000
33	Capital One Financial Corp	$206,019,000
34	Lincoln National Corp.	$202,906,000
35	Wal-Mart Stores, Inc.	$193,406,000
36	SLM Corp.	$193,345,000
37	NW Mutual Life Ins.	$189,645,000
38	Pfizer Inc	$188,002,000
39	Ally Financial Inc	$184,059,000
40	BlackRock, Inc.	$179,896,000
41	Ford Motor Co. (DE)	$178,348,000
42	Suntrust Banks, Inc.	$176,859,000
43	Apple Inc	$176,064,000
44	BB&T Corp.	$174,579,000
45	MetLife Ins. Co of CT	$171,771,000
46	Fed Reserve Bank Of Chica	$166,980,000
47	Comcast Corp	$157,818,000
48	American Express Co.	$153,337,000
49	ConocoPhillips	$153,230,000
50	Principal Financial Group, I	$148,298,000
51	General Motors Co.	$144,603,000
52	Ameriprise Financial Inc	$133,986,000
53	Procter & Gamble Co.	$132,244,000
54	Regions Financial Corp	$127,050,000
55	Allstate Corp.	$125,563,000
56	Microsoft Corporation	$121,271,000
57	Liberty Mutual Holding Co	$117,131,000
58	AFLAC Inc.	$117,102,000
59	Fifth Third Bancorp (Cincinn	$116,967,000
60	Pacific Mutual Holding Co	$116,811,000
61	Intl Bus Machines Corp.	$116,433,000
62	Genworth Financial Inc	$114,302,000
63	Johnson & Johnson	$113,644,000
64	Fed Home Loan Bank of SF	$113,552,000
65	Fed Reserve Bank of Dallas	$113,107,000
66	Annaly Capital Mgmt Inc.	$109,630,002
67	Hewlett-Packard Co	$108,768,000
68	Schwab (Charles) Corp.	$108,553,000
69	Fed Reserve Bank Of Bosto	$107,345,000
70	Fed Reserve Bank Of Phila	$106,541,000
71	RiverSource Life Ins. Co	$105,380,000
72	Merck & Co., Inc	$105,128,000
73	Travelers Co Inc (The)	$104,602,000
74	Ford Motor Credit Co LLC.	$100,242,000
75	Northern Trust Corp.	$100,223,700
76	Fed Home Loan Bank NY	$97,662,340
77	Mondelez International Inc	$93,837,000
78	Cisco Systems, Inc.	$91,759,000
79	Toyota Motor Credit Corp.	$88,913,000
80	KeyCorp	$88,785,000
81	Fed Reserve Bank of Cleve	$84,053,000
82	Caterpillar Inc.	$81,446,000
83	Santander Holdings USA Inc.	$80,565,199
84	Boeing Co.	$79,986,000
85	Coca-Cola Co (The)	$79,974,000
86	Oracle Corp.	$78,327,000
87	M & T Bank Corp	$77,924,287
88	Loews Corp.	$75,375,000
89	Disney (Walt) Co. (The)	$74,898,000
90	ING Life Insurance & Annuity	$74,628,900
91	Fed Reserve Bank of Kansas	$74,607,000
92	Pepsico Inc.	$72,882,000
93	Google Inc	$72,574,000
94	Intel Corp	$71,119,000
95	Dow Chemical Co.	$69,224,000
96	Burlington N. & Santa Fey	$68,987,000
97	Discover Financial Services	$68,783,937
98	International Finance Corp.	$68,490,000
99	UnitedHealth Group Inc	$67,889,000
100	Time Warner Inc	$67,801,000

If less than 5 years of data are available, growth is for the years available.

SOURCE: MERGENT INC., DATABASE, 2012

The Mergent 500 Largest US Corporations

Rank	Company	Sales ($ thous.)
1	Exxon Mobil Corp.	$486,429,000
2	Wal-Mart Stores, Inc.	$446,950,000
3	Chevron Corporation	$241,909,000
4	Phillips 66	$182,922,000
5	Apple Inc	$156,508,000
6	General Motors Co.	$152,256,000
7	General Electric Co	$147,359,000
8	Berkshire Hathaway Inc.	$143,688,000
9	Fannie Mae	$137,451,000
10	Ford Motor Co. (DE)	$134,252,000
11	AT&T Inc	$127,434,000
12	Valero Energy Corp.	$125,987,000
13	CVS Caremark Corporation	$123,133,000
14	McKesson Corp.	$122,734,000
15	Hewlett-Packard Co	$120,357,000
16	Verizon Comm Inc	$115,846,000
17	Bank of America Corp.	$115,074,000
18	JPMorgan Chase & Co.	$110,838,000
19	UnitedHealth Group Inc	$110,618,000
20	Cardinal Health, Inc.	$107,552,000
21	Intl Bus Machines Corp.	$104,507,000
22	Citigroup Inc	$102,587,000
23	Costco Wholesale Corp	$99,137,000
24	Express Scripts Holding Co	$93,858,100
25	Kroger Co.	$90,374,000
26	Archer Daniels Midland Co.	$89,038,000
27	Freddie Mac	$88,262,000
28	Federal Reserve System	$88,027,000
29	Wells Fargo & Co.	$87,597,000
30	Prudential Financial, Inc.	$84,815,000
31	Procter & Gamble Co.	$83,680,000
32	Boeing Co. (The)	$81,698,000
33	AmerisourceBergen Corp.	$79,489,596
34	Marathon Petroleum Corp.	$78,759,000
35	Philip Morris International Inc	$77,393,000
36	Microsoft Corporation	$73,723,000
37	Walgreen Co.	$71,633,000
38	Home Depot Inc	$70,395,000
39	MetLife Inc	$70,262,000
40	Target Corp	$69,865,000
41	INTL FCStone Inc.	$69,249,000
42	Pfizer Inc	$67,425,000
43	Johnson & Johnson	$67,224,000
44	Caterpillar Inc.	$65,875,000
45	Amer Intl Group Inc	$65,656,000
46	PepsiCo Inc.	$65,492,000
47	Comcast Corp	$62,570,000
48	Dell Inc	$62,071,000
49	ConocoPhillips	$62,004,000
50	WellPoint Inc	$61,711,700
51	Amazon.com Inc.	$61,093,000
52	United Technologies Corp.	$57,708,000
53	Dow Chemical Co.	$56,786,000
54	Intel Corp	$53,341,000
55	United Parcel Service Inc	$53,105,000
56	Best Buy Inc	$50,705,000
57	Lowe's Companies Inc	$50,208,000
58	Google Inc	$50,175,000
59	Merck & Co., Inc	$48,047,000
60	Coca-Cola Co (The)	$46,542,000
61	Lockheed Martin Corp.	$46,499,000
62	Cisco Systems, Inc.	$46,061,000
63	Enterprise Prod Partners L.P.	$44,313,000
64	Safeway Inc.	$44,206,500
65	FedEx Corp	$42,680,000
66	Sysco Corp.	$42,380,939
67	Disney (Walt) Co. (The)	$42,278,000
68	Johnson Controls Inc	$41,955,000
69	Sears Holdings Corp	$41,567,000
70	CHS Inc	$40,599,286
71	Abbott Laboratories	$39,873,910
72	Fed Reserve Bank of NY	$39,655,000
73	Humana Inc.	$39,126,000
74	Hess Corp	$37,871,000
75	Honeywell International, Inc.	$37,665,000
76	Oracle Corp.	$37,121,000
77	United Contl Holdings Inc	$37,110,000
78	Goldman Sachs Group, Inc.	$36,793,000
79	Delta Air Lines, Inc. (DE)	$36,670,000
80	Aetna Inc.	$36,595,900
81	Ingram Micro Inc.	$36,328,701
82	Deere & Co.	$36,157,100
83	SUPERVALU INC	$36,100,000
84	Du Pont de Nemours&Co	$35,310,000
85	Mondelez International Inc	$35,015,000
86	Lib Mutual Holding Co., Inc.	$34,671,000
87	World Fuel Services Corp.	$34,622,854
88	Plains All Amer Pipeline, L.P.	$34,275,000
89	American Express Co.	$33,808,000
90	News Corp	$33,706,000
91	Sprint Nextel Corp	$33,679,000
92	Allstate Corp.	$33,315,000
93	Tyson Foods, Inc.	$33,278,000
94	Tesoro Corporation	$32,974,000
95	Morgan Stanley	$32,036,000
96	General Dynamics Corp.	$31,513,000
97	3M Co	$29,904,000
98	DIRECTV	$29,740,000
99	HCA Holdings Inc	$29,682,000
100	Time Warner Inc	$28,729,000
101	Halliburton Company	$28,503,000
102	International Paper Co.	$27,833,000
103	Murphy Oil Corp	$27,745,549
104	Fluor Corp.	$27,577,135
105	McDonald's Corp	$27,567,000
106	Publix Super Markets, Inc.	$27,178,764
107	Tech Data Corp.	$26,488,124
108	Macys Inc	$26,405,000
109	Rite Aid Corp.	$26,121,222
110	Travelers Cos Inc (The)	$25,740,000
111	Avnet Inc	$25,707,522
112	Northrop Grumman Corp	$25,218,000
113	Teachers Ins & Ann Assn.	$25,120,000
114	Staples Inc	$25,022,192
115	AMR Corp. (DE)	$24,855,000
116	Raytheon Co.	$24,414,000
117	Emerson Electric Co.	$24,412,000
118	Occidental Petroleum Corp	$24,253,000
119	NIKE, Inc	$24,128,000
120	Altria Group Inc	$23,800,000
121	Alcoa, Inc.	$23,700,000
122	NW Mutual Life Ins Co.	$23,595,000
123	Exelon Corp.	$23,489,000
124	TJX Companies, Inc.	$23,191,455
125	Lilly (Eli) & Co.	$22,603,400
126	Xerox Corp	$22,390,000
127	U.S. Bancorp (DE)	$22,202,000
128	AFLAC Inc.	$22,171,000
129	Cigna Corp	$21,998,000
130	Hartford Fin Svcs Group Inc.	$21,859,000
131	Time Warner Cable Inc	$21,386,000
132	Baker Hughes Inc.	$21,361,000
133	Kimberly-Clark Corp.	$21,063,000
134	Goodyear Tire & Rubber Co.	$20,992,000
135	Union Pacific Corp	$20,926,000
136	ManpowerGroup	$20,678,000
137	Arrow Electronics, Inc.	$20,405,128
138	National Oilwell Varco Inc	$20,041,000
139	Nucor Corp.	$20,023,564
140	EMC Corp. (MA)	$20,007,588
141	United States Steel Corp.	$19,328,000
142	Burlington N & Santa Fe Rail	$19,229,000
143	Qualcomm, Inc.	$19,121,000
144	Kohl's Corp.	$18,804,000
145	Kraft Foods Group Inc	$18,655,000
146	Capital One Financial Corp	$18,525,000
147	Danaher Corp.	$18,260,400
148	Whirlpool Corp	$18,143,000
149	Freeport-McMoRan Co&Go	$18,010,000
150	Illinois Tool Works, Inc.	$17,924,000
151	Southern Company (The)	$17,657,000
152	Bristol-Myers Squibb Co.	$17,621,000
153	AbbVie Inc.	$17,443,951
154	Cummins, Inc.	$17,334,000
155	AES Corp.	$17,274,000
156	Penney (J.C.) Co.,Inc.	$17,260,000
157	Jabil Circuit, Inc.	$17,151,941
158	Southwest Airlines Co	$17,088,000
159	Colgate-Palmolive Co.	$17,085,000
160	Progressive Corp. (OH)	$17,083,900
161	Apache Corp.	$16,888,000
162	General Mills, Inc.	$16,657,900
163	PACCAR Inc.	$16,355,200
164	Marathon Oil Corp.	$16,221,000
165	Medtronic, Inc.	$16,184,000
166	Eaton Corp plc	$16,049,000
167	Computer Sciences Corp.	$15,877,000
168	PNC Fin Svcs Group (The)	$15,820,000
169	Bank of NY Mellon Corp	$15,804,000
170	AutoNation, Inc.	$15,668,800
171	Amgen Inc	$15,582,000
172	HollyFrontier Corp.	$15,439,528
173	CenturyLink, Inc.	$15,351,000
174	NextEra Energy Inc	$15,341,000
175	FirstEnergy Corp.	$15,303,000
176	PPG Industries, Inc.	$15,200,000
177	L-3 Comm Hldngs, Inc.	$15,169,000
178	PG&E Corp. (Holding Co.)	$15,040,000
179	Amer Electric Power Co, Inc.	$14,945,000
180	Global Partners LP	$14,835,729

SOURCE: MERGENT, 2012

The **Mergent** 500 Largest US Corporations (continued)

Rank	Company	Sales ($ thou)
181	Dollar General Corp	$14,807,188
182	Lear Corp.	$14,567,000
183	Loews Corp.	$14,552,000
184	The Gap, Inc.	$14,549,000
185	Duke Energy Corp	$14,529,000
186	Dominion Resources Inc	$14,379,000
187	Dish Network Corp	$14,266,492
188	Omnicom Group, Inc.	$14,219,400
189	Kellogg Co	$14,197,000
190	Baxter International Inc.	$14,190,000
191	CBS Corp	$14,089,000
192	eBay Inc.	$14,072,000
193	Viacom Inc	$13,887,000
194	US Airways Group Inc	$13,831,000
195	Waste Mgmt, Inc. (DE)	$13,649,000
196	Yum! Brands, Inc.	$13,633,000
197	Comm Health Systems, Inc.	$13,626,168
198	Chubb Corp.	$13,585,000
199	Monsanto Co.	$13,504,000
200	Anadarko Petroleum Corp	$13,411,000
201	Ally Financial Inc	$13,332,000
202	Starbucks Corp.	$13,299,500
203	ConAgra Foods, Inc.	$13,262,600
204	Parker Hannifin Corp.	$13,145,942
205	Smithfield Foods, Inc.	$13,094,300
206	Dean Foods Co.	$13,055,493
207	Genuine Parts Co.	$13,013,868
208	Navistar International Corp.	$12,948,000
209	West End IN Bancshares Inc.	$12,887,027
210	Texas Instruments Inc.	$12,825,000
211	PPL Corp	$12,737,000
212	Oneok Inc.	$12,632,559
213	Western Digital Corp.	$12,478,000
214	Textron Inc.	$12,237,000
215	Consolidated Edison, Inc.	$12,188,000
216	Coventry Health Care Inc.	$12,186,683
217	Health Net, Inc.	$11,901,036
218	Edison International	$11,862,000
219	Icahn Enterprises L P	$11,855,000
220	Ecolab, Inc.	$11,838,700
221	Marriott International, Inc.	$11,814,000
222	CSX Corp.	$11,756,000
223	Thermo Fisher Scientific Inc	$11,725,900
224	Whole Foods Market, Inc.	$11,698,828
225	EOG Resources, Inc.	$11,682,636
226	Heinz (H.J.) Co.	$11,649,079
227	Chesapeake Energy Corp.	$11,635,000
228	Penske Automotive Group Inc	$11,556,232
229	Marsh & McLennan Cos Inc.	$11,526,000
230	Aon Plc	$11,514,000
231	ONEOK Partners LP	$11,322,607
232	Avon Products, Inc.	$11,291,600
233	Praxair, Inc.	$11,252,000
234	Entergy Corp.	$11,229,073
235	Tennessee Valley Authority	$11,220,000
236	Huntsman Corp	$11,187,000
237	Mosaic Co (The)	$11,107,800
238	Norfolk Southern Corp.	$11,040,000
239	Sunoco Log Partners L.P.	$10,918,000

Rank	Company	Sales ($thous)
240	Jacobs Eng. Group, Inc.	$10,893,778
241	Nordstrom, Inc.	$10,877,000
242	Office Depot, Inc.	$10,695,652
243	Aut Data Processing Inc.	$10,665,200
244	Lincoln National Corp.	$10,636,000
245	Florida Power & Light Co.	$10,613,000
246	Donnelley (R.R.) & Sons Co.	$10,611,000
247	SAIC Inc	$10,587,000
248	Science App Intl Corp.	$10,587,000
249	Southern CA Edison Co.	$10,577,000
250	Unum Group	$10,515,400
251	Cons Edison Co. of NY, Inc.	$10,484,000
252	Visa Inc	$10,421,000
253	Limited Brands Inc.	$10,364,000
254	Genworth Financial Inc	$10,344,000
255	Robinson (C.H.) Worldwide,	$10,336,346
256	Exelon Generation Co LLC	$10,308,000
257	Synnex Corp	$10,285,507
258	Ameriprise Financial Inc	$10,192,000
259	Stanley Black & Decker, Inc.	$10,190,500
260	Xcel Energy, Inc.	$10,128,223
261	State Street Corp.	$10,125,000
262	Fed Reserve Bank of Rich,	$10,043,000
263	Sempra Energy	$10,036,000
264	Carmax Inc.	$10,003,599
265	BB&T Corp.	$9,998,000
266	Newmont Mining Corp.	$9,868,000
267	Pub Svc Enterprise Group Inc.	$9,781,000
268	Lauder (Estee) Cos., Inc.	$9,713,600
269	Liberty Interactive Corp	$9,616,000
270	Air Products & Chemicals, Inc.	$9,611,700
271	SunTrust Banks, Inc.	$9,602,000
272	GameStop Corp	$9,550,500
273	URS Corp	$9,545,000
274	Liberty Global Inc	$9,510,800
275	Devon Energy Corp.	$9,502,000
276	Bed, Bath & Beyond, Inc.	$9,499,890
277	VF Corp.	$9,459,232
278	Las Vegas Sands Corp	$9,410,745
279	Family Dollar Stores, Inc.	$9,331,005
280	KBR Inc	$9,261,000
281	Principal Financial Group, Inc.	$9,215,100
282	Rock-Tenn Co.	$9,207,600
283	Leucadia National Corp.	$9,193,689
284	Tenet Healthcare Corp.	$9,119,000
285	BlackRock, Inc.	$9,081,000
286	NRG Energy Inc	$9,079,000
287	Western Refining Inc	$9,071,037
288	Discover Financial Services	$8,984,000
289	CNA Financial Corp.	$8,947,000
290	Schein (Henry), Inc.	$8,939,967
291	Fed Res Bank of San Fran	$8,863,000
292	Caesars Entertainment Corp	$8,834,500
293	Reinsurance Grp of Amer, Inc.	$8,829,538
294	Georgia Power Co.	$8,800,000
295	DTE Energy Co.	$8,791,000
296	AGCO Corp.	$8,773,200
297	Sherwin-Williams Co.	$8,765,699
298	Ball Corp	$8,735,700

Rank	Company	Sales ($ thous)
299	Applied Materials, Inc.	$8,719,000
300	Motorola Solutions Inc.	$8,698,000
301	Crown Holdings Inc	$8,644,000
302	Owens & Minor, Inc.	$8,627,912
303	Ross Stores, Inc.	$8,608,291
304	AutoZone, Inc.	$8,603,863
305	MetLife Insurance Co of CT	$8,529,000
306	Assurant Inc	$8,508,270
307	Cameron International Corp	$8,502,100
308	CenterPoint Energy, Inc	$8,450,000
309	Gilead Sciences, Inc.	$8,385,385
310	Stryker Corp.	$8,307,000
311	Reynolds American Inc	$8,304,000
312	Hertz Global Holdings Inc	$8,298,380
313	Kinder Morgan Inc.	$8,264,900
314	Pantry Inc. (The)	$8,253,243
315	Energy Transfer Equity L P	$8,240,703
316	Micron Technology Inc.	$8,234,000
317	Autoliv Inc.	$8,232,400
318	Hormel Foods Corp.	$8,230,670
319	Aecom Technology Corp (DE)	$8,218,180
320	Kinder Morgan Energy Prtnrs	$8,211,200
321	Ashland Inc	$8,206,000
322	Oshkosh Corp	$8,180,900
323	Toyota Motor Credit Corp.	$8,146,000
324	Reliance Steel & Aluminum Co.	$8,134,700
325	Republic Services, Inc.	$8,118,300
326	Core Mark Holding Co Inc	$8,114,900
327	Dover Corp	$8,104,339
328	Grainger (W.W.) Inc.	$8,078,185
329	Peabody Energy Corp	$8,077,500
330	Coca-Cola Enterprises Inc	$8,062,000
331	Visteon Corp.	$8,047,000
332	Corning, Inc.	$8,012,000
333	Broadcom Corp.	$8,006,000
334	Darden Restaurants, Inc.	$7,998,700
335	Steel Dynamics Inc.	$7,997,500
336	Spectrum Group Intl Inc	$7,974,830
337	Williams Cos Inc (The)	$7,930,000
338	TravelCenters of America LLC	$7,888,857
339	Sonic Automotive, Inc.	$7,871,274
340	MGM Resorts International	$7,849,312
341	Commercial Metals Co.	$7,828,440
342	Masco Corp.	$7,745,000
343	Becton, Dickinson and Co.	$7,708,382
344	Campbell Soup Co.	$7,707,000
345	Dana Holding Corp	$7,592,000
346	Pilgrims Pride Corp.	$7,535,698
347	Ameren Corp.	$7,531,000
348	Quest Diagnostics, Inc.	$7,510,490
349	Universal Health Services, Inc.	$7,500,198
350	WellCare Health Plans Inc	$7,409,032
351	MasterCard Inc	$7,391,000
352	Avis Budget Group Inc	$7,357,000
353	Santander Holdings USA Inc.	$7,249,685
354	Boston Scientific Corp.	$7,249,000
355	Virginia Electric & Power Co.	$7,246,000
356	Dole Food Co., Inc.	$7,223,836
357	Fed Res Bank of Atlanta,	$7,222,000

The Mergent 500 Largest US Corporations (continued)

Rank	Company	Sales ($ thous)
358	Precision Castparts Corp.	$7,214,600
359	Tenneco Inc	$7,205,000
360	Charter Communications Inc	$7,204,000
361	Delek US Holdings Inc	$7,198,200
362	Alon USA Energy Inc	$7,186,257
363	Borg Warner Inc	$7,183,200
364	Eastman Chemical Co.	$7,178,000
365	Barnes & Noble Inc	$7,129,199
366	Alpha Natural Resources Inc	$7,109,186
367	Fifth Third Bancorp	$7,106,000
368	Franklin Resources, Inc.	$7,101,000
369	Weyerhaeuser Co.	$7,059,000
370	Energy Future Holdings Corp	$7,040,000
371	Owens-Illinois, Inc.	$7,000,000
372	Targa Resources Corp	$6,994,500
373	Casey's General Stores, Inc.	$6,987,804
374	Targa Resources Partners LP	$6,987,100
375	DaVita HealthCare Partners Inc	$6,982,214
376	Interpublic Grp of Comps Inc.	$6,956,200
377	OfficeMax Inc (DE)	$6,920,384
378	Federal-Mogul Corp.	$6,910,000
379	Ralph Lauren Corp	$6,859,500
380	Agilent Technologies, Inc.	$6,858,000
381	Energy Transfer Partners L P	$6,850,440
382	Southern Copper Corp	$6,818,721
383	Credit Suisse (USA) Inc	$6,738,000
384	Symantec Corp.	$6,730,000
385	Williams Partners L.P.	$6,729,000
386	NII Holdings Inc.	$6,719,344
387	Enbridge Energy Partners, L.P.	$6,706,100
388	Cablevision Systems Corp.	$6,700,848
389	Jarden Corp.	$6,679,900
390	Hershey Company (The)	$6,644,252
391	Qwest Corp	$6,635,000
392	Dollar Tree, Inc.	$6,630,500
393	Lorillard, Inc.	$6,623,000
394	Virgin Media Inc	$6,609,459
395	Hartford Life Insurance Co	$6,603,000
396	NuStar Energy L.P.	$6,575,255
397	Huntington Ingalls Industries,	$6,575,000
398	UGI Corp.	$6,519,200
399	Terex Corp.	$6,504,600
400	AK Steel Holding Corp.	$6,468,000
401	PPL Energy Supply, LLC	$6,429,000
402	Celanese Corp (DE)	$6,418,000
403	Dillard's Inc.	$6,399,765
404	Starwood Htls & Res WW Inc	$6,321,000
405	Mattel Inc	$6,266,037
406	Rockwell Automation, Inc.	$6,259,400
407	Ryder System, Inc.	$6,256,967
408	Consumers Energy Co.	$6,253,000
409	CMS Energy Corp	$6,253,000
410	McGraw-Hill Cos., Inc. (The)	$6,246,000
411	Netapp, Inc.	$6,233,200
412	Ingredion Inc	$6,219,000
413	Advance Auto Parts Inc	$6,170,462
414	CC Media Holdings Inc	$6,161,352
415	Omnicare Inc.	$6,160,388
416	Windstream Corp	$6,156,300
417	FMC Technologies, Inc.	$6,151,400
418	Expeditors Intl of Wash, Inc.	$6,150,498
419	Anixter International Inc	$6,146,900
420	PSEG Power LLC	$6,143,000
421	Mylan Inc	$6,129,825
422	Wesco International, Inc.	$6,125,718
423	Cognizant Techn Sols Corp.	$6,121,156
424	PETsMART, Inc.	$6,113,304
425	SLM Corp.	$6,110,000
426	CenterPoint Energy Res Corp.	$6,102,000
427	CF Industries Holdings Inc	$6,097,900
428	Sanmina Corp	$6,093,334
429	Group 1 Automotive, Inc.	$6,079,765
430	Avery Dennison Corp.	$6,026,300
431	Eastman Kodak Co.	$6,022,000
432	Regions Financial Corp	$6,003,000
433	Dr Pepper Snapple Group Inc	$5,995,000
434	Mutual of Omaha Ins Co. (NE)	$5,974,057
435	Vanguard Health Systems, Inc.	$5,949,000
436	Pepco Holdings Inc.	$5,920,000
437	CBRE Group Inc	$5,905,411
438	PVH Corp	$5,890,624
439	Cliffs Natural Resources, Inc.	$5,872,700
440	General Cable Corp. (DE)	$5,866,700
441	Newell Rubbermaid, Inc.	$5,864,600
442	Pacific Mutual Holding Co.	$5,862,000
443	Booz Allen Ham Hldng Corp.	$5,859,218
444	Exelis Inc.	$5,839,000
445	Fidelity Natl Info Services Inc	$5,807,600
446	Allergan, Inc	$5,806,100
447	Health Mgmt Associates, Inc.	$5,804,451
448	O'Reilly Automotive, Inc.	$5,788,816
449	Seaboard Corp.	$5,746,902
450	Alabama Power Co.	$5,702,000
451	HSBC USA, Inc.	$5,695,000
452	Lab Corp. of Amer Hldngs	$5,671,400
453	Western Union Co.	$5,664,800
454	Joy Global Inc	$5,660,889
455	Mohawk Industries, Inc.	$5,642,258
456	Sealed Air Corp.	$5,640,900
457	Foot Locker, Inc.	$5,623,000
458	EMCOR Group, Inc.	$5,613,459
459	Domtar Corp	$5,612,000
460	Fed Res Bank of Chicago,	$5,586,000
461	Harley-Davidson Inc	$5,580,506
462	Kelly Services, Inc.	$5,551,000
463	Smucker (J.M.) Co.	$5,525,782
464	Kindred Healthcare Inc	$5,521,763
465	Biogen Idec Inc	$5,516,461
466	Celgene Corp.	$5,506,713
467	St. Jude Medical, Inc.	$5,503,000
468	Calpine Corp	$5,478,000
469	Clorox Co.	$5,468,000
470	MeadWestvaco Corp.	$5,459,000
471	Harris Corp.	$5,451,300
472	NCR Corp.	$5,443,000
473	Ohio Power Company	$5,431,111
474	CONSOL Energy Inc	$5,430,307
475	Advanced Micro Devices, Inc.	$5,422,000
476	Live Nation Entertainment, Inc.	$5,383,998
477	Graybar Electric Co., Inc.	$5,374,800
478	Tele & Data Systems, Inc.	$5,345,277
479	Centene Corp	$5,340,582
480	Owens Corning	$5,335,000
481	Bemis Co Inc	$5,322,670
482	Con-Way Inc	$5,289,953
483	Insight Enterprises Inc.	$5,287,228
484	Host Hotels & Resorts Inc	$5,286,000
485	Wynn Resorts Ltd	$5,269,792
486	Frontier Communications Corp	$5,243,043
487	Gannett Co Inc	$5,239,989
488	United Natural Foods Inc.	$5,236,021
489	Dick's Sporting Goods, Inc	$5,211,802
490	Momentive Spec Chems Inc	$5,207,000
491	Big Lots, Inc.	$5,202,269
492	Susser Holdings Corp	$5,194,168
493	Allegheny Technologies, Inc	$5,183,000
494	Berkley (W. R.) Corp.	$5,155,984
495	Detroit Edison Co.	$5,152,000
496	SPX Corp.	$5,100,200
497	Facebook, Inc.	$5,089,000
498	Spectra Energy Corp	$5,075,000
499	NiSource Inc. (Holding Co.)	$5,061,200
500	SanDisk Corp.	$5,052,509

Hoover's Handbook of

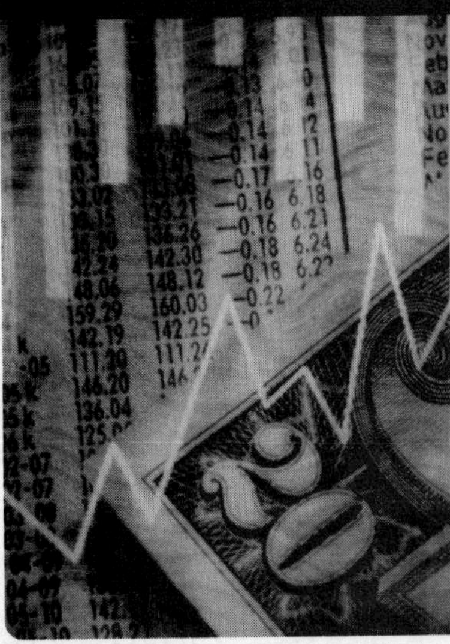

American Business

The Companies

1st Source Corp.

Need a bank? Don't give it a 2nd thought. Contact 1st Source Corporation parent of 1st Source Bank which provides commercial and consumer banking services through more than 75 branches in northern Indiana and southwestern Michigan. The bank offers deposit accounts; business agricultural and consumer loans; residential and commercial mortgages; credit cards; and trust services. Its specialty finance group provides financing for aircraft automobile fleets trucks and construction and environmental equipment through about two-dozen offices nationwide; such loans account for nearly half of 1st Source's portfolio.

The company offers mutual funds through an agreement with Wasatch Advisors which acquired its 1st Source Monogram family of funds (now the Wasatch - 1st Source Funds) in 2008. Bank subsidiary 1st Source Insurance sells corporate and personal property/casualty coverage and group and individual life and health insurance.

1st Source has expanded its aircraft leasing business which accounts for the largest portion of its specialty finance activities into Brazil and Mexico and may be looking to expand into other selected markets in South America. The bank however has seen a rise in repossessions amid the sputtering economy. Nonetheless the company was able to grow its earnings in 2011 thanks in part to improved interest rate margins and fewer loan losses in other parts of its loan portfolio.

EXECUTIVES

President and COO Specialty Finance Group 1st Source Bank, Allen R. Qualey, age 59, $220,000 total compensation

Vice Chairman, Wellington D. (Duke) Jones III, age 67, $388,385 total compensation

SVP CFO and Treasurer 1st Source Corporation and 1st Source Bank, Larry E. Lentych, age 65, $238,846 total compensation

Chairman President and CEO; Chairman and CEO 1st Source Bank, Christopher J. (Chris) Murphy III, age 65, $684,554 total compensation

SVP Funds Management Division 1st Source Bank, James S. Jackson

EVP 1st Source Bank, Steven J. Wessell

EVP Secretary and General Counsel 1st Source Corporation and 1st Source Bank, John B. Griffith, age 54, $292,471 total compensation

SVP Marketing Division 1st Source Bank, Melissa A. Collins

President 1st Source Bank, James R. Seitz

SVP Human Resources Division 1st Source Bank, Tina H. Perkins

SVP Operations Group 1st Source Bank, Donald E. Miller

SVP Business Banking Group 1st Source Bank, Joseph T. Kuzmitz

SVP and Chief Credit Officer 1st Source Bank, Jeffrey L. Buhr

Vice Chairman, Wellington D. (Duke) Jones III, age 67

Director, Daniel B. Fitzpatrick, age 54

Director, Craig A. Kapson, age 61

Director, Rex Martin, age 60

Director, William P. Johnson, age 69

Director, Lawrence E. Hiler, age 66

Director, Timothy K. Ozark, age 62

Director, John T. Phair, age 62

Director, Mark D. Schwabero, age 59

Director, Allison Nickle Egidi

Director, Najeeb A. Khan

Director, Christopher J. Murphy IV

Auditors: Ernst&YoungLLP

LOCATIONS

HQ: 1st Source Corporation
100 N. Michigan St., South Bend IN 46601
Phone: 574-235-2000 **Fax:** 574-235-2882
Web: www.1stsource.com

PRODUCTS/OPERATIONS

2011 Sales

	$ mil.	% of total
Interest		
Loans & leases	164	61
Investment securities	22	8
Other	1	-
Noninterest		
Equipment rental	23	9
Service charges on deposit accounts	18	7
Trust fees	16	6
Insurance commissions	4	2
Mortgage banking	3	2
Other	14	5
Total	**268**	**100**

Select Subsidiaries

1st Source Bank
- 1st Source Commercial Aircraft Leasing
- 1st Source Corporation Investment Advisors Inc.
- 1st Source Insurance Inc.
- 1st Source Specialty Finance Inc.
- Michigan Transportation Finance Corporation
- SFG Aircraft Inc.
- SFG Equipment Leasing Corporation I

1st Source Funding LLC
1st Source Intermediate Holding LLC
1st Source Leasing Inc.
1st Source Master Trust

COMPETITORS

Bank of America
Fifth Third
Huntington Bancshares
JPMorgan Chase
KeyCorp
MainSource Financial
Old National Bancorp
PNC Financial
U.S. Bancorp
Wells Fargo

HISTORICAL FINANCIALS

Company Type: Public

Income Statement FYE: December 31

	ASSETS ($ mil.)	NET INCOME ($ mil.)	INCOME AS % OF ASSETS	EMPLOYEES
12/11	4,374	48	1.1%	1,160
12/10	4,445	41	0.9%	1,160
12/09	4,542	25	0.6%	1,170
12/08	4,464	33	0.7%	1,280
12/07	4,447	30	0.7%	1,350
Annual Growth	(0.4%)	12.1%	—	(3.7%)

2011 Year-End Financials

Debt ratio: 2.90%
Return on equity: 9.20%
Cash ($ mil.): 114
Current ratio: —
Long-term debt ($ mil.): 126
No. of shares (mil.): 24
Dividends
Yield: —
Payout: 32.65%
Market value ($ mil.): 613

	STOCK PRICE ($) FY Close	P/E High/Low		PER SHARE ($) Earnings	Dividends	Book Value
12/11	25.33	13	9	1.96	0.00	21.64
12/10	20.24	17	12	1.21	0.61	20.12
12/09	16.09	30	18	0.79	0.59	23.65
12/08	23.63	20	11	1.37	0.58	18.62
12/07	17.31	25	13	1.28	0.56	17.66
Annual Growth	10.0%	—	—	11.2%	—	5.2%

3M Co

Loath to be stuck on one thing 3M makes everything from tape to high-tech security gear. The diversified company makes products through six operating segments: Consumer and Office; Display and Graphics; Electro and Communications; Health Care (through 3M Health Care); Industrial and Transportation; and Safety Security and Protection Services. Well-known brands include Post-it notes Scotch tapes Scotchgard fabric protectors Scotch-Brite scouring pads and Filtrete home air filters. 3M has operations in more than 65 countries. About two-thirds of its sales are made outside the US. It sells products directly to users and through numerous wholesalers retailers distributors and dealers worldwide.

HISTORY

Five businessmen in Two Harbors Minnesota founded Minnesota Mining and Manufacturing (3M) in 1902 to sell corundum to grinding-wheel manufacturers. The company soon needed to raise working capital. Co-founder John Dwan offered his friend Edgar Ober 60% of 3M's stock. Ober persuaded Lucius Ordway VP of a plumbing business to help underwrite 3M. In 1905 the two took over the company and moved it to Duluth.

In 1907 future CEO William McKnight joined 3M as a bookkeeper. Three years later the plant moved to St. Paul. The board of directors declared a dividend to shareholders in the last quarter of 1916 and 3M hasn't missed a dividend since. The next two products 3M developed –Scotch-brand masking tape (1925) and Scotch-brand cellophane tape (1930) –assured its future.

McKnight introduced one of the first employee pension plans in 1931 and in the late 1940s he implemented a vertical management structure. 3M introduced the first commercially viable magnetic recording tape in 1947.

In 1950 after a decade of work and $1 million in development costs 3M employee Carl Miller completed the Thermo-Fax copying machine which was the foundation of 3M's duplicating division.

Products in the 1960s included 3M's dry-silver microfilm photographic products carbonless papers overhead projection systems and medical and dental products. The company moved into pharmaceuticals radiology energy control and office markets in the 1970s and 1980s.

A 3M scientist developed Post-it Notes (1980) because he wanted to attach page markers to his church hymnal. Recalling that a colleague had developed an adhesive that wasn't very sticky he brushed some on paper and began a product line that now generates hundreds of millions of dollars each year.

In 1990 the company bought sponge maker O-Cel-O. But not all of its inventions have brought 3M good news. In 1995 along with fellow silicone breast-implant makers Baxter International and Bristol-Myers Squibb it agreed to settle thousands of personal-injury claims related to implants. The companies paid an average of $26000 per claim.

3M spun off its low-profit imaging and data-storage businesses in 1996 as Imation Corp. and closed its audiotape and videotape businesses. The next year 3M sold its National Advertising billboard business to Infinity Outdoor for $1 billion and its Media Network unit (a printer of advertising inserts) to Time Warner.

The company created the 3M Nexcare brand for its line of first-aid and home health products in 1998. To regain earnings growth 3M closed about 10% of its plants in the US and abroad; it also discontinued unprofitable product lines. The next year 3M sold its heart-surgery-equipment health care unit to Japan's Terumo and its Eastern Heights Bank subsidiary to Norwest Bank of Minnesota. It also bought out Hoechst AG's 46% stake in Dyneon LLC a fluorine elastomer joint venture between the two companies.

3M bought Polaroid's Technical Polarizer and Display Films business and a controlling stake in Germany-based Quante AG (telecom systems) in 2000. In addition the company decided to halt the manufacture of many of its Scotchgard-brand repellent products due to research revealing that one of the compounds (perfluorooctane sulfonate) used in the manufacturing process is "persistent and pervasive" in the environment and in people's bloodstreams. As 2000 drew to a close 3M named GE executive James McNerney to succeed L. D. DeSimone as its chairman and CEO. With the sale of Eastern Heights and several health care businesses (including its cardiovascular systems unit) 3M was rewarded with its second-best financial performance in 14 years.

3M then bought Robinson Nugent (electronic connectors) and MicroTouch Systems (touch screens) in 2001. It also announced plans to cut 6000 jobs and authorized a stock buy-back program of up to $2.5 billion.

The company changed its legal name from Minnesota Mining and Manufacturing Company to 3M Company that year. Also in 2002 3M restructured its business segments around end uses rather than products or raw materials. So the Health Care segment encompassed everything from transdermal skin patches to software for hospital coding and classification. Similarly the Consumer and Office Business unit became responsible for Post-its O-Cel-O sponges wood-finishing materials and air conditioner filters. By the end of that year the company had cut more than 8500 jobs 11% of its total workforce.

Nevertheless a strong year in 2003 emboldened the company to look to expand. 3M closed a deal to buy fellow Minnesota resident HighJump Software a maker of supply chain software for businesses in February 2004. CEO McNerney left 3M in 2005 to join Boeing in the same capacity and was replaced by George Buckley formerly of the Brunswick Corporation.

That year the company made a billion-dollar acquisition of liquid filtration producer CUNO. 3M's own filtration products business –primarily air filters –amounted to more than $1 billion in annual sales before the deal and the deal added nearly half that. (3M eventually changed CUNO's name to 3M Purification.)

The company signaled a new strategic direction in 2006 when it broke up its pharmaceutical unit along geographic lines and sold it in pieces. In total 3M got $2.1 billion for the sale of its pharmaceutical operations. The next year it sold HighJump Software. High-tech venture capital firm Battery Ventures bought HighJump to set it up as a stand-alone company.

The company then ran through another string of acquisitions in 2007 buying companies such as Unifam Lingualcare Innovative Paper Technologies and Diamond Productions.

Its 2008 acquisition of protection products maker Aearo Technologies helped 3M's sales growth in the area of safety security and protection services. It added to the unit with the purchase (through its 3M Canada subsidiary) of Toronto-based MTI PolyFab which makes thermal and acoustic insulation for aerospace products. 3M also capitalized on its purchase of Beiersdorf subsidiary Futuro which makes medical products such as wraps elastic bandages and compression hosiery.

3M made two moves into the high-tech security field in 2010. The company acquired Cogent Inc. for $943 million. Known as Cogent Systems the firm provides finger palm face and iris biometric systems for governments law enforcement agencies and commercial enterprises. 3M also acquired Attenti Ltd. an Israeli manufacturer of people-tracking technology for $230 million. Attenti makes remote monitoring devices to track people awaiting trial or on probation as well as for elder-care facilities to monitor patient safety.

The company expanded its consumer and office business line in 2010 by acquiring a majority stake in Japanese company A-One the top office label brand in Asia and the second-largest label business worldwide. It also acquired Alpha Beta Enterprise a manufacturer of box sealing tape and masking tape headquartered in Taiwan. Both acquisitions will expand 3M's presence in the global packaging market.

Also in 2010 3M acquired J.R. Phoenix Ltd. a manufacturer of hand hygiene and skin care products for health care and professional use. The majority of J.R. Phoenix products are sold under the Laura Line brand in Canada. The deal expanded 3M's line of hand hygiene skin care products to the healthcare market in Canada. The company also acquired UK-based Dailys Ltd. a global supplier of non-woven disposable chemical protective coveralls for industrial use.

The company made several acquisitions in 2010 including Minnesota-based Arizant which manufactures forced-air warming garments designed to prevent hypothermia in surgical settings a growing international market estimated at some $1 billion per year.

EXECUTIVES

Chairman, George W. Buckley, age 65, $1,720,000 total compensation
SVP Legal Affairs and General Counsel, Marschall I. Smith, age 68
VP and CIO, Ernest (Ernie) Park, age 58
EVP Research and Development and CTO, Frederick J. Palensky, age 62, $481,000 total compensation
President CEO and Director, Inge G. Thulin, age 59, $594,000 total compensation
Deputy General Counsel and Secretary, Gregg M. Larson
SVP Corporate Supply Chain Operations, John K. Woodworth, age 61
EVP Electro and Communications Business, Joaquin Delgado, age 52
VP Latin America, Rosa M. Miller
EVP International Operations, Hak Cheol (H. C.) Shin, age 55
EVP Health Care Business, Brad T. Sauer, age 53, $572,400 total compensation
SVP Asia/Pacific, Jay V. Ihlenfeld, age 61
EVP Consumer and Office Business, Joseph E. (Joe) Harlan, age 53, $532,950 total compensation
Assistant Secretary, Steven J. Beilke
SVP Marketing and Sales, Ian F. Hardgrove, age 61
VP Europe Middle East and Africa, Paul D. Rosso
SVP Strategy and Corporate Development, Roger H. D. Lacey, age 62
SVP West Europe, Patrick Deconinck
EVP Display and Graphics Business, Michael A. Kelly, age 55
EVP Safety Security and Protection Services Business, Julie L. Bushman
SVP Human Resources, Angela S. Lalor, age 47
SVP Finance and CFO, David W. Meline, age 54
General Auditor, David G. Werpy
Assistant Secretary, Robert W. Sprague
EVP Industrial and Transportation Business, Christopher D. (Chris) Holmes, age 53
Assistant Secretary, Michael M. Dai
Public Relations, Connie Thompson
VP 3M Middle East and Africa, Irfan Malik
VP Corporate Controller and Chief Accounting Officer, Nicholas C. Gangestad, age 47
EVP Consumer and Office Business, Michael G. Vale, age 46
VP and Treasurer, Scott D. Krohn, age 41
SVP Human Resources, Marlene M. McGrath, age 50
Senior Vice President - Legal Affairs; General Counsel, Ivan Fong
Director, Robert J. (Bob) Ulrich, age 68
Director, W. James (Jim) Farrell, age 69
Director, Herbert L. (Herb) Henkel, age 64
Director, Vance D. Coffman, age 67
Director, Edward M. Liddy, age 66
Director, Michael L. (Mike) Eskew, age 62
Director, Linda G. Alvarado, age 60
Director, Aulana L. Peters, age 70
President CEO and Director, Inge G. Thulin, age 59
Director, Robert S. (Bob) Morrison, age 69
Auditors: PricewaterhouseCoopersLLP

LOCATIONS

HQ: 3M Company
3M Center, St. Paul MN 55144-1000
Phone: 651-733-1110 **Fax:** 651-733-9973
Web: www.mmm.com

2011 Sales

	$ mil.	% of total
US	10,028	34
Europe Africa & Middle East	7,076	24
Adjustments	(12)	-

PRODUCTS/OPERATIONS

2011 Sales

	$ mil.	% of total
Industrial & Transportation	10,073	34
Consumer & Office	4,153	14
Display & Graphics	3,674	12
Corporate	11	-
Adjustments	(458)	-

Selected Segments and Products

Industrial and Transportation
- Automotive aftermarket products
- Automotive products
- Closures for disposable diapers
- Coated and nonwoven abrasives
- Films
- Filtration products
- Specialty adhesives
- Tapes

Health Care
- Dental products
- Drug delivery systems
- Health information systems
- Infection prevention
- Medical and surgical supplies
- Microbiology products
- Skin health products

Safety Security and Protection
- Commercial cleaning products
- Consumer safety products
- Corrosion protection products
- Floor matting
- Occupational health and safety products
- Safety and security products
- Track and trace products

Consumer and Office
- Carpet and fabric protectors

- Commercial cleaning products
- Fabric protectors (Scotchgard)
- High-performance cloth (Scotch-Brite)
- Home-improvement products
- Repositionable notes (Post-it)
- Scour pads (Scotch-Brite)
- Sponges (O-Cel-O)
- Tape (Scotch)

Display and Graphics
- Commercial graphics systems
- Optical films for electronic display
- Specialty film and media products
- Traffic control materials

Electro and Communications
- Insulating and splicing products for electronics telecommunications and electrical industries
- Packaging and interconnection devices

COMPETITORS

ACCO Brands
Avery Dennison
BASF SE
Bayer AG
Beiersdorf
Bostik
Corning
DuPont
GE
H.B. Fuller
Henkel
Honeywell International
Illinois Tool Works
Johnson & Johnson
Kimberly-Clark
Ricoh Company
RPM International
S.C. Johnson
Sealed Air Corp.
Sika

HISTORICAL FINANCIALS

Company Type: Public

Income Statement FYE: December 31

	REVENUE ($ mil.)	NET INCOME ($ mil.)	NET PROFIT MARGIN	EMPLOYEES
12/11	29,611	4,283	14.5%	84,198
12/10	26,662	4,085	15.3%	80,057
12/09	23,123	3,193	13.8%	74,835
12/08	25,269	3,460	13.7%	79,183
12/07	24,462	4,096	16.7%	76,239
Annual Growth	4.9%	1.1%	—	2.5%

2011 Year-End Financials

Debt ratio: 16.59%
Return on equity: 27.78%
Cash ($ mil.): 2,219
Current ratio: 224.96
Long-term debt ($ mil.): 4,563
No. of shares (mil.): 694
Dividends
Yield: —
Payout: 36.91%
Market value ($ mil.): 56,800

	STOCK PRICE ($) FY Close	P/E High/Low		PER SHARE ($) Earnings	Dividends	Book Value
12/11	81.73	16	12	5.96	0.00	22.19
12/10	86.30	16	13	5.63	2.10	22.00
12/09	82.67	18	9	4.52	2.04	17.96
12/08	57.54	17	11	4.89	2.00	14.24
12/07	84.32	17	13	5.60	1.92	16.56
Annual Growth	(0.8%)	—	—	1.6%	—	7.6%

Abbott Laboratories

Filling baby bottles and soothing aching joints are a habit for Abbott. Abbott Laboratories is a top health care products manufacturer. Its pharmaceuticals include HIV treatments Norvir and Kaletra rheumatoid arthritis therapy Humira and Lupron to treat endometriosis and prostate cancer. Its nutritional products division makes such well-known brands as Similac infant formula and the Ensure line of nutrition supplements. The company also makes diagnostic instruments (including tests and assays) vascular medical devices such as its Xience drug-eluting stents and the FreeStyle diabetes care line as well as products for the eye. Abbott has announced it will split apart its medical products and research drug units.

HISTORY

Dr. Wallace Abbott started making his dosimetric granule (a pill that supplied uniform quantities of drugs) at his home outside Chicago in 1888. Aggressive marketing earned Abbott the American Medical Association's criticism though much of the medical profession supported him.

During WWI Abbott scientists synthesized anesthetics previously available only from Germany. Abbott improved its research capacity in 1922 by buying Dermatological Research Laboratories; in 1928 it bought John T. Milliken and its well-trained sales force. Abbott went public in 1929.

Salesman DeWitt Clough became president in 1933. International operations began in the mid-1930s with branches in Argentina Brazil Cuba Mexico and the UK.

Abbott was integral to the WWII effort; the US made only 28 pounds of penicillin in 1943 before the company began to ratchet up production. Consumer infant and nutritional products (such as Selsun Blue shampoo Murine eye drops and Similac formula) joined the roster in the 1960s. The FDA banned Abbott's artificial sweetener Sucaryl in 1970 saying it might be carcinogenic and in 1971 millions of intravenous solutions were recalled following contamination deaths.

Robert Schoellhorn became CEO in 1979; profits increased but research and development was cut. In the 1980s Abbott began selling Japanese-developed pharmaceuticals in the US.

Duane Burnham became CEO in 1989; under his conservative management the company received FDA approvals to market insomnia treatment ProSom (1990) hypertension drug Hytrin for enlarged prostates (1994) and ulcer treatment Prevacid and central nervous system disorder treatment Depakote (1995).

Abbott bought MediSense a maker of blood sugar self-tests for diabetics in 1996; it also paid $32.5 million to settle claims by 17 states of infant formula price-fixing. In 1997 FTC action prompted Abbott to stop claiming that doctors recommended its Ensure nutritional supplement for healthy adults. That year the FDA allowed Abbott to use Norvir to treat HIV and AIDS in children after approving its use in adults in a record 72 days in 1996. In 1998 the company pulled blood-clot dissolver Abbokinase off the market to address manufacturing problems.

In 1999 Abbott agreed to buy pharmaceutical research company ALZA but the deal fell through in part because of FTC antitrust concerns. That year the FDA fined the company $100 million and pulled 125 of its medical diagnostic kits off the market citing quality assurance problems. Abbott later purchased arterial device closure maker Perclose and part of the anesthesia business of what is now GlaxoSmithKline.

The company sold its agricultural products business to Sumitomo Chemical in 2000. That year the FDA approved Gengraf a drug that fights organ transplant rejection and Kaletra a promising protease inhibitor designed to combat AIDS.

Insider Miles White was named chairman and CEO in 2001. That same year Abbott bought Knoll Pharmaceuticals a pharmaceutical unit of German chemicals giant BASF and also purchased Vysis thereby acquiring that company's worldwide distribution network and adding its products for the evaluation and management of cancer prenatal disorders and other genetic diseases to its portfolio of diagnostics.

The FDA thwarted the company's launch of new diagnostic products in 2002 by declaring that Abbott's Chicago manufacturing plant was not up to snuff. Attempting to move forward in the test market despite the setback the company licensed a patent to OraSure Technologies and made plans to jointly distribute OraSure's rapid HIV diagnostic test. It also struck an alliance with Celera to develop molecular diagnostic tests. That same year the FDA approved the company's Synthroid thyroid treatment which had already been on the market for nearly 50 years.

In 2004 Abbott spun off its hospital products division Hospira into a separate company.

Abbot ceased selling attention deficit drug Cylert in early 2005 citing declining sales concurrent with a consumer advocacy group's complaint that the drug caused more than 20 cases of liver failure. The FDA withdrew approval for the drug later that year.

Though diagnostics (including lab tests for HIV cancer and pregnancy) were once the core of Abbott's product line acquisitions have shifted the company's focus toward pharmaceuticals. As part of this refocusing Abbott sold its Abbott Spine subsidiary to Zimmer Holdings in 2008 for $360 million.

In addition to keep drug development focused on its core areas (immunology oncology neuroscience metabolic disorders and infectious disease) Abbott sold its share of TAP Pharmaceutical Products to Takeda Pharmaceutical in 2008. Abbott and Takeda had formed the joint venture in 1977 to market Takeda's drugs in the US. Takeda paid more than $1.5 billion for Abbott's share in TAP which was broken up through the deal taking home best-selling acid-reflux treatment Prevacid and the TAP development. Abbott retained rights to oncology drug Lupron and will continue to receive payments on current and future TAP products.

Until mid-2009 Abbott was embroiled in a decade-long intellectual property rights lawsuit with Medtronic over certain patents related to coronary stent and stent-delivery systems. Medtronic eventually agreed to pay $400 million to Abbott to settle the lawsuit. Also under terms of the agreement both parties agreed not to sue the other in the field of coronary stents for at least 10 years.

EXECUTIVES

VP Corporate Marketing, Susan M. Widner, age 55
VP Government Affairs, Elaine R. Leavenworth, age 53
Chairman and CEO, Miles D. White, age 57, $1,852,319 total compensation
EVP Pharmaceutical Products Group; President Abbott Ventures Inc., Richard A. (Rick) Gonzalez, age 58
VP and Controller, Greg W. Linder, age 55
SVP Medical Optics, James V. (Jim) Mazzo, age 54, $640,866 total compensation
VP Corporate Regulatory and Quality Science, Michael G. Beatrice, age 64
EVP Finance and CFO, Thomas C. (Tom) Freyman, age 57, $914,461 total compensation
SVP Human Resources, Stephen R. (Steve) Fussell, age 54, $454,689 total compensation
SVP Vascular, Robert B. (Chip) Hance, age 52

SVP Pharmaceuticals Research and Development, John M. Leonard, age 55
EVP Diagnostics, Edward L. Michael, age 55
EVP Medical Devices, John M. Capek, age 50, $679,383 total compensation
EVP Global Nutrition, John C. Landgraf, age 59
SVP Global Strategic Marketing and Services Pharmaceutical Products Group, Mary T. Szela, age 48
VP Taxes, A. J. Shoultz, age 56
SVP Diabetes Care, Heather L. Mason, age 51
VP Quality Medical Products, Cecilia L. Kimberlin
EVP Corporate Development, Richard W. Ashley, age 68
VP Molecular Diagnostics, Stafford O'Kelly, age 50
EVP General Counsel and Secretary, Laura J. Schumacher, age 49, $799,350 total compensation
VP Investor Relations and Public Affairs, John B. Thomas
VP and Treasurer, Valentine Yien, age 58
VP Strategic Initiatives Pharmaceutical Products Group, Glenn S. Warner, age 45
Manager Public Affairs Mexico, Jorge Solorzano
VP Point of Care Diagnostics, Greg E. Arnsdorff
VP and Chief Ethics and Compliance Officer, Robert E. Funck
VP Information Technology, Preston T. Simons
VP Pharmaceuticals Clinical Development, Eugene Sun
Senior Director External Communications Science Corporate Public Affairs, Kelly Morrison
VP and Associate General Counsel Corporate Transactions, Honey Lynn Goldberg
Divisional VP External Communications Corporate Public Affairs, Melissa Brotz
SVP Proprietary Pharmaceutical Products Global Commercial Operations, Carlos Alban, age 49
VP Established Products Operations, Steven J. Lichter
WVP Established Products Pharmaceutical Products Group, Michael J. Warmuth, age 49
Director External Communications Financial and Litigation Corporate Public Affairs, Scott Stoffel
Director Public Affairs Diabetes Care Medical Products, Greg Miley
Senior Director Public Affairs Diagnostics Medical Products, Don Braakman
Senior Director Public Affairs Vascular Medical Products, Jonathon Hamilton
Divisional VP Global Public Affairs Abbot Nutrition, Jennifer Smoter
Director Public Affairs US Nutrition, Tami Jones
SVP US Nutrition, J. Scott White, age 43
Director Public Affairs International Pharmaceuticals, Dirk van Eeden
VP Internal Audit, Thomas A. Hurwich
VP Nutrition Supply Chain, John F. Ginascol
VP Diabetes Care Commercial Operations, Robert B. Ford
VP Pharmaceuticals Japan, Gary M. Winer
VP Corporate Engineering Services, Corlis D. Murray
VP Nutrition Pacific Asia and Africa, Ramachandran Rajamanickam
VP Pharmaceuticals Western Europe and Canada, Pascale Richetta
VP Pharmaceuticals Discovery, James P. Sullivan
VP Pharmaceuticals Latin America, Santiago Luque
VP Sales and Marketing Pharmaceutical Operations, John R. Schilling
Manager External Communications, Adelle Infante
SVP Diagnostics, Brian J. Blaser, age 47
SVP International Nutrition, David Forrest, age 50
Senior Director External Communications Global Citizenship and Policy Corporate Public Affairs, Scott Davies
Director and Head Public Affairs International Nutrition, Steve Collens
Director Public Affairs International Pharmaceuticals, Ana Paula Barboza
Senior Manager Public Affairs International Pharmaceuticals, Elizabeth Hoff
Head Corporate Communications Australia, Jennifer Stevenson
Manager Public Affairs Brazil, Patricia Sant'Anna
Director Public Affairs China, Ling Wang
Director Communications France, Francoise Poterre
Director Public Affairs Italy, Alesia Scott
Director Public Affairs Japan, Seiko Noma
Manager Communications Spain, Javier Boix
Senior Vice President; Chief Marketing Officer, Paul Magill
Director, Roxanne S. Austin, age 51
Director, H. Laurance (Larry) Fuller, age 73
Director, W. James (Jim) Farrell, age 69
Director, Glenn F. Tilton, age 64
Director, William A. Osborn, age 64
Director, Edward M. Liddy, age 66
Director, Samuel C. (Sam) Scott III, age 68
Director, Roy S. Roberts, age 73
Director, Rt. Hon. David A. L. Owen, age 73
Director, William D. (Bill) Smithburg, age 74
Director, Phebe N. Novakovic, age 54
Director, Robert J. Alpern, age 62
Independent Director, Sally Blount
Independent Director, Nancy Mckinstry
Auditors: Deloitte&ToucheLLP

LOCATIONS

HQ: Abbott Laboratories
100 Abbott Park Rd., Abbott Park IL 60064-6400
Phone: 847-937-6100 **Fax:** 910-739-0024
Web: www.acmepowerdist.com

2012 Sales

US	16,784	42
Japan	2,441	6
Germany	1,740	4
Canada	1,253	3
Italy	1,127	3
India	933	2
Total	**39,874**	**100**

PRODUCTS/OPERATIONS

2012 Sales

	$ mil.	% of total
Proprietary pharmaceuticals (AbbVie)	18,012	45
Nutritionals	6,471	16
Established pharmaceuticals	5,121	13
Diagnostics	4,292	11
Vascular	3,071	8
Other	2,907	7
Total	**39,874**	**100**

Selected Products

Nutritional
- Alimentum (infant formula)
- EAS nutritional brands
  - AdvantEdge (nutritional supplements)
  - Myoplex (nutritional supplements)
- Ensure (adult nutrition)
- Freego (enteral pump)
- Glucerna (nutritional beverage for diabetics)
- Isomil (soy-based infant formula)
- Jevity (liquid food for enteral feeding)
- NeoSure (infant formula)
- Osmolite
- Pedialyte (pediatric electrolyte solution)
- PediaSure (children' s nutrition)
- Similac (infant formula)
- Zone Perfect (nutritional bars)

Established Pharmaceuticals (branded generics)
- Creon (pancreatic enzyme replacement therapy)
- Duphaston (progesterone deficiency)
- Klacid (macrolide antibiotic)

Diagnostic
- Abbott PRISM (high-volume blood-screening system)
- ARCHITECT (clinical chemistry system)
- AxSYM (clinical chemistry system)
- Cell-Dyn (hematology systems and reagents)
- Diagnostic and screening assays
- Informatics and automation solutions for lab use
- i-STAT (blood analyzer)
- m2000 (instrument that detects and measures infectious agents)
- Vysis (genomic-based tests)
  - PathVysion (breast cancer diagnostic test)
  - UroVysion (bladder cancer)

Medical Devices (former vascular division)
- Absorb (vascular scaffold)
- Acculink/Accunet (carotid stent)
- Asahi (coronary guidewires licensed from Asahi Intecc)
- Hi-Torque Balance Middleweight (coronary guidewire licensed from Asahi Intecc)
- MitraClip (valve repair)
- Multi-Link 8 Multi-Link Mini Vision and Multi-Link Vision (coronary metallic stents)
- Perclose (vessel closure)
- StarClose (vessel closure)
- Trek (balloon dilation)
- Xience V Xience nano and Xience Prime (drug-eluting stents)
- Voyager (balloon dilation)

Selected Acquisitions

2012
- STARLIMS Technologies ($123 million Tel Aviv laboratory information management systems)

2010
- Branded generics unit of Piramal Healthcare ($4 billion India 350 branded generic products in international markets)
- Facet Biotech ($450 million US biotech drug development)
- Solvay Pharmaceuticals (E4.5 billion or $6.2 billion Belgium therapies for cardiovascular gastrointestinal and neurological ailments as well as hormone therapies)

COMPETITORS

Amgen
Angiotech Pharmaceuticals
AstraZeneca
Bard
Baxter International
Bayer AG
Becton Dickinson
Boston Scientific
Bristol-Myers Squibb
Cordis
Crucell
Eli Lilly
Genentech
GlaxoSmithKline
GNC
Johnson & Johnson
LifeScan
Medtronic CardioVascular
Merck
Mylan
Nestle
Novartis
Pfizer
Roche Holding
Sandoz International GmbH
Sanofi
Shionogi & Co.
Solvay
Teva
Watson Pharmaceuticals

HISTORICAL FINANCIALS

Company Type: Public

Income Statement

FYE: December 31

	REVENUE ($ mil.)	NET INCOME ($ mil.)	NET PROFIT MARGIN	EMPLOYEES
12/11	38,851	4,728	12.2%	91,000
12/10	35,166	4,626	13.2%	90,000
12/09	30,764	5,745	18.7%	73,000
12/08	29,527	4,880	16.5%	69,000
12/07	25,914	3,606	13.9%	68,000
Annual Growth	10.7%	7.0%	—	7.6%

2011 Year-End Financials

Debt ratio: 25.57%
Return on equity: 19.35%
Cash ($ mil.): 6,812
Current ratio: 153.54
Long-term debt ($ mil.): 12,039

No. of shares (mil.): 1,570
Dividends
Yield: —
Payout: 62.46%
Market value ($ mil.): 88,302

	STOCK PRICE ($) FY Close	P/E High/Low		PER SHARE ($) Earnings	Dividends	Book Value
12/11	56.23	19	15	3.01	0.00	15.56
12/10	47.91	19	15	2.96	1.72	14.47
12/09	53.99	15	11	3.69	1.56	14.73
12/08	53.37	19	16	3.12	1.41	11.26
12/07	56.15	25	21	2.31	1.27	11.47
Annual Growth	0.0%	—	—	6.8%	—	7.9%

AbbVie Inc.

LOCATIONS

HQ: AbbVie Inc.
1 North Waukegan Road, Chicago, IL 60064
Phone: 847 932-7900
Web: www.abbvie.com

2011 Sales

	$ mil.	% of total
US	9,712	56
The Netherlands	904	5
Germany	701	4
Japan	616	4
Spain	569	3
France	516	3
UK	496	3
Canada	446	3
Italy	428	2
Brazil	382	2
Rest of the world	2,674	15
Total	**17,444**	**100**

PRODUCTS/OPERATIONS

2011 Sales

	$ mil.	% of total
Humira	7,932	46
TriCor/Trilipix	1,372	8
Kaletra	1,170	7
Niaspan	976	5
AndroGel	874	5
Lupron	810	5
Synagis	792	4
Sevoflurane	665	4
Synthroid	522	3
Norvir	419	2
Zemplar	409	2
Creon	332	2
Other	1,171	7
Total	**17,444**	**100**

HISTORICAL FINANCIALS

Company Type:

Income Statement

FYE: December 31

	REVENUE ($ mil.)	NET INCOME ($ mil.)	NET PROFIT MARGIN	EMPLOYEES
12/11	17,443	3,433	19.7%	30,000
12/10	15,637	4,177	26.7%	0
12/09	14,214	4,636	32.6%	0
Annual Growth	10.8%	(14.0%)	—	—

2011 Year-End Financials

Debt ratio: —
Return on equity: 28.09%
Cash ($ mil.): 27
Current ratio: 124.72
Long-term debt ($ mil.): —

Dividends
Yield: —
Payout: —
Market value ($ mil.): —

Abercrombie & Fitch Co.

Trading on its century-old name Abercrombie & Fitch (A&F) sells upscale men's women's and kids' casual clothes and accessories —quite a change from when the company outfitted Ernest Hemingway and Teddy Roosevelt for safari. A&F operates about 1045 stores in Asia throughout North America and in Europe and also sells via catalog and online. Its carefully selected college-age sales staff and use of 20-something models imbue its stores with an upscale fraternity-house feel. A&F runs a fast-growing chain of some 570 teen stores called Hollister and a chain targeted at boys and girls ages seven to 14 called abercrombie. Its Aussie-inspired just-for-girls brand Gilly Hicks has about 20 stores.

After a rough patch during the recession during which shoppers shunned its pricey apparel A&F has logged its second consecutive year of strong sales growth. In fiscal 2012 (ends January) sales popped 20% vs. the prior year and same-store sales (those at stores open for at least a year) grew by 5% after rising 7% in fiscal 2011. Double-digit sales increases from its international and direct-to-consumer operations up 74% and 36% respectively were growth drivers for the company. By comparison sales at its stores in the US rose just 6% in fiscal 2012 vs. 2011.

While the sales picture was rosy net income fell 15%. (Write downs costs associated with closing underperforming US stores and other charges hurt profitability.) A&F has been closing unprofitable stores in the US while expanding its international presence. New markets for the company include Austria China Belgium Hong Kong and Singapore. A&F began its international expansion when sales headed south in the US and continues to look abroad for growth even as its sales rebound at home. Indeed international expansion is key to the retailer's growth strategy.

A&F has aggressively culled its US store count closing more than 100 locations over the past two years including all of its high-end RUEHL chain stores (launched in 2005). Hollister which accounts for nearly half of the company's sales is A&F's fastest-growing chain both at home and abroad. Since its launch in 2008 Gilly Hicks –an Aussie-inspired purveyor of bras and underwear for young women. –has grown to nearly 20 locations including several overseas. The chain competes with Victoria's Secret Pink line of intimate apparel for young women.

The investment firm FMR LLC owns about 15% of the company's shares.

HISTORY

Scotsman David Abercrombie began selling camping equipment in Lower Manhattan in 1892. Joined by lawyer Ezra Fitch Abercrombie & Fitch (A&F) soon established itself as the purveyor of outdoors equipment for the very rich. A&F supplied Theodore Roosevelt and Ernest Hemingway for safaris and provided gear for Charles Lindbergh and polar explorer Richard Byrd. In 1917 the company moved into a 12-story edifice in Manhattan that included a log cabin (which Fitch lived in) and a casting pool.

A&F thrived through the 1960s. Mounted animal heads adorned its New York store which offered 15000 types of lures and 700 different shotguns. However by the 1970s A&F's core customers were as extinct or endangered as the animals they had hunted and the company struggled to find new markets. In 1977 A&F filed for bankruptcy. Sports retailer Oshman's (now The Sports Authority) bought the company a year later and expanded the number of stores while providing an eclectic assortment of goods. In 1988 clothing retailer The Limited bought A&F then with about 25 stores and shifted the company's emphasis to apparel.

Michael Jeffries took over in 1992 and transformed the still money-losing chain into an outfitter for college students. The new "jefe" micromanaged issuing a 29-page book on everything from how A&F salespeople (who earned around $6 an hour) must look to exactly how many sweaters can be placed in a stack. Draconian perhaps but the strategy worked and A&F returned to profitability in fiscal 1995. The company went public in 1996 with more than 110 stores.

In 1998 The Limited spun off its remaining 84% stake. Also that year A&F sued rival American Eagle Outfitters claiming it illegally copied A&F's clothing and approach (the suit was dismissed in 1999) and it raised the hackles of Mothers Against Drunk Driving with a catalog article entitled "Drinking 101." The company got attention of a different sort in 1999 when the SEC launched an investigation after A&F leaked sales figures to an analyst before they were made available to the public. In 2000 A&F launched its new teen store concept called Hollister Co.

A&F continued to push the envelope with its A&F Quarterly in summer 2001. Under the theme "Let Summer Begin" the catalog featured naked and half-naked models having "wet 'n' wild summer fun" and T-shirts logos that read "I Have a Big One" and "Get on the Stick."

The company pushed a little further in spring 2002 with a line of T-shirts portraying Asian caricatures. Vocal protests from Asian groups forced A&F to pull the shirts from its shelves and issue an apology. Later that spring A&F may have pushed a little too hard. A line of children's-sized thong underwear bearing sexually suggestive messages caused a furor among family-advocacy groups.

In 2003 Abercrombie & Fitch toned down with the discontinuation of its popular and racy A&F Quarterly magazine which targeted consumers aged 18-24. the following year it launched a young professionals' brand called RUEHL.The stores target customers aged 22 to 30 traditionally J. Crew and Banana Republic customers offering hip styles at lower prices.

A&F established a Japanese subsidiary company called ANF in May 2005. In November the company opened its first RUEHL Accessories store a tiny (600 sq. ft.) shop on Manhattan's Bleecker Street. That month the company opened its first off-mall flagship store on New York's Fifth Avenue at 56th Street.

In late 2007 the retailer launched an e-commerce site for its RUEHL concept. Soon after in January 2008 the company launched its newest brand Gilly Hicks with a store opening in Natick Massachusetts. The company also opened its first Hollister stores in British malls in 2008.

In January 2010 the company shut down the last of its RUEHL stores as well as the e-commerce site.

In 2011 A&F opened about 40 Hollister stores overseas including its first stores in China and Hong Kong. Also five Abercrombie & Fitch stores opened in Paris Madrid Dusseldorf Brussels and Singapore.

EXECUTIVES

EVP and CFO, Jonathan E. Ramsden, age 47, $700,000 total compensation
EVP Planning and Allocation, Leslee K. Herro, age 51, $923,446 total compensation
SVP Real Estate, David L. Leino, age 45, $473,077 total compensation
EVP Sourcing, Diane Chang, age 56, $923,446 total compensation
Chairman and CEO, Michael S. (Mike) Jeffries, age 67, $1,500,000 total compensation
SVP and CIO, John M. Deane
SVP Store Operations, Lawrence E. (Larry) Honig, age 64
SVP Diversity and Inclusion, Todd Corley
VP Brand Protection, Shane Berry
Senior Director Brand Protection, John Carriero
SVP Allocation, Rebecca F. Lee
Senior Counsel, David S. Cupps, age 75, $474,338 total compensation
SVP Human Resources, Ron Grzymkowski
SVP Design, Molly Hunt
SVP Technical Design, Mark D. Kabbes
SVP Store Construction, Abed W. Karaze
SVP Supply Chain, John A. Singleton
SVP Store Operations, Amy L. Zehrer
VP Finance, Brian P. Logan, $246,462 total compensation
Director Treasury, Scott Lipesky
Manager Investor Relations, Eric M. Cerny
SVP General Counsel and Secretary, Ronald A. Robins Jr., age 48
VP, Jon Rudy
Director, Lauren J. Brisky, age 61
Director, Michael E. Greenlees, age 65
Director, John W. (Jack) Kessler, age 76
Director, Craig R. Stapleton, age 67
Director, Elizabeth M. Lee, age 68
Auditors: PricewaterhouseCoopersLLP

LOCATIONS

HQ: Abercrombie & Fitch Co.
6301 Fitch Path, New Albany OH 43054
Phone: 614-283-6500 **Fax:** 614-283-6710
Web: www.abercrombie.com

2012 Stores

	No.
US	946
International	
UK	29
Canada	19
Germany	15
Spain	9
Italy	7
France	5
Austria	3
Belgium	3
China	3
Japan	2
Sweden	2
Denmark	1
Ireland	1
Hong	1
Singapore	1
Total	**1,047**

PRODUCTS/OPERATIONS

2012 Stores

	No.
Hollister	571
Abercrombie &	294
abercrombie	159
Gilly	21
Total	**1,045**

2012 Sales

	$ mil.	% of total
Hollister	2,022	49
Abercrombie & Fitch	1,665	40
abercrombie	397	9
Gilly Hicks	73	2
Total	**4,158**	**100**

Selected Products

Backpacks
Belts
Caps
Fleece
Footwear
Fragrances
Hats
Jackets
Jeans
Outerwear
Pants
Shirts
Shorts
Skirts
Sweaters
Swimwear
Tank tops
Underwear

COMPETITORS

Aeropostale
American Eagle Outfitters
Bath & Body Works
Benetton
Body Shop
Dillard' s
Express
Forever 21
French Connection
Guess?
H&M
J. Crew
L.L. Bean
La Senza
Lands' End
Levi Strauss
Macy' s
Nordstrom
Pacific Sunwear
Quiksilver
Ralph Lauren
Target Corporation
The Buckle
The Gap
Tommy Hilfiger
Urban Outfitters
Victoria' s Secret Stores
Wet Seal
Zara

HISTORICAL FINANCIALS

Company Type: Public

Income Statement

FYE: January 28

	REVENUE ($ mil.)	NET INCOME ($ mil.)	NET PROFIT MARGIN	EMPLOYEES
01/12	4,158	127	3.1%	90,000
01/11	3,468	150	4.3%	85,000
01/10	2,928	0	0.0%	80,000
01/09*	3,540	272	7.7%	83,000
02/08	3,749	475	12.7%	99,000
Annual Growth	2.6%	(28.0%)	—	(2.4%)

*Fiscal year change

2012 Year-End Financials

Debt ratio: 1.90%
Return on equity: 6.85%
Cash ($ mil.): 583
Current ratio: 211.07
Long-term debt ($ mil.): 57
No. of shares (mil.): 85
Dividends
Yield: —
Payout: 48.95%
Market value ($ mil.): 4,045

	STOCK PRICE ($) FY Close	P/E High/Low		PER SHARE ($) Earnings	Dividends	Book Value
01/12	47.23	52	30	1.43	0.00	21.75
01/11	48.36	34	18	1.67	0.00	21.67
01/10	31.54	—	—	(0.00)	0.00	20.78
01/09*	17.85	26	5	3.05	0.00	21.06
02/08	82.06	16	13	5.20	0.00	18.78
Annual Growth	(12.9%)	—	—	(27.6%)	—	3.7%

*Fiscal year change

ABM Industries, Inc.

Many businesses hope to clean up but diversified facilities services contractor ABM counts on it. The company primarily offers janitorial services to owners and operators of office buildings hospitals manufacturing plants schools shopping centers and transportation facilities throughout the US and in Canada and Puerto Rico. Through other units ABM provides security services and maintains mechanical electrical and plumbing systems. Its Ampco System Parking operates more than 1800 parking lots and garages mainly at airports across 35 states while ABM Security Services provides security officers and security systems monitoring services.

Like other conglomerates in the business services sector ABM has grown mainly by acquiring local and regional operating companies and their client rosters. It has also stayed focused on strengthening its core cleaning parking and security services operations. ABM generates cost savings by centralizing many business functions such as marketing sales and accounting.

This strategy also allows ABM to increase sales by more effectively leveraging its diverse portfolio of service offerings. Such a strategy appears to be working. In 2011 ABM reported an increase in earnings by $4.4 million (or 6.8%) to $68.5 million up from $64.1 million in 2010 primarily related to revenues associated with several recent acquisitions.

In a transaction it hopes will vault the company into the Fortune 500 in the coming years ABM purchased California-based facilities services company The Linc Group for nearly $300 million in cash in 2011. ABM rolled TLG's operations into its engineering division. The combined engineering operations boasts close to $1 billion in annual revenues.

ABM strengthened its janitorial segment through the 2010 acquisition of Diversco a provider of outsourced facility services serving industrial and manufacturing clients for about $30 million. The deal broadened the segment's client base and geographic reach and added security services to its list of offerings. Also in 2010 Ampco System Parking purchased the assets of several small parking companies. The acquisitions stretched the reach of Ampco's service in major urban areas such as Chicago Philadelphia and Boston.

HISTORY

Morris Rosenberg invested $4.50 in a bucket and cleaning tools and began cleaning San Francisco storefront windows in 1909. Later that year he purchased Chicago Window Cleaning for $300 and armed with new supplies and a Ford Model T began offering annual cleaning contracts. He changed the company's name to American Building Maintenance in 1913 to emphasize its broadening services. By 1920 the company had established three west coast offices and it became the first contractor to clean a major college campus when it signed an agreement with Stanford University in 1921.

The company added cleaning supplies to its offerings in 1927 with the acquisition of Easterday Janitorial Supply Company and continued to grow even during the Great Depression by providing cleaning services cheaper than its clients could provide for themselves. ABM expanded to the East Coast in 1932. Morris Rosenberg died in 1935 leaving the company to his oldest son Theodore who bought electrical services company Alta Electric the following year. During WWII ABM cleaned Navy ships and wired amphibious vehicles called Water Buffaloes. By the end of the war it operated 17 offices in the US and Canada.

Now called American Building Maintenance Industries the company went public in 1962 with Theodore serving as chairman and younger brother Sydney as CEO. To diversify its services ABM Industries stepped up its acquisition pace in the late 1960s buying Ampco Auto Parks (1967 parking facilities) Commercial Air Conditioning (1968 equipment maintenance) and General Elevator Corporation (1969 elevator maintenance and repair).

ABM Industries continued to expand its business into diverse services and regions through a three-decade buying spree. In 1981 the company combined its air-conditioning elevator lighting and energy services into American Technical Services Company (Amtech) to better focus on the high-growth tech and energy businesses. A management-led buyout of the company failed in 1990 on opposition from the Rosenberg brothers. Although ABM Industries' president stepped down and several lawsuits were filed following the aborted LBO the company continued to post impressive sales and profit numbers.

The company shortened its name to ABM Industries in 1994 the same year William Steele was named CEO. Sydney Rosenberg retired as chairman in 1997 marking the end of family control. The following year the company formed a Facility Services division to provide one-stop shopping for all of its services. It moved into landscaping services in 1999 with the purchase of Commercial Landscape Systems. The following year Steele stepped down as CEO and Henrik Slipsager a former executive of Dutch services giant ISS was tapped as the company's new chief.

In 2001 ABM sold off its Easterday Janitorial Supply subsidiary to AmSan West. ABM acquired six companies in 2001 and 2002 including Lakeside Building Maintenance a large Midwestern janitorial contractor. In 2003 the company sold its Amtech Elevator Services to Otis Elevator Company for $112 million. Two years later the company sold its CommAir Mechanical Services unit to Carrier Corp.

In 2005 ABM sold the last of its mechanical operations divesting its water treatment business to San Joaquin Chemicals. ABM made one of the biggest deals in its history in 2007 when it obtained rival facility services company OneSource Services paying about $390 million. The operations of OneSource including more than 10000 commercial accounts in the US Canada and Puerto Rico were integrated into those of ABM Janitorial throughout 2008.

In order to focus on its core operations in late 2008 the company sold the operating assets of its Amtech Lighting Services business to a unit of OSRAM SYLVANIA for about $34 million. ABM acquired several companies in 2009 and 2010 including Diversco and The Linc Group. It also snatched up several cleaning and engineering businesses –Control Building Services Control Engineering Services and TTF Assets –located primarily in New Jersey and New York. Collectively these businesses generate annual revenues of about $50 million and cater to the commercial institutional and pharmaceutical industries.

EXECUTIVES

President CEO and Director, Henrik C. Slipsager, age 57, $765,000 total compensation
EVP and CFO, James S. Lusk, age 56, $434,700 total compensation
Chairman, Maryellen C. Herringer, age 68
EVP; President ABM Janitorial Services, James P. (Jim) McClure, age 55, $550,000 total compensation
Chief Marketing Officer; President ABM Facility Services, Steven M. Zaccagnini, age 50, $434,700 total compensation
SVP Investor Relations, David L. Farwell, age 51
Senior Vice President, Erin M. Andre, age 53
VP Corporate Communications, Anthony (Tony) Mitchell
President Ampco System Parking, Mark Muglich
SVP General Counsel and Secretary, Sarah H. McConnell, age 47, $340,000 total compensation
SVP Mergers and Acquisitions and Treasurer, D. Anthony Scaglione
President ABM Security Services, Chris Hansen
SVP Controller and Chief Accounting Officer, Dean A. Chin, age 44
EVP; President ABM Facility Solutions, Tracy K. Price
VP and CIO, Doug Gilbert
SVP Human Resources, Angelique Carbo
President CEO and Director, Henrik C. Slipsager, age 57
Director, William W. (Bill) Steele, age 75
Director, Anthony G. (Tony) Fernandes, age 66
Director, Dan T. Bane
Director, Linda L. Chavez, age 65
Director, J. Philip (Phil) Ferguson
Independent Director, Sudhakar Kesavan
Auditors: KPMGLLP

LOCATIONS

HQ: ABM Industries Incorporated
551 5th Ave. Ste. 300, New York NY 10176
Phone: 212-297-0200 **Fax:** 614-716-1823
Web: www.aep.com

PRODUCTS/OPERATIONS

2011 Sales

	$ mil.	% of total
Janitorial	2,380	56
Engineering	899	21
Security	350	8
Corporate	1	-

Selected Services

Janitorial
Parking & transportation
Security
Engineering
Facility services
Energy
Landscape & golf
Electrical & lighting
HVAC & mechanical
Maintenance & repair

COMPETITORS

AlliedBarton Security
ARAMARK
Central Parking
Comfort Systems USA
Guardsmark
Healthcare Services
Impark
ISS A/S
ServiceMaster
Sodexo USA
Standard Parking
Temco Service Industries
UGL Services UNICCO

HISTORICAL FINANCIALS

Company Type: Public

Income Statement

FYE: October 31

	REVENUE ($ mil.)	NET INCOME ($ mil.)	NET PROFIT MARGIN	EMPLOYEES
10/12	4,300	62	1.5%	95,000
10/11	4,246	68	1.6%	96,000
10/10	3,495	64	1.8%	96,000
10/09	3,481	54	1.6%	91,000
10/08	3,623	45	1.3%	100,000
Annual Growth	4.4%	8.3%	—	(1.3%)

2012 Year-End Financials

Debt ratio: 11.50%
Return on equity: 7.36%
Cash ($ mil.): 43
Current ratio: 161.94
Long-term debt ($ mil.): 215
No. of shares (mil.): 54
Dividends
Yield: 3.05%
Payout: 50.88%
Market value ($ mil.): 1,033

	STOCK PRICE ($) FY Close	P/E High/Low		PER SHARE ($) Earnings	Dividends	Book Value
10/12	19.00	21	15	1.14	0.58	15.63
10/11	20.22	21	13	1.27	0.56	14.92
10/10	22.55	19	15	1.23	0.00	14.04
10/09	18.78	22	11	1.05	0.00	13.29
10/08	16.33	30	15	0.88	0.50	12.64
Annual Growth	3.9%	—	—	6.7%	3.8%	5.5%

Activision Blizzard, Inc.

When it comes to making cool video games Activision Blizzard aims to be sub-zero. The #2 global video game publisher (#1 in consoles and handheld games in the US) is best known for industry-dominating franchises such as World of Warcraft from Blizzard Entertainment and Call of Duty through Activision. The latter division also makes games based on licensed properties from Marvel (Spider-Man and X-Men) DreamWorks Animation (Shrek) MGM and the UK's EON Productions (James Bond) Hasbro (Transformers) as well as professional skateboarder Tony Hawk. Its games are produced for console systems and handheld devices from Sony Microsoft and Nintendo as well as for PC and mobile phones and tablets.

Activision Blizzard is moving away from casual and music-based games and –like many of its competitors –continuing to publish fewer more focused titles as fewer titles dominate more of both the company's and total industry sales. The top 10 titles in the industry accounted for more than a quarter of all sales in 2011 up from 23% in 2010. More than 60% of Activision Blizzard's sales came from just two franchises in 2010 –genre dominators subscription-based massively-multiplayer online role-playing game (MMORPG) World of Warcraft (WoW) and military-focused first-person shooter Call of Duty (CoD). By the end of 2011 those two along with the newly introduced Skylanders Spyro's Adventure accounted for nearly three-quarters of Activision Blizzard's total sales. This new reality has meant the cancellation of even once-hit franchise Guitar Hero as the popularity of that genre has faded.

Despite the move to streamline its catalog the company's strategy still includes acquiring and creating franchises as the introduction of Skylanders attests but in tandem with a disciplined selection and development rigor with an eye to enhancing operating profit and revenue predictability. Skylanders incorporates the use of toys offering an extra revenue stream. That propelled it to being a top-ten selling game and #1 selling kids' game in dollars during the quarter of its release in North America and Europe. It was the #10 best-selling title overall in dollars for the year.

CoD installment Black Ops released in 2010 was the top-selling video game in the US that year raking in more than $1 billion in worldwide sales. The series' Modern Warfare 3 (MW3) launched in November 2011 pulled in $775 million in its first five days driving it to be the #1 best-selling game of 2011 in dollars while Black Ops came in at #5. MW3 went on to surpass $1 billion in sales in 16 days the fastest of any entertainment property breaking the 17-day record held by the Twentieth Century Fox movie Avatar. Activision also produces subsequent downloadable content for current CoD games initially releasing them on Microsoft's Xbox Live and later on other platforms.

Both Activision's CoD and Blizzard's WoW depend on a robust social gaming community for their success so maintaining and enhancing that aspect is also a core component of the company's strategy.

The most current installments in Blizzard's two current franchises World of Warcraft: Cataclysm and Starcraft II: Wings of Liberty (both released in 2010) were both top-ten PC titles in North America and Europe for 2011. That partially made up for the lack of any new releases from the company that year but total revenues for Blizzard still fell 25%. The company's third franchise Diablo is yet another popular and critically acclaimed series. The first and most recent sequel Diablo II was released back in 2000 but the third installment is nearing completion and is targeted for release in the first half of 2012.

Those are Blizzard's three currently active franchises but it has talked about a fourth game it is developing a casual online multiplayer project reportedly given the working title Titan. The company announced in 2012 that it was laying off 600 employees about 10% coming from active game development. The company was quick to reassure though that the cuts would not knock current projects off track.

In 2010 Activision established a 10-year partnership with Bungie Inc. the creators of the mega-hit franchise Halo for exclusive rights to distribute and publish all games based on a new future property from the developer.

Another major industry trend affecting Activision Blizzard's business model is the escalation of online connectivity speeds and the proliferation of connected devices. The increasingly connected world continues to cause the digital distribution of its software to replace physical disc-based distribution. Digital online revenues increased nearly 15% in 2011 and are now more than a third of sales at more than $1.5 billion. Activision Blizzard expects this trend to continue.

Like many major video game publishers Activision Blizzard also maintains a distribution business that provides warehousing logistical and distribution services for its own games as well as for third-party publishers. The company's distribution operations are focused on European markets.

HISTORY

James Levy and four former Atari software designers founded Activision in 1979 to supply game cartridges to Atari. The company went public in 1983. Despite Activision's initial success Atari's downfall in the 1980s left the company struggling to stay afloat. Levy departed in 1987 and in 1988 new management renamed the company Mediagenic and attempted to transform it into a maker of PC software. Three years later BHK headed by Robert Kotick bought a controlling interest in Mediagenic. The company then reorganized under Chapter 11 bankruptcy and changed its name back to Activision.

By 1996 Activision's heavy investment in game development put the company back in the black. The company enhanced its international profile the next year through acquisitions of Take Us! Marketing & Consulting (software for German markets) and UK software distributor CentreSoft. Activision's growth continued in 1998 with its acquisition of Head Games Publishing (sports-oriented CD-ROM games). That year Activision obtained the rights to distribute LucasArts' PC and PlayStation games and expanded its list of game titles through agreements with companies such as Disney Marvel and Viacom.

The company's acquisitive streak continued in 1999 with purchases of Expert Software (budget-priced game software) and Elsinore Multimedia (Windows-based games). That year it introduced "Tony Hawk's Pro Skater" which went on to sell more than 3.5 million copies. Its successes did not keep the company from posting a loss in 2000 however and as its stock price began sinking Activision restructured its operations and closed Expert Software. With a focus on its existing brands and other proven properties including new Tony Hawk titles"" the company experienced record growth while the rest of the industry suffered from sluggish sales. Activision also began developing titles for next-generation game systems such as Sony's PlayStation 2 and Microsoft's Xbox.

In 2001 the company bought action and action-sports game developer Treyarch Invention. The following year Activision bought the remaining 60% of Grey Matter Interactive Studios it didn't already own.

In 2002 Activision acquired 30% of Infinity Ward the developer of Call of Duty; in 2003 the company bought the other 70%.

In 2007 the company acquired Bizarre Creations (the company behind the Project Gotham Racing and Geometry Wars franchises) and Red Octane (Guitar Hero). It also purchased network middleware developer DemonWare.

Vivendi acquired a majority stake in Activision in a deal valued at $9.8 billion; it then combined the company with Vivendi Games (and its Blizzard Entertainment division) to form Activision Blizzard. Part of Vivendi's strategy behind the Activision purchase was to leverage Activision's existing relationships with movie and media companies which can lead to profitable video game tie-ins to films and their sequels. It was a natural fit as Vivendi itself is a significant media holder with besides its existing games division companies such as top French pay-TV provider CANAL+ and Universal Music Group. The addition of Activision's mega-hit Guitar Hero franchise made the deal irresistable. The deal helped propel the company ahead of former world #2 Electronic Arts but still kept it a distant second to industry icon Nintendo.

In 2008 Activision Blizzard sold its game studio Massive Entertainment (publishers of the World in Conflict franchise) to UbiSoft. It also sold Swordfish Studios and Wanako Studios and closed Sierra Entertainment. That same year Activision Blizzard beefed up its music genre offerings with the purchase of Freestyle Games and also strengthened its development capabilities for Nintendo titles with the acquisition of Budcat Creations.

Continuing to pare down its operations in 2009-2010 the company closed its RedOctane Luxoflux and Shaba Games studios. In 2011 it announced it would close its Guitar Hero division and discontinue development of the game; it later recanted somewhat saying it would continue to provide downloadable content in response to outcry from fans.

EXECUTIVES

Co-Chairman, Brian G. Kelly, age 49, $875,387 total compensation
President CEO and Director, Robert A. (Bobby) Kotick, age 49, $953,654 total compensation
EVP and Chief Public Policy Officer, George L. Rose, age 50, $330,000 total compensation
CEO Activision Publishing, Eric Hirshberg, age 44
Chief Human Resources Officer, Ann E. Weiser, age 54
Vice Chairman, Michael J. (Mike) Griffith, age 55, $686,000 total compensation
Co-Chairman, Jean-Bernard Levy, age 57
President and CEO Blizzard Entertainment, Michael (Mike) Morhaime, age 44, $514,814 total compensation
Chief Legal Officer, Chris B. Walther, age 45, $94,231 total compensation
COO, Thomas Tippl, age 45, $726,423 total compensation
SVP and Managing Director European Publishing, Thibaud de Saint-Quentin
Chief Customer Officer, Brian Hodous, age 48, $533,365 total compensation
CFO, Dennis Durkin, age 41
COO Guitar Hero, David Haddad
Chief Accounting Officer, Stephen Wereb, age 47
Chief Strategy and Talent Officer, Humam Sakhnini
Director, Richard Sarnoff, age 53
Director, Robert J. Corti, age 62
President CEO and Director, Robert A. (Bobby) Kotick, age 49
Director, Robert J. Morgado, age 69
Vice Chairman, Michael J. (Mike) Griffith, age 55
Co-Chairman, Jean-Bernard Levy, age 57
Director, Regis Turrini, age 53
Director, Lucian Grainge, age 51
Director, Stephane Roussel, age 50
Director, Philippe G. H. Capron, age 54
Director, Frederic R. Crepin, age 42
Auditors: PricewaterhouseCoopersLLP

LOCATIONS

HQ: Activision Blizzard Inc.
3100 Ocean Park Blvd., Santa Monica CA 90405
Phone: 310-255-2000 **Fax:** 310-255-2100
Web: www.activisionblizzard.com

2011 Sales

	$ mil.	% of total
North America	2,405	51
Europe	1,990	42
Asia/Pacific	360	7
Total	**4,755**	**100**

PRODUCTS/OPERATIONS

2010 Sales by Type

	$ mil.	% of total
Product sales	3,257	68
Subscription licensing & other	1,498	32
Total	**4,755**	**100**

2011 Sales by Segment

	$ mil.	% of total
Activision	2,828	59
Blizzard	1,243	26
Distribution	418	9
Adjustments	266	6
Total	**4,755**	**100**

2011 Sales by Platform

	$ mil.	% of total
Console		
Xbox 360	1,140	24
PlayStation 3	935	20
Wii	351	7
PlayStation 2	13	-
Online subscriptions	1,357	29
Distribution	418	9
PC and other	374	8
Handheld	167	3
Total	**4,755**	**100**

Selected Titles and Franchises

Activision
- Bakugan (Japanese-style RPG for Nintendo DS)
- Band Hero
- Cabela' s Big Game Hunter
- Cabela' s Survival: Shadows of Katmai
- Call of Duty
- DJ Hero
- GoldenEye 007: Reloaded
- NASCAR Unleashed
- Prototype
- Rapala for Kinect (fishing game)
- Spider-Man
- Skylanders Spyro' s Adventure
- Tony Hawk
- Transformers
- True Crime
- X-Men: Destiny

Blizzard
- Diablo
- Starcraft
- World of Warcraft

Selected Production Studios

Bizarre Creations (Blur Geometry Wars: Retro Evolved 2)
FreeStyleGames (DJ Hero)
Infinity Ward (Call of Duty Call of Duty 2 Call of Duty 4: Modern Warfare)
Neversoft (Guitar Hero Band Hero Tony Hawk' s Pro Skater Tony Hawk' s Underground)
Radical Entertainment (Crash Bandicoot: Mind Over Mutant Prototype)
Treyarch (Call of Duty 3 Call of Duty: World at War Quantum of Solace Spider-Man)

COMPETITORS

Capcom
Disney Interactive Studios
Electronic Arts
Konami
Lucasfilm Entertainment
Microsoft
Namco Limited
Nintendo
SEGA
Sony
Square Enix
Take-Two
THQ
Turbine Inc.
Ubisoft
Valve Corporation
ZeniMax Media

HISTORICAL FINANCIALS

Company Type: Public

Income Statement

FYE: December 31

	REVENUE ($ mil.)	NET INCOME ($ mil.)	NET PROFIT MARGIN	EMPLOYEES
12/11	4,755	1,085	22.8%	7,300
12/10	4,447	418	9.4%	7,600
12/09	4,279	113	2.6%	7,000
12/08*	3,026	(107)	—	7,000
03/08	2,898	344	11.9%	2,640
Annual Growth	13.2%	33.2%	—	29.0%

*Fiscal year change

2011 Year-End Financials

Debt ratio: —
Return on equity: 10.34%
Cash ($ mil.): 3,165
Current ratio: 210.49
Long-term debt ($ mil.): —
No. of shares (mil.): 1,133
Dividends
Yield: —
Payout: 17.93%
Market value ($ mil.): 13,963

	STOCK PRICE ($) FY Close	P/E High/Low		PER SHARE ($) Earnings	Dividends	Book Value
12/11	12.32	15	11	0.92	0.00	9.26
12/10	12.44	37	29	0.33	0.15	8.62
12/09	11.11	145	91	0.09	0.00	8.60
12/08*	8.64	—	—	(0.11)	0.00	8.87
03/08	27.31	25	14	1.10	0.00	6.61
Annual Growth	(18.0%)	—	—	(4.4%)	—	8.8%

*Fiscal year change

Adobe Systems, Inc.

Adobe Systems is the house that desktop publishing software built. Now the company helps its customers create distribute and manage digital content in a variety of ways. Among the company's marquee brands are Acrobat Photoshop Flash and Dreamweaver. Adobe serves customers such as content creators and Web application developers with its digital media products and marketers advertisers publishers and others with its digital marketing business. Adobe not only offers its products in traditional software packages but some such as its Creative Suite which combines many of its digital media products are also available as cloud-based versions.

While its print and publishing segment (about 5% of sales) has remained intact Adobe consolidated its several other segments into two in 2012: digital media and digital marketing. Digital media includes products such as Flash Photoshop and Illustrator. Like digital media's Creative Suite digital marketing's more simply named Digital Marketing Suite houses a number of this segment's products that allow customers to collect data access reporting and analytics and assemble and access content.

In 2012 Adobe enhanced its digital marketing suite with the purchase of marketing management services provider Efficient Frontier. The acquisition brings ad campaign analytics and performance capabilities such as social ad buying for Facebook as well as brand management and other multi-channel optimization functions. It also bought Behance a social media platform Adobe plans to utilize in the cloud.

In 2011 Adobe bought advertising data management software developer Demdex to further improve the strategic marketing features of its software. Also that year Adobe acquired EchoSign a Web-based provider of electronic signatures as well as mobile applications creation software company Nitobi. Vancouver-based Nitobi's PhoneGap platform is an open source tool for mobile application developers to build with HTML5 and JavaScript. In total Adobe spent about $330 million on acquisitions in 2011.

In 2010 the company purchased Day Software Holding for about $240 million; that deal expanded Adobe's enterprise content management product line and added tools for social collaboration and digital asset management.

Among what is now Adobe's digital media segment is the former creative and interactive solutions which rose nearly 10% in 2011 on the strength of demand for the newest version of Creative Suite. The new segment also includes the former digital media solutions which was up 5% and Knowledge Worker which grew 13%.

Digital marketing products posted even stronger growth including Omniture which increased 20% mainly due to strong demand for its Online Marketing Suite and the former enterprise segment which climbed more than 25% due mainly to the acquisition of Day Software. Print and publishing was the only weak spot dropping 3% as demand weakened for its Shockwave product.

Adobe growth strategy will rely on a mix of more minor product releases more content capabilities for tablets and hosted online programs larger customers and more cloud-based options. The company is also looking to the subscription model to entice customers with more appealing pricing and provide a predictable stream of revenue.

Adobe sells directly and through distributors and resellers. Ingram Micro accounted for about 15% of the company's sales in each of the past three fiscal years.

HISTORY

When Charles Geschke hired John Warnock as chief scientist for Xerox's new graphics and imaging lab he set the stage for one of the world's largest software makers. While at the Xerox lab the pair developed the PostScript computer language which tells printers how to reproduce digitized images on paper. When Xerox refused to market it the duo left that company and started Adobe (named after a creek near their homes in San Jose California) in 1982.

Their original plan was to produce an electronic document processing system based on PostScript but the company changed direction when Apple whiz Steve Jobs hired it to co-design the software for his company's LaserWriter printer. A year later Adobe went public. Meanwhile PostScript was pioneering the desktop publishing industry by enabling users to laser print nearly anything they created on a computer.

In 1987 the company branched into the European market with the establishment of subsidiary Adobe Systems Europe. It also entered the PC market by adapting PostScript for IBM's operating system. Two years later the company began marketing its products in Asia.

Adobe grew throughout the 1990s by acquiring other software firms including OCR Systems and Nonlinear Technologies (1992) and AH Software and Science & Art (1993). In 1993 the company began licensing its PostScript software to printer manufacturers; it also started marketing its Acrobat software.

Adobe bought Aldus (1994) whose PageMaker software had been instrumental in establishing the desktop publishing market. (PageMaker's success depended on the font software that Adobe made and the two companies had a history of cooperation.) Next the company bought Frame Technology (FrameMaker publishing software 1995) but that acquisition proved disastrous. Frame sales plummeted partly the result of Adobe's move to eliminate Frame's technical support operations. Adobe's purchase of Web toolmaker Ceneca Communications that year was more fruitful.

In 1996 Adobe spun off its pre-press applications operations as Luminous. That year its licensing sales suffered a blow when one of its largest customers Hewlett-Packard introduced a clone version of PostScript. Also in 1997 for the first time Adobe's revenues from Windows-based software exceeded those of its once-dominant Macintosh-based software.

In 1998 a takeover attempt by competitor Quark proved unsuccessful. Drooping sales that year which Adobe blamed on the Asian crisis (but which some analysts blamed on its product strategy) prompted the company to shed a layer of executives 10% of its workforce and its Adobe Enterprise Publishing Services and Image Club Graphics units. Its 1999 acquisition of GoLive Systems expanded its Web publishing product line. That year Adobe released professional page layout application InDesign which immediately spurred the biggest backlog in the company's history.

The company boosted its electronic book offerings by acquiring software maker Glassbook. In 2002 in a move to expand its ePaper division Adobe purchased electronic forms provider Accelio for $72 million.

In early 2003 the company restructured its divisions creating its Creative Professional segment to replace the Cross-media Publishing division and its Digital Imaging and Video unit to replace its former Graphics division. This realignment was a part of Adobe's plan to focus on its core market of creative professionals. In order to expand its digital video offerings the company also acquired the assets of digital audio tools-maker Syntrillium Software that year.

In 2004 the company acquired OKYZ a Paris-based maker of 3D collaboration software; the acquisition added 3D technology to Adobe's Intelligent Document Platform.

Adobe acquired rival Macromedia for approximately $3.4 billion in stock late in 2005. Macromedia's popular website design and animation tools included Dreamweaver and Flash. Adobe acquired Trade and Technologies France (TTF) a developer of CAD data interoperability software in 2006.

Adobe acquired publishing software provider Scene7 in 2007. It also purchased online word processing software developer Virtual Ubiquity.

Though products designed for creative professionals remained Adobe's bread and butter the company continued to expand its market focus. Adobe launched a beta version of Acrobat.com an online collaboration service for the enterprise market in 2008. The following year it moved the site to a subscription-based model charging for shared access to PDF creation applications and other productivity tools.

Web analytics provider Omniture was acquired in 2009 for $1.8 billion. Adobe used Omniture's technology to bolster the functionality of its integrated marketing product suite to create manage and track the usage and performance of a wide variety of Web-based content including videos Web pages and podcasts.

EXECUTIVES

SVP and CTO, Kevin M. Lynch, age 45, $421,000 total compensation
SVP General Counsel and Secretary, Karen O. Cottle, age 62, $423,333 total compensation
Co-Chairman, Charles M. (Chuck) Geschke, age 72
Co-Chairman, John E. Warnock, age 71
SVP Global Marketing, Ann Lewnes
SVP and CIO, Gerri Martin-Flickinger
SVP and General Manager Digital Enterprise Solutions Group, Robert M. (Rob) Tarkoff, age 43
EVP and CFO, Mark S. Garrett, age 54, $510,000 total compensation
President CEO and Director, Shantanu Narayen, age 50, $875,000 total compensation
SVP Human Resources, Donna Morris
SVP Worldwide Field Operations, Matthew A. (Matt) Thompson, age 54, $450,500 total compensation
VP Corporate Controller and Principal Accounting Officer, Richard T. Rowley, age 55
SVP and Chief Software Architect Advanced Technology Labs, Tom Malloy
SVP Print and Publishing Business Unit; Managing Director Adobe India, Naresh Gupta
SVP Engineering Technologies Group, Digby Horner
VP Investor Relations, Mike Saviage
SVP Corporate Development, Paul Weiskopf
SVP and General Manager Digital Media, David Wadhwani, age 40
SVP and General Manager Digital marketing, Brad Rencher
VP Government Affairs and Public Policy, Jace Johnson
SVP General Counsel and Corporate Secretary, Michael Dillon
Director, Robert K. (Rob) Burgess, age 54
Co-Chairman, John E. Warnock, age 71
Director, Michael R. (Mike) Cannon, age 59
Director, James E. (Jim) Daley, age 70
Director, Daniel L. (Dan) Rosensweig, age 50
Director, Edward W. (Ned) Barnholt, age 69
President CEO and Director, Shantanu Narayen, age 50
Director, Robert Sedgewick, age 65
Auditors: KPMGLLP

LOCATIONS

HQ: Adobe Systems Incorporated
345 Park Ave., San Jose CA 95110-2704
Phone: 408-536-6000 **Fax:** 408-537-6000
Web: www.adobe.com

2011 Sales

	$ mil.	% of total
Americas	2,044	49
Europe Middle East & Africa	1,317	31
Asia	854	20
Total	**3,800**	**100**

PRODUCTS/OPERATIONS

2011 Sales by Segment

	$ mil.	% of total
Creative & interactive solutions	1,713	41
Digital enterprise solutions		
Knowledge worker	740	18
Enterprise	442	15
Digital media solutions	625	11
Omniture	476	10
Print & publishing	218	5
Total	**4,216**	**100**

2011 Sales by Type

	$ mil.	% of total
Product	3,424	81
Subscription (hosted offerings)		
Omniture	387	9
Other	63	2
Services & support	341	8
Total	**4,216**	**100**

Selected Products

Digital media
- Acrobat (PDF management)
- Audition (audio editing)
- Dreamweaver (software development)
- Flash (Internet application and video creation)
- Illustrator (graphic artwork creation)
- Photoshop
- Premiere (video editing)

Digital marketing
- AudienceManager
- Connect (enterprise collaboration and communication)
- CRX (enterprise content management)
- DataWarehouse
- Scene7 (merchandising system)

Print and publishing
- Authorware (tutorial creation)
- Font Folio
- PageMaker (document creation and page layout)
- RoboHelp (help system creation)
- Shockwave (media player)

COMPETITORS

ACD Systems
Apple Inc.
ArcSoft
Autodesk
Avid Technology
Bare Bones Software
Canon
Cisco WebEx
Citrix Systems
Corel
Coremetrics
Dell
Eastman Kodak
Google
Hewlett-Packard
IBM
Microsoft
Monotype
Nexaweb
Nikon
Nuance Communications
Oracle
Pegasystems
Quark
RealNetworks
Rovi
SAS Institute
Sony
TIBCO Software
Ultimus
Webtrends
Xara
Yahoo!
Zinio Systems

HISTORICAL FINANCIALS

Company Type: Public

Income Statement FYE: December 2

	REVENUE ($ mil.)	NET INCOME ($ mil.)	NET PROFIT MARGIN	EMPLOYEES
12/11	4,216	832	19.8%	9,925
12/10*	3,800	774	20.4%	9,117
11/09	2,945	386	13.1%	8,660
11/08	3,579	871	24.4%	7,335
11/07	3,157	723	22.9%	6,959
Annual Growth	7.5%	3.6%	—	9.3%

*Fiscal year change

2011 Year-End Financials

Debt ratio: 16.84%
Return on equity: 14.40%
Cash ($ mil.): 989
Current ratio: 301.53
Long-term debt ($ mil.): 1,505
No. of shares (mil.): 491
Dividends
Yield: —
Payout: —
Market value ($ mil.): 13,326

	STOCK PRICE ($) FY Close	P/E High/Low		PER SHARE ($) Earnings	Dividends	Book Value
12/11	27.11	21	14	1.65	0.00	11.77
12/10*	29.14	25	17	1.47	0.00	10.35
11/09	35.38	50	22	0.73	0.00	9.36
11/08	23.16	28	13	1.59	0.00	8.38
11/07	42.14	39	30	1.21	0.00	8.14
Annual Growth	(10.4%)	—	—	8.1%	—	9.7%

*Fiscal year change

Advance Auto Parts Inc

Advance Auto Parts (AAP) has turned auto parts retailing into less of a one-company race. Comfortably in 2nd place (AutoZone is #1) AAP operates nearly 3700 stores under the Advance Auto Parts Advance Discount Auto Parts and Western Auto banners in about 40 states Puerto Rico and the Virgin Islands as well as an e-commerce site. Its stores carry brand-name replacement parts batteries maintenance items and automotive chemicals. AAP's Autopart International (AI) unit operates more than 200 locations and primarily serves commercial customers including garages service stations and auto dealers. Commercial customers account for around 35% of AAP's revenues while do-it-yourselfers generate the balance.

Operations

The company's main segments are parts (alternators batteries belts and hoses engines and engine parts and spark plugs and wires) accessories (floor mats mirrors vent shades and MP3 and cell phone accessories) chemicals (antifreeze brake and power steering fluid freon and windshield washer fluid) and oil (transmission fluid and other automotive petroleum products). The parts segment accounted for close to 65% of sales in 2011. Accessories accounted for about 15% of sales and both the chemicals and oil segments represented about 10% in 2011.

Sales & Marketing

Advance Auto Parts builds it marketing and advertising campaigns around radio direct marketing digital and local marketing. The company also employs Spanish-language television radio and outdoor ads to reach Latinos. In early 2011 the firm launched its "Service is our best part" campaign nationwide. The campaign targets core DIY customers and emphasizes service.

Financial Analysis

The company fared well amid the recent deep recession in the US. AAP's top line continued to climb steadily in 2011 when revenue reached $6.1 billion –a nearly 5% improvement from $5.9 billion in 2010. (Since 2007 when sales were $4.8 billion AAP has grown its revenues by more than 25%.) Profit growth has been even more impressive. The company logged about $395 million in net income in 2011 about a 15% gain over 2010. (Profits have risen by around 60% from $238 million since 2007.) Interestingly it has been the tough economic environment that has helped to pump up AAP's earnings. With disposable incomes falling and the unemployment rate remaining relatively high Americans are hanging on to their cars longer and relying more on mechanics for maintenance and repairs to keep vehicles in good working condition. (Professional mechanics are part of AAP's commercial customer segment.)

Strategy

AAP is looking to the commercial market for growth opportunities and hopes to eventually generate 50% of its sales from the segment. To better serve commercial customers AAP in 2011 added more parts from key manufacturers to its inventory and expanded its workforce with parts professionals delivery drivers and sales representatives.

To drive sales among DIY customers AAP has focused on improving customer service. In recent years the company introduced more structured training programs and it has been assessing the effectiveness of its staffing model. In 2011 AAP rolled out the "Service is our best part" advertising campaign emphasizing the retailer's commitment to providing higher quality service.

Both commercial and DIY customers are benefiting from AAP's store network expansion in both new and existing markets. In 2011 the company opened about 105 stores. During 2010 the retailer added nearly 150 more locations.

If customers would rather not stop by one of AAP's stores they can place their orders through the company's e-commerce site which began operating in 2009. Shoppers can search through AAP's inventory of more than 100000 parts and accessories as well as choose from in-store pickup and delivery options. Admittedly late to online retailing the company said its e-commerce platform has had a positive impact on revenue and is expected to be a significant sales driver in the years ahead.

Company Background

Founded as Advance Stores Company in 1929 AAP was a general merchandise retailer until the '80s. From there the company shifted its focus to automotive parts retailing targeting DIY customers.

EXECUTIVES

President, Jim L. Wade, age 57, $450,008 total compensation
SVP Store Support, Michael W. (Mike) Marolt
EVP and CFO, Michael A. (Mike) Norona, age 48, $450,008 total compensation
COO, Kevin P. Freeland, age 54, $450,008 total compensation
Chief Development Officer, Tamara A. (Tami) Kozikowski, age 50, $230,772 total compensation
President CEO and Director, Darren R. Jackson, age 48, $700,000 total compensation
SVP Supply Chain, Charles A. (Chas) Scheiderer
SVP Team Member Excellence, Donna J. Broome
Chairman, John C. (Jack) Brouillard, age 63, $23,077 total compensation
SVP and General Manager E-Commerce, Scott Bauhofer
SVP Operations Florida, Kurt R. Schumacher
SVP Information Technology and CIO, Ricardo S. (Rick) Coro
SVP and Controller, Jill A. Livesay, age 43
SVP Real Estate, Randall A. (Randy) Young
Senior Vice President - Merchandising and Marketing, Charles E. Tyson, age 49
SVP Operations East, Derrick Thomas
SVP Market Strategy, Gregory N. (Greg) Johnson, age 44
SVP National Operations and Customer Experience, Carl Hauch
SVP Finance, Judd Nystrom
SVP General Counsel and Corporate Secretary, Sarah E. Powell, age 45
President Autopart International, Jim Durkin
Manager Public Communications, Shelly Whitaker
SVP Operations, Mike Pack
SVP DIY and Commercial Operations Support, Bill Carter
Area Senior Vice President, Rusty Tweedy
Director, Carlos A. Saladrigas, age 63
President CEO and Director, Darren R. Jackson, age 48
Director, John F. Bergstrom, age 65
Director, Fiona P. Dias, age 46
Director, Gilbert T. Ray, age 67
Director, William S. Oglesby, age 52
Director, J. Paul (Paul) Raines, age 48
Director, Frances X. Frei, age 48
Auditors: Deloitte&ToucheLLP

LOCATIONS

HQ: Advance Auto Parts Inc.
5008 Airport Rd., Roanoke VA 24019
Phone: 540-362-4911 **Fax:** 540-561-1448
Web: corp.advanceautoparts.com

2011 AAP Locations

	No.
Florida	465
North	242
Georgia	233
Ohio	209
Pennsylvania	179
Virginia	177
Texas	174
Tennessee	138
New	133
South	128
Alabama	121
Michigan	112
Illinois	109
Indiana	107
Kentucky	102
Maryland	84
Massachusetts	70
West	69
New	65
Louisiana	61
Mississippi	57
Wisconsin	53
Colorado	50
Missouri	43
Connecticut	41
Oklahoma	31
Arkansas	28
Iowa	27
Kansas	25
Puerto	25
Nebraska	21
New	15
Maine	14
Minnesota	14
Rhode	11
Vermont	8
Delaware	7
South	7
Wyoming	3
New	1
Virgin	1
Total	**3,460**

2011 AI Locations

	No.
Florida	44
Massachusetts	32
New	24
Pennsylvania	23
Connecticut	17
New	17
Maryland	13
Virginia	11
New	8
Maine	4
Rhode	4
Alabama	1
Delaware	1
Georgia	1
North	1
Vermont	1
Total	**202**

PRODUCTS/OPERATIONS

2011 Sales

	$ mil.	% of total
Parts & batteries	3,887	63
Accessories	863	14
Chemicals	678	11
Oil	617	10
Other	123	2
Total	**6,170**	**100**

Selected Brands

Bosch
Castrol
Dayco
Monroe
Moog
Prestone
Purolator
Sylvania
Trico
Wagner

COMPETITORS

AutoZone
CARQUEST
CSK Auto
Fisher Auto Parts
Genuine Parts
Keystone Automotive Operations
O' Reilly Automotive
Pep Boys
Replacement Parts
Sears
Somerset Tire Service
U.S. Auto Parts
VIP
Wal-Mart
Whitney Automotive Group

HISTORICAL FINANCIALS

Company Type: Public

Income Statement

FYE: December 31

	REVENUE ($ mil.)	NET INCOME ($ mil.)	NET PROFIT MARGIN	EMPLOYEES
12/11*	6,170	394	6.4%	53,000
01/11	5,925	346	5.8%	51,000
01/10	5,412	270	5.0%	49,000
01/09	5,142	238	4.6%	47,582
12/07	4,844	238	4.9%	44,055
Annual Growth	6.2%	13.4%	—	4.7%

*Fiscal year change

2011 Year-End Financials

Debt ratio: 11.38%
Return on equity: 46.55%
Cash ($ mil.): 57
Current ratio: 104.84
Long-term debt ($ mil.): 415
No. of shares (mil.): 72
Dividends
Yield: —
Payout: 4.70%
Market value ($ mil.): 5,069

	STOCK PRICE ($) FY Close	P/E High/Low		PER SHARE ($) Earnings	Dividends	Book Value
12/11*	69.63	14	10	5.11	0.00	11.65
01/11	66.15	17	10	3.95	0.00	12.68
01/10	40.48	17	11	2.83	0.00	13.70
01/09	34.14	18	10	2.50	0.00	11.34
12/07	38.17	18	13	2.28	0.00	10.34
Annual Growth	16.2%	—	—	22.4%	—	3.0%

*Fiscal year change

Advanced Micro Devices, Inc.

Advanced Micro Devices (AMD) made some advances in its battle against Intel but has yet to capitalize on those gains. AMD ranks #2 in PC and server microprocessors far behind its archrival. Though Intel commands the world processor market AMD has at times eroded that market share thanks to the popularity of its Athlon and Opteron processor families as well as its Fusion and Radeon chips. The company also makes embedded processors and other chips for communications graphics storage networking and other applications. Hewlett-Packard is its largest customer. AMD gets a majority of its sales from international customers; those in China account for more than half of the company's sales.

HISTORY

Silicon Valley powerhouse Fairchild Camera & Instrument axed marketing whiz Jerry Sanders reportedly for wearing a pink shirt on a sales call to IBM. In 1969 Sanders and seven friends started a semiconductor company (just as his former boss Intel co-founder Robert Noyce had done a year earlier) based on chip designs licensed from other companies.

Advanced Micro Devices (AMD) went public in 1972. Siemens eager to enter the US semiconductor market paid $30 million for nearly 20% of AMD in 1977. (Siemens had sold off its stake by 1991). In 1982 AMD inked a deal with Intel that let AMD make exact copies of Intel's iAPX86 microprocessors used in IBM and compatible PCs.

By the mid-1980s the company was developing its own chips. In 1987 AMD sued Intel for breaking the 1982 agreement that allowed AMD to second-source Intel's new 386 chips. Intel countersued for copyright infringement when AMD introduced versions of Intel's 287 math coprocessor (1990) 386 chip (1991) and 486 chip (1993).

AMD acquired Monolithic Memories in 1987 broadening its portfolio of memory devices. The company began work on its Submicron Development Center at headquarters in Sunnyvale California where crucial work on future products would be done.

In 1993 AMD formed a joint venture with Fujitsu to make flash memory devices. (Ten years later the two companies formed a separate company to pool their flash operations.) After a federal jury decided in AMD's favor in the 287 math coprocessor case in 1994 AMD and Intel settled their legal differences in 1995. Each agreed to pay damages and AMD won a perpetual license to the microcode of Intel's 386 and 486 chips. AMD's K5 microprocessor (a rival of Intel's Pentium) hit the market in 1996 –more than a year late.

In 1996 AMD bought microprocessor developer NexGen Microsystems and its technology for use in the K6 chip. That year AMD restructured its programmable logic chip unit as subsidiary Vantis. AMD unveiled its K6 microprocessor the next year but had trouble increasing production to meet demand. In 1999 AMD sold Vantis to Lattice Semiconductor netting $500 million. The company debuted its Athlon (K7) chip in 1999 to positive reviews and soon won Compaq Computer and IBM as customers.

Early in 2000 AMD named Hector Ruiz president and COO. Also in 2000 AMD sold 90% of its communications circuits business (chips for telephony and Internet access) to Francisco Partners for $375 million; the deal called for AMD to provide manufacturing services to the new company which was renamed Legerity. (The arrangement ended in 2002 when AMD shut down the fabrication plant that had supported it.)

Improved manufacturing processes increased sales of high-end Athlons and a worldwide shortage of flash memory helped AMD turn a profit (and a big one) in 2000 its first since 1995. In the face of a dismal slump in the global chip business though AMD cut costs in 2001 by closing two chip plants in Texas and by cutting about 2300 jobs – 15% of its total workforce –there and in Malaysia.

In 2002 AMD acquired Alchemy Semiconductor a maker of embedded microprocessors for wireless networking applications for $50 million in cash. Sanders handed over the CEO reins to Ruiz that year.

In 2003 AMD joined long-time joint-venture partner Fujitsu in forming a new company called FASL (later renamed Spansion) to pool the two chip makers' flash memory operations. (AMD subsequently bought chip startup Coatue which made memory cell arrays and folded it into Spansion.) AMD also bought National Semiconductor's Information Appliance unit which made the Geode line of system-on-a-chip devices. AMD broke ground on a new wafer fabrication plant or fab in Germany late that year.

By mid-2004 industry watchers were crediting the company's existing German production center with helping AMD find solid footing against manufacturing powerhouse Intel. AMD further expanded production capacity through a deal with chip foundry Chartered Semiconductor in 2004. The following year AMD filed an antitrust suit against Intel alleging that the chip giant had used improper subsidies and coercion to secure sales.

In 2004 Ruiz succeeded Sanders as chairman as well; Sanders retired from the board after 35 years and was named to the honorary post of chairman emeritus.

In 2006 AMD started shipping AMD64 processors from its Fab 36 facility in Dresden Germany adjacent to Fab 30. Also that year AMD sold its Alchemy processor line and related operations to Raza Microelectronics a fabless semiconductor firm then headed by former AMD COO Atiq Raza. The company also made an equity investment in Raza Micro.

Later that year AMD acquired ATI Technologies for about $5.4 billion in cash and stock. AMD exchanged around $4.3 billion in cash and 58 million shares of its common stock for ATI's shares and stock options. The company integrated its operations with ATI's by combining platform development and technical support teams in Shanghai and Taipei. Those centers then coordinated with design teams in Austin and Toronto.

A year later AMD wrote off $1.3 billion in impaired goodwill on the deal and took an impairment charge of $349 million on acquisition-related intangible assets of ATI.

The European Commission the antitrust regulator for the European Union nations brought formal charges against Intel on behalf of AMD in 2007. The company accused its rival of securing sales by use of coercion and improper subsidies. Two years later the commission found in AMD's favor fining Intel for alleged anticompetitive behavior.

In 2007 AMD launched its Opteron Quad-Core processor code-named Barcelona as its latest entry in the server processor market. Barcelona differed from Intel's competing Xeon 5300 quad-core processor in that it combined four processing cores onto one chip while Intel put two dual-core processors in a multichip module. Multiple processing cores offer not only faster performance since they can divide various processing chores; they also need less power to operate and don't require the extensive chip-cooling features that AMD and Intel needed for earlier processors.

After seven consecutive quarters of losses Hector Ruiz stepped aside as CEO in 2008. He remained executive chairman until 2010. Dirk Meyer was promoted to CEO to succeed him; Meyer a 13-year veteran of AMD was promoted to president and COO of the company in 2006.

In 2007 a unit of Mubadala Development Company bought 49 million new shares of AMD's common stock for about $622 million taking an equity stake of about 8% in the chip maker. AMD used the proceeds for general corporate purposes including R&D. Mubadala Development is the strategic-investment arm of Abu Dhabi's government part of the United Arab Emirates.

Seeing sales slow across all business segments in 2008 as did many chip makers AMD cut about 13% of its global workforce more than 2200 employees. The company eliminated another 1100 jobs in early 2009 900 through layoffs and the remainder through attrition and the sale of a business unit.

The company agreed in 2008 to sell its digital TV (DTV) chip product line to Broadcom in order to raise funds to pay off debt. Due to lower sales for the unit AMD reduced the price for the DTV product line by more than $50 million when the transaction closed in late 2008 to $141.5 million in cash from $192.8 million.

In 2009 the company sold graphics and multimedia assets from its handheld electronics business to QUALCOMM for $65 million in cash.

The company reached a $1.25 billion legal settlement with Intel in 2009 resolving a longstanding antitrust lawsuit which accused its rival of using improper subsidies and coercion methods to secure sales from computer makers. Also that year the European Commission fined Intel about $1.44 billion based on complaints brought by AMD alleging that Intel paid hidden rebates to PC makers to use only Intel processors in their products and not AMD's processors.

EXECUTIVES

Chairman, Bruce L. Claflin, age 61
SVP and CIO, Mike Wolfe, age 53
SVP Corporate Controller and Interim CFO, Devinder Kumar
SVP General Counsel and Corporate Secretary, Harry A. Wolin, age 49
SVP and CFO, Thomas J. Seifert, age 48, $121,152 total compensation
Senior Vice President; Chief Marketing Officer, Colette LaForce, age 37
SVP and General Manager Global Business Units, Lisa Su, age 42
SVP and General Manager Technology Group, Chekib Akrout, age 54
SVP; President Greater China, David Tang
SVP Human Resources and Chief Talent Officer, Allen Sockwell
SVP and Chief Sales Officer, Emilio Ghilardi, age 53, $514,195 total compensation
SVP and CTO, Mark Papermaster, age 50
SVP and General Manager Products Group, Rick Bergman, age 48
VP and General Manager Latin America, Ronaldo Miranda, age 51
VP Worldwide Business Management (WBM), Hans Erickson
President CEO and Director, Rory P. Read, age 50
SVP and Chief Strategy Officer, Rajan Naik
SVP and Chief Sales Officer, John Byrne
Director, Nicholas M. (Nick) Donofrio, age 66
Director, W. Michael (Mike) Barnes, age 69
Director, Craig A. Conway, age 57
Director, Henry W. K. Chow, age 66
Director, Robert B. Palmer, age 71
Director, John E. Caldwell, age 62
Director, Paulett Eberhart, age 58
Director, Waleed Ahmed Al Mokarrab Al Muhairi, age 37
President CEO and Director, Rory P. Read, age 50
Auditors: Ernst&YoungLLP

LOCATIONS

HQ: Advanced Micro Devices Inc.
One AMD Place, Sunnyvale CA 94088
Phone: 408-749-4000 **Fax:** 860-975-3110
Web: www.aetna.com

2012 Sales

	$ mil.	% of total
China	3,131	58
Singapore	856	16
Europe	469	9
US	407	7
Japan	305	5
Other regions	254	5
Total	**5,422**	**100**

PRODUCTS/OPERATIONS

2012 Sales

	$ mil.	% of total
Computing solutions	4,005	74
Graphics & other	1,417	26
Total	**6,422**	**100**

Selected Products

Computing
- Accelerated processing units (APUs; Fusion combines central processing and graphics processing units on a single chip)
- Microprocessors (Athlon Opteron Phenom Sempron and Turion lines)
- Motherboard reference design kits and chipsets

Graphics
- Embedded graphics processing units
- Macintosh notebook and desktop PC graphics processors (Radeon)
- Motherboard chipsets (for AMD and Intel processors)
- Server and workstation graphics processing units

Personal connectivity
- Embedded processors
- Networking chips

COMPETITORS

Analog Devices
ARM Holdings
Atmel
Broadcom
Centaur Technology
Freescale Semiconductor
Hitachi
IBM
Intel
LSI Corp.
Marvell Technology
Matrox Electronic Systems
MediaTek
NVIDIA
NXP Semiconductors
Samsung Electronics
SANYO Semiconductor
Sigma Designs
Silicon Image
Silicon Integrated Systems
Silicon Motion
STMicroelectronics
Texas Instruments
VIA Technologies

HISTORICAL FINANCIALS

Company Type: Public

Income Statement

FYE: December 31

	REVENUE ($ mil.)	NET INCOME ($ mil.)	NET PROFIT MARGIN	EMPLOYEES
12/11	6,568	491	7.5%	11,100
12/10	6,494	471	7.3%	11,100
12/09	5,403	293	5.4%	10,400
12/08	5,808	(3,098)	—	14,700
12/07	6,013	(3,379)	—	16,420
Annual Growth	2.2%	—	—	(9.3%)

2011 Year-End Financials

Debt ratio: 40.69%
Return on equity: 30.88%
Cash ($ mil.): 869
Current ratio: 182.02
Long-term debt ($ mil.): 1,527
No. of shares (mil.): 698
Dividends
Yield: —
Payout: —
Market value ($ mil.): 3,769

	STOCK PRICE ($) FY Close	P/E High	P/E Low	PER SHARE ($) Earnings	Dividends	Book Value
12/11	5.40	14	7	0.66	0.00	2.28
12/10	8.04	15	9	0.64	0.00	1.48
12/09	9.91	22	4	0.45	0.00	0.97
12/08	2.18	—	—	(5.10)	0.00	(0.13)
12/07	7.32	—	—	(6.06)	0.00	4.93
Annual Growth	(7.3%)	—	—	—	—	(17.5%)

Aecom Technology Corp (DE)

AECOM Technology means never having to say Architecture Engineering Consulting Operations and Maintenance. One of the world's leading engineering and design groups AECOM provides planning consulting and construction management services for civil and infrastructure construction to government and private clients. It is a top design firm operating in Asia Africa Europe the Middle East and Australia/New Zealand. The group offers services through two divisions: Professional Technical Services (PTS) and Management Support Services (MSS). AECOM Technology projects have included project management for the Saadiyat Island Cultural District in Abu Dhabi and master planning for the 2012 London Olympics.

The company's PTS segment which accounted for some 86% of AECOM's 2011 revenues provides planning consulting architectural engineering program management and construction management services while MSS offers facilities management as well as training and consulting services primarily for the US government. Domestic and foreign governments together account for about two-thirds of the company's business which could make it vulnerable to government spending cuts or political unrest. However as the world's infrastructure needs grow AECOM stands to benefit from the resulting increase in project opportunities.

Growth by acquisition is a large part of its strategy as it enables the company to cement its leadership position in its existing markets. AECOM has acquired more than 35 companies in the last

10 years expanding geographically and filling out its operations with like-minded companies absorbing them into its existing units.

In 2010 AECOM continued its buying spree with a series of deals including the $245 million purchase of real estate company Tishman's construction business. It expanded its presence in Europe when it bought Spain-based INOCSA Ingenieria a specialist in high-speed rail energy and water projects. AECOM also bought government national security intelligence services firm McNeil Technologies for $355 million and project management consultancy Davis Langdon for some $325 million. The acquisition of Montreal-based RSW boosted AECOM's global energy business.

AECOM acquired Spectral Services a consulting firm based in India in 2011. The addition helped deepen the company's presence across India and Asia and fell in line with AECOM's strategy to expand in emerging markets. Other deals that year included the purchase of four international consulting firms operating under the Davis Langdon name and Canadian engineering firm RSW. After a relatively quiet year with smaller acquisitions the company is likely to go back into active buying mode. In early 2012 AECOM bought Chinese environmental specialist Capital Engineering Corporation further expanding its presence in Asia.

Largely due to the acquisitions the company has made AECOM's revenues have been growing year over year. Revenues grew 23% in 2011 to $8 billion and profits rose 16% to $275.8 million. These gains were offset by a decrease in business for certain governments. For example unrest in Libya caused AECOM to temporarily pull out of an infrastructure project in that country that year. Additionally a contract with the US government to provide combat support services in the Middle East was completed in 2011. The company also exited certain operations in Western Europe as that region struggled. On the other hand the company has secured numerous projects in Asia and Australia where it is a leading design firm so those areas have experienced growth.

EXECUTIVES

President Americas and Government, James M. (Jim) Jaska, age 55
Vice Chairman, Daniel R. (Dan) Tishman, age 56
Chairman Emeritus, Richard G. Newman, age 77, $935,981 total compensation
Chief Executive AECOM Capital, John T. Livingston
Director; Vice Chairman, Francis S. Y. Bong, age 69, $390,943 total compensation
SVP Finance and Chief Strategy Officer, Glenn R. Robson, age 49, $357,505 total compensation
CEO Environment, Robert C. (Bob) Weber
Chairman and CEO, John M. Dionisio, age 63, $978,479 total compensation
COO, Jane A. Chmielinski, age 58
President Corporate Development, Frederick W. (Fred) Werner, age 58
SVP Corporate Finance, Eric Chen
President Strategic Development, Alan P. Krusi, age 56
VP and Director US Tolling Services Transportation, James J. (J.J.) Eden
VP and Corporate Secretary, Christina Ching
Vice Chairman Operations, James R. (Jim) Royer, age 65, $543,389 total compensation
President Global Geographies, Nigel C. Robinson, age 58, $493,250 total compensation
Chairman Asia, Anthony C. K. (Tony) Shum
Chief Executive Building Engineering, Kennedy F. (Ken) Dalton
SVP Human Resources, Ian R. MacLeod
President, Michael S. (Mike) Burke, age 49, $561,776 total compensation
SVP Corporate Communications and Chief Communications Officer, Paul J. Gennaro Jr.
Chief Executive Construction Services; CEO Tishman Construction, Daniel P. McQuade
Group Chief Executive Global Transportation, Elliot G. (Lee) Sander
SVP and CIO, Raul A. Cruz
VP Safety Health and Environmental, Gary Beswick
CEO North America, John L. Kinley
Chief Innovation Officer, Joseph E. Brown
Chief Executive Europe, Stephen (Steve) Morriss
VP External Communications, Paul Dickard
SVP and Chief Risk Officer; CEO AECOM Enterprises, Regis Damour
VP Assistant General Counsel Global Compliance, Susan Frank
EVP and CFO, Stephen M. (Steve) Kadenacy
SVP Operations and Chief Integration Officer, Robert (Bob) Pell
SVP Corporate Services, Gregory Sauter
SVP and CTO, James T. (Jim) Walsh
Global Managing Director Water, Robert Andrews
Chief Executive Middle East, David Barwell
Global Managing Director Energy, Luc Benoit
Global Managing Director Transportation, Graham Hooper
Chief Executive Australia and New Zealand, Richard Jackson
Chief Executive Federal Services Group, Al Konvicka
SVP and Director Program Management, Timothy C. McManus
Chief Executive International Government Services, James F. Thompson
VP Investor Relations, Paul Cyril
Director Corporate Communications, Edward (Ed) Mayer
SVP Legal and General Counsel, Nancy Laben
VP and Assistant General Counsel, David Y. Gan
VP and Chief Sustainability Officer, Gary Lawrence
Director Global IT Infrastructure, Hugo Lopez
Director Information Security, Dan Rathbun
SVP Corporate Services Asia, Christine Cheung
Chief Executive Program Cost Consultancy; Global Chief Executive Davis Langdon, Jeremy Horner
Chief Executive Asia, Dickson Lo
Managing Director Africa, Indresen Pillay
Chief Executive Planning Design + Development, Jason Prior
Resident Engineer and Site Supervisor, Dave Wilkinson
SVP Corporate Controller and Principal Accounting Officer, Ronald E. Osborne
SVP and CIO, Thomas (Tom) Peck
Vice Chairman, Daniel R. (Dan) Tishman, age 56
Chairman Emeritus, Richard G. Newman, age 77
Director, Rob J. Routs, age 65
Director, William G. Ouchi, age 68
Director, Linda M. Griego, age 64
Director, William P. (Bill) Rutledge, age 70
Director; Vice Chairman, Francis S. Y. Bong, age 69
Director, Robert J. (Bob) Lowe, age 72
Chairman and CEO, John M. Dionisio, age 63
Director, James H. Fordyce, age 53
Director, S. Malcolm Gillis, age 71
Auditors: Ernst&YoungLLP

LOCATIONS

HQ: AECOM Technology Corporation
555 S. Flower St. Ste. 3700, Los Angeles CA 90071-2300
Phone: 213-593-8000 **Fax:** 213-593-8730
Web: www.aecom.com

2011 Sales

	$ mil.	% of total
US	4,806	60
Asia/Pacific	1,421	18
Canada	686	8
Europe	643	8
Other	480	6
Total	**8,037**	**100**

PRODUCTS/OPERATIONS

2011 Sales by Segment

	$ mil.	% of total
Professional Technical Services	6,877	86
Management Support Services	1,160	14
Total	**8,037**	**100**

2011 Sales By Client

	$ mil.	% of total
Government		
US federal		
MSS	1,151	14
PTS	640	8
US state & local	1,453	18
Non-US	1,931	24
Private	2,860	36
Total	**8,037**	**100**

COMPETITORS

ABB
AMEC
Bechtel
Black & Veatch
CH2M HILL
Fluor
Foster Wheeler
Henkels & McCoy
Jacobs Engineering
KBR
Louis Berger
MWH Global
Parsons Brinckerhoff
Parsons Corporation
Skidmore Owings
STV
Terracon
Tutor Perini
URS

HISTORICAL FINANCIALS

Company Type: Public

Income Statement

FYE: September 30

	REVENUE ($ mil.)	NET INCOME ($ mil.)	NET PROFIT MARGIN	EMPLOYEES
09/12	8,218	(58)	—	46,800
09/11	8,037	275	3.4%	45,000
09/10	6,545	236	3.6%	48,100
09/09	6,119	189	3.1%	43,200
09/08	5,194	147	2.8%	43,000
Annual Growth	12.2%	—	—	2.1%

2012 Year-End Financials

Debt ratio: 18.88%
Return on equity: (-2.70)%
Cash ($ mil.): 593
Current ratio: 151.43
Long-term debt ($ mil.): 907
No. of shares (mil.): 107
Dividends
Yield: —
Payout: —
Market value ($ mil.): 2,265

	STOCK PRICE ($) FY Close	P/E High	P/E Low	PER SHARE ($) Earnings	Dividends	Book Value
09/12	21.16	—	—	(0.52)	0.00	20.27
09/11	17.67	13	8	2.33	0.00	20.66
09/10	24.26	15	11	2.05	0.00	18.12
09/09	27.14	19	9	1.73	0.00	15.60
09/08	24.44	26	16	1.41	0.00	13.82
Annual Growth	(3.5%)	—	—	—	—	10.0%

AEROTEK INC.

EXECUTIVES

President and CEO, Thomas M. (Tom) Thornton
VP Marketing and Communications, Todd Gardner
President, Todd M. Mohr
CFO, Thomas B. (Tom) Kelly
Director Communications, Erin Mulgrew
SVP Strategic Sales & Operations, Chad Koele
SVP Recruiting Operations, John Flanigan
VP HR, Rodney H. Scaife

LOCATIONS

HQ: Aerotek Inc.
7301 Parkway Dr., Hanover MD 21076
Phone: 410-694-5100 **Fax:** 410-540-7055
Web: www.aerotek.com

PRODUCTS/OPERATIONS

Selected Industries

Accounting and Finance
Administrative
Aerospace & Defense
Architecture
Automotive
Aviation
Call Center
Clinical Research
Construction
Energy
Engineering
Environmental
Labor
Manufacturing
Mortgage
Scientific

COMPETITORS

Adecco
AMN Healthcare
Bryant Bureau
CDI
COMFORCE
Kelly Services
Kforce
ManpowerGroup
Medical Staffing Network
MSX International
On Assignment
Pinnacle Staffing
Randstad Holding
Robert Half

HISTORICAL FINANCIALS

Company Type: Subsidiary

Income Statement FYE: December 31

	REVENUE ($ mil.)	NET INCOME ($ mil.)	NET PROFIT MARGIN	EMPLOYEES
12/11	4,481	226	5.0%	4,200
12/10	3,446	193	5.6%	0
12/09	2,372	87	3.7%	0
12/08	2,838	167	5.9%	0
Annual Growth	16.4%	10.5%	—	—

2011 Year-End Financials

Debt ratio: —
Return on equity: 5.00%
Cash ($ mil.): 6
Current ratio: 3.30
Long-term debt ($ mil.): —
Dividends
Yield: —
Payout: —
Market value ($ mil.): —

AES Corp.

The right place at the right time –Is it kismet? No it's AES one of the world's leading independent power producers. The company has interests in 98 generation facilities in 27 countries throughout the Americas Asia Africa Europe and the Middle East that gave it a net generating capacity of 44200 MW in 2011. AES sells electricity to utilities and other energy marketers through wholesale contracts or on the spot market. AES also sells power directly to customers worldwide through stakes in distribution utilities mainly in Latin America. The company has 2400 MW of power plants under development in eight countries. In 2011 AES acquired DPL in a $4.7 billion deal.

HISTORY

Applied Energy Services (AES) was founded in 1981 three years after passage of the Public Utilities Regulation Policies Act which enabled small power firms to enter electric generation markets formerly dominated by utility monopolies. Cofounders Roger Sant and Dennis Bakke who had served in President Nixon's Federal Energy Administration saw that an independent power producer (IPP) could make money by generating cheap power in large volumes to sell to large power consumers and utilities.

AES set about building massive cogeneration plants (producing both steam and electricity) in 1983. The first plant Deepwater went into operation near Houston in 1986. By 1989 AES had three plants on line and it then opened plants in Connecticut and Oklahoma. In 1991 the company formally renamed AES went public but one plant's falsified emissions reports caused AES's stock to plummet in 1992.

Facing environmental groups' opposition to new power plant construction and an overall glut in the US power market AES bought interests in two Northern Ireland plants in 1992 and began expanding into Latin America in 1993. Also in 1993 AES set up a separately traded subsidiary AES China Generating Co. to focus on Chinese development projects. AES won a plant development contract with the Puerto Rico Electric Power Authority (1994) and a bid to privatize an Argentine hydrothermal company (1995).

In 1996 AES began adding stakes in electric utility and distribution companies to its portfolio including interests in formerly state-owned Brazilian electric utilities Light-Servicos de Eletricidade (1996) and CEMIG (1997); one Brazilian and two Argentine distribution companies (1997); and a distribution company in El Salvador (1998).

AES almost doubled its revenues after buying Destec Energy's international operations from NGC (now Dynegy) in 1997. By the next year prospects in international markets were dimming so AES turned to the US market again. It bought three California plants from Edison International and arranged for The Williams Companies to supply natural gas to the facilities and market the electricity generated. AES also won a bid to buy six plants from New York State Electric & Gas (now Energy East) affiliate NGE.

Also in 1998 despite black days in many world markets AES bought 90% of Argentine electric distribution company Edelap and a 45% stake in state-owned Orissa Power Generation in India. Its moves paid off: AES posted a 70% gain in sales that year.

It bought CILCORP an Illinois utility holding company in an $886 million deal in 1999. Boosting its presence in the UK AES bought the Drax power station a 3960-MW coal-fired plant from National Power. It also bought a majority stake in Brazilian data transmission company Eletronet from Brazil's government-owned utility ELETROBRAS. In 2000 AES increased its interests in Brazilian power distributors. It also gained a 73% stake (later expanded to 87%) in Venezuelan electric utility Grupo EDC in a $1.5 billion hostile takeover.

The next year AES bought IPALCO the parent of Indianapolis Power & Light in a $3 billion deal. Also in 2001 AES acquired the outstanding shares of Chilean generation company Gener in which it previously held a 60% stake.

That year AES moved to take control of CANTV Venezuela's #1 telecom company. Through Grupo EDC which already owned 6.9% of CANTV AES offered to buy 43.2% of the company. But AES withdrew the offer after the CANTV board rejected it. (AES sold Grupo EDC's stake in CANTV the following year.) AES also sold some generation assets in Argentina to TOTAL FINA ELF (now TOTAL) for about $370 million.

In 2002 AES sold its 24% interest in Light Servicos de Eletricidade (Light) to Electricite de France (EDF) in exchange for a 20% stake in Brazilian utility Eletropaulo (increasing its stake in Eletropaulo to 70%). In that same year the company sold its retail energy marketing unit (AES NewEnergy) to Constellation Energy Group for $240 million and its CILCORP subsidiary which holds utility Central Illinois Light to Ameren.

In 2007 the company acquired two 230 MW petroleum coke-fired power generation facilities in Tamuin Mexico for $611 million. It also bought a 51% stake in Turkish power generator IC ICTAS Energy Group.

AES has faced controversy in Brazil where an unstable power market has caused the company to default on debts incurred from its purchases of stakes in local utilities (as well as bankrupt telecom firm Eletronet) in recent years. To restructure its debt with Banco Nacional de Desenvolvimento Economico e Social (BNDES) AES completed a deal in 2007 in which the firm's interests in AES Eletropaulo AES Uruguaiana AES Tiete and AES Sul was placed into a new holding company (Brasiliana Energia). AES owns 50.1% of that company while BNDES holds 49.9%.

To raise cash in 2008 and 2009 AES sold the AES Ekibastuz power plant and Maikuben coal mine in Kazakhstan to Kazakhmys PLC for $1.1 billion. The assets were no longer considered to be a viable part of its long term energy portfolio.

In 2008 the company boosted it assets in the Philippines acquiring the 660 MW Masinloc coal-fired power plant in Barangay Bula Zambales Province Luzon for $930 million. It began an $800 million expansion of that facility in 2010.

In 2008 it formed AES Solar Energy a joint venture with investment firm Riverstone Holdings. The project has begun commercial operations at nine solar plants in Spain generating some 33 MW of power.

To reduce carbon emissions the company is developing alternative energy power plants including wind hydro and biomass. In 2010 AES Wind Generation had 30 plants with more than 1400 MW of generating capacity in operation in four countries. The company is one of the largest producers of wind power in the US.

EXECUTIVES

Plant Manager AES Huntington Beach, David Stone
Chairman, Philip A. Odeen, age 76
EVP and CFO, Thomas M. (Tom) O'Flynn, age 51
VP and Controller, Mary E. Wood, age 56
EVP CFO and President Global Business Services, Victoria D. Harker, age 47, $600,000 total compensation
President CEO and Director, Andres R. Gluski, age 54, $670,000 total compensation
EVP; COO Global Generation, Edward (Ned) Hall, age 52, $440,000 total compensation
EVP General Counsel and Corporate Secretary, Brian A. Miller, age 46, $463,000 total compensation
EVP and Global Commercial Support, Richard (Rich) Santoroski
EVP; COO Global Utilities, Andrew M. Vesey, age 56
SVP Global Business Services and CIO, Elizabeth Hackenson, age 51
Managing Director Mergers and Acquisitions, Ahmed Pasha
President AES Southland, Eric Pendergraft
Director External Communications, Meghan Dotter
President and Plant Manager AES Alamitos, Tony Chavez
CFO and Financial Manager AES Southland, Minh Hoang
Director Government and Regulatory Affairs AES Southland, Julie Gill
Plant Manager AES Redondo Beach, Buck Hunt
CEO Greenhouse Gas Services, Mauricio Vargas
CFO and Chief Risk Officer Greenhouse Gas Services, Joseph DeNicola
Managing Director Carbon Project Development Greenhouse Gas Services, Mark A. Miller
Senior Director Construction Operations and Engineering Greenhouse Gas Services, Mark Stanski
General Counsel and Corporate Secretary Greenhouse Gas Services, Robert A. Kohn
Managing Director Construction Operations and Policy Greenhouse Gas Services, Derek Porter
Managing Director Project Development Greenhouse Gas Services, Brandon Moffatt
Managing Director Commercial and Canada Business Greenhouse Gas Services, Christopher (Chris) Guillon
Media Contact Greenhouse Gas Services, Alison Carr
Coordinator External Communications, Lucas Bushman
VP Investor Relations, Joel Abramson
VP Human Resources and Internal Communications Safety and AES Performance Excellence, Rita Trehan, age 44
SVP Strategy, Gardner W. Walkup Jr.
Director, John B. (Jay) Morse Jr., age 65
Director, Philip Lader, age 66
Director, Sandra O. Moose, age 70
Director, Sven Sandstrom, age 70
President CEO and Director, Andres R. Gluski, age 54
Director, Charles O. Rossotti, age 71
Director, John A. Koskinen, age 73
Director, Samuel W. Bodman III, age 72
Director, Tarun Khanna, age 45
Auditors: Ernst&YoungLLP

LOCATIONS

HQ: The AES Corporation
4300 Wilson Blvd. 11th Fl., Arlington VA 22203
Phone: 703-522-1315 **Fax:** 703-528-4510
Web: www.aes.com

2011 Sales

	$ mil.	% of total
Latin America		
Utilities	7,374	42
Generation	4,982	29
North America		
Generation	1,465	8
Utilities	1,326	8
Europe		
Generation	1,550	9
Asia		
Generation	625	4
Adjustments	(48)	-
Total	17,274	100

PRODUCTS/OPERATIONS

2011 Sales

	$ mil.	% of total
Regulated	9,504	55
Non-regulated	7,770	45
Total	17,274	100

Selected Electric Utilities and Distribution Companies

AES CLESA (electric utility El Salvador)
AES Edelap (electric utility Argentina)
AES Eden (electric utility Argentina)
AES Edes (electric utility Argentina)
AES Gener (electric generation Chile)
AES India Private Ltd.
AES SeaWest Inc.
Brasiliana Energia
  AES Sul Distribuidora Gaucha de Energia SA (AES Sul electric utility Brazil)
  AES Tiete (power generation Brazil)
  AES Uruguaiana (power generation Brazil)
  Eletropaulo Metropolitana Eletricidade de S?o Paulo S.A. (AES Electropaulo electric distribution Brazil)
CAESS (electric utility El Salvador)
Companhia Energetica de Minas Gerais (CEMIG Brazil)
EEO (electric utility El Salvador)
IC ICTAS Energy Group (power generation Turkey)
IPALCO Enterprises Inc. (holding company)

COMPETITORS

Alliant Energy
Bonneville Power
Calpine
CenterPoint Energy
CMS Energy
CPFL Energia
Duke Energy
Dynegy
E.ON UK
Edison International
El Paso Corporation
Endesa S.A.
Energias de Portugal
Energy Future
Enersis
Entergy
Exelon
GenOnEnergy
Huadian Power
IBERDROLA
Indeck Energy
International Power
MidAmerican Energy
NextEra Energy
Nicor Gas
NRG Energy
PG&E Corporation
Public Service Enterprise Group
Sempra Energy
Siemens AG
Tractebel Engineering
Xcel Energy

HISTORICAL FINANCIALS

Company Type: Public

Income Statement FYE: December 31

	REVENUE ($ mil.)	NET INCOME ($ mil.)	NET PROFIT MARGIN	EMPLOYEES
12/11	17,274	58	0.3%	27,000
12/10	16,647	9	0.1%	29,000
12/09	14,119	658	4.7%	27,000
12/08	16,070	1,234	7.7%	25,000
12/07	13,588	(95)	—	28,000
Annual Growth	6.2%	—	—	(0.9%)

2011 Year-End Financials

Debt ratio: 49.79%
Return on equity: 0.96%
Cash ($ mil.): 1,710
Current ratio: 109.26
Long-term debt ($ mil.): 20,116
No. of shares (mil.): 765
Dividends
  Yield: —
  Payout: —
Market value ($ mil.): 9,060

	STOCK PRICE ($) FY Close	P/E High/Low	PER SHARE ($) Earnings	Dividends	Book Value
12/11	11.84	191135	0.07	0.00	7.87
12/10	12.18	1413890	0.01	0.00	8.30
12/09	13.31	15 5	0.98	0.00	7.09
12/08	8.24	12 3	1.82	0.00	5.54
12/07	21.39	— —	(0.14)	0.00	4.72
Annual Growth	(13.7%)	— —	—	—	13.6%

Aetna Inc.

Life death health or injury —Aetna's got an insurance policy to cover it. The company one of the largest health insurers in the US also offers life and disability insurance as well as retirement savings products. Its health care division offers HMO PPO point of service (POS) health savings account (HSA) and traditional indemnity coverage along with dental vision behavioral health and Medicare and Medicaid plans to groups and individuals. The health care segment covers some 18.5 million medical members. Aetna's group insurance segment sells life and disability insurance nationwide and its large case pensions segment offers pensions annuities and other retirement savings products.

HISTORY

Hartford Connecticut businessman and judge Eliphalet Bulkeley started Connecticut Mutual Life Insurance in 1846. Agents gained control of the firm the following year. Undeterred Bulkeley and a group of Hartford businessmen founded Aetna Life Insurance in 1853 as a spinoff of Aetna Fire Insurance. Among its offerings was coverage for slaves a practice for which the company apologized in 2000.

A nationwide agency network fueled early growth at Aetna which expanded in the 1860s by offering a participating life policy returning dividends to policyholders based on investment earnings. (This let Aetna compete with mutual life insurers.) In 1868 Aetna became the first firm to offer renewable term life policies.

Eliphalet's son Morgan became president in 1879. Aetna moved into accident (1891) health (1899) workers' compensation (1902) and auto and other property insurance (1907) during his 43-year tenure. He served as Hartford mayor Connecticut governor and US senator all the while leading Aetna.

By 1920 the company sold marine insurance and by 1922 it was the US's largest multiline insurer. Aetna overexpanded its nonlife lines (particularly autos) during the 1920s threatening its solvency. It survived the Depression by restricting underwriting and rebuilding reserves.

After WWII the firm expanded into group life health and accident insurance. In 1967 it reorganized into holding company Aetna Life and Casualty.

The 1960s 1970s and 1980s were go-go years: The company added lines and bought and sold everything from an oil services firm to commercial real estate. The boom period led to a bust and a 1991 reorganization in which Aetna eliminated 8000 jobs withdrew from such lines as auto insurance and sold its profitable American Reinsurance.

To take advantage of the boom in retirement savings in 1995 it got permission to set up bank AE Trust to act as a pension trustee.

With its health care business accounting for some 60% of sales by 1995 the company restructured in the late 1990s. Aetna sold its property/casualty behavioral managed care (1997) and individual life insurance (1998) businesses. It then expanded overseas and bought U.S. Healthcare and New York Life's NYLCare managed health business (1998).

Controversy marred 1998. Contract terms –including a "gag" clause against discussing uncovered treatments –prompted 400 Texas doctors to leave its system; defections followed in Kentucky and West Virginia. Consumers balked over Aetna's refusal to cover some treatments including experimental procedures and advanced fertility treatments. One group sued for false advertising.

The American Medical Association that year decried Aetna's plan to buy Prudential's health care unit as anticompetitive; in 1999 the government required Aetna to sell operations including NYLCare (completed 2000) to gain approval. Also in 1999 Aetna became the second insurer (after Humana) to be sued for misleading clients about treatment decisions; it reached a settlement the next year with the State of Texas over capitation physician incentives and other matters.

In 2000 Aetna restated earnings for seven previous quarters at the behest of the SEC. Flagging earnings prompted CEO Richard Huber to resign; William Donaldson one of the founders of Donaldson Lufkin & Jenrette now Credit Suisse First Boston (USA) took his place. Also in 2000 Aetna went through major restructuring and sold its financial services and international divisions to Netherlands-based ING Groep.

John "Jack" Rowe took over the helm as CEO in 2001 and announced that Aetna may require two years to recover from turbulent changes and rising medical costs. In 2002 the company returned to operating profitability after reducing its workforce raising premiums and restructuring critical operations. Also that year Aetna expanded its pharmacy benefits management operations.

The following year it bought a mail-order pharmacy facility from Eckerd Health Services and in 2004 formed Aetna Specialty Pharmacy a joint venture with Priority Healthcare (later named CuraScript) to provide mail-order drugs to consumers with chronic diseases.

In 2005 Aetna acquired health technology company ActiveHealth. It also brought its behavioral health care services in-house; the firm formerly contracted with Magellan Health Services but bought those operations in late 2005 rebranding the business as Aetna Behavioral Health.

It bought out CuraScript's share of Aetna Specialty Pharmacy in early 2006 as part of that company's merger with Express Scripts. Later that year Ronald Williams succeeded Jack Rowe as CEO.

In 2007 the company expanded its health care offerings for expatriates by acquiring Goodhealth an underwriting agent for international private medical insurance. Goodhealth became part of the Aetna Global Benefits division (which was renamed as Aetna International in 2011). Aetna also acquired Medicaid provider Schaller Anderson in 2007.

To expand its offerings for expatriates Aetna Global Benefits unit positioned the group to take a major leap forward when it set up a representative office in China in mid-2008 the beginning of a two-year process of becoming licensed to sell insurance in the world's largest market. It also signed contracts with the Dubai government that year. Aetna also added a direct provider network in Africa in 2009.

To build up its workplace products the company paid $70 million in 2009 to buy employee assistance program (EAP) provider Horizon Behavioral Services from Psychiatric Solutions (now part of Universal Health Services).

Williams retired from the CEO post in 2010 after about a decade with the company. He was replaced by Mark Bertolini who retained his role as president of Aetna a position held since 2007. Bertolini started with Aetna in 2003.

EXECUTIVES

Head Strategic Diversification, Charles E. (Chuck) Saunders
SVP Human Resources, Elease E. Wright
SVP and General Counsel, William J. Casazza, age 56, $498,129 total compensation
VP New Businesses, Andrew Lee, age 39
SVP and Head Health Care Management and the Regions, Jeff D. Emerson, age 62
Chairman President and CEO, Mark T. Bertolini, age 56, $932,414 total compensation
EVP Operations and Technology, Margaret M. (Meg) McCarthy, age 58
SVP and Head National Government and Specialty Products, Patricia A. (Pat) Farrell
SVP Marketing Product and Communications, Robert E. Mead
SVP and Chief Medical Officer, Lonny Reisman, age 56, $547,893 total compensation
SEVP CFO and Chief Enterprise Risk Officer, Joseph M. Zubretsky, age 56, $725,211 total compensation
President and CEO Schaller Anderson, Thomas L. (Tom) Kelly, age 58
Managing Director Aetna Global Benefits (AGB), David Corkum
CEO and President ActiveHealth Management, Gregory (Greg) Steinberg
Media and Public Relations, Fred Laberge
Head New Product Business, Dan Fishbein
VP and CIO, Michael G. Mathias, age 53
Head Public and Labor, Cain Hayes
President Aetna International, Sandip Patel, age 45
Chief Nursing Officer, Susan M. Kosman
Chief of Staff Office of the Chairman and CEO; Head Mergers and Acquisitions Integration and Head Health Care Reform Project Management Office, Kay Mooney
National Medical Director Racial and Ethnic Equality, Wayne Rawlins
Managing Director Greater China, Hocking Cheng
Managing Director Southeast Asia, Derek Goldberg
Head Brand and Consumer Marketing, Belinda Lang
SVP Local Employers & Consumers, Frank G. McCauley
President Aetna Student Health, Chekesha C. Kidd
VP Account Management Aetna Student Health, Philip Chambers
VP National Sales Aetna Student Health, Paul Correia
VP Operations Aetna Student Health, Don Harrington
VP Finance Aetna Student Health, Maryellen Pease
Head Network Access and Health Plan Services Emerging Businesses Unit, Michael Ciarrocchi
Investor Relations, Tom Cowhey
CTO, Richard J. (Rich) Leonard, age 58
VP and Head Sales Latin America International, Krishnan Sridharan
Executive Vice President; Head - Specialty Products, Karen Rohan
Executive Vice President of Aetna Government Services, Kristi A. Matus
Director, Frank M. Clark Jr., age 66
Director, Edward J. (Ed) Ludwig, age 61
Director, Richard J. (Dick) Harrington, age 65
Director, Betsy Zubrow Cohen, age 71
Director, Ellen M. Hancock, age 68
Director, Earl G. Graves Sr., age 77
Director, Roger N. Farah, age 59
Director, Gerald Greenwald, age 76
Director, Jeffrey E. Garten, age 65
Director, Barbara Hackman Franklin, age 72
Director, Joseph P. Newhouse, age 70
Director, Molly J. Coye, age 65
Independent Director, Betsy Cohen
Independent Director, Fernando Aguirre
Auditors: KPMGLLP

LOCATIONS

HQ: Aetna Inc.
151 Farmington Avenue, Hartford, CT 06156
Phone: 860 273-0123
Web: www.aetna.com

PRODUCTS/OPERATIONS

2012 Sales

	$ mil.	% of total
Health care		
Commercial premiums	20,944	57
Medicare premiums	6,250	17
Medicaid premiums	1,677	5
Fees & other	4,133	11
Group insurance	2,145	6
Large case pensions	1,444	4
Total	**36,595**	**100**

Selected Products and Services

Behavioral and Mental Health Plans
Dental Plans
Disability Insurance
Health Expense Funds
Life Insurance
Medicaid
Medical Plans
Medicare
Pharmacy
Student Health
Support Programs
Vision Plans
Wellness Programs and Discounts

Selected Acquisitions

2011
Continental Life ($290 million US Medicare supplement business of Genworth)
Indian Health Organization (IHO medical and dental plans India)
Medicity ($500 million US health information exchange platforms)
PayFlex ($202 million US consumer spending account administration)
Prodigy Health Group ($600 million US third party administrator of self-funded health and dental plans)

COMPETITORS

ACE Limited
AMERIGROUP
BioScrip
Blue Cross
Blue Shield Of
Health Net
HealthSpring
Highmark
Humana
Independence Blue

California
Catalyst Health Solutions
Centene
CIGNA
Coventry Health Care
DeCare Dental
Delta Dental Plans
Express Scripts
Guardian Life
HCSC
Cross
Kaiser Foundation Health Plan
Magellan Health
MetLife
Molina Healthcare
Principal Financial
Prudential
UnitedHealth Group
USAA
WellPoint

HISTORICAL FINANCIALS

Company Type: Public

Income Statement FYE: December 31

	ASSETS ($ mil.)	NET INCOME ($ mil.)	INCOME AS % OF ASSETS	EMPLOYEES
12/11	38,593	1,985	5.1%	33,300
12/10	37,739	1,766	4.7%	34,000
12/09	38,550	1,276	3.3%	35,000
12/08	35,852	1,384	3.9%	35,500
12/07	50,724	1,831	3.6%	35,200
Annual Growth	(6.6%)	2.0%	—	(1.4%)

2011 Year-End Financials

Debt ratio: 10.31%
Return on equity: 19.62%
Cash ($ mil.): 679
Current ratio: —
Long-term debt ($ mil.): 3,977
No. of shares (mil.): 349
Dividends
Yield: —
Payout: 8.62%
Market value ($ mil.): 14,754

	STOCK PRICE ($) FY Close	P/E High/Low		PER SHARE ($) Earnings	Dividends	Book Value
12/11	42.19	9	6	5.22	0.00	28.94
12/10	30.51	8	6	4.18	0.04	25.73
12/09	31.70	12	7	2.84	0.04	22.06
12/08	28.50	20	6	2.83	0.04	17.94
12/07	57.73	17	11	3.47	0.04	20.23
Annual Growth	(7.5%)	—	—	10.7%	—	9.4%

AFLAC Inc.

Would you buy insurance from a duck? Aflac counts on it! To soften the financial stresses during periods of disability or illness Aflac sells supplemental health and life insurance policies including coverage for accidents intensive care dental vision and disability as well as for specific conditions primarily cancer. It is a leading supplier of supplemental insurance in the US and is an industry leader in Japan's cancer-insurance market (with 14 million policies in force). Aflac which is marketed through –and is an acronym for –American Family Life Assurance Company sells policies that pay cash benefits for hospital confinement emergency treatment and medical appliances.

Geographic Reach

Despite its US roots Aflac makes 75% of its insurance sales in Japan where its policies fill in gaps not covered by the national health insurance system.

Sales & Marketing

In Japan Aflac primarily sells through an agency system in which a corporation forms a subsidiary to sell Aflac insurance to its employees. In the face of Japan's deregulated life insurance industry the company has also had a marketing alliance with Dai-ichi Life Insurance one of the country's largest life insurers since 2000. Changes in regulations now allow the company to sell through banks and post offices and it has also opened retail shops where consumers can purchase directly from sales associates.

In the US Aflac sells mainly through the workplace with employers deducting premiums from paychecks. Building on its strong brand recognition –due largely to the company's popular TV ads featuring a valiant spokes-duck –Aflac has invested in its US business by adding more sales associates and expanding its distribution to include insurance brokers.

Financial Analysis

Its reliance on Japan has a downside: The company is vulnerable to currency fluctuations between the dollar and yen. It also faces increased competition due to deregulation of Japan's insurance industry. However as in the US Japanese consumers are seeing more health care costs being shifted onto their shoulders making Aflac's products more attractive.

Strategy

Aflac has created new life insurance products for the Japanese market. In addition to standard life insurance it has also introduced child endowment products that pay out part of the benefit when the child enters high school and then functions like an annuity for four years during college.

Aflac paddled seemingly unperturbed through the economic recession in its major markets. It is also remaining unruffled by the potential changes in the US health care insurance industry. As it is already familiar with operating in a market with a national health care system and as it does not pay for any actual health care it does not expect to see major changes in its products. If anything the company anticipates a potential increase in demand for its products should the US adopt a more comprehensive major medical health insurance plan.

Mergers & Acquisitions

To build up its US large-group business in late 2009 Aflac paid $100 million to purchase Continental American Insurance Company. Rebranded as Aflac Group Insurance the business offers payroll-deducted voluntary group insurance products for large employers.

Ownership

Chairman and CEO Dan Amos holds 9% of the company his father and uncles founded. His son Paul Amos serves as the company's president.

HISTORY

American Family Life Assurance Company (AFLAC) was founded in Columbus Georgia in 1955 by brothers John Paul and William Amos to sell life health and accident insurance. Competition was fierce and the little company did poorly. With AFLAC nearing bankruptcy the brothers looked for a niche.

The polio scares of the 1940s and 1950s had spawned insurance coverage written especially against that disease; the Amos brothers (whose father was a cancer victim) took a cue from that concept and decided to sell cancer insurance. In 1958 they introduced the world's first cancer-expense policy. It was a hit and by 1959 the company had written nearly a million dollars in premiums and expanded across state lines.

The enterprise grew quickly during the 1960s especially after developing its cluster-selling approach in the workplace where employers were usually willing to make payroll deductions for premiums. By 1971 the company was operating in 42 states.

While visiting the World's Fair in Osaka in 1970 John Amos decided to market supplemental cancer coverage to the Japanese whose national health care plan left them exposed to considerable expense from cancer treatment. After four years the company finally won approval to sell in Japan since the policies did not threaten existing markets and because the Amoses found notable backers in the insurance and medical industries. AFLAC became one of the first US insurance companies to enter the Japanese market and it enjoyed an eight-year monopoly on the cancer market. Back in the US in 1973 AFLAC organized a holding company and began buying television stations in the South and Midwest.

The 1980s were marked by US and state government inquiries into dread disease insurance. Critics said such policies were a poor value because they were relatively expensive and covered only one disease. However the inquiries led nowhere and demand for such insurance increased bringing new competition. In the 1980s AFLAC's scales tilted: US growth slowed while business grew in Japan which soon accounted for most of the company's sales.

In 1990 John Amos died of cancer and was replaced as CEO by his nephew Dan. Two years later the company officially renamed itself Aflac (partly because Dan planned to increase the company's US profile and so many US companies already used the name "American").

Aflac has sought to supplement its cancer insurance by introducing new products and improving old ones to encourage policyholders to add on or trade up. Its Japanese "living benefit" product which includes lump sum payments for heart attacks and strokes struck a chord with the aging population.

Connecticut in 1997 repealed its ban on specified-disease insurance; New York eventually followed suit. Also that year Aflac sold its seven TV stations to Raycom Media to focus on insurance.

The company boosted its name recognition in the US from 2% in 1990 to more than 56% primarily through advertising including slots during the 1998 Olympic Winter Games and NASCAR races.

Accident/disability premiums surpassed cancer premiums in the US for the first time in the company's history in 2000. The Aflac duck made its first appearance in a 2001 Japanese commercial for accident insurance. Shortly thereafter it debuted in the US where it quickly achieved advertising-icon status.

EXECUTIVES

EVP and Deputy CFO, Kenneth S. (Ken) Janke Jr., age 53

EVP General Counsel and Corporate Secretary, Joey M. Loudermilk, age 58, $518,700 total compensation

President CFO Treasurer and Director; EVP Aflac, Kriss Cloninger III, age 64, $883,500 total compensation

Chairman and CEO, Daniel P. (Dan) Amos, age 60, $1,378,400 total compensation

SVP and Director Governmental Relations, Phillip J. (Jack) Friou

Chairman Aflac Japan, Charles D. Lake II, age 50, $333,333 total compensation

EVP Corporate Services, Audrey Boone Tillman, age 47

SVP and CIO, Michael B. Boyle

SVP Customer Assurance Organization, Laree R. Daniel

President and Director; COO Aflac US, Paul S. Amos II, age 36, $515,000 total compensation

EVP; Chief Administrative Officer Aflac U.S., Teresa L. White, age 45
SVP and Director Human Resources, Janet P. Baker
SVP Fixed Income Investments, W. Jeremy (Jerry) Jeffery, age 61
SVP Strategic Management Aflac International, John A. Moorefield
EVP and Corporate Actuary; First SVP Aflac Japan, Susan R. Blanck, age 45
President and COO Aflac Japan, Tohru Tonoike, age 61, $597,925 total compensation
SVP and Director U.S. Sales, Thomas R. Giddens
SVP and Chief Marketing Officer US, Michael W. Zuna
SVP Financial Services and International Financial Reporting Standards and Chief Accounting Officer, June P. Howard, age 46
SVP and Global Chief Investment Officer, Eric M. Kirsch
Director, E. Stephen Purdom, age 64
President CFO Treasurer and Director; EVP Aflac, Kriss Cloninger III, age 64
Director, Elizabeth J. Hudson, age 62
Director, John Shelby Amos II, age 59
Director, Michael H. Armacost, age 74
Director, Joe Frank Harris, age 76
Director, Charles B. Knapp, age 65
Director, Barbara K. Rimer, age 63
Director, Marvin R. Schuster, age 74
Director, Robert L. Wright, age 74
Director, Robert B. Johnson, age 67
Director, Douglas W. (Doug) Johnson, age 68
President and Director; COO Aflac US, Paul S. Amos II, age 36
Director, David G. Thompson, age 65
Director, Takuro Yoshida
Auditors: KPMGLLP

LOCATIONS

HQ: Aflac Incorporated
1932 Wynnton Rd., Columbus GA 31999
Phone: 706-323-3431 **Fax:** 706-324-6330
Web: www.aflac.com

PRODUCTS/OPERATIONS

2012 Sales

Aflac Japan	20,053	77
Corporate	262	1
Realized investment losses	(349)	-
Total	**25,364**	**100**

COMPETITORS

American Fidelity Assurance Company
American National Insurance
Asahi Mutual Life
CNO Financial
Colonial Life & Accident
Meiji Yasuda Life
MetLife
Nippon Life Insurance
Taiyo Life
Torchmark
Unum Group

HISTORICAL FINANCIALS

Company Type: Public

Income Statement FYE: December 31

	ASSETS ($ mil.)	NET INCOME ($ mil.)	INCOME AS % OF ASSETS	EMPLOYEES
12/11	117,102	1,964	1.7%	8,562
12/10	101,039	2,344	2.3%	8,211
12/09	84,106	1,497	1.8%	8,057
12/08	79,331	1,254	1.6%	7,949
12/07	65,805	1,634	2.5%	8,048
Annual Growth	15.5%	4.7%	—	1.6%

2011 Year-End Financials

Debt ratio: 2.81%
Return on equity: 14.54%
Cash ($ mil.): 2,249
Current ratio: —
Long-term debt ($ mil.): 3,285
No. of shares (mil.): 466
Dividends
Yield: —
Payout: 29.43%
Market value ($ mil.): 20,173

	STOCK PRICE ($) FY Close	P/E High	P/E Low	PER SHARE ($) Earnings	Dividends	Book Value
12/11	43.26	14	7	4.18	0.00	28.96
12/10	56.43	12	8	4.95	1.14	23.54
12/09	46.25	15	4	3.19	1.12	17.96
12/08	45.84	26	11	2.62	0.96	14.23
12/07	62.63	19	14	3.31	0.80	18.08
Annual Growth	(8.8%)	—	—	6.0%	—	12.5%

AGCO Corp.

AGCO's annual harvests may be smaller than those of major rivals John Deere and CNH Global but it reaps some healthy profits worldwide. AGCO makes tractors combines hay and forage tools sprayers and replacement parts for agricultural end-uses. It sells through a global network of some 3100 dealers and distributors spanning 140 countries. It also builds diesel engines gears and generators through its AGCO Sisu Power unit. Its four core machinery brands include Massey Ferguson Challenger Valtra (Finland-based) and Fendt (Germany). The company offers financing services to retail customers and dealers via a venture with Dutch company Rabobank.

HISTORY

In 1861 American Edward Allis purchased the bankrupt Reliance Works a leading Milwaukee-based manufacturer of sawmills and flour-milling equipment. Under shrewd management The Reliance Works of Edward P. Allis & Co. weathered financial troubles - bankruptcy in the Panic of 1873 —but managed to renegotiate its debt and recover. By the time Allis died in 1889 Reliance Works employed some 1500 workers.

The company branched into different areas of manufacturing in the late 19th century and by the 20th century the Edward P. Allis Co. (as it was then known) was the world leader in steam engines. In 1901 the company merged with another manufacturing giant Fraser & Chalmers to form the Allis-Chalmers Company. In the 1920s and 1930s Allis-Chalmers entered the farm equipment market.

Although overshadowed by John Deere and International Harvester (IH) Allis-Chalmers made key contributions to the industry —the first rubber-tired tractor (1932) and the All-Crop harvester. Allis-Chalmers spun off its farm equipment business in the 1950s and phased out several unrelated products. The company with its orange-colored tractors expanded and prospered from the 1940s through the early 1970s. Then the chafing farm economy of the late 1970s and early 1980s hurt Allis-Chalmers' sales.

After layoffs and a plant shutdown in 1984 the company was purchased in 1985 by German machinery maker Klockner-Humbolt-Deutz (KHD) who moved the company (renamed Deutz-Allis) to Georgia. In the mid-1980s low food prices hurt farmers and low demand hurt the equipment market. KHD was never able to bring profits up to a satisfactory level and in 1990 the German firm sold the unit to the US management in a buyout led by Robert Ratliff. Ratliff believed the company could succeed by acquiring belly-up equipment makers turning them around and competing on price.

Renamed AGCO the company launched a buying spree in 1991 that included Fiat's Hesston (1991) White Tractor (1991) the North American distribution rights for Massey Ferguson (1993) and White-New Idea (1993). The bumper crop of product growth enabled it to slice into the market share of competitors Deere and Case. AGCO went public in 1992. Its 1994 purchase of the remainder of Massey Ferguson (with 20% of the world market) vaulted AGCO to prominence among the world's leading farm equipment makers.

In 1996 AGCO launched a five-year plan for European growth. In 1997 the company acquired German farm equipment makers Fendt and Dronniberg. It also picked up Deutz Argentina a supplier of agricultural equipment engines and vehicles as part of an effort to expand into Latin and South America.

AGCO entered the agricultural sprayer market in 1998 by acquiring the Spra-Coupe line from Ingersoll-Rand and the Willmar line from Cargill. A worldwide drop in farm equipment sales caused AGCO to cut about 10% of its workforce.

To further overcome stalled sales and slumping profits in 1999 the company announced it was permanently closing an Ohio plant and would cease production at a Texas plant. The next year AGCO closed its Missouri plant and trimmed its workforce by about 5%.

In 2001 AGCO acquired fertilizer equipment manufacturer Ag-Chem Equipment and the next year it completed the purchase of certain assets relating to the design assembly and marketing of the MT 700 and MT 800 series of Caterpillar's Challenger rubber-tracked farm tractors.

AGCO added to its harvesting equipment segment in 2002 by purchasing Beloit-based Sunflower Manufacturing for an undisclosed price. That year AGCO suffered a tragic loss when president and CEO John Shumejda and SVP Ed Swingle were killed in an airplane accident in the UK.

The company added Valtra in early 2004 a global tractor and off-road engine maker to its fold for about $750 million. In 2004 chairman Robert Ratliff handed Martin Richenhagen the president and CEO titles he had taken on after the death of Shumejda.

AGCO announced late in 2006 a new growth initiative dubbed "Always Growing." The strategy makes some basic assumptions about the trends emerging in global agriculture. They include the increase in mega-farms exponential growth in certain developing countries increased demand for biofuels in developed nations and increasingly advanced technology.

In 2007 it bought Industria Agricola Fortaleza Limitada a leading Brazilian maker of farm implements and purchased a 50% stake in Laverda an Italian harvesting equipment producer to further expand its overseas presence.

It partnered with Topcon and Sauer-Danfoss in 2008 to provide steering technology for its professional farming equipment. The company formed a joint venture with one of Russia's leading industrial equipment producers CTP to assemble engines.

AGCO has taken advantage of public funding too. In 2009 the company was selected by the US Department of Energy for a $5 million grant to determine whether a hay product can be used to supply large biomass feedstock to biofuel processors. AGCO is working with renewable fuel companies and industry experts to develop an efficient method of collecting and transporting biomass to production plants.

In an effort to reduce costs and selling and administrative expenses as well as align inventory supply with global market demand AGCO restructured during 2010 and 2009. The company cut headcount and closed and consolidated manufacturing facilities in the US UK France Germany Spain Finland and Denmark. AGCO also instituted temporary plant shutdowns in all of its factories and cut production reducing both its company and dealer inventories.

Filling a regional product niche AGCO in late 2010 purchased UK-based Sparex from Rubicon Partners Industries for #53 million (more than $75 million). Sparex is a global distributor of tractor replacement parts; it extends AGCO's portfolio of accessories as well as its reach into for the agricultural aftermarket.

EXECUTIVES

Director, Luiz Fernando Furlan, age 66
Senior VP; CEO GSI, Scott G. Clawson, age 46
SVP and CFO, Andrew H. (Andy) Beck, age 48, $418,850 total compensation
SVP - Engineering Projects, Garry L. Ball, age 64, $286,650 total compensation
SVP and General Manager Europe Africa and Middle East, Hubertus M. Muehlhaeuser, age 42, $472,004 total compensation
SVP - Materials Projects, David L. Caplan, age 64
SVP; General Manager Asia/Pacific, Gary L. Collar, age 55, $320,000 total compensation
SVP - Global Sales Marketing and Product Management, Randall G. (Randy) Hoffman, age 60
Chairman President and CEO, Martin H. Richenhagen, age 59, $1,054,000 total compensation
VP and CIO, Robert (Bob) Greenberg, age 58
SVP and General Manager North America, Robert B. Crain, age 52, $306,667 total compensation
SVP; General Manager South America, Andre M. Carioba, age 61, $375,081 total compensation
VP General Counsel and Corporate Secretary, Debra Kuper
SVP and Chief Supply Chain Officer, Hans-Bernd Veltmaat, age 57, $448,972 total compensation
SVP Human Resources, Lucinda B. Smith, age 45
Director Investor Relations, Greg Peterson
Administrator AGCOmediaplace, Stephanie Buskell
Manager Communications AGCO Tractors AGCO Hesston Gleaner Sunflower White Planters, Reid Hamre
Manager Communications Massey Ferguson, Meghann McNally
Manager Communications Challenger, Allison Bass
Manager Communications Ag-Chem Spra-Coupe, Chris Lund
Manager Communications AGCO Parts, Tony Solon
VP and Managing Director China and India, Andreas Georg Weishaar
SVP Engineering Worldwide, Helmut R. Endres, age 56
Director, Gerald L. (Gerry) Shaheen, age 67
Director, Daniel C. (Dan) Ustian, age 61
Director, Gerald B. Johanneson, age 71
Director, Wolfgang Deml, age 66
Director, Luiz Fernando Furlan, age 66
Director, H. (Henk) Visser, age 68
Director, George E. Minnich, age 62
Director, P. George Benson, age 65
Director, Thomas W. LaSorda, age 57
Director, Mallika Srinivasan
Auditors: KPMGLLP

LOCATIONS

HQ: AGCO Corporation
4205 River Green Pkwy., Duluth GA 30096
Phone: 770-813-9200 **Fax:** 770-813-6118
Web: www.agcocorp.com

2011 Sales

	$ mil.	% of total
Europe		
Germany	1,067	12
Finland & Scandinavia	835	10
France	825	10
UK & Ireland	449	5
Other Europe	1,403	16
US	1,363	15
Canada	315	4
Middle East & Africa	266	3
Australia & New Zealand	187	2
Mexico Central America & Caribbean	111	1
Total	**8,773**	**100**

PRODUCTS/OPERATIONS

2011 Sales

	$ mil.	% of total
Tractors	5,779	66
Combines	610	7
Other machinery	762	9

Selected Mergers and Acquisitions

FY2012
- Santal Equipamentos (60% share; $31 million; Ribeir?o Preto Brazil; planting harvesting and handling equipment)

FY2011
- Laverda S.p.A (Breganze Italy; combine harvester manufacturer)
- GSI Holdings Corp. ($928 million; Assumption Illinois; grain conditioning and drying material handling and bulk storage equipment)

FY2010
- Sparex ($75 million; UK; distributor of tractor replacement parts)

Selected Products

Application equipment
Combine Harvesters
Grounds care
Hay and forage
Implements attachments and material handling
Power generation
Seeding and tillage
Tractors

COMPETITORS

Buhler Industries
Caterpillar
CNH Global
Deere
Komatsu
Kubota
Mahindra
Toro Company

HISTORICAL FINANCIALS

Company Type: Public

Income Statement

FYE: December 31

	REVENUE ($ mil.)	NET INCOME ($ mil.)	NET PROFIT MARGIN	EMPLOYEES
12/11	8,773	585	6.7%	17,400
12/10	6,896	220	3.2%	14,300
12/09	6,630	135	2.0%	14,456
12/08	8,424	400	4.7%	15,600
12/07	6,828	246	3.6%	13,700
Annual Growth	6.5%	24.2%	—	6.2%

2011 Year-End Financials

Debt ratio: 20.25%
Return on equity: 19.54%
Cash ($ mil.): 724
Current ratio: 166.08
Long-term debt ($ mil.): 1,409
No. of shares (mil.): 97
Dividends
Yield: —
Payout: —
Market value ($ mil.): 4,176

	STOCK PRICE ($) FY Close	P/E High	P/E Low	PER SHARE ($) Earnings	Dividends	Book Value
12/11	42.97	10	5	5.95	0.00	30.82
12/10	50.66	21	11	2.29	0.00	28.54
12/09	32.34	23	10	1.44	0.00	25.98
12/08	23.59	16	4	4.09	0.00	21.31
12/07	67.98	26	11	2.55	0.00	22.30
Annual Growth	(10.8%)	—	—	23.6%	—	8.4%

Agilent Technologies, Inc.

Products from Agilent Technologies have a measurable effect on the scientific world. A leading maker of scientific testing equipment Agilent supplies a slew of analytical and measurement instruments including oscilloscopes gas chromatographs mass spectrometers vacuum pumps and nuclear magnetic resonance imaging systems. Its operations include products used in electronic test and measurement life sciences and chemical analysis. Its Agilent Research Laboratories unit develops technologies used to create new products. Agilent's customers include such global giants as Cisco Dow Chemical GlaxoSmithKline Intel Merck and Samsung. The company gets about 70% of sales from outside the US.

HISTORY

Agilent Technologies was formed in 1999 when Hewlett-Packard (HP) split off its measurement business. But Agilent's roots run as deep as HP's —Agilent's core products served as the original business of Stanford-trained electrical engineers William Hewlett and David Packard. The friends started HP in 1939 as a test and measurement equipment maker. Their first product developed in Packard's garage (Hewlett was living in a rented cottage behind Packard's house) was an audio oscillator for testing sound equipment; Walt Disney Studios bought eight to help make the animation classic "Fantasia."

Demand for electronic test equipment during WWII pushed sales from $34000 in 1940 (when

HP had three employees and eight products) to nearly $1 million three years later. The company entered the microwave field in 1943 creating signal generators for the Naval Research Laboratory. Its postwar line of microwave test products made it a market leader for signal generation equipment.

Expanding beyond the US in the late 1950s HP established a plant in West Germany. The company went public in 1957. It entered the medical field in 1961 with the purchase of Sanborn and the analytical instrumentation business in 1965 with the purchase of F&M Scientific. In the 1970s president Hewlett and chairman Packard began shifting HP's focus toward the computer market. Late in that decade they stepped back from day-to-day management (they would retire in 1987 and 1992 respectively).

Sales hit $3 billion in 1980. In 1991 HP broadened its communications component offerings when it bought Avantek. HP moved into the DNA analysis field in 1994 with pharmaceutical research and health care products. Packard died in 1996. In 1997 HP bought Heartstream maker of an automatic external defibrillator.

In 1999 HP formed Agilent as a separate company for its test and measurement and other noncomputer operations which by then accounted for 16% of sales. Edward Barnholt a 30-year HP veteran was named CEO of the new company. In a move to energize its computer business HP spun off 15% of Agilent to the public in November 1999. The remainder was distributed to HP shareholders in mid-2000.

In 2000 Agilent bought Salient 3's subsidiary SAFCO Technologies (engineering services analysis tools and wireless network planning software) for $120 million. Later that year Philips Electronics agreed to buy Agilent's Healthcare Solutions unit for $1.7 billion. (After lengthy scrutiny from US and European regulators the deal was completed in mid-2001.)

In a move to bolster its networking business Agilent completed its $665 million acquisition of network management software maker Objective Systems Integrators in early 2001. The company also implemented cost-cutting measures such as temporary pay cuts. Later that year in the face of harsh market conditions Agilent announced two separate layoffs of 4000 employees each representing a total staff reduction of about 18%. Hewlett died that same year.

In 2002 the company announced plans to consolidate the operations of three older California fabs (wafer fabrication plants) into a facility in Colorado; the Colorado fab specialized in chips made from high-performance indium phosphide (InP) rather than silicon.

In 2004 Agilent acquired privately held Silicon Genetics (genomics data analysis and management software) broadening its life sciences offerings. Agilent also entered the flat-panel display test market with the acquisition of IBM's thin-film transistor array test and charge test product line assets.

Barnholt retired early in 2005; Agilent's COO Bill Sullivan was tapped to replace him as president and CEO.

That year Agilent completed the sale of its camera module business to Flextronics and purchased Wavics a Korean maker of power amplifiers for mobile handsets. The company also acquired Scientific Software a developer of chromatography data systems and content and business process management applications and Molecular Imaging a maker of measurement tools used by nanotechnology researchers.

Also in 2005 Agilent announced a divestiture plan designed to help it focus on its measurement products. The company sold its semiconductor operations which produced such products as application-specific integrated circuits (ASICs) optoelectronic components and radio-frequency chipsets. The semiconductor operations renamed Avago Technologies were acquired by two buyout firms —KKR and Silver Lake Partners —for approximately $2.7 billion. Agilent sold its stake in Lumileds Lighting (light-emitting diodes or LEDs) to Philips for $950 million. It also spun off its memory and system-on-a-chip (SoC) test system operations with an IPO in 2006; the company was called Verigy.

Late in 2007 and into 2008 Agilent began expanding its product portfolio primarily to grow its newly created Life Sciences and Chemical Analysis business. Through a serious of acquisitions including Till Photonics RVM Scientific and the Nano Instruments division of MTS Systems Agilent added laboratory robotics optical microscopy gas chromatography and nanoindentation solutions products.

In mid-2007 Agilent acquired Stratagene a developer of life science research and diagnostic products for about $252 million in cash. In one of the largest acquisitions Agilent made in its short history as a stand-alone company the instrument maker bolstered its product offerings in life sciences for genomics and proteomics with the Stratagene portfolio particularly among academic and government research customers. Agilent's substantial sales organization was expected to pay benefits for Stratagene as well.

It also acquired in late 2007 the operations of Velocity11 which made laboratory robotics for the life sciences market. That acquisition strengthened Agilent's life sciences suite of automation products.

In 2009 Agilent bought the the radio-frequency (RF) product line of electrical test instrument and system provider Keithley Instruments for about $9 million expanding its RF measurement portfolio. The following year Agilent purchased digital multimeter (DMM) and modular switch device maker Signametrics bolstering its existing DMM and switch product lines.

In response to lower sales in 2009 the company restructured its operations with a goal of shrinking expenses by some $300 million a year. The cost cuts came primarily from reductions in pay and wages in its electronic measurement segment. The company cut about 2800 positions a reduction in force of about 14%. Most of the restructuring was completed in fiscal 2010 and wage reductions were restored by the beginning of that fiscal year. Agilent has also increased its use of outsourcing to cut costs and abandoned some facilities which had lease payments due through 2014.

The company also exited businesses that were not performing well in 2009. It trimmed its N2X family of products for Internet protocol (IP) performance testing and sold the Data Network Testing family to Ixia for $44 million. The company also dropped its automated optical and X-ray inspection product lines from the semiconductor and board test segment.

Agilent bought digital multimeter (DMM) instrument and modular switch device maker Signametrics in late 2010. The acquisition complemented Agilent's existing DMM and switch product lines.

In a transformational deal and the largest in its history at the time Agilent in 2010 bought Varian a maker of instruments for measuring biological and physical attributes for about $1.5 billion in cash. The acquisition diversified Agilent's product portfolio into such fields as nuclear magnetic resonance and imaging and vacuum technology which target the energy life sciences and environmental industries. In order to satisfy antitrust regulators Agilent sold Varian's micro gas chromatography business to INFICON while Bruker bought three of Varian's instrument businesses —inductively coupled plasma mass spectrometry laboratory gas chromatography and gas chromatography/triple-quadruple mass spectrometry.

Agilent continued to divest operations considered noncore in 2010 as well. The company sold its Hycor Biomedical subsidiary which manufactured in-vitro diagnostics products as part of the company's life sciences business to Linden a Chicago-based private equity health care firm. It also sold its Network Solutions business (including network protocol test and drive test products) in 2010 to JDS Uniphase (JDSU) for $165 million in cash.

EXECUTIVES

President and Chief, William P. (Bill) Sullivan, age 61, $907,500 total compensation

President and COO, Ronald S. (Ron) Nersesian, age 52, $413,125 total compensation

SVP Human Resources, Jean M. Halloran, age 60, $399,996 total compensation

VP and General Manager Worldwide Sales Life Sciences Group, John R. Pouk, age 57

Chairman, James G. Cullen, age 69

SVP and CTO, Darlene J. S. Solomon

SVP; President Life Sciences Group, Nicholas H. (Nick) Roelofs, age 53, $334,583 total compensation

SVP and CFO, Didier Hirsch, age 60

SVP; President Chemical Analysis Group, Michael R. (Mike) McMullen, age 50, $334,583 total compensation

VP and Treasurer, Hilliard C. Terry III, age 43

VP Service Solutions, Steve Aleshire

VP and General Manager Sales Service and Support Chemical Analysis Group, Lonnie G. (Lon) Justice

VP and General Manager Electronic Instrument Business Unit Electronic Measurement Group, Gooi Soon Chai, age 50

SVP and Chief Infrastructure Officer, Rick Burdsall, age 49

VP and General Manager Columns and Supplies Division, Helen Stimson

VP Corporate Development and Strategy, Shiela Barr Robertson

SVP General Counsel and Secretary, Marie Oh Huber, age 50

VP and General Manager Sales Service and Support Electronic Measurement Group, Saleem N. Odeh, age 61

SVP; President Electronic Measurement Group, Guy Sene

VP Technology Leadership, Bob Witte

VP and General Manager Oscilloscopes, Jay Alexander

VP System Products Division, Gary Whitman

VP Basic Instruments Division, Ee Huei Sin

VP and General Manager Genomics, Robert Schueren

VP and General Manager Component Test Division, Gregg Peters

VP and General Manager Research Products Division, Regina Schuck

President Life Sciences Group, Nick Roelofs

VP Measurement Systems Division, Daniel Mak

Country General Manager Agilent Technologies India, Parmeet Ahuja

VP Gas Chromatography Systems and Workflow Automation, Shanya Kane

SVP, Nicolas Roelofs

Director, Heidi Fields, age 57

President and Chief, William P. (Bill) Sullivan, age 61
Director, Paul N. Clark, age 65
Director, Robert J. (Bob) Herbold, age 69
Director, David M. Lawrence, age 71
Director, Tadataka (Tachi) Yamada, age 66
Director, Koh Boon Hwee, age 61
Director, A. Barry Rand, age 67
Auditors: PricewaterhouseCoopersLLP

LOCATIONS

HQ: Agilent Technologies Inc.
5301 Stevens Creek Blvd., Santa Clara CA 95051
Phone: 408-345-8886 **Fax:** 408-345-8474
Web: www.agilent.com

2011 Sales

	$ mil.	% of total
US	2,016	30
China	1,035	16
Japan	700	11
Other countries	2,864	43
Total	**6,615**	**100**

PRODUCTS/OPERATIONS

2011 Sales

	$ mil.	% of total
Electronic measurement	3,316	50
Life sciences	1,788	27
Chemical analysis	1,511	23
Total	**6,615**	**100**

2011 Sales

	$ mil.	% of total
Products	5,482	83
Services & other	1,133	17
Total	**6,615**	**100**

Selected Products

Electronic Test and Measurement
- Generators sources supplies
  - AC power sources / power analyzers
  - Data generators and analyzers
  - DC electronic loads
  - DC power supplies
  - Function / Arbitrary waveform generators
  - Pulse pattern generators
  - Signal generators
- Oscilloscopes analyzers meters
  - Bit error ratio test (BERT) solutions
  - DC power analyzers
  - Digital multimeters voltmeters
  - Digitizers
  - Dynamic signal analyzers mechanical and physical test
  - EMI/EMC phase noise physical layer test
  - Frequency counters and time-to-digital converts
  - Impedance analyzers
  - LCR and resistance meters
  - Logic Analyzers
  - Network analyzers
  - Noise figure analyzers and noise sources
  - Oscilloscopes
  - Parameter and device analyzers curve tracers
  - Power meters and power sensors
  - Protocol analyzers and exercisers
  - Signal and spectrum analyzers
- Software
  - Agilent EEsof EDA design and simulation software
  - Agilent IO libraries suite
  - Agilent license manager
  - Agilent VEE
  - Calibration and adjustment software
  - Fault detective
  - Instrument connectivity
  - Instrument software
  - Test optimization and diagnostics

Life Sciences and Chemical Analysis
- Clinical diagnostics
  - Allergy testing
  - Autoimmune testing
  - Infectious disease
  - Urinalysis
- Columns and supplies
- Informatics and software
- Instruments and systems
  - Automation solutions
  - DNA microarrays
  - Electrophoresis
  - Gas chromatography
  - ICP-MS
  - Lab-on-a-chip
  - Liquid chromatography
  - Mass spectrometry
  - PCR and QPCR
  - Spectroscopy
- Reagents standards and kits
  - Cloning and competent cells
  - DNA microarrays
  - DNA target enrichment
  - Instrument standards and kits
  - Mutagenesis
  - Nucleic acid purification and analysis
  - PCR and reverse transcription
  - Protein expression and analysis
  - Protein preparation
  - Real-time/quantitative PCR
  - Total RNA and cDNA libraries

COMPETITORS

Advantest
Aeroflex
Affymetrix
AMETEK
Anritsu
Ansoft
Applied Materials
AWR
Beckman Coulter
Bio-Rad Labs
Bruker
Danaher
Fluke Corporation
GE Healthcare
HEIDENHAIN Corp.
IBM Software
Life Technologies Corporation
National Instruments
PerkinElmer
Rohde & Schwarz
Shimadzu
Spirent
Teledyne LeCroy
telent
Teradyne
Thermo Fisher Scientific
W. R. Grace
Waters Corp.
Yokogawa Electric
Zygo

HISTORICAL FINANCIALS

Company Type: Public

Income Statement FYE: October 31

	REVENUE ($ mil.)	NET INCOME ($ mil.)	NET PROFIT MARGIN	EMPLOYEES
10/12	6,858	1,153	16.8%	20,500
10/11	6,615	1,012	15.3%	18,700
10/10	5,444	684	12.6%	18,500
10/09	4,481	(31)	—	16,800
10/08	5,774	693	12.0%	2,495
Annual Growth	4.4%	13.6%	—	69.3%

2012 Year-End Financials

Debt ratio: 22.42%
Return on equity: 22.25%
Cash ($ mil.): 2,351
Current ratio: 244.53
Long-term debt ($ mil.): 2,112
No. of shares (mil.): 346
Dividends
Yield: 0.83%
Payout: 9.17%
Market value ($ mil.): 12,470

	STOCK PRICE ($) FY Close	P/E High/Low	PER SHARE ($) Earnings	Dividends	Book Value
10/12	35.99	14 10	3.27	0.30	14.96
10/11	37.07	18 10	2.85	0.00	12.44
10/10	34.80	19 13	1.94	0.00	9.33
10/09	24.74	— —	(0.09)	0.00	7.24
10/08	22.19	20 10	1.87	0.00	7.32
Annual Growth	12.9%	— —	15.0%	—	19.6%

Air Products & Chemicals, Inc.

Air Products and Chemicals looks for its profits to expand like the gases it sells. The company provides gases such as argon hydrogen nitrogen and oxygen to manufacturers health care facilities and other industries. Air Products' largest segment is Merchant Gases which manufactures atmospheric process and specialty gases delivered from tanker truck trailer or on-site. The company's Tonnage Gases segment serves the global refining and chemical industries while its Electronics and Performance Materials unit serves electronics and other manufacturing companies. Air Products also makes gas containers and equipment that separates air purifies hydrogen and liquefies gas.

HISTORY

In the early 1900s Leonard Pool the son of a boilermaker began selling oxygen to industrial users. By the time he was 30 he was district manager for Compressed Industrial Gases. In the late 1930s Pool hired engineer Frank Pavlis to help him design a cheaper more efficient oxygen generator. In 1940 they had the design and Pool established Air Products in Detroit (initially sharing space with the cadavers collected by his brother who was starting a mortuary science college). The company was based on a simple breakthrough concept: the provision of on-site gases. Instead of delivering oxygen in cylinders Pool proposed to build oxygen-generating facilities near large-volume gas users and then lease them reducing distribution costs.

Although industrialists encouraged Pool to pursue his ideas few orders were forthcoming and the company faced financial crisis. The outbreak of WWII got the company out of difficulty as the US military became a major customer. During the war the company moved to Chattanooga Tennessee for the available labor.

The end of the war brought with it another downturn as demand dried up. By waiting at the Weirton Steel plant until a contract was signed Pool won a contract for three on-site generators. Weirton was nearly the company's only customer. Pool relocated the company to Allentown Pennsylvania to be closer to the Northeast's industrial market where he could secure more contracts with steel companies.

The Cold War and the launching of the Sputnik satellite in 1957 propelled the company's growth. Convinced that Soviet rockets were powered by liquid hydrogen the US government asked Air Products to supply it with the volatile fuel. The company entered the overseas market that year through a joint venture with Butterley (UK) to which it licensed its cryogenic processes and equipment. The company went public in 1961 and formed a subsidiary in Belgium in 1964.

Air Products diversified into chemicals when it bought Houdry Process (chemicals and chemical-plant maintenance 1962) and Airco's chemicals and plastics operations in the 1970s. The company continued to diversify in the mid-1980s as it built large-scale plants for its environmental- and energy-systems business and added Anchor Chemical and the industrial chemicals unit of Abbott Labs.

In 1995 and 1996 Air Products expanded into China and other countries by winning 20 contracts with semiconductor makers. It bought Carburos Metalicos Spain's #1 industrial gas supplier in 1996. To focus on its core gas and chemical lines the company shed most of its environmental- and energy-systems business.

Expanding further in Europe Air Products bought the methylamines and derivatives unit of UK-based Imperial Chemical Industries (ICI) in 1997. The company sold its remaining interest in American Ref-Fuel (a waste-to-energy US operation).

In 1998 Air Products bought Solkatronic Chemicals and opened a methylamines plant in Florida to complement its ICI purchase. To further target semiconductor makers it formed Air Products Electronic Chemicals and allied with AlliedSignal Chemical (now part of Honeywell International).

The next year Air Products and France's L'Air Liquide agreed to buy and break up BOC Group. European Union regulators initially approved the deal but in 2000 the companies shelved the plan when other regulatory issues arose. Also in 2000 Air Products sold its polyvinyl alcohol business to Celanese for about $326 million. The company boosted its European presence in 2001 with the acquisition of Messer Griesheim's (Germany) respiratory home-care business and 50% of AGA's Netherlands industrial gases operations.

Air Products was hurt by the slowdown in manufacturing primarily in the electronics and steel industries which are major customers for gases. Its chemical revenues also were hurt by pressure on pricing. To improve profits the company initiated cost cuts including job cuts (about 10% of its employees) and divestitures such as its US packaged gas business.

The company broadened its health care operations in late 2002 by acquiring American Homecare Supply. It appeared briefly that Air Products wanted to devote a great deal of attention to the health care business. The company had created its Air Products Healthcare unit in 1999 and expanded it greatly three years later with the acquisition of American Homecare Supply. Air Products proceeded to add to the division through subsequent acquisitions; however the US portion of the business never performed to the company's expectations and Air Products sold the domestic operations of the health care unit in 2008 and 2009.

It also decided to divest its chemicals operations in the latter half of the decade. Those operations included the production of catalysts surfactants and intermediates derived from vinyl acetate monomer (VAM) all of which it sold in 2008. Air Products had sold its amines business to chemical company Taminco in 2006. The company's polymers operations which were run through a joint venture with Wacker-Chemie called Air Products Polymers were divested in 2008. The company sold most of its holdings in the JV to Wacker for $265 million though two facilities that had belonged to the joint venture were sold to Ashland Performance Materials.

In 2007 Air Products made a small but strategic move into Eastern Europe. The company took advantage of Linde's selloff of some BOC assets after the German company bought BOC in 2006. Air Products acquired the Polish Gazy SP for just under $500 million with the hopes of moving into the Central and Eastern European markets to take advantage of the migration of manufacturing to the region.

In 2010 the company made a major bid to buy rival Airgas but it was rejected. The Airgas board considered the $5.1 billion offer too low. Air Products extended its tender offer to Airgas stockholders several times making its "best and final offer" of $70 a share in December 2010. Airgas also rejected that offer.

EXECUTIVES

VP and Chief Commercial Counsel, Diane L. Sheridan
VP Energy and Materials, Laurie K. Stewart
Chairman President and CEO, John E. McGlade, age 58, $1,200,000 total compensation
SVP and CFO, Paul E. Huck, age 62, $650,000 total compensation
VP and General Manager Tonnage Gases, Jeffry L. Byrne
VP and General Manager Sales and Operations Electronics Division, Bruce C. Hargus
VP Energy Businesses, David J. Taylor, age 56
VP and General Manager Global Healthcare Europe, Caroline Lloyd
VP and General Manager Packaged Gases Europe, Jeffrey Kramer
SVP Corporate Strategy Technology and Supply Chain, Corning F. Painter, age 49
VP Continuous Improvement, Alexander W. Masetti
VP Global Business Support Services (GBSS), Wayne M. Mitchell
Manager Communications Merchant Gases, Arthur (Art) George
SVP and General Manager Merchant Gases, John W. Marsland, age 46
VP International, Michael A. Olivares
VP and General Manager Merchant Gases Asia, Ivo Bols
VP Global Operations, Joseph M. Pietrantonio, age 53
VP Liquid Bulk Europe, Graham M. Rhodes
VP North America Tonnage Gases, Wilbur W. Mok
SVP Human Resources and Communications, Lynn C. Minella, age 54, $440,000 total compensation
VP Tonnage Development Asia, Philip C. (Phil) Sproger
VP Platform Renewal Merchant Gases, Thomas J. Ward
VP Treasurer and Chief Risk Officer, George G. Bitto
SVP and General Manager Tonnage Gases Equipment and Energy and China President, Stephen J. Jones, age 51, $400,000 total compensation
VP Information Technology and CIO, Richard Boocock
VP Global Engineering Europe, David R. Edmondson
VP Human Resources Air Products Asia, Jennifer Woo
VP and General Manager Performance Materials Division, Patricia A. (Pam) Mattimore
VP Environment Health Safety and Quality, Patrick F. Loughlin
Manager Corporate Public Relations, Beth K. Mentesana
VP North America Merchant Gases, Nelson J. Squires III
VP and CTO, Montgomery (Monty) Alger
VP and Corporate Controller, M. Scott Crocco, age 48
VP Taxes, Charles G. Stinner
VP Engineering Global, Deborah A. McCullough, age 55
Regional VP Tonnage Gases Europe and Middle East, Howard Castle-Smith
VP Corporate Communications, Elizabeth L. (Betsy) Klebe
SVP and General Counsel, John D. Stanley, age 54
Corporate Secretary and Chief Governance Officer, Mary Afflerbach
Regional VP Tonnage Gases Asia, Douglas J. Hayes
Regional VP and General Manager Performance Materials Asia, Craig R. Williams
VP Human Resources Europe, Laure Swift
President Air Products Japan, Eugene Crossland
President Air Products Korea, Soo-Yon Lee
VP Base Gas Taiwan, Jerry Shih Ming Huang
VP China Government Relations, Matthew Mao
President Air Products San Fu Co. Ltd., John Chieh Jung Tsai
Senior Communications Specialist Financial Electronics and Performance Materials, Robert (Rob) Brown
Communications Specialist Merchant Gases, Debbie Bauer
Director Investor Relations, Simon R. Moore
VP Engineering North America and Energy Product Supply, Thomas E. Mutchler
VP Liquid Bulk and Generated Gases Asia, Chong Seong Saw
Manager Communications Asia, Jessica S. Cheng
Vice President - Information Technology, Kevin B. Michaelis
Vice President Energy and Materials, Laurie K. Stew
Senior Vice President; General Manager - Electronics; Performance Materials; Strategy and Technology, Guillermo Novo
Director, Ursula O. Fairbairn, age 69
Director, William L. Davis III, age 68
Director, Lawrence S. Smith, age 65
Director, Evert Henkes, age 69
Director, Michael J. Donahue, age 54
Director, Edward E. (Ed) Hagenlocker, age 72
Director, Margaret G. (Margie) McGlynn, age 53
Director, Mario L. Baeza, age 61
Director, W. Douglas (Doug) Ford, age 68
Director, Chadwick C. (Chad) Deaton, age 59
Independent Director, Susan Carter
Auditors: KPMGLLP

LOCATIONS

HQ: Air Products and Chemicals Inc.
7201 Hamilton Blvd., Allentown PA 18195-1501
Phone: 610-481-4911 **Fax:** 610-481-5900
Web: www.airproducts.com

2012 Sales

North America		
Canada	267	3
Asia	2,304	24
Total	**9,611**	**100**

PRODUCTS/OPERATIONS

2012 Sales

Merchant Gases	3,662	38
Electronics & Performance Materials	2,322	24
Total	**9,611**	**100**

Selected Products and Services

Industrial Gases
- Argon
- Carbon dioxide
- Carbon monoxide
- Helium
- Hydrogen
- Nitrogen
- Oxygen
- Synthesis gas

Equipment and Services
- Air-pollution control systems
- Air-separation equipment
- Hydrogen-purification equipment
- Natural gas-liquefaction equipment

COMPETITORS

Aceto
Airgas
BASF SE
Bayer AG
L' Air Liquide
Messer Group
Praxair
Taiyo Nippon Sanso
The Linde Group

HISTORICAL FINANCIALS

Company Type: Public

Income Statement FYE: September 30

	REVENUE ($ mil.)	NET INCOME ($ mil.)	NET PROFIT MARGIN	EMPLOYEES
09/12	9,611	1,167	12.1%	21,300
09/11	10,082	1,224	12.1%	18,900
09/10	9,026	1,029	11.4%	18,300
09/09	8,256	631	7.6%	18,900
09/08	10,414	909	8.7%	21,100
Annual Growth	(2.0%)	6.4%	—	0.2%

2012 Year-End Financials

Debt ratio: 31.24%
Return on equity: 18.02%
Cash ($ mil.): 454
Current ratio: 126.99
Long-term debt ($ mil.): 4,584
No. of shares (mil.): 212
Dividends
Yield: —
Payout: 45.96%
Market value ($ mil.): 17,572

	STOCK PRICE ($) FY Close	P/E High/Low		PER SHARE ($) Earnings	Dividends	Book Value
09/12	82.70	17	13	5.44	0.00	30.48
09/11	76.37	17	13	5.63	2.23	27.57
09/10	82.82	17	13	4.74	1.92	25.94
09/09	77.58	27	14	2.96	1.79	22.68
09/08	68.49	25	15	4.15	1.70	24.03
Annual Growth	4.8%	—	—	7.0%	—	6.1%

Airgas Inc.

Airgas has floated to the top of the industrial gas distribution industry by buying more than 400 companies since its founding in 1986. Its North American network of more than 1100 locations includes retail stores gas fill plants specialty gas labs production facilities and distribution centers. Airgas distributes argon carbon dioxide hydrogen nitrogen oxygen and a variety of medical and specialty gases as well as dry ice and protective equipment (hard hats goggles). Its gases production unit operates air-separation plants that produce oxygen nitrogen and argon. Airgas also sells welding machines. Founder and CEO Peter McCausland and his wife control about 20% of Airgas.

Airgas is the largest distributor of packaged gases in the US with a 25% market share. Outside of the US it conducts operations mostly in Canda but also operates in Dubai Mexico Russia and parts of Europe.

The industrial manufacturing and repair and maintenance industries account for about a quarter each of the company's sales; customers primarily make fabricated metal products industrial transportation and equipment chemical products and primary metal products. Other industries served include medical and health services agriculture mining repair and maintenance and wholesale trade.

Its distribution business accounts for about 90% of the company's sales. Almost all of its sales come from distributing bulk gases (nitrogen oxygen argon helium) gas cylinders and welding equipment. Airgas also produces gases to supply its regional distribution companies. Its other operations consist of six business units that manufacture and/or distribute carbon dioxide dry ice nitrous oxide ammonia and refrigerant gases.

The company continually strives to grow its operations through acquisitions in its core businesses adding seven to 10 companies annually. It focuses on high-growth products with strong cross-selling opportunities.

In fiscal 2012 the company added eight businesses with total annual sales of about $106 million. The largest of the businesses acquired were ABCO Gases Welding and Industrial Supply Company (ABCO); Pain Enterprises; and Industrial Welding Supplies of Hattiesburg (doing business as Nordan Smith). Connecticut-based ABCO has 12 industrial and gas welding supply locations throughout New England. Indiana-based Pain operates 20 dry ice and liquid carbon dioxide production and distribution sites. Mississippi-based Nordan Smith has 17 locations that distribute industrial medical and specialty gases and supplies thoughout Alabama Arkansas and Mississippi.

Airgas posted sales of $4.75 billion in fiscal 2012 a 12% increase over the previous year's sales. The strong performance resulted from a 2% increase in sales from the company's recent acquisitions and a 10% increase in its same-store sales with hardgoods up 14% and gas and rentals up 7%. Demand from customers that year strengthened particularly in large manufacturing petrochemical and energy sectors; even demand from the hard-hit construction sector saw some improvement. The company also recorded a net income of $313.4 million in fiscal 2012 a hike of more than 25% over the previous year.

In 2011 Airgas reorganized its 12 regional segments into four new business support divisions – North South Central and West –to leverage a new SAP information systems platform in 2011. Each of the units is headed by a division president. The new company structure is designed to accelerate sales growth and pricing management and create operating efficiencies.

HISTORY

In the early 1980s Peter McCausland was a corporate attorney involved in mergers and acquisitions for Messer Griesheim a large German industrial gas producer. When the German firm declined McCausland's recommendation in 1982 to buy Connecticut Oxygen he raised money from private sources and bought it himself. He acquired other distributors and then left Messer Griesheim in 1987 to run Airgas full-time.

Airgas began buying mostly small local and regional gas distributors in the US. By 1994 strategy shifted to purchasing larger "superregional" distributors such as Jimmie Jones Co. and Post Welding Supply of Alabama which added about $70 million combined to the company's revenues.

Airgas then began "rolling up" additional similar businesses. In 1995 it bought more than 25 companies and two years later it added more than 20 gas distributors. Also in 1997 Airgas expanded its manufacturing capabilities by building five plants that could fast-fill whole pallets of gas cylinders (the old manual system rolls cylinders two at a time). By 2000 the company had about 100 cylinder fill plants.

Struggling to integrate acquisitions while dealing with softening markets Airgas began a companywide realignment in 1998. To that end it sold its calcium carbide and carbon products operations to former partner Elkem ASA later that year; the company also consolidated 34 hubs into 16 regional companies and sold its operations in Poland and Thailand to Germany-based Linde in 1999.

In 2000 Airgas acquired distributor Mallinckrodt's Puritan-Bennett division (gas products for medical uses) with 36 locations in the US and Canada. The company also acquired the majority of Air Products' US packaged gas business excluding its electronic gases and magnetic resonance imaging-related helium operations in 2002.

In 2004 and 2005 it bought units from giants like Air Products and Chemicals BOC and LaRoche Industries. In 2006 Airgas continued to build with the purchase of 10 businesses including Union Industrial Gas which supplies Texas and much of the Southwest and then Linde's US bulk gas business for $495 million the next year. Linde in the process of integrating its 2006 acquisition of BOC then sold to Airgas a portion of its US packaged gas business for $310 million.

Rival Air Products had made a major bid to buy Airgas in 2010 but was rebuffed. Air Products extended its tender offer to Airgas stockholders several times and made a "best and final offer" of $70 a share (almost $6 billion) in December 2010. Airgas said it was holding out for $78 a share and rejected that offer too. In early 2011 a Delaware judge ruled for Airgas in a suit brought by Air Products to set aside a "poison pill" defense used by the Airgas board to fend off the takeover try. Following the verdict Air Products dropped its bid.

Airgas acquired six businesses in 2010 including Tri-Tech an independent distributor with 16 locations throughout Florida Georgia and South Carolina and annual sales of $31 million.

EXECUTIVES

President Process Gases and Chemicals Division, Andrew R. (Andy) Cichocki
SVP Corporate Accounts, Patrick M. Visintainer, age 48
SVP Product Management Vendor Relationships and Marketing Refrigerants; President Refron, Jay Kestenbaum
President Airgas Specialty Products, Ted R. Schulte, age 61, $274,411 total compensation
Chairman and CEO, Peter McCausland, age 62, $812,500 total compensation
SVP Human Resources, Dwight T. Wilson, age 56
SVP Sales and Marketing, Ronald J. (Ron) Stark
EVP and COO, Michael L. (Mike) Molinini, age 61, $477,167 total compensation
SVP and CIO, Robert A. Dougherty, age 54
Division President East, B. Shaun Powers, age 60, $295,215 total compensation
Director, John P. Clancey, age 67
SVP and CFO, Robert M. (Bob) McLaughlin, age 55, $320,190 total compensation
SVP Medical, Kelly P. Justice
VP and Treasurer, Joseph C. Sullivan
SVP Tonnage and Merchant Gases, Thomas S. Thoman
VP Tax, Carey M. Verger
President Airgas/Carbonic Dry Ice, Philip J. (Phil) Filer
SVP Specialty Gases and Life Sciences, James A. Muller
President Oilind Safety, Henry B. (Rusty) Coker III
President Mid America, J. Robert (Bob) Hilliard
VP Hardgoods, David E. Levin
President Airgas Safety, Donald S. Carlino Jr.

SVP Distribution Operations, Michael E. Rohde
President Southwest, J. Brent Sparks
President West Division, Max D. Hooper, age 52
President Red-D-Arc, Mitch M. Imielinski
President Airgas National Welders, Steve Marinelli
President South, L. Jay Sullivan
SVP Corporate Development, Leslie J. Graff, age 51, $264,003 total compensation
VP and Controller, Thomas M. Smyth, age 58
President Airgas Refrigerants, Charles E. (Chuck) Broadus Jr.
President Intermountain, Douglas L. (Doug) Jones
VP Communications and Investor Relations, R. Jay Worley
President Great Lakes, Kevin M. McBride
President East, Frederick E. (Fred) Manley
SVP and General Counsel, Robert H. Young Jr., age 61
Director Internal Audit, E. David Coyne
President Mid South, Terry Lodge
President West, J. Samuel (Sam) Thompson
VP Construction, John J. (Jack) Appolonia
VP Technology Refron, Jerry Kestenbaum
Director Investor Relations, Barry Strzelec
President Northern California and Nevada, Michael T. (Mike) Chandler
President Nor Pac, Edward A. (Eddie) Richards
President North Central, Pamela M. Swanson
Presiding Independent Director, John Roden
Director, Ellen C. Wolf, age 58
Director, Robert L. Lumpkins, age 68
Director, Lee M. Thomas, age 67
Director, Paula A. Sneed, age 64
Director, John C. van Roden Jr., age 63
Director, Ted B. Miller Jr., age 61
Director, David M. Stout, age 57
Director, John P. Clancey, age 67
Director, James W. Hovey, age 65
Auditors: KPMGLLP

LOCATIONS

HQ: Airgas Inc.
259 N. Radnor-Chester Rd. Ste. 100, Radnor PA 19087-5283
Phone: 610-687-5253 **Fax:** 610-687-1052
Web: www.airgas.com

PRODUCTS/OPERATIONS

2012 Sales

	$ mil.	% of total
Distribution	4,234	89
Adjustments	(37.8)	-

2012 Sales

Gas & Rentals	2,967	63
Hardgoods	1,778	37
Total	**4,746**	**100**

Selected Products and Services

Products
- Carbon dioxide
- Dry ice
- Industrial gases
- Argon
- Helium
- Hydrogen
- Liquid oxygen
- Nitrogen
- Nitrous oxide
- Oxygen
- Safety equipment
- Specialty gases

Services
- Container rental
- Welding equipment rental

Selected Subsidiaries

Airgas Canada
Airgas Carbonic
Airgas East
Airgas Great Lakes
Airgas Intermountain
Airgas Medical Services
Airgas Mid America
Airgas Mid South
Airgas Nitrous Oxide
Airgas Nor Pac
Airgas North Central
Airgas Northern California & Nevada
Airgas Refrigerant
Airgas Safety
Airgas South
Airgas Southwest
Airgas Specialty Gases
Airgas Specialty Products
Airgas West
National Welders Supply Company dba Airgas National Welders
Nitrous Oxide Corp.
Red-D-Arc
WorldWide Welding LLC

COMPETITORS

Air Products
American Air Liquide
L' Air Liquide
Lincoln Electric
Matheson Tri-Gas
Praxair Distribution
Valley National Gases
W.W. Grainger

HISTORICAL FINANCIALS

Company Type: Public

Income Statement FYE: March 31

	REVENUE ($ mil.)	NET INCOME ($ mil.)	NET PROFIT MARGIN	EMPLOYEES
03/12	4,746	313	6.6%	15,000
03/11	4,251	249	5.9%	14,000
03/10	3,864	196	5.1%	14,000
03/09	4,349	261	6.0%	14,000
03/08	4,017	223	5.6%	14,500
Annual Growth	4.3%	8.8%	—	0.9%

2012 Year-End Financials

Debt ratio: 40.61%
Return on equity: 17.90%
Cash ($ mil.): 44
Current ratio: 137.00
Long-term debt ($ mil.): 1,761
No. of shares (mil.): 76
Dividends
Yield: —
Payout: 31.25%
Market value ($ mil.): 6,821

	STOCK PRICE ($) FY Close	P/E High/Low	PER SHARE ($) Earnings	Dividends	Book Value
03/12	88.97	22 14	4.00	0.00	22.83
03/11	66.42	24 20	2.93	1.01	21.80
03/10	63.62	27 14	2.34	0.76	21.57
03/09	33.81	20 8	3.12	0.56	19.31
03/08	45.47	20 15	2.66	0.39	17.18
Annual Growth	18.3%	— —	10.7%	—	7.4%

AK Steel Holding Corp.

Automobile sales help AK Steel's business keep rolling though it also has operations in the infrastructure and manufacturing industries. The company manufactures carbon stainless and electrical steel. It sells hot- and cold-rolled carbon steel to construction companies steel distributors and service centers and automotive and industrial machinery producers. AK Steel also sells cold-rolled and aluminum-coated stainless steel to automakers. The company produces electrical steels (iron-silicon alloys with unique magnetic properties) for makers of power transmission and distribution equipment. AK Steel has seven steel-making and finishing plants located across Indiana Kentucky Ohio and Pennsylvania.

Financial Analysis

The company has been buffeted by a difficult economic environment and factors beyond its control (such as high prices in raw materials). Strategically the company is focused on cost competitiveness and ready to capitalize on an economic recovery. AK Steel saw a significant increase in its revenues in 2010 up more than 46% over recession-shrouded 2009. Sales volumes began to pick up during the second half of the year though prices continued to be stuck in the low range. Net income remained in the loss column in 2010 due primarily to the rise in the cost of raw materials brought on by increased demand in China and other growing markets.

Strategy

The steel industry has been consolidating for years as troubled companies have been snapped up by market leaders. AK Steel has maintained its independence however in part because of its status as a leading supplier of some high-grade niche products such as components of stainless steel exhaust systems for carmakers.

In recent years the company has increased the production capacity at many of its facilities. Total investments in its US plants have been about $268 million. The company also operates subsidiaries in the UK the Netherlands Italy France Germany and other countries.

HISTORY

George Verity who was in the roofing business in Cincinnati around the turn of the century often had trouble getting sheet metal so in 1900 he founded his own steel company American Rolling Mill. His first plant in Middletown Ohio was followed by a second production facility 11 years later in Ashland Kentucky. Plant superintendent John Tytus whose family was in paper milling applied those rolling techniques to make American Rolling Mill's steel more uniform in thickness.

In 1926 Columbia Steel developed a process to overcome several production problems inherent in the Tytus method and in 1930 American Rolling Mill bought Columbia Steel. The company changed its name to Armco Steel in 1948.

Armco began diversifying in the 1950s and continued diversifying until the early 1980s. Subsidiaries were involved in coal oil and gas-drilling equipment and insurance and financial services among other things. In 1978 the company changed its name to Armco Inc.

Armco began shedding subsidiaries in the early 1980s. Sales and market share increased as the company approached the billion-dollar mark at the end of the decade. In 1989 Armco formed Armco Steel Company with Japan's Kawasaki Steel Corporation.

The company's sales reached $1.3 billion in 1991 though the high operating expenses in the steel industry of the 1990s kept profits low. Armco began looking outside the company for help and in 1992 it persuaded retired steel executive Tom Graham to head the company. Graham brought with him another industry veteran Richard Wardrop who would succeed Graham as CEO in 1995. After evaluating the company's holdings the two divested more than 10 subsidiaries and divisions. Armco also worked on improving quality and customer service with special emphasis placed on timely delivery.

In 1994 Armco's limited partnership with Kawasaki was altered and AK Steel Holding Corporation was formed with AK Steel Corporation as its main subsidiary and the Middletown and Ashland plants as its production base. The holding company went public the same year raising more than $650 million enabling the company to pay off its debt.

AK Steel Holding moved its headquarters to Middletown Ohio in 1995. Despite many naysayers Graham then pushed a plan to build a state-of-the-art $1.1 billion steel production facility. Many doubted the wisdom of going into long-term debt so soon after coming out of the hole –especially when a similar facility had produced lackluster results for Inland Steel. Graham stuck by his plant and in 1997 ground was broken on the facility in Spencer County near Rockport Indiana (Rockport Works). Graham retired that year and Wardrop took over as chairman.

In 1998 the company opened its Rockport Works cold-rolling mill and began operating a hot-dip galvanizing and galvannealing line. The next year AK Steel bought former parent Armco for $842 million. AK Steel acquired welded steel tubing maker Alpha Tube Corporation (renamed AK Tube LLC) in 2001. In late 2001 the company took a charge of $194 million for losses in its pension fund which had been battered by a weak stock market and lowered interest rates.

AK Steel sold its Sawhill Tubular Division to John Maneely Company (Collingswood NJ) for roughly $50 million in 2002.

AK Steel offered to purchase National Steel which was operating under Chapter 11 bankruptcy protection. However AK Steel's bid was trumped in 2003 by one from U.S. Steel that included a ratified labor agreement with the United Steelworkers of America. AK Steel also lost out in an effort to acquire Rouge Industries (later Severstal North America).

Chairman and CEO Wardrop and president John Hritz left their posts in September 2003. CFO James Wainscott was named president and CEO and Robert Jenkins became chairman. (Wainscott succeeded Jenkins as chairman in January 2006.)

In an effort to reduce its debt AK Steel in 2004 sold its Douglas Dynamics unit a maker of snow and ice removal equipment for $260 million and its Greens Port Industrial Park a 600-acre development in Houston for $75 million.

In 2007 the company moved its corporate headquarters to West Chester Ohio.

EXECUTIVES

VP Human Resources, Lawrence F. Zizzo Jr., age 63
EVP and Operating Officer, John F. Kaloski, age 62, $481,250 total compensation
VP Government and Public Relations, Alan H. McCoy, age 60
Chairman President and CEO, James L. (Jim) Wainscott, age 55, $1,010,625 total compensation
SVP Corporate Strategy and Investor Relations, Albert E. Ferrara Jr., age 63, $433,125 total compensation
EVP General Counsel and Secretary, David C. Horn, age 60, $553,430 total compensation
VP Finance and CFO, Roger K. Newport, age 47
General Manager Strategic Planning and Financial Analysis, Christopher J. Ross
General Manager Public Relations, Barry Racey
VP Carbon Steel Operations, Keith J. Howell
VP Specialty Steel Operations, Kirk W. Reich, age 44
VP Sales and Customer Service, Gary T. Barlow
Assistant Treasurer, Douglas O. Mitterholzer
VP Engineering Raw Materials and Energy, Maurice A. Reed
Director, Ralph S. (Mike) Michael III, age 57
Director, Bonnie G. Hill, age 70
Director, John S. Brinzo, age 69
Director, Robert H. Jenkins, age 69
Director, Richard A. (Dick) Abdoo, age 68
Director, William K. (Bill) Gerber, age 58
Director, James A. Thomson, age 67
Director, Shirley D. Peterson, age 70
Director, Dennis C. Cuneo, age 62
Auditors: Deloitte&ToucheLLP

LOCATIONS

HQ: AK Steel Holding Corp.
9227 Centre Pointe Drive, West Chester, OH 45069
Phone: 513 425-5000 **Fax:** 513 425-5220
Web: www.aksteel.com

2010 Sales

US	5,145	86
Total	5,968	100

PRODUCTS/OPERATIONS

2010 Sales

	$ mil.	% of total
Carbon steel	3,620	60
Tubular steel & other	211	4

2010 Sales (by Market)

Distributors & converters	39
Industry & manufacturing	25

COMPETITORS

ArcelorMittal USA
Dofasco
Feralloy
Kobe Steel USA
Nucor
Steel Dynamics
Union Electric Steel
United States Steel
Worthington Industries

HISTORICAL FINANCIALS

Company Type: Public

Income Statement

FYE: December 31

	REVENUE ($ mil.)	NET INCOME ($ mil.)	NET PROFIT MARGIN	EMPLOYEES
12/11	6,468	(155)	—	6,600
12/10	5,968	(128)	—	6,600
12/09	4,076	(74)	—	6,500
12/08	7,644	4	0.1%	6,800
12/07	7,003	387	5.5%	6,900
Annual Growth	(2.0%)	—	—	(1.1%)

2011 Year-End Financials

Debt ratio: 20.24%
Return on equity: (-40.05)%
Cash ($ mil.): 42
Current ratio: 112.07
Long-term debt ($ mil.): 650
No. of shares (mil.): 110
Dividends
Yield: —
Payout: —
Market value ($ mil.): 911

	STOCK PRICE ($) FY Close	P/E High/Low	PER SHARE ($) Earnings	Dividends	Book Value
12/11	8.26	— —	(1.41)	0.00	3.52
12/10	16.37	— —	(1.17)	0.20	5.86
12/09	21.35	— —	(0.68)	0.20	8.05
12/08	9.32	1822131	0.04	0.20	8.77
12/07	46.24	15 5	3.46	0.00	7.85
Annual Growth	(35.0%)	— —	—	—	(18.2%)

Alabama Power Co.

Alabama Power powers up Southern Rockers and others in the heart of Dixie. The Southern Company subsidiary provides electricity to nearly 1.4 million residential and business customers in Alabama. The utility operates almost 92000 miles of transmission and distribution lines and it has nuclear hydroelectric and fossil-fueled power plant interests that give it a generating capacity of more than 12200 MW. Alabama Power sells wholesale power to more than 15 municipal and rural distribution utilities; it also provides steam transmission (used for heating and cooling buildings) in downtown Birmingham Alabama and sells electric appliances (such as thermostats ovens and washing machines).

In 2009 Alabama Power began was exploring the possibility of generating power by burning wood and other renewable fuels at one of its coal-fired plants in repsonse to government regulations calling for lower carbon emissions. In 2010 the company teamed up with The Westervelt Company agreeing to buy biomass-fuel (waste wood material) from the timber company.

In 2011 Alabama Power was also completing a six-year $1.7 billion clean air project that calls for the installation of scrubbers (air pollution control devices) at all seven of its largest coal fired plants in Alabama. By 2010 six scrubbers were in operation at four power plants in Jefferson Shelby Walker and Mobile counties.

Growing its green energy portfolio in 2012 the company agreed to buy 202 MW of power from a Kansas wind park being developed by TradeWind Energy and which is expected to commence operations in 2014.

A warmer-the-usual summer and a colder-than-normal winter helped increase power demand. This and a rate increase helped to lift retail revenues and overall net income in 2010. The improving economy saw industrial demand pick up as well. However wholesale sales took a dip in 2010 due to the end of a number of long-term unit power sales contracts which expired mid-year and became available for retail service.

EXECUTIVES

President CEO and Director, Charles D. McCrary, age 60, $687,713 total compensation
EVP Customer Service, Steven R. (Steve) Spencer, age 56, $393,771 total compensation
VP Birmingham Division, Barbara J. (Bobbie) Knight
VP Eastern Division, Julia H. Segars
SVP, Robert Holmes Jr.
VP Corporate Secretary and Assistant Treasurer, William E. Zales Jr.
VP, Marsha S. Johnson
SVP and General Counsel, Gordon G. Martin
VP, William B. Johnson
Assistant Secretary, Celia H. Shorts
Assistant Secretary, Kay I. Worley
Assistant Treasurer, J. Randy DeRieux
EV CFO and Treasurer, Philip C. Raymond, age 52
SVP and Senior Production Officer, Theodore J. (Ted) McCullough, age 48
VP, Nick C. Sellers
VP, J. Leigh Davis-Perry
VP, Greg Barker
Assistant Comptroller, Ronald Q. Patterson
Assistant Comptroller, Anita Allcorn-Walker
EVP External Affairs, Zeke W. Smith, age 52
VP, Myrna J. Pittman

VP and CIO, Kathleen S. King
VP, Matthew W. Bowden
VP, Leslie L. Sanders
Assistant Secretary and Assistant Treasurer, Melissa K. Caen
VP, Daniel K. Glover
VP, Richard J. Mandes Jr.
President CEO and Director, Charles D. McCrary, age 60
Director, David M. Ratcliffe, age 63
Director, John D. Johns, age 59
Director, James W. Wright, age 68
Director, Malcolm Portera, age 65
Director, James K. Lowder, age 62
Director, Whit Armstrong, age 64
Director, David J. Cooper Sr., age 66
Director, Patricia M. King, age 66
Director, C. Dowd Ritter, age 64
Director, James H. Sanford, age 67
Director, John C. Webb IV, age 69
Director, Ralph D. Cook, age 67

LOCATIONS

HQ: Alabama Power Co.
600 North 18th Street, Birmingham, AL 35203
Phone: 205 257-1000
Web: www.alapower.com

PRODUCTS/OPERATIONS

2010 Sales

	$ mil.	% of total
Retail		
Residential	2,283	38
Commercial	1,535	26
Industrial	1,231	21
Other retail	27	-
Wholesale	701	12
Other	199	3
Total	**5,976**	**100**

COMPETITORS

Alabama Gas
Duke Energy
Entergy

HISTORICAL FINANCIALS

Company Type: Subsidiary

Income Statement

FYE: December 31

	REVENUE ($ mil.)	NET INCOME ($ mil.)	NET PROFIT MARGIN	EMPLOYEES
12/11	5,702	747	13.1%	6,632
12/10	5,976	746	12.5%	6,552
12/09	5,528	709	12.8%	6,842
12/08	6,076	655	10.8%	6,997
12/07	5,359	615	11.5%	6,980
Annual Growth	1.6%	5.0%	—	(1.3%)

2011 Year-End Financials

Debt ratio: 30.48%
Return on equity: 12.39%
Cash ($ mil.): 344
Current ratio: 121.58
Long-term debt ($ mil.): 5,632
No. of shares (mil.): 30
Dividends
Yield: —
Payout: 109.32%
Market value ($ mil.): 2,822

	STOCK PRICE ($) FY Close	P/E High/Low	PER SHARE ($) Earnings	Dividends	Book Value
12/11	92.40	— —	(0.00)	0.00	197.36
12/10	80.00	— —	(0.00)	1.30	199.03
12/09	78.00	— —	(0.00)	1.30	193.91
12/08	76.00	— —	(0.00)	1.30	217.45
12/07	83.00	— —	(0.00)	1.30	283.40
Annual Growth	2.7%	— —	—	—	(8.6%)

Alaska Air Group, Inc.

Whether you want to capture a Kodiak moment or down a daiquiri by the Sea of Cortez an Alaska Air Group airplane can fly you there. Operating through primary subsidiary Alaska Airlines and regional carrier Horizon Air the group flies more than 24 million passengers to 100+ destinations in the US (mainly western states including Alaska and Hawaii) Canada and Mexico. The group's primary hub is Seattle (accounting for almost two-thirds of passengers) but it also flies out of key markets such as Portland Oregon; Los Angeles; and Anchorage Alaska. Alaska Airlines has a fleet of more than 115 Boeing 737 jets. Horizon Air operates about 50 Bombardier Q400 turboprops.

Accounting for 92% of revenue the passenger segment's Alaska line is divided into Alaska Mainline which makes flights with average stage lengths that are more than 1000 miles and Alaska Regional for shorter distances. Regional airline Horizon sells all of its capacity to Alaska under a capacity purchase agreement. Mainline operations carried about 18 million revenue passengers while regional operations which includes Horizon carried about seven million revenue passengers mainly in Washington Oregon Idaho and California.

As its name would imply the airline transports more passengers between Alaska and the US mainland than any other airline. Besides its own flights the segment provides passenger service through contracts with SkyWest Airlines and Peninsula Airways. Carrying about 4% of all US domestic passenger traffic the segment also includes such non-ticket revenue as reservations fees ticket change fees and charges for baggage service.

Freight and mail account for 2% of revenue. The Other segment 6% of revenue includes the Mileage Plan on-board food and beverages commissions from car and hotel vendors and travel insurance. The Mileage Plan awards miles for flights on Alaska Horizon and partner airlines and sells miles to third parties.

Revenue rose about 13% in 2011 compared with 2010. In the Passenger segment Mainline revenue increased about 15% over the same period thanks to an 8% jump in capacity and about a 6% bump in passenger revenue per available seat mile (PRASM). Regional revenue was up about 7% as the result of of a 13% rise in PRASM which itself resulted from a 9% increase in ticket yield and a 3% jump in load factor. The Freight and Mail segment inched up just 2% on freight fuel surcharge increases. The Other segment enjoyed an uptick of about 9% mainly because of more Mileage Plan revenue and food and beverage sales. Net income however fell from more than $251 million in 2010 to more than $244 million in 2011.

Besides focusing on key markets such as Seattle and Los Angeles another important component of Alaska Air's strategy includes marketing alliances with other airlines for reciprocal frequent flyer mileage credit and codesharing. Alaska has relationships with about a dozen major airlines such as AMR's American Airlines Air France Delta Air Lines and Qantas as well as two other regional airlines besides SkyWest and Peninsula Air: Era Alaska and Kenmore Air.

Like the airline industry as a whole Alaska Air has been challenged by rising fuel costs which have been known to head up even higher in Alaska's operating territory of the West Coast than in the Gulf and East coasts. Alaska cushions itself against such volatility with crude oil call options jet fuel refining margin swap contracts and the acquisition of more fuel-efficient aircraft including the Boeing 737-800 and 737-900ER. Fuel costs represented about 34% of total operating expenses in 2011 up from 27% in 2010.

For customer service Alaska Air offers a Baggage Service Guarantee and recently introduced Android and iPhone mobile applications for the airline's passengers. The company will continue focusing on improving its customers' experience especially in the airport. Onboard Alaska tries to set itself apart by not only providing Wi-Fi on most flights but also by serving Starbucks coffee on some flights.

HISTORY

Pilot Mac McGee started McGee Airways in 1932 to fly cargo between Anchorage and Bristol Bay Alaska. He joined other local operators in 1937 to form Star Air Lines which began airmail service between Fairbanks and Bethel in 1938. In 1944 a year after buying three small airlines Star adopted the name Alaska Airlines.

The company expanded to include freight service to Africa and Australia in 1950. This expansion coupled with the seasonal nature of the airline's business caused losses in the early 1970s. Developer Bruce Kennedy gained control of the board turning the firm around by the end of 1973. But the Civil Aeronautics Board forced the carrier to drop service to northwestern Alaska in 1975 and by 1978 it served only 10 Alaskan cities and Seattle.

Kennedy became CEO the next year. The 1978 Airline Deregulation Act allowed Alaska Air to move into new areas as well as regain the routes it had lost. By 1982 it was the largest airline flying between Alaska and the lower 48 states.

In 1985 the airline reorganized forming Alaska Air Group as its holding company. The next year Alaska Air Group bought Jet America Airlines (expanding its routes eastward to Chicago St. Louis and Dallas) and Seattle-based Horizon Air Industries (which served 30 Northwest cities). When competition in the East and Midwest cut profits in 1987 Kennedy shut down Jet America to focus on West Coast operations.

To counterbalance summer traffic to Alaska the airline began service to two Mexican resorts in 1988. Fuel prices and sluggish traffic hurt 1990 earnings but Alaska Air Group stayed in the black unlike many other carriers. Kennedy retired as chairman and CEO in 1991.

That year the airline began service to Canada and seasonal flights to two Russian cities. Neil Bergt's MarkAir airline declared war cutting fares and horning in on Alaska Air Group's territory. Alaska Air Group's profits were slashed and MarkAir went into bankruptcy.

Alaska Air extended Russian flights to year-round in 1994. The airline began service to Vancouver in 1996. That year it became the first major US carrier to use the GPS satellite navigation system. In 1997 it added service to more than a dozen new cities but halted service to Russia because of that country's economic woes in 1998.

Alaska Air Group and Dutch airline KLM agreed to a marketing alliance in 1998 that included reciprocal frequent-flier programs and code-sharing and in 1999 it added code-sharing agreements with several major airlines including American and Continental. Alaska Airlines developed an online check-in system a first among US carriers.

In 2000 an Alaska Airlines MD-83 crashed into the Pacific Ocean near Los Angeles killing all 88 people on board. A federal investigation of Alaska Airlines' maintenance practices found deficiencies but the FAA eventually accepted the airline's plan to tighten safety standards.

Like most carriers in the latter part of 2001 Alaska Airlines cut back its flights as a result of reduced demand after the September 11 terrorist attacks. As demand slowly returned in 2002 Alaska Airlines began to add new destinations and increase the number of flights on some established routes.

In 2005 Alaska Airlines announced plans to buy 35 Boeing 737-800s between 2006 and 2011.

EXECUTIVES

President Horizon Air, Glenn S. Johnson, age 53, $311,537 total compensation
President CEO and Director, Bradley D. (Brad) Tilden, age 51, $353,074 total compensation
VP Legal and Corporate Affairs General Counsel and Corporate Secretary, Keith Loveless, age 55
Chairman, William S. (Bill) Ayer, age 57, $373,846 total compensation
VP Safety, Thomas W. (Tom) Nunn
VP Maintenance and Engineering Alaska Airlines, Frederick L. Mohr
VP Flight Operations Alaska Airlines, Gary L. Beck
VP Marketing Alaska Airlines, Joseph A. (Joe) Sprague
Managing Director Loyalty Marketing and Customer Advocacy Alaska Airlines, Caroline Boren
Managing Director Corporate Affairs and Assistant Corporate Secretary, Shannon K. Alberts
VP Information and Technology Alaska Airlines, Kris M. Kutchera
Managing Director Brand and Product Marketing Alaska Airlines, Greg Latimer
Director Corporate Real Estate Alaska Airlines, Karen A. Gruen
Managing Director Taxes, Laurie Sands
Managing Director Strategic and Corporate Communications Alaska Airlines, Paul McElroy
VP Finance and CFO, Brandon S. Pedersen, age 45
Vice President - Human Resources of Alaska Airlines; Inc, Kelley J. Dobbs, age 45
VP Planning and Revenue Management Alaska Airlines, Andrew R. Harrison
Associate General Counsel and Assistant Corporate Secretary, Irving S. Bertram
VP Customer Service Airports Alaska Airlines, Jeffrey M. Butler
Chief Risk Compliance and Ethics Officer, Wendy Jones
COO and EVP Operations Alaska Airlines, Benito (Ben) Minicucci, age 45, $259,610 total compensation
Managing Director Airport Services Alaska Airlines, Sandy Stelling
Managing Director Labor Relations Alaska Air Group, Elizabeth Ryan
Director Cargo Sales Alaska Air Cargo, Joe Samudovsky
VP Strategic Sourcing and Supply Chain Management Alaska Airlines, Ann E. Ardizzone
Managing Director Investor Relations, Chris Berry
Managing Director Accounting and Controller, George Newman
Managing Director Privacy and Security and Associate General Counsel, Aileen Cronin
Vice President Customer Service, Diana Shaw
Vice President - Human Resources, Tammy Young
Director, J. Kenneth Thompson, age 60
Director, Phyllis J. Campbell, age 60
Director, Dennis F. Madsen, age 63
Director, Byron I. Mallott, age 69
Director, Jessie J. Knight Jr., age 61
Director, R. Marc Langland, age 70
Director, Marion C. Blakey
Director, Patricia M. Bedient, age 58
Auditors: KPMGLLP

LOCATIONS

HQ: Alaska Air Group Inc.
19300 International Blvd., Seattle WA 98188
Phone: 206-392-5040 **Fax:** 206-392-2804
Web: www.alaskaair.com

PRODUCTS/OPERATIONS

2012 Sales

Passenger Revenue — Mainline	3,284	71
Freight & mail	111	2
Other	516	11

2012 Sales

Alaska	4,650	93
Adjustments	(369.0)	-

COMPETITORS

ACE Aviation
Aeromexico
Air Canada
Allegiant Travel
AMR Corp.
Delta Air Lines
Hawaiian Holdings
JetBlue
Mesa Air
SkyWest
Southwest Airlines
United Continental
US Airways
Virgin America
WestJet

HISTORICAL FINANCIALS

Company Type: Public

Income Statement FYE: December 31

	REVENUE ($ mil.)	NET INCOME ($ mil.)	NET PROFIT MARGIN	EMPLOYEES
12/11	4,317	244	5.7%	12,806
12/10	3,832	251	6.6%	12,039
12/09	3,399	121	3.6%	12,440
12/08	3,662	(135)	—	14,143
12/07	3,506	125	3.6%	14,710
Annual Growth	5.3%	18.3%	—	(3.4%)

2011 Year-End Financials

Debt ratio: 25.16%
Return on equity: 20.84%
Cash ($ mil.): 102
Current ratio: 105.69
Long-term debt ($ mil.): 1,099
No. of shares (mil.): 70
Dividends
Yield: —
Payout: —
Market value ($ mil.): 5,328

	STOCK PRICE ($) FY Close	P/E High/Low		PER SHARE ($) Earnings	Dividends	Book Value
12/11	75.09	22	15	3.33	0.00	16.54
12/10	56.69	17	9	3.42	0.00	15.39
12/09	34.56	21	8	1.68	0.00	12.25
12/08	29.25	—	—	(1.87)	0.00	9.12
12/07	25.01	29	14	1.55	0.00	13.46
Annual Growth	31.6%	—	—	21.1%	—	5.3%

Alcoa, Inc.

While many of its aluminum products may be lightweight Alcoa is anything but. The company is among the world's top producers of alumina (aluminum's principal ingredient from bauxite) and aluminum. Operations include bauxite mining alumina refining and aluminum smelting; primary products include alumina and alumina-based chemicals automotive components and sheet aluminum for beverage cans. Markets include the aerospace automotive and construction industries. Non-aluminum products include precision castings and aerospace and industrial fasteners. Although a global company Alcoa does about half of its business in the US; Australia Brazil and European countries make up its largest international markets.

HISTORY

In 1886 two chemists one in France and one in the US simultaneously discovered an inexpensive process for aluminum production. The American Charles Hall pursued commercial applications. Two years later with an investor group led by Captain Alfred Hunt Hall formed the Pittsburgh Reduction Company. Its first salesman Arthur Davis secured an initial order for 2000 cooking pots.

In 1889 the Mellon Bank loaned the company $4000. In 1891 the firm recapitalized with the Mellon family holding 12% of the stock.

Davis led the business after Hunt died in 1899 and stayed on until 1957 (he died in 1962 at age 95). The company introduced aluminum foil (1910) and found applications for aluminum in new products such as airplanes and cars. It became the Aluminum Company of America in 1907.

By the end of WWI Alcoa had integrated backward into bauxite mining and forward into end-use production. By the 1920s the Mellons had raised their stake to 33%.

The government and Alcoa had debated antitrust issues in court for years since the smelting patent expired in 1912. Finally a 1946 federal ruling forced the company to sell many operations built during WWII as well as its Canadian subsidiary (Alcan).

In the competitive aluminum industry of the 1960s Alcoa's lower-cost production helped it seize market share especially in beverage cans. In the 1970s Alcoa began offering engineered products such as aerospace components and in the 1980s it invested in research acquisitions and plant modernization.

Paul O'Neill (former president of International Paper) arrived as CEO in 1987 and shifted the company's focus back to aluminum. Sales and earnings set records the next two years but plunged afterward reflecting a weak global economy and record-low aluminum prices. Then the fall of the Soviet Union in the early 1990s led to a worldwide glut as Russian exports soared.

In 1994 Alcoa cut its production as part of a two-year accord with Western and Russian producers. That year the company agreed to pool its alumina and chemical operations with Australia's Western Mining Corp.

Alcoa formed a joint venture with Shanghai Aluminum Fabrication Plant in China. The company expanded in Europe in 1996 acquiring Italy's state-run aluminum business followed by the purchase of Inespal Spain's state-run aluminum operations in 1998. Alcoa also bought #3 US aluminum producer Alumax for $3.8 billion in 1998 but only after divesting its cast-plate operations.

Known by the nickname "Alcoa" since the late 1920s the company adopted that as its official name in 1999. O'Neill retired as CEO in 1999; COO Alain Belda succeeded him. Later that year Alcoa bought the 50% of aluminum auto parts maker A-CMI that it did not already own from Hayes Lemmerz International.

In 2000 Alcoa bought aluminum extrusion maker Excel Extrusions from Noranda (now called Falconbridge) and paid $4.5 billion for Reynolds Metals after agreeing to divest some assets –including all of Reynolds' alumina refineries –to satisfy regulators. The same month Alcoa acquired Cordant Technologies. Alcoa also assumed Cordant's 85% ownership of Howmet International (castings) as a result of the transaction –and later acquired the remainder of Howmet. Late in 2000 President-elect George W. Bush named Alcoa's chairman Paul O'Neill to be treasury secretary. (O'Neill subsequently resigned the post in December 2002.)

Alcoa sold its majority stake in the Worsley alumina refinery (Australia) to BHP Billiton in 2001 for about $1.5 billion as part of its refinery divestments. Treasury Secretary O'Neill completed the sale of his more than $90 million worth of Alcoa stock and options in June. In late November Alcoa and BHP Billiton combined their North American metals distribution businesses to create Integris Metals –a joint venture with revenues of about $1.5 billion. (The two subsequently sold the JV to Ryerson in 2005.)

Late in the year Alcoa agreed to buy an 8% stake in Aluminium Corporation of China (Chinalco). The deal gave Alcoa a seat on the board and 27% of Chinalco's initial public offering.

Early in 2002 Alcoa made a bid to acquire Elkem a Norway-based metals producer for $850 million; Elkem spurned the offer. Later that year Alcoa bought Elkem shares in the open market increasing its ownership to around 46%. Alcoa also purchased Ivex Packaging (Chicago-based industrial packaging group) which excluded Ivex's 48% stake in Packaging Dynamics for an estimated $790 million in cash and assumed debt. The company raised its stake in Shibazaki Seisakusho (plastic and aluminum closures and caps Japan) from 70% to around 95%. At the close of 2002 Alcoa bought Fairchild Fasteners (aerospace and industrial fastening) a unit of The Fairchild Corporation for roughly $657 million.

The acquisitions kept apace into the next year. In 2003 Alcoa acquired Camargo Correa Group's 41% stake in the South American businesses of Alcoa including its largest subsidiary in the group –Alcoa Aluminio S.A. (Brazil) –and operations in Argentina Chile Colombia Peru Uruguay and Venezuela.

Faced with lower aluminum prices in its aerospace industrial-gas-turbine and nonresidential construction markets Alcoa decided to divest under-performing businesses primarily in its automotive packaging and specialty chemicals units. It sold off its Alumax Foils facilities (Russellville Arkansas and St. Louis Missouri) to JW Aluminum. As part of that divestment strategy in early 2004 Alcoa sold its automotive fastener unit to privately held Kaminski Holdings for an undisclosed price. That same year the company sold its specialty chemicals unit for $342 million to Rhone Capital LLC and Teachers' Merchant Bank.

Alcoa and Fujikura Ltd. had shared a joint venture called Alcoa Fujikura. The two JV partners disbanded Alcoa Fujikura in 2005 though splitting it evenly between the parents. Alcoa acquired the automotive cable operations based in Detroit and Fujikura kept the telecommunications unit that is based in Nashville. Later in the year Alcoa decided to sell its rail unit –comprised of four railroad companies in Arkansas New York and Texas –to RailAmerica for about $77 million; the two companies signed an agreement allowing service through the railroads.

In 2006 the company sold its Home Exteriors unit to Ply Gem Industries; it also sold its aerospace service business to ThyssenKrupp. In the latter half of that decade the company also divested its packaging unit and its wire harness and electrical distribution business. The company sold its stake in Chinalco in a 2007 private offering that garnered Alcoa $2 billion.

In 2007 Alcoa also offered to buy what was then the world's #3 aluminum producer Alcan for $33 billion but was trumped by Rio Tinto's $40 billion offer. The merger of Russian aluminum giants RUSAL and Sual (along with Glencore's alumina operations) earlier that year briefly created the world's largest aluminum company pushing Alcoa and Alcan down a notch each. With the formation of Rio Tinto Alcan RUSAL abdicated the title and became the #2 aluminum producer.

Alcoa formed a soft-alloy extrusion joint venture with Sapa Group (part of Orkla) in 2008 called Sapa AB. It was the world's largest aluminum shaper and was originally owned equally by Orkla and Alcoa. The two companies also co-owned a joint venture through Orkla subsidiary Elkem called Elkem Aluminum. In 2009 Alcoa and Orkla exchanged ownership stakes in the two JVs with Alcoa taking full ownership of Elkem Aluminum and Orkla doing the same with Sapa AB.

In 2010 Alcoa added to its building products portfolio when it acquired Pennsylvania-based commercial window and door maker Traco. The family-owned company became part of Alcoa's building and constructon business.

EXECUTIVES

VP Secretary and Corporate Governance Counsel, Donna C. Dabney, age 61
VP Human Resources, John D. (Jack) Bergen
President Canada, Pierre Morin
Senior Counsel and Assistant Secretary, Janet F. Duderstadt
VP Sustainability and Environment Health and Safety, William J. (Bill) O'Rourke Jr., age 64
Chairman and CEO, Klaus Kleinfeld, age 54, $1,400,000 total compensation
EVP; President Engineered Products and Solutions, Olivier M. Jarrault, age 50
Executive Vice President; Chief Legal and Compliance Officer, Kurt R. Waldo, age 57
Senior Counsel and Assistant Secretary, Brenda A. Hart
President Alcoa Power and Propulsion, Michael A. Pepper
VP; Regional CEO Latin America and Caribbean, Franklin L (Frank) Feder, age 61
VP Internal Audit, Julie A. Caponi, age 50
President Alcoa Defense, David C. (Dave) Dobson, age 59
VP Corporate Affairs, Nicholas J. (Nick) Ashooh
VP; President Alcoa Power and Propulsion, Raymond B. (Ray) Mitchell
President Energy, Rick A. Bowen, age 57
EVP and CFO, Charles D. (Chuck) McLane Jr., age 59, $600,000 total compensation
COO Global Primary Products, William F. (Bill) Oplinger, age 45
EVP; President Global Rolled Products, Kay Meggers
Assistant General Counsel and Director Global Compliance, Judith L. (Judi) Nocito
Assistant General Counsel, Dale C. Perdue
VP; President Global Primary Products Australia, Alan Cransberg
EVP and Chief Legal and Compliance Officer, Audrey Strauss
VP; CFO Engineered Products and Solutions, Tony R. Thene, age 51
President Global Packaging, Andrey Donets, age 50
President European Mill Products, Ingrid Muehlboeck, age 43
VP and Chief Sustainability Officer, Kevin J. Anton, age 54
VP and Treasurer, Peter Hong, age 54
Assistant Treasurer, Paul A. Hayes
Assistant General Counsel; Group Counsel Global Rolled Products, Paula J. Jesion
VP; President Asia Pacific Region, Jinya Chen, age 60
VP; President Global Primary Metals Technology and Manufacturing, Jean-Pierre Gilardeau, age 60
VP; President Global Primary Products - Growth Bauxite and Africa, Kenneth (Ken) Wisnoski, age 57
Manager Corporate Communications, Joyce Saltzman
President Consumer Electronics and President Alcoa China Rolled Products, Jiming Zhu, age 51
Director Communications Global Rolled Products, Kevin Lowery
President Oil and Gas, Mary Zappone
President Wheel and Transportation Products, Tim D. Myers, age 46
Assistant Treasurer; Chief Investment Officer Pension Plan Investments, Ronald E. Barin
Assistant Controller, Robert S. Collins
President Materials Management, Timothy D. (Tim) Reyes, age 45
EVP; President Global Primary Products, Chris L. Ayers
President Fastening Systems, Vitaliy V. Rusakov
President Alcoa Building and Construction Systems, Glen G. Morrison
President Global Primary Products - Latin America and the Caribbean, Marcos R. Ramos, age 53
VP; President Alcoa Foundation, Paula Davis
VP and Controller, Graeme W. Bottger
CFO Global Primary Products, Roy Harvey
VP Corporate Development and Global Public and Government Affairs, Daniel Cruise
VP Tax, John Kenna, age 51
CFO Global Rolled Products and Asia, Vanessa Lau, age 40
VP Program Office, Matthias Obermayer, age 43
VP and General Counsel, Max W. Laun
President Forgings and Extrusions, Eric V. Roegner, age 43
President Global Primary Products ? U.S.A., Bob Wilt
Director Communications Global Primary Products, Sonya Elam Harden
Director Communications Engineered Products and Solutions, Jean Moorman
Director Marketing Communications and Branding, Dina Shapiro
EVP and CTO, Raymond (Ray) Kilmer
EVP; President Global Business Services, Mark Davies
President Global Aerospace Ground Transportation and Industrial and Specialty Products, Mark Vrablec
President European Region and Global Primary Products Europe, Tomas Mar Sigurdsson
Acting President Alcoa Russia, Maxim Smirnov
CIO, Nancy Wolk
Chief Diversity Officer, Gena Lovett
Assistant Corporate Secretary; Director - Executive Communications, Esra Ozer
Director, James W. (Jim) Owens, age 66
Director, Arthur D. (Art) Collins Jr., age 64
Director, Michael G. (Mike) Morris, age 65
Director, Ratan N. Tata, age 74
Director, Patricia F. (Pat) Russo, age 59

Director, Judith M. Gueron, age 70
Director, Ernesto Zedillo, age 60
Director, Kathryn S. Fuller, age 65
Director, E. Stanley (Stan) O'Neal, age 60
Independent Director, Martin Sorrell
Independent Director, Stanley Neal
Independent Director, Stanley ONeal
Auditors: PricewaterhouseCoopersLLP

LOCATIONS

HQ: Alcoa Inc.
390 Park Ave., New York NY 10022-4608
Phone: 212-836-2600 **Fax:** 212-836-2815
Web: www.alcoa.com

2010 Sales

	$ mil.	% of total
US	12,295	49
Spain	1,487	6
The Netherlands	1,025	4
Total	**24,951**	**100**

PRODUCTS/OPERATIONS

2011 Sales

	$ mil.	% of total
Primary Metals	8,240	33
Engineered Products & Solutions	5,345	21
Total	**24,951**	**100**

Selected Products

Commercial windows and doors
Engineering
Extruding
Finishing and electrostatic painting
Glass cutting
Insulating
Tempering
Flat-rolled products
Light gauge sheet products
 Rigid container sheet and foil (packaging market)
 Sheet and plate mill products (transportation and construction markets)
Primary aluminum
Smelted from alumina which is derived from bauxite
Engineered products and solutions
Aluminum wheels castings fasteners forgings
Alumina and chemicals
Alumina
Alumina-based chemicals
Bauxite
Transportation services for alumina and bauxite

COMPETITORS

BHP Billiton
Chinalco
Crown Holdings
Hayes Lemmerz
Hydro Aluminium
National Aluminium
Nippon Light Metal
Quanex Building Products
Rio Tinto Alcan
RUSAL
Superior Industries

HISTORICAL FINANCIALS

Company Type: Public

Income Statement FYE: December 31

	REVENUE ($ mil.)	NET INCOME ($ mil.)	NET PROFIT MARGIN	EMPLOYEES
12/11	24,951	611	2.4%	61,000
12/10	21,013	254	1.2%	59,000
12/09	18,439	(1,151)	—	59,000
12/08	26,901	(74)	—	87,000
12/07	30,748	2,564	8.3%	107,000
Annual Growth	(5.1%)	(30.1%)	—	(13.1%)

2011 Year-End Financials

Debt ratio: 23.36%	No. of shares (mil.): 1,064
Return on equity: 4.41%	Dividends
Cash ($ mil.): 1,939	Yield: —
Current ratio: 128.27	Payout: 21.82%
Long-term debt ($ mil.): 8,640	Market value ($ mil.): 9,207

	STOCK PRICE ($) FY Close	P/E High/Low		PER SHARE ($) Earnings	Dividends	Book Value
12/11	8.65	32	15	0.55	0.00	13.01
12/10	15.39	70	40	0.24	0.12	13.32
12/09	16.12	—	—	(1.23)	0.26	12.79
12/08	11.26	—	—	(0.09)	0.68	14.66
12/07	36.55	16	10	2.95	0.68	19.36
Annual Growth	(30.3%)	—	—	(34.3%)	—	(9.5%)

Aleris International Inc (New)

LOCATIONS

HQ: Aleris International Inc (New)
25825 Science Park Drive, Suite 400, Cleveland, OH 44122-7392
Phone: 216 910-3400
Web: www.aleris.com

HISTORICAL FINANCIALS

Company Type:

Income Statement FYE: December 31

	REVENUE ($ mil.)	NET INCOME ($ mil.)	NET PROFIT MARGIN	EMPLOYEES
12/11	4,826	161	3.3%	6,900
12/10*	2,474	71	2.9%	0
05/10	1,643	2,204	134.2%	0
12/09	2,996	(1,187)	—	0
Annual Growth	17.2%	—	—	—

*Fiscal year change

2011 Year-End Financials

Debt ratio: 29.54%	No. of shares (mil.): 0
Return on equity: 28.89%	Dividends
Cash ($ mil.): 231	Yield: —
Current ratio: 233.73	Payout: 132.01%
Long-term debt ($ mil.): 595	Market value ($ mil.): —

Alleghany Corp.

After a spell as a conglomerate with interests ranging from minerals to steel fasteners Alleghany found that it really prefers property/casualty insurance with a smattering of good old real estate. Alleghany's subsidiaries include Capitol Transamerica (property/casualty fidelity and surety insurance) and RSUI Group (wholesale specialty insurance). The company distributes its insurance products through independent insurance brokers in the US. Its Pacific Compensation Corporation (PCC) unit handles workers' compensation insurance in California where Alleghany also has commercial and residential real estate interests. Its Transatlantic Holdings subsidiary offers property/casualty reinsurance globally.

HISTORY

Alleghany was formed in 1929 by Clevelanders Mantis and Oris Van Sweringen as a pyramid railroad holding company. It collapsed in 1934 and after passing through several hands it was bought in 1937 by speculator Robert Young with backing from Woolworth heir Allan Kirby.

Young resurrected the company's Chesapeake and Ohio railroad but another holding Missouri Pacific Railroad (Mo-Pac) failed to thrive and Young embarked on a 40-year struggle to maximize Mo-Pac's value. Young focused on railroads even as the industry declined but he also made other investments including a chunk of IDS (which became the US's largest mutual fund company) and real estate. He also trimmed company holdings from nearly 70 to about 10. By the time Young committed suicide in 1958 Alleghany was in trouble and Kirby who had always kept to the shadows took over.

In his first three years at the helm Kirby fought a takeover attempt by Abraham Sonnabend and a proxy fight with investors John and Clint Murchison. After being ousted briefly in 1961 Kirby reemerged in control of the company. Allan suffered a stroke in 1965 and his son Fred Morgan "F. M." Kirby II took over.

In 1966 the company sold its interest in the New York Central railroad (bought in 1945) and eight years later finally emerged from the Mo-Pac mess with about $42 million in cash and some stock. Alleghany used the cash to buy metal fabricating company MSL Industries and the rest of IDS.

Fred Kirby's mantra was flexibility and in 1984 he sold IDS to American Express for a then-flabbergasting $800 million including a pile of stock. Kirby used these proceeds to buy Chicago Title & Trust the same year. Two years later he liquidated the old Alleghany and reincorporated Alleghany Financial CT&T's parent as Alleghany Corporation.

Kirby used the cash from the American Express deal to buy and then spin off a construction company. Other purchases followed in the 1990s including more title operations a California thrift and in 1991 Celite which produced filtration materials. This line was expanded the next year with the purchase of Harborlite. After several purchases in direct insurance (quickly flipped for a profit) in 1993 Alleghany bought Underwriters Re.

In 1994 and 1995 the company bought up shares of Burlington Northern Railroad which merged with Santa Fe in 1995.

In the 1990s CT&T lost market share through industry consolidation so in 1998 Alleghany spun off CT&T's title operations (later acquired by Fidelity National Financial). The next year hit by a down market in reinsurance Alleghany agreed to sell Underwriters Re to Swiss Reinsurance keeping its hand in the market via Alleghany Underwriting Holdings Ltd. (AUL).

In 1999 the company bulked up its asset management operations through acquisitions and in 2000 its industrial fastener business Heads & Threads International bought Acktion's Reynold's Fasteners unit. In 2001 Alleghany sold Lloyd's reinsurer Alleghany Underwriting to Bermuda-based Talbot Holdings and Dutch bank ABN Amro bought the company's asset management business.

The company built up its insurance operations with the purchase of Resurgens Specialty Underwriting (RSUI Group) a subsidiary of British insurance powerhouse Royal & Sun Alliance. It also expanded insurance operations with the 2004 acquisitions of Capitol Transamerica and Darwin National Assurance Company (formerly known as U.S. AEGIS Energy Insurance Company) later renamed as Darwin Professional Underwriters. In early 2006 it took Darwin through an initial public offering and used the funds to reduce its equity interest while retaining majority ownership. (Alleghany's 55% stake in Darwin was sold to Allied World Assurance in 2008.)

While Alleghany collected insurance firms it shed other operations. The company sold Heads & Threads to a management-led investors group in 2004. In 2005 it sold its World Minerals subsidiary (diatomite production) to the US branch of Imerys in a deal valued at about $217 million.

Hurricane Katrina took a serious bite out of profits in 2005. In response Alleghany Insurance Holdings created AIHL Re a reinsurance subsidiary to provide reinsurance directly to RSUI while RSUI worked to reduce its exposure and increased its prices on property insurance. Once the reinsurance market settled down AIHL Re was allowed to go dormant in 2008.

During the quieter 2006 and 2007 hurricane seasons Alleghany found it still had an appetite for insurance providers. The company plunked down $120 million in cash to purchase 33% of monoline homeowners insurance provider Homesite Group in 2006 and spent $198 million to acquire Employers Direct in 2007.

Alleghany held 55% of Darwin Professional Underwriters a specialty property/casualty insurance writer but in 2008 sold it to Allied World Assurance for approximately $300 million.

F. M. Kirby retired as chairman at the end of 2006. His brother Allan Kirby retired from the board in 2010 leaving Jefferson Kirby F. M.'s son as the last family member on the board as directors. F. M. died at the age of 91 in early 2011.

EXECUTIVES

VP Controller Assistant Secretary and Treasurer, Peter R. Sismondo, age 54, $239,455 total compensation
Vice Chairman, John J. Burns Jr., age 80, $1,009,284 total compensation
President CEO and Director, Weston M. Hicks, age 55, $1,000,000 total compensation
President and CEO Alleghany Properties, David J. Bugatto, age 47
Chairman and CEO Capitol Transamerica Corporation, David F. (Dave) Pauly
SVP Finance and Investments and CFO, Roger B. Gorham, age 49, $530,000 total compensation
VP General Counsel and Secretary, Christopher K. Dalrymple, age 44, $300,000 total compensation
VP and General Auditor, Susan E. Giarrusso
Chairman RSUI Group, E.G. Lassiter
Chairman, Jefferson W. Kirby, age 50
VP Finance and Chief Accounting Officer, Jerry G. Borrelli, age 46, $350,000 total compensation
VP and Tax Director, John Carr
VP Planning and Corporate Development, William M. Wilt
Chairman President and CEO Employers Direct, James E. Little
Executive Vice President, Joseph Brandon
Vice Chairman, John J. Burns Jr., age 80
Director, Thomas S. (Tom) Johnson, age 71
Director, Dan R. Carmichael, age 67
President CEO and Director, Weston M. Hicks, age 55
Director, James F. Will, age 73
Director, Rex D. Adams, age 72
Director, William K. Lavin, age 67
Director, Phillip M. Martineau, age 64
Director, Raymond L.M. Wong, age 59
Director, Karen Brenner, age 56
Independent Director, Ian Chippendale
Independent Director, John Foos
Independent Director, Stephen Bradley
Auditors: Ernst&YoungLLP

LOCATIONS

HQ: Alleghany Corporation
7 Times Square Tower, New York NY 10036
Phone: 212-752-1356 **Fax:** 212-759-8149
Web: www.alleghany.com

PRODUCTS/OPERATIONS

2011 Revenues

	$ mil.	% of total
Premiums		
RSUI Group	593	60
Capitol Transamerica Corporation (CATA)	149	15
Pacific Compensation Corporation (PCC)	4	1
Capital gains	127	13
Investment income	108	11
Other than temporary impairment losses	(3.6)	-
Other income	1	-
Total	**981**	**100**

Selected Subsidiaries

Alleghany Capital Corporation (equity investment management)
Alleghany Insurance Holdings LLC
 Capitol Transamerica Corporation (property/casualty insurance)
 Pacific Compensation Corporation (workers' compensation insurance)
 Platte River Insurance Company
 RSUI Group Inc. (specialty insurance)
  Resurgens Specialty Underwriting Inc.
  RSA Surplus Lines Insurance Services Inc.
  RSUI Indemnity CompanyCovington Specialty Insurance CompanyLandmark American Insurance Company
Alleghany Properties Holdings LLC
 Alleghany Properties LLC (real estate ownership and management)
MSL Property Holdings Inc.
Transatlantic Holdings Inc. (global reinsurance organization)

COMPETITORS

AIG
California Casualty
Chubb Corp
CNA Surety
Liberty Mutual Agency
Nationwide
Ohio Casualty
State Compensation Insurance Fund
State Farm
Travelers Companies
Unico American

HISTORICAL FINANCIALS

Company Type: Public

Income Statement FYE: December 31

	ASSETS ($ mil.)	NET INCOME ($ mil.)	INCOME AS % OF ASSETS	EMPLOYEES
12/11	6,478	143	2.2%	763
12/10	6,431	198	3.1%	745
12/09	6,192	271	4.4%	748
12/08	6,181	147	2.4%	826
12/07	6,733	305	4.5%	951
Annual Growth	(1.0%)	(17.2%)	—	(5.4%)

2011 Year-End Financials

Debt ratio: 4.62%
Return on equity: 4.90%
Cash ($ mil.): 84
Current ratio: —
Long-term debt ($ mil.): 299
No. of shares (mil.): 8
Dividends
 Yield: —
 Payout: —
Market value ($ mil.): 2,440

	STOCK PRICE ($) FY Close	P/E High	P/E Low	PER SHARE ($) Earnings	Dividends	Book Value
12/11	285.29	21	17	16.20	0.00	342.12
12/10	306.37	14	12	21.85	0.00	325.31
12/09	276.00	10	8	28.51	0.00	294.80
12/08	282.00	28	13	14.82	0.00	301.48
12/07	402.00	13	11	30.86	0.00	316.34
Annual Growth	(8.2%)	—	—	(14.9%)	—	2.0%

Allegheny Technologies, Inc

Allegheny Technologies Inc. (ATI) is on a roll when it comes to producing metals. The company manufactures stainless and specialty steels nickel- and cobalt-based alloys and superalloys titanium and titanium alloys tungsten materials and such exotic alloys as niobium and zirconium. The company's flat-rolled products (sheet strip and plate) account for about 60% of its sales. Its high-performance metals unit produces metal bar coil foil ingot plate rod and wire. ATI's largest markets include aerospace the chemical process and oil and gas industries. Two-thirds of its sales are in the US with the rest spread among industrial countries in Europe and Asia.

Financial Analysis

ATI's sales plummeted in 2009 as a global recession saddled the company with the twin burdens of low prices for its products and a slump in demand especially of its flat-rolled products. However revenues rebounded in 2010 up some 33% over the previous year on strong sales gains in its engineered products (up 56%) and flat-rolled products (up 54%) segments. After significant losses during the recession net income rose 123% in 2010 driven primarily by gains made through improved manufacturing processes and aggressive cost-cutting.

The company saw significant gains in several key markets including aerospace and defense electrical energy and the chemical process industry. However growth was the strongest in the medical market which was up 90% and the oil and gas market which grew 55%.

Strategy

ATI plans to continue its restructuring strategy. The company spent about $350 million in capital expenditures in 2011 to modernize its operations and drive efficiencies.

The company anticipated strong sales in the aerospace oil and gas and chemical processing markets in 2012. Those predictions were contingent on the fortunes of customers such as Boeing and Airbus who were scheduled to ramp up production of products such as the 787 Dreamliner and A380 jumbo jet. The company also anticipated record capital spending on deepwater oil and gas exploration and new technology to develop shale reserves.

Mergers & Acqusitions

Boosting its specialty products portfolio ATI acquired the Research and Compaction Metals divisions of Crucible Materials in 2009 for about $40 million. The company won the rights to the division at auction; Crucible entered Chapter 11 bankruptcy protection earlier in 2009. ATI combined the units to form a new subsidiary called ATI Powder Metals.

In a strategic 2011 move to bolster its engineered product offerings ATI acquired high-end manufacturer Ladish for some $778 million in stock. Wisconsin-based Ladish produces advanced metal components for the jet engine aerospace and industrial markets.

Company Background

ATI was formed from the 1996 merger of Teledyne and stainless-steel producer Allegheny Ludlum.

HISTORY

Allegheny Ludlum Steel began in 1938 when Allegheny Steel Company (founded in Pennsylvania in 1898) and Ludlum Steel Company (founded in New Jersey in 1854) merged. Allegheny Steel veteran W. F. Detwiler became Allegheny Ludlum Steel's first chairman. During WWII the company developed heat-resisting alloys for aircraft turbine engines.

After the war the focus was on stainless steel and flat-rolled silicon electrical steel used to make electrical transformers. In 1956 the company doubled its capacity for making specialty alloys and installed the industry's first semi-automated system for working hot steel. It expanded outside the US by opening a plant in Belgium in the 1960s.

The company adopted the name Allegheny Ludlum Industries in 1970 and after diversifying sold its specialty steel division in a management-led buyout that formed Allegheny Ludlum Steel (1980). In 1986 it became Allegheny Ludlum Corp. It went public in 1987.

Henry Singleton and George Kozmetsky former Litton Industries executives invested $225000 each in 1960 to found Teledyne to make electronic aircraft components. First year sales of $4.5 million grew to nearly $90 million by 1964. Kozmetsky left the firm in 1966.

Under Singleton Teledyne bought more than 100 successful manufacturing and technology firms in defense-related areas such as engines unmanned aircraft specialty metals and computers. Teledyne also moved into offshore oil-drilling equipment insurance and finance and the Water Pik line of oral-care products.

Teledyne spun off its Argonaut Insurance unit in 1986 and left the insurance business entirely with its 1990 spinoff of Unitrin. Its defense businesses were caught in a 1989 fraud probe and the company paid $4.4 million in restitution. In 1991 Teledyne consolidated its 130 operations into 21 companies. It paid a $13 million fine in 1995 on charges of knowingly selling zirconium to a Chilean arms manufacturer for use in cluster bombs sold to Iraq.

Despite Teledyne's rebuff of holding company WHX's 1994 takeover offer in 1996 WHX came back with a new proposal that led to the $3.2 billion merger of Teledyne and Allegheny Ludlum in 1997. Also in 1997 CEO William Rutledge was succeeded by former Allegheny Ludlum CEO Richard Simmons. Allegheny and Bethlehem Steel entered into a bidding war for steelmaker Lukens. Bethlehem won but in 1998 granted exclusive access to or sold most of Lukens' stainless-steel operations to Allegheny. The company also bought UK-based Sheffield Forgemasters Group's aerospace division and titanium producer Oregon Metallurgical.

Allegheny restructured to focus on specialty metals in 1999 changing its name to Allegheny Technologies. The company sold Ryan Aeronautical (aerial drones) to Northrop Grumman its mining equipment business to Astec Industries and its lift-truck-making business to Terex. It spun off its consumer oral-hygiene business as Water Pik Technologies and its remaining aerospace businesses as Teledyne Technologies. Lockheed Martin executive Thomas Corcoran became president and CEO in 1999 but abruptly resigned in late 2000. That same year the company bought Baker Hughes' tungsten carbide products unit. VC Robert Bozzone served as chairman and CEO until insider James Murdy was named CEO in 2001.

In order to cut costs in 2001 Allegheny Technologies closed a plant in Pennsylvania made workforce cuts and sold its North American titanium distribution operations to management.

In 2002 the company had another round of workforce cuts (around 275 employees) mostly in its flat-rolled products unit. The following year Allegheny Technologies formed a joint venture with Russian-based VSMPO AVISMA to make a range of commercially pure titanium products.

Patrick Hassey a retired Alcoa EVP took over as CEO in 2003 and became charirman as well the next year. He retired in 2011.

Allegheny Technologies purchased J&L Specialty Steel one of its competitors for an undisclosed price in 2004. Other buys that year included two plants in Pennsylvania and Ohio from Arcelor. Still it initiated cost-cutting efforts aimed at saving $200 million a year announcing in 2004 cuts of more than 950 jobs at Allegheny Ludlum. The plants acquired from Arcelor lost more than 300 of their workforce.

To offset rapidly rising costs in raw materials energy health care and transportation the company increased prices on several of its metal grades. Those price increases helped ATI achieve record sales in 2006 and 2007.

EXECUTIVES

Chairman President and CEO, Richard J. (Rich) Harshman, age 56, $428,000 total compensation
EVP Finance and CFO, Dale G. Reid, age 56
EVP Human Resources Chief Legal and Compliance Officer General Counsel and Corporate Secretary, Jon D. Walton, age 69, $428,000 total compensation
EVP High Performance Forgings and Castings; President ATI Ladish, Gary J. Vroman, age 52
Director Investor Relations and Corporate Communications, Dan Greenfield
Business Unit President ATI Tungsten Materials, Robert (Bob) Wetherbee, age 53
EVP Long Products and President ATI Allvac, Hunter R. Dalton, age 57
EVP Flat-Rolled Products and President ATI Allegheny Ludlum, Terry L. Dunlap, age 52, $400,000 total compensation
Group President ATI Engineered Products and Business Unit President ATI Metalworking Products, David M. (Dave) Hogan, age 64
VP International, Carl R. Moulton, age 64
EVP Primary Metals and Exotic Alloys; President ATI Wah Chang, John D. Sims
Controller and Principal Accounting Officer, Karl Schwartz, age 48
SVP General Counsel Chief Compliance Officer and Corporate Secretary, Elliot S. Davis
VP Human Resources, Mary Beth Moore, age 43
VP Labor Relations and Assistant General Counsel, Lauren S. McAndrews
Treasurer, Rose Marie Manley
Corporate Strategic Sourcing, Bhart Sarin
Manager Corporate Strategic Sourcing, Kathi M. Jobkar
Manager Corporate Strategic Sourcing, Jason Farmerie
Strategic Sourcing Specialist, James Lee
Director, Barbara S. Jeremiah, age 60
Director, James E. (Jim) Rohr, age 63
Director, James C. Diggs, age 63
Director, Diane C. Creel, age 63
Director, J. Brett Harvey, age 61
Director, John D. Turner, age 66
Director, L. Patrick (Pat) Hassey, age 66
Director, Michael J. Joyce, age 70
Director, Louis J. Thomas, age 69
Auditors: Ernst&YoungLLP

LOCATIONS

HQ: Allegheny Technologies Incorporated
1000 Six PPG Place, Pittsburgh PA 15222-5479
Phone: 412-394-2800 **Fax:** 412-394-3034
Web: www.atimetals.com

2010 Sales

	$ mil.	% of total
US	2,764	68
Asia/Pacific	336	8
South America Midle East other	108	3

PRODUCTS/OPERATIONS

2010 Sales

Flat-Rolled Products	2,338	59
Engineered Products	371	7

Selected Operations and Products

Flat-Rolled Products
- Allegheny Ludlum (stainless steel nickel-based alloys titanium silicon electrical steels tool steels high-tech alloy and titanium plate)
- Allegheny Rodney (stainless steel strip)
- Shanghai STAL Precision Stainless Steel Company Ltd. (60% with Baosteel Group; precision-rolled strip stainless steel)
- Uniti LLC (50% owned jointly with the Russian metals maker VSMPO-AVISMA; industrial titanium)

High-Performance Metals
- Allvac (nickel-based alloys and superalloys cobalt-based alloys and superalloys titanium and titanium-based alloys specialty steel)
- Allvac Ltd. (UK) (nickel-based alloys and superalloys cobalt-based alloys and superalloys specialty steel)
- Wah Chang/Oremet (zirconium zirconium chemicals hafnium niobium tantalum titanium and titanium-based alloys)

Engineered Products
- Casting Service (large gray iron castings large ductile iron castings)
- Metalworking Products (cutting tools and tungsten carbide products)
- Portland Forge (carbon forgings alloy steel forgings nonferrous forgings)
- Rome Metals (processor of titanium zirconium nickel alloy and other specialty metals)

COMPETITORS

A. M. Castle
AK Steel Holding Corporation
Carpenter Technology
Eramet
Gerdau Ameristeel
Kennametal
Nippon Steel & Sumitomo Metal Corporation
Nucor
Olympic Steel
Ryerson
Special Metals

ThyssenKrupp Steel
Timken
Titanium Metals
United States Steel

HISTORICAL FINANCIALS

Company Type: Public

Income Statement FYE: December 31

	REVENUE ($ mil.)	NET INCOME ($ mil.)	NET PROFIT MARGIN	EMPLOYEES
12/11	5,183	214	4.1%	11,400
12/10	4,047	70	1.7%	9,200
12/09	3,054	31	1.0%	8,500
12/08	5,309	565	10.7%	9,600
12/07	5,452	747	13.7%	9,700
Annual Growth	(1.3%)	(26.8%)	—	4.1%

2011 Year-End Financials

Debt ratio: 24.96%
Return on equity: 8.66%
Cash ($ mil.): 380
Current ratio: 298.15
Long-term debt ($ mil.): 1,482
No. of shares (mil.): 106
Dividends
Yield: —
Payout: 36.55%
Market value ($ mil.): 5,084

	STOCK PRICE ($) FY Close	P/E High/Low		PER SHARE ($) Earnings	Dividends	Book Value
12/11	47.80	35	16	1.97	0.00	23.27
12/10	55.18	81	54	0.72	0.72	20.71
12/09	44.77	139	53	0.32	0.72	20.52
12/08	25.53	15	3	5.67	0.72	20.15
12/07	86.40	16	11	7.26	0.57	21.89
Annual Growth	(13.8%)	—	—	(27.8%)	—	1.5%

ALLEGIS GROUP INC.

EXECUTIVES

EVP Human Resources, Neil Mann
CIO, Kevin Apperson
General Counsel, Randall (Randy) Sones
President and CEO Aerotek, Thomas M. (Tom) Thornton
CEO, Michael (Mike) Salandra
Chairman, James C. (Jim) Davis
CFO, Paul Bowie

LOCATIONS

HQ: ALLEGIS GROUP INC.
7301 PARKWAY DR, HANOVER, MD 210761159
Phone: 4105793000
Web: WWW.ALLEGISGROUP.COM

PRODUCTS/OPERATIONS

Selected Subsidiaries

Aerotek
- Aerotek Automotive
- Aerotek Aviation LLC
- Aerotek Canada
- Aerotek CE
- Aerotek Commercial Staffing
- Aerotek E&E
- Aerotek Energy Services
- Aerotek Germany
- Aerotek Netherlands
- Aerotek Professional Services
- Aerotek Scientific LLC
- Aerotek United Kingdom

Allegis Group Canada
Allegis Group Europe
Allegis Group India
Allegis Group Services
InSearch Worldwide
Major Lindsey & Africa
MarketSource Inc
Stephen James Associates
TEKsystems
- TEKsystems Canada
- TEKsystems Germany
- TEKsystems Netherlands
- TEKsystems United Kingdom

COMPETITORS

Adecco
ASG Renaissance
CDI
Curran Partners
ExecuNet
Heidrick & Struggles
Horton International
Innovative Management Solutions Group
Kelly Services
Korn/Ferry
ManpowerGroup
Randstad Holding
RDL Corporation
Robert Half
Snelling Staffing
Volt Information

HISTORICAL FINANCIALS

Company Type: Private

Income Statement FYE: December 31

	REVENUE ($ mil.)	NET INCOME ($ mil.)	NET PROFIT MARGIN	EMPLOYEES
12/11	8,275	438	5.3%	85,000
12/10	6,405	406	6.3%	0
12/09	4,880	316	6.5%	0
12/08	5,737	378	6.6%	0
Annual Growth	13.0%	5.0%	—	—

2011 Year-End Financials

Debt ratio: —
Return on equity: 5.30%
Cash ($ mil.): 190
Current ratio: 2.80
Long-term debt ($ mil.): —
Dividends
Yield: —
Payout: —
Market value ($ mil.): —

Allergan, Inc

Vanity thy true name be Profits –at least for Allergan. The company is a leading maker of eye care skin care and aesthetic products including best-selling pharmaceutical Botox. Originally used to treat muscle spasms (as well as eye spasms and misalignment) Botox found another more popular application in diminishing facial wrinkles. Allergan's eye care products include medications for glaucoma allergic conjunctivitis and chronic dry eye. Skin care products include treatments for acne wrinkles and psoriasis. Allergan also sells breast augmentation implants and the Lap-Band system used in weight-loss surgery. Its products are sold in more than 100 countries via direct sales and distributors.

Geographic Reach

The US is Allergan's largest market accounting for more than 60% of sales.

Operations

Allergan's eye care segment featuring such products as Alphagan Restasis and Refresh comprises almost half of Allergan's product sales.

With a nod to vertical integration Allergan manufactures most of its products as well as the plastic parts and bottles used in its ophthalmic solutions. While it purchases most of its raw materials it does brew up the botulinum toxin for its Botox products.

Sales and Marketing

The company targets its marketing efforts toward specialty medical practitioners and hospitals as well as directly to consumers. It distributes its products through drug wholesalers and directly to hospitals retailers group purchasing organizations and retailers.

Financial Analysis

Approximately 40% of Allergan's products are not reimbursable by governmental or other health care plans meaning consumers must pay out of pocket for them. In theory this would make the company particularly vulnerable in times of economic uncertainty when consumers limit non-essential spending. And to be cautious during the worst of the economic recession Allergan reduced its own expenses with selective workforce reductions and the closure of a manufacturing facility in Ireland. However it never experienced a significant drop in revenues during those times. That said while its sales remained steady the company did see its income drop sharply in 2010 as a result of a legal settlement (to the tune of $609 million) following a US Department of Justice investigation into Allergan's sales and marketing practices with Botox.

Strategy

To maintain a robust product pipeline Allergan relies on a regimen of acquisitions and in-house development of its niche pharmaceuticals. It also has had success in discovering new uses for its existing drugs. Its glaucoma drug Lumigan stimulated eyelash growth so the company ran it through testing and received FDA approval for that use. The drug was renamed Latisse and launched in 2008. As competition from other anti-wrinkle drugs ramped up the company found new uses for Botox including as a treatment for excessive underarm sweating migraines and urinary incontinence in adults with neurological conditions such as spinal cord injury or multiple sclerosis. Allergan is still looking for new ways to apply Botox including as a possible treatment for children with cerebral palsy or to alleviate post-herpetic neuralgia.

To share the cost of drug development Allergan actively seeks out licensing agreements and partnerships. It currently has development agreements withMAP Pharmaceuticals (inhaled migraine treatment) Molecular Partners (retinal disease) and Serenity Pharmaceuticals (treatment for nighttime urinary incontinence). It also rakes in royalties from the licensing of its own products to other companies.

Mergers and Acquisitions

Acquisitions have plumped up the company's pipeline with potential new products and technologies. To expand its range of skin care products in 2012 Allergan acquired rival dermatology company SkinMedica for $350 million upfront and an additional $25 million if certain sales goals are met. The acquisition expanded Allergan's product portfolio with prescription treatments to reduce female facial hair and lotions to reduce the appearance of wrinkles. Following the transaction SkinMedica operates as an independent subsidiary of Allergan continuing to market its own offerings; SkinMedica will also eventually take over sales efforts on Allergan's Vivite and Latisse product lines.

Other recent acquisitions made by Allergan include its 2011 purchase of Vicept Therapeutics to gain its drug candidate in development to treat erythema (facial redness) from rosacea and its 2010 buy of Serica Technologies' cosmetic and reconstructive surgery unit which brought in biodegradable scaffolds made from silk used in skin grafting breast augmentation and reconstructive surgery.

HISTORY

Gavin Herbert set up a small ophthalmic business in 1950 above one of his drugstores in Los Angeles. Chemist Stanley Bly invented the company's first product antihistamine eye drops called Allergan. The company adopted the name of the eye drops and expanded the business and the product range. Herbert's son Gavin Jr. then a USC student helped with the business.

By 1960 Allergan was a $1 million company; it moved into the contact lens solution market with its Liquifilm product that year. In 1964 it developed its first foreign distributorship in Iraq and the following year it started its first foreign subsidiary in Canada. International expansion and limited competition for hard contact lens care products sustained sales growth around 20% throughout the 1960s.

Allergan went public in 1971. During the 1970s the company became Bausch & Lomb's contractual supplier of Hydrocare lens solution and enzymatic cleaner for soft contact lenses. By 1975 Allergan had about a third of the hard contact lens care market. When Gavin Sr. died in 1978 Gavin Jr. succeeded him as president and CEO and also became chairman. By 1979 revenues topped $62 million.

SmithKline bought Allergan in 1980 just as the soft contact lens market boomed. In 1984 SmithKline acquired International Hydron the #2 soft contact lens maker behind Bausch & Lomb; International Hydron became part of Allergan in 1987.

The next year the company acquired the rights to a botulinum toxin product called Oculinum which would later evolve into Botox.

In 1989 SmithKline merged with Beecham and spun off Allergan.

By the early 1990s the contact lens and lens care markets had begun to mature leading to a company restructuring and a new focus on specialty pharmaceuticals. In 1992 Allergan sold its North and South American contact lens businesses; the rest of its contact lens businesses were sold in 1993.

The company boosted its presence in the intraocular lens market with the 1994 purchase of Ioptex Research. Also in 1994 Allergan and joint venture partner Ligand Pharmaceuticals made their enterprise an independently operating company Allergan Ligand Retinoid Therapeutics (ALRT). The next year Allergan recalled about 400000 bottles of contact lens solution because of potential eye irritation.

In 1995 Allergan acquired cataract surgery equipment maker Optical Micro Systems and the contact lens care business of Pilkington Barnes Hind. That year the government probed the company for exporting the botulism toxin in Botox –it feared the product's use in biological weapons – but did not press charges.

The company's 1995 income was hurt by a $50 million contribution to ALRT; its 1996 income was the result of a $70 million write-off for restructuring. In 1996 it was discovered that Allergan's Botox could be used to lessen facial wrinkles.

In 1997 Allergan received approval for a handful of new products including its multifocus eye lens for cataract patients acne and psoriasis treatment Tazorac and glaucoma treatment Alphagan. That year Allergan and Ligand acquired the assets of ALRT and formed subsidiary Allergan Specialty Therapeutics to research and develop new drugs. The unit was spun off in 1998 but Allergan bought it back again in 2001.

The company restructured in 1998 cutting jobs and closing about half of its manufacturing plants. In 2000 Botox was approved by the FDA to treat cervical dystonia.

In 2003 Allergan bought ophthalmic drug company Oculex Pharmaceuticals which makes the Posurdex implanted drug delivery device and Bardeen Sciences which had a complementary drug pipeline. Subsidiary Advanced Medical Optics was spun off in 2004.

The company acquired private firm Esprit Pharma which marketed overactive bladder treatment Sanctura through a partnership with Indevus for $370 million in 2007.

EXECUTIVES

Vice Chairman, Herbert W. Boyer, age 75
Chairman President and CEO, David E. I. Pyott, age 58, $1,300,000 total compensation
EVP; President Europe Africa Middle East, Douglas S. Ingram, age 49, $540,000 total compensation
SVP Treasury and Investor Relations, James M. (Jim) Hindman
EVP Finance and Business Development and CFO, Jeffrey L. Edwards, age 51, $495,000 total compensation
SVP and Corporate Controller, James F. Barlow, age 53
Investor Relations, Joann Bradley
EVP Research and Development and Chief Scientific Officer, Scott M. Whitcup, age 52, $540,000 total compensation
EVP General Counsel and Assistant Secretary, Arnold A. Pinkston, age 53
EVP Global Technical Operations, Raymond H. (Ray) Diradoorian, age 54
Global Corporate Communications, Caroline Van Hove
Media Contact Topical Aesthetics and Breast Aesthetics, Heather Katt
Media Contact Neurosciences and Eye Care, Crystal Muilenburg
Media Contact Obesity Intervention and Eye Care, Cathy Taylor
European Corporate Communications, Janet Kettels
Media Contact Facial Aesthetics, Kellie Lao
Canadian Corporate Communications, Amanda Mills-Sirois
EVP Human Resources, Scott D. Sherman, age 46
SVP and CIO, Sue Jean Lin
Senior Director Enterprise Architecture/Portfolio Management, Fred Orensky
VP Information Services Regulatory Affairs and Safety Corporate Enterprise Architecture Portfolio Management Office, Steve Plank
Senior Director IS Infrastructure and Operations, Ed Ryan
Corporate VP; President Allergan Medical Asia Pacific and Latin America, David J. Endicott
Corporate VP; President North America, Julian S. Gangolli, age 54
Vice President General Counsel Secretary, Matthew J. Maletta
Sr. Vice President Chief Compliance Officer, Rose Swanson
Vice Chairman, Herbert W. Boyer, age 75
Director, Leonard D. Schaeffer, age 66
Director, Louis J. Lavigne Jr., age 64
Director, Michael R. Gallagher, age 66
Director, Stephen J. Ryan, age 71
Director, Robert A. (Bob) Ingram, age 69
Director, Dawn E. Hudson, age 54
Director, Russell T. Ray, age 64
Director, Deborah Dunsire, age 49
Director, Trevor M. Jones, age 69
Auditors: Ernst&YoungLLP

LOCATIONS

HQ: Allergan Inc.
2525 Dupont Dr., Irvine CA 92612
Phone: 714-246-4500 **Fax:** 714-246-6987
Web: www.allergan.com

2011 Sales

	$ mil.	% of total
US		60
Asia/Pacific		8
Other regions		5

PRODUCTS/OPERATIONS

2011 Sales

	$ mil.	% of total
Specialty pharmaceut		
Botox/neuromodulator	1,594	29
Urologics	56	1
Facial aesthetics	362	7
Obesity intervention	203	4
Total	**5,419**	**100**

Selected Products

Specialty Pharmaceuticals
- Eye care
  - Acuvail (post-surgery pain)
  - Alphagan (glaucoma)
  - Botox (eye twitching)
  - Combigan (glaucoma ocular hypertension)
  - Elestat (allergic conjunctivitis)
  - Ganfort (glaucoma)
  - Lastacaft (allergic conjunctivitis)
  - Lumigan (glaucoma)
  - Ozurdex (macular edema)
  - Pred Forte (inflammation)
  - Refresh (chronic dry eye disease)
  - Restatis (chronic dry eye disease)
  - Zymaxia (bacterial conjunctivitis)
- Neuromodular
  - Botox (neuromuscular disorder chronic migraine treatment)
  - Botox Cosmetic (wrinkle reduction)
- Skin care
  - Aczone (acne treatment)
  - Avage (skin wrinkles or discoloration)
  - Azelex (acne treatment)
  - Botox (excessive sweating)
  - Fluoroplex (keratoses)
  - Latisse (eyelash growth)
  - Tazorac (treatment for acne and psoriasis)
  - Vivite (skin care products)
- Urologics
  - Botox (urinary incontinence)
  - Sanctura (overactive bladder)

Medical devices
- Breast aesthetics (saline silicone)
  - CUI (implants)
  - Inspira (implants)
  - Natrelle (implants)
  - Tissue expanders (reconstruction)
- Obesity intervention
  - Lap-Band (stomach implant)
  - Orbera (intragastric balloon system)
- Facial aesthetics
  - Juvederm (dermal fillers)
  - Latisse (eyelash enhancer)

COMPETITORS

Abbott Labs
Alcon
Apotex
Astellas
Bausch & Lomb
Galderma Laboratories
Genentech
GlaxoSmithKline
Inspire Pharmaceuticals
Ipsen
ISTA Pharmaceuticals
Johnson & Johnson
L' Oreal
Medicis Pharmaceutical
Merck
Merz Pharmaceuticals
Novartis
Obagi Medical
Pfizer
Roche Holding
Sandoz
SkinMedica
Stiefel Laboratories
Valeant Pharmaceuticals
Warner Chilcott
Watson Pharmaceuticals

HISTORICAL FINANCIALS

Company Type: Public

Income Statement FYE: December 31

	REVENUE ($ mil.)	NET INCOME ($ mil.)	NET PROFIT MARGIN	EMPLOYEES
12/11	5,419	934	17.2%	10,000
12/10	4,919	0	0.0%	9,200
12/09	4,503	621	13.8%	8,300
12/08	4,403	578	13.1%	8,740
12/07	3,938	499	12.7%	7,886
Annual Growth	8.3%	17.0%	—	6.1%

2011 Year-End Financials

Debt ratio: 17.81%
Return on equity: 17.60%
Cash ($ mil.): 2,406
Current ratio: 423.91
Long-term debt ($ mil.): 1,515
No. of shares (mil.): 305
Dividends
Yield: —
Payout: 6.65%
Market value ($ mil.): 26,785

	STOCK PRICE ($) FY Close	P/E High/Low		PER SHARE ($) Earnings	Dividends	Book Value
12/11	87.74	29	22	3.01	0.00	17.39
12/10	68.67	—	—	(0.00)	0.20	15.57
12/09	63.01	31	18	2.03	0.20	15.84
12/08	40.32	36	16	1.89	0.20	13.19
12/07	64.24	76	35	1.62	0.20	12.22
Annual Growth	8.1%	—	—	16.8%	—	9.2%

Alliant Techsystems Inc.

LOCATIONS

HQ: Alliant Techsystems Inc.
1300 Wilson Boulevard, Suite 400, Arlington, VA 22209-2307
Phone: 703 412-5960
Web: www.atk.com

PRODUCTS/OPERATIONS

2012 Sales

	$ mil.	% of total
Armament systems	1,580	34
Aerospace systems	1,347	29
Security & sporting	1,002	22
Missile products	682	15
Total	**4,613**	**100**

2012 Sales

% of total	
Government customers	
US	28
US	12
NASA	10
US Air	6
Other government	9
Commercial & foreign	35
Total	**100**

HISTORICAL FINANCIALS

Company Type:

Income Statement FYE: March 31

	REVENUE ($ mil.)	NET INCOME ($ mil.)	NET PROFIT MARGIN	EMPLOYEES
03/12	4,613	262	5.7%	17,000
03/11	4,842	313	6.5%	15,000
03/10	4,807	278	5.8%	18,000
03/09	4,583	155	3.4%	19,000
03/08	4,171	222	5.3%	17,000
Annual Growth	2.5%	4.2%	—	0.0%

2012 Year-End Financials

Debt ratio: 28.67%
Return on equity: 21.41%
Cash ($ mil.): 568
Current ratio: 218.50
Long-term debt ($ mil.): 1,272
No. of shares (mil.): 33
Dividends
Yield: —
Payout: 10.09%
Market value ($ mil.): 1,661

	STOCK PRICE ($) FY Close	P/E High/Low		PER SHARE ($) Earnings	Dividends	Book Value
03/12	50.12	10	6	7.93	0.00	37.02
03/11	70.67	9	6	9.32	0.20	34.51
03/10	81.30	11	8	8.33	0.00	24.17
03/09	66.98	24	13	4.56	0.00	18.76
03/08	103.53	18	13	6.32	0.00	22.60
Annual Growth	(16.6%)	—	—	5.8%	—	13.1%

Allstate Corp.

Ya gotta hand it to Allstate. The "good hands" company has managed to work its way to the top of the property/casualty insurance pile. The company is the second-largest personal lines insurer in the US just behind rival State Farm. Its Allstate Protection segment sells auto homeowners property/casualty and life insurance products in Canada and the US. Allstate Financial provides life insurance through subsidiaries Allstate Life American Heritage Life and Lincoln Benefit Life. It also provides investment products targeting affluent and middle-income consumers. Allstate Motor Club provides emergency road service.

Allstate Protection's property/casualty operations account for more than 90% of the entire company's total premiums. California Florida New York Pennsylvania and Texas make up more than 40% of Allstate Protection's sales. Catastrophe management is a key part of the company's stability. To limit its exposure to catastrophic claims Allstate has quit writing new homeowners policies in some coastal areas including California and Florida that are vulnerable to hurricane wind storms and earthquakes. While it still renews existing homeowners policies in California the company tweaked its underwriting to reduce exposure to claims for fires following earthquakes.

These and other changes to reduce its exposure are reflective of Allstate's coming to terms with the increase in severe weather events in recent years. While not directly linking the change to anything more specific than warmer ocean water in 2011 CEO Thomas Wilson stated that the company now considers such severe weather to be permanent rather than anomalous. As evidence of the seriousness of the matter tornados in Alabama and Missouri during 2011 resulted in the company's biggest losses since Hurricane Katrina in 2005.

All of the company's life insurance annuities and banking services operate through Allstate Financial. While these sales account for less than 10% of the company's total revenue Allstate considers them to be useful for deepening relationships with Allstate Protection customers. These financial products are sold through its exclusive agencies independent agents banks and broker dealers. Allstate Financial is also looking to boost sales of its workplace products offered through Allstate Benefits.

Allstate maintains a network of about 11500 exclusive agencies which sell its Allstate-branded insurance products. Independent agencies sell the company's Encompass-branded products as well as its Allstate lines.

To better compete with its faster-growing direct-to-consumer competitors Progressive and GEICO Allstate has been expanding its marketing efforts to reach younger consumers who like to compare and purchase insurance online. It entered that market with a bang in 2011 by purchasing auto insurer Esurance and insurance agency Answer Financial from White Mountains Insurance Group for about $1 billion. Both Esurance and Answer Financial operate online and in 2010 had a combined customer base of close to 840000 and growing (an increase of more than 8% compared to the prior year). The purchase which included $700 million cash plus the book value of the companies made Allstate a formidable competitor in the online insurance marketplace.

Prior to the deal such direct-channel sales accounted for only 3% of Allstate Protection premiums. It's yet to be seen just how much the addition of Esurance and Answer Financial will add to that channel over time. Allstate (and its agents) are hoping that as younger consumers acquire more property they'll start appreciating the convenience (and discounts) of buying multiple policies from one company and the personal accessibility of agents.

Previously the company operated the nationwide online Allstate Bank. In 2011 Allstate determined that banking wasn't really part of its core products and announced plans to exit that business. Its initial plans were to sell most of Allstate Bank's deposits to Discover Financial Services. However the deal died when Discover was unable to secure regulatory approvals. Allstate remained certain of its decision and continued to wind down the banking operations through the end of the year.

The company has disposed of the majority of its operations outside North America (including Allstate Investments in Japan and the direct auto business in Germany and Italy) focusing on its core markets in Canada and the US.

HISTORY

Allstate traces its origins to a friendly game of bridge played in 1930 on a Chicago-area commuter train by Sears president Robert Wood and a friend insurance broker Carl Odell. The insurance man suggested Sears sell auto insurance through the mail. Wood liked the idea financed the company and in 1931 put Odell in charge (that hand of bridge must have shown Wood that Odell was no dummy). The company was named Allstate after one of Sears' tire brands. Allstate was born just as Sears was beginning its push into retailing and Allstate went with it selling insurance out of all the new Sears stores.

Growth was slow during the Depression and WWII but the postwar boom was a gold mine for both Sears and Allstate. Suburban development made cars a necessity; 1950s prudence necessitated car insurance; and Sears made it easy to buy the insurance at their stores and increasingly at freestanding agencies.

In the late 1950s Allstate added home and other property/casualty insurance lines. It also went into life insurance –in-force policies zoomed from zero to $1 billion in six years the industry's fastest growth ever.

Sears formed Allstate Enterprises in 1960 as an umbrella for all its noninsurance operations. In 1970 that firm bought its first savings and loan (S&L). The insurer continued to acquire other S&Ls and to add subsidiaries throughout the 1970s and 1980s.

This strategy dovetailed with Sears' strategy which was to become a diversified financial services company. In 1985 Sears introduced the Discover Card through Allstate's Greenwood Trust Company. However by the late 1980s it was obvious Sears would never be a financial services giant. Moreover it was losing so much in retailing that by 1987 Allstate was the major contributor to corporate net income. Sears began to dismantle its financial empire in the 1990s.

Allstate also suffered from a backlash against high insurance rates. When Massachusetts instituted no-fault insurance in 1989 Allstate stopped writing new auto insurance there. Later the company had to refund $110 million to customers to settle a suit with California over rate rollbacks required by 1988's Proposition 103.

Allstate went public in 1993 when Sears sold about 20% of its stake. That year it began reducing its operations in Florida to protect itself against high losses from hurricanes. Two years later the retailer sold its remaining interest to its shareholders. Also in 1995 Allstate sold 70% of PMI its mortgage insurance unit to the public.

In 1996 Allstate worked to reduce its exposure to hurricane and earthquake losses. (Together Hurricane Andrew and the Northridge quake helped account for almost $4 billion in casualty losses.) It created a Florida-only subsidiary that would buy reinsurance to protect against losses that could arise from another major hurricane. That year Allstate sold its Northbrook (property/casualty) and Allstate Reinsurance operations to St. Paul and SCOR respectively.

In 1998 Allstate sold its real estate portfolio for nearly $1 billion and opened a savings bank. In 2000 Allstate restructured adding online and telephone distributions to increase its sales and buying Provident National Assurance Co. from UNUMProvident. Reducing expenses Allstate cut some 10% of its staff (some 4000 jobs) that year and turned its agents into independent contractors. With its purchase of Sterling Collision Centers Allstate entered the car repair business in 2001.

In coastal counties of New York Allstate attempted to limit homeowner policies by only renewing the policies of customers who also held other types of insurance with the company. The New York Insurance Superintendent found the company to be in violation with the state's insurance laws in mid-2007 and pressured Allstate to offer quotes to more than 55000 former customers who had been dropped.

Despite trying to slim down and refocus as the US economy weakened Allstate Financial suffered right alongside its financial services brethren taking a loss of $1.72 billion in 2008. However when the US Treasury offered Allstate a piece of the Troubled Asset Relief Program in 2009 the insurer politely turned it down citing its strong capital and liquidity. Instead the company undertook a number of initiatives to reduce its financial risk especially in the area of natural catastrophes.

Allstate expanded its roadside assistance unit in 2008 when it bought the Partnership Marketing Group (PMG) of GE Consumer Finance. In addition to roadside assistance PMG brought along its legal services benefit plans to member-based affinity groups in the US. The businesses were then housed within the company's Allstate Protection segment.

EXECUTIVES

Senior Group VP and Controller The Allstate Corporation and Allstate Insurance Company, Samuel H. (Sam) Pilch, age 65
EVP Claims Allstate Insurance Company, Michael J. Roche, age 60
Chairman President and CEO, Thomas J. Wilson II, age 54, $1,100,769 total compensation
President Allstate Auto Home and Agencies, Matthew E. (Matt) Winter, age 55
EVP and CFO and President Allstate Financial, Don Civgin, age 51, $571,154 total compensation
EVP Corporate Relations Allstate Insurance, Joan H. Walker, age 64
President Allstate Protection South Regions, Catherine S. Brune, age 58
SEVP and Chief Marketing Officer Allstate Insurance, Mark R. LaNeve, age 52
EVP and Chief Administrative Officer Allstate Insurance Company, James D. DeVries, age 48
EVP Emerging Businesses, Donald J. (Don) Bailey, age 47
EVP Product Operations Allstate Insurance, Steven P. Sorenson, age 47
EVP and General Counsel, Michele C. Mayes, age 62, $573,930 total compensation
EVP and Chief Investment Officer Allstate Insurance Company, Judith P. (Judy) Greffin, age 51, $480,235 total compensation
EVP Technology and Operations, Suren Gupta
Field SVP Southwest Region Allstate Insurance Company, Denis Bailey
President Allstate New Jersey Insurance Company., William Ballinger
Field SVP California Region Allstate Insurance Company., Robert H. Barge III
Field SVP Midwest Region Allstate Insurance Company., Alice Byrne
Field SVP North Central Region Allstate Insurance Company., Thomas F. Clarkson
Field SVP New York Region Allstate Insurance Company, Vincent A. Fusco
Field SVP New York Region Allstate Insurance Company, Bob Holden
President Allstate Canada, Chris Kiah
Field SVP Texas Region Allstate Insurance Company, Philip Lawson
Field SVP Northwest Region Allstate Insurance Company, Michelle Lee
Field SVP Southern Region Allstate Insurance Company, Michael McKinney
Field SVP Capital Region Allstate Insurance Company, David Prendergast
Field SVP Northeast Region Allstate Insurance Company, David Schwartzer
Field SVP Florida Region Allstate Insurance Company, Mike Sheely
President Central/West Regions Allstate Protection, Katherine (Kathy) Mabe
CFO, Steve Shebik
Chief Risk Officer, Steve Verney
Director, F. Duane Ackerman, age 69
Director, H. John Riley Jr., age 71
Director, W. James (Jim) Farrell, age 69
Director, Jack M. Greenberg, age 69
Director, Ronald T. LeMay, age 66
Director, Mary Alice Taylor, age 62
Director, Judith A. (Judy) Sprieser, age 58
Director, Robert D. Beyer, age 52
Director, Joshua I. Smith, age 71
Director, Andrea Redmond, age 56
Auditors: Deloitte&ToucheLLP

LOCATIONS

HQ: The Allstate Corporation
2775 Sanders Rd., Northbrook IL 60062-6127
Phone: 847-402-5000 **Fax:** 866-532-3029
Web: www.allstate.com

PRODUCTS/OPERATIONS

2011 Revenues

	$ mil.	% of total
Property/liability insurance premiums		
Allstate brand	24,663	76
Encompass brand	1,078	3
Esurance brand	201	-
Net investment income	3,971	12
Life & annuity premiums & contract charges	2,238	7
Realized capital gains & losses	503	2
Total	**32,654**	**100**

2011 Property/Liability Premiums

Standard auto	64	
Non-standard auto	3	
Total	**0**	**100**

Selected Subsidiaries

Allstate Insurance Company of Canada
Allstate Life Insurance Company
Allstate Motor Club
American Heritage Life Insurance Company
Encompass Insurance Company
Esurance Insurance Company
Kennett Capital Inc.
Lincoln Benefit Life Company
Northbrook Indemnity Company
Pafco Insurance Company (Canada)
Sterling Collision Centers Inc.

COMPETITORS

Chubb Corp
Farmers Group
GEICO
Hanover Insurance
Liberty Mutual
MetLife
Nationwide
Progressive Corporation
Prudential
State Farm
The Hartford
Torchmark
Travelers Companies
USAA

HISTORICAL FINANCIALS

Company Type: Public

Income Statement FYE: December 31

	ASSETS ($ mil.)	NET INCOME ($ mil.)	INCOME AS % OF ASSETS	EMPLOYEES
12/11	125,563	788	0.6%	37,600
12/10	130,874	928	0.7%	35,700
12/09	132,652	854	0.6%	36,800
12/08	134,798	(1,679)	—	38,900
12/07	156,408	4,636	3.0%	39,000
Annual Growth	(5.3%)	(35.8%)	—	(0.9%)

2011 Year-End Financials

Debt ratio: 4.71%
Return on equity: 4.22%
Cash ($ mil.): 776
Current ratio: —
Long-term debt ($ mil.): 5,908
No. of shares (mil.): 501
Dividends
Yield: —
Payout: 55.63%
Market value ($ mil.): 13,732

	STOCK PRICE ($) FY Close	P/E High/Low		PER SHARE ($) Earnings	Dividends	Book Value
12/11	27.41	23	15	1.51	0.00	37.27
12/10	31.88	21	16	1.71	0.80	35.68
12/09	30.04	21	9	1.58	0.80	31.08
12/08	32.76	—	—	(3.07)	1.64	23.58
12/07	52.23	8	6	7.77	1.52	38.81
Annual Growth	(14.9%)	—	—	(33.6%)	—	(1.0%)

Ally Financial Inc

Ally Financial wants to be your friend in the financing business. Formerly GMAC the firm opted for the friendlier-sounding name in 2010 after it converted to a bank holding company. In addition to owning Ally Bank the company provides auto financing for some 21000 auto dealerships (mostly General Motors (GM) and Chrysler) and their customers around the world. Its Residential Capital (ResCap) subsidiary issues residential mortgages in the US and Canada. Ally Financial also provides financing services for large- and mid-market companies around the world through Ally Commercial Finance (formerly GMAC Commercial Finance). The US government owns about 74% of Ally Financial but is selling off its stake in stages.

The US Treasury earned its stake in Ally after providing $17 billion in aid to the company as it recovered from the global financial crisis; subprime mortgages held by ResCap hit Ally particularly hard. Part of the government's plan to exit its holding in Ally was to come through an initial public offering (IPO) of the company. However the IPO which was originally expected to take place in 2011 has been put on hold primarily due to ResCap's troubled mortgage loans. In mid-2012 ResCap filed for Chapter 11 bankruptcy as part of a plan to sell itself off. With its mortgage issues out of the way Ally will be able to concentrate on its auto financing operations and proceed with its IPO plans.

To begin unwinding its holdings in Ally the Treasury received $2.7 billion in a sale of all of its trust-preferred securities in 2011. As with the planned IPO proceeds from the transaction did not go to Ally but instead were used to begin paying down the government bailout.

The economic recession also rocked Ally's longtime partner and former majority owner GM. Although GM owns a small stake (about 10%) in Ally the lender was not included in GM's 2009 Chapter 11 bankruptcy reorganization. The federal funds were intended to fuel lending for both GM and Chrysler vehicles as part of the government-backed restructuring of the automakers. The government also gave Ally Financial access to its debt guarantee program despite its having low ratings in a controversial move that gave the lender an advantage over other auto finance firms.

Ally Financial is in the midst of its own reorganization with a renewed focus on its core automotive lending business. The company has been positioning itself to benefit from the recovery in the auto industry and economy. As a whole Ally sold off 15 noncore operations in 2010 alone including its North American factoring operations to Wells Fargo and its GMAC Insurance to property/casualty insurer AmTrust Financial Services. In 2012 it agreed to sell another insurance unit UK-based Car Care Plan to AmTrust for some $70 million.

To cash out of its Canadian arm Ally Financial in late 2012 agreed to sell its auto finance and deposit business in Canada to Royal Bank of Canada (RBC) in a deal valued at $1.4 billion. Expected to close during the first quarter of 2013 the sale will boost RBC's financial services capacity in Canada.

Ally Financial also has been streamlining its mortgage business. It laid off some 5000 ResCap employees or 60% of the unit's workforce in 2009. It sold the company's real estate brokerage business to Brookfield Asset Management and in 2010 ResCap sold its European operations to Fortress Investment Group.

In addition to slashing its mortgage operations the group has streamlined its auto finance business. It consolidated its business offices to five regional centers and cut back its workforce by 15%. Although Ally Financial temporarily offered subprime auto loans during the credit crisis to spur the nation's economic recovery it later limited lending to US consumers with credit scores of 700 or higher.

The company has diversified its automotive service customer base by establishing agreements with other auto manufacturers (besides GM and Chrysler). In 2010 Ally Financial began offering financing to Swedish Automobile's Saab dealers. Ally also was chosen to offer financing for Thor Industries' recreation vehicles.

Internationally Ally Financial offers car loans in 15 countries. The company streamlined its global business in 2009 and 2010 to focus on five key international markets: Germany the UK Brazil Mexico and China.

In 2009 it revamped its GMAC Bank online banking unit and renamed it Ally Bank. The fresh start and new name helped the company raise cash through retail deposit growth. Now Ally Bank is a leading online retail bank franchise which reported 17% loan growth in 2010. As online banking continued gaining traction with consumers the company reported 27% loan growth the following year.

All of the changes helped. The company's net income rebounded in 2010 to about $1 billion up from a net loss of $10 billion the prior year. However Ally reported a net loss on continuing operations of $112 million in 2011 as lowered interest rates impacted its net servicing income and loan sales brought lower gains. The sale of insurance operations and lower earnings on its US servicing income (as a result of slower vehicle sales) also led to a decrease in revenues that year.

Further impacting the company's bottom line Ally Financial in 2012 was one of five banks to sign on to a $25 billion out-of-court settlement with 49 state attorneys general over the banks' deceptive foreclosure practices. Ally's share of the settlement payment came to $110 million; it will also pay $200 million (a figure which could possibly rise) towards borrower relief programs.

Ally Financial was founded as a GM subsidiary in 1919. It was owned by GM until 2006. That year the automaker sought new ways to raise money and sold 51% of Ally to a Cerberus Capital Management-led investment group for some $7 billion.

EXECUTIVES

President and Head Global Automotive Services, William F. (Bill) Muir, age 58, $850,000 total compensation
President GMAC Mortgage Operations, Steven M. (Steve) Abreu, age 47
CEO, Michael A. (Mike) Carpenter, age 64, $119,726 total compensation
Chief Marketing Officer, Sanjay Gupta, age 43, $430,769 total compensation
Chief Administrative Officer, Barbara A. Yastine, age 52
VP Corporate Controller and Chief Accounting Officer, David J. (Dave) DeBrunner, age 46
Chief Human Resources Officer, James J. (Jim) Duffy, age 57
EVP GMAC International Automotive Finance Operations, Mark F. Bole, age 49
Regional VP, David L. Brinkman
President Ally Credit Canada Limited, Thomas E. Dickerson, age 59
VP Strategic Planning and Implementation International Operations, John R. Jones
VP - Alliance Sales, James A. Kucharski
General Counsel, William B. Solomon Jr., age 60, $306,025 total compensation
Corporate Secretary, Cathy L. Quenneville, age 52
Managing Director Corporate Strategy ? Finance, Linda K. Zukauckas, age 51
EVP NAO/IO Asset Performance Integration, Lee McCarty
EVP GMAC North American Automotive Finance Operations, Tim M. Russi
CEO Mortgage Operations and Capital Markets Executive, Thomas (Tom) Marano, age 51, $2,419,231 total compensation
CFO Mortgage Operations Ally Financial Inc. and Residential Capital LLC, James N. Young
VP and Associate General Counsel, Gregory Merryman
Chief Risk Executive, Karin Hirtler-Garvey, age 55
Regional VP NAO Automotive Finance Southeast Regional Business Center, Doug Timmerman
Head Corporate Debt and Equity, Corey Pinkston, age 46
President Ally Servicing, Evan Noulas
SEVP Finance and Corporate Planning, Jeffrey J. Brown, age 39
Chief Risk Officer Global Automotive Finance, Brian Gunn
Managing Director SmartAuction, Mark Newman, age 49
Director Risk ? International Operations, Alex M. Sarafian
Chief Investment Officer, Jon Centurino
President and CEO Ally Bank, Mark B. Hales, age 58
CTO and COO, Cliff Skelton, age 56
General Auditor, Mark H. Weintraub, age 43
Chairman, Franklin W. (Fritz) Hobbs, age 64
President and CEO Ally Commercial Finance, William (Bill) Hall Jr., age 52
VP Government Relations, Michele E. Lieber

VP and Chief Communications Officer, Gina Proia, age 40
CFO, James G. Mackey, age 44
Executive Director Global Communications North American Automotive Financing Insurance Remarketing Commercial Finance, Sue Mallino
President and CEO ResMor Trust Company, Johanne Brossard
President Ally Insurance, Tom Callahan
Senior Managing Director and Head Corporate Strategy, Michael Constantino III
Deposits and Product Innovation Executive, Diane Morais
Chief Compliance Officer, Dan Soto
President Structured Finance GMAC Commercial Finance, George Triebenbacher
CFO, Craig Winterfield
Treasurer, Christopher Halmy, age 43
Director, Robert T. (Bob) Blakely, age 70
CEO, Michael A. (Mike) Carpenter, age 64
Director, Marjorie (Marge) Magner, age 62
Director, Stephen A. Feinberg, age 51
Director, Mayree C. Clark, age 54
Director, John D. Durrett Jr., age 64
Director, Kim S. Fennebresque, age 61
Director, Jack Stack, age 65
Auditors: Deloitte&ToucheLLP

LOCATIONS

HQ: Ally Financial Inc.
200 Renaissance Center, Detroit MI 48265-2000
Phone: 866-710-4623 **Fax:** 815-282-6156
Web: www.ally.com

PRODUCTS/OPERATIONS

2011 Sales

	$ mil.	% of total
Financing revenue & other interest income		
Interest & fees on finance receivables & loans	6,635	47
Operating leases	2,298	16
Interest & dividends on available-for-sale investment securities	398	3
Interest on loans held-for-sale	332	2
Other	73	1
Insurance premiums & service revenue earned	1,573	11
Servicing fees	1,358	10
Net gain on mortgage & automotive loans	470	3
Other	1,048	7
Adjustments	(853)	-
Total	**13,332**	**100**

Selected Operations

Automotive
- Commercial finance
- Consumer finance
- Dealer inventory insurance
- Extended service contracts
- Loan servicing
- Vehicle remarketing services

Corporate
- Asset-based lending
- Health capital
- Resort finance
- Structured finance

Mortgage
- Loan servicing
- Residential mortage loans
- Other lending

COMPETITORS

Bank of America
Citigroup
Ford Motor Credit
Mercedes-Benz Credit
Mercedes-Benz Financial Services USA
Mitsubishi Motors Credit of America
Toyota Motor Credit
Volkswagen Financial Services

HISTORICAL FINANCIALS

Company Type: Private

Income Statement FYE: December 31

	REVENUE ($ mil.)	NET INCOME ($ mil.)	NET PROFIT MARGIN	EMPLOYEES
12/11	13,332	(157)	—	14,800
12/10	16,768	1,075	6.4%	14,400
12/09	17,517	(10,298)	—	18,800
12/08	33,325	1,868	5.6%	0
Annual Growth	(26.3%)	—	—	—

2011 Year-End Financials

Debt ratio: 54.59%
Return on equity: (-0.81)%
Cash ($ mil.): 13,035
Current ratio: 31.47
Long-term debt ($ mil.): 92,794
No. of shares (mil.): 1
Dividends
Yield: —
Payout: —
Market value ($ mil.): 24

	STOCK PRICE ($) FY Close	P/E High/Low		PER SHARE ($) Earnings	Dividends	Book Value
12/11	18.39	—	—	(691.00)	0.00	14,554.05
Annual Growth	—	—	—	—	—	—

Alon USA Energy Inc

Could anything be finer than FINA? Alon USA Energy is the driving force behind FINA-branded marketing and refining operations throughout the US Southwest. The company provides fuel to more than 630 FINA-branded retail sites. It owns or operates more than 300 convenience stores under the 7-Eleven and FINA brands. It also sub-licenses the FINA brand to distributors supplying about 260 additional locations. Alon USA Energy's refineries in Texas (one) California (two) Louisiana (one) and Oregon (one) have a combined throughput capacity of 250000 barrels per day. Alon USA Energy is also a top asphalt producer. Alon Israel Oil owns 76% of Alon USA Energy.

Alon USA Energy is the largest 7-Eleven licensee in the US and a leading convenience store operator in the Texas cities of El Paso Big Spring Lubbock Midland and Odessa.

The company has pursued a strategy of consolidating regional market share through acquisitions of both gas stations/convenience stores and refineries. In 2007 it acquired Abilene Texas-based Skinny's Inc. chain of stores (which it rebranded as 7-Eleven) for $75.3 million. In 2008 Alon USA Energy bought Valero Energy's Krotz Springs Louisiana refinery for $333 million.

In a setback to its refinery segment in 2008 an explosion and fire shut down the company's refinery in Big Spring for several weeks and forced the shutdown of its alkylation unit (used to process premium gasolines) for almost two years.

Refinery shutdowns in 2008 (including hurricane damage to its Louisiana refinery) and the global downturn in 2009 with its resulting low commodity prices and weak demand saw the company's revenues and income drop dramatically in 2009.

Looking to recover and ramp up its refinery capacity in 2010 Alon USA Energy acquired the 70000-barrels-per-day Bakersfield California refinery from bankrupt Pilot Flying J for $40 million. The deal enabled the company to avoid a costly planned expansion involving the building of a hydrocracker unit at its nearby Paramount California refinery.

Higher refined product prices and increased motor fuel volumes help lift Alon USA Energy's revenues in 2010. However lower refinery throughput and margins and weaker asphalt sales volumes increased the company's net loss for the year.

Alon Israel Oil formed Alon USA Energy in 2000 to acquire FINA Inc.'s downstream assets.

EXECUTIVES

Vice Chairman, Jeff D. Morris, age 60, $333,100 total compensation
SVP, Claire A. Hart, age 56, $176,723 total compensation
President and CEO, W. Paul Eisman, age 57
Chairman, David Wiessman, age 57, $288,000 total compensation
President and CEO Alon Brands, Kyle C. McKeen, age 48
SVP Refining, Joseph A. (Joe) Concienne, age 61, $202,223 total compensation
President and CEO Southwest Convenience Stores, Joseph Lipman, age 66
SVP and CFO, Shai Even, age 44, $268,300 total compensation
VP Refining Big Spring, Jimmy C. Crosby, age 53
COO, Joseph Israel, age 40, $257,981 total compensation
SVP Supply, Alan P. Moret, age 58
SVP Mergers and Acquisitions, Michael Oster, age 40, $225,000 total compensation
VP Refining Krotz Springs, William Wuensche, age 51
VP Asphalt Operations, William L. Thorpe, age 65
VP Refining Paramount, Ed Juno, age 59
Vice Chairman, Jeff D. Morris, age 60
Director, Ronald W. (Ron) Haddock, age 72
Director, Shlomo Even, age 56
Director, Itzhak Bader, age 66
Director, Boaz Biran, age 48
Director, Yeshayahu Pery, age 78
Director, Avraham B. Shochat, age 75
Director, Zalman Segal, age 75
Director, Avinadav (Nadav) Grinshpon, age 40
Auditors: KPMGLLP

LOCATIONS

HQ: Alon USA Energy Inc
7616 LBJ Freeway, Suite 300, Dallas, TX 75251
Phone: 972 367-3600
Web: www.alonusa.com

PRODUCTS/OPERATIONS

2011 Sales

	$ mil.	% of total
Refining & unbranded marketing	5,194	72
Retail & branded marketing	1,437	20
Asphalt	554	8
Total	**7,186**	**100**

Selected Subsidiaries

Alon Asphalt Bakersfield Inc.
Alon Assets Inc.
Alon Pipeline Logistics LLC
Alon USA Asphalt Inc.
Alon USA Capital Inc.
Alon USA Delaware LLC
Alon USA GP LLC
Alon USA Inc.
Alon USA Interests LLC
Alon USA LP

Alon USA Operating Inc.
Alon USA Partners LP (82%)
Alon USA Pipeline Inc.
Alon USA Refining Inc.
Paramount Petroleum Corporation
Skinny' s LLC
Southwest Convenience Stores LLC

COMPETITORS

BP
Chevron
ConocoPhillips
Exxon Mobil
Hess Corporation
HollyFrontier
Koch Industries Inc.
Marathon Petroleum
Shell Oil Products
Valero Energy

HISTORICAL FINANCIALS

Company Type: Public

Income Statement FYE: December 31

	REVENUE ($ mil.)	NET INCOME ($ mil.)	NET PROFIT MARGIN	EMPLOYEES
12/11	7,186	43	0.6%	2,824
12/10	4,030	(132)	—	2,821
12/09	3,915	(102)	—	2,825
12/08	5,156	82	1.6%	2,760
12/07	4,542	103	2.3%	2,697
Annual Growth	12.2%	(19.5%)	—	1.2%

2011 Year-End Financials

Debt ratio: 45.07%
Return on equity: 11.05%
Cash ($ mil.): 157
Current ratio: 119.50
Long-term debt ($ mil.): 930
No. of shares (mil.): 56
Dividends
Yield: —
Payout: 23.19%
Market value ($ mil.): 489

	STOCK PRICE ($) FY Close	P/E High/Low		PER SHARE ($) Earnings	Dividends	Book Value
12/11	8.71	19	7	0.69	0.00	7.06
12/10	5.98	—	—	(2.27)	0.16	6.31
12/09	6.84	—	—	(2.46)	0.16	7.80
12/08	9.15	15	4	1.72	0.16	11.03
12/07	27.18	21	11	2.16	0.16	8.28
Annual Growth	(24.8%)	—	—	(24.8%)	—	(3.9%)

Alpha Natural Resources Inc

Alpha Natural Resources doesn't mind going underground. The company produces steam and metallurgical coal at some 145 mines and 35 preparation plants primarily in central and northern Appalachia and the Powder River Basin. Alpha became one of the largest coal producers in the US in 2011 when it acquired coal miner Massey Energy creating a $15 billion energy behemoth. Alpha's sales are split between low-sulfur steam coal used mainly for electricity generation and metallurgical coal used primarily for steelmaking. The combined companies produce about 100 million tons of coal per year. Alpha controls about 5 billion tons of proved and probable reserves.

The $8.5 billion acquisition of Massey made Alpha the second-largest publicly traded coal company in the US (behind Peabody) as measured by its 2011 consolidated revenues of $7.1 billion. The acquisition also elevated it to the world's third-largest supplier of coking coal with the largest port capacity of any US producer.

Geographic Reach

The company's coal reserves are in the US states of Illinois Kentucky Pennsylvania Virginia West Virginia and Wyoming. More than 40% of its coal revenues and freight and handling sales come from customers outside the US mostly in Brazil India Italy the Netherlands and Turkey.

Operations

The company operates through two main segments: Eastern Coal Operations (mines in North and Central Appalachia coal brokerage activities and road construction) and Western Coal Operations (two Powder River Basin mines in Wyoming). Its All Other segment includes an idled Illinois mine other closed mines equipment and filter sales revenues and royalties from coalbed methane and natural gas sales and mineral rights leasing. Alpha also has a joint venture with Rice Energy to develop its Marcellus Shale natural gas resource in southwestern Pennsylvania.

Financial Analysis

Steam coal used by Alpha's large utility and industrial customers accounted for about 82% of the company's 2011 coal sales volume. Met coal used to produce coke as a raw material in steelmaking accounted for the remaining 18%. Met coal generally sells at a higher price because of its higher quality but demand for steel has softened recently and therefore production has slowed.

In 2011 the company sold 106.3 million tons of both steam and met coal generating revenues of $6.2 billion. Of those totals the Massey acquisition contributed 20.9 million tons and $1.9 billion in coal revenues. The company also purchased about 6 million tons of coal from third parties which it usually processes and blends with its own coal to make a higher selling product.

Prior to its acquisition by Alpha Massey had been struggling since 29 miners died in a 2010 explosion at its Upper Big Branch mine in West Virginia. Massey was under investigation by federal mining officials for the incident. In 2011 Alpha agreed to a record $209 million settlement for the explosion. The settlement allocated $46.5 million to families of the victims but did not protect individual Massey executives from criminal prosecution. The Mine Safety and Health Administration also imposed the largest fine in its history $10.8 million on the company. As part of the agreement Alpha is also investing $80 million over the next two years toward improving miner health and safety.

Following the acquisition of Massey Alpha generated net sales of $7.1 billion in fiscal 2011 soaring 82% above the 2010 net sales of $3.9 billion. Its net income however plummeted to $677.4 million from the previous year due to costs associated with a $745 million charge related to weakened demand for coal and stricter environmental regulations.

Strategy

Although the company experienced record growth in 2011 by 2012 it responded to softened demand by reducing production volumes by some 4 million tons of domestic steam coal and planned to make more reductions if necessary. Despite the volatility of coal prices during the past several years Alpha believes it maintains a balanced approach to selling that includes its long-term contracts and the control of production levels according to demand.

It sees its increased geographic presence the ability to produce in three major coal regions in the US its access to export terminal capacity and its expected growth in international coal consumption as factors that position it well for long-term growth.

HISTORY

Alpha made another big move when it bought Foundation Coal in 2009 creating a major US coal producer. The company had already tried a deal the previous year when iron miner Cliffs Natural Resources had agreed to buy Alpha for about $8 billion but the deal fell through.

Prior to the Foundation Coal acquisition its operations had been made up mainly of assets acquired from Pittston Coal Coastal Coal American Metals & Coal International and Mears Enterprises. Alpha was formed in 2002 by private equity group First Reserve.

Since then Alpha Natural Resources has expanded through acquisitions of coal reserves and related assets from Nicewonder Coal three small subsidiaries of Progress Fuels that controlled some 75 million tons of reserves and more coal operations from Arch Coal.

In 2010 Alpha entered into a 50-50 joint venture with Rice Energy to produce natural gas from the Marcellus Shale region in Pennsylvania where the venture controls about 20000 acres.

EXECUTIVES

President, Paul H. Vining, age 57
EVP and Running Right Officer, Randy L. McMillion, age 55, $148,076 total compensation
EVP Secretary and General Counsel, Vaughn R. Groves, age 55, $218,566 total compensation
President, Kurt D. Kost, age 55, $505,649 total compensation
EVP and Chief Administrative Officer, Michael R. Peelish, age 50, $262,358 total compensation
Chairman, Michael J. (Mike) Quillen, age 62, $689,423 total compensation
Chairman and CEO, Kevin S. Crutchfield, age 50, $336,538 total compensation
EVP and Chief Risk Officer, Eddie W. Neely, age 60
EVP and CFO, Frank J. Wood, age 59, $366,254 total compensation
EVP Sales; President Alpha Coal Sales, A. Scott Pack Jr., age 52
VP Investor Relations, Todd Allen
EVP and Chief Strategy Officer, Philip J. Cavatoni, age 48
Recruitment Coordinator, Christopher (Chris) Matras
Recruitment Coordinator, Jessica Stallings
EVP and Chief Commercial Officer, Brian D. Sullivan
Director, Glenn A. Eisenberg, age 50
Director, E. Linn Draper Jr., age 69
Director, Joel Richards III, age 64
Director, P. Michael Giftos, age 65
Director, Ted G. Wood, age 74
Director, James F. Roberts, age 62
CEO and Director, Kevin S. Crutchfield, age 50
Director, William J. Crowley Jr., age 66
Auditors: KPMGLLP

LOCATIONS

HQ: Alpha Natural Resources Inc.
1 Alpha Place, Bristol VA 24209
Phone: 276-619-4410 **Fax:** 208-837-6254

PRODUCTS/OPERATIONS

2011 Sales

	$ mil.	% of total
Coal		
Metallurgical	3,104	44

Eastern steam	2,488	35
Western steam	596	8
Other	257	4

COMPETITORS

Alliance Resource
Arch Coal
Cloud Peak Energy
CONSOL Energy
James River Coal
Patriot Coal
Peabody Energy
Westmoreland Coal

HISTORICAL FINANCIALS

Company Type: Public

Income Statement FYE: December 31

	REVENUE ($ mil.)	NET INCOME ($ mil.)	NET PROFIT MARGIN	EMPLOYEES
12/11	7,109	(677)	—	14,500
12/10	3,917	95	2.4%	6,500
12/09	2,495	58	2.3%	6,400
12/08	2,554	165	6.5%	3,779
12/07	1,877	27	1.5%	3,640
Annual Growth	39.5%	—	—	41.3%

2011 Year-End Financials

Debt ratio: 17.98%
Return on equity: (-9.12)%
Cash ($ mil.): 585
Current ratio: 140.45
Long-term debt ($ mil.): 2,922
No. of shares (mil.): 219
Dividends
Yield: —
Payout: —
Market value ($ mil.): 4,491

	STOCK PRICE ($) FY Close	P/E High	P/E Low	PER SHARE ($) Earnings	Dividends	Book Value
12/11	20.43	—	—	(3.76)	0.00	33.80
12/10	60.03	75	40	0.79	0.00	22.04
12/09	43.38	72	23	0.63	0.00	21.51
12/08	16.19	43	6	2.36	0.00	10.29
12/07	32.48	79	29	0.43	0.00	5.79
Annual Growth	(10.9%)	—	—	—	—	55.4%

Altria Group Inc

The house the Marlboro Man built Altria Group owns the largest cigarette company in the US. Altria operates through subsidiary Philip Morris USA which sells Marlboro –the world's #1-selling cigarette brand. Altria controls about half of the US tobacco market. It manufactures cigarettes under the Parliament Virginia Slims and Basic brands among many. Altria however is diversifying from solely a cigarette maker to a purveyor of cigars and pipe tobacco through John Middleton Co. smokeless tobacco products through UST and wine through UST subsidiary Ste. Michelle Wine Estates. Another subsidiary Philip Morris Capital Corp. holds a group of finance leases. Altria also owns a 27% stake in SABMiller.

HISTORY

Philip Morris opened his London tobacco store in 1847 and by 1854 was making his own cigarettes. Morris died in 1873 and his heirs sold the firm to William Thomson just before the turn of the century. Thomson introduced his company's cigarettes to the US in 1902. American investors bought the rights to leading Philip Morris brands in 1919 and in 1925 the new company Philip Morris & Co. introduced Marlboro which targeted women smokers and produced modest sales.

When the firm's larger competitors raised their prices in 1930 Philip Morris Companies countered by introducing inexpensive cigarettes that caught on with Depression-weary consumers. By 1936 it was the fourth-biggest cigarette maker.

The firm acquired Benson & Hedges in 1954. It signed ad agency Leo Burnett which promptly initiated the Marlboro Man campaign. Under Joseph Cullman (who became president in 1957) Philip Morris experienced tremendous growth overseas. After dipping to sixth place among US tobacco companies in 1960 it rebounded at home thanks to Marlboro's growing popularity among men (Marlboro became the #1 cigarette brand in the world in 1972).

In 1970 Philip Morris bought the nation's seventh-largest brewer Miller Brewing and with aggressive marketing it vaulted to #2 among US beer makers by 1980. To protect itself against a shrinking US tobacco market in 1985 Philip Morris paid $5.6 billion for General Foods (Kool-Aid Post Stove Top). In 1988 it bought Kraft (Miracle Whip Velveeta). The next year Philip Morris joined Kraft with General Foods.

In 1994 Australian Geoffrey Bible became CEO. By late 1998 the company and its rivals had settled tobacco litigation with most states agreeing to pay about $250 billion over 25 years to receive protection from further state suits.

In 1999 Philip Morris bought three cigarette brands (L&M Chesterfield and Lark) from the Brooke Group. The US government filed a massive lawsuit against Big Tobacco and Philip Morris admitted –no kidding –that smoking increases the risk of getting cancer and other illnesses.

In 2000 Philip Morris vowed to appeal after a state court awarded $74 billion in punitive damages to Florida smokers. The court later ruled that Philip Morris Lorillard and the Liggett Group would pay at least $709 million in the case regardless of the outcome but would not have to pay damages until after the appeals are resolved. A Los Angeles jury awarded Richard Boeken $3 billion in punitive damages. The company appealed even after Boeken later agreed to reduced damages of $100 million. (Boeken died in 2002.)

In December 2000 Philip Morris completed its purchase of Nabisco Holdings for $18.9 billion. In June 2001 Philip Morris spun off Kraft Foods in what was the second-largest IPO in US history; it retained an 84% stake in the company and 97% of the voting rights.

In April 2002 CFO Louis Camilleri succeeded Bible as CEO; in September Camilleri became chairman upon Bible's retirement. In July 2002 Philip Morris sold Miller Brewing to South African Breweries for $5.6 billion ($3.6 billion in SAB stock and the assumption of $2 billion in Miller debt) in July 2002.

In the ongoing saga of tobacco-related litigation Philip Morris said it would appeal an October 2002 verdict by a California jury that ordered the company to pay $28 billion in punitive damages the most ever in an individual tobacco liability lawsuit (later reduced to $28 million). In January 2003 Philip Morris changed its name to Altria Group in an effort to distance itself from its tobacco litigation. In April a Florida appeals court threw out the state's multibillion-dollar judgment (made in 2000) against Philip Morris USA and four other US tobacco companies stating that thousands of Florida smokers could not lump their complaints together in a single case.

In March 2003 Philip Morris USA lost an Illinois lawsuit which claimed the company's use of the word "light" was misleading and violated Illinois consumer fraud laws. The judge ordered Philip Morris USA to pay damages of $10 billion and post a $12 billion bond. The Illinois Supreme Court has lowered the bond to $7 billion and agreed to hear Philip Morris USA's appeal of the original verdict.

In 2005 Altria purchased a $4.8 billion stake in Indonesia's third-largest tobacco firm PT Hanjaya Mandala Sampoerna which makes kreteks or clove cigarettes. Also in 2005 the company formed a long-term alliance with China National Tobacco Corp.

In mid-2006 Altria unseated Roger Deromedi from Kraft's top spot and appointed Irene Rosenfeld to head the company. The executive realignment was part of Altria's plan to spin off Kraft. Deromedi a 28-year Kraft veteran had been under fire for the unit's stale sales since taking over as sole CEO in 2003. Rosenfeld spent more than 20 years at Kraft and exited the firm in mid-2003 as president of Kraft Foods North America. The former chairman and CEO of Frito-Lay Rosenfeld is known for her integration expertise as well as restructuring and turning around companies.

In March 2007 Altria completed the spinoff of Kraft Foods to Altria shareholders. Also in 2007 Altria bought US cigar maker John Middleton from privately held Bradford Holdings. Based in Pennsylvania John Middleton specializes in machine-made cigars –most notably the Black & Mild brand. The deal was valued at $2.2 billion. A year later in March 2008 Altria spun off its Philip Morris International arm also to shareholders and moved its headquarters from New York City's Park Avenue to Richmond Virginia to be closer to its bread and butter operations. (As part of the move Altria in late 2007 agreed to sell the headquarters that has housed the firm since 1982 to a unit of privately held Global Holdings for some $525 million. Altria relocated about 100 of its about 500 employees in the move from New York City to Richmond.)

In January 2009 the company purchased smokeless tobacco maker UST as well as its wine business. The $11 billion deal gave Altria a significant foothold in the US smokeless tobacco market garnering popular brands Copenhagen and Skoal into Altria's fold. Following the acquisition Altria consolidated the sales forces of UST's U.S. Smokeless Tobacco brands and Philip Morris USA and relocated U.S. Smokeless Tobacco Company to Richmond Virginia. Altria has since launched a new versions of certain brands designed to compete with value-priced brands such as Reynolds American's Grizzly and Swedish Match AB's Timber Wolf.

In June 2009 the passage of the Family Smoking and Tobacco Control Act by the US Congress gave the U.S. Food and Drug Administration unprecedented authority to regulate tobacco products including the authority to regulate marketing ban candy flavorings and reduce nicotine in tobacco products.

EXECUTIVES

EVP and CTO, John R. (Jack) Nelson Jr., age 60, $770,000 total compensation

Chairman and CEO, Michael E. (Mike) Szymanczyk, age 63, $1,283,333 total compensation

Chairman and CEO, Martin J. (Marty) Barrington, age 58, $700,333 total compensation

President and CEO Ste. Michelle Wine Estates, Theodor P. (Ted) Baseler, age 57

EVP and CFO Ste. Michelle Wine Estates, Sheila A. Newlands

EVP Sales and Marketing Ste. Michelle Wine Estates, Glenn D. Yaffa

SVP Regulatory Administrative Affairs Altria Client Services, James E. (Jim) Dillard III
President and COO, David R. (Dave) Beran, age 57, $759,500 total compensation
President and CEO Altria Group Distribution, Craig A. Johnson, age 59, $735,958 total compensation
SVP Manufacturing Operations Philip Morris USA, Gary R. Ruth
VP Manufacturing U.S. Smokeless Tobacco Company, Mary A. Gordon
EVP and CFO, Howard A. Willard III, age 48
President and CEO U.S. Smokeless Tobacco, Brian W. Quigley
SVP Marketing Ste. Michelle Wine Estates, Martin Johnson
President and CEO U.S. Smokeless Tobacco Company, Peter P. Paoli
President and CEO Philip Morris Capital Corporation, John J. Mulligan
VP and Controller, Linda M. Warren, age 63
VP California Operations Ste. Michelle Wine Estates and General Manager of Stag?s Leap Wine Cellars, Jeff McBride
President and CEO Philip Morris USA Inc., William F. (Billy) Gifford Jr., age 41
EVP and General Counsel, Denise F. Keane, age 60, $700,333 total compensation
SVP Marketing Altria Client Services, Nancy B. Lund, age 59
SVP and Associate General Counsel Altria Client Services, Murray R. Garnick
SVP Procurement Altria Client Services, Henry P. Long Jr.
SVP Tobacco Regulatory and Health Sciences Altria Client Services, Jane Y. Lewis
SVP and CIO Altria Client Services, Joseph S. (Joe) Amado
VP Investor Relations Altria Client Services, Clifford B. Fleet
Corporate Secretary and Senior Assistant General Counsel, W. Hildebrandt (Brandt) Surgner
SVP Human Resources and Compliance Altria Client Services, Charles N. (Charlie) Whitaker
VP and Treasurer, Salvatore Mancuso
President and CEO John Middleton, Craig G. Schwartz
SVP and General Manager Altria Sales and Distribution, Miguel Martin
VP Corporate Governance and Associate General Counsel, Louanna O. Heuhsen
SVP External Affairs Altria Client Services, Bruce A. Gates
EVP Winemaking Vineyards and Operations Ste. Michelle Wine Estates, Doug Gore
VP Marlboro Philip Morris USA, Francisca Rahardja
VP Brand Management U.S. Smokeless Tobacco Company, Jen P. Campbell
Director Marketing John Middleton, William J. Dartnall
SVP Human Resources and Environmental Affairs Ste. Michelle Wine Estates, Susan Reams
SVP and General Counsel Ste. Michelle Wine Estates, Tom Rowland
SVP and Manager National Sales Ste. Michelle Wine Estates, Frank Genovese
Director, Thomas F. Farrell II, age 58
Director, John T. Casteen III, age 69
Director, Thomas W. (Tom) Jones, age 62
Director, Gerald L. Baliles, age 72
Director, Elizabeth E. (Betsy) Bailey, age 73
Director, Robert E. R. Huntley, age 82
Director, Dinyar S. Devitre, age 65
Director, Nabil Y. Sakkab, age 65
Director, George Mu?oz, age 61
Auditors: PricewaterhouseCoopersLLP

LOCATIONS

HQ: Altria Group Inc.
6601 W. Broad St., Richmond VA 23230-1723
Phone: 804-274-2200 **Fax:** 804-484-8231
Web: www.altria.com

PRODUCTS/OPERATIONS

2011 Sales

	$ mil.	% of total
Cigarettes	21,403	89
Smokeless products	1,627	7
Cigars	567	2
Wine	516	2
Financial services	(313)	
Excise taxes of products	(7181)	-
Total	**16,619**	**100**

Selected Subsidiaries

F.W. Rickard Seeds Inc.
International Wine & Spirits Ltd.
John Middleton Co.
Philip Morris Capital Corp.
Philip Morris USA Inc.
Stag' s Leap Wine Cellars LLC
Ste. Michelle Wine Estates Ltd.
U.S. Smokeless Tobacco Co. LLC
UST LLC

COMPETITORS

Altadis
Anheuser-Busch
Anheuser-Busch InBev
British American Tobacco
Constellation Brands
E. & J. Gallo
Heineken
Japan Tobacco
Loews
Lorillard
Molson Coors
North Atlantic Trading
Ravenswood Winery
Reynolds American
Sebastiani Vineyards
Swedish Match
Treasury Wine Estates Americas
Vector Group

HISTORICAL FINANCIALS

Company Type: Public

Income Statement FYE: December 31

	REVENUE ($ mil.)	NET INCOME ($ mil.)	NET PROFIT MARGIN	EMPLOYEES
12/11	23,800	3,390	14.2%	9,900
12/10	24,363	3,905	16.0%	10,000
12/09	23,556	3,206	13.6%	10,000
12/08	19,356	4,930	25.5%	10,400
12/07	73,801	9,786	13.3%	84,000
Annual Growth	(24.6%)	(23.3%)	—	(41.4%)

2011 Year-End Financials

Debt ratio: 37.04%
Return on equity: 92.12%
Cash ($ mil.): 3,270
Current ratio: 93.30
Long-term debt ($ mil.): 13,089
No. of shares (mil.): 2,044
Dividends
Yield: —
Payout: 96.34%
Market value ($ mil.): 60,617

	STOCK PRICE ($) FY Close	P/E High	P/E Low	PER SHARE ($) Earnings	Dividends	Book Value
12/11	29.65	18	14	1.64	0.00	1.80
12/10	24.62	14	10	1.87	1.46	2.49
12/09	19.63	13	9	1.54	1.32	1.96
12/08	15.06	33	6	2.36	1.68	1.37
12/07	75.58	19	14	4.62	3.05	8.80
Annual Growth	(20.9%)	—	—	(22.8%)	—	(32.7%)

Amazon.com Inc.

What began as Earth's biggest bookstore has become Earth's biggest everything store. Expansion has propelled Amazon.com in innumerable directions. While the website still offers millions of books movies games and music electronics and other general merchandise categories including apparel and accessories auto parts home furnishings health and beauty aids toys and groceries ring up about 60% of sales. Shoppers can also download e-books games MP3s and films to their computers or handheld devices including Amazon's own portable e-reader the Kindle. Amazon also offers products and services such as self-publishing online advertising e-commerce platform hosting and a co-branded credit card.

HISTORY

Jeff Bezos was researching the Internet in the early 1990s for hedge fund D.E. Shaw. He realized that book sales would be a perfect fit with e-commerce because book distributors already kept meticulous electronic lists. Bezos who as a teen had dreamed of entrepreneurship in outer space took the idea to Shaw. The company passed on the idea but Bezos ran with it trekking cross country to Seattle (close to a facility owned by major book distributor Ingram) and typing up a business plan along the way.

Bezos founded Amazon.com in 1994. After months of preparation he launched a website in July 1995 (Douglas Hofstadter's "Fluid Concepts and Creative Analogies" was its first sale); it had sales of $20000 a week by September. Bezos and his team kept working with the site pioneering features that now seem mundane such as one-click shopping customer reviews and e-mail order verification.

Amazon went public in 1997. Moves to cement the Amazon.com brand included becoming the sole book retailer on AOL's website and Netscape's commercial channel.

In 1998 the company launched its online music and video stores and it began to sell toys and electronics. Amazon also expanded its European reach with the purchases of online booksellers in the UK and Germany and it acquired the Internet Movie Database. Bezos also expanded the company's base of online services buying Junglee (comparison shopping) and PlanetAll (address book calendar reminders).

By midyear Amazon.com had attracted so much attention that its market capitalization equaled the combined values of profitable bricks-and-mortar rivals Barnes & Noble and Borders Group even though their combined sales were far greater than the upstart's. Late that year Amazon formed a promotional link with Hoover's publisher of this profile.

After raising $1.25 billion in a bond offering early in 1999 Amazon.com began a spending spree with deals to buy all or part of several dot-coms. However some have since been sold (HomeGrocer.com) and others have gone out of business or bankrupt —Pets.com living.com (furniture). It also bought the catalog businesses of Back to Basics and Tool Crib of the North.

Amazon.com began conducting online auctions in early 1999 and partnered with venerable auction house Sotheby's. Also that year Amazon added distribution facilities including one each in England and Germany.

In 2000 the company inked a 10-year deal with Toysrus.com to set up a co-branded toy and video game store. (The partnership came to a bitter end in 2006 after Toys "R" Us sued Amazon.com when it began selling toys from other companies.) Also that year Amazon.com added foreign-language sites for France and Japan.

In 2001 Amazon cut 15% of its workforce as part of a restructuring plan that also forced a $150 million charge. That year the company also made a deal with Borders to provide inventory fulfillment content and customer service for borders.com. As part of a deal to expand their marketing partnership AOL invested $100 million in Amazon.com in 2001. Later that year Amazon purchased some assets from Egghead.com (which filed for Chapter 11 in August) and relaunched the site.

In 2002 the firm introduced clothing sales featuring hundreds of retailers including names such as The Gap Nordstrom and Lands' End. Amazon.com received accreditation from ICANN (the Internet Corporation for Assigned Names and Numbers) as an Internet domain name registrar becoming one of about 160 entities permitted to register Internet addresses.

The company launched its Search Inside the Book feature in 2003. The tool allows customers to search the text inside books for more relevant search returns. At launch the search feature covered more than 120000 books from over 190 publishers. Amazon expanded into China in 2004 with the purchase of Joyo.com. (It renamed the unit Joyo Amazon in 2007.)

In 2005 Amazon launched Amazon Prime a two-day shipping service for an annual fee of $79.

Amazon.com began testing the online dry grocery waters in 2006. It launched the Amazon Fresh delivery service for the Seattle area a year later to include perishables.

The company acquired shopping site Shopbop.com in 2006 boosting its apparel offerings. Also that year IBM filed a pair of patent infringement lawsuits alleging that Amazon.com has been violating at least five of its patents –including technologies that govern how the online retailer handles product recommendations and displays advertising –for about four years. In 2007 the two companies settled the litigation and signed a long-term patent cross-license agreement.

The Internet bookseller in November 2007 introduced the Kindle an electronic portable book reader. The launch Amazon's first foray into the tech hardware market is aimed at kindling demand for electronic books.

Also in 2007 Amazon launched Endless.com which sells shoes and accessories; Askville.com where users can solicit answers from others on the site; and the Amazon MP3 site which offers digital music free of copyright restrictions. In addition Amazon acquired audiobook publisher Brilliance Audio.

Amazon stayed focused on entertainment in 2008. The company launched Amazon Video On Demand a service that gives customers the option to stream or download ad-free digital movies and TV shows on Macs or PCs. It also purchased AbeBooks an online retailer of more than 110 million primarily used rare and out-of-print books as well as Shelfari a social-networking site for booklovers. Additionally Amazon.com sold its UK and German online DVD rental services to Internet movie-rental company LOVEFiLM International in exchange for stock. The deal gave Amazon about a 40% stake in LOVEFiLM.

Shopping was also at the top of Amazon's list in 2008. In May the company invested in The Talk Market a user-generated TV Shopping Channel. In June Amazon launched an online office supplies store and sewed up the acquisition of the online fabrics retailer Fabrics.com.

In June 2009 Amazon agreed to pay Toys "R" Us $51 million to settle a dispute dating back to 2004. The settlement was related to a partnership that gave the toy seller exclusive rights to supply some of the toys on Amazon's site. In November Amazon completed its $888 million acquisition of shoe e-tailer Zappos.com –the #1 online shoe and apparel retailer. (Besides footwear and clothing Zappos also sells handbags housewares and beauty products.) The purchase allowed Amazon to boost its sales and expand its products portfolio by leveraging Zappos' widely recognized customer service expertise.

In mid-2010 Amazon acquired Woot Inc. a pioneer in the deal-of-the-day genre of online retailing. While neither Amazon or Woot would disclose the selling price reports valued the deal at about $110 million in cash.

In January 2011 Amazon completed its move to a new corporate headquarters in Seattle's South Lake Union neighborhood. Also in early 2011 the company acquired the remaining shares it didn't already own in LOVEFiLM International.

EXECUTIVES

CEO Zappos, Anthony C. (Tony) Hsieh, age 38
SVP Consumer Business, Jeffrey A. (Jeff) Wilke, age 46, $155,000 total compensation
Chairman President and CEO, Jeffrey P. (Jeff) Bezos, age 48, $81,840 total compensation
SVP International Consumer Business, Diego Piacentini, age 51, $175,000 total compensation
SVP Worldwide Operations, Marc A. Onetto, age 62, $157,500 total compensation
SVP Ecommerce Platform, H. Brian Valentine, age 53, $157,500 total compensation
SVP General Counsel and Secretary, L. Michelle Wilson, age 49
Media Relations, Mary Osako
SVP and CFO, Thomas J. (Tom) Szkutak, age 51, $160,000 total compensation
SVP Seller Services, Sebastian J. Gunningham, age 50, $160,000 total compensation
SVP Business Development, Jeffrey M. Blackburn, age 43
SVP Web Services, Andrew R. Jassy, age 45
SVP Worldwide Digital Media, Steven Kessel, age 47
VP Worldwide Controller and Principal Accounting Officer, Shelley L. Reynolds, age 48, $160,000 total compensation
VP Product Management and Developer Relations Amazon Web Services, Adam Selipsky
VP Kindle Content, Russell (Russ) Grandinetti
VP and CTO, Werner Vogels
VP Books, Jeff Belle
CEO IMDb.com, Col Needham
Director Amazon Kindle Amazon Digital Services, Jay Marine
Senior Manager Music, Craig Pape
VP Consumer Electronics, Paul Ryder
Director, Jonathan J. (Jon) Rubinstein, age 55
Director, William B. (Bing) Gordon, age 61
Director, Thomas O. (Tom) Ryder, age 67
Director, Patricia Q. (Patty) Stonesifer, age 55
Director, John Seely Brown, age 71
Director, Tom A. Alberg, age 72
Director, Alain Monie, age 61
Independent Director, Alain Monie
Auditors: Ernst&YoungLLP

LOCATIONS

HQ: Amazon.com Inc.
410 Terry Ave. North, Seattle WA 98109-5210
Phone: 206-266-1000 **Fax:** 512-344-5080
Web: www.txlottery.org

2011 Sales

	$ mil.	% of total
North America	26,705	56
Other countries	21,372	44
Total	**48,077**	**100**

PRODUCTS/OPERATIONS

2011 Sales

	$ mil.	% of total
Electronics & other general merchandise	28,712	60
Media	17,779	37
Other	1,586	3
Total	**48,077**	**100**

Selected Departments

Apparel shoes and jewelry
Books
- Books
- Kindle e-books
- Textbooks
- Magazines

Computers and office
- Computers and accessories
- Computer components
- Office products and supplies
- PC games
- Software

Digital downloads
- Amazon shorts
- Game downloads
- Kindle Store
- MP3 downloads

Electronics
- Audio TV and home theater
- Camera photo and video
- Car electronics and GPS
- Cell phones and service
- Home appliances
- MP3 and media players
- Musical instruments
- Video games

Grocery health and beauty
- Beauty
- Diapers
- Gourmet food
- Grocery
- Health and personal care
- Natural and organic

Home and garden
- Bedding and bath
- Furniture and decor
- Home appliances
- Home improvement
- Kitchen and dining
- Patio lawn and garden
- Pet supplies
- Sewing craft and hobby
- Vacuums and storage

Kindle
- Books
- Blogs
- Magazines
- Newspapers

Movies music and games
- Blu-ray
- Movies and TV
- Music
- Musical instruments
- Video games
- Video On Demand

Sports and outdoors
- Action sports
- Camping and hiking
- Cycling
- Exercise and fitness
- Fan gear
- Golf

Team sports
Tools auto and industrial
Automotive
Home improvement
Industrial and scientific
Lighting and electrical
Motorcycle and ATV
Outdoor power equipment
Plumbing fixtures
Power and hand tools
Toys kids and baby
Apparel (kids and baby)
Baby
Books
Movies
Music
Software
Toys and games
Video games

Selected Operations

A9.com (search technology development)
Amazon.ca (Canada)
Amazon.cn (China)
Amazon.de (Germany)
Amazon.fr (France)
Amazon.co.jp (Japan)
Amazon.co.uk (UK)
Audible (audiobooks and other recorded content)
Endless (shoes and handbags)
Internet Movie Database (IMDb)
IVONA Software
Joyo (China)
LOVEFiLM International Ltd.
Woot.com (US)
Zappos.com (US)

COMPETITORS

Apple Inc.
AutoNation
AutoZone
Barnes & Noble
Best Buy
Bidz.com
Blockbuster
Bluefly
Books-A-Million
Buy.com
Collective Brands
Columbia House
Costco Wholesale
DSW
eBay
Finish Line
Foot Locker
Google
Hastings Entertainment
Hollywood Media
Home Depot
HSN
IAC
Indigo Books & Music
J. C. Penney
Lowe' s
Macy' s
Netflix
Nine West
Office Depot
OfficeMax
Overstock.com
Peapod LLC
PPR SA
Provide Gifts
Rack Room Shoes
Sears
Shoe Carnival
shoebuy.com
Staples
Target Corporation
The Gap
TJX Companies
Walmart.com
Yahoo!

HISTORICAL FINANCIALS

Company Type: Public

Income Statement FYE: December 31

	REVENUE ($ mil.)	NET INCOME ($ mil.)	NET PROFIT MARGIN	EMPLOYEES
12/11	48,077	631	1.3%	56,200
12/10	34,204	1,152	3.4%	33,700
12/09	24,509	902	3.7%	24,300
12/08	19,166	645	3.4%	20,700
12/07	14,835	476	3.2%	17,000
Annual Growth	34.2%	7.3%	—	34.8%

2011 Year-End Financials

Debt ratio: 5.60%
Return on equity: 8.14%
Cash ($ mil.): 9,576
Current ratio: 117.41
Long-term debt ($ mil.): 1,415
No. of shares (mil.): 455
Dividends
Yield: —
Payout: —
Market value ($ mil.): 78,761

	STOCK PRICE ($) FY Close	P/E High/Low		PER SHARE ($) Earnings	Dividends	Book Value
12/11	173.10	177	116	1.37	0.00	17.05
12/10	180.00	72	42	2.53	0.00	15.22
12/09	134.52	68	23	2.04	0.00	11.84
12/08	51.28	63	23	1.49	0.00	6.24
12/07	92.64	88	32	1.12	0.00	2.88
Annual Growth	16.9%	—	—	5.2%	—	56.0%

Ambac Financial Group, Inc.

Ambac Financial Group used to give an A+ to school bonds until its own ratings fell to C's. Ambac Assurance the holding company's primary subsidiary sold financial guarantee insurance and other credit enhancement products for municipal bonds in the US market. However the company has halted all new business and has placed its remaining business in "run-off" –meaning it is only taking in premium payments and paying out claims as it is able. Already operating under "rehabilitation" by Wisconsin regulators Ambac Financial filed for Chapter 11 bankruptcy in 2010.

In better days the company also insured infrastructure and utility finance deals internationally. Its Ambac Financial Services unit offered interest rate swaps credit swaps and investment management primarily to states and municipal authorities tied to their bond financing.

How did a once-solid municipal bond insurer fall so hard? Along with other US bond insurers including FGIC and MBIA the US subprime mortgage meltdown knocked the wind out of Ambac. Its financial guarantee business had slowed to a trickle by late 2007 when the company posted losses of $3.5 billion for the last quarter of that year. And the company's portfolio bulged with collateralized debt obligations of asset-backed securities –the financial equivalent of a sack of rotten potatoes.

The large rating houses took a dim view of Ambac's weakening reserves prompting the company to scramble for a plan in late 2007. It scrapped one plan to split apart its municipal bond business from its increasingly risky US mortgage securities then hit on another plan to raise $1.5 billion through stock sales.

To steady itself during 2008 the company took a few deep breaths quit underwriting certain types of structured finance business (especially asset- and mortgage-backed securities) dropped its dividends down to a penny per share promoted its Chief Risk Officer David Wallis to serve as CEO and pinned its future on its public finance business.

Despite all of these efforts the company's ratings slid down from "AAA" in early 2007 to "CC" in 2010 putting a serious crimp on its ability to write new business. By 2010 with no new business coming in the company resigned itself to mitigating its losses and trying to coax better yields from its investment portfolio. Its stinkier holdings were sent off to auction with any proceeds earmarked to pay interest on the company's remaining debts.

In late 2010 after missing a scheduled interest payment and failing to reach an agreement for a prepackaged bankruptcy proceeding with its creditors the company voluntarily filed for Chapter 11 bankruptcy protection. Through the filing Ambac hopes to restructure more than $1.6 billion in outstanding debt. The company is also haggling with the IRS over $700 million in potentially improper tax refunds between 2003 and 2008.

By 2011 the independent ratings houses of Standard and Poors and Moodys had withdrawn all formal ratings of Ambac. David Wallis announced his resignation in mid-2011 along with the company's General Counsel. Internal executive Diana Adams was tapped to serve as president and CEO.

Before the subprime mortgage mess ruptured in the US Ambac Financial was looking overseas for growth. Spurred by an increase in public/private partnerships in the UK and Western Europe the company broadened its presence there. However by 2009 Ambac UK's new business was curtailed. An earlier alliance with Sompo Japan was meant to give Ambac access to Japan but it was terminated in 2008.

HISTORY

Mortgage Guaranty Insurance Corporation (MGIC) in 1971 founded American Municipal Bond Assurance Corporation (Ambac Indemnity) in Milwaukee. That year Ambac wrote the very first municipal bond insurance policy –for a bond to fund a medical building and a sewage treatment facility in Juneau Alaska. New York City's 1975 moratorium on debt payments helped make the new product more attractive. The company wrote the first insurance policies for mutual funds (1977) and secondary market municipal bonds (1983). In 1981 Ambac moved to New York; four years later it became a Citibank subsidiary. It went public in 1991.

In 1995 Ambac and rival MBIA allied to offer bond insurance overseas. Two years later the company formed a UK subsidiary to serve Europe. In recognition of the growing market the joint venture was amended in 2000 to provide for individual operations by the two partners in Europe though they continue to reinsure each other there and to work jointly in Japan. Ambac went on a buying spree in 1996 and 1997 buying the investment advisory and broker dealer operations of Cadre and Construction Loan Insurance (renamed Connie Lee Holdings) a guarantor of college bonds and hospital infrastructure bonds.

In 1998 as Ambac lost share in the US municipal bond market because it declined to cut premiums the company began concentrating on asset-backed securities and international bonds. Two years later Ambac entered the Japanese market through a joint venture with Yasuda Fire & Marine.

The company sold its Cadre Financial Services and Ambac Securities divisions in 2004 but kept Connie Lee for the future. In the middle of the recession in 2008 Ambac went back and reactivated a somewhat dusty Connie Lee with the hopes that guaranteeing municipal construction bonds would be a stable business. To get Construction Loan Insurance Company ready for its debut Ambac tucked $850 million of capital into its pocketbook. In 2009 it changed Connie Lee's name to Everspan Financial Guarantee but was unable to raise additional capital and eventually put the whole plan back on the shelf indefinitely.

EXECUTIVES

Managing Director Corporate Secretary and Assistant General Counsel, Anne Gill Kelly
Senior Managing Director and Chief Accounting Officer, Robert B. Eisman, age 44
Managing Director and Director Tax, Wes Kirchhoff
Senior Managing Director and CFO, David Trick, age 40
Managing Director and Chief Investment Officer, Rodney D. Kumasaki
Managing Director Fixed Income Investor Relations Ambac UK and Europe, Miguel Sanchez
President CEO and Director, Diana Adams, age 49
Managing Director Investor and Media Relations, Michael Fitzgerald
Senior Managing Director and General Counsel, Stephen M. Ksenak, age 46
Director, Henry D. G. Wallace, age 66
Director, Philip N. Duff, age 54
Director, Jill M. Considine, age 67
Director, Laura S. Unger, age 51
Director, Thomas C. Theobald, age 74
Director, Paul R. DeRosa, age 70
Director, David W. Wallis, age 52
Auditors: KPMGLLP

LOCATIONS

HQ: Ambac Financial Group Inc.
1 State Street Plaza, New York NY 10004
Phone: 212-668-0340 **Fax:** 212-509-9190
Web: www.ambac.com

COMPETITORS

Assured Guaranty
FGIC
MBIA

HISTORICAL FINANCIALS

Company Type: Public

Income Statement FYE: December 31

	ASSETS ($ mil.)	NET INCOME ($ mil.)	INCOME AS % OF ASSETS	EMPLOYEES
12/11	27,113	(1,960)	—	227
12/10	29,047	(753)	—	243
12/09	18,886	(14)	—	293
12/08	17,256	(5,609)	—	328
12/07	23,565	(3,248)	—	367
Annual Growth	3.6%	—	—	(11.3%)

2011 Year-End Financials

Debt ratio: 53.52%
Return on equity: 987650001000000.00%
Cash ($ mil.): 16
Current ratio: —
Long-term debt ($ mil.): 14,512
No. of shares (mil.): 302
Dividends
Yield: —
Payout: —
Market value ($ mil.): 6

	STOCK PRICE ($) FY Close	P/E High/Low	PER SHARE ($) Earnings	Dividends	Book Value
12/11	0.02	— —	(6.48)	0.00	(12.61)
12/10	0.11	— —	(2.56)	0.00	(6.65)
12/09	0.83	— —	(0.05)	0.03	(7.96)
12/08	1.30	— —	(22.31)	0.10	(13.17)
12/07	25.77	— —	(31.56)	0.78	22.45
Annual Growth	(83.3%)	— —	—	—	—

Ameren Corp.

Ameren provides the power that makes much of the American Midwest run. The holding company distributes electricity to 2.4 million customers and natural gas to 900000 customers in Missouri and Illinois through utility subsidiaries. Ameren has a generating capacity of 16000 MW (primarily coal-fired) most of which is controlled by utility Union Electric (which does business as Ameren Missouri) and nonregulated subsidiary AmerenEnergy Resources Generating Company. Ameren which also supplies merchant generation power to third parties operates a nuclear power facility three hydroelectric plants and several coal-fired plants and turbine combustion facilities. It also purchases power including windpower.

Operations

In addition to operating power plants Ameren procures natural gas for its affiliated companies builds new power plants and provides long-term energy supply contracts. It also markets and trades electricity to wholesale and retail customers and provides risk management and other energy-related services.

Financial Analysis

Ameren's overall revenues dipped in 2011. While increased rates helped to lift Ameren Missouri's revenues in 2011 Ameren Illinois' regulated segment and the merchant generation segment both reported a drop in revenues. In particular low gas prices and a warm winter hurt gas revenues. However lower purchased power and resale gas coupled with a drop in goodwill impairment and other charges helped to lift Ameren's net income for the year.

Favorable weather conditions (which increased energy demand) and rate increases help to lift the company's revenues in 2010. However impairment of goodwill intangible assets and long-lived assets in the merchant generation segment (due to the sustained decline in market prices for electricity) dragged down Ameren's operating income.

Strategy

In 2010 the company combined AmerenIP AmerenCIPS and AmerenCILCO into one entity Ameren Illinois in order to streamline operations and reduce confusion among customers. The three Illinois utilities have operated as a single business since 2004 and deliver energy to more than 1100 communities. Ameren Illinois also operates some 21400 miles of natural gas distribution and transmission lines.

To comply with federal requirements to separate ownership of power generation and transmission businesses the operations of Ameren subsidiaries' transmission assets are under the control ofMidwest Independent Transmission System Operator a regional transmission organization that coordinates power across 15 Midwestern states and one Canadian Province.

HISTORY

More than 30 St. Louis companies had built a chaotic grid of generators and power lines throughout the city by 1900. Two years later many of them merged into the Union Company which attracted national notice when it lit the St. Louis World's Fair in the first broad demonstration of electricity's power. In 1913 the company by then named Union Electric (UE) began buying electricity from an Iowa dam 150 miles away –the greatest distance power had ever been transmitted in such quantity.

UE pushed into rural Missouri and began buying and building fossil-fuel plants. Despite a slowdown during the Depression UE built Bagnell Dam on Missouri's Osage River in the early 1930s to gather power for a hydroelectric plant. At the onset of WWII construction began on new plants with larger generators and lower production costs; however demand for electricity lagged. In the late 1940s UE compensated by joining a "power pool" a system of utilities with interconnected transmission lines that shared electricity.

Growth in the 1950s came from acquisitions including Missouri Power & Light (1950) and Missouri Edison (1954). During the 1960s and 1970s UE built five new plants including the Labadie plant (2300 MW) one of the largest coal-fired plants in the US.

UE began producing nuclear energy in 1984 at its Callaway nuke. High costs and the expenses of a scrapped second plant caused UE to battle the Missouri Public Service Commission throughout the 1980s for rate increases.

Charles Mueller became president in 1993 and CEO one year later. He oversaw continued staff reductions and cost cutting through the 1990s in an increasingly competitive market. In 1997 UE expanded into Illinois through its purchase of CIPSCO which owned utility Central Illinois Public Service Company (CIPS).

CIPS began as a Mattoon Illinois streetcar company in the early 1900s. The firm bought Mattoon's electric power plant in 1904 and began growing its power business buying small electric companies in the 1920s and 1930s. CIPS built five generating units in the 1940s and 1950s and became part-owner (along with UE) of Electric Energy Inc. which built a power plant on the Ohio River. The company bought Illinois Electric and Gas Company in the 1960s and the state's Gas Utilities in the 1980s. To prepare for competition under deregulation CIPS created holding company CIPSCO in the 1990s to diversify.

UE's purchase of CIPSCO expanded its geographic scope and the new company was named Ameren in 1997 to reflect its American energy focus. The next year the company committed to adding generating capacity through several natural gas-fired combustion turbines. It joined nine other utilities to form the Midwest Independent System Operator to manage their transmission needs.

In 1999 Ameren bought a 245-mile railroad line between St. Louis and Kansas City to help the area's economic development. Looking for new opportunities in deregulated energy markets the company purchased Data & Metering Specialties.

In 2000 Ameren created subsidiary AmerenEnergy Generating to operate its nonregulated power plants and affiliate AmerenEnergy Marketing to sell the generating facilities' power. When deregulation took effect in Illinois in 2002 the company transferred AmerenCIPS' power plants to AmerenEnergy Generating. In 2003 Ameren acquired CILCORP the holding company for electric and gas utility Central Illinois Light (now operating as AmerenCILCO) from independent power producer AES in a $1.4 billion deal. To further expand its utility operations Ameren acquired power and gas utility Illinois Power from Dynegy in a $2.3 billion deal in 2004. As part of the agreement Ameren gained Dynegy's 20% stake in power generator Electric Energy in which Ameren already held a 60% stake.

In 2007 Ameren subsidiary AmerenUE moved into wind power operations by contracting to buy

100 MW of wind power from Horizon Wind Energy's Rail Splitter Wind Farm located near Delavan Illinois.

EXECUTIVES

President and CEO Ameren Illinois, Scott A. Cisel, age 58, $387,000 total compensation
President and CEO Ameren Missouri, Warner L. Baxter, age 50, $569,600 total compensation
VP and Treasurer, Jerre E. Birdsong, age 57
SVP CFO and Principal Accounting Officer, Martin J. Lyons Jr., age 45, $364,867 total compensation
President and CEO Ameren Services, Daniel F. Cole, age 58, $292,000 total compensation
Chairman President and CEO Ameren Energy Company, Steven R. Sullivan, age 51, $417,133 total compensation
SVP Customer Operations Ameren Missouri, Richard J. Mark, age 56
Chairman President CEO and Director, Thomas R. Voss, age 64, $660,733 total compensation
Media Contact Ameren Missouri, Rita Holmes-Bobo
VP Environmental Services Ameren Services, Michael L. Menne, age 54
SVP and General Counsel, Gregory L. Nelson, age 52
President Ameren Energy Fuels and Services, Michael G. Mueller, age 48
SVP Customer Operations Ameren Illinois, Michael L. Moehn, age 42
Media Contact Corporate, Susan Gallagher
VP and Controller, Bruce Steinke
VP Strategic Initiatives Ameren Services, Shawn E. Schukar, age 48
Media Contact Illinois, Leigh Morris
SVP Generation and Environmental Projects Ameren Missouri, Charles D. Naslund, age 59, $427,267 total compensation
VP Energy Delivery Technical Services Ameren Services, David J. Schepers, age 55
VP Supply Services Ameren Services, Dennis W. Weisenborn, age 54
President Ameren Energy Marketing, Andrew M. Serri, age 50
Director Coal Supply and Transportation Ameren Energy Fuels and Services, Robert K. Neff, age 56
President and CEO Ameren Transmission, Maureen A. Borkowski, age 52
VP Federal Legislative and Regulatory Affairs Ameren Services, Joseph M. (Joe) Power
SVP and Chief Nuclear Officer Ameren Missouri, Adam C. Heflin
VP Information Technology and Ameren Services Center, Mary P. Heger
VP Internal Audit Ameren Services, S. Mark Brawley
VP Corporate Project Risk Management Ameren Services, Kevin DeGraw
VP Generation Technical Services Ameren Energy Resources, Christopher A. Iselin
VP and Deputy General Counsel Ameren Services, James A. Sobule
VP Energy Delivery-Distribution Services AmerenUE, David N. Wakeman
Manager Supplier Diversity, Adriene Bruce
Managing Supervisor Cyber Security, Chris Sawall
Director, James C. Johnson, age 59
Director, Ellen M. Fitzsimmons, age 51
Director, Walter J. Galvin, age 65
Director, Patrick T. (Pat) Stokes, age 69
Director, Stephen R. Wilson, age 63
Director, Steven H. Lipstein, age 55
Chairman President CEO and Director, Thomas R. Voss, age 64
Director, Gayle P. W. Jackson, age 65
Director, Stephen F. Brauer, age 66
Director, Jack D. Woodard, age 68
Auditors: PricewaterhouseCoopersLLP

LOCATIONS

HQ: Ameren Corporation
1901 Chouteau Ave., St. Louis MO 63103
Phone: 314-621-3222 **Fax:** 314-554-3801
Web: www.ameren.com

PRODUCTS/OPERATIONS

2011 Sales

	$ mil.	% of total
Electric	6,530	87
Total	**7,531**	**100**

2011 Sales

	% of total
Coal	85
Nuclear	12
Renewables	2
Natural	1
Total	**100**

COMPETITORS

AES
Atmos Energy
CenterPoint Energy
Empire District Electric
Exelon
Great Plains Energy
MidAmerican Energy
Midwest Generation
Nicor Gas
Southern Union

HISTORICAL FINANCIALS

Company Type: Public

Income Statement FYE: December 31

	REVENUE ($ mil.)	NET INCOME ($ mil.)	NET PROFIT MARGIN	EMPLOYEES
12/11	7,531	519	6.9%	9,323
12/10	7,638	139	1.8%	9,474
12/09	7,090	612	8.6%	9,780
12/08	7,839	605	7.7%	9,524
12/07	7,546	618	8.2%	9,069
Annual Growth	(0.0%)	(4.3%)	—	0.7%

2011 Year-End Financials

Debt ratio: 29.62%
Return on equity: 6.55%
Cash ($ mil.): 255
Current ratio: 128.57
Long-term debt ($ mil.): 6,677
No. of shares (mil.): 242
Dividends
Yield: —
Payout: 72.33%
Market value ($ mil.): 8,037

	STOCK PRICE ($) FY Close	P/E High/Low	PER SHARE ($) Earnings	Dividends	Book Value
12/11	33.13	16 12	2.15	0.00	32.64
12/10	28.19	51 41	0.58	1.54	32.15
12/09	27.95	13 7	2.78	1.54	33.08
12/08	33.26	19 10	2.88	2.54	33.72
12/07	54.21	18 16	2.98	2.54	33.35
Annual Growth	(11.6%)	— —	(7.8%)	—	(0.5%)

American Electric Power Company, Inc.

American Electric Power (AEP) takes its slice of the US power pie out of Middle America. The holding company is one of the largest power generators and distributors in the US. AEP owns the nation's largest electricity transmission system a network of almost 39000 miles. It also has 223000 miles of distribution lines. Its electric utilities have 5.3 million customers in 11 states and have about 36500 MW of largely coal-fired generating capacity. AEP is a top wholesale energy company; it markets electricity in the US. Other operations include coal and bulk commodities barge transportation services.

HISTORY

In 1906 Richard Breed Sidney Mitchell and Henry Doherty set up American Gas & Electric (AG&E) in New York to buy 23 utilities from Philadelphia's Electric Company of America. With properties in seven northeastern US states AG&E began acquiring and merging small electric properties creating the predecessors of Ohio Power (1911) Kentucky Power (1919) and Appalachian Power (1926). AG&E also bought the predecessor of Indiana Michigan Power (1925).

By 1926 the company was operating in Indiana Kentucky Michigan Ohio Virginia and West Virginia. In 1935 AG&E engineer Philip Sporn later known as the Henry Ford of power introduced his high-voltage high-velocity circuit breaker. AG&E picked up Kingsport Power in 1938.

Becoming president in 1947 Sporn began an ambitious building program that continued through the 1960s. Plants designed by AG&E (renamed American Electric Power in 1958) were among the world's most efficient and electric rates stayed 25%-38% below the national average.

AEP bought Michigan Power in 1967 six years after Donald Cook succeeded Sporn as president. Cook who refused to attach scrubbers to the smokestacks of coal-fired plants was criticized in the early 1970s by environmental protesters. AEP's first nuclear plant named in Cook's honor went on line in Michigan in 1975. He retired in 1976.

The firm moved from New York to Columbus Ohio in 1980 after buying what is now Columbus Southern Power (formed in 1883). It set up AEP Generating in 1982 to provide power to its electric utilities.

AEP began converting its second nuke Zimmer to coal in 1984. In 1992 AEP finally began installing scrubbers at its coal-fired Gavin plant in Ohio after being ordered to comply with the Clean Air Act. It also cleaned up its image by planting millions of trees in 1996.

The company formed AEP Communications after Congress passed the Telecommunications Act of 1996. The next year AEP jumped into the UK's deregulated electric market; AEP and New Century Energies (now Xcel Energy) bought Yorkshire Electricity (later Yorkshire Power Group) for $2.8 billion. However a $109 million UK windfall tax on the transaction –and increased wholesale competition –hurt AEP's bottom line.

As the normally staid electric industry succumbed to merger mania AEP agreed in 1997 to buy Central and South West (CSW) of Texas in a

$6.6 billion deal. AEP's sales would nearly double and CSW was to bring its own UK utility SEEBOARD and other overseas holdings.

In 1998 AEP bought a 20% stake in Pacific Hydro an Australian power producer and CitiPower an Australian electric distribution company. AEP also bought Equitable Resources' Louisiana natural gas midstream operations including an intrastate pipeline. In 1999 China's Pushan Power Plant (70%-owned by AEP) began operations. Environmental concerns resurfaced that year when the EPA sued the utility alleging its old coal-powered plants which had been grandfathered from the Clean Air Act had been quietly upgraded to extend their lives.

Regulators approved the company's acquisition of CSW in 2000 but AEP had to agree to relinquish control of its 22000 miles of transmission lines to an independent operator. The CSW deal closed later that year. (However the SEC's approval of the deal was challenged by a federal appeals court in 2002.)

AEP sold its 50% stake in Yorkshire Power Group to Innogy (now RWE npower) in 2001; it also purchased Houston Pipe Line Co. (which it later sold in early 2005) from Enron for $727 million. AEP became one of the largest US barge operators that year when it bought MEMCO Barge Line from Progress Energy. It also purchased two UK coal-fired power plants (4000 MW) from Edison Mission Energy a subsidiary of Edison International in a $960 million deal.

In 2002 AEP sold its UK utility SEEBOARD to Electricite de France in a $2.2 billion deal; it also sold its Australian utility CitiPower to a consortium led by Cheung Kong Infrastructure and Hongkong Electric for $855 million. The following year the company sold two of its competitive Texas retail electric providers (WTU Retail Energy and CPL Retail Energy) to UK utility Centrica. It also divested its power plant development subsidiary AEP Pro Serv and its stakes in telecom firms C3 Communications and AFN.

The company sold two UK power plants to Scottish and Southern Energy for $456 million in 2004 and it sold a 50% stake in a third UK plant to Scottish Power in a $210 million deal. AEP also sold four independent power plants in Florida and Colorado to Bear Stearns for $156 million that year.

In 2006 the company sold its Plaquemine cogeneration plant to Dow Chemical for $64 million. Also that year it formed a joint venture company with MidAmerican Energy Holdings to build and own new electric transmission assets within the Electric Reliability Council of Texas.

AEP settled an eight-year lawsuit with the US government in 2007 and agreed to pay more than $4.6 billion to reduce hazardous air pollution from 16 coal-burning power plants.

EXECUTIVES

SVP and Chief Administrative Officer, Lana L. Hillebrand
EVP and COO, Robert P. (Bob) Powers, age 57, $511,961 total compensation
President and COO Southwestern Electric Power, Venita McCellon-Allen, age 52
Chairman, Michael G. (Mike) Morris, age 65, $1,254,808 total compensation
President Transmission, Susan Tomasky, age 58, $511,961 total compensation
EVP and Chief External Officer, Dennis E. Welch, age 60
SVP Chief Accounting Officer and Controller, Joseph M. Buonaiuto
VP Strategic Initiatives and Chief Risk Officer, Stephan T. Haynes
VP Corporate Communications, Dale E. Heydlauff, age 52
SVP Regulatory Services, Richard E. (Rich) Munczinski, age 59
Managing Director Investor Relations, Bette Jo Rozsa
Director Corporate Media Relations, Pat D. Hemlepp
President and COO AEP Ohio, Joseph (Joe) Hamrock, age 48
SVP Engineering Projects and Field Services, William L. (Bill) Sigmon Jr.
VP Strategic Policy Analysis, Bruce H. Braine
VP Enterprise Risk and Insurance, Laura J. Thomas
Senior Manager Corporate Media Relations and Policy Communications, Melissa McHenry
President and COO Appalachian Power, Charles R. Patton, age 53
SVP Investor Relations and Treasurer, Charles E. (Chuck) Zebula, age 52
EVP and CFO, Brian X. Tierney, age 45, $401,539 total compensation
President and COO Public Service Company of Oklahoma, J. Stuart Solomon, age 50
President CEO and Director, Nicholas K. (Nick) Akins, age 51
VP Supply Chain Procurement and Fleet, Craig T. Rhoades
SVP Transmission, Michael (Mike) Heyeck
Investor Relations, Kathleen Kozero
SVP General Counsel and Secretary, David M. Feinberg, age 42
SVP Governmental Affairs, Anthony P. Kavanagh
VP Audit Services, Richard A. Mueller
Director Investor Relations, Julie Sherwood
SVP Repositioning and Program Management Office, Barbara Radous
EVP Generation, Mark McCullough, age 54
SVP Corporate Planning and Budgeting, Lonni L. Dieck, age 53
President and COO Indiana Michigan Power, Paul Chodak III, age 48
VP and CIO, Pablo A. Vegas, age 39
SVP Fuel Emissions and Logistics, Timothy K. Light, age 54
VP Site Support Services Cook Nuclear Plant, Raymond A. (Ray) Hruby, age 52
Assistant Secretary, Thomas G. Berkemeyer
SVP Commercial Operations, Todd D. Busby
VP and Chief Compliance Officer, Sandra K. (Sandy) Williams, age 53
SVP and Chief Nuclear Officer Cook Nuclear Plant, Lawrence J. (Larry) Weber, age 62
President and COO AEP Texas, A. Wade Smith, age 48
VP Engineering Services, Tim Riordan, age 49
President and COO Kentucky Power, Gregory G. Pauley, age 60
EVP Transmission, Lisa Barton, age 46
VP Human Resources, Tracy A. Elich
VP and CIO, Alberto G. Ruocco
Managing Director Labor Relations, Thomas P. Householder
Director, David J. (Dave) Anderson, age 62
Director, Ralph D. Crosby Jr., age 65
Director, Richard C. (Dick) Notebaert, age 65
Director, Linda A. Goodspeed, age 51
Director, Thomas E. (Tom) Hoaglin, age 62
Director, Kathryn D. Sullivan, age 61
Director, Lester A. Hudson Jr., age 72
Director, Richard L. Sandor, age 71
Director, James F. (Jim) Cordes, age 71
Director, Lionel L. Nowell III, age 57
President CEO and Director, Nicholas K. (Nick) Akins, age 51
Director, John F. Turner, age 70
Director, Sara Martinez Tucker, age 56
Independent Director, Sandra Lin
Independent Director, Steve Rasmussen
Auditors: Deloitte&ToucheLLP

LOCATIONS

HQ: American Electric Power Company, Inc.
1 Riverside Plaza, Columbus, OH 43215-2373
Phone: 614 716-1000 **Fax:** 614 223-1823
Web: www.aep.com

PRODUCTS/OPERATIONS

2012 Sales

	$ mil.	% of total
Retail	11,259	75
Wholesale	2,210	15
Other	1,476	10
Total	**14,945**	**100**

Selected Subsidiaries

AEP Energy Services Inc. (energy marketing and trading)
AEP Generating Co. (electricity generator marketer)
AEP Retail Energy (retail energy marketing in deregulated territories)
AEP Texas Central Company (formerly Central Power and Light electric utility)
AEP Texas North Company (formerly West Texas Utilities electric utility)
AEP Towers (wireless communications towers)
Appalachian Power Company (electric utility)
Columbus Southern Power Company (electric utility)
Indiana Michigan Power Company (electric utility)
Kentucky Power Company (electric utility)
Kingsport Power Company (electric utility)
Ohio Power Company (electric utility)
Public Service Company of Oklahoma (electric utility)
Southwestern Electric Power Company (electric utility)
Wheeling Power Company (electric utility)
Utility Distribution/Customer Service Divisions
AEP Ohio (handles distribution customer service and external affairs functions for Columbus Southern Power Company Ohio Power Company and Wheeling Power Company)
AEP Texas (handles distribution customer service and external affairs functions for AEP Texas Central Company and AEP Texas North Company)
Appalachian Power (handles distribution customer service and external affairs functions for Appalachian Power Company and Kingsport Power Company)
Indiana Michigan Power (handles distribution customer service and external affairs functions for Indiana Michigan Power Company)
Kentucky Power (handles distribution customer service and external affairs functions for Kentucky Power Company)
Public Service Company of Oklahoma (handles distribution customer service and external affairs functions for Public Service Company of Oklahoma)
Southwestern Electric Power Company (handles distribution customer service and external affairs functions for Southwestern Electric Power Company)

COMPETITORS

BP
Calpine
CenterPoint Energy
CMS Energy
Constellation Energy Group
Delmarva Power
Dominion Resources
DTE
Duke Energy
Dynegy
El Paso Corporation
Energy Future
Entergy
Exelon
FirstEnergy
GenOnEnergy
NiSource
PG&E Corporation
Sempra Energy
Southern Company
TVA
UTC Power
Xcel Energy

HISTORICAL FINANCIALS

Company Type: Public

Income Statement FYE: December 31

	REVENUE ($ mil.)	NET INCOME ($ mil.)	NET PROFIT MARGIN	EMPLOYEES
12/11	15,116	1,946	12.9%	18,710
12/10	14,427	1,214	8.4%	18,712
12/09	13,489	1,360	10.1%	21,763
12/08	14,440	1,380	9.6%	21,912
12/07	13,380	1,089	8.1%	20,861
Annual Growth	3.1%	15.6%	—	(2.7%)

2011 Year-End Financials

Debt ratio: 34.79%
Return on equity: 13.27%
Cash ($ mil.): 582
Current ratio: 63.26
Long-term debt ($ mil.): 15,083
No. of shares (mil.): 483
Dividends
Yield: —
Payout: 46.02%
Market value ($ mil.): 19,970

	STOCK PRICE ($) FY Close	P/E High/Low		PER SHARE ($) Earnings	Dividends	Book Value
12/11	41.31	10	8	4.02	0.00	30.33
12/10	35.98	15	12	2.53	1.71	28.46
12/09	34.79	12	8	2.96	1.64	27.61
12/08	33.28	14	8	3.42	1.64	26.48
12/07	46.56	19	15	2.72	1.58	25.32
Annual Growth	(2.9%)	—	—	10.3%	—	4.6%

American Express Co.

LOCATIONS

HQ: American Express Co.
World Financial Center, 200 Vesey Street, New York, NY 10285
Phone: 212 640-2000
Web: www.americanexpress.com

HISTORICAL FINANCIALS

Company Type:

Income Statement FYE: December 31

	REVENUE ($ mil.)	NET INCOME ($ mil.)	NET PROFIT MARGIN	EMPLOYEES
12/11	32,282	4,935	15.3%	62,500
12/10	30,242	4,057	13.4%	61,000
12/09	26,730	2,130	8.0%	58,300
12/08	31,920	2,699	8.5%	66,000
12/07	31,557	4,012	12.7%	67,700
Annual Growth	0.6%	5.3%	—	(2.0%)

2011 Year-End Financials

Debt ratio: 41.08%
Return on equity: 26.26%
Cash ($ mil.): 24,893
Current ratio: 121.26
Long-term debt ($ mil.): 59,570
No. of shares (mil.): 1,164
Dividends
Yield: —
Payout: 17.48%
Market value ($ mil.): 54,906

	STOCK PRICE ($) FY Close	P/E High/Low		PER SHARE ($) Earnings	Dividends	Book Value
12/11	47.17	13	10	4.12	0.00	16.15
12/10	42.92	14	11	3.35	0.72	13.56
12/09	40.52	27	7	1.54	0.72	12.09
12/08	18.55	22	7	2.33	0.72	10.21
12/07	52.02	19	15	3.36	0.60	9.52
Annual Growth	(2.4%)	—	—	5.2%	—	14.1%

American Financial Group, Inc (Holding Co.)

American Financial Group (AFG) insures American businessmen in pursuit of the great American Dream. Through the Great American Insurance Group of companies and its flagship Great American Insurance Company AFG offers commercial property/casualty insurance focused on specialties such as workers' compensation professional liability ocean and inland marine and multiperil crop insurance. The company also provides surety coverage for contractors and risk management services. For individuals and employers AFG provides a wide range of annuity policies sold through its Great American Financial Resources (GAFRI) subsidiary.

HISTORY

When his father became ill in the mid-1930s Carl Lindner Jr. dropped out of high school to take over his family's dairy business. He built it into a large ice-cream store chain called United Dairy Farmers. Lindner branched out in 1955 with Henthy Realty and in 1959 he bought three savings and loans. The next year Lindner changed the company's name to American Financial Corp. (AFC). He took it public in 1961 using the proceeds to buy United Liberty Life Insurance (1963) and Provident Bank (1966).

Lindner also formed the American Financial Leasing & Services Company in 1968 to lease airplanes computers and other equipment. In 1969 the company acquired Phoenix developer Rubenstein Construction and renamed it American Continental. AFC bought several life casualty and mortgage insurance firms in the 1970s including National General parent of Great American Insurance Group later the core of AFC's insurance segment. The company also moved into publishing by buying 95% of the "Cincinnati Enquirer" paperback publisher Bantam Books and hardback publisher Grosset & Dunlap.

But the publishing interests soon went back on the block as Lindner concentrated on insurance which was then suffering from an industry wide slowdown. In addition to selling the "Enquirer" AFC spun off American Continental in 1976. American Continental's president was Charles Keating who had joined AFC in 1972 and whose brother published the "Enquirer." Keating (who was later jailed released then eventually pleaded guilty in connection with the failure of Lincoln Savings) underwent an SEC investigation during part of his time at AFC for alleged improprieties at Provident Bank. The bank was spun off in 1980.

Lindner took AFC private in 1981. That year following a strategy of bottom-feeding the firm began building its interest in the non-railroad assets of Penn Central the former railroad that had emerged from bankruptcy as an industrial manufacturer. Later that decade AFC increased its ownership in United Brands (later renamed Chiquita Brands International) from 29% to 45%. Lindner installed himself as CEO and reversed that company's losses. In 1987 AFC acquired a TV company Taft Communications (renamed Great American Communications) entailing a heavy debt load. To reduce its debt AFC trimmed its holdings including Circle K Hunter S&L and an interest in Scripps Howard Broadcasting.

Great American Communications went bankrupt in 1992 and emerged the next year as Citicasters Inc. (sold 1996). In 1995 Lindner created American Financial Group to effect the merger of AFC and Premier Underwriters of which he owned 42%. The result was American Financial Group (AFG).

Lindner's bipartisan political donations gained publicity when it became known that his gifts to Republicans had brought support in a dispute with the European Union over the banana trade. The next year AFG sold some noncore units including software consultancy Millennium Dynamics and its commercial insurance operations. In 1999 AFG bought direct-response auto insurer Worldwide Insurance Company as part of its efforts to build depth in the highly commodified auto insurance market.

In 2000 American Financial Group agreed to pay $75 million over the next 30 years to get its name on the Cincinnati Reds' new stadium known as Great American Ball Park. In 2001 AFG sold its Japanese property/casualty division to Japanese insurer Mitsui Marine & Fire (now Mitsui Sumitomo Insurance).

AFG's results in the 1990s were uneven and it typically did not make an underwriting profit. In 2003 the insurer kept operating expenses down (partly by merging two of its holding company subsidiaries into AFG) and swung to a profit even though premium revenue was down.

The company shed some commercial lines to concentrate on its property/casualty and life and annuities businesses. To refine its mix AFG transferred Atlanta Casualty Company Infinity Insurance Company Leader Insurance Company and Windsor Insurance Company into 40%-owned Infinity Property and Casualty which went public in 2003. In 2004 the business exchanged its stake in Provident Financial Group for a holding in National City Corporation.

In 2006 AFG expanded its Great American Financial Resources (GAFRI) unit through the purchase of a block of fixed annuity products from Old Standard Life Insurance. GAFRI also acquired Ceres Group and its health insurance subsidiary Continental General Insurance. To balance things out GAFRI sold its Great American Life Assurance of Puerto Rico unit to Triple-S Management that year.

In 2008 the company purchased 67% of medical malpractice insurer and Lloyd's of London member Marketform Group for $75 million; AFG stopped writing new malpractice policies through Marketform the following year. The company also acquired Louisiana-based workers' compensation provider Strategic Comp Holdings in 2008.

Founder and chairman Carl Lindner retired as CEO in 2005 and died in 2011. No one was named to replace him as chairman but two of his sons Carl Lindner III and Craig Lindner carried on as co-CEOs.

EXECUTIVES

VP Taxes, Kathleen J. Brown
VP and Controller, Robert H. Ruffing
SVP Taxes, Thomas E. Mischell, age 64, $590,000 total compensation
SVP General Counsel and Director, James E. Evans, age 66, $1,066,150 total compensation
Co-President Co-CEO and Director; President and CEO Great American Financial Resources; President American Money Management, S. Craig Lindner, age 57, $1,144,250 total compensation
Co-President Co-CEO and Director, Carl H. Lindner III, age 58, $1,144,250 total compensation
SVP and CFO, Keith A. Jensen, age 61, $634,150 total compensation
VP and CIO, Piyush K. Singh
VP Assistant General Counsel and Secretary, Karl J. Grafe
VP Internal Audit, Robert E. Dobbs
VP, Sandra W. Heimann
VP, Karen Holley Horrell, age 56
VP and Treasurer, David J. Witzgall
VP and Chief Administrative Officer, Michelle A. (Shelly) Gillis
Assistant VP Investor Relations, Diane P. Weidner
SVP and General Counsel, Vito C. Peraino
VP Tax, H. Kim Baird
Director, Terry S. Jacobs, age 70
SVP General Counsel and Director, James E. Evans, age 66
Co-President Co-CEO and Director; President and CEO Great American Financial Resources; President American Money Management, S. Craig Lindner, age 57
Co-President Co-CEO and Director, Carl H. Lindner III, age 58
Director, John I. Von Lehman, age 60
Director, William W. (Will) Verity, age 53
Director, Kenneth C. Ambrecht, age 66
Director, Gregory G. Joseph, age 49
Auditors: Ernst&YoungLLP

LOCATIONS

HQ: American Financial Group Inc.
1 E. 4th St., Cincinnati OH 45202-3715
Phone: 513-579-2121 **Fax:** 513-412-0200
Web: www.afginc.com

PRODUCTS/OPERATIONS

Selected Subsidiaries

Property/Casualty
- American Empire Surplus Lines Insurance Company
- Great American Insurance Company
- Mid-Continent Casualty Company
- National Interstate Insurance Company
- Republic Indemnity Company of America

Annuities and Life Insurance
- Great American Financial Resources Inc. (GAFRI)
  - Annuity Investors Life Insurance
  - Great American Life Insurance Company

Real estate investments
- Charleston Harbor Resort and Marina
- Mountain View Grand Resort
- Sailfish Marina and Resort
- Skipjack Cove Yachting Resort and Bay Bridge Marina

COMPETITORS

ACE Limited
AIG
Midland National Life
Munich Re Group
Allianz
Arch Capital
Aviva
Chubb Corp
Cincinnati Financial
CNA Financial
HCC Insurance
ING
Liberty Mutual
LSW
Markel
MetLife
Mutual of Omaha
Philadelphia Insurance Companies
RLI
The Hartford
Travelers Companies
W. R. Berkley
Wells Fargo
XL Group plc
Zenith National
Zurich Financial Services

HISTORICAL FINANCIALS

Company Type: Public

Income Statement

FYE: December 31

	ASSETS ($ mil.)	NET INCOME ($ mil.)	INCOME AS % OF ASSETS	EMPLOYEES
12/11	36,042	343	1.0%	6,500
12/10	32,454	479	1.5%	6,450
12/09	27,683	519	1.9%	6,200
12/08	26,427	195	0.7%	6,200
12/07	25,807	383	1.5%	5,800
Annual Growth	8.7%	(2.7%)	—	2.9%

2011 Year-End Financials

Debt ratio: 2.59%
Return on equity: 7.55%
Cash ($ mil.): 1,324
Current ratio: —
Long-term debt ($ mil.): 934
No. of shares (mil.): 97
Dividends
Yield: —
Payout: 19.89%
Market value ($ mil.): 3,610

	STOCK PRICE ($) FY Close	P/E High/Low		PER SHARE ($) Earnings	Dividends	Book Value
12/11	36.89	11	9	3.33	0.00	46.45
12/10	32.29	7	6	4.33	0.58	42.50
12/09	24.95	6	3	4.45	0.52	33.35
12/08	22.88	19	9	1.67	0.50	21.54
12/07	28.88	11	8	3.10	0.40	26.84
Annual Growth	6.3%	—	—	1.8%	—	14.7%

American International Group Inc

Even to this day American International Group (AIG) is one of the world's largest insurance firms. While it held the spotlight for staggering losses and government bailouts the company's subsidiaries have steadily provided general property/casualty insurance life insurance and retirement services financial services and residential mortgage guaranty insurance to commercial institutional and individual customers in the US and more than 130 countries around the world. In exchange for $161.3 billion in bailouts at one point the US government held more than 90% of AIG. An exit plan of repayments and stock sales gradually shrunk that number with the US Treasury announcing the final sale of AIG shares in late 2012.

HISTORY

Former ice cream parlor owner Cornelius Starr founded property/casualty insurer American Asiatic Underwriters in Shanghai in 1919. After underwriting business for other insurers Starr began selling life insurance policies to the Chinese in 1921 (foreign companies were loath to do so despite the longevity of the Chinese). In 1926 he opened a New York office specializing in foreign risks incurred by American companies. As WWII loomed Starr moved his base to the US; when the war cut off business in Europe he focused on Latin America. After a brief postwar return to China the company was kicked out by the communist government.

In the 1950s the company began providing disability health and life insurance and pension plans for employees who moved from country to country. Starr chose his successor Maurice "Hank" Greenberg in 1967 and died the next year. Greenberg who had come aboard in 1960 to develop overseas operations took over the newly formed American International Group a holding company for Starr's worldwide collection of insurance concerns. Greenberg's policy of achieving underwriting profits forced the company to use tight fiscal discipline. AIG went public in 1969.

By 1975 AIG was the largest foreign life insurer in much of Asia and the only insurer with global sales and support facilities. The 1980s saw AIG begin investment operations in Asia increase its presence in health care and form a financial services group. AIG soon moved into parts of Eastern Europe. The company resumed its Chinese operations in 1993 after triumphing over stiff opposition from state-owned monopolies.

With a strong presence in many developing nations AIG began cross-selling an array of financial products in those markets. It launched a mutual fund for individual investors and acquired aconsumer and commercial finance company with offices in the Philippines Taiwan and Thailand.

Throughout the late 1990's AIG continued to live up to the "international" in its name. The company won licenses to begin insurance businesses in Azerbaijan Romania Bulgaria and Sri Lanka. As part of a crackdown on foreign insurers the Chinese government in 1999 stopped AIG from selling what it considered group policies –historically the sole province of Chinese companies; however a U.S.-China pact reached later that year set out plans to allow foreign firms gradual entry to the group-policy market.

In 2001 AIG agreed to be the business sponsor for the troubled Chiyoda Mutual Life Insurance Company (now AIG Star Life Insurance); it also bought American General wooing the insurer away from rival suitor Prudential plc to bolster AIG's share of the lucrative US retirement-planning market. Taking advantage of rising premiums AIG (along with Goldman Sachs and specialty insurer Chubb) formed Bermuda-based insurer Allied World Assurance in 2001.

The insurer paid out about $800 million in claims related to the attacks on the World Trade Center. Even though rate increases helped AIG's premium revenues grow capital losses and the weak stock market dragged the company's net result down in 2002. The company known for making an underwriting profit chalked up a $1.2 billion underwriting loss on its general insurance operations that year.

Legal settlements forced the company to take a $1.8 billion charge in 2003 in a move that surprised analysts and sent shock waves throughout the industry causing other large insurance stocks to plummet. The company said the charge would be used to bolster reserves used for paying claims.

Legal woes continued to befall AIG in 2004 when two company executives pleaded guilty to charges of involvement in an alleged price-fixing scheme that also involved insurance broker Marsh and insurer ACE USA. AIG also reached a $126 million settlement with federal regulators in 2004 over allegations the insurer sold products and services used to help customers improve their financial appearance. Scrutiny from insurance regulators in the US also led the company to shut down operations of its reinsurance unit based in Bermuda Richmond Insurance after questions were raised regarding the business relationship of the company and its parent.

Hank Greenberg led the company for more than three decades becoming a financial legend in the process. Greenberg appeared to be building a family dynasty but those plans unraveled when son Evan left the company in 2001 and joined smaller rival ACE Ltd. as CEO. (Another Greenberg son Jeff was CEO at Marsh & McLennan until he resigned under pressure in 2004.) After Evan's departure no heir was apparent at AIG. Then the unthinkable occurred: AIG came under investigation by the Office of the Attorney General for the State of New York the New York Insurance Department and the SEC into possible accounting irregularities and the company's use of offshore reinsurers. In early 2005 Greenberg was forced to step down as CEO. Former vice chairman and co-COO Martin Sullivan was named to succeed him. Soon after Greenberg —the man most associated with the company —was forced to give up his chairman's seat as well. He stepped down from the board later that year.

As a result of the allegations which included accounting irregularities fraud and bid-rigging and along with acknowledging some wrong-doing in 2006 the company agreed to pay a $1.6 billion settlement to the three agencies.

Seizing a moment in early 2007 AIG Investments snapped up the US port operations of Dubai-based DP World and renamed the business Ports America. DP World had bought the operations in 2006 only to find that the deal attracted too much attention from US lawmakers fearful that such ownership might compromise US security. From that acquisition AIG apparently developed a taste for ports and shortly thereafter purchased North American port operation companies AMPORTS and MTC Holdings. MTC brought with it operations at 32 US ports primarily based on the West coast. Ultimately all of the port holdings were sold to private investment firm Highstar Capital.

While AIG had long been a leader in insuring risk for institutions worldwide it also led the industry in the practice of investing in murky assets to bring a little zest to the otherwise dull world of insurance. In 2008 as US subprime mortgages turned septic AIG's large banking customers who carried default insurance on those risky investments submitted claims and demanded huge payments to cover their growing losses. Simultaneously AIG's own risky investments brought home billions of dollars in losses and the company's liquidity seized up like cold gravy.

By early September 2008 AIG was laying out plans to jettison several of its most valuable businesses such as its domestic auto insurance and annuities units. However the mention of those sales alone were not enough and despite a desperate scramble to raise capital from various sources the company's credit ratings were cut. Credit ratings are the foundation of confidence that supports all insurance and the cuts effectively doomed the company's ability to underwrite.

With insolvency only days away the US Federal Reserve stepped up with an $85 billion loan. The original loan was intended to reassure investors and allow AIG to sell off its assets in an orderly fashion. But investors continued to clamor for collateral to back up AIG's credit default swaps and buyers weren't lining up fast enough to buy off AIG assets. The company continued to struggle and the Fed restructured and augmented its loans several times over.

Even with the US government holding nearly 80% of the company AIG had trouble stemming its losses. In early March of 2009 amid swirling speculation of a possible bankruptcy the government apparently figuring "in for a penny in for a pound" agreed to give the company access to another $30 billion from its Troubled Asset Relief Program bringing its total offer of support of AIG up to $182 billion. However in the end AIG only wound up taking $161.3 billion in government assistance.

Just before things got dicey in 2008 chairman Robert Willumstad stepped in as CEO but he only held the steering wheel a few short months before the company collided with the iceberg of insolvency awaiting it. As part of the government bailout agreement later that year former Allstate executive Edward Liddy took over both the chairman and CEO titles from Willumstad. Nine months into the job after leading AIG's first round of restructuring measures Liddy announced his retirement. Robert Benmosche replaced him in 2009.

After his 2005 ouster former CEO Hank Greenberg held on to 11% of the company through his C.V. Starr & Co. brokerage business and continued to aim potshots at the company with critical comments on its management. As AIG was blinking into the abyss of insolvency in 2008 he made a short-lived pitch to regain control. Following the government's takeover of the company Greenberg remained feistily attentive to the company he helped build and kept up a steady volley of legal disputes over everything from alleged financial misrepresentation to oriental rugs he was forced to leave behind in the company's headquarters. While his immediate successors did their best to keep Greenberg at bay CEO Robert Benmosche reversed that strategy and drew him slightly closer. As a result by late 2009 Greenberg and AIG had dropped their collective disputes.

Among the many assets disposed to repay its debts its international wealth management arm AIG Private Bank was bought up by United Arab Emirates-based Aabar Investments for $253 million in 2009 while the company's grand old HSB Group (industrial equipment insurance) was sold to Munich Re for $739 million. Bank of Montreal paid $263 million for AIG Life of Canada while Zurich Financial Services paid $1.9 billion for US personal auto insurer 21st Century Insurance. The company then handed over its US life insurance finance businesses to First Insurance Funding in exchange for $679 million.

After agreeing that it needed to let go of its Asian assets AIG sold American Life Insurance Company to MetLife in 2010 for $7.2 billion in cash and $9 billion in equity —briefly giving AIG a 20% stake in MetLife. The company held on to that equity until 2011 when it sold a combination of stock and equity units for $9.6 billion —$6.9 billion of which was promptly used to pay down debt. Meanwhile during 2010 the UK's Prudential plc offered $35.5 billion to acquire AIG's China-based American International Assurance (AIA). However while AIG and Prudential were happy with the deal Prudential's investors were not and they pitched a collective fit which killed the deal. AIG then returned to an earlier plan and in late 2010 took the business public on the Hong Kong stock exchange as AIA Group Ltd. The gross proceeds of the sale brought in over $20 billion while the company indirectly held on to a 33% equity stake.

The Federal Reserve Bank of New York the body that has held most of the company's securities waited until an auspicious moment in 2011 and then began selling off bits and bonds from the AIG portfolio. AIG offered $15.7 billion to buy back a significant chunk but the Fed coolly rejected it preferring to auction off the securities to eager investors for a modest profit.

EXECUTIVES

EVP Financial Services and Investments; CEO Asset Management, William N. (Bill) Dooley, age 59
Vice Chairman Chartis, Kristian P. Moor, age 52, $915,385 total compensation
EVP; President and CEO Domestic Life and Retirement Services, Jay S. Wintrob, age 54, $775,000 total compensation
Chairman, Robert S. (Steve) Miller Jr., age 70
President CEO and Director, Robert H. (Bob) Benmosche, age 67, $1,153,964 total compensation
EVP Legal Compliance Regulatory Affairs and Government Affairs and General Counsel, Thomas A. (Tom) Russo, age 68
EVP and CFO, David L. Herzog, age 52, $625,000 total compensation
Vice Chairman and Chief Distribution Officer Chartis, Nicholas C. (Nick) Walsh, age 61, $698,077 total compensation
EVP Treasury and Capital Markets, Brian T. Schreiber, age 46
CEO Global Consumer Business Chartis, Jeffrey L. Hayman, age 52
VP and Chief Operations and Systems Officer, Robert Dickie, age 52
SVP and Deputy CFO, Jeffrey M. (Jeff) Farber, age 47
Senior Vice President Corporate Communications, Christina Pretto
VP and Head Investor Relations, Elizabeth A. Werner
CEO Global Commercial Business Chartis, John Q. Doyle
SVP Human Resources and Communications, Jeffrey J. Hurd, age 45
CEO Chartis, Peter D. Hancock, age 53
SVP and Head Asset Management, Monika Machon, age 51
VP and Head Strategic Planning, Peter Juhas
SVP and Chief Administrative Officer, Michael R. Cowan
SVP and Chief Risk Officer, Sid Sankaran
SVP Corporate Chief Actuary, Charlie Shamieh
SVP and Director of Internal Audit, Paulette E. Mullings Bradnock
Chief Financial Officer, James Bracken
Chairman Managing Director, Miller Buckfire
Director, Laurette T. Koellner, age 58
Director, Donald H. (Don) Layton, age 61
Director, Douglas M. (Doug) Steenland, age 60
President CEO and Director, Robert H. (Bob) Benmosche, age 67
Director, Ronald A. (Ron) Rittenmeyer, age 65
Director, John H. Fitzpatrick, age 55
Director, Morris W. Offit, age 75
Director, Henry S. Miller, age 66
Director, Arthur C. Martinez, age 72
Director, George L. Miles Jr., age 70
Director, Christopher S. Lynch, age 54
Director, Suzanne Nora Johnson, age 54
Director, W. Don Cornwell, age 64
Auditors: PricewaterhouseCoopersLLP

LOCATIONS

HQ: American International Group Inc.
180 Maiden Ln., New York NY 10038
Phone: 212-770-7000 **Fax:** 303-645-7679
Web: www.apl.com

2011 Revenues

US	40,234	63
Other	15,884	25

PRODUCTS/OPERATIONS

2011 Revenues

	$ mil.	% of total
Chartis		
Commercial	25,544	40
Consumer	13,678	21
Other	1,480	2
SunAmerica		
Life insurance	8,282	13
Retirement services	7,033	11
Aircraft leasing	4,457	7
Other operations	4,079	6
Consolidation & eliminations	(316)	-
Total	**64,237**	**100**

Selected Subsidiaries

Chartis
AIU Insurance Company (AIUI)
American Home Assurance Company
Chartis Europe Holdings Limited
Chartis Europe S.A.
Chartis Overseas Ltd.
Lexington Insurance Company
National Union Fire Insurance Company of Pittsburgh Pa (National Union)
New Hampshire Insurance Company
SunAmerica
American General Life and Accident Insurance Company (AGLA)
American General Life Insurance Company (American General)
SunAmerica Retirement Markets
The Variable Annuity Life Insurance Company (VALIC)
Western National Life Insurance Company (Western National)
Aircraft Leasing
International Lease Finance Corporation (ILFC)
Other operations
Mortgage Guaranty
United Guaranty Corporation
Global Capital Markets
AIG Markets
AIG Financial Products Corp
AIG Trading Group Inc.

COMPETITORS

ACE Limited
AEGON
Allianz
American Financial Group
AXA
Berkshire Hathaway
Chubb Corp
CNA Financial
Fairfax Financial Holdings
General Re
Genworth Financial
Hanover Insurance
ING
John Hancock Financial Services
Liberty Mutual
Manulife Financial
MetLife
Nationwide
New York Life
Northwestern Mutual
Prudential
The Hartford
Tokio Marine
Travelers Companies
Zurich Financial Services

HISTORICAL FINANCIALS

Company Type: Public

Income Statement FYE: December 31

	ASSETS ($ mil.)	NET INCOME ($ mil.)	INCOME AS % OF ASSETS	EMPLOYEES
12/11	555,773	17,798	3.2%	57,000
12/10	683,443	7,786	1.1%	63,000
12/09	847,585	(10,949)	—	96,000
12/08	860,418	(99,289)	—	116,000
12/07	1,060,505	6,200	0.6%	116,000
Annual Growth	(14.9%)	30.2%	—	(16.3%)

2011 Year-End Financials

Debt ratio: 13.54%
Return on equity: 16.96%
Cash ($ mil.): 1,474
Current ratio: —
Long-term debt ($ mil.): 75,253
No. of shares (mil.): 1,896
Dividends
Yield: —
Payout: —
Market value ($ mil.): 44,006

	STOCK PRICE ($) FY Close	P/E High	P/E Low	PER SHARE ($) Earnings	Dividends	Book Value
12/11	23.20	6	2	9.44	0.00	55.33
12/10	57.62	5	2	11.60	0.00	607.41
12/09	29.98	—	—	(90.48)	0.00	516.94
12/08	1.57	—	—	(756.80)	0.00	391.94
12/07	58.30	2	1	47.80	0.00	758.24
Annual Growth	(20.6%)	—	—	(33.3%)	—	(48.0%)

American National Insurance Co. (Galveston, TX)

True to its name American National Insurance offers agricultural commercial and personal property/casualty insurance as well as life insurance annuities supplemental health credit and other types of insurance throughout the US Puerto Rico and other territories. The company's subsidiaries include Garden State Life Insurance Standard Life and Accident Insurance and Farm Family Holdings. It markets its life and pension products to small businesses and individuals through brokers and agents. The company distributes its property/casualty products through its exclusive agency force as well as career agents. The company's direct-to-consumer division sells life and health products.

While the company considers its life insurance and annuities segments to be its main focus it earns more of its premiums from property/casualty insurance. Together both groups make up half of the company's total revenues. However a high number of weather-related catastrophes have driven up property/casualty claims in recent years thus weakening the profitability of that segment. Investments account for about a third of the company's revenues.

Based in hurricane-prone Galveston Texas American National knows firsthand the importance of property/casualty insurance and how to evaluate risk. The company did not incur damaging losses during the calamitous 2005 US hurricane season but nonetheless withdrew from writing some policies along the Atlantic and Gulf coasts. In early 2008 the company moved its processing facilities further inland to San Antonio. That facility is also able to serve as temporary headquarters in case the Galveston offices are evacuated due to catastrophic weather.

Economic turmoil dampened the company's equity holdings in 2008 but the company maintained sufficient assets to cover its liabilities. To reach a new market and comply with local regulations American National launched the American National Life Insurance Company of New York in 2010.

Reassessing its exposure American National ended its life insurance operations in Mexico in 2009. In late 2010 the company arranged the sale of its investment advisor and broker dealer subsidiary. Having occupied a distant branch on the company's organizational chart the pruning of Securities Management and Research did not impact American National's earnings.

In fiscal 2011 American National's revenues were essentially flat at $3 billion dropping less than 2% from $3.1 billion in 2010. Its net income continued to grow increasing 35% from 2010 to more than $193 million mainly due to increased income from investments and gains on investments.

In its quest to be a leading financial products and services provider now and for years to come American National's strategy is to maintain the conservative business practices it has upheld for more than a century. Additionally it is commited to providing exemplary customer service along with competitively priced diversified products to meet the needs of its policyholders and agents and build shareholder value. Profitable growth is essential for its financial strength as it enables the company to grow internally through investments in its distribution channels and markets (its main avenue of growth) and externally through acquisitions of like-minded businesses.

American National was founded by Galveston businessman W. L. Moody in 1905. Robert Moody Sr. a descendent of his serves as the company's chairman and CEO. His children Russell Moody and Frances Anne Moody-Dahlberg serve as directors and his son Robert Moody Jr. serves as an advisory director. The Moody Foundation a charitable trust controlled by Robert Moody and his family and the Moody National Bank together own 70% of the company.

EXECUTIVES

EVP Independent Marketing Group; COO Garden State Life Insurance Company, David A. Behrens, age 49
EVP and Director Multiple Line; Chairman President and CEO American National Property And Casualty Companies, Gregory V. Ostergren, age 56
SVP Life Policy Administration, Albert L. Amato Jr., age 63
EVP Investments and Treasurer, Michael W. McCroskey, age 68
SVP Health Insurance Operations, Steven H. Schouweiler, age 65
SEVP and Chief Administrative Officer, James E. Pozzi, age 61, $412,425 total compensation
President COO and Director, G. Richard Ferdinandtsen, age 75, $1,000,000 total compensation
SEVP Chief Actuary and Corporate Risk Officer, Ronald J. Welch, age 66, $408,887 total compensation
Chairman and CEO, Robert L. Moody Sr., age 76, $2,000,000 total compensation

President and CEO Farm Family Companies, Timothy A. Walsh, age 48
VP Information Security and Enterprise Architecture, Donald French
VP Payroll Deduction Independent Marketing Group, Franklin J. Gerren
Secretary, J. Mark Flippin
EVP CFO and Treasurer, John J. Dunn Jr., age 52
SVP CIO Chief Innovation Officer Multiple Line, Bernard S. Gerwel, age 53
SVP Credit Insurance Division, James W. Pangburn, age 55
SVP and Corporate Controller, William F. Carlton
VP and Assistant Controller, Richard T. Crawford
Assistant VP Accounting Control, John T. Burchett
Assistant VP Finance Operations, Donna L. Daulong
Assistant VP Tax Finance Operations, Larry E. Linares
Assistant Treasurer, Victor J. Krc
SVP and Actuary, Frank V. Broll Jr., age 62
SVP and and Corporate Chief Information Officer, Rex D. Hemme, age 63
Assistant VP and Illustration Actuary, Joseph J. Cantu
VP and Actuary, Gerald A. Schillaci
VP and Actuary, John O. Norton
Assistant VP Corporate Research Corporate Planning, Deborah K. Janson
VP Career Sales and Service Division, Wayne A. Smith
SVP Corporate Affairs; Chief Compliance Officer, Dwain A. Akins, age 60
Assistant VP Corporate Compliance, Judith L. Regini
Assistant Secretary, Jeanette E. Cernosek
Assistant VP Human Resources, Carol A. Kratz
VP and General Auditor, George A. Macke
Assistant VP and Associate General Auditor Corporate Audit Services, Michael S. Nimmons
SVP Stock/Bond Investments, Gordon D. Dixon, age 66
SVP Real Estate and Mortgage Loan Investments, Scott F. Brast, age 48
VP Real Estate Investments, Robert J. Kirchner
VP Life Policy Administration, E. Bruce Pavelka
Assistant VP Pension Administration Life Insurance Administration, Nancy M. Day
Assistant VP Life Insurance Systems IT Services, James A. Tyra
VP Life New Business Life Insurance Administration, D. Lanette Leining
VP Life and Annuity Claims Life Insurance Administration, Bradley W. Manning
VP and Medical Director, Harry B. Kelso Jr.
VP Application Development and Support IT Services, Meredith M. Mitchell
Assistant VP Enterprise Financial Systems IT Services, Barbara J. Huerta
Assistant VP and Advisory Systems Engineer IT Services, Kenneth J. Juneau
VP and Director Telecommunications IT Services, James B. McEniry
Assistant VP Life and Annuity Systems IT Services, Katherine S. Meisetschlaeger
SVP and Chief Marketing Officer Career Life Agencies, Ronald C. Price, age 60
VP and Chief Life Marketing Officer MLEA Multiple Line Marketing, James A. Collura
Assistant VP and Director Advanced Life Sales Multiple Line Marketing, J. Wayne Cucco
Assistant VP Creative Services Multiple Line Marketing, John D. Ferguson
Assistant VP and Director Marketing and Career Development Career Sales and Service Division, Raymond E. Pittman Jr.
VP Brokerage Sales Independent Marketing Group, George C. Crume
VP Financial Institution Independent Marketing Group, Douglas A. Culp
VP Broker Dealer Marketing Independent Marketing Group, Steven L. Dobbe
VP Pension Sales Independent Marketing Group, J. Truitt Smith
VP Financial Marketing Credit Insurance Operations, Dwight D. Judy
VP and Chief Health Actuary Health Insurance Division, William H. Watson III
VP and Group Actuary Health Insurance Division, Joseph F. Grant Jr.
VP Health Underwriting and New Business Health Insurance Division, Charles J. Jones
VP Group and Health Compliance Health Insurance Division, James P. Stelling
VP and Assistant Actuary Health Insurance Division, Clarence E. Tipton
Assistant VP Director Health Systems Administration and HIPAA Security Officer Health Insurance Division, Ronald J. Ostermayer
VP Group and MGU Operations Health Insurance Division, Michael C. Paetz
SVP Human Resources, Bruce M. LePard, age 55
VP Fixed Income Investments, Anne M. LeMire
VP Mortage Loan Production, E. Vince Matthews III
SVP and Corporate CIO, Johnny D. Johnson, age 59
VP Marketing Training and Development MLEA Multiple Line Marketing, William C. Ray
VP Computing Services, Brian N. Bright
SVP and Chief Multiple Line Marketing Officer, Shannon L. Smith, age 52
EVP Career Sales and Service Division, Hoyt J. Strickland, age 55
VP and Director Corporate Treasury Services, Brian K. Weyer
Assistant VP and Life Product Actuary, Douglas R. Brown
Assistant VP and Assistant Actuary, Sara L. Latham
Assistant VP Criminal Investigations and Corporate Security Internal Audit, James J. Fish
VP and Assistant Corporate Treasurer, Brenda T. Koelemay
Assistant VP Mortgage Loan Production, Denny W. Fisher Jr.
Assistant VP Life and Annuity Claims Life Insurance Administration, Thomas R. LeGrand
Assistant VP Life New Business Life Insurance Administration, Michael S. Marquis
Assistant VP and Associate Medical Director, John F. White III
Assistant VP Field Systems IT Services, Deanna L. Walton
Assistant VP National Business Development Executive Multiple Line Marketing, Emerson V. Unger
VP Direct Marketing and Sales Independent Marketing Group, Richard S. Katz
VP Advanced Sales and Marketing Independent Marketing Group, Robert W. Schefft
Assistant VP Health and HIPAA Compliance Health Insurance Division, William J. Hogan
Assistant VP Health Business Vision Coordinator Health Insurance Division, Tracy L. Milina
President COO and Director, G. Richard Ferdinandtsen, age 75
Director, William L. Moody IV, age 87
Director, Frances A. Moody-Dahlberg, age 42
Director, Russell S. Moody, age 50
Director, James D. Yarbrough, age 56
Director, Arthur O. Dummer, age 78
Director, Shelby M. Elliott, age 85
Director, Frank P. Williamson, age 79
Auditors: KPMGLLP

LOCATIONS

HQ: American National Insurance Co. (Galveston, TX)
One Moody Plaza, Galveston, TX 77550-7999
Phone: 409 763-4661 **Fax:** 409 766-6502
Web: www.anico.com

PRODUCTS/OPERATIONS

2011 Revenue

	$ mil.	% of total
Premiums		
Property & casualty	1,144	38
Life	277	9
Accident & health	231	8
Annuity	94	3
Other policy revenues	189	6
Net investment income	968	32
Realized investment gains	100	3
Other-than-temporary impairments	(9.5)	-
Other income	25	1
Total	**3,023**	**3,032**

Selected Subsidiaries

American National Life Insurance Company of Texas (ANTEX)
American National Life Insurance Company of New York
American National Property and Casualty Company (ANPAC)
ANICO Financial Services Inc.
Farm Family Casualty Insurance Company
Farm Family Life Insurance Company
Garden State Life Insurance Company
Pacific Property and Casualty Company
Standard Life and Accident Insurance Company
United Farm Family Insurance Company

COMPETITORS

Allstate
American Financial Group
CNO Financial
Farmers Group
Mutual of Omaha
National Western
Nationwide
New York Life
Penn Mutual
Prudential
State Farm
Torchmark
USAA

HISTORICAL FINANCIALS

Company Type: Public

Income Statement

FYE: December 31

	ASSETS ($ mil.)	NET INCOME ($ mil.)	INCOME AS % OF ASSETS	EMPLOYEES
12/11	22,524	192	0.9%	3,207
12/10	21,413	144	0.7%	3,251
12/09	20,149	15	0.1%	3,211
12/08	18,379	(154)	—	0
12/07	18,464	240	1.3%	0
Annual Growth	5.1%	(5.5%)	—	—

2011 Year-End Financials

Debt ratio: 0.26%
Return on equity: 5.26%
Cash ($ mil.): 102
Current ratio: —
Long-term debt ($ mil.): 58

No. of shares (mil.): 26
Dividends
Yield: —
Payout: 42.78%
Market value ($ mil.): 1,959

	STOCK PRICE ($) FY Close	P/E High	P/E Low	PER SHARE ($) Earnings	Dividends	Book Value
12/11	73.03	12	9	7.20	0.00	136.35
12/10	85.62	22	14	5.40	3.08	135.44
12/09	119.44	205	59	0.59	3.08	129.02
12/08	73.73	—	—	(5.82)	3.08	116.85
12/07	121.24	17	12	9.04	3.05	141.12
Annual Growth	(11.9%)	—	—	(5.5%)	—	(0.9%)

Ameriprise Financial Inc

It's no surprise that Ameriprise Financial is a leading provider of financial advice. The company offers financial planning products and services to individual and institutional investors. Through Ameriprise Financial Columbia Management RiverSource and other affiliates and brands the company provides access to insurance mutual funds savings plans personal trust services retail brokerage and other financial products and services. Its Ameriprise Bank subsidiary offers deposits and loans. Ameriprise which has about $630 billion of assets under management distributes its products primarily through a network of more than 9700 financial advisors.

The company has been sharpening its focus on its branded adviser network. It sold its Securities America independent broker-dealer subsidiary to Ladenburg Thalmann for some $150 million in 2011. Shortly before the sale of the troubled unit Ameriprise agreed to pay $160 million to settle claims that Securities America brokers sold securities in fraudulent companies.

Ameriprise has been steadily boosting its assets under management and growing its client base (focusing on the affluent and mass affluent with at least $100000 in investable assets). The company also is focused on geographic areas where those clients are congregated and has closed or consolidated offices in areas with less potential. While Columbia Management covers Ameriprise's main asset management market in the US the company is increasing its global presence through its Threadneedle brand overseas. Ameriprise plans to grow its asset management operations in Europe as well as in Australia the Middle East and Asia.

Ameriprise's strategies have paid off. Volatile financial market conditions which negatively impacted all of the company's operations led to a decline in revenue in 2008 and 2009. However the company returned to success in 2010 and revenues grew by more than 20% that year. Poor economic conditions continued in 2011. However Ameriprise's operating net revenues climbed that year by about 10%. The boost was due to strong growth in the company's fee-based advisory and asset management businesses.

Ameriprise Financial which was founded in 1894 was spun off from American Express in 2005.

EXECUTIVES

Chairman and CEO, James M. (Jim) Cracchiolo, age 53, $850,000 total compensation
EVP Service Delivery and Technology, Glen Salow, age 55, $475,000 total compensation
President The Personal Advisors Group, Donald E. (Don) Froude, age 56, $400,000 total compensation
CEO U.S. Asset Management; President Annuities, William F. (Ted) Truscott, age 51, $450,000 total compensation
EVP and CFO, Walter S. Berman, age 69, $450,000 total compensation
EVP Human Resources, Kelli A. Hunter, age 50
EVP Financial Planning and Wealth Strategies and Chief Marketing Officer, Kim Sharan, age 54
President Advice and Wealth Management Products and Services, Joseph (Joe) Sweeney, age 50, $375,000 total compensation
President Insurance and Chief Strategy Officer, John R. Woerner, age 43
EVP and General Counsel, John C. Junek, age 62, $375,000 total compensation
SVP and Controller, David K. Stewart, age 59
EVP Corporate Communications and Community Relations, Deirdre Davey McGraw, age 41
CEO Threadneedle Asset Management Holdings, Crispin Henderson
VP Retirement Wealth Strategies, Craig Brimhall
SVP Chief Governance Officer and Secretary, Thomas R. Moore
Director, Siri S. Marshall, age 63
Director, Robert F. (Rob) Sharpe Jr., age 60
Director, Jeffrey (Jeff) Noddle, age 66
Director, Lon R. Greenberg, age 61
Director, Warren D. Knowlton, age 65
Director, H. Jay Sarles, age 66
Director, William H. Turner, age 72
Director, W. Walker Lewis, age 67
Auditors: PricewaterhouseCoopersLLP

LOCATIONS

HQ: Ameriprise Financial Inc.
1099 Ameriprise Financial Center, Minneapolis MN 55474
Phone: 612-671-3131 **Fax:** 612-671-5112
Web: www.ameriprise.com

PRODUCTS/OPERATIONS

2011 Sales

	$ mil.	% of total
Management & financial advice fees	4,537	45
Distribution fees	1,573	15
Other	863	8
Total	**10,239**	**100**

2011 Sales by Segment

	$ mil.	% of total
Advice & wealth management	2,925	29
Asset management	2,811	27
Annuities	2,379	23
Protection	2,035	20
Corporate & other	189	1
Total	**10,239**	**100**

Selected Subsidiaries and Affiliates

American Enterprise Investment Services Inc.
Ameriprise Financial Services Inc.
Ameriprise Bank FSB
Ameriprise Certificate Company
Ameriprise Trust Company
Columbia Management Investment Advisers LLC
Columbia Management Investment Distributors Inc.
IDS Property Casualty Insurance Company
J. & W. Seligman & Co. Incorporated
RiverSource Distributors Inc.
RiverSource Life Insurance Co. of New York
Threadneedle Asset Management Holdings

COMPETITORS

Allstate
AXA Financial
Bank of America
Bank of New York Mellon
Calamos Asset Management
Capital Group
Charles Schwab
Citigroup
First Eagle Investment Mangement
FMR
John Hancock Financial Services
Lincoln Financial Group
MassMutual
Merrill Lynch
MetLife
Nationwide Financial
New York Life
Northwestern Mutual
PNC Financial
Primerica
Principal Financial
Prudential
Regions Financial
State Street
TIAA-CREF
U.S. Bancorp

HISTORICAL FINANCIALS

Company Type: Public

Income Statement

FYE: December 31

	REVENUE ($ mil.)	NET INCOME ($ mil.)	NET PROFIT MARGIN	EMPLOYEES
12/11	10,192	1,076	10.6%	11,139
12/10	9,976	1,097	11.0%	10,472
12/09	7,805	722	9.3%	9,793
12/08	6,970	(38)	—	11,093
12/07	8,654	814	9.4%	8,750
Annual Growth	4.2%	7.2%	—	6.2%

2011 Year-End Financials

Debt ratio: 6.03%
Return on equity: 10.49%
Cash ($ mil.): 3,251
Current ratio: 77.67
Long-term debt ($ mil.): 7,571
No. of shares (mil.): 221
Dividends
Yield: —
Payout: 19.91%
Market value ($ mil.): 11,017

	STOCK PRICE ($) FY Close	P/E High	P/E Low	PER SHARE ($) Earnings	Dividends	Book Value
12/11	49.64	15	8	4.37	0.00	46.21
12/10	57.55	14	8	4.18	0.71	43.47
12/09	38.82	13	5	2.95	0.68	36.35
12/08	23.36	—	—	(0.17)	0.64	28.53
12/07	55.11	19	16	3.39	0.56	34.29
Annual Growth	(2.6%)	—	—	6.6%	—	7.7%

Ameris Bancorp

Ameris Bancorp enjoys the financial climate of the Deep South. It is the holding company of Ameris Bank which serves retail and consumer customers through more than 60 branches in Alabama Georgia South Carolina and northern Florida. The bank provides standard products and services including checking and savings accounts money market accounts CDs IRAs and credit cards; it offers investment services through an agreement with Raymond James Financial. Loans secured by commercial real estate and farmland account for approximately half of the company's loan portfolio while residential mortgages account for about a quarter.

Acquisitions helped boost Ameris' revenues by more than 25% in 2011 from $154.3 million to nearly $194 million. The company also returned to profitability after two consecutive years of losses posting nearly $18 million in net income. Higher interest margins and lower expenses contributed to its improved results as well.

Georgia's economy was one of the hardest hit in the US during the recession and Ameris has taken advantage of the plethora of banks seized by regulators in the state. Since 2009 the company has acquired about 10 failed banks in Georgia though FDIC-assisted transactions adding some 20 branches to its network. Ameris also snagged the failed First Bank of Jacksonville in Florida which had two locations.

EXECUTIVES

President and Director Brunswick Georgia, Michael D. Hodges, age 58
President and COO Ameris Bank, Andrew B. (Andy) Cheney, age 62

Chairman, Daniel B. Jeter, age 60
Director; Chairman Ameris Bank - Brunswick Georgia, Jimmy D. Veal, age 63
EVP and Director Credit Administration, Jon S. Edwards, age 50, $176,188 total compensation
EVP Chief Administrative Officer and Corporate Secretary, Cindi H. Lewis, age 58, $90,333 total compensation
President CEO and Director; CEO Ameris Bank, Edwin W. (Ed) Hortman Jr., age 58, $400,000 total compensation
President and Director Moultrie Georgia, Ronnie F. Marchant
President and Director Cordele Georgia, Robert L. Evans
President and Director Tifton Georgia, Lawton E. Bassett III
City President Douglas Georgia, David B. Batchelor
President and Director Albany Georgia, Don Monk
President and Director Alabama and Director Colquitt and Donalsonville Georgia, Harris O. Pittman III
EVP and CFO, Dennis J. Zember Jr., age 42, $215,000 total compensation
President and Director St. Marys Georgia, R. Edwin Haworth
President and Director Orange Park Florida, Timothy M. O'Keefe
President and Director Thomasville Georgia, Ronald K. Bell Sr.
EVP and COO, Marc J. Bogan, age 45, $177,400 total compensation
President and Director Cairo Georgia, Robert S. VanLandingham
City President and Director Donalsonville, Nancy S. Jernigan
President and Director Trenton Florida, Michael E. McElroy
City President and Chairman Beaufort South Carolina, John R. Perrill
SVP and Director Retail Investments, R. Wayne Martin
President and Director Valdosta Georgia, Austen D. Caroll
President and Director Crawfordville Florida, J. Martin Stubblefield
Investor Relations Officer, Cara Horne
Executive Vice President; Chief Risk Officer, Stephen Melton
Director, Daniel B. Jeter, age 60
Director, J. Raymond Fulp, age 67
Director, Robert P. Lynch, age 48
Director; Chairman Ameris Bank - Brunswick Georgia, Jimmy D. Veal, age 63
President CEO and Director; CEO Ameris Bank, Edwin W. (Ed) Hortman Jr., age 58
Director, Brooks Sheldon, age 66
Director, V. Wayne Williford
Director, R. Dale Ezzell
Auditors: PorterKeadleMooreLLP

LOCATIONS

HQ: Ameris Bancorp
310 1st St. SE, Moultrie GA 31768
Phone: 229-890-1111 **Fax:** 229-890-2235
Web: www.amerisbank.com

PRODUCTS/OPERATIONS

2011 Sales

	% mil.	% of total
Interest		
Loans including fees	128	66
Securities	11	6
Other	0	-
Noninterest		
Gain on acquisitions	26	14
Service charges on deposit accounts	18	9
Mortgage banking	3	2
Other	4	3
Total	**193**	**100**

Selected Acquisitions

American United Bank
Central Bank of Georgia
Darby Bank & Trust
First Bank of Jacksonville
High Trust Bank
Montgomery Bank & Trust
One Georgia Bank
Satilla Community Bank
Tifton Banking Company
United Security Bank

COMPETITORS

BancTrust Financial
Bank of America
Capital City Bank
Colony Bankcorp
Community Capital Bancshares
Compass Bancshares
First South Bancorp (NC)
Regions Financial
Southwest Georgia Financial
SunTrust
Thomasville Bancshares

HISTORICAL FINANCIALS

Company Type: Public

Income Statement FYE: December 31

	ASSETS ($ mil.)	NET INCOME ($ mil.)	INCOME AS % OF ASSETS	EMPLOYEES
12/11	2,994	21	0.7%	746
12/10	2,972	(3)	—	709
12/09	2,423	(41)	—	615
12/08	2,407	(3)	—	595
12/07	2,112	15	0.7%	620
Annual Growth	9.1%	8.6%	—	4.7%

2011 Year-End Financials

Debt ratio: 2.08%
Return on equity: 7.18%
Cash ($ mil.): 266
Current ratio: —
Long-term debt ($ mil.): 62
No. of shares (mil.): 23
Dividends
Yield: —
Payout: —
Market value ($ mil.): 244

	STOCK PRICE ($) FY Close	P/E High/Low	PER SHARE ($) Earnings	Dividends	Book Value
12/11	10.28	15 11	0.76	0.00	12.37
12/10	10.54	— —	(0.35)	0.00	11.56
12/09	7.16	— —	(3.23)	0.19	13.92
12/08	11.85	— —	(0.30)	0.37	17.33
12/07	16.85	26 13	1.09	0.54	13.84
Annual Growth	(11.6%)	— —	(8.6%)	—	(2.8%)

AmerisourceBergen Corp.

AmerisourceBergen is "the" source for many of North America's pharmacies and health care providers. The distribution company serves as a go-between for drug makers and the pharmacies doctors' offices hospitals and other health care providers that dispense drugs. Operating primarily in the US and Canada it distributes generic branded and over-the-counter pharmaceuticals as well as some medical supplies and other products using its network of more than two dozen facilities. Its specialty distribution unit focuses on sensitive and complex biopharmaceuticals. Other operations include pharmaceutical packaging. AmerisourceBergen also provides commercialization and consulting services to its customers.

HISTORY

In 1977 Cleveland millionaire and horse racing enthusiast Tinkham Veale went into the drug wholesaling business. His company Alco Standard (now IKON Office Solutions) already owned chemical electrical metallurgical and mining companies but by the late 1970s the company was pursuing a strategy of zeroing in on various types of distribution businesses.

Alco's first drug wholesaler purchase was The Drug House (Delaware and Pennsylvania); the next was Duff Brothers (Tennessee). The company then bought further wholesalers in the South East and Midwest. Its modus operandi was to buy small well-run companies for cash and Alco stock and leave the incumbent management in charge.

By the early 1980s Alco was the US's third-largest wholesale drug distributor and growing quickly (28% between 1983 and 1988) at a time of mass consolidation in the industry (the number of wholesalers dropped by half between 1980 and 1992). In 1985 Alco Standard spun off its drug distribution operations as Alco Health Services retaining 60% ownership.

Alco Health boosted its sales above $1 billion mostly via acquisitions and expanded product lines. The company offered marketing and promotional help to its independent pharmacy customers (which were beleaguered by the growth of national discounters) and also targeted hospitals nursing homes and clinics.

The US was in the midst of its LBO frenzy in 1988 but an Alco management group failed in its attempt. Rival McKesson then tried to acquire Alco Health but that deal fell through for antitrust reasons. Later in 1988 management turned for backing to Citicorp Venture Capital in another buyout attempt. This time the move succeeded and a new holding company Alco Health Distribution was formed.

In 1993 Alco Health was named as a defendant in suits by independent pharmacies charging discriminatory pricing policies; a ruling the next year limited its liability. To move away from a reliance on independent drugstores Alco Health began targeting government entities and others.

Alco Health went public as AmeriSource Health in 1995. Throughout the next year AmeriSource made a series of acquisitions to move into related areas including inventory management technology drugstore pharmaceutical supplies and disease-management services for pharmacies.

In 1997 AmeriSource acquired Alabama-based Walker Drug for $140 million adding 1500 independent and chain drugstores in the Southeast to its customer list. That same year McKesson once again made an offer to buy AmeriSource this time for $2.4 billion while two other major wholesale distributors Cardinal Health and Bergen Brunswig reached a similar pact. The deals were scrapped in 1998 when the Federal Trade Commission voted against both pacts and a federal judge supported that decision.

Later that year AmeriSource signed a five-year deal to become the exclusive pharmaceutical supplier to not-for-profit Sutter Health; in 1999 it renewed similar contracts with the US Department of Veterans Affairs and Pharmacy Provider Services Corporation. That year AmeriSource bought Midwest distributor C.D. Smith Healthcare.

In 2001 AmeriSource bought Bergen Brunswig and the combined company renamed itself AmerisourceBergen.

In 2005 the company acquired Trent Drugs (Wholesale) a Canadian pharmaceutical wholesaler and renamed it AmerisourceBergen Canada. The following year it acquired Canadian pharmaceutical distributors Asenda Pharmaceutical Supplies (Western Canada) and Rep-Pharm (Central and Eastern Canada). In late 2006 it then acquired Canada's Access M.D. (pharmaceutical support services) to expand its specialty services into Canada.

Back in the US during 2005 the company sold its Bridge Medical subsidiary which provides medication and laboratory specimen tracking via bar codes to Cerner. Group purchasing organization United Drug Stores had been a significant customer but terminated its contract with AmerisourceBergen in 2005

AmerisourceBergen was highly acquisitive throughout 2006. That year it acquired I.G.G. of America a specialty pharmacy focusing on blood derivative IVIG. It also purchased medical education and analytical research firm Network for Medical Communications & Research LLC (NMCR); NMCR became part of AmerisourceBergen's manufacturer services business. That March AmerisourceBergen acquired UK-based pharmaceutical packaging manufacturer Brecon Pharmaceuticals. It also purchased Florida-based Health Advocates which provides cost containment services to insurance payors for $83 million.

AmerisourceBergen spun off its long-term care institution drug dispensing services as PharMerica Long-term Care in 2007. The business was merged with Kindred Healthcare's institutional pharmacy unit to form PharMerica entity. The combined entity became the second-largest institutional pharmacy operator in the US.

To further narrow its focus on its core pharmaceutical distribution operations AmerisourceBergen sold its PMSI unit in 2008 for $34 million. PMSI provided workers' compensation services to insurance companies and other health care payers.

EXECUTIVES

SVP and President AmerisourceBergen Drug Corporation, David W. (Dave) Neu
SVP and CIO, Thomas H. (Tom) Murphy
VP and Corporate Treasurer, J. F. (Jack) Quinn
SVP Human Resources, June B. Barry, age 60
SVP Supply Chain Management, Antonio R. (Tony) Pera, age 55
President CEO and Director, Steven H. Collis, age 51, $572,669 total compensation
SVP Strategy and Corporate Development, David M. Senior
SVP and CFO, Tim G. Guttman
VP Corporate and Investor Relations, Barbara A. Brungess
Chief Marketing Officer, Gina K. Clark
Director Shareholder Relations and Assistant Secretary, Vicki L. Bausinger
EVP General Counsel and Secretary, John G. Chou, age 56, $310,160 total compensation
Chairman, Richard C. Gozon, age 73
SVP AmerisourceBergen Corporation; President AmerisourceBergen Specialty Distribution and Services, James D. Frary, age 39
VP Informaton Technology Specialty Group, Richard Burk
SVP Business Development; President AmerisourceBergen Consulting Services, Peyton Howell
Senior Vice President and Chief Information OfficerDale, Dale Danilewitz
Vice President and Corporate ControllerLazarus, Lazarus Krikorian
Director, Michael J. (Mike) Long, age 53
Director, Charles H. Cotros, age 74
Director, Richard W. Gochnauer, age 62
Director, Edward E. (Ed) Hagenlocker, age 72
Director, Kathleen W. (Kathi) Hyle, age 53
President CEO and Director, Steven H. Collis, age 51
Director, Jane E. Henney, age 64
Director, Henry W. McGee, age 58
Director Shareholder Relations and Assistant Secretary, Vicki L. Bausinger
Auditors: Ernst&YoungLLP

LOCATIONS

HQ: AmerisourceBergen Corporation
1300 Morris Dr., Chesterbrook PA 19087-5594
Phone: 610-727-7000 **Fax:** 610-727-3600
Web: www.amerisourcebergen.com

PRODUCTS/OPERATIONS

Selected Acquisitions

InstrinsiQ LLC (2011 information technology)
Premier Source (2011 consulting & reimbursement servcies)
TheraCom (2011 drug commercialization support services)
Innomar Strategies Inc. (2009 Canadian pharmaceutical services)

Selected Subsidiaries and Units

AmerisourceBergen Consulting Services
- Anderson Packaging
- Brecon Pharmaceuticals
- Lash Group
- TheraCom
- Xcenda

AmerisourceBergen Drug Corporation
- AmerisourceBergen Canada Corporation
- American Health Packaging

AmerisourceBergen Specialty Group

COMPETITORS

BioScrip
Cardinal Health
Express Scripts
FFF Enterprises
H. D. Smith Wholesale Drug
Henry Schein
McKesson
Medline Industries
Owens & Minor
PSS World Medical
Quality King
Roadnet
US Oncology
Watson Pharmaceuticals

HISTORICAL FINANCIALS

Company Type: Public

Income Statement FYE: September 30

	REVENUE ($ mil.)	NET INCOME ($ mil.)	NET PROFIT MARGIN	EMPLOYEES
09/12	79,489	718	0.9%	14,500
09/11	80,217	706	0.9%	10,300
09/10	77,953	636	0.8%	10,000
09/09	71,759	503	0.7%	10,300
09/08	70,189	250	0.4%	10,900
Annual Growth	3.2%	30.2%	—	7.4%

2012 Year-End Financials

Debt ratio: 9.37%
Return on equity: 29.27%
Cash ($ mil.): 1,066
Current ratio: 97.97
Long-term debt ($ mil.): 1,446
No. of shares (mil.): 235
Dividends
Yield: —
Payout: 18.57%
Market value ($ mil.): 9,112

	STOCK PRICE ($) FY Close	P/E High	P/E Low	PER SHARE ($) Earnings	Dividends	Book Value
09/12	38.71	15	13	2.80	0.00	10.44
09/11	37.27	17	12	2.54	0.43	10.98
09/10	30.66	15	10	2.22	0.32	10.65
09/09	22.38	23	10	1.66	0.21	9.44
09/08	37.65	61	48	0.77	0.15	8.67
Annual Growth	0.7%	—	—	38.1%	—	4.8%

Amgen Inc

Amgen is among the biggest of the biotech big'uns and it's determined to get even bigger. The company uses cellular biology and medicinal chemistry to target cancers kidney ailments inflammatory disorders and metabolic diseases. Its top protein-based therapeutic products include Neulasta and Neupogen (both used as anti-infectives in cancer patients) Aranesp and Epogen (used to fight anemia in chronic kidney disease and cancer patients) and Enbrel for rheumatoid arthritis. In addition Amgen has extensive drug research and development programs. Its products are marketed in 50 countries (primarily in North America and Europe) to doctors hospitals pharmacies and other health care providers.

HISTORY

Amgen was formed as Applied Molecular Genetics in 1980 by a group of scientists and venture capitalists to develop health care products based on molecular biology. George Rathmann a VP at Abbott Laboratories and researcher at UCLA became the company's CEO and first employee. Rathmann decided to develop a few potentially profitable products rather than conduct research. The company initially raised $19 million.

Amgen operated close to bankruptcy until 1983 when company scientist Fu-Kuen Lin cloned the human protein erythropoietin (EPO) which stimulates the body's red blood cell production. Amgen went public that year. It formed a joint venture with Kirin Brewery in 1984 to develop and market EPO. The two firms also collaborated on recombinant human granulocyte colony stimulating factor (G-CSF later called Neupogen) a protein that stimulates the immune system.

Amgen joined Johnson & Johnson subsidiary Ortho Pharmaceutical (later Ortho-McNeil Pharmaceutical) in a marketing alliance in 1985 and created a tie with Roche in 1988. Fortunes soared in 1989 when the FDA approved Epogen (the brand name of EPO) for anemia. (It is most commonly used to counter side effects of kidney dialysis.)

In 1991 Amgen received approval to market Neupogen to chemotherapy patients. A federal court ruling also gave it a US monopoly for EPO. The following year Amgen won another dispute forcing a competitor to renounce its US patents for G-CSF.

As the company grew it needed to transform itself from startup to going concern; to do so Amgen hired MCI veteran Kevin Sharer as president in 1992. Neupogen's usage was expanded in 1993 to include treatment of severe chronic neutropenia (low white-blood-cell count).

In 1993 Amgen became the first American biotech to gain a foothold in China through an agreement with Kirin Pharmaceuticals to sell Neupogen (under the name Gran) and Epogen there. The purchase of Synergen in 1994 added another research facility accelerating the pace of and increasing the number of products in research and clinical trials.

Although Amgen had two proven sellers in Epogen and Neupogen its growth lay in its pipeline. In 1997 Amgen and partner Regeneron Pharmaceuticals reported the failure of human trials for a drug to treat Lou Gehrig's disease. Still its new drug Stemgen for breast cancer patients undergoing chemotherapy was recommended for approval by an FDA advisory committee in 1998.

Amgen had to swallow a couple of tough legal pills in 1998. First a dispute with J&J over Amgen's 1985 licensing agreement with Ortho Pharmaceutical ended when an arbiter ordered Amgen to pay about $200 million. Later that year however Amgen won a legal battle with J&J over the rights to a promising anemia drug.

Work on its product pipeline continued in 1999: Amgen ended development of obesity and Parkinson's disease drugs after clinical trials produced discouraging results while it began human tests with partner Guilford Pharmaceuticals on a drug designed to regenerate damaged nerve cells in the brains of Parkinson's disease patients. (Guildford and Amgen ended the collaboration in 2001.)

In 2000 the firm resumed its battle to keep its stranglehold on the Epogen market: It sued Transkaryotic Therapies and Aventis (later Sanofi-Aventis) for alleged patent violations over its Epogen product in both the US and the UK. Although it initially won its case in the UK that verdict was overturned in 2002 making Amgen vulnerable to competition before Epogen's patents expire in 2004. That year it won EU and US approval for Aranesp an updated version of Epogen; Amgen in 2002 teamed with former J&J marketing partner Fresenius to sell Aranesp in Germany and take some market share away from J&J. Meanwhile an arbitration committee found J&J had breached its contract with Amgen when it sold Procrit to the dialysis market which Amgen had reserved for itself in their 1985 licensing deal.

In 2003 the company bought leukemia and rheumatoid arthritis drugs maker Immunex. As part of the FTC's blessing on the $10.3 billion union Amgen and Immunex licensed some technologies to encourage competition. Merck Serono gained access to Enbrel data and Regeneron Pharmaceuticals licensed some interleukin inhibitor rights.

The next year Amgen spent $1.3 billion to purchase the remaining 79% of cancer treatment technology maker Tularik that it did not already own.

In 2006 Amgen acquired Abgenix a company that manufactures human therapeutic antibodies. Vectibix Abgenix's treatment for colorectal cancer was approved by the FDA that year. The company also acquired private company Avidia a developer of treatments for inflammation and autoimmune diseases.

The company completed the acquisition of two privately held firms to expand its product pipeline in mid-2007: Ilypsa a biotech working in renal disease care and Alantos which has been working on therapies for rheumatoid arthritis and for Type II diabetes.

Amgen then saw some trouble with one of its best sellers Aranesp which experienced a drop in sales following damaging reports of adverse effects of the drug on the heart as well as increased risks for cancer patients. As a result of the reports the FDA required changes in Aranesp's and Epogen's warning labels and Medicare restricted Aranesp's use in chemotherapy patients during 2007. Revenues from Aranesp dropped from $3.6 billion in 2007 to $2.6 billion in 2009.

Amgen undertook restructuring plans to help absorb the sales losses. The company cut its workforce by about 15% between mid-2007 and the end of 2009; it also rationalized its manufacturing facilities and reduced R&D efforts. In 2008 Amgen sold two noncore oncology products (Kepivance and Stemgen) and licensed rights to rheumatoid arthritis drug Kineret to Swedish firm Biovitrum for $130 million plus potential milestone payments. It also sold its Japanese unit and formed a co-development partnership with that country's top drugmaker Takeda Pharmaceutical in a deal worth up to $1.2 billion.

Amgen founder George Rathmann died in 2012.

EXECUTIVES

EVP Operations, Fabrizio Bonanni, age 65, $795,000 total compensation
Chairman and CEO, Kevin W. Sharer, age 64, $1,682,308 total compensation
EVP and CFO, Jonathan M. Peacock, age 54
SVP Manufacturing, Madhavan Balachandran
SVP Research, David L. (Dave) Lacey
SVP and Chief Compliance Officer, Anna S. Richo, age 51
SVP Global Government and Corporate Affairs, David W. Beier, age 63
SVP Human Resources, Brian M. McNamee, age 55
SVP Research and Development, Joseph P. (Joe) Miletich, age 60
EVP Global Commercial Operations, Anthony C. (Tony) Hooper, age 57
SVP Global Value and Access, Joshua J. Ofman
SVP General Counsel and Secretary, David J. Scott, age 59
SVP International Commercial Operations, Rolf K. Hoffmann
SVP North America Commercial Operations, James M. (Jim) Daly
VP International Finance, Michael A. Kelly, age 55
EVP Research and Development, Sean E. Harper, age 49
President and COO, Robert (Bob) Bradway, age 49, $883,096 total compensation
Media Contact Government Policy/Reimbursement, Kelley Davenport
Media Contact, Christine Regan
SVP Global Regulatory Affairs and Safety, Paul R. Eisenberg
VP Finance and Chief Accounting Officer, Thomas Dittrich, age 48
SVP and CIO, Diana McKenzie
SVP Global Development and Corporate Chief Medical Officer, Michael Severino
SVP and Chief Compliance Officer, Cynthia Patton
Director, Gilbert S. Omenn, age 70
Director, Leonard D. Schaeffer, age 66
Director, Vance D. Coffman, age 67
Director, Frank C. Herringer, age 69
Director, Judith C. (Judy) Pelham, age 66
Director, Frederick W. (Fred) Gluck, age 76
Director, Jerry D. Choate, age 73
Director, David Baltimore, age 74
Director, Adm. J. Paul Reason, age 71
Director, Frank J. Biondi Jr.
Director, Francois de Carbonnel, age 64
Director, Rebecca M. Henderson, age 52
Auditors: Ernst&YoungLLP

LOCATIONS

HQ: Amgen Inc.
1 Amgen Center Dr., Thousand Oaks CA 91320-1799
Phone: 805-447-1000 **Fax:** 805-447-1010
Web: www.amgen.com

2011 Sales

	$ mil.	% of total
US	11,985	77
Other countries	3,597	23
Total	**15,582**	**100**

PRODUCTS/OPERATIONS

2011 Sales

	$ mil.	% of total
Product sales		
Enbrel	3,701	24
Aranesp	2,303	15
Sensipar/Mimpara	808	5
XGEVA	351	2
Vectibix	322	2
Nplate	297	2
Prolia	203	2
Other	287	2

Top Selling Products
Neupogen/Neulasta (chemotherapy-induced neutropenia - low white blood cells and cancer-related infections
Enbrel (rheumatoid arthritis psoriasis)
Aranesp (chemotherapy-induced anemia and chronic renal failure anemia sustained duration Epogen)
Epogen (anemia in chronic renal failure)
Sensipar/Mimpara (also known as Mimpara chronic kidney disease)
Xgeva (to prevent bone fractures)
Vectibix (monoclonal antibody for colorectal cancer)
Nplate (romiplostim for autoimmune bleeding disorder ITP or immune thrombocytopenic purpura)
Prolia (postmenopausal osteoporos

COMPETITORS

Abbott Labs
Affymax
Apotex
AstraZeneca
Bayer HealthCare Pharmaceuticals Inc.
Bristol-Myers Squibb
Celgene
Chugai
Eli Lilly
Fresenius Medical Care
GlaxoSmithKline
Hospira
Johnson & Johnson
Merck
Merck KGaA
Nektar Therapeutics
Novartis
Pfizer
Roche Holding
Sanofi
Shire
Takeda Pharmaceutical
Teva
UCB

HISTORICAL FINANCIALS

Company Type: Public

Income Statement

FYE: December 31

	REVENUE ($ mil.)	NET INCOME ($ mil.)	NET PROFIT MARGIN	EMPLOYEES
12/11	15,582	3,683	23.6%	17,800
12/10	15,053	4,627	30.7%	17,400
12/09	14,642	4,605	31.5%	17,200
12/08	15,003	4,196	28.0%	16,900
12/07	14,771	3,166	21.4%	17,500
Annual Growth	1.3%	3.9%	—	0.4%

2011 Year-End Financials

Debt ratio: 43.85%
Return on equity: 19.35%
Cash ($ mil.): 6,946
Current ratio: 479.54
Long-term debt ($ mil.): 21,344
No. of shares (mil.): 795
Dividends
Yield: —
Payout: 13.86%
Market value ($ mil.): 51,085

	STOCK PRICE ($) FY Close	P/E High/Low		PER SHARE ($) Earnings	Dividends	Book Value
12/11	64.21	16	12	4.04	0.00	23.92
12/10	54.90	13	10	4.79	0.00	25.69
12/09	56.57	14	10	4.51	0.00	22.78
12/08	57.75	17	10	3.90	0.00	19.47
12/07	46.44	27	17	2.82	0.00	16.44
Annual Growth	8.4%	—	—	9.4%	—	9.8%

AMR Corp. (DE)

AMR knows America's spacious skies –and lots of others. Its main subsidiary is American Airlines one of the largest airlines in the world. Together with sister company American Eagle and a regional carrier that operates as AmericanConnection under contract American Airlines serves more than 250 destinations in 50+ countries in the Americas Europe and Asia/Pacific. The overall fleet exceeds 900 aircraft; American Airlines operates about 610 jets. The carrier extends its geographic reach through code-sharing arrangements and is part of the oneworld Alliance along with British Airways Cathay Pacific Iberia Qantas and others. The company filed for Chapter 11 bankruptcy protection in November 2011.

HISTORY

In 1929 Sherman Fairchild created a New York City holding company called the Aviation Corporation (AVCO) combining some 85 small airlines in 1930 to create American Airways. In 1934 the company had its first dose of financial trouble after the government suspended private airmail for months. Corporate raider E. L. Cord took over and named the company American Airlines.

Cord put former AVCO manager C. R. Smith in charge and American became the leading US airline in the late 1930s. The Douglas DC-3 built to Smith's specifications was introduced by American in 1936 and became the first commercial airliner to pay its way on passenger revenues alone.

After WWII American bought Amex Airlines which flew to northern Europe but another financial crisis prompted Amex's sale in 1950. The airline introduced Sabre the first automated reservations system in 1964. Smith left American four years later to serve as secretary of commerce in the Johnson administration.

In 1979 the year after airline industry deregulation American moved to Dallas/Fort Worth. Former CFO Bob Crandall became president in 1980 (and later CEO). Using Sabre to track mileage he introduced the industry's first frequent-flier program (AAdvantage). In 1982 American created AMR as its holding company. After acquiring commuter airline Nashville Eagle in 1987 AMR established American Eagle.

After ducking a 1989 takeover bid by Donald Trump AMR bought routes to Japan Latin America and London from other carriers. American's 1994 attempt to simplify pricing led to a fare war that hurt industry profits.

In 1996 AMR spun off nearly 20% of Sabre and announced plans for a code-sharing pact with British Airways (BA) that sparked a wave of alliances including oneworld which took effect in 1999. American's code-sharing deal with BA however ran into opposition from regulators who were concerned about the airlines' dominance of landing slots at London's Heathrow airport.

Crandall retired in 1998 (after a major airline strike was averted by President Clinton's intervention) and was replaced by Donald Carty. Looking to replace its turboprops American Eagle rolled out its first regional jets that year. American also bought Reno Air and concerns about integrating the smaller airline (completed in 1999) culminated in American pilots calling in sick for a week in 1999. The union was later ordered to pay almost $46 million in compensation.

To focus on its airlines AMR sold its executive aviation services ground services and call center units in 1999. That year nine people died when an American jet tried to land in Arkansas during a storm and slid off the runway. The Justice Department dealt another blow in 2000 when it filed a suit accusing American of predatory pricing to fend off low-fare startups. (A federal judge dismissed the case in 2001 however.) Also in 2000 AMR sold its Canadian Airlines stake (bought in 1994) to Air Canada and spun off the rest of Sabre.

In 2001 AMR moved to become a stronger competitor to United Continental formerly UAL Corporation by buying the assets of troubled rival TWA for $742 million. Later that year American and BA revived plans to seek regulatory clearance for a code-sharing deal.

Also in 2001 American Airlines lost two aircraft that were used in the September 11 terrorist attacks on the World Trade Center in New York and the Pentagon in Washington DC. In anticipation of reduced demand for air travel AMR announced a 20% reduction in flights and layoffs of at least 20000 employees. Later that year another American Airlines jet crashed in New York killing all 260 passengers. Unlike peers such as Delta United Continental's United Airlines and Continental and US Airways AMR was able to navigate the airline industry downturn that followed the September 11 2001 terrorist attacks without making a stop in bankruptcy court. In 2002 the carrier set about reducing its capacity by 9% and reducing its workforce by some 7000 employees and won concessions from its unions. It also simplified its fleet by retiring its Fokker-100 jets ahead of schedule.

American Airlines' planned partnership with BA which the airlines had been negotiating since 1996 received conditional approval from the US Department of Transportation (DOT) in 2002 only to be abandoned by the airlines. The DOT wanted the airlines to give up 224 slots at London's Heathrow airport something they were not willing to do.

Carty resigned in 2003 after rankling union leaders by failing to disclose executive compensation perquisites during labor negotiations aimed at keeping the airline giant out of bankruptcy. Carty was replaced as CEO by former president and COO Gerard Arpey. Director Edward Brennan a former chairman and CEO of Sears Roebuck & Co. was named non-executive chairman. Brennan relinquished the chairman role to Arpey in 2004 but remained a director.

To take advantage of demand for travel to the Asia/Pacific region American Airlines began nonstop service from Chicago to Shanghai in April 2006 making it the first US airlines to offer nonstop service to Shanghai.

AMR lost money for five straight years –and piled up debt –before posting profits in 2006 and 2007. Short lived the gains were followed by alarming net losses of more than $2 billion in 2008 and $1.5 billion in 2009 primarily driven by a drop in traffic and passenger yields (tied to ticket discounting) and a sharp rise in fuel costs.

Even as the company worked to cut costs and shore up revenue the carrier had to address maintenance issues. After an inspection by the Federal Aviation Administration (FAA) found problems with the way wiring was bundled in aircraft wheel wells American Airlines canceled more than 3000 flights over several days in April 2008 in order to re-inspect its fleet of MD-80s. The cancellations affected hubs in Chicago and Dallas and had repercussions nationwide. In a separate case the FAA in August 2008 proposed a $7.1 million fine against American Airlines for allegedly flying airplanes that had not been properly maintained and for allegedly failing to follow drug- and alcohol-testing procedures for employees. The carrier contested the agency's findings.

As part of an effort to strengthen its balance sheet and to concentrate on airline operations AMR sold a controlling interest in its American Beacon Advisors asset management business in 2008 for $480 million to two private equity firms Pharos Capital and TPG Capital. It also announced plans to shed its American Eagle operations.

These moves followed American Airlines 12% cut in late 2008 which targeted the retirement of about 75 aircraft and the elimination of thousands of jobs. Starting that year the company implemented a slate of passenger service charges. "Other revenues" was the sole revenue growth segment for AMR in 2009 increasing about 5% from 2008. In 2009 the carrier reduced its mainline seating capacity by 7% including grounding its Airbus A300 fleet and clipping the wings of some of its Embraer RJ-135 aircraft.

In 2010 the legacy airline agreed to a limited partnership with the younger low-cost carrier JetBlue. The two began sharing customer "interline" duties in New York and Boston including one-stop booking and check-in and bag transfers for connecting flights.

Also in 2010 American Airlines exchanged eight pairs of its take-off and landing slots at Ronald Reagan Washington National Airport to gain 12 pairs of JetBlue's slots at John F. Kennedy International Airport.

With China in its sites American Airlines launched a Chicago-to-Beijing route in 2010. Also that year the carrier allied with British Airways Iberia Finnair and Royal Jordanian on flights between North America and Europe. This joint business agreement goes beyond code-sharing by enabling the carriers to pool and share some revenues and costs.

American Airlines and JAL began joint sales of airfares in 2011 the same year American began a Los Angeles-to-Shanghai service.

EXECUTIVES

SVP and CFO AMR and American Airlines, Isabella D. (Bella) Goren, age 52

SVP Mexico Caribbean and Latin America American Airlines, Peter J. Dolara, age 75

EVP AMR and American Airlines; President and CEO American Eagle, Daniel P. Garton, age 54, $527,865 total compensation

Chairman CEO, Gerard J. Arpey, age 53, $666,348 total compensation

SVP Operations American Airlines, James B. (Jim) Ream, age 56

VP Customer Technology American Airlines, Andrew O. Watson

Chairman President and CEO AMR and American Airlines, Thomas W. (Tom) Horton, age 51, $615,090 total compensation

SVP Government Affairs AMR and American Airlines, William K. (Will) Ris Jr., $385,102 total compensation
President Cargo Division American Airlines, David R. (Dave) Brooks
SVP Airport Services American Airlines, Thomas R. (Tom) Del Valle
VP Operations Finance and Strategy Planning American Airlines, Douglas G. Herring
VP Airport Services American Airlines, Timothy J. Ahern
VP Safety Security and Environmental American Airlines, David L. (Dave) Campbell
SVP General Counsel and Chief Compliance Officer AMR and American Airlines, Gary F. Kennedy Sr., age 56, $486,238 total compensation
SVP Customer American Airlines, Craig S. Kreeger
VP Purchasing and Transportation American Airlines, John R. MacLean
VP New York American Airlines, Arthur J. Torno
SVP Human Resources American Airlines, Jeffery J. Brundage, age 59
VP Diversity and Leadership Strategies American Airlines, Lauri L. Curtis
VP Corporate Human Resources American Airlines, Carolyn E. (Carol) Wright
VP Corporate Development and Treasurer; Chief Restructuring Officer, Beverly K. (Bev) Goulet
VP Corporate Real Estate American Airlines, Laura A. Einspanier
VP State and Community Affairs American Airlines, Kevin E. Cox
VP Information Technology American Airlines, Susan B. Garcia
VP Operations Planning and Performance American Airlines, Jonathan D. (Jon) Snook
VP International American Airlines, Kurt Stache, age 41
VP Airport Services American Airlines Miami Hub, Marilyn DeVoe
VP People, Denise Lynn
VP and Controller American Airlines, Brian J. McMenamy
VP Dallas/Fort Worth American Airlines, Arthur (Art) Pappas
Corporate Secretary AMR and American Airlines, Kenneth W. Wimberly
CFO and SVP Planning American Eagle, John T. Hutchinson
VP Marketing American Airlines, Robert J. (Rob) Friedman
SVP Technical Operations American Eagle, Fred E. Cleveland
VP Airport Services Planning American Airlines, Mark E. DuPont
SVP Technology and CIO American Airlines, Maya Leibman
VP Line Maintenance American Airlines, Ken Durst
SVP and Chief Commercial Officer American Airlines, Virasb Vahidi
VP Strategic Alliances American Airlines, Kenji Hashimoto
VP Revenue Management American Airlines, Don B. Casey
Managing Director Investor Relations, Chris Ducey
VP Base Maintenance American Airlines, William Collins
VP Information Technology Services American Airlines, Patrick O'Keeffe
Director Sales New York American Airlines, Johna Johnson
VP Sales Eastern Division American Airlines, Jim Carter
VP Engineering Performance Improvement Strategies and Quality Assurance American Airlines, William M. (Bill) Cavitt
VP Sales American Airlines, Derek DeCross
VP Flight American Airlines, Capt. John Hale
VP Chicago American Airlines, Franco Tedeschi
VP Network Planning American Airlines, Charles Schubert
VP Corporate Communications American Airlines, Andrew Backover
SVP Customer Service American Eagle, Pedro Fabregas
President of AAdvantage American Airlines, Suzanne Rubin
Vice President Business Technology Services, Daniel P. Henry
Vice President Airline Operations Technology, Patrick J. OKeeffe
Director, Matthew K. (Matt) Rose, age 53
Director, Philip J. (Phil) Purcell, age 68
Director, Michael A. Miles, age 72
Director, Judith (Judy) Rodin, age 67
Director, John W. Bachmann, age 72
Director, Roger T. Staubach, age 70
Director, Ann McLaughlin Korologos, age 70
Director, Armando M. Codina, age 65
Director, Ray M. Robinson, age 64
Director, Alberto Ibarguen, age 68
Auditors: Ernst&YoungLLP

LOCATIONS

HQ: AMR Corporation
4333 Amon Carter Blvd., Fort Worth TX 76155
Phone: 817-963-1234 **Fax:** 609-716-8255
Web: amrepcorp.com

2011 Sales

	$ mil.	% of total
DOT Domestic	13,804	58
DOT Latin America	5,460	22
DOT Atlantic	3,499	15
DOT Pacific	1,216	5
Total	**23,979**	**100**

Selected Hub Locations

Chicago (O' Hare)
Dallas/Fort Worth (DFW)
Los Angeles
Miami
New York City

PRODUCTS/OPERATIONS

2011 Sales

	$ mil.	% of total
Passenger		
American Airlines	17,947	75
Regional affiliates	2,724	11
Cargo	703	3
Other	2,605	11
Total	**23,979**	**100**

COMPETITORS

Air France-KLM
AirTran Airways
Alaska Air
China Southern Airlines
Continental Airlines
Delta Air Lines
FedEx
Frontier Airlines
Greyhound
Hawaiian Holdings
JetBlue
Lufthansa
Mesa Air
Pinnacle Airlines
SkyWest
Southwest Airlines
Spirit Airlines
United Air Lines
United Continental
UPS
US Airways
Virgin Atlantic Airways

HISTORICAL FINANCIALS

Company Type: Public

Income Statement FYE: December 31

	REVENUE ($ mil.)	NET INCOME ($ mil.)	NET PROFIT MARGIN	EMPLOYEES
12/11	23,979	(1,979)	—	80,100
12/10	22,170	(471)	—	78,250
12/09	19,917	(1,468)	—	78,900
12/08	23,766	(2,071)	—	84,100
12/07	22,935	504	2.2%	85,500
Annual Growth	1.1%	—	—	(1.6%)

2011 Year-End Financials

Debt ratio: 34.47%
Return on equity: 987650001000000.00%
Cash ($ mil.): 1,021
Current ratio: 78.30
Long-term debt ($ mil.): 6,702
No. of shares (mil.): 335
Dividends
Yield: —
Payout: —
Market value ($ mil.): 117

	STOCK PRICE ($) FY Close	P/E High/Low		PER SHARE ($) Earnings	Dividends	Book Value
12/11	0.35	—	—	(5.91)	0.00	(21.21)
12/10	7.79	—	—	(1.41)	0.00	(11.83)
12/09	7.73	—	—	(4.99)	0.00	(10.49)
12/08	10.67	—	—	(7.98)	0.00	(10.52)
12/07	14.03	20	7	1.78	0.00	10.65
Annual Growth	(60.3%)	—	—	—	—	—

AmTrust Financial Services Inc

Insurance holding company AmTrust Financial Services likes a mix of businesses on its plate. Its subsidiaries offer a range of commercial property/casualty insurance products for small and midsized customers including workers' compensation products auto and general liability and extended service and warranty coverage of consumer and commercial goods. It also provides a small amount of personal auto reinsurance. It operates in Bermuda Ireland the UK and the US and distributes its products through brokers agents and claims administrators. The company's customers include restaurants retail stores physicians' offices auto and consumer electronics manufacturers and trucking operations.

Operations Historically AmTrust's premium revenue was fairly evenly split among three segments: Small Commercial Business Specialty Risk and Extended Warranty and Specialty Middle Market Business. In 2010 it added a Personal Lines Reinsurance segment when it acquired a minority stake in GMAC Insurance Personal Lines the former US consumer property/casualty insurance business of GMAC (now known as Ally Financial). That stake gave the company access to writing 10% of the reinsurance on GMAC's US personal auto insurance. While that business only accounts for a small portion of AmTrust's premiums it gave it access to a distribution network of more than 10000 independent agents and helped to diversify the company's revenue streams.

Financial Analysis AmTrust reported 2011 revenue of nearly $1.4 billion up more than a third from the previous year. The company saw strong double-digit growth across all segments including nearly 50% growth in its largest segment (specialty risk and extended warranty) because of a new reinsurance program for the company's European medical liability business among other factors. AmTrust's newest and smallest segment (personal lines reinsurance) nearly doubled from the previous year as 2011 was the first full year of results. It also benefitted from the 2011 acquisition of business from Majestic Insurance Company. Net income in 2011 was up nearly 20% to $170 million. Strategy Key to AmTrust's overall business strategy is keeping its portfolio diversified by both business line and geography. For example in 2012 the company expanded its six-year strategic partnership with CNH Capital by establishing a long-term licensing and service agreement with the company and acquiring its affiliate agencies CNH Capital Insurance Agency and CNH Capital Canada Insurance Agency. The companies will collaborate to expand CNH Capital's offering of equipment extended service contracts and other insurance products to equipment dealers in the US and Canada including CNH-affiliated companies Case New Holland and Kobelco. Mergers and Acquisitions The company has been able to expand its product offerings and geographic reach through acquisitions of smaller competitors though it approaches its purchases with a conservative eye avoiding huge financial investments. To diversify its product offerings the company has made investments in a range of businesses including a 60% stake in Tiger Capital which acquires life settlement contracts and an 80% stake in Risk Services a captive management provider during 2010. In other instances the company simply acquires the renewal rights to blocks of policies issued by other companies. It acquired the renewal rights to Unitrin's Business Insurance unit in 2008 and picked up a block of workers' compensation policies from Majestic Insurance Company in 2011. In early 2012 AmTrust added coverage for community banks when it acquired renewal rights to the in-force policies of Oklahoma-based BancInsure. The company took a larger bite out of the warranty business through the purchase of Warrantech in 2010. AmTrust previously held a minority stake in Warrantech; it made the third-party warranty administration company a wholly owned subsidiary by purchasing the 73% interest held by H.I.G. Capital through a $35 million cash and debt transaction. AmTrust will expand further in the warranty market through the purchase of UK-based Car Car Plan which it agreed to acquire from Ally Financial for $70 million in 2012. Ownership Chairman Michael Karfunkel and his brother George each hold about 25% of AmTrust; Michael's son-in-law CEO Barry Zyskind holds 10%.

EXECUTIVES

VP Investor Relations, Hilly Gross
President CEO and Director, Barry D. Zyskind, age 40, $637,019 total compensation
COO, Michael J. Saxon, age 53, $509,615 total compensation
CFO, Ronald E. Pipoly Jr., age 45, $407,962 total compensation
CIO, Christopher M. Longo, age 38, $306,250 total compensation
General Counsel and Secretary, Stephen B. Ungar
CEO AmTrust Europe; President AmTrust International Insurance, Max G. Caviet, age 59, $365,475 total compensation
Chairman, Michael Karfunkel, age 69
Investor Relations, Ellen Taylor
President CEO and Director, Barry D. Zyskind, age 40
Director, Donald T. DeCarlo, age 73
Director, George Karfunkel, age 64
Director, Abraham Gulkowitz, age 64
Director, Jay J. Miller, age 80
Auditors: BDOSeidmanLLP

LOCATIONS

HQ: AmTrust Financial Services Inc.
59 Maiden Ln. 6th Fl., New York NY 10038
Phone: 212-220-7120 **Fax:** 212-220-7130
Web: www.amtrustgroup.com

PRODUCTS/OPERATIONS

2011 Earned Premiums

	% of total
Specialty risk & extended	43
Small commercial	31
Specialty	17
Personal lines	9
Total	**100**

Selected Acquisitions

2012
- Builders & Tradesmen' s Insurance Services
- Car Car Plan (UK; warranty administration; $70 million)

Selected Subsidiaries

AmTrust Europe Ltd. (specialty risk and extended warranty coverage EU)
AmTrust International Insurance Ltd. (reinsurance Bermuda)
AmTrust International Underwriters Limited (specialty risk and extended warranty coverage EU)
Associated Industries Insurance Company Inc. (workers' compensation)
Milwaukee Casualty Insurance Company (small commercial business)
Rochdale Insurance Company (specialty property/casualty specialty risk and extended warranty workers' compensation)
Security National Insurance Company (small commercial business)
Technology Insurance Company Inc. (specialty property/casualty specialty risk and extended warranty workers' compensation)
Wesco Insurance Company (specialty property/casualty specialty risk and extended warranty workers' compensation)

COMPETITORS

AIG
Allianz Insurance
Amica Mutual
Bankers Financial
Berkshire Hathaway
FCCI
Liberty Mutual
National Indemnity Company
The Hartford
Travelers Companies

HISTORICAL FINANCIALS

Company Type: Public

Income Statement FYE: December 31

	ASSETS ($ mil.)	NET INCOME ($ mil.)	INCOME AS % OF ASSETS	EMPLOYEES
12/11	5,682	170	3.0%	1,900
12/10	4,182	142	3.4%	1,400
12/09	3,400	103	3.0%	1,000
12/08	3,143	82	2.6%	900
12/07	2,322	90	3.9%	625
Annual Growth	25.1%	17.3%	—	32.0%

2011 Year-End Financials

Debt ratio: 7.88%
Return on equity: 19.14%
Cash ($ mil.): 406
Current ratio: —
Long-term debt ($ mil.): 447
No. of shares (mil.): 66
Dividends
Yield: —
Payout: 12.27%
Market value ($ mil.): 1,570

	STOCK PRICE ($) FY Close	P/E High	P/E Low	PER SHARE ($) Earnings	Dividends	Book Value
12/11	23.75	11	7	2.52	0.00	13.47
12/10	17.50	8	5	2.15	0.29	10.94
12/09	11.82	8	4	1.56	0.23	8.73
12/08	11.60	14	5	1.25	0.18	5.94
12/07	13.77	15	6	1.36	0.11	5.92
Annual Growth	14.6%	—	—	16.7%	—	22.8%

Anadarko Petroleum Corp

Anadarko Petroleum has ventured beyond its original area of operation –the Anadarko Basin – to explore for develop produce and market oil natural gas natural gas liquids and related products worldwide. In 2011 the large independent company reported proved reserves (90% of which is located in the US) of 1.1 billion barrels of crude oil and NGLs and 8.4 trillion cu. ft. of natural gas. Additional assets include coal trona (natural soda ash) and other minerals. Anadarko operates a handful of gas-gathering systems in the Mid-Continent. Internationally the company has substantial oil and gas interests in Algeria. It also has holdings in Brazil China Indonesia Mazambique and West Africa.

Financial Analysis

That year higher oil and NGL prices helped to lift the company's overall revenues despite weak natural gas commodity prices. However Anadarko's settlement with BP created a major net loss for the company in 2011. The company held a minority stake in BP's ill-fated Macondo well in the Gulf of Mexico. Despite attempts by BP to make Anadarko liable for part of the clean up costs related to destruction of that rig in 2010 and the devastating oil spill that followed Anadarko initially rebuffed such claims citing BP's negligence. It did reach a settlement with BP in 2011 transferring its minority stake in the Macondo well to BP and paying that company $4 billion.

In 2010 the company reported a 9% growth in sales volumes while it cut oil and gas operating expenses by 7%. Higher commodity prices and increased production volumes (coupled with cost-cutting measures) lifted Anadarko's revenues and net income in 2010.

Strategy

In 2012 the company resolved a tax dispute allowing it to resume full operations in Algeria. (Algeria accounted for 15% of Anadarko's total revenues in 2011).

Anadarko added a total of 392 million barrels of oil equivalent reserves in 2011. Taking advantage of a low priced assets that year Anadarko and Newfield Exploration bought properties in the Maverick Basin in Texas for $310 million from bankrupt TXCO.

To raise cash to help it exploit its US shale assets (a growth segment) in 2011 the company closed a joint venture deal with Korea National Oil (KNOC) under which KNOC agreed to pay $1.6 billion over serveral years for one-third of Anadarko's holdings in the lucrative Eagle Ford shale play in South Texas.

HISTORY

In 1959 the Panhandle Eastern Pipe Line Company set up Anadarko (named after the Anadarko Basin) to carry out its gas exploration and production activities. The new company was also formed to take advantage of a ruling by the Federal Power Commission (now the Federal Energy Regulatory Commission) to set lower price ceilings for producing properties owned by pipeline companies.

The company grew rapidly during the early 1960s largely because of its gas-rich namesake. It bought Ambassador Oil of Fort Worth Texas in 1965 –adding interests in 19 states in the US and Canada. The firm also relocated from Kansas to Fort Worth.

Anadarko began offshore exploration in the Gulf of Mexico in 1970 and focused there early in the decade. After moving to Houston in 1974 Anadarko increased its oil exploration activities when the energy crisis led to higher gas prices. A deal with Amoco (now part of BP) led to major finds on Matagorda Island off the Texas coast in the early 1980s.

To realize shareholder value Panhandle spun off Anadarko in 1986 –separating transmission from production. At the time more than 90% of Anadarko's reserves were natural gas. The next year Anadarko made new discoveries in Canada.

Low domestic natural gas prices led Anadarko overseas. It signed a production-sharing agreement with Algeria's national oil and gas firm SONATRACH in 1989. The deal covered 5.1 million acres in the Sahara. Two years later Anadarko began operating in the South China Sea and in Alaska's North Slope.

Back home the company spent $190 million in 1992 for properties in West Texas and in 1993 Anadarko began divesting noncore assets. Along with some of its partners the company also discovered oil in the Mahogany Field offshore Louisiana. Production from Mahogany began in 1996.

In 1997 Anadarko added exploration acreage in the North Atlantic and Tunisia. The next year it made two major oil and gas discoveries in the Gulf of Mexico. Anadarko decided to sell some of its noncore Algerian assets in 1999 and teamed up with Texaco (later acquired by Chevron) in a joint exploration program in the Gulf of Mexico offshore Louisiana. The next year the company acquired Union Pacific Resources in a $5.7 billion stock swap.

Anadarko expanded its presence in western Canada in 2001 by buying Berkley Petroleum for more than $1 billion in cash and assumed debt; a smaller purchase that year Gulfstream Resources Canada landed Anadarko in the Persian Gulf and added 70 million barrels of oil equivalent to its reserves.

Expanding its presence and asset base in the lucrative resource plays in the Rocky Mountains and the deepwater Gulf of Mexico in 2006 Anadarko acquired midstream operator Western Gas and fellow explorer Kerr-McGee for about $26 billion.

To create greater financial flexibility in 2008 Anadarko spun off midstream unit Western Gas Partners though it still held on to about 60% of the company. The deal allowed Anadarko to focus on its core exploration and production operations while generating cash from the midstream unit through its ownership stake.

Anadarko bulked up its core assets in 2009 announcing nine major deepwater discoveries (primarily in the Gulf of Mexico) and adding some 314 million barrels of oil equivalent in proved reserves. The additional reserves helped fulfill the company's plans for future revenue growth partially mitigating a poor financial performance in 2009 which saw a decline in total revenues caused by the economic recession low commodity prices and the global slump in oil demand.

EXECUTIVES

VP, Albert L. (Al) Richey, age 64
VP Information Technology Services and CIO, Mario M. Coll III, age 51
VP Government Relations, Gregory M. (Greg) Pensabene, age 62
Chairman, James T. (Jim) Hackett, age 58, $1,567,500 total compensation
SVP General Counsel and Chief Administrative Officer, Robert K. (Bobby) Reeves Sr., age 54, $503,846 total compensation
VP Finance and Treasurer, Bruce W. Busmire, age 55
President CEO and Director, R. A. (Al) Walker, age 55, $685,192 total compensation
VP Deputy General Counsel and Corporate Secretary, David L. Siddall
SVP Worldwide Exploration, Robert P. (Bob) Daniels, age 53, $575,000 total compensation
VP Gulf of Mexico, Darrell E. Hollek
VP Operations, James J. (Jim) Kleckner
VP Marketing, A. Scott Moore
SVP Worldwide Operations, Charles A. (Chuck) Meloy Sr., age 52, $575,000 total compensation
SVP Finance and CFO, Robert G. Gwin, age 49, $569,231 total compensation
VP International Exploration, Frank J. Patterson
VP Midstream, Danny J. Rea
Corporate Controller, Michael C. Pearl, age 40
VP Investor Relations and Communications, John Colglazier
Director External Communications, John Christiansen
Manager Public Affairs Alaska, Mark Hanley
VP Operations, Donald H. MacLiver
VP and Chief Accounting Officer, M. Cathy Douglas, age 56
General Manager Gulf of Mexico Operations, Danny Hart
VP Corporate Development, Robert D. Abendschein
VP Corporate Audit, Larry J. Abston
VP Exploration and Production Services and Minerals, David C. Bretches
VP Operations, R. Douglas (Doug) Lawler
VP Human Resources, Julia A. Struble
Senior Staff Public Affairs Representative, Matt Carmichael
VP; President and CEO Western Gas Holdings, Donald R. Sinclair
VP Exploration, Douglas P. Hazlett
Manager Investor Relations, Dean Hennings
VP Gulf of Mexico Exploration and Corporate Development, Ernest A. Leyendecker
Director, Paula R. Reynolds, age 54
Director, Luke R. Corbett, age 65
President CEO and Director, R. A. (Al) Walker, age 55
Director, Rt. Hon. Preston M. (Pete) Geren III, age 60
Director, Peter J. Fluor, age 64
Director, John R. Butler Jr., age 73
Director, John R. Gordon, age 63
Director, Paulett Eberhart, age 58
Director, Gen. Kevin P. Chilton, age 57
Auditors: KPMGLLP

LOCATIONS

HQ: Anadarko Petroleum Corporation
1201 Lake Robbins Dr., The Woodlands TX 77380-1046
Phone: 832-636-1000 **Fax:** 781-937-1078
Web: www.analog.com

2011 Sales

	% of total
US	76
Algeria	16
Other	8
Total	**100**

PRODUCTS/OPERATIONS

2011 Sales

	$ mil.	% of total
Oil & condensate	8,072	58
Natural gas	3,300	24
NGLs	1,462	10
Gathering processing & marketing	1,048	7
Gains on divestitures	85	1

COMPETITORS

Adams Resources
Apache
BP
Cabot Oil & Gas
Chesapeake Energy
Chevron
Cimarex
ConocoPhillips
Devon Energy
EOG
Exxon Mobil
Hunt Consolidated
Jones Energy
Key Energy
National Fuel Gas
Noble Energy
Pioneer Natural Resources
Royal Dutch Shell

HISTORICAL FINANCIALS

Company Type: Public

Income Statement FYE: December 31

	REVENUE ($ mil.)	NET INCOME ($ mil.)	NET PROFIT MARGIN	EMPLOYEES
12/11	13,967	(2,649)	—	4,800
12/10	10,984	761	6.9%	4,400
12/09	9,000	(135)	—	4,300
12/08	15,723	3,261	20.7%	4,300
12/07	15,892	3,781	23.8%	4,000
Annual Growth	(3.2%)	—	—	4.7%

2011 Year-End Financials

Debt ratio: 29.41%
Return on equity: (-14.63)%
Cash ($ mil.): 2,697
Current ratio: 141.48
Long-term debt ($ mil.): 15,060
No. of shares (mil.): 498
Dividends
Yield: —
Payout: —
Market value ($ mil.): 38,043

	STOCK PRICE ($) FY Close	P/E High	P/E Low	PER SHARE ($) Earnings	Dividends	Book Value
12/11	76.33	—	—	(5.32)	0.00	36.33
12/10	76.16	49	23	1.52	0.36	41.68
12/09	62.42	—	—	(0.28)	0.36	40.45
12/08	38.55	11	4	6.97	0.36	40.87
12/07	65.69	8	5	8.08	0.36	34.97
Annual Growth	3.8%	—	—	—	—	1.0%

Anchor BanCorp Wisconsin, Inc

Anchor BanCorp Wisconsin is the holding company for AnchorBank which has more than 50 branches across the Badger State. The thrift courts individuals and local businesses offering checking and savings accounts credit cards CDs and IRAs as well as insurance and investment products. Founded in 1919 AnchorBank is predominantly a real estate lender with residential and commercial mortgages and construction and land loans accounting for the majority of its loan portfolio. Like many other banks though AnchorBank is struggling with its capital levels due to real estate-related losses. The company has sold some of its branches to raise capital.

A decrease in real estate loan demand due to a weakened economy put a dent in Anchor BanCorp Wisconsin's revenue in fiscal 2012. Although it was able to decrease its provisions for loan losses that year compared to the previous three loan-related losses nonetheless contributed to an overall net loss of $36.7 million for the company. It was the fourth consecutive fiscal year that Anchor BanCorp Wisconsin finished in the red. Revenues also fell for the fourth year declining 21% from $222.3 million to $176.6 million.

The company holds a significant amount of senior debt and preferred debt obligations. To concentrate on its primary market of southern Wisconsin (and to raise funds) AnchorBank sold 11 bank branches in the northwestern part of the state to Royal Credit Union in 2010. It also sold four branches in Green Bay to Nicolet National Bank closed a lending-only location and is exploring other strategic alternatives including obtaining funding from outside investors.

EXECUTIVES

Chairman Anchor BanCorp Wisconsin and AnchorBank, David L. Omachinski, age 60

EVP Commercial Lending AnchorBank, Daniel K. Nichols, age 56, $179,400 total compensation

SVP Treasurer and CFO, Dale C. Ringgenberg, age 63, $148,800 total compensation

President CEO and Director; CEO AnchorBank, Chris M. Bauer, age 63

Director, Donald D. Parker, age 73

Director, James D. Smessaert, age 74

Director, Greg M. Larson, age 62

Director, Pat Richter, age 70

Director, Richard A. Bergstrom, age 62

Director, Holly Cremer Berkenstadt, age 56

Director, Donald D. Kropidlowski, age 70

President CEO and Director; CEO AnchorBank, Chris M. Bauer, age 63

Auditors: McGladreyLLP

LOCATIONS

HQ: Anchor BanCorp Wisconsin Inc.
25 W. Main St., Madison WI 53703-3374
Phone: 608-252-8700 **Fax:** 608-252-1806
Web: www.anchorbank.com

PRODUCTS/OPERATIONS

2012 Sales

	$ mil.	% of total
Interest		
Loans	116	66
Investments and Federal Home Loan Bank stock	9	6
Deposits	0	-
Noninterest		
Net gain on sale of loans	17	10
Service charges on deposits	11	6
Net gain on sale of investment securities	6	4
Net gain on sale of other real estate owned	6	3
Other	9	5
Adjustments	(1.4)	-
Total	**176**	**100**

COMPETITORS

Associated Banc-Corp
Bank Mutual
CIB Marine Bancshares
Citizens Republic Bancorp
First Business Financial
Harris
Mound City Financial Services
TCF Financial
U.S. Bancorp

HISTORICAL FINANCIALS

Company Type: Public

Income Statement FYE: March 31

	ASSETS ($ mil.)	NET INCOME ($ mil.)	INCOME AS % OF ASSETS	EMPLOYEES
03/12	2,789	(36)	—	738
03/11	3,394	(41)	—	817
03/10	4,416	(177)	—	1,063
03/09	5,273	(228)	—	1,169
03/08	5,149	31	0.6%	1,153
Annual Growth	(14.2%)	—	—	(10.6%)

2012 Year-End Financials

Debt ratio: 17.07%
Return on equity: 987650001000000.00%
Cash ($ mil.): 242
Current ratio: —
Long-term debt ($ mil.): 476
No. of shares (mil.): 21
Dividends
Yield: —
Payout: —
Market value ($ mil.): 21

	STOCK PRICE ($) FY Close	P/E High/Low	PER SHARE ($) Earnings	Dividends	Book Value
03/12	1.00	— —	(2.37)	0.00	(1.39)
03/11	0.99	— —	(2.57)	0.00	(0.61)
03/10	1.10	— —	(8.97)	0.00	1.39
03/09	1.35	— —	(10.83)	0.29	9.91
03/08	18.97	20 12	1.48	0.71	16.17
Annual Growth	(52.1%)	— —	—	—	—

Andersons, Inc.

The Andersons earns its daily bread on a mix of grains trains and corncobs. The agricultural company's main business –the Grain & Ethanol Group –consists of the buying conditioning and reselling of corn soybeans and wheat which it acquires from US grain farmers and stores using a system of elevators and terminals located in the Midwest. The company has six operating segments. Its segments comprise Grain Ethanol Plant Nutrient Group the Retail Group the Turf & Specialty Group and the Rail Group. The Andersons has operations in 16 US states and Puerto Rico as well as rail-leasing interests in Canada and Mexico.

The company's main agricultural operations are located in Ohio Indiana Illinois and Michigan. In total it has a grain-storage capacity of about 350 million bushels. About 95% of the grain sold by the company in 2011 was purchased by US grain processors and feeders and approximately 5% was exported (mainly to Canada).

Growing this business in 2012 the company acquired 12 grain elevators in northwestern Iowa and western Tennessee from Green Plains Renewable Energy for $133.1 million. Also it acquired the assets of Mt. Pulaski Products adding a pair of mills in Illinois and bolstering its cob supply. The two facilities are operated by The Andersons's Turf & Specialty Group

The Andersons jointly owns three ethanol facilities. It holds a 50% interest in The Andersons Albion Ethanol and a 38% interest in The Andersons Clymers Ethanol. It also holds a 50% interest (with Marathon Oil) in The Andersons Marathon Ethanol LLC. In all the company has an ethanol manufacturing capacity of 275 million gallons.

The Plant Nutrient Group has farm centers located throughout Michigan Indiana Ohio and Florida. The farm centers offer agricultural fertilizer chemicals seeds supplies and custom fertilizer application. The group also makes liquid anti-icers and deicers for use on roads and runways. It is now the company's second largest sales segment having generated 15% of The Andersons' sales in 2011.

The Andersons' Retail Group runs large retail home-center stores that serve the Toledo and Columbus Ohio areas. The stores sell home-improvement products nursery stock groceries beverages and other items. The Retail Group brought in about 3% of The Andersons' 2011 sales.

The Turf and Specialty operations of The Andersons at 3% of 2011 sales purchases stores formulates manufactures and sells dry and liquid fertilizer to dealers and farmers; provides warehousing and services; and distributes seeds and various other farm supplies such as corncobs that have been shredded into animal bedding pet litter and turf materials.

The company's Rail Group at 3% of 2011 sales sells leases repairs and reconfigures railcars and locomotives. The group also provides fleet management services and operates a custom steel-fabrication business. The company also owns around a 50% stake in Iowa Northern Railway Company (IANR) a 163-mile short-line railroad which runs through Iowa from northwest to southeast.

EXECUTIVES

VP Corporate Operations Services and President Retail Group, Daniel T. Anderson, age 56, $211,998 total compensation

Chairman President and CEO, Michael J. (Mike) Anderson, age 60, $519,231 total compensation

Chairman Emeritus, Richard P. (Dick) Anderson, age 82

President Grain Group, Dennis J. Addis, age 59, $275,192 total compensation

COO, Harold M. (Hal) Reed, age 55, $295,904 total compensation

President Rail Group, Rasesh H. Shah, age 57, $290,077 total compensation

Manager Corporate Communications, Debra A. (Debbie) Crow

VP Human Resources, Arthur D. DePompei, age 58

VP General Counsel and Corporate Secretary, Naran U. Burchinow, age 58, $169,749 total compensation

President Turf and Specialty Group, Thomas L. (Tom) Waggoner, age 57

VP Corporate Business and Financial Analysis, Tamara S. Sparks, age 43

VP Finance and Treasurer, Nicholas C. (Nick) Conrad, $160,929 total compensation

President Ethanol Group, Neill C. McKinstray
President Plant Nutrients Group, William J. Wolf
VP and Corporate Controller, Anne G. Rex
Director Corporate Business Development and Public Policy, Joseph W. Needham
Director, Robert J. (Bob) King Jr., age 56
Director, Gerard M. (Gerry) Anderson, age 54
Director, Ross W. Manire, age 60
Chairman Emeritus, Richard P. (Dick) Anderson, age 82
Director, David L. Nichols, age 71
Director, Jacqueline F. Woods, age 64
Director, Donald L. Mennel, age 65
Director, Catherine M. (Cathy) Kilbane, age 49
Director, John T. Stout Jr., age 58
Auditors: PricewaterhouseCoopersLLP

LOCATIONS

HQ: The Andersons Inc.
480 W. Dussel Dr., Maumee OH 43537
Phone: 419-893-5050 **Fax:** 713-220-4285
Web: www.akllp.com

PRODUCTS/OPERATIONS

2011 Sales

	$ mil.	% of total
Grain	2,849	62
Plant nutrition	690	15
Ethanol	641	14
Retail	157	3
Turf & specialty	129	3
Rail	107	3
Total	**4,576**	**100**

Selected Subsidiaries

The Andersons Agriculture Group L.P.
The Andersons ALACO Lawn Inc.
The Andersons Rail Operating I LLC
The Andersons ECO Services LLC
The Andersons Ethanol Champaign LLC
The Andersons Ethanol Investment LLC
The Andersons Ethanol Investment II LLC
The Andersons Farm Development LLC
The Andersons Lawn Fertilizer Division Inc.
The Andersons Winona Terminal LLC
Liqui Fert Corporation
Metamora Commodity Company Incorporated
Mineral Processing Company
NuRail Canada ULC
NuRail USA LLC

COMPETITORS

ADM
Ag Processing Inc.
Agrial
Bartlett and Company
Bunge Limited
Cargill
CHS
Costco Wholesale
DeBruce Grain
Food Corporation of India
GROWMARK
Home Depot
Louis Dreyfus Group
Lowe' s
Scoular
Southern States
Viterra Inc.
Wal-Mart
Wilbur-Ellis

HISTORICAL FINANCIALS

Company Type: Public

Income Statement FYE: December 31

	REVENUE ($ mil.)	NET INCOME ($ mil.)	NET PROFIT MARGIN	EMPLOYEES
12/11	4,576	95	2.1%	2,985
12/10	3,393	64	1.9%	2,943
12/09	3,025	38	1.3%	2,862
12/08	3,489	32	0.9%	2,741
12/07	2,379	68	2.9%	2,953
Annual Growth	17.8%	8.4%	—	0.3%

2011 Year-End Financials

Debt ratio: 19.76%
Return on equity: 18.15%
Cash ($ mil.): 20
Current ratio: 139.40
Long-term debt ($ mil.): 238
No. of shares (mil.): 18
Dividends
Yield: —
Payout: 9.43%
Market value ($ mil.): 808

	STOCK PRICE ($) FY Close	P/E High	P/E Low	PER SHARE ($) Earnings	Dividends	Book Value
12/11	43.66	10	6	5.09	0.00	28.32
12/10	36.35	12	7	3.48	0.38	24.49
12/09	25.82	18	5	2.08	0.35	21.52
12/08	16.48	26	6	1.79	0.33	19.49
12/07	44.80	13	10	3.75	0.25	19.13
Annual Growth	(0.6%)	—	—	7.9%	—	10.3%

Anixter International Inc

When it comes to getting wired Anixter International's got the connections. The company is a distributor of communication products used to connect voice video data and security systems. It sells 450000-plus products including electrical and electronic wire cable fasteners and security system components to some 100000 customers in a host of industries. Anixter operates primarily through several special sales forces –Electric and Electronic Wire and Cable Enterprise Cabling and Security Solutions and Fasteners –operating from about 300 warehouses and sales centers in 50 countries. Although Anixter gets its products from thousands of suppliers almost one-third come from just five companies.

Geographic Reach

Anixter operates through a network of warehouses and sales offices consisting of 155 locations in the US more than 15 in Canada 30 in the UK and 35 throughout the rest of Europe 30 in Latin America almost 20 in Asia and 5 spanning Australia and New Zealand.

Sales & Marketing

More than two dozen industries are represented among Anixter customers –markets such as education government health care manufacturing retail and transportation. Anixter also serves contractors and integrators who install and maintain communications networks and data centers. International national regional and local OEMs number among Anixter's customers as well procuring wire cable fasteners and other small components to help finish the manufacturing of their own products typically with short lead times.

Operations

Anixter's massive distribution capacity is central to delivering goods whenever and wherever its customers demand. In addition to turn-on-a-dime delivery the company's reach has cultivated a broad customer base; no one customer accounts for more than 2% of sales. Not content however to rest on its distribution might Anixter moves beyond solely aggregating and marketing products to offering a slate of inventory management services for customers as well as testing facilities for its suppliers.

Financial Analysis

The company has enjoyed steady growth over the last three years. From 2010 to 2011 its revenues increased by almost 17% while its profits skyrocketed by 73%. The spike in total sales was due to favorable foreign exchange rates and higher revenue generated from Clark Security Products a previous acquisition.

It also enjoyed a rise in demand for its products across North America Latin America and the Asia/Pacific. Total sales increased in Europe due to higher sales in the OEM Supply end sector and growth in the Enterprise Cabling and Security end market. Anixter derives more than 40% of its revenue from outside the US.

Strategy

The company's operations are driven organically through both product and service expansions. At the same time Anixter doesn't hesitate to go after niche acquisition opportunities that promise to expand its technical expertise and geographic reach. For example in mid-2012 it purchased Jorvex S.A. a distributor of electrical wire cable and fasteners based in Lima Peru. In late 2010 it paid $36.4 million in cash for the operations of San Diego-based security products distributor Clark Security Products and the assets and operations of General Lock.

In addition to South America Anixter is looking to extend its reach in the Middle East. It entered a partnership in early 2012 with Mohawarean Trading Company to form Anixter Saudi Arabia Limited. The new entity will allow Anixter to distribute its electrical products throughout Saudi Arabia and other regions.

Focusing on its core operations Anixter in 2011 sold its Aerospace Hardware division to Greenbriar Equity for about $155 million. Customer and supplier consolidation and increasing demands for capital have caused the division to become a poor fit for Anixter.

Ownership

Billionaire financier Samuel Zell Anixter's chairman since 1985 holds 15% of Anixter through various family trusts.

HISTORY

Anixter International was founded in 1957 by two brothers Alan and Bill Anixter along with a small group of employees in Evanston Illinois. The company was known as Anixter Brothers at the time and it supplied distributors and wholesalers looking for an alternative to buying wire and cable in bulk quantities directly from manufacturers.

The company went public on the American Stock Exchange in 1967. Anixter became an international company when Anixter United Kingdom was formed in 1972. That decade saw its continued growth throughout North America.

In 1987 holding company Itel bought Anixter which had since moved into the data communications business to round out its expertise in electrical wire and cable. Itel was led by Chicago financier Samuel Zell who had become chairman in 1985.

Zell and vice chairman Rod Dammeyer former Household International CFO acquired Great Lakes International (marine dredging 1986) Anixter Bros. (wire and cable 1986) Pullman (railcars 1988) and a minority stake in Santa Fe Southern Pacific (railroad 1988). Other acquisitions included Flexi-Van Leasing (1987) the assets of Evans Asset Holding (railcars 1987) and B.C. Hydro (rail freight line 1988). By 1988 Itel was North America's leading railcar leasing company.

In the 1990s Itel repositioned itself selling its container-leasing business (1990) and its Itel Distribution Systems and Great Lakes Dredge & Deck Co. (1991). When the smoke cleared Anixter was the company's core operation. Anixter spun off its cable television products subsidiary ANTEC in 1993. Also that year Dammeyer replaced Zell as Itel's CEO.

Itel began focusing on developing new markets in the burgeoning global communications industry. The company sold its remaining rail leasing interests in 1994. The next year Itel sold its stake in Santa Fe Energy Resources and changed its name to Anixter.

When an ANTEC subsidiary merged with cable TV equipment firm TSX Corp. in 1997 Anixter's ownership in ANTEC was reduced to 19%. That year the company joined with security software maker Check Point Software Technologies to provide network security products in Europe.

Anixter sold its ANTEC holdings in 1998 to finance the repurchase of its common stock and bought Pacer Electronics an electrical and data cabling distributor. Also that year company veteran Robert Grubbs became CEO.

The next year Anixter sold its European network integration business to Persetel Q Data Holdings of South Africa and its data network design and consulting unit to Ameritech for $200 million in cash. It also sold North America Integration and Asia Pacific Integration completing the dissolution of its integration segment by the close of 1999.

Anixter formed a consortium in 2000 with Panduit Rockwell Automation and Siemens for the production of industrially hardened Ethernet connectors. Anixter signed an agreement to distribute network cabling products for IBM in 2001.

In 2002 Anixter was named as a "Forbes" "Platinum 400" company chosen by the magazine's editors as one of America's "best-performing" corporations by industry. Later that year it acquired Pentacon (which became Anixter Pentacon) a fastener distribution company. More fastener acquisitions followed: Walters Hexagon in 2003 DDI in 2004 Infast Group in 2005 MFU in 2006 and Eurofast and Total Supply Solutions in 2007. (Anixter combined Anixter Pentacon and Anixter Eurofast into a single brand forming Anixter Aerospace Hardware) in 2009.)

Robert Grubbs retired as president and CEO in mid-2008. The board designated EVP/COO Robert Eck a 17-year veteran of Anixter as his successor. Also that year Anixter acquired the assets and operations of Quality Screw & Nut (now Anixter Fasteners) and its Quality Screw de Mexico subsidiary for about $80 million. The acquisition augmented Anixter's geographic reach with the addition of nearly 20 facilities in the US and Mexico and it boosted manufacturing capacity in bolts screws and cold formed components. Anixter also benefited from an enhanced portfolio that courted manufacturers in a variety of vertical markets.

Later in 2008 the company purchased the assets and operations of Wisconsin's World Class Wire & Cable for some $62 million and it bought France's Sofrasar and Germany's Camille Gergen. The European fastener distributors gave subsidiaries Anixter Fasteners and Anixter Aerospace Hardware more muscle to supply fasteners and aerospace hardware respectively to manufacturers throughout the world.

Anixter obtained in 2010 San Diego-based security products distributor Clark Security Products and the assets and operations of General Lock. The purchase price was roughly $36 million.

EXECUTIVES

Chairman, Samuel (Sam) Zell, age 70
VP General Counsel and Secretary, John A. Dul, age 50, $310,000 total compensation
VP Taxes, Philip F. Meno, age 53, $158,000 total compensation
VP and Controller, Terrance A. Faber, age 60, $262,000 total compensation
VP and Treasurer, Rodney A. Shoemaker, age 54, $189,000 total compensation
EVP and CFO, Theodore A. (Ted) Dosch, age 52, $325,096 total compensation
EVP and CIO, Dave Lemme
VP Human Resources, Rodney A. Smith, age 54, $245,000 total compensation
President CEO and Director, Robert J. Eck, age 54, $630,000 total compensation
VP Internal Audit, Nancy C. Ross-Dronzek, age 51
VP Marketing Communications, Dawn Marks
VP and Internal Audit, Mary Kate Powell, age 39
Chairman, Samuel (Sam) Zell, age 70
Director, Robert W. Grubbs Jr., age 55
Director, F. Philip Handy, age 67
Director, Melvyn N. Klein, age 70
Director, Linda Walker Bynoe, age 59
Director, Matthew M. Zell, age 45
Director, Lord James Blyth, age 71
Director, Frederic F. (Jake) Brace, age 54
Director, George Mu?oz, age 61
President CEO and Director, Robert J. Eck, age 54
Auditors: Ernst&YoungLLP

LOCATIONS

HQ: Anixter International Inc.
2301 Patriot Blvd., Glenview IL 60026
Phone: 224-521-8000 **Fax:** 972-431-1362
Web: www.jcpenney.net

2011 Sales

North America	4,302	70
Other regions	694	11

PRODUCTS/OPERATIONS

2011 Sales by Markets

Enterprise cabling & security	53
Original equipment manufacturing	15

Selected Products & Services

Products
- Electrical wire and cable (power cable)
- Electronic wire and cable (coax)
- Fasteners and connectors (" C" class)
- Industrial networking communications
- Network cabling (copper and fiber)
- Networking wireless and voice electronics
- Security (video surveillance access control)

Supply chain services
- Database tracking
- Deployment
- Inventory management
- Logistics
- Product enhancement and packaging
- Sourcing

COMPETITORS

Agilysys
Arrow Electronics
Avnet
Border States Electric
Consolidated Electrical
Crescent Electric Supply
Fastenal
Gexpro
Graybar Electric
Ingram Micro
Kirby Risk
Lawson Products
MSC Industrial Direct
Park-Ohio Holdings
Precision Industries
Premier Farnell
Rexel
Richardson Electronics
Sonepar
Tech Data
TESSCO
W.W. Grainger
WESCO International

HISTORICAL FINANCIALS

Company Type: Public

Income Statement

FYE: December 31

	REVENUE ($ mil.)	NET INCOME ($ mil.)	NET PROFIT MARGIN	EMPLOYEES
12/11	6,146	188	3.1%	8,200
12/10*	5,472	108	2.0%	7,989
01/10	4,982	(29)	—	7,811
01/09	6,136	195	3.2%	8,645
12/07	5,852	253	4.3%	8,000
Annual Growth	1.2%	(7.2%)	—	0.6%

*Fiscal year change

2011 Year-End Financials

Debt ratio: 26.69%	No. of shares (mil.): 33
Return on equity: 18.80%	Dividends
Cash ($ mil.): 106	Yield: —
Current ratio: 234.00	Payout: —
Long-term debt ($ mil.): 806	Market value ($ mil.): 1,982

	STOCK PRICE ($) FY Close	P/E High	P/E Low	PER SHARE ($) Earnings	Dividends	Book Value
12/11	59.64	14	8	5.36	0.00	30.13
12/10*	59.73	19	12	3.05	3.25	29.45
01/10	47.10	—	—	(0.83)	0.00	29.51
01/09	32.17	13	4	5.07	0.00	29.32
12/07	62.27	13	7	6.00	0.00	28.84
Annual Growth	(1.1%)	—	—	(2.8%)	—	1.1%

*Fiscal year change

Annaly Capital Management Inc

Annaly cannily invests its capital. A real estate investment trust (REIT) Annaly Capital Management invests in and manages a portfolio of mortgage-backed securities including mortgage pass-through certificates collateralized mortgage obligations and agency callable debentures. It primarily invests in high-quality securities issued or guaranteed by the likes of Freddie Mac Fannie Mae and Ginnie Mae and backed by single-family residential mortgages. As agency mortgage-backed securities Annaly's assets carry an implied AAA rating. Subsidiaries Fixed Income Discount Advisory Company (FIDAC) and Merganser provide investment advisory and asset management services; RCap Securities operates as a broker/dealer.

All three subsidiaries are also structured as REITs. FIDAC and Merganser manage some $20 billion in gross assets for clients including pension plans endowments and funds. The units provide Annaly with additional service offerings broadening its revenue base.

The REIT has established other new entities too. In 2010 it formed Shannon Funding to provide warehouse financing to residential mortgage originators and corporate middle market lending specialist Charlesfort Capital Management. The following year it created European advisory arm FIDAC Europe and security investor FIDAC FSI.

Annaly Capital is a self-advised and self-managed REIT.

Unlike many mortgage REITs Annaly doesn't own actual real estate. The company makes its money based on the interest rate spread: When interest rates go down Annaly's returns tend to go up. It does this by borrowing short-term loans which typically carry lower interest rates and using that money to invest in mortgage-backed securities which typically carry higher rates. As such the troubled economy actually benefitted the REIT as lowered short-term interest rates widened the interest rate spread which translates into higher interest income. That combined with the company's interest rate hedging strategy contributed to 2009 profits of $2 billion a more than 200% increase over 2008.

However revenues and profits have declined since then. In 2011 sales fell 57% to $1.1 billion while net income plummeted 73% to $344.5 million. The declines were attributed to losses on interest rate swaps. Also contributing to the declines Fannie Mae and Freddie Mac began buying up delinquent loans cutting into the REIT's principal repayments income. Annaly is exploring the impact that the possible winding down of the agencies might have on its business.

Partially offsetting the losses the REIT's interest earnings grew 33% in 2011 largely due to growth in its interest-earning portfolio of mortgage-backed securities and US Treasury notes and bonds. The company maintains a conservative investment and divestiture strategy.

EXECUTIVES

CFO and Treasurer Annaly and FIDAC, Kathryn F. Fagan, age 45, $972,000 total compensation
Vice Chairman Chief Investment Officer and COO; Chief Investment Officer and COO FIDAC, Wellington J. Denahan-Norris, age 48, $2,430,000 total compensation
Chairman President and CEO Annaly and FIDAC, Michael A. J. Farrell, age 60, $2,430,000 total compensation
Managing Director Head of Liabilities and Chief of Staff; Managing Director FIDAC, James P. Fortescue, age 38, $500,000 total compensation
Managing Director Head of Research and Corporate Communications, Jeremy Diamond, age 48, $500,000 total compensation
Managing Director and Head of Asset Management Group, Ronald Kazel, age 44, $500,000 total compensation
Managing Director and Head Portfolio Manager, Kristopher R. Konrad, age 37, $500,000 total compensation
Managing Director and Chief Investment Officer FIDAC, Rose-Marie Lyght, age 38
EVP General Counsel Corporate Secretary and Chief Compliance Officer Annaly and FIDAC, R. Nicholas Singh, age 53
Managing Director and Chief Risk Officer Annaly and FIDAC, Eric Szabo
Managing Director and Head of Business Development, Matthew J. Lambiase, age 45
Director, Michael E. (Mike) Haylon, age 54
Vice Chairman Chief Investment Officer and COO; Chief Investment Officer and COO FIDAC, Wellington J. Denahan-Norris, age 48
Director, E. Wayne Nordberg, age 74
Director, Kevin P. Brady, age 56
Director, Donnell A. Segalas, age 54
Director, Jonathan D. (Jon) Green, age 65
Director, John A. Lambiase, age 72
Auditors: Deloitte&ToucheLLP

LOCATIONS

HQ: Annaly Capital Management Inc.
1211 Avenue of the Americas Ste. 2902, New York NY 10036
Phone: 212-696-0100 **Fax:** 212-696-9809
Web: www.annaly.com

PRODUCTS/OPERATIONS

2011 Sales

	$ mil.	% of total
Interest		
Investment securities	3,558	91
US Treasury securities	14	-
Securities loaned	6	-
Net gains on sale of mortgage-backed securities & agency debentures		206
5		
Investment advisory & other fee income	79	2
Dividends	31	1
Net gains on trading assets	21	1
Underwriting	5	-
Adjustments	(2804.2)	-
Total	**1,120**	**100**

COMPETITORS

AG Mortgage Investment Trust
Capstead Mortgage
Impac Mortgage Holdings
Institutional Financial Markets
iStar Financial Inc
JAVELIN Mortgage
MFA Financial
Newcastle Investment
Redwood Trust

HISTORICAL FINANCIALS

Company Type: Public

Income Statement FYE: December 31

	ASSETS ($ mil.)	NET INCOME ($ mil.)	INCOME AS % OF ASSETS	EMPLOYEES
12/11	109,630	344	0.3%	147
12/10	83,026	1,267	1.5%	114
12/09	69,376	1,961	2.8%	87
12/08	57,597	346	0.6%	65
12/07	53,903	414	0.8%	39
Annual Growth	19.4%	(4.5%)	—	39.3%

2011 Year-End Financials

Debt ratio: 1.23%
Return on equity: 2.18%
Cash ($ mil.): 994
Current ratio: —
Long-term debt ($ mil.): 1,344
No. of shares (mil.): 970
Dividends
Yield: —
Payout: 532.10%
Market value ($ mil.): 15,484

	STOCK PRICE ($) FY Close	P/E High/Low		PER SHARE ($) Earnings	Dividends	Book Value
12/11	15.96	51	42	0.37	0.00	16.28
12/10	17.92	9	7	2.04	2.65	15.68
12/09	17.35	6	4	3.52	2.54	17.39
12/08	15.87	33	18	0.64	2.08	13.44
12/07	18.18	14	10	1.31	1.04	13.23
Annual Growth	(3.2%)	—	—	(27.1%)	—	5.3%

Anworth Mortgage Asset Corp.

What's an Anworth? Depends on the mortgage market. A self-managed real estate investment trust (REIT) Anworth Mortgage invests in mortgage-related assets primarily mortgage-backed securities (MBS) guaranteed by the US government or federally sponsored entities like Fannie Mae and Freddie Mac. As a REIT the company must invest at least three-quarters of its assets in real estate government securities cash or cash-equivalents and it more than complies: More than 99% of Anworth Mortgage's assets are invested in agency-backed MBS; the remainder is invested in non-agency collateralized mortgage obligations (CMOs). The company funds its investment activities mainly through short-term loans.

Anworth Mortgage hopes to diversify its portfolio by taking advantage of reduced competition in the secondary mortgage market due to mergers bankruptcies or market jitters.

EXECUTIVES

EVP Chief Investment Officer and Director, Joseph E. McAdams, age 43, $700,000 total compensation
VP and Portfolio Manager, Evangelos Karagiannis, age 50, $39,985 total compensation
EVP, Heather U. Baines, age 70, $50,495 total compensation
Chairman President and CEO, Lloyd McAdams, age 66, $925,000 total compensation
CFO Treasurer and Secretary, Thad M. Brown, age 62, $275,000 total compensation
VP and Director Investor Relations, John T. Hillman
SVP and Portfolio Manager, Bistra Pashamova, age 41, $275,000 total compensation
SVP Finance and Assistant Secretary, Charles J. Siegel, age 62, $250,000 total compensation
VP and Controller, Angelina Greve
EVP Chief Investment Officer and Director, Joseph E. McAdams, age 43
Director, Lee A. Ault III, age 75
Director, Joe E. Davis, age 77
Director, Charles H. Black, age 85
Director, Robert C. Davis, age 67
Auditors: McGladreyLLP

LOCATIONS

HQ: Anworth Mortgage Asset Corporation
1299 Ocean Ave. 2nd Fl., Santa Monica CA 90401
Phone: 310-255-4493 **Fax:** 310-434-0070
Web: www.anworth.com

PRODUCTS/OPERATIONS

COMPETITORS

Annaly Capital Management
ARMOUR Residential REIT
Capstead Mortgage
DVL
Huntington Preferred Capital
Impac Mortgage Holdings
Institutional Financial Markets
MFA Financial
Newcastle Investment
Redwood Trust
Webster Preferred Capital

HISTORICAL FINANCIALS

Company Type: Public

Income Statement FYE: December 31

	ASSETS ($ mil.)	NET INCOME ($ mil.)	INCOME AS % OF ASSETS	EMPLOYEES
12/11	8,813	122	1.4%	0
12/10	7,790	110	1.4%	12
12/09	6,526	130	2.0%	12
12/08	5,477	62	1.1%	12
12/07	4,797	(156)	—	12
Annual Growth	16.4%	—	—	—

2011 Year-End Financials

Debt ratio: 0.42%
Return on equity: 12.17%
Cash ($ mil.): 8
Current ratio: —
Long-term debt ($ mil.): 37

No. of shares (mil.): 134
Dividends
Yield: —
Payout: 104.44%
Market value ($ mil.): 842

	STOCK PRICE ($) FY Close	P/E High/Low		PER SHARE ($) Earnings	Dividends	Book Value
12/11	6.28	8	7	0.90	0.00	7.53
12/10	7.00	8	7	0.87	0.97	7.39
12/09	7.00	7	5	1.16	1.18	8.04
12/08	6.43	15	6	0.69	1.00	6.46
12/07	8.26	—	—	(3.47)	0.27	7.50
Annual Growth	(6.6%)	—	—	—	—	0.1%

Apache Corp.

There's more than only a patch of oil for Apache. The oil and gas exploration and production company has onshore and offshore operations in major oil patches around the world in North America as well as in Argentina Australia Egypt and the UK North Sea. Its five North American regions include the Gulf of Mexico the Gulf Coast of Texas and Louisiana the Permian Basin in West Texas the Anadarko Basin in Oklahoma and Canada's Western Sedimentary Basin. In 2011 the company reported estimated proved reserves of about 3 billion barrels of oil equivalent. Apache spreads its production risks both through geographic diversification and through mixing low- and higher-risk properties in its portfolio.

Financial Analysis

Boosted by its acquisitions and stronger oil prices in 2010 the company reported a surge in revenues. Its net income was also up dramatically (Apache's 2009 results were negatively impacted by an almost $2 billion after-tax write-down of the carrying value of proved property). Increased production and higher oil prices lifted Apache's revenues and net income further in 2011.

Strategy

While the US represents almost 40% of the company's production Apache is well aware that growth can not come from drilling simply more wells in its existing US mature and declining fields. With that in mind Apache seeks domestic and international expansion through acquisitions. In 2010 it seized on one such opportunity buying Gulf of Mexico shelf assets from Devon Energy (which is shedding assets to raise cash) for $1 billion. The acquisition added some 41 million barrels of proved reserves and some 477200 acres to Apache's asset base.

It also acquired Mariner Energy for $2.7 billion (including Mariner Energy's debt of $1.6 billion) giving the company an entry into the deepwater Gulf of Mexico. Mariner's deepwater portfolio includes 125 blocks seven discoveries under development and more than 50 prospects. The deal is a natural extension of Apache's commitment to develop the Gulf of Mexico as a primary area of production and anticipates a rebounding economy and an increasing demand for oil.

With BP looking to raise cash to defray the cost of its rig disaster in the Gulf of Mexico in 2010 Apache took the opportunity to buy BP assets in Canada Egypt and the US (Permian Basin) for about $7 billion. The deal boosted Apache's estimated proved reserves by 385 million barrels of oil equivalent.

In Canada the company moved in 2010 to expand its supply base buying 51% of a proposed liquefied natural gas (LNG) export terminal in British Columbia operated by Kitimat LNG Inc.

The company grew its North Sea assets further in 2012 buying Exxon Mobil's Beryl field and related properties for about $1.75 billion.

Growing its unconventional assets in the US that year the company acquired Cordillera Energy Partners for $2.85 billion. The privately held company owned 254000 net acres of tight sand plays in Oklahoma and Texas. In 2012 it also bought 49% of Burrup Holdings an ammonia fertilizer plant in Western Australia for $439 million. The deal with one of the world's largest ammonia plants secures a long-term market for Apache's natural gas production in the region.

HISTORY

Originally Raymond Plank wanted to start a magazine. Then it was an accounting and tax-assistance service. Plank and his co-founding partner Truman Anderson had no experience in any of these occupations but their accounting business succeeded. In the early 1950s Plank and Anderson branched out again founding APA a partnership to invest in new ventures including oil and gas exploration. The partnership founded Apache Oil in Minnesota in 1954. Investors put up the money and Apache managed the drilling spreading the risk over several projects.

As problems with government regulations in the oil industry mounted during the 1960s Apache diversified into real estate. The real estate operations were pivotal in driving a wedge between Plank and Anderson. In 1963 Anderson called a board meeting to ask the directors to fire Plank. Instead Anderson resigned and Plank took over.

Apache's holdings soon encompassed 24 firms including engineering electronics farming and water-supply subsidiaries. Understanding that its fortunes were tied to varying oil and gas prices the company reassessed its diversified structure in the 1970s. When the energy crisis rocketed oil prices skyward Apache sold its non-energy operations which would have been hurt by the price increases.

Apache formed Apache Petroleum in 1981 as an investment vehicle to take advantage of tax laws favoring limited partnerships. Initially the strategy was a success but it fell victim in the mid-1980s to a one-two punch: Oil prices sank like a rock and Congress put an end to the tax advantage. After suffering its first loss in 1986 Apache reorganized into a conventional exploration and production company.

Still under Plank's leadership the company began steadily buying oil and gas properties and companies in 1991. That year it purchased oil and gas sites with more than 100 million barrels of reserves from Amoco and put the wells back into production. By buying Hadson Energy Resources which operated fields in western Australia Apache gained entry into the relatively unexplored region in 1993.

In 1995 Apache merged with Calgary Canada-based DEKALB Energy (later renamed DEK Energy) and continued picking up properties. It bought $600 million worth of US reserves from Texaco (acquired by Chevron in 2001) that year. In 1996 it expanded its Chinese operations and bought Phoenix Resource Companies which operated solely in Egypt. A 1998 agreement with Texaco expanded its Chinese acreage thirtyfold. Apache also bought oil and gas properties and production facilities in waters off western Australia from a Mobil unit.

Apache joined with FX Energy and Polish Oil & Gas in 1998 to begin exploratory drilling in Poland. It also worked with XCL and China National Oil & Gas Exploration & Development in Bohai Bay though the project was slowed by a dispute between Apache and XCL over costs. In 1999 Apache bought Gulf of Mexico assets from a unit of Royal Dutch Shell and acquired oil and gas properties in western Canada from Shell Canada. That year Apache sold its Ivory Coast oil and gas holdings for $46 million.

Still shopping however Apache agreed in 2000 to buy assets in western Canada and Argentina with proved reserves of more than 700 billion cu. ft. of natural gas equivalent from New Zealand's Fletcher Challenge Energy. To help pay for the $600 million acquisition which closed in 2001 Apache sold $100 million in stock to Shell which acquired other Fletcher Challenge Energy assets. Apache bought the Canadian assets of Phillips Petroleum (later ConocoPhillips) for $490 million in 2000 and acquired the Egyptian assets of Repsol YPF for $410 million in 2001.

Late in 2002 in a move aimed at boosting its natural gas production by more than 10% Apache acquired 234000 net acres of land in southern Louisiana for $260 million. That year the company also announced three oil discoveries in the Carnarvon Basin offshore Western Australia.

Apache acquired UK and US oil and gas assets in 2003 from BP for $1.3 billion. The main prize was the Forties field one of the North Sea's oldest discoveries (dating back to the early 1970s) and its largest.

In 2004 it acquired more than two dozen mature US and Canadian fields from Exxon Mobil for $347 million and Gulf of Mexico properties from Anadarko Petroleum for $525 million. In 2005 Hurricane Katrina destroyed eight of its 241 Gulf rigs.

In 2009 Apache founder Raymond Plank retired as chairman of the company. He had been its chief executive from Apache's founding in 1954 until his retirement in 2002 when he remained as chairman. CEO Steven Farris took up the additional title of chairman when Plank stepped down completely.

The company bounced back from a sup-par 2009 when the global recession low commodities prices and a slump in demand suppressed its revenues.

EXECUTIVES

EVP and CTO, Michael S. (Mike) Bahorich, age 55, $447,288 total compensation

Corporate Secretary, Cheri L. Peper, age 58

VP Information Technology, Aaron S. G. Merrick, age 49

SVP Treasury and Administration, Matthew W. (Matt) Dundrea, age 59
President and Chief Corporate Officer, Roger B. Plank, age 55, $578,598 total compensation
SVP Global Communications and Corporate Affairs, Robert J. (Bob) Dye, age 57
Chairman and CEO, G. Steven (Steve) Farris, age 64, $1,387,500 total compensation
EVP and General Counsel, P. Anthony Lannie, age 58
Regional VP and Managing Director Apache North Sea, James L. (Jim) House, age 51
President and COO, Rodney J. Eichler, age 63, $557,722 total compensation
EVP Gulf of Mexico Operations, Jon A. Jeppesen, age 64, $318,750 total compensation
VP Tax, Jon W. Sauer, age 51
SVP Human Resources, Margery M. (Margie) Harris, age 51
EVP and CFO, Thomas P. (Tom) Chambers, age 57
SVP Gas Monetization, Janine J. McArdle, age 51
Region VP Central Region, Robert V. (Rob) Johnston, age 57
Director Public Affairs, William (Bill) Mintz
VP Permian Region, John J. Christmann IV, age 44
EVP Corporate Reservoir Engineering, W. Kregg Olson, age 58
Editor Arrows Apache's Employee Newsletter, Lisa Nutting
VP Security, Alex C. De Alvarez, age 48
SVP Policy and Governance, Sarah B. Teslik, age 58
VP Chief Accounting Officer and Controller, Rebecca A. (Becky) Hoyt, age 48
VP Liquefied Natural Gas Projects, Graham Lawton
Region VP and General Manager Apache Egypt Companies, Thomas E. Voytovich, age 55
President Apache Canada; Region VP Canada Apache Energy, Timothy O. (Tim) Wall, age 50
VP Worldwide Exploration and New Ventures, John R. Bedingfield, age 56
VP Environmental Health and Safety Organization, Jon Graham, age 58
VP Government Affairs, Urban F. (Obie) O'Brien, age 58
VP Australia Region and Managing Director Apache Energy Ltd., Thomas M. (Tom) Maher, age 55
VP Business Development, David L. French, age 42
Manager e-Communications, Anne Hedrich
Manager Environmental, John Williams
Community Outreach Contact Argentina, Claudio Barone
Community Outreach Contact Australia, Carol Foster
Community Outreach Contact Egypt, Glenn Joyce
Community Outreach UK North Sea, Donna McLennan
Community Outreach Contact US Central, Kellie Muckleroy
Supervisor Corporate Services Procurement, Toya Shepard
Manager Strategic Sourcing, Mark Hood
VP Environmental Health and Safety, David Carmony
VP Gulf Coast Onshore Region, Paul McKinney, age 53
VP and Associate General Counsel, Dominic Ricotta, age 46
VP Audit, Rodney A. (Rod) Gryder, age 64
VP Planning and Strategy, Alfonso Leon, age 36
VP International Marketing, David (Dave) Gilbronson, age 54
VP North America Oil and Gas Marketing, Mark Bright, age 50
Manager Public Affairs, Patrick Cassidy
Region VP Gulf of Mexico Shelf, Mark Bauer
Region VP and Country Manager Argentina, Michael Bose
VP LNG Marketing and Shipping Apache Energy, Kenny Paterson
Director, Frederick M. (Fred) Bohen, age 74
Director, Randolph M. Ferlic, age 74
Director, Eugene C. Fiedorek, age 80
Director, John A. Kocur, age 83
Director, George D. Lawrence Jr., age 61
Director, F. H. Merelli, age 76
Director, Rodman D. Patton, age 68
Director, Charles J. Pitman, age 69
Director, Lori Holland, age 54
Director, A. D. Frazier Jr., age 67
Director, Scott D. Josey, age 54
Director, Patricia A. Graham, age 76
Director, Chansoo Joung, age 52
Auditors: Ernst&YoungLLP

LOCATIONS

HQ: Apache Corporation
2000 Post Oak Blvd. Ste. 100, Houston TX 77056-4400
Phone: 713-296-6000 **Fax:** 713-296-6496
Web: www.apachecorp.com

2011 Sales

	$ mil.	% of total
US	6,104	36
UK (North Sea)	2,091	13
Canada	1,617	10
Adjustments	78	-

PRODUCTS/OPERATIONS

2011 Production Sales

	$ mil.	% of total
% of total		
Vitol		13
Royal Dutch		11
Other		76
Total		**100**

COMPETITORS

Abraxas Petroleum
Adams Resources
Anadarko Petroleum
BP
Brigham Exploration
Chesapeake Energy
Chevron
Devon Energy
El Paso Corporation
EOG
Exxon Mobil
Forest Oil
Helmerich & Payne
Hess Corporation
Jones Energy
Pioneer Natural Resources
Qatargas
Range Resources
Royal Dutch Shell
Santos Ltd
XTO Energy

HISTORICAL FINANCIALS

Company Type: Public

Income Statement FYE: December 31

	REVENUE ($ mil.)	NET INCOME ($ mil.)	NET PROFIT MARGIN	EMPLOYEES
12/11	16,888	4,584	27.1%	5,299
12/10	12,092	3,032	25.1%	4,449
12/09	8,614	(284)	—	3,452
12/08	12,389	711	5.7%	3,639
12/07	9,977	2,812	28.2%	3,521
Annual Growth	14.1%	13.0%	—	10.8%

2011 Year-End Financials

Debt ratio: 13.86%
Return on equity: 15.81%
Cash ($ mil.): 295
Current ratio: 96.78
Long-term debt ($ mil.): 6,785
No. of shares (mil.): 384
Dividends
Yield: —
Payout: 5.23%
Market value ($ mil.): 34,793

	STOCK PRICE ($) FY Close	P/E High	P/E Low	PER SHARE ($) Earnings	Dividends	Book Value
12/11	90.58	11	7	11.47	0.00	75.48
12/10	119.23	14	10	8.46	0.60	63.75
12/09	103.17	—	—	(0.87)	0.60	46.90
12/08	74.53	70	29	2.09	0.70	49.32
12/07	107.54	13	7	8.39	0.60	46.19
Annual Growth	(4.2%)	—	—	8.1%	—	13.1%

Apollo Group, Inc.

Apollo's creed could be that we all deserve the chance to advance. The for-profit Apollo Group provides educational programs through a number of subsidiaries including online stalwart University of Phoenix. The largest private university in the US the University of Phoenix accounts for more than 90% of Apollo's sales and has an enrollment of 400000 students in degree programs ranging from associate's to doctoral. Other schools include Western International University (graduate and undergraduate courses) and UK-based BPP Holdings a provider of legal and financial professional training. Founder and chairman John Sperling and his son vice chairman Peter Sperling together own a controlling stake in Apollo.

Other Apollo Group subsidiaries include The College for Financial Planning Institutes which offers financial planner certification and graduate programs and Institute for Professional Development which consults with schools seeking to expand and develop programs for working adults. In 2011 Apollo Group sold its Insights Schools unit which provided online high school education for homeschooled students for about $25 million (including $15 million working capital consideration and $3 million to be held in escrow for a year). The same year the company shuttered its Meritus University which was established in 2008 to offer online degree programs in Canada.

Apollo Group pursues growth through acquisitions and via organic growth into new markets. Its majority-owned Apollo Global subsidiary formed in 2007 focuses on both online and on-site expansion in additional international markets. In Latin America the unit acquired Chile's Universidad de Artes Ciencias y Comunicacion in 2008 and Mexico's Universidad Latinoamericana in 2009. Also in 2009 it acquired UK-based BPP Holdings; following the purchase Apollo Global is investing in BPP's growth enabling it to expand its degree program offerings in the UK and throughout Europe. In 2010 Apollo Group transferred its Western International University unit to Apollo Global as well.

While cramming really isn't a good study strategy it's a quick way to build out a company. In 2011 Apollo Group paid $75 million to acquire K-12 math curricula publisher Carnegie Learning from Carnegie Mellon University. It also paid an additional $21.5 million to acquire related technology to support Carnegie Learning and carry the company into the the elementary education market.

The company's rapid success as a leading online educational services provider –its University of Phoenix has grown to become the largest for-profit college in the US –has put Apollo Group in the public eye and not all of the attention has been positive. A number of government institutions have launched inquiries into its business practices including an investigation by the Florida Attorney General into possible deceptive trade practices and an informal SEC investigation over Apollo Group's insider trading practices. The US Education Department is also looking into how the University of Phoenix disburses federal student loans.

These investigations have contributed to major changes at the university. The changes while improving transparency place the institution in a transitional phase since a drop in admissions and finances stands to follow suit. The plan however is that long-term growth of a higher quality will result. Some of the changes have included altering its marketing practices so that potential students are fully informed about their educational options and the associated costs providing heightened training for its financial counselors and developing financial literacy tools to aid students. Compensation practices regarding admittance personnel were also reviewed. Additionally the university developed a free three-week program piloted and implemented in 2010 to give prospective students the chance before enrolling and taking on debt to determine if the experience was right for them.

Charles Edelstein formerly an investment banker with Credit Suisse was named Apollo Group's CEO in 2008. The following year global strategy leader Gregory Capelli was named co-CEO to share leadership duties with Edelstein.

HISTORY

The son of Missouri sharecroppers John Sperling had an early interest in higher education for the working class. Following WWII he attended Reed College on the GI Bill and eventually received a PhD in economic history from Cambridge. He started the Institute for Professional Development in 1973 to offer nontraditional programs designed for working adults. Sperling's program was rejected by San Jose State University where he was a tenured professor so he took his idea to the University of San Francisco. There he designed a curriculum program for firefighters police officers and other workers. Within two years the program had 2500 students but the regional accrediting board accused him of running a diploma mill and yanked his accreditation.

Sperling moved to Arizona (which falls under a different accrediting board) where he founded The University of Phoenix in 1976. The university received accreditation in 1978; its first graduating class had eight students. It expanded into new states through the 1980s and in 1989 it added distance learning to its services using its own dial-up computer network. The company went public as Apollo Group in 1994.

To further expand its reach Apollo bought Western International University (founded in 1978) in 1995 and the College for Financial Planning from National Endowment of Financial Education in 1997. That year it formed Apollo Learning Group to offer high-tech training programs. The University of Phoenix received approval to offer its first doctoral program in 1998 a doctor of management degree. The next year Apollo made its first entry into the northeastern US when it was approved by the State of Pennsylvania. It also expanded and upgraded its online operations in 1999 centralizing its operations in Phoenix.

In 2001 the university introduced FlexNet courses that combined classroom and online instruction. The weakening economy in 2001 and 2002 benefited Apollo: As jobs became more scarce many professionals sought further education as a competitive advantage. In 2003 the school received state approval to offer courses in New Jersey.

Although it denied the claims in 2004 Apollo agreed to pay almost $10 million in fines after a US Department of Education inquiry claimed that University of Phoenix recruiters had used unethical or illegal tactics to enroll unqualified students.

Longtime chairman and CEO Todd Nelson resigned two years later. Founder John Sperling was appointed acting chairman and Brian Mueller president of The University of Phoenix became the company's president and principal executive.

The company also entered the K-12 market in 2006 when it acquired Insight Schools an online education content provider for home-schooled students.

Apollo Group joined together with private equity firm Carlyle Group in 2007 to create international arm Apollo Global. In 2009 Apollo Group upped its stake in Apollo Global from 80% to 86%.

Brian Mueller left as the company's president in 2008 to head the much-smaller Grand Canyon Education. Investment banker Charles Edelstein was named CEO (a position that had been vacant for more than two years). Apollo Group named Gregory Cappelli as co-CEO in 2009 to share leadership duties with Edelstein.

EXECUTIVES

SVP and Chief Human Resources Officer, Frederick J. (Fred) Newton III, age 56
Vice Chairman, Peter V. Sperling, age 52
Chairman, John G. Sperling, age 91, $850,000 total compensation
EVP and Chief Innovation Officer, Robert W. (Rob) Wrubel, age 50, $350,000 total compensation
EVP Integrated Academic Strategies Senior Advisor to the CEO and Director, Terri C. Bishop, age 58
Co-CEO and Director, Charles B. (Chas) Edelstein, age 52, $600,000 total compensation
President University of Phoenix, William J. (Bill) Pepicello, age 62
President, Joseph L. (Joe) D'Amico, age 62, $500,000 total compensation
SVP and CFO, Brian L. Swartz, age 39, $337,808 total compensation
Co-CEO and Director; Chairman Apollo Global, Gregory W. Cappelli, age 44, $535,616 total compensation
VP Chief Accounting Officer and Controller, Gregory J. Iverson, age 36
COO University of Phoenix, Dianne Pusch
Director Investor Relations, Jeremy Davis
SVP General Counsel and Secretary, Sean B.W. Martin
VP Public Relations, Alex Clark
VP Investor Relations, Beth Coronelli
President Apollo Global, Timothy F. Daniels
Chief Administrative Officer; Chief of Staff Office of the CEO, Jeff Langenbach
Director, George A. Zimmer, age 63
Director, James R. Reis, age 54
Vice Chairman, Peter V. Sperling, age 52
Director, Samuel A. (Sam) DiPiazza Jr., age 61
Director, Ann Kirschner, age 61
Director, Dino J. DeConcini, age 77
Director, Manuel F. (Manny) Rivelo, age 48
Director, Roy A. Herberger Jr., age 69
EVP Integrated Academic Strategies Senior Advisor to the CEO and Director, Terri C. Bishop, age 58
Co-CEO and Director, Charles B. (Chas) Edelstein, age 52
Director, K. Sue Redman, age 54
Co-CEO and Director; Chairman Apollo Global, Gregory W. Cappelli, age 44
Director, Darby E. Shupp, age 36
Auditors: Deloitte&ToucheLLP

LOCATIONS

HQ: Apollo Group Inc.
4025 S. Riverpoint Pkwy., Phoenix AZ 85040
Phone: 480-966-5394 **Fax:** 617-572-2427
Web: www.bain.com

2011 Sales

	$ mil.	% of total
US	4,437	94
Latin America	50	1
Total	**4,733**	**100**

PRODUCTS/OPERATIONS

2011 Sales

	$ mil.	% of total
Tuition & educational services	4,571	92
Services	76	2
Adjustments	(258.4)	-

2011 Sales by Segment

	$ mil.	% of total
University of Phoenix	4,322	91
Apollo Global		
BPP	244	5
Other Apollo Global	75	2
Other schools	88	2
Corporate	1	-
Total	**4,733**	**100**

Selected Subsidiaries

Apollo Development Corp.
Apollo Education Services LLC
Apollo Global Inc. (86%)
  Apollo UK Acquisition Company Limited
    BPP Holdings plcBPP Services Ltd.BPP College of Professional Studies Ltd.Mander Portman Woodward Ltd.
  Cooperatieve Apollo Global Netherlands U.A.
    Apollo Global Chile S.A.Apollo Chile Comunicaciones LimitadaInstituto Superior de Artes y Ciencias de la Comunicacion S.A.Sociedad de Transportes Trans-Guil Limitada (Trans-Guil)Universidad de Artes Ciencias y Comuncacion
    Apollo Global Mexico S. de R.L. de C.V.Apollo Global Mexico Sub S. de R.L. de C.V.Universidad Latinoamericana S.C.
  Western International University Inc.
Apollo Group China LLC
Apollo Investments Inc.
Apollo NB Holding Company
Aptimus Inc.
Carnegie Learning Inc.
The College for Financial Planning Institutes Corporation
Institute for Professional Development
The University of Phoenix Inc.

COMPETITORS

American Public Education
Bridgepoint Education
Capella Education
Career Education
Corinthian Colleges
DeVry
Education Management
Grand Canyon Education
ITT Educational
Laureate Education
Strayer Education
UTI

HISTORICAL FINANCIALS

Company Type: Public

Income Statement FYE: August 31

	REVENUE ($ mil.)	NET INCOME ($ mil.)	NET PROFIT MARGIN	EMPLOYEES
08/12	4,253	422	9.9%	49,992
08/11	4,733	572	12.1%	56,743
08/10	4,925	553	11.2%	57,414
08/09	3,974	598	15.1%	53,498
08/08	3,140	476	15.2%	44,647
Annual Growth	7.9%	(3.0%)	—	2.9%

2012 Year-End Financials

Debt ratio: 25.10%
Return on equity: 45.53%
Cash ($ mil.): 1,594
Current ratio: 117.10
Long-term debt ($ mil.): 81
No. of shares (mil.): 112
Dividends
Yield: —
Payout: —
Market value ($ mil.): 3,014

	STOCK PRICE ($) FY Close	P/E High/Low		PER SHARE ($) Earnings	Dividends	Book Value
08/12	26.85	17	7	3.45	0.00	8.27
08/11	46.83	13	8	4.04	0.00	9.51
08/10	42.49	21	11	3.62	0.00	9.18
08/09	64.84	24	13	3.75	0.00	7.48
08/08	63.68	28	14	2.87	0.00	5.25
Annual Growth	(19.4%)	—	—	4.7%	—	12.0%

Apple Inc

Apple has an "i" for revolutionary technology. Since its release the company's iPhone has spurred a revolution in cell phones and mobile computing. It also continues to innovate its core Mac desktop and laptop computers all of which feature its OS X operating system including the iMac all-in-one desktop for the consumer and education markets the MacBook Air ultra-portable laptop and the high-end Mac Pro and MacBook Pro for consumers and professionals. Apple scored a runaway hit with its digital music players (iPod) and online music store (iTunes). Its iPad tablet computer has become another game-changer in the consumer market. Apple gets nearly 40% of sales from customers in the US.

HISTORY

College dropouts Steve Jobs (1955-2011) and Steve Wozniak founded Apple in 1976 in California's Santa Clara Valley. After Jobs' first sales call brought an order for 50 units the duo built the Apple I in his garage and sold it without a monitor keyboard or casing. Demand convinced Jobs there was a distinct market for small computers and the company's name (a reference to Jobs' stint on an Oregon farm) and the computer's user-friendly look and feel set it apart from others.

By 1977 Wozniak added a keyboard color monitor and eight peripheral device slots (which gave the machine considerable versatility and inspired numerous third-party add-on devices and software). Sales jumped from $7.8 million in 1978 to $117 million in 1980 the year Apple went public. In 1983 Wozniak left the firm and Jobs hired PepsiCo's John Sculley as president. Apple rebounded from failed product introductions that year by unveiling the Macintosh in 1984. After tumultuous struggles with Sculley Jobs left in 1985 and founded NeXT a designer of applications for developing software. That year Sculley ignored Microsoft founder Bill Gates' appeal for Apple to license its products and make the Microsoft platform an industry standard.

Apple blazed the desktop publishing trail in 1986 with its Mac Plus and LaserWriter printers. The following year it formed the software firm that later became Claris (and ultimately FileMaker). The late 1980s brought new competition from Microsoft whose Windows operating system (OS) featured a graphical interface akin to Apple's. Apple sued but lost its claim to copyright protection in 1992.

In 1993 Apple unveiled the Newton handheld computer but sales were slow. Earnings fell drastically so the company trimmed its workforce. (Sculley was among the departed.) In 1994 Apple cried "uncle" and began licensing clones of its OS hoping a flurry of cheaper Mac-alikes would encourage software developers. By 1996 struggling Apple realized Mac clones were stealing sales. That year it hired Gilbert Amelio formerly of National Semiconductor as CEO.

The company bought NeXT in 1997 but sales kept dropping and it subsequently cut about 30% of its workforce canceled projects and trimmed research costs. Meanwhile Apple's board ousted Amelio and Jobs took the position back on an interim basis. The CEO forged a surprising alliance with Microsoft which included releasing a Mac version of Microsoft's popular office software. To protect market share Jobs also stripped the cloning license from chief imitator Power Computing and put it out of business.

In 1998 Apple jumped back into the race with its colorful cocktail of iMacs and its first server software the Mac OS X. That year the company also revamped its profitable Claris unit (by cutting 300 employees shifting most operations to Apple and renaming it FileMaker) and stopped making its Newton handheld device and printer products.

Apple in 1999 opened a new chapter in portable computing with the introduction of its iBook laptop and (taking a cue from Dell) began selling built-to-order systems online. In 2000 after two and a half years as the semipermanent executive in charge Jobs took the "interim" out of his title and revamped the company's Web site around a suite of consumer Internet services. Jobs unveiled overhauled desktop lines later that year including an eight-inch cube-shaped G4. The company ended 2000 on a sour note as an industrywide slowdown and poor response to the G4 cube resulted in Apple's first unprofitable quarter in years.

Apple opened 2001 with another round of product upgrades including faster processors components such as CD and DVD burners and an ultra-slim version of its PowerBook called Titanium. The company also made a move to reclaim some of its slipping share in the education market purchasing software maker PowerSchool. Soon Apple confirmed a long-rumored plan to open a chain of retail stores in the US. The company then acquired DVD authoring software maker Spruce Technologies. In line with its strategy to market Macs as "digital hubs" for devices such as cameras and other peripherals Apple closed the year with the introduction of a digital music player called the iPod.

In 2002 Apple introduced a new look for its iMac line; featuring a half-dome base and a flat-panel display supported by a pivoting arm the redesign was the first departure from the original (and at the time radical) all-in-one design since iMac's debut in 1998. Looking to reclaim market share in the education sector Apple then introduced the eMac –a computer similar to the iMac to be sold only to students and educators (Apple later introduced a retail version). It continued its product push that year with the announcement that it would begin offering a rack-mount server called Xserve. In 2004 Apple debuted a streamlined iMac design powered by its G5 processor.

Apple announced it would begin incorporating Intel processors into its PC lines in 2005 ending more than a decade of using PowerPC microprocessors; the transition was completed the following year. Also that year Apple Motorola and Cingular Wireless (now AT&T Mobility) announced the debut of a mobile phone with iTunes functionality. Apple also unveiled the iPod nano an updated (and even smaller) version of its miniature iPod model as well as an iPod capable of playing video. In 2006 Apple reached a settlement in a dispute with Creative Technology over technology used in digital music players; Apple agreed to pay the company $100 million in exchange for a license to use Creative's patent related to navigation and organization.

The company also launched an online movie service in 2006 and previewed a device called iTV for watching downloaded content on televisions. (Apple announced availability of its television device redubbed Apple TV early the following year.)

Apple unveiled a mobile phone offering called the iPhone in 2007. To reflect the growing breadth of its product portfolio the company announced it would change its name from Apple Computer to simply Apple. The company kicked off 2008 with the release of an updated Apple TV device in conjunction with an iTunes movie rental service.

Looking toward the continued development of its mobile devices Apple purchased P.A. Semi a developer of low-power processors in 2008. In another move intended to bring more of its chip design in-house Apple bought Intrinsity a provider of chip design software in 2010.

After beginning 2011 with a leave of absence and then stepping down as CEO Steve Jobs died on October 5 2011. COO Tim Cook had been named CEO after Jobs' resignation though Jobs retained the chairman title until his death.

EXECUTIVES

Chairman, Arthur D. (Art) Levinson, age 61
CEO and Director, Timothy D. (Tim) Cook, age 51, $800,400 total compensation
SVP Retail, John Browett
SVP Worldwide Product Marketing, Philip W. Schiller, age 51, $494,942 total compensation
SVP Software Engineering, Craig Federighi
SVP General Counsel and Secretary, D. Bruce Sewell, age 53
VP Software Technology, Guy (Bud) Tribble
SVP and CFO, Peter Oppenheimer, age 49, $700,398 total compensation
VP Worldwide Corporate Communications, Katie Cotton
SVP Internet Software and Services, Eduardo H. (Eddy) Cue, age 48
VP iAD, Todd Teresi
VP Marketing, Greg Joswiak
SVP Industrial Design, Jonathan Ive
Senior Product Manager Security, Window Snyder
VP Sales, Zane C. Rowe, age 41
SVP iOS Software, Scott Forstall, age 43, $600,396 total compensation
SVP Hardware Engineering, Robert (Bob) Mansfield, age 51, $600,396 total compensation
SVP Operations, Jeffrey E. (Jeff) Williams, age 48

Director Global Security, David Rice
Director Core Security, Ivan Krstic
Director, Andrea Jung, age 53
Director, Millard S. (Mickey) Drexler, age 67
Director, Robert A. (Bob) Iger, age 59
CEO and Director, Timothy D. (Tim) Cook, age 51
Director, Ronald D. (Ron) Sugar, age 64
Auditors: Ernst&YoungLLP

LOCATIONS

HQ: Apple Inc.
1 Infinite Loop, Cupertino CA 95014
Phone: 408-996-1010 **Fax:** 408-974-2113
Web: www.apple.com

2011 Sales

	$ mil.	% of total
Americas	38,315	35
Asia/Pacific		
Japan	5,437	5
Other countries	22,592	21
Europe	27,778	26
Retail	14,127	13
Total	**108,249**	**100**

PRODUCTS/OPERATIONS

2011 Sales

	$ mil.	% of total
iPhone & related products & services	47,057	43
Computers		
Portable	15,344	14
Desktop	6,439	6
iPad & related products & services	20,358	19
Music-related products		
iPod	7,453	7
Other music-related products & services	6,314	6
Peripherals & other hardware	2,330	2
Software services & other	2,954	3
Total	**108,249**	**100**

Selected Products

Hardware
- Desktop computers (iMac Mac mini Mac Pro)
- Displays (Cinema Thunderbolt)
- External hard drives (Time Capsule)
- Keyboards
- Media devices (Apple TV)
- Mice (Mighty Mouse)
- Mobile phones (iPhone)
- Portable computers (MacBook MacBook Air MacBook Pro)
- Portable digital music player (iPod iPod nano iPod shuffle iPod touch)
- Rack-mount servers (Xserve)
- Stereo systems (iPod Hi-Fi)
- Storage systems (Xserve RAID)
- Tablet computers (iPad)
- Web cams (iSight)
- Wireless networking systems (AirPort)

Software
- MultimediaDVD Studio Pro FinalCut GarageBand iDVD iLife suite iMovie iPhoto iTunes Quicktime Soundtrack)
- Networking (Apple Remote Desktop AppleShare IP)
- Operating system (OS X)
- Personal productivity (AppleWorks FileMaker iWork Keynote Pages)
- Server (Mac OS X Server)
- Storage area network (SAN) file system (Xsan)
- Web browser (Safari)

Online Services
- Applications for iPad iPhone iPod touch (App Store)
- Applications for Mac (Mac App Store)
- Cloud service (iCloud)
- E-books (iBooks)
- Electronic greeting cards (iCard)
- E-mail (Webmail)
- Online multimedia store (iTunes)
- Personal Web page creation (HomePage)
- Remote network storage (iDisk)
- Software (antivirus backup)
- Technical support (AppleCare)

COMPETITORS

Acer
Adobe Systems
Amazon.com
Best Buy
Blockbuster
Bose
Cisco Systems
Comcast
Creative Technology
D-Link
Dell
eMusic.com
Ericsson
Fujitsu Technology Solutions
Google
Hewlett-Packard
HTC Corporation
IBM
Iriver
Kyocera
Lenovo
LG Electronics
MediaNet Digital
Microsoft
MTV Networks
Napster
NEC
Netflix
Nokia
Panasonic Corp
Philips Electronics
RealNetworks
Red Hat
Research In Motion
Samsung Electronics
SanDisk
Seagate Technology
Sharp Electronics
Sony
Sony Mobile
Target Corporation
Time Warner Cable
Toshiba
Wal-Mart
Yahoo!

HISTORICAL FINANCIALS

Company Type: Public

Income Statement FYE: September 29

	REVENUE ($ mil.)	NET INCOME ($ mil.)	NET PROFIT MARGIN	EMPLOYEES
09/12	156,508	41,733	26.7%	76,100
09/11	108,249	25,922	23.9%	63,300
09/10	65,225	14,013	21.5%	49,400
09/09	36,537	5,704	15.6%	36,800
09/08	32,479	4,834	14.9%	35,100
Annual Growth	48.2%	71.4%	—	21.3%

2012 Year-End Financials

Debt ratio: —
Return on equity: 35.30%
Cash ($ mil.): 10,746
Current ratio: 149.58
Long-term debt ($ mil.): —
No. of shares (mil.): 939
Dividends
Yield: —
Payout: 6.00%
Market value ($ mil.): 626,555

	STOCK PRICE ($) FY Close	P/E High/Low		PER SHARE ($) Earnings	Dividends	Book Value
09/12	667.11	16	8	44.15	0.00	125.86
09/11	404.30	15	10	27.68	0.00	82.45
09/10	292.32	19	12	15.15	0.00	52.18
09/09	182.37	29	12	6.29	0.00	30.93
09/08	128.24	36	22	5.36	0.00	23.67
Annual Growth	51.0%	—	—	69.4%	—	51.9%

Applied Materials, Inc.

Today semiconductor manufacturing; tomorrow the world –of alternative energy sources. Applied Materials is by far the world's largest maker of semiconductor production equipment. With the acquisition of Applied Films the company moved into the market for equipment used in making solar power cells. Applied's machines vie for supremacy in many segments of the chip-making process including deposition (layering film on wafers) etching (removing portions of chip material to allow precise construction of circuits) and semiconductor metrology and inspection equipment. About 70% of Applied's sales come from the Asia/Pacific region with China leading the way at nearly a quarter.

HISTORY

Applied Materials was founded in 1967 in Mountain View California as a maker of chemical vapor deposition systems for fabricating semiconductors. After years of rapid growth the company went public in 1972. Two years later it purchased wafer maker Galamar Industries.

In 1975 Applied Materials suffered a 45% drop in sales as the semiconductor industry (and the US economy) contracted. Financial and managerial problems plagued the company following the recession so in 1976 James Morgan a former division manager for conglomerate Textron was chosen to replace founder Michael McNeilly as CEO. Two years later Morgan also became chairman.

After selling Galamar (1977) and other noncore units and extending the company's line of credit Morgan announced a plan to move into Japan. The company's first joint venture Applied Materials Japan was set up in 1979.

Applied got into the ion implanter market in 1980 through its acquisition of the UK's Lintott Engineering.

Morgan's hunch that Japan would become a semiconductor hub paid off. His early arrival plus his attention to Japanese ways of doing business put Applied way ahead of its American competitors. Morgan wrote "Cracking the Japanese Market" about his experiences doing business in Japan which came to account for one-sixth of the company's sales.

When another slump hit the chip industry in 1985 Morgan revved up research and development. With two separate manufacturing technologies poised to compete Morgan essentially bet on the fast but unproven one-at-a-time multiple-chamber method (as opposed to the existing batch process system). The resulting Precision 5000 series machines revolutionized the industry and catapulted Applied Materials to the top of it. Applied's sales passed the $1 billion mark for the first time in 1993.

Shaking off an industry slump in 1996 Applied acquired two Israeli companies Opal (scanning electronic microscopes used in wafer inspection) and Orbot Instruments (wafer and photomask inspection systems) to grab nearly 5% of the crowded chip inspection tools market. In 1998 the company bought Consilium a maker of factory floor management software as well as Obsidian a maker of chemical mechanical polishing systems.

In early 2000 Applied began its move into photolithography –one of the few industry segments in which it didn't operate –by acquiring Etec Systems a leading maker of semiconductor mask pattern generation equipment for nearly $2 billion.

A sharp global downturn in the chip industry led the company in early 2001 to take a variety of cost-cutting measures (including executive pay cuts a voluntary separation plan and temporary plant shutdowns) that stopped short of layoffs. Later that year though Applied let go about 2000 employees –about 10% of its workforce –in response to continuing poor conditions in the chip market.

Also in 2001 Applied bought Schlumberger's electron-beam wafer inspection business as well as privately held Global Knowledge Services a provider of data-mining services for chip factory yield enhancement. Late that year the company enacted another 10% layoff this one affecting 1700 workers. It repeated the move late in 2002 as the chip industry's worst-ever slump stretched across two full years.

In 2003 longtime Intel executive Michael Splinter succeeded Morgan as CEO; Morgan remained chairman (until 2009 when Splinter became chairman as well) .

Also in 2003 Applied bought privately held Boxer Cross which made monitoring equipment that regulated semiconductor manufacturing processes. In mid-2004 Applied acquired atomic layer deposition specialist TORREX.

Applied acquired Metron Technology for about $85 million in cash in late 2004 further expanding its global service portfolio.

In mid-2005 Applied filed to create a holding company in China to coordinate its efforts in the giant economy. Marketing semiconductor equipment in China since 1984 the company had more than 300 employees at five locations in the People's Republic and it established a Global Development Capability center in China a facility that provided engineering and software support services to customers around the world.

Late in 2005 Applied shut down Etec Systems (laser and electron-beam pattern-making equipment) and folded its etching cleaning and inspection products into other divisions.

In early 2006 the company set plans to sell or shut down facilities it no longer needed in California (the former Etec Systems plant) Massachusetts and Oregon and well as overseas in Japan and South Korea. It took asset impairment and restructuring charges of about $212 million including $122 million in asset write-offs as a result.

In 2006 Applied Ventures the venture capital arm of the company invested $3 million in Soliacx a supplier of single-crystal silicon wafers for the solar photovoltaic industry. The same year Applied acquired Applied Films a supplier of thin-film deposition equipment for around $464 million in cash. Following the acquisition of Applied Films the company created a new product segment Adjacent Technologies (later called Energy & Environmental Solutions) that covered equipment used to fabricate solar photovoltaic cells flexible electronics and energy-efficient glass.

The company delved further into the solar energy market with the 2007 acquisition of HCT Shaping Systems for about $483 million. HCT supplied equipment for making the crystalline silicon wafers that go into producing solar cells. Applied expected the acquisition to help reduce the cost of manufacturing photovoltaic (PV) solar cells.

In 2007 the company acquired the Brooks Software division of competitor Brooks Automation for $125 million in cash. The transaction broadened Applied's portfolio of factory control software for the wafer fabrication plant. Brooks Software became part of the Applied Global Services organization.

Holding up closing of the Brooks Software acquisition was a request for more information from the US Department of Justice's Antitrust Division. Despite the regulatory delay the parties were able to complete the transaction during the first quarter of 2007. The US government finally gave its clearance on the sale in late March 2007.

In 2007 Applied gave up on the ion implantation equipment market where it was a perennial #3 (behind Varian Semiconductor Equipment Associates and Axcelis Technologies with its SEN Corp. joint venture). The company closed its Applied Implant Technologies operations in Horsham England at the end of 2007 with about 270 employees there losing their jobs. Applied continued to supply new and refurbished implanters for customers' capacity requirements. Other support for customers including field support and spare parts was provided through the Applied Global Services group.

Although the company held the top competitive spot in most of its semiconductor production equipment categories it was never able to take market share away from Varian and Axcelis (an Eaton spinoff). Applied blamed the "commoditization" of the implant equipment market and the projected financial performance of Applied Implant Technologies for its decision to stop development of new implant equipment.

In mid-2008 Applied made an unsolicited bid to acquire the atomic layer deposition and plasma-enhanced chemical vapor deposition equipment lines of ASM International (ASMI) offering between $400 million and $500 million for the product lines. Under pressure from shareholders to take action on its unprofitable front-end equipment business ASMI rejected Applied's offer but stated it was open to discussions between the companies on alternatives. Applied then made a combined offer with Francisco Partners to buy all of ASMI's front-end equipment lines for up to $800 million. ASMI rejected that offer as well saying it was not in the best interest of its shareholders employees and other stakeholders.

More than four months later Applied and Francisco notified ASMI that they were no longer interested in pursuing the buyout offer —not a surprising development in light of the challenging business conditions unfolding in the worldwide semiconductor equipment market.

Applied continued to add to its solar equipment portfolio however adding Baccini SpA (material handling automation systems for ultrathin silicon wafers) in 2008 at a cost of about $224 million. The following year Applied bought Advent Solar which develops processes and technologies used to streamline PV module production.

Late in 2009 Applied purchased Semitool for about $364 million in cash. The acquisition of Semitool which makes electrochemical plating and wafer surface preparation equipment gave Applied a broader range of products and access to new customers in the semiconductor packaging market.

EXECUTIVES

Fellow, Avi Tepman
Chairman Emeritus, James C. (Jim) Morgan, age 73
SVP and Chief of Staff, Manfred Kerschbaum, age 57, $419,040 total compensation
SVP General Counsel and Corporate Secretary, Joseph J. Sweeney, age 63
Chairman President and CEO, Michael R. (Mike) Splinter, age 61, $814,154 total compensation
EVP and General Manager Silicon Systems, Randhir Thakur, age 49
VP Global IS Planning and Strategy, Stephen C. (Steve) Finnerty
EVP and CFO, George S. Davis, age 54, $426,185 total compensation
VP Global Human Resources, Mary E. Humiston, age 47
EVP; General Manager Energy and Environmental Solutions and Display, Mark R. Pinto, age 52, $456,923 total compensation
Group VP and General Manager Applied Global Services, Charlie Pappis
SVP Worldwide Operations and Supply Chain, Joseph G. (Joe) Flanagan, age 40
Managing Director Global Community Affairs, Mark Walker
Group VP Corporate Initiatives, Chris Bowers, age 51
Fellow, Juergen Frosien
Fellow, Tetsuya Ishikawa
CTO, Omkaram (Om) Nalamasu
Fellow, Ken Collins
Fellow, Prabu Raja
Fellow, John White
VP and Deputy CIO, Jay Kerley
Chairman President and CEO, Michael R. (Mike) Splinter, age 61
Director, Willem P. (Wim) Roelandts, age 67
Director, Aart J. de Geus, age 57
Director, James E. (Jim) Rogers, age 64
Director, Robert H. (Bob) Swan, age 51
Director, Stephen R. Forrest, age 61
Director, Gerhard H. (Gerry) Parker, age 68
Director, Dennis D. Powell, age 63
Director, Thomas J. (Tom) Iannotti, age 55
Director, Alexander A. (Andy) Karsner, age 44
Director, Susan M. James, age 65
Auditors: KPMGLLP

LOCATIONS

HQ: Applied Materials Inc.
3050 Bowers Ave., Santa Clara CA 95052-8039
Phone: 408-727-5555 **Fax:** 408-748-9943
Web: www.appliedmaterials.com

2011 Sales

	$ mil.	% of total
Asia/Pacific		
China	2,574	24
Taiwan	2,093	20
South Korea	1,263	12
Japan	912	9
Other countries	592	6
North America	1,963	19
Europe	1,120	10
Total	**10,517**	**100**

PRODUCTS/OPERATIONS

2011 Sales

	$ mil.	% of total
Silicon Systems	5,415	51
Applied Global Services	2,413	23
Energy & Environmental Solutions	1,990	19
Display	699	7
Total	**10,517**	**100**

Selected Products

Chemical mechanical polishing/planarization systems (wafer polishing)
Deposition systems (deposit layers of conducting and insulating material on wafers)
  Dielectric deposition (chemical vapor deposition or CVD)
  Metal (CVD electroplating or physical vapor deposition)
  Silicon and thermal deposition
  Sputtering (physical vapor deposition) for solar cells
  Thin-film silicon solar cells
  Web coating for flexible solar cells
Etch systems (remove portions of a wafer surface for circuit construction)
Inspection systems (defect review for reticles — patterned plates which hold precise images of chip circuit patterns —and wafers)
Ion implant systems (implant ions into wafer surface to change conductive properties)
Manufacturing process optimization software
Metrology systems
  CD-SEM (scanning electron microscope system)
Optical monitoring systems (for glass or web coating systems)
Rapid thermal processing systems (heat wafers to change electrical characteristics)

COMPETITORS

AIXTRON
ASM International
Aviza Technology
Lam Research
Mattson Technology
Micronic Laser Systems

Axcelis Technologies
CollabRx
Dainippon Screen
Ebara
EG Systems
FEI
FSI International
GT Advanced Technologies
Hitachi
Hitachi Kokusai Electric
Intevac
KLA-Tencor
Nanometrics
Nikon
Novellus
Rudolph Technologies
Spire Corp.
Sumitomo Heavy Industries
Sumitomo Metal Industries
Tokyo Electron
ULVAC
Veeco Instruments
Zygo

HISTORICAL FINANCIALS

Company Type: Public

Income Statement FYE: October 28

	REVENUE ($ mil.)	NET INCOME ($ mil.)	NET PROFIT MARGIN	EMPLOYEES
10/12	8,719	109	1.3%	15,000
10/11	10,517	1,926	18.3%	13,900
10/10	9,548	937	9.8%	14,325
10/09	5,013	(305)	—	13,032
10/08	8,129	960	11.8%	15,410
Annual Growth	1.8%	(42.0%)	—	(0.7%)

2012 Year-End Financials

Debt ratio: 16.08%
Return on equity: 1.51%
Cash ($ mil.): 1,392
Current ratio: 225.25
Long-term debt ($ mil.): 1,946
No. of shares (mil.): 1,197
Dividends
Yield: —
Payout: 377.78%
Market value ($ mil.): 12,748

	STOCK PRICE ($) FY Close	P/E High/Low	PER SHARE ($) Earnings	Dividends	Book Value
10/12	10.65	147111	0.09	0.00	6.04
10/11	12.62	12 7	1.45	0.00	6.74
10/10	12.35	21 15	0.70	0.00	5.68
10/09	12.95	— —	(0.23)	0.00	5.29
10/08	11.40	30 16	0.70	0.00	5.67
Annual Growth	(1.7%)	— —	(40.1%)	—	1.6%

ARAMARK Corp.

LOCATIONS

HQ: ARAMARK Corp.
ARAMARK Tower, 1101 Market Street, Philadelphia, PA 19107
Phone: 215 238-3000
Web: www.aramark.com

HISTORICAL FINANCIALS

Company Type:

Income Statement FYE: September 30

	REVENUE ($ mil.)	NET INCOME ($ mil.)	NET PROFIT MARGIN	EMPLOYEES
09/11*	13,082	100	0.8%	250,000
10/10	12,571	30	0.2%	254,000
10/09	12,297	(6)	—	255,000
10/08	13,470	39	0.3%	260,000
09/07	8,438	16	0.2%	250,000
Annual Growth	11.6%	58.0%	—	0.0%

*Fiscal year change

2011 Year-End Financials

Debt ratio: 53.64%
Return on equity: 6.93%
Cash ($ mil.): 213
Current ratio: 103.89
Long-term debt ($ mil.): 5,588
No. of shares (mil.): 0
Dividends
Yield: —
Payout: 131.33%
Market value ($ mil.): —

Arch Coal, Inc.

What powers your power company? Perhaps Arch Coal. About half of the electricity generated in the US comes from coal and Arch Coal is one of the country's largest coal producers by volume behind industry leader Peabody Energy. Arch Coal sold about 155 million tons of coal in 2011 from 24 mining complexes in every major coal supply basin in the US. It produces thermal (steam) coal used by electric utilities to produce steam in boilers and metallurgical coal used to make steel products. To store and ship its Appalachian coal it operates the Arch Coal Terminal near the Ohio River. In 2011 Arch Coal acquired rival International Coal Group for $3.4 billion which hiked its coal reserves to 5.5 billion tons.

The International Coal Group (ICG) deal made Arch Coal one of the world's largest coal producers and the second-largest metallurgical coal producer in the US. The acquisition extended Arch Coal's reach into every major coal-producing basin in North America and added its low-cost high-quality met coal to its product lines. With the purchase came 12 mining complexes in Appalachia making that region the company's largest revenue generator.

Arch Coal's strategy is to operate mines with access to export facilities that enable Arch Coal to ship to most of the major coal-fueled power plants industrial facilities and steel mills within the US and on four continents. Despite an expected drop in coal demand in the US the company sees worldwide demand increasing in the next decade particularly in developing countries such as China and India.

To enhance its shipping capabilities in early 2012 Arch signed a long-term throughput agreement with Kinder Morgan Energy Partners to support Kinder Morgan's expansion of its export facilities along the Gulf Coast. After terminal upgrades are completed Arch Coal will ship coal at minimum volume levels through KMP's terminals. The expansion of KMP's terminal network will also help boost Arch's growing seaborne coal volumes. Upon completion KMP's Deepwater terminal is projected to have a throughput capacity of 10 million tons of coal per year.

In addition to acquiring ICG in 2011 Arch Coal strengthened its presence in overseas markets with new offices in Asia and Europe. That year it also increased its port access in the US on all coasts. In addition it was awarded a federal coal lease in Wyoming to mine an estimated 222 million tons of coal reserves adjacent to its Black Thunder mining complex.

However the US coal market that year weakened after a very mild weather and a slowdown in economic growth caused demand to dip. Arch Coal responded by scaling back on its production in some areas. The company also looked to global markets where demand in energy has been growing.

HISTORY

Raised in the Oklahoma oil patch Fred Miles founded the Swiss Drilling Company in 1910 and started wildcatting oil wells. Unable to compete against the low prices offered by Standard Oil Miles moved his company in 1916 to eastern Kentucky and acquired control of 200000 acres of oil land. With powerful backers such as the Armours of Chicago Swiss Oil Company soon became one of the leading oil companies in Kentucky.

In the early 1920s the company's oil wells started to play out during a postwar depression. Miles fought back by expanding into refining buying Tri-State Refining in 1930. The company changed its name in 1936 to Ashland Oil and Refining Company a business that turned a profit even during the darkest days of the Depression. Miles didn't survive the transition however. By 1926 Ashland was outperforming its parent and investors eased Miles out the corporate door.

Pearl Harbor only brought more success to a business the American war machine needed to fuel its ships planes and tanks. Although peace brought the inevitable recession America's postwar love affair with the automobile helped Ashland continue to thrive.

During the 1950s Ashland's refineries ran at near capacity. In 1969 Merle Kelce and Guy Heckman along with help from Ashland formed Arch Mineral. Ashland had decided that it needed to diversify and lessen its dependence on oil refining. The Hunt family of Dallas put its money into the venture in 1971 and in the following years the company bought Southwestern Illinois Coal Corporation USX's Lynch Properties Diamond Shamrock Coal and Lawson-Hamilton Properties. By the end of 1996 the company owned some 1.5 billion tons of recoverable coal reserves.

Ashland struck out on its own in the coal business in 1975 forming Ashland Coal. Ashland Coal then began a series of acquisitions lasting 15 years. The company bought Addington Brothers Mining (1976) Hobet Mining and Construction (1977) Saarbergwerke (1981) Coal-Mac (1989) Mingo Logan (1990) and Dal-Tex Coal (1992). Growing through that binge of acquisitions the company went public in 1988.

In 1997 Arch Mineral and Ashland Coal merged into Arch Coal an entity that consolidated Ashland's coal assets. Ashland kept a 58% stake. In 1998 Arch Coal purchased Atlantic Richfield's (ARCO) US coal operations for $1.14 billion making itself the second-largest coal producer in the US. That year Arch Coal also created Arch Western Resources a joint venture in which Arch Coal owns 99% and ARCO owns 1%.

Regulatory pressures and low coal prices in 1999 forced the company to close three mines — the Dal-Tex in West Virginia and two surface mines in Kentucky.

Arch Coal recorded a $346 million loss in 1999. To recover from the profit plunge and benefit from increased demand as utilities complied with Clean Air Act mandates the company boosted production at its low-sulfur coal Black Thunder mine in Wyoming. In 2000 Ashland reduced its stake in Arch Coal to 12%; it sold the remainder of its stock the next year.

In 2002 Arch Coal and WPP Group formed a partnership Natural Resource Partners which went public that October. The next year Arch Coal sold a portion of its stake back to Natural Resource's management for $115 million and by 2004 it had divested its remaining holdings in the partnership.

Arch Coal sold four of its mining operations in southern West Virginia in 2005 to Magnum Coal a company backed by affiliates of investment firm ArcLight Capital. The sale was part of Arch Coal's strategy of focusing on its core areas the Central Appalachian Basin and the Powder River Basin. In 2004 the company acquired Triton Coal and its mines in the Powder River Basin. Conversely Arch Coal dipped its toe into the increasingly important Illinois Basin region with the acquisition of a one-third interest in Knight Hawk Coal.

The company acquired Rio Tinto's Jacobs Ranch mine in the Powder River Basin of Wyoming for $760 million in 2009. The mine had been included in the Rio Tinto spinoff of Cloud Peak Energy. Arch Coal later combined the Jacobs Ranch mine with its own Black Thunder property thereby creating one of the world's largest coal-mining complexes.

In 2010 Arch Coal exchanged more than 68 million tons of coal reserves in the Illinois Basin to increase its ownership interest in Knight Hawk Holdings LLC to 42% then later to 49% in a cash transaction. The deal for Knight Hawk a midwestern coal producer netted Arch Coal almost $42 million that year. Also that year Arch Coal acquired a 35% stake in Tenaska's Trailblazer Energy Center project in West Texas in 2010.

EXECUTIVES

VP Business Development, David B. Peugh, age 57, $230,000 total compensation
President CEO and Director, John W. Eaves, age 54, $535,000 total compensation
Chairman, Steven F. Leer, age 59, $850,000 total compensation
VP Human Resources, Sheila B. Feldman, age 57
SVP Law Secretary and General Counsel, Robert G. (Bob) Jones, age 55, $315,000 total compensation
SVP Strategic Development, C. Henry Besten Jr., age 63, $290,000 total compensation
VP Federal Government Affairs, Thomas Altmeyer
VP and Chief Accounting Officer, John W. Lorson
Treasurer, James E. Florczak
SVP Strategy and Public Affairs, Deck S. Slone, age 48
VP Tax, C. David Steele
VP Human Resources, John Ziegler Jr.
SVP Marketing and Trading, David N. Warnecke, age 56, $370,000 total compensation
EVP and COO, Paul A. Lang, age 51, $380,000 total compensation
VP Safety, Anthony S. Bumbico
SVP and CFO, John T. Drexler, age 42, $360,000 total compensation
VP Market Research, Andy Blumenfeld
Corporate Controller, Gregory A. Szczepan
VP and CIO, David E. Hartley
Director Otter Creek Operations, William M. (Mike) Rowlands
Director Internal Audit, Casey Warner
Media Contact, Kim Link
President Western Operations, Kenneth (Ken) Cochran
VP External Affairs Western Region, Greg Schaefer
President Eastern US Operations, Gary L. Bennett
General Manager Coal-Mac, J. Chris Sykes
VP Business Development and Strategy, Jeffrey W. Strobel
President CEO and Director, John W. Eaves, age 54
Director, James R. Boyd, age 65
Director, Brian J. Jennings, age 51
Director, Theodore D. Sands, age 66
Director, Robert G. Potter, age 72
Director, Douglas H. (Doug) Hunt, age 59
Director, A. Michael Perry, age 75
Director, Thomas A. Lockhart, age 76
Director, Patricia F. (Pat) Godley, age 63
Director, Wesley M. Taylor, age 69
Director, David D. Freudenthal, age 61
Director, J. Thomas Jones
Director, Peter I. Wold
Auditors: Ernst&YoungLLP

LOCATIONS

HQ: Arch Coal Inc.
1 CityPlace Dr. Ste. 300, St. Louis MO 63141
Phone: 314-994-2700 **Fax:** 314-994-2878
Web: www.archcoal.com

PRODUCTS/OPERATIONS

2012 Sales

Appalachia	1,793	43
Western Bituminous	728	17
Total	**4,159**	**100**

Selected Operations

Appalachia
Coal-Mac (West Virginia)
Lone Mountain (Kentucky)
Western US
Arch of Wyoming
Black Thunder/Jacobs Ranch (Wyoming)
Coal Creek (Wyoming)
Dugout Canyon (Utah)
Skyline (Utah)
SUFCO (Utah)
West Elk (Colorado)

Selected Mergers and Acquisitions

FY2011
International Coal Group ($3.4 billion; West Virginia; coal producer)

COMPETITORS

Alliance Resource
Alpha Natural Resources
Cloud Peak Energy
CONSOL Energy
Drummond Company
James River Coal
Patriot Coal
Peabody Energy
Penn Virginia

HISTORICAL FINANCIALS

Company Type: Public

Income Statement FYE: December 31

	REVENUE ($ mil.)	NET INCOME ($ mil.)	NET PROFIT MARGIN	EMPLOYEES
12/11	4,285	141	3.3%	7,442
12/10	3,186	158	5.0%	4,700
12/09	2,576	42	1.6%	4,601
12/08	2,983	354	11.9%	4,300
12/07	2,413	174	7.2%	4,030
Annual Growth	15.4%	(5.1%)	—	16.6%

2011 Year-End Financials

Debt ratio: 39.58%
Return on equity: 3.96%
Cash ($ mil.): 138
Current ratio: 115.88
Long-term debt ($ mil.): 3,762
No. of shares (mil.): 211
Dividends
Yield: —
Payout: 58.11%
Market value ($ mil.): 3,071

	STOCK PRICE ($) FY Close	P/E High	P/E Low	PER SHARE ($) Earnings	Dividends	Book Value
12/11	14.51	48	18	0.74	0.00	16.90
12/10	35.06	36	20	0.97	0.39	13.76
12/09	22.25	90	43	0.28	0.36	13.02
12/08	16.29	31	4	2.45	0.34	12.10
12/07	44.93	37	22	1.21	0.27	10.70
Annual Growth	(24.6%)	—	—	(11.6%)	—	12.1%

Archer Daniels Midland Co.

A daily grind is the secret to Archer-Daniels-Midland's (ADM) success. It's one of the world's largest processors of agricultural commodities. Its main products which represent roughly 10% of sales are soybeans and soybean meal and corn. Corn is converted into sweeteners starches and bio-products among many. ADM produces wheat flour for bakeries; cocoa and chocolate for confectioners; animal-feed ingredients for farmers; and malt for brewers. Oilseeds are processed into vegetable oils and protein meals. ADM has a US grain elevator and global transportation network that buys stores transports and resells feed commodities for the ag processing industry. Overseas demand generates nearly half of all sales.

HISTORY

John Daniels began crushing flaxseed to make linseed oil in 1878 and in 1902 he formed Daniels Linseed Company in Minneapolis. George Archer another flaxseed crusher joined the company the following year. In 1923 the company bought Midland Linseed Products and became Archer Daniels Midland (ADM). ADM kept buying oil processing companies in the Midwest during the 1920s. It also started to research the chemical composition of linseed oil.

ADM entered the flour milling business in 1930 when it bought Commander-Larabee (then the #3 flour miller in the US). In the 1930s the company discovered a method for extracting lecithin (an emulsifier food additive used in candy and other products) from soybean oil significantly lowering its price.

The enterprise grew rapidly following WWII. By 1949 it was the leading processor of linseed oil and soybeans in the US and was fourth in flour milling. During the early 1950s ADM began foreign expansion in earnest.

In 1966 the company's leadership passed to Dwayne Andreas a former Cargill executive who had purchased a block of Archer family stock. Andreas focused ADM on soybeans including the production of textured vegetable protein a cheap soybean by-product used in foodstuffs.

Andreas' restructuring paved the way for productivity and expansion. In 1971 the company acquired Corn Sweeteners (glutens high-fructose syrups). Other acquisitions included Tabor (grain 1975) and Colombian Peanut (1981). ADM formed a grain-marketing joint venture with GROWMARK in 1985.

The company continued to expand its global presence in the early 1990s. In 1992 ADM bought Canadian Ogilvie Mills. During the 1992 presidential race the Andreas family made substantial donations to both parties in hopes that the winner would support the use of ethanol in gasoline. Two years later the EPA required that 10% of all gas sold in the US be blended with ethanol.

In 1995 the FBI —aided by ADM executive-turned-informer Mark Whitacre —joined a federal investigation of lysine and citric acid price-fixing by the company. The next year ADM agreed to plead guilty to two criminal charges of price-fixing and paid $100 million in penalties a record at that time for a US criminal antitrust case. Whitacre later lost his immunity when convicted of defrauding ADM out of $9 million. He and two other ADM executives including onetime ADM heir apparent Michael Andreas (son of one-time chairman emeritus Dwayne Andreas and cousin of then-chairman Allen Andreas) were tried and convicted in 1998 and sentenced to prison in 1999.

Meanwhile ADM continued to grow. In 1997 it acquired W. R. Grace's cocoa business and after naming Allen Andreas (Dwayne's nephew) as CEO bought 42% of Canada-based United Grain Growers. Also that year it bought a minority stake in pork and beef packer Tyson Fresh Meats and purchased soybean processor Moorman Manufacturing (renamed Moorman's). The following year ADM sold its Harvest Burger line of meat-replacement products to Worthington Foods (Harvest Burger is now owned by Kellogg Company).

Dwayne turned over the chairman post to Allen in early 1999. In 2000 ADM was again cited for involvement in the price-fixing of lysine and was fined $45 million by the European Commission.

The company took control of Farmland Industries' grain operations in 2001 through a new ADM subsidiary that shares profits with Farmland. Later that year the company merged its two animal feed divisions Consolidated Nutrition and Moorman's into a new subsidiary ADM Alliance Nutrition.

In December 2001 in a move to help Mexico's domestic sugar industry the Mexican government imposed a 20% tax on soft drinks made with corn-syrup sweeteners of which ADM's plant in Guadalajara is a major producer. However amid political controversy Mexican President Vicente Fox suspended the tax until the end of September 2002. In July 2002 the tax was ordered reinstated by the Mexican Supreme Court.

In 2002 the company entered into a joint venture with Greatocean Oils & Grains Industries to start soy crushing operations in China and announced the formation of the ADM Specialty Oils and Fats Group which provides vegetable-oil-based products for the food pharmaceutical and personal care industries. The company also sold its Martha Gooch and LaRosa pasta brands to American Italian Pasta.

Also in 2002 ADM acquired Minnesota Corn Processors (MCP). MCP was the company's chief competitor in the ethanol market and the addition of MCP increased ADM's ethanol production making it a top player in the US market. Later in 2002 ADM launched the now discontinued Enova brand cooking oil which because of its manufacturing process was metabolized differently than other oils and was said to help reduce both body weight and fat mass.

In 2003 ADM purchased the remaining interest in UK oils and fats company Pura for $69 million. Prior to the buyout ADM owned a 28% stake in Pura which had about a 30% market share of the UK edible oil market. Also in 2003 ADM reached a settlement with the US government regarding violations of the Clean Air Act and agreed to pay approximately $340 million to clean up air pollution at 52 of its food-processing plants in the Midwest.

ADM announced a joint research agreement with Volkswagen AG in 2004 in order to develop next-generation clean renewable biodiesel fuels for the auto industry. That year it also announced a joint venture with Japanese grain trader Marubeni to market specialty grains in Japan. The company also formed a joint venture with Lesaffre et Cie to produce Red Star Yeast for the North American market.

With trade ties improving between the US and Cuba in 2004 ADM signed a $9 million contract to supply corn to Cuba. In mid-2004 ADM agreed to shell out $400 million to settle a class-action antitrust lawsuit claiming the company conspired to fix the price of high fructose corn syrup between the years of 1991 and 1995. Syrup customers involved in the suit included Coca-Cola and PepsiCo. Faced with potential damage awards of nearly $5 billion the company chose to settle before going to trial.

Marking its first venture into the condiment sector in 2005 ADM acquired the mayonnaise sauces and other salad food products of Sunlight Foods and formed ADM Sunlight Foods. On the disposition side of the business ADM sold its 6% interest in UK sugar and sweetener company Tate & Lyle in 2005.

President and COO Paul Mulhollem retired from the company in 2005. Chairman and CEO G. Allen Andreas assumed Mulhollem's duties until a replacement was found. In 2006 the company named Patricia Woertz as president CEO and director. Woertz joined ADM after having served as an EVP at energy giant Chevron. With her appointment ADM became the largest publicly traded US company to be headed by a woman.

In 2006 ADM (along with two Dutch companies Akzo Nobel and Avebe) was found guilty of price fixing in the cleaning agent sodium gluconate sector by an EU court. ADM was fined almost $13 million. Also that year it bought Canadian bio-based absorbent polymer company Groupe Lysac as well as UK chocolate company Classic Couverture. It also bought out Lesaffre's 50% share of the companies' 50-50 joint venture International Malting (IMC) in 2006. IMC supplies malt to the brewing distilling and food industries worldwide and has plants in Australia Canada New Zealand and the US.

In 2007 long-time chairman G. Allen Andreas stepped down and was replaced by company CEO and president Patricia Woertz who before joining ADM worked for Chevron.

In August 2011 ADM acquired English River Pellets Inc. a grain elevator and animal feed maker with two locations in Iowa.

EXECUTIVES

Chairman President and CEO, Patricia A. (Pat) Woertz, age 59, $1,300,000 total compensation
EVP Secretary and General Counsel, David J. Smith, age 57, $901,400 total compensation
SVP Toepfer and ADM Value Creation Team, Lewis W. Batchelder, age 67, $768,000 total compensation
SEVP Performance and Growth, Steven R. (Steve) Mills, age 57, $750,000 total compensation
Vice Chairman and EVP Commercial and Production, John D. Rice, age 58, $885,400 total compensation
VP, Mark J. Cheviron, age 63
SVP and Senior Advisor Global Corn, Edward A. Harjehausen, age 62, $652,000 total compensation
Senior Director Governmental Affairs, Anthony Reed
President Rail Container and Supply Chain Transportation, Scott B. Frederickson
SVP; President Agricultural Services, Craig E. Huss, age 60
VP Compliance and Ethics, Scott A. Roney, age 48
VP and General Auditor, Marc A. Sanner, age 59
SVP; President Corn, Mark A. Bemis, age 51
Assistant Secretary and Assistant General Counsel, Scott A. Roberts, age 52
VP Captive Insurance, Michael Lusk, age 63
Assistant Treasurer, Ronald S. Bandler, age 51
President Natural Health & Nutrition, Janice K. Binger, age 46
Director Employee Benefits, Teresa Hicks
VP Investor Relations, Dwight E. Grimestad
VP Environmental, Mark E. Calmes
VP Safety and Health, Gene F. Smith
VP; Chairman Alfred C. Toepfer International, Gary L. Towne, age 57
President ADM Research, Thomas P. Binder
President ADM Rice Inc., Christian Bonnesen
President ADM Trucking Inc., William Patterson
SVP; President Oilseeds, Matthew J. (Matt) Jansen, age 46
President American River Transportation Co., Royce C. Wilken
Director Chocolate ADM Cocoa International, Benoit Villers, age 56
VP; President Grain, Joseph D. (Joe) Taets
VP Oilseeds Processing, Kevin L. Hess, age 52
VP Mergers and Acquisitions, A. James Shafter, age 65
Director Protein Research, Russ Egbert
SVP and CFO, Ray G. Young, age 50
VP Global Oleo Chemicals, Mike Livergood
President ADM Investor Services, Thomas R. Kadlec
SVP Human Resources, Michael (Mike) D'Ambrose, age 55, $700,000 total compensation
President ADM/Farmland, Pete Goetzmann
President Hickory Point Bank and Trust, Corydon C. Nicholson
VP; President ADM Corn Processing, Dennis C. Riddle, age 65
VP Global Oilseeds, Mark N. Zenuk, age 45
VP Human Resources Canada and Cost Management, Crocifissa (Croci) Mandraccia
Director Archer Financial Services, Greg Grow
Senior Manager Information Technology, Gary Mruz
VP Finance and Treasurer, Vikram Luthar, age 45
President ADM Alliance Nutrition, Terry Myers
VP, Ismael Roig, age 45
VP Global Benefits, Randall J. (Randy) Moon, age 53
Director Executive Talent Development, Kelly Mirsky
VP Government Affairs, Shannon S. Herzfeld, age 60
VP; President Milling and Cocoa, Mark Kolkhorst
VP North American Food Oils, Tedd Kruse
VP Human Resources, F. Kathie Whitley
VP Sales Fuel Ethanol, Kyle James
VP and Controller, John P. Stott, age 45
VP Product and Market Development - Corn Processing Natural Health and Nutrition and Specialty Food Ingredients, Doug Millar
VP Manufacturing ADM Milling, John Little
VP Manufacturing Operations North American Oilseed, Bruno Ejankowski
VP Manufacturing Operations BioProducts, John Hanson
VP General Manager BioProducts - Feed, Kevin Moore
VP State Government Relations, Greg Webb
President Almex, Chris Cuddy
President Milling, Kris Lutt
VP Sales and Marketing Corn Processing Division; General Manager Glacial Technologies, Rodney Schanefelt
VP; President South American Operations, Domingo A. Lastra, age 44
VP Corn Processing, Mathew Bruns
VP Transportation and Logistics Grain Group, Thomas Ames
VP Economic Policy, Michael R. (Mike) Baroni, age 57
Manager Media Relations, Roman Blahoski
Director International Sales, Gerd Mueller
Business Director Natural Health and Nutrition, Greg Dodson
Senior Group Controller, Rene Brand

EVP and COO, Juan R. Luciano
Group Controller Corporate Accounting, Amy Rambo
Chief Communications Officer, Victoria A. Podesta, age 56
Assistant Secretary and Assistant General Counsel, Stuart E. (Stu) Funderburg
VP Refined Oils Operations, John Guymon
General Manager Packaged Oils, Kevin Swanson
Director Retail Confectionary Sales and Marketing ADM Cocoa, John Zima
VP Biofuels and Biochemical Research, Todd Werpy
VP Global Tax, Marc Hinch
VP Safety and Health, Peter Taschner
Director Innovation and Marketing ADM Cocoa International, Steven Laning
General Manager Telles, Robert E. (Bob) Engle, age 49
CIO, Martin Schoenthaler
VP Investor Services, Chris Damilatis
Director Business Development Europe Telles, Stan Haftka
VP Corn Processing, Randall R. Kampfe, age 65
Director External Communications, David Weintraub
Coordinator Media Relations, Beth Chandler
Director European Marketing and Communications, Sara Vermeulen-Anastasi
VP Procurement, Steven J. Cassady
VP Export Trading, Kent Soellner
VP Sweetener Sales, Conrad Givers
Advisor Office of the Chairman, Chris Boerm
Director, George W. Buckley, age 65
Vice Chairman and EVP Commercial and Production, John D. Rice, age 58
Director, Patrick J. Moore, age 58
Director, Victoria F. Haynes, age 64
Director, Donald E. Felsinger, age 65
Director, Pierre Dufour, age 57
Director, Mollie H. Carter, age 50
Director, Thomas F. O'Neill, age 65
Director, Antonio Maciel Neto, age 55
Auditors: Ernst&YoungLLP

LOCATIONS

HQ: Archer-Daniels-Midland Company
4666 Faries Pkwy., Decatur IL 62525
Phone: 217-424-5200 **Fax:** 217-424-6196
Web: www.admworld.com

2011 Sales

	$ mil.	% of total
US	42,390	53
Switzerland	8,413	10
Germany	6,217	8
Other countries	23,656	29
Total	**80,676**	**100**

PRODUCTS/OPERATIONS

2011 Sales

	$ mil.	% of total
Agricultural services	37,927	47
Oilseeds processing	26,662	33
Corn processing	9,908	12
Other	6,179	8
Total	**80,676**	**100**

Selected Commodities

Barley
Corn
Milo (sorghum)
Oats
Oilseeds
Rice
Rye
Wheat

Selected Brands

Consumer food
- Casa (canned refried beans)
- Commander (wheat flour)
- Five Roses (wheat flour)
- Gigantic (wheat flour)
- Midland Harvest (rice)
- Novasoy (soy supplement)
- Top King (wheat flour)
- VegeFull (cooked ground beans)

Industrial food
- Ambrosia (chocolate)
- CardioAid (plant sterol)
- deZaan (cocoa powder)
- EnviroStrip (dry-stripping)
- Evolution Chemicals (sustainable alternative chemical)
- Merckens (chocolate)
- NovaLipid (fats and oils)
- NovaSoy (isoflavones)
- VegeFull (dried bean-based food ingredient)

Selected Products

Agricultural
- Fertilizer

Feed ingredients
- Animal nutrition
- Corn co-products
- Milling products
- Oils/energy products
- Premixes
- Specialty feed ingredients

Food
- Acidulants
- Beverage alcohol
- Cocoa and chocolate products
- Edible beans and bean ingredients
- Fiber
- Flour and whole grains
- Lecithin
- Natural-source vitamin E
- Oils
- Plant sterols
- Polyols and gums
- Proteins
- Rice
- Soy isoflavones
- Starches
- Sweeteners

Fuel
- Biodiesel
- Ethanol

Industrials
- Acidulants
- De-icers
- Dispersants
- Dust control products
- Emulsifiers and thickeners
- Fermentation nutrients
- Fertilizers
- Industrial oils
- Polyols
- Propylene glycol
- Solvents
- Starches
- Superabsorbents

Selected Services

Agriculture
- Grain merchandising
- Grain milling
- Grain processing

Information
- Billing and invoicing
- Inventory
- Logistics
- Payment
- Product search

Transportation
- Land
  - Rail
  - Truck
- Water
  - Ocean
  - River

Selected Subsidiaries Joint Ventures and Other Holdings

Almidones Mexicanos S.A. (50% wet corn milling plant Mexico)
Alfred C. Toepfer International (80% agricultural commodities trading and processed products Germany)
Compagnie Industrielle et Financiere des Produits Amylaces SA (Luxembourg) (42% joint venture investments in food feed ingredients and bioenergy)
Eaststarch C.V. (50% wet corn milling plants Netherlands)
Edible Oils Limited (50% procure package sell edible oils UK)
Golden Peanut LLC (100% peanut hulls oil meal and seed)
Gruma S.A.B. de C.V (23% corn flour and corn tortilla manufacturer Mexico)
Kalama Export Company (45% grain export elevator)
Red Star Yeast LLC (40% joint venture fresh and dry yeast manufacturer US and Canada)
Stratas Foods LLC (50% procure package sell edible oils North America)
Telles LLC (50% market sell corn-based bioplastic)

COMPETITORS

Abengoa Bioenergy
Ag Processing Inc.
AGRI Industries
Agrium
Ajinomoto
Andersons
Barry Callebaut
Bartlett and Company
Bayer CropScience
BioFuel Energy
Brenntag North America
Buckeye Technologies
Bunge Limited
Cargill
CHS
Cosun
CP Kelco
Danisco A/S
Dow AgroSciences
DuPont Agriculture
General Mills
Green Plains
Hain Celestial
Hershey
Ingredion
Liberty Vegetable Oil
LifeLine
Little Sioux Corn Processors
Louis Dreyfus Commodities
Louis Dreyfus Group
Malt Products Corporation
MGP Ingredients
Monsanto Company
Nestle
Nisshin Oillio
Northern Growers
Omega Protein
Pacific Ethanol
Pioneer Hi-Bred
Renewable Energy Group
Riceland Foods
Scoular
Sudzucker
Syngenta
Tate & Lyle
Viterra Inc.

HISTORICAL FINANCIALS

Company Type: Public

Income Statement

FYE: June 30

	REVENUE ($ mil.)	NET INCOME ($ mil.)	NET PROFIT MARGIN	EMPLOYEES
06/12	89,038	1,223	1.4%	30,000
06/11	80,676	2,036	2.5%	30,700
06/10	61,682	1,930	3.1%	29,300
06/09	69,207	1,707	2.5%	28,200
06/08	69,816	1,802	2.6%	27,600
Annual Growth	6.3%	(9.2%)	—	2.1%

2012 Year-End Financials

Debt ratio: 24.84%
Return on equity: 6.81%
Cash ($ mil.): 1,291
Current ratio: 184.29
Long-term debt ($ mil.): 6,535
No. of shares (mil.): 659
Dividends
Yield: —
Payout: 37.23%
Market value ($ mil.): 19,454

	STOCK PRICE ($) FY Close	P/E High/Low		PER SHARE ($) Earnings	Dividends	Book Value
06/12	29.52	18	13	1.84	0.00	27.27
06/11	30.15	12	8	3.13	0.62	27.82
06/10	25.82	11	8	3.00	0.58	22.86
06/09	26.77	13	6	2.65	0.54	21.03
06/08	33.75	17	11	2.79	0.49	20.95
Annual Growth	(3.3%)	—	—	(9.9%)	—	6.8%

Arrow Electronics, Inc.

LOCATIONS

HQ: Arrow Electronics, Inc.
7459 S. Lima Street, Englewood, CO 80112
Phone: 303 824-4000
Web: www.arrow.com

HISTORICAL FINANCIALS

Company Type:

Income Statement FYE: December 31

	REVENUE ($ mil.)	NET INCOME ($ mil.)	NET PROFIT MARGIN	EMPLOYEES
12/11	21,390	598	2.8%	15,700
12/10	18,744	479	2.6%	12,700
12/09	14,684	123	0.8%	11,300
12/08	16,761	(613)	—	12,700
12/07	15,984	407	2.6%	12,600
Annual Growth	7.6%	10.1%	—	5.7%

2011 Year-End Financials

Debt ratio: 19.96%
Return on equity: 16.32%
Cash ($ mil.): 396
Current ratio: 177.44
Long-term debt ($ mil.): 1,927
No. of shares (mil.): 111
Dividends
Yield: —
Payout: —
Market value ($ mil.): 4,183

	STOCK PRICE ($) FY Close	P/E High/Low		PER SHARE ($) Earnings	Dividends	Book Value
12/11	37.41	9	5	5.17	0.00	32.81
12/10	34.25	8	5	4.01	0.00	28.36
12/09	29.61	29	15	1.03	0.00	24.34
12/08	18.84	—	—	(5.08)	0.00	22.44
12/07	39.28	13	10	3.28	0.00	28.92
Annual Growth	(1.2%)	—	—	12.0%	—	3.2%

Asbury Automotive Group, Inc

Asbury Automotive Group has made a living out of being large. The company oversees about 80 dealerships which operate around 100 auto franchises in about a dozen states including the Carolinas Florida Texas and Virginia. The dealerships sell some 30 different brands of US and foreign new and used vehicles. Asbury also offer parts service and collision repair as well as financing and insurance. The auto dealer has grown by acquiring large locally-branded dealership groups as well as smaller groups and individually-owned dealerships throughout the US. Customers include individual buyers and fleet operators.

Aside from the Carolinas Florida Texas and Virginia Asbury has dealerships in Arkansas Georgia Mississippi Missouri and New Jersey.

Revenues increased by some 10% in 2011 vs. 2010 and net income grew by close to 80%. Revenues in 2011 came in at $4.3 billion compared to $3.9 billion in 2010 and cash flow from operations increased to $135 million in 2011 from $23 million in 2010.

The company's luxury and mid-line import vehicles comprised 84% of revenues; while its domestic vehicles 16% of revenues in 2011. The company also operates some 25 collision repair centers which accounted for around 15% of revenues.

On the operational side Asbury Automotive responded by selling assets and shuttering or selling franchises. In early 2011 the firm sold its heavy truck business in Georgia and a Peterbilt franchise there to Rush Enterprises. (The sale marked the firm's exit from the heavy truck business which included seven brands of heavy trucks among them Hino Isuzu Truck Volvo and Workhorse.) Previous divestments include a Chrysler and two GM dealerships following the twin bankruptcy filings. The closures were part of the Chrysler and GM's dealer consolidation plans. The Chrysler dealership was located in Roswell Georgia and the GM locations were in Kissimmee Florida. Historically-acquisitive Asbury Automotive also temporarily stopped buying dealerships while it struggled to manage its existing business.

The company believes its current mix of luxury and mid-line import vehicles will continue to grow over the long term but are influenced by potential downturns in the economy cost structure and brand mix.

Investment firm FMR LLC owns about 13% of Asbury's shares while MSD Capital (tech-mogul Michael Dell's personal investment vehicle) owns about 11%.

EXECUTIVES

Chairman, Thomas C. DeLoach Jr., age 65
VP and Chief Human Resources Officer, Joseph G. (Joe) Parham Jr., age 62
President CFO and Director, Craig T. Monaghan, age 55, $568,345 total compensation
SVP and CFO, Scott J. Krenz, age 60
VP Corporate Development and Real Estate, George C. Karolis, age 37
VP Field Human Resources, Kenneth E. Jackson, age 53
EVP COO and Director, Michael S. Kearney, age 60, $600,000 total compensation
VP Manufacturer Relations, Matthew J. Mees, age 54
VP Operations, Keith R. Style, age 39, $236,923 total compensation
VP General Counsel and Corporate Secretary, Elizabeth B. (Beth) Chandler, age 48, $209,423 total compensation
Chief Accounting Officer and Controller, Bryan Hanlon, age 35
VP and Treasurer, Ryan T. Marsh
Manager Public Relations and Communications, Melissa Corey
Chief Audit Executive, Barbara Jesup
VP and CIO, Teresa Devine
Director, Vernon E. Jordan Jr., age 76
Director, Philip F. (Flip) Maritz, age 51
President CFO and Director, Craig T. Monaghan, age 55
Director, Janet M. Clarke, age 59
Director, Michael J. (Mike) Durham, age 61
Director, Jeffrey I. Wooley, age 67
Director, Dennis E. Clements, age 67
EVP COO and Director, Michael S. Kearney, age 60
Director, Eugene S. Katz, age 66
Director, Juanita T. James, age 60
Auditors: Ernst&YoungLLP

LOCATIONS

HQ: Asbury Automotive Group Inc.
2905 Premiere Pkwy. NW Ste. 300, Duluth GA 30097
Phone: 770-418-8200 **Fax:** 260-434-4707
Web: www.drivekelley.com

PRODUCTS/OPERATIONS

2011 Sales

	$ mil.	% of total
New vehicles	2,307	54
Used vehicles	1,250	29
Parts & service	577	14
Finance & insurance	141	3
Total	**4,276**	**100**

2011 New Vehicle Sales

	% of total
Luxury	44
Mid-line	40
Mid-line	15
Total	**99**

COMPETITORS

AutoNation
Buchanan Automotive
CarMax
Ferman Automotive
Group 1 Automotive
Hendrick Automotive
Island Lincoln-Mercury
Penske Automotive Group
Ron Tonkin Family of Dealerships
Scott-McRae
Sonic Automotive

HISTORICAL FINANCIALS

Company Type: Public

Income Statement FYE: December 31

	REVENUE ($ mil.)	NET INCOME ($ mil.)	NET PROFIT MARGIN	EMPLOYEES
12/11	4,276	67	1.6%	6,800
12/10	3,936	38	1.0%	7,100
12/09	3,650	13	0.4%	6,600
12/08	4,619	(338)	—	7,300
12/07	5,712	50	0.9%	8,300
Annual Growth	(7.0%)	7.4%	—	(4.9%)

2011 Year-End Financials

Debt ratio: 62.89%
Return on equity: 20.79%
Cash ($ mil.): 11
Current ratio: 124.55
Long-term debt ($ mil.): 439
No. of shares (mil.): 31
Dividends
Yield: —
Payout: —
Market value ($ mil.): 675

	STOCK PRICE ($) FY Close	P/E High/Low		PER SHARE ($) Earnings	Dividends	Book Value
12/11	21.56	10	7	2.08	0.00	10.43
12/10	18.48	16	8	1.14	0.00	8.75
12/09	11.53	35	5	0.41	0.00	7.51
12/08	4.57	—	—	(10.66)	0.68	6.97
12/07	15.05	19	9	1.53	0.85	18.50
Annual Growth	9.4%	—	—	8.0%	—	(13.3%)

Ashland Inc

Ashland's four business units are built on chemicals and cars. Ashland Performance Materials makes specialty resins polymers and adhesives. Ashland's Water Technologies unit provides papermaking chemicals and specialty chemicals to markets such as pulp and paper food and beverage municipal and mining. Consumer Markets led by subsidiary Valvoline runs an oil-change chain in the US and sells Valvoline oil and Zerex antifreeze. In 2011 Ashland acquired International Specialty Products (ISP) and combined it with Ashland Aqualon Functional Ingredients to make up its Ashland Specialty Ingredients unit. The unit produces polymers and additives for the food personal care pharmaceutical and other industries.

HISTORY

After moving to Kentucky in 1917 Fred Miles formed the Swiss Oil Company. In 1924 Swiss Oil bought a refinery in Catlettsburg a rough town near sedate Ashland and created a unit called Ashland Refining. Miles battled Swiss Oil directors for control lost and resigned in 1927.

Swiss Oil bought Tri-State Refining in 1930 and Cumberland Pipeline's eastern Kentucky pipe network in 1931. Swiss Oil changed its name to Ashland Oil and Refining in 1936. After WWII it bought small independent oil firms acquiring the Valvoline name in 1950 by buying Freedom-Valvoline.

The firm formed Ashland Chemical in 1967 after buying Anderson-Prichard Oil (1958) United Carbon (1963) and ADM Chemical (1967). Ashland Chemical changed its name to Ashland Oil. It added the SuperAmerica convenience store chain (1970) and started exploring for oil in Nigeria after OPEC nations raised oil prices.

Scandal hit in 1975 the year Ashland Coal was formed. CEO Orin Atkins admitted to ordering Ashland executives to make illegal contributions to the 1972 Nixon presidential campaign. Atkins was deposed in 1981 after the company made questionable payments to highly placed "consultants" with connections to oil-rich Middle Eastern governments. In 1988 Atkins was arrested for trying to fence purloined documents regarding litigation between Ashland and the National Iranian Oil Company (NIOC). Ashland which launched the federal investigation that led to Atkins' arrest settled with NIOC in 1989. Atkins pleaded guilty and received probation.

Ashland went on a shopping spree in the 1990s. The company bought Permian (crude oil gathering and marketing) in 1991 and merged it into Scurlock Oil. In 1992 Ashland Chemical bought most of Unocal's chemical distribution business and two years later it bought two companies that produce chemicals for the semiconductor industry. Also in 1994 Ashland made a promising oil discovery in Nigeria.

The company by then named Ashland Inc. spent $368 million on 14 acquisitions to expand its energy and chemical divisions in 1995. It received a $75 million settlement with Columbia Gas System (now Columbia Energy Group) for abrogated natural gas contracts resulting from Columbia's bankruptcy.

In 1996 president Paul Chellgren became CEO and with the company under shareholder fire began a major reorganization. The next year Arch Mineral and Ashland Coal combined to form Arch Coal with Ashland owning 58%. Also that year Ashland made more than a dozen acquisitions to bolster its chemical and construction businesses. Its exploration unit renamed Blazer Energy was sold to Norway's Statoil for $566 million.

Ashland joined USX-Marathon (now Marathon Oil) in 1998 to create Marathon Ashland Petroleum (now called Marathon Petroleum). It bought 20 companies including Eagle One Industries a maker of car-care products and Masters-Jackson a group of highway construction companies. Ashland reduced its holdings in Arch Coal from 58% to 12% in 2000; it sold the remainder in early 2001.

In 2002 the company was jolted when Chellgren was forced to retire after violating a company policy prohibiting romantic office relationships. James O'Brien replaced Chellgren.

Ashland had a record year in 2001 but was hampered in 2002 by smaller profits from MAP which was hurt by reduced demand for petroleum products and tighter margins. Ashland Distribution also hurt the bottom line which led Ashland to reorganize that unit's management and sales teams.

After that record year Ashland came back to earth with much smaller profits in 2002 and the next year; APAC particularly was hit hard in 2003. The construction division swung from $120 million in profits in 2002 to a loss of more than $40 million in 2003; the company attributes the decline to unusual weather conditions which can greatly affect the construction business more than others. (The pendulum swung back into the black in 2004 with more than $100 million in operating income.)

The company commenced a grand reorganization of its business soon after that. Beginning in 2005 it sold its former petroleum refining joint venture (with Marathon Oil) re-named Marathon Petroleum Company; acquired car cleaning products maker Car Brite for Valvoline; purchased Degussa's water treatment business (operating as Stockhausen); and bought adhesives and coatings company Northwest Coatings. Another big deal though provided a complementary book end to the sale of Marathon Petroleum. In 2006 Ashland sold construction unit APAC (which supplied highway materials built bridges and paved streets) to Oldcastle Materials for $1.3 billion. The move coming as it did on the heels of the divestiture of MAP transformed Ashland into solely a chemicals company.

In 2008 Ashland paid $3.3 billion to buy specialty chemicals company Hercules which added greatly to its water treatment and resins businesses. That move was just the latest in a series of transactions in the latter half of the decade that transformed Ashland from a multi-industry conglomerate into strictly a chemicals operations. Among other moves the company sold its half of a refining joint venture with Marathon Oil and construction unit APAC. The deal provided Ashland already with a healthy international business with even more of a global presence.

Ashland formed a 50-50 joint venture with Sud-Chemie AG in 2010 to produce foundry chemicals. Sud-Chemie manages the operation called ASK Chemicals GmbH which is headquartered in Germany.

EXECUTIVES

Chairman and CEO, James J. (Jim) O'Brien Jr., age 57, $1,127,363 total compensation
VP and Chief Information and Administrative Services Officer, Anne T. Schumann, age 52
SVP; President Ashland Consumer Markets, Samuel J. (Sam) Mitchell Jr., age 51, $343,418 total compensation
VP and Chief Human Resources and Communications Officer, Susan B. Esler, age 51
Assistant General Counsel and Corporate Secretary, Linda L. Foss
VP and Controller, J. William Heitman, age 57
SVP and CFO, Lamar M. Chambers, age 58, $461,252 total compensation
VP and Chief Growth Officer, Walter H. Solomon, age 52
VP Environmental Health and Safety, Karen T. Murphy
SVP; President Global Supply Chain; and President Performance Materials, Theodore L. (Ted) Harris, age 47, $330,372 total compensation
VP and Treasurer, J. Kevin Willis
VP Corporate Development, John W. (Jack) Joy
SVP; President Water Technologies, Paul C. Raymond III, age 50
SVP and General Counsel, Peter J. Ganz, age 50
SVP; President Specialty Ingredients, John E. Panichella, age 53, $364,500 total compensation
General Auditor, John F. Guldig
Manager Public Relations, James E. (Jim) Vitak
VP; President Ashland Distribution, Robert M. Craycraft II, age 43
Director Investor Relations, Eric N. Boni
VP Tax, Scott A. Gregg
Global New Product Leader Personal Care and Functional Ingredients, Dianne Leipold
Global Business Manager Fertilizer Products Ashland Hercules Water Technologies, Brine Ranson
VP Operations and Environmental Health and Safety, Steven E. (Steve) Post
Director, Theodore M. (Tim) Solso, age 65
Director, Barry W. Perry, age 65
Director, Roger W. Hale, age 68
Director, Mark C. Rohr, age 60
Director, Michael J. Ward, age 61
Director, Kathleen A. Ligocki, age 56
Director, George A. Schaefer Jr., age 67
Director, John F. Turner, age 70
Director, Vada O. Manager, age 51
Auditors: PricewaterhouseCoopersLLP

LOCATIONS

HQ: Ashland Inc.
50 E. RiverCenter Blvd., Covington KY 41012-0391
Phone: 859-815-3333 **Fax:** 859-815-5053
Web: www.ashland.com

2011 Sales

	$ mil.	% of total
% of total		
North		54
Europe		26
Asia/Pacific		13
Latin America &		7
Total		**100**

PRODUCTS/OPERATIONS

2011 Sales

	$ mil.	% of total
% of total		
Consumer		30
Water		29
Performance		21
Specialty		20
Total		**100**

COMPETITORS

Aceto
Chemtura

Arkema	Cytec
BASF SE	DuPont
BP Lubricants USA	HELM U.S.
Brenntag	Momentive

HISTORICAL FINANCIALS

Company Type: Public

Income Statement FYE: September 30

	REVENUE ($ mil.)	NET INCOME ($ mil.)	NET PROFIT MARGIN	EMPLOYEES
09/12	8,206	26	0.3%	15,000
09/11	6,502	414	6.4%	15,000
09/10	9,012	332	3.7%	14,500
09/09	8,106	71	0.9%	14,700
09/08	8,381	167	2.0%	11,900
Annual Growth	(0.5%)	(37.2%)	—	6.0%

2012 Year-End Financials

Debt ratio: 28.66%	No. of shares (mil.): 79
Return on equity: 0.65%	Dividends
Cash ($ mil.): 523	Yield: —
Current ratio: 167.75	Payout: 242.42%
Long-term debt ($ mil.): 3,131	Market value ($ mil.): 5,656

	STOCK PRICE ($) FY Close	P/E High	P/E Low	PER SHARE ($) Earnings	Dividends	Book Value
09/12	71.60	233	130	0.33	0.00	51.00
09/11	44.14	13	8	5.17	0.65	53.01
09/10	48.77	15	8	4.18	0.45	48.14
09/09	43.22	46	6	0.96	0.30	47.79
09/08	29.24	25	10	2.63	1.10	50.83
Annual Growth	25.1%	—	—	(40.5%)	—	0.1%

Associated Banc-Corp.

A lot of Midwesterners are associated with Associated Banc-Corp the holding company for Associated Bank.One of the largest banks based in Wisconsin the operates about 250 branches in that state as well as Illinois and Minnesota. Catering to consumers and local businesses it offers deposit accounts loans mortgage banking credit and debit cards and leasing. The bank's wealth management division offers investments trust services brokerage insurance and employee group benefits plans. Commercial loans including agricultural construction and real estate loans make up nearly 60% of bank's loan portfolio. The bank also writes residential mortgages consumer loans and home equity loans.

Hampered by one of the worst economic environments in recent history the bank saw increase in nonperforming loans (particularly business- and housing-related loans) and more than tripled its provision for loan losses from 2008 to 2009. The company cut its losses in 2010 and nearly turned a profit as it concentrated on improving its credit quality. It moved away from construction lending and its nonperforming loans and its provisions for loan losses decreased.

Even though 2011 revenues were down Associated Banc-Corp returned to profitability as credit quality continued to improve. The company hopes to keep the momentum going via organic growth including increasing its fee income and commercial deposits among other measures. It is also remodeling or relocating many of its branches.

EXECUTIVES

EVP and Chief Risk Officer, Arthur G. (Art) Heise, age 54
President CEO and Director, Philip B. (Phil) Flynn, age 54, $186,092 total compensation
Chairman, William R. Hutchinson, age 69
EVP and Chief Audit Executive, Patrick J. Derpinghaus
EVP and Director Retail Banking, David L. Stein, age 48
EVP CIO and COO Associated Banc-Corp and Associated Bank, Mark D. Quinlan, age 51, $310,000 total compensation
EVP and Chief Human Resources Officer, Judith M. Docter, age 51
CFO, Christopher (Chris) Del Moral-Niles
EVP and Chief Credit Officer Associated Banc-Corp and Associated Bank, Scott S. Hickey, age 56, $350,000 total compensation
EVP and Chief Strategy Officer Associated Banc-Corp and Associated Bank National Association, Oliver Buechse, age 43
EVP and Head Commercial Real Estate, Breck F. Hanson
SVP and Director Public Relations, Autumn Latimore
EVP and Head Commercial Middle Market and Regional Banking, Donna N. Smith
EVP and Head Specialized Industries and Commercial Financial Services, John A. Utz
EVP and Head Wealth Management, Timothy J. Lau
VP Finance, Tim Sedabres
VP and Public Relations Manager, Jennifer Kaminski
Director, Richard T. (Rick) Lommen, age 67
Director, John F. Bergstrom, age 65
Director, Ruth M. Crowley, age 52
Director, John C. Seramur, age 69
President CEO and Director, Philip B. (Phil) Flynn, age 54
Director, Ronald R. Harder, age 68
Director, J. Douglas Quick, age 65
Director, Karen T. Van Lith, age 52
Director, Eileen A. Kamerick, age 53
Directors, John B. (Jay) Williams, age 60
Director, Robert (Bob) Jeffe
Auditors: KPMGLLP

LOCATIONS

HQ: Associated Banc-Corp
1200 Hansen Rd., Green Bay WI 54304-3307
Phone: 920-491-7000 **Fax:** 920-491-7090
Web: www.associatedbank.com

PRODUCTS/OPERATIONS

2011 Sales

	$ mil.	% of total
Interest		
Loans including fees	582	57
Investment securities including dividends	153	15
Other	5	1
Noninterest		
Service charges on deposit accounts	75	7
Retail commissions	62	6
Card-based & other nondeposit fees	57	6
Trust service fees	39	4
Other	46	4
Total	**1,024**	**100**

COMPETITORS

Anchor BanCorp	KeyCorp
Bank Mutual	Northern Trust
Citizens Republic Bancorp	TCF Financial
Harris	U.S. Bancorp

HISTORICAL FINANCIALS

Company Type: Public

Income Statement FYE: December 31

	ASSETS ($ mil.)	NET INCOME ($ mil.)	INCOME AS % OF ASSETS	EMPLOYEES
12/11	21,924	139	0.6%	5,100
12/10	21,785	(0)	—	4,894
12/09	22,874	(131)	—	4,784
12/08	24,192	168	0.7%	5,140
12/07	21,592	285	1.3%	5,110
Annual Growth	0.4%	(16.4%)	—	(0.0%)

2011 Year-End Financials

Debt ratio: 5.37%	No. of shares (mil.): 174
Return on equity: 4.88%	Dividends
Cash ($ mil.): 609	Yield: —
Current ratio: —	Payout: 6.06%
Long-term debt ($ mil.): 1,177	Market value ($ mil.): 1,950

	STOCK PRICE ($) FY Close	P/E High	P/E Low	PER SHARE ($) Earnings	Dividends	Book Value
12/11	11.17	23	14	0.66	0.00	16.41
12/10	15.15	—	—	(0.18)	0.04	18.17
12/09	11.01	—	—	(1.26)	0.47	21.33
12/08	20.93	22	11	1.29	1.27	22.45
12/07	27.09	16	11	2.23	1.22	18.30
Annual Growth	(19.9%)	—	—	(26.2%)	—	(2.7%)

ASSOCIATED WHOLESALE GROCERS INC.

EXECUTIVES

SVP Grocery Products, Dennis Kinser, age 67
SVP General Counsel and Corporate Secretary, Frances Pellegrino Puhl, age 62
VP Corporate Sales, Bill Lancaster, age 72
President and CEO, Jerry Garland, age 61
EVP and CFO, Robert C. (Bob) Walker
SVP Real Estate and Store Engineering, Scott Wilmoski, age 59
COO, Michael (Mike) Rand
VP Corporate Sales Development, Stephen G. (Steve) Dillard
SVP Perishables, Lucky Hicks
SVP and Division Manager Kansas City, William A. (Bill) Quade
SVP and Division Manager Kansas City, Gary Jennings
SVP and Division Manager Nashville, Milton Milam
VP and CIO, Keith Martin
VP Distribution, John F. Lane
Corporate Executive Director Risk Management and Loss Prevention, Chuck Dillion
VP Sales Valu Merchandisers, Joe Busch

Assistant Electronic Data Interchange, Cari Carpenter
Chairman, Bob Hufford
Director of Training and Development, Pat Carr
Auditors: GrantThorntonLLP

LOCATIONS

HQ: Associated Wholesale Grocers Inc.
5000 Kansas Ave., Kansas City KS 66106
Phone: 913-288-1000 **Fax:** 913-288-1587
Web: www.awginc.com

Selected States Served

Alabama
Arkansas
Florida
Georgia
Illinois
Indiana
Iowa
Kansas
Kentucky
Louisiana
Michigan
Mississippi
Missouri
Nebraska
New Mexico
North Carolina
Oklahoma
Ohio
South Carolina
Tennessee
Texas
Virginia
West Virginia
Wisconsin

COMPETITORS

Affiliated Foods
Affiliated Foods Midwest
Alex Lee
Associated Grocers Inc.
C&S Wholesale
Central Grocers
Dearborn Wholesale Grocers
GSC Enterprises
H. T. Hackney
Kroger
McLane
Nash-Finch
Spartan Stores
SUPERVALU
Wakefern Food
Wal-Mart

HISTORICAL FINANCIALS

Company Type: Private - Cooperative

Income Statement FYE: December 31

	REVENUE ($ mil.)	NET INCOME ($ mil.)	NET PROFIT MARGIN	EMPLOYEES
12/11	7,766	169	2.2%	5,500
12/10	7,251	164	2.3%	0
12/09	7,057	147	2.1%	0
12/08	6,853	134	2.0%	0
Annual Growth	4.3%	8.0%	—	—

2011 Year-End Financials

Debt ratio: —
Return on equity: 2.20%
Cash ($ mil.): 82
Current ratio: 0.50
Long-term debt ($ mil.): —
Dividends
Yield: —
Payout: —
Market value ($ mil.): —

Assurant Inc

From credit cards to trailer parks Assurant provides a range of specialty insurance products. Through Assurant Solutions and Assurant Specialty Property the company offers such products as credit protection insurance manufactured home coverage creditor-placed homeowners insurance pre-need funeral policies and extended warranties for electronics appliances and vehicles. Individuals and small employer groups can choose from several types of health coverage offered by Assurant Health while group life dental and disability products are available through the Assurant Employee Benefits segment. Assurant's products are distributed through sales offices and independent agents across the US and abroad.

More than 80% of Assurant's sales are in the US but the company also operates in Canada and Mexico as well as in the Caribbean and select Latin American European and Asian countries. International sales are focused on extended service contracts and credit insurance (debt protection coverage for unemployment death or other events) through partnering retail and institutional distributors. The company also offers funeral policies (used to fund funeral expenses) in Canada.

To expand its business Assurant pursues a conservative acquisition strategy investing in small purchases that neatly complement its existing offerings. In 2011 for instance the Specialty Property division acquired SureDeposit which provides security deposit alternatives for rental property owners across the US for some $45 million. The purchase expanded the unit's service offerings for the multifamily housing market.

Assurant also partners with other companies to expand its reach. For example in 2012 Assurant Solutions partnered with Best Buy's wholly owned affiliate Jiangsu Five Star a leading electronics retailer in China to provide extended protection products and services for electronics and appliances at more than 200 stores in China.

The company built up the domestic warranty operations of Assurant Solutions through historical acquisitions adding a niche provider of handset repair and protection insurance services for wireless companies and a provider of appliance and electronics warranties in 2008. In addition Assurant Solutions has formed agreements to provide warranty services for companies such as GE and Whirlpool.

With a wary eye on pending US health care reform the company has begun to streamline its group and individual health insurance operations in the hopes that it can cash in on any industry opportunities that might arise. It started offering more low-cost insurance products such as high-deductable low-premium health plans with limited benefits to meet current market needs.

In 2010 the company resolved a nearly three-year-long SEC investigation into the company's finances. The investigation was part of a more widespread SEC investigation into the use by several companies (including Assurant) of finite reinsurance contracts which if manipulated can fraudulently lead investors into misunderstanding a company's bottom line. Assurant was never charged with fraud; but the company paid $3.5 million to settle non-fraud-related violations and settle the investigation without admitting or denying wrongdoing.

While its sales have declined slightly in recent years (including a drop of 3% from $8.5 billion in 2010 to $8.3 billion in 2011 due to customer non-renewals and increased catastrophe losses) Assurant's net income sagged heavily for a few years (2008-2010) from a variety of expenses including the loss of a large service contract business a steady decline in the credit insurance market and settlement of the SEC investigation. Net income recovered in 2011 jumping from $279 million to $546 million primarily due to a lack of impairment charges incurred the previous year.

The company formerly known as Fortis Inc. was spun off by the Fortis group (now known as Ageas) in 2004 and became publicly traded. The Fortis group owned 36% of Assurant until 2005 when it further reduced its stake to about 16% through a secondary public offering; the group gradually sold off the rest of its shares in the following years.

EXECUTIVES

Chief Compliance Officer, Jay M. Cohen, age 60
EVP Chief Legal Officer and Secretary, Bart R. Schwartz, age 59, $500,000 total compensation
President CEO and Director, Robert B. (Rob) Pollock, age 57, $950,000 total compensation
EVP and CFO, Michael J. (Mike) Peninger, age 57, $500,000 total compensation
EVP Human Resources and Development, Sylvia R. Wagner, age 63
SVP Federal Government Relations, Ronny B. Lancaster, age 60
Chairman, Elaine D. Rosen, age 59
EVP Marketing and Business Development, Alan B. Colberg, age 50
SVP Investor Relations, Melissa Kivett, age 41
EVP Treasurer and Chief Investment Officer; President Assurant Asset Management, Christopher J. (Chris) Pagano, age 48
SVP Controller and Principal Accounting Officer, John A. Sondej, age 47
VP Investor Relations, Brian D. Koppy, age 43
President and CEO Assurant Solutions, S. Craig Lemasters, age 51, $475,000 total compensation
President and CEO Assurant Specialty Property, Gene E. Mergelmeyer, age 53, $500,000 total compensation
President and CEO Assurant Employee Benefits, John S. Roberts, age 56, $500,000 total compensation
President and CEO Assurant Health, Adam Lamnin, age 48
SVP Chief Corporate Counsel and Assistant Secretary, Stephen W. Gauster, age 42
VP Corporate Communications, Shawn M. Kahle
Director Media Relations and Financial Communications, Vera Carley
Director, Paul J. Reilly, age 55
Director, David B. Kelso, age 59
Director, Lawrence V. Jackson, age 59
Director, Charles J. (Bud) Koch, age 65
Director, Beth L. Bronner, age 61
Director, John A. Swainson
Director, John M. Palms, age 77
Director, Allen R. Freedman, age 72
President CEO and Director, Robert B. (Rob) Pollock, age 57
Director, Juan N. Cento, age 60
Director, Howard L. Carver, age 67
Director, H. Carroll Mackin, age 71
Director, Elyse Douglas, age 55
Auditors: PricewaterhouseCoopersLLP

LOCATIONS

HQ: Assurant Inc.
1 Chase Manhattan Plaza 41st Fl., New York NY 10005
Phone: 212-859-7000 **Fax:** 212-859-7010
Web: www.assurant.com

2011 Sales

	$ mil.	% of total
US	7,233	87
Total	**8,272**	**100**

PRODUCTS/OPERATIONS

2011 Sales

	$ mil.	% of total
Solutions	3,097	37
Health	1,798	22
Corporate & other	70	1

Business Segments & Products
Assurant Solutions
Credit insurance (domestic and internatio
Debt protection
Preneed life insurance (pre-funded funeral insurance)
Warranties and Extended Service Contracts (ESCs domestic and internatio
Assurant Specialty Property
Homeowners insurance (creditor-placed and voluntary)
Manufactured housing insurance (creditor-placed and voluntary)
Other specialty property personal lines (primarily flood and renters insurance)
Assurant Health
Health Savings Accounts and Health Reimbursement Accounts (HSAs and HRAs)
Individual health insurance
Short-term health and student insurance
Small employer group health insurance
Assurant Employee Benefits
Group disability
Group dental
Group life

COMPETITORS

Aetna
Allstate
American Home Shield
Americo
AmTrust Financial
Asurion
Bankers Financial
CIGNA
Delta Dental Plans
Fidelity National Financial
First American
Great American Insurance Company
Home Buyers Warranty
Homesteaders Life
Humana
Maiden Holdings
Monumental Life
Mutual of Omaha
Nationwide
NGL Insurance
QBE First
State Farm
The Warranty Group
United Concordia
UnitedHealth Group
Warrantech
WellPoint

HISTORICAL FINANCIALS

Company Type: Public

Income Statement FYE: December 31

	REVENUE ($ mil.)	NET INCOME ($ mil.)	NET PROFIT MARGIN	EMPLOYEES
12/11	8,272	545	6.6%	14,100
12/10	8,527	279	3.3%	14,000
12/09	8,700	430	4.9%	15,000
12/08	8,601	447	5.2%	15,000
12/07	8,453	653	7.7%	14,000
Annual Growth	(0.5%)	(4.4%)	—	0.2%

2011 Year-End Financials

Debt ratio: 3.59%
Return on equity: 10.86%
Cash ($ mil.): 1,166
Current ratio: 1612.76
Long-term debt ($ mil.): 972
No. of shares (mil.): 88
Dividends
Yield: —
Payout: 12.54%
Market value ($ mil.): 3,635

	STOCK PRICE ($) FY Close	P/E High	P/E Low	PER SHARE ($) Earnings	Dividends	Book Value
12/11	41.06	7	6	5.58	0.00	56.79
12/10	38.52	17	12	2.50	0.63	46.87
12/09	29.48	9	5	3.63	0.59	41.61
12/08	30.00	18	3	3.77	0.54	31.61
12/07	66.90	13	9	5.38	0.46	34.71
Annual Growth	(11.5%)	—	—	0.9%	—	13.1%

Astoria Financial Corp.

Astoria Financial is the holding company for Astoria Federal Savings and Loan one of the largest thrifts in the US. The thrift has more than 80 branches in and around New York City and Long Island encompassing Brooklyn Queens Nassau Suffolk and Westchester counties in addition to a network of third-party mortgage brokers spanning more than a dozen states and Washington DC. It offers standard deposit products such as CDs and checking savings and retirement accounts. With these funds Astoria Federal primarily writes loans and invests in mortgage-backed securities. Subsidiary AF Insurance Agency sells life and property/casualty coverage to Astoria Federal customers.

One- to four-family residential mortgages account for approximately three-quarters of Astoria Financial's loan portfolio.The bulk of these are jumbo prime hybrid adjustable-rate mortgages. Multifamily and commercial real estate loans most of which are subject to rent control or stabilization make up nearly 20% of the portfolio. The thrift halted its multifamily and commercial lending due to the difficult economic environment but resumed originating those loans in late 2011. The company actively sells nonperforming assets to get them off of its books.

Despite the high concentration of home loans Astoria Financial remained largely shielded from the mortgage meltdown thanks to its strict underwriting standards and the geographic diversity of its lending activities. Like many of its peers however the bank has also seen loan volumes decline and delinquencies increase. Benefitting from its conservative strategy the bank remained profitable during the recession. However as a result of a slowdown in lending activities revenues fell 18% in 2011 to $764.2 million and net income fell 9% to $67.2 million.

Astoria Financial prefers to grow organically rather than through acquisitions or by opening new branches.

The company's employee pension plan owns 11% of Astoria Financial.

EXECUTIVES

Vice Chairman and Chief Administrative Officer Astoria Financial and Astoria Federal, Gerard C. Keegan, age 65, $544,000 total compensation
EVP General Counsel and Secretary Astoria Financial and Astoria Federal, Alan P. Eggleston, age 58, $445,000 total compensation
EVP and Assistant Secretary Astoria Financial and Astoria Federal, Arnold K. Greenberg, age 71, $483,000 total compensation
President and CEO Astoria Financial and Astoria Federal, Monte N. Redman, age 61, $825,000 total compensation
Chairman Astoria Financial and Astoria Federal, George L. Engelke Jr., age 73, $1,142,000 total compensation
Vice Chairman Astoria Financial, John J. Conefry Jr., age 68
Chairman Astoria Financial and Astoria Federal, Ralph F. Palleschi, age 65
SVP and Director Multi-family/Commercial Real Estate Lending Astoria Federal Savings, Gary M. Honstedt, age 62
SVP and CIO Astoria Financial and Astoria Federal, Robert J. DeStefano
EVP and Managing Director Retail Banking Group, Brian T. Edwards
EVP CFO and Treasurer, Frank E. Fusco, age 48, $465,000 total compensation
EVP, Gary T. McCann, age 57, $500,000 total compensation
First VP and Director Investor Relations, Peter J. Cunningham
Vice Chairman and Chief Administrative Officer Astoria Financial and Astoria Federal, Gerard C. Keegan, age 65
Vice Chairman Astoria Financial, John J. Conefry Jr., age 68
Director, Denis J. Connors, age 70
Director, Peter C. Haeffner Jr., age 73
Director, Ralph F. Palleschi, age 64
Director, Thomas V. Powderly, age 74
Director, Brian M. Leeney, age 62
Director, John R. Chrin, age 49
Auditors: KPMGLLP

LOCATIONS

HQ: Astoria Financial Corp.
One Astoria Federal Plaza, Lake Success, NY 11042-1085
Phone: 516 327-3000 **Fax:** 516 327-7860
Web: www.astoriafederal.com

PRODUCTS/OPERATIONS

2011 Sal

	$ mil.	% of total
Interest		
One- to four family mortgage loans	434	57
Multifamily commercial real estate & construction mortgage loans 21	162	
Securities	82	11
Consumer & other loans	9	1
Other	6	1
Noninterest		
Customer service fees	46	6
Net mortgage banking income	10	1
Other	12	2
Total	**764**	**100**

COMPETITORS

Apple Bank for Savings
Bank of America
Capital One
Citibank
Dime Community Bancshares
Flushing Financial
HSBC USA
JPMorgan Chase
New York Community Bancorp
TD Bank USA

HISTORICAL FINANCIALS

Company Type: Public

Income Statement FYE: December 31

	ASSETS ($ mil.)	NET INCOME ($ mil.)	INCOME AS % OF ASSETS	EMPLOYEES
12/11	17,022	67	0.4%	1,730
12/10	18,089	73	0.4%	1,662
12/09	20,252	27	0.1%	1,699
12/08	21,982	75	0.3%	1,685
12/07	21,719	124	0.6%	1,735
Annual Growth	(5.9%)	(14.3%)	—	(0.1%)

2011 Year-End Financials

Debt ratio: 14.23%
Return on equity: 5.37%
Cash ($ mil.): 132
Current ratio: —
Long-term debt ($ mil.): 2,421
No. of shares (mil.): 98
Dividends
Yield: —
Payout: 74.29%
Market value ($ mil.): 837

	STOCK PRICE ($) FY Close	P/E High	P/E Low	PER SHARE ($) Earnings	Dividends	Book Value
12/11	8.49	22	9	0.70	0.00	12.70
12/10	13.91	22	15	0.78	0.52	12.69
12/09	12.43	56	20	0.30	0.52	12.45
12/08	16.48	34	17	0.83	1.04	12.33
12/07	23.27	22	17	1.36	1.04	12.65
Annual Growth	(22.3%)	—	—	(15.3%)	—	0.1%

AT&T Inc

Through its subsidiaries affiliates and operating companies holding company AT&T is the industry-leading provider of wireline voice communications services in the US. Customers in 22 states use AT&T-branded telephone Internet and VoIP services; it also sells digital TV under the U-verse brand. Key markets include California Illinois and Texas. The company's corporate government and public sector clients use its conferencing managed network and wholesale communications services. Subsidiary AT&T Mobility is the second-largest US mobile carrier by both sales and subscriptions (after Verizon Wireless). It provides mobile voice and data services to more than 100 million subscribers.

HISTORY

In 1878 a dozen customers signed up for the first telephone exchange in St. Louis (later Bell Telephone Company of Missouri). That exchange and the Missouri and Kansas Telephone Company later merged into Southwestern Bell which became a regional arm of the AT&T monopoly in 1917.

The old AT&T was broken up in 1984 and Southwestern Bell emerged as a regional Bell operating company (RBOC) with local phone service rights in five states a cellular company a directory business and a stake in R&D arm Bellcore (now Telcordia). In 1987 the company bought paging and cellular franchises from Metromedia.

Edward Whitacre a Texan who worked his way from measuring phone wire to an executive spot at Southwestern Bell became CEO in 1990. That year the RBOC joined with France Telecom and Mexican conglomerate Grupo Carso to purchase 20% of Telefonos de Mexico (Telmex) the former state monopoly.

Renamed SBC Communications in 1994 the company hired lobbyists the next year to coax the Texas Legislature to pass a bill that would deter local phone competitors. It worked: New entrants had to build a phone network to serve every house in a 27-mile square.

The federal Telecommunications Act passed in 1996 and the following year SBC acquired Pacific Telesis the parent of Pacific Bell and Nevada Bell. That year the FCC denied SBC's request to enter Oklahoma's long-distance market saying the company had not done enough to encourage competition. Undeterred SBC launched a legal assault on the Telecom Act itself which proved to be unsuccessful.

SBC bought Southern New England Telecommunications (SNET) in 1998 gaining a foothold on the East Coast. The next year the company bought Comcast's cellular operations and took a minority stake in Williams Communications Group (now WilTel Communications) –the first significant investment in a long-distance carrier by a Baby Bell.

SBC completed the $62 billion purchase of Ameritech in 1999 after weathering a year-long regulatory review. The acquisition extended SBC's local access dominance into five Midwestern states but about half of Ameritech's wireless business was sold as a condition of the deal. SBC agreed to provide competitive local phone service in 30 cities outside its home territory by 2002 to win regulatory approval. Also in 1999 the company announced plans to spend $6 billion over three years to make its networks capable of delivering high-speed DSL Internet access to 80% of its customers.

In 2000 SBC combined its US wireless operations with those of BellSouth to form Cingular Wireless a carrier with operations in 38 states. The company also combined its consumer and small-business Internet access operations with those of Prodigy Communications gaining a minority stake in Prodigy (SBC took full ownership of Prodigy in 2001). Also in 2000 the FCC approved SBC's application to sell long-distance service in Texas and the company racked up more than a million long-distance customers in less than six months.

In 2001 SBC won approval to offer long-distance in Arkansas Kansas Missouri and Oklahoma but was fined by the FCC –it paid $69 million between December 2000 and August 2001 –for failing to meet standards for opening its local networks to competitors. The company expanded its long-distance network to include Texas and Connecticut and entered the lucrative California market after receiving regulatory approval on a 3-1 vote by the FCC in 2002. The company in 2003 gained approval to offer long-distance in Illinois Indiana Ohio and Wisconsin filling out the company's 13-state home territory.

The recession and what SBC officials called an "outmoded regulatory scheme" drove the company to cut expenses including deep cuts in its workforce in 2002 and 2003. It sold its 16% stake in Bell Canada to BCE for $3.2 billion and in 2003 it sold its 15% stake in France's Cegetel (now SFR) to Vodafone Group. It also sold stakes in international holdings including Denmark's TDC (for about $2.1 billion) and South African carrier Telkom SA.

In 2004 Cingular Wireless acquired AT&T Wireless in a cash deal valued at $41 billion creating the #1 US wireless operator toppling former market leader Verizon Wireless (now Cellco Partnership). (By 2007 the combined company came to be known as AT&T Mobility). Also in 2004 the company sold its interest in a directory publishing partnership in Illinois and Indiana to partner R. H. Donnelly (now Dex One) for about $1.45 billion. It also teamed up with BellSouth to purchase Internet directory publisher YellowPages.com.

Former Baby Bell SBC Communications bought AT&T Corp. the original Ma Bell in 2005 for some $16 billion creating the largest telecom outfit in the US. The cash and stock deal added valuable industry-leading enterprise customers (a space that SBC had trouble making inroads into with a brand that was little-known outside of its region) to the company's strong repertoire of consumer offerings. After the merger SBC adopted the globally familiar AT&T name.

In 2006 the company purchased southern RBOC BellSouth in the largest telecommunications takeover in US history valued at $86 billion. The BellSouth deal gave AT&T complete control of mobile phone service provider Cingular Wireless formerly a joint venture between the two companies. The subsequent reorganization and absorption of BellSouth resulted in the elimination of about 10000 jobs.

The company made a move to build its base of cellular customers in rural areas with the $2.8 billion purchase of Dobson Communications in 2007. AT&T acquired private specialized business software provider USinternetworking for $300 million as well. The Annapolis Maryland-based firm known as USi developed applications used to automate functions related to human resources customer relations and e-commerce. CEO Whitacre handed over the reins to COO Randall Stephenson that year. AT&T bought Easterbrooke Cellular and Windstream Wireless the following year.

In 2009 AT&T paid $275 million in cash to acquire Texas-based Wi-Fi services provider Wayport. The purchase expanded AT&T wireless hot spot coverage particularly in retail locations and hotels. The company also bought Centennial Communications (a provider of wireless and broadband services to the Midwest and Southeast US as well as parts of the Caribbean) for $920 million late that year. The deal boosted AT&T's subscriber base by about 900000 and extended its service area to include rural areas of Louisiana Michigan and Texas. Outside of the US the company bolstered its position in Puerto Rico and the US Virgin Islands.

EXECUTIVES

SEVP External and Legislative Affairs AT&T Services Inc., James W. (Jim) Cicconi, age 59, $800,000 total compensation

President and CEO AT&T Labs, Krish A. Prabhu, age 57

President and CEO AT&T Mobility, Ralph de la Vega, age 60, $800,000 total compensation

SEVP Human Resources, William A. (Bill) Blase Jr., age 56

SEVP and CFO, John J. Stephens, age 52

Chairman President and CEO, Randall L. Stephenson, age 51, $1,450,000 total compensation

SEVP and Global Marketing Officer, Catherine M. (Cathy) Coughlin, age 54

Group President and Chief Strategy Officer, John T. Stankey, age 49, $830,000 total compensation

VP Internet and Mobile Sales AT&T Advanced Ad Solutions, Michael Rosen

SEVP Executive Operations, Ronald E. (Ron) Spears, age 63

SEVP AT&T Technology and Network Operations, John M. Donovan

SEVP and General Counsel, D. Wayne Watts, age 58

SVP Talent Development and Chief Diversity Officer, Debbie Storey
Chief Medical Information Officer, Geeta Nayyar
Senior Executive Vice President ? AT&T Business and Home Solutions, Andrew M. Geisse, age 55
Director, Scott T. Ford, age 48
Director, Matthew K. (Matt) Rose, age 53
Director, James H. (Jim) Blanchard, age 70
Director, Jon C. Madonna, age 69
Director, James P. (Jim) Kelly, age 68
Director, John B. McCoy, age 68
Director, Jaime Chico Pardo, age 62
Director, Laura D. Tyson, age 65
Director, Reuben V. Anderson, age 69
Director, Gilbert F. (Gil) Amelio, age 69
Director, Joyce M. Roche, age 65
Auditors: Ernst&YoungLLP

LOCATIONS

HQ: AT&T Inc
208 S. Akard St., Dallas, TX 75202
Phone: 210 821-4105
Web: www.att.com

PRODUCTS/OPERATIONS

2011 Sales

	$ mil.	% of total
% of total		
Wireless		50
Wireline		47
Advertising &		3
Total		100

Selected Acquisitions

Plusmo (2009 cross-platform mobile application solutions)
Centennial Communications (2008 wireless and wired communications provider)
Ingenio (2008 pay per call technology)
Interwise (2007 communications provider)
Dobson Communications (2007 wireless communications services)
Daniel IT (2007 WebSphere Commerce consulting)

Selected Services

Voice
- Local
- Long-distance
- Wholesale

Data
- Application management
- Data equipment sales
- Data storage
- Database management
- Dedicated Internet service
- Digital television
- Directory and operator assistance
- Disaster recovery
- Enterprise networking
- Hardware and operating system management
- Internet access and network integration
- Managed Web hosting
- Network design
- Network implementation
- Network installation
- Network integration
- Network management
- Outsourcing
- Packet services
- Private lines
- Satellite video
- Switched and dedicated transport
- Voice-over-IP networks
- Wholesale networking
- WiFi

COMPETITORS

Cablevision Systems
CenturyLink
Level 3 Communications
SAVVIS
Charter Communications
Comcast
Consolidated Communications
Cox Communications
DIRECTV
DISH Network
EarthLink
Equinix
Frontier Communications
Sprint Nextel
T-Mobile USA
TDS Metrocom
Telephone & Data Systems
Time Warner Cable
tw telecom
U.S. Cellular
Verizon
XO Holdings

HISTORICAL FINANCIALS

Company Type: Public

Income Statement

FYE: December 31

	REVENUE ($ mil.)	NET INCOME ($ mil.)	NET PROFIT MARGIN	EMPLOYEES
12/11	126,723	3,944	3.1%	256,420
12/10	124,280	19,864	16.0%	266,590
12/09	123,018	12,535	10.2%	282,720
12/08	124,028	12,867	10.4%	301,000
12/07	118,928	11,951	10.0%	310,000
Annual Growth	1.6%	(24.2%)	—	(4.6%)

2011 Year-End Financials

Debt ratio: 23.95%—
Return on equity: 3.74%
Cash ($ mil.): 3,185
Current ratio: 74.78
Long-term debt ($ mil.): 61,300
Dividends
Yield: —
Payout: 260.61%
Market value ($ mil.): —

	STOCK PRICE ($) FY Close	P/E High/Low		PER SHARE ($) Earnings	Dividends	Book Value
12/11	30.24	48	41	0.66	0.00	17.81
12/10	29.38	9	7	3.35	1.68	18.89
12/09	28.03	14	10	2.12	1.64	17.27
12/08	28.50	19	10	2.16	1.60	16.35
12/07	41.56	22	17	1.94	1.42	19.09
Annual Growth	(7.6%)	—	—	(23.6%)	—	(1.7%)

Autoliv Inc.

LOCATIONS

HQ: Autoliv Inc.
Vasagatan 11, 7th Floor, SE-111 20, Box 70381,
Phone: (46) 8 587 20 600
Web: www.autoliv.com

2010 Sales

	$ mil.	% of total
Europe	2,741	38
North America	2,054	29
Japan	791	11
Other regions	1,585	22
Total	7,171	100

PRODUCTS/OPERATIONS

2010 Sales

	$ mil.	% of total
Airbags & associated products	4,807	67
Seatbelts & associated products	2,364	33
Total	7,171	100

Selected Products

Anti-whiplash seats
Child restraints
Electronics
Frontal airbags
Inflators
Leg airbags
Seat belts
Side-impact airbags
Steering wheels

Selected Subsidiaries and Affiliates

Airbags International Ltd (UK)
Autoflator AB
Autoliv AB
Autoliv Argentina SA
Autoliv ASP BV (The Netherlands)
Autoliv ASP Inc. (US)
Autoliv Australia Proprietary Ltd
Autoliv Autosicherheitstechnik GmbH (Germany)
Autoliv BKI SA (Spain)
Autoliv BV (The Netherlands)
Autoliv Canada Inc
Autoliv Cankor Otomotiv Emniyet Sistemleri Sanayi Ve (Turkey)
Autoliv China Electronics Co. Ltd
Autoliv do Brasil Ltda.
Autoliv East Europe AB
Autoliv Electronics AB
Autoliv Electronics SAS (France)
Autoliv France SNC
Autoliv Holding BV (The Netherlands)
Autoliv Holding Inc. (US)
Autoliv Holding Ltd. (UK)
Autoliv Italia S.P.A.
Autoliv Japan Ltd
Autoliv KFT (Hungary)
Autoliv KLE SAU (Spain)
Autoliv Ltd (UK)
Autoliv Nichiyo Co. (Japan)
Autoliv Overseas BV (The Netherlands)
Autoliv Poland Sp zoo
Autoliv Romania SA
Autoliv Safety Technology Inc. (US)
Autoliv Sicherheitstechnik GmbH (Germany)
Autoliv Southern Africa Pty Ltd
Autoliv Stakupress GmbH (Germany)
Autoliv Sverige AB
Autoliv Thailand Ltd
Autoliv UK Holding Ltd
Marling BV (The Netherlands)
Mei-An Autoliv Co. (59% Taiwan)
Nanjing Hongguang Autoliv Vehicle Safety Co. Ltd. (50% China)
NSK Safety Technology (Thailand) Co. Ltd.
OEA Inc. (US)
Svensk Airbag AB
Van Oerle Alberton BV (The Netherlands)
Van Oerle Alberton Holding BV (The Netherlands)
Van Oerle Webco Pty Ltd (Australia)

HISTORICAL FINANCIALS

Company Type:

Income Statement

FYE: December 31

	REVENUE ($ mil.)	NET INCOME ($ mil.)	NET PROFIT MARGIN	EMPLOYEES
12/11	8,232	623	7.6%	47,900
12/10	7,170	590	8.2%	43,300
12/09	5,120	10	0.2%	37,900
12/08	6,473	164	2.5%	37,300
12/07	6,769	287	4.3%	41,900
Annual Growth	5.0%	21.3%	—	3.4%

2011 Year-End Financials

Debt ratio: 10.89%
Return on equity: 18.70%
Cash ($ mil.): 739
Current ratio: 143.84
Long-term debt ($ mil.): 363
No. of shares (mil.): 89
Dividends
Yield: —
Payout: 26.02%
Market value ($ mil.): 4,776

STOCK PRICE ($) FY Close	P/E High/Low		PER SHARE ($) Earnings	Dividends	Book Value
12/11 53.49	12	7	6.65	0.00	37.33
12/10 78.94	12	6	6.39	0.65	32.90
12/09 43.36	370	103	0.12	1.03	28.06
12/08 21.46	27	7	2.28	1.60	30.11
12/07 52.71	17	14	3.68	1.54	31.83
Annual Growth 0.4%	—	—	15.9%	—	4.1%

Automatic Data Processing Inc.

The original outsourcer Automatic Data Processing (ADP) has still got it. ADP is one of the largest payroll and tax filing processors in the world serving about 535000 clients. Employer services (payroll processing tax and benefits administration services) account for the majority of the company's sales and its PEO (professional employer organization) services are provided through ADP TotalSource. ADP also provides inventory and other computing and data services to some 25000 auto motorcycle truck and recreational vehicle dealers. Other offerings include accounting auto collision estimates for insurers employment background checks desktop support and business development training services.

HISTORY

In 1949 22-year-old Henry Taub started Automatic Payrolls a manual payroll preparation service in Paterson New Jersey. Taub's eight accounts created gross revenue of around $2000 that year. In 1952 his brother Joe joined the company and a childhood friend Frank Lautenberg took a pay cut to become its first salesman.

Automatic Payrolls grew steadily during the 1950s. In 1961 the company went public and changed its name to Automatic Data Processing (ADP). The next year it offered back-office services to brokerage houses and bought its first computer. The company's sales reached $1 million in 1962.

During the 1970s ADP bought more than 30 companies in Brazil the UK and the US —all involved in data and payroll processing or financial services. Its stock began trading on the NYSE in 1970. By 1971 revenue had reached $50 million. Lautenberg became CEO in 1975.

ADP bought more than 25 businesses during the 1980s in Canada Germany and the US. Its purchases of stock information provider GTE Telenet (1983) and Bunker Ramo's information system business (1986) brought the company 45000 stock quote terminals in brokerages such as E.F. Hutton Dean Witter and Prudential-Bache. When Lautenberg resigned to become one of New Jersey's US senators in 1983 Josh Weston who had joined the company as a VP in 1970 replaced him.

By 1985 ADP sales had climbed to $1 billion. That year Taub retired. The company installed 15000 computer workstations at brokerages in 1986; it began installing more than 38000 new integrated workstations at Merrill Lynch and Shearson Lehman three years later. ADP shed units including its Canadian stock quote and Brazilian businesses in 1989 and 1990.

After being deterred from major acquisitions by the inflated prices of the late 1980s the company bought BankAmerica's 17000-client Business Services division (1992) and Industry Software's back-office and international equities business (1993).

In 1994 the company purchased Peachtree Software (accounting and payroll software for small companies) National Bio Systems (medical bill auditing) and V-Crest (auto dealership management systems). ADP acquired chief rival AutoInfo and its network of 3000 salvage yards the next year and further expanded into Western Europe with its purchase of Paris-based computing services firm GSI.

The buying binge continued in 1996 with acquisitions including Global Proxy Services (proxy processing services) Health Benefits America (benefits management) and Merrin Financial (automated securities trade order management). Former Deloitte & Touche partner Arthur Weinbach an ADP executive since 1980 was named CEO that year. ADP was ordered in an antitrust settlement in 1997 to help re-create AutoInfo as a viable competitor to its salvage yard business.

Among its dozen acquisitions in 1998 was Swiss Reinsurance's European collision estimates business. The company also sold its money-losing stock quote business that year to financial information provider Bridge Information Systems. Weston retired in 1998; Weinbach was named chairman. The company also filed to spin off Peachtree to the public but in early 1999 it sold the unit to UK-based software firm The Sage Group. The buying spree continued that year; ADP's largest purchase was The Vincam Group an employment management contractor for about $295 million.

In 2000 the company acquired Cunningham Graphics a provider of printing services to the financial services industry and Traver Technologies which offers consulting and training services to automobile dealers in the US. The following year it acquired Avert a provider of employment screening services and the output services business of IBM Global Services specializing in printing and distributing communications for the financial services industry. In 2003 the company bought ProBusiness Services a payroll and human resource processing service provider for about $500 million. The next year ADP purchased EDS's Automotive Retail Group a provider of dealer management systems as well as ProQuest Business Solutions' DMS business.

In August 2006 Weinbach retired as chairman and CEO and former president and COO Gary Butler was elevated to top executive at that time. The same year ADP sold its Claims Services Group (CSG) to Solera and GTCR Golder Rauner for $975 million. Later one of ADP's divisions bought Employease a provider of Web-based human resources and benefits management software. Maintaining this software expansion strategy in October 2006 ADP snatched up VirtualEdge a software designer specializing in recruitment/pre-employment screening tools and services.

At the time ADP also concentrated on boosting its tax compliance services capabilities. In obtained Taxware LP (from First Data Corp.) and Mintax; both were businesses used to assist with tax calculations and related services. In 2007 ADP spun off its brokerage services division Broadridge Financial Solutions.

ADP set its sights on China in 2009 when it purchased a majority share in ChinaLink Professional Services a firm providing outsourced human resources based in Shanghai. Also that year ADP snatched up HRinterax an HR support services firm catering exclusively to small businesses.

After years of navigating successfully through the stormy clouds of the recession the company appointed Carlos Rodriguez as its new CEO in late 2011.

EXECUTIVES

Corporate VP; President Dealer Services, Steven J. Anenen, age 59
President CEO and Director, Carlos A. Rodriguez, age 48, $433,333 total compensation
Corporate VP, John W. P. Holt
Staff VP, Gary E. Tarino
Chairman, Leslie A. (Les) Brun, age 60
VP and Chief Human Resources Officer, Dermot J. O'Brien
Corporate VP and CFO, Christopher R. (Chris) Reidy, age 55, $532,400 total compensation
VP and CFO, Jan Siegmund, age 48
President ? National Account Services Major Account Services Benefits Services Canada and GlobalView, Regina R. Lee, age 55, $441,667 total compensation
VP Corporate Controller and Principal Accounting Officer, Alan Sheiness, age 54
Corporate VP, Alfred A. Nietzel, age 49
VP and CIO, Michael L. Capone, age 45
EVP Worldwide Sales and Marketing, Edward B. Flynn III, age 52
President Employer Services Small Business Services TotalSource and Retirement Services, Anish D. Rajparia, age 41
VP and Treasurer, Michael C. Eberhard, age 50
President Employer Services International, Mark D. Benjamin
Corporate VP, Kris D. Borkovich
Corporate VP, Laurie J. Eldridge
Corporate VP, Robert N. Karp
VP General Counsel and Secretary, Michael A. Bonarti, age 47
Staff VP, Stephen A. Doherty
Staff VP, David H. Garfinkel
Staff VP, Charles Gibbons
Corporate VP, Timothy T. Clifford
Director, Gregory L. Summe, age 55
Director, Eric C. Fast, age 63
Director, Gregory D. (Greg) Brenneman, age 50
President CEO and Director, Carlos A. Rodriguez, age 48
Director, Enrique T. Salem, age 46
Director, Leon G. Cooperman, age 69
Director, Linda R. Gooden, age 59
Director, Sharon T. Rowlands, age 54
Director, R. Glenn Hubbard, age 54
Auditors: Deloitte&ToucheLLP

LOCATIONS

HQ: Automatic Data Processing Inc.
One ADP Boulevard, Roseland, NJ 07068
Phone: 973 974-5000 **Fax:** 973 974-5390
Web: www.adp.com

2011 Sales

	$ mil.	% of total
US	7,930	80
Canada	428	5
Total	**9,879**	**100**

PRODUCTS/OPERATIONS

2011 Sales

Employer services	6,861	68
Dealer services	1,494	15
Adjustments	(212.9)	-

Selected Services

Dealer Services
- Business management
- Computer systems sales
- Employee productivity training
- Hardware maintenance
- Manufacturer and dealer data communications networks
- Software licensing and support
- Vehicle registration services

Employer Services
- 401(k) record keeping and reporting
- Benefits administration and outsourcing
- Employment screening and background checks
- Human resource record keeping and reporting
- Payroll processing
- Tax filing
- Unemployment compensation management

Selected Mergers & Acquisitions

2011
- AdvancedMD Software (Salt Lake City; electronic health records)

2010
- The Cobalt Group ($400 million; Seattle; car marketing)
- DO2 Technolologies (Calgary; electronic invoicing software)
- Workscape (Marlborough MA; HR and benefits software)

COMPETITORS

Avatar Systems
CBIZ
Ceridian
Computer Sciences Corp.
Enertia Software
Global Payments
HP Enterprise Services
Insperity
Intuit
Oasis Outsourcing
Paychex
Reynolds and Reynolds
Total System Services
TriNet Group
Ultimate Software

HISTORICAL FINANCIALS

Company Type: Public

Income Statement

FYE: June 30

	REVENUE ($ mil.)	NET INCOME ($ mil.)	NET PROFIT MARGIN	EMPLOYEES
06/12	10,665	1,388	13.0%	57,000
06/11	9,879	1,254	12.7%	51,000
06/10	8,927	1,211	13.6%	47,000
06/09	8,867	1,332	15.0%	45,000
06/08	8,776	1,235	14.1%	47,000
Annual Growth	5.0%	3.0%	—	4.9%

2012 Year-End Financials

Debt ratio: 0.05%
Return on equity: 22.71%
Cash ($ mil.): 1,548
Current ratio: 108.25
Long-term debt ($ mil.): 16
No. of shares (mil.): 484
Dividends
Yield: —
Payout: 54.79%
Market value ($ mil.): 26,951

	STOCK PRICE ($) FY Close	P/E High/Low		PER SHARE ($) Earnings	Dividends	Book Value
06/12	55.66	20	16	2.82	0.00	12.63
06/11	52.68	22	15	2.52	1.42	12.25
06/10	40.26	19	14	2.40	1.35	11.14
06/09	35.44	17	12	2.63	1.28	10.61
06/08	41.90	21	16	2.34	1.10	9.97
Annual Growth	7.4%	—	—	4.8%	—	6.1%

AutoNation, Inc.

AutoNation wants to instill patriotic fervor in the fickle car-buying public. The brainchild of entrepreneur and ex-chairman Wayne Huizenga (Waste Management Blockbuster) AutoNation is the #1 auto dealer in the US (ahead of Penske Automotive Group and Sonic Automotive). The firm owns more than 250 new-vehicle franchises (down from 300 in 2008) in 15 states and it conducts online sales through AutoNation.com and individual dealer websites. AutoNation operates under about 15 different brands in local markets (including Mike Shad in Jacksonville Florida and GO in Colorado). In addition to auto sales AutoNation provides maintenance and repair services sells auto parts and finances and insures vehicles.

Financial Analysis

After being stuck in a ditch as the deep recession and credit crunch in the US discouraged car sales in 2008 and 2009 AutoNation's sales have recovered and are growing at double-digit rates. Sales were up 11% in 2011 vs. 2010 after posting a nearly 17% increasing in the previous annual comparison. Both used and new vehicles sales rose by more than 12%. Sales of used vehicles slightly outpaced new vehicle sales. The lag in new vehicle sales which account for more than 50% of the company's total revenue relative to used cars continued the pattern observed during the recession when consumers who had to replace a vehicle eschewed new cars in favor of lower-priced used models. The lingering preference for used over new is a problem for AutoNation because new vehicle sales are much more profitable. Indeed gross profit on a new car sales was about 21% in 2011 vs. just 7% for used cars. After two years of improvement the company expects the favorable sales trend to continue over the next few years.

Strategy

AutoNation seeks to capture an increasing share of vehicle sales through a two-pronged strategy: building powerful local brands while increasing consumer awareness of the AutoNation brand. The company relies on its 15 local brands in key metropolitan markets such as GO in Denver and Champion in South Texas to connect with car buyers. Indeed stores operated under its 15 local brands accounted for about 70% of total revenue in 2011. Using its website store signage and media presence AutoNation is also working to familiarize car buyers with the AutoNation brand. A key element of the firm's business strategy is its diversified portfolio of 30-plus brands spanning imports (37% of new vehicle sales) premium luxury vehicles (28%) and domestic autos (34%). Over the past decade AutoNation has increased the percentage of import and luxury cars it sells.

Mergers and Acquisitions

The economic turmoil caused AutoNation and other megadealers to put the brakes on acquisitions and divest domestic brand dealerships. Historically AutoNation has been a driving force in the consolidation of the US car sales business. It clusters dealerships within markets so that they can share inventory cross-sell to customers and reduce marketing costs –basically cutting and combining costs in an attempt to become the auto industry's Wal-Mart. As the economy improves AutoNation is again looking for acquisition and new store opportunities. In 2011 it acquired one automotive retail franchise five in 2010 and one in 2009.

Ownership

Billionaire investor and former AutoNation director Edward Lampert has been steadily increasing his stake in AutoNation through his hedge fund ESL Investments which owns nearly 53% of the company's shares. Cascade Investment LLC the investment vehicle owned by Bill Gates III owns about 14% of the company's shares.

HISTORY

AutoNation started in 1980 as Republic Resources which brokered petroleum leases did exploration and production and blended lubricants. In 1989 after oil prices crashed and a stockholder group tried to force Republic into liquidation Browning-Ferris Industries (BFI) founder Thomas Fatjo gained control of the company and refocused it on a field he knew well –solid waste. He renamed the firm Republic Waste.

Michael DeGroote founder of BFI rival Laidlaw bought into Republic in 1990. (Fatjo left the next year.) DeGroote's investment funded more acquisitions. Republic moved into hazardous waste in 1992 just before the industry nosedived due to stringent new environmental rules. In 1994 Republic spun off its hazardous-waste operations as Republic Environmental Systems and Republic's stock began rising immediately.

That attracted the attention of Wayne Huizenga who had founded Waste Management and Blockbuster Video. To him Republic was not merely a midsized solid-waste firm. No Huizenga saw Republic as a publicly traded vehicle that could allow him to tap into the stock market to fund his latest project: an integrated nationwide auto dealer –a first for the highly fragmented and localized industry.

In 1995 Republic bought Hudson Management a trash business owned by Huizenga's brother-in-law and Huizenga bought a large interest in Republic. As a result Huizenga took control of Republic's board. The firm became Republic Industries and DeGroote stepped back from active management.

Huizenga's investment helped Republic acquire more waste businesses and his name brought a flood of new investors. The firm diversified with electronic security acquisitions but growth in this field faltered with a failed bid to buy market leader ADT in 1996. (Republic sold its security division to Ameritech in 1997.)

By 1996 Huizenga's still-separate auto concept AutoNation was operational with 55 automobile franchises and seven used-car stores. Republic bought Alamo Rent A Car and National Car Rental System and in 1997 AutoNation was bought by Republic. The combined company continued buying dealerships and car rental firms at a sizzling rate.

Republic spun off its solid-waste operations to the public in 1998 as Republic Services. That year Republic bought or agreed to buy 181 new-car franchises opened nine AutoNation USA dealerships and opened 62 CarTemps USA insurance-replacement locations.

Republic became AutoNation in 1999 and announced plans to spin off its rental division. In September 1999 Mike Jackson the former president and CEO of Mercedes-Benz USA was named CEO of AutoNation. In December the company closed most of its poorly performing used-car superstores and laid off about 1800 employees.

In May 2000 AutoNation acquired AutoVantage an online car-buying service linking more than 900 dealerships and inked a deal to be America Online's (once a division of Time Warner) exclusive auto retailer. Later the company completed its spinoff of ANC Rental (Alamo National and CarTemps with more than 3400 rental car locations worldwide) making AutoNation a pure-play auto retailer.

Due to guarantees related to the spinoff AutoNation took a $20 million charge after ANC Rental filed for Chapter 11 bankruptcy protection in 2001. Also that year AutoNation closed its auto-loan unit to further focus on car sales. Huizenga retired as chairman of the company at the end of 2002. Jackson assumed the chairmanship while continuing in his role as CEO.

In March 2003 AutoNation agreed to pay the IRS about $470 million in relation to the tax treatment of some 1997-1999 transactions. It bought a dealership that accounts for some 10% of Mercedes-Benz USA sales Glauser Mercedes-Benz in Sarasota Florida in May 2004. The dealership is now called Mercedes-Benz of Sarasota.

In 2007 AutoNation sold about 540000 new and used vehicles. However the company's revenue declined relative to 2006 as the weak economy particularly in California and Florida curtailed sales.

In early 2008 the company acquired Don Mackey BMW in Tucson Arizona and renamed the dealership BMW Tucson. It's the AutoNation's 23rd new vehicle franchise in Arizona and its 13th BMW dealership nationwide.

The Chrysler and GM bankruptcies were a major headache for the autodealer. It saw seven of its 16 Chrysler dealerships close in 2009 as a result of the automaker's shuttering of nearly 800 dealerships nationwide. Also the company has closed four of its GM dealerships in 2010.

EXECUTIVES

President COO and Director, Michael E. (Mike) Maroone, age 58, $1,000,000 total compensation
Chairman and CEO, Michael J. (Mike) Jackson, age 63, $1,150,000 total compensation
EVP Secretary and General Counsel, Jonathan P. Ferrando, age 46, $561,000 total compensation
EVP and CFO, Michael J. (Mike) Short, age 50, $561,000 total compensation
SVP Corporate Communications and Public Policy, Marc Cannon
VP Investor Relations and Treasurer, Cheryl Scully
SVP eCommerce, Gary Marcotte
President Florida Region, James (Jim) Bender
President Central Region, Hank Phillips
VP Media Services, Ed Cicale
VP Human Resources, Julie Staub
VP and Corporate Controller, Michael J. Stephan, age 49
SVP Franchise Operations, Donna Parlapiano
Senior Director Investor Relations, Kate Keyser
President Western Region, Bill Berman
SVP Sales, David L. (Dave) Koehler
SVP Customer Care, Alan J. McLaren
President Texas Region, Dave Casto
SVP Legal, Coleman Edmunds
SVP Strategy, Scot Eisenfelder
President COO and Director, Michael E. (Mike) Maroone, age 58
Director, Robert J. Brown, age 77
Director, Rick L. Burdick, age 60
Director, Michael Larson, age 52
Director, William C. Crowley, age 55
Director, David B. Edelson, age 52
Director, Robert R. Grusky, age 55
Director, Carlos A. Migoya, age 61
Director, Alison H. Rosenthal
Auditors: KPMGLLP

LOCATIONS

HQ: AutoNation Inc.
200 SW 1st Ave., Fort Lauderdale FL 33301
Phone: 954-769-6000 **Fax:** 954-769-6537
Web: corp.autonation.com

2011 Stores

	Owned	Franchised
Florida	58	66
Texas	34	42
California	36	43
Colorado	17	24
Arizona	13	15
Nevada	10	11
Georgia	10	11
Washington	12	19
Illinois	5	5
Tennessee	7	8
Ohio	4	4
Minnesota	1	1
Virginia	2	2
Maryland	4	5
Alabama	2	2
Total	**215**	**258**

PRODUCTS/OPERATIONS

2011 Sales

	$ mil.	% of total
New vehicle	7,498	54
Used vehicle	3,512	25
Parts & service	2,293	17
Finance & insurance	474	4
Other	53	-
Total	**13,832**	**100**

2011 Sales

	$ mil.	% of total
Domestic	4,655	34
Import	51,210	37
Luxury	3,908	28
Corporate & other	147	1
Total	**13,832**	**100**

COMPETITORS

Asbury Automotive
Brown Automotive
CarMax
Ed Morse Auto
Group 1 Automotive
Hendrick Automotive
Holman Enterprises
JM Family Enterprises
Lithia Motors
Penske Automotive Group
Potamkin Automotive
Sonic Automotive

HISTORICAL FINANCIALS

Company Type: Public

Income Statement FYE: December 31

	REVENUE ($ mil.)	NET INCOME ($ mil.)	NET PROFIT MARGIN	EMPLOYEES
12/11	13,832	281	2.0%	19,400
12/10	12,461	226	1.8%	19,000
12/09	10,757	198	1.8%	18,000
12/08	14,131	(1,243)	—	20,000
12/07	17,691	278	1.6%	25,000
Annual Growth	(6.0%)	0.2%	—	(6.1%)

2011 Year-End Financials

Debt ratio: 26.57%
Return on equity: 14.85%
Cash ($ mil.): 86
Current ratio: 108.67
Long-term debt ($ mil.): 1,634
No. of shares (mil.): 135
Dividends
Yield: —
Payout: —
Market value ($ mil.): 5,006

	STOCK PRICE ($) FY Close	P/E High/Low		PER SHARE ($) Earnings	Dividends	Book Value
12/11	36.87	21	14	1.91	0.00	13.95
12/10	28.20	20	12	1.43	0.00	14.01
12/09	19.15	19	7	1.12	0.00	13.41
12/08	9.88	—	—	(6.99)	0.00	12.43
12/07	15.66	16	11	1.39	0.00	19.26
Annual Growth	23.9%	—	—	8.3%	—	(7.7%)

AutoZone, Inc.

Imagine that you are in your garage making some weekend car repairs. The wheel cylinders are leaking ... the brake shoe adjuster nut is rusted solid ... you're about to enter ... the AutoZone. With more than 4500 stores in the US and Puerto Rico it's the nation's #1 auto parts chain. It also operates some 280 stores in Mexico. AutoZone stores sell hard parts (alternators engines batteries) maintenance items (oil antifreeze) accessories (car stereos floor mats) and non-automotive merchandise under brand names as well as under private labels including Duralast and Valucraft. AutoZone's commercial sales program distributes parts and other products to garages dealerships and other businesses.

Geographic Reach

The company's subsidiary in Mexico AutoZone de Mexico operates about 280 stores. AutoZone has two store support centers south of the border in Monterrey and Chihuahua. The firm does not break out sales by region.

Financial Analysis

AutoZone is in the fast lane to growth. Even the recent recession didn't slow it down. On the contrary it was good for business as cash-strapped consumers deferred new car purchases in favor of keeping old clunkers on the road. Now with the economy on the mend AutoZone's sales and earnings growth are accelerating. In fiscal 2011 (ends August) sales and net income were up nearly 10% and 15% respectively vs. the year earlier period. Sales topped $8 billion and the company added about 185 stores including about 40 locations in Mexico.

Strategy

AutoZone has grown quickly through a series of acquisitions over the past several years but now is focused on internal growth and development. Among the factors AutoZone considers when opening new stores –at a rate of 150 to 200 per year –is how many cars in an area are OKVs or "our kind of vehicles" that is cars older than seven years and no longer under their manufacturers' warranty. (With the US auto industry in the tank more and more consumers are driving older cars.) AutoZone is also growing quickly in Mexico where cars are even older –and in need of more repairs –than in the US. The auto parts retailer also loans tools and sells merchandise and diagnostic and repair advice online. In addition to parts the stores also offer diagnostic testing for starters alternators and batteries. (The shops do not sell tires or perform general auto repairs.) AutoZone's ALLDATA unit sells automotive diagnostic and repair software to more than 70000 repair facilities.

Ownership

ESL Partners controlled by the hedge fund manager Edward Lampert owns about 22% of the company (down from about 41% in 2009). In late 2011 ESL sold AutoZone shares to meet client redemptions related to setbacks at Sears Holdings Corp. Lampert who began accumulating AutoZone shares in 1998 stepped down from AutoZone's board several years ago sparking speculation that ESL might sell its stake in the company. However Lampert has said that ESL plans to remain a significant shareholder in AutoZone for the foreseeable future.

HISTORY

Joseph "Pitt" Hyde took over the family grocery wholesale business Malone & Hyde (established 1907) in 1968. He expanded into specialty retailing opening drugstores sporting goods stores and supermarkets but his fortunes began to race on Independence Day 1979 when he opened his first Auto Shack auto parts store in Forrest City Arkansas.

Using retailing behemoth Wal-Mart as a model Hyde concentrated on smaller markets in the South and Southeast emphasizing everyday low prices and centralized distribution operations. He stressed customer service to provide his do-it-yourself customers with expert advice on choosing parts. While a number of retailers have tried to copy Wal-Mart's successful model Hyde had an inside track: Before starting Auto Shack he served on Wal-Mart's board for seven years.

Auto Shack had expanded into seven states by 1980 and by 1983 it had 129 stores in 10 states. The next year Malone & Hyde's senior management with investment firm Kohlberg Kravis Roberts (KKR) took the company private in an LBO. Auto Shack continued to expand reaching 192 stores in 1984.

A year later Auto Shack introduced its Express Parts Service the first service in the industry to offer a toll-free number and overnight delivery of parts. The following year it introduced another first: a limited lifetime warranty on its merchandise. Also in 1986 Auto Shack introduced its own Duralast line of auto products.

The company was spun off to Malone & Hyde's shareholders in 1987 and Malone & Hyde's other operations were sold. Auto Shack brought its electronic parts catalog online that year. The company changed its name to AutoZone in 1987 in part to settle a lawsuit with RadioShack. By this time it had 390 stores in 15 states.

The company went public in 1991. By the end of that year it had nearly 600 stores and five distribution centers. The company topped $1 billion in sales in 1992. The next year it opened new distribution centers in Illinois and Tennessee and closed its Memphis operation.

AutoZone began selling to commercial customers such as service stations and repair shops in 1996. It also acquired auto diagnostic software company ALLDATA. Hyde stepped down as CEO that year and as chairman in 1997 and was replaced by COO Johnston (John) Adams.

The company made several key purchases in 1998. It acquired Chief Auto Parts for $280 million adding 560 stores (most in California) that were converted to AutoZones in 1999. It also purchased Adap and its 112 Auto Palace stores in the Northeast heavy-duty truck parts distributor TruckPro and (from Pep Boys) 100 Express stores. Also in 1998 AutoZone opened its first store in Mexico (Nuevo Laredo).

Hyde sold much of his stake by early 1999. Late that year AutoZone expanded its board of directors to 10 members making room for increasingly active longtime shareholder Edward Lampert.

In January 2001 Steve Odland formerly COO at supermarket retailer Ahold USA succeeded Adams as chairman and CEO. In December 2001 AutoZone sold its TruckPro subsidiary to an investor group led by Paratus Capital Management of Boston and New York.

Odland resigned in 2005 to become CEO of Office Depot. He was replaced by Bill Rhodes AutoZone's former EVP of Store Operations and Commercial.

In fiscal 2009 the company opened 40 new stores in Mexico more than doubling its presence there since 2005.

EXECUTIVES

EVP Secretary and General Counsel, Harry L. Goldsmith, age 61, $385,154 total compensation
CFO and EVP Finance IT and Store Development, William T. (Bill) Giles, age 53, $458,308 total compensation
Chairman President and CEO, William C. (Bill) Rhodes III, age 47, $752,385 total compensation
Corporate Development Officer, Robert D. (Bob) Olsen, age 59, $445,385 total compensation
SVP Marketing, Lisa R. Kranc, age 59
SVP Commercial, Larry M. Roesel, age 55
SVP and Controller, Charlie Pleas III, age 47
SVP and CIO, Jon A. Bascom, age 55
SVP Human Resources, Timothy W. Briggs, age 51
SVP Merchandising, Mark A. Finestone, age 51
SVP Supply Chain, William W. Graves, age 52
SVP Store Operations, Thomas B. Newbern, age 50
SVP and CIO, Ron Griffin
Director, Sue E. Gove, age 54
Director, George R. Mrkonic Jr., age 60
Director, W. Andrew McKenna, age 66
Director, Joseph R. (J. R.) Hyde III, age 69
Director, Theodore W. (Ted) Ullyot, age 44
Director, William C. Crowley, age 55
Director, Robert R. Grusky, age 55
Director, Earl G. (Butch) Graves Jr., age 50
Director, Luis P. (Lou) Nieto Jr., age 57
Auditors: Ernst&YoungLLP

LOCATIONS

HQ: AutoZone Inc.
123 S. Front St., Memphis TN 38103
Phone: 901-495-6500 **Fax:** 901-495-8300
Web: www.autozone.com

2011 Stores

	No.
US	
Texas	547
California	478
Florida	233
Ohio	233
Illinois	221
North	181
Georgia	180
Tennessee	157
Michigan	155
Indiana	144
New	129
Pennsylvania	121
Arizona	119
Louisana	112
Missouri	104
Virginia	101
Alabama	98
Mississippi	85
Kentucky	84
South	79
Massachusetts	71
New	70
Washington	69
Colorado	67
Oklahoma	67
New	62
Arkansas	59
Nevada	53
Wisconsin	52
Maryland	45
Utah	40
Kansas	38
Connecticut	37
Oregon	34
Minnesota	30
Puerto	27
West	26
Iowa	23
New	20
Idaho	19
Rhode	15
Nebraska	14
Delaware	13
Maine	6
Washington	6
Wyoming	5
South	2
Montana	1
North	1
Vermont	1
Mexico	279
Total	**4,813**

PRODUCTS/OPERATIONS

2011 Sales

	$ mil.	% of total
Auto parts stores	7,906	98
Other	166	2
Total	**8,073**	**100**

2011 Store Sales by Product Grouping

	$ mil.	% of total
Failure	3,530	45
Maintenance	3,051	38
Discretionary	1,324	17
Total	**7,906**	**100**

Selected Merchandise

Accessories
- Car stereos
- Floor mats
- Lights
- Mirrors

Hard Parts
- Alternators
- Batteries
- Brake shoes and pads
- Carburetors
- Clutches
- Engines
- Spark plugs
- Starters
- Struts
- Water pumps

Maintenance Items
- Antifreeze
- Brake fluid
- Engine additives
- Oil
- Power steering fluid
- Transmission fluid
- Waxes
- Windshield wipers

Other
- Air fresheners
- Dent filler
- Hand cleaner
- Paint
- Repair manuals
- Tools

Selected Brands

ALLDATA
AutoZone
Duralast
Duralast Gold
Valucraft

COMPETITORS

Advance Auto Parts
CARQUEST
Costco Wholesale
Fisher Auto Parts
Genuine Parts
Goodyear Tire & Rubber
Kmart
O' Reilly Automotive
Pep Boys
Sears
Target Corporation
Wal-Mart

HISTORICAL FINANCIALS

Company Type: Public

Income Statement FYE: August 25

	REVENUE ($ mil.)	NET INCOME ($ mil.)	NET PROFIT MARGIN	EMPLOYEES
08/12	8,603	930	10.8%	70,000
08/11	8,072	848	10.5%	65,000
08/10	7,362	738	10.0%	63,000
08/09	6,816	657	9.6%	60,000
08/08	6,522	641	9.8%	57,000
Annual Growth	7.2%	9.7%	—	5.3%

2012 Year-End Financials

Debt ratio: 60.14%
Return on equity: 987650001000000.00%
Cash ($ mil.): 103
Current ratio: 81.49
Long-term debt ($ mil.): 3,718
No. of shares (mil.): 37
Dividends
Yield: —
Payout: —
Market value ($ mil.): 13,518

	STOCK PRICE ($) FY Close	P/E High/Low		PER SHARE ($) Earnings	Dividends	Book Value
08/12	365.08	17	12	23.48	0.00	(41.81)
08/11	301.30	15	11	19.47	0.00	(31.27)
08/10	214.65	14	9	14.97	0.00	(16.38)
08/09	148.45	14	7	11.73	0.00	(8.53)
08/08	137.23	14	10	10.04	0.00	3.85
Annual Growth	27.7%	—	—	23.7%	—	—

Avery Dennison Corp.

Avery Dennison is easy to label: It's a global leader in the making of adhesive labels used on packaging mailers and other items. Pressure-sensitive adhesives and materials account for more than half of its sales. Under the Avery Dennison and Fasson brands it makes papers films and foils coated with adhesive and sold in rolls to printers. Perhaps its most widely used products are the self-adhesive stamps used by the US Postal Service since 1974. The company also makes retail branding and security tags printer systems and fasteners. In 2011 it agreed to sell its Office and Consumer Products segment to 3M for $550 million. The segment makes school and office products (Avery Marks-A-Lot HI-LITER).

Operations

Its Pressure-sensitive Materials unit is split into two other units: Label and Packaging Materials (LPM) and Graphics and Reflective Solutions (GRS). LPM the larger unit has differentiated products but its film products have the fastest growth. It launched almost 20 products in 2011 elevating Avery to leadership positions in several key markets. Avery plans to continue the unit's growth with more new products in targeted markets such as its Avery Dennison Shrink PS for food labeling and Global MDO film for home and personal care products. The GRS unit is also innovative; more than half of its sales growth in 2011 came from its cast films which consist of new or reformulated products.

The Retail Branding and Information Solutions (RBIS) unit provides global branding and supply chain services and products for the retail apparel industry. RBIS operates facilities in more than 40 countries to check the quality of branding on apparel. It also offers labeling technology to check inventory and pricing accuracy. It is a leader in RFID (Radio Frequency Identification) tagging for retailers and its apparel-related RFID sales grew more than 60% in 2011. The unit has a new line of heat transfer products for printing graphics on apparel.

Avery also holds specialty converting businesses that use its expertise in one market to develop products for other markets.

Geographic Reach

The company expanded its operations in Asia Latin America and Eastern Europe in 2010. By the end of 2011 it operated about 200 manufacturing and distribution facilities in more than 60 countries.

Financial Analysis

Despite a challenging year in 2011 Avery posted revenues of $6.03 billion about 4% higher than the $5.78 billion it reported the previous year. It offset a $200 million increase in raw material costs with price increases and cost reduction measures. Sales of the company's largest unit Pressure-sensitive Materials rose 2% from the previous year with both LPM and GRS realizing growth. Sales in its RBIS unit declined however because of lower demand from the US and Europe. Sales in its Other Specialty Converting Businesses unit also dipped 6%. Net income declined from $316.9 million in 2010 to $190.1 million in 2011 due to restructuring costs and foreign exchange translations.

Strategy

The company follows a strategy of trying to obtain leading share positions in global markets. It attempts to leverage its global reach and scale and its product expertise to sustain competitive advantages in its core businesses. It focuses on increased productivity cost reductions and pricing to counteract softened demand caused by the global economic recession. The company also seeks continued growth of its key global brands in both new and emerging markets.

With the sale of the Office and Consumer Products unit Avery will focus on its Pressure-sensitive Materials and Retail Branding and Information Solutions businesses. It plans to use the proceeds from the deal to invest in its two core businesses and reduce debt and pension liability.

In 2011 Avery also decided to divest its Metalure pigments business which it sold to the Eckart Effect Pigments division of ALTANA. Eckart had been the distributor of the PVD-type aluminum pigments for more than 20 years.

HISTORY

Avery Dennison was created in 1990 by the merger of Avery International and Dennison Manufacturing. In 1935 Stanton Avery founded Kum-Kleen Products which would become Avery International. After a fire destroyed the plant's equipment in 1938 Avery who had renamed the company Avery Adhesives improved the machinery used in making the labels.

During and after WWII Avery Adhesives shifted toward the industrial market for self-adhesives. The company incorporated in 1946. At that time Avery Adhesives sold 80% of its production consisting of industrial labels to manufacturers that labeled their own products.

The company lost its patent rights for self-adhesive labels in 1952 transforming the firm and the entire industry. As a result a new division was created —the Avery Paper Company (later renamed Fasson) —to produce and market self-adhesive base materials.

Avery Adhesives went public in 1961. Three years later it had four divisions: label products base materials Rotex (hand-operated embossing machines) and Metal-Cal (anodized and etched aluminum foil for nameplates). Renamed Avery International in 1976 the company closed some manufacturing facilities and cut 8% of its workforce in the late 1980s.

In 1990 Avery International merged with Dennison Manufacturing. Dennison was started in 1844 by the father-and-son team of Andrew and Aaron Dennison to produce jewelry boxes. By 1849 Aaron's younger brother Eliphalet Whorf (E.W.) was running the business and expanding it into tags labels and tissue paper. Dennison was incorporated in 1878 with $150000 in capital.

By 1911 Dennison sold tags gummed labels paper boxes greeting cards sealing wax and tissue paper and it had stores in Boston Chicago New York City Philadelphia St. Louis and London. Henry Dennison E.W.'s grandson was president from 1917 to 1952.

From the 1960s to the 1980s Dennison spent heavily on research and development and helped to develop such products as electronic printers and pregnancy test supplies. In the mid-1980s the firm reorganized its operations selling seven businesses closing four others and focusing on stationery systems and packaging.

In addition to office products and product identification and control systems the 1990 merger combined Dennison's office products operations in France (Doret and Cheval Ordex) with Avery International's sizable self-adhesive base materials business.

Avery Dennison sold its 50% interest in a Japanese label converting company Toppan in 1996 clearing the way to develop its own businesses in Asia. In 1997 an alliance with Taiwanese rival Four Pillars turned sour when Avery Dennison accused the company of stealing trade secrets. (Two executives at Four Pillars were convicted of corporate espionage in 1999.)

President and COO Philip Neal was promoted to CEO in 1998. (He became chairman in 2000.) In 1999 adhering to its goal of global expansion Avery Dennison formed office products joint ventures in Germany with Zweckform Buro-Produkte and in Japan with Hitachi Maxell. Record 1998 sales and earnings were dampened by the news of slowing growth and in 1999 Avery Dennison closed five plants and began laying off workers. Later that year the company bought Stimsonite a maker of reflective highway safety products.

In early 2000 Avery Dennison began a $40 million expansion of its Chinese manufacturing operations while eliminating 1500 jobs worldwide. Later in the year the company agreed to jointly package instant imaging and labeling products with Polaroid. Several acquisitions in 2001 included CD Stomper (CD and DVD labels and software). Avery Dennison continued its acquisitive ways in 2002 acquiring Jackstadt (German maker of pressure-sensitive adhesive materials) RVL Packaging (maker of woven and printed labels and other tags for the apparel and retail industries) and L&E Packaging (key supplier and printer for RVL).

In 2003 the company sold its European package label converting business (including plants in Denmark and France) to label and packaging company CCL Industries. As part of the deal Avery Dennison began to supply pressure-sensitive base materials to CCL Industries. The divestiture was part of the company's strategy to concentrate its efforts in adhesive materials office products and retail information services.

Phillip Neal retired as chairman and CEO in 2005 and was replaced by director Kent Kresa as chairman and by Dean Scarborough as president and CEO.

The company completed a restructuring program in 2010 it began in 2008 that generated a total of $180 million in cost savings. It also paid down some $300 million in debt during that same period.

EXECUTIVES

Chairman President and CEO, Dean A. Scarborough, age 56, $945,000 total compensation
President Retail Branding and Information Solutions, R. Shawn Neville, age 49
President Specialty Materials and New Growth Platforms, Timothy S. Clyde, age 49, $500,000 total compensation
VP and Treasurer, Karyn E. Rodriguez, age 52
Group VP Office Products, Timothy G. (Tim) Bond, age 54
SVP and CIO, Richard W. (Rich) Hoffman
SVP and Chief Human Resources and Communications Officer, Anne Hill, age 52
VP and CTO, David N. Edwards
SVP General Counsel and Secretary, Susan C. Miller, age 52
SVP and CFO, Mitchell R. Butier, age 40
President Label and Packaging Materials, Donald A. (Don) Nolan, age 51, $500,000 total compensation
VP Global Operations and Supply Chain, Gregory E. Temple
Director, David E. I. Pyott, age 58
Director, Julia A. Stewart, age 56
Director, Kenneth C. (Ken) Hicks, age 59
Director, Rolf Borjesson, age 69
Director, Peter K. Barker, age 63
Director, Peter W. Mullin, age 71
Director, Patrick T. Siewert, age 56
Director, John T. Cardis, age 70
Auditors: PricewaterhouseCoopersLLP

LOCATIONS

HQ: Avery Dennison Corporation
150 N. Orange Grove Blvd., Pasadena CA 91103-3596
Phone: 626-304-2000 **Fax:** 626-304-2192
Web: www.averydennison.com

2010 Sales

	$ mil.	% of total
Europe	2,007	33
Asia	1,533	26
Other regions	359	6

PRODUCTS/OPERATIONS

2011 Sales

	$ mil.	% of total
Pressure-Sensitive Materials	3,971	66
Total	6,026	100

Selected Brands

Avery
Avery Dennison
Avery Graphics
Fasson

COMPETITORS

3M
ACCO Brands
Beam
Bemis
Bostik
Brady Corporation
Checkpoint Systems
Esselte
H.B. Fuller
Newell Rubbermaid
Standard Register
UPM-Kymmene

HISTORICAL FINANCIALS

Company Type: Public

Income Statement

FYE: December 31

	REVENUE ($ mil.)	NET INCOME ($ mil.)	NET PROFIT MARGIN	EMPLOYEES
12/11*	6,026	190	3.2%	30,400
01/11	6,512	316	4.9%	32,100
01/10	5,952	(746)	—	31,300
12/08	6,710	266	4.0%	35,700
12/07	6,307	303	4.8%	37,300
Annual Growth	(1.1%)	(11.0%)	—	(5.0%)

*Fiscal year change

2011 Year-End Financials

Debt ratio: 23.76%
Return on equity: 11.46%
Cash ($ mil.): 178
Current ratio: 134.71
Long-term debt ($ mil.): 954
No. of shares (mil.): 106
Dividends
Yield: —
Payout: 56.18%
Market value ($ mil.): 3,048

	STOCK PRICE ($) FY Close	P/E High/Low		PER SHARE ($) Earnings	Dividends	Book Value
12/11*	28.68	24	13	1.78	0.00	15.61
01/11	42.34	14	10	2.97	0.00	15.62
01/10	36.49	—	—	(7.21)	0.00	12.94
12/08	31.53	20	9	2.70	0.00	17.79
12/07	53.41	23	16	3.07	0.00	20.22
Annual Growth	(14.4%)	—	—	(12.7%)	—	(6.3%)

*Fiscal year change

Avis Budget Group Inc

Whether you're a business traveler on an expense account or a family on vacation counting every penny Avis Budget Group has a car rental brand for you. The company's Avis Rent A Car unit which targets corporate and leisure travelers at the high end of the market has 5200 locations in the Americas Europe and the Asia/Pacific region. Budget Rent A Car marketed to those who watch costs closely rents cars from some 3050 locations in more than 120 countries and trucks from 2600 dealers in the US. Avis Budget Group in 2011 acquired its formerly independent licensee Avis Europe boosting its worldwide presence to some 10000 rental locations in more than 175 countries.

HISTORY

Cendant began life through the 1997 merger of CUC International and HFS. A giant in hospitality HFS was cobbled together as Hospitality Franchise Systems by LBO specialist Blackstone Group in 1992. With brands including Days Inn Ramada and Howard Johnson HFS went public that year. In 1995 HFS bought real estate firm Century 21. The next year it added Electronic Realty Associates (ERA) and Coldwell Banker. Also in 1996 HFS acquired the Super 8 Motels brand as well as car-rental firm Avis (founded by Warren Avis in 1946 it went through a succession of owners until acquired by HFS). The next year HFS sold 75% of Avis' #1 franchisee to the public and later bought relocation service firm PHH.

In an attempt to leverage the power of his brands HFS CEO Henry Silverman began looking at direct marketing giant CUC International. CUC was founded in 1973 as Comp-U-Card America by Walter Forbes and other investors envisioning a computer-based home shopping network. During the 1980s CUC developed as a discount direct marketer and catalog-based shopping club. It went public in 1983 with 100000 members. CUC saw explosive growth as it signed up 7.6 million members between 1989 and 1993. In 1996 CUC acquired Rent Net an online apartment rental service and later bought entertainment software publishers Davidson & Associates and Sierra On-Line. In 1997 CUC bought software maker Knowledge Adventure and launched online shopping site NetMarket.

CUC and HFS completed their $14.1 billion merger in December 1997 with Silverman as CEO and Forbes as chairman. While the name Cendant was derived from "ascendant" the marriage quickly headed in the opposite direction. Accounting irregularities from before the merger that had inflated CUC's revenue and pretax profit by about $500 million were revealed in 1998. Cendant's stock price tumbled taking a $14 billion hit in one day. Forbes resigned that summer. Silverman quickly took action and began to sell off operations. Cendant Software National Leisure Group (now World Travel Holdings) National Library of Poetry and Match.com all were sold that year for a total of about $1.4 billion. The company also acquired Jackson Hewitt the US's #2 tax-preparation firm and UK-based National Parking.

Through 1999 the company continued to sell assets. Cendant sold its fleet business –including PHH Vehicle Management Services –to Avis Rent A Car for $5 billion and sold its Entertainment Publications unit the world's largest coupon book marketer and publisher to The Carlyle Group. Cendant later paid $2.8 billion in one of the largest shareholder class action lawsuit settlements. (Accounting firm Ernst & Young also settled with Cendant shareholders for $335 million.)

In 2000 Cendant introduced Move.com a relocation and real estate Internet portal. Also that year the company launched Cendant Internet Group to help cement its presence on the Web and bought the brand name and franchising rights of AmeriHost Inns from AmeriHost Properties. Later in 2000 cable programming company Liberty Media (now Liberty Interactive) invested $400 million in Cendant. The next year the company began licensing and outsourcing its Incentives and Marketing Services business (practically all of the businesses that made up the former CUC International) to Trilegiant a new company formed by the units' management.

In 2001 after selling Move.com to Homestore (later called Move) for $761 million Cendant sought to expand its travel holdings with a slew of acquisitions. Its purchases included timeshare resort firm Fairfield Communities ($690 million); travel services firm Galileo International ($2.4 billion); online travel reservation service Cheap Tickets ($425 million); and vacation timeshare marketer Equivest Finance ($100 million). In late 2001 Cendant cut some 6000 jobs to improve its bottom line and announced that during the next year or so it would cut an additional 10000 jobs and eliminate about 7% of its franchised hotels.

In 2002 the company sold its UK-based National Car Park unit which accounted for 3% of sales as part of its strategy to sell off noncore businesses. In June Cendant bought TRUST International from Bertelsmann and later that year purchased car-rental company Budget Rent A Car for about $110 million then slashed costs by closing facilities and laying off more than 450 employees. The company also purchased Novasol AS which rented out private vacation homes in Northern Europe.

Cendant terminated its licensing and services agreements with Trilegiant in January 2004 and in February Sotheby's Holdings sold its 15 Sotheby's International Realty offices (along with the brand's licensing rights) to the company for about $100 million. In March Cendant's Jackson Hewitt subsidiary filed for its IPO. In May the company purchased Dutch vacation rental company Landal Green Parks (LGP) for about $150 million. Also that month former chairman Walter Forbes and former vice chairman E. Kirk Shelton went on trial for federal fraud and conspiracy stemming from the pre-merger accounting irregularities. (Shelton was found guilty of multiple counts of fraud in early 2005.) In October CFO Ronald Nelson was named president taking over for Henry Silverman who remained chairman and CEO.

In 2004 Cendant acquired online travel firm Orbitz in a deal valued at about $1.25 billion. Quick on the heels of the Orbitz deal the company Cendant also purchased ebookers (a European online travel site now called Flightbookers) in a deal worth about $400 million and acquired two travel groups collectively known as Gullivers for about $1.1 billion.

As 2004 wound to a close Cendant completed the acquisition of the Ramada International Hotels & Resorts brand and franchising operations from Marriott International. Cendant already owned the rights to the brand and franchising operations in the US and Canada which included some 820 US properties and about 70 Canadian properties. In 2005 Cendant acquired the Wyndham hotel brand from Wyndham International Inc. for $101 million. The deal included the franchise agreements for 82 hotels and the management contracts for another 29 hotels but not the actual properties which were located in the US Mexico and the Caribbean. The next year Cendant acquired the Baymont Inn & Suites brand of limited-service midscale lodging from Blackstone's La Quinta Corporation (now LQ Management). The Baymont Inn & Suites brand covered 115 franchised properties; the properties themselves were not included in the deal.

Cendant in 2005 spun off its mortgage operations PHH Mortgage (formerly Cendant Mortgage) and fleet management (PHH Arval) businesses under the PHH Corporation umbrella. Also that year Cendant spun off Wright Express (payment processing and information services for fleet management) in an IPO and sold its marketing services division to Apollo Management for about $1.8 billion.

The divestitures that began in 2005 culminated in the unwinding of the Cendant conglomerate the next year. The company spun off its hotel and real estate operations and sold its travel services division in 2006 reconfiguring itself around its rental car businesses and renaming itself Avis Budget Group. Silverman became chairman and CEO of the company's real estate business Realogy and Nelson took over as chairman and CEO of the slimmed-down Avis Budget Group which took on its new name in September 2006.

Warren Avis the founder of Avis Rent A Car died in April 2007 at the age of 92. In October the company acquired a 48% stake in chauffeured transportation company Carey International for $60 million. (In 2009 due to losses at Carey it wrote down its investment in the company to zero.)

Avis Budget Group acquired Avis Europe plc in October 2011.

EXECUTIVES

Chairman and CEO, Ronald L. (Ron) Nelson, age 60, $1,000,000 total compensation
SEVP and CFO, David B. Wyshner, age 45, $525,000 total compensation
Vice Chairman, F. Robert (Bob) Salerno, age 58, $700,000 total compensation
EVP and Chief Administrative Officer, Mark J. Servodidio, age 46, $372,549 total compensation
President Latin America/Asia Pacific, Patric Siniscalchi, age 62, $322,212 total compensation
EVP Strategy, W. Scott Deaver, age 60
President North America, Thomas M. (Tom) Gartland, age 54, $448,692 total compensation
President EMEA, Larry De Shon, age 52, $420,000 total compensation
SVP and CIO, Gerard Insall
EVP and General Counsel, Michael K. Tucker
Vice Chairman, F. Robert (Bob) Salerno, age 58
Director, Leonard S. Coleman Jr., age 63
Director, Martin L. Edelman, age 70
Director, Mary C. Choksi, age 61
Director, Eduardo G. Mestre, age 63
Director, Stender E. Sweeney, age 73
Director, Lynn Krominga, age 61
Director, John D. (Jack) Hardy Jr., age 68
Auditors: Deloitte&ToucheLLP

LOCATIONS

HQ: Avis Budget Group Inc
6 Sylvan Way, Parsippany, NJ 07054
Phone: 973 496-4700
Web: www.avisbudget.com

2011 Car Rental Sales

	$ mil.	% of total
% of total		
Airport		74
Off-airport		26
Total		**100**

2011 Sales

	$ mil.	% of total
North America car rental	4,495	76
International car rental	1,028	18
Truck rental	376	6
Corporate & other	1	-
Total	**5,900**	**100**

2011 Locations

	Avis	Budget
North America		
Company-operated	1,200	850
Licensees	300	400
International		
Company-operated	900	250
Licensees	2,800	1,550
Total	**5,200**	**3,050**

PRODUCTS/OPERATIONS

2011 Sales by Brand

	$ mil.	% of total
Avis		64
Budget		30
Budget		6
Total		**100**

COMPETITORS

Dollar Thrifty Automotive
Enterprise Rent-A-Car
Europcar
Hertz
Penske Truck Leasing
Ryder System
Zipcar

HISTORICAL FINANCIALS

Company Type: Public

Income Statement — FYE: December 31

	REVENUE ($ mil.)	NET INCOME ($ mil.)	NET PROFIT MARGIN	EMPLOYEES
12/11	5,900	(29)	—	28,000
12/10	5,185	54	1.0%	21,000
12/09	5,131	(47)	—	22,700
12/08	5,984	(1,124)	—	26,000
12/07	5,986	(916)	—	30,000
Annual Growth	(0.4%)	—	—	(1.7%)

2011 Year-End Financials

Debt ratio: 67.78%
Return on equity: (-7.04)%
Cash ($ mil.): 534
Current ratio: 104.83
Long-term debt ($ mil.): 8,732
No. of shares (mil.): 105
Dividends
Yield: —
Payout: —
Market value ($ mil.): 1,131

	STOCK PRICE ($) FY Close	P/E High/Low	PER SHARE ($) Earnings	Dividends	Book Value
12/11	10.72	— —	(0.28)	0.00	3.91
12/10	15.56	31 16	0.49	0.00	3.95
12/09	13.12	— —	(0.46)	0.00	2.17
12/08	0.70	— —	(11.04)	0.00	0.91
12/07	13.00	— —	(8.88)	0.00	14.09
Annual Growth	(4.7%)	— —	—	—	(27.4%)

Avnet Inc

If you need an electronic component Avnet probably has it. The company is one of the world's largest distributors of electronic components and computer products alongside rival Arrow Electronics. Its suppliers include 300-plus component and systems makers; Avnet distributes products to some 100000 manufacturers and resellers worldwide. Avnet Electronics Marketing the larger of the company's two major operating units offers semiconductors and other components to industrial commercial and military customers. Avnet Technology Solutions provides computer products and services to resellers large end-users systems integrators and software vendors. More than 60% of sales comes from customers outside the US.

HISTORY

In 1921 before the advent of commercial battery-operated radios Charles Avnet started a small ham radio replacement parts distributorship in Manhattan selling parts to designers inventors and ship-to-shore radio users on docked ships. The stock market crash in 1929 left the business strapped; it went bankrupt in 1931. A few years later Avnet founded another company making car radio kits and antennas. But competition got the best of him and that company also went bankrupt.

During WWII Charles joined by his sons Lester and Robert founded Avnet Electronic Supply to sell parts to government and military contractors. After the war the company bought and sold surplus electrical and electronic parts. A contract from Bendix Aviation spurred company growth and Avnet opened a West Coast warehouse. In 1955 it incorporated as Avnet Electronics Supply with Robert as chairman and CEO and Lester as president. Sales reached $1 million that year although the company lost $17000. It changed its name to Avnet Electronics in 1959.

In 1960 Avnet made its first acquisition British Industries and went public. Acquisitions continued throughout the 1960s with Hamilton Electro (1962) Fairmount Motor Products (1963) Carol Wire & Cable (1968) and Time Electronic Sales (1968).

To acknowledge its diversification into motors and other products the company again changed its name to Avnet Inc. in 1964. Robert Avnet died the next year and Lester took over as chairman; Lester died in 1970.

In 1973 Intel which introduced the microprocessor signed Avnet as a distributor and by 1979 Avnet's sales topped $1 billion. A soft 1982 market caused price declines that led Avnet to sell its wire and cable business. The company consolidated many of its operations to its Arizona headquarters in 1987.

During 1991 and 1992 Avnet spent more than $100 million for acquisitions strategic to the European market. In 1993 it bought the US's third-largest distributor Hall-Mark Electronics and acquired Penstock the top US distributor of microwave radio-frequency products in 1994. Avnet was Europe's #2 electronics distributor by 1994 despite having had almost no European operations prior to 1990. The company continued to expand globally acquiring Hong Kong-based distributor WKK Semiconductor in 1995 among others. Also that year Avnet began selling off its non-electronics operations.

In 1998 it reorganized around separate global computer and electronics businesses. Also that year president and COO Roy Vallee became chairman and CEO. As part of its restructuring the company sold its Allied Electronics subsidiary to UK-based components distributor Electrocomponents in 1999 for $380 million. That year Avnet acquired rival Marshall Industries in a deal valued at about $760 million.

In 2000 Avnet acquired IBM midrange server distributor Savoir Technology Group in a $140 million deal making Avnet the leading distributor of IBM midrange products. Later that year it acquired a part of Germany-based EBV Group (semiconductor distribution) and RKE (computer products and services) both from German utility giant E.ON in a cash deal worth about $740 million. In 2001 Avnet acquired smaller rival Kent Electronics for about $600 million.

In 2003 it combined its Computer Marketing Group and its Applied Computing Group to form Avnet Technology Solutions. The next year it launched Avnet Logistics as a separate business unit to provide assembly asset management distribution programming and warehousing services to its customers.

In 2005 it established Avnet Managed Technologies (AMT) to offer IT services to small and midsized businesses. Operating directly and with other providers of products and services AMT was set up to provide data center managed services help desk support and Microsoft Exchange mailbox hosting.

Avnet acquired semiconductor distributor Memec Group Holdings for $663 million in 2005. Later that year the company sold the assets of its radio-frequency and microwave components business to Teledyne Technologies. To focus the operations of Avnet Technology Solutions on distribution Avnet sold its Hewlett-Packard end-user business to Logicalis and its Avnet Enterprise Solutions business to networking firm Calence. Both transactions closed in 2006.

In 2007 Avnet acquired Access Distribution the computer products distribution business of General Electric for about $410 million in cash. Access Distribution which specialized in computer hardware made by Sun Microsystems was integrated into Avnet Technology Solutions. Also that year the company acquired the European Enterprise Infrastructure division of Magirus Group and integrated it into the European operations of Avnet Technology Solutions.

Later in 2007 Avnet bought the IT Solutions division of Acal for about $83 million in cash and integrated into the European operations of Avnet Technology Solutions. Horizon Technology Group bought in 2008 for about E98.5 million ($150 million) in cash also became part of Technology Solutions in Europe. And Mumbai-based Ontrack Solutions became part of Avnet Technology Solutions Asia/Pacific.

In 2008 Avnet acquired Nippon Denso Industry Co. Ltd.which doubled Electronics Marketing's business in Japan. The purchase of Source Electronics boosted the geographic reach of Avnet Electronics Marketing in South America through operations in Brazil.

In 2009 which saw sales drop almost 10% for the first time in years Avnet continued acquisitions in international markets. It bought Abacus Group a European component distributor based in the UK for $61 million in cash. Avnet made Abacus part of Electronics Marketing EMEA forming Avnet Abacus.

The company's business in Asia was relatively strong during 2009 with sales there nearly doubling for the year. Avnet acquired certain assets of Vietnam-based IT distributor Sunshine Joint Stock Company and integrated it into its Technology Solutions Asia business. Additionally the company bought a controlling interest in Vanda Group a systems integrator and software applications developer based in China from Hutchison Whampoa. Vanda complemented Avnet Technology Solutions' recently launched distribution business in China adding a vertically integrated service offering and extensive base of customers in the banking financial services telecommunications and government markets. It also let Avnet expand its reach across China Hong Kong and Macau where Vanda had a strong local brand.

Teaming with Sanko Holding Group Avnet picked up a more than 50% interest in a joint venture in Turkey in 2009. The operation Avnet Technology Solutions Sanayi ve Ticaret A.S. is one of the largest IT distributors in Turkey.

In 2010 it bought a handful of companies the largest being rival Bell Microproducts for about $630 million in assumed debt and cash. Avnet was attracted to Bell Micro's strong presence in fast-growing Latin America as well as its position in data center products and embedded systems. Avnet combined Bell Micro's Latin American and European businesses and its North American data center business into Avnet Technology Solutions. Bell Micro's North American embedded components business was integrated into Avnet Electronics Marketing. (Acquired in the Bell Micro deal VAR and IT infrastructure solutions provider New ProSys was sold in early 2011.)

In another 2010 acquisition Avnet bought a majority stake in Asian distributor Unidux continuing a run of acquisitions in the region from the previous year and tripling the business of Avnet Electronics Marketing in Japan. China-based Eurotone Electric Limited added a line of components for solar and wind power applications for the fast-growing alternative energy market in the region.

Continuing its shopping spree Avnet also bought Broadband Integrated Resources that year. The company is a small provider of technical repair and logistics services to US cable companies including Time Warner Comcast and Charter Communications. The purchase was part of Avnet's strategy to expand into adjacent value-added service areas through acquisitions of companies with an established North American customer base. Broadband became part of Avnet Logistics Services.

In 2011 Avnet president and COO Rick Hamada succeeded long-time CEO Roy Vallee who remained chairman.

EXECUTIVES

VP; EVP Business Development Innovation Worldwide, Gregory A. (Greg) Frazier

VP and Director Global Financial Operations, John T. Clark

President Avnet Technology Solutions EMEA, Graeme A. Watt, age 51

SVP; Chief Business Development and Planning Officer; and President Avnet Integrated Resources, Steven C. (Steve) Church, age 63, $525,000 total compensation

SVP and General Counsel, David R. Birk, age 65, $475,000 total compensation

SVP and CFO, Raymond (Ray) Sadowski, age 58, $485,000 total compensation

Chairman, Roy A. Vallee, age 60, $1,050,000 total compensation

VP and Chief Communications Officer, Allen W. (Al) Maag

SVP; President Avnet Electronics Marketing Global, Harley M. Feldberg, age 59, $520,000 total compensation

SVP; President Avnet Technology Solutions, Philip R. (Phil) Gallagher, age 51, $420,000 total compensation

SVP; SVP and Director Administrative Services Shared Business Services, Patrick (Pat) Jewett

CEO and Director, Richard P. (Rick) Hamada, age 54, $610,000 total compensation

Director, William H. (Bill) Schumann III, age 61

SVP; General Manager IBM Solutions Avnet Technology Solutions Americas, Fred J. Cuen

SVP and Chief Human Resources Officer, MaryAnn G. Miller, age 55

VP and Director Corporate Audit, Bob Brown

VP; President Electronics Marketing Europe Middle East and Africa, Patrick Zammit

SVP Avnet Technology Solutions Europe Middle East and Africa, Gary Coburn, age 46

VP; President Avnet Electronics Marketing Americas, Edward J. (Ed) Smith

VP; President Avnet Technology Solutions Americas, Jeff Bawol

SVP and CIO, Stephen R. (Steve) Phillips, age 49

VP Investor Relations, Vincent (Vince) Keenan

VP; SVP Avnet Embedded Avnet Electronics Marketing Americas, Jeffrey (Jeff) Ittel

VP; SVP Global Business Development Avnet Electronics Marketing President & Representative Director Avnet EM Holdings Japan, Tom McCartney

VP; President Electronics Marketing Asia, Stephen Wong

Director Marketing Avnet Technology Solutions Europe, Linda Patterson

VP Public Relations, Michelle Gorel
Director Marketing Avnet Technology Solutions Asia/Pacific, Michael Costigan
VP; President Avnet Logistics, James N. (Jim) Smith, age 66
VP; President Avnet Technology Solutions Asia/Pacific, K. P. Tang
VP Assistant General Counsel and Secretary, Jun Li
VP Community Relations, Teri Radosevich
VP and Chief Tax Officer, Jill M. Wysolmierski
VP Global Transportation Avnet Logistics, Danny Stephens
VP; Group Finance Officer Avnet Technology Solutions, Rusty Murdaugh
VP and General Manager Avnet Technology Solutions Canada, Brian Aebig
VP Defense and Aerospace, Bryan Brady
VP; SVP and Group Financial Officer Avnet Electronics Marketing, Bill Crowell
SVP Global Communications Avnet Electronics Marketing North America, Sean Fanning
VP Communications Avnet Electronics Marketing Europe Middle East and Africa, Georg Steinberger
Director Marketing and Communications Avnet Electronics Marketing Japan, Bob Hackett
Director Communications Avnet Technology Solutions North America, Joal Redmond
VP Vertical Market Solutions Avnet Technology Solutions Americas, Michael Houghton
SVP and General Manager HP Solutions Avnet Technology Solutions Americas, Tony Vottima
Manager Marketing Communications Avnet Electronics Marketing Asia, Jaime Chan
Director Marketing and Communications Avnet Electronics Marketing North America, Heidi Elliott
Chief Global Logistics and Operations Officer, Gerry Fay
Director, William P. (Bill) Sullivan, age 61
CEO and Director, Richard P. (Rick) Hamada, age 54
Director, William H. (Bill) Schumann III, age 61
Director, Frank R. Noonan, age 70
Director, Gary L. Tooker, age 72
Director, Ray M. Robinson, age 64
Director, Eleanor Baum, age 72
Director, J. Veronica Biggins, age 66
Director, Ehud Houminer, age 72
Auditors: KPMGLLP

LOCATIONS

HQ: Avnet Inc.
2211 S. 47th St., Phoenix AZ 85034
Phone: 480-643-2000 **Fax:** 480-643-7370
Web: www.avnet.com

2012 Sales

	$ mil.	% of total
Americas		45
Europe Middle East &		29
Asia/Pacific		26
Total		**100**

PRODUCTS/OPERATIONS

2012 Sales by Operating Group

	$ mil.	% of total
Electronics Marketing (EM)		
Americas	5,678	22
Asia/Pacific	5,051	20
Europe Middle East & Africa	4,203	16
Technology Solutions (TS)		
Americas	5,820	23
Europe Middle East & Africa	3,205	12
Asia/Pacific	1,748	7
Total	**25,707**	**100**

2012 Sales by Product Category

	$ mil.	% of total
Semiconductors	13,461	52
Computer products	9,984	39
Passives electromechanical & other	1,594	6
Connectors	667	3
Total	**25,707**	**100**

COMPETITORS

Arrow Electronics
Digi-Key
Future Electronics
Heilind Electronics
Ingram Micro
N.F. Smith
Premier Farnell
SYNNEX
Tech Data
TTI Inc.
WPG Holdings

HISTORICAL FINANCIALS

Company Type: Public

Income Statement

FYE: June 30

	REVENUE ($ mil.)	NET INCOME ($ mil.)	NET PROFIT MARGIN	EMPLOYEES
06/12*	25,707	567	2.2%	19,100
07/11	26,534	669	2.5%	17,600
07/10	19,160	410	2.1%	14,200
06/09	16,229	(1,122)	—	12,900
06/08	17,952	499	2.8%	12,800
Annual Growth	9.4%	3.2%	—	10.5%

*Fiscal year change

2012 Year-End Financials

Debt ratio: 21.09%
Return on equity: 14.52%
Cash ($ mil.): 1,006
Current ratio: 172.02
Long-term debt ($ mil.): 1,271
No. of shares (mil.): 142
Dividends
Yield: —
Payout: —
Market value ($ mil.): 4,399

	STOCK PRICE ($) FY Close	P/E High/Low	PER SHARE ($) Earnings	Dividends	Book Value
06/12*	30.86	10 6	3.79	0.00	27.40
07/11	32.55	9 5	4.34	0.00	26.55
07/10	23.98	12 7	2.68	0.00	19.82
06/09	21.52	— —	(7.44)	0.00	18.28
06/08	27.55	13 8	3.27	0.00	27.49
Annual Growth	2.9%	— —	3.8%	—	(0.1%)

*Fiscal year change

Avon Products, Inc.

Avon calling –calling for a younger crowd overseas reps and improved global operational efficiencies. Avon Products the world's top direct seller of cosmetics and beauty-related items is busy building a global brand and enticing more consumers to buy its products. Direct selling remains its modus operandi; sales also come from catalogs and a website. Its lineup includes cosmetics fragrances toiletries jewelry apparel home furnishings and more. Avon which owns Silpada jewelry boasts about 6.4 million independent representatives. With sales and distribution operations in some 110 countries the company continues to transform its business following a multiyear turnaround and a takeover bid by Coty.

Operations

Smaller rival Coty a privately held maker of such fragrances as Calvin Klein and Kenneth Cole in May 2012 raised its original $10 billion unsolicited offer (which Avon rejected in April) to $10.7 billion. Backing Coty's sweetened offer is Berkshire Hathaway run by famed investor Warren Buffett. (The addition of Buffett is designed to bring Avon to the negotiating table.) To spur a turnaround in the meantime Avon has purged staff streamlined manufacturing and narrowed its supply chain with regard to procurement and distribution. Avon plans to shut down plants in Ohio and another in Germany by 2013. It also moved its New York headquarters in 2011 lured by a lease allowing one year of free rent. Other cost-saving measures include freezing salaries and bolstering its recruitment of sales representatives. The cost of the reorganization estimated at $700 million a year factors in savings from simplifying its product line and making sourcing improvements. Avon is using the savings to fund investments in consumer research product innovation and advertising. Stubborn unemployment in the US and other countries has created a line of new recruits. Its ranks of independent representatives swelled from 5.8 million (in 2008) to 6.4 million (2011). While its number of sales reps grew its office staff has shrunk. By 2008 the company had trimmed its employee ranks by 10% and management by nearly 30%. Avon later purged another 4000 jobs. Job eliminations hit Avon's global direct-selling operations hardest notably in Germany. As a result the beauty company is outsourcing transactional and other services where necessary and navigating toward countries with lower operating costs. Avon has focused on building its group of independent sales representatives particularly in Russia and China and less so the UK.

Geographic Reach

Avon has grown its business on North American soil but the beauty company counts on more of its revenue beyond its roots from operations overseas; it now generate 83% of its sales outside the US. It operates in Brazil Russia China the UK and Germany among other countries.

Financial Analysis

The beauty company logged a 4% increase in revenue in 2011. The modest gains can be attributed to Avon's efforts to ramp up its largest market Brazil. While the company saw lower than normal sales there it has not been able to see traction as it invests in implementing an Enterprise Resource Planning system in the country. The effort has weakened results in the interim. Besides Brazil whose beauty business stalled during the second half of 2011 Avon's 2011 global growth was further bogged down by a weak beauty market in Russia during the year. Avon has found its calling in China. Despite resistance from the country Avon persisted in knocking on the Asian giant's door and eventually gained entrance. In 1998 China banned direct-selling citing consumer confusion in distinguishing between companies that direct sell and those with pyramid schemes. Nonetheless in 2005 Avon was given approval from the government to test its direct selling in parts of China specifically the cities of Beijing and Tianjin and the province of Guangdong. Happily Avon has since retained a direct-selling license. Pulling out of the Japanese market was part of the company's decision to double up on its efforts in China. To this end it sold its 75% stake in Avon Japan to private equity firm TPG for $90 million in 2010. The move also was part of the beauty products maker's plan to refocus on direct sales. (The Japanese unit typically generated more than half its revenues through direct mail.)

Sales & Marketing

Competition from mass merchandisers and specialty and department stores however has spurred Avon to not only spend many millions on consumer research market intelligence and product innovation but set aside just as much to launch a global ad campaign intended to boost sales of fragrances (Today Tomorrow Always) and skin care (Anew anti-aging). The company's recent reorganization has freed up many millions of dollars with which Avon plans to use to fund the company's investment in consumer research product innovation and advertising (for selling products and recruiting sales reps).

Mergers & Acquisitions

The company has expanded its product lineup through an investment in acquisitions and alliances. Avon bought Silpada Designs a Kansas-based direct seller of sterling silver jewelry with operations in the US Canada and the UK for $650 million. The 2010 acquisition was the company's largest in more than a decade. Silpada's higher-priced jewelry offerings were expected to boost margins. However in 2011 the jewelry brand delivered weaker than expected performance spurring Avon to lower its revenue and earnings projections. Not helping Avon or Silpada is that silver prices nearly doubled since the acquisition; this was paired with the negative impact of pricing on revenues and margins. The Silpada deal followed a pair of purchases earlier in the year: UK-based Liz Earle Beauty which develops skin care products made of botanical ingredients and the Tiny Tillia brand engaged in bath and body care products for babies. Both purchases help to broaden Avon's brand portfolio in the growing markets of natural personal care products and baby care.

Strategy

Avon's alliances have included a global licensing agreement with Finnish clothing design firm Marimekko to create a color collection. In addition Avon has made a Bond Girl 007 fragrance under license and signed on award-winning singer Fergie to develop a signature fragrance. Other partnerships have involved French designer Emanuel Ungaro for two fragrances (U by Ungaro for Her and U by Ungaro for Him) and the New York Yankees' Derek Jeter for "Driven" men's fragrance and a personal grooming line of products.

HISTORY

In the 1880s book salesman David McConnell gave small bottles of perfume to New York housewives who listened to his sales pitch. The perfume was more popular than the books so in 1886 McConnell created the California Perfume Company and hired women to sell door-to-door. (He renamed the company Avon Products in 1939 after being impressed by the beauty of Stratford-upon-Avon in England.) Through the 1950s these women mostly housewives seeking extra income made Avon a major force in the cosmetics industry.

From the 1960s until the mid-1980s Avon was the world's largest cosmetics company known for its appeal to middle-class homemakers. But the company hit hard times in 1974 –a recession made many of its products too pricey for blue-collar customers and women were leaving home for the workforce. Discovering that Avon's traditional products had little appeal for younger women Avon began an overhaul of its product line introducing the Colorworks line for teenagers with the slogan "It's not your mother's makeup."

Avon acquired prestigious jeweler Tiffany & Co. in 1979 (sold 1984) to help improve the company's image. To boost profits it entered the retail prestige fragrance business by launching a joint venture with Liz Claiborne (1985) and buying Giorgio Armani (1987 the Giorgio Beverly Hills retail operations were sold in 1994). But Liz Claiborne dissolved the joint venture when Avon bought competitor Parfums Stern in 1987 (sold 1990). It sold 40% of Avon Japan (begun 1969) to the Japanese public that year.

Avon Color cosmetics were introduced in 1988 and sleepwear preschool toys and videos followed in 1989. The company introduced apparel in 1994 and the next year worked with designer Diane Von Furstenberg to launch a line of clothing.

Mattel and Avon joined forces in 1996 to sell toys –Winter Velvet Barbie became Avon's most successful product introduction ever. In 1997 the company launched a new home furnishings catalog and bought direct seller Discovery Toys (sold 1999). Late in 1997 it began a $400 million restructuring program.

Passing over several high-ranking female executives (the company felt they weren't ready) Avon made Charles Perrin its CEO in mid-1998. Andrea Jung the brain behind the makeover became president. Avon also began selling makeup in 1998 at mall kiosks and through a catalog. Late that year The Avon Centre day spa opened in Manhattan.

In 1999 Jung became Avon's first female CEO by replacing the retiring Perrin. Former Goodyear and Rubbermaid CEO Stanley Gault was elected chairman of the board. In March 2000 Avon announced an alliance with Swiss pharmaceutical group Roche to develop a line of women's vitamins and nutritional products (its first) launched in 2001.

In June 2001 the company relaunched its Web site; the site allows Avon representatives to transact business through their own personal Web pages. In September Jung was elected chairman of the board. That year Avon also ceased marketing its beComing line in Penney's stores and added the brand to its direct-selling line of products.

In 2002 as part of a move to improve operating efficiencies Avon closed its jewelry manufacturing plant in San Sebastian Puerto Rico. The closure marked Avon's exit from jewelry manufacturing. It now outsources its full jewelry line by purchasing finished goods from Asia. In another cost-cutting move Avon laid off 3500 employees or 8% of its workforce that March saying that the economic recession in Argentina which accounts for about 5% of Avon's sales made the layoffs necessary. The next month Avon announced the closing of production operations in Northampton UK and a shift of these operations to its facility in Garwolin Poland reflecting what the company called a continuation of its plan to improve efficiency and integration.

As part of its focus on the younger market in 2003 Avon launched a new cosmetics line called "mark." –targeted to the 16-24 age group. Named for young women making their mark on the world the line includes 300 products such as cosmetics skin care fragrance accessories jewelry and handbags.

In 2004 Avon agreed to pay some $50 million for a 20% stake in its two Chinese joint ventures with Masson Group.

EXECUTIVES

Senior Vice President - Human Resources; Chief People Officer, Scott A. Crum, age 56

EVP Developing Market Group, Charles M. Herington, age 52, $627,322 total compensation

Chairman, Andrea Jung, age 53, $1,375,000 total compensation

Chairman, Fred Hassan, age 66

SVP Global Supply Chain and Process Excellence, John F. Owen, age 54

SVP and Global Brand President, Jeri B. Finard, age 52

VP Corporate Communications, Victor Beaudet

SVP Human Resources and Corporate Responsibility, Lucien Alziari, age 52

SVP Global Communications, Nancy Glaser

EVP and CFO, Kimberly A. Ross, age 47

SVP General Counsel Corporate Secretary and Chief Compliance Officer, Kim K.W. Rucker, age 45

SVP and President Asia Pacific, Bob Briddon, age 58

SVP; President Europe Middle East and Africa, John P. Higson, age 53

SVP, Geralyn R. Breig, age 49

CEO and Director, Sherilyn S. (Sheri) McCoy, age 54

SVP and CIO, Donagh Herlihy, age 48

SVP and President Western Europe Middle East & Africa, Anna Segatti, age 59

SVP and President Central and Eastern Europe, Srdjan Mijuskovic, age 56

General Manager Russia, Angela Cretu, age 37

Group VP and Corporate Controller, Stephen Ibbotson, age 52

SVP Global Insights and Marketing Intelligence, Michael (Mike) Schwartz

Vice President - Global Corporate Relations; Chief Communications Officer, Cheryl Heinonen

SVP and President North America, Jorge Martinez-Quiroga, age 56

President Mark Brand, Vanessa Reggiardo

Senior Manager Corporate Communications, Jennifer Dwyer Vargas

Director Public Relations North America, Claudia Shaum

Senior Manager Public Relations and Promotions, Jennifer Iino-Harvey

Senior Manager Public Relations and Communications Avon Foundation for Women, Karyn Margolis

SVP Chief Marketing Officer and President Global Brand & Category, Patricia Perez-Ayala

Senior Vice President; President; Latin America, Fernando J. Acosta

Senior Vice President; General Counsel, Jeff Benjamin

Director, Gary M. Rodkin, age 60

Director, V. Ann Hailey, age 60

Director, Paul S. Pressler, age 55

Director, Lawrence A. (Larry) Weinbach, age 72

Director, W. Don Cornwell, age 65

Director, Fred Hassan, age 66

Director, Paula Stern, age 67

Director, Ann S. Moore, age 62

Director, Maria Elena (Mel) Lagomasino, age 62

CEO and Director, Sherilyn S. (Sheri) McCoy, age 54

Independent Director, Douglas Conant

Auditors: PricewaterhouseCoopersLLP

LOCATIONS

HQ: Avon Products Inc.
1345 Avenue of the Americas, New York NY 10105-0196

Phone: 212-282-5000 **Fax:** 212-282-6049

Web: www.avoncompany.com

2011 Sales

	$ mil.	% of total
Latin America	5,116	45
North America	2,110	19
Central & Eastern Europe	1,580	14
Western Europe Middle East & Africa	1,542	14
Asia/Pacific	942	8
Total	**11,291**	**100**

2011 Sales

	$ mil.	% of total
Brazil	2,316	21
US	1,748	15
Other	7,226	64
Total	**11,291**	**100**

PRODUCTS/OPERATIONS

2011 Sales

	$ mil.	% of total
Beauty	8,067	71
Fashion	1,995	18
Home	1,048	9
Other	179	2
Total	**11,291**	**100**

Selected Collections

Advance Techniques
Anew
Avon Color
Avon Naturals
Avon Solutions
Avon Wellness
Beyond Color
Fragrance
 Christian LaCroix Absynthe
 Christian Lacroix Rouge
 Derek Jeter Driven
 Extraordinary
 mark
 Today Tomorrow Always
 U by Ungaro for Her
 U by Ungaro for Him
Skin So Soft

COMPETITORS

Alticor
Amway China
Bath & Body Works
BeautiControl
Beiersdorf
Body Shop
Carolee
Chanel
Clarins
Colgate-Palmolive
Coty Inc.
Dana Classic Fragrances
Dillard' s
Elizabeth Arden Inc
Enesco
Estee Lauder
Forever Living
Fossil Inc.
Hanover Direct
J. C. Penney
Jafra
James Avery
Johnson & Johnson
Johnson Publishing
Jostens
Kracie
L' Oreal
LJ International
LVMH
Macy' s
Mary Kay
Murad Inc.
Nu Skin
Perrigo
Prestige Cosmetics
Procter & Gamble
Revlon
Sara Lee
Shaklee
Shiseido
Target Corporation
Tiffany & Co.
Tupperware Brands
Unilever
Wal-Mart
Zale

HISTORICAL FINANCIALS

Company Type: Public

Income Statement FYE: December 31

	REVENUE ($ mil.)	NET INCOME ($ mil.)	NET PROFIT MARGIN	EMPLOYEES
12/11	11,291	513	4.5%	40,600
12/10	10,862	606	5.6%	42,000
12/09	10,382	625	6.0%	41,000
12/08	10,690	875	8.2%	42,000
12/07	9,938	530	5.3%	42,000
Annual Growth	3.2%	(0.8%)	—	(0.8%)

2011 Year-End Financials

Debt ratio: 42.77%
Return on equity: 32.71%
Cash ($ mil.): 1,245
Current ratio: 141.78
Long-term debt ($ mil.): 2,459
No. of shares (mil.): 430
Dividends
 Yield: —
 Payout: 77.97%
Market value ($ mil.): 7,526

	STOCK PRICE ($) FY Close	P/E High/Low		PER SHARE ($) Earnings	Dividends	Book Value
12/11	17.47	26	14	1.18	0.00	3.65
12/10	29.06	25	18	1.39	0.88	3.86
12/09	31.50	25	10	1.45	0.84	2.98
12/08	24.03	22	9	2.04	0.80	1.58
12/07	39.53	34	26	1.21	0.74	1.66
Annual Growth	(18.5%)	—	—	(0.6%)	—	21.8%

Baker Hughes Inc.

Baker Hughes cooks up a baker's dozen of products and services for the global petroleum market. Through its Drilling and Evaluation segment Baker Hughes makes products and services used to drill oil and natural gas wells. Through its Completion and Production segment the company provides equipment and services used from the completion phase through the productive life of oil and natural gas wells. It also makes bits and drilling fluids and submersible pumps. Its Industrial service segment provides equipment and services for the refining process and pipeline industries. Since 1944 Baker Hughes has published a weekly report that counts active drilling rigs and which serves as a barometer for the industry.

HISTORY

Howard Hughes Sr. and partner Walter Sharp opened a plant in Houston and their company Sharp & Hughes soon had a near monopoly on rock bits. When Sharp died in 1912 Hughes bought his partner's half of the company incorporating as Hughes Tool. Hughes held 73 patents when he died in 1924; the company passed to Howard Hughes Jr.

It is estimated that between 1924 and 1972 Hughes Tool provided Hughes Jr. with $745 million in pretax profits which he used to diversify into movies (RKO) airlines (TWA) and Las Vegas casinos. In 1972 he sold the company to the public for $150 million. After 1972 the company expanded into tools for aboveground oil production. In 1974 under the new leadership of chairman James Leach Hughes bought the oil field equipment business of Borg-Warner.

In 1913 drilling contractor Carl Baker organized the Baker Casing Shoe Company in California to collect royalties on his three oil tool inventions. The firm began to make its own products in 1918 and during the 1920s it expanded nationally opened global trade and formed Baker Oil Tools (1928). The company grew in the late 1940s and the 1950s as oil drilling boomed.

During the 1960s Baker prospered despite fewer US well completions. Foreign sales increased. From 1963 to 1975 Baker bought oil-related companies Kobe Galigher Ramsey Engineering and Reed Tool.

US expenditures for oil services fell between 1982 and 1986 from $40 billion to $9 billion. In 1987 both Baker and Hughes faced falling revenues. The two companies merged to form Baker Hughes. By closing plants and combining operations the venture became profitable by the end of 1988. The company bought Eastman Christensen (the world leader in directional and horizontal drilling equipment) and acquired the instrumentation unit of Tracor Holdings in 1990.

Baker Hughes spun off BJ Services (pumping services) to the public in 1991 and sold the Eastern Hemisphere operations of Baker Hughes Tubular Services (BHTS) to Tuboscope. It sold the Western Hemisphere operations of BHTS to ICO the following year.

Also in 1992 Baker Hughes bought Teleco Oilfield Services a pioneer in directional drilling techniques from Sonat. The next year the company consolidated its drilling-technology businesses into a single unit Baker Hughes INTEQ.

The company continued expanding internationally in 1994 and in 1995 Baker Hughes sold EnviroTech Pumpsystems to the Weir Group of Glasgow Scotland. In 1996 company veteran Max Lukens became CEO. He replaced James Woods as chairman the next year.

Baker Hughes allied with Schlumberger's oil field service operations in 1996. In a move to boost its oil field chemicals business the company bought Petrolite in 1997 and rival Western Atlas for $3.3 billion in 1998 strengthening its land-based seismic data business (#1 in that market) and testing business. A downturn in the Asian economy disruptions from tropical storms and slumping oil prices caused oil companies to reduce demand for Baker Hughes' products. The company suffered a big loss in 1998 and in response trimmed its workforce by about 15% in 1999. It also put its separation-equipment business up for sale.

In 2000 Lukens stepped down after accounting blunders caused the company to restate earnings. Company director and Newfield Exploration Company CEO Joe Foster replaced him as acting CEO until Michael Wiley was named to that office. Baker Hughes combined its seismic oil and gas exploration business with that of Schlumberger to create WesternGeco in early 2001.

In 2002 Baker Hughes completed the sale of its Baker Process segment's EIMCO division. It also discontinued its oil producing operations in West Africa.

That next year the company formed QuantX a wellbore instrumentation joint venture company with Expro International. Cornerstone Pipeline Management was acquired in an effort to expand the pipeline inspection services provided by its Baker Petrolite division. Continuing with its acquisition run Baker Hughes purchased the remaining 10% interest in Compagnie Generale de Geophysique's (CGG) borehole seismic processing business. Following the acquisition Baker Hughes and CGG formed joint venture company VSFusion.

In 2004 Baker Hughes exited its Process division when it completed the sale of its Bird Machine subsidiary to Austrian-based machinery manufacturer Andritz. It also sold its water separation technology firm Petreco to Cooper Cameron. Later that year the company formed a new division Baker Hughes Drilling Fluids by separating its INTEQ business from its Oilfield segment. Baker Hughes then sold its discontinued Baker Hughes Mining Tools unit which formerly operated under its Hughes Christensen division to Atlas Copco USA Holdings (then operating as Atlas Copco North America). Michael Wiley retired from his position as chairman and CEO of Baker Hughes. Chad Deaton formerly president and CEO of

Hanover Compressor was named chairman and CEO to replace him.

In late 2005 the company acquired Scotland-based Zeroth Technologies a company that manufactures expandable metal sealing elements.

In early 2006 Baker Hughes acquired Nova Technology a Louisiana-based company that supplies monitoring and chemical injection systems for use in offshore gas and oil well operations.

To raise cash in 2006 Baker Hughes divested its 30% stake in seismic services provider WesternGeco selling out to joint-venture partner Schlumberger.

EXECUTIVES

VP and Controller, Alan J. Keifer, age 57, $191,386 total compensation
SVP and General Counsel, Alan R. Crain Jr., age 60, $473,000 total compensation
VP Chief Executive Office, John A. (Andy) O'Donnell, age 63, $374,173 total compensation
VP Corporate Development, David E. Emerson
Corporate Secretary, Sandra E. Alford
Chairman, Chadwick C. (Chad) Deaton, age 59, $1,155,000 total compensation
VP Technology Porfolio Management, Michael Sanders
President US Land, Paul S. Butero, age 55
President and CEO, Martin S. Craighead, age 52, $573,077 total compensation
President Gulf of Mexico, Richard L. Williams, age 56
President Canada, F. Mike Davis, age 57
SVP and CFO, Peter A. Ragauss, age 54, $618,622 total compensation
VP Global Sales, Gary G. Rich, age 53
VP Human Resources, Didier Charreton, age 48
VP Legal Western Hemisphere, William D. (Will) Marsh
VP; President Eastern Hemisphere Operations, Belgacem Chariag, age 49
VP and Treasurer, Jan Kees van Gaalen, age 55
Senior Executive Advisor, D. Nathan Meehan, age 56
President Reservoir Development Services, John Harris
President Western Hemisphere Operations, Derek Mathieson, age 41
VP and Chief Security Officer, Russell J. (Russ) Cancilla, age 60
President Global Products and Services, Arthur L. (Art) Soucy, age 49
VP Internal Audit, Ronald E. Martz
President Completion and Production, Neil Harrop
President Russia and Caspian, Dmitry Kuzevenkov
President Industrial Services Portfolio, Patrick (Pat) Marfone
President Middle East, Khaled Nouh
VP Reliability, Randolph (Randy) Phillips
President Drilling and Evaluation, Scott Schmidt
President Africa, Tom Thissen
President Asia Pacific, Richard Ward
VP Global Marketing, Maria Claudia Borras
VP Legal Eastern Hemisphere, Michael (Mike) Rasmuson
President Pressure Pumping, Lindsay Link
President Latin America, Rod Larson
VP Tax, Alexander Peng
Director, Larry D. Brady, age 69
Director, H. John Riley Jr., age 71
Director, J. Larry Nichols, age 69
Director, Charles L. (Chuck) Watson, age 62
Director, Pierre H. Jungels, age 68
Director, Anthony G. (Tony) Fernandes, age 66
Director, Clarence P. Cazalot Jr., age 61
Director, Claire W. Gargalli, age 69
Director, James A. Lash, age 67
Director, J. W. Stewart, age 68
Auditors: Deloitte&ToucheLLP

LOCATIONS

HQ: Baker Hughes Incorporated
2929 Allen Pkwy. Ste. 2100, Houston TX 77019-2118
Phone: 713-439-8600 **Fax:** 713-439-8699
Web: www.bakerhughes.com

2012 Sales

North America	11,501	54
Middle East & Asia/Pacific	3,443	16
Latin America	2,436	11
Total	**21,361**	**100**

PRODUCTS/OPERATIONS

Selected Operations

Drilling and Evaluation
- Drill bits
- Drilling and completion fluids
- Drilling services
- Wireline services

Completion and Production
- Artificial lift
- Completion systems
- Intelligent production systems
- Pressure pumping
- Upstream chemicals
- Wellbore intervention

Industrial Services and Other

COMPETITORS

Aker Solutions
CE Franklin
CGGVeritas
FMC
Halliburton
John Wood Group
Nabors Well Services
Nalco
National Oilwell Varco
Petroleum Geo-Services
Precision Drilling
Pride International
Schlumberger
Technip
TETRA Technologies
Weatherford International
Wenzel Downhole Tools

HISTORICAL FINANCIALS

Company Type: Public

Income Statement FYE: December 31

	REVENUE ($ mil.)	NET INCOME ($ mil.)	NET PROFIT MARGIN	EMPLOYEES
12/11	19,831	1,739	8.8%	57,700
12/10	14,414	812	5.6%	53,100
12/09	9,664	421	4.4%	34,400
12/08	11,864	1,635	13.8%	39,800
12/07	10,428	1,513	14.5%	35,800
Annual Growth	17.4%	3.5%	—	12.7%

2011 Year-End Financials

Debt ratio: 16.38%
Return on equity: 11.04%
Cash ($ mil.): 1,050
Current ratio: 279.75
Long-term debt ($ mil.): 3,845
No. of shares (mil.): 437
Dividends
Yield: —
Payout: 15.11%
Market value ($ mil.): 21,256

	STOCK PRICE ($) FY Close	P/E High/Low		PER SHARE ($) Earnings	Dividends	Book Value
12/11	48.64	20	11	3.97	0.00	36.03
12/10	57.17	28	17	2.06	0.60	32.64
12/09	40.48	35	20	1.36	0.60	23.35
12/08	32.07	17	5	5.30	0.56	22.03
12/07	81.10	21	13	4.73	0.52	19.99
Annual Growth	(12.0%)	—	—	(4.3%)	—	15.9%

Ball Corp

The well-rounded Ball Corporation pitches packaging to companies producing food beverage and household goods. Food and beverage packaging includes steel cans and aluminum slugs. Ball's packaging revenue derives primarily from long-term contracts with a relatively few customers such as MillerCoors and bottlers of Pepsi-Cola and Coca-Cola brands in Argentina Brazil China Europe and North America. Ball Aerospace & Technologies manufactures an array of aerospace systems from satellites to tactical antennas as well as providing systems engineering services. The Department of Defense NASA and their prime contractors represent 87% of this segment's sales.

HISTORY

The Ball Corporation began in 1880 when Frank Ball and his four brothers started making wood-jacket tin cans to store and transport kerosene and other materials. In 1884 the company switched to tin-jacketed glass containers for kerosene lamps. The lamps however were soon displaced by Thomas Edison's electric light bulb.

The Ball brothers then learned that the patent to the original sealed-glass storage container (the Mason jar) had expired. By 1886 the brothers had entered the sealed-jar business and imprinted their jars with the Ball name. In their first year they made 12500 jars and sparked a patent war with the two reigning jar producers who asserted that they controlled the correct patents and threatened to sue. The Ball lawyers proved that the patents had expired and the jar remained Ball's mainstay for many years.

The company began diversifying but a 1947 antitrust ruling prohibited it from buying additional glass subsidiaries. Ball decided to take advantage of the space race by buying Control Cells (aerospace science research) in 1957; that operation became Ball Brothers Research Corporation (later Ball Aerospace Systems Division). The Soviets launched Sputnik that year igniting a massive US scientific effort in 1958 and Ball won federal contracts to make equipment for the US space program.

Ball established its metal beverage-container business in 1969 when it bought Jeffco Manufacturing of Colorado. The operation soon won contracts to supply two-piece cans to Budweiser Coca-Cola Dr Pepper Pepsi and Stroh's Beer.

John Fisher became president and CEO in 1971. The last company president who was a member of the Ball family Fisher wanted Ball to diversify. He took it public in 1972 to fund his efforts. That year he acquired a Singapore-based petroleum equipment company. Next he led Ball into agricultural irrigation systems and prefabricated housing. In 1974 Ball acquired a small California computer firm which formed the basis of its telecommunications division.

Fisher retired in 1981. Ball's metal-container business suffered in the late 1980s from overcapacity and price wars in its industry. In 1989 the company's aerospace division was hard hit by $10 million in losses on an Air Force contract and by cuts in defense spending.

Ball spun off its Alltrista canning supplies subsidiary to shareholders in 1993 and purchased Heekin Can a manufacturer for the food pet food and aerosol markets. That year Ball's $50 million mirror system corrected the Hubble Space Telescope's blurred vision. The company entered the polyethylene terephthalate (PET) container business in 1995 and placed its glass-container business into a newly formed company Ball-Foster Glass Container and the next year sold its stake to its partner French materials company Saint-Gobain Group. Also in 1995 the company's aerospace division became subsidiary Ball Aerospace & Technologies Corporation.

Ball sold its aerosol-can business to BWAY Corp in 1996. It acquired M.C. Packaging of Hong Kong in 1997. Ball popped the top on another big deal in 1998 when it bought Reynolds Metals' aluminum-can business (Reynolds is now owned by Alcoa). In 1999 and 2000 the company closed four can plants in an effort to improve an imbalance in supply and demand.

In 2001 Ball and ConAgra Grocery Products formed a joint venture Ball Western Can Company to make metal food containers. Also that year subsidiary Ball Aerospace & Technologies landed a $260 million contract with the US Air Force and Ball's president and COO David Hoover was named CEO. That November Ball entered into a joint venture with Coors Brewing Co. called Rocky Mountain Metal Container to operate Coors' can facilities making 4.5 billion cans per year. The company also acquired Wis-Pak Plastics Inc. adding to its plastic container operations.

Ball finalized its purchase of German can maker Schmalbach-Lubeca (renamed Ball Packaging Europe) in 2003 for about $890 million. The deal made Ball the second-largest can maker in Europe.

Before the economy turned south Ball made several sizeable acquisitions. It acquired US Can's US and Argentinean operations for $550 million. The deal which included 10 US plants and two in Argentina made Ball the US's largest maker of aerosol cans. Ball also supplemented its plastic bottle manufacturing operations buying three facilities from Alcan for about $180 million.

However in 2008 Ball was forced to make a number of hard choices. It exited a custom and decorative tinplate can business in Maryland and closed a plastic-packaging plant in Ontario. It sold off its plastic pail business too for about $32 million to BWAY Corp. In its aerospace and technologies business segment Ball's Australian subsidiary was put on the sale rack. QinetiQ Group a British defense company pocketed it.

In 2009 Ball purchased four US beverage can plants in Florida Georgia Ohio and Wisconsin from Anheuser-Busch InBev for $576 million.

Among its significant decisions in 2010 the company sold off its Plastic Packaging Americas business for $280 million to Amcor Australia's packaging giant.

EXECUTIVES

SVP and CFO, Scott C. Morrison, age 50
EVP and COO Global Packaging, Raymond J. Seabrook, age 61, $490,500 total compensation
Chairman, R. David (Dave) Hoover, age 67, $1,130,000 total compensation
Chief Commercial Officer Global Metal Beverage, Michael D. Herdman, age 62
President CEO and Director, John A. Hayes, age 47, $575,000 total compensation
VP Financial Reporting and Tax, Douglas K. Bradford, age 55
President and CEO Ball Aerospace & Technologies, David L. (Dave) Taylor, age 60
SVP Human Resources and Administration, Lisa A. Pauley, age 50
VP General Counsel and Corporate Secretary, Charles E. Baker, age 55
Director Corporate Relations, Scott McCarty
Director Investor Relations, Ann T. Scott
SVP and COO Global Metal Food and Household Packaging, Michael W. Feldser, age 61
VP Information Technology and Services, Leroy J. Williams Jr., age 47
SVP and COO. Global Metal Beverage Packaging, Gerrit Heske, age 48
President Ball Metal Beverage Packaging Division Americas, Michael L. Hranicka, age 44
VP and Controller, Shawn M. Barker, age 45
VP and Treasurer, Jeff A. Knobel, age 41
President Ball Packaging Europe, Colin Gillis, age 58
Media Relations Ball Aerospace & Technologies, Roz Brown
Public Relations Ball Packaging Europe, Sylvia Bloemker
President Ball Asia Pacific, Gihan Atapattu, age 46
VP Marketing and Corporate Affairs, James N. Peterson, age 43
Manager Sustainability Europe, Bjorn Kulmann
Director Environment and Recycling Asia, Major Deng
Director Environmental Health and Safety and System Safety Engineering Aerospace, Laura Davis
Vice President of Corporate Purchasing Brewing Operation Group, Jimmy Jiaping
Vice President and Chief Sustainability Officer, John Gardner
Senior Director Marketing & Corporate Communications, Laura Olson-Reyes
Vice President of Treasury and Investor Relations, Michael Carlotti
PresidentLatapack-Ball Embalagens Ltda., Tony Barnett, age 47
Director, Theodore M. (Tim) Solso, age 65
Director, John F. Lehman Jr., age 69
Director, Robert W. (Bob) Alspaugh, age 65
Director, Georgia R. Nelson, age 62
Director, Hanno C. Fiedler, age 67
President CEO and Director, John A. Hayes, age 47
Director, Stuart A. Taylor II, age 51
Director, Jan Nicholson, age 67
Director, Erik H. van der Kaay, age 72
Director, George M. Smart, age 66
Advisory Director, Pedro Henrique Mariani
Independent Director, Erik Kaay
Auditors: PricewaterhouseCoopersLLP

LOCATIONS

HQ: Ball Corporation
10 Longs Peak Dr., Broomfield CO 80021-2510
Phone: 303-469-3131 **Fax:** 303-460-2127
Web: www.ball.com

2011 Sales

	$ mil.	% of total
US	5,370	62
Other countries	3,260	38
Total	**8,630**	**100**

PRODUCTS/OPERATIONS

2011 Sales

	$ mil.	% of total
Metal beverage packaging Americas & Asia	4,415	51
Metal beverage packaging Europe	2,017	23
Metal food & household products packaging Americas	1,426	17
Aerospace & technologies	784	9
Corporate & intercompany eliminations	(13.5)	-
Total	**8,630**	**100**

Selected Products

Aerospace & technologies
- Aerospace technology & components
- Antennas & microwave systems
- Satellites & spacecraft
- Space-based instruments & sensors
- Tactical instruments & sensors
- Technical services

Packaging
- Aerosol cans
- Beverage cans
- Food cans
- Paint & general line cans

COMPETITORS

Alcoa
Amcor
Anchor Glass
Boeing
BWAY
CLARCOR
Consolidated Container
Constar International
Crown Holdings
Orbital Sciences
Owens-Illinois
Rexam
Rio Tinto Alcan
Rockwell Collins
Saint-Gobain Containers
Sequa
Silgan
Teledyne Technologies
Tetra Laval

HISTORICAL FINANCIALS

Company Type: Public

Income Statement FYE: December 31

	REVENUE ($ mil.)	NET INCOME ($ mil.)	NET PROFIT MARGIN	EMPLOYEES
12/11	8,630	444	5.1%	15,000
12/10	7,630	468	6.1%	14,000
12/09	7,345	387	5.3%	10,500
12/08	7,561	319	4.2%	14,500
12/07	7,389	281	3.8%	15,500
Annual Growth	4.0%	12.1%	—	(0.8%)

2011 Year-End Financials

Debt ratio: 43.16%
Return on equity: 36.42%
Cash ($ mil.): 165
Current ratio: 125.10
Long-term debt ($ mil.): 2,696
No. of shares (mil.): 160
Dividends
Yield: —
Payout: 10.65%
Market value ($ mil.): 5,725

	STOCK PRICE ($) FY Close	P/E High/Low		PER SHARE ($) Earnings	Dividends	Book Value
12/11	35.71	28	11	2.63	0.00	7.60
12/10	68.05	27	19	2.55	0.20	8.82
12/09	51.70	25	18	2.04	0.20	8.41
12/08	41.59	34	17	1.65	0.20	5.79
12/07	45.00	40	32	1.37	0.20	6.70
Annual Growth	(5.6%)	—	—	17.7%	—	3.2%

BancFirst Corp. (Oklahoma City, Okla)

This Oklahoma bank wants to be more than OK. It wants to be super. BancFirst Corporation is the holding company for BancFirst a super-community bank that emphasizes decentralized management and centralized support. BancFirst operates about 100 locations in some 50 Oklahoma communities. It serves individuals and small to midsized businesses offering traditional deposit products such as checking and savings accounts CDs and IRAs. Commercial real estate lending (including farmland and multifamily residential loans) makes up more than a third of the bank's loan portfolio while one-to-four family residential mortgages represent about 20%. The bank also issues business construction and consumer loans.

The company's BancFirst Insurance Services arm sells property/casualty coverage while the bank's trust and investment management division oversees some $1.5 billion of assets on behalf of clients. Bank subsidiaries Council Oak Investment Corporation and Council Oak Real Estate focus on small business and property investments respectively.

Bank acquisitions in 2010 and 2011 helped BancFirst grow its loan portfolio which in turn brought in more interest-related income. The company reported approximately 7% increases in revenues (from nearly $241 million to some $259 million) and earnings ($42.3 million to $45.6 million) for 2011.

The company has been buying smaller banks to expand in Oklahoma. In 2011 it acquired FBC Financial Corporation and its subsidiary bank 1st Bank Oklahoma with about five branches throughout the state. In 2010 BancFirst acquired Union Bank of Chandler Okemah National Bank and Exchange National Bank of Moore adding about another five branches. It acquired First State Bank Jones in 2009 to expand in eastern Oklahoma.

President and CEO David Rainbolt owns some 40% of BancFirst Corporation.

EXECUTIVES

SVP Investments, Robert M. Neville, age 56
EVP Asset Quality BancFirst, Dale E. Petersen, age 61
EVP Financial Services BancFirst, D. Jay Hannah, age 56
EVP Chief Risk Officer and Treasurer, Randy P. Foraker, age 56
Vice Chairman, James R. Daniel, age 72, $223,000 total compensation
Member of the Executive Committee, Robert A. Gregory, age 76
Vice Chairman BancFirst Corp. and BancFirst, K. Gordon Greer, age 75
Chairman, H. E. (Gene) Rainbolt, age 83
SVP Human Resources, J. Michael Rogers, age 68
EVP CFO and Corporate Secretary, Joe T. Shockley Jr., age 60, $178,000 total compensation
President CEO and Director, David E. Rainbolt, age 56, $350,000 total compensation
Regional Executive BancFirst, E. Wayne Cardwell, age 71
EVP and Head Operions BancFirst, Scott Copeland, age 47
SEVP; President and CEO BancFirst, Dennis L. Brand, age 64, $350,000 total compensation
Vice Chairman BancFirst Corp. and BancFirst; CEO Council Oak Partners, William O. Johnstone, age 64, $200,000 total compensation
Regional Executive BancFirst, Roy C. Ferguson, age 65
Regional Executive BancFirst, Karen James, age 56
EVP and Director Community Banking, Darryl Schmidt, age 50, $254,000 total compensation
Regional Executive BancFirst, David M. Seat, age 61
EVP and CTO BancFirst, David Westman, age 56
Regional Executive BancFirst, Marion McMillian, age 59
Regional Executive BancFirst, Kendal W. Starks, age 58
Regional Executive BancFirst, David R. Harlow, age 49
SVP, Terry Croll
Regional Executive of BancFirst, Harvey Robinson
Regional Executive of BancFirst, Marion McMillan
Vice Chairman, James R. Daniel, age 72
Vice Chairman BancFirst Corp. and BancFirst, K. Gordon Greer, age 75
President CEO and Director, David E. Rainbolt, age 56
Director, Ronald J. Norick, age 70
Director, David E. Ragland, age 69
Director, William H. Crawford, age 74
Vice Chairman BancFirst Corp. and BancFirst; CEO Council Oak Partners, William O. Johnstone, age 64
Director, Melvin Moran, age 81
Director, Paul B. Odom Jr., age 83
Director, C. L. Craig Jr., age 67
Director, John C. Hugon, age 57
Director, J. Ralph McCalmont, age 76
Director, David R. Lopez, age 60
Director, Donald B. Halverstadt, age 77
Director, G. Rainey Williams Jr., age 51
Director, Tom H. McCasland III, age 53
Director, Michael K. Wallace, age 59
Director, F. Ford Drummond
Independent Director, Cynthia Ross
Auditors: GrantThorntonLLP

LOCATIONS

HQ: BancFirst Corporation
101 N. Broadway Ste. 200, Oklahoma City OK 73102
Phone: 405-270-1086 **Fax:** 405-270-1089
Web: www.bancfirst.com

PRODUCTS/OPERATIONS

2011 Sales

	$ mil.	% of total
Interest		
Loans including fees	164	63
Securities	14	5
Other	3	1
Noninterest		
Service charges on deposits	42	17
Insurance commissions	10	4
Cash management	7	3
Trust revenue	6	3
Other	9	4
Total	**258**	**100**

Selected Subsidiaries

BancFirst
- BancFirst Agency Inc. (credit life insurance)
- BancFirst Community Development Corporation
- Council Oak Investment Corporation (small business investments)
- Council Oak Real Estate Inc. (real estate investments)

Council Oak Partners LLC
BancFirst Insurance Services Inc.

COMPETITORS

Arvest Bank
Bank of America
BOK Financial
International Bancshares
Midland Financial
Southwest Bancorp
UMB Financial
Wells Fargo

HISTORICAL FINANCIALS

Company Type: Public

Income Statement

FYE: December 31

	ASSETS ($ mil.)	NET INCOME ($ mil.)	INCOME AS % OF ASSETS	EMPLOYEES
12/11	5,608	45	0.8%	1,641
12/10	5,060	42	0.8%	1,533
12/09	4,416	32	0.7%	1,428
12/08	3,867	44	1.1%	1,457
12/07	3,743	53	1.4%	1,443
Annual Growth	10.6%	(3.7%)	—	3.3%

2011 Year-End Financials

Debt ratio: 0.97%
Return on equity: 9.45%
Cash ($ mil.): 1,707
Current ratio: —
Long-term debt ($ mil.): 54
No. of shares (mil.): 15
Dividends
Yield: —
Payout: 35.49%
Market value ($ mil.): 568

	STOCK PRICE ($) FY Close	P/E High	P/E Low	PER SHARE ($) Earnings	Dividends	Book Value
12/11	37.54	15	10	2.93	0.00	31.95
12/10	41.19	17	13	2.70	0.96	29.84
12/09	37.04	25	14	2.09	0.90	28.14
12/08	52.92	25	13	2.85	0.84	27.08
12/07	42.85	16	12	3.33	0.76	24.44
Annual Growth	(3.3%)	—	—	(3.1%)	—	6.9%

BancorpSouth Inc.

Like Elvis Presley BancorpSouth has grown beyond its Tupelo roots. It's the holding company for BancorpSouth Bank which operates nearly 300 branches in eight southern and midwestern states. Catering to consumers and small and midszed businesses the bank offers checking and savings accounts loans credit cards and commercial banking services. BancorpSouth also sells insurance and provides brokerage investment advisory and asset management services throughout most of its market area. Real estate loans including consumer and commercial mortgages and home equity construction and agricultural loans comprise approximately three-quarters of its loan portfolio.

BancorpSouth Bank operates in Alabama Arkansas Florida Louisiana Mississippi Missouri Tennessee and Texas. BancorpSouth's insurance and financial advisory businesses also operate in Illinois and Florida respectively.

Since the credit crunch began in 2007 the company had been stockpiling provisions for loan losses to cover sour real estate construction acquisition and development loans. After three consecutive years of increasing its provisions it reduced them in 2011 a move that helped the company's bottom line. In order to cut costs the bank closed or divested some two dozen low-volume branches in 2011.

To reduce its reliance on interest-related revenue BancorpSouth hopes to diversify its revenue stream by increasing the amount it generates from mortgage lending insurance brokerage and securities activities. To this end subsidiary BancorpSouth Insurance Services has acquired small insurance agencies in Arkansas Missouri and Texas.

EXECUTIVES

EVP; Vice Chairman and Chief Lending Officer BancorpSouth Bank, Wayne Gregg Cowsert, age 64, $325,000 total compensation
SVP, W. O. Jones
Chairman and CEO BancorpSouth and BancorpSouth Bank, Aubrey B. Patterson Jr., age 69, $783,500 total compensation
EVP; Vice Chairman BancorpSouth Bank, Gordon Lewis, age 62, $325,000 total compensation
President COO and Director; President and COO BancorpSouth Bank, James Virgil (Jim) Kelley, age 62, $500,000 total compensation
EVP; Vice Chairman BancorpSouth Bank, W. James Threadgill Jr., age 57, $291,000 total compensation
EVP and Corporate Secretary BancorpSouth and BancorpSouth Bank, Cathy S. Freeman, age 46
CEO and Director, James D. (Dan) Rollins III, age 53
CFO and Treasurer; EVP CFO and Cashier BancorpSouth Bank, William L. (Bill) Prater, age 52, $275,000 total compensation
EVP; Vice Chairman BancorpSouth Bank, Larry Bateman, age 62, $283,959 total compensation
SVP and Principal Accounting Officer, Gary C. Bonds
EVP Audit and Loan Review and BancorpSouth Bank, Carol Waddle
First VP and Director Investor Relations, Will Fisackerly
EVP Vice Chairman and Chief Lending Officer, James R. Hodges
Director, Larry G. Kirk, age 65
Director, Wilbert G. (Mickey) Holliman, age 74
Director, R. Madison Murphy, age 54
President COO and Director; President and COO BancorpSouth Bank, James Virgil (Jim) Kelley, age 62
Director, Robert C. Nolan, age 70
Director, W. Cal Partee Jr., age 67
Director, Turner O. Lashlee, age 75
Director, Alan W. Perry, age 64
Director, Hassell H. Franklin, age 76
Director, Guy W. Mitchell III, age 68
CEO and Director, James D. (Dan) Rollins III, age 53
Director, James E. (Jim) Campbell III, age 62
Auditors: KPMGLLP

LOCATIONS

HQ: BancorpSouth Inc.
One Mississippi Plaza, 201 South Spring Street, Tupelo, MS 38804
Phone: 662 680-2000 **Fax:** 601 680-2570
Web: www.bancorpsouth.com

PRODUCTS/OPERATIONS

2011 Sales

	$ mil.	% of total
Interest		
Loans & leases	461	58
Securities	73	9
Other	3	-
Noninterest		
Insurance commissions	86	11
Service charges	66	8
Credit card debit card & merchant fees	42	5
Mortgage lending	17	2
Other	57	7
Total	**808**	**100**

Selected Subsidiaries

BancorpSouth Bank
BancorpSouth Insurance Services Inc.
BancorpSouth Investment Services Inc.
BancorpSouth Municipal Development Corporation
Century Credit Life Insurance Company
Personal Finance Corporation

COMPETITORS

Capital One
Compass Bancshares
First Horizon
Great Southern Bancorp
Hancock Holding
Regions Financial
Renasant
SunTrust
Trustmark

HISTORICAL FINANCIALS

Company Type: Public

Income Statement

FYE: December 31

	ASSETS ($ mil.)	NET INCOME ($ mil.)	INCOME AS % OF ASSETS	EMPLOYEES
12/11	12,995	37	0.3%	4,244
12/10	13,615	22	0.2%	4,311
12/09	13,167	82	0.6%	4,450
12/08	13,480	120	0.9%	4,500
12/07	13,189	137	1.0%	4,400
Annual Growth	(0.4%)	(27.8%)	—	(0.9%)

2011 Year-End Financials

Debt ratio: 1.49%
Return on equity: 2.98%
Cash ($ mil.): 499
Current ratio: —
Long-term debt ($ mil.): 193
No. of shares (mil.): 83
Dividends
Yield: —
Payout: 31.11%
Market value ($ mil.): 920

	STOCK PRICE ($) FY Close	P/E High/Low		PER SHARE ($) Earnings	Dividends	Book Value
12/11	11.02	37	19	0.45	0.00	15.13
12/10	15.95	87	45	0.27	0.88	14.64
12/09	23.46	25	17	0.99	0.88	15.29
12/08	23.36	21	11	1.45	0.87	14.92
12/07	23.61	16	13	1.69	0.83	14.54
Annual Growth	(17.3%)	—	—	(28.2%)	—	1.0%

Bank Mutual Corp

Bank Mutual Corporation is the holding company for Bank Mutual which serves consumers and businesses through about 80 branches in Wisconsin and one in Minnesota. Founded in 1892 the bank offers standard products such as checking and savings accounts CDs and credit cards. The company mainly uses funds gathered from deposits to originate a variety of loans and to invest in mortgage-backed securities and US government securities. Bank subsidiary BancMutual Financial and Insurance Services offers mutual funds annuities insurance and brokerage and investment advisory services.

Bank Mutual is primarily a real estate lender: Residential and commercial mortgages dominate its lending activities representing about 70% of the company's loan portfolio. Consumer loans are nearly 20%. To a lesser extent the bank also originates construction and business loans.

Until 2010 Bank Mutual had remained profitable through the credit crisis that began in 2007. However the economic downturn led the company to increase its provisions for loan losses more than sevenfold from 2008 to 2009 then triple that figure in 2010. The loan losses coupled with losses related to an early repayment of an above-market interest rate loan from the Federal Home Loan Bank of Chicago and an increase in foreclosed real estate contributed to the net loss for the year. Though it remained in the red (in part due to a writedown of goodwill) Bank Mutual was able to cut its loss in 2011 as it reduced its provisions for loan losses more than 85% amid an improving economy even though revenues were down.

The bank is looking to increase market share in financial and insurance services and among middle market businesses with up to $100 million in annual revenue. To woo consumers it forged an agreement with PULSE to offer its customers surcharge-free access to that firm's ATM network. Bank Mutual has enhanced technological offerings such as online bill payment.

Despite its name Bank Mutual is not mutually owned. The holding company whose shares are publicly traded owns all of the bank's outstanding stock.

EXECUTIVES

SVP and CFO Bank Mutual Corporation and Bank Mutual, Michael W. (Mike) Dosland, age 53, $63,308 total compensation
Chairman and CEO Bank Mutual Corporation and Bank Mutual, Michael T. Crowley Jr., age 67, $709,500 total compensation
SVP Retail and Operations Bank Mutual, P. Terry Anderegg, age 61, $193,300 total compensation
SVP Lending Bank Mutual, Christopher J. Callen, age 68, $191,000 total compensation
VP Human Resources, Diane Selfworth
Director and President Bank Mutual Corporation and Bank Mutual, David A. Baumgarten, age 61
Director Investment Real Estate Lending, Thomas H. (Tom) Koepp, age 64
VP Marketing and Communications, Jack Steinbrecker
VP Information Systems, Jerry Arata
VP Controller and Principal Accounting Officer, Richard L. Schroeder, age 54
VP and Secretary, James P. Carter
Director, J. Gus Swoboda, age 77
Director, Mark C. Herr, age 59
Director, Thomas J. Lopina Sr., age 74
Director, Robert B. Olson, age 74
Director, Thomas H. Buestrin, age 75
Director, William J. Mielke, age 64
Director and President Bank Mutual Corporation and Bank Mutual, David A. Baumgarten, age 61
Director, David C. Boerke, age 66
Director, Richard A. Brown, age 63
Auditors: Deloitte&ToucheLLP

LOCATIONS

HQ: Bank Mutual Corporation
4949 W. Brown Deer Rd., Milwaukee WI 53223
Phone: 414-354-1500 **Fax:** 414-354-5450
Web: www.bankmutualcorp.com

PRODUCTS/OPERATIONS

2011 Sales

	$ mil.	% of total
Interest		
Loans	69	62
Mortgage-related securities	16	15
Investment securities	2	3
Other	0	-
Noninterest		
Service charges on deposits	6	6
Net gain on loan sales activities	6	5
Brokerage & insurance commissions	2	2
Other	7	7
Total	**112**	**100**

COMPETITORS

Anchor BanCorp
Associated Banc-Corp
CIB Marine Bancshares
Citizens Republic Bancorp
Harris
TCF Financial
U.S. Bancorp
Wells Fargo

HISTORICAL FINANCIALS

Company Type: Public

Income Statement FYE: December 31

	ASSETS ($ mil.)	NET INCOME ($ mil.)	INCOME AS % OF ASSETS	EMPLOYEES
12/11	2,498	(47)	—	719
12/10	2,591	(72)	—	764
12/09	3,512	13	0.4%	815
12/08	3,489	17	0.5%	769
12/07	3,488	17	0.5%	746
Annual Growth	(8.0%)	—	—	(0.9%)

2011 Year-End Financials

Debt ratio: 6.13%
Return on equity: (-17.90)%
Cash ($ mil.): 120
Current ratio: —
Long-term debt ($ mil.): 153
No. of shares (mil.): 46
Dividends
Yield: —
Payout: —
Market value ($ mil.): 147

	STOCK PRICE ($) FY Close	P/E High/Low	PER SHARE ($) Earnings	Dividends	Book Value
12/11	3.18	— —	(1.03)	0.00	5.75
12/10	4.78	— —	(1.59)	0.20	6.84
12/09	6.93	40 24	0.29	0.34	8.72
12/08	11.54	34 25	0.35	0.36	8.38
12/07	10.57	38 31	0.31	0.33	8.63
Annual Growth	(25.9%)	— —	—	—	(9.7%)

Bank of America Corp.

Welcome to the machine. One of the largest banks in the US by assets (along with JPMorgan Chase and Citigroup) Bank of America also boasts one of the country's most extensive branch networks with some 5700 locations and more than 17000 ATMs throughout the US. The bank's core services include consumer and small business banking corporate banking credit cards mortgage lending and asset management. Thanks largely to its 2009 acquisition of Merrill Lynch Bank of America is also one of the world's leading wealth managers with more than $2 trillion under management. The addition of the once-mighty investment bank known as "The Bull" also beefed up Bank of America's trading and international businesses.

HISTORY

Bank of America predecessor NationsBank was formed as the Commercial National Bank in 1874 by citizens of Charlotte North Carolina. In 1901 George Stephens and Word Wood formed what became American Trust Co. The banks merged in 1957 to become American Commercial Bank which in 1960 merged with Security National to form North Carolina National Bank.

In 1968 the bank formed holding company NCNB which by 1980 was the largest bank in North Carolina. Under the leadership of Hugh McColl who became chairman in 1983 NCNB became the first southern bank to span six states.

NCNB profited from the savings and loan crisis of the late 1980s by managing assets and buying defunct thrifts at fire-sale prices. The company nearly doubled its assets in 1988 when the FDIC chose it to manage the shuttered First Republicbank then Texas' largest bank. The company renamed itself NationsBank in 1991.

In 1993 the company bought Chicago Research & Trading a government securities dealer and provider of oil and gas financing. A 1993 joint venture with Dean Witter and Discover to open securities brokerages in banks led to complaints that customers were not fully informed of the risks of some investments and that brokers were paying rebates to banking personnel for customer referrals. Dean Witter withdrew from the arrangement in 1994 and SEC investigations and a class-action lawsuit ensued. NationsBank settled the lawsuit for about $30 million the next year. (The company agreed to pay nearly $7 million to settle similar charges in 1998.)

NationsBank scooped up St. Louis-based Boatmen's Bancshares and Montgomery Securities (now Banc of America Securities) in 1997. The next year it bought Barnett Banks Florida's #1 bank.

Enter BankAmerica. Founded in 1904 as Bank of Italy BankAmerica had once been the US's largest bank but had fallen behind as competitors consolidated. The company's board of directors was pondering ways to become more competitive and in 1998 decided a merger was the best way. With the ink barely dry on its Barnett Banks deal NationsBank obliged.

After the merger the combined firm announced it would write down a billion-dollar bad loan to D.E. Shaw & Co. which followed the same Russian-investment-paved path of descent as Long-Term Capital Management. David Coulter (head of the old BankAmerica which made the loan) took the fall for the loss resigning as president; the balance of power shifted to the NationsBank side in 1999 when Kenneth Lewis took the post.

The Russian debacle and merger hiccups led the firm in early 1999 to reorganize and reduce overseas operations; it sold its private banking operations in Europe and Asia to UBS. Also that year it bought the recreational-vehicle financing unit of Associates First Capital (now part of Citigroup) 50% of Denver-based mutual fund firm Marsico Capital Management (it bought the rest in 2001) and BA Merchant Services. The bank also changed its name to Bank of America and began offering online banking through America Online. To avoid a court battle the bank settled charges that it retained proceeds from unclaimed bonds in California.

In 1999 the company earned the ire of labor officials for a program in which employees were recruited to maintain ATMs without being paid or provided supplies. EVP Frank Gentry who crafted the NationsBank/BankAmerica deal retired in 2000 signaling an end to the company's buying spree. Its focus turned inward as it set about the difficult integration of the two firms.

McColl retired as chairman in 2001. Later that year the company announced it would cease its subprime lending and car leasing operations.

In 2003 Bank of America's mutual fund chief Robert Gordon was among several employees who left the firm amidst a New York attorney general's investigation into hedge fund client Canary Capital Partners which allegedly had access to Bank of America's trading platform to make illegal after-hours trades of the company's erstwhile Nations Funds. Bank of America also paid $10 million for failing to provide documents to the SEC during its investigation of the scandal the largest-ever fine levied by the regulatory body for such an infraction.

The company sold its securities clearing and broker/dealer services units to ADP in 2004. In early 2005 the company struck a deal with regulators to implement tighter controls cut fees charged to investors exit the mutual fund clearing business and pay more than $500 million in fines including $140 million to settle complaints against FleetBoston. Also that year Bank of America remitted about another $460 million to settle investor claims that it did not adequately conduct due diligence when underwriting bonds of doomed telecom firm WorldCom in 2001 and 2002. (The claim involved 17 other investment banks as well; Citigroup paid more than $2.2 billion to clear itself of similar charges in late 2004).

Bank of America previously fattened up by purchasing northeastern banking behemoth FleetBoston for some $50 billion in 2004 and credit card giant MBNA for approximately $35 billion in cash and stock in early 2006. The latter deal roughly doubled the bank's credit card customer base (as well as its income from credit card fees) and gave the bank access to some 5000 organizations and institutions with which MBNA had affinity marketing relationships.

In early 2007 the company shed its venture capital arm BA Venture Partners (now Scale Venture Partners) to focus on middle-market private equity investments carried out by its BA Capital Investors unit.

In 2007 Bank of America bought U.S. Trust from Charles Schwab for more than $3 billion and acquired Chicago-based LaSalle Bank from Netherlands-based ABN AMRO for some $21 billion. Following the acquisition of U.S. Trust Bank of America merged the asset manager with its private banking and wealth management business to form U.S. Trust Bank of America Private Wealth Management. Prior acquisitions include credit card giant MBNA in 2006 a deal that doubled the bank's credit card customer base and its income from credit card fees.

In an effort to boost the economy and stimulate lending the US government in 2008 bought some $250 billion worth of preferred shares in the country's top banks. Approximately $45 billion of that was slated for Bank of America ($20 billion more than the original investment total). As a result of the government intervention US Treasury official (and so-called "pay czar") ordered then-CEO Lewis to receive no salary in 2009 and slashed compensation for other highly paid employees. Bank of America finished paying back the debt in late 2009.

As the global economy reeled from a credit freeze and subsequent recession in 2008 Bank of America added to its coffers by buying up troubled mortgage lender Countrywide Financial and investment bank Merrill Lynch. Countrywide had fallen on hard times as one of the hardest-hit victims of the subprime mortgage crisis. The deal was initially for $4 billion in stock but was finalized at around $2.5 billion as the economic climate sunk.

The Countrywide purchase made Bank of America the largest residential mortgage lender and servicer in the US. The company also settled a lawsuit contending that Countrywide engaged in deceptive lending practices. Bank of America agreed to pay more than $8 billion toward reductions on interest rates and principals of some 400000 troubled mortgage accounts. To avoid the stigma of the subprime loan crisis Countrywide was renamed Bank of America Home Loans in 2009.

Bank of America paid some $50 billion in stock to buy Merrill Lynch which had been crippled by the global credit crisis. Hoping to increase its up-front account fee revenues Bank of America began making a concerted push to cross-promote Merrill Lynch's wealth management business to the bank's affluent clients.

However the Merrill Lynch deal also brought its fair share of headaches. With the approval of Bank of America leadership the failed investment bank gave early bonuses worth billions to its executives prompting angry Bank of America shareholders and lawmakers to cry foul. The Securities and Exchange Commission slapped Bank of America with a $33 million fine for misleading shareholders about the bonuses. That fine was rejected by a federal judge in 2009 and the matter was ordered to go to trial. Bank of America ultimately agreed to pay $150 million in a settlement. In another Merrill Lynch-related settlement Bank of America agreed to pay $315 million in 2011 for claims that Merrill Lynch made false and misleading statements about its mortgage-backed securities sold to investors.

Then-CEO Ken Lewis in particular came under fire for not disclosing how bleak Merrill Lynch's financial condition was prior to the purchase; Lewis in turn said he had been implicitly pressured by the government to keep the troubles under wraps to prevent the deal from collapsing. A push to oust Lewis at the company's annual meeting in 2009 didn't pass but shareholders split the chairman and CEO positions to provide more accountability to the public. Director Walter Massey was named chairman and Lewis stepped down at the end of the year. Brian Moynihan the head of consumer and small business banking succeeded Lewis as CEO. Longtime Dupont CEO Charles Holliday took over as chairman in 2010 replacing the retiring Massey.

EXECUTIVES

Vice Chairman, Charles H. (Chuck) Noski, age 59
Chairman, Charles O. (Chad) Holliday Jr., age 65
SVP and Global Strategy and Marketing Officer, Anne M. Finucane, age 58
President CEO and Director, Brian T. Moynihan, age 52, $800,000 total compensation
President Global Technology and Operations, Catherine P. (Cathy) Bessant
SVP; President Home Loans, Barbara J. Desoer, age 59, $800,000 total compensation
Global Chief Legal Compliance and Regulatory Relations, Gary G. Lynch, age 61
EVP; President Legacy Asset Servicing, Terrence P. (Terry) Laughlin, age 57
Co-COO, Thomas K. (Tom) Montag, age 55
Co-COO, David C. Darnell, age 59
Chief Accounting Officer, Neil A. Cotty
Global Compliance Executive, Paula Dominick
Bank Spokesman, Scott Silvestri
CFO, Bruce R. Thompson, age 47
General Counsel, Edward (Ed) O'Keefe, age 56
EVP and Global Head Human Resources, Andrea B. Smith, age 44
Chief Risk Officer, Terrence P. (Terry) Laughlin, age 57
Media Relations EMEA Research, Tomos Rhys Edwards
Country Manager Mexico, Tito Vidaurri
Small Business Banker Region Executive Pacific Southwest Region, Lynn Fernandez
Corporate Secretary, Lauren A. Mogensen
Executive Shared Technology Infrastructure and CTO Global Wealth and Investment Management, David Reilly
CIO Global Wealth and Investment Management, Mark Alexander
CIO, Laurie Readhead
Corporate General Auditor, Christine P. Katziff
Legacy Asset Servicing Executive, Ron D. Sturzenegger
Director, Linda P. Hudson, age 62
Vice Chairman, Charles H. (Chuck) Noski, age 59
Director, Thomas J. (Tom) May, age 64
Director, D. Paul Jones Jr., age 69
Director, Susan S. Bies, age 64
Director, Jack O. Bovender Jr., age 67
Director, R. David (Dave) Yost, age 65
Director, Charles K. (Chad) Gifford, age 69
Director, Mukesh D. Ambani, age 54
Director, Frank P. Bramble Sr., age 63
President CEO and Director, Brian T. Moynihan, age 52
Director, Virgis W. Colbert, age 73
Director, Monica C. Lozano, age 55
Director, Sharon L. Allen, age 60
Director, Charles O. Rossotti, age 71
Director, Donald E. (Don) Powell, age 70
Director, Robert W. (Bob) Scully, age 62
Auditors: PricewaterhouseCoopersLLP

LOCATIONS

HQ: Bank of America Corporation
100 N. Tryon St., Charlotte NC 28255
Phone: 704-386-5681 **Fax:** 972-459-4800
Web: www.ushomesystems.com

PRODUCTS/OPERATIONS

2011 Sales

	$ mil.	% of total
Interest		
Loans & leases including fees	44,966	36
Debt securities	9,521	8
Trading account assets	5,961	5
Federal funds sold & securities borrowed or purchased under agreements to resell	2,147	2
Other	3,641	3
Noninterest		
Investment & brokerage services	11,826	9
Service charges	8,094	6
Equity investment income	7,360	6
Card income	7,184	6
Trading account profits	6,697	5
Investment banking	5,217	4
Gains on sale of debt securities	3,374	3
Insurance	1,346	1
Other	6,930	6
Adjustments	(9190)	-
Total	**115,074**	**100**

COMPETITORS

Bank of New York Mellon
BB&T
Capital One
Citigroup
Goldman Sachs
HSBC
HSBC USA
JPMorgan Chase
KeyCorp
Morgan Stanley
PNC Financial
RBC Financial Group
RBS Citizens Financial Group
State Street
SunTrust
U.S. Bancorp
UnionBanCal
Wells Fargo

HISTORICAL FINANCIALS

Company Type: Public

Income Statement FYE: December 31

	ASSETS ($ mil.)	NET INCOME ($ mil.)	INCOME AS % OF ASSETS	EMPLOYEES
12/11	2,129,046	1,446	0.1%	282,000
12/10	2,264,909	(2,238)	—	288,000
12/09	2,223,299	6,276	0.3%	284,000
12/08	1,817,943	4,008	0.2%	243,000
12/07	1,715,746	14,982	0.9%	210,000
Annual Growth	5.5%	(44.3%)	—	7.6%

2011 Year-End Financials

Debt ratio: 17.49%—
Return on equity: 0.63%
Cash ($ mil.): 120,102
Current ratio: —
Long-term debt ($ mil.): 372,265
Dividends
Yield: —
Payout: 400.00%
Market value ($ mil.): —

	STOCK PRICE ($)	P/E	PER SHARE ($)		
	FY Close	High/Low	Earnings	Dividends	Book Value
12/11	5.56	1525499	0.01	0.00	21.84
12/10	13.34	— —	(0.37)	0.04	22.63
12/09	15.06	— —	(0.29)	0.04	26.76
12/08	14.08	80 20	0.55	2.24	35.29
12/07	41.26	16 12	3.30	2.40	33.08
Annual Growth	(39.4%)	— —	(76.5%)	—	(9.9%)

Bank of Hawaii Corp

Bank of Hawaii knows there's no place like home. The corporation is the holding company for Bank of Hawaii (familiarly known as Bankoh) which has about 70 branches in its home state plus an additional dozen in American Samoa Guam Palau and Saipan. Founded in 1897 the bank operates through four business segments: retail banking for consumers and small businesses in Hawaii; commercial banking including property/casualty insurance for middle-market and large corporations (this segment also includes the bank's activities beyond the state); investment services such as trust asset management and private banking; and treasury which performs corporate asset and liability management services.

Banking in paradise isn't always easy: Hawaii is known for its high cost of living and its reliance upon the tourism industry. As the second-largest bank on the archipelago Bankoh's performance often mirrors that of the state since loans secured by homes and new home construction represent the largest portion of the company's lending. Due the recent economic environment in the state the bank has curtailed its lending activities which cut into its bottom line. Its 2011 results were also negatively impacted by a federal law that went into effect the previous year that puts caps on overdraft fees.

The company's growth —limited by geography —comes methodically. Bankoh has more than 500 ATMs in its market and continuously looks for ways to expand. It has installed some 60 ATMs inside McDonald's restaurants throughout Hawaii and in 2009 it introduced ATMs inside McDonald's restaurants in Guam. In addition to growing its ATM network Bankoh has also introduced a special mobile banking fleet which includes shuttle-sized vehicles that offer ATMs and wireless technology inside.

HISTORY

Bank of Hawaii was chartered in 1897 and initially capitalized at $400000. The company opened its first branch in 1903 on neighboring island Kauai and over the next 20 years branches were added on the other islands. It had branches on every major island in the archipelago by 1930 the same year it bought Bank of Maui.

During WWII Bank of Hawaii provided banking services to soldiers and sailors on their way to the Pacific theater. In 1959 Hawaii became a state and Bank of Hawaii became a member of the FDIC. In its first forays out of state it opened branches on Midway Island and Kwajalein Atoll followed by branches in American Samoa Guam the Marshall Islands Ponape Saipan and Yap. The company also established alliances with Credit Lyonnais and the Bank of New Zealand setting up outposts in New Caledonia Tahiti Tonga and Western Samoa (now simply Samoa). In 1968 the company formed its Bank of Hawaii International subsidiary to hold its foreign operations.

Bank of Hawaii reorganized as a bank holding company Hawaii Bancorporation in 1971. It continued its westward expansion acquiring substantial stakes in Banque de Nouvelle Caledonie and Bank of Tonga. The company moved into leasing operations in 1973 and changed its name to Bancorp Hawaii in 1979.

During the 1980s the company began to grow via acquisitions. It established a Tokyo branch in 1981 merged with the Hawaiian Trust Company (1985) and made its first appearance on the US mainland by buying First National Bank of Arizona (1989). In 1990 the company acquired FirstFed America a holding company for banks in Hawaii and Guam.

Coinciding with the state's economic slump Bancorp Hawaii began fiddling with its subsidiaries in a search for the right mix of businesses. It consolidated units (such as American Trust and Bishop Trust with Hawaiian Trust Company) and branches and dissolved certain operations (Pacific Century Asset Management; founded 1994 closed 1997). It also reactivated some other operations such as its Bankoh Corporation in 1994 dormant since 1984 when it was established as Hawaiian Hong Kong Holdings. The company entered insurance brokerage with Pacific Century Insurance Agency formerly Pan-Ocean Insurance in 1995.

In 1997 Bancorp Hawaii bought CU Bancorp holding company for California United Bank (renamed Pacific Century Bank) giving it access to the manic California banking market. That year the company also changed its name to Pacific Century Financial Corporation to better reflect its geographic diversity.

In 1998 Pacific Century in response to the Asian economic crisis announced that it was cutting jobs and writing off around $17 million in bad loans which resulted in slumping earnings that year. The company remained eager to grow however purchasing two South Seas banks from Paribas and expanding its insurance offerings through the purchase of broker Triad/AIG Insurance Agency. The bank also increased its stake in Australia's Bank of Queensland. But the next year the bank cut more than 1000 jobs.

In 2000 Bank of Hawaii unveiled televised tellers that allowed bank workers to serve two customers at once. In other cost-saving moves Pacific Century sold its credit card portfolio to American Express and sold its stakes in Bank of Tonga Samoa-based Pacific Commercial Bank Banque de Tahiti Bank of Hawaii-Nouvelle Caledonie (New Caledonia) and Australia's Bank of Queensland in 2001.

The company then unloaded its Pacific Century Bank franchise selling its Arizona branches to Zions Bancorporation and its Southern California offices to U.S. Bancorp. It also sold its branches in Fiji Papua New Guinea and Vanuatu to Australia and New Zealand Banking Group. France's La Caisse Nationale des Caisses d'Epargne et de Prevoyance (CNCE) bought Bank of Hawaii Corporation's operations in Tahiti and New Caledonia. The company closed offices in Hong Kong Seoul Singapore and Taipei as well.

After divesting most of its South Pacific business Pacific Century Financial reverted to the Bank of Hawaii moniker in 2002.

EXECUTIVES

Vice Chairman Client Relations Bank of Hawaii, Alton T. Kuioka, age 65, $375,001 total compensation
Vice Chairman and CFO, Kent T. Lucien, age 58, $340,000 total compensation
EVP Board Secretary and Assistant Corporate Secretary, Cynthia G. (Cindy) Wyrick
Vice Chairman and Client and Community Relations Bank of Hawaii, Donna A. Tanoue, age 57, $315,000 total compensation
SEVP and Treasurer Bank of Hawaii, Dean Y. Shigemura
Chairman President and CEO, Peter S. Ho, age 47, $625,000 total compensation
SEVP and CIO, Derek A. Baughman
EVP Corporate Communications and Government Relations, Stafford Kiguchi
Vice Chairman and Chief Risk Officer, Mary E. Sellers, age 55, $310,000 total compensation
SEVP Consumer Deposits Bank of Hawaii, Peter M. Biggs
SEVP Institutional Client Services Bank of Hawaii, Tobias M. (Toby) Martyn
Vice Chairman and Chief Fiduciary Officer, Shelley B. Thompson
SEVP and Manager of Operations Group Administration Bank of Hawaii, Sharon M. Crofts
SEVP and Chief Lending Officer Bank of Hawaii, James C. (Jim) Polk
Vice Chairman Chief Administrative Officer General Counsel and Corporate Secretary, Mark A. Rossi, age 63, $360,000 total compensation
Vice Chairman and Chief Commercial Officer, Wayne Y. Hamano
SEVP Mortgage Banking Bank of Hawaii, Lee Y. Moriwaki
SEVP Controller and Principal Accounting Officer, Derek J. Norris, age 62
SEVP Asset Management Group, Vincent E. Barfield
SEVP Retail Delivery Channels Bank of Hawaii, Thomas J. (Tom) Koide
SEVP and Division Manager Consumer Lending Administration Bank of Hawaii, Jill F. S. Higa
Director, Martin A. Stein, age 71
Vice Chairman and CFO, Kent T. Lucien, age 58
Director, David A. Heenan, age 71
Director, Robert A. (Bob) Huret, age 66
Director, Michael J. Chun, age 68
Director, Mary G. F. Bitterman, age 67
Director, Donald M. Takaki, age 70
Director, Clinton R. Churchill, age 68
Director, Robert W. Wo Jr., age 59
Director, S. Haunani Apoliona, age 62
Director, Barbara J. Tanabe, age 62
Vice Chairman and Chief Risk Officer, Mary E. Sellers, age 55
Vice Chairman Chief Administrative Officer General Counsel and Corporate Secretary, Mark A. Rossi, age 63
Director, Mark A. Burak, age 63
Auditors: Ernst&YoungLLP

LOCATIONS

HQ: Bank of Hawaii Corporation
130 Merchant St., Honolulu HI 96813
Phone: 888-643-3888 **Fax:** 662-678-7299
Web: www.bancorpsouth.com

PRODUCTS/OPERATIONS

2011 Sales

	$ mil	% of total
Interest		
Loans & leases including fees	262	41
Investment securities	175	28
Other	1	-
Noninterest		
Fees exchange & other service charges	60	10
Trust & asset management	45	7
Service charges on deposit accounts	38	6
Mortgage banking	14	2
Insurance	11	2
Investment securities gains net	6	1
Other	21	3
Total	**637**	**100**

Selected Subsidiaries

Bank of Hawaii
- Bank of Hawaii Leasing Inc.
  - BNE Airfleets Corporation (Barbados)
  - Pacific Century Leasing International Inc.
- Bank of Hawaii Insurance Services Inc.
- Bank of Hawaii International Inc.
- Bankoh Investment Partners LLC
- Bankoh Investment Services Inc.
- BOH Wholesale Insurance Agency Inc.
- Pacific Century Advisory Services Inc.
- Pacific Century Insurance Services Inc.
- Pacific Century Life Insurance Corporation

COMPETITORS

American Savings Bank
Australia and New Zealand Banking
Bank of America
Central Pacific Financial
First Hawaiian Bank
HSBC
Territorial Bancorp
Westpac Banking

HISTORICAL FINANCIALS

Company Type: Public

Income Statement FYE: December 31

	ASSETS ($ mil.)	NET INCOME ($ mil.)	INCOME AS % OF ASSETS	EMPLOYEES
12/11	13,846	160	1.2%	2,400
12/10	13,126	183	1.4%	2,400
12/09	12,414	144	1.2%	2,400
12/08	10,763	192	1.8%	2,600
12/07	10,472	183	1.8%	2,600
Annual Growth	7.2%	(3.4%)	—	(2.0%)

2011 Year-End Financials

Debt ratio: 0.22%
Return on equity: 15.96%
Cash ($ mil.): 157
Current ratio: —
Long-term debt ($ mil.): 30
No. of shares (mil.): 45
Dividends
Yield: —
Payout: 53.10%
Market value ($ mil.): 2,044

	STOCK PRICE ($) FY Close	P/E High/Low		PER SHARE ($) Earnings	Dividends	Book Value
12/11	44.49	14	10	3.39	0.00	21.82
12/10	47.21	14	11	3.80	1.80	21.02
12/09	47.06	16	9	3.00	1.80	18.66
12/08	45.17	17	9	3.99	1.77	16.56
12/07	51.14	15	12	3.69	1.67	15.44
Annual Growth	(3.4%)	—	—	(2.1%)	—	9.0%

Bank of New York Mellon Corp

Big Apple meet Iron City. The Bank of New York Mellon (BNY Mellon) is the result of the 2007 marriage of Bank of New York and Mellon Financial. It is one of the largest securities servicing companies in the world as well as a leader in asset management and corporate trust and treasury services. BNY Mellon has approximately $26 trillion in assets under custody and administration and more than $1 trillion of assets under management. Its Pershing unit is a leading securities clearing firm. Subsidiaries BNY Mellon Asset Management and Mellon Capital Management serve institutional investors while the company's wealth management business courts high-net-worth individuals and families endowments and foundations.

HISTORY

In 1784 Alexander Hamilton (at 27 already a Revolutionary War hero and economic theorist) and a group of New York merchants and lawyers founded New York City's first bank The Bank of New York (BNY). Hamilton saw a need for a credit system to finance the nation's growth and to establish credibility for the new nation's chaotic monetary system.

Hamilton became US secretary of the treasury in 1789 and soon negotiated the new US government's first loan –for $200000 –from BNY. The bank later helped finance the War of 1812 by raising $16 million and the Civil War by loaning the government $150 million. In 1878 BNY became a US Treasury depository for the sale of government bonds.

The bank's conservative fiscal policies and emphasis on commercial banking enabled it to weather economic turbulence in the 19th century. In 1922 it merged with New York Life Insurance and Trust (formed in 1830 by many of BNY's directors) to form Bank of New York and Trust. The bank survived the crash of 1929 and remained profitable paying dividends throughout the Depression. In 1938 it reclaimed its Bank of New York name.

During the mid-20th century BNY expanded its operations and its reach through acquisitions including Fifth Avenue Bank (trust services 1948) and Empire Trust (serving developing industries 1966). In 1968 the bank created holding company The Bank of New York Company to expand statewide with purchases such as Empire National Bank (1980).

BNY relaxed its lending policies in the 1980s and began to build its fee-for-service side boosting its American Depositary Receipts business by directly soliciting European companies and seeking government securities business. The bank bought New York rival Irving Trust in a 1989 hostile takeover and in 1990 began buying other banks' credit card portfolios.

As the economy cooled in the early 1990s BNY's book of highly leveraged transactions and nonperforming loans suffered so the company sold many of those loans.

In the mid-1990s BNY bought processing and trust businesses and continued to build its retail business in the suburbs. It pared noncore operations selling its mortgage banking unit (and in 1998 moved its remaining mortgage operations into a joint venture with Alliance Mortgage); credit card business (1998); and factoring and asset-based lending operations (1999). In late 1997 and again in 1998 the bank tried to woo Mellon Bank (now Mellon Financial) into a merger but was rejected; it had better luck in 2006.

The growth of the firm's custody services accelerated in the late 1990s. In 1997 BNY bought operations from Wells Fargo Signet Bank (later part of First Union) and NationsBank (now Bank of America). By 1998 BNY had bought some two dozen corporate trust businesses. Two years later it acquired the trust operations of Royal Bank of Scotland and Barclays Bank.

During this period BNY also built its other operations largely through purchases. It bought the Bank of Montreal's UK-based fiscal agency business (1998) and Eastbrook Capital Management which manages assets for businesses and wealthy individuals (1999).

Scandal rocked the firm in 1999 when the US began investigating the possible flow of money related to Russian organized crime; the following year a former bank executive admitted to having laundered about $7 billion through BNY. The bank reached a non-prosecution agreement in the US in 2005 and four years later agreed to a $14 million settlement with Russia.

In 2000 BNY bought the corporate trust business of Dai-Ichi Kangyo Bank (now part of Mizuho Financial) and Harris Trust and Savings Bank. It also purchased a trio of securities clearing and processing firms in addition to hedge fund manager Ivy Asset Management. The next year BNY bought the corporate trust operations of U.S. Trust.

Purchases in 2002 included equity research firm Jaywalk institutional trader Francis P. Maglio & Co. and a pair of Boston-area asset managers for high-net-worth individuals Gannet Welsh & Kotler and Beacon Fiduciary Advisors. BNY bought Pershing from Credit Suisse First Boston in 2003.

Fallout from the money laundering scandal lingered. In 2006 the Federal Reserve accused the bank of not tightening its own controls to prevent a recurrence of illegal activity. But there were apparently no hard feelings between BNY and the federal government who tapped the company in 2008 to act as custodian for the US Treasury's $700 million Troubled Asset Relief Program (TARP) meant to provide liquidity to banks.

The Bank of New York jettisoned much of its traditional banking services for more lucrative fee-based securities and financial services swapping virtually all its retail branches in metropolitan New York for JPMorgan Chase's corporate trust business in 2006. Both units were valued at more than $2 billion each and JPMorgan Chase paid an additional $150 million in cash to make up the difference.

In 2007 Bank of New York merged with Mellon Financial to create BNY Mellon). It was the New York company's third attempt to acquire the Pittsburgh-based firm. The deal cemented the company's status as one of the largest securities servicing companies in the world and augmented its other other areas of focus including asset management and corporate trust and treasury services.

The company followed that transaction with the sale of Mellon 1st Business Bank to U.S. Bancorp in 2008.

In 2009 the company acquired Insight Investment Management which specializes in liability-driven investment services fixed income products and alternative investments from Lloyds Bank for some $387 million. Also that year BNY Mellon bought analytics firm Portsmouth Financial Systems. The acquisition offered customers more transparency in structured credit portfolios.

EXECUTIVES

Chairman President and CEO, Gerald L. Hassell, age 60, $800,000 total compensation
Comptroller; EVP The Bank of New York, Thomas J. Mastro, age 60
CFO, Thomas P. (Todd) Gibbons, age 55, $650,000 total compensation
Head Global Operations and Technology and Chief Administrative Officer, Kurt D. Woetzel, age 56
EVP and COO, Edward G. (Ed) Watson, age 50
Chief of Staff, Richard F. (Rich) Brueckner, age 62
SEVP and Chief Human Resources Officer, Lisa B. Peters, age 54
EVP and Chief Corporate Affairs Officer Corporate Affairs, R. Jeep Bryant
CEO Global Client Management and Liquidity Services, James P. (Jim) Palermo, age 56
Chief Risk Officer, Brian G. Rogan, age 54, $510,000 total compensation
Global Business Head Derivatives360(SM), Patrick Tadie
SEVP; CEO Global Markets, Arthur (Art) Certosimo, age 56
CEO BNY Mellon Asset Servicing, Timothy F. (Tim) Keaney, age 50
CEO Financial Markets and Treasury Services, Karen B. Peetz, age 56
EVP Broker-Dealer Services & Alternative Investment Services, Andrew M. Gordon
CEO Asia-Pacific, Alan J. Harden, age 54
EVP and Treasurer, Scott Freidenrich
CEO BNY Mellon Wealth Management, Lawrence (Larry) Hughes
President Investment Management, Mitchell E. Harris
CEO BNY Mellon Corporate Trust, Eric D. Kamback
CEO Alternative Investment Services, Brian A. Ruane
Global Head Securities Lending, James E.R. Slater
SEVP and General Counsel, Jane C. Sherburne, age 61
CEO Investment Management, Curtis Arledge, age 47
CEO The Dreyfus Corporation, Jon Baum
EVP International Wealth Management and Client Segments; President BNY Mellon of Pennsylvania, Donald J. (Don) Heberle
Head Cash Investment Strategies, Jeffrey D. (Jeff) Landau
SVP Global Client Management Group, Christopher R. (Chris) Sturdy
EVP and Head National Banking BNY Mellon Wealth Management, Bill E. Sappington
Managing Director and Head Investor Services Asia-Pacific The Bank of New York, Chong Jin Leow

EVP and Deputy General Counsel Global Litigation and Regulatory Enforcement, J. Kevin McCarthy, age 47
Chief Auditor; EVP and Chief Auditor The Bank of New York, James (Jim) Vallone
Chief Investment Officer BNY Mellon Wealth Management, Leo P. Grohowski
Head Treasury Services Japan, Robert L. Whittemore
EVP and Head Global Sales and Relationship Management Treasury Services, David Cruikshank
President Eagle Investment Systems BNY Mellon Asset Servicing, John Lehner
CEO and CIO Franklin Portfolio Associates, Oliver Buckley
President and COO Franklin Portfolio Associates, Paul F. Healey
President BNY Mellon Capital Markets, Gary Strumeyer
Managing Director and President Bank of New York Securities Company Japan, Makoto Saji
Chairman Asia-Pacific, Stephen Lackey
EVP and Head Enterprise-Wide Market Risk, Robert R. Rupp, age 58
Head Treasury Services Asia, Richard Brown
Chairman Latin America; Head Global Client Management Latin America, Rene Boettcher
President Mexico; General Manager Corporate Trust Mexico, Juan Carlos Morales
EVP and Controller, John A. Park, age 59
CEO BNY Mellon Shareowner Services, Samir Pandiri, age 49
Corporate Secretary, Arlie R. Nogay
Vice Chairman Europe and Chief Administrative Officer EMEA Region BNY Mellon - Europe, William A. (Woody) Kerr
Senior Director Asset Services, Michael Onders
Head Client Management United States and Europe, Frank Froud
EVP European Client Management; Chairman Middle East and Africa, Hani Kablawi
CEO Broker-Dealer Services, James Malgieri
CTO Eagle Investment Systems, Marc Firenze
Managing Director and Head Asset Allocation Research Mellon Capital Management, Anjun Zhou
Managing Director and Head Multi-Strategy Mellon Capital, Jeff Zhang
Global Product Manager Depository Receipts, Christopher Kearns
Head Depositary Receipts Asia Pacific, Greg Roath
CEO Depositary Receipts, Michael Cole-Fontayn
VP and Senior Relationship Manager India, Nisha Pereira
Head Treasury Services India, Aneish Kumar
Corporate Communications, Ronald R. (Ron) Gruendl
President and CEO Japanese Trust Bank, Dominick Falco
Head International Corporate Trust, James Maitland
CEO I(3) Advisors, June Ntazinda
Head Relationship Management and Sales Treasury Services Middle East and Africa, Mark Fenner
Head Global Sales and Relationship Management, Alan Verschoyle-King
Managing Director and Head Treasury Services Latin America, Dino Sani Jr.
Country Executive Japan; General Manager Tokyo, Thom Fisher
Head Global Operations Japan; Deputy General Manager Tokyo, Malcolm Podmore
Head Global Product Management Alternative Investment Services, Alan Flanagan
Regional President Ohio BNY Mellon Wealth Management, Ronald S. Ambrogio
President US Markets East BNY Mellon Wealth Management, Timothy Tully Jr.
Business Manager Derivatives360 Europe Middle East and Africa (EMEA) and Asia-Pacific Regions, Jonathan Bowler
Business Manager Derivatives360 North and Latin America Regions, Chris Coleman
Chief Administrative Officer Derivatives360, Laure Scala
COO Asia-Pacific, Daniel J. Smith
General Manager Mexico, Jorge Garay
COO Securities Lending, David DiNardo
Managing Director Lending U.S. and Corporate Securities Securities Lending, Robert Chiuch
Head Global Product Management and Strategic Development Treasury Services, Susan Skerritt
Chief Administrative Officer Financial Markets and Treasury Services, Jean Wynn
CIO, Suresh Kumar
Director, Nicholas M. (Nick) Donofrio, age 66
Director, Wesley W. von Schack, age 66
Director, Richard J. Kogan, age 70
Director, Michael J. Kowalski, age 59
Director, John A. Luke Jr., age 63
Director, Edmund F. (Ted) Kelly, age 66
Director, Catherine A. Rein, age 69
Director, Mark A. Nordenberg, age 63
Director, William C. (Bill) Richardson, age 71
Director, Samuel C. (Sam) Scott III, age 68
Vice Chairman and CFO, Thomas P. (Todd) Gibbons, age 55
Director, Ruth E. Bruch, age 59
Director, John P. Surma Jr., age 57
Vice Chairman; CEO Global Client Management and Liquidity Services, James P. (Jim) Palermo, age 56
Vice Chairman and Chief Risk Officer, Brian G. Rogan, age 54
Vice Chairman; CEO BNY Mellon Asset Servicing, Timothy F. (Tim) Keaney, age 50
Vice Chairman; CEO Financial Markets and Treasury Services, Karen B. Peetz, age 56
Vice Chairman; CEO Investment Management, Curtis Arledge, age 47
Auditors: KPMGLLP

LOCATIONS

HQ: Bank of New York Mellon Corp
One Wall Street, New York, NY 10286
Phone: 212 495-1784
Web: www.bnymellon.com

PRODUCTS/OPERATIONS

2011 Sales

	$ mil.	% of total
Investment servicing fees		
Asset servicing	3,697	24
Issuer services	1,445	9
Clearing services	1,159	8
Treasury services	535	4
Interest	3,588	23
Asset & wealth management fees	3,002	20
Foreign exchange & other trading revenue	848	5
Investment income	258	2
Consolidated investment management funds	200	1
Distribution & servicing	187	1
Financing-related fees	170	1
Other	245	2
Total	**15,334**	**100**

Selected Subsidiaries and Business Lines

Alcentra Investment Limited (sub-investment-grade debt asset management Bermuda)
Ankura Capital (Australian equities)
BNY Mellon Asset Management International Holdings Limited (institutional asset management UK)
The Boston Company Asset Management LLC (equity asset management)
The Dreyfus Corporation (mutual funds)
EACM Advisors LLC (fund of funds)
Ivy Asset Management (fund of hedge funds management)
Mellon Capital Management Corporation
Newton Investment Management Limited (active investment management UK)
Pershing Group LLC (securities clearing)
Urdang (global real estate investment management)
Walter Scott & Partners Limited (global equity investment management Scotland)
WestLB Mellon Asset Management KAG (European and global fixed income UK 50%)

COMPETITORS

Bank of America
Barclays
BlackRock
Citigroup
Credit Suisse (USA)
Deutsche Bank
HSBC
JPMorgan Chase
Northern Trust
PNC Financial
State Street
UBS

HISTORICAL FINANCIALS

Company Type: Public

Income Statement

FYE: December 31

	ASSETS ($ mil.)	NET INCOME ($ mil.)	INCOME AS % OF ASSETS	EMPLOYEES
12/11	325,266	2,569	0.8%	48,700
12/10	247,259	2,581	1.0%	48,000
12/09	212,224	(1,083)	—	42,200
12/08	237,512	1,419	0.6%	42,900
12/07	197,656	2,039	1.0%	42,100
Annual Growth	13.3%	5.9%	—	3.7%

2011 Year-End Financials

Debt ratio: 6.13%
Return on equity: 7.69%
Cash ($ mil.): 130,739
Current ratio: —
Long-term debt ($ mil.): 19,933
No. of shares (mil.): 1,209
Dividends
Yield: —
Payout: 23.65%
Market value ($ mil.): 24,085

	STOCK PRICE ($) FY Close	P/E High	P/E Low	PER SHARE ($) Earnings	Dividends	Book Value
12/11	19.91	16	9	2.03	0.00	27.62
12/10	30.20	16	12	2.05	0.36	26.06
12/09	27.97	—	—	(1.16)	0.51	23.99
12/08	28.33	41	19	1.20	0.96	24.42
12/07	48.76	23	18	2.18	0.48	25.66
Annual Growth	(20.1%)	—	—	(1.8%)	—	1.9%

Bank of the Ozarks, Inc.

Bank of the Ozarks is the holding company for the bank of the same name which has more than 110 branches in Arkansas Texas Georgia Florida the Carolinas and Alabama. Focusing on individuals and small to midsized businesses the bank offers traditional deposit and loan services in addition to personal and commercial trust services retirement and financial planning and investment management. Commercial real estate and construction and land development loans make up the largest portion of Bank of the Ozarks' loan portfolio followed by residential mortgage business and agricultural loans.

The expansion strategy of Bank of the Ozarks - which had only five branches less than twenty years ago –centered on opening new locations in smaller communities in Arkansas. But after tasting success in larger markets like Little Rock and Fort Smith the company began targeting Bentonville Arkansas (home of Wal-Mart's headquarters) and the Dallas metropolitan area for further growth. More recently it has agreed to buy Genala Banc in Alabama. The deal valued at nearly $14 million is expected to close in late 2012 or early 2013.

The company then expanded further with a series of FDIC-assisted transactions to take over failed banks; In 2010 Bank of the Ozarks entered Georgia South Carolina Alabama and Florida by purchasing Unity National Horizon Bank Woodlands Bank and Chestatee State Bank. The deals which included loss-sharing agreements with the regulator added than 20 locations. In 2011 Bank of the Ozarks acquired three more failed Georgia institutions Oglethorpe Bank Park Avenue Bank and First Choice Community Bank adding nearly 20 more branches in the state and one in Florida. The bank hasn't forgot about its earlier ambitions either as it continues to open new branches in Arkansas and Texas including Austin.

Gains on the FDIC-assisted acquisitions along with improved interest rate spreads boosted Bank of the Ozarks' results in 2010 and contributed to record earnings in 2011.

Chairman and CEO George Gleason owns nearly 15% of Bank of the Ozarks. He initially bought the bank more than three decades ago at age 25.

EXECUTIVES

EVP Human Resources, Diane Hilburn
President Central Division and Co-Chairman of the Loan Committee Bank of the Ozarks, Darrel Russell, age 58, $175,980 total compensation
President Western Arkansas Division, Susan Grobmyer
Vice Chairman President and COO Bank of the Ozarks Inc. and Bank of the Ozarks, Mark Ross, age 56, $277,311 total compensation
Chairman and CEO Bank of the Ozarks Inc. and Bank of the Ozarks, George G. Gleason, age 58, $819,837 total compensation
President Western Division Bank of the Ozarks, C.E. Dougan, age 65, $148,192 total compensation
President Leasing Division Bank of the Ozarks, Scott Hastings, age 54, $181,925 total compensation
President Mortgage Division Bank of the Ozarks, Gene Holman, age 64, $150,042 total compensation
President Trust and Wealth Management Division Bank of the Ozarks, Rex Kyle, age 55, $125,297 total compensation
President Eastern Division Bank of the Ozarks, Fred Campbell
President Southwest and Coastal Divisions, Rick Wisdom
CIO, Ron Kuykendall
President Real Estate Specialties Group Bank of the Ozarks, Dan Thomas
President Conway Division Bank of the Ozarks, Sarah Shaw
President Metro Dallas Division Bank of the Ozarks, Dennis James
President Hot Springs Arkansas Northwest Georgia and Florida Division, John Davis
CFO and Chief Accounting Officer Bank of the Ozarks Inc. and Bank of the Ozarks, Greg McKinney, age 44, $248,077 total compensation
Chief Banking Officer, Tyler Vance, age 37
President Northwest Division Bank of the Ozarks, Harvey Williams
President Northern Division Bank of the Ozarks, Joe Willis
President Cabot Bank of the Ozarks, Audwin Vaughn
President Greater Little Rock, Matt Reddin
President Johnson County. Bank of the Ozarks, Gary Miller
President River Valley Arkansas Division, Larry Dicks
President Baxter and Marion County, Steven Dunn
President Saline County, Alan Jessup
President Boone County, Jack Mays
Director, R. L. Qualls, age 78
Vice Chairman President and COO Bank of the Ozarks Inc. and Bank of the Ozarks, Mark Ross, age 56
Director, Jean Arehart, age 71
Director, Robert East, age 64
Director, Linda Gleason, age 57
Director, Henry Mariani, age 73
Director, Kennith Smith, age 80
Director, Richard Cisne, age 61
Director, James Matthews, age 50
Auditors: CroweHorwathLLP

LOCATIONS

HQ: Bank of the Ozarks, Inc.
17901 Chenal Parkway, Little Rock, AR 72223
Phone: 501 978-2265 **Fax:** 501 978-2224
Web: www.bankozarks.com

PRODUCTS/OPERATIONS

2011 Sales

	$ mil.	% of total
Interest		
Loans & leases	113	36
Covered loans	66	21
Tax-exempt investment securities	16	5
Other	3	1
Noninterest		
Gains on FDIC-assisted transactions	65	21
Service charges on deposit accounts	18	6
Net accretion of FDIC loss share receivable	10	3
Other loss share income net	6	2
Other	16	5
Total	**316**	**100**

COMPETITORS

Arvest Bank
BancorpSouth
Bank of America
BOK Financial
First Federal Bancshares of Arkansas
Home BancShares
IBERIABANK
Regions Financial
Simmons First
Wells Fargo

HISTORICAL FINANCIALS

Company Type: Public

Income Statement FYE: December 31

	ASSETS ($ mil.)	NET INCOME ($ mil.)	INCOME AS % OF ASSETS	EMPLOYEES
12/11	3,839	101	2.6%	1,084
12/10	3,273	63	2.0%	881
12/09	2,770	43	1.6%	707
12/08	3,233	34	1.1%	705
12/07	2,710	31	1.2%	689
Annual Growth	9.1%	33.7%	—	12.0%

2011 Year-End Financials

Debt ratio: 9.55%
Return on equity: 23.86%
Cash ($ mil.): 58
Current ratio: —
Long-term debt ($ mil.): 366
No. of shares (mil.): 34
Dividends
Yield: —
Payout: 12.59%
Market value ($ mil.): 1,021

	STOCK PRICE ($) FY Close	P/E High	P/E Low	PER SHARE ($) Earnings	Dividends	Book Value
12/11	29.63	18	7	2.94	0.00	12.32
12/10	43.35	24	15	1.88	0.30	9.39
12/09	29.27	27	16	1.09	0.26	7.96
12/08	29.64	32	14	1.02	0.25	9.61
12/07	26.20	35	28	0.95	0.22	5.67
Annual Growth	3.1%	—	—	32.6%	—	21.4%

Banner Corp.

Flagging bank accounts? See Banner Corporation. Banner is the holding company for Banner Bank which serves the Pacific Northwest through about 90 branches and loan production offices in Washington Oregon and Idaho. The company also owns Islanders Bank which operates three branches in Washington's San Juan Islands. The banks offer standard products such as deposit accounts credit cards and business and consumer loans. Commercial loans including business agriculture construction and multifamily mortgage loans account for about 90% of the company's portfolio. Bank subsidiary Community Financial writes residential mortgage and construction loans.

Islanders Bank was acquired in 2007 the same year Banner acquired F&M Bank and NCW Community Bank of Wenatchee both also based in Washington. After the spate of acquisitions the company focused on opening branches in 2008 and 2009 when it added six new locations. In all Banner has added more than two dozen branches since 2005. The company continues to look for acquisition opportunities with an eye on banks shut down by regulators.

After the economy fell into crisis in 2008 Banner saw a jump in loan delinquencies as well as the commensurate increase in provisions for expected loan losses which cut into the company's bottom line. The troubled real estate market also impacted the bank as property values sunk and new construction slowed down. Banner reported losses for each year from 2008 to 2010 and in the latter year entered into a memorandum of understanding with regulators to improve its asset quality profitability and capital position and to reduce its exposure to commercial real estate.

EXECUTIVES

EVP and CFO Banner Corporation and Banner Bank, Lloyd W. Baker, age 63, $220,000 total compensation
Vice Chairman Banner Corporation and Banner Bank, Jesse G. Foster, age 73, $195,000 total compensation
President Mortgage Banner Bank, Michael K. Larsen, age 69, $248,667 total compensation
VP and Director Human Resources Banner Bank, Debi Sapp
Chairman Banner Corporation and Banner Bank, Gary L. Sirmon, age 68, $275,000 total compensation

EVP Retail Banking and Administration, Cynthia D. Purcell, age 54, $257,650 total compensation
EVP Corporate Lending Banner Corporation and Banner Bank, John R. Neill, age 63
EVP Commercial Banking, Paul E. Folz, age 57, $257,500 total compensation
EVP and Chief Lending Officer Banner Bank, Richard B. Barton, age 68, $236,250 total compensation
President CEO and Director Banner Corporation and Banner Bank, Mark J. Grescovich, age 47
EVP and Real Estate Lending Manager Banner Bank, Douglas M. Bennett, age 59
Corporate Secretary, Albert H. Marshall
EVP Risk Management and Compliance Officer Banner Bank, Tyrone J. Bliss, age 54
EVP and Chief Information Officer, Steven W. (Steve) Rust, age 64
EVP Retail Products and Services, Gary W. Wagers, age 51
EVP, John T. Wagner
Senior Credit Officer Banner Bank, Jill Rice
Sales Manager of Engineering, Chris Dales
Business Development Manager, Mark Lampert
Director of Marketing, Bob Durkee
Business Development Manager, Darvin Kaelberer
Director, Robert J. Lane, age 66
Vice Chairman Banner Corporation and Banner Bank, Jesse G. Foster, age 73
Director, D. Michael Jones, age 70
Director, Wilbur E. Pribilsky, age 78
Director, Robert D. Adams, age 70
Director, Dean W. Mitchell, age 77
Director, Brent A. Orrico, age 62
Director, David B. Casper, age 75
Director, Gordon E. Budke, age 70
President CEO and Director Banner Corporation and Banner Bank, Mark J. Grescovich, age 47
Director, Edward L. Epstein, age 75
Director, Michael M. Smith, age 57
Director, Constance H. (Connie) Kravas, age 65
Director, David A. Klaue, age 69
Director, John R. Layman, age 53
Auditors: MossAdamsLLP

LOCATIONS

HQ: Banner Corporation
10 S. 1st Ave., Walla Walla WA 99362
Phone: 509-527-3636 **Fax:** 509-526-8898
Web: www.banrbank.com

PRODUCTS/OPERATIONS

2010 Sales

	$ mil.	% of total
Interest		
Loans receivable	205	83
Securities & cash equivalents	8	3
Mortgage-backed securities	4	2
Noninterest		
Deposit fees & other service charges	22	9
Mortgage banking	6	3
Other	0	-
Total	**247**	**100**

COMPETITORS

BancWest
Bank of America
Columbia Banking
Glacier Bancorp
KeyCorp
Sound Financial
Sterling Financial (WA)
U.S. Bancorp
Washington Federal
Wells Fargo

HISTORICAL FINANCIALS

Company Type: Public

Income Statement FYE: December 31

	ASSETS ($ mil.)	NET INCOME ($ mil.)	INCOME AS % OF ASSETS	EMPLOYEES
12/11	4,257	5	0.1%	1,111
12/10	4,406	(61)	—	1,092
12/09	4,722	(35)	—	1,098
12/08	4,584	(127)	—	1,140
12/07	4,492	36	0.8%	1,178
Annual Growth	(1.3%)	(38.0%)	—	(1.5%)

2011 Year-End Financials

Debt ratio: 5.00%
Return on equity: 1.03%
Cash ($ mil.): 132
Current ratio: —
Long-term debt ($ mil.): 212
No. of shares (mil.): 17
Dividends
Yield: —
Payout: —
Market value ($ mil.): 300

	STOCK PRICE ($) FY Close	P/E High/Low		PER SHARE ($) Earnings	Dividends	Book Value
12/11	17.15	—	—	(0.15)	0.00	30.39
12/10	2.32	—	—	(7.21)	0.00	31.71
12/09	2.68	—	—	(16.31)	0.00	133.15
12/08	9.41	—	—	(55.58)	0.00	179.37
12/07	28.73	3	2	17.43	0.00	191.25
Annual Growth	(12.1%)	—	—	—	—	(36.9%)

Barnes & Noble Inc

Barnes & Noble does business –big business – by the book and the NOOK. As the #1 bookstore chain in the US it operates about 1335 bookstores including some 690 Barnes & Noble superstores and another 665 college bookstores in all 50 states and Washington DC. Stores range in size from 3000 sq. ft. to 60000 sq. ft. and stock between 60000 and 200000 book titles. It also sells books and other media online. The company's newly digital subsidiary NOOK Media develops supports and creates digital content and products for the digital reading and digital education markets. Stalwart Barnes & Noble is attempting to make the case for traditional bookstores while growing its digital business.

Barnes & Noble put itself up for sale in mid-2010 but has yet to find a buyer. An approach by media conglomerate Liberty Media in 2011 resulted in an investment of $204 million rather than a sale. As a result Liberty Media owns roughly 16% of Barnes & Noble and received two seats on the bookseller's board. Barnes & Noble is using the proceeds to further expand its NOOK e-reader and digital book businesses. The lengthy and as yet unsuccessful search for a buyer by the #1 US bookstore chain reflects the uncertain outlook for bookstores.

Operations

Seismic changes in the book industry have led Barnes & Noble to reconfigure its business from a store-based model to a multi-channel strategy centered on its retail stores the Internet and digital commerce. While the traditional retail operation soldiers on (although with a dwindling number of bookstores) the bookseller has been rapidly expanding its digital business since the launch of its NOOK e-reader in 2009. The nascent NOOK segment is rapidly approaching $1 billion in sales and accounted for 12% of its parent company's total sales in fiscal 2012 (ends April). In a vote of confidence in Barnes & Noble's digital strategy Microsoft invested $300 million in its NOOK business in return of a 17% share in a newly-formed subsidiary: Nook Media LLC. The new unit includes Barnes & Noble's digital reading and digital education businesses and will launch a new application called "NOOK reading" for Windows 8. B&N reunited with its sister company Barnes & Noble College Booksellers making it a wholly-owned subsidiary. (The two companies had operated independently since Barnes & Noble went public in 1993.) B&N College which accounts for nearly a quarter of Barnes & Noble's total sales operates more than 645 bookstores at colleges and universities across the US that sell and rent new and used textbooks including e-textbooks and course-related materials. B&N College has expanded its electronic textbooks and other course materials through its proprietary digital platform NOOK Study. Other operations include Sterling Publishing the company's general trade book publishing arm and the e-commerce site.

Financial Analysis

Barnes & Noble's sales topped $7 billion in fiscal 2012 (ends April) a nearly 2% increase vs. the prior year. Same-store sales at Barnes & Noble stores increased 1.4% vs. the prior year (buoyed by reduced competition following the liquidation of rival Borders) while the College division posted a negative annual sales comparison. The company blamed the decrease in the College division's sales on increased textbook rentals which cost less than new or used textbooks.) NOOK sales increased 34% on higher sales of digital content and hardware. But while NOOK is the company's sales growth engine it's a big drain on profits due to the heavy investment required to develop new digital products to compete with Apple and Amazon. Indeed the company lost nearly $69 million in 2012 marking the fifth consecutive year of declining or negative net income.

Strategy

Barnes & Noble's strategy is to continue to invest heavily in the digital business to fuel NOOK and content sales while leveraging the Barnes & Noble brand to drive traffic to its stores and attract customers to its multi-platform offering. Indeed the bookstores house NOOK boutiques where shoppers can try out the company's growing line of NOOK e-readers and tablets and become familiar with the digital offering. Increasingly the company is delivering content to customers wirelessly and online. Barnes & Noble is also partnering with hardware and software companies and other retailers. The NOOK is sold at the company's own stores and at Best Buy and now at Wal-Mart Stores.

Ownership

Company founder and chairman Leonard Riggio owns about 30% of Barnes & Noble's shares. Liberty Media owns 16.7 % followed by JANA Partners with 10%.

HISTORY

Barnes & Noble dates back to 1873 when Charles Barnes went into the used-book business in Wheaton Illinois. By the turn of the century he was operating a thriving bookselling operation in Chicago. His son William took over as president in 1902. William sold his share in the firm in 1917 (to C. W. Follett who built Follett Corp.) and moved to New York City where he bought an interest in established textbook wholesalers Noble & Noble.

The company was soon renamed Barnes & Noble. It first sold mainly to colleges and libraries providing textbooks and opening a large Fifth Avenue shop. Over the next three decades Barnes & Noble became one of the leading booksellers in the New York region.

Enter Leonard Riggio who worked at a New York University bookstore to help pay for night school. He studied engineering but got the itch for bookselling. In 1965 at age 24 he borrowed $5000 and opened Student Book Exchange NYC a college bookstore. Beginning in the late 1960s he expanded by buying other college bookstores.

In 1971 Riggio paid $1.2 million for the Barnes & Noble store on Fifth Avenue. He soon expanded the store and in 1974 he began offering jaw-dropping competitor-maddening discounts of up to 40% for best-sellers. Acquiring Marlboro Books five years later the company entered the mail-order and publishing business.

By 1986 Barnes & Noble had grown to about 180 outlets (including 142 college bookstores). Along with Dutch retailer Vendex that year it bought Dayton Hudson's B. Dalton mall bookstore chain (about 800 stores) forming BDB Holding Corp. (Vendex had sold its shares by 1997.) In 1989 the company acquired the Scribner's Bookstores trade name and the Bookstop/Bookstar superstore chain. BDB began its shift to superstore format and streamlined its operations to integrate Bookstop and Doubleday (acquired in 1990) into its business.

BDB changed its name to Barnes & Noble in 1991. With superstore sales booming the retailer went public in 1993 (the college stores remained private). It bought 20% of Canadian bookseller Chapters (now Indigo Books) in 1996 (sold in 1999).

The bookseller went online in 1997 and in 1998 sold a 50% stake in its Web operation subsidiary to Bertelsmann (which it re-purchased in 2003) in an attempt to strengthen both companies in the battle against online rival Amazon.com.

Also in 1998 Barnes & Noble agreed to buy #1 US book distributor Ingram Book Group but the deal was called off in 1999 because of antitrust concerns. Also in 1999 barnesandnoble.com went public and Barnes & Noble bought small book publisher J.B. Fairfax International USA which included coffee-table book publisher Michael Friedman Publishing Group. Later that year the company bought a 49% stake in book publishing portal iUniverse.com (later reduced to 22%). It also bought Riggio's financially struggling Babbage's Etc. a chain of about 500 Babbage's Software Etc. and GameStop stores for $215 million.

Subsidiary Babbage's Etc. (renamed GameStop Inc.) acquired video game retailer Funco for $161.5 million in 2000. In 2001 Barnes & Noble joined barnesandnoble.com in acquiring a majority stake in magazine subscription seller enews.com.

The company completed an IPO of its GameStop unit in 2003 reducing its ownership interest to about 63%. Leonard also handed over the CEO title to his brother Steve Riggio. Another development during that busy year included shutting down enews.com due to repeated quarterly losses.

In 2003 the company beefed up its self-publishing efforts with the purchase of Sterling Publishing a specialist in how-to and craft books. In addition Barnes & Noble's half-owned BOOK magazine shut down. The next year saw Barnes & Noble exit the video game retailing business when it spun off its remaining shares in GameStop.

In 2009 the firm sold its majority interest in Calendar Club for $7 million.

CEO Steve Riggio was replaced by William Lynch president of Barnes&Noble.com in 2010. Riggio remained chairman of the company. Barnes & Noble closed the last of its small-format B. Dalton bookstores in early 2010. (B. Dalton which once numbered more than 900 stores had been closing stores since 1989.) Later in the year hedge fund manager William Ackman offered to finance a $960 million merger of Barnes & Noble and its smaller rival Borders but nothing came of it.

EXECUTIVES

SVP Corporate Communications and Public Affairs, Mary Ellen Keating, age 55, $508,462 total compensation
VP Development, David S. Deason, age 53, $490,000 total compensation
CFO, Michael P. Huseby, age 57
VP of Human Resources, Michelle Smith, age 59
CEO Barnes & Noble Retail Group, Mitchell S. (Mitch) Klipper, age 54, $812,308 total compensation
VP Author Relations, Brenda Marsh
Founder and Chairman of the Board, Leonard S. (Len) Riggio, age 71, $300,000 total compensation
Vice Chairman, Stephen (Steve) Riggio, age 57, $800,000 total compensation
President Barnes & Noble.com, John Foley
President Sterling Publishing, Marcus E. Leaver, age 42
VP and Corporate Controller, Allen W. Lindstrom, age 45
Director Corporate Communications, Carolyn J. Brown
Director Investor Relations, Andy Milevoj
VP and Director of Stores, Mark Bottini, age 52
VP Retention and Loyalty Marketing, Marc Parrish
CEO and Director, William J. Lynch Jr., age 42, $812,308 total compensation
VP General Counsel and Corporate Secretary, Eugene V. (Gene) DeFelice, age 51
Chief Merchandising Officer, Jaime Carey, age 51
General Manager Digital Newsstand and Emerging Content, Jonathan Shar
EVP Operations and Customer Service, Dan Gilbert
President Digital Products, Jamie Iannone, age 39
VP and CIO, Christopher (Chris) Troia, age 60
VP Search Marketing, Jeff Day
VP Acquisition Marketing Barnes & Noble.com, Sasha Norkin
VP Digital Content, Theresa Horner
VP Digital Products Hardware Engineering, Bill Saperstein
VP Software Development, Ravi Gopalakrishnan
Chief Architect Software Development, Roger Webster
VP General Counsel and Corporate Secretary, Gene DeFelice
VP Marketing, Patricia Bostelman
VP and CIO, Christopher Grady-Troia, age 60
Director, David G. (Dave) Golden, age 54
Director, William (Bill) Dillard II, age 67
Vice Chairman, Stephen (Steve) Riggio, age 57
Director, Gregory B. (Greg) Maffei, age 50
Director, Irene R. Miller, age 59
Director, Margaret T. Monaco, age 64
Director, George Campbell Jr., age 66
Director, Patricia L. Higgins, age 62
Director, Mark D. Carleton, age 51
CEO and Director, William J. Lynch Jr., age 42
Director, David A. Wilson, age 71
Auditors: BDOSeidmanLLP

LOCATIONS

HQ: Barnes & Noble Inc.
122 5th Ave., New York NY 10011
Phone: 212-633-3300 **Fax:** 212-675-0413
Web: www.barnesandnobleinc.com

2012 US Retail Stores

	No.
Alabama	7
Alaska	2
Arizona	18
Arkansas	5
California	80
Colorado	17
Connecticut	13
Delaware	2
District of	2
Florida	44
Georgia	21
Hawaii	3
Idaho	3
Illinois	30
Indiana	12
Iowa	7
Kansas	4
Kentucky	7
Louisiana	7
Maine	1
Maryland	13
Massachusetts	18
Michigan	21
Minnesota	20
Mississippi	3
Missouri	14
Montana	4
Nebraska	4
Nevada	5
New	4
New	24
New	3
New	46
North	21
North	3
Ohio	19
Oklahoma	5
Oregon	7
Pennsylvania	27
Rhode	3
South	11
South	1
Tennessee	8
Texas	56
Utah	10
Vermont	1
Virginia	25
Washington	18
West	1
Wisconsin	11
Wyoming	1
Total	**691**

PRODUCTS/OPERATIONS

2012 Stores

	No.
B&N	691
B&N	647
Total	**1,338**

2012 Sales

	$ mil.	% of total
B&N Retail	4,852	68
B&N College	1,743	24
NOOK	933	13
Adjustment (400.9) (5)		
Total	**7,129**	**100**

COMPETITORS

Amazon.com
Apple Inc.
Best Buy
Books-A-Million
Buy.com
Costco Wholesale
Half Price Books
Hastings Entertainment
Sony
Target Corporation
Wal-Mart

HISTORICAL FINANCIALS

Company Type: Public

Income Statement FYE: April 28

	REVENUE ($ mil.)	NET INCOME ($ mil.)	NET PROFIT MARGIN	EMPLOYEES
04/12	7,129	(68)	—	30,000
04/11*	6,998	(73)	—	35,000
05/10	5,810	36	0.6%	40,000
05/09	1,105	(2)	—	0
01/09	5,121	75	1.5%	37,000
Annual Growth	8.6%	—	—	(5.1%)

*Fiscal year change

2012 Year-End Financials

Debt ratio: 8.61%
Return on equity: (-9.21)%
Cash ($ mil.): 54
Current ratio: 109.33
Long-term debt ($ mil.): 324
No. of shares (mil.): 57
Dividends
Yield: —
Payout: —
Market value ($ mil.): 789

	STOCK PRICE ($) FY Close	P/E High/Low		PER SHARE ($) Earnings	Dividends	Book Value
04/12	13.68	—	—	(1.41)	0.00	12.97
04/11*	10.99	—	—	(1.31)	0.00	14.37
05/10	22.04	42	26	0.63	0.00	16.19
05/09	25.59	—	—	(0.05)	0.00	16.53
01/09	16.42	25	9	1.32	0.00	16.87
Annual Growth	(4.5%)	—	—	—	—	(6.4%)

*Fiscal year change

BATTELLE MEMORIAL INSTITUTE INC

LOCATIONS

HQ: BATTELLE MEMORIAL INSTITUTE INC
505 KING AVE, COLUMBUS, OH 432012681
Phone: 6144246424
Web: WWW.BATTELLE.ORG

HISTORICAL FINANCIALS

Company Type:

Income Statement FYE: September 30

	REVENUE ($ mil.)	NET INCOME ($ mil.)	NET PROFIT MARGIN	EMPLOYEES
09/11	5,499	27	0.5%	7,457
09/10	5,547	0	0.0%	0
09/09	4,878	31	0.6%	0
09/07	4,180	8	0.2%	0
Annual Growth	9.6%	48.8%	—	—

2011 Year-End Financials

Debt ratio: —
Return on equity: 0.50%
Cash ($ mil.): 55
Current ratio: 1.40
Long-term debt ($ mil.): —
Dividends
Yield: —
Payout: —
Market value ($ mil.): —

Baxter International Inc.

Why choose between making drugs and making medical equipment when you can do both? Baxter International makes a wide variety of medical products and medicines through two divisions. The company is a leading manufacturer of intravenous (IV) fluids and systems via its Medical Products division. The medical segment also makes infusion pumps prefilled syringes and inhaled anesthetics as well as dialyzers and other products for the treatment of end-stage renal disease (ESRD). Baxter's BioScience division makes protein and plasma therapies to treat hemophilia and immune disorders as well as vaccines and biological sealants used to close surgical wounds.

HISTORY

Idaho surgeon Ralph Falk his brother Harry and California physician Donald Baxter formed Don Baxter Intravenous Products in 1931 to distribute the IV solutions Baxter made in Los Angeles. Two years later the company opened its first plant located outside Chicago. Ralph Falk bought Baxter's interest in 1935 and began R&D efforts leading to the first sterilized vacuum-type blood collection device (1939) which could store blood for weeks instead of hours. Product demand during WWII spurred sales above $1.5 million by 1945.

In 1949 the company created Travenol Laboratories to make and sell drugs. Baxter went public in 1951 and began an acquisition program the next year. In 1953 failing health caused both Falks to give control to William Graham a manager since 1945. Under Graham's leadership Baxter absorbed Wallerstein (1957); Fenwal Labs (1959); Flint Eaton (1959); and Dayton Flexible Products (1967).

In 1975 Baxter's headquarters moved to Deerfield Illinois. In 1978 the company debuted the first portable dialysis machine and had $1 billion in sales. Vernon Loucks Jr. became CEO two years later. Baxter claimed the title of the world's leading hospital supplier in 1985 when it bought American Hospital Supply (a Baxter distributor from 1932 to 1962). Offering more than 120000 products and an electronic system that connected customers with some 1500 vendors Baxter captured nearly 25% of the US hospital supply market in 1988. That year it became Baxter International.

In 1992 Baxter spun off Caremark (home infusion therapy and mail-order drugs) but kept a division that controlled 75% of the world's dialysis machine market.

In 1993 Baxter pleaded guilty (and was temporarily suspended from selling to the Veterans Administration) to bribing Syria to remove Baxter from a blacklist for trading in Israel.

The company entered the US cardiovascular perfusion services market in 1995 with the purchases of PSICOR and SETA. Baxter along with two other silicone breast-implant makers agreed to settle thousands of claims (at an average of $26000 each) from women suffering side-effects from the implants. The next year Baxter spun off its cost management and hospital supply business as Allegiance (sold to Cardinal Health in 1999).

Buys in 1997 boosted Baxter's presence in Europe and its share of the open-heart-surgery devices market. That year it agreed to pay about 20% of a $670 million legal settlement in a suit relating to hemophiliacs infected with HIV from blood products.

In response to concerns posed by shareholders Baxter in 1999 said it would phase out the use of PVC (polyvinyl chloride) in some products by 2010. In 2000 the firm spun off its underperforming cardiovascular unit as Edwards Lifesciences. To strengthen core operations it lined up a number of purchases including North American Vaccine.

Purchases in 2001 included the cancer treatment unit of chemicals firm Degussa. Also that year Baxter withdrew dialysis equipment from Spain and Croatia after patients who used its products died. It also ended production of two types of dialyzers that were sold there. As the number of deaths mounted to more than 50 in seven countries Baxter began facing lawsuits; it later settled with the families of many of the patients. In September 2002 the FDA issued a warning when several patients died after using Baxter's Meridian dialysis machines. The same year Baxter bought Fusion Medical to expand its BioScience unit.

Robert L. Parkinson Jr. took over as chairman and CEO in April 2004. Parkinson succeeded Harry M. Jansen Kraemer Jr. William Graham who remained on the Baxter board of directors as honorary chairman emeritus after his official retirement in 1996 died in 2006.

In 2005 the FDA seized Baxter's existing inventories of previously recalled 6000 Colleague Volumetric Infusion Pumps and nearly 1000 Syndeo PCA Syringe Pumps; the federal agency resorted to these measures after the company did not fix production and design problems with the pumps in a suitable amount of time after batches of the product had been recalled earlier that year.

Baxter's product troubles didn't end there. In 2008 Baxter halted production of heparin after hundreds of bad reactions (including several deaths) occurred in patients using the drug. Subsequent investigations focused on raw heparin supplied to Baxter by a Chinese factory which apparently added a cheaper ingredient into the drug which contaminated it. Heparin-related litigation continued for Baxter in following years.

In 2009 the company acquired the hemofiltration (renal replacement therapy) product line of Edwards Lifesciences in a $65 million deal.

To meet increasing demand Baxter also expanded its infusion systems portfolio that year by entering an agreement to distribute medical device maker SIGMA's Spectrum large volume infusion pumps domestically and internationally. The deal also gave Baxter a 40% stake in the company (with the option to buy the rest) as well as access to future products under development. In 2012 Baxter exercised its right to buy and paid $90 million in cash for the remaining 60% of the company.

The addition of the Spectrum system was especially helpful when the FDA ordered the company to recall all of its Colleague infusion pumps in the US market in 2010. Patients were given the option of receiving Spectrum pumps to replace the Colleague systems.

EXECUTIVES

Corporate VP Manufacturing, James Michael Gatling, age 62, $376,154 total compensation

Corporate VP and Chief Scientific Officer, Norbert G. Riedel, age 54

Corporate VP; President Asia Pacific, Gerald Lema, age 51

Chairman and CEO, Robert L. Parkinson Jr., age 61, $1,342,000 total compensation
VP: President International, Jean-Luc Butel, age 55
Corporate VP and CIO, Paul E. Martin
Corporate VP Human Resources, Jeanne K. Mason, age 56
Corporate VP Investor Relations, Mary Kay Ladone
Corporate VP and President Medical Products, Robert M. Davis, age 45, $576,923 total compensation
Corporate/General Media Contact, Deborah Spak
Corporate VP and Controller, Michael J. Baughman, age 47
Corporate VP and General Counsel, David P. Scharf, age 44
Corporate VP; President Europe, Peter Nicklin
Corporate VP; President Renal Business, Carlos Alonso
Corporate VP and CFO, Robert J. Hombach, age 46
Corporate VP and President BioScience, Ludwig N. Hantson, age 49
Corporate VP Associate General Counsel and Corporate Secretary, Stephanie A. Shinn
Corporate VP Quality, Phillip L. Batchelor, age 50
Corporate VP; President Latin America and Canada, Wolf F. Kupatt
VP Information Technology, Paul Nielander
Director, Thomas T. (Tom) Stallkamp, age 66
Director, Wayne T. Hockmeyer, age 67
Director, Carole J. Shapazian, age 68
Director, Walter E. Boomer, age 73
Director, Albert P. L. (Al) Stroucken, age 64
Director, Peter S. Hellman, age 62
Director, Kornelis J. (Kees) Storm, age 70
Director, Gail D. Fosler, age 64
Director, James R. Gavin III, age 66
Director, Joseph B. Martin, age 73
Director, John D. Forsyth, age 64
Director, Blake E. Devitt, age 65
Auditors: PricewaterhouseCoopersLLP

LOCATIONS

HQ: Baxter International Inc.
1 Baxter Pkwy., Deerfield IL 60015-4625
Phone: 847-948-2000 **Fax:** 847-948-2016
Web: www.baxter.com

2011 Sales

	$ mil.	% of total
US	5,709	41
Total	13,893	100

PRODUCTS/OPERATIONS

2011 Sales

	$ mil.	% of total
Medical Products		
Renal	2,530	18
Global injectables	2,004	15
IV therapies	1,802	13
Infusion systems	901	7
Anesthesia	537	4
Other Medical Products	30	-
Recombinants	2,212	16
Antibody therapy	1,541	11
Plasma proteins	1,440	10
Regenerative medicine	580	4
Other BioScience	280	2
Total	13,893	100

Selected Products

Medical Products
- Hemodialysis equipment
- Infusion pumps
- Inhaled anesthesia
- Injectable anesthesia
- IV fluids and medications
- IV tubing and access devices
- Parenteral nutrition products
- Peritoneal dialysis equipment

BioScience
- Advate (hemophilia A)
- Aralast (hereditary emphysema)
- Biosurgical sealants
- IGIV therapies (immune disorders)
- Vaccines

COMPETITORS

Amgen
APP Pharmaceuticals
Bayer HealthCare
Becton Dickinson
Biogen Idec
CareFusion
Covidien
CSL
CSL Behring
Fresenius Medical Care
Gambro AB
Genzyme
Grifols
Hospira
Kimberly-Clark Health
Novartis
Novo Nordisk
Sanofi Pasteur
Terumo
ZymoGenetics

HISTORICAL FINANCIALS

Company Type: Public

Income Statement FYE: December 31

	REVENUE ($ mil.)	NET INCOME ($ mil.)	NET PROFIT MARGIN	EMPLOYEES
12/11	13,893	2,224	16.0%	48,500
12/10	12,843	1,420	11.1%	48,000
12/09	12,562	2,205	17.6%	49,700
12/08	12,348	2,014	16.3%	48,500
12/07	11,263	1,707	15.2%	46,000
Annual Growth	5.4%	6.8%	—	1.3%

2011 Year-End Financials

Debt ratio: 27.24%
Return on equity: 33.77%
Cash ($ mil.): 2,905
Current ratio: 178.09
Long-term debt ($ mil.): 4,749
No. of shares (mil.): 560
Dividends
Yield: —
Payout: 32.60%
Market value ($ mil.): 27,757

	STOCK PRICE ($) FY Close	P/E High/Low		PER SHARE ($) Earnings	Dividends	Book Value
12/11	49.48	16	12	3.88	0.00	11.74
12/10	50.62	26	17	2.39	1.18	11.31
12/09	58.68	17	13	3.59	1.07	11.97
12/08	53.59	22	15	3.16	0.91	10.11
12/07	58.05	23	17	2.61	0.72	10.91
Annual Growth	(3.9%)	—	—	10.4%	—	1.9%

BB&T Corp.

Big Bold & Temerarious? That might be an apt description of BB&T the banking company that covers the Southeast like kudzu. It serves consumers small to midsized businesses and government entities through more than 1800 branches in more than a dozen states and Washington DC. Its flagship subsidiary Branch Banking and Trust (also known as BB&T) is one of North Carolina's oldest banks and a leading originator of residential mortgages in the Southeast. The company also operates investment bank Scott & Stringfellow. BB&T expanded its banking franchise in Florida through the 2012 acquisition of BankAtlantic a deal that brought in nearly 80 branches.

In addition to standard services like deposits and loans BB&T also offers insurance mutual funds discount brokerage wealth management financial planning and business services such as leasing and venture capital. BB&T's bulk allows it to trump smaller competitors yet the company maintains decentralized regional management of its banks giving them a community bank feel. Once a serial acquirer of smaller banks throughout the Southeast BB&T has cooled its jets in recent years amid the sputtering economy. Until the BankAtlantic deal its recent acquisitions have primarily come in the form of FDIC-assisted transactions.

In 2008 BB&T bought failed Haven Trust Bank in Georgia. In another FDIC-assisted acquisition of a failed bank albeit on a much larger scale BB&T assumed ownership of more than 350 bank branches in Alabama Florida Georgia Texas and Nevada as well as assets and customer deposits from Colonial BancGroup which was shut down by regulators in 2009. In early 2010 BB&T sold the Nevada assets deposits and branches from that transaction to U.S. Bancorp. The Colonial deal proved to be positive for BB&T's earnings and helped the company enter new attractive markets such as Texas.

Insurance services account for more than 10% of BB&T's revenue. The company remains an inveterate buyer of small insurance agencies (about 85 acquired since 1995) and asset managers throughout the Southeast casting itself as a one-stop financial products shop. It additionally has insurance operations in California a market it entered in 2008. In one of its largest purchases in the segment to date BB&T in 2012 bought the life and property/casualty division of New Jersey-based wholesale insurance brokerage Crump Group. BB&T has also continued its strategy of purchasing niche financial services companies that offer other products that can be sold at its bank branches.

The company has made a point to reduce its exposure to real estate by disposing of problem assets and boost lending in less volatile sectors such as commercial lending. Other growth areas for BB&T include large corporate banking specialized lending wealth management and payment services.

HISTORY

In 1872 Alpheus Branch son of a wealthy planter founded Branch and Company a mercantile business in Wilson North Carolina. He and Thomas Jefferson Hadley who was organizing a public school system created the Branch and Hadley bank later that same year. The private bank helped rebuild farms and small businesses after the Civil War.

In 1887 Branch bought out Hadley and changed the bank's name to Branch and Company Bankers. Two years later Branch secured a state trust charter for the Wilson Banking and Trust Company. He never got the business running however and died in 1893. The trust charter was amended to change the name to Branch Banking and Company and Branch and Company Bankers was folded into it in 1900.

In 1907 the bank finally got its trust operations running and began calling itself Branch Banking and Trust Company. In 1922 it opened its first insurance department; the next year it started its mortgage loan activities.

BB&T survived the 1929 stock market crash with the help of the Post Office. Nervous customers withdrew their funds from BB&T and other banks and deposited them in postal savings accounts unaware that BB&T was the local Post Office's bank and the withdrawn funds went right back to the bank. BB&T opened six more branches between 1929 and 1933.

After WWII consumerism skyrocketed resulting in more car loans and mortgages. During the 1960s and 1970s the bank embarked on a series of mergers and acquisitions forming the thin end of a buying wedge that would widen significantly in the coming decades.

By 1994 BB&T was the fourth-largest bank in North Carolina. In 1995 it merged with North Carolina's fifth-largest bank Southern National Corp. founded in 1897.

With banking regulations loosening to allow different types of operations BB&T in 1997 made several acquisitions including banks thrifts and securities brokerage Craigie.

BB&T's 1998 activities included three bank acquisitions that pushed it into metro Washington DC. The company also increased holdings in fields such as insurance sales venture capital for Southern businesses and investment banking (through its acquisition of Scott & Stringfellow Financial the South's oldest NYSE member).

In 1999 Craigie was melded into Scott & Stringfellow. That year BB&T bought several insurance companies and small banks. The company continued its march through the South the following year buying several Georgia banks and Tennessee's BankFirst. In 2001 BB&T purchased South Carolina's FirstSpartan Financial multibank holding company Century South Banks Maryland-based FCNB Corporation and western Georgia's Community First Banking Company. To bolster its presence in the Washington DC market it bought Virginia Capital Bancshares and F&M National.

BB&T purchased Alabama-based Cooney Rikard & Curtin a wholesale insurance broker active in 45 states in 2002. Also that year it added about 100 branches in Kentucky after buying MidAmerica Bancorp and AREA Bancshares and entered the coveted Florida market following its purchase of Regional Financial the privately held parent of First South Bank.

Acquisitions continued the following three years as the bank swallowed First Virginia Banks among other targets. It took a break in 2005 to assimilate its holdings before joining the acquisition hunt in 2006 with deals for banks in Georgia (Main Street Banks) and Tennessee (First Citizens Bancorp) and in South Carolina (Coastal Financial) in 2007.

EXECUTIVES

Regional President Southwest Virginia Region, Charles L. Robbins III, age 60
Group/State President and Regional President Central Region West Virginia, Phyllis H. Arnold, age 64
Group/State President and Regional President Midlands Region South Carolina, Michael R. (Mike) Brenan, age 60
SEVP and Manager Operations Division, C. Leon Wilson III, age 57, $469,350 total compensation
SEVP; Manager Administrative Services; President Branch Banking and Trust Company, Robert E. (Rob) Greene, age 62, $469,350 total compensation
Chairman and CEO, Kelly S. King, age 64, $900,000 total compensation
Group/State President and Regional President South Florida Region, Michael L. (Mike) Oster, age 60
Regional President Central Kentucky Region, F. Lee (Lee) Hess, age 66
Group/State President and Regional President Hampton Roads Region Virginia, Robert M. (Bob) Boyd, age 55
SEVP; President Community Banking, Ricky K. Brown, age 56
Regional President Blue Ridge Region Virginia, John C. Williams, age 66
Group/State President and Eastern Regional President North Carolina, R. W. (Danny) Daniels Jr., age 64
Group/State President and Regional President Southeast Region North Carolina, Jeff D. Etheridge Jr., age 63
Regional President Northeast Region North Carolina, Stephen L. Medlin, age 62
Group/Regional President and Charlotte Metro Regional President, C. Louis Moore Jr., age 56
Regional President South Central Region North Carolina, W. Vince Nelson Jr., age 67
SEVP; Chief Marketing Officer; and Manager Lending Group, Steven B. (Steve) Wiggs, age 54
Regional President Coastal Region South Carolina, J. Frank (Frank) Bullard III, age 53
Group/State President and Regional President Charlotte Metro Region, Wesley M. (Wes) Beckner, age 54
COO, Christopher L. (Chris) Henson, age 51, $500,000 total compensation
Regional President Gulf Coast Region, J. Kenneth (Ken) Coppedge, age 58
Regional President North Georgia Region, Robert Perry (Perry) Tomlinson, age 57
Regional President Washington DC Region, Luis G. Lobo, age 52
Group State President North Florida Region, James T. (Jim) Daly, age 52
Triad Regional President North Carolina, J. Cantey Alexander, age 48
SEVP and Enterprise Risk Manager, Barbara F. Duck, age 46
President BB&T of Florida; Group/State President Florida, William R. (Bill) Klich, age 68
Regional President Mid-South Georgia Region, David S. Lanier, age 56
Regional President Western Kentucky Region, Hoyt W. Almond, age 66
Group/State President and Regional President Central Virginia, S. Anderson (Andy) Hughes, age 57
Regional President Western Region North Carolina, Michael J. Willett, age 52
Regional President Texas, Kay St. John
Regional President Upstate South Carolina, Scott P. Evans, age 51
Regional President North Atlanta Region, Robert (Bobby) Blakley, age 46
Regional President Central Florida Region, Nan C. Hillis, age 58
SVP Investor Relations, Tamera Gjesdal, age 49
SEVP and Manager Deposit Services, Donna C. Goodrich, age 49
SEVP and Chief Risk Officer, Clarke R. Starnes III, age 53
Regional President Fairfax Region Virginia, Don Strehle, age 56
Regional President East Tennessee Region, Martha S. (Missy) Wallen, age 59
Manager Media Relations, A.C. McGraw
Regional President South Alabama, Jodie E. Hughes, age 43
SEVP and CFO, Daryl N. Bible, age 51, $350,000 total compensation
State President Maryland and Regional President Baltimore Metro Region, Brant Standridge, age 36
Group/State President and Regional President North Alabama Region, Donta L. Wilson, age 36
EVP and Corporate Controller, Cynthia B. (Cindy) Powell
EVP Corporate Branding Product Marketing and Advertising and Chief Communications Officer, Cynthia Williams
Group/State President Greater Washington DC Region, Daniel G. Waetjen, age 61
EVP and Manager Business Loan Administration, Steven L. Alexander
EVP and CTO, Gary R. Coleman
Regional President Triangle Region, David H. Weaver, age 45
Regional President West Virginia North, Calvin E. Barker Jr., age 48
EVP and Treasurer, Hal S. Johnson
EVP and Manager Decathlon, Leland A. (Allen) White
EVP and BLA Senior Loan Administrator, Rayford L. (Ray) Barnes
EVP and Director Retail and Commercial Marketing Strategy, Jon L. Bass
EVP and Chief Loan Operations Officer, Carla D. Fox
EVP and Manager Employee Relations, Henry M. Skinner
EVP and Manager Compensation and Benefits, John F. Sapp
EVP and Manager Management Reporting, Dale A. Davies
Regional President Southwest Florida Region, Scott M. Greer, age 53
SVP and Manager CM Corporate Banking Division, Boyte P. Cory
EVP and Manager Processing Services, Joseph E. Brannan
EVP Payment Solution Sales and Consulting Manager, Garrett B. Thompson
SVP and Manager Electronic Delivery Channel, Howard S. Brooks
Regional President Chesapeake Region, Richard C. (Rick) Springer, age 53
EVP and Manager Loan Services, David L. Burris
SVP and Director Wealth Management Sales and Service, Eric B. Housman
EVP and Director CRA/Community Development Management, Sharon Jeffries-Jones
EVP and CIO, Paul W. Johnson
Insurance Chief Administrative Officer BB&T Insurance Services and Vice Chairman, David M. Pruett
SVP and Manager International Banking Services, John B. Morton III
EVP and Manager Senior Consumer Credit Risk, Ernest S. Picciolil
President South Atlanta Region, William H. (Bill) Kilburg, age 48
General Counsel Secretary and Chief Corporate Governance Officer, Robert J. Johnson Jr.
Regional President North Florida, Scott P. Keith
Director, Stephen T. Williams, age 52
Director, Thomas E. (Tom) Skains, age 56
Director, John A. Allison IV, age 63
Director, Jennifer S. Banner, age 52
Director, Ronald E. Deal, age 68
Director, J. Holmes Morrison, age 70
Director, Nido R. Qubein, age 63
Director, Jane P. Helm, age 69
Director, John P. Howe III, age 69
Director, Anna R. Cablik, age 59
Director, Thomas N. (Tommy) Thompson, age 63
Director, J. Littleton Glover, age 69
Director, K. David Boyer Jr., age 60
Auditors: PricewaterhouseCoopersLLP

LOCATIONS

HQ: BB&T Corporation
200 W. 2nd St., Winston-Salem NC 27101
Phone: 336-733-2000 **Fax:** 336-733-2470
Web: www.bbt.com

2011 Branches

Virginia		387
Florida		268
Georgia		167
South Carolina		116
Kentucky		88
Alabama		87
Tennessee		56
Texas		24
Washington DC		12
Indiana		2
Total	**0**	**1,779**

PRODUCTS/OPERATIONS

2011 Sales

	$ mil.	% of total
Interest		
Loans & leases including fees	6,119	61
Securities & other	766	8
Noninterest		
Insurance	1,044	10
Service charges on deposits	563	6
Mortgage banking	436	4
Investment banking & brokerage fees & commissions	333	3
Checkcard fees	271	3
Bankcard fees & merchant discounts	204	2
Trust & investment advisory	173	2
Other	89	1
Total	**9,998**	**100**

Selected Subsidiaries and Affiliates

American Coastal Insurance Company
BB&T Equipment Finance Corporation
BB&T Financial FSB
Sheffield Financial
BB&T Insurance Services Inc.
BB&T Investment Services Inc.
Branch Banking and Trust Company
Clearview Correspondent Services
CRC Insurance Services
Grandbridge Real Estate Capital LLC
Lendmark Financial Services Inc.
McGriff Seibels & Williams Inc.
MidAmerica Gift Certificate Company
Prime Rate Premium Finance Corporation Inc.
AFCO Credit Corporation
Regional Acceptance Corporation
Scott & Stringfellow LLC
Stanley Hunt DuPree & Rhine Inc.
Sterling Capital Management LLC

COMPETITORS

Bank of America
Capital One
Fifth Third
First Citizens BancShares
First Horizon
JPMorgan Chase
PNC Financial
Regions Financial
SunTrust
Synovus
United Bankshares
Wells Fargo

HISTORICAL FINANCIALS

Company Type: Public

Income Statement FYE: December 31

	ASSETS ($ mil.)	NET INCOME ($ mil.)	INCOME AS % OF ASSETS	EMPLOYEES
12/11	174,579	1,332	0.8%	31,800
12/10	157,081	854	0.5%	31,400
12/09	165,764	877	0.5%	32,400
12/08	152,015	1,519	1.0%	29,600
12/07	132,618	1,734	1.3%	29,400
Annual Growth	7.1%	(6.4%)	—	2.0%

2011 Year-End Financials

Debt ratio: 12.66%
Return on equity: 7.65%
Cash ($ mil.): 4,762
Current ratio: —
Long-term debt ($ mil.): 22,099
No. of shares (mil.): 697
Dividends
Yield: —
Payout: 34.97%
Market value ($ mil.): 17,547

	STOCK PRICE ($) FY Close	P/E High/Low		PER SHARE ($) Earnings	Dividends	Book Value
12/11	25.17	16	10	1.83	0.00	24.98
12/10	26.29	30	19	1.16	0.60	23.67
12/09	25.37	25	11	1.15	1.24	23.47
12/08	27.46	15	7	2.71	1.86	28.68
12/07	30.67	14	10	3.14	1.76	23.14
Annual Growth	(4.8%)	—	—	(12.6%)	—	1.9%

BBCN Bancorp Inc.

LOCATIONS

HQ: BBCN Bancorp Inc.
3731 Wilshire Boulevard, Suite 1000, Los Angeles, CA 90010
Phone: 213 639-1700 **Fax:** 213 235-3033
Web: www.bbcnbank.com

PRODUCTS/OPERATIONS

HISTORICAL FINANCIALS

Company Type:

Income Statement FYE: December 31

	ASSETS ($ mil.)	NET INCOME ($ mil.)	INCOME AS % OF ASSETS	EMPLOYEES
12/11	5,166	27	0.5%	678
12/10	2,963	(7)	—	376
12/09	3,227	(5)	—	337
12/08	2,672	2	0.1%	366
12/07	2,423	33	1.4%	404
Annual Growth	20.8%	(4.9%)	—	13.8%

2011 Year-End Financials

Debt ratio: 7.67%
Return on equity: 3.41%
Cash ($ mil.): 299
Current ratio: —
Long-term debt ($ mil.): 396
No. of shares (mil.): 77
Dividends
Yield: —
Payout: —
Market value ($ mil.): 737

	STOCK PRICE ($) FY Close	P/E High/Low		PER SHARE ($) Earnings	Dividends	Book Value
12/11	9.45	20	11	0.53	0.00	10.21
12/10	9.86	—	—	(0.30)	0.00	9.44
12/09	11.34	—	—	(0.35)	0.08	9.73
12/08	9.83	167	82	0.09	0.11	11.05
12/07	11.67	16	9	1.25	0.11	8.48
Annual Growth	(5.1%)	—	—	(19.3%)	—	4.8%

BBX Capital Corp

BankAtlantic Bancorp is the holding company for BankAtlantic which operates about 80 branches in Florida with a focus on the Miami metropolitan area. The bank offers standard services like deposit accounts and credit cards in addition to investments through and agreement with LPL Financial. Residential mortgages make up about 40% of its loan portfolio while commercial mortgage are about 25% and home equity loans are nearly 20%. The bank also originates business and personal loans. BankAtlantic which has struggled with loan losses and declining revenues is being acquired by Southeast banking giant BB&T.

BankAtlantic Bancorp is currently owned by holding company BFC Financial headed by company chairman Alan Levan and vice chairman John Abdo. BFC Financial also controls Woodbridge Holdings and indirectly Bluegreen.

The battered commercial and residential real estate market in Florida brought problems for BankAtlantic during the recession. Nonperforming loans increased as unemployment rose and the bank's loan portfolio and earnings suffered. The company responded by making several changes to its operations. In 2009 it began diversifying its loan portfolio by originating fewer real estate loans and more small-business and middle-market commercial loans. BankAtlantic also stopped buying risky bulk residential loans on the secondary market.

BankAtlantic sold off assets in order to pay down debts and improve liquidity and capital ratios during the recession. However fewer earning assets also meant reduced net interest income for the company in 2008 and 2009. BankAtlantic delayed its plans to expand its retail network and decreased operating expenses by lowering advertising and marketing budgets and reducing store and call center hours. In 2011 the company sold about 20 locations in the Tampa-St. Petersburg area to PNC Financial Services. The deal resulted in a net gain of nearly $40 million and allowed BankAtlantic to redouble its efforts in southeastern Florida.

Other moves to reverse its losses included rights offerings in order to raise capital. The bank also moved more than $100 million in nonperforming loans to a newly created subsidiary of BankAtlantic Bancorp in exchange for $95 million in cash in an effort to isolate troubled loans. After the acquisition of BankAtlantic by BB&T is complete the holding company will change its name to BBX Capital and continue to manage the loans. It may eventually engage in real estate investment or specialty finance using proceeds from the sale of the assets.

In 2011 BankAtlantic Bancorp entered into an Order to Cease and Desist with the Office of Thrift Supervision that called for the bank to improve its capital position among other measures. The company was able to cut its losses last year thanks in part to the sale of branches to PNC as well as a reduction in expenses and provisions for loan losses. In all BankAtlantic Bancorp lost more than a half-billion dollars from 2008 through 2011.

EXECUTIVES

EVP and COO BankAtlantic Bancorp and BankAtlantic, Lloyd B. DeVaux, age 59, $465,763 total compensation
EVP and Chief Investment Officer BankAtlantic, Lewis F. Sarrica, age 68, $234,834 total compensation
Vice Chairman BankAtlantic Bancorp and BankAtlantic, John E. (Jack) Abdo, age 69, $540,859 total compensation
EVP and Chief Talent Officer BankAtlantic Bancorp and BankAtlantic, Susan D. McGregor, age 51
Chairman and CEO; Chairman BankAtlantic, Alan B. Levan, age 67, $540,859 total compensation
President and Director; President and CEO BankAtlantic, Jarett S. Levan, age 38, $430,969 total compensation
SVP Community Relations; Executive Director BankAtlantic Foundation, Marcia Barry-Smith
EVP and Chief Corporate Banking Executive, Douglas K. (Doug) Freeman, age 61
President Tampa Bay Region, Douglas A. Tuttle, age 53
EVP and CFO BankAtlantic Bancorp and BankAtlantic, Valerie C. Toalson, age 46, $293,782 total compensation
SVP and Investor Relations Officer, Leo Hinkley Jr.
EVP and Chief Risk Officer BankAtlantic, Jay C. McClung, age 63
VP Media Relations, Sharon Lyn
Assistant VP Investor Relations and Corporate Communications, Donna Rouzeau
EVP Retail Banking Division of BankAtlantic, Patricia M. Lefebvre, age 60
Branch Manager Hollywood, Georgia Rozakis
SVP and Director Financial Intelligence, Michelle Kulzer
VP and Relationship Manager BankAtlantic, Nancy L. Merolla
Vice Chairman BankAtlantic Bancorp and BankAtlantic, John E. (Jack) Abdo, age 69
President and Director; President and CEO BankAtlantic, Jarett S. Levan, age 38
Director, Steven M. Coldren, age 64
Director, Bruno L. Digiulian, age 78
Director, Charlie C. Winningham II, age 79
Director, David A. Lieberman, age 76
Director, D. Keith Cobb, age 71
Director, Willis N. (Will) Holcombe, age 66
Auditors: PricewaterhouseCoopersLLP

LOCATIONS

HQ: BBX Capital Corporation
2100 W. Cypress Creek Rd., Fort Lauderdale FL 33309
Phone: 954-940-5000 **Fax:** 954-940-5250
Web: www.bbxcapital.com

PRODUCTS/OPERATIONS

2011 Sales

	$ mil.	% of total
Interest		
Loans including fees	127	47
Securities including dividends	9	4
Tax certificates	4	2
Noninterest		
Service charges on deposits	42	16
Gain on sale of Tampa branches	38	14
Other service charges & fees	26	10
Other	19	7
Total	**268**	**100**

COMPETITORS

1st United Bank
Bank of America
Bank of Tampa
BankUnited
BB&T
Capital City Bank
CenterState Banks
Comerica
OptimumBank
Seacoast Banking
SunTrust

HISTORICAL FINANCIALS

Company Type: Public

Income Statement FYE: December 31

	ASSETS ($ mil.)	NET INCOME ($ mil.)	INCOME AS % OF ASSETS	EMPLOYEES
12/11	3,678	(29)	—	1,036
12/10	4,509	(144)	—	1,372
12/09	4,815	(185)	—	1,644
12/08	5,814	(202)	—	1,847
12/07	6,378	(22)	—	2,569
Annual Growth	(12.9%)	—	—	(20.3%)

2011 Year-End Financials

Debt ratio: 9.76%
Return on equity: 987650001000000.00%
Cash ($ mil.): 770
Current ratio: —
Long-term debt ($ mil.): 359
No. of shares (mil.): 15
Dividends
Yield: —
Payout: —
Market value ($ mil.): 53

	STOCK PRICE ($) FY Close	P/E High/Low	PER SHARE ($) Earnings	Dividends	Book Value
12/11	3.38	— —	(2.04)	0.00	(1.08)
12/10	1.15	— —	(12.90)	0.00	1.14
12/09	1.30	— —	(39.35)	0.00	14.38
12/08	5.80	— —	(90.25)	0.00	108.59
12/07	4.10	— —	(9.50)	0.00	204.79
Annual Growth	(4.7%)	— —	—	—	—

Becton, Dickinson and Co.

Don't worry you'll only feel a slight prick if Becton Dickinson (BD) is at work. The company's BD Medical segment is one of the top global manufacturers of syringes and other injection and infusion devices. BD Medical also makes IV catheters and syringes prefillable drug delivery systems self-injection devices for diabetes patients and related supplies such as anesthesia trays and sharps disposal systems. The BD Diagnostics segment offers tools for collecting specimens and the equipment and reagents to detect diseases in them. Finally BD caters to researchers through its BD Biosciences unit which makes reagents antibodies cell imaging systems and labware used in basic and clinical research.

HISTORY

Maxwell Becton and Fairleigh Dickinson established a medical supply firm in New York in 1897. In 1907 the company moved to New Jersey and became one of the first US firms to make hypodermic needles.

During WWI Becton Dickinson (BD) made all-glass syringes and introduced the cotton elastic bandage. After the war its researchers designed an improved stethoscope and created specialized hypodermic needles. The company supplied medical equipment to the armed forces during WWII. Becton and Dickinson helped establish Fairleigh Dickinson Junior College (now Fairleigh Dickinson University) in 1942. The company continued to develop products such as the Vacutainer blood-collection apparatus its first medical laboratory aid.

After the deaths of Dickinson (1948) and Becton (1951) their respective sons Fairleigh Jr. and Henry took over. The company introduced disposable hypodermic syringes in 1961. BD went public in 1963 to raise money for new expansion. In the 1960s the company opened plants in Brazil Canada France and Ireland and climbed aboard the conglomeration bandwagon by diversifying into such businesses as industrial gloves (Edmont 1966) and computer systems (Spear 1968). BD also went on a major acquisition spree in its core fields during the 1960s and 1970s buying more than 25 medical supply testing and lab companies by 1980.

Wesley Howe successor to Fairleigh Dickinson Jr. expanded the company's foreign sales in the 1970s. Howe thwarted a takeover by the diversifying oil giant Sun Company (now Sunoco) in 1978 and began to sell BD's nonmedical businesses in 1983 ending with the 1989 sale of Edmont. Acquisitions including Deseret Medical (IV catheters surgical gloves and masks; 1986) sharpened BD's focus on medical and surgical supplies.

In the 1990s BD formed a number of alliances and ventures including a 1991 agreement to make and market Baxter International's InterLink needleless injection system which reduces the risk of accidental needle sticks and a 1993 joint venture with NeXagen (now part of Gilead Sciences) to make and market in vitro diagnostics. As tuberculosis reemerged in the US as a serious health threat the firm improved its TB-detection and drug-resistance test systems which cut testing time from as much as seven weeks to less than two.

In 1996 BD introduced GlucoWatch (a glucose monitoring device developed by Cygnus) and acquired the diagnostic business and brand name of MicroProbe (now Epoch Pharmaceuticals).

Previously known on Wall Street as a homely company that focused on cutting costs BD changed its image with a string of acquisitions beginning in 1997. The firm acquired PharMingen (biomedical research reagents) and Difco Laboratories (microbiology media) which broadened its product lines. BD also collaborated with Nanogen on diagnosis products for infectious disease.

In 1998 BD bought The BOC Group's medical devices business. The company also settled a lawsuit by a health care worker claiming that BD continued selling conventional syringes that could spread disease through accidental needle sticks instead of promoting safer technology. BD still faced several lawsuits from health workers who had sustained needle sticks. In 1999 the firm joined forces with Millennium Pharmaceuticals to develop cancer tests and treatments; it also bought genetic test maker Clontech Laboratories.

BD sold its Clontech division (part of BD Biosciences) to Takara Bio part of Takara Holdings in 2005.

During 2006 the company acquired GeneOhm Sciences which develops molecular diagnostic testing systems specifically for the rapid detection of bacterial organisms that cause healthcare-associated infections in hospitalized patients including MRSA (methicillin resistant "Staphylococcus aureus") and Group B Strep (rapid testing for bacteria). That same year the company also acquired the 93% of TriPath Imaging that it didn't already own for $350 million. TriPath brought with it a line of cancer management products.

In another strategic move of 2006 BD announced it would discontinue its line of blood glucose monitors and test strips citing fierce competition in the market. (Rivals Lifescan and Abbott Labs capitalized on BD's exit by offering free monitors to former BD customers.) BD continued to make its other diabetes-related products such as prefilled insulin syringes.

The company expanded the Biosciences unit through the 2008 purchase of Cytopeia a maker of flow cytometry instruments for $43 million and the 2007 acquisition of cell culture tool development firm Plasso Technology for $10 million.

To further this goal in 2009 BD acquired test and processing equipment maker Handylab for $275 million. The purchase enhanced its infection-testing operations and expanded its position in the molecular (gene-based) diagnostic testing market.

The company sold one of its more well-known products –ACE brand elastic bandages –in 2009 to 3M for $51 million. BD first started manufacturing ACE in 1914 but decided to sell the line and its related thermometer product line to focus on other core business segments. The divestiture marks BD Medical's exit from its former home health care product line.

EXECUTIVES

EVP and COO, William A. Kozy, age 60, $567,154 total compensation
Chairman President and CEO, Vincent A. (Vince) Forlenza, age 59, $622,538 total compensation
EVP, Gary M. Cohen, age 53, $545,685 total compensation
Executive Chairman, Edward J. (Ed) Ludwig, age 60, $1,070,000 total compensation
VP and Treasurer, Richard K. Berman
SVP Corporate Medical Affairs, David T. Durack, age 67
SVP Corporate Regulatory and External Affairs, Patricia B. Shrader, age 62
SVP and General Counsel, Jeffrey S. Sherman, age 57
VP Corporate Secretary and Public Policy, Dean J. Paranicas
SVP and Controller, William A. Tozzi
SVP Integrated Supply Chain, Stephen (Steve) Sichak, age 54
VP and CIO, J. Peter Natale
SVP Human Resources, Donna M. Boles, age 58
VP Chief Intellectual Property Counsel and Assistant Secretary, David W. Highet
Director Corporate Communications, Colleen T. White
EVP and CFO, David V. Elkins, age 44, $413,462 total compensation
VP Investor Relations, Zachary A. (Zac) Nagle
SVP and Chief Marketing Officer, Nabil Shabshab, age 46
SVP and CTO, Scott P. Bruder, age 50
Assistant Secretary, Richard A. Carbone
Assistant Secretary, Gary M. DeFazio
Assistant Secretary, Patricia A. Walesiewicz
Assistant Treasurer, Kenneth Monkowski
VP and Chief Ethics and Compliance Officer, Patti E. Russell
Investor Relations, Sherry L. Bertner
VP Tax, Antoinette F. Segreto
VP Global Sustainability, Glenn Barbi
SVP Corporate Strategy and Development, William E. Rhodes, age 57
President BD Diagnostic Systems, Thomas Polen
Director Worldwide Public Relations, Maj. Jeff Ezell
Manager Corporate Communications, Elizabeth (Liz) Ryan Sax
Director, Edward F. DeGraan, age 67
Director, Marshall O. Larsen, age 63
President CEO and Director, Vincent A. (Vince) Forlenza, age 58
Director, Basil L. Anderson, age 65
Director, Gary A. Mecklenburg, age 66
Director, James F. Orr, age 65
Director, Adel A. F. Mahmoud, age 69
Director, Henry P. Becton Jr., age 67
Director, Willard J. (Mike) Overlock Jr., age 64
Director, Cathy E. Minehan, age 63
Director, Alfred Sommer, age 68
Director, Claire M. Fraser-Liggett, age 55
Director, Bertram L. (Bert) Scott, age 59
Director, Christopher Jones, age 57
Auditors: Ernst&YoungLLP

LOCATIONS

HQ: Becton Dickinson and Company
1 Becton Dr., Franklin Lakes NJ 07417-1880
Phone: 201-847-6800 **Fax:** 201-847-6475
Web: www.bd.com

2011 Sales

	$ mil.	% of total
US	3,355	43
Asia/Pacific	817	10
Other	1,158	15

PRODUCTS/OPERATIONS

2011 Sales

	$ mil.	% of total
BD Medical		
Pharmaceutical systems	1,059	14
Preanalytical systems	1,277	16
BD Bioscience		
Discovery labware	316	4
Total	**7,828**	**100**

Selected Acquisitions

2012
- Sirigen Group Limited (polymer dyes for flow cytometry)

2011
- KIESTRA Lab Automation BV (Netherlands automated laboratory technology)
- Carmel Pharma ($287 million Sweden drug handing safety equipment)
- Accuri Cytometers ($205 million flow cytometry)Selected Products

Medical
- Anesthesia needles and trays
- Hypodermic needles and syringes
- Intravenous catheters
- Insulin syringes and pen needles
- Prefillable drug-delivery systems
- Prefillable IV flush syringes
- Safety needles and syringes
- Sharps disposal systems

Diagnostics
- Bar-code systems for patient identification and data capture
- Blood culturing systems
- Cytology systems (for cervical cancer screening)
- Drug susceptibility systems
- Immunodiagnostic test kits
- Microorganism identification systems
- Molecular diagnostics (for infectious disease and hospital infection testing)
- Plated media
- Rapid diagnostic assays
- Safety-engineered blood collection devices
- Sample collection products
- Specimen management systems

Biosciences
- Cell culture media
- Cell sorters and analyzers
- Cell growth and screening products
- Cellular imaging systems
- Clinical and research laboratory software
- Diagnostic assays
- Labware (tubes pipettes Petri dishes etc.)
- Molecular biology reagents (for study of genes)
- Monoclonal antibodies (for biomedical research)
- Other research reagents

COMPETITORS

Abbott Labs
Affymetrix
Agilent Technologies
Alere
B. Braun Melsungen
Bard
Baxter International
Beckman Coulter
Bio-Rad Labs
bioMerieux
Boston Scientific
CareFusion
Covidien
Dako
Fresenius
Gen-Probe
Harvard Bioscience
Hologic
Hospira
Johnson & Johnson
Kimberly-Clark Health
Life Technologies Corporation
Meridian Bioscience
Novo Nordisk
Retractable Technologies
Roche Diagnostics
Safety Syringes
Sekisui Diagnostics
Siemens Healthcare Diagnostics
Terumo
Thermo Fisher Scientific
Third Wave Technologies
Trinity Biotech
Unilife

HISTORICAL FINANCIALS

Company Type: Public

Income Statement

FYE: September 30

	REVENUE ($ mil.)	NET INCOME ($ mil.)	NET PROFIT MARGIN	EMPLOYEES
09/12	7,708	1,169	15.2%	29,555
09/11	7,828	1,270	16.2%	29,369
09/10	7,372	1,317	17.9%	28,803
09/09	7,160	1,231	17.2%	29,116
09/08	7,155	1,127	15.7%	28,277
Annual Growth	1.9%	0.9%	—	1.1%

2012 Year-End Financials

Debt ratio: 36.67%
Return on equity: 28.29%
Cash ($ mil.): 1,671
Current ratio: 269.06
Long-term debt ($ mil.): 3,761
No. of shares (mil.): 196
Dividends
Yield: —
Payout: 32.20%
Market value ($ mil.): 15,469

	STOCK PRICE ($) FY Close	P/E High/Low		PER SHARE ($) Earnings	Dividends	Book Value
09/12	78.56	14	12	5.59	0.00	21.00
09/11	73.32	16	13	5.62	1.64	22.48
09/10	74.10	14	12	5.49	1.48	23.65
09/09	69.75	16	12	4.99	1.32	21.69
09/08	80.26	20	17	4.46	1.14	20.30
Annual Growth	(0.5%)	—	—	5.8%	—	0.9%

Bed, Bath & Beyond, Inc.

Bed Bath & Beyond (BBB) has everything you need to play "house" for real. It's the nation's #1 superstore domestics retailer with about 1000 BBB stores throughout the US Puerto Rico and Canada. The stores' floor-to-ceiling shelves stock better-quality (brand-name and private-label) goods in two main categories: domestics (bed linens bathroom and kitchen items) and home furnishings (cookware and cutlery small household appliances picture frames and more). BBB also operates three smaller specialty chains: about 70 Christmas Tree Shops; 65 buybuy BABY stores; and 45 Harmon discount health and beauty shops. The home goods retailer bought its smaller rival Cost Plus for $495 million in cash in 2012.

Geographic Reach

Beyond the US the domestics retailer is growing in Canada and Mexico. BBB opened its first international store in Richmond Hill Ontario in 2007 and now has more than 25 stores in several Canadian provinces. It also has a joint venture with Mexican retailer Home & More. BBB anticipates the joint venture will be a springboard for future growth in Mexico.

Sales & Marketing

The company relies primarily on word-of-mouth to boost sales and the mailing of advertising pieces. In fiscal 2012 (ends February) BBB reported a relative decrease in advertising expenses ($192.5 million in 2012 vs. more than $198 million in 2011) resulting from a reduction in the distribution of advertising pieces.

Operations

Beyond its main BBB chain of 1000 stores the company operates 258 stores under the names World Market Cost Plus World Market and World Market Stores banners. It also operates 70-plus Christmas Tree Shops about 70 buybuy BABY shops and more than 45 stores under the names Harmon and Harmon Face Values.

Financial Analysis

In fiscal 2012 (ends February) sales increased more than 8% vs. the prior year after growing more than 12% in the previous annual comparison. Same-store sales (generally considered the best indicator of a retailer's health) increased by 6% in fiscal 2012 compared with an increase of nearly 8% in fiscal 2011. Net income increased by 25% and 31% in fiscal 2012 and 2011 respectively. Indeed the company has no long-term debt and is looking to make strategic acquisitions.

The retailer's decentralized structure allows store managers to have more control than their peers at other retailers (and the company has less manager turnover). BBB cuts costs by locating its stores in strip shopping centers freestanding buildings and off-price malls rather than in pricier regional malls. To cut costs further its vendors ship merchandise directly to the stores eliminating the expense of a central distribution center and reducing warehousing costs. The chain relies exclusively on circulars mailings and word-of-mouth for advertising.

Strategy

BBB is reaping the benefits from its former archrival Linens 'n Things' demise and the sustained strong rebound in demand for home goods following the recent deep recession. To capitalize BBB is growing organically and through acquisitions. In 2012 it bought Cost Plus which operates nearly 260 stores in 30 states under the World Market Cost Plus World Market and Cost Plus Imports banners. The acquisition followed an 18-month partnership between the two chains during which specialty food departments were added to some BBB stores. BBB is looking to boost foot traffic and fend off online and discount retail competitors by adding food and drink to its merchandise menu. (About 40% of Cost Plus sales come from food and drink.) The tender offer for the shares of Cost Plus was completed in late June. Also in June the retailer acquired New Jersey-based Linen Holdings a privately-held distributor of bath bed and table linens for about $105 million. Linen Holdings' customers include hotels cruise lines food service establishments and health care operators.

Ownership

The investment firms Davis Selected Advisers and FMR LLC both own about 10% of BBB's stock.

HISTORY

Warren Eisenberg and Leonard Feinstein both employed by a discounter called Arlan's brainstormed an idea in 1971 for a chain of stores offering only home goods. They were betting that customers were in Feinstein's words interested in a "designer approach to linens and housewares." The two men started two small linens stores (about 2000 sq. ft) named bed n bath one in New York and one in New Jersey.

Expansion came at a fairly slow pace as the company moved only into California and Connecticut by 1985. By then the time was right for such a specialty retailer: Department stores were cutting back on their houseware lines to focus on the more profitable apparel segment and baby boomers were spending more leisure time at their homes (and more money on spiffing them up). Eisenberg and Feinstein opened a 20000-sq.-ft. superstore in 1985 that offered a full line of home furnishings. The firm changed its name to Bed Bath & Beyond (BBB) two years later in order to reflect its new offerings.

With the successful superstore format the company built all new stores in the larger design. BBB grew rapidly; square footage quadrupled between 1992 and 1996. The company went public in 1992. That year it eclipsed the size of its previous stores when it opened a 50000-sq.-ft. store in Manhattan. (It later enlarged this store to 80000 sq. ft.; the company's stores now average 42000 sq. ft.)

BBB's management has attributed its success in part to the leeway it gives its store managers who monitor inventory and have the freedom to try new products and layouts. One example often cited by the company is the case of a manager who decided to sell glasses by the piece instead of in sets. Sales increased 30% and the whole chain incorporated the practice.

The retailer opened 28 new stores in 1996 33 in 1997 (its first-ever billion-dollar sales year) and 45 in 1998.

In 1999 the company dipped a toe into the waters of e-commerce by agreeing to buy a stake in Internet Gift Registries which operates the WeddingNetwork website. The company later began offering online sales and bridal registry services. Keeping up its rapid expansion pace the company opened 70 stores in 1999 85 in 2000 and 95 in 2001.

In 2002 BBB acquired Harmon Stores a health and beauty aid retailer with 29 stores in three states. It acquired Christmas Tree Shops a giftware and household items retailer with 23 stores in six states for $200 million in 2003.

In March 2007 BBB acquired buybuy BABY which operates eight stores on the East Coast for $67 million. The retailer opened its first Canadian location in Ontario north of Toronto in December. In 2008 BBB added three more stores in Canada and its first locations in Mexico via a joint venture there under the Home & More banner.

EXECUTIVES

CFO and Treasurer; President Buy Buy Baby, Eugene A. (Gene) Castagna, age 46, $840,000 total compensation
VP Legal and General Counsel, Allan N. Rauch
VP Corporate Development; President Harmon Stores, G. William Waltzinger Jr.
President and Chief Merchandising Officer, Arthur (Art) Stark, age 57, $1,055,000 total compensation
SVP Stores, Matthew Fiorilli, age 55, $686,000 total compensation
CEO and Director, Steven H. (Steve) Temares, age 53, $1,500,000 total compensation
Co-Chairman, Leonard (Lenny) Feinstein, age 75, $1,100,000 total compensation
Co-Chairman, Warren Eisenberg, age 81, $1,100,000 total compensation
VP Corporate Operations and Chief Strategy Officer; President BBB Canada, Richard C. (Rich) McMahon
Director Public Relations, Bari Fagin
Manager Public Relations, Rachael Risinger
CEO and Director, Steven H. (Steve) Temares, age 53
Co-Chairman, Leonard (Lenny) Feinstein, age 75
Co-Chairman, Warren Eisenberg, age 81
Director, Klaus Eppler, age 82
Director, Victoria A. (Vicki) Morrison, age 59
Director, Dean S. Adler, age 55
Director, Stanley F. Barshay, age 72
Director, Patrick R. Gaston, age 54
Director, Jordan Heller, age 51
Auditors: KPMGLLP

LOCATIONS

HQ: Bed Bath & Beyond Inc.
650 Liberty Ave., Union NJ 07083
Phone: 908-688-0888 **Fax:** 908-688-6483
Web: www.bedbathandbeyond.com

2012 Stores

	No.
California	116
New	91
Texas	81
Florida	80
New	80
Illinois	44
Massachusetts	43
Pennsylvania	42
Ohio	40
Michigan	37
North	33
Virginia	33
Georgia	30
Arizona	27
Colorado	25
Connecticut	23
Indiana	23
Washington	23
Maryland	20
Tennessee	20
Alabama	16
Missouri	16
South	15
New	14
Louisiana	13
Utah	13
Minnesota	12
Wisconsin	11

Oregon	10
Kansas	9
Kentucky	9
Iowa	8
Maine	8
Nevada	8
Oklahoma	8
Arkansas	7
Idaho	7
Mississippi	7
Montana	6
Nebraska	5
New	5
Rhode	5
Delaware	3
Puerto	3
Vermont	3
West	3
Alaska	2
District of	2
North	2
South	2
Wyoming	2
Hawaii	1
Canada	27
Total	1,173

PRODUCTS/OPERATIONS

2012 Stores

	No.
Bed Bath &	993
Christmas Tree	71
buybuy	64
Harmon Face	45
Total	1,173

Selected Merchandise

- Domestics
  - Bath accessories
    - Hampers
    - Shower curtains
    - Towels
  - Bed linens
    - Bedspreads
    - Pillows
    - Sheets
  - Kitchen textiles
    - Cloth napkins
    - Dish towels
    - Placemats
    - Tablecloths
  - Window treatments
- Home Furnishings
  - Basic housewares
    - Accessories (lamps chairs accent rugs)
    - General housewares (brooms ironing boards)
    - Small appliances (blenders coffeemakers vacuums)
    - Storage items (hangers organizers shoe racks)
  - General home furnishings
    - Artificial plants and flowers
    - Candles
    - Gift wrap
    - Picture frames
    - Seasonal merchandise
    - Wall art
  - Kitchen and tabletop items
    - Cookware
    - Cutlery
    - Flatware
    - Gadgets
    - Glassware
    - Serveware

COMPETITORS

Amazon.com
Anna' s Linens
Art.com
Babies " R" Us
Burlington Coat Factory
Container Store
Cost Plus
Dillard' s
Euromarket Designs
Garden Ridge
Gymboree
IKEA
J. C. Penney
Kmart
Macy' s
Pier 1 Imports
Ross Stores
Sears
Sensational Beginnings
Target Corporation
The Children' s Place
TJX Companies
Tuesday Morning Corporation
Wal-Mart
Williams-Sonoma

HISTORICAL FINANCIALS

Company Type: Public

Income Statement FYE: February 25

	REVENUE ($ mil.)	NET INCOME ($ mil.)	NET PROFIT MARGIN	EMPLOYEES
02/12	9,499	989	10.4%	48,000
02/11	8,758	791	9.0%	45,000
02/10	7,828	600	7.7%	41,000
02/09*	7,208	425	5.9%	37,000
03/08	7,048	562	8.0%	39,000
Annual Growth	7.7%	15.2%	—	5.3%

*Fiscal year change

2012 Year-End Financials

Debt ratio: —
Return on equity: 25.23%
Cash ($ mil.): 1,003
Current ratio: 309.38
Long-term debt ($ mil.): —
No. of shares (mil.): 235
Dividends
Yield: —
Payout: —
Market value ($ mil.): 14,213

	STOCK PRICE ($) FY Close	P/E High/Low		PER SHARE ($) Earnings	Dividends	Book Value
02/12	60.35	15	11	4.06	0.00	16.66
02/11	47.85	16	12	3.07	0.00	15.62
02/10	41.61	18	8	2.30	0.00	13.89
02/09*	21.30	21	10	1.64	0.00	11.55
03/08	28.34	20	12	2.10	0.00	9.89
Annual Growth	20.8%	—	—	17.9%	—	13.9%

*Fiscal year change

Bemis Co Inc

Thanks to companies like Bemis delicacies such as potato chips and snack cakes have a longer shelf life than most marriages. Bemis makes a broad line of flexible packaging materials including polymer films barrier laminates and paper-bag packaging about 65% of which are used by the food industry to bundle a diversity of edibles. Flexible packaging accounts for about 90% of sales. Bemis also produces pressure-sensitive products ranging from label paper and graphic films to thin-film adhesives. In addition to the food industry the company sells to the agricultural chemical medical personal care and printing industries. With 80 facilities in 13 countries North America represents two-thirds of sales.

Sales & Marketing

Bemis' major customers —including Kimberly-Clark Procter & Gamble Sara Lee Nestle Kraft General Mills Energizer Batteries and Hormel Foods —are themselves engaged in a fiercely competitive market where packaging can make the difference in consumer buying decisions.

Financial Analysis

The global recession hurt even the food industry a business environment traditionally immune to economic boom and bust cycles. Worldwide consumer demand which plunged during 2009 gradually picked up in 2010. Sales of Bemis' flexible packaging products increased more than 40% over 2009 and pressure sensitive materials almost 6%. All told the company's consolidated year-over-year sales rose more than 35% in 2010. Earnings in 2010 improved by nearly 40% over 2009 results. Cash generated from operations decreased due to changes in working capital hit by a rise in raw material costs.

Strategy

Bemis' rebound and expansion is in large part driven by a series of strategic acquisitions that have broadened its manufacturing footprint. In 2011 Bemis took over China-based Mayor Packaging a maker of consumer packaging. Hard on its heels Bemis's Dendron Participacoes subsidiary upped its stake in Dixie Toga from 86% to 99%. Bemis in a more significant acquisition purchased Alcan Packaging Food Americas from mining group Rio Tinto for $1.2 billion in spring 2010. The deal —which adds 23 flexible packaging facilities in Argentina Brazil Mexico as well as New Zealand Canada and the US —was conditioned upon Bemis' divestment of certain US assets. As ordered by US Department of Justice Bemis sold its discontinued cheese and meat packaging operations in Menasha Wisconsin and Tulsa Oklahoma to Exopack Holding Corp. an affiliate of Sun Capital Partners for approximately $82 million.

HISTORY

Judson Moss Bemis founded J. M. Bemis and Company Bag Manufacturers in St. Louis in 1858. The 25-year-old received advice and equipment from cousin Simeon Farwell who owned an established bag-making factory. St. Louis' role as a trading center supported by major railroads and the Mississippi River helped Bemis' business. The company introduced preprinted and machine-sewn flour sacks to the city's millers and by the end of its first year it was making about 4000 sacks a day. In its second year Edward Brown a relative of Farwell's became Bemis' partner and the company was renamed Bemis and Brown.

During the Civil War Brown opened an office in Boston to make the most of fluctuating exchange rates. Bemis also began trading in raw cotton (priced sky-high because of the war) and it started recycling burlap shipping bags into gunnysacks. The company soon began producing its own burlap sacks from imported jute.

Stephen Bemis Judson's brother became a partner in the firm in 1870 and took over its St. Louis operations. Judson joined Brown in Boston where he could be involved in commodity purchases and financial operations. Soon after he bought out Brown's share of the firm for an amount considered extravagant at the time - $300000.

By the early 1880s Bemis Bros. and Co. was the US's #2 bag maker. It opened a second factory in 1881 in Minneapolis which was home to such companies as General Mills and Pillsbury. During the late 1800s and the early 1900s Bemis opened plants throughout the US.

Judson retired in 1909 but the company continued to be run by Bemis family members. In 1914 the company entered the emerging industry of paper milling and paper-bag making but it continued to focus on textile packaging until WWII when shortages of cotton and jute expanded the role of paper packaging and led to the development of polyethylene packaging. By the 1950s Bemis' core products were paper and plastic packaging. In 1959 the company opened its own R&D facility. During the late 1950s and 1960s Bemis made several important acquisitions including Curwood (packaging for medical products) and MACtac (pressure-sensitive materials). The company was renamed Bemis Company in 1965.

Bemis sold more than $100 million of noncore businesses during the 1970s and 1980s. In its effort to become an industry leader the company began a major capital expansion program. Bemis' sales topped $1 billion in 1988.

Bemis bought candy-packaging producer Milprint Inc. in 1990; Princeton Packaging's bakery-packaging business in 1993; and Banner Packaging in 1995. In 1996 Bemis introduced the on-battery tester developed with Eveready. Bemis' medical packaging segment was rejuvenated that year with the purchase of Malaysia-based Perfecseal. The company sold its packaging-equipment business in 1997 and began closing plants and consolidating operations.

In 1998 Bemis purchased a one-third interest in Brazil-based Dixie Toga's flexible-packaging operations. That year it also acquired Belgium's Techy International which became Bemis' base for sales and distribution in Europe.

Bemis invested more than $100 million to modernize its packaging manufacturing and printing operations in 1999. The next year it acquired Arrow Industries' flexible packaging operations Viskase's plastic-films business and Kanzaki Specialty Papers' pressure sensitive materials business. Bemis acquired plastic film maker Duralam in 2001.

The company opened its pocketbook again in 2002 purchasing the Clysar shrink film business of DuPont (with operations in both the US and Europe) for more than $140 million. The purchase gave Bemis a worldwide reach for its shrink bags film and heat-set packaging products. Later that year Bemis acquired the Walki Films business of UPM-Kymmene for about $69 million.

In 2003 Bemis expanded its operations in Europe through the acquisition of Multi-Fix's pressure sensitive materials business for about $11 million. The next year Bemis acquired flexible packaging assets in Mexico from Masterpak S.A. de C.V. The company also restructured its Pressure Sensitive Materials division which included the closing of two facilities.

Bemis restructured its operations to reduce costs during 2006; the move primarily consisted of manufacturing facility consolidations that resulted in seven plant closings.

Intent on strengthening its market presence in South America Bemis bought a majority stake in Brazil-based Dixie Toga one of the country's largest packaging companies. Bemis had originally purchased a one-third interest in Dixie Toga as far back as 1998.

Bemis acquired in 2009 the South American-based rigid packaging business of Huhtamaki Oyj for about $43 million. That transaction included three facilities (two in Brazil and one in Argentina) that sell primarily to the dairy and food service markets complementing Bemis' existing South American activities.

EXECUTIVES

Chairman, William J. Bolton, age 65
VP Operations, William F. Austen, age 53, $460,000 total compensation
VP and Treasurer, Melanie E. R. Miller, age 48
President CEO and Director, Henry J. Theisen, age 58, $875,000 total compensation
President Milprint/Banner, Donald E. Nimis
VP Operations, James W. (Jim) Ransom, age 52
President Milprint, Gregory J. Derhaag
President Bemis Flexible Packaging Europe, Marc Dussart
President Polyethylene Packaging Division, Peter R. Mathias
President Perfecseal North America, Paul R. Verbeten
VP and CFO, Scott B. Ullem, age 45, $450,000 total compensation
VP General Counsel and Secretary, Sheri H. Edison, age 55
President Bemis Mexico, Robert Mescal
President Dixie Toga, Nelson Fazenda
President MACtac Americas, James Peruzzi
Regional President Bemis Asia Pacific, B. L. Lim
President Bemis Clysar, Steve Moore
VP; General Manager Bemis Asia-Pacific, Christopher C. Martin
Public Relations Specialist, Kristi Pavletich
VP Human Resources, Timothy S. Fliss
VP and Controller, Jerry S. Krempa, age 51
Director, Philip G. (Phil) Weaver, age 59
Director, David S. (Dave) Haffner, age 59
Director, Timothy M. (Tim) Manganello, age 62
Director, Roger D. O'Shaughnessy, age 69
Director, Edward N. Perry, age 65
Director, David T. (Dave) Szczupak, age 57
Director, Barbara L. Johnson, age 61
President CEO and Director, Henry J. Theisen, age 58
Director, William J. (Bill) Scholle, age 65
Director, Paul S. Peercy, age 72
Director, Holly A. Van Deursen, age 53
Auditors: PricewaterhouseCoopersLLP

LOCATIONS

HQ: Bemis Company Inc.
1 Neenah Center 4th Fl., Neenah WI 54957-0669
Phone: 920-727-4100 **Fax:** 513-419-3394
Web: www.greyhound.com

2011 Sales

North America	3,592	68
Europe	548	10
Total	**5,322**	**100**

PRODUCTS/OPERATIONS

2011 Sales

Flexible packaging	4,747	89

Selected Products

Flexible Packaging Segment
- Bag closing materials
- Blown & cast stretch film
- Carton sealing tapes & application equipment
- Custom thermoformed & injection molded plastic packaging
- Laminates
- Multilayer flexible polymer film structures
- Multiwall paper bags
- Printed paper roll stock

Pressure Sensitive Materials Segment
- Graphic markets
  - Photographic over-laminate & mounting materials (optically clear films)
  - Pressure sensitive films
- Label markets
  - Film & metalized film printing stocks (high-speed printing & die-cutting)
  - Narrow-web rolls of pressure sensitive paper
- Technical markets
  - Micro-thin film adhesives
  - Pressure sensitive applications utilizing foam & tape based stocks (fastening & mounting)

COMPETITORS

3M
Amcor
Avery Dennison
Bryce Corporation
Cantex
Pactiv
Pliant Corporation
Printpack
Ricoh Americas
RockTenn CP
Dow Chemical
DuPont
Exopack
Green Bay Packaging
Hood Packaging
International Paper
Intertape Polymer
Sealed Air Corp.
Sonoco Products
Southern Film Extruders
UPM-Kymmene
Wausau Paper
Winpak

HISTORICAL FINANCIALS

Company Type: Public

Income Statement FYE: December 31

	REVENUE ($ mil.)	NET INCOME ($ mil.)	NET PROFIT MARGIN	EMPLOYEES
12/11	5,322	184	3.5%	20,000
12/10	4,835	205	4.2%	19,796
12/09	3,514	147	4.2%	20,400
12/08	3,779	166	4.4%	15,400
12/07	3,649	181	5.0%	15,678
Annual Growth	9.9%	0.3%	—	6.3%

2011 Year-End Financials

Debt ratio: 36.34%
Return on equity: 11.64%
Cash ($ mil.): 109
Current ratio: 227.14
Long-term debt ($ mil.): 1,554
No. of shares (mil.): 102
Dividends
Yield: —
Payout: 55.49%
Market value ($ mil.): 3,098

	STOCK PRICE ($) FY Close	P/E High/Low		PER SHARE ($) Earnings	Dividends	Book Value
12/11	30.08	20	16	1.73	0.00	15.36
12/10	32.66	18	14	1.85	0.92	17.46
12/09	29.65	22	12	1.38	0.90	16.67
12/08	23.68	18	13	1.65	0.88	13.50
12/07	27.38	21	15	1.74	0.84	15.54
Annual Growth	2.4%	—	—	(0.1%)	—	(0.3%)

Beneficial Mutual Bancorp Inc

You would expect something beneficial from the city of brotherly love. Beneficial Mutual Bancorp is the holding company for Beneficial Bank which serves the greater Philadelphia area and southern New Jersey through about 65 branches. Founded in 1853 as Beneficial Mutual Savings Bank the bank provides traditional deposit products such as checking savings and money market accounts; IRAs; and CDs. Commercial real estate business and construction loans together account for nearly half of the company's loan portfolio; consumer loans (nearly 30%) and residential mortgages (almost 25%) round out its lending activities. The bank is looking to grow its commercial loan portfolio.

Beneficial Mutual sells insurance and offers investment advisory services through subsidiaries Beneficial Insurance Services and Beneficial Advisors. The company seeks to differentiate itself by promoting financial education for its customers. It also eyes expansion through acquisitions. In 2012 it acquired SE Financial the holding company for St. Edmond's Federal Savings Bank for more than $30 million. The deal added five branches in the greater Philadelphia area.

Although its revenue was down in 2011 Beneficial Mutual Bancorp returned to profitability after a year in the red as it was able to cut its provisions for credit losses by nearly half. However the company expects elevated levels of charged-off loans to continue and has implemented a plan to reduce expenses to offset possible loan losses.

Mutual holding company Beneficial Savings Bank MHC owns more than 55% of Beneficial Mutual Bancorp.

EXECUTIVES

EVP Community Banking, Denise Kassekert, age 60, $192,000 total compensation
EVP and Chief Lending Officer, Andrew J. Miller, age 56, $280,800 total compensation
EVP and CFO, Thomas D. Cestare, age 43
VP and Manager Customer Contact, James J. Fecca
VP and Regional Officer Community Banking Division, Brian C. Miller
Chairman President and CEO, Gerard P. Cuddy, age 52, $475,000 total compensation
EVP, Robert J. Bush, age 53, $312,000 total compensation
SVP and Chief Accounting Officer, Amy J. Hannigan
Director, Elizabeth H. Gemmill, age 66
Director, Michael J. Morris, age 77
Director, Edward G. Boehne, age 71
Director, Roy D. Yates, age 49
Director, Donald F. (Don) Gayhardt, age 47
Director, George W. Nise, age 69
Director, Frank A. Farnesi, age 64
Director, Thomas F. Hayes, age 89
Director, Charles Kahn Jr., age 87
Director, Joseph J. McLaughlin, age 83
Director, Donald F. O'Neill, age 72
Director, Thomas J. Lewis, age 59
Director, Karen D. Buchholz, age 44
Auditors: KPMGLLP

LOCATIONS

HQ: Beneficial Mutual Bancorp Inc.
510 Walnut St. 19th Fl., Philadelphia PA 19106
Phone: 215-864-6000 **Fax:** 215-864-6177
Web: www.thebeneficial.com

PRODUCTS/OPERATIONS

2011 Sales

	$ mil.	% of total
Interest		
Loans including fees	139	68
Securities including dividends	39	19
Other	0	-
Noninterest		
Insurance & advisory commissions & fees	7	4
Service charges & other	17	9
Total	**205**	**100**

COMPETITORS

Bank of America
Firstrust Savings Bank
National Penn Bancshares
PNC Financial
Prudential Bancorp
RBS Citizens Financial Group
Republic First Bank
TD Bank USA

HISTORICAL FINANCIALS

Company Type: Public

Income Statement FYE: December 31

	ASSETS ($ mil.)	NET INCOME ($ mil.)	INCOME AS % OF ASSETS	EMPLOYEES
12/11	4,596	11	0.2%	842
12/10	4,929	(8)	—	965
12/09	4,673	17	0.4%	965
12/08	4,002	16	0.4%	970
12/07	3,557	(1)	—	912
Annual Growth	6.6%	—	—	(2.0%)

2011 Year-End Financials

Debt ratio: 5.45%
Return on equity: 1.75%
Cash ($ mil.): 347
Current ratio: —
Long-term debt ($ mil.): 250
No. of shares (mil.): 80
Dividends
Yield: —
Payout: —
Market value ($ mil.): 671

	STOCK PRICE ($) FY Close	P/E High	P/E Low	PER SHARE ($) Earnings	Dividends	Book Value
12/11	8.36	66	51	0.14	0.00	7.84
12/10	8.83	—	—	(0.12)	0.00	7.63
12/09	9.84	51	38	0.22	0.00	7.78
12/08	11.25	60	42	0.21	0.00	7.42
12/07	9.72	—	—	(0.03)	0.00	7.53
Annual Growth	(3.7%)	—	—	—	—	1.0%

Berkley (W. R.) Corp.

W. R. Berkley is a holding company with a full basket. The firm offers an assortment of commercial property/casualty insurance across five segments. Its specialty insurance segment underwrites complex third-party liability risks especially excess and surplus lines professional liability and commercial transportation insurance. Its regional segment offers commercial insurance focused on small to midsized business customers and state and local governments through regional subsidiaries. The alternative markets segment develops self-insuring programs aimed at employers and employer groups. Berkley also does a bit of reinsurance and increasingly international property/casualty underwriting in about 40 countries.

Each of the company's decentralized units focus on specific niches. Berkley's specialty insurance segment accounts for a little more than 30% of revenues; its high-risk coverage products are sold directly and through brokers to a wide variety of clients. New units created to serve niches include Gemini Transportation Underwriters (2009) to provide excess liability coverage for trucking and railroad operators and Verus Underwriting Managers (2010) to provide excess and surplus lines.

Its regional products segment accounts for more than 20% of sales. Its product offerings are sold through a network of independent agents. The segment is divided into geographic regions led by Continental Western Group in the Midwest Acadia Insurance in New England Union Standard Insurance Group in the South and Berkley Mid Atlantic Group in the mid-Atlantic region. A fifth regional unit was formed to cover the Northwest in 2009 when Berkley North Pacific Group was split off from Continental Western. The regional division also offers some surety bonds and commercial excess and surplus coverage nationwide through regional offices and contracted agents.

Although international business accounts for a modest portion of Berkley's revenues it has steadily increased and in 2011 accounted for about 13% of total revenues. The segment's South American business writes both commercial and personal insurance while its business in the UK and other European countries offers only commercial property/casualty products. In 2009 the company formed a Canadian subsidiary and it added a Lloyd's of London property/casualty underwriting syndicate to its European division the previous year.

In fiscal 2011 the company's revenues of $5.16 billion represented a more than 9% increase over 2010. Berkley's net income declined by 12% to $394.8 million. The increase in revenues was largely due to new product offerings and expansion into new markets an 8% increase in premiums earned increased business in its international and specialty segments and increased gains on investments which more than doubled from the previous year. The drop in net income was attributable to decreased underwriting income due to increased catastrophe losses of $72 million and a $52 million decrease in favorable prior-year reserve development.

Strategically Berkley's decentralized structure promotes the development of specialized expertise in a range of areas and enables the company to adapt to cyclical market conditions and insulate itself from great risk. While the company has made a handful of acquisitions through the years it prefers to expand by forming new operating units after identifying needs in specific areas. The company also focuses on such growing world markets as South America Australia the Asia/Pacific region and Norway. Additionally Berkley exercises insightful discretion in exiting insurance lines as demand diminishes.

Chairman and CEO William R. Berkley founded the enterprise in 1967 and owns almost 19% of the company. His son W. Robert Berkley Jr. is the firm's president and COO.

EXECUTIVES

VP Taxes, Scott A. Siegel
VP and Controller, Clement P. Patafio, age 47
SVP Regional Operations, Robert P. Cole, age 62
SVP Investments; President Berkley Dean & Company, James G. Shiel, age 52, $555,000 total compensation
SVP Reinsurance Operations, C. Fred Madsen, age 58
SVP General Counsel and Corporate Secretary, Ira S. Lederman, age 59, $555,000 total compensation
VP Investments, Edward F. Linekin
SVP and Chief Corporate Actuary, Paul J. Hancock, age 50
VP Human Resources, Joseph M. Pennachio
Chairman and CEO, William R. Berkley, age 66, $1,000,000 total compensation
VP Information Technology, Harry J. Berkley
VP Senior Counsel and Assistant Secretary, Josephine A. Raimondi
SVP and CFO, Eugene G. Ballard, age 59, $555,000 total compensation
President Riverport Insurance Services, Douglass E. Pfeifer
President COO and Director, W. Robert Berkley Jr., age 39, $700,000 total compensation
SVP Excess and Surplus Lines, Robert C. Hewitt, age 51
AVP and Corporate Actuarial, Thomas P. Boyle

Assistant VP and Director Internal Audit, Raymond J. O'Brien
Assistant VP and Counsel, Bruce I. Weiser
Assistant Corporate Controller, Jean P. Milot
Assistant Treasurer, George K. Richardson
Assistant Secretary, Janet L. Shemanske
Assistant Corporate Controller Financial Reporting, John E. Warycha
Director Investment Accounting, Dawn M. Callahan
President and CEO Admiral Insurance Group, James S. Carey
President and CEO Berkley Risk Solutions, Jeffrey E. Vosburgh
President and CEO Carolinas Casualty Insurance, Douglas J. Powers
President Monitor Liability Managers, Sandra C. Nelson
SVP Insurance Risk Management, Robert W. Gosselink, age 58
President and CEO Berkley Specialty Underwriting Managers, Steven S. Zeitman
SVP, Philip S. Welt, age 52
SVP Alternative Markets Operations, Robert D. Stone, age 47
President and CEO Berkley Mid-Atlantic Group, Kevin W. Nattrass
Assistant VP Analytics, Arthur Gurevitch
VP and Senior Counsel, Jane B. Parker
President and CEO Nautilus Insurance Group, Thomas M. (Tom) Kuzma
EVP and Chief Underwriting Officer Nautilus Insurance Group, Richard P. (Rich) Shemitis
CEO and Chief Underwriting Officer W. R. Berkley Insurance (Europe), Stuart Wright
President and CEO Continental Western Group, Bradley S. Kuster
President Union Standard Insurance Group, Craig W. Sparks
Chairman Preferred Employers Insurance Company, Linda R. Smith
President B F Re Underwriters, Daniel L. Avery
President and CEO Berkley Underwriting Partners, John S. Diem
President and CEO Berkley International Latinoamerica S.A. and Berkley International Seguros S.A.; President Berkley International Aseguradora de Riesgos del Trabajo S.A. and Berkley International Seguros S.A. (Uruguay), Eduardo I. Llobet
SVP Human Resources, Carol J. LaPunzina, age 50
SVP, Peter L. Kamford, age 57
VP External Financial Communications, Karen A. Horvath
EVP and Chief Underwriting Officer Facultative ReSources, James H. Crutchley
President Berkley Net Underwriters, John K. Goldwater
President Berkley Capital, Frank T. Medici, age 47
President Berkley Surety Group, Steven F. Coward
SVP Information Technology, Kevin H. Ebers, age 54
VP, Joan E. Kapfer
SVP and Chief Underwriting Officer Berkley Life Sciences, Emily J. Urban
General Manager and Underwriter W. R. Berkley Insurance Australia, Christian Garling
President Clermont Specialty Managers, William J. Johnston
SVP Underwriting, James W. McCleary
COO Accident and Health, Donato (Don) Gasparro
President Berkley Risk Administrators, J. Michael Foley
Chairman and CEO Key Risk Insurance, Joe W. Sykes
President and COO Midwest Employers Casualty Group, Melodee J. Saunders
President Facultative ReSources, Gerald S. (Jerry) King
SVP International Operations, Steven W. Taylor, age 52
VP and Corporate Actuary, Jessica L. Somerfeld
SVP; President Acadia Insurance Group, William M. Rohde Jr.
President Berkley North Pacific Group, Jeffrey R. (Jeff) Dehn
President Vela Insurance Services, David A. Jordan
VP Investment and Controller, Richard K. Altorelli
VP Internal Audit, Michele Fleckenstein
VP Insurance Risk Management, David Gronski
Assistant VP and Corporate Actuary, Bryan V. Spero
SVP CFO and Treasurer Admiral Insurance Group, Thomas C. Grilli Jr.
President Berkley Life Sciences, Jill W. Wadlund
VP and CFO Berkley Life Sciences, Spencer J. Page
VP and Chief Claims Officer Berkley Life Sciences, Sharon C. McDermott
VP and CIO Berkley Life Sciences, Scott Rosenberg
President Berkley Select, Joseph G. (Joe) Shores
CFO Berkley Select, Joseph N. (Joe) Smith
EVP and COO Berkley Specialty Underwriting Managers, Rick Bak
VP and CFO Berkley Specialty Underwriting Managers, Patrick K. London
President FinSecure, Annette Merz
CFO and Treasurer FinSecure; EVP and CFO Berkley Underwriting Partners, Joseph L. Mathews
SVP CFO and Treasurer Nautilus Insurance Group, Miklos F. (Mick) Kallo
VP and CFO Vela Insurance Services, Gerald P. Kalvaitis Jr.
President and CEO American Mining Insurance Group, Chandler F. Cox Jr.
EVP and CFO American Mining Insurance Group, Dominick Giovannelli
President Berkley Asset Protection Underwriting Managers, Joseph P. Dowd
President Berkley Aviation, Jason R. Niemela
VP and CFO Berkley Aviation, Alan C. Hair
President Berkley Offshore Underwriting Managers, Frank A. Costa
EVP Berkley Offshore Underwriting Managers UK, R. Christian Walker
President Berkley Professional Liability, John R. Benedetto
President Gemini Transportation Underwriters, Rocco P. Modafferi
CFO Clermont Specialty Managers, Richard Pellegrino
VP and CFO Continental Western Group, Ann M. Collins
President Berkley Agribusiness Risk Specialists, Terry L. Shaw
VP CFO and Treasurer Union Standard Insurance Group, John E. Gray
Chairman and President Berkley Regional Specialty, Bill Thornton
COO and CFO Key Risk Insurance, Rebecca H. (Becky) Karr
SVP CFO and Treasurer Midwest Employers Casualty Group, Peter W. Shaw
VP Treasurer and CFO Preferred Employers Group, Timothy J. Wiebe
President and CEO Signet Star Re, Jon A. Schriber
SVP and CFO Signet Star Re, Mark G. Davidowitz
VP and CFO Berkley Facultative Reinsurance Services, Pasquale Tomaino
CFO Berkley International Latinoamerica S.A., Marcelo R. Crespo
CEO Berkley International do Brasil Seguros S.A., Jose Marcelino Risden
Chief Marketing Officer Berkley International do Brasil Seguros S.A., Luciana Natividade Motta de Souza
SVP Berkley International Seguros S.A., Osvaldo P. Borghi
CEO Berkley International Seguros S.A. (Uruguay), Alvaro A. Miguel
President Berkley Canada, Michael S. McLachlan
CFO W. R. Berkley Insurance (Europe), Paul Hosking
COO W. R. Berkley Insurance (Europe), Graham Dennis
Chief Executive W. R. Berkley Syndicate, Michael A. Sibthorpe
President and CEO Berkley Re Asia and Berkley Re Australia, K. Grant Robson
Chief Underwriting Officer Berkley Re Asia and Berkley Re Australia, Gerald MacDonald
CFO Berkley Re Australia, Shaun A. West
General Manager Berkley Re Asia, Eric Chan
General Manager Berkley Re Australia, Peter R. Nickerson
President Accident and Health, Christopher C. (Chris) Brown
Executive President Sucursal en Espa?a Insurance (Europe), Javier Esteban
SVP Enterprise Risk Management, Gillian James, age 46
President Berkley Specialty Underwriting Managers LLC Environmental Division, Kenneth J. Berger
President Berkley Medical Excess Underwriters, Collin J. Suttie
SVP Berkley Medical Excess Underwriters, W. Matthew Fessler
SVP, Jeffrey M. (Jeff) Hafter
SVP, Lucille T. Sgaglione
VP and Treasurer, Richard M. Baio
Tax Counsel, Richard A. Jordan Jr.
Assistant Tax Director, John S. Navratil
President Preferred Employers Insurance Company, Steven A. (Steve) Gallacher
SVP Claims, Nelson Tavares
VP and Senior Counsel, Rajiv N. Raval
Vice President, Aaron Larson
Non-Executive Chairman of the Board, Alan Beckett
Non-Executive Independent Director, Egon Vetter
Non-Executive Independent Director, Grantly Anderson
Director, Jack H. Nusbaum, age 71
Director, Mark E. Brockbank, age 60
President COO and Director, W. Robert Berkley Jr., age 39
Director, George G. Daly, age 71
Director, Mark L. Shapiro, age 68
Director, Ronald E. (Ron) Blaylock, age 52
Director, Rodney A. Hawes Jr., age 74
Director, Mary C. Farrell, age 62
Auditors: KPMGLLP

LOCATIONS

HQ: W. R. Berkley Corporation
475 Steamboat Rd., Greenwich CT 06830
Phone: 203-629-3000 **Fax:** 203-629-3073
Web: www.wrbc.com

PRODUCTS/OPERATIONS

2011 Revenues by Segment

Specialty	1,620	31
Alternative markets	819	16
International	656	13
Total	**5,156**	**100**

2011 Premiums Written

	% of total
Specialty	36
Regional	24
International	16
Alternative	14
Reinsurance	10
Total	**100**

Selected Property/Casualty Segments

Specialty includes excess and surplus lines and admitted specialty lines
Regional commercial lines property/casualty
Alternative markets includes excess workers' compensation monoline workers' compensation accident and health and insurance services
Reinsurance on both a facultative and treaty basis and participates in business written through Lloyd' s of London
International business in selected regions throughout the world

Selected Subsidiaries and Affiliates

Berkley International LLC
Berkley Surety Group Inc.
J/I Holding Corporation:
Admiral Insurance Company
Admiral Indemnity Company
Berkley London Holdings Inc.W. R. Berkley Insurance (Europe) Limited
Carolina Casualty Insurance CompanyBerkley Assurance Company
Clermont Insurance Company
Nautilus Insurance CompanyGreat Divide Insurance Company
Signet Star Holdings Inc.
Berkley Insurance Company
Berkley Regional Insurance CompanyAcadia Insurance CompanyAmerican Mining Insurance Company Inc.Berkley National Insurance CompanyBerkley Regional Specialty Insurance CompanyContinental Western Insurance CompanyFiremen's Insurance Company of Wa
Gemini Insurance Company
Key Risk Insurance Company
Midwest Employers Casualty CompanyPreferred Employers Insurance Company
Riverport Insurance Company
StarNet Insurance Company

COMPETITORS

ACE Limited
AIG
Allied Group
Allied World Assurance
American Financial Group
Arch Capital
Berkshire Hathaway
CNA Financial
Everest Re
Farmers Group
General Re
HCC Insurance
Liberty Mutual
Munich Re America
Munich Re Group
Nationwide
Ohio Casualty
Old Republic
PartnerRe
Selective Insurance
Swiss Re
Transatlantic Reinsurance
Travelers Companies
White Mountains Insurance Group

HISTORICAL FINANCIALS

Company Type: Public

Income Statement

FYE: December 31

	ASSETS ($ mil.)	NET INCOME ($ mil.)	INCOME AS % OF ASSETS	EMPLOYEES
12/11	18,487	394	2.1%	6,642
12/10	17,528	449	2.6%	6,253
12/09	17,328	309	1.8%	6,072
12/08	16,121	281	1.7%	5,768
12/07	16,832	743	4.4%	5,494
Annual Growth	2.4%	(14.6%)	—	4.9%

2011 Year-End Financials

Debt ratio: 9.43%
Return on equity: 9.85%
Cash ($ mil.): 911
Current ratio: —
Long-term debt ($ mil.): 1,743
No. of shares (mil.): 137
Dividends
Yield: —
Payout: 11.44%
Market value ($ mil.): 4,729

	STOCK PRICE ($) FY Close	P/E High	P/E Low	PER SHARE ($) Earnings	Dividends	Book Value
12/11	34.39	13	9	2.71	0.00	29.15
12/10	27.38	9	8	2.90	0.27	26.26
12/09	24.64	16	10	1.86	0.24	22.97
12/08	31.00	18	11	1.62	0.23	18.87
12/07	29.81	9	7	3.78	0.20	19.80
Annual Growth	3.6%	—	—	(8.0%)	—	10.2%

Berkshire Hathaway Inc.

Berkshire Hathaway is where Warren Buffett the world's third-richest man (behind Mexican billionaire Carlos Slim and Warren's good buddy Bill Gates) spreads his risk by investing in a variety of industries from insurance and utilities to apparel and food and building materials to jewelry and furniture retailers. Its core insurance subsidiaries include GEICO National Indemnity and reinsurance giant General Re. The company's other largest holdings include Marmon Group McLane Company MidAmerican Energy and Shaw Industries. Known as the Oracle of Omaha Buffett holds more than 20% of Berkshire Hathaway which owns a majority of more than 70 firms in all and has stakes in more than a dozen others.

HISTORY

Warren Buffett bought his first stock —three shares of Cities Service —at age 11. In the 1950s he studied at Columbia University under famed investor Benjamin Graham. Graham's axioms: Use quantitative analysis to discover companies whose intrinsic worth exceeds their stock prices; popularity is irrelevant; the market will vindicate the patient investor.

In 1956 Buffett then 25 founded Buffett Partnership. Its $105000 in initial assets multiplied as the company bought Berkshire Hathaway (textiles 1965) and National Indemnity (insurance 1967). When Buffett nixed the partnership in 1969 because he believed stocks were overvalued value per share had risen 30-fold.

Buffett continued investing under the Berkshire Hathaway name looking for solid businesses such as See's Candies (1972) advertising agencies (Interpublic Ogilvy & Mather) newspapers ("Washington Post" "Boston Globe" and "Buffalo News") and television (Capital Cities/ABC 1985).

Buffett bought Nebraska Furniture Mart (1983) and Scott Fetzer ("World Book" encyclopedias and Kirby vacuum cleaners 1986). The scale of investments grew as the company bought stakes in Salomon Brothers (investment banking 1987) Gillette (1989) American Express (1991) Coca-Cola (1988-89) and Wells Fargo (1989-91).

In the 1990s Buffett sought strong brands and services including shoes (H. H. Brown 1991) furniture jewelry retailing and pilot-training (FlightSafety International 1996).

When Salomon was investigated by the federal government in 1991 for submitting false bids in US Treasury auctions Buffett was solicited to save the company —and Berkshire's $700 million stake. In an unusual move for him he took over the daily operations of the company. He mandated openness with government investigators and reined in some of Salomon's unorthodox trading practices. He is widely credited with having saved the firm from nearly certain demise; several years later it was bought by Travelers.

Buffett increased Berkshire Hathaway's insurance holdings including an 82% stake in Central States Indemnity (credit insurance 1992) and a total buyout of GEICO (1996).

In 1996 as the company's share price soared toward $35000 —easily the highest per-share priced security in the US outsiders threatened to start a mutual fund to invest in Berkshire Hathaway stock. In response Buffett created a class B stock that was 1/30th the price of the class A.

Continuing to invest in what he knew Buffett bought General Re and time-share private jets through NetJets (called Executive Jet in 1998). Berkshire also increased its holdings in Dairy Queen that year.

In 2000 the company's purchases included Ben Bridge Jeweler; furniture rental company CORT Business Services; boot maker Justin Industries; paint maker Benjamin Moore and Co.; and more than 80% of Shaw Industries the world's largest carpet maker. The company also bought shares of Wells Fargo and Costco Wholesale.

The next year Buffett did a little housekeeping: He dumped 80% of his Disney stock after Mickey's earnings slipped and sold most of the firm's holdings in Fannie Mae and Freddie Mac.

Berkshire Hathaway also teamed with financial services firm Leucadia National to bail out FINOVA but later exited that project in response to uncertainty after the terrorist attacks on September 11 2001.

Berkshire's insurance and reinsurance businesses —especially General Re —took a hard hit from the 9/11 terrorist attacks. In a mea culpa that's rare for modern CEOs but not for him Buffett said in his annual letter to shareholders that he had considered the risk of terrorism but hadn't adequately acted upon it.

Berkshire went on to acquire Albecca Fruit of the Loom (pulling the garment company out of chapter 11) Garan The Pampered Chef and CTB during 2002.

In an interesting and contrary (and it turns out profitable) move Berkshire Hathaway began investing in foreign currencies in 2002 as a result of the US's trade deficit and the weak value of the dollar. It expanded this position in 2003 encompassing some $12 billion in exchange contracts. Berkshire bought grocery distributor McLane Company from Wal-Mart for $1.5 billion the same year.

The following year the company unloaded holdings in Dun & Bradstreet Duke Energy and the former Great Lakes Chemical as well as Gap HCA Dover Corporation NIKE and H&R Block.

Buffett's wife Susan died in 2004. She had been a member of the board of directors and owned about 3% of the company.

After failing to make any large acquisitions that year the company in 2005 bought GE's Medical Protective Corp. a provider of liability insurance to physicians and dentists and Forest River a maker of RVs buses trailers manufactured homes and boats.

In 2006 it bought press release distributor Business Wire sportswear company Russell and 80% of ISCAR Metalworking an Israel-based maker of metal-cutting tools and the first foreign company in which Berkshire has a controlling stake.

Also in 2006 Buffett announced a donation of 85% of his Berkshire Hathaway stock (worth some $44 billion) to five charitable organizations with the Bill & Melinda Gates Foundation led by his close friends getting the largest portion by far. Buffett married longtime companion Astrid Menks on his 76th birthday in August of that year.

Berkshire Hathaway's Class A shares were the first ever to breach the $100000 per-share price in 2006 and touched $150000 the following year. Relatively quiet for much of 2007 the company announced on Christmas Day of that year that it would buy a 60% stake in manufacturing and service conglomerate The Marmon Group from the founding Pritzker family for some $4.5 billion the largest cash purchase in Berkshire's history. The initial transaction closed in 2008 and Berkshire announced plans to acquire the remaining 40% in stages over the next several years.

Berkshire Hathaway endured its worst-ever year in 2008 partially because of declines in its residential construction and retail businesses and an ill-timed investment in ConocoPhillips as oil and gas prices spiked. Nonetheless most mere mortals would accept Berkshire's lot as the company still outperformed the S&P 500.

The company was in on the massive Mars buyout of Wrigley in 2008 which netted Berkshire a more than 10% stake in Wrigley. The company also formed bond insurer Berkshire Hathaway Assurance to compete with the likes of MBIA and Ambac after attempts to acquire those companies' public finance business were rebuffed. (In retrospect Buffett said that being turned down was "very good news.")

In late 2009 Berkshire Hathaway joined with occasional investment partner Leucadia –forming a joint enterprise called Berkadia Commercial Mortgage –to acquire the loan servicing business of bankrupt Capmark for some $468 million.

EXECUTIVES

Chairman President and CEO General Re Corp., Franklin (Tad) Montross IV
VP and Controller, Daniel J. Jaksich
Secretary, Forrest N. Krutter, age 57
SVP and CFO, Marc D. Hamburg, age 62, $862,500 total compensation
Vice Chairman; Chairman President and CEO Wesco Financial, Charles T. (Charlie) Munger, age 88, $100,000 total compensation
Chairman President and CEO GEICO, Olza M. (Tony) Nicely, age 69
Chairman and CEO, Warren E. Buffett, age 82, $100,000 total compensation
Director Internal Auditing, Rebecca K. Amick
VP, Mark D. Millard
President Buffett Farms and Director, Howard G. Buffett, age 57
Chairman President and CEO MidAmerican Energy Holdings, Gregory E. (Greg) Abel, age 49
Director Taxes, Jo Ellen Rieck
Chairman President and CEO Johns Manville, Todd Raba
VP, Sharon L. Heck
Chairman and CEO NetJets, Jordan Hansell
Treasurer, Kerby S. Ham
Director, Stephen B. (Steve) Burke, age 53
Vice Chairman; Chairman President and CEO Wesco Financial, Charles T. (Charlie) Munger, age 88
Director, J. Walter (Walter) Scott Jr., age 80
Director, William H. (Bill) Gates III, age 57
Director, Susan L. Decker, age 49
President Buffett Farms and Director, Howard G. Buffett, age 57
Director, Ronald L. (Ron) Olson, age 70
Director, Donald R. (Don) Keough, age 85
Director, David S. Gottesman, age 85
Director, Thomas S. Murphy, age 86
Director, Charlotte Guyman, age 55
Auditors: Deloitte&ToucheLLP

LOCATIONS

HQ: Berkshire Hathaway Inc.
3555 Farnam St., Omaha NE 68131
Phone: 402-346-1400 **Fax:** 402-346-3375
Web: www.berkshirehathaway.com

PRODUCTS/OPERATIONS

2011 Sales

	$ mil.	% of total
Insurance & other		
Sales & service revenues	72,803	51
Insurance premiums earned	32,075	22
Other investment income	5,857	4
Railroad utilities & energy	30,839	21
Finance & financial products	2,114	2
Total	**143,688**	**100**

2011 Sales by Segment

	$ mil.	% of total
McLane Company	33,279	23
Burlington Northern Santa Fe	19,548	14
GEICO	15,363	11
MidAmerican	11,291	8
Berkshire Hathaway Reinsurance Group	9,147	6
Marmon	6,925	5
General Re	5,816	4
Investment income	4,746	3
Finance & financial products	4,014	3
Berkshire Hathaway Primary Group	1,749	1
Other	31,810	22
Total	**143,688**	**100**

Major Equity Investment
American Express (13%)
Coca-Cola (8.8%)
ConocoPhillips (2.3%)
International Business Machines (5.5%)
Kraft Foods (4.5%)
Munich Re (11.3%)
POSCO (5.1%)
Procter & Gamble (2.6%)
Tesco plc (3.6%)
U.S. Bancorp (4.1%)
Wells Fargo & Co. (7.6%)

Subsidiaries and Selected Holdings
Acme Building Brands (face brick and other building materials)
Albecca (custom framing products)
Applied Underwriters (workers' compensati
Ben Bridge Jeweler (jewelry retailer)
Benjamin Moore (architectural and industrial paint)
Berkshire Hathaway Assurance Corporatio
Berkshire Hathaway Credit Corporatio
Berkshire Hathaway International Insurance Limited (UK)
Berkshire Hathaway Life Insurance Company of Nebraska
BH Finance (proprietary investment strategies
Boat America Corporation (insurance
Borsheim Jewelry Company (jewelry retailer)
The Buffalo News (newspaper
Burlington Northern Santa Fe (railroad)
Business Wire (news service)
California Insurance Company
Central States Indemnity Co. of Omaha (credit and disability insurance)
Clayton Homes (manufactured housing and financing)
CORT (provider of rental furniture accessories and related services)
CTB International (manufacturer of equipment and systems for poultry hog and egg production
Cypress Insurance Company
The Fechheimer Brothers (uniforms and accessorie
FlightSafety International (high technology training to operators of aircraft and ships)
Forest River (recreational vehicles)
Fruit of the Loom (apparel)
Garan (apparel)
GEICO (property/casualty insurance)
General Re Corporation (property/casualty reinsuranc
H.H. Brown Shoe Company
Helzberg's Diamond Shops (jewelry retailer)
International Dairy Queen Inc. (licensing and servicing Dairy Queen Stores)
Iscar (cutting tools Israel)
Johns Manville (building and equipment insulation
Jordan's Furniture (retailing home furnishing
Justin Brands (western footwear and apparel)
Kansas Bankers Surety Company
Lubrizol (specialty chemicals)
Marmon Holdings (manufacturing and service)
McLane Company (wholesale distribution of groceries and non-food items)
Medical Protective Company (Med Pro; professional liability insurer)
MidAmerican Energy Holdings Company
HomeServices of America Inc. (residential real estate brokerage)
Kern River Gas Transmission Company
Northern Electric
Northern Natural Gas
Pacific Power
Rocky Mountain Power
Yorkshire Electricit
MiTek (building components
National Indemnity Company (specialty insurance)
Nebraska Furniture Mart (retailing home furnishing
NetJets (fractional ownership programs for general aviation aircraft)
The Pampered Chef (kitchenware and housewares
Precision Steel Warehouse (steel service center)
R.C. Willey Home Furnishings (home furnishings retailer)
Richline Group (jewelry manufactur
Russell Corporation (sportswea
Scott Fetzer Company (manufacture and distribution of diversified products)
See's Candies (boxed chocolates and other confectionery products)
Shaw Industries (carpets and rugs)
Star Furniture (home furnishings retailer)
TTI Inc. (electronics distributi
Wesco Financial (investment holdings)
Wells Lamont (glove manufactur
World Book (encyclope
XTRA Corporation (transportation equipment)

COMPETITORS

AEA Investors
Allstate
Apollo Global Management
Bain Capital
Blackstone Group
Chubb Corp
CIGNA
CNA Financial
HM Capital Partners
KKR
Lincoln Financial Group
Loews
Progressive Corporation
State Farm
The Carlyle Group
The Hartford
TPG

HISTORICAL FINANCIALS

Company Type: Public

Income Statement

FYE: December 31

	ASSETS ($ mil.)	NET INCOME ($ mil.)	INCOME AS % OF ASSETS	EMPLOYEES
12/11	392,647	10,254	2.6%	271,000
12/10	372,229	12,967	3.5%	260,000
12/09	297,119	8,055	2.7%	222,000
12/08	267,399	4,994	1.9%	246,000
12/07	273,160	13,213	4.8%	233,000
Annual Growth	9.5%	(6.1%)	—	3.8%

2011 Year-End Financials

Debt ratio: 15.38%
Return on equity: 6.22%
Cash ($ mil.): 37,299
Current ratio: —
Long-term debt ($ mil.): 60,384
No. of shares (mil.): 1
Dividends
Yield: —
Payout: —
Market value ($ mil.): 126

	STOCK PRICE ($) FY Close	P/E High/Low		PER SHARE ($) Earnings	Dividends	Book Value
12/11	76.30	0		06,215.00	0.00	99,860
12/10	80.11	0		07,928.00	0.00	95,453
12/09	3,286.00	1		05,193.00	0.00	84,486
12/08	3,214.00	1		13,224.00	0.00	70,529
12/07	4,736.00	1		08,548.00	0.00	78,008
Annual Growth	(64.4%)	—	—	(7.7%)	—	6.4%

Berkshire Hills Bancorp, Inc.

Berkshire Hills Bancorp is the holding company for Berkshire Bank which serves individuals and small businesses through some 60 branches in Massachusetts New York Connecticut and Vermont. Established in 1846 the bank provides standard deposit products such as savings checking and money market accounts CDs and IRAs in addition to credit cards investments private banking wealth management and lending services. Real estate mortgages make up nearly three-quarters of Berkshire Hills Bancorp's loan portfolio which also includes business and consumer loans. In addition to its banking activities Berkshire Hills also owns insurance agency Berkshire Insurance Group.

Berkshire Bank is transition into a regional bank and is growing its geographic footprint by acquiring other banks. On the heels of its 2011 acquisitions of Rome Bancorp and Legacy Bancorp Berkshire Hills Bancorp bought The Connecticut Bank and Trust which gave the company its first eight branches in Connecticut. The previous acquisitions expanded Berkshire's presence in Massachusetts and New York two target markets in which it has also opened new branches. (However the company sold four branches from the Legacy deal to NBT Bancorp in order to satisfy antitrust concerns.) Berkshire Hills also is eyeing further expansion into Connecticut and other parts of New England and New York by opening new branches and through acquisitions.

The company which was established in 1846 believes one of its competitive advantages is the regional niche it serves which has been relatively unscathed by the recession compared to other parts of the country. The bank's performance has been boosted by an increase in business development in the company's market area in addition to growth in its asset-based lending and private banking businesses. The bank also has grown its loans and deposits and has plans to grow its insurance and wealth management operations as well.

Berkshire reported a more than 20% increase in revenues in 2011 and a 28% jump in net income. The company's 2011 acquisitions for Rome Bancorp and Legacy Bancorp as well as organic growth helped boost revenues. Berkshire now plans to buy Beacon Federal Bancorp in a $132 million deal that will add seven branches serving primarily the Syracuse market.

HISTORY

.

EXECUTIVES

President CEO and Director Berkshire Hills Bancorp and Berkshire Bank, Michael P. Daly, age 50, $450,000 total compensation
Chairman, Lawrence A. (Larry) Bossidy, age 77
EVP Human Resources, Linda A. Johnston
SVP Commercial Lending, Michael J. Ferry
SVP Wealth Management and Trust, Thomas W. Barney
EVP Integrated Services Berkshire Hills Bancorp and Berkshire Hills Bank, David B. (Dave) Farrell, age 56
EVP, Michael J. (Mike) Oleksak, age 53, $225,000 total compensation
President and CEO Berkshire Insurance Group, John S. Millet, age 47, $150,000 total compensation
EVP Retail Banking, Sean A. Gray
EVP CFO Treasurer and Secretary, Kevin P. Riley, age 52, $250,000 total compensation
EVP and Chief Risk Officer, Richard M. Marotta
VP Marketing, Fedelina Madrid
Director, Rodney C. Dimock, age 65
Director, Cornelius D. Mahoney, age 66
President CEO and Director Berkshire Hills Bancorp and Berkshire Bank, Michael P. Daly, age 50
Director, Catherine B. Miller, age 70
Director, Corydon L. Thurston, age 59
Director, D. Jeffrey Templeton, age 70
Director, David E. Phelps, age 59
Director, Robert M. Curley
Director, John B. Davis, age 62
Director, Wallace W. Altes, age 70
Director, Susan M. Hill, age 62
Auditors: PricewaterhouseCoopersLLP

LOCATIONS

HQ: Berkshire Hills Bancorp Inc.
24 North St., Pittsfield MA 01201
Phone: 413-443-5601 **Fax:** 413-443-3587
Web: www.berkshirebank.com

PRODUCTS/OPERATIONS

2011 Sales

	$ mil.	% of total
Interest		
Loans	124	71
Securities & other	13	8
Noninterest		
Deposit related fees	13	8
Insurance commissions & fees	11	7
Wealth management fees	5	3
Loan related fees	3	2
Other	2	1
Total	174	100

COMPETITORS

Bank of America
Hudson City Bancorp
KeyCorp
Pathfinder Bancorp
RBS Citizens Financial Group
Sovereign Bank
TD Bank USA

HISTORICAL FINANCIALS

Company Type: Public

Income Statement FYE: December 31

	ASSETS ($ mil.)	NET INCOME ($ mil.)	INCOME AS % OF ASSETS	EMPLOYEES
12/11	3,991	17	0.4%	760
12/10	2,880	13	0.5%	599
12/09	2,700	(16)	—	622
12/08	2,666	22	0.8%	610
12/07	2,513	13	0.5%	560
Annual Growth	12.3%	6.8%	—	7.9%

2011 Year-End Financials

Debt ratio: 5.70%
Return on equity: 3.18%
Cash ($ mil.): 75
Current ratio: —
Long-term debt ($ mil.): 227
No. of shares (mil.): 21
Dividends
Yield: —
Payout: 66.33%
Market value ($ mil.): 469

	STOCK PRICE ($) FY Close	P/E High/Low		PER SHARE ($) Earnings	Dividends	Book Value
12/11	22.19	24	18	0.98	0.00	26.17
12/10	22.11	23	17	0.99	0.64	27.56
12/09	20.68	—	—	(1.52)	0.64	27.64
12/08	30.86	15	10	2.06	0.63	33.33
12/07	26.00	24	17	1.44	0.58	31.15
Annual Growth	(3.9%)	—	—	(9.2%)	—	(4.3%)

Best Buy Inc

Best Buy wants to be the best consumer electronics outlet in the US and beyond. The multinational retailer sells both products and services through three primary channels: retail stores online and call centers. Its branded store banners include Best Buy Best Buy Mobile The Carphone Warehouse The Phone House Five Star Future Shop Geek Squad Magnolia Audio Video and Pacific Sales. Its stores sell a variety of electronic gadgets movies music computers mobile phones and appliances. On the services side it offers installation and maintenance technical support and subscriptions for mobile phone and Internet services. Amid a decline in its business Best Buy's founder has offered to take it private.

HISTORY

Tired of working for a father who ignored his ideas on how to improve the business (electronics distribution) Dick Schulze quit. In 1966 with a partner he founded Sound of Music a Minnesota home/car stereo store. Schulze bought out his partner in 1971 and began to expand the chain. While chairing a school board Schulze saw declining enrollment and realized his target customer group 15- to 18-year-old males was shrinking. In the early 1980s he broadened his product line and targeted older more affluent customers by offering appliances and VCRs.

After a 1981 tornado destroyed his best store (but not its inventory) Schulze spent his entire marketing budget to advertise a huge parking-lot sale. The successful sale taught him the benefits of strong advertising and wide selection combined with low prices. In 1983 Schulze changed the company's name to Best Buy and began to open larger superstores. The firm went public two years later.

Buoyed by the format change and the fast-rising popularity of the VCR Best Buy grew rapidly. Between 1984 and 1987 it expanded from eight stores to 24 and sales jumped from $29 million to $240 million. In 1988 another 16 stores opened and sales jumped by 84%. But Best Buy began to butt heads with many expanding consumer electronics retailers and profits took a beating.

To set Best Buy apart from its competitors in 1989 Schulze introduced the Concept II warehouse-like store format. Thinking that customers could buy products without much help Schulze cut payroll by taking sales staff off commission and reducing the number of employees per store by about a third. The concept proved to be such a hit in the company's home territory Minneapolis/St. Paul that it drove major competitor Highland Appliance to bankruptcy. Customers were happy but many of Best Buy's suppliers believing sales help was needed to sell products pulled their products from Best Buy stores. The losses didn't seem to hurt Best Buy; it took on Sears and Montgomery Ward in the Chicago market in 1989 and continued expanding.

In 1994 the company debuted Concept III an even larger store format. Best Buy opened 47 new stores in 1995 but found itself swimming in debt. Earnings plummeted in fiscal 1997 partly due to a huge PC inventory made obsolete by Intel's newer product. Best Buy started selling CDs on its website in 1997. That year it realized it had overextended itself with its expansion super-sized stores and financing promotions. Best Buy underwent a speedy massive makeover by scaling back expansion and doing away with its policy of "no money down no monthly payments no interest" (and next-to-no profits).

In 1999 Best Buy began to enter new markets (including New England) and introduced its Concept IV stores which highlighted digital products and featured stations for computer software and DVD demonstrations. Also in 1999 Best Buy formed a separate subsidiary for its online operations (BestBuy.com Inc.) and invested $10 million in consumer electronics information website etown.com (etown.com closed down in February 2001).

In 2000 Best Buy agreed to pay $88 million for Seattle-based Magnolia Hi-Fi a privately held chain of 13 high-end audio and video stores. In early 2001 Best Buy bought The Musicland Group (at the time operator of more than 1300 Sam Goody Suncoast On Cue and Media Play music stores) for about $425 million. The company began its international expansion in November 2002 with its $377 million acquisition of Future Shop Canada's leading consumer electronics retailer. Over the next year Best Buy opened eight of its own Best Buy stores in Ontario Canada.

In June 2002 Schulze turned over his responsibilities as CEO to vice chairman Brad Anderson; Schulze remained as chairman of the board. Best Buy acquired Geek Squad a computer support provider for $3 million the same year.

Best Buy shut down more than 100 Musicland stores (90 Sam Goody music stores and 20 Suncoast video stores) and laid off about 700 employees in January 2003; in June it sold the entire Musicland subsidiary (then about 1100 stores) to an affiliate of investment firm Sun Capital Partners. Three years later Best Buy purchased Pacific Sales Kitchen and Bath Centers which sells appliances and offers assistance on residential remodeling for $410 million.

Philip Schoonover a top executive in charge of customer segments defected to rival Circuit City in 2004. The company also dismissed Ernst & Young as its independent auditor after a former board member disclosed personal business dealings with the firm.

In 2006 the chain acquired home appliance and remodeling retailer Pacific Sales Kitchen and Bath Centers for about $410 million.

To facilitate its expansion in China Best Buy purchased a 75% stake in Jiangsu Five Star Appliance Co. in May 2006 and later opened the first Best Buy store in China in Shanghai.

To enhance its technology product offering for small businesses Best Buy in fiscal 2008 acquired Seattle-based Speakeasy a provider of broadband voice data and IT services. The deal valued at some $97 million made Speakeasy a wholly owned subsidiary that operates through the Best Buy for Business unit. Speakeasy CEO Bruce Chatterley as well as his management team was retained to run the Speakeasy operation once the deal closed. In a bid to add digital music downloads to its playlist Best Buy acquired a majority stake in Napster for about $127 million. The retailer's 2008 purchase of the music-swapping service included Napster's approximately 700000 digital entertainment subscribers.

In June 2008 Best Buy acquired a 50% stake in Carphone Warehouse's European and US retail interests for about $2.2 billion. In late October the company acquired digital music pioneer Napster for about $127 million via a tender offer for the firm's shares.

In early 2009 the retailer acquired the 25% of China's Jiangsu Five Star Appliance that it didn't already own. It also entered the Mexican market with its first store there.

CEO Brad Anderson retired in mid-2009 and COO and longtime employee Brian Dunn took over as CEO. Dunn's stint as chief executive lasted about three years. The 28-year company veteran stepped down in April 2012 handing his CEO title in the interim to board director Mike Mikan.

EXECUTIVES

SVP Communications Public Affairs and Corporate Responsibility, Paula Prahl
Chairman, Richard M. (Dick) Schulze, age 70, $150,000 total compensation
Chairman, Hatim A. Tyabji, age 67
President and COO Best Buy Canada, Michael J. (Mike) Pratt, age 44
President CEO and Director, Hubert Joly, age 53
COO Best Buy Europe, Andrew Harrison, age 41
EVP Finance and CFO, James L. (Jim) Muehlbauer, age 50, $622,616 total compensation
SVP; CFO U.S. Strategic Business Unit, Ryan D. Robinson, age 46
VP Investor Relations, Bill Seymour
EVP Enterprise; President Asia, Kalendu (Kal) Patel, age 48
SVP Entertainment, Gary L. Arnold
SVP Merchandising, Michael Mohan
Senior Director and Global Lead Public Relations, Susan Busch
EVP; President Best Buy U.S., Michael A. (Mike) Vitelli, age 56, $553,445 total compensation
EVP; President Best Buy International, Shari L. Ballard, age 45, $650,001 total compensation
Director Investor Relations, Mollie O'Brien
Director Public Relations, Lisa Hawks
VP and Creative Director Best Buy On, William (Bill) Anderson
EVP and Chief Marketing Officer, Barry Judge, age 49
Interim CEO and Director, G. Mike Mikan III, age 40
VP Controller and Chief Accounting Officer, Susan S. Grafton, age 55
Connected World Strategies, Julie Owen, age 46
EVP Enterprise and Chief Administrative Officer, Timothy R. (Tim) Sheehan, age 47
VP and Territory General Manager, Bill Thompson
SVP Growth Operations and Assimilation, Neil McPhail
General Manager Napster Inc, Christopher W. Allen, age 46
EVP; President Digital and Global Business Services, Stephen Gillett
VP Enterprise Customer Care, Lisa Smith
SVP Enterprise, Sean Skelley, age 45
SVP Human Capital US Channels, Steve Hurst
President Best Buy Mobile, Shawn Score
SVP Business Customer Lead, Glen Swanson
VP and Territory General Manager Southeastern US, Mary Stoddart
VP Merchandising and Global Vendor Capabilities, Liz Haesler
VP and Territory General Manager, Monica Hubbard
VP and Territory General Manager, David Pullen
VP and Territory General Manager, Dean Kimberly
Senior Director Investor Relations, Andrew Lacko
VP Best Buy Capital, Kuk Yi
EVP and Chief Human Resources Officer, Carol A. Surface, age 46
SVP Consumer Insights, Bill Hoffman
SVP and Chief Design Officer, Aura Oslapas, age 55
VP Computing, Jason Bonfig
VP Finance and Treasurer, Chris Gould, age 43
Director Investor Relations, Adam Hauser
SVP US Marketing, Drew Panayiotou
EVP and General Counsel, Keith Nelson, age 48
Director, Rogelio M. Rebolledo, age 67
Director, Richard M. (Dick) Schulze, age 71
Director, Hatim A. Tyabji, age 66
Director, Matthew H. (Matt) Paull, age 61
Director, Gerard R. Vittecoq, age 63
Director and Board Secretary, Elliot S. Kaplan, age 75
President CEO and Director, Hubert Joly, age 53
Director, Kathleen J. (Kathy) Higgins Victor, age 55
Director, Ronald James, age 61
Director, Sanjay Khosla, age 60
Director, Lisa M. Caputo, age 48
Director, G. Mike Mikan III, age 40
Auditors: Deloitte&ToucheLLP

LOCATIONS

HQ: Best Buy Inc
7601 Penn Avenue South, Richfield, MN 55423
Phone: 612 291-1000
Web: www.bestbuy.com

2012 Sales

	$ mil.	% of total
US	37,615	74
Canada	5,635	11
Europe	5,228	10
China	2,069	4
Other	158	1
Total	**50,705**	**100**

2012 US Stores

	Best Buy	Best Buy Mobile	Pacific Sales	Magnolia Audio
Alabama	15	5	-	-
Alaska	2	-	-	-
Arizona	26	-	2	-
Arkansas	9	4	-	-
California	126	29	31	3
Colorado	23	5	-	-
Connecticut	12	3	-	-
Delaware	4	-	-	-

District of Columbia	2	1	-	-
Florida	67	30	-	-
Georgia	30	6	-	-
Hawaii	2	-	-	-
Idaho	5	-	-	-
Illinois	58	14	-	-
Indiana	23	11	-	-
Iowa	13	-	-	-
Kansas	10	2	-	-
Kentucky	9	5	-	-
Louisiana	16	6	-	-
Maine	6	-	-	-
Maryland	25	11	-	-
Massachusetts	29	11	-	-
Michigan	34	10	-	-
Minnesota	28	9	-	-
Mississippi	9	2	-	-
Missouri	21	7	-	-
Montana	3	-	-	-
Nebraska	6	3	-	-
Nevada	10	4	1	-
New Hampshire	6	3	-	-
New Jersey	27	7	-	-
New Mexico	5	1	-	-
New York	55	13	-	-
North Carolina	34	14	-	-
North Dakota	4	-	-	-
Ohio	39	10	-	-
Oklahoma	13	3	-	-
Oregon	12	3	-	-
Pennsylvania	38	12	-	-
Puerto Rico	4	-	-	-
Rhode Island	2	-	-	-
South Carolina	15	4	-	-
South Dakota	2	1	-	-
Tennessee	17	6	-	-
Texas	110	25	-	-
Utah	10	-	-	-
Vermont	1	-	-	-
Virginia	37	10	-	-
Washington	20	4	-	2
West Virginia	5	-	-	-
Wisconsin	23	10	-	-
Wyoming	1	1	-	-
Total			**34**	**5**

PRODUCTS/OPERATIONS

2012 Sales

	$ mil.	% of total
Domestic	37,615	74
International	13,090	26
Total	**50,705**	**100**

2012 Sales by Domestic Category

% of total	
Products	
Computing & mobile	40
Consumer	36
Entertainment	12
Appliances	5
Services	6
Other	1
Total	**100**

2012 Sales by International Category

% of total	
Products	
Computing & mobile	56
Consumer	20
Appliances	10
Entertainment	5
Services	9
Total	**100**

2012 US Stores by Brand

	No.
Best	1,103
Best Buy	305
Pacific	34
Magnolia Audio	5
Total	**1,447**

2012 International Stores by Brand

	No.
Best Buy	2,393
Canada	
Future	149
Best	77
Best Buy	30
China	
Five	204
Mexico	
Best	8
Total	**2,861**

Selected Brands

Domestic
- Best Buy
- Best Buy Mobile
- Geek Squad
- Magnolia Audio Video
- Pacific Sales

International
- Canada
  - Best Buy
  - Best Buy Mobile
  - Cell Shop
  - Connect Pro
  - Future Shop
  - Geek Squad
- China
  - Five Star
- Europe
  - The Carphone Warehouse
  - The Phone House
  - Geek Squad
- Mexico
  - Best Buy
  - Geek Squad

Selected Products

Consumer Electronics
- Audio
  - Car stereos
  - Home theater audio systems
  - MP3 players
  - Satellite radio systems
- Video
  - Digital cameras and camcorders
  - DVD players
  - Televisions

Computing and mobile phones
- Computers
- Networking equipment
- Office furniture
- Printers
- Scanners
- Supplies
- Telephones

Entertainment
- CDs
- Computer software
- DVDs
- Subscription plans
- Video game hardware and software

Appliances
- Dishwashers
- Microwave ovens
- Refrigerators
- Stoves and ranges
- Vacuum cleaners
- Washers and dryers

COMPETITORS

Amazon.com
Apple Inc.
ARTISTdirect
Audible Inc.
Barnes & Noble
Brilliant Digital Entertainment
Brookstone
Buy.com
Buzz Media
Conn' s
Costco Wholesale
Darty
Dell
Dixons Retail
eMusic.com
Home Depot
Lowe' s
MediaNet Digital
METRO AG
MSN
Myspace
Office Depot
OfficeMax
RadioShack
RealNetworks
Sears Holdings
Sony Music
Staples
Systemax
Target Corporation
Trans World Entertainment
Fry' s Electronics
Gateway Inc.
Hastings Entertainment
HMV
Virgin Group
Wal-Mart
Yahoo!

HISTORICAL FINANCIALS

Company Type: Public

Income Statement FYE: March 3

	REVENUE ($ mil.)	NET INCOME ($ mil.)	NET PROFIT MARGIN	EMPLOYEES
03/12*	50,705	(1,231)	—	167,000
02/11	50,272	1,277	2.5%	180,000
02/10	49,694	1,317	2.7%	180,000
02/09	45,015	1,003	2.2%	155,000
03/08	40,023	1,407	3.5%	150,000
Annual Growth	6.1%	—	—	2.7%

*Fiscal year change

2012 Year-End Financials

Debt ratio: 13.80%
Return on equity: (-32.87)%
Cash ($ mil.): 1,199
Current ratio: 116.28
Long-term debt ($ mil.): 1,685
No. of shares (mil.): 341
Dividends
Yield: —
Payout: 1036.36%
Market value ($ mil.): 8,299

	STOCK PRICE ($) FY Close	P/E High	P/E Low	PER SHARE ($) Earnings	Dividends	Book Value
03/12*	24.31	—	—	(3.36)	0.00	10.97
02/11	32.37	15	10	3.08	0.00	16.82
02/10	36.50	14	8	3.10	0.00	15.09
02/09	28.82	20	7	2.39	0.00	11.22
03/08	43.01	17	13	3.12	0.00	10.92
Annual Growth	(13.3%)	—	—	—	—	0.1%

*Fiscal year change

BFC Financial Corp.

Holding company BFC Financial controls Florida-based BankAtlantic and investment firm Woodbridge Holdings (formerly Levitt Corporation) which has holdings in real estate companies Core Communities and Bluegreen Corporation and restaurant franchise Pizza Fusion. (Famous for constructing Levittown New York —widely regarded as the first planned community in the US —Levitt filed for Chapter 11 bankruptcy protection in 2007 and re-emerged the following year as Woodbridge.) BFC also owns a minority stake in Asian-themed restaurant chain Benihana. Chairman president and CEO Alan Levan and vice chairman Jack Abdo control BFC Financial.

The company has felt the sting of the economic downturn particularly in its real estate holdings and from its stake in BankAtlantic which operates in the hard-hit Florida market. Nonetheless BFC in 2009 upped its stakes in both the bank and Bluegreen and it acquired the remaining stock in Woodbridge that it did not already own after abandoning plans for a similar deal two years earlier. The Bluegreen acquisition which was accounted for as a "bargain purchase" using fair-value estimates helped BFC return to profitability in 2009 after two years of losses. The company's Woodbridge subsidiary now plans to acquire the remaining 46% stake in Bluegreen it does not already own.

Its positive results were short-lived however and BFC reported losses of more than $100 million in 2010 as its subsidiaries continued to struggle. That year Pizza Fusion expressed doubts about its ability to continue as a going concern (for its part BFC said it would not make any new investments in the company after writing off its initial investment in 2009) and Benihana announced its intent to evaluate its strategic alternatives including a sale of the company.

In 2011 BankAtlantic entered into a Order to Cease and Desist with the Office of Thrift Supervision that stipulates that the bank improve its capital position. Later that year Southeast banking giant BB&T agreed to acquire BankAtlantic. Following the completion of the deal the bank's holding company BankAtlantic Bancorp will change its name to BBX Capital and continue to manage a portfolio of distressed assets transferred from the bank. It may eventually engage in real estate investment or specialty finance using proceeds from the sale of the assets.

There was a bright spot for BFC in 2011. Revenues were up and the company reported (only) a $12 million loss for the year mostly related to discontinued operations as its real estate business turned a profit.

EXECUTIVES

Vice Chairman BFC Financial and BankAtlantic, John E. (Jack) Abdo, age 69, $660,739 total compensation
Chairman President and CEO; Chairman and CEO BankAtlantic Bancorp, Alan B. Levan, age 67, $677,375 total compensation
EVP and CFO, John K. Grelle, age 68, $192,166 total compensation
SVP Investor Relations, Leo Hinkley Jr.
EVP and Director, Seth M. Wise, age 42
VP and Investor Relations Officer, Sharon Lyn
Chief Accounting Officer, Maria R. Scheker, age 54, $215,000 total compensation
EVP and Director, Jarett S. Levan, age 38
Vice Chairman BFC Financial and BankAtlantic, John E. (Jack) Abdo, age 69
Director, Darwin C. Dornbush, age 82
Director, D. Keith Cobb, age 71
EVP and Director, Seth M. Wise, age 42
Director, Oscar J. Holzmann, age 69
EVP and Director, Jarett S. Levan, age 38
Director, James J. Blosser, age 74
Auditors: PricewaterhouseCoopersLLP

LOCATIONS

HQ: BFC Financial Corporation
2100 W. Cypress Creek Rd., Fort Lauderdale FL 33309
Phone: 954-940-4900 **Fax:** 954-940-4910
Web: www.bfcfinancial.com

PRODUCTS/OPERATIONS

2011 Sales

	$ mil.	% of total
Real Estate & Other		
Sales of real estate	170	24
Interest	88	13
Other resorts fee-based revenue	71	10
Other	74	11
Financial Services		
Interest	143	20
Service charges on deposits	42	6
Gain on sale of Tampa branches	38	5
Other service charges & fees	26	4
Other non-interest income	19	3
Other	25	4
Total	**699**	**100**

COMPETITORS

Bank of America
BKF Capital Group
H.I.G. Capital
Huizenga Holdings
St. Joe
Sun Capital

HISTORICAL FINANCIALS

Company Type: Public

Income Statement FYE: December 31

	ASSETS ($ mil.)	NET INCOME ($ mil.)	INCOME AS % OF ASSETS	EMPLOYEES
12/11	4,778	(11)	—	5,119
12/10	5,813	(103)	—	5,084
12/09	6,047	25	0.4%	5,368
12/08	6,395	(58)	—	1,969
12/07	7,114	(30)	—	2,742
Annual Growth	(9.5%)	—	—	16.9%

2011 Year-End Financials

Debt ratio: 22.27%
Return on equity: (-8.62)%
Cash ($ mil.): 858
Current ratio: —
Long-term debt ($ mil.): 1,063
No. of shares (mil.): 77
Dividends
Yield: —
Payout: —
Market value ($ mil.): 27

	STOCK PRICE ($) FY Close	P/E High/Low	PER SHARE ($) Earnings	Dividends	Book Value
12/11	0.35	— —	(0.16)	0.00	1.70
12/10	0.37	— —	(1.39)	0.00	2.04
12/09	0.37	2 0	0.44	0.00	3.40
12/08	0.25	— —	(1.32)	0.00	2.75
12/07	1.51	— —	(0.81)	0.00	4.08
Annual Growth	(30.6%)	— —	—	—	(19.7%)

Big Lots, Inc.

Big Lots believes that a product's shelf life depends solely on which shelf it's on. The company is North America's #1 broadline closeout retailer with more than 1500 Big Lots stores in 48 US states and seven provinces in Canada. (About a third of its stores are located in California Florida Ohio and Texas.) It sells a variety of brand-name products including consumables furniture housewares seasonal items and toys that have been overproduced returned discontinued or result from liquidations typically at 20%-40% below discounters' prices. Its wholesale division sells its discounted merchandise to a variety of retailers manufacturers distributors and other wholesalers.

Geographic Reach

Big Lots entered the Canadian market in mid-2011 with its acquisition of the Liquidation World chain there for about $1.8 million plus debt. The purchase formed the foundation of the retailer's new Canadian subsidiary Big Lots Canada. The addition of the Canadian stores contributed an additional $62 million to Big Lots coffers in fiscal 2012 (ends January).

Financial Analysis

Big Lots sales grew by about 5% in fiscal 2012 (ends January) vs. the prior year driven by the addition of the Canadian stores. However the acquisition of Liquidation World proved to be a drain on profits. Indeed Liquidation World posted an operating loss of about $12 million for the year contributing to Big Lot's 7% decline in net income in fiscal 2012 vs. 2011. The company is forecasting fiscal 2013 sales in Canada of $140 million to $150 million.

Strategy

Big Lots has been working hard to rebound from declining growth in the US. The company has lost business to dollar store rivals such as Dollar Tree and Dollar General as well as other discount stores. To compensate it has focused on getting the most bang for its buck from its real estate and store locations. Indeed since the beginning of early 2009 the retailer has opened 224 new stores and closed about half a many in the US. The new Big Lots locations have produced positive performances and the company's gamble on high-dollar "A" locations as they've been deemed have exceeded its expectations. While these locations come with higher occupancy costs they often offer a market's best retail centers co-tenant mix and demographics. As of early 2012 the retailer had 66 "A" locations and is looking to add between 15 to 20 more in the coming year. Another key to the retailer's turnaround is its What's Important Now Strategy (or WIN strategy) which focuses on merchandising real estate and cost structure. Big Lots credits WIN with increasing its profitability. It has increased its sales per square foot from $146 per square foot in 2005 to $166 per square foot at present while also boosting gross margin dollars from $1.7 billion in 2005 to more than $2 billion in 2011. Now in the growth phase of the WIN strategy Big Lots plans to expand its net store network during fiscal 2013 by opening about 90 stores and shuttering 45 in the US.

Operations

Big Lots boasts five regional distribution centers one each in Alabama California Oklahoma Ohio and Pennsylvania to receive process and distribute the majority of its merchandise to its retail locations nationwide. (The retailer acquires a quarter of its merchandise from overseas vendors including about 20% from vendors in China.)

HISTORY

As a kid growing up in Columbus Ohio Russian-born Sol Shenk (pronounced "Shank") couldn't stand to pay full price for anything. His frugality blossomed into a knack for buying low and wholesaling. After a failed effort to make auto parts Shenk began the precursor to Consolidated Stores in 1967 backed by brothers Alvin Saul and Jerome Schottenstein.

The company started by wholesaling closeout auto parts and buying retailers' closeout items to sell to other retailers. By 1971 Shenk had branched into retailing selling closeout auto parts through a small chain of Corvair Auto Stores.

One of Shenk's sons suggested they devote space in the Corvair stores to closeout merchandise other than car parts. Sales surged and Shenk decided to sell the Corvair outlets and focus on closeout stores. The first Odd Lots opened in 1982. Consolidated grew more than 100% annually for the next three years. By 1986 the year after it went public the company was opening two stores a week in midsized markets around the Midwest.

Shenk found that people would buy anything as long as the price was right. Two years after the mania for Rubik's Cubes ended Odd Lots bought 6 million of the puzzles (once priced at $8) at 8 cents apiece marked them up 500% and sold them all.

By 1987 the company had nearly 300 Odd Lots/Big Lots stores. But runaway growth had created massive inventory shortages and losses as disappointed customers stopped browsing the company's sparsely stocked shelves. The woes coincided with a falling-out with the Schottensteins. Shenk retired in 1989.

Apparel and electronics retail executive William Kelley was named chairman and CEO the next year. Kelley returned Consolidated to its closeout roots and increased sales through acquisitions and creating new discount chains.

Consolidated doubled its size in 1996 with the $315 million purchase of more than 1000 struggling Kay-Bee Toys (now KB Toys) stores from Melville Corp. The expansion continued with the 1998 purchase of top closeout competitor Mac Frugal's Bargains - Closeouts. (Mac Frugal's had nearly bought Consolidated in 1989 before Consolidated board members vetoed the deal.) The $1 billion acquisition of Mac Frugal's gave Consolidated another 326 western stores under the Pic 'N' Save and Mac Frugal's names.

In 1999 Consolidated combined its online toy sales operations with those of BrainPlay.com to form KBkids.com. In mid-2000 Kelley was ousted as CEO handing the title over to CFO Michael Potter.

In December 2000 the company sold KB Toys (including KBkids.com) to a group led by KB management and global private equity firm Bain Capital for about $300 million. In mid-2001 the company changed its name to Big Lots and began converting all stores to that name to establish a national brand. Big Lots bought the inventory of bankrupt Internet home furnishings giant Living.com in June.

In 2002 the company completed converting 434 stores to the Big Lots banner including 380 stores previously operating under the names of Odd Lots Mac Frugal's and Pic 'N' Save. The name changes were part of a larger initiative to broaden the appeal of closeout retailing and to establish a unified national brand. During the year Big Lots opened 87 new stores and closed 42 others.

In 2003 Big Lots continued to remodel stores opened 86 new locations and closed 36 others. In 2004 the company opened about 100 new stores and continued to add furniture departments to its existing stores. Potter stepped down in July 2005. He was succeeded by Steven S. Fishman who became the company's chairman CEO and president. Fishman is a veteran of the Pamida Frank's Nursery & Crafts and Rhodes Furniture retail chains. Also that year Kelley unsuccessfully sought to join the Big Lots' board by asking large shareholders to elect him. Overall the company shuttered 174 stores in 2005 including 43 Big Lots Furniture stores and exited the frozen food business. Store closures continued in 2006 with a net loss of 25 locations.

In late 2006 the company reached tentative settlements of two employee-related class action suits including one by some 1400 Big Lots employees in Louisiana and Texas who alleged that they were wrongly classified as managers so that they could be denied overtime pay. The settlements amounted to nearly $10 million. (In 2004 Big Lots settled a similar suit brought by more than 1000 California employees by agreeing to pay $10 million.)

In July 2011 Big Lots acquired the Ontario Canada-based Liquidation World chain of 89 stores marking its entry into Canada.

EXECUTIVES

SVP Distribution and Transportation Services, Harold A. (Hal) Wilson, age 63
EVP Merchandising, Douglas N. (Doug) Wurl, age 50
EVP COO and CTO, Lisa M. Bachmann, age 50, $440,000 total compensation
EVP and Chief Administrative Officer, Charles W. Haubiel II, age 46
EVP and CFO; President Canada, Joe R. Cooper, age 54, $440,000 total compensation
SVP Big Lots Capital and Wholesale, Norman J. (Norm) Rankin, age 55
Chairman President and CEO, Steven S. (Steve) Fishman, age 60, $1,200,000 total compensation
VP and Divisional Merchandise Manager, Fred L. Fox, age 53
VP Loss Prevention, Kevin R. Wolfe
VP Transportation Services, Kathryn A. Keane
VP Divisional Merchandise Manager, Kim K. Horner
VP Store Operations Support, Timothy C. Anderson
VP Store Operations, William Coney
VP Real Estate, Kevin R. Day
VP Store Operations, Mollie M. Hall
VP Store Projects, Gary E. Huber
VP Wholesale, Steven B. Marcus
VP Distribution Support Services, Todd A. Noethen
VP Human Resources Services, Jo L. Roney
SVP Human Resources, Michael A. (Mike) Schlonsky
VP Tax, L. Michael Watts
VP Divisional Merchandise Manager, Robert Strenski
EVP Administration, John C. Martin, age 61, $520,000 total compensation
VP Merchandise Planning, Craig A. Hart
SVP and CFO, Timothy A. (Tim) Johnson, age 44
SVP and General Merchandise Manager Consumables Hardlines and Play and Wear, Steven R. Smart, age 52
VP Technology and Data Services, Richard L. Fannin
SVP and General Merchandise Manager Furniture Seasonal and Home Divisions, Robert S. (Bob) Segal, age 57
VP Allocation, Sharon A. Smith
VP Divisional Merchandise Manager, Wayne W. Stockton
VP Merchandise Support, Stewart Wenerstrom
SVP Marketing, Robert C. Claxton, age 57
VP and Controller, Paul A. Schroeder, age 46
VP Global Sourcing, Charles Ellis
VP Advertising, Shelley L. Rubin
VP Information Technology Development, Gregory W. Wilmer
Senior Buyer, Patrick S. Finley
VP Divisional Merchandise Manager, Karen L. Lutz-Lento
VP Store Operations, Thomas R. Myron
VP and Treasurer, Jared A. Poff
SVP Store Operations, Christopher T. (Chris) Chapin, age 48
VP Store Operations, Brian M. Bade
VP Divisional Merchandise Manager, L. Stephanie Brown
VP Store Operations, Virginia A. Chase
VP Real Estate Administration, Shawn F. Clancy
Director, Russell Solt, age 64
Director, James R. (Jim) Tener, age 62
Director, David T. Kollat, age 73
Director, Philip E. Mallott, age 54
Director, Brenda J. Lauderback, age 62
Director, Peter J. Hayes, age 70
Director, Dennis B. Tishkoff, age 68
Director, Jeffrey P. (Jeff) Berger, age 62
Auditors: Deloitte&ToucheLLP

LOCATIONS

HQ: Big Lots Inc.
300 Phillipi Rd., Columbus OH 43228-5311
Phone: 614-278-6800 **Fax:** 614-278-6676
Web: www.biglots.com

2012 US Stores

	No.
California	174
Texas	117
Florida	109
Ohio	108
Pennsylvania	70
North	68
Georgia	60
New	54
Michigan	48
Tennessee	47
Indiana	46
Kentucky	40
Virginia	37
Arizona	36
Illinois	34
South	34
Alabama	28
Missouri	28
Louisiana	23
Washington	23
Colorado	20
Massachusetts	20
Maryland	19
New	18
West	18
Oklahoma	17
Mississippi	14
Arkansas	13
Oregon	13
Nevada	12
New	12
Connecticut	11
Utah	11
Wisconsin	10
Kansas	9
Maine	7
Minnesota	7
New	7
Idaho	6
Delaware	4
Nebraska	4
Vermont	4
Iowa	3
Montana	2
North	2
Wyoming	2
Rhode	1
South	1
Total	**1,451**

2012 Canada Stores

	No.
Alberta	13
British	16
Manitoba	4
New	2
Nova	4
Ontario	37
Saskatchewan	6
Total	**82**

PRODUCTS/OPERATIONS

2012 US Sales

	$ mil.	% of total
Consumables	1,571	31
Furniture	883	17
Home	799	16
Play n' wear	776	15
Seasonal	683	13
Hardlines & other	425	8
Total	**5,140**	**100**

COMPETITORS

99 Cents Only
Amazon.com
BJ' s Wholesale Club
Costco Wholesale
Dollar General
Dollar Tree
Family Dollar Stores
Fred' s
Michaels Stores
Quality King
Ross Stores
Salvation Army
Sears
Simply Amazing
Target Corporation
TJX Companies

Goodwill Industries	Tuesday Morning Corporation
Gordon Brothers Group	Variety Wholesalers
J. C. Penney	Wal-Mart
Jo-Ann Stores	Walgreen
Kmart	

HISTORICAL FINANCIALS

Company Type: Public

Income Statement FYE: January 28

	REVENUE ($ mil.)	NET INCOME ($ mil.)	NET PROFIT MARGIN	EMPLOYEES
01/12	5,202	207	4.0%	37,400
01/11	4,952	222	4.5%	35,600
01/10	4,726	200	4.2%	35,600
01/09*	4,645	151	3.3%	37,000
02/08	4,656	158	3.4%	38,153
Annual Growth	2.8%	6.9%	—	(0.5%)

*Fiscal year change

2012 Year-End Financials

Debt ratio: 4.02%
Return on equity: 25.15%
Cash ($ mil.): 68
Current ratio: 172.13
Long-term debt ($ mil.): 65
No. of shares (mil.): 63
Dividends
Yield: —
Payout: —
Market value ($ mil.): 2,544

	STOCK PRICE ($) FY Close	P/E High/Low		PER SHARE ($) Earnings	Dividends	Book Value
01/12	40.00	15	10	2.99	0.00	12.94
01/11	31.82	14	10	2.83	0.00	12.81
01/10	28.41	13	5	2.42	0.00	12.22
01/09*	13.45	19	7	1.85	0.00	9.53
02/08	17.51	23	8	1.55	0.00	7.72
Annual Growth	22.9%	—	—	17.9%	—	13.8%

*Fiscal year change

Bilfinger SE

LOCATIONS

HQ: Bilfinger SE
Carl-Reiss-Platz 1-5,
Phone: (49) 6 21 459 0 **Fax:** (49) 6 21 459 23 66
Web: www.bilfingerberger.com

HISTORICAL FINANCIALS

Company Type:

Income Statement FYE: December 31

	REVENUE ($ mil.)	NET INCOME ($ mil.)	NET PROFIT MARGIN	EMPLOYEES
12/11	10,617	509	4.8%	59,210
12/10	10,715	380	3.5%	58,182
12/09	13,801	201	1.5%	60,838
12/08	13,641	280	2.1%	60,923
12/07	12,710	197	1.6%	52,723
Annual Growth	(4.4%)	26.8%	—	2.9%

2011 Year-End Financials

Debt ratio: 8.94%
Return on equity: 28.51%
Cash ($ mil.): 1,095
Current ratio: 97.09
Long-term debt ($ mil.): 672
No. of shares (mil.): 46
Dividends
Yield: —
Payout: —
Market value ($ mil.): 870

	STOCK PRICE ($) FY Close	P/E High/Low		PER SHARE ($) Earnings	Dividends	Book Value
12/11	18.91	4	3	11.55	0.00	50.25
12/10	15.14	5	3	8.61	0.00	52.43
12/09	15.50	9	4	5.46	0.00	48.15
Annual Growth	10.5%	—	—	45.4%	—	2.2%

Biogen Idec Inc

With its pipeline full of biotech drugs Biogen Idec aims to meet the unmet needs of patients around the world. The biotech giant is focused on developing treatments in the areas of immunology and neurology. Its product roster includes best-selling Avonex a popular drug for the treatment of relapsing multiple sclerosis (MS); Tysabri a drug treatment for MS and Crohn's disease (developed with Elan); Rituxan a monoclonal antibody developed jointly with Genentech that treats non-Hodgkin's lymphoma and rheumatoid arthritis; and Fumaderm a psoriasis drug marketed in Germany. Biogen Idec serves customers in more than 90 countries.

Operations

The company's top selling drug Avonex accounts for more than half of annual revenues. Avonex is marketed through Biogen Idec's direct sales force to specialist physicians and hospitals in North America Europe and select other countries around the globe. The firm started marketing the Avonex pen a single-use autoinjector version of the drug for once-weekly dosing in the EU and Canada in 2011. The device gained FDA approval for US marketing in early 2012.

The company also handles most of the global marketing efforts for the Elan-partnered MS therapy Tysabri which brings in about 20% of revenues —despite the drug's troubled regulatory history. Biogen Idec and Elan had to temporarily stop selling Tysabri in 2005 after several patients died from a rare neurological condition. The companies were allowed to reintroduce the drug in 2006 (when it was also launched in Europe) under a strict risk management plan that insured sufficient doctor and patient education about risks and proper usage. Despite its side effects Tysabri was approved as a treatment for Crohn's disease in the US in 2008 (under a similar patient monitoring program) and the companies continue to pursue additional uses for the drug.

Because Genentech handles sales and marketing duties for Rituxan Biogen Idec's Rituxan sales (accounting for another 20% of revenues) are counted as "unconsolidated joint business." In addition to non-Hodgkin's lymphoma and rheumatoid arthritis Rituxan was approved by the FDA to treat leukemia in 2010 and follicular lymphoma and two forms of vasculitis in 2011.

Another partnership this time with Acorda Therapeutics proved successful in 2011 when Biogen Idec gained approval to sell MS treatment Fampyra in the European Union. Biogen Idec expanded the drug's reach when it launched Fampyra in Canada in early 2012. Acorda sells the drug as Ampyra in the US market.

In addition to gaining revenue from the development and sales of its products (both directly and through partnerships) Biogen Idec receives royalties on some patents it has licensed to other companies. For instance The Medicines Company pays royalties on sales of anticoagulant Angiomax.

Strategy

Biogen Idec's pipeline of drug candidates is focused on treatments for central nervous system ailments including Alzheimer's MS amyotrophic lateral sclerosis (ALS) hemophilia neuropathic pain and lupus. The company has collaborative development candidates with Genentech and other drugmakers and it continuously looks to expand its pipeline through acquisitions and partnerships.

In 2011 the company partnered with Portola Pharmaceuticals on new lupus and rheumatoid arthritis treatments in a deal worth up to $550 million and in 2012 Biogen Idec entered a collaboration worth up to $300 million with Isis Pharmaceuticals to partner on Isis' spinal muscular atrophy candidate. Also in 2012 Biogen Idec formed a collaborative research project to research thegenetic causes of ALS with a number of research institutions that aim to map the genomes of hundreds of ALS patients.

Branching out in a new direction Biogen Idec entered a joint venture agreement with Samsung BioLogics in late 2011 with the goal of developing and selling biosimilars (generic biologic drugs). The venture named Samsung Bioepis was formally established in early 2012; construction was also started on a research and development center in Korea that year to serve as a headquarters for the venture.

Mergers and Acquisitions

In 2012 Biogen Idec expanded its immunology pipeline when it acquired biotech R&D firm Stromedix for $75 million in upfront cash with additional contingent value payments of up to $490 million. Stromedix focuses on developing antibody therapies for conditions including fibrosis and organ failure.

In 2011 Biogen Idec moved to expand its direct commercial presence to about 30 countries (with hopes of bolstering international sales) by buying out long-time partner Dompe Group's shares in their joint ventures in Italy and Switzerland for an undisclosed price. It renamed the affiliate offices Biogen Idec Italia and Biogen Idec Switzerland.

In 2010 the company expanded its neurological pipeline by acquiring Panima Pharmaceuticals a subsidiary of Neurimmune for $33 million (plus another $395 million in potential milestone payments).

Company Background

Activist investor Carl Icahn held a minority stake in the company for several years and kept a watchful eye over his investment in Biogen Idec until he sold his shares in the firm in 2011. In 2007 he bullied the company to put itself up for sale but no buyer came through. Then he began a series of proxy battles in an attempt to stack the board with his own nominees to gain further control. By 2010 he had secured three seats on the board filled with his own representatives and resumed talk of seeing Biogen Idec broken into parts and/or sold to a larger pharmaceutical company.

Ichan's persistence might have contributed to the retirement of Biogen Idec's long-time CEO James Mullen in mid-2010 with George Scangos (former CEO of Exelixis) stepping in as Mullen's replacement. Scangos implemented sharp changes in late 2010 launching a reorganization plan aimed at reducing operational costs and increasing efficiencies. The plan included a 13% workforce reduction and a streamlining of R&D programs to focus primarily on neurological disease. Biogen Idec halted or licensed out its oncology and cardiovascular development programs and consolidated a number of US sites. As a sign that he was pleased with Mullen's work in early 2011 Icahn reduced his ownership stake and did not seek to gain control of more board seats; he sold his remaining interests in the firm in mid-2011.

Biogen Idec was formed out of the 2003 merger of IDEC Pharmaceuticals and Biogen.

EXECUTIVES

CEO and Director, George A. Scangos, age 64
EVP Research and Development, Douglas E. (Doug) Williams, age 53
EVP Corporate Development, Steven H. Holtzman, age 57
Chairman, William D. Young, age 67
EVP General Counsel and Corporate Secretary, Susan H. Alexander, age 55, $518,173 total compensation
EVP Human Resources, Kenneth A. (Ken) DiPietro, age 53
EVP Finance and CFO, Paul J. Clancy, age 50, $524,231 total compensation
EVP Global Commercial Operations, Tony Kingsley, age 48
EVP Pharmaceutical Operations and Technology, John G. Cox, age 49
VP Chief Accounting Officer and Controller, Robert E. Gagnon, age 37
Director, Caroline Dorsa, age 52
CEO and Director, George A. Scangos, age 64
Director, Stelios Papadopoulos, age 64
Director, Stephen A. (Steve) Sherwin, age 63
Director, Nancy L. Leaming, age 64
Director, Robert W. Pangia, age 60
Director, Lynn Schenk, age 67
Director, Brian S. Posner, age 50
Director, Alexander J. (Alex) Denner, age 42
Director, Richard C. Mulligan
Director, Eric K. Rowinsky, age 55
Auditors: PricewaterhouseCoopersLLP

LOCATIONS

HQ: Biogen Idec Inc.
133 Boston Post Rd., Weston MA 02493
Phone: 781-464-2000 **Fax:** 408-513-1600
Web: www.zilog.com

2011 Sales

	$ mil.	% of total
US	3,020	60
Europe		
Germany	378	8
Other European countries	1,221	24
Asia	119	2
Other regions & countries	309	6
Total	**5,048**	**100**

PRODUCTS/OPERATIONS

2011 Sales

	$ mil.	% of total
Products		
Tysabri	1,079	21
Unconsolidated joint business (Genentech collaboration)	996	20
Total	**5,048**	**100**

Selected Products

Approved
- Avonex (multiple sclerosis)
- Fampyra (multiple sclerosis with Acorda Therapeutics)
- Fumaderm (severe psoriasis in Germany only)
- Rituxan (non-Hodgkin' s lymphoma chronic lymphocytic leukemia follicular lymphoma rheumatoid arthritis vasculitis)
- Tysabri (multiple sclerosis Crohn' s disease; with Elan Pharmaceuticals)

In development
- BG-12 (relapsing multiple sclerosis)
- Daclizumab (multiple sclerosis)
- Dexpramipexole (amyotrophic lateral sclerosis)
- GA101 (leukemia)
- Factor V111 Fc (hemophilia A)
- Factor IX Fc (hemophilia B)
- PEGylated interferon beta 1a (multipler sclerosis)

COMPETITORS

Abbott Labs
Amgen
Bayer HealthCare Pharmaceuticals
Bristol-Myers Squibb
Cephalon
Genmab
GlaxoSmithKline
Johnson & Johnson
Merck Serono
Millennium: The Takeda Oncology Company
Novartis
Pfizer
Roche Holding
Sanofi
Teva
UCB

HISTORICAL FINANCIALS

Company Type: Public

Income Statement

FYE: December 31

	REVENUE ($ mil.)	NET INCOME ($ mil.)	NET PROFIT MARGIN	EMPLOYEES
12/11	5,048	1,234	24.5%	5,000
12/10	4,716	1,005	21.3%	4,850
12/09	4,377	970	22.2%	4,750
12/08	4,097	783	19.1%	4,700
12/07	3,171	638	20.1%	4,300
Annual Growth	12.3%	17.9%	—	3.8%

2011 Year-End Financials

Debt ratio: 11.76%
Return on equity: 19.21%
Cash ($ mil.): 514
Current ratio: 325.94
Long-term debt ($ mil.): 1,060
No. of shares (mil.): 242
Dividends
Yield: —
Payout: —
Market value ($ mil.): 26,645

	STOCK PRICE ($) FY Close	P/E High/Low		PER SHARE ($) Earnings	Dividends	Book Value
12/11	110.05	23	13	5.04	0.00	26.54
12/10	67.05	17	12	3.94	0.00	22.44
12/09	53.50	16	13	3.35	0.00	22.64
12/08	47.63	27	15	2.65	0.00	20.16
12/07	56.92	41	21	1.99	0.00	18.72
Annual Growth	17.9%	—	—	26.2%	—	9.1%

BlackRock, Inc.

Now this is the kind of coal you want in your stocking. BlackRock with more than $3.5 trillion under management is the world's largest money manager. The firm specializes in equity and fixed income products as well as alternative and multi-class instruments which it invests in on behalf of institutional and retail investors worldwide; it does not engage in proprietary trading. Clients include pension plans governments insurance companies mutual funds endowments foundations and charities. BlackRock also provides risk management services through BlackRock Solutions and is a leading provider of exchange-traded funds (ETFs) through iShares. BlackRock has offices in some 25 countries.

CEO Laurence Fink who has overseen a string of major acquisitions in recent years engineered a blockbuster merger with Barclays Global Investors (BGI) in 2009. In the deal which was several years in the making BlackRock bought Barclays Global Investors from UK banking giant Barclays for some $15 billion. The deal resulted in a new company operating under the BlackRock name. Barclays Bank retained a 20% stake in the combined firm but Fink remained in charge of the enterprise.

The merger nearly tripled BlackRock's assets under management and propelled the company to the top of the international money management industry by enhancing its investment and risk management capabilities. The deal also gave BlackRock a much larger footprint outside the US and added more than 3500 new employees. Revenues nearly doubled in the year after the merger.

Growth continued in 2011 when the company reported $9.1 billion in revenues (a rise of 5%) and net income of $2.3 billion (a rise of 13%). BlackRock has benefitted from unrest in the global markets as clients move their funds into more passive investments like equity and fixed income assets.

Even prior to the Barclays Global deal BlackRock was growing rapidly through acquisitions gobbling up smaller firms and other opportunities in the marketplace. The growth has continued albeit on a smaller scale post-merger. In 2012 BlackRock expanded in Canada through the acquisition of fund manager Claymore Investments. Also that year the company agreed to buy Swiss Re Private Equity Partners the European private equity and infrastructure fund of funds business of Swiss Re which will expand its own private equity fund of funds group into infrastructure investing as well as broadening its presence in Europe and Asia.

Stateside BlackRock acquired most of the assets of South Carolina-based Helix Financial Group in 2010. The deal enhanced BlackRock's real estate analytics capabilities in addition to adding offices and personnel in the US and India. BlackRock also oversees the operations of publicly traded real estate investment trust Anthracite Capital.

The company has amassed quite an impressive portfolio of holdings and is often the largest shareholder of entities it invests in (including General Electric Exxon Mobil and BP.) BlackRock traditionally focused investments on developed economies but the company has broadened its sights to include emerging markets in Asia the Middle East and Latin America. The firm plans to expand its client base further to the point where it does more than half of its business outside the US. (Approximately 44% of its client assets under management come from outside the US.)

BlackRock Realty partnered with Tishman Speyer to buy Stuyvesant Town-Peter Cooper Village in New York City from Met Life for $5.4 billion in 2006. The deal was one of the largest in US history but proved unfortunate in the wake of the real estate and credit market crashes. In 2010 BlackRock and Tishman Speyer defaulted on the $4.4 billion debt used to finance the transaction and the property was handed over to creditors.

Bank of America gained a 34% stake in BlackRock when it acquired Merrill Lynch (and its BlackRock holdings) in 2009. The bank reduced its stake in BlackRock to less than 10% in 2010 and announced plans to sell the remainder of its holdings to the company for more than $2.5 billion the following year. PNC Financial Services Group is the company's largest shareholder owning 24% of its voting common shares.

EXECUTIVES

VP Corporate Communications Hong Kong, Sabrina Leung

President and Director, Robert S. (Rob) Kapito, age 54, $400,000 total compensation
Chairman and CEO, Laurence D. (Larry) Fink, age 59, $500,000 total compensation
Vice Chairman and Global Chief Investment Officer Equitiy, Robert C. (Bob) Doll, age 57, $400,000 total compensation
Senior Managing Director and Head Global Client Group, Robert W. (Rob) Fairbairn, age 46
Senior Managing Director and Chief Risk Officer, Bennett W. Golub, age 54
Senior Managing Director and COO, Charles S. Hallac, age 47, $300,000 total compensation
Senior Managing Director and Head Portfolio Management Group, J. Richard Kushel, age 45
Managing Director and Chief Accounting Officer, Joseph Feliciani Jr.
Managing Director and CIO, Thomas M. Fortin
Chief Performance Officer Fixed Income, Andrew J. Phillips
Deputy Chief Investment Officer Fixed Income Fundamental Portfolios; Head European and Non-US Fixed Income, Scott F. Thiel
Managing Director and Co-Head FMA Portfolio Management, Roland E. Villacorta
Managing Director and Co-Head FMA Portfolio Management, Ryan Marshall
Managing Director Fundamental Equity and Chief Investment Officer Europe Middle East Africa and Pacific Equity, Quintin Price
Vice Chairman, Susan L. Wagner, age 49, $300,000 total compensation
Vice Chairman, Kendrick R. Wilson III, age 65
Managing Director and Head US Fiduciary Management Solutions, Nancy C. Everett
Managing Director and Global Head Financial Markets Advisory Group, Craig S. Phillips
Managing Director and Head of UK Institutional Account Management, Juliet Bullick
Managing Director Client Advisory Services Financial Markets Advisory Group, Debra Huddleston
Managing Director Corporate Global, Bobbie Collins
Director Corporate, Brian Beades
Director Corporate and iShares London, Emma Phillips
Managing Director Corporate and iShares Asia, Katherine Cheung
Director Corporate Taiwan, Stephanie Chang
Head Retail Business UK, Alex Hoctor-Duncan
Chief Investment Officer Fixed Income Fundamental Portfolios; Head Corporate Credit Multi Sector and Mortgage Group, Rick M. Rieder
Senior Managing Director and Global Head Marketing and Communications, Linda Gosden Robinson, age 59
Senior Managing Director and CFO, Ann Marie Petach, age 51, $450,000 total compensation
Director iShares Hong Kong, Angela Yeung
VP Media Relations Melbourne Australia, Libby O'Sullivan
Managing Director iShares San Francisco, Lance Berg
Director iShares San Francisco, Christine Hudacko
Director Media Relations London, Rebecca Nelson
Director Corporate and iShares London, Caroline Hancock
Director Media Relations Tokyo, Tomoko Yamaki
Director Corporate and iShares Sydney, Debbie Pearce
Managing Director and Head BlackRock Solutions EMEA, Maarten Slendebroek
Managing Director Client Advisory Services FMA Group, Zach Buchwald
Managing Director Client Advisory Services FMA Group, Samuel (Sam) Coleman
Managing Director Client Advisory Services FMA Group, Martin Small
Managing Director and Head Financial Institutions, Kevin Holt
Managing Director and Head Municipal Bonds, Peter Hayes
Managing Director and CIO Fixed Income Index and Model-Based Portfolios; Head Index and Model-Based Fixed Income, Peter Knez
Head Trading for Fixed Income, Richard Prager
Managing Director and Country Head Brazil, Luiz F. Pinheiro de Andrade, age 58
Global Head iShares, Mike Latham, age 46
Senior Managing Director and Chairman Europe Middle East & Africa, N. James Charrington, age 59
Senior Managing Director and Head Human Resources, Jeffrey A. Smith, age 41
Head Latin America and Iberia, Daniel Gamba
Chief Investment Officer US Fundamental Equity, Chris Leavy
Senior Managing Director; Chairman Asia Pacific, Mark McCombe, age 45
Senior Managing Director and General Counsel, Matthew J. Mallow, age 68
Director, Mathis Cabiallavetta, age 67
Director, Sir Deryck Maughan, age 64
Director, Robert E. (Bob) Diamond Jr., age 60
Director, Murry S. Gerber, age 59
Director, Dennis D. Dammerman, age 66
Director, David H. Komansky, age 72
Director, James E. (Jim) Rohr, age 63
Director, Thomas H. O'Brien, age 75
President and Director, Robert S. (Rob) Kapito, age 54
Director, John S. Varley, age 55
Director, Ivan G. Seidenberg, age 65
Director, James Grosfeld, age 74
Director, William S. (Bill) Demchak, age 49
Director, Thomas K. (Tom) Montag, age 55
Vice Chairman, Susan L. Wagner, age 49
Vice Chairman, Kendrick R. Wilson III, age 65
Director, Abdlatif Y. Al-Hamad, age 74
Director, Marco Antonio Slim Domit, age 44
Auditors: Deloitte&ToucheLLP

LOCATIONS

HQ: BlackRock Inc.
55 E. 52nd St., New York NY 10055
Phone: 212-810-5300 **Fax:** 212-810-8760
Web: www.blackrock.com

2011 Sales by Region

	$ mil.	% of total
Americas	6,064	67
Europe	2,517	28
Asia/Pacific	500	5
Total	**9,081**	**100**

PRODUCTS/OPERATIONS

2011 Sales

	$ mil.	% of total
Investment advisory securities lending & administration fees		
Related parties	5,303	58
Other third parties	2,593	29
BlackRock Solutions & advisory	510	6
Investment advisory performance fees	371	4
Distribution fees	100	1
Other	204	2
Total	**9,081**	**100**

2011 Sales by Business Line

	$ bil.	% of total
Investment advisory administration fees & securities lending		
Equity	4,447	49
Fixed income	1,659	18
Multi-asset class	914	10
Alternative investments	864	10
Cash management	383	4
BlackRock Solutions & advisory	510	6
Distribution fees	100	1
Other	204	2
Total	**9,081**	**100**

COMPETITORS

Allianz Global Investors
Bank of New York Mellon
Charles Schwab
Dimensional Fund Advisors
Federated Investors
Legg Mason
Morgan Stanley
Principal Global
State Street
UBS
Waddell & Reed

HISTORICAL FINANCIALS

Company Type: Public

Income Statement

FYE: December 31

	REVENUE ($ mil.)	NET INCOME ($ mil.)	NET PROFIT MARGIN	EMPLOYEES
12/11	9,081	2,337	25.7%	10,100
12/10	8,612	2,063	24.0%	9,127
12/09	4,700	875	18.6%	8,629
12/08	5,064	786	15.5%	5,341
12/07	4,844	995	20.5%	5,952
Annual Growth	17.0%	23.8%	—	14.1%

2011 Year-End Financials

Debt ratio: 2.66%
Return on equity: 9.33%
Cash ($ mil.): 3,506
Current ratio: 225.12
Long-term debt ($ mil.): 4,690
No. of shares (mil.): 138
Dividends
Yield: —
Payout: 44.46%
Market value ($ mil.): 24,680

	STOCK PRICE ($) FY Close	P/E High	P/E Low	PER SHARE ($) Earnings	Dividends	Book Value
12/11	178.24	16	11	12.37	0.00	180.90
12/10	190.58	23	13	10.55	4.00	198.86
12/09	232.20	39	15	6.11	3.12	393.06
12/08	134.15	38	16	5.91	3.12	102.87
12/07	216.80	29	19	7.53	2.68	99.92
Annual Growth	(4.8%)	—	—	13.2%	—	16.0%

BNC Bancorp

BNC Bancorp knows the ABCs of the financial world. The firm is the holding company for Bank of North Carolina which has about 35 locations in both North and South Carolina. The bank offers community-oriented services to local business and retail customers providing checking savings and money market accounts credit cards and certificates of deposit. Its loan portfolio is mainly composed of residential and commercial mortgages and construction loans. Bank of North Carolina also offers insurance retirement planning and other investment products and services. BNC Bancorp is buying First Trust Bank which has three branches in the Charlotte area for some $35 million.

The deal is the latest in a string of acquisitions for BNC Bancorp. In 2010 the company acquired the failed Beach First National Bank in an FDIC-facilitated transaction expanding Bank of North Carolina's branch network into South Carolina. The 2012 acquisitions of Regent Bank further extended the bank's reach in the state. BNC Bancorp acquired another failed bank in 2011 with assistance from the FDIC Blue Ridge Savings Bank in North Carolina. The following year it bought the single-branch KeySource Financial also in North Carolina.

In 2010 Aquiline Capital Partners a private equity firm specializing in the financial services industry invested nearly $35 million in BNC Bancorp. The transaction netted the investor approximately 10% of the bank holding company as well as convertible shares that could equate to an additional 15% stake.

EXECUTIVES

Chairman Emeritus, W. Groome Fulton Jr., age 73
President CEO and Director; President and CEO Bank of North Carolina, W. Swope Montgomery Jr., age 63, $345,200 total compensation
EVP COO and Director; EVP and COO Bank of North Carolina, Richard D. Callicutt II, age 52, $268,650 total compensation
EVP and CFO BNC and Bank of North Carolina, David B. Spencer, age 49, $251,200 total compensation
Secretary and Director, Richard F. Wood, age 67
SVP and City Executive Lexington Bank of North Carolina, William H. McMurray III, $141,600 total compensation
Chairman of the Board, Thomas R. Sloan, age 67
SVP Bank of North Carolina, Thomas N. Nelson, $172,800 total compensation
President CEO and Director; President and CEO Bank of North Carolina, W. Swope Montgomery Jr., age 63
EVP COO and Director; EVP and COO Bank of North Carolina, Richard D. Callicutt II, age 52
Director, Robert A. Team Jr., age 56
Director, Larry L. Callahan, age 64
Director, Joseph M. Coltrane Jr., age 65
Director, Lenin J. Peters, age 60
Director, Thomas R. Smith, age 63
Director, D. Vann Williford, age 63
Secretary and Director, Richard F. Wood, age 67
Director, Charles T. Hagan III, age 63
Chairman of the Board, Thomas R. Sloan, age 67
Director Emeritus, Bob M. Burleson
Director Emeritus, John J. Collett Jr.
Director Emeritus, Lloyd M. Higgins
Auditors: CherryBekaert&HollandLLP

LOCATIONS

HQ: BNC Bancorp
831 Julian Ave., Thomasville NC 27360
Phone: 336-476-9200 **Fax:** 336-476-5818
Web: www.bankofnc.com

PRODUCTS/OPERATIONS

2008 Sales

	$ mil.	% of total
Interest		
Loans including fees	64	85
Debt securities	5	7
Other	0	1
Noninterest		
Service charges	3	4
Mortgage fees	0	1
Other	1	2
Total	**76**	**100**

COMPETITORS

Bank of America
Bank of the Carolinas
BB&T
Carolina Bank
First Bancorp (NC)
First Citizens BancShares
FNB United
NewBridge Bancorp
Piedmont Federal
Southern Community
Financial
Wells Fargo

HISTORICAL FINANCIALS

Company Type: Public

Income Statement FYE: December 31

	ASSETS ($ mil.)	NET INCOME ($ mil.)	INCOME AS % OF ASSETS	EMPLOYEES
12/11	2,454	6	0.3%	455
12/10	2,149	7	0.4%	372
12/09	1,634	6	0.4%	262
12/08	1,572	3	0.3%	222
12/07	1,130	7	0.7%	223
Annual Growth	21.4%	(1.8%)	—	19.5%

2011 Year-End Financials

Debt ratio: 3.82%
Return on equity: 4.23%
Cash ($ mil.): 55
Current ratio: —
Long-term debt ($ mil.): 93
No. of shares (mil.): 9
Dividends
Yield: —
Payout: 44.44%
Market value ($ mil.): 66

	STOCK PRICE ($) FY Close	P/E High/Low		PER SHARE ($) Earnings	Dividends	Book Value
12/11	7.25	20	14	0.45	0.00	18.00
12/10	9.00	17	11	0.61	0.20	16.81
12/09	7.59	13	8	0.62	0.20	17.19
12/08	7.51	32	14	0.52	0.20	16.42
12/07	16.91	19	15	1.05	0.18	11.90
Annual Growth	(19.1%)	—	—	(19.1%)	—	10.9%

Boeing Co. (The)

Boeing has built a big name for itself as one of the world's largest aerospace companies. It is the #2 maker of large commercial jets behind Airbus and the #2 defense contractor behind Lockheed Martin. In addition to commercial jet aircraft like the much anticipated 787 Dreamliner the company manufactures military aircraft including the Apache the Chinook and the Osprey. It also produces satellites missile defense systems and launch systems. These products are rounded out by a portfolio of services. Major customers include the US Department of Defense and NASA. Additionally Boeing provides airplane financing and leasing services to both commercial and military customers.

HISTORY

Bill Boeing who had already made his fortune in Washington real estate built his first airplane in 1916 with naval officer Conrad Westervelt. His Seattle company Pacific Aero Products changed its name to Boeing Airplane Company the next year. During WWI Boeing built training planes for the US Navy and began the first international airmail service (between Seattle and Victoria British Columbia). The company added a Chicago-San Francisco route in 1927 and established an airline subsidiary Boeing Air Transport. The airline's success was aided by Boeing's Model 40A the first plane to use Frederick Rentschler's new air-cooled engine.

Rentschler and Boeing combined their companies as United Aircraft and Transport in 1929 and introduced the all-metal airliner in 1933. The next year new antitrust rules forced United Aircraft and Transportation to sell portions of its operations as United Air Lines and United Aircraft (later United Technologies). This left Boeing Airplane (as it was known until 1961) with the manufacturing concerns.

During WWII Boeing produced such planes as the B-17 "Flying Fortress" and B-29 bombers. At one point the company was producing 362 planes per month for the war effort.

Between 1935 and 1965 Boeing's commercial planes included the Model 314 Clipper the Model 307 Stratoliner (with the first pressurized cabin) and the 707 (the first successful jetliner) and 727. In the 1960s it built the rockets used in the Apollo space program. The company delivered the first 737 in 1967. The 747 (the first jumbo jet) also went into production in the late 1960s.

Boeing expanded its information services and aerospace capabilities by establishing Boeing Computer Services in 1970. World fuel shortages and concern over aircraft noise prompted Boeing to design the efficient 757 and 767 models in the late 1970s.

The company's wide-body 777 made its maiden flight in 1995. Boeing bought Rockwell's aerospace and defense operations in 1996. The next year it purchased rival and leading military aircraft maker McDonnell Douglas for $16 billion.

Boeing's commercial rocket program was thrown into turmoil after its Delta III rocket exploded in 1998 during its maiden launch. However the US Air Force awarded the bulk of a satellite-launching contract to Boeing over rival Lockheed Martin. In 1999 Boeing stole another major government contract from Lockheed Martin –an estimated $4.5 billion job to make spy satellites for the CIA.

Boeing acquired Hughes Electronics' satellite-making unit (now The DIRECTV Group) in a $3.85 billion deal in 2000. It also signed an $8.9 billion contract to provide the Navy with 222 of Boeing's new F/A-18E/F Super Hornet fighter aircraft.

In 2001 the company stopped development of its 747X (no customers had ordered the super-jumbo) to focus on the smaller faster and longer-range 20XX which featured a double delta wing and two smaller wings near the nose of the plane enabling it to travel at Mach 0.95. However in a nod to the heavy-jetliner market the company also announced plans to build a larger longer-range 747-400.

Boeing officially moved its corporate headquarters from Seattle to Chicago in September 2001. The airline industry was rocked on the 11th of that month when terrorists crashed hijacked commercial jets in New York City near Washington DC and in rural Pennsylvania. As airlines reduced their flight schedules in the aftermath Boeing announced that it would lay off 25000-30000 people (about 30% of its commercial aviation workforce) by the end of 2002 (12000 by the end of 2001 and 8000 more by mid-2002). When it rains it pours: In October of 2001 it was announced that Boeing lost out to Lockheed Martin for the Joint Strike Fighter contract.

Early in 2002 Boeing cut a deal with Ryanair for 100 new aircraft with options on another 50 potentially worth around $9 billion. That July Boeing combined its space and defense units in a bid to boost efficiency. The next month Boeing and the Air Force signed a $9.7 billion deal for 60 C-17 Globemaster III transport aircraft. Boeing narrowly avoided a strike in September when 61% of its machinists union members voted to strike rather than to ratify a new contract. Since union rules required that 67% vote in favor of a strike the contract was automatically accepted.

After scrapping plans for the Sonic Cruiser late in 2002 Boeing announced the following year that it was working on the 7E7 (now renamed the 787) a long-range super-efficient mid-size plane able to seat as many as 250 passengers.

Boeing was found to have obtained a 1998 launch contract with the help of confidential Lockheed Martin documents and in 2003 was barred from bidding on launch contracts for almost two years. Even higher-profile was the scandal in which Boeing recruited Darleen Druyun —then the Air Force's #2 procurement officer —for a high-level position with Boeing thus violating conflict of interest laws. She reportedly shared inside information with Boeing and helped the company land a contract for 100 767 refueling tankers. The deal eventually collapsed under the weight of the scandal. Michael Sears Boeing's former CFO was sentenced to four months in prison for his role in the incident; Druyun received nine months. Chairman and CEO Phil Condit resigned in the wake of the scandals and was replaced by Harry Stonecipher in late 2003.

The US Army canceled the Comanche scout helicopter program in early 2004. Boeing and partner Sikorsky expected to deliver more than 600 of the craft during the course of the $38 billion program. Later that year Boeing sold 50 of its 787 Dreamliners to All Nippon Airways in a deal worth about $6 billion at list prices. Boeing formally launched the Dreamliner upon receipt of the order. In June Boeing was selected as the prime contractor for a new maritime multi-role airplane to replace the aging P-3 Orion beating out rival Lockheed Martin. The design contract was worth almost $4 billion.

Later that year the US Congress nixed a controversial $23 billion deal for Boeing to lease refueling tankers to the military. Refueling tankers were still needed but Boeing was likely to see a smaller deal and competition from Airbus. Boeing announced in 2004 that it would build a cargo version of its 777 plane for flight in 2008.

Boeing ended production of the 717 in 2005 and took a $615 million charge. The company landed a huge deal soon after when six Chinese airlines agreed to buy 60 Dreamliners worth more than $7 billion at list prices. Also that year Boeing sold its Rocketdyne business to Pratt & Whitney for about $700 million. It sold three manufacturing plants in Kansas and Oklahoma to Canadian investment company Onex Corporation for about $1.2 billion ($900 million cash and the assumption of $300 million in liabilities). The Onex deal guaranteed that the plants would still make parts and structures for Boeing but also freed up the facilities to seek business from other aircraft makers. Irish airline Ryanair ordered 140 737 planes (70 firm orders and 70 options) in a deal worth about $4 billion. Around the same time Boeing completed the sale of its Electron Dynamic Devices business to L-3 Communications.

Though CEO Stonecipher announced he would step down in 2006 at the age of 70 he was forced to resign in 2005 when an internal investigation revealed that he had been having an extramarital relationship with another Boeing executive. CFO James Bell served as interim president and CEO until W. James McNerney Jr. former head of 3M was named chairman president and CEO in the summer of 2005. Before joining 3M in 2001 McNerney spent 19 years with General Electric including a stint as CEO of its GE Aircraft Engines unit.

Also in 2005 more than 18000 Boeing machinists went on strike bringing commercial aircraft production to a halt but a sweetened deal brought machinists back in less than a month. Two months later Boeing reached an agreement with Chinese officials to sell 70 airplanes to China.

In early in 2006 China tentatively agreed to buy an additional 80 737s. Later that year Boeing bought aviation services and parts distributor Aviall Inc. for $1.7 billion. Aviall became a wholly owned subsidiary of Boeing within the aerospace giant's commercial aviation services division. Also in 2006 Boeing acquired Carmen Systems a provider of software and systems primarily used by the transportation industry to optimize productivity. Carmen was absorbed into Jeppesen Sanderson a subsidiary of Boeing Commercial Airplanes a unit of Boeing Commercial Airplanes.

That same year Boeing announced it would shut down its Connexion broadband Internet business due to lack of demand. Airlines such as Lufthansa and Singapore Airlines offered their customers in-flight high-speed Internet service through Connexion but cash-strapped US carriers were reluctant to buy in. Late in the year Boeing was awarded a $67 million federal contract to build a "virtual fence" along a 28-mile stretch along Arizona's border with Mexico.

The company bought C-Map a provider of digital maritime cartography in 2007. C-Map became part of Jeppesen. The following year labor troubles arose yet again when the aerospace company's machinist union went on strike. Some estimates had the strike costing Boeing upwards of $100 million per day. Spirit AeroSystems one of Boeing's primary suppliers reduced Boeing-related production as a result of the strike which ended after eight weeks with a new contract ratified. The strike however created additional delays to the troubled 787 Dreamliner's production schedule pushing delivery into late 2009 or 2010. Boeing selected North Charleston as its second 787 assembly line.

The machinist union however has not been the only labor issue in the public eye. A terminated employee blew the whistle on Boeing for scalping taxpayers; he claimed that the company padded billing records at a San Antonio maintenance plant for Air Force planes. Despite denying that it inflated the hours of non-routine repairs and maintenance on the KC-135 tankers Boeing settled the lawsuit in 2009 by paying $2 million to the US Justice Department.

The 787 Dreamliner took its inaugural flight in mid-December 2009 from Paine Field in Washington State. The last inaugural flight of a Boeing airplane was in 1994. The 787 was decked out with a plethora of sensors to relay data to the ground engineers during its three-hour test flight. That same year the Air Force awarded Boeing a contract valued at up to $3 billion for 15 C-17 military cargo aircraft in 2009. Congress approved the acquisition of the planes as part of a supplemental defense spending bill funding operations in Iraq and Afghanistan. The funding extended the C-17 production line through 2010.

In 2009 the company acquired its remaining 50% stake in Global Aeronautica from Alenia North America (part of Italy-based Finmeccanica). Global Aeronautica is a South Carolina-based company responsible for the sub-assembly of the 787's fuselage. Boeing had acquired its initial 50% stake in Global Aeronautica from Vought Aircraft (now Triumph Aerostructures - Vought Aircraft Division) the year prior.

The US federal government under the Obama administration has delivered some bad news to defense contractors like Boeing which took a direct hit when the Army's Future Combat Systems program was cancelled in late 2010.

As NASA's prime contractor for the Space Shuttle Boeing supported the Endeavour's final launch in spring 2011. Boeing designed and manufactured the space shuttle orbiters and had been a major subcontractor to the United Space Alliance (USA) NASA's prime contractor for space shuttle operations providing engineering support including launch as well as overall shuttle systems and payload integration services. Though the Space Shuttle was retired in 2011 Boeing is working on other services for NASA. In 2012 the company completed the second parachute drop test for its Crew Space Transportation (CST) spacecraft that is intended to transport US astronauts to and from low-Earth orbit and the International Space Station.

EXECUTIVES

EVP; President and CEO Commercial Airplanes, James F. (Jim) Albaugh, age 61, $952,382 total compensation

SVP Commercial Aviation Services Commercial Airplanes, Louis J. (Lou) Mancini

VP Global Corporate Citizenship, Anna E. (Anne) Roosevelt

Chairman President and CEO, W. James (Jim) McNerney Jr., age 62, $1,930,000 total compensation

CFO International Finance, R. Paul Kinscherff

VP Advanced 737 Product Development Boeing Commercial Airplanes, Michael B. (Mike) Bair, age 56

President Network and Space Systems Defense Space & Security, Roger A. Krone, age 56

VP Business Development Commercial Airplanes, Nicole W. Piasecki, age 49

President Boeing Australia and South Pacific, Ian Thomas, age 46

SVP Government Operations, Timothy J. (Tim) Keating, age 50

SVP; President Capital, Michael J. (Mike) Cave, age 52

President Shared Services Group, Robert J. (Rob) Pasterick, age 56

VP National Security and Space Group Government Operations, Leo A. Brooks Jr.

SVP Human Resources and Administration, Richard D. (Rick) Stephens, age 59, $486,308 total compensation

SVP Engineering Operations and Technology and CTO, John J. Tracy, age 57

VP Public Policy Advocacy Government Operations, Robert J. (Bob) Vilhauer, age 57

VP Sales Commercial Airplanes, Marlin Dailey, age 55

VP Environment Health and Safety, Mary Armstrong

SVP Business Development and Strategy; President Boeing International, Shepard W. (Shep) Hill, age 59, $503,598 total compensation

VP Program Management Commercial Airplanes, Howard E. Chambers

EVP and General Counsel, J. Michael (Mike) Luttig, age 57, $736,160 total compensation

St. Louis Regional Executive Boeing Defense Space & Security; VP State and Local Government Operations Government Operations, George C. Roman

SVP Communications, Thomas J. (Tom) Downey, age 47

VP; General Manager Information Solutions Boeing Defense Space and Security, John Hinshaw, age 42

SVP Office of Internal Governance, Wanda Denson-Low, age 55

VP and General Manager Airplane Programs Boeing Commercial Airplanes, Patrick M. (Pat) Shanahan, age 50
VP and General Manager 787 Program Boeing Commercial Airplanes, Scott Fancher, age 54
VP and General Manager Supply Chain Management and Operations Boeing Commercial Airplanes, Raymond L. (Ray) Conner, age 57
Lean+ Enterprise Initiative Leader; VP Supply and Operations Chain Boeing Defense Space & Security, William (Bill) Schnettgoecke Jr., age 51
EVP; President and CEO Boeing Defense Space and Security, Dennis A. Muilenburg, age 48
President Boeing Military Aircraft Boeing Defense Space & Security, Christopher M. (Chris) Chadwick, age 51
President Phantom Works Boeing Defense Space & Security, Darryl W. Davis
VP and General Manager Boeing Research and Technology, Matthew (Matt) Ganz, age 52
VP Finance and Treasurer, David Dohnalek, age 54
VP and General Manager 747-8 Program, Elizabeth Lund, age 47
President Boeing Japan, Mike Denton
Media Contact Europe, Chantal Dorange, age 47
VP and Managing Director Boeing Defence Australia, John Duddy
President Boeing India, Dinesh Keskar, age 58
Corporate VP Legislative Branch Authorizations and Appropriations Government Operations, David H. (Dave) Morrison
VP Communications Government Operations, Sean I. McCormack
President Global Services and Support Boeing Defense Space & Security, Anthony M. (Tony) Parasida, age 56
VP Final Assembly 787 Program Commercial Airplanes, John Cornish
VP Engineering Commercial Airplanes, Mike Delaney
VP Freighter Conversions Commercial Aviation Services Boeing Commercial Airplanes, Dan da Silva
VP Fleet Services Commercial Aviation Services, Dennis Floyd
VP and General Manager 737 Program Commercial Airplanes, Beverly Wyse
VP Advanced 777 Product Development Commercial Airplanes, Lars Andersen
VP Sales Asia Pacific Commercial Airplanes, John Wojick
Media Contact Commercial Airplanes, Jim Proulx
EVP and CFO, Gregory D (Greg) Smith, age 45
Corporate Controller, Diana Sands, age 46
VP Test and Evaluation, Dennis O'Donoghue
VP and CFO Boeing Commercial Airplanes, Ray Ferrari
VP Executive/Legislative and Regulatory Affairs Government Operations, Theodore (Ted) Austell
VP Strategy Government Operations, Andrew K. (Andy) Ellis
VP International Operations and Policy Government Operations, Jeff S. Hofgard
Director Operations Government Operations, Frank Silverio
VP Global Trade Controls Office of Internal Governance, Kathryn (Kathie) Greaney
VP and Assistant General Counsel Government Operations, Richard Hauser
Director Human Resources Government Operations, Gary L. Moore
VP International Government Relations Government Operations, Stanley O. Roth
VP Enterprise Technology Strategy Engineering Operations & Technology, Amy L. Buhrig
VP Boeing Commercial Aviation Services Information Services, Per A. Noren
VP Information Technology and CIO, Kim Hammonds, age 44
President Boeing Middle East, Jeffrey Johnson
President Boeing China, Marc Allen, age 38
VP and General Manager 767 Program, Kim Pastega
President and CEO Tapestry Solutions, R. Sam DeFord Jr.
President and CEO Insitu, Steve Morrow
VP Ethics and Business Conduct Office of Internal Governance, Mike Mesick
Chief of Staff Government Operations, Jennifer Lowe
VP International Business Development Boeing Space and Security India, Dennis D. Swanson
Director, Ronald A. (Ron) Williams, age 62
Director, John F. McDonnell, age 73
Director, Arthur D. (Art) Collins Jr., age 64
Director, Edward M. Liddy, age 65
Director, John H. Biggs, age 75
Director, Mike S. Zafirovski, age 58
Director, Linda Z. Cook, age 53
Director, David L. (Dave) Calhoun, age 55
Director, Kenneth M. (Ken) Duberstein, age 67
Director, Prof Susan C. Schwab, age 57
Director, Edmund P. Giambastiani Jr., age 62
Auditors: Deloitte&ToucheLLP

LOCATIONS

HQ: Boeing Co. (The)
100 N. Riverside Plaza, Chicago, IL 60606-1596
Phone: 312 544-2000
Web: www.boeing.com

2011 Sales

	$ mil.	% of total
US	34,391	51
Asia		
China	4,779	7
Other Asia	7,438	11
Europe	9,850	14
Middle East	5,477	8
Oceania	3,067	4
Africa	1,759	2
Latin American Caribbean and other	1,356	2
Canada	618	1
Total	**68,735**	**100**

PRODUCTS/OPERATIONS

2011 Sales

	$ mil.	% of total
Commercial Airplanes	36,171	53
Defense Space & Security		
Military Aircraft	14,947	22
Network & Space Systems	8,673	13
Global Services & Support	8,356	12
Boeing Capital	532	-
Other	138	-
Adjustments	(82)	-
Total	**68,735**	**100**

2011 Sales

	$ mil.	% of total
Products	57,401	84
Services	11,334	16
Total	**68,735**	**100**

Selected Products and Services

Commercial Airplanes
Products
737 Next Generation (short-to-medium-range two-engine jet)
747 (long-range four-engine jet)
767 (medium-to-long-range two-engine jet)
777 (long-range two-engine jet)
Boeing Business Jet
787 Dreamliner (in development; long-range super-efficient 200-250 passenger capacity)
747-8 (in development;
Services
Engineering modification and logistics
Maintenance repair and overhaul
Boeing Training & Flight Services
Defense Space & Security
Military Aircraft
AH-64 Apache
B-1B Lancer
B-2 Spirit
F/A-18 Hornet
F-15E Strike Eagle
F-22 Raptor
T-45 Flight Training System
A160 Hummingbird
Harpoon
Insitu
C-17 Globemaster III
CH-47D/F Chinook
V-22 Osprey
Global Services & Support
Integrated logistics
Maintenance modifications and upgrades
Training systems
Government services
Network & Space Systems
Electronic and mission
Cyber security
Infrastructure
Intelligence
Logistics command and control
Satellite and ground operations
Space exploration

COMPETITORS

AgustaWestland
Airbus
BAE SYSTEMS
Bombardier
COMAC
Dassault Aviation
EADS
Embraer
Finmeccanica
GE Aviation
General Dynamics
Goodrich Corp.
Kaman
Lockheed Martin
Northrop Grumman
Raytheon
Rockwell Collins
Textron
Thales
United Technologies

HISTORICAL FINANCIALS

Company Type: Public

Income Statement FYE: December 31

	REVENUE ($ mil.)	NET INCOME ($ mil.)	NET PROFIT MARGIN	EMPLOYEES
12/11	68,735	4,018	5.8%	171,700
12/10	64,306	3,307	5.1%	160,500
12/09	68,281	1,312	1.9%	157,100
12/08	60,909	2,672	4.4%	162,200
12/07	66,387	4,074	6.1%	159,300
Annual Growth	0.9%	(0.3%)	—	1.9%

2011 Year-End Financials

Debt ratio: 15.47%
Return on equity: 114.31%
Cash ($ mil.): 10,049
Current ratio: 120.68
Long-term debt ($ mil.): 10,018
No. of shares (mil.): 744
Dividends
Yield: —
Payout: 31.46%
Market value ($ mil.): 54,624

	STOCK PRICE ($) FY Close	P/E High/Low		PER SHARE ($) Earnings	Dividends	Book Value
12/11	73.35	15	11	5.34	0.00	4.72
12/10	65.26	17	12	4.45	1.68	3.76
12/09	54.13	30	16	1.84	1.68	2.82
12/08	42.67	24	10	3.67	1.60	(1.78)
12/07	87.46	20	16	5.28	1.40	11.72
Annual Growth	(4.3%)	—	—	0.3%	—	(20.3%)

BOK Financial Corp.

Will your money BOK? Multibank holding company BOK Financial tries to make sure it is. With seven principal banking divisions in eight midwestern and southwestern states BOK offers a range of financial services to consumers and regional businesses. In addition to traditional deposit lending and trust services the banks provide investment management wealth advisory and mineral and real estate management services through a network of about 200 branches in Arizona Arkansas Colorado Kansas Missouri New Mexico Oklahoma and Texas. Brokerage subsidiary BOSC underwrites public private and municipal securities. BOK also owns electronic funds network TransFund and institutional asset manager Cavanal Hill.

BOK emphasizes local decision-making at its flagship subsidiary Bank of Oklahoma and its operating divisions Bank of Texas Bank of Albuquerque Bank of Arkansas Colorado State Bank Bank of Kansas City and Bank of Arizona. Commercial loans primarily to the energy services health care and wholesale and retail industries make up the majority of the company's loan portfolio. Commercial real estate residential mortgage car and consumer loans round out its lending activities.

With nearly half of its business in its home state of Oklahoma BOK is looking to metropolitans areas such as Dallas/Fort Worth Houston Denver Kansas City and Phoenix for expansion either through acquisitions or by opening new branches. The company is also focused on diversifying its revenue stream by growing its mortgage banking brokerage and wealth management operations. (In 2012 it acquired Denver-based The Milestone Group which oversees some $1.3 billion for wealthy investors.) The strategy has paid off in 2010 and 2011 as fee income increased both years. An improved economic environment which led to more favorable interest rate spreads and better credit quality in the bank's portfolio also contributed to a 16% increase in net income for BOK in 2011.

Oilman and company chairman George Kaiser owns about 60% of BOK Financial.

EXECUTIVES

Chairman, George B. Kaiser, age 69
President CEO and Director; President and CEO BOKF, Stanley A. (Stan) Lybarger, age 62, $828,600 total compensation
Director; Chairman Bank of Texas, C. Frederick (Fred) Ball Jr., age 67, $300,000 total compensation
SEVP BOKF, Steven G. (Steve) Bradshaw, age 52, $440,000 total compensation
SVP and Chief Accounting Officer, John C. Morrow, age 56
EVP and CFO BOK Financial and BOKF, Steven E. Nell, age 50, $388,749 total compensation
SEVP BOKF, Daniel H. (Dan) Ellinor, age 50, $442,500 total compensation
EVP and Chief Credit Officer BOKF, Charles E. (Chuck) Cotter, age 58
EVP and CIO, Donald T. (Don) Parker, age 51, $366,250 total compensation
Chairman and CEO Bank of Texas, Norman P. Bagwell, age 49
Director, Chester (Chet) Cadieux III, age 45
Director, V. Burns Hargis, age 66
President CEO and Director; President and CEO BOKF, Stanley A. (Stan) Lybarger, age 62
Director, Joseph W. Craft III, age 61
Director; Chairman Bank of Texas, C. Frederick (Fred) Ball Jr., age 67
Director, Peter C. Boylan III, age 47
Director, Steven J. (Steve) Malcolm, age 64
Director, Robert J. LaFortune, age 85
Director, William E. Durrett, age 81
Director, John W. Gibson, age 59
Director, Sharon J. Bell, age 60
Director, E. Carey Joullian IV, age 51
Director, David F. Griffin, age 46
Director, Gregory S. Allen, age 49
Director, E. C. Richards, age 62
Auditors: Ernst&YoungLLP

LOCATIONS

HQ: BOK Financial Corporation
Bank of Oklahoma Tower, Tulsa OK 74192
Phone: 918-588-6000 **Fax:** 918-588-6853
Web: www.bokf.com

PRODUCTS/OPERATIONS

2011 Sales

	$ mil.	% of total
Interest		
Loans	505	37
Available-for-sale securities	262	19
Other	44	3
Noninterest		
Transaction card revenue	116	8
Brokerage & trading	104	8
Deposit service charges & fees	95	7
Mortgage banking	91	7
Trust fees & commissions	73	5
Net gain on available-for-sale securities	34	2
Other	56	4
Total	**1,372**	**100**

Selected Banking Subsidiaries

Bank of Albuquerque National Association
Bank of Arizona National Association
Bank of Arkansas National Association
Bank of Kansas City National Association
Bank of Oklahoma National Association
Bank of Texas National Association
Colorado State Bank & Trust

COMPETITORS

Bank of America
Bank of the West
CoBiz Financial
Comerica
Commerce Bancshares
Compass Bancshares
First National of Nebraska
JPMorgan Chase
Regions Financial
UMB Financial
Wells Fargo
Zions Bancorporation

HISTORICAL FINANCIALS

Company Type: Public

Income Statement FYE: December 31

	ASSETS ($ mil.)	NET INCOME ($ mil.)	INCOME AS % OF ASSETS	EMPLOYEES
12/11	25,493	285	1.1%	4,511
12/10	23,941	246	1.0%	4,432
12/09	23,516	200	0.9%	4,355
12/08	22,734	153	0.7%	4,300
12/07	20,839	217	1.0%	4,110
Annual Growth	5.2%	7.1%	—	2.4%

2011 Year-End Financials

Debt ratio: 1.86%
Return on equity: 10.39%
Cash ($ mil.): 976
Current ratio: —
Long-term debt ($ mil.): 473
No. of shares (mil.): 68
Dividends
Yield: —
Payout: 27.10%
Market value ($ mil.): 3,744

	STOCK PRICE ($) FY Close	P/E High/Low		PER SHARE ($) Earnings	Dividends	Book Value
12/11	54.93	13	11	4.17	0.00	40.36
12/10	53.40	15	12	3.61	0.99	36.97
12/09	47.52	16	8	2.96	0.95	32.53
12/08	40.40	27	17	2.27	0.88	27.36
12/07	51.70	17	15	3.22	0.75	28.75
Annual Growth	1.5%	—	—	6.7%	—	8.9%

Booz Allen Hamilton Holding Corp.

For almost a century consultants at Booz Allen Hamilton have been helping US government agencies operate more efficiently at home and abroad. The firm provides a wide range of management consulting and technology integration services; its specialties include information technology operations organization and change program management strategy training programs and systems engineering. Booz Allen has long-established relationships with such agencies as the Department of Defense the Federal Aviation Administration and the Internal Revenue Service. Investment firm The Carlyle Group owns a majority interest in the consulting firm which was founded in 1914. In late 2010 Booz Allen launched an IPO.

IPO

The consulting firm used more than $250 million of the proceeds from its IPO to pay down debt. (Carlyle still controls a collective voting power of about 70% in Booz Allen.)

Strategy

The consulting firm plans to continue to grow its client base (about 1200 in the US operating under more than 5800 contracts) across a wide spectrum of government agencies and departments. Though almost entirely focused on US government clients (98% of revenue) Booz Allen undertakes a variety of engagements. Key markets include civil government agencies responsible for energy finance health and transportation as well as defense and national security agencies.

Booz Allen is also focused on enhancing its cyber-security products and services in the commercial market. In addition the consulting firm acts to take advantage of a rising need for health care consulting services as a result of the 2010 passage of The Patient Protection and Affordable Care Act and other recent acts of health care reform legislation.

Mergers & Acquisitions

In late 2012 Booz Allen acquired the Defense Systems Engineering & Support (DSES) division of ARINC Incorporated for approximately $154 million in cash. The deal brought capabilities in advanced aviation and maritime engineering advanced weapons modernization and sustainment and advanced systems engineering and integration to complement Booz Allen's existing services.

Company Background

Booz Allen formerly worked for commercial as well as government clients. But the firm separated its commercial- and government-related businesses in 2008 as part of a deal in which The Carlyle Group paid about $2.5 billion for control of the government arm which retained the Booz Allen name. The firm's commercial arm was spun off as a separate entity Booz & Company which is owned by its officers. The goal of the separation was to enable each operating business to better focus on its core market. Just as the commercial and government units did when they operated under common ownership however Booz Allen and Booz & Company also work together on engagements when it makes sense to do so.

HISTORY

Edwin Booz graduated from Northwestern University in 1914 with degrees in economics and psychology and started a statistical analysis firm in Chicago. After serving in the army during WWI he returned to his firm renamed Edwin Booz Surveys. In 1925 Booz hired his first full-time assistant George Fry and in 1929 he hired a second James Allen. By then the company had a long list of clients including U.S. Gypsum the "Chicago Tribune" and Montgomery Ward which was losing a retail battle with Sears Roebuck and Co.

In 1935 Carl Hamilton joined the partnership and a year later it was renamed Booz Fry Allen & Hamilton. The firm prospered well into the next decade by providing advice based on "independence that enables us to say plainly from the outside what cannot always be said safely from within" according to a company brochure.

During WWII the firm worked increasingly on government and military contracts. Fry opposed the pursuit of such work for consultants and left in 1942. The firm was renamed Booz Allen & Hamilton. Hamilton died in 1946 and the following year Booz retired (he died in 1951) leaving Allen as chairman. He successfully steered the firm into lucrative postwar work for clients such as Johnson Wax RCA and the US Air Force.

A separate company Booz Allen Applied Research Inc. (BAARINC) was formed in 1955 for technical and government consulting including missile and weaponry work as well as consulting with NASA. By the end of the decade "Time" had dubbed Booz Allen "the world's largest most prestigious management consultant firm." The partnership was incorporated as a private company in 1962 and in 1967 commissioner Pete Rozelle requested its services for the merger of the National Football League and American Football League.

When Allen retired in 1970 Charlie Bowen became the new chairman and the company went public. However as the economy stalled during the energy crisis spending for consultants plunged. Jim Farley replaced Bowen in 1975 and the company was taken private again in 1976. A turnaround was engineered and the firm was soon helping Chrysler through its 1979 bailout and developing strategies for the breakup of AT&T in 1984.

Booz Allen again experienced trouble in the 1980s after Farley instituted a competition to select his successor. Michael McCullough was eventually chosen in 1984 but the 10-month election process turned into a dogfight that pitted partner against partner taking an enormous toll on morale. McCullough began restructuring the firm along industry lines creating a department store of services in an industry characterized by boutique houses. The turmoil was too much and by 1988 nearly a third of the partners had quit.

William Stasior became chairman in 1991 and reorganized Booz Allen yet again splitting it down public and private sector lines. Allen died in 1992 the same year the firm moved to McLean Virginia. The company began privatization work in the former Soviet Union and in Eastern Europe in 1992 and continued to emphasize government business including contracts with the IRS (1995) for technology modernization and with the General Services Administration (1996) to provide technical and management support for all federal telecommunications users.

In 1998 the company won a 10-year $200 million contract with the US Defense Department to establish a scientific and technical data warehouse. Ralph Shrader was appointed CEO in early 1999; Stasior retired as chairman later that year. Booz Allen acquired Scandinavian consulting firm Carta in 1999 and formed a venture capital firm for startups with Lehman Brothers in 2000. The company announced in late 2000 that it would spin off Aestix its e-commerce business but reconsidered amid a general economic slowdown and hostile IPO market. (The unit was integrated back into Booz Allen in 2002.)

Booz Allen saw an increase in work related to defense and national security after the terrorist attacks of September 11 2001. Engagements included work related to the reconstruction of Iraq (as a subcontractor on telecommunications projects managed by Lucent) and in 2003 Booz Allen was awarded a contract from the US Health Resources and Services Administration to help establish and operate a bioterrorism technical support center.

In 2008 Booz Allen spun off its commercial consulting business as an independent firm Booz & Company. The spinoff was part of a transaction in which investment firm The Carlyle Group acquired a controlling interest in the Booz Allen's government-related consulting business which retained the Booz Allen name.

Striving to alleviate debt Booz Allen launched an initial public offering on the New York Stock Exchange in November 2010.

EXECUTIVES

Chairman President and CEO, Ralph W. Shrader, age 68, $1,162,500 total compensation
SVP, Gary D. Labovich
SVP, Peter B. Trick
EVP, Reggie Van Lee
SVP, David A. (Dave) Mader
SVP, Dov S. Zakheim
EVP and COO, Horacio D. Rozanski, age 44
EVP CFO Chief Administrative Officer and Director, Samuel R. (Sam) Strickland, age 61, $825,000 total compensation
SVP, James (Jim) Manchisi
EVP, Mark J. Gerencser
EVP, John M. (Mike) McConnell, age 68, $1,505,000 total compensation
SVP, Ronald T. (Ron) Kadish, age 63
VP, Gary Lance
SVP, Henry A. (Trey) Obering III
EVP, Joseph E. Garner, age 64, $1,050,000 total compensation
EVP General Counsel Chief Legal Officer and Secretary, C. G. Appleby, age 65, $1,050,000 total compensation
SVP and CIO, Frank S. Smith III
SVP, Nancy Hardwick
EVP, Gary D. Mather
EVP, Ghassan Salameh
EVP, Ken Wiegand
EVP, Francis J. (Jimmy) Henry Jr., age 60
EVP, Lloyd W. Howell Jr., age 50
SVP, Christopher M. (Chris) Kelly
EVP, Joseph W. (Joe) Mahaffee, age 55
EVP, John D. Mayer, age 66
SVP, Carl Salzano
SVP, Donald L. (Don) Pressley
EVP, Patrick F. Peck, age 54
EVP, Neil Gillespie
SVP, William (Bill) Bastedo
SVP, Fred K. Blackburn
SVP, Cindy Broyles
SVP, Douglas (Doug) Carter
VP, Drew Cohen
SVP, Gary C. Cubbage
SVP, Karen Dahut
SVP, Maria Darby
SVP, Paul M. Doolittle
SVP, Judith H. (Judi) Dotson
SVP, Lee J. Falkenstrom
SVP, Michael Farber
SVP, Molly Finn
SVP, Margo Fitzpatrick
SVP, Art Fritzson
SVP, Thomas (Tom) Fuhrman
SVP, Laurie Gallo
SVP, Natalie M. Givans
SVP, Patricia Goforth
SVP, Tom Greenspon
SVP, Gregory Harrison
EVP, Mark Herman
SVP, Ronald (Ron) Hodge
SVP, Gordon S. Holder
SVP, David F. Humenansky
SVP, Mike W. Jones
SVP, David J. (Dave) Karp
SVP, Jeffrey J. Kibben
SVP, David Kletter
SVP, Frederick (Fred) Knops
SVP, Robert J. (Bob) Lamb
SVP, Douglas J. Lane
SVP, Christopher Ling
EVP, Joseph (Joe) Logue, age 47
SVP, John Lueders
SVP, Janet Lyman
SVP, Herbert MacArthur
SVP, Robert Makar
SVP, Joseph (Joe) Martha
SVP, Angela M. (Angie) Messer
SVP, Anthony (Tony) Mitchell
SVP, Sharon L. Muzik
SVP, Catherine Nelson
SVP, Robert W. Noonan Jr.
SVP, Susan L. Penfield
SVP, Sam Porgess
SVP, Robin L. Portman
SVP, Robert (Bob) Post
SVP, Gary Rahl
SVP, Larry D. Scheuble
SVP, George M. Schu
SVP, Gary Schulman
SVP, Joseph F. (Joe) Sifer
SVP, Ted Sniffin
VP, Bob Sogegian
SVP, Carol Staubach
SVP, Kurt B. Stevens
SVP, William Stewart
SVP, Bill A. Thoet
SVP, John A. Thomas
SVP, Betty Thompson
SVP, Emile Trombetti
SVP, Laurie S. Villano
SVP, William J. Wansley
SVP, Jack D. Welsh Jr.
SVP, Gregory G. (Greg) Wenzel
EVP, Richard J. Wilhelm
SVP, Charles P. Zuhoski
SVP, Christopher Pierce
SVP, James Allen
SVP, Eugene Bounds
SVP, Joan A. Dempsey
SVP, Nicole Funk
SVP, John Feeney

SVP, Corrine Kosar
SVP, Thomas Pfeifer
SVP, Donald Schaefer
SVP, Stephen Soules
SVP, Lee Wilbur
SVP, Abram Zwany
SVP, Kristine Martin Anderson
SVP, Thomas Crabtree
SVP, David Rubin
Senior Executive Advisor, Dennis O. Doughty
Senior Executive Advisor, Marty Hill
Senior Executive Advisor, Charlie R. Jones Jr.
Senior Executive Advisor, Pamela M. Lentz
Senior Executive Advisor, Tom Moorman
Senior Executive Advisor, Donald J. Vincent
Senior Executive Advisor, R. James Woolsey
VP, Mickie Bolduc
VP, Cathy Breeze
VP, Rene Castro
VP, Keith Catanzano
VP, Kevin Cook
VP, Leslie DiFonzo
VP, Jay Dodd
VP, Jeane Dolan
VP, Alexis Feringa
VP, Robert E. Furtado
VP, James Gibbons
VP, Dennis Gibson
VP, Lesley Gilbert
VP, Dorothy (Dee Dee) Helfenstein
VP, Mark Himler
VP, Rick Holley
VP Contracts and Pricing, Joan Hyde
VP, Andrea Inserra
VP, Mark (Jake) Jacobsohn

VP, Brian M. Legan
VP Marketing and Communications, Marie L. Lerch
VP, Judy Merkel
VP, Bill Meyers
VP, Ken Mills
VP, Bruce R. Orjada
VP, Mike Otten
VP, Tom Russell
VP, Roy K. Salomon
VP, Rick Saunders
VP, Robert Silverman
VP, Gale N. Smith
VP, Thomas (Craig) Starnes
VP Human Resources, Sarah St. Clair
VP, Jerry Vevon
VP, Kevin Vigilante
VP, Gary Voellger
VP, Joan Wolfle
VP, Joanne Yuvanc
SVP Cyber Security, Roger W. Cressey
Senior Manager Media Relations, James Fisher
Senior Vice President, William Stew
Vice President General Counsel Corporate Secretary, Douglas Manya
Vice President specializing in the Human Capital, Grant McLaughlin
Vice President who leads the firm s United, Jennifer Swindell
Senior Vice President, Kristine Anderson
Vice President, Reggie Lee
Vice President, Scott D. Welles
Executive Vice President, Rich WilhelmFor
Director, Daniel F. (Dan) Akerson, age 63
Director, Peter J. Clare, age 47
Director, Charles O. Rossotti, age 71
EVP CFO Chief Administrative Officer and Director, Samuel R. (Sam) Strickland, age 61
Director, Ian I. Fujiyama, age 39
Director, Philip A. Odeen, age 76
Auditors: Ernst&YoungLLP

LOCATIONS

HQ: Booz Allen Hamilton Holding Corporation
8283 Greensboro Dr., McLean VA 22101
Phone: 703-902-5000 **Fax:** 703-902-3333
Web: www.boozallen.com

PRODUCTS/OPERATIONS

Selected Markets Served

Civil government
- Benefits and entitlements
- Federal finance
- International development and diplomacy

Defense
- Air Force
- Army
- Joint staff and combatant commands
- Navy and Marine Corps
- Office of the Secretary of Defense and defense agencies
- Space

Energy
Environment
Health
- Health informatics
- Health not-for-profit/nongovernmental organizations
- International public health
- US public health

Homeland security
Intelligence
Law enforcement
Not-for-profit/nongovernmental organizations
Transportation
- Aviation infrastructure
- Highways and automotive technology
- Passenger rail and mass transit

Selected Practice Areas

Assurance and resilience
Economic and business analysis
Information technology
Modeling and simulation
Organization and strategy
Supply chain and logistics
Systems engineering and integration

COMPETITORS

A.T. Kearney
Accenture
BAE SYSTEMS
Bain & Company
Boeing
Boston Consulting
CACI International
Capgemini
Computer Sciences Corp.
Deloitte Consulting
General Dynamics
HP Enterprise Services
IBM
L-3 Communications
Lockheed Martin
ManTech
MAXIMUS
McKinsey & Company
Northrop Grumman
PA Consulting
PRTM Management
Raytheon
SAIC
SRA International
Unisys

HISTORICAL FINANCIALS

Company Type: Public

Income Statement

FYE: March 31

	REVENUE ($ mil.)	NET INCOME ($ mil.)	NET PROFIT MARGIN	EMPLOYEES
03/12	5,859	239	4.1%	25,000
03/11	5,591	84	1.5%	25,000
03/10	5,122	25	0.5%	23,315
03/09*	2,941	(38)	—	21,614
07/08	1,409	(1,245)	—	0
Annual Growth	42.8%	—	—	—

*Fiscal year change

2012 Year-End Financials

Debt ratio: 29.12%
Return on equity: 20.25%
Cash ($ mil.): 484
Current ratio: 181.28
Long-term debt ($ mil.): 922
No. of shares (mil.): 142
Dividends
Yield: —
Payout: 5.29%
Market value ($ mil.): 2,428

	STOCK PRICE ($) FY Close	P/E High/Low		PER SHARE ($) Earnings	Dividends	Book Value
03/12	17.03	11	7	1.70	0.00	8.31
03/11	18.01	27	24	0.66	0.00	6.47
Annual Growth	(5.4%)	—	—	157.6%	—	28.4%

Borg Warner Inc

If suburbanites need four-wheel-drive vehicles to turbocharge their urban drive that's OK with BorgWarner. The company is a leading maker of engine and drivetrain products for the world's major automotive manufacturers. Products include turbochargers air pumps timing chain systems four-wheel-drive and all-wheel-drive transfer cases (primarily for light trucks and SUVs) and transmission components. Its largest customers include Volkswagen Ford and Daimler. BorgWarner operates nearly 60 manufacturing and technical facilities worldwide. The company nets around 75% of sales from outside the US; more than half of sales come from its European operations.

Financial Analysis

The worldwide economic downturn coupled with the financial crisis that started in 2008 and accelerated in 2009 obliterated optimistic projections for BorgWarner. Following an earnings high in 2007 the company suffered a small loss in 2008 mainly attributable restructuring and goodwill impairment charges its first loss since 2002. After a full year of declining consumer demand for light vehicles BorgWarner' sales in 2009 slumped about 25% from 2008. Nonetheless the company returned to profitability citing strict cost controls and improved liquidity. More significant results were realized in 2010 as the economy recovered and consumers were given a cash-for-clunkers incentive to buy a fuel efficient vehicle; the company's sales jumped more than 40% over the prior year and net income soared nearly 14-fold.

Strategy

Going forward BorgWarner will target new business as it focuses on more fuel-efficient and environmentally friendly technologies (turbochargers and dual-clutch transmissions) as well as international opportunities. (The company plans to release 80% of its new products from Asia and Europe.) It enjoys a strong slate of orders from Ford Chrysler Opel and Hyundai.

The engine maker's strategy is to follow market share as it shifts away from Detroit and toward Asia and Europe. BorgWarner generates more business from Volkswagen and Daimler than it does from General Motors and Chrysler and sales in Germany outstrip those in the US. Manufacturing operations are situated close to demand enabling the company to ship products directly from its plant to the customer. Western automotive companies are scrambling to grab a piece of the market in Asia particularly in China which is signaling to overtake the US as the largest automotive market in the world. BorgWarner like many of its peers has steadily increased its presence in South Korea (where Hyundai and Kia reside) and crossed into China. It is also investing in India Brazil and Eastern Europe.

Mergers & Acquisitions

Expanding its product line BorgWarner in early 2011 acquired Sweden-based Traction Systems a division of Haldex Group. The $205 million acquisition is anticipated to accelerate BorgWarner's share of the all-wheel drive market. In spring 2010 the company purchased BERU Eichenauer a maker of electric cabin heaters from former JV partner Eichenauer Heizelemente. Hard on its heels BorgWarner bought Spanish emissions equipment maker Dytech ENSA. In addition to Spain Dytech has locations in Portugal and India and sells to an array of customers in Europe and Asia.

HISTORY

BorgWarner traces its roots to the 1928 merger of major Chicago auto parts companies Borg & Beck (clutches) Warner Gear (transmissions) Mechanics Universal Joint and Marvel Carburetor. The newly named Borg-Warner Corporation quickly began buying other companies including Ingersoll Steel & Disc (agricultural blades and discs) and Norge (refrigerators).

The company survived the Depression largely through the contributions of its Norge and Ingersoll divisions. In the latter 1930s the company purchased Calumet Steel (1935) and US Pressed Steel (1937) along with several other companies.

During the early 1940s Borg-Warner made parts for planes trucks and tanks. Between 1942 and 1945 it produced more than 1.6 million automotive transmissions and gained the experience and manufacturing capacity to handle the postwar car boom. Its 1948 contract with Ford Motor to build half of its transmissions resulted in massive growth.

Roy Ingersoll president of the Ingersoll Steel & Disc division assumed leadership of Borg-Warner in 1950 and embarked on a major diversification program. Borg-Warner's 1956 purchases included York Humphreys Manufacturing Industrial Crane & Hoist Dittmer Gear and the Chemical Process Company among others. James Bert became president in 1968 and continued diversification.

Borg-Warner entered the security business in 1978 by buying Baker Industries (armored transport under the Wells Fargo name). In 1980 Borg-Warner sold its Ingersoll Products division. It acquired Burns International Security Services in 1982 and spun off York to its shareholders in 1986.

In the face of a 1987 takeover attempt Merrill Lynch Capital Partners organized an LBO and took the company private assuming $4.5 billion in debt. Borg-Warner then sold everything but its automotive and security units including its chemical group to General Electric for $2.3 billion (1988) and its credit unit Chilton to TRW for $330 million (1989).

The company went public again in 1993 as Borg-Warner Security; it spun off Borg-Warner Automotive to its shareholders. (Borg-Warner Security changed its name to Burns International Services in 1999.) In 1995 Borg-Warner Automotive formed a joint venture in India (Divgi-Warner) to make transmissions and purchased the precision-forged products division of Federal-Mogul.

To expand its air- and fluid-control business the company acquired Holley Automotive Coltec Automotive and Performance Friction Products from component maker Coltec Industries in 1996. The following year Borg-Warner Automotive sold its money-losing manual-transmission business to Transmisiones y Equipos Mecanicos of Mexico.

Reduced production of Ford trucks a weak Asian economy and a strike at General Motors hurt 1998 sales. The following year the company bought diesel-engine component maker Kuhlman and then sold Kuhlman's electrical transformer and wire/cable businesses. Borg-Warner Automotive also sold its interests in joint ventures Warner-Ishi and Warner-Ishi Europe to partner Ishikawajima-Harima Heavy Industries (now IHI Corp.).

In 1999 Borg-Warner Automotive bought the Fluid Power Division (automotive cooling systems) of Eaton for $130 million. The company changed its name to BorgWarner in 2000. Early the next year BorgWarner sold its fuel systems interests to private equity group TMB Industries.

In 2005 BorgWarner purchased a controlling 60% stake in Germany's BERU AG at a price of about $290 million.

Although it attempted to insulate itself from Detroit's woes few could have predicted the massive 2006 production cuts at Chrysler Ford and GM. To adjust late in 2006 BorgWarner said it would cut about 800 jobs at 19 facilities in the US Canada and Mexico –or about 13% of its total North American workforce.

Soon after the job cut announcement BorgWarner purchased Eaton's European Transmission and Engine Controls product lines for nearly $64 million net of cash acquired. Products included high-pressure control solenoids for automated transmissions as well as for rail diesel and gasoline engines.

In 2007 BorgWarner increased its stake in BERU to 80% and took control of the company the following year. Towards the end of 2009 BERU was delisted and integrated into BorgWarner. The company's name changed to BorgWarner BERU Systems GmbH.

The company's recessionary controls included eliminating about 4400 jobs (around one-quarter of the worldwide workforce) putting European plants on four-day work weeks and shutting down all operations for a month at the end of 2008. In 2009 the company cut an additional 760 jobs worldwide.

EXECUTIVES

VP and Chief Procurement Officer, John J. McGill, $247,600 total compensation
VP and Chief Compliance Officer, Laurene H. Horiszny
Chairman and CEO, Timothy M. (Tim) Manganello, age 62, $946,458 total compensation
EVP; Group President and General Manager Drivetrain Group, John G. Sanderson, age 59, $322,878 total compensation
Vice Chairman EVP and Chief Administrative Officer, Robin J. Adams, age 58, $486,135 total compensation
VP and Controller, Jan A. Bertsch, age 55
VP General Counsel and Secretary, John J. Gasparovic, age 54
VP Internal Audit, Anthony D. Hensel, age 53
VP; President and General Manager BorgWarner Thermal Systems, Daniel J. (Dan) CasaSanta, age 57
VP; President and General Manager BorgWarner Transmissions Systems, Robin Kendrick, age 47
VP and CIO, Jamal M. Farhat
VP Business Development and M&A, Christopher H. (Chris) Vance
VP; President and General Manager BorgWarner BERU Systems and BorgWarner Emissions Systems, Thomas Waldhier, age 48, $429,660 total compensation
Managing Director China, Tom Tan
VP Marketing Public Relations Communications and Government Affairs, Scott D. Gallett, age 46
Director Investor Relations, Ken Lamb
Director Marketing and Public Relations, Erika Nielsen
CFO, Ronald T. (Ron) Hundzinski, age 53
President and COO, James R. Verrier, age 49
VP Human Resources, Janice K. (Jan) McAdams, age 53
VP Advanced Engine Engineering, Wolfgang Bullmer
VP Advanced Drivetrain Engineering, Bill Kelley
VP; President and General Manager BorgWarner BERU Systems and Emissions Systems, Brady D. Ericson, age 40
VP; President and General Manager BorgWarner TorqTransfer Systems, Joseph F. Fadool, age 45
VP; President and General Manager BorgWarner Turbo Systems Commercial Diesel Products, Pete B. Kohler, age 56
VP; President and General Manager BorgWarner Turbo Systems Passenger Car Products, Frederic B. Lissalde, age 44
Director, Thomas T. (Tom) Stallkamp, age 66
Director, Jere A. Drummond, age 72
Director, David T. (Dave) Brown, age 64
Director, John R. McKernan Jr., age 64
Director, Alexis P. Michas, age 54
Vice Chairman EVP and Chief Administrative Officer, Robin J. Adams, age 58
Director, Phyllis O. Bonanno, age 69
Director, Richard O. Schaum, age 65
Director, Ernest J. Novak Jr., age 67
Director, Dennis C. Cuneo, age 62
Director, Jan Carlson, age 52
Auditors: PricewaterhouseCoopersLLP

LOCATIONS

HQ: BorgWarner Inc.
3850 Hamlin Rd., Auburn Hills MI 48326
Phone: 248-754-9200 **Fax:** 248-754-9397
Web: www.bwauto.com

2010 Sales

	$ mil.	% of total
Europe		
Germany	1,839	32
Hungary	418	7
France	318	6
Other countries	546	10
US	1,451	26
South Korea	358	6
China	330	6
Other regions	390	7
Total	**5,652**	**100**

PRODUCTS/OPERATIONS

2010 Sales

	$ mil.	% of total
Engine	4,060	72
Drivetrain	1,611	28
Adjustments	(19.4)	-
Total	**5,652**	**100**

2010 Sales by Market

% of total	
Light vehicle	77
Commercial truck bus construction & agricultural vehicle	16
Distributors of aftermarket replacement	7
Total	**100**

Selected Mergers & Acquisitions

FY2011

Haldex Traction Systems ($205 million; Sweden; all-wheel drive systems)

FY2010

BERU Eichenauer GmbH (Germany; maker of electric cabin heaters)

Dytech ENSA SL (Spain; emissions equipment maker)

Selected Products

Engine Group
- Air-control valves
- Chain tensioners and snubbers
- Complete engine induction systems
- Complex solenoids and multi-function modules
- Crankshaft and camshaft sprockets
- Diesel cabin heaters
- Diesel cold starting systems (glow plugs and instant starting systems)
- Electric air pumps
- Engine hydraulic pumps
- Exhaust gas-recirculation (EGR) coolers modules tubes and valves
- Fan clutches
- Fans and fan drives
- Front-wheel and four-wheel-drive chain and timing-chain systems
- High-temperature sensors (for exhaust gas aftertreatment systems)
- Ignition coils
- Intake manifolds
- On-off fan drives
- Single-function solenoids
- Throttle bodies
- Throttle position sensors
- Tire pressure sensors
- Transfer cases
- Turbochargers

Drivetrain Group
- Four-wheel-drive and all-wheel-drive transfer cases
- Friction plates
- One-way clutches
- Torque converter lock-up clutches
- Transmission bands

Selected Joint Ventures

BERU Korea Co. Ltd. (51% South Korea ignition coils and pumps)

Borg-Warner Shenglong (Ningbo) Co. Ltd. (70% China fans and fan drives)

BorgWarner TorqTransfer Systems Beijing Co. Ltd. (80% China transfer cases)

BorgWarner Transmission Systems Korea Inc. (60% South Korea transmission components)

BorgWarner United Transmission Systems Co. Ltd. (66% China transmission components)

BorgWarner-Vikas Emissions Systems India Private Limited (60% India EGR coolers)

Divgi-Warner Limited (60% India transfer cases and automatic locking hubs)

SeohanWarner Turbo Systems Ltd. (71% South Korea turbochargers)

COMPETITORS

Dana Holding
Delphi Automotive Systems
DENSO
Eaton
GKN
Honeywell International
IHI Corp.
JTEKT
Kolbenschmidt Pierburg
Magna Powertrain
Meritor
Mitsubishi Heavy Industries
NGK SPARK PLUG
Renold
Robert Bosch
Schaeffler Technologies
Tsubaki Nakashima
Valeo
Visteon

HISTORICAL FINANCIALS

Company Type: Public

Income Statement

FYE: December 31

	REVENUE ($ mil.)	NET INCOME ($ mil.)	NET PROFIT MARGIN	EMPLOYEES
12/11	7,114	550	7.7%	19,250
12/10	5,652	377	6.7%	17,500
12/09	3,961	27	0.7%	12,500
12/08	5,263	(35)	—	13,800
12/07	5,328	288	5.4%	17,700
Annual Growth	7.5%	17.5%	—	2.1%

2011 Year-End Financials

Debt ratio: 22.31%
Return on equity: 23.04%
Cash ($ mil.): 359
Current ratio: 112.20
Long-term debt ($ mil.): 751
No. of shares (mil.): 108
Dividends
Yield: —
Payout: —
Market value ($ mil.): 6,917

	STOCK PRICE ($) FY Close	P/E High/Low	PER SHARE ($) Earnings	Dividends	Book Value
12/11	63.74	16 11	4.45	0.00	22.01
12/10	72.36	22 10	3.07	0.00	20.11
12/09	33.22	156 66	0.23	0.34	18.70
12/08	21.77	— —	(0.31)	0.44	17.36
12/07	48.41	42 19	2.45	0.34	19.99
Annual Growth	7.1%	— —	16.1%	—	2.4%

Boston Private Financial Holdings, Inc.

Boston Private —isn't that an old David Kelley TV series? Not exactly. The holding company owns Boston Private Bank & Trust which operates nearly 20 branches in the Boston Los Angeles and Seattle metropolitan areas and its Boral Private Bank & Trust division with about five locations in northern California. Boston Private also owns five other money management firms. The company offers private banking wealth advisory investment management deposits and lending and trust services to wealthy individuals corporations and institutional clients. All told Boston Private and its affiliates have some $20 billion in managed or advised assets.

Since its founding in 1987 Boston Private has had a voracious appetite for acquiring smaller trust companies private banks and wealth managers. However the firm put the brakes on its expansion and shifted strategies in 2009 amid the economic recession. Since then it has divested about a half-dozen money management subsidiaries as way to raise capital and reduce risk. In 2011 the company consolidated its four banking charters into Boston Private Bank & Trust to simplify its structure and cut costs. The bank is also shifting its focus away from commercial real estate lending and concentrating on relatively less risky residential mortgages and client-oriented commercial and industrial loans.

The moves helped the company to return to profitability in 2011 when it recorded net income of more than $38 million (though revenues were slightly down) after reporting losses each year from 2008 to 2010. Boston Private continues to open branches in its key markets has enhanced its online banking systems and expanded its investment management wealth advisory and trust services.

EXECUTIVES

EVP and Chief Lending Officer Borel Private Bank & Trust, Bruce K. Farrell

EVP and Director Marketing and Private Banking Borel Private Bank & Trust, Barbara L. Evers, age 59

EVP Senior Operations Officer and Security Officer Borel Private Bank & Trust, Carol J. Olson, age 57

Director; Chairman Boston Private Bank & Trust Company, Eugene S. Colangelo, age 64

Chairman Borel Private Bank & Trust, Sherie S. Dodsworth

EVP General Counsel Secretary and Chief Legal Officer, Margaret W. (Megan) Chambers, age 52, $283,500 total compensation

CEO Private Banking Group; President and CEO Boston Private Bank & Trust, Mark D. Thompson

EVP, James D. (Jim) Dawson, age 60, $412,885 total compensation

President and CEO Borel Private Bank & Trust Company, James C. (Jim) Garvey, age 55

EVP and Chief Credit Officer First Private Bank & Trust, Edwin J. (Ed) Fix Jr., age 64

EVP Investment Management Boston Private Bank & Trust, James D. Henderson

EVP CFO and Chief Administrative Officer Boston Private Bank & Trust, Anne L. Randall

CEO West Coast Private Banking Group and First Private Bank & Trust, V. Charles (Charlie) Jackson

SVP Human Resources Boston Private Bank & Trust, Pilar Pueyo

EVP Deposit and Cash COO and Treasurer Deposit Management Boston Private Bank & Trust, George G. Schwartz

Chairman, Stephen M. Waters, age 65

EVP and Chief Lending Officer Commercial Banking Boston Private Bank & Trust, James C. Brown

EVP and Manager Residential Lending Boston Private Bank & Trust, John J. Sullivan

Co-Managing Principal and COO Bingham Osborn & Scarborough, Carol L. Benz

Co-Managing Principal Bingham Osborn & Scarborough, William R. (Bill) Urban

CEO Dalton Greiner Hartman Maher & Co., Bruce H. Geller

EVP and CFO, David J. Kaye, age 47, $325,000 total compensation

Chairman Dalton Greiner Hartman Maher & Co., Timothy G. (Tim) Dalton

EVP and COO First Private Bank & Trust, Mary K. Fischer

EVP and Director Human Capital Resources, Martha T. Higgins, age 48

EVP and Chief Risk Officer, George L. Alexakos

EVP CFO and Secretary Borel Private Bank & Trust, Stephen A. Rossi

EVP Human Resources and Strategic Development Borel Private Bank & Trust, Constance I. Katsaros

SVP and Chief Risk Officer Boston Private Bank & Trust, Robert C. Buffum Jr.

SVP and CIO Boston Private Bank & Trust, Gary L. Garber

EVP and Chief Credit Officer Charter Bank, Andrew (Andy) Niemer

SVP and CTO Charter Bank, Tom Robertson

VP and Chief Administrative Officer Charter Bank, Theresa Stauch

EVP and CFO First Private Bank & Trust, Mike Winiarski
SVP and Technology Manager First Private Bank & Trust, Judith Breen
SVP and Chief Compliance Officer First Private Bank & Trust, Timothy Richey
CEO and Principal Davidson Trust, Alvin A. (Al) Clay III
Managing Director Business Development KLS Professional Advisors, Georgia Pangle
SVP and Director Marketing Anchor Capital Advisors, Robert F. Croce
President and Treasurer Anchor Capital Advisors, William P. Rice, age 68
SVP Corporate Communications, Catharine Sheehan
President and CEO, Clayton G. (Clay) Deutsch
SVP and Controller, William A. Gratrix
EVP and Chief Lending Officer Commercial Banking First Private Bank & Trust, John Tellenbach
Director; Chairman Boston Private Bank & Trust Company, Eugene S. Colangelo, age 64
Director, Allen L. Sinai, age 72
Director, Herbert S. Alexander, age 69
Director, Lynn Thompson Hoffman, age 63
Director, William J. (Bill) Shea, age 64
Director, Deborah F. Kuenstner, age 53
Director, John Morton III, age 68
Auditors: KPMGLLP

LOCATIONS

HQ: Boston Private Financial Holdings Inc.
10 Post Office Sq., Boston MA 02109
Phone: 617-912-1900 **Fax:** 617-912-4550
Web: www.bostonprivate.com

PRODUCTS/OPERATIONS

2011 Sales

	$ mil.	% of total
Interest and dividend income		
Loans	212	60
Investment securities	9	3
Mortgage-backed securities	7	2
Federal funds sold and other	1	-
Fees and other income		
Investment management & trust fees	63	18
Wealth advisory fees	41	11
Other	20	6
Total	**354**	**100**

Selected Subsidiaries & Affiliates

Anchor Capital Advisors LLC
Bingham Osborn & Scarborough LLC
Borel Private Bank & Trust Company
Boston Private Bank & Trust Company
Dalton Greiner Hartman Maher & Co. LLC
KLS Professional Advisors Group LLC

COMPETITORS

Bank of America
Brown Brothers Harriman
Central Bancorp
Century Bancorp (MA)
Citigroup
FMR
JPMorgan Chase
Morgan Stanley
RBS Citizens Financial Group
Sovereign Bank
TD Bank USA
Wells Fargo

HISTORICAL FINANCIALS

Company Type: Public

Income Statement FYE: December 31

	ASSETS ($ mil.)	NET INCOME ($ mil.)	INCOME AS % OF ASSETS	EMPLOYEES
12/11	6,048	39	0.6%	878
12/10	6,152	(10)	—	890
12/09	6,049	5	0.1%	859
12/08	7,266	(388)	—	1,220
12/07	6,818	4	0.1%	1,166
Annual Growth	(3.0%)	75.0%	—	(6.8%)

2011 Year-End Financials

Debt ratio: 11.64%
Return on equity: 6.91%
Cash ($ mil.): 203
Current ratio: —
Long-term debt ($ mil.): 703
No. of shares (mil.): 78
Dividends
Yield: —
Payout: 8.70%
Market value ($ mil.): 620

	STOCK PRICE ($) FY Close	P/E High/Low	PER SHARE ($) Earnings	Dividends	Book Value
12/11	7.94	16 10	0.46	0.00	7.26
12/10	6.55	— —	(0.29)	0.04	6.80
12/09	5.77	— —	(0.52)	0.04	9.48
12/08	6.84	— —	(8.87)	0.22	10.79
12/07	27.08	275223	0.11	0.36	17.68
Annual Growth	(26.4%)	— —	43.0%	—	(19.9%)

Boston Scientific Corp.

Boston Scientific knows that nothing is simple in matters of the heart. The company makes medical supplies and devices used to diagnose and treat conditions in a variety of medical fields with an emphasis on cardiovascular products and cardiac rhythm management. It also makes devices used for endoscopy urology and women's health pain management (neuromodulation) and electrophysiology. Its 13000-plus products made in 15 factories worldwide include defibrillators catheters coronary and urethral stents pacemakers biopsy forceps and needles and urethral slings. Boston Scientific markets its wares in about 100 countries mainly through its own direct sales staff which is active in more than 40 countries.

HISTORY

Many medical companies start near a hospital but Boston Scientific's roots sprouted at a children's soccer game where two dads found common ground. John Abele and Peter Nicholas had complementary interests: Wharton MBA Nichols wanted to run his own company; philosophy and physics graduate Abele wanted a job that would help people.

In 1979 the two men founded Boston Scientific to buy medical device maker Medi-Tech. Abele and Nicholas had to borrow half a million dollars from a bank and raise an additional $300000. Medi-Tech's primary product was a steerable catheter a soft-tipped device that could be maneuvered within the body. The catheter revolutionized gallstone operations in the early 1970s and Boston Scientific expanded on the success of the product. The company adapted it for a slew of new procedures for the heart lungs intestines and other organs.

Boston Scientific's sales were healthy in 1983 but the firm still lacked funds. It eagerly accepted $21 million from Abbott Laboratories in exchange for a 20% stake. New FDA regulations slowed product introduction and put a crimp in the company's growth. Boston Scientific found a legal loophole in the late 1980s to avoid lengthy delays: The company described its products in the vaguest possible terms so upgraded devices were considered similar enough to predecessors to escape the in-depth scrutiny of the new approval process. Still Abele and Nicholas had to mortgage their personal properties to stay afloat before this linguistic legerdemain helped to clear government red tape. Boston Scientific returned to profitability in 1991 and went public the next year buying back Abbott Laboratories' interest in the company as well.

Boston Scientific acquired a bevy of medical device companies throughout the late 1990's which expanded its range of cardiology products and doubled sales. Among them were SCIMED Life Systems Heart Technology Meadox Medicals EP Technologies and Symbiosis Target Therapeutics and Pfizer's catheter stent and angioplasty equipment business.

Late in 1998 news came out that Boston Scientific's Japanese subsidiary had inflated sales over several years by as much as $90 million. Restated earnings subsequently revealed a loss compounding the company's assimilation and recall problems.

Takeover rumors started to fly as well. The 1998 purchase of stent maker Schneider Worldwide fattened Boston Scientific's pipeline and payroll; the company cut 14% of its workers in 1999. That same year a federal judge ruled that the company's Bandit PTCA catheter infringed on a Guidant patent. Boston Scientific settled with Guidant and the two companies agreed to license products to each other.

The firm racked up 22 FDA approvals and a half dozen acquisitions in 2001. Its efforts to buy Israel-based Medinol (in which it already had a minority stake) dissolved when Medinol sued the firm alleging that Boston Scientific had tried to use Medinol's technology for its own purposes. Boston Scientific answered with a countersuit. (The two dissolved their partnership and settled their dispute in late 2005 with Boston Scientific agreeing to pay $750 million.) In late 2002 the company bought Inflow Dynamics and Smart Therapeutics.

Throughout 2003 and 2004 the company's Taxus drug-coated stent systems were big news despite recalls of the system. Controversy over the use of stents began to hurt the product segment's sales in 2006.

In spite of ongoing patent infringement suits Boston Scientific continued to develop new products and acquire smaller companies. In 2005 the firm bought Advanced Stent Technologies to gain its technology for stents for bifurcated heart vessels (a condition caused by the branching of one vessel into two).

Boston Scientific acquired CryoVascular Systems which produced an angioplasty device used to treat atherosclerotic disease that was distributed by Boston Scientific. Boston Scientific also acquired a portfolio of endoscopic (throat and esophageal) stents from Teleflex subsidiary Willy Rusch GmbH in 2005.

In 2006 the company made a major purchase with the $22 billion acquisition of Guidant a maker of vascular and endovascular products including implantable cardioverter defibrillators (ICDs) pacemaker systems and surgical ablation products. The acquisition came after Boston Scientific won a bidding battle with rival Johnson & Johnson and the company had to pay a $700 million breakup fee to Johnson & Johnson as a result. However Guidant had recalled over 100000 faulty defibrillators in 2005 and shortly after its purchase Boston Scientific was hit with more than 2000 lawsuits including more than 70 class-action suits over the products.

In response to the defibrillator troubles as well as controversy that emerged over its drug-coated stent products the company launched a restructuring of its operations in 2007. Its efforts included job cuts plant closures and the sale of noncore assets although it still managed to continue acquiring businesses.

Sales included its cardiac surgery and vascular surgery businesses to Swedish firm Getinge for $750 million in cash in early 2008 and the sale of the auditory (deafness treatment) and drug pump development portions of its neuromodulation segment to management members of former subsidiary Advanced Bionics. The company sold its fluid management business (angiography and angioplasty products) and its venous access business which makes blood stream access implants to Avista Capital Partners for $425 million. Avista then combined the two business units into a new independent company named Navilyst Medical.

Acquisitions in 2007 included carotid (neck) stent maker EndoTex Interventional Systems which signaled its entry into the carotid artery treatment field and Rubicon Medical which brought non-invasive stent delivery systems and other less-invasive endovascular devices to the company's product portfolio. As luck would have it Boston Scientific had to recall most of its EndoTex's NexStent products in 2008 due to a faulty delivery system.

Despite setbacks from its Guidant purchase Boston Scientific remained committed to its cardiac rhythm management segment and in 2008 the company paid $21 million to purchase CryoCor. Boston Scientific integrated its balloon catheter system with CryoCor's cryoablation system to treat cardiac arrhythmias by using extreme cold to destroy targeted tissue.

At the same time that Guidant's defibrillators were in the news drug-coated stents began drawing negative attention —including many made by Boston Scientific. Stents small implanted devices that prop open blood vessels and arteries were part of the company's interventional cardiology business and a key source of revenues. Drug-coated stents that can hold open blood vessels and slowly dispense plaque-fighting drugs were touted as a one-two punch to fight atherosclerosis and Boston Scientific was among the first heavyweights in the ring. However a few years after they were introduced safety concerns were raised over the possibility that the devices posed a risk for increased blood clots and the company saw sales of its drug-coated stents dip. Nonetheless it remained committed to cardiovascular stents with or without drug coatings and in 2008 spent $17 million to acquire Labcoat to obtain its work in improving the drug-coating process for stent systems.

The company spent some $193 million to acquire Asthmatx (2010) and its newly-approved Alair system which uses heat to reduce the amount of smooth muscle in the airways of severe asthma patients.

In 2010 Boston Scientific settled a chunk of stent-related patent litigation (including battles over its TAXUS Express and TAXUS Liberte patents) by paying competitor Johnson & Johnson (J&J) a whopping $1.7 billion. Boston Scientific had already taken a financial hit in 2008 when it lost a patent infringement suit filed by J&J over a coronary stent and was fined $700 million by a US District Court. After its failed appeal the company paid $716 million in exchange for a partial settlement with J&J.

EXECUTIVES

EVP and COO, Samuel R. (Sam) Leno, age 66, $625,000 total compensation
Chairman, Peter M. (Pete) Nicholas, age 70, $700,003 total compensation
SVP Global Sales Operations, Stephen F. (Steve) Moreci, age 60, $427,450 total compensation
EVP and CFO, Jeffrey D. (Jeff) Capello, age 47
Director Corporate Communications, Erik Kopp
President CEO and Director, Michael F. (Mike) Mahoney, age 47
SVP; President Cardiac Rhythm Management, Joseph M. (Joe) Fitzgerald
SVP Human Resources, Otha T. (Skip) Spriggs III
SVP Corporate Communications, Denise Kaigler
EVP Global Quality Medical Safety and Regulatory Affairs, Brian R. Burns, age 47
EVP Global Operations and Technology, Kenneth J. (Ken) Pucel, age 45
CEO and Director, William H. (Hank) Kucheman, age 62
Director Media Relations Cardiac Rhythm Management, Annette Ruzicka
SVP; President EMEA (Europe the Middle East and Africa), J. Michael Onuscheck, age 45
SVP; President Neuromodulation, Maulik Nanavaty
SVP; President Urology and Women's Health, John B. Pedersen, age 49
EVP; President Medical Surgical (MedSurg), Michael P. (Mike) Phalen, age 52
EVP Chief Administrative Officer Secretary and General Counsel, Timothy A. (Tim) Pratt, age 62, $525,000 total compensation
SVP and Chief Compliance Officer, Jean Fitterer Lance, age 50
SVP and Global Medical Officer, Keith D. Dawkins
Manager Media Relations Cardiac Rhythm Management, Dave Knutson
EVP; President Asia-Pacific, Supratim Bose
SVP; President Endoscopy Division, David A. (Dave) Pierce
SVP; President Emerging Markets, Lawrence R. (Larry) Neuman
Director, Bruce L. Byrnes, age 64
Director, Ernest Mario, age 73
Director, Kristina M. Johnson, age 54
Director, Uwe E. Reinhardt, age 74
Director, J. Raymond (Ray) Elliott, age 62
President CEO and Director, Michael F. (Mike) Mahoney, age 47
CEO and Director, William H. (Hank) Kucheman, age 62
Director, Katharine T. (Kate) Bartlett, age 65
Director, John E. Sununu, age 47
Director, Nelda J. Connors, age 47
Auditors: Ernst&YoungLLP

LOCATIONS

HQ: Boston Scientific Corporation
1 Boston Scientific Place, Natick MA 01760-1537
Phone: 508-650-8000 **Fax:** 508-650-8910
Web: www.bostonscientific.com

2011 Sales

	$ mil.	% of total
US	4,010	53
Europe Middle East & Africa	1,742	23
Japan	951	12
Intercontinental	778	10
Divested businesses	141	2
Total	**7,622**	**100**

PRODUCTS/OPERATIONS

2011 Sales

	$ mil.	% of total
Interventional cardiology	2,495	33
Cardiac rhythm management	2,087	27
Endoscopy	1,187	16
Peripheral interventions	731	10
Urology/Women's Health	498	6
Neuromodulation	336	4
Electrophysiology	147	2
Divested businesses	141	2
Total	**7,622**	**100**

Selected Products

Cardiovascular
- Interventional Cardiology
  - PolarCath peripheral dilation system
  - PROMUS drug-eluting stents
  - TAXUS drug-eluting stents
  - VeriFLEX bare-metal stents
  - WALLSTENT carotid artery stents
- Cardiac Rhythm Management (CRM)
  - ACUITY steerable ventricular leads
  - COGNIS cardiac resynchronization defibrillator
  - LATITUDE remote patient monitoring system
  - TELIGEN implantable cardiac defbrillator
- Other cardiovascular
  - Cutting Balloon dilation device
  - FilterWire EZ embolic protection system
  - iLab ultrasound imaging catheter system
  - Maverick balloon catheters

Endoscopy
- Radial Jaw 4 single-use biopsy forceps (gastrointestinal)
- RX Biliary System (bile duct surgeries)
- SpyGlass direct visualization system (pancreatic system)

Urology/Women' s Health
- Genesys Hydro ThermAblator (endometrial ablation system)

Neuromodulation
- Precision Spinal Cord Stimulation system (chronic pain)

Electrophysiology
- Blazer Prime temperature ablation catheters

Selected Acquisitions

2012
- BridgePoint Medical Inc. (undisclosed price; Minneapolis; developer of a catheter system to treat blocked coronary arteries)
- Rhythmia Medical Inc. ($90 million including potential milestone payments; Burlington MA; developer of mapping and navigational software used in procedures that treat abnormal heart rhythms)
- Cameron Health Inc. ($1.3 billion including potential milestone payments; San Clemente CA; subcutaneous ICD)

2011
- Atritech ($375 million including potential milestone payments; development-stage minimally invasive atrial closure device for fibrillation or stroke)
- Intelect Medical ($78 million deep brain stimulation (DBS) technologies)
- Sadra Medical ($386 million including potential milestone payments; Lotus Valve System an aortic valve replacement implant system)

2010
- Asthmatx ($193 million Alair asthma treatment system)

COMPETITORS

Abbott Labs
American Medical Systems
Bard
Cook Group
Covidien
Edwards Lifesciences
ev3
Hologic
Johnson & Johnson
LeMaitre Vascular
Medtronic
St. Jude Medical
ZOLL

HISTORICAL FINANCIALS

Company Type: Public

Income Statement FYE: December 31

	REVENUE ($ mil.)	NET INCOME ($ mil.)	NET PROFIT MARGIN	EMPLOYEES
12/11	7,622	441	5.8%	24,000
12/10	7,806	(1,065)	—	25,000
12/09	8,188	(1,025)	—	26,000
12/08	8,050	(2,036)	—	24,800
12/07	8,357	(495)	—	27,500
Annual Growth	(2.3%)	—	—	(3.3%)

2011 Year-End Financials

Debt ratio: 20.01%
Return on equity: 3.88%
Cash ($ mil.): 267
Current ratio: 171.83
Long-term debt ($ mil.): 4,257
No. of shares (mil.): 1,449
Dividends
Yield: —
Payout: —
Market value ($ mil.): 7,738

	STOCK PRICE ($) FY Close	P/E High/Low	PER SHARE ($) Earnings	Dividends	Book Value
12/11	5.34	27 18	0.29	0.00	7.84
12/10	7.57	— —	(0.70)	0.00	7.43
12/09	9.00	— —	(0.68)	0.00	8.14
12/08	7.74	— —	(1.36)	0.00	8.77
12/07	11.63	— —	(0.33)	0.00	10.12
Annual Growth	(17.7%)	— —	—	—	(6.2%)

Bristol-Myers Squibb Co.

Bristol-Myers Squibb (BMS) may be a giant in transition but its still a pharmaceutical giant. The company's blockbuster cardiovascular lineup includes heart disease drug Plavix and Avapro for hypertension. BMS also makes antipsychotic medication Abilify and HIV treatments Reyataz and Sustiva. Most of its sales come from products in the therapeutic areas of cardiovascular care immunoscience metabolics neuroscience oncology and virology. BMS has global R&D facilities and manufacturing plants mainly in the US and Europe and its products are marketed to health care practitioners hospitals and managed care providers in 100 countries.

HISTORY

Bristol-Myers Squibb is the product of a merger of rivals.

Squibb was founded by Dr. Edward Squibb in New York City in 1858. He developed techniques for making pure ether and chloroform; he turned the business over to his sons in 1891.

Sales of $414000 in 1904 grew to $13 million by 1928. The company supplied penicillin and morphine during WWII. In 1952 it was bought by Mathieson Chemical which in turn was bought by Olin Industries in 1953 forming Olin Mathieson Chemical. Squibb maintained its separate identity.

From 1968 to 1971 Olin Mathieson went through repeated reorganizations and adopted the Squibb name. Capoten and Corgard two major cardiovascular drugs were introduced in the late 1970s. Capoten was the first drug engineered to attack a specific disease-causing mechanism. Squibb formed a joint venture with Denmark's Novo (now Novo Nordisk) in 1982 to sell insulin.

William Bristol and John Myers founded Clinton Pharmaceutical in Clinton New York in 1887 (renamed Bristol-Myers in 1900) to sell bulk pharmaceuticals. The firm made antibiotics after the 1943 purchase of Cheplin Biological Labs. It began expanding overseas in the 1950s and eventually bought Clairol (1959); Mead Johnson (drugs infant and nutritional formula; 1967); and Zimmer (orthopedic implants 1972). Bristol-Myers launched new drugs to treat cancer (Platinol 1978) and anxiety (BuSpar 1986). That year it acquired biotech companies Oncogen and Genetic Systems.

The firm bought Squibb in 1989. In 1990 the new company bought arthroscopy products and implant business lines and joined Eastman Kodak and Elf Aquitaine to develop new heart drugs in 1993. Despite these initiatives earnings slipped. In 1994 company veteran Charles Heimbold became CEO and moved to increase profits. BMS in 1995 bought wound and skin care products firm Calgon Vestal Laboratories. Also that year the company along with fellow silicone breast implant makers 3M and Baxter International agreed to settle thousands of personal injury claims at an average of $26000 per claim.

Facing an antitrust suit filed by independent drugstores BMS and other major drugmakers agreed in 1996 to charge pharmacies the same prices as managed care groups for medications. That year the company formed a generic drug unit and launched Pravachol.

Over the next two years BMS tweaked its product line buying drug cosmetics and consumer products companies and brands. Having refined its product line the firm began a series of officer reassignments that were widely interpreted as an effort to find a successor for Heimbold who retired in 2001.

In 1999 the firm pulled its backing for EntreMed after the biotech had problems duplicating results for a cancer drug candidate. BMS helped market promising diabetes drug Avandia (from GlaxoSmithKline which ended the deal in 2002) and teamed with Millennium Pharmaceuticals to study the genetic makeup of tumors.

As the company entered the 21st century it began streamlining. It sold its Sea Breeze skin care brand (1999); Matrix Essentials hair care products unit (2000); and Clairol hair and personal care products business (2001). BMS also spun off its Zimmer orthopedic implant unit in 2001. More changes came in 2004: The firm sold its Mead Johnson Adult Nutritional business.

In 2002 BMS was dealt a blow when a judge ruled that the company had illegally blocked Mylan Labs and Watson Pharmaceuticals from selling generic versions of BuSpar.

The firm bought a 20% stake in ImClone to collaborate on the development of cancer drug Erbitux and to stay on top of the cancer drug market. Instead BMS found itself embroiled in the controversy over insider information and stock deals surrounding the biotech. Persistence paid off however; Erbitux was approved by the FDA in 2004.

During 2005 the company cleaned out parts of its medicine cabinet. Analgesics Excedrin and Bufferin had made the company a household name but in 2005 the company sold its US and Canadian consumer products operations to Novartis. The deal also meant saying goodbye to such brands as Comtrex (cold medications) Choice (blood sugar monitoring supplies) and Keri (lotions skin care). Sales for the its US and Canadian consumer products operations reached about $270 million in 2004.

That same year BMS sold Oncology Therapeutics Network which distributes cancer drugs to oncology doctors to private equity firm One Equity Partners. The unit had accounted for about 13% of sales in 2004.

As part of an agreement with the New Jersey US Attorney's office in 2005 to settle an investigation into inventory control and accounting practices the company split the role of chairman and CEO into two separate offices. Long-time BMS director James Robinson III was elected the company's new chairman with Peter Dolan in the CEO role. James Cornelius took over as CEO in 2006 and became chairman in 2008 bring the two roles back together.

While the patent expiration on blockbuster Plavix was still five years off in mid-2006 Canadian generics maker Apotex managed to flood the market with a generic version of Plavix for several weeks. The release of the drug followed bungled attempts by BMS to negotiate a deal with Apotex that would have kept it off the market. The debacle led to federal investigations into whether that deal violated anti-trust laws (among other things) and also resulted in the ouster of CEO Peter Dolan (replaced by James Cornelius). Though a judge put a halt to the manufacturing of the generic until the courts could straighten the whole thing out the short-term generic competition hurt Plavix sales to the tune of more than $1 billion. BMS ultimately wound up paying more than $150 million to settle lawsuits and agreed that it would report any future deals struck with generics makers.

As part of its efforts to remake itself into a purely biopharmaceutical player BMS began jettisoning its non-pharmaceutical businesses. During 2008 the company sold its Medical Imaging unit to private equity firm Avista Capital Partners for $525 million and Avista Capital Partners and Nordic Capital paid $4.1 billion to acquire BMS' ConvaTec ostomy and wound-care subsidiary. Then in 2009 the company divested its Mead Johnson subsidiary which sold Enfamil infant formula and other nutritional products for children.

In 2008 the company made a pair of splashy – but ultimately unsuccessful –bids to acquire ImClone Systems first for $4.5 billion and then for $4.7 billion. BMS had owned about 17% of ImClone and the two companies have spent years working together on the commercialization of profitable cancer therapy Erbitux. However ImClone's board (led by chairman Carl Icahn) rejected both bids in favor of a higher $6.5 billion offer from Eli Lilly. BMS then sold its ImClone stake for about $1 billion to Eli Lilly and continue its role as the North American marketing partner for Erbitux.

Focusing on its string of pearls strategy to acquire biotech drugs through acquisitions and licensing deals BMS acquired oncology drug developers Kosan Biosciences ($190 million 2008) and Medarex ($2.4 billion 2009). Medarex had been collaborating with BMS to develop ipilimumab an antibody candidate in late-stage trials for melanoma and other cancers.

In anticipation of the day when it would need to manufacture a variety of the more complicated biologic drugs BMS built a new plant in Massachusetts in 2010.

EXECUTIVES

SVP Corporate and Business Communications and Chief Communications Officer, Robert T. (Bob) Zito, age 58

General Counsel and Corporate Secretary, Sandra Leung, age 51
Chairman, James M. (Jim) Cornelius, age 68, $1,500,000 total compensation
EVP Chief Scientific Officer and Director; President Research and Development, Elliott Sigal, age 60, $1,014,846 total compensation
CEO and Director, Lamberto Andreotti, age 61, $1,244,730 total compensation
VP Investor Relations, John Elicker
President Mead Johnson Nutritionals, Stephen W. (Steve) Golsby, age 57
President Technical Operations and Global Support Functions, Carlo de Notaristefani, age 54
SVP Human Resources Public Affairs and Philanthropy, John E. Celentano, age 52
SVP Global Regulatory Services, Richard L. Wolgemuth, age 66
SVP Human Resources, Anthony McBride
President BMS Foundation, John Damonti
SVP Global Development and Medical Affairs Research and Development, Brian Daniels
VP Human Resources, Sandra J. Holleran
VP and Treasurer, Jeffrey Galik
VP and General Manager Devens Biologic Manufacturing Facility, Christopher Perley
VP Global Development Oncology Global Clinical Research, Renzo Canetta
Senior Director Work/Life and Diversity Programs, Stacey Gibson
President and General Manager Bristol-Myers Squibb Puerto Rico and the Caribbean, Edda Guerrero
Corporate and Financial Media Contact, Brian Henry
Director Business Communications, Jennifer Fron Mauer
Director Community Affairs, Fred Egenolf
Director Business Communications, Laura Hortas
Cardiovascular & Metabolics Contact, Ken Dominski
Virology & Neuroscience Contact, Sonia Choi
Director Business Communications, Linda Jordan
Senior Director International Communications, Patrice Grand
Philanthropy & Social Responsibility Contact, Tracy Furey
VP Global Clinical Research Neuroscience and Virology, Doug Manion
VP and Therapeutic Area Head Global Clinical Research Neuroscience, Howard Feldman
SVP and Chief Procurement Officer, Quentin L. Roach
EVP Commercial Operations, Beatrice Cazala, age 55
President US Pharmaceuticals, Giovanni Caforio, age 47
EVP and CFO, Charles A. Bancroft, age 52
Director Investor Relations, Teri Loxam
Director Investor Relations, Suketu Desai
SVP Research and Development, Francis Cuss, age 57
SVP and CIO, Paul von Autenried, age 50
SVP and Corporate Controller, Joseph C. Caldarella, age 56
President Technical Operations, Louis S. Schmukler, age 56
Director, Alan J. Lacy, age 58
Director, Lewis B. Campbell, age 66
Director, Vicki L. Sato, age 63
Director, Laurie Heinz Glimcher, age 60
Director, Michael Grobstein, age 69
Director, Togo Dennis West Jr., age 69
Director, Louis J. Freeh, age 62
EVP Chief Scientific Officer and Director; President Research and Development, Elliott Sigal, age 60
CEO and Director, Lamberto Andreotti, age 61
Director, Robert Sanders (Sandy) Williams, age 63
Auditors: Deloitte&ToucheLLP

LOCATIONS

HQ: Bristol-Myers Squibb Company
345 Park Ave., New York NY 10154-0037
Phone: 212-546-4000 **Fax:** 212-546-4020
Web: www.bms.com

2011 Sale

	$ mil.	% of total
US	13,845	65
Europe	3,667	17
Japan Asia/Pacific & Canada	1,862	9
Latin America Middle East & Africa	894	4
Emerging markets (Brazil Russia India China & Turkey) & other	976	5
Total	**21,244**	**100**

PRODUCTS/OPERATIONS

2011 Sales

	$ mil.	% of total
Plavix	7,087	33
Abilify	2,758	13
Reyataz	1,569	7
Sustiva franchise	1,485	7
Baraclude	1,196	6
Avapro/Avalide	952	5
Orencia	917	4
Sprycel	803	4
Erbitux	691	3
Onglyza/Kombiglyze	473	2
Yervoy	360	2
Nulojix	3	-
Mature products & other	2,950	14
Total	**21,244**	**100**

Selected Pharmaceuticals

Cardiovascular
- Avalide (irbesartan hydrochlorothiazide)
- Avapro (irbesartan)
- Plavix (clopidogrel bisulfate)

Immunology
- Kombiglyze (saxagliptin and metformin hydrochloride extended-release)
- Nulojix (belatacept)
- Onglyza (saxagliptin)
- Orencia (abatacept)

Psychiatric disorders
- Abilify (aripiprazole)

Oncology
- Erbitux (cetuximab)
- Ixempra (ixabepilone)
- Sprycel (dasatinib)
- Yervoy (ipilimumab)

Virology
- Atripla (efavirenz/emtricitabine/tenofovir disoproxil fumarate)
- Baraclude (entecavir)
- Reyataz (atazanavir sulfate)
- Sustiva (efavirenz)

Selected Subsidiaries

Adnexus (research and development)
Allard Labs Acquisition G.P.
Apothecon Inc.
Bristol Laboratories Inc.
Bristol Laboratories Medical Information Systems Inc.
GenPharm International Inc.
Grove Insurance Company Ltd.
Heyden Farmaceutica Portugesa Limitada
Inhibitex Inc.
Kosan Biosciences Incorporated
Lawrence Laboratories
Linson Investments Limited
Medarex Inc.
Princeton Pharmaceutical Products Inc.
Route 22 Real Estate Holding Corporation
Swords Laboratories
Tri-Supply Limited
ZymoGenetics Inc.

COMPETITORS

Abbott Labs
Amgen
Apotex
AstraZeneca
Biogen Idec
Boehringer Ingelheim
Eli Lilly
Forest Labs
Genentech
GlaxoSmithKline
Johnson & Johnson
Merck
Mylan
Novartis
Pfizer
Ranbaxy Laboratories
Roche Holding
Sandoz International GmbH
Sanofi
Teva
Watson Pharmaceuticals

HISTORICAL FINANCIALS

Company Type: Public

Income Statement FYE: December 31

	REVENUE ($ mil.)	NET INCOME ($ mil.)	NET PROFIT MARGIN	EMPLOYEES
12/11	21,244	3,709	17.5%	27,000
12/10	19,484	3,102	15.9%	27,000
12/09	18,808	10,612	56.4%	28,000
12/08	20,597	5,247	25.5%	35,000
12/07	19,348	2,165	11.2%	42,000
Annual Growth	2.4%	14.4%	—	(10.5%)

2011 Year-End Financials

Debt ratio: 16.31%
Return on equity: 23.25%
Cash ($ mil.): 5,776
Current ratio: 196.89
Long-term debt ($ mil.): 5,376
No. of shares (mil.): 1,690
Dividends
Yield: —
Payout: 61.11%
Market value ($ mil.): 59,556

	STOCK PRICE ($) FY Close	P/E High	P/E Low	PER SHARE ($) Earnings	Dividends	Book Value
12/11	35.24	16	11	2.16	0.00	9.44
12/10	26.48	16	12	1.79	1.28	9.22
12/09	25.25	5	3	5.34	1.25	8.66
12/08	23.25	10	7	2.63	1.24	6.19
12/07	26.52	29	24	1.09	1.12	5.34
Annual Growth	7.4%	—	—	18.6%	—	15.3%

Broadcom Corp.

As a semiconductor supplier for the global wired and wireless communications industry Broadcom's reach is far and wide. With sales and marketing offices and R&D centers around the globe Broadcom manufactures about two billion chips annually and is one of the top 10 semiconductor companies by revenue. Its System-on-a-Chip (SoC) technologies and software products deliver voice video data and multimedia in several major market segments: home and office (cable modems DSL and set-top boxes) mobile (Bluetooth and GPS) and infrastructure (controllers embedded processors and security). Broadcom's customer roster includes such elite technology names as Apple Cisco Dell Samsung and ZTE.

HISTORY

Henry Samueli and Henry Nicholas began their partnership at UCLA as professor and student respectively although the two had earlier worked together as product designers for technology specialist TRW's military integrated circuit operation. In

1988 Samueli helped found copper line-based data transmission firm PairGain Technologies (which later became part of ADC Telecommunications). Though only in his 20s Nicholas was PairGain's director of microelectronics.

Convinced that the fastest microchip would own the market for devices combining computers TVs and phones Samueli and Nicholas left PairGain in 1991 to found Broadcom. The duo accepted no venture capital; they wanted to be able to offer head-turning amounts of stock options to potential employees.

Broadcom's pioneering chip efforts soon attracted the attention of larger companies. In 1993 Broadcom introduced an advanced chip for cable boxes that was chosen by Scientific-Atlanta (now part of Cisco Systems) for use in its pioneering interactive cable television trials for Time Warner. The company began shipping production quantities of its chips in 1994. Other early customers included Analog Devices Intel Rockwell and the US Air Force.

Intel invested $5 million in Broadcom in 1994 and Broadcom formed chip development alliances with Hewlett-Packard in 1995 and with Northern Telecom (now Nortel Networks) in 1996.

In 1997 Broadcom unveiled chipsets that enabled different manufacturers' cable modem equipment to work together; the chips soon became the industry standard. The company went public in 1998 in an IPO that made more than 200 of its employees millionaires (and made Samueli and Nicholas billionaires).

Flush with IPO cash in 1999 Broadcom began beefing up its technology through acquisitions. The spree continued through 2000 and into 2001 as the company spent around $10 billion to round out its product offerings and acquire new engineering talent.

For most of 2001 and early 2002 Broadcom stayed silent on the acquisition front as it weathered the worst year ever for the global chip industry. In 2002 though the company acquired Mobilink Telecom a maker of chipsets for wireless devices in a deal initially valued at about $190 million. Late that year the company laid off about 500 workers —a sixth of its staff —in the face of brutal industry conditions.

In 2003 the company reorganized its business units. Just after that the intensely driven and energetic Nicholas resigned as president and CEO citing his wish to stave off divorce. (Nicholas retired from the company's board later that year.) Board member and interim COO Alan Ross succeeded Nicholas as president and CEO. Also in 2003 Broadcom acquired the assets of Gadzoox Networks a maker of storage area network (SAN) hardware and software for about $6 million.

When the market picked up by 2004 Broadcom picked up the pace of its acquisitions. It bought RAIDCore a privately held company that produced software for RAID (redundant array of independent disks) storage applications for $16 million; Sand Video which designed video compression chips for $80 million; WIDCOMM for nearly $50 million; Zyray Wireless which designed baseband co-processor chips for $80 million; and Alphamosaic which designed multimedia processors for $120 million. Early in 2005 it acquired wireless chip designer Zeevo for $32 million in cash and stock. It then purchased Siliquent Technologies a developer of processors used in network interface controllers for about $76 million in cash. It also acquired Athena Semiconductors for about $21 million.

Philips Semiconductors (now NXP) president and CEO Scott McGregor succeeded Ross as president and CEO in 2005. The following year Broadcom purchased Sandburst a designer of networking chipsets for about $77 million.

In 2006 the company announced that an internal investigation revealed potential problems with the backdating of stock options during 2000; the company said that it would likely take a $750 million charge and would need to restate five years' worth of financial statements.

Broadcom later doubled the size of the estimated non-cash charge against earnings it would need to take to $1.5 billion and finally disclosed in 2007 that the charge would total around $2.2 billion. CFO William Ruehle decided to move up his retirement. The internal investigation later revealed backdating problems existed from June 1998 to May 2003. In addition an informal inquiry by the SEC was upgraded to a formal investigation and the company was cooperating with federal prosecutors as well.

Later in 2007 Broadcom disclosed that chairman/CTO Henry Samueli and David Dull SVP and general counsel received Wells notices from the staff of the SEC a notification that the securities regulators might seek civil charges against the company and the executives related to past practices in granting stock options. Dull headed up Broadcom's highly successful patent litigation against QUALCOMM.

In 2007 Broadcom acquired LVL7 Systems a developer of networking software for about $62 million in cash. The chip firm saw LVL7's FASTPATH software enhancing its offerings for small to medium-sized businesses since the software enabled OEMs and original design manufacturers (ODMs) to develop networking products quicker and more efficiently.

Aiming to widen its offerings for the cable-based home networking market Broadcom that year acquired Octalica a fabless semiconductor startup for about $31 million in cash. Octalica developed networking technologies based on the Multimedia over Coax Alliance (MoCA) standard specifications created by an industry group of cable system operators and chip companies.

Also in 2007 the company paid about $143 million in cash to buy Global Locate a developer of Global Positioning System (GPS) and assisted GPS semiconductors and software. Global Locate's products were used in wireless handsets and in personal navigation devices made by TomTom a leading GPS product vendor.

In 2008 Broadcom acquired AMD's digital TV (DTV) chip line. Broadcom already served many top-tier manufacturers in the DTV market and the purchase supplemented its offerings for DTV sets. Because the DTV chip product line had lower than expected sales AMD reduced the price from $192.8 million to $141.5 million in cash.

In 2008 the SEC charged the company with falsifying its reported income by backdating stock-option grants over five years from 1998 to 2003. Without admitting or denying the charges Broadcom agreed to settle the case and to pay a penalty of $12 million. The SEC earlier reached a settlement with Nancy Tullos the company's former VP of human resources and Tullos pleaded guilty to a single criminal charge of obstructing justice; she cooperated with federal prosecutors as part of her plea arrangement and her guilty plea was dismissed by a federal judge in 2010.

The SEC brought civil charges against Samueli Dull Ruehle and Nicholas alleging multiple violations of the Securities Act of 1933 the Securities Exchange Act of 1934 and the Sarbanes-Oxley Act of 2002. Samueli and Dull took leaves of absence from their executive posts while remaining employees of Broadcom and Samueli resigned from the board of directors. John Major a Broadcom director since 2003 was named nonexecutive chairman to succeed Samueli.

Federal prosecutors next unsealed criminal charges alleging conspiracy securities fraud and other violations of securities law against Nicholas and Ruehle. They both pleaded not guilty to the charges. (All civil and criminal securities charges were dismissed against both men in 2009.) Nicholas was also indicted on a variety of federal drug charges; those charges were dismissed in 2010.

Samueli then pleaded guilty to a federal felony charge of lying to SEC investigators regarding a statement he made in a 2007 deposition. Under a plea deal with federal prosecutors the billionaire philanthropist owner of the Anaheim Ducks hockey team and UCLA engineering professor was expected to be sentenced to five years of probation while paying a penalty of $12 million and a fine of $250000.

The US District Court judge hearing the case rejected the plea deal however saying it gave the impression that justice was for sale. Samueli appealed the judge's decision; in 2009 another US District Court judge ruled that Samueli's statements to regulators were "ambiguous and evasive" though not materially false and as such not a crime. Charges against the executive were dismissed.

Criminal and civil charges brought against Nicholas Samueli and other executives related to alleged backdating of stock option grants were all dismissed in 2009 as a federal judge found there were insufficient legal grounds for the cases. A separate sensational case alleging that Nicholas helped distribute illicit drugs was dismissed in 2010 with both criminal and civil charges dropped.

Also in 2009 Broadcom reached a legal settlement with rival QUALCOMM agreeing to dismiss their patent litigation and granting each other certain rights under their patent portfolios. Among other terms QUALCOMM agreed to pay Broadcom $891 million in cash over four years.

Broadcom had a busy 2009 with attempted takeovers lawsuits and legal settlements. Late in the year the company acquired Dune Networks for about $178 million. Dune Networks was a privately held fabless semiconductor company that developed switch fabric products for data center networking equipment. The acquisition beefed up Broadcom's network equipment product line.

EXECUTIVES

EVP Global Human Resources, Terri L. Timberman, age 54

EVP Worldwide Sales, Thomas F. (Tom) Lagatta, age 54, $298,385 total compensation

Chairman and Chief Technical Officer, Henry Samueli, age 57, $1 total compensation

EVP & General Manager Broadband Communications Group, Daniel A. (Dan) Marotta, age 51, $325,000 total compensation

EVP and CFO, Eric K. Brandt, age 49, $360,000 total compensation

Chairman, John E. Major, age 66

President CEO and Director, Scott A. McGregor, age 55, $682,500 total compensation

EVP Corporate Services and CIO, Kenneth E. (Ken) Venner, age 49

EVP & General Manager Mobile & Wireless Group, Robert A. (Bob) Rango, age 54, $325,000 total compensation

EVP Operations and Central Engineering, Neil Y. Kim, age 53

Media Relations Asia, Mike He

EVP General Counsel and Corporate Secretary, Arthur Chong, age 59, $59,231 total compensation
Media Contact Broadband Communications, Dana Brzozkiewicz
SVP Mobile Platforms, Scott A. Bibaud, age 49
SVP Corporate Controller and Principal Accounting Officer, Robert L. Tirva, age 45, $219,213 total compensation
VP Global Communications, Karen Kahn
EVP and General Manager Infrastructure and Networking Group, Rajiv Ramaswami, age 46
Media Contact Mobile and Wireless Group, Susan Vander May
Media Contact Infrastructure and Networking Group, Tamara Snowden
Director Investor Relations, Chris Zegarelli
Manager Corporate Public Relations, Jennifer (Jen) Baumgartner
Director, Nancy H. Handel, age 60
Director, Robert E. (Bob) Switz, age 65
Director, Eddy W. Hartenstein, age 61
CTO and Director, Henry Samueli, age 57
Director, John E. Major, age 66
Director, John A. Swainson
Director, Robert J. (Bob) Finocchio Jr., age 59
President CEO and Director, Scott A. McGregor, age 55
Director, Maria M. Klawe, age 60
Director, William T. (Bill) Morrow, age 52
Auditors: KPMGLLP

LOCATIONS

HQ: Broadcom Corporation
5300 California Ave., Irvine CA 92617-3038
Phone: 949-926-5000 **Fax:** 949-926-6589
Web: www.broadcom.com

PRODUCTS/OPERATIONS

2011 Sales

	$ mil.	% of total
Mobile & wireless	3,484	47
Broadband communications	2,039	28
Infrastructure & networking	1,658	22
Other	208	3
Total	**7,389**	**100**

2011 Sales

	$ mil.	% of total
Product revenue	7,160	97
Income from QUALCOMM agreement	207	3
Licensing revenue	22	-
Total	**7,389**	**100**

Selected Products

Broadband processors
Cable modems
Cable set-top boxes
Carrier access
Digital subscriber lines (DSL)
Enterprise networking
Home networking
Optical networking
Servers
Software
Wireless communications

Selected Mergers & Acquisitions

2012
BroadLight Inc. (networking and fiber access PON processor provider)
NetLogic Microsystems Inc. (intelligent semiconductor provider)
2011
SC Square Ltd (security software developer)
Provigent Ltd. (provider of mixed signal semiconductors for microwave backhaul systems)

COMPETITORS

Airvana
AMD
Analog Devices
Applied Micro Circuits
Cirrus Logic
Conexant Systems
CSR plc
Cypress Semiconductor
Emulex
Entropic Communications
Freescale Semiconductor
Fujitsu Semiconductor
Gennum
Himax
IBM Microelectronics
Infineon Technologies
Intel
Intersil
LSI Corp.
Marvell Technology
MediaTek
Mindspeed
NVIDIA
NXP Semiconductors
Oki Semiconductor
PMC-Sierra
QLogic
QUALCOMM
RF Micro Devices
Samsung Electronics
ST-Ericsson
STMicroelectronics
Symmetricom
Texas Instruments
Toshiba Semiconductor & Storage Products
VIA Technologies
Zarlink

HISTORICAL FINANCIALS

Company Type: Public

Income Statement

FYE: December 31

	REVENUE ($ mil.)	NET INCOME ($ mil.)	NET PROFIT MARGIN	EMPLOYEES
12/11	7,389	927	12.5%	9,590
12/10	6,818	1,081	15.9%	8,950
12/09	4,490	65	1.5%	7,407
12/08	4,658	214	4.6%	7,402
12/07	3,776	213	5.6%	6,347
Annual Growth	18.3%	44.4%	—	10.9%

2011 Year-End Financials

Debt ratio: 13.23%
Return on equity: 14.22%
Cash ($ mil.): 4,146
Current ratio: 523.38
Long-term debt ($ mil.): 1,196
No. of shares (mil.): 545
Dividends
Yield: —
Payout: 21.82%
Market value ($ mil.): 16,001

	STOCK PRICE ($) FY Close	P/E High/Low	PER SHARE ($) Earnings	Dividends	Book Value
12/11	29.36	28 16	1.65	0.00	11.97
12/10	43.55	22 13	1.99	0.32	10.82
12/09	31.47	248118	0.13	0.00	7.85
12/08	16.97	71 32	0.41	0.00	7.38
12/07	26.14	109 67	0.37	0.00	7.51
Annual Growth	2.9%	— —	45.3%	—	12.4%

Brookline Bancorp Inc (DE)

Brookline Bancorp is the holding company for Brookline Bank Bank Rhode Island (BankRI) and The First National Bank of Ipswich which operate more than 40 branches in eastern Massachusetts and Rhode Island. Commercial and multifamily mortgages backed by real estate such as apartments condominiums and office buildings account for the largest portion of the company's loan portfolio followed by indirect auto loans commercial loans and consumer loans. Most of Brookline's commercial loans are offered through Eastern Funding a majority-owned firm that specializes in financing coin-operated laundry dry cleaning and convenience store equipment in the New York City metropolitan area.

Brookline Bancorp has been making acquisitions to grow geographically. In 2011 it acquired The First National Bank of Ipswich a six-branch bank serving Massachusetts' North Shore. The $19.7 million transaction gave First National Bank of Ipswich a much-needed boost as that bank had been struggling with loan losses during the recession. It also expanded Brookline Bancorp's market area as there was no overlap between the two banks.

The following year the company completed the acquisition of Bancorp Rhode Island for $234 million in cash and stock adding 17 branches in that state. BankRI retained its brand and operates as a separate subsidiary of Brookline Bancorp.

The acquisitions helped to boost the company's deposit base. Brookline Bancorp also reported higher earnings in 2011 as interest rate margins improved and the company grew its loan portfolio across all sectors. It plans to continue to increase its commercial lending.

Brookline Bancorp's board rejected a takeover offer by an unnamed suitor in early 2010. Two directors had voted to accept the bid however including former longtime chairman Richard Chapman. Both resigned in the aftermath of the vote.

EXECUTIVES

President CEO and Director, Paul A. Perrault, age 61
SVP CFO and Treasurer; EVP CFO and Treasurer Brookline Bank, Paul R. Bechet, age 69, $242,500 total compensation
Acting Chairman, Joseph J. Slotnik, age 75
VP and Relationship Manager Brookline Bank, Lori B. Leeth
SVP Commercial Banking Brookline Bank, William R. MacKenzie
President and CEO Eastern Funding, Michael J. Fanger, age 54, $275,500 total compensation
Regional VP Retail Banking Brookline Bank, James A. Albridge
SVP Community Banking Brookline Bank, Jane M. Wolchonok, age 63
SVP Commercial Lending Brookline Bank, Joseph Cavallini
VP Commercial Lending Brookline Bank, Douglas Stevens
VP Commercial Lending Brookline Bank, Gretchen Annese
VP and Relationship Manager Brookline Bank, William Henning
VP Commercial Banking Brookline Bank, Warren Ramirez

President CEO and Director, Paul A. Perrault, age 61
Director, Charles H. Peck, age 71
Director, David C. Chapin, age 75
Director, John L. Hall II, age 72
Director, Hollis W. Plimpton Jr., age 81
Director, Rosamond B. Vaule, age 74
Director, William V. Tripp III, age 73
Director, Peter O. Wilde, age 72
Director, John A. Hackett, age 71
Director, John J. Doyle Jr., age 79
Auditors: KPMGLLP

LOCATIONS

HQ: Brookline Bancorp Inc (DE)
131 Clarendon Street, Boston, MA 02117-9179
Phone: 617 425-4600
Web: www.brooklinebank.com

PRODUCTS/OPERATIONS

2011 Sales

	$ mil.	% of total
Interest		
Loans	133	92
Debt securities	6	4
Other	0	-
Noninterest		
Fees charges & other	5	4
Gains on sales of securities	0	-
Investments in affordable housing projects	(0.7)	-
Total	**145**	**100**

COMPETITORS

Bank of America
Boston Private
Central Bancorp
Century Bancorp (MA)
Eastern Bank
RBS Citizens Financial Group
Sovereign Bank
TD Bank USA

HISTORICAL FINANCIALS

Company Type: Public

Income Statement FYE: December 31

	ASSETS ($ mil.)	NET INCOME ($ mil.)	INCOME AS % OF ASSETS	EMPLOYEES
12/11	3,299	27	0.8%	358
12/10	2,720	26	1.0%	266
12/09	2,615	19	0.7%	245
12/08	2,613	12	0.5%	245
12/07	2,418	17	0.7%	243
Annual Growth	8.1%	11.7%	—	10.2%

2011 Year-End Financials

Debt ratio: 15.11%
Return on equity: 5.48%
Cash ($ mil.): 106
Current ratio: —
Long-term debt ($ mil.): 498
No. of shares (mil.): 59
Dividends
Yield: —
Payout: 72.34%
Market value ($ mil.): 500

	STOCK PRICE ($) FY Close	P/E High/Low	PER SHARE ($) Earnings	Dividends	Book Value
12/11	8.44	24 15	0.47	0.00	8.50
12/10	10.85	25 19	0.46	0.34	8.39
12/09	9.91	37 23	0.33	0.54	8.26
12/08	10.65	60 41	0.22	0.74	8.46
12/07	10.16	45 32	0.30	0.74	8.95
Annual Growth	(4.5%)	— —	11.9%	—	(1.3%)

Buckeye Partners, L.P.

Buckeye Partners serves the Buckeye State and then some. Its main subsidiary Buckeye Pipe Line stretches about 2700 miles from Massachusetts to Illinois. Other pipelines include Laurel Pipe Line (Pennsylvania) Everglades Pipe Line (Florida) and Wood River Pipe Lines (Illinois Indiana Missouri and Ohio). It owns a major natural gas storage facility in northern California and markets refined petroleum products in a number of the geographic areas served by its pipeline and terminal operations. In the US Buckeye Partners operates about 5400 miles of pipeline and nearly 70 storage terminals capable of holding more than 53 million barrels of refined petroleum. It also has storage assets in the Bahamas.

Buckeye Partners also operates about 2600 miles of other pipelines under long-term arrangements with major oil and chemical companies.

The company has grown through acquisitions and internal investments including the 2009 purchase of product terminals and pipeline assets in the East St. Louis Illinois and East Chicago Indiana markets from ConocoPhillips for $47.1 million and the completion in 2009 of the Kirby Hills Phase II (Lodi California) expansion project which added 100000 million cu. ft. per day of natural gas storage capacity. In a major geographic expansion it acquired a leading gas storage terminal operator in Northern California –Lodi Gas –in 2008 for $442 million.

The global recession and lower commodity prices hurt the company's financial performance in 2009. In a move to lower the company's cost of equity capital and increase its liquidity Buckeye Partners acquired Buckeye GP Holdings the parent of its general partner in 2010 and subsequently subsumed its operations. A recovering economy and higher commodity prices saw the company's revenues spike in 2010 led by the performance of the Energy Services segment (the wholesale distribution of refined petroleum products). However net income slid that year as the result of increased expenses and a jump in debt and interest expenses.

To grow its refining capacity in 2010 it acquired a petroleum terminal in Puerto Rico from a unit of Royal Dutch Shell for an undisclosed price. It also greatly boosted its storage assets in early 2011 buying Bahamas Oil Refining Company International (which has an oil and petroleum products storage terminal with 21.6 million barrels of storage capacity) for about $1.7 billion. It subsequently acquired a number of BP terminal assets in the US (including 33 refined petroleum products terminals with a storage capacity of more than 10 million barrels) for $165 million. It also bought two petroleum products terminals in Maine and a 124-mile pipeline that connects them from affiliates of Exxon Mobil.

Growing its Northeast assets in 2012 Buckeye Partners acquired a liquid petroleum products marine terminal facility in New York Harbor from Chevron for $260 million.

EXECUTIVES

VP Customer Services, Robert A. Malecky, age 48, $243,706 total compensation
Director Customer Services Buckeye Development and Logistics, Bill Lehner
VP Controller and Principal Accounting Officer, Jeffrey I. Beason, age 63
SVP and CFO, Keith E. St. Clair, age 55, $325,000 total compensation
Chairman and CEO, Forrest E. Wylie, age 48, $400,000 total compensation
VP Corporate Development, Khalid A. Muslih, age 40, $223,261 total compensation
VP and General Counsel, William H. Schmidt Jr., age 39
Director Marketing, Marc Davidson
Director Marketing, Patrick Tucker
President and COO, Clark C. Smith, age 57, $280,000 total compensation
VP Commercial Operations, Todd G. Johnson
VP Commercial Strategy, Corey C. Ayers
VP Human Resources, Wayne St. Claire
Director Financial Planning and Analysis and Investor Relations, Mark Stockard
Director Corporate Development, Dan Ownby
VP Terminal Commercial Operations, Robert T. Ingalls
VP Terminal Commercial Operations East, Daryl J. Hackman
CIO, Kathleen J. (Kathy) Sinatore
Director, Oliver G. (Rick) Richard III, age 59
Director, C. Scott Hobbs, age 58
Director, Robb E. Turner, age 49
Director, Michael B. Goldberg, age 65
Director, Irvin K. Culpepper Jr., age 63
Director, Mark C. McKinley, age 55
Auditors: Deloitte&ToucheLLP

LOCATIONS

HQ: Buckeye Partners L.P.
1 Greenway Plaza Ste. 600, Houston TX 77046
Phone: 832-615-8600 **Fax:** 817-352-7171
Web: www.bnsf.com

PRODUCTS/OPERATIONS

2010 Sales

	$ mil.	% of total
Energy services	2,481	78
Pipeline	400	12
Terminalling & storage	175	6
Natural gas storage	95	3
Development & logistics	37	1
Adjustments	(39.2)	-
Total	**3,151**	**100**

Selected Subsidiaries

Buckeye Gas Storage LLC
Buckeye Energy Holdings LLC
Buckeye Pipe Line Company L.P.
Buckeye Pipe Line Transportation LLC
Everglades Pipe Line Company L.P.
Laurel Pipe Line Company L.P.
Wood River Pipe Lines LLC

COMPETITORS

AmeriGas Partners
CMS Energy
Duke Energy
El Paso Corporation
Enbridge
Enbridge Energy
Ferrellgas Partners
Plains All American Pipeline
Sunoco Logistics
Williams Companies

HISTORICAL FINANCIALS

Company Type: Public

Income Statement FYE: December 31

	REVENUE ($ mil.)	NET INCOME ($ mil.)	NET PROFIT MARGIN	EMPLOYEES
12/11	4,759	108	2.3%	1,029
12/10	3,151	43	1.4%	859
12/09	1,770	140	8.0%	846
12/08	1,896	184	9.7%	1,040
12/07	519	155	29.9%	920
Annual Growth	74.0%	(8.6%)	—	2.8%

2011 Year-End Financials

Debt ratio: 47.48%
Return on equity: 4.71%
Cash ($ mil.): 12
Current ratio: 112.80
Long-term debt ($ mil.): 2,393
No. of shares (mil.): 93
Dividends
Yield: —
Payout: 335.42%
Market value ($ mil.): 5,968

	STOCK PRICE ($) FY Close	P/E High/Low		PER SHARE ($) Earnings	Dividends	Book Value
12/11	63.98	57	48	1.20	0.00	24.69
12/10	66.83	42	32	1.65	3.83	19.49
12/09	54.45	30	18	1.84	3.63	23.51
12/08	32.25	16	8	3.15	3.43	24.18
12/07	49.41	18	15	3.03	3.23	23.72
Annual Growth	6.7%	—	—	(20.7%)	—	1.0%

Burlington Northern & Santa Fe Railway Co. (The)

BNSF Railway operates one of the largest railroad networks in North America. A wholly-owned subsidiary of Burlington Northern Santa Fe the company provides freight transportation over a network of about 32000 route miles of track across two-thirds of the western US and two provinces in Canada. About 23000 miles of that track are company owned while the remainder is owned and permitted by other railroads. BNSF Railway owns or leases a fleet of about 6700 locomotives. It also has some 30 intermodal facilities that help to transport agricultural consumer and industrial products as well as coal. In addition to major cities and ports BNSF Railway serves smaller markets in alliance with short-line partners.

BNSF Railway's freight revenues are well diversified among consumer products such as appliances clothing and shoes electronics toys and games and home decor items; coal; agricultural products such as wheat corn soybeans feeds malt ethanol and fertilizer; and industrial products including construction and building materials petroleum chemicals plastics and food and beverages.

BNSF Railway announced a planned 2011 capital program valued at $3.5 billion to strengthen its infrastructure. The largest component of the plan is spending $2 billion on its core network and related technology assets. It also plans to spend about $450 million to acquire about 230 locomotives and another $350 million on freight car and other equipment acquisitions. The company hopes these measures will improve the efficiency of its freight transportation operations and help it gain more rail market share. This capital commitment follows one of the deepest recessions in US history and cost-cutting measures including layoffs and the curtailment of intermodal hub expansion projects undertaken by BNSF Railway in 2009.

EXECUTIVES

VP and General Tax Counsel, Shelley J. Venick
Chairman and CEO, Matthew K. (Matt) Rose, age 53
President and COO, Carl R. Ice, age 55
EVP and CFO, Thomas N. (Tom) Hund, age 58
VP Network Strategy, Dean H. Wise, age 58
General Director External Relations, Steve Forsberg
EVP Operations, Gregory C. (Greg) Fox
EVP and Chief Marketing Officer, John P. Lanigan Jr., age 56
VP and General Regulatory Counsel, Richard E. (Rick) Weicher
VP Coal Marketing, George T. Duggan
Group VP Consumer Products, Stephen G. (Steve) Branscum
Group VP Coal, Stevan B. (Steve) Bobb
Group VP Industrial Products, David L. Garin
VP Corporate Audit Services, David W. Stropes
VP Domestic Intermodal, Kathryn M. (Katie) Farmer
Director Public Affairs Alabama Arkansas Louisiana Mississippi New Mexico Oklahoma Tennessee and Texas, Joe Faust
Director Public Affairs Arizona California Colorado Nevada and Utah, Lena Kent
Director Public Affairs Idaho Montana Oregon Washington Wyoming and Canada, Gus Melonas
Director Media Relations, Suann Lundsberg
VP Technology Services and CIO, Josephine M. (Joann) Olsovsky
EVP Law and Secretary, Roger Nober, age 47
VP Government Affairs, Amy C. Hawkins
VP Engineering, Dave Freeman
Assistant VP Government Affairs, Andrew K. Johnsen
VP Planning and Studies and Controller, Julie A. Piggott
VP Corporate Relations, John O. Ambler
VP and General Counsel, Charles W. Shewmake
Assistant VP Finance and Treasurer, C. Alec Vincent
Director Public Affairs Iowa Illinois Kentucky Minnesota North Dakota South Dakota and Wisconsin, Amy McBeth
Director Public Affairs Kansas Missouri Nebraska, Andy Williams
VP Industrial Products Sales, Tom G. Williams
Auditors: Deloitte&ToucheLLP

LOCATIONS

HQ: BNSF Railway Company
2650 Lou Menk Dr., Fort Worth TX 76131-2830
Phone: 800-795-2673 **Fax:** 301-610-4301
Web: www.americatel.com

PRODUCTS/OPERATIONS

2010 Sales

	$ mil.	% of total
Consumer products	5,031	30
Coal	4,348	26
Agricultural products	3,493	21
Industrial products	3,460	21
Other revenues	271	2
Total	**16,603**	**100**

COMPETITORS

American Commercial Lines
Canadian National Railway
Canadian Pacific Railway
CSX Transportation
Ingram Industries
J.B. Hunt
Kansas City Southern Railway
Kirby Corporation
Landstar System
Norfolk Southern
Schneider National
Union Pacific Railroad
Werner Enterprises

HISTORICAL FINANCIALS

Company Type: Subsidiary

Income Statement FYE: December 31

	REVENUE ($ mil.)	NET INCOME ($ mil.)	NET PROFIT MARGIN	EMPLOYEES
12/11	19,229	3,273	17.0%	39,000
12/10*	14,835	2,382	16.1%	38,000
02/10	1,768	282	16.0%	0
12/09	13,848	2,014	14.5%	35,000
12/08	17,787	2,362	13.3%	40,000
Annual Growth	2.0%	8.5%	—	(0.6%)

*Fiscal year change

2011 Year-End Financials

Debt ratio: 3.00%
Return on equity: 7.47%
Cash ($ mil.): 293
Current ratio: 83.82
Long-term debt ($ mil.): 1,845
No. of shares (mil.): 0
Dividends
Yield: —
Payout: —
Market value ($ mil.): —

CA Inc

CA wants to give your IT some TLC. One of the world's largest software companies CA provides tools for managing networks databases applications storage security and other systems. Primarily serving large enterprises its applications work across both mainframes and distributed computing environments including cloud computing products. Most of its software license sales come from subscriptions (primarily 1- to 5-year terms). The company also offers consulting implementation and training services. It sells worldwide to businesses government agencies and schools directly and through various resale channels. Revenue from international customers represents more than 40% of sales.

HISTORY

Born in Shanghai Charles Wang fled Communist China with his family in 1952 and grew up in Queens New York. After working in sales for software developer Standard Data Wang started a joint venture in 1976 with Swiss-owned Computer Associates (CA) to sell software in the US. He started with four employees and one product a file organizer for IBM storage systems. It was a great success and in 1980 Wang bought out his Swiss partners. CA went public in 1981.

Wang realized that a far-flung distribution and service network (continuously fed by new products) was the key to success. Acquiring existing software (and its customers) reduced risky in-house development and moved products to market sooner.

The company expanded its offerings by buying the popular SuperCalc spreadsheet in 1984. The 1987 purchase of chief utilities rival UCCEL gave investor Walter Haefner what remained the largest individual stake in CA.

CA's purchases of mostly struggling software firms made it in 1989 the first independent software company to reach $1 billion in sales. The $300 million acquisition of Cullinet that year added database and banking applications to CA's product line.

By the early 1990s CA's acquisition methods had developed a reputation that were seen by some as ruthless –swoop in gobble up cut costs and get rid of employees. As a new owner CA strongly defended its licensing contracts –often in court.

In 1994 CA the appointment of a new company president led to a shift away from older systems to focus on network software reflected by the acquisitions of ASK Group (1994) Legent (1995) and network management expert Cheyenne Software (1996). CA continued its practice of buying in cash to avoid diluting stock.

Acquisition-related charges caused losses for fiscal 1996. With its lack of a major service operation taking a bite out of potential business CA made a $9.8 billion hostile takeover offer for consulting firm Computer Sciences Corp. (CSC) in 1998. CA soon dropped its bid in the face of CSC's fierce opposition and later acquired smaller computer service specialist Realogic.

The acquisitions helped cause a drop in profits for fiscal 1999. Later that year the company bought database management software company PLATINUM technology for about $3.5 billion.

In 2000 CA acquired business software specialist Sterling Software in a deal valued at nearly $4 billion. Later that year the company began spinning off some of its promising software businesses; Wang stepped down as CEO to focus on new opportunities for CA as chairman.

Alleging corporate mismanagement in 2001 Sam Wyly (co-founder of Sterling Software) initiated a proxy fight designed to elect a new board of directors. Wyly's bid failed however as it was voted down by shareholders. He initiated a second proxy fight in 2002 but abandoned it after reaching a settlement with the company which included a $10 million payment. Later in 2002 Wang retired.

An SEC investigation into the company's accounting practices led to the resignation of CA's CFO in 2003. The investigation continued into 2004 resulting in additional executive resignations. That year CA agreed to pay $225 million to shareholders in order to avoid criminal prosecution by the SEC and the US Justice Department for fraudulently recording and reporting revenues. Shortly after the settlement was announced former CEO Sanjay Kumar and former EVP Stephen Richards were indicted on charges of securities fraud conspiracy and obstruction of justice. Kumar resigned as chairman president and CEO in 2004 (he left the company entirely after a brief stint as chief software architect). IBM veteran John Swainson was named CEO.

Also in 2004 the company expanded its desktop management product line through the purchase of Miramar Systems and it bulked up its security software portfolio with the purchases of eSecurity Online Silent Runner and Netegrity. It sold its ACCPAC subsidiary to Sage Group for about $110 million in 2004.

In 2005 it acquired network management specialist Concord Communications for about $330 million. CA also acquired firewall developer Tiny Software IT management software maker Niku and document security software provider iLumin Software Services that year.

The company purchased application management specialist Wily Technology for $375 million in 2006. It then acquired job scheduling software developer Cybermation for $75 million in cash enterprise records management software maker MDY and data recovery specialist XOsoft. Also that year Computer Associates International officially changed its name to CA.

It acquired identity management software developer Eurekify in 2008 and data loss prevention specialist Orchestria in 2009. CA also purchased some of Cassatt's data center automation assets in 2009 as well as buying IT management software provider NetQoS for $200 million in cash.

Swainson retired as CA's CEO at the end of 2009. Replacing him in 2010 was another ex-IBMer William McCracken who spent 36 years with Big Blue.

EXECUTIVES

Chairman, Arthur F. Weinbach, age 69
SVP and General Manager Public Sector, Patrick J. Gnazzo, age 63
EVP Worldwide Human Resources, Andrew (Andy) Goodman, age 53
CEO and Director, William E. (Bill) McCracken, age 69, $1,114,584 total compensation
EVP Technology and Development Group, Ajei S. Gopal, age 50
SVP Security Strategy, Bill Mann
SVP Worldwide Public Relations, Daniel (Dan) Kaferle, age 60
EVP Worldwide Sales and Marketing, George J. Fischer, age 49
Chief Marketing Officer, Andrew Wittman
EVP, Donald R. (Don) Friedman, age 66
EVP Strategy and Corporate Development, Jacob Lamm, age 47
EVP; Group Executive Customer Solutions Group, David Dobson, age 49
SVP Global CA Technologies Support, Leo Annab
EVP Growth and Emerging Markets, John Ruthven
Program Manager Investor Relations, Carol Lu
EVP Cloud Products and Solutions Business Line, Chris O'Malley, age 49
Chief Communications Officer, William L. (Bill) Hughes, age 52
EVP and CFO, Richard J. Beckert, age 50
SVP Corporate Governance and Secretary, C.H.R. DuPree
EVP Worldwide Sales and General Manager; Managing Director North America and Europe, Mark Thompson
Chief Compliance Officer and Chief Counsel Litigation Law Department, Gary Brown
Chief Ethics Officer Law Department, Joel Katz
Chief Marketing Officer, Marianne Budnik
SVP and CIO, Stephen Savage
SVP and General Manager Service Assurance, Cliff Meltzer
EVP and General Counsel, Amy Fliegelman Olli, age 48, $550,000 total compensation
EVP Risk and Chief Administrative Officer, Phillip Harrington, age 55
EVP and CTO, Donald Ferguson
EVP Enterprise Products and Solutions Business Line, Thomas W. (Tom) Kendra
SVP and General Manager CA Technologies Recovery Management and Data Modeling Customer Solutions, Adam Famularo
SVP and General Manager ecoSoftware, Terrence Clark
SVP Cloud Products and Solutions, David Hodgson
SVP Sales North America, Jon Hunter
SVP Investor Relations, Kelsey R. Doherty
Senior Principal Investor Relations, Jonathan Doros
Director, Richard (Rich) Sulpizio, age 63
Director, Christopher B. Lofgren
Director, Renato (Ron) Zambonini, age 65
Director, Gary J. Fernandes, age 68
Director, Kay Koplovitz, age 68
Director, Laura S. Unger, age 51
CEO and Director, William E. (Bill) McCracken, age 69
Director, Rohit Kapoor, age 47
Director, Raymond J. Bromark, age 66
EVP Worldwide Sales and General Manager; Managing Director North America and Europe, Mark Thompson
Auditors: KPMGLLP

LOCATIONS

HQ: CA Inc.
1 CA Plaza, Islandia NY 11749
Phone: 800-225-5224 **Fax:** 631-342-6800
Web: www.ca.com

2012 Sales

	$ mil.	% of total
US	2,812	58
Other countries	2,002	42
Total	**4,814**	**100**

PRODUCTS/OPERATIONS

2012 Sales by Revenue Type

	$ mil.	% of total
Subscriptions & maintenance	4,021	83
Software fees & other	411	9
Professional services	382	8
Total	**4,429**	**100**

2012 Sales by Segment

	$ mil.	% of total
Mainframe	2,612	54
Enterprise	1,820	38
Services	382	8
Total	**4,814**	**100**

Selected Acquisitions

Base Technologies (2011 government consultancy)
Interactive TKO (2011 solutions for developing applications in cloud and composite environments)
Watchmouse (2011 SaaS-based monitoring for cloud mobile and traditional Web applications)
Hyperformix (2010 capacity management software)
Arcot Systems (2010 technology for fraud prevention)
4Base Technology (2010 virtualization and cloud infrastructure consulting)
3Tera (2010 solutions for building cloud services)
Nimsoft (2010 IT performance and availability monitoring solutions)

Selected Product Groups

Application performance management
Cloud Computing
Database management
Infrastructure and operations management
IT service and asset management
Mainframe
Project portfolio and financial management
Security management (identity and access management)
Virtualization and Service Automation

COMPETITORS

BMC Software
Check Point Software
Cisco Systems
Compuware
EMC
Hewlett-Packard
IBM
McAfee
Microsoft
Novell
Oracle
RSA Security
SAP
Symantec
VMware

HISTORICAL FINANCIALS

Company Type: Public

Income Statement FYE: March 31

	REVENUE ($ mil.)	NET INCOME ($ mil.)	NET PROFIT MARGIN	EMPLOYEES
03/12	4,814	951	19.8%	13,600
03/11	4,429	827	18.7%	13,400
03/10	4,353	771	17.7%	13,800
03/09	4,271	694	16.2%	13,200
03/08	4,277	500	11.7%	13,700
Annual Growth	3.0%	17.4%	—	(0.2%)

2012 Year-End Financials

Debt ratio: 10.84%
Return on equity: 17.62%
Cash ($ mil.): 2,679
Current ratio: 105.71
Long-term debt ($ mil.): 1,287
No. of shares (mil.): 466
Dividends
Yield: —
Payout: 20.73%
Market value ($ mil.): 12,848

	STOCK PRICE ($) FY Close	P/E High/Low		PER SHARE ($) Earnings	Dividends	Book Value
03/12	27.56	14	10	1.93	0.00	11.58
03/11	24.18	16	11	1.61	0.16	11.19
03/10	23.47	16	11	1.47	0.16	9.78
03/09	17.61	20	11	1.29	0.20	8.45
03/08	22.50	29	22	0.93	0.16	7.28
Annual Growth	5.2%	—	—	20.0%	—	12.3%

Cablevision Systems Corp.

Cablevision thinks it's the ideal choice for cable TV service. Through the Optimum and iO brands the company provides cable services such as basic and digital video programming high-speed data and voice. Mostly in the New York City (NYC) metro area more than 3.6 million subscribers receive at least one of these services. Subsidiary Optimum Lightpath (about 5% of sales) serves commercial broadband Internet users in the area. Cablevision also owns NYC newspaper publisher Newsday and Clearview Cinemas which operates nearly 50 tri-state area movie theaters including the Ziegfeld Theater. Founder and chairman Charles Dolan and his family control about 72% of the company.

HISTORY

In 1954 Charles Dolan helped form Sterling Manhattan Cable which won the cable-TV franchise for lower Manhattan in 1965. It began broadcasting pro basketball and hockey courtesy of Madison Square Garden (MSG) in 1967. In 1970 Dolan started Home Box Office (HBO) the first nationwide pay-TV channel and hired Gerald Levin to run it.

Dolan took the company public as Sterling Communications; its partner media giant Time (now part of Time Warner) came to own 80% of Sterling. Costs mounted however and in 1973 Time liquidated Sterling (but kept HBO).

Dolan bought back the New York franchises and formed Long Island Cable Communications Development. He changed its name to Cablevision and expanded around New York and Chicago. In 1980 Cablevision formed Rainbow Programming which soon included the American Movie Classics and Bravo channels; in 1983 it launched the popular SportsChannel (now Fox Sports New York). Cablevision went public in 1986 and bought two Connecticut cable systems that year and one in Massachusetts the next.

In 1989 the company helped NBC launch the CNBC cable network but sold its interest to NBC in 1991. Cablevision began offering cable phone service to businesses on Long Island two years before the Telecommunications Act of 1996 was passed. Subsidiary Cablevision Lightpath a competitive local-exchange carrier signed a groundbreaking co-carrier agreement with Baby Bell NYNEX (now part of Verizon) in 1995.

To get a grip on NYC entertainment Cablevision partnered with ITT in 1995 to buy the MSG properties. (Three years later Starwood acquired ITT.) Meanwhile on-again off-again merger talks with U S WEST Media stalled over Dolan's high asking price. In 1996 Charles' son James became CEO.

In 1997 Cablevision began dumping cable holdings which were spread over 19 states to focus on New York City and the upgrading of its cable infrastructure. It began a series of swaps with TCI to cluster its cable systems (As a result TCI which was bought by AT&T held 33% of Cablevision stock by 1999. AT&T sold the stake in 2001.) Cablevision traded its Boston-area subscribers to MediaOne (also acquired by AT&T) for more NYC customers (2001) and sold its Cleveland cable system to Adelphia and its Kalamazoo Michigan cable system to Charter (2000).

Cablevision sold 40% of Rainbow's regional sports business to Fox/Liberty (now Fox Sports Net owned by News Corp.) to create a rival to Disney's ESPN. Fox/Liberty got 40% of MSG and Cablevision got Fox Sports Net a chain of 22 regional sports networks. MSG also bought Radio City Entertainment (and the famed Rockettes) in 1997.

In 1998 Cablevision sold cable systems in 10 states to Mediacom. That year it bought beleaguered electronics retailer Nobody Beats The Wiz (aiming to sell cable modems and HDTV alongside TVs) Clearview Cinema and 16 New York theaters from Loews Cineplex. It also began offering business phone service in Connecticut and residential service on Long Island.

The company began a $70 million renovation of Radio City Music Hall in 1999 and agreed to buy 3 million interactive set-top boxes from Sony for about $1 billion.

In 2001 MGM paid $825 million for a 20% stake in four of Rainbow's national networks. But the recession forced the company to take steps to improve operations including the elimination of 5000 jobs.

The next year the company battled with the Yankees Entertainment & Sports Network (YES Network) over the rights to broadcast New York Yankees games. Also in 2002 Cablevision sold its Bravo network to NBC a subsidiary of GE. Cablevision decided to get out of electronics retailing in 2003 closing down the Wiz stores.

Cablevision reorganized some of its assets in 2004 creating subsidiary Rainbow Media Holdings —which included a number of cable channels satellite-TV service VOOM and Rainbow Movies — preparing to spin the properties off but these plans fell apart in 2005. Later Cablevision announced its intention to shut down the financially challenged VOOM satellite service; Charles Dolan unsuccessfully tried to buy VOOM himself but son James Cablevision's CEO sided with the board of directors and favored shuttering the unit resulting in a bit of a family feud. Charles responded to the decision by tossing three Cablevision directors and installing five new ones who were more aligned with his interests. Not surprisingly the company gave him more time to come up with the money to make another bid for VOOM yet the effort turned out to be futile and Cablevision eventually axed the service.

In a move that would have expanded the company's cable systems outside the New York City metro area Cablevision in 2005 made a failed bid for troubled rival Adelphia's cable systems. The company also wanted to buy Adelphia in an effort to keep rivals Time Warner Cable and Comcast from growing bigger but the two industry leaders eventually won the bidding war after all.

In 2005 the Dolan family abandoned an offer to take the company private for $7.9 billion citing an overall decline of value in the communications sector. However the following year the Dolans made another offer to take the company private for the same amount. In 2007 their bid was raised to $8.9 billion. Both parties finally agreed on a deal worth $10.6 billion that would give the Dolans full control of the company but shareholders rejected the bid later that year.

Also that year Cablevision restructured its Madison Square Garden partnership with News Corp. resulting in Rainbow Media owning 100% of the sports and entertainment company. Cablevision also sold two regional sports networks to Comcast in 2007 for about $570 million. The deal included Cablevision's 60% stake in FSN Bay Area and its 50% stake in FSN New England.

In 2008 it bought 97% of metro NYC newspaper publishers Newsday from Tribune Company for $650 million the same year Tribune filed for bankruptcy.

In October 2012 Cablevision signed a distribution with The Walt Disney Company to deliver Disney's sports news and other entertainment programming to its customers across TV Internet tablets and handheld devices.

EXECUTIVES

President News 12 Networks and Director, Patrick F. Dolan, age 60

EVP Strategy and Development and Director, Thomas C. Dolan, age 59, $384,615 total compensation

President CEO and Director, James L. Dolan, age 56

Chairman, Charles F. Dolan, age 85, $46,000 total compensation

SVP Controller and Principal Accounting Officer, Victoria Mink, age 43

SVP Financial Planning And Control, Donna Coleman

Senior Advisor Engineering and Technology, Wilton (Wilt) Hildenbrand, age 64, $750,000 total compensation

President Cable and Communications, John R. Bickham, age 60

Vice Chairman, Hank J. Ratner, age 53

SVP, Charles (Charlie) Schueler

EVP and General Counsel, David G. Ellen, age 47

Director Investor Relations, Ken Martin

President Local Media, Tad Smith, age 52

SVP Deputy General Counsel and Secretary, Victoria D. Salhus, age 62

SVP Marketing Local Media, Valerie (Val) Green

VP Business and Voice Product Management, Joseph Varello

EVP and CFO, Gregg G. Seibert, age 56

EVP Product Management and Marketing, Patricia Gottesmann
SVP eMedia and Director, Brian G. Sweeney, age 47
EVP, Barry Frey
SVP Investor Relations, Patricia Armstrong
SVP and Treasurer, Kevin F. Watson, age 45
EVP Advanced Advertising Strategy & Operations, Kim Norris
SVP Sales Optimum Lightpath, Phil DeCabia
SVP Business Planning Intercarrier and Administration Optimum Lightpath, Joe Caruso
SVP, Carolyn Dursi
SVP Technology Local Media, Tom Donohue
SVP Strategic Product Development and Director, Kristin A. Dolan, age 45
SVP Strategic Product Development, Patrick Donoghue
SVP Strategic Product Advancement, Jonathan Greenfield
Coordinator, Rosemary E. Aigner
President Optimum Lightpath, Dave Pistacchio, age 51
SVP and Associate General Counsel Business Affairs, Todd Brecher
EVP Corporate Engineering and Technology, James A. (Jim) Blackley
VP Multimedia Services and Director, Edward C. Atwood, age 75
President News 12 Networks and Director, Patrick F. Dolan, age 60
EVP Strategy and Development and Director, Thomas C. Dolan, age 59
President CEO and Director, James L. Dolan, age 56
Director, Leonard Tow, age 83
Vice Chairman, Hank J. Ratner, age 53
Director, Rand V. Araskog, age 80
Director, Vincent S. Tese, age 69
Director, Frank J. Biondi Jr.
Director, Thomas V. Reifenheiser, age 76
Director, Vice Adm. John R. Ryan, age 66
Director, Zachary W. Carter, age 62
SVP eMedia and Director, Brian G. Sweeney, age 47
Director, Kathleen M. Dolan, age 49
Director, Deborah Dolan-Sweeney, age 48
SVP Strategic Product Development and Director, Kristin A. Dolan, age 45
VP Multimedia Services and Director, Edward C. Atwood, age 75
Auditors: KPMGLLP

LOCATIONS

HQ: Cablevision Systems Corporation
1111 Stewart Ave., Bethpage NY 11714
Phone: 516-803-2300 **Fax:** 516-803-3134
Web: www.cablevision.com

PRODUCTS/OPERATIONS

2012 Sales

	$ mil.	% of total
Telecommunications services		
Cable television		
Video	3,443	51
High-speed data	1,366	20
Voice	906	13
Advertising	167	2
Other	105	2
Optimum Lightpath	323	5
Other	435	7
Adjustments	(41.3)	-
Total	**6,705**	**100**

COMPETITORS

AT&T
Charter Communications
Comcast
Cox Communications
DIRECTV
DISH Network
EchoStar
RCN Corporation
Time Warner Cable
Verizon
Vonage

HISTORICAL FINANCIALS

Company Type: Public

Income Statement FYE: December 31

	REVENUE ($ mil.)	NET INCOME ($ mil.)	NET PROFIT MARGIN	EMPLOYEES
12/11	6,700	291	4.4%	17,815
12/10	7,231	360	5.0%	19,065
12/09	7,773	285	3.7%	27,940
12/08	7,230	(227)	—	27,413
12/07	6,484	218	3.4%	22,935
Annual Growth	0.8%	7.5%	—	(6.1%)

2011 Year-End Financials

Debt ratio: 156.21%
Return on equity: 987650001000000.00%
Cash ($ mil.): 611
Current ratio: 84.93
Long-term debt ($ mil.): 10,792
No. of shares (mil.): 274
Dividends
Yield: —
Payout: 56.37%
Market value ($ mil.): 3,901

	STOCK PRICE ($) FY Close	P/E High	P/E Low	PER SHARE ($) Earnings	Dividends	Book Value
12/11	14.22	36	12	1.02	0.00	(20.33)
12/10	33.84	28	18	1.20	0.48	(21.33)
12/09	25.82	27	10	0.96	0.40	(17.07)
12/08	16.84	—	—	(0.78)	0.20	(18.05)
12/07	24.50	51	32	0.74	0.00	(17.33)
Annual Growth	(12.7%)	—	—	8.4%	—	—

Caesars Entertainment Corp

Caesars Entertainment Corporation (formerly Harrah's Entertainment) likes to spread its bets. The firm owns and/or operates more than 50 casinos (under such names as Harrah's Horseshoe and Rio) in 12 US states and seven countries. Altogether its facilities –including hotels dockside and riverboat casinos and Native American gaming establishments –boast more than 3 million sq. ft. of casino space and some 43000 hotel rooms. Among its many locations on the Vegas Strip are Caesars Palace Paris Las Vegas and Planet Hollywood. The company went public in 2012 more than a year after it cancelled a previous IPO.

HISTORY

William Harrah and his father founded their first bingo parlor in Reno Nevada in 1937. Using the income from that business Harrah opened his first casino Harrah's Club in downtown Reno in 1946. In 1955 and 1956 he bought several clubs in Stateline Nevada (near Lake Tahoe). Harrah built the company by using promotions to draw middle-class Californians to his clubs.

During the 1960s the entrepreneur expanded his operations in Lake Tahoe and in 1968 he built a 400-room hotel tower in Reno. Harrah's went public in 1971. After Harrah's death in 1978 the company expanded outside Nevada by building a hotel and casino in Atlantic City New Jersey.

Holiday Inns bought Harrah's in 1980 for about $300 million. The hotelier already owned a 40% interest in River Boat Casino which operated a casino next to a Holiday Inn in Las Vegas. When Holiday Inns acquired the other 60% of the casino/hotel in 1983 Harrah's took over its management. Holiday Inns became Holiday Corporation in 1985. The following year UK brewer Bass PLC put up $100 million for 10% of Holiday Corporation.

In 1990 Bass acquired the Holiday Inn hotel chain for $2.2 billion. The rest of Holiday Corporation including Harrah's was renamed Promus under chairman Michael Rose.

In the early 1990s Harrah's built a casino on Ak-Chin Indian land near Phoenix and opened riverboat casinos in Joliet Illinois; Shreveport Louisiana; and North Kansas City Missouri. In 1995 Promus spun off its hotel operations as Promus Hotel Corporation and changed the name of its casino business to Harrah's Entertainment. (Promus was acquired by Hilton Hotels later called Hilton Worldwide in 1999.)

Also in 1995 Harrah's gambled and lost. Big. Its New Orleans casino was shelved even before it was finished –a victim of Louisiana's Byzantine politics. Eager for the right to build what would be a $395 million 200000-sq.-ft. casino in the heart of the city Harrah's had made a number of ill-advised concessions to state and municipal officials. It agreed not to offer hotel rooms or food at the casino (forgoing about 20% of anticipated revenues) and promised to make an annual $100 million minimum payment to the state in addition to 19% of the casino's revenues. In the end the fiasco's price tag reached $900 million (only half of which went to casino construction costs) and Harrah's put the project into bankruptcy to stop the bleeding. (It resumed construction in 1999 and finally opened the casino at the end of the year.)

In 1997 Rose retired as chairman and was replaced by CEO Philip Satre. In 1998 Harrah's bought competitor Showboat with properties in Las Vegas and Atlantic City and management of a New South Wales Australia casino. A Louisiana Supreme Court ruling that year allowed the company to resume work on the New Orleans casino (albeit with a stake of less than 45% which was later increased to 63%). Harrah's also invested in Las Vegas-based National Airlines that year.

In early 1999 Harrah's bought Rio Hotel & Casino (also a partner in National Airlines) which operates one upscale casino on the Las Vegas Strip for about $525 million. In 2000 the company bought riverboat casino operator Players International for $425 million. Also that year Harrah's had to write off about $39 million in investments and loans to National Airlines which filed for bankruptcy. The company had a 48% stake in the airline.

Harrah's continued its acquisition streak in 2001 with the purchase of Harveys Casino Resorts with four locations in Colorado Iowa and Nevada for $675 million. (It sold the Colorado location in 2002.) The 452-room Harrah's Atlantic City hotel tower was opened in 2002. Also that year the company began construction of a second 800-room tower at its Atlantic City Showboat casino. Later in 2002 Harrah's acquired the shares of JCC Holding company it didn't already own for $54.1 million. It also acquired Louisiana Downs a Thoroughbred racetrack in Bossier City for $157 million. Harrah's subsequently turned Louisiana Downs into a full-blown casino.

In 2004 Harrah's acquired casino operator Horseshoe Gaming for $1.45 billion. The purchase added several properties to Harrah's portfolio (in Hammond Indiana; Bossier City Louisiana; and Tunica Mississippi). In order to gain regulatory approval for the purchase Harrah's later sold its Harrah's Shreveport casino to Boyd Gaming for $190 million. The sale was intended to limit Harrah's exposure in the Louisiana market.

The following year Harrah's completed a monster-sized deal the $9.4 billion acquisition of rival Caesars Entertainment Inc. which rocketed the company to the top of the gaming world. To appease regulators the company sold its Harrah's Tunica and East Chicago casinos to Colony Capital. In 2005 Harrah's bought the Imperial Palace one of the last few independent casinos on the Las Vegas Strip for $370 million.

The effects of Hurricane Katrina were felt at the company's Biloxi and Gulfport Mississippi locations which suffered extensive damage. Harrah's sold the Gulfport location such as it was and rebuilt the Biloxi site which re-opened in 2006. Also that year Harrah's acquired the remaining assets of Casino Magic Biloxi from Pinnacle Entertainment; Harrah's sold two subsidiaries that own businesses in Lake Charles Louisiana. In addition to the Casino Magic assets Pinnacle paid Harrah's some $25 million in the deal.

In 2006 Harrah's sold its Flamingo Laughlin hotel-casino and an undeveloped land parcel in Atlantic City to American Real Estate Partners. It also purchased casino operator London Clubs International for $586 million. London Clubs operates seven UK casinos as well as two in Egypt and one in South Africa.

The company acquired Macau Orient Golf one of only two golf courses in Macau China in 2007 for some $577 million. It subsequently re-branded the property Caesars Macau Golf. Caesars made the deal to enter the popular Chinese market joining rivals Las Vegas Sands Wynn Resorts and MGM Resorts International which already own casinos in Macau. In 2008 the company ceased to be a publicly traded company after being bought out by two private equity firms.

In 2010 Harrah's purchased the beleaguered Planet Hollywood Resort & Casino in Las Vegas. (The property is separate from Planet Hollywood International). Harrah's was attracted to Planet Hollywood proximity to its other resorts on the Strip as well as its strong brand name. The deal – the company's first new Vegas property since it bought Caesars Palace in 2005 –gave the firm its eighth connected property on the Strip's east side.

Also in 2010 the company filed to go public. However later that year it cancelled the IPO due to unfavorable market conditions and weak investor demand. In addition to its massive debt Harrah's lacked interest from investors due to the fact that its holdings are focused on domestic markets and the company has no plans to expand in the fast-growing Chinese market of Macau where its competitors have had much success.

After cancelling the IPO the company changed its name from Harrah's Entertainment to Caesars Entertainment Corporation. Though it continues to use the Harrah's brand at one of its bigger properties the company made the identity change to capitalize on the Caesar's name which it sees as "the world's preeminent and most respected casino brand."

The company went public in 2012 raising little more than $16 million in a small IPO.

EXECUTIVES

EVP Communications and Government Relations, Janis L. (Jan) Jones, age 62
President Strategy and Development, Peter E. Murphy, age 49, $225,962 total compensation
Chairman President and CEO, Gary W. Loveman, age 51, $1,919,231 total compensation
EVP and CFO, Donald A. Colvin, age 59
EVP General Counsel Chief Regulatory and Compliance Officer, Timothy R. (Tim) Donovan, age 56
President Operations, Thomas M. (Tom) Jenkin, age 57, $1,151,538 total compensation
SVP and Chief Marketing Officer, David W. Norton, age 43
President Eastern Division, Donald P. (Don) Marrandino, age 52
EVP and CFO, Jonathan S. Halkyard, age 47, $605,731 total compensation
SVP and CTO, Katrina R. Lane, age 46
SVP and General Manager Harrah's Laughlin, Wade Faul
EVP Human Resources, Mary H. Thomas, age 45
President Enterprise Shared Services, John W. R. Payne, age 43, $887,645 total compensation
SVP Enterprise Effectiveness, John W. Baker
VP Finance and Treasurer, Eric Hession
SVP and General Manager Harrah's New Orleans, Dan Real
President International Development, Steven M. Tight, age 56
CEO Interactive Entertainment, Mitch Garber
Director, Jeffrey D. Benjamin, age 50
Director, Marc J. Rowan, age 50
Director, Lynn C. Swann, age 60
Director, Christopher J. (Chris) Williams, age 54
Director, Eric L. Press, age 46
Director, Kelvin L. Davis, age 48
Director, Jinlong Wang, age 54
Director, Karl Peterson, age 41
Director, Jonathan J. Coslet, age 47
Director, David B. Sambur, age 31
Auditors: Deloitte&ToucheLLP

LOCATIONS

HQ: Caesars Entertainment Corporation
1 Caesars Palace Dr., Las Vegas NV 89109
Phone: 702-407-6000 **Fax:** 702-407-6037
Web: www.caesars.com/corporate/

2011 Sales

	$ mil.	% of total
Nevada		
Las Vegas	3,013	34
Other	450	5
Atlantic City	1,839	21
Louisiana & Mississippi	1,104	13
Illinois & Indiana	1,059	12
Iowa & Missouri	724	8
Other markets	644	7
Total	**8,834**	**100**

PRODUCTS/OPERATIONS

2011 Sales

	$ mil.	% of total
Casino	6,637	66
Food & beverage	1,534	15
Rooms	1,208	12
Management fees	35	-
Other	682	7
Promotional allowances	(1263.5)	-
Total	**8,834**	**100**

Selected US Properties

Atlantic City NJ
- Bally' s Atlantic City
- Caesars Atlantic City
- Harrah' s Atlantic City
- Showboat Atlantic City

Bossier City LA
- Horseshoe Bossier City
- Louisiana Downs

Chicago area
- Harrah' s Joliet (Illinois)
- Horseshoe Southern Indiana

Council Bluffs IA
- Harrah' s Council Bluffs
- Horseshoe Council Bluffs

Indiana
- Horseshoe Southern Indiana

Lake Tahoe NV
- Harrah' s Lake Tahoe
- Harveys Lake Tahoe

Las Vegas
- Bally' s Las Vegas
- Bill' s Gamblin' Hall & Saloon
- Caesars Palace
- Flamingo Las Vegas
- Harrah' s Las Vegas
- Imperial Palace
- Paris Las Vegas
- Planet Hollywood Resort and Casino
- Rio

Laughlin NV
- Harrah' s Laughlin

Reno NV
- Harrah' s Reno

Metropolis IL
- Harrah' s Metropolis

Mississippi Gulf Coast
- Grand Casino Biloxi

New Orleans
- Harrah' s New Orleans

Tunica MS
- Harrah' s Tunica
- Horseshoe Tunica

Selected International Properties

Egypt
- Caesars Cairo
- London Clubs Cairo-Ramses

Ontario Canada
- Caesars Windsor

South Africa
- Emerald Safari

UK
- Alea Glasgow
- Alea Nottingham
- The Casino at the Empire
- Golden Nugget
- Manchester235
- Rendezvous Brighton
- Rendezvous Casino
- Rendezvous Southend-on-Sea
- The Sportsman

Other Selected Operations

Casinos managed for Indian tribes
- Harrah' s Ak-Chin (Phoenix)
- Harrah' s Cherokee (North Carolina)
- Harrah' s Rincon (San Diego)

Macau Orient Golf (on Cotai Strip in Macao)

Racetracks
- Bluegrass Downs (Paducah KY)
- Thistledown Racetrack (Cleveland OH)
- Turfway Park (50%; Simpson County KY)

World Series of Poker

COMPETITORS

Ameristar Casinos
Boyd Gaming
Isle of Capri Casinos
Kerzner International
Las Vegas Sands
Mashantucket Pequot
MGM Resorts
Pinnacle Entertainment
Station Casinos
Tropicana Entertainment
Trump Resorts
Wynn Resorts

HISTORICAL FINANCIALS

Company Type: Public

Income Statement FYE: December 31

	REVENUE ($ mil.)	NET INCOME ($ mil.)	NET PROFIT MARGIN	EMPLOYEES
12/11	8,834	(687)	—	70,000
12/10	8,818	(831)	—	69,000
12/09	8,907	827	9.3%	0
12/08*	9,366	(5,096)	—	0
01/08	760	(100)	—	0
Annual Growth	84.6%	—	—	—

*Fiscal year change

2011 Year-End Financials

Debt ratio: 69.44%
Return on equity: (-68.30)%
Cash ($ mil.): 904
Current ratio: 114.62
Long-term debt ($ mil.): 19,759

No. of shares (mil.): 125
Dividends
Yield: —
Payout: —
Market value ($ mil.): —

Calpine Corp

Calpine may get hot but it also knows how to blow off some steam. In 2012 the independent power producer and marketer controlled almost 29000 MW of generating capacity through interests in more than 90 primarily natural gas-fired power plants in 20 US states and Canada. This fleet also includes 15 geothermal power plants in California. Calpine the leading geothermal power producer in North America owns 725 MW of capacity at the largest geothermal facility in the US –the Geysers in northern California and which accounts for more than 20% of the state's renewable energy. The company has major presence in the wholesale power markets in California the Mid-Atlantic and Texas.

Operations

Calpine sells electricity to utilities wholesalers and end-users primarily through long-term contracts; the firm also trades power on the wholesale market. Other Calpine operations include construction consulting and management services; turbine component manufacturing; and critical power provision for high-tech companies.

Financial Analysis

In 2011 the company reported higher output and revenues thanks to the Conectiv acquisition and bringing York Energy Center (a 565-MW plant in Pennsylvania) on line. However higher fuel and purchased power costs coupled with poor hedging returns resulted in the company posting a net loss for the year.

An improving economy and the Conectiv purchase lifted commodity sales in 2010 despite a drag from hedging losses. The company's overall revenues and net income were essentially flat in 2010 following a 34% drop in revenues in 2009 (due to the collapse of commodity prices caused by the global recession).

Cash flow has steadily improved since Calpine emerged from bankruptcy in 2008 having filed for Chapter 11 protection in 2005.

Strategy

The company has disposed of most of its natural gas reserves and gathering and transportation assets in order to focus on power generation.

Gearing up to grow its national footprint as the economy began to pick up in 2010 Calpine sold two of its gas-fired power plants to Xcel Energy for $739 million in order to generate cash. The two plants located near Denver were already providing power to Public Service Company of Colorado an Xcel subsidiary under a contract agreement. It also sold a 25% stake in a Texas power plant to Rayburn Country Electric Cooperative for $215 million.

That year the company purchased 4490 MW of power plants from Pepco Holdings for about $1.7 billion. The acquisition added Conectiv Energy's power plants (18 operating and one under construction) to Calpine's fleet helping to strengthen its market position in the Eastern US.

Although Calpine had scaled back on new plant development due to low demand –it had about 584 MW under construction in late 2011 –it has a call option to purchase the 775-MW power plant in Riverside County California for the Inland Empire Energy Center. The plant completed in 2010 is based on General Electric's latest gas turbine technology.

Growing its generating capacity in 2012 the company acquired an 800-MW natural gas-fired combined-cycle power plant in Central Texas from Bosque Power Co. for $432 million.

EXECUTIVES

VP Corporate Communications, Norma F. Dunn
President CEO and Director, Jack A. Fusco, age 49, $1,015,269 total compensation
EVP Chief Legal Officer and Secretary, W. Thaddeus Miller, age 61, $723,366 total compensation
SVP and CIO, Dennis Fishback
SVP Government and Regulatory Affairs, Joseph E. (Joe) Ronan Jr.
SVP Power Operations, John Adams
EVP and COO, John B. (Thad) Hill III, age 45, $609,904 total compensation
SVP Internal Audit and Chief Compliance Officer, Kevin G. McMahon, age 44
Manager Investor Relations, Christine Parker
SVP Government Affairs and Managing Counsel, Sarah Novosel
EVP and Chief Risk Officer, Gary M. Germeroth, age 53
SVP Geothermal Operations, Michael D. (Mike) Rogers, $455,192 total compensation
EVP and CFO, Zamir Rauf, age 52, $484,135 total compensation
VP Controller and Interim Chief Accounting Officer, Kenneth A. (Ken) Graves, age 47
SVP and Chief Accounting Officer, Jim D. Deidiker, age 56
Chairman, J. Stuart Ryan, age 53
VP Finance and Investor Relations, Andre K. Walker
SVP Human Resources, Hether Benjamin-Brown
Director, Frank Cassidy, age 65
President CEO and Director, Jack A. Fusco, age 49
Director, W. Benjamin (Ben) Moreland, age 48
Director, William E. Oberndorf, age 59
Director, Robert A. Mosbacher Jr., age 60
Director, Denise M. O'Leary, age 55
Director, Robert C. Hinckley, age 64
Director, David C. Merritt, age 57
Auditors: PricewaterhouseCoopersLLP

LOCATIONS

HQ: Calpine Corporation
717 Texas Ave. Ste. 1000, Houston TX 77002
Phone: 713-830-2000 **Fax:** 713-830-2001
Web: www.calpine.com

2011 Sales

	$ mil.	% of total
West	2,372	35
Texas	2,306	34
North	1,336	20
Southeast	786	11
Total	**6,800**	**100**

PRODUCTS/OPERATIONS

COMPETITORS

AEP
AES
CMS Energy
Covanta
Duke Energy
Edison International
Enel North America
GenOnEnergy
MidAmerican Energy
PG&E Corporation
PSEG Power
Sempra Energy

HISTORICAL FINANCIALS

Company Type: Public

Income Statement FYE: December 31

	REVENUE ($ mil.)	NET INCOME ($ mil.)	NET PROFIT MARGIN	EMPLOYEES
12/11	6,800	(190)	—	2,101
12/10	6,545	31	0.5%	2,142
12/09	6,564	149	2.3%	2,046
12/08	9,937	10	0.1%	2,049
12/07	7,970	2,693	33.8%	2,080
Annual Growth	(3.9%)	—	—	0.3%

2011 Year-End Financials

Debt ratio: 60.01%
Return on equity: (-4.41)%
Cash ($ mil.): 1,252
Current ratio: 164.75
Long-term debt ($ mil.): 10,321

No. of shares (mil.): 481
Dividends
Yield: —
Payout: —
Market value ($ mil.): 7,867

	STOCK PRICE ($) FY Close	P/E High/Low	PER SHARE ($) Earnings	Dividends	Book Value
12/11	16.33	— —	(0.39)	0.00	8.93
12/10	13.34	234180	0.06	0.00	10.45
12/09	11.00	47 15	0.31	0.00	10.04
12/08	7.28	1150326	0.02	0.00	10.19
Annual Growth	30.9%	— —	—	—	(4.3%)

Cameron International Corp

Cameron International knows how to work under pressure. A leading manufacturer provider and servicer of oil and gas industry equipment the company makes products that control pressure at oil and gas wells including blowout preventers chokes controls wellheads and valves. It also makes integral and separable reciprocating engines and compressors used in oil and gas and power-generation applications. Cameron International sells its products which are used for offshore onshore and subsea applications under more than 60 brand names including Ajax Cameron Cooper-Bessemer Demco LeTourneau Natco Petreco and Willis.

Operations

The company provides oil and gas production systems used to control the pressure and flows of oil and gas wells. Through its Valves segment Cameron International provides valves and other equipment used to control the flow of oil and gas through wellheads gathering lines and transmission systems. Through its compression segment formed from the merger of the company's Cooper Energy Services and Cooper Turbocompressor businesses Cameron International provides aftermarket parts engine compressors turbo chargers and controls.

Financial Analysis

In 2010 a BP rig in the Gulf of Mexico exploded and sank spewing oil into the Gulf. The blowout preventer on the system made by Cameron International failed to work properly. A board of inquiry was set up to find out the cause of the disaster and a separate government report found that the company's blowout preventer proved incapable of stopping the high-pressure flow from the doomed well. The company claimed that its equipment met industry standards and it was not found liable in any legal proceeding although it did pay $82.5 million to settle with BP.

Despite this incident Cameron International reported a major growth in revenue and income in 2010 thanks to a rebounding global economy high oil prices and increased demand for oil and gas exploration and production activity especially in the shallow shelf Gulf of Mexico and West Africa. An increase in demand for valves for pipeline and refinery projects globally also drove up the company's revenues.

Cameron International reported robust revenue growth in 2011 reflecting a strong global oil and gas exploration market (especially in North America) which resulted in increased demand for the company's products across all of its business segments. But higher operating costs and litigation and settlement costs related to the BP well incident dragged down the firm's net income in 2011.

Strategy

Cameron International has pursued a strategy of growth through joint ventures and the acquisition of companies that complement its existing core businesses. In 2012 the company formed a 60%-owned joint venture with Halliburton OneSubsea to make and develop products systems and services for the subsea oil and gas market. Cameron will contribute its existing subsea division and receive $600 million from Schlumberger. Schlumberger will contribute its Framo Surveillance Flow Assurance and Power and Controls businesses.

Cameron International moved into the lucrative shale market in the US Northeast in 2011 through the acquisition of West Virginia-based Industrial Machine & Fabrication a leading aftermarket service provider for reciprocating engines and compressors.

That year it also expanded its drilling equipment portfolio buying LeTourneau Technologies Drillings Systems and Offshore Products divisions from Joy Global for $375 million.

Company Background

Cameron International traces its roots to the mid-1800s when it made steam engines to generate power for plants and textile and rolling mills.

EXECUTIVES

SVP and CFO, Charles M. Sledge, age 46, $450,000 total compensation
EVP and COO, John D. Carne, age 63, $540,000 total compensation
SVP and General Counsel, William C. Lemmer, age 67, $420,000 total compensation
President Flow Control, Stuart C. Nelson
Chairman President and CEO, Jack B. Moore, age 59, $900,000 total compensation
VP Development and Technology, John C. Bartos
VP Investor Relations, Jeffrey G. (Jeff) Altamari
VP Aftermarket Sales Process & Compression Systems, Ronald J. (Ron) Flecknoe
VP Aftermarket, Edward E. (Ed) Roper
VP; President Surface Systems, Gary M. Halverson
VP Global Business Development, Hal J. Goldie
VP; President Drilling Systems, Glenn Chiasson
CIO, Hunter W. Jones
VP Business Development Valves & Measurement, W. B. (Willy) Findlay
President Measurement Systems, Patrick C. Holley
VP Engineering Valves & Measurement, Dave Mefford
VP Finance Drilling & Production Systems, R. A. (Rick) Steans
VP; President Process & Compression Systems, Joseph H. Mongrain, age 54
SVP; President Valves and Measurement, James E. (Jim) Wright, age 58, $375,000 total compensation
VP Chief Accounting Officer and Controller, Christopher A. Krummel, age 43
VP Operations Integrity, Stephen P. Tomlinson
President Distributed Valves, Mark T. Cordell
VP Human Resources, Roslyn R. (Roz) Larkey, age 53
VP Tax, Stuart Taylor, age 50
VP and Treasurer, H. Keith Jennings, age 42
Corporate Secretary and Chief Governance Officer, Grace B. Holmes
VP; President Subsea Systems, Owen A. Serjeant
Director Information Technology, Carl Sackett
VP Marketing and Strategy, Edward E. Will
Chief Compliance Officer, Celine Gerson
VP Total Rewards, Amber J. Macksey
VP HR Regional Operations and Services, Kevin Fleming
VP Quality and Customer Experience, Gary F. Devlin
Director, Douglas L. (Doug) Foshee, age 52
Director, C. Baker Cunningham, age 70
Director, Sheldon R. (Shel) Erikson, age 70
Director, Michael E. Patrick, age 68
Director, David A. Ross III, age 71
Director, Bruce W. Wilkinson, age 67
Director, Peter J. Fluor, age 64
Director, Jon E. Reinhardsen, age 55
Auditors: Ernst&YoungLLP

LOCATIONS

HQ: Cameron International Corporation
1333 West Loop South Ste. 1700, Houston TX 77027
Phone: 713-513-3300 **Fax:** 713-513-3456
Web: www.c-a-m.com

2011 Sales

	$ mil.	% of total
North America	3,084	44
Asia & Middle East	1,270	18
Africa	1,002	15
Europe	753	11
South America	647	9
Other regions	200	3
Total	**6,959**	**100**

PRODUCTS/OPERATIONS

2011 Sales

	$ mil.	% of total
Drilling & production systems	4,061	58
Valve & measurement	1,663	24
Compression systems	1,234	18
Total	**6,959**	**100**

COMPETITORS

ABB Inc.
Aker Solutions
Atlas Copco
CIRCOR International
Dresser Inc.
Dresser-Rand
Dril-Quip
Ebara
Flotek
FMC
GE Oil
Ingersoll-Rand Industrial Technologies
McDermott
National Oilwell Varco
Tyco
Weatherford International

HISTORICAL FINANCIALS

Company Type: Public

Income Statement FYE: December 31

	REVENUE ($ mil.)	NET INCOME ($ mil.)	NET PROFIT MARGIN	EMPLOYEES
12/11	6,959	521	7.5%	22,500
12/10	6,134	562	9.2%	19,500
12/09	5,223	475	9.1%	18,100
12/08	5,848	593	10.2%	17,100
12/07	4,666	500	10.7%	15,400
Annual Growth	10.5%	1.0%	—	9.9%

2011 Year-End Financials

Debt ratio: 16.93%
Return on equity: 11.09%
Cash ($ mil.): 898
Current ratio: 217.46
Long-term debt ($ mil.): 1,574
No. of shares (mil.): 245
Dividends
Yield: —
Payout: —
Market value ($ mil.): 12,078

	STOCK PRICE ($) FY Close	P/E High/Low		PER SHARE ($) Earnings	Dividends	Book Value
12/11	49.19	29	19	2.09	0.00	19.17
12/10	50.73	22	14	2.27	0.00	18.01
12/09	41.80	20	8	2.11	0.00	16.02
12/08	20.50	21	6	2.60	0.00	10.69
12/07	48.13	46	22	2.16	0.00	9.61
Annual Growth	0.5%	—	—	(0.8%)	—	18.8%

Campbell Soup Co.

Soup boils down to M'm! M'm! Money! at the world's #1 soup maker Campbell Soup. The company's most popular selections among its 90-variety soup portfolio in the US include chicken noodle tomato and cream of mushroom. Campbell also makes and markets meal kits SpaghettiOs canned pasta Pace picante sauce V8 beverages and Pepperidge Farm baked goods (including those popular Goldfish crackers). Campbell's Australian division produces snack foods such as the Aussie favorite Arnott's biscuits. The food manufacturer which sells its products in more than 160 countries boasts facilities throughout the world. In addition to North America its principal markets are Australia Belgium France and Germany.

Strategy

The company is working to boost profits by focusing on three categories worldwide: simple meals baked snacks and healthy beverages. Campbell is working to increase product innovation and consumer marketing initiatives for products in the Campbell's Swanson Pace Prego Liebig Erasco Pepperidge Farm Goldfish Arnott's and V8 lines that fall under the three categories. Currently the company looks to stabilize and boost the profitability of its North American soup and simple meals businesses. For its healthy beverages unit it's pursuing fast-growing product segments such as energy drinks and juices while also growing this business outside the US. To set up its baked snacks for growth Campbell is building a 34000-sq.-ft. innovation center at the Pepperidge Farm headquarters. Funding the initiatives will negatively affect financial performance for that year but help set the stage for profitability in 2013 onward.

Geographic Reach

The company operates manufacturing facilities in 14 US states and 10 foreign countries. Campbell is focused on boosting its presence in international markets with existing products in Europe and Asia Pacific. It also hopes to capture market share in fast-growing markets in Asia and Latin America through acquisitions and strategic alliances such as joint ventures. With China having one of the world's highest rates of per-capita soup consumption Campbell has been focusing its efforts on the Guangdong province and Shanghai. Campbell formed a joint venture with its Chinese distribution partner Swire Pacific Limited in 2011 to chase after the commercial soup market. Named Campbell Swire the venture is controlled by Campbell which retains a 60% interest and based in Campbell's Shanghai offices.

Sales & Marketing

Wal-Mart is Campbell's largest customer accounting for 17% of sales. Addressing changing consumer tastes the company has been reducing the salt content of its foods across some of its best-selling brands including its iconic tomato soup along with V8 Healthy Request Chunky and Goldfish products. Challenged in quality and sales by rival General Mills' Progresso-brand soups Campbell has enhanced the taste of its products by adding more vegetables to its vegetable soup and making its cream soups creamier.

Mergers & Acquisitions

Meanwhile Campbell has expanded its brand portfolio through acquisitions. The soup giant in 2012 purchased Bolthouse Farms for about $1.55 billion from Madison Dearborn Partners. Bolthouse known for selling fresh carrots beverages and salad dressings is expected to further fuel Campbell's US beverage division which has benefitted from the rising popularity of the V8 juice brand. Campbell also acquired Ecce Panis a maker of artisan breads in 2009; it has since been folded into its Pepperidge Farm operations and has given Campbell entry into the growing higher-margin artisanal bread sector. Previously Campbell acquired the Wolfgang Puck soup label from Country Gourmet Foods in 2008 and inked a licensing deal with Wolfgang Puck Worldwide to use the celebrity chef's name on additional broth and stock products.

Divestitures

Campbell simultaneously has shed non-core lines; it sold its premium chocolate maker Godiva to Turkish food company Ulker. Campbell pocketed $850 million from the 2008 sale and used the proceeds to repurchase shares. The company also divested its French sauce and mayonnaise business which was marketed under the "Lesieur" brand for $42 million and axed some of its Australian salty snack brands including Cheezels Thins Tasty Jacks French Fries and Kettle Chips. The French and Australian divestitures were cited as part of Campbell's operational-efficiency and long-term restructuring initiative which began that year. Whittling down manufacturing costs Campbell in mid-2010 also sold its German Village Products pasta facility in Ohio to Philadelphia Macaroni which has in turn agreed to supply pasta to Campbell.

Financial Analysis

Campbell has grown slowly during the past few years. Revenue has remained relatively flat as net income dipped some 5% in 2012 vs. 2011. It's also down $379 million in cash in 2012 as compared to 2011. The company points to International Simple Meals and Beverages and US Simple Meals (due to US sauces) for the sales decreases as it logged increases among its Global Baking and Snacking (due to Pepperidge Farm offsetting Arnott's declines) US Beverages (V8 Splash beverages and V8 V-Fusion beverages) and North America Foodservice (due to refrigerated soup) units. Campbell cites increases in marketing and selling expenses for its net income boost as well as a $3 million impairment charge associated with the (Swedish) Bl? trademark used in the International Simple Meals and Beverages segment.

Ownership

The descendants of John Dorrance the inventor of condensed soup and founder of the company own approximately 42% of Campbell.

HISTORY

Campbell Soup Company began in Camden New Jersey in 1869 as a canning and preserving business founded by icebox maker Abram Anderson and fruit merchant Joseph Campbell. Anderson left in 1876 and Arthur Dorrance took his place. The Dorrance family assumed control after Campbell retired in 1894.

Arthur's nephew John Dorrance joined Campbell in 1897. The young chemist soon found a way to condense soup by eliminating most of its water. Without the heavy bulk of water-filled cans distribution was cheaper; Campbell products quickly spread.

In 1904 the firm introduced the Campbell Kids characters. Entering the California market in 1911 Campbell became one of the first US companies to achieve national distribution of a food brand. It bought Franco-American the first American soup maker in 1915.

The company's ubiquity in American kitchens made its soup can an American icon (consider Andy Warhol's celebrated 1960 print) and brought great wealth to the Dorrance family.

With a reputation for conservative management Campbell began to diversify acquiring V8 juice (1948) Swanson (1955) Pepperidge Farm (1961) Godiva Chocolatier (33% in 1966 full ownership in 1974) Vlasic pickles (1978) and Mrs. Paul's seafood (1982). It introduced Prego spaghetti sauce and LeMenu frozen dinners in the early 1980s.

Much of Campbell's sales growth in the 1990s came not from unit sales but from increasing its prices. In 1993 it took a $300 million restructuring charge and over the next two years it sold poor performers at home and abroad. John Sr.'s grandson Bennett Dorrance took up the role of vice chairman in 1993 becoming the first family member to take a senior executive position in 10 years.

Two years later Campbell paid $1.1 billion for Pace Foods (picante sauce) and acquired Fresh Start Bakeries (buns and muffins for McDonald's) and Homepride (popular cooking sauce in the UK).

As part of its international expansion in 1996 the firm acquired Erasco a top German soup maker and Cheong Chan a food manufacturer in Malaysia. However back at home it sold Mrs. Paul's. In 1997 Campbell sold its Marie's salad dressing operations and bought Groupe Danone's Liebig (France's leading wet-soup brand). Also that year Dale Morrison a relative newcomer to the firm succeeded David Johnson as president and CEO. To reduce costs and focus on other core segments in 1998 Campbell spun off Swanson frozen foods and Vlasic pickles into Vlasic Foods International. (Vlasic later filed bankruptcy and was snapped up in a leveraged buyout.) In 1999 Campbell redesigned its soup can labels altering an American icon.

Morrison resigned abruptly as president and CEO in 2000; Johnson returned to the helm during the search for a permanent chief. In early 2001 Douglas Conant previously of Nabisco Foods joined Campbell as president and CEO. A fresh plan was introduced to spend up to $600 million on marketing product development and quality upgrades (at the expense of shareholder dividends). In 2001 Campbell also bought the Batchelors Royco and Heisse Tasse brands of soup as well as the OXO brand of stock cubes from Unilever for about $900 million. The deal made Campbell the leading soup maker in Europe. In 2003 Campbell bought Snack Foods Limited a leading snack food maker in Australia and Irish dry soup maker Erin Foods from Greencore.

Campbell reorganized its North American business in 2004 into the following units: US Soup Sauces and Beverages; Campbell Away From Home and Canada Mexico and Latin America; Pepperidge Farm; and Godiva Worldwide. (In response to dietary trends the company announced that year that it was removing all trans-fatty acids from its Pepperidge Farm breads.) The company retired the Franco-American brand in 2004; products that carried the brand (most notably SpaghettiOs) now bear the Campbell brand. Also that year company chairman George M. Sherman retired and was replaced by Harvey Golub.

In 2006 Campbell sold its UK and Irish businesses to Premier Foods for about $870 million. Brands involved in the sale included Homepride sauces OXO stock cubes and Batchelors McDonnells and Erin soups.

Denise Morton succeeded Douglas Conant as CEO of Campbell in August 2011.

In August 2012 Campbell acquired California-based Bolthouse Farms for roughly $1.55 billion from the private equity firm Madison Dearborn Partners. The company is a leading producer of fresh-cut carrots as well as chilled juices and smoothies.

EXECUTIVES

SVP Law and Government Affairs, Ellen Oran Kaden, age 60, $627,000 total compensation

Chairman, Paul R. Charron, age 70

President CEO and Director, Denise M. Morrison, age 58, $650,000 total compensation

SVP CFO and Chief Administrative Officer, B. Craig Owens, age 57, $780,000 total compensation

SVP Finance, Anthony P. DiSilvestro, age 53, $384,124 total compensation

Chief Marketing Officer, Michael P. (Mike) Senackerib, age 46

SVP Global Supply Chain, David R. White, age 57

President Campbell Company of Canada, Phillip E. Donne

President Pepperidge Farm, Patrick J. (Pat) Callaghan, age 61

SVP and CIO, Joseph C. (Joe) Spagnoletti, age 47

President Asia Pacific, Gareth Edgecombe

President Greater Europe, John Sechi, age 55
President Campbell North America, Mark Alexander, age 48
SVP Global Research and Development and Quality, George Dowdie, age 57
SVP Global Baking and Snacking, Irene Chang Britt, age 49
VP Finance and Strategy International, Andy Ridler
VP Corporate Development, Raymond Liguori, age 54
SVP and Chief Human Resources Officer, Bob Morrissey
President Asia, Daniel Saw
Director, Les C. Vinney, age 63
Director, Randall W. (Randy) Larrimore, age 65
Director, William D. (Bill) Perez, age 64
Director, Lawrence C. Karlson, age 69
President CEO and Director, Denise M. Morrison, age 58
Director, Archbold D. (Archie) van Beuren, age 55
Director, Sara S. Mathew, age 56
Director, Edmund M. Carpenter, age 70
Director, Bennett Dorrance, age 66
Director, Mary Alice D. Malone, age 62
Director, Charles R. Perrin, age 67
Director, Charlotte C. Weber, age 69
Director, Nick Shreiber, age 63
Director, A. Barry Rand, age 67
Auditors: PricewaterhouseCoopersLLP

LOCATIONS

HQ: Campbell Soup Company
1 Campbell Place, Camden NJ 08103-1799
Phone: 856-342-4800 **Fax:** 856-342-3878
Web: www.campbellsoup.com

2011 Sales

	$ mil.	% of total
US	5,309	69
Australia & Asia Pacific	1,138	15
Europe	596	8
Other	676	8
Total	**7,719**	**100**

PRODUCTS/OPERATIONS

2011 Sales

	$ mil.	% of total
US Simple Meals	2,751	35
Global Baking & Snacking	2,156	28
International Simple Meals & Beverages	1,463	19
US Beverages	751	10
North America Foodservice	590	8
Total	**7,719**	**100**

2011 Sales

	$ mil.	% of total
Simple Meals	4,437	58
Baked Snacks	2,321	30
Beverages	961	12
Total	**7,719**	**100**

Selected Brand Names

Domestic
- Away From Home
- Bolthouse Farms
- Campbell
- Ecce Panis
- Pace
- Pepperidge Farm
- Prego

Select Harvest

- StockPot
- Swanson
- V8 and V8 Splash
- Wolfgang Puck

International
- Arnott' s (Asia)
- Bl? (Sweden)
- DeliSoup (the Netherlands)
- Devos Lemmens (France and the Netherlands)
- Erasco (Germany)
- Heisse Tasse (Germany)
- Lacroix (Belgium and France)
- Liebig (France)
- Royco (France and the Netherlands)
- Touch of Taste (Sweden)

Selected Subsidiaries

Arnott' s Biscuits Limited (Australia)
Ecce Panis Inc.
Eugen Lacroix GmbH (Germany)
Grundstuecksverwaltungsgesellschaft GmbH (Germany)
Lacroix GmbH (Germany)
Pepperidge Farm Incorporated
Players Group Limited (Australia)
Royco Voedingsmiddelenfabrieken B.V. (the Netherlands)
Sinalopasta S.A. de C.V. (Mexico)
Stockpot Inc.

COMPETITORS

Associated British Foods
B&G Foods
Barbara' s Bakery
Baxters
Bush Brothers
Canyon Creek Food
ConAgra
Del Monte Foods
Dole Food
Faribault Foods
Frito-Lay
General Mills
Golden Enterprises
Grimmway Enterprises
Hanover Foods
Harry' s Fresh Foods
Heinz
Hormel
Kellogg U.S. Snacks
Mondelez International
Morgan Foods
Nestle
NORPAC
Odwalla
Pacific Coast Producers
Peter Rabbit Farms
Red Gold
Reily Foods
Renee' s Gourmet Foods
Snyder' s-Lance
Unilever
Walkers Snack Foods

HISTORICAL FINANCIALS

Company Type: Public

Income Statement

FYE: July 29

	REVENUE ($ mil.)	NET INCOME ($ mil.)	NET PROFIT MARGIN	EMPLOYEES
07/12	7,707	774	10.0%	17,700
07/11*	7,719	805	10.4%	17,500
08/10	7,676	844	11.0%	18,400
08/09	7,586	736	9.7%	18,700
08/08	7,998	1,165	14.6%	19,400
Annual Growth	(0.9%)	(9.7%)	—	(2.3%)

*Fiscal year change

2012 Year-End Financials

Debt ratio: 42.73%
Return on equity: 86.19%
Cash ($ mil.): 335
Current ratio: 85.56
Long-term debt ($ mil.): 2,004
No. of shares (mil.): 312
Dividends
Yield: —
Payout: 48.13%
Market value ($ mil.): 10,333

	STOCK PRICE ($) FY Close	P/E High	P/E Low	PER SHARE ($) Earnings	Dividends	Book Value
07/12	33.12	14	12	2.41	0.00	2.88
07/11*	33.05	15	13	2.42	0.00	3.40
08/10	35.90	15	12	2.42	0.00	2.76
08/09	31.03	19	12	2.06	0.00	2.12
08/08	35.85	12	10	3.06	0.00	3.70
Annual Growth	(2.0%)	—	—	(5.8%)	—	(6.1%)

*Fiscal year change

Capital City Bank Group, Inc.

Capital City Bank Group is the holding company for Capital City Bank which serves individuals businesses and institutions from some 70 branches in northern Florida plus portions of Alabama and Georgia. It offers checking savings and money market accounts; CDs; IRAs; Internet banking; and debit and credit cards. Commercial real estate mortgages account for about a third of its loan portfolio; residential real estate loans are about a quarter. The bank also originates business loans and consumer loans including credit cards. Capital City also performs data processing services for other financial institutions in its market area.

Subsidiary Capital City Trust provides trust and asset management services. Capital City Banc Investments offers investments retirement plans and life and long-term care insurance through an agreement with third-party provider INVEST Financial Corporation a subsidiary of Jackson National Life Insurance Company.

Capital City was founded in 1982 to acquire six banks and has never looked back. The company has continued its acquisition strategy buying 15 banks since 1984; it has also expanded by opening new offices. However its home state of Florida was one of the hardest hit during the recession. High unemployment levels contributed to an increase in nonperforming loans in the bank's portfolio which in turn translated to net losses in 2009 and 2010. Capital City is focusing on diversifying its portfolio and reducing problem assets.

President and CEO William Smith Jr. and his brother Robert own about 20% of Capital City Bank Group.

EXECUTIVES

EVP and CFO; EVP and CFO Capital City Bank, J. Kimbrough Davis, age 58, $239,000 total compensation
Treasurer and Director; President Capital City Bank, Thomas A. (Tom) Barron, age 59, $245,000 total compensation
Chairman President and CEO; Chairman Capital City Bank, William G. Smith Jr., age 58, $285,000 total compensation
President Capital City Banc Investments, William L. Moor Jr.
President Capital City Trust, Randolph M. (Randy) Pople
EVP Commercial Real Estate Lending Capital City Bank, Edward G. (Ed) Canup
EVP Metro Community Banking Capital City Bank; President Leon County, William D. (Bill) Colledge
EVP Community Banking Capital City Bank, Mitchell R. (Mitch) Englert
EVP Residential Lending Capital City Bank, Karen H. Love
EVP Credit Administration. Capital City Bank, Dale A. Thompson
EVP Sales Leadership Capital City Bank, Edwin N. (Ed) West Jr.
EVP; President Capital City Services, Cynthia Y. (Cindy) Pyburn
Chief People Officer Capital City Bank, Beth H. Corum
Treasurer and Director; President Capital City Bank, Thomas A. (Tom) Barron, age 59
Director, DuBose (Duby) Ausley, age 74

Director, J. Everitt Drew, age 56
Director, Cader B. Cox III, age 62
Director, Lina S. Knox, age 67
Director, John K. Humphress, age 63
Director, Frederick Carroll III, age 61
Director, Henry Lewis III, age 62
Auditors: Ernst&YoungLLP

LOCATIONS

HQ: Capital City Bank Group Inc.
217 N. Monroe St., Tallahassee FL 32301
Phone: 850-402-7000 **Fax:** 850-878-9150
Web: www.ccbg.com

PRODUCTS/OPERATIONS

2011 Sales

	$ mil.	% of total
Interest		
Loans including fees	94	60
Investment securities	4	3
Funds sold	0	-
Noninterest income		
Service charges on deposit accounts	25	16
Bank card fees	10	6
Asset management fees	4	3
Retail brokerage fees	3	2
Data processing fees	3	2
Mortgage banking fees	2	2
Other	9	6
Total	**158**	**100**

COMPETITORS

Ameris
Bank of America
BBX Capital
Delta Community Credit Union
Regions Financial
SunTrust
Thomasville Bancshares

HISTORICAL FINANCIALS

Company Type: Public

Income Statement

FYE: December 31

	ASSETS ($ mil.)	NET INCOME ($ mil.)	INCOME AS % OF ASSETS	EMPLOYEES
12/11	2,641	4	0.2%	959
12/10	2,622	(0)	—	975
12/09	2,708	(3)	—	1,006
12/08	2,488	15	0.6%	1,042
12/07	2,616	29	1.1%	1,097
Annual Growth	0.2%	(36.3%)	—	(3.3%)

2011 Year-End Financials

Debt ratio: 4.07%
Return on equity: 1.94%
Cash ($ mil.): 385
Current ratio: —
Long-term debt ($ mil.): 107
No. of shares (mil.): 17
Dividends
Yield: —
Payout: 103.45%
Market value ($ mil.): 164

	STOCK PRICE ($) FY Close	P/E High/Low		PER SHARE ($) Earnings	Dividends	Book Value
12/11	9.55	47	33	0.29	0.00	14.68
12/10	12.60	—	—	(0.02)	0.49	15.15
12/09	13.84	—	—	(0.20)	0.76	15.73
12/08	27.24	39	22	0.89	0.75	16.28
12/07	28.22	21	15	1.66	0.71	17.03
Annual Growth	(23.7%)	—	—	(35.3%)	—	(3.6%)

Capital One Financial Corp

Capital One isn't just concerned with what's in your wallet; it's interested in your bank account as well. The company is best known as one of the largest issuers of Visa and MasterCard credit cards in the US but it also boasts a banking network of approximately 1000 branches mainly in New York New Jersey Louisiana Texas and the Washington DC area. Subsidiary ING Direct offers online and direct banking without branches. Capital One which serves more than 50 million customers in the US Canada and the UK also has units that offer auto financing write home loans sell insurance and manage assets for institutional and high-net-worth clients.

Capital One's credit card business makes up its largest business segment (contributing around 65% of revenues). The company works hard to cater to its credit card customers and tries to keep the "custom" in customer. Cardholders can customize their cards' appearance rates and rewards. Products range from platinum and gold cards for preferred customers to secured cards for customers with poor or limited credit histories. Capital One is focused on growing its customer base and strengthening its loan portfolios.

Much of its recent growth has been through acquisitions. In 2011 the company boosted its credit card business with the acquisition of GE Capital's $1.3 billion Hudson's Bay credit card portfolio tripling the number of Canadian customer accounts Capital One services. That year Capital One also acquired Kohl's existing $3.7 billion private-label credit card portfolio. Capital One grew its US credit card business once again with the 2012 acquisition of HSBC's US card portfolio for some $2.6 billion.

The company's foray into banking which began in 2005 has allowed it to use deposits to fund its lending rather than relying on capital markets. The company's focus on consumer lending has shielded it somewhat from the downturn in commercial markets. Capital One added more than 7 million new banking customers and increased loans and deposits in 2012 when it bought online bank ING Direct from ING Groep for some $9 billion in cash and stock. The deal gave ING Groep ownership of about 10% of Capital One.

Company performance in 2011 was bolstered by lower credit costs due to improved loan credit quality. Net income increased by 15% that year as Capital One also reduced provisions for mortgage repurchase losses.

HISTORY

Capital One Financial is a descendant of the Bank of Virginia which was formed in 1945. The company began issuing products similar to credit cards in 1953 and was MasterCard issuer #001. Acquisitions and mergers brought some 30 banks and several finance and mortgage companies under the bank's umbrella between 1962 and 1986 when Bank of Virginia became Signet Banking.

Signet's credit card operations had reached a million customers in 1988 when the bank hired consultants Richard Fairbank and Nigel Morris (Fairbank is now chairman and CEO) to implement their "Information-Based Strategy." Under the duo's leadership the bank began using sophisticated data-collection methods to gather massive amounts of information on existing or prospective customers; it then used the information to design and mass-market customized products to the customer.

In 1991 –after creating an enormous database and developing sophisticated screening processes and direct-mail marketing tactics –Signet escalated the credit card wars luring customers from its rivals with its innovative balance-transfer credit card. The card let customers of other companies transfer what they owed on higher-interest cards to a Signet card with a lower introductory rate.

The new card immediately drew imitators (by 1997 balance-transfer cards accounted for 85% of credit card solicitations). After skimming off the least risky customers Fairbank and Morris began going after less desirable credit customers who could be charged higher rates. The result was what they call second-generation products –secured and unsecured cards with lower credit lines and higher annual percentage rates and fees for higher-risk customers.

The credit card business had grown to 5 million customers by 1994 but at a high cost to Signet which had devoted most of its resources to finding and servicing credit card holders. That year Signet spun off its credit card business as Capital One to focus on banking. (Signet was later acquired by First Union.)

The company moved into Florida and Texas in 1995 and into Canada and the UK in 1996; that year it established its savings bank mainly to offer products and services to its cardholders. In 1997 the company used this unit to move into deposit accounts buying a deposit portfolio from J. C. Penney. In 1998 the company began marketing its products to such clients as immigrants and high school students (whose parents must co-sign for the card). The company also expanded in terms of products and geography acquiring auto lender Summit Acceptance and opening a new office in Nottingham England.

In 1999 the firm's growth continued. The company stepped up its marketing efforts and was rewarded with significant boosts to its non-interest income and customer base. The next year the company launched The Capital One Place an Internet shopping site. In 2001 the company acquired AmeriFee which provides loans for elective medical and dental surgery; and PeopleFirst Inc. the nation's largest online provider of direct motor vehicle loans.

In response to industry-wide concern over subprime lending Capital One agreed in 2002 to beef up reserves on its subprime portfolio. Also in 2002 the company's UK operations proved profitable for the first time.

The company expanded into banking in 2005 and 2006 with the acquisitions of Hibernia and North Fork Bancorporation respectively. The deals gave it a boost in the banking sector expanding its presence both geographically in the Northeast and in the South and turning the company into one of the top bank holding companies in the US. The $13.2 billion stock-and-cash North Fork deal gave the company more than 300 bank branches in New York New Jersey and Connecticut.

The 2005 purchase of New Orleans-based Hibernia was a stock-and-cash transaction valued at some $5 billion nearly 10% less than the originally agreed-upon price. The transaction was delayed then renegotiated after Hurricane Katrina devastated Hibernia's home city. Hibernia which relocated to Houston adopted the Capital One moniker.

Capital One closed wholesale lender GreenPoint Mortgage Funding acquired as part of its acquisition of North Fork in 2007. The unit suffered from the credit woes that have plagued the subprime mortgage industry.

The company expanded its franchise into the Washington DC market in 2009 by buying Chevy Chase Bank for some $475 million in cash and stock.

EXECUTIVES

Chief Risk Officer, Peter A. Schnall, age 48, $2,350,000 total compensation
EVP General Counsel and Corporate Secretary, John G. Finneran Jr., age 62, $2,300,000 total compensation
Chairman President and CEO, Richard D. (Rich) Fairbank, age 61
EVP and CFO, Gary L. Perlin, age 60, $3,175,000 total compensation
President Capital One Banking, Lynn A. Carter, age 55, $2,625,000 total compensation
EVP Finance and Principal Officer, R. Scott Blackley, age 44
Chief Human Resources Officer, Jory A. Berson, age 41
CIO, Robert M. Alexander, age 47
Managing VP Investor Relations, Jeff Norris
President Commercial Banking, Michael C. Slocum, age 58
President Financial Services, Sanjiv Yajnik, age 55
President Card, Ryan M. Schneider, age 42
President Retail and Direct Banking, Jonathan W. Witter, age 42
Chief Enterprise Services Officer and Chief of Staff to the CEO, Frank G. LaPrade III
Director, Edward R. (Bo) Campbell, age 71
Director, Pierre E. Leroy, age 63
Director, Mayo A. Shattuck III, age 57
Director, Bradford H. (Brad) Warner, age 60
Director, Lewis (Lew) Hay III, age 56
Director, Patrick W. (Pat) Gross, age 67
Director, W. Ronald Dietz, age 69
Director, Ann Fritz Hackett, age 58
Auditors: Ernst&YoungLLP

LOCATIONS

HQ: Capital One Financial Corporation
1680 Capital One Dr., McLean VA 22102-3407
Phone: 703-720-1000 **Fax:** 818-841-4291
Web: www.haskel.com

PRODUCTS/OPERATIONS

2011 Sales

	$ mil.	% of total
Interest		
Loans held for investment including past-due fees	13,774	74
Investment securities	1,137	6
Other	76	-
Noninterest		
Service charges & other customer fees	1,979	11
Interchange fees	1,318	7
Other	372	2
Adjustments	(131)	-
Total	**18,525**	**100**

COMPETITORS

American Express
Bank of America
Citigroup
Credit Acceptance
Discover
GM Financial
HSBC USA
JPMorgan Chase
PNC Financial
Regions Financial
Wells Fargo

HISTORICAL FINANCIALS

Company Type: Public

Income Statement FYE: December 31

	ASSETS ($ mil.)	NET INCOME ($ mil.)	INCOME AS % OF ASSETS	EMPLOYEES
12/11	206,019	3,147	1.5%	31,542
12/10	197,503	2,743	1.4%	27,826
12/09	169,646	883	0.5%	28,000
12/08	165,913	(46)	—	25,800
12/07	150,590	1,570	1.0%	27,000
Annual Growth	8.2%	19.0%	—	4.0%

2011 Year-End Financials

Debt ratio: 19.20%
Return on equity: 10.61%
Cash ($ mil.): 5,496
Current ratio: —
Long-term debt ($ mil.): 39,561
No. of shares (mil.): 459
Dividends
Yield: —
Payout: 2.94%
Market value ($ mil.): 19,451

	STOCK PRICE ($) FY Close	P/E High	P/E Low	PER SHARE ($) Earnings	Dividends	Book Value
12/11	42.29	8	5	6.80	0.00	64.50
12/10	42.56	8	6	6.01	0.20	58.07
12/09	38.34	55	11	0.74	0.53	58.42
12/08	31.89	—	—	(0.21)	1.50	67.92
12/07	47.26	21	11	3.97	0.11	65.16
Annual Growth	(2.7%)	—	—	14.4%	—	(0.3%)

CapitalSource Inc

LOCATIONS

HQ: CapitalSource Inc
633 West 5th Street, 33rd Floor, Los Angeles, CA 90071
Phone: 213 443-7700
Web: www.capitalsource.com

HISTORICAL FINANCIALS

Company Type:

Income Statement FYE: December 31

	ASSETS ($ mil.)	NET INCOME ($ mil.)	INCOME AS % OF ASSETS	EMPLOYEES
12/11	8,300	(52)	—	564
12/10	9,445	(109)	—	625
12/09	12,246	(869)	—	665
12/08	18,414	(222)	—	716
12/07	18,040	176	1.0%	562
Annual Growth	(17.6%)	—	—	0.1%

2011 Year-End Financials

Debt ratio: 15.96%
Return on equity: (-3.30)%
Cash ($ mil.): 458
Current ratio: —
Long-term debt ($ mil.): 1,324
No. of shares (mil.): 256
Dividends
Yield: —
Payout: —
Market value ($ mil.): 1,716

	STOCK PRICE ($) FY Close	P/E High	P/E Low	PER SHARE ($) Earnings	Dividends	Book Value
12/11	6.70	—		(0.17)	0.00	6.15
12/10	7.10	—	—	(0.34)	0.04	6.36
12/09	3.97	—	—	(2.84)	0.04	6.76
12/08	4.62	—	—	(0.89)	1.30	10.04
12/07	17.59	31	15	0.91	2.38	11.70
Annual Growth	(21.4%)	—	—	—	—	(14.9%)

Capstead Mortgage Corp.

Capstead Mortgage is holding steady in a turbulent real estate market. To stay the course the self-managed real estate investment trust (REIT) makes leveraged investments in single-family residential adjustable-rate mortgage securities issued and backed by government agencies such as Fannie Mae Freddie Mac and Ginnie Mae; it occasionally makes limited investments in credit-sensitive commercial mortgage assets as well. The REIT typically funds its investment activities through short-term borrowings or equity offerings. Its portfolio is worth approximately $8.5 billion.

Established in 1985 Capstead is one of the oldest publicly traded mortgage REITs in the US. The company initially was a conduit for nonconforming loans but adopted its current strategy in 2000 and now invests only in securities with implied AAA ratings especially in light of credit troubles of the last few years.

Not that the economy has negatively affected Capstead. Though revenues have been down from prior levels 2011 was the fourth year in a row with earnings above $125 million the best four-year period in the company's history. Lower interest rate spreads and charges taken to reduce exposure to investments in commercial real estate loans have contributed to the dip in Capstead's overall results but the REIT's revenues did begin recovering in 2011 growing 22% to $243.6 million.

The REIT's strategy is to invest in highly rated securities that produce returns over the long haul. Most of the securities in its portfolio are backed by loans with interest rates that reset annually or after an initial fixed-rate period of five years thereby minimizing exposure to interest rate fluctuations. The company believes that its investments are less risky than others because they are guaranteed by government-sponsored entities.

HISTORY

Former Chairman and CEO Ronn Lytle formed Capstead Mortgage (originally called Lomas Mortgage Corp.) and took it public in 1985 to structure and manage mortgage investments. Lytle had previously been an SVP at mortgage banking firm Lomas & Nettleman Co. (later Lomas Mortgage USA) which provided initial funding and some management services.

In 1989 the firm became Capstead Mortgage and acquired Strategic Mortgage Investment. Capstead Mortgage entered the mortgage servicing business in 1992 and acquired Tyler Cabot Mortgage Securities Fund. The company severed its ties to Lomas after 1992.

As market conditions changed the company adjusted its strategy. In 1994 Capstead Mortgage stopped issuing collateralized mortgage obligations and instead began acquiring interest-only mortgage securities. In 1996 the investor reduced its commitment to adjustable-rate mortgage securities and increased its investments in interest-only mortgage securities.

By early 1998 the firm had serviced more than 400000 mortgage loans and developed a mortgage investment portfolio worth more than $10 billion. Capstead Mortgage even ventured into originating mortgages. With its servicing income threatened by prepayments the firm sold its mortgage servicing and writing operations that year.

In 1999 the company began rebuilding its investment portfolio which had lost value due to mortgage investment market conditions and accepted a $51 million cash infusion from privately held real estate investor Fortress Investment in return for a share of Capstead Mortgage's stock. As part of the deal Fortress Investment chairman and CEO Wesley Edens was appointed to the same position in Capstead Mortgage's management.

The following year Capstead Mortgage sold off $1.4 billion in medium-term and fixed-rate securities opting instead to invest in adjustable-rate securities. The company also selected a new board of seven directors four of whom were chosen by Fortress Investment.

In 2003 Mr. Edens resigned and Andrew Jacobs was named as the President and CEO.

Capstead made its first direct investment in real estate in 2002 investing in a portfolio of seven senior living properties in Georgia Florida Ohio Virginia and Texas. It sold one property about five months after the purchase and the rest at the end of 2005.

EXECUTIVES

EVP and Director Residential Mortgage Investments, Robert R. Spears Jr., age 50, $695,500 total compensation
EVP CFO and Secretary, Phillip A. Reinsch, age 51, $532,000 total compensation
President CEO and Director, Andrew F. Jacobs, age 52, $908,000 total compensation
SVP Asset and Liability Management and Treasurer, Michael W. Brown, age 45, $318,500 total compensation
SVP Financial Accounting and Reporting, D. Christopher Sieber
VP Asset and Liability Management, Richard A. Wolf
Chairman, Jack Biegler, age 68
SVP and Director Commercial Mortgage Investments, Anthony R. Page, age 48, $240,000 total compensation
VP Financial Accounting and Reporting, Diane F. Wilson
President CEO and Director, Andrew F. Jacobs, age 52
Director, Paul M. Low, age 81
Director, Michael G. (Mike) O'Neil, age 69
Director, Mark S. Whiting, age 55
Director, Gary Keiser, age 68
Director, Christopher W. (Chris) Mahowald, age 50
Auditors: Ernst&YoungLLP

LOCATIONS

HQ: Capstead Mortgage Corporation
8401 N. Central Expwy. Ste. 800, Dallas TX 75225
Phone: 214-874-2323 **Fax:** 214-874-2398
Web: www.capstead.com

PRODUCTS/OPERATIONS

COMPETITORS

AG Mortgage Investment Trust
Annaly Capital Management
Anworth Mortgage Asset
ARMOUR Residential REIT
Dynex Capital
Impac Mortgage Holdings
JAVELIN Mortgage
MFA Financial
Redwood Trust
Walter Investment Management

HISTORICAL FINANCIALS

Company Type: Public

Income Statement FYE: December 31

	ASSETS ($ mil.)	NET INCOME ($ mil.)	INCOME AS % OF ASSETS	EMPLOYEES
12/11	12,844	160	1.2%	15
12/10	8,999	126	1.4%	16
12/09	8,628	129	1.5%	16
12/08	7,729	125	1.6%	17
12/07	7,208	24	0.3%	15
Annual Growth	15.5%	59.6%	—	0.0%

2011 Year-End Financials

Debt ratio: 0.80%
Return on equity: 12.39%
Cash ($ mil.): 426
Current ratio: —
Long-term debt ($ mil.): 103
No. of shares (mil.): 88
Dividends
Yield: —
Payout: 100.57%
Market value ($ mil.): 1,098

	STOCK PRICE ($) FY Close	P/E High/Low		PER SHARE ($) Earnings	Dividends	Book Value
12/11	12.44	8	6	1.75	0.00	14.64
12/10	12.59	9	7	1.52	1.51	14.62
12/09	13.65	9	6	1.66	2.24	14.63
12/08	10.77	9	4	1.94	2.02	12.04
12/07	13.19	72	41	0.19	0.34	13.74
Annual Growth	(1.5%)	—	—	74.2%	—	1.6%

Cardinal Financial Corp

Cardinal Financial can help you keep out of the red. The holding company owns Cardinal Bank which operates nearly 30 branches in northern Virginia and the Washington DC metropolitan area. Serving commercial and retail customers it offers such deposit options as checking savings and money market accounts; IRAs; and CDs as well as trust services. Commercial real estate loans make up more than 40% of Cardinal Financial's loan portfolio; residential mortgages construction loans business loans and home equity and consumer loans round out the bank's lending activities. Subsidiary Cardinal Wealth Services provides brokerage and investment services through an alliance with Raymond James Financial.

Other units include money manager Wilson/Bennett Capital Management which focuses on value-oriented investing and large-cap stocks and George Mason Mortgage which originates residential mortgages for sale into the secondary market through about 15 branches in Cardinal Bank's market area.

As many of its peers struggled Cardinal Financial reported record earnings for three consecutive years from 2009 to 2011. Net income for the latest period was some $28 million a nearly 35% increase from the previous year. Key factors for the company's results include the relative strength of the Washington DC market (one of the wealthiest regions in the US) and growth in the company's commercial banking and mortgage banking segments.

EXECUTIVES

Regional President Cardinal Bank Washington D.C., Kathleen (Kate) Walsh Carr, age 65
EVP and Chief Compliance Officer Cardinal Financial Corporation and Cardinal Bank, Eleanor D. Schmidt, age 48
EVP Chief Credit Officer and Chief Risk Officer; Regional President Cardinal Bank, Christopher W. Bergstrom, age 52, $185,000 total compensation
Regional President Cardinal Bank, F. Kevin Reynolds, age 52, $155,546 total compensation
Vice Chairman, John H. Rust Jr., age 64
EVP and COO Cardinal Financial Corporation and Cardinal Bank, Alice P. Frazier, age 46
Regional President Cardinal Bank, Kendal E. Carson, age 55, $250,000 total compensation
Chairman and CEO Cardinal Finanial Corporation and Cardinal Bank, Bernard H. Clineburg, age 63, $350,000 total compensation
EVP Real Estate Lending Group Cardinal bank, Dennis M. Griffith, age 63, $154,985 total compensation
EVP Cardinal Bank, Todd W. Hewitt
Chief Accounting Officer and Secretary, Jennifer L. Deacon
EVP and Treasurer Cardinal Financial Corporation and Cardinal Bank, Robert E. (Bob) Bradecamp, age 57
Vice Chairman Cardinal First Mortgage and George Mason Mortgage, D. Gene Merrill, age 66
President George Mason Mortgage, H. Ed Dean, age 41
Assistant Secretary, Janice A. Cross
EVP Cardinal Bank, Guy S. Johnston
CFO George Mason Mortgage, Daniel V. Lawson
EVP and CFO Cardinal Financial Corporation and Cardinal Bank, Mark A. Wendel, age 53, $185,000 total compensation
President Trust and Investment Cardinal Bank; Chief Investment Officer Wilson/Bennett Capital Management, Betsy Piper-Bach, age 59
SVP and Senior Portfolio Manager Wilson/Bennett Capital Management, James S. O'Donnell
Managing Director Cardinal Wealth Services, Steven F. Collins
President Wealth Management Services and EVP Cardinal Bank, John Mockoviak, age 68
VP Portfolio Manager Wilson/Bennett Capital Management, Benjamin V. Hill
Vice Chairman, John H. Rust Jr., age 64
Director, George P. Shafran, age 85
Director, James D. Russo, age 65
Director, J. Hamilton Lambert, age 71
Director, Sidney O. (Sid) Dewberry, age 84
Director, B. G. Beck, age 75
Director, Michael A. Garcia, age 52
Director, Alice M. Starr, age 63
Director, William E. Peterson, age 50
Director, William G. Buck, age 65

Director, Alan G. Merten, age 70
Auditors: KPMGLLP

LOCATIONS

HQ: Cardinal Financial Corporation
8270 Greensboro Dr. Ste. 500, McLean VA 22102
Phone: 703-584-3400 **Fax:** 616-554-8608
Web: www.familychristian.com

PRODUCTS/OPERATIONS

2011 Sales

	$ mil.	% of total
Interest		
Loans	89	65
Investment securities	13	10
Other	0	-
Noninterest		
Mortgage banking activities	20	15
Management fees	3	2
Loan fees	2	2
Investment fees	2	2
Net gains on securities available for sale	2	2
Other	2	2
Total	**124**	**100**

COMPETITORS

Access National
Bank of America
BB&T
Burke & Herbert Bank
Capital One
Millennium Bankshares
PNC Financial
SunTrust
United Bankshares
Virginia Commerce Bancorp

HISTORICAL FINANCIALS

Company Type: Public

Income Statement FYE: December 31

	ASSETS ($ mil.)	NET INCOME ($ mil.)	INCOME AS % OF ASSETS	EMPLOYEES
12/11	2,602	28	1.1%	510
12/10	2,072	18	0.9%	417
12/09	1,976	10	0.5%	368
12/08	1,743	0	0.0%	352
12/07	1,690	4	0.3%	364
Annual Growth	11.4%	58.1%	—	8.8%

2011 Year-End Financials

Debt ratio: 12.13%
Return on equity: 10.86%
Cash ($ mil.): 16
Current ratio: —
Long-term debt ($ mil.): 315
No. of shares (mil.): 29
Dividends
Yield: —
Payout: 12.77%
Market value ($ mil.): 314

	STOCK PRICE ($) FY Close	P/E High/Low		PER SHARE ($) Earnings	Dividends	Book Value
12/11	10.74	13	9	0.94	0.00	8.83
12/10	11.63	19	14	0.62	0.08	7.75
12/09	8.74	24	13	0.37	0.04	7.12
12/08	5.69	965440		0.01	0.04	6.58
12/07	9.32	60	48	0.18	0.04	6.59
Annual Growth	3.6%	—	—	51.2%	—	7.6%

Cardinal Health, Inc.

When your local pharmacy runs low on drugs or supplies it probably calls Cardinal Health. The company is a top distributor of pharmaceuticals and other medical supplies and equipment in the US. Its pharmaceutical division provides supply chain services including branded and generic prescription and OTC drug distribution. It also franchises Medicine Shoppe retail pharmacies. Its medical division parcels out medical laboratory and surgical supplies and provides logistics consulting and data management. Customers include retail pharmacies hospitals nursing homes doctor's offices and other health care businesses.

HISTORY

Cardinal Health harks back to Cardinal Foods a food wholesaler named for Ohio's state bird. In 1971 Robert Walter then 26 and with the ink still fresh on his Harvard MBA acquired Cardinal in a leveraged buyout. He hoped to grow Cardinal by acquisitions but was frustrated when he found that the food distribution industry was already highly consolidated.

In 1980 Cardinal moved into pharmaceuticals distribution with the acquisition of Zanesville. It went public in 1983 as Cardinal Distribution and Walter began looking for more acquisitions. Cardinal soon expanded nationwide by swallowing other distributors. During the 1980s these purchases included two pharmaceuticals distributors headquartered in New York and a Massachusetts-based pharmaceuticals and food distributor.

In 1988 Cardinal sold its food group including Midland Grocery and Mr. Moneysworth to Roundy's and narrowed its focus to pharmaceuticals.

Drug distributors joined the rest of the pharmaceutical industry in its rush toward consolidation during the 1990s. Cardinal's acquisitions in those years included Ohio Valley-Clarksburg (1990 the Mid-Atlantic) Chapman Drug Co. (1991 Tennessee) PRN Services (1993 Michigan) Solomons Co. (1993 Georgia) Humiston-Keeling (1994 Illinois) and Behrens (1994 Texas).

One of Cardinal's most important acquisitions during this period was its cash purchase of Whitmire Distribution in 1994. Formerly Amfac Health Care Whitmire had been a subsidiary of Amfac one of Hawaii's "Big Five" landholders. When Amfac Health Care was spun off in 1988 its president Melburn Whitmire led a management group that acquired a majority interest. When Cardinal bought it Whitmire was the US's #6 drug wholesaler; the purchase bumped Cardinal up to #3. At that time the company changed its name to Cardinal Health and Melburn Whitmire became Cardinal's vice chairman.

In 1995 Cardinal made its biggest acquisition yet when it purchased St. Louis-based Medicine Shoppe International the US's largest franchisor of independent retail pharmacies. Founded by two St. Louis obstetricians in 1970 the Medicine Shoppe had 987 US outlets and 107 abroad at the time of its purchase by Cardinal (for $348 million in stock).

Over the next few years Cardinal continued to grow through acquisitions including automatic drug-dispensing system maker Pyxis pharmaceutical packaging company PCI Services and pharmacy management services company Owen Healthcare (now Cardinal Health Pharmacy Management).

In 1998 however plans to acquire Bergen Brunswig were blocked by the Federal Trade Commission along with rival McKesson's bid to buy AmeriSource Health. (AmeriSource later became AmerisourceBergen after boosting itself into the top drug-distributor ranks by purchasing Bergen Brunswig.) This did not deter Cardinal from its strategy; it acquired surgical equipment distribution company Allegiance Healthcare about a year later.

In 2001 Cardinal purchased pharmaceuticals distributor Bindley Western and it bought contract drug developer Magellan Labs the following year. The company made several acquisitions in 2003 including UK contract manufacturer Intercare Group radiopharmaceuticals firm Syncor International and pharmacy franchiser Medicap. It made a $2 billion purchase of IV medication safety products maker Alaris Medical Systems in 2004; it also purchased drug development consulting firm Beckloff Associates that year.

Founder Robert Walter stepped aside as CEO in 2006 to make room for Kerry Clark to take over the role; the following year Clark assumed the founder's chairman role as well. Also in 2006 the company acquired generic drug distributor ParMed Pharmaceuticals and in 2007 it purchased specialty medication distributor SpecialtyScripts.

The company unloaded its healthcare marketing services unit and its UK Intercare distribution business in 2007. Even more significantly Cardinal Health sold its Pharmaceutical Technologies and Services division which offered drug delivery systems packaging services and development services to The Blackstone Group for $3.3 billion. As part of the deal Cardinal retained two businesses that complement its generic pharmaceutical operations.

In 2007 the company dropped about $1.5 billion on medical equipment manufacturer VIASYS Healthcare. The following year the company added to its infection prevention line by acquiring private health care firm Enturia maker of the ChloraPrep brand line of skin disinfectant products for $490 million. Both acquisitions were integrated into Cardinal Health's medical equipment business. In 2008 Cardinal divested two former VIASYS businesses Tecomet (orthopedic implants) and MedSystems (feeding tubes).

Cardinal also reorganized its operations in 2008 to create a new Clinical and Medical Products division which was later renamed CareFusion. Its pharmaceutical and medical distribution businesses were temporarily lumped into a Healthcare Supply Chain Services division. CareFusion was spun off into a separate publicly traded company in 2009 at which time Clark retired and company executive George Barrett moved into the chairman and CEO roles. The company organized its operations as pharmaceutical and medical divisions.

The company made a large move to simplify its operations in 2009 when it completed a spinoff its medical equipment manufacturing and clinical technologies operations into CareFusion in 2009. After distributing a majority stake (81%) in CareFusion to its shareholders in August 2009; Cardinal Health sold its remaining 19% stake in CareFusion to Morgan Stanley for $706 million the following year. Cardinal Health aimed to increase shareholder value and growth prospects for both Cardinal Health and CareFusion by separating the businesses; it also hoped to improve customer relationships across the board.

The company experienced a dip in revenues and net income in 2010. Further paring efforts that year included the sale of its SpecialtyScripts business (a specialty medication distributor acquired in 2007) and its UK-based Martindale injectable drug manufacturing unit.

On the expansion side Cardinal Health acquired Healthcare Solutions Holding in a deal worth roughly $670 million in 2010. Healthcare Solutions Holding was the parent company for a number of subsidiaries including P4 Pathways and P4 Healthcare that provided data and claims management tools for specialty care doctors payers and drugmakers. The P4 units were integrated into the Cardinal Health Specialty Solutions division.

For instance in 2010 Cardinal Health expanded its retail distribution business by acquiring private wholesaler Kinray for some $1.3 billion. Kinray supplied generic branded and private-label drugs to thousands of independent pharmacies in the eastern US (especially in New York City). The purchase significantly increased Cardinal Health's customer base in the independent retail pharmacy market as well as its presence in the Northeast region.

EXECUTIVES

Chief Human Resources Officer, Carole S. Watkins, age 52
EVP and CIO, Patricia B. (Patty) Morrison, age 52
Chairman and CEO, George S. Barrett, age 57, $1,162,397 total compensation
CFO, Jeffrey W. (Jeff) Henderson, age 47, $700,000 total compensation
CEO Medical Segment, Michael A. (Mike) Lynch, age 51, $600,000 total compensation
President Specialty Group, Meghan M. FitzGerald, age 41
EVP Public Affairs, Shelley Bird
CEO Pharmaceutical Segment, Michael C. (Mike) Kaufmann, age 49, $567,452 total compensation
Chief Customer Officer, Mark Rosenbaum
Chief Legal and Compliance Officer, Craig S. Morford, age 53, $450,000 total compensation
EVP Global Manufacturing and Supply Chain, Mike Duffy
President and General Manager Nuclear and Specialty Pharmacy Services, John Rademacher
EVP Strategy and Corporate Development, Mark R. Blake, age 41
EVP General Counsel and Corporate Secretary, Stephen T. (Steve) Falk, age 47
EVP Sales Officer of Customer Experience, Anthony (Tony) Caprio
President U.S. Pharmaceutical Distribution, Jon Giacomin
President Channel Management Medical Segment, Steve Inacker
SVP Operational Excellence, Bill Owad
SVP Investor Relations, Sally J. Curley
SVP and General Manager P4 Healthcare, Jeffrey Scott
VP Category Leader, Brodie Bauders
President Category Management Medical Segment, Lisa Ashby
Director Investor Relations, Matt Blake
Director, Bruce L. Downey, age 64
Director, David W. Raisbeck, age 62
Director, Gregory B. Kenny, age 59
Director, Carrie S. Cox, age 54
Director, Richard C. (Dick) Notebaert, age 64
Director, Glenn A. Britt, age 63
Director, John F. Finn, age 64
Director, Colleen F. Arnold, age 55
Director, Jean G. Spaulding, age 65
Auditors: Ernst&YoungLLP

LOCATIONS

HQ: Cardinal Health Inc.
7000 Cardinal Place, Dublin OH 43017
Phone: 614-757-5000 **Fax:** 706-576-2812
Web: www.carmike.com

2012 Sales

	$ mil.	% of total
US	105,205	98
Other countries	2,347	2
Total	**107,552**	**100**

PRODUCTS/OPERATIONS

2012 Sales

	$ mil.	% of total
Pharmaceutical	97,925	91
Medical	9,642	9
Adjustments	(15)	-
Total	**107,552**	**100**

Top Customers
CVS Caremark Corp. (22%)
Walgreen Co. (21%)

Selected Acquisitions

2012
- Futuremed Healthcare ($125 million Canadian nursing home medical supplies)

2010
- Healthcare Solutions Holding ($670 million; Ellicott City Maryland; P4 specialty distribution data and claims management tools)
- Kinray Inc. ($1.3 billion; Whitestone New York; pharma distribution in Northeast)
- Yong Yu ($460 million; China drug importation unit of Zuellig Pharma renamed Cardinal Health China)

Selected Subsidiaries Divisions and Brands

Cardinal Health Medical
- Endura (performance apparel/scrubs)
- Presource (OR procedures packs)
- ValueLink (inventory management)

Cardinal Health Pharmaceutical
- Beckloff Associates Inc. (regulatory and scientific consulting)
- Cardinal Health China
- Cardinal Health Canada Inc.
- Cardinal Health Pharmacy Solutions (pharmacy management services)
- Leader Drugstores Inc.
- Medicine Shoppe International Inc.
  - Medicap Pharmacies Incorporated
- Cardinal Health Specialty Solutions (specialty drug distribution and services)
- VitalSource (specialty pharmaceuticals group purchasing)

COMPETITORS

AmerisourceBergen
Ansell
CVS Caremark
Deroyal Industries
Franz Haniel
H. D. Smith Wholesale Drug
Henry Schein
Kimberly-Clark
McKesson
Medical Action Industries
Medline Industries
Molnlycke
Moore Medical
Omnicare
Owens & Minor
PharMerica
PSS World Medical
Quality King
Rite Aid
Thermo Fisher Scientific
Walgreen

HISTORICAL FINANCIALS

Company Type: Public

Income Statement

FYE: June 30

	REVENUE ($ mil.)	NET INCOME ($ mil.)	NET PROFIT MARGIN	EMPLOYEES
06/12	107,552	1,069	1.0%	32,500
06/11	102,644	959	0.9%	31,900
06/10	98,502	642	0.7%	31,200
06/09	99,512	1,151	1.2%	46,500
06/08	91,091	1,300	1.4%	47,600
Annual Growth	4.2%	(4.8%)	—	(9.1%)

2012 Year-End Financials

Debt ratio: 11.93%
Return on equity: 17.12%
Cash ($ mil.): 2,274
Current ratio: 123.54
Long-term debt ($ mil.): 2,418
No. of shares (mil.): 343
Dividends
Yield: —
Payout: 28.84%
Market value ($ mil.): 14,406

	STOCK PRICE ($) FY Close	P/E High/Low		PER SHARE ($) Earnings	Dividends	Book Value
06/12	42.00	15	12	3.06	0.00	18.20
06/11	45.42	17	11	2.72	0.80	16.66
06/10	33.61	20	14	1.77	0.72	14.80
06/09	30.55	18	9	3.18	0.60	24.24
06/08	51.58	20	14	3.57	0.50	21.70
Annual Growth	(5.0%)	—	—	(3.8%)	—	(4.3%)

Carmax Inc.

To the greatest extent possible CarMax helps drivers find late-model used autos. The US's largest specialty used-car retailer buys reconditions and sells cars and light trucks at more than 100 superstores in 25 US states mainly in the Southeast and Midwest; CarMax also operates four new-car franchises and sells older vehicles through about 263000 in-store auctions each year at some 50 stores. CarMax sells vehicles that are generally fewer than six years old with less than 60000 miles. It also sells older cars and trucks with higher mileage via its ValuMax program. The company's website lets customers search CarMax outlets nationwide for a particular model. Its CarMax Auto Finance unit offers financing.

Operations

The company's financing activities conducted through CarMax Auto Finance have been a profit center for the firm which began offering loans to customers at rates of 9% or more. Also with an average selling price of more than $17000 for one of its late-model used vehicles and its "no-haggle" pricing policy CarMax realizes a hefty $2000 gross profit on each sale. Despite sales of more than 415000 vehicles a year CarMax has less than 3% of the late-model used-car market.

Financial Analysis

CarMax's sales hit $10 billion in fiscal 2012 (ends February) up more than 11% vs. the prior year. Net income increased by nearly 9% over the same period. Sales and profit growth have accelerated in recent years as the economy picks up speed. Cash flow however continued its steep three-year decline.

Strategy

CarMax's used-vehicle niche was a buffer for the firm during the deep recession and credit crisis which negatively impacted both new- and used-car sales. Indeed used vehicles account for more than 75% of total sales. While the number of vehicles sold at auction to represent 14% of its revenue new car sales declined for the fifth consecutive year. To make room for more used-car sales CarMax has divested half of its new-car franchises and may sell more. New vehicles account for only 3% of CarMax's retail vehicle unit sales. Historically fast-growing CarMax which increased its store count from 58 locations in 2005 to 100 in 2009 put the brakes on new superstore openings after a dramatic drop in sales. However given the recent improvement in the economy credit markets and retail scene the used-car dealer has begun growing again with eight new locations opened in the past two years and as many as 10 new superstores slated to open in 2012. With a presence more than 50 metropolitan markets nationwide CarMax feels it has plenty of room to grow. Also in the wake of the worst financial crisis since the Great Depression CarMax believes that many newly thrifty consumers will buy a used vehicle when the time comes to replace their current ride.

Ownership

Capital World Investors owns 12% of CarMax.

HISTORY

Looking for new retailing channels to conquer in 1993 Circuit City Stores began test-driving the used-car concept when it opened its first CarMax outlet in Richmond Virginia. Richard Sharp who was named Circuit City's CEO in 1986 became the chairman and CEO for CarMax Group as well.

A pioneer in the car industry CarMax offered computerized shopping play areas for children and no-haggle pricing. Competing car dealers criticized CarMax's TV ads which tarred rivals with a stereotype of sleaze and greed. Some dealers disputed CarMax's low-price claims.

The company extended its geographical reach into North Carolina Georgia and Florida in 1995 and 1996. In 1996 CarMax began selling new cars at an Atlanta store.

No longer riding it as a test-drive Circuit City spun off about 25% of CarMax to the public in 1997. The following year it moved into Illinois.

Also in 1998 CarMax bought a new-car Toyota dealership in Maryland and the multi-make Mauro Auto Mall of Wisconsin. It entered South Carolina that year and added a Georgia Mitsubishi dealership in early 1999. The company acquired two new-car franchises in the competitive Los Angeles market in mid-1999.

In mid-2001 Circuit City reduced its share in CarMax from 75% to about 65% having sold some stock to help remodel the company's electronics stores. Circuit City then spun off CarMax as an independent company in October 2002. President Austin Ligon took the CEO title at that time (Sharp remained chairman).

CarMax opened five superstores but sold four new-car dealerships in 2003.

Ligon retired as CEO in June 2006. He was succeeded by EVP Thomas J. Folliard a 13-year company veteran who was named president CEO and a director of the company.

EXECUTIVES

SVP CarMax Auto Finance, Angela Chattin
VP Store Administration, Fred Wilson
VP Human Resources, Scott A. Rivas
SVP Marketing and Strategy, Joseph S. Kunkel, age 49, $547,409 total compensation
President CEO and Director, Thomas J. (Tom) Folliard, age 47, $850,000 total compensation
EVP and Chief Administrative Officer, Michael K. (Mike) Dolan, age 62, $581,622 total compensation
EVP Finance and Director, Keith D. Browning, age 58, $615,835 total compensation
Chairman, William R. Tiefel, age 78
SVP Service Operations, Edwin J. (Ed) Hill
SVP General Counsel and Secretary, Eric M. Margolin, age 58, $350,000 total compensation
VP and Controller, Kim D. Orcutt
VP Information Technology, David D. Banks
VP Advertising and VP Public Affairs, Laura R. Donahue
VP Information Technology, Barbara B. Harvill
VP Consumer Finance, Robert W. (Rob) Mitchell
VP Real Estate, K. Douglass Moyers
SVP and CIO, Richard M. Smith, age 54, $338,308 total compensation
SVP and CFO, Tom Reedy
VP Business Strategy, Anu Agarwal
Assistant VP Media, John L. Montegari
Assistant VP Sales Operations, Daniel J. (Dan) Johnston
EVP Human Resources and Administration, William D. (Bill) Nash
VP Construction and Facilities, Dan Bickett
Assistant VP CarMax Auto Finance, Michael (Mike) Callahan
Assistant VP Service Operations Human Resources, Edward Fabritiis
Assistant VP and Deputy General Counsel, Michelle Halasz
Assistant VP Auction Services and Buyer Development, Joseph (Joe) Wilson
Assistant VP Process Engineering, Gary Sheehan
Assistant VP and Assistant Controller, Veronica Hinckle
VP Business Operations, Lynn Mussatt
VP CarMax Auto Finance, John Daniels
VP Human Resource Development, Roberta Douma
VP Marketing, Rob Sorenson
VP Investor Relations, Katharine Kenny
Assistant VP Information Technology, Troy Downs
Assistant VP Procurement, Dodie Fix
Assistant VP Human Resources, Chad Kulas
Assistant VP Human Resources, Kim Ross
Assistant VP Sales Development, Brian Stone
Assistant VP and Assistant Controller, Natalie Wyatt
Assistant VP Logistics, Mark Adams
Director Selection and Recruiting, Pam Hill
EVP Stores, William C. (Cliff) Wood Jr., age 45
Manager Investor Relations, Celeste Gunter
Assistant VP and Deputy General Counsel, Diane Cafritz
Director Public Affairs and Communication, Trina Lee
Manager Public Relations, Britt Farrar
Public Relations, Elia Imler
Foundation and Community Affairs Coordinator, Michelle Ellwood
Director, Rakesh Gangwal, age 58
Director, Thomas G. (Tom) Stemberg, age 63
President CEO and Director, Thomas J. (Tom) Folliard, age 47
EVP Finance and Director, Keith D. Browning, age 58
Director, Jeffrey E. Garten, age 65
Director, Beth A. Stewart, age 55
Director, Shira D. Goodman, age 51
Director, Ronald E. (Ron) Blaylock, age 52
Director, W. Robert (Bob) Grafton, age 71
Director, Vivian M. Stephenson, age 75
Director, Edgar H. (Ed) Grubb, age 72
Director, Mitchell D. Steenrod
Auditors: KPMGLLP

LOCATIONS

HQ: Carmax Inc.
12800 Tuckahoe Creek Parkway, Richmond, VA 23238
Phone: 804 747-0422
Web: www.carmax.com

2012 Stores

	No.
California	14
Texas	12
Florida	10
North	8
Virginia	8
Georgia	6
Illinois	6
Tennessee	5
Maryland	4
Ohio	4
Arizona	3
South	3
Wisconsin	3
Alabama	2
Connecticut	2
Indiana	2
Kansas	2
Kentucky	2
Nevada	2
Oklahoma	2
Colorado	1
Louisiana	1
Massachusetts	1
Mississippi	1
Missouri	1
Nebraska	1
New	1
Utah	1
Total	**108**

PRODUCTS/OPERATIONS

2012 Sales

	$ mil.	% of total
Used vehicles	7,826	78
Wholesale vehicles	1,721	17
New vehicles	200	2
Other sales & revenue	254	3
Total	**10,003**	**100**

COMPETITORS

Asbury Automotive
AutoNation
AutoTrader
Brown Automotive
Danner Company
DriveTime Automotive
Ed Morse Auto
Group 1 Automotive
Hendrick Automotive
Holman Enterprises
Internet Brands
JM Family Enterprises
Manheim
McCombs Enterprises
Penske Automotive Group
Serra Automotive
Sonic Automotive

HISTORICAL FINANCIALS

Company Type: Public

Income Statement FYE: February 29

	REVENUE ($ mil.)	NET INCOME ($ mil.)	NET PROFIT MARGIN	EMPLOYEES
02/12	10,003	413	4.1%	16,460
02/11	8,975	380	4.2%	15,565
02/10	7,470	281	3.8%	13,439
02/09	6,973	59	0.8%	13,035
02/08	8,199	182	2.2%	15,637
Annual Growth	5.1%	22.8%	—	1.3%

2012 Year-End Financials

Debt ratio: 60.65%
Return on equity: 15.48%
Cash ($ mil.): 442
Current ratio: 286.77
Long-term debt ($ mil.): 4,863
No. of shares (mil.): 227
Dividends
Yield: —
Payout: —
Market value ($ mil.): 6,970

	STOCK PRICE ($) FY Close	P/E High	P/E Low	PER SHARE ($) Earnings	Dividends	Book Value
02/12	30.69	19	13	1.79	0.00	11.77
02/11	35.37	22	11	1.67	0.00	10.15
02/10	20.19	19	7	1.26	0.00	8.67
02/09	9.43	80	23	0.27	0.00	7.23
02/08	18.36	65	20	0.83	0.00	6.81
Annual Growth	13.7%	—	—	21.2%	—	14.7%

Casey's General Stores, Inc.

Casey's General Stores makes sure that small towns in the Midwest get their fill of convenient shopping. It operates about 1700 company-owned convenience stores mostly in Illinois Iowa and Missouri but also in a dozen states overall in the Midwest all within about 500 miles of its headquarters and distribution center. Towns with 5000 people or fewer where rent is low are home to about 60% of the chain's stores. Casey's sells lots of gasoline (more than 70% of total sales) as well as beverages groceries and fresh prepared foods including from-scratch pizza donuts and hot sandwiches. It also sells tobacco products automotive goods and other nonfood items such as ammunition and photo supplies.

Financial Analysis

Fiscal 2012 (ends April) sales at Casey's General Stores increased by 24% vs. the prior year approaching $7 billion. Gasoline sales accounted for just more than $5 billion of that. The sharp rise was primarily due to a 20% increase in average gas prices as well as the number of gallons sold. Beyond the pump increasing same-store sales of groceries prepared foods and other in-store items boosted sales as did the expansion of the chain's pizza delivery service and the addition of about 65 new stores. Net income increased by about 23% over the same period. However rising gas prices put pressure on gasoline profit margins as the company tried to keep prices competitive to retain customers.

Strategy

Casey's seeks to meet the needs of its small town clientele by combining the features of a general store and convenience store. The stores which offer more than 3000 food and nonfood products carry a broader selection than a typical convenience store. It addition to low-margin food and grocery items the stores offer lots of prepared foods which sell at higher markups. Indeed while sales of products other than gasoline account for about 30% of its total revenue they contribute nearly three-quarters of the chain's gross profit. To make more room for food the convenience store operator has been opening larger (about 3800 sq. ft.) "O-shaped" stores. The format (launched in 2008)devotes additional space to food and beverages allowing for a wider selection of beer energy drinks and other high-margin items. Still gasoline sales account for a growing share of the company's revenue: 73% in fiscal 2012 up from about 68% two years ago. Over the same period however the gross profit on gas has declined from 5.6% in 2010 to just 4.4% in 2012. Volatile gas prices result in pressure to sell gas a competitive prices putting pressure on margins. Acquisitive Casey's added about 35 stores through acquisitions and built another 30 locations in 2012. More recently Casey's recently broke ground on its first stores in Kentucky and Tennessee.

Mergers & Acquisitions

The company's annual goal is to increase its store count by 4% to 6%. To that end Casey's has been expanding in existing markets and broadening its presence by acquiring other Midwestern chains. During fiscal 2012 the company acquired 35 stores including 22 locations most in rural Iowa from rival Kum & Go. Previously it bought five convenience stores from rival QuikTrip located in the Springfield Missouri metropolitan area. Also in 2011 Casey's purchased about a dozen NuMart convenience stores in Minnesota from NuWay Co-operative and it completed the acquisition of about 45 stores in Nebraska Kansas and Oklahoma (a new market) from Kabredlo's.

HISTORY

Donald Lamberti who had run his family's grocery store founded Casey's General Stores with Kurvin C. "K. C." Fish. The men converted a gas station into the first Casey's convenience store in 1968. To expand and build brand recognition the company began franchising outlets two years later. By focusing on small towns the company avoided competition and expensive building and property costs. A significant growth spurt in 1979 took Casey's from 119 stores to 226. Fish retired the following year.

The company went public in 1983 and began to curtail its franchising efforts in favor of more profitable company-owned stores (at the time there were about 190 company-owned stores and about 215 franchised outlets; today only about 130 are franchised). Casey's introduced carry-out pizza in 1984 and sandwiches two years later. Fueled by another stock offering in 1985 the company continued to grow quickly. It opened its 500th store that year and by 1990 had stores in eight states.

By 1996 Casey's had 1000 stores and it continued to add about 70 stores a year. After 30 years at the helm in 1998 Lamberti retired as CEO; president Ronald Lamb took his place. In 2000 Casey's continued to expand at a rate of about 85 stores per year.

The company was accused of charging up to $5 a gallon for gas at 25 Casey's stores in Illinois on September 11 2001 the day of terrorist attacks in New York City and Washington DC. Casey's agreed the next month to pay $25000 to the Red Cross and $5000 to the state of Illinois. It also agreed to refund customers who were overcharged for gas. In fiscal 2002 the company opened more than 50 company-owned stores.

In fiscal 2003 the company built 15 new stores and purchased another. In April 2003 co-founder Lamberti retired from the company and Ronald Lamb added chairman to his title in May.

In early 2006 the company acquired 51 convenience stores in Nebraska from Gas 'N Shop for about $29 million. In June COO Robert Myers was named CEO of Casey's succeeding Ronald Lamb who held onto the chairman's title. In October the company acquired 33 HandiMart convenience stores in Iowa from Nordstrom Oil for about $63 million.

Prior to those deals Casey's acquired about a dozen convenience stores in fiscal 2008 and about 50 stores including 30-plus HandiMart convenience stores and a truck stop in Iowa in 2007.

In 2008 the company rolled out a new store format. Casey's first "O-shaped" store opened in Des Moines Iowa. The format is larger (about 3800 sq. ft.) than typical Casey's stores and devotes more space to food and beverages offering plenty of room for beer energy drinks and other high-margin items. The cashier is positioned in the center of the store.

In March 2009 Casey's ended its franchising program begun in the 1970s. (At its peak Casey's had a total of 230 franchised stores.) As a result all of its convenience stores are and will be company-owned going forward. Also in 2009 Casey's acquired about 15 stores including nine Bullseye locations in Missouri and the three-store Green Lantern chain in Kansas.

In 2010 Casey's bought half a dozen Short Stop convenience stores in Iowa from J.D. Carpenter Companies 10 Holiday convenience stores in Iowa and Nebraska from Holiday Companies and about 20 On the Way locations in Illinois from Harper Oil. In October Casey's completed its acquisition of six Short Stop convenience stores in Iowa (formerly owned by J.D. Carpenter Companies) and 19 On The Way convenience stores in Illinois (owned by Harper Oil). Also that year Casey's became the target of a hostile takeover by Canada's Alimentation Couche-Tard which ultimately abandoned its takeover attempt late in the year.

EXECUTIVES

SVP and CFO, William J. (Bill) Walljasper, age 47, $300,000 total compensation
VP Marketing, Michael R. (Mike) Richardson, $195,000 total compensation
President CEO and Director, Robert J. (Bob) Myers, age 65, $660,000 total compensation
COO, Terry W. Handley, age 52, $365,000 total compensation
VP Support Services, Hal D. Brown
SVP Logistics and Acquisitions, Sam J. Billmeyer, age 55, $300,000 total compensation
VP Food Services, Darryl F. Bacon
SVP Corporate General Counsel and Human Resources, Julie L. Jackowski
VP and Treasurer, Russell D. Sukut
VP and Corporate Counsel, Eli J. Wirtz
VP Store Operations, Robert C. Ford
VP Transportation and Distribution, Jay F. Blair
VP Finance and Corporate Secretary, Brian J. Johnson
President CEO and Director, Robert J. (Bob) Myers, age 65
Director, Kenneth H. Haynie, age 79
Director, H. Lynn Horak, age 66
Director, Diane C. Bridgewater, age 49
Director, Johnny A Danos, age 72
Director, Jeffrey M. (Jeff) Lamberti, age 49
Director, Richard A. Wilkey, age 72
Auditors: KPMGLLP

LOCATIONS

HQ: Casey' s General Stores Inc.
1 Convenience Blvd., Ankeny IA 50021
Phone: 515-965-6100 **Fax:** 515-965-6160
Web: www.caseys.com

2012 Stores

	No.
Iowa	453
Illinois	400
Missouri	299
Kansas	133
Nebraska	126
Minnesota	98
Indiana	66
South	37
Wisconsin	10
Arkansas	1
Oklahoma	1
Total	**1,699**

PRODUCTS/OPERATIONS

2012 Sales

	$ mil.	% of total
Gasoline	5,092	73
Grocery & other merchandise	1,365	20
Prepared food & fountain	499	7
Other	30	-
Total	**6,987**	**100**

Selected Merchandise

Ammunition
Automotive products
Beverages
Food including fresh foods
Gasoline (self-service)
Health and beauty aids
Housewares
Pet products
Photo supplies
School supplies
Tobacco products

COMPETITORS

7-Eleven
Chevron
Couche-Tard
CVS Caremark
Exxon Mobil
Holiday Companies
Hy-Vee
IGA
Krause Gentle
Kroger
Kwik Trip
Martin & Bayley
McDonald's
Pizza Hut
QuikTrip
Royal Dutch Shell
Walgreen

HISTORICAL FINANCIALS

Company Type: Public

Income Statement FYE: April 30

	REVENUE ($ mil.)	NET INCOME ($ mil.)	NET PROFIT MARGIN	EMPLOYEES
04/12	6,987	116	1.7%	24,726
04/11	5,635	94	1.7%	22,157
04/10	4,637	116	2.5%	19,434
04/09	4,687	85	1.8%	18,780
04/08	4,827	84	1.8%	17,983
Annual Growth	9.7%	8.3%	—	8.3%

2012 Year-End Financials

Debt ratio: 38.24%
Return on equity: 23.08%
Cash ($ mil.): 55
Current ratio: 91.08
Long-term debt ($ mil.): 667
No. of shares (mil.): 38
Dividends
Yield: 1.07%
Payout: 19.74%
Market value ($ mil.): 2,149

	STOCK PRICE ($) FY Close	P/E High/Low		PER SHARE ($) Earnings	Dividends	Book Value
04/12	56.35	19	13	3.04	0.60	13.27
04/11	39.03	20	16	2.22	0.00	10.64
04/10	38.63	17	11	2.29	0.34	16.19
04/09	26.61	18	11	1.68	0.30	14.18
04/08	22.13	19	13	1.67	0.26	12.76
Annual Growth	26.3%	—	—	16.2%	23.3%	1.0%

Caterpillar Inc.

Caterpillars may crawl but this company isn't fuzzy about earthmoving machinery and agricultural equipment. Considered #1 in the world Caterpillar (Cat) makes construction and mining machinery; diesel and natural gas engines; underground mining equipment; industrial gas turbines; and electrical power generation systems. It operates plants worldwide and sells equipment through some 3500 offices in more than 180 countries. It also provides rental services through 1300-plus outlets and offers financing and insurance for dealers and customers. Caterpillar Power Ventures invests in power projects that use Caterpillar power generation equipment. Cat Logistics offers supply chain services.

HISTORY

In 1904 in Stockton California combine maker Benjamin Holt modified the farming tractor by substituting a gas engine for steam and replacing iron wheels with crawler tracks. This improved the tractor's mobility over dirt.

The British adapted the "caterpillar" (Holt's nickname for the tractor) design to the armored tank in 1915. Following WWI the US Army donated tanks to local governments for construction work. The caterpillar's efficiency spurred the development of earthmoving and construction equipment.

Holt merged with Best Tractor in 1925. The company renamed Caterpillar moved to Peoria Illinois in 1928. Cat expanded into foreign markets in the 1930s and phased out combine production to focus on construction and road-building equipment.

Sales volume more than tripled during WWII when Cat supplied the military with earthmoving equipment. Returning GIs touted Cat durability and quality and high demand continued. Cat held a solid first place in the industry far ahead of #2 International Harvester.

Moving beyond US borders Cat established its first overseas plant in the UK (1951). In 1963 it entered a joint venture with Japanese industrial titan Mitsubishi. Cat bought Solar Turbines (gas turbine engines) in 1981. Fifty consecutive years of profits ended however when Cat ran up $953 million in losses between 1982 and 1984 as equipment demand fell and foreign competition intensified. Cat doubled its product line between 1984 and 1989 and shifted production toward smaller equipment.

In 1990 CEO Donald Fites reorganized Cat along product lines. The next year the company clashed with the UAW over wage and health benefits. A strike resulted and Cat reported its first annual loss since 1984. Most of the striking workers returned to work without a contract by mid-1992.

The firm completed a six-year $1.8 billion modernization program in 1993 that automated many of its plants. That investment benefited the company when almost two-thirds of Cat's UAW employees at eight plants in Colorado Illinois and Pennsylvania went on strike in 1994. Company management hired replacement workers and used its foreign factories to help fill orders. In 1995 after two years of record earnings at Cat the UAW called off the strike. Cat set up a holding company Caterpillar China Investment Co. Ltd. in 1996 for joint ventures in China.

In 1998 Cat and the UAW (with federal mediation) hammered out their first contract agreement in more than six years. That year Cat paid $1.33 billion for LucasVarity's UK-based Perkins Engines expanding its capacity to produce small and midsize diesel engines.

Fites retired in 1999; vice chairman Glen Barton succeeded him. Cat cut back its workforce and production after slowdowns in the agricultural mining and oil exploration industries reduced machinery orders. The company sold subsidiary Kato Engineering (electric generators) to Emerson Electric in exchange for Emerson's stake in F.G. Wilson a generator-set packaging firm.

In 2000 Cat expanded the range of its marine power systems to include engines below 300 bhp with its purchase of family-owned Sabre Engines Ltd. a UK maker of high-performance marine diesel engines. Late that year the company announced an alliance with DaimlerChrysler (now Daimler AG) to make and market medium-duty engines worldwide. In 2001 Caterpillar announced a restructuring that involved facility consolidation the retirement of several executives and the sale of the high-tech MT series tractor line to AGCO Corp. A deal to sell the company's rubber-belted track component business to Canada-based Camoplast was completed in late 2002.

Caterpillar received certification by the US Environmental Protection Agency in early 2003 for its ACERT-equipped engine (Advanced Combustion Emission Reduction Technology) for the North American trucking bus construction and mining industries. The technology also positioned Caterpillar to meet emissions regulations for both on- and off-highway engines. That same year the company inked a deal with diversified global resources company BHP Billiton to supply an estimated $1.5 billion in equipment and support to its operations. Additionally Caterpillar and Eaton Corporation formed joint venture Intelligent Switchgear Organization LLC (Georgia) to produce Cat-branded electrical distribution switching products with Eaton controlling 51% of the venture and Caterpillar 49%.

Jim Owens became CEO in early 2004 and Caterpillar increased its stake in A.S.V. Inc. (rubber-tracked all-purpose crawlers and undercarriages accessories and attachments) to roughly 22%. Later that year Caterpillar acquired Swiss industrial gas turbine packager Turbomach S.A. In the same year RV manufacturer Fleetwood Enterprises announced that it would equip all of its diesel-powered vehicles with Caterpillar engines by the end of 2005. Williams Technology a transmission remanufacturing company was acquired by Caterpillar from Remy International in late 2004.

Caterpillar bought Progress Rail in early 2004 from One Equity Partners for about $1 billion in cash Caterpillar stock and the assumption of long-term debt. Also in 2006 Caterpillar agreed to acquire the rail and non-Cat engine component remanufacturing business of O.E.M. Remanufacturing Company a subsidiary of Caterpillar distributor Finning. The following year it completed the acquisition of French company Eurenov which greatly enhanced its remanufacturing unit's reach into the European market. In 2008 Caterpillar acquired MGE Equipamentos & Servicos Ferroviarios. The Brazil-based locomotive component manufacturer became part of Caterpillar's Progress Rail Services unit.

Despite the depth and breadth of its manufacturing reach Caterpillar has been hurt by the decrease in infrastructure activity due to the global economic crisis in 2008 and 2009. Its sales in 2009 were beaten down by 37% over 2008 –the worst erosion in single year sales since the 1940s. The company offset the decline by squeezing manufacturing costs by about $2 billion from 2008 levels. Caterpillar also countered rising expenses from retiree pension health care and related benefits moving the funded status from 61% in 2008 to 76% by year-end 2009.

Further cost-cutting efforts included the training of the company trimmed executive pay by half and salaried employee pay by as much as 15%. Workforce reductions included cuts at five plants in Illinois Indiana and Georgia dropping 2500 workers. Caterpillar eliminated more than 22000 workers from its payroll a reduction in force of around 20%.

In mid-2010 outgoing board chairman and CEO James Owens' retired. Doug Oberhelman a Caterpillar veteran assumed the CEO position. Oberhelman who served as CFO and a group president of the company has a background in international business primarily in Asia and Latin America regions.

Caterpillar scored in mid-2011 with its $8.8 billion acquisition of Wisconsin-based Bucyrus International. Caterpillar integrated Bucyrus into its newly created Mining Equipment Group comprising Integrated Manufacturing Operations Division (global manufacturing operations); Mining Sales and Marketing; and Mining Products (mining product strategy development and product design). Bucyrus products assumed the Caterpillar trade name.

EXECUTIVES

VP and Chief Procurement Officer, Frank J. Crespo
Group President Customer and Dealer Support, Stuart L. Levenick, age 59, $729,996 total compensation
Chairman and CEO, Douglas R. (Doug) Oberhelman, age 59, $729,996 total compensation
VP Customer Services Support Division, Stephen A. (Steve) Gosselin
VP Large Power Systems & Growth Markets Division, Gary A. Stroup
Group President Resource Industries, Steven H. Wunning, age 61, $729,996 total compensation
Group President, Gerard R. Vittecoq, age 63, $895,957 total compensation
Construction Industries Group President, Edward J. (Ed) Rapp, age 54, $584,004 total compensation
Group President, Richard P. (Rich) Lavin, age 59, $584,004 total compensation
SVP Legal Services Division and Chief Legal Officer, James B. (Jim) Buda, age 64
VP; Chairman Caterpillar Japan, Ali M. Bahaj
VP Diversified Products Division, William F. (Bill) Springer
VP Europe South America Operations Division, Cristiano V. (Chris) Schena
Assistant Treasurer, Robin D. Beran
Assistant Secretary, Laurie J. Huxtable
VP and President and CEO Progress Rail Services, William P. (Billy) Ainsworth, age 56
Corporate Public Affairs, Bridget Young
Corporate Public Affairs, Rusty Dunn
VP and President and CEO Caterpillar Financial Services, Kent M. Adams
Treasurer, Edward J. (Ed) Scott
VP Building Construction Products Division, Mary H. Bell, age 51
VP Advanced Components and Systems Division, Hans A. Haefeli
VP and CIO, John S. Heller
VP Global Mining Division, Christopher C. Curfman
VP Construction Industries Sales & Marketing, Paolo Fellin
VP Electric Power Division, William J. Rohner
VP Large Power Systems and Growth Markets Division (LPSD), Steven L. (Steve) Fisher
VP Excavation Division, Gary A. Stampanato, age 55
Country Manager UK and VP Industrial Power Systems and Growth Markets, Tana L. Utley, age 48
VP and Chairman and President Caterpillar Logistics Services, Stephen P. (Steve) Larson
VP Earthmoving Division, Thomas J. (Tom) Bluth
VP Marine and Petroleum Power Division, Richard J. Case
Corporate Controller and Chief Accounting Officer, Jananne A. Copeland, age 49
CFO and President Corporate Services, Bradley M. Halverson, age 51
CTO and VP Product Development & Global Technology, Gwenne A. Henricks
VP Asia Pacific Distribution Services Division, Robert B. (Rob) Charter, age 49
VP Remanufacturing and Components Division, Gregory S. (Greg) Folley, age 53
VP Integrated Manufacturing Operations Division, David P. Bozeman, age 44
Chief Ethics and Compliance Officer, Christopher C. Spears
President Energy & Power Systems, D. James (Jim) Umpleby
VP and Chief HR Officer, Kimberly S. (Kim) Hauer
VP Americas Distribution Services Division, William E. (Bill) Finerty
Corporate Public Affairs, Kate Kenny
Corporate Public Affairs, Dan Bozung
Chief Corporate Spokesperson, Jim Dugan
VP Marine and Petroleum Power Division, Tom Frake
President Caterpillar Japan, Noriyuki Takeuchi
VP Europe South America Operations Division, Mark Sweeney
VP China Operations, Olivia Chen
Director, Jesse J. Greene Jr.
Director, Miles D. White, age 57
Director, John T. Dillon, age 72
Director, David R. Goode, age 70
Director, William A. Osborn, age 64
Director, Edward B. (Ed) Rust Jr., age 61
Director, Peter A. Magowan, age 70
Director, David L. (Dave) Calhoun, age 55
Director, W. Frank Blount, age 72
Director, Lord Charles D. Powell, age 70
Director, Eugene V. Fife, age 72
Director, Prof Susan C. Schwab, age 57
Director, John R. Brazil, age 66
Director, Juan Gallardo, age 64
Director, Joshua I. Smith, age 71
Director, Daniel M. Dickinson, age 50
Director, Dennis A. Muilenburg, age 48
Director, Jon M. Huntsman Jr., age 51
Auditors: PricewaterhouseCoopersLLP

LOCATIONS

HQ: Caterpillar Inc.
100 NE Adams St., Peoria IL 61629
Phone: 309-675-1000 **Fax:** 309-675-1182
Web: www.caterpillar.com

2011 Sales

	$ mil.	% of total
North America	21,733	36
Asia/Pacific	14,993	25
Europe/Africa/Middle East	14,739	25
Latin America	8,673	14
Total	**60,138**	**100**

PRODUCTS/OPERATIONS

2011 Sales

	$ mil.	% of total
Machinery & Power Systems		
Power Systems	20,114	33
Construction Industries	19,667	33
Resource Industries	15,629	26
Other	2,021	3
Corporate items & eliminations (39)		
Financial products	3,003	5
Corporate items & eliminations (257)		
Total	**60,138**	**100**

Selected Products

Engines
- Engines for Caterpillar machinery
- Engines for electric power generation systems
- Engines for marine petroleum construction industrial and agricultural applications
- Engines for on-highway trucks and locomotives

Financing and insurance services
- Financing to customers and dealers
- Insurance to customers and dealers

Machinery
- Articulated trucks
- Backhoe loaders
- Log loaders
- Log skidders
- Mining shovels
- Motor graders
- Off-highway trucks
- Paving products
- Pipelayers
- Related parts
- Skid steer loaders
- Telescopic handlers
- Track and wheel excavators
- Track and wheel loaders
- Track and wheel tractors
- Wheel tractor-scrapers

Mining
- Surface mining
  - Draglines
  - Drills
  - Electric mining shovels
  - Highwall miners
  - Hydraulic excavators
  - Off-highway haul trucks
- Underground mining
  - Longwall equipmentArmored face conveyorsAutomated plow systemsHydraulic roof supportsLongwall shearers
  - Room and pillar miningContinuous haulage systemsContinuous minersFeeder breakersUnderground haulage and utility vehicles

Selected Brands

Anchor Coupling
AsiaTrak
Balderson
Barber-Greene
Cat Financial
Cat Logistics
Cat Reman
Cat Rental Store
FG Wilson
MaK
Olympian
Perkins
Prentice
Progress Rail
Solar Turbines
Turbomach
Turner Powertrain Systems
Verachtert
Xpart

COMPETITORS

Atlas Copco
Bombardier
Charles Machine Works
CNH Global
Cummins
Deere
Detroit Diesel
DHL
Doosan Infracore
Dresser Inc.
GE
GENCO Distribution System
Generac Holdings
Hitachi Construction Machinery
J C Bamford Excavators
Joy Mining
Kawasaki Heavy Industries
Komatsu
Kubota
Kuehne + Nagel
MAN
Menlo Worldwide
Mitsubishi Heavy Industries
Multiquip
Navistar International
Nortrak
Rolls-Royce
Sandvik
Siemens Energy
Sumitomo Heavy Industries
Terex
Tognum
UPS Supply Chain Solutions
Volvo
Wartsila
Wells Fargo Equipment Finance
Woods Equipment

HISTORICAL FINANCIALS

Company Type: Public

Income Statement FYE: December 31

	REVENUE ($ mil.)	NET INCOME ($ mil.)	NET PROFIT MARGIN	EMPLOYEES
12/11	60,138	4,928	8.2%	125,099
12/10	42,588	2,700	6.3%	104,490
12/09	32,396	895	2.8%	93,813
12/08	51,324	3,557	6.9%	112,887
12/07	44,958	3,541	7.9%	101,333
Annual Growth	7.5%	8.6%	—	5.4%

2011 Year-End Financials

Debt ratio: 42.47%
Return on equity: 38.25%
Cash ($ mil.): 3,057
Current ratio: 133.50
Long-term debt ($ mil.): 24,944
No. of shares (mil.): 647
Dividends
Yield: —
Payout: 24.32%
Market value ($ mil.): 58,667

	STOCK PRICE ($) FY Close	P/E High/Low		PER SHARE ($) Earnings	Dividends	Book Value
12/11	90.60	15	9	7.40	0.00	19.90
12/10	93.66	22	12	4.15	1.72	16.94
12/09	56.99	42	15	1.43	1.68	13.99
12/08	44.67	15	6	5.66	1.56	10.12
12/07	72.56	16	10	5.37	1.32	14.24
Annual Growth	5.7%	—	—	8.3%	—	8.7%

Cathay General Bancorp

Cathay General Bancorp is the holding company for Cathay Bank which mainly serves Chinese and Vietnamese communities from some 30 branches in California and about 20 more in Illinois New Jersey New York Massachusetts Washington and Texas. It also has a branch in Hong Kong and offices in Shanghai and Taipei. Catering to small businesses and low- to middle-income consumers the bank offers standard deposit services and loans. Commercial mortgages account for more than half of the bank's portfolio; business loans comprise more than 20%. The bank's Cathay Wealth Management unit offers online stock trading mutual funds and other investment products and services through an agreement with PrimeVest.

Although revenues remained rather steady the company reported a net loss in 2009 mainly attributable to an increase in credit losses. Many of Cathay General's loans are secured by real estate in California and the downturn in the real estate market hurt the company as the value of the collateral underlying the loans plummeted. In 2010 the company entered into a memorandum of understanding with the FDIC to reduce its concentration of commercial real estate loans improve its capital ratios reduce overall risk and strengthen asset quality. The moves helped the company to cut its losses that year even though revenues were down.

Despite its troubles in the loan department Cathay General has been growing deposits. It has also expanded geographically beyond its home state of California mainly through acquisitions. The company bought New York's Great Eastern Bank and Illinois-based New Asia Bancorp in 2006 while the 2007 purchase of United Heritage Bank gave the company its first branch in New Jersey. However as part of its agreement with the FDIC Cathay General is restricted from opening new branches or entering new business lines until the memorandum is lifted.

EXECUTIVES

EVP and Manager Corporate Commercial Real Estate and Construction Loan Cathay Bank, Eddie Chang
Vice Chairman and COO Cathay General Bancorp and Cathay Bank, Peter Wu, age 63, $438,000 total compensation
EVP and Chief Risk Officer Cathay Bank, Irwin Wong, age 63, $241,000 total compensation
EVP and Director; SEVP Chief Lending Officer and Director Cathay Bank; Trustee and VP Cathay Real Estate Investment Trust, Anthony M. Tang, age 58, $313,000 total compensation
Chairman President and CEO Cathay General Bancorp and Cathay Bank, Dunson K. Cheng, age 67, $1,000,000 total compensation
SVP and Director Business Development Cathay Bank, Shu-Yuan Lai
EVP CFO and Treasurer Cathay General Bancorp; EVP and CFO Cathay Bank; VP and CFO Cathay Real Estate Investment Trust, Heng W. Chen, age 59, $312,000 total compensation
EVP and Assistant to Chief Lending Officer Cathay Bank, James P. Lin
SVP and District Administrator Southern California Region II Cathay Bank, Alex Lee
SVP General Counsel and Secretary Cathay General Bancorp and Cathay Bank, Perry P. Oei, age 49
EVP and General Manager East and Midwest Region Cathay Bank, Pin Tai
SVP and District Administrator Southern California Region I Cathay Bank, Wilson Tang
EVP and Chief Credit Officer Cathay Bank, Kim R. Bingham, age 55
SVP and Director Human Resources Cathay Bank, Jennifer Laforcarde
SVP and Manager Corporate Lending Northern California Region Cathay Bank, Dominic Li
SVP and Operations Administrator Cathay Bank, Olivia DeRossi
SVP and Chief Risk Officer Cathay Bank, Jose Jiminez
SVP and Treasurer Cathay Bank, Dennis Kwok
SVP and District Administrator Southern California Region III Cathay Bank, Shu Lee
SVP and Manager Multi-Cultural Corporate Lending Group Cathay Bank, Esther Wee
SVP and District Administrator New York and New Jersey Regions Cathay Bank, Veronica Tsang
SVP and CIO Cathay Bank, Robert Romero
SVP Loan Officer and Manager Other Real Estate Owned Department Cahthay Bank, Gary Cook
SVP and Manager Corporate Lending New York and New Jersey Regions Cathay Bank, Peggy Chan
SVP and Assistant Manager Corporate Commercial Real Estate and Construction Lending Cathay Bank, Angela Hui
SVP and Bank Secrecy Act Officer Cathay Bank, Marisa DeRojas
Vice Chairman and COO Cathay General Bancorp and Cathay Bank, Peter Wu, age 63
EVP and Director; SEVP Chief Lending Officer and Director Cathay Bank; Trustee and VP Cathay Real Estate Investment Trust, Anthony M. Tang, age 58
Director, Kelly L. Chan, age 65
Director, Joseph C. H. Poon, age 65
Director, Michael M. Y. Chang, age 74
Director, Patrick S. D. Lee, age 77
Director, Thomas G. Tartaglia, age 88
Director, Thomas C. T. Chiu, age 64
Director, Ting Y. Liu, age 75
Director, Nelson Chung, age 59
Auditors: KPMGLLP

LOCATIONS

HQ: Cathay General Bancorp
777 N. Broadway, Los Angeles CA 90012
Phone: 213-625-4700 **Fax:** 213-625-1368
Web: www.cathaybank.com

2011 Branch Offices

	No.
California	31
New	8
Illinois	3
Washington	3
Texas	2
Massachusetts	1
New	1
Hong	1
Total	**50**

PRODUCTS/OPERATIONS

2011 Sales

	$ mil.	% of total
Interest & dividends		
Loans receivable	364	72
Taxable investment securities	83	17
Other	6	1
Noninterest		
Net securities gains	21	4
Letter of credit commissions	5	1
Depository service fees	5	1
Other	18	4
Total	**504**	**100**

COMPETITORS

Bank of America
BBCN
Citibank
East West Bancorp
Far East National Bank
Grandpoint Bank
Hanmi Financial
U.S. Bancorp
Wilshire Bancorp

HISTORICAL FINANCIALS

Company Type: Public

Income Statement FYE: December 31

	ASSETS ($ mil.)	NET INCOME ($ mil.)	INCOME AS % OF ASSETS	EMPLOYEES
12/11	10,644	100	0.9%	1,018
12/10	10,801	11	0.1%	1,010
12/09	11,588	(67)	—	986
12/08	11,582	50	0.4%	1,044
12/07	10,402	125	1.2%	1,156
Annual Growth	0.6%	(5.5%)	—	(3.1%)

2011 Year-End Financials

Debt ratio: 3.91%
Return on equity: 6.65%
Cash ($ mil.): 412
Current ratio: —
Long-term debt ($ mil.): 415
No. of shares (mil.): 78
Dividends
Yield: —
Payout: 3.77%
Market value ($ mil.): 1,174

	STOCK PRICE ($) FY Close	P/E High/Low		PER SHARE ($) Earnings	Dividends	Book Value
12/11	14.93	18	10	1.06	0.00	19.16
12/10	16.70	—	—	(0.06)	0.04	18.18
12/09	7.55	—	—	(1.59)	0.21	20.55
12/08	23.75	29	10	1.00	0.42	26.11
12/07	26.49	14	11	2.46	0.41	19.70
Annual Growth	(13.4%)	—	—	(19.0%)	—	(0.7%)

CBRE Group Inc

CBRE (formerly CB Richard Ellis Group) is all about location location location —not to mention "ubicacion" "l'emplacement" "posizione" and "Standort." One of the world's largest commercial real estate services companies CBRE operates more than 300 offices in 60 countries. Services include property and facilities management leasing brokerage valuation asset management financing and market research. The company manages about 1.3 billion sq. ft. of commercial space for third-party owners and occupants. Subsidiary Trammell Crow provides property development services for corporate and institutional clients primarily in the US. CBRE Global Investors manages real estate investments for institutional clients.

CBRE operates in five segments: the Americas; Europe the Middle East and Africa (EMEA); the Asia/Pacific region; global investment management (handled by CBRE Global Investors); and development services (handled by Trammell Crow). The Americas division which includes the US Canada and Latin America is its largest accounting for more than 60% of all sales.

CBRE continues to expand its geographic reach and broaden its service offerings by making fill-in acquisitions in regional markets that complement or expand existing operations. The company's strategy is to be the leading firm in each of its major business lines.

After several years of limiting its investments due to the recession CBRE in 2011 made one of its largest deals in several years. The company bolstered its global real estate investment management business with the acquisition of ING Groep's real estate investment management operations for some $940 million. The Dutch firm's real estate investment management business in Asia and Europe was merged into CBRE Global Investors and more than doubled the size of the unit. The transaction also included US-based Clarion Real Estate Securities and interests in commercial real estate co-investments.

The ING deal helped boost CBRE's investment management revenue by more than 30% in 2011. Most of the company's other business lines also saw double-digit positive revenue growth. That coupled with expense management helped CBRE's overall revenues to increase by 15% in 2011. Trends that began in 2010 continued the following year. Commercial real estate markets stabilized. Vacancy rates decreased rents stabilized or edged up credit became more widely available and property sales and leasing activity increased. As conditions improve the company expects acquisitions to once again drive growth.

Private equity firm Blum Capital Partners owns about 7% of CBRE. Blum is headed by Richard Blum who is also the chairman of CBRE.

HISTORY

Colbert Coldwell and Albert Tucker started real estate brokerage Tucker Lynch & Coldwell in 1906 in San Francisco. In 1922 the company expanded to Los Angeles where it began developing real estate in 1933 with a 60-acre subdivision in the burgeoning city.

Having profited from California's rapid growth in the 1950s and 1960s the firm expanded out of state. The partnership incorporated in 1962 as Coldwell Banker which went public in 1968. Sears Roebuck & Co. bought the company in 1981 for 80% above its market price. But by 1991 Sears had abandoned aims to become a financial services giant and sold Coldwell Banker's commercial operations to The Carlyle Group as CB Commercial Real Estate Services Group.

Free of Sears but $56 million in the red the company didn't return to profitability until 1993. Two years later it embarked on a shopping spree in real estate services buying tenant representatives Langon Rieder and Westmark Realty. In 1996 the company went public and bought mortgage banker L. J. Melody & Company (which was renamed CBRE | Melody); it purchased Koll Real Estate Services in 1997.

In 1998 the company widened its global scope with the acquisition of REI Limited the non-UK operations of Richard Ellis; it was renamed CB Richard Ellis Services. CB Richard Ellis also bought Hillier Parker May & Rowden (now operating in the UK as CB Hillier) a London-based provider of commercial property services.

CB Richard Ellis experienced a revenue crunch in 1999 and responded by restructuring its North American operations into three divisions (transaction financial and management services) and cutting management ranks by 30%. Growth continued in 1999 with the purchase of Pittsburgh-based Gold & Co. the addition of an office in Venezuela and a fat contract to manage more than 1100 locations for Prudential.

In 2000 the company committed significant resources to the Internet inking a deal to offer the lease management services of MyContracts.com and investing in Canadian real estate transaction tracker RealNet Canada.

A group of investors including then-CEO Ray Wirta chairman Richard Blum (and his BLUM Capital Partners) and Freeman Spogli took the company private in 2001. Blum Capital Partners bought the 60% of publicly traded CBRE that it did not already own forming CBRE Holding. Three years later the company went public once again.

In 2003 CBRE merged with top commercial real estate broker and property manager Insignia Financial. The next year the company changed its name to CB Richard Ellis Group and went public. It bought rival Trammell Crow in 2006 as well as a dozen or so other companies as it sought to fill in its holdings. The acquisitions deepened CBRE's outsourcing services especially project and facilities management for corporate and institutional clients in the US.

CBRE spun off former subsidiary Realty Finance Corporation in 2008 after the real estate investment trust continued to post losses in a troubled credit market.

Also in 2008 it opened its first offices in Bahrain and joined forces with Vanke to provide residential property management services in China. The following year CBRE expanded its existing UK-based investment banking business (advisory and restructuring services for real estate hospitality and gaming companies) to the Americas.

In November 2012 CBRE acquired EA Shaw. a independent commercial and residential property partnership specializing in central London. The purchase significantly enhanced the firm's business in central London.

EXECUTIVES

EVP and CFO, Gil Borok, age 44, $412,806 total compensation

Global Director Facilities Management, Maureen A. Ehrenberg, age 53

Chairman, Richard C. Blum, age 76

President, Robert E. (Bob) Sulentic, age 55, $520,673 total compensation

President Global Corporate Services, William F. (Bill) Concannon, age 56

President Americas Brokerage and Capital Markets, Christopher R. Ludeman

CEO and Director, W. Brett White, age 52, $781,346 total compensation

Chairman Global Brokerage, Stephen B. (Steve) Siegel, age 67

Managing Director Tucson, Timothy J. (Tim) Prouty

President Eastern Division, James A. (Jim) Reid

Global Strategy and Chief Investment Officer, James R. (Jim) Groch

CEO New York Tri-State Region Brokerage Services, Mary Ann Tighe

Vice Chairman Investment Properties, Darcy A. Stacom

Group President-Global Services, Calvin W. (Cal) Frese Jr., age 55, $562,038 total compensation

COO New York Tri-State Region, Cherrie L. Nanninga, age 63

Vice Chairman and Managing Director Investment Properties Institutional Group, Jack C. Fraker

President Capital Markets, Brian F. Stoffers

COO Americas, Steven A. (Steve) Swerdlow

Chief Accounting Officer, Arlin E. Gaffner, age 55

President-Americas, Michael J. (Mike) Lafitte, age 51

Vice Chairman Brokerage Services, Patrick Murphy

Vice Chairman Investment Properties, William M. (Bill) Shanahan, age 55

Director Distance Learning Training and Development Corporate Human Resources, Gail Austin

President-Asia Pacific, Robert (Rob) Blain, age 56, $488,500 total compensation

Senior Managing Director Capital Markets Multi-Housing Group, Peter F. Donovan

President-Europe Middle East and Africa, Michael J. (Mike) Strong, age 64, $450,371 total compensation

President Strategic Partners U.S., Vance G. Maddocks

Executive Managing Director Office Services The Americas, John D. Frager

EVP Office and Commercial Properties, Jeffrey S. Pion

President and CEO Tri-State Region, Mitchell (Mitch) Rudin

Global Director Human Resources, J. Christopher (Chris) Kirk

Senior Managing Director Corporate Communications, Steven (Steve) Iaco

EVP General Counsel and Secretary, Laurence H. Midler, age 47, $325,000 total compensation

Vice Chairman Global Corporate Services, John G. Nugent, age 48

Senior Director Corporate Communications, Robert W. (Bob) McGrath

Managing Director Private Client Group, Jennifer Pierson

Vice Chairman Brokerage Services; Co-Head Consulting Group Midtown Manhattan, Michael Geoghegan, age 52
SVP Brokerage Services, Keith Caggiano
SVP Brokerage Services, Edward E. (Ned) Midgley
President Global Asset Services, Tony Long
Global CIO, Donald B. (Don) Goldstein
Associate Investment Properties Institutional Group, Jonathan Bryan
Vice Chairman Brokerage Services, R. Todd Doney
SVP Brokerage Services, Benjamin (Ben) Friedland
SVP Brokerage Services, Matthew McBride
EVP Brokerage Services, Paul Muratore
SVP Brokerage Services, Rand W. Pear
First VP Valuation and Advisory Services Group, Edward R. Eschmann
VP Brokerage Services, Alan Friedman
SVP Global Corporate Services, David Kleinhandler
VP Brokerage Services, Kevin M. Powderly
SVP, Sacha M. Zarba, age 33
SVP Brokerage Services, Sinclair Li
SVP Brokerage Services, Roshan Shah
EVP Brokerage Services, Peter C. Turchin
SVP Brokerage Services, James C. Ackerson
SVP Brokerage Services, Brad Needleman
SVP Investor Relations, Nicholas M. (Nick) Kormeluk
First VP Industrial/Brownfield Services, Paul D. Cohen
Global Chief Economist, Raymond (Ray) Torto
General Manager Asset Services, David A. Ayres
First VP Brokerage Services, Jeremy S. Shyk
Executive Managing Director Public Institutions and Education Solutions The Americas, Theodore N. (Ted) Carter
CEO CB Richard Ellis Investors, Matt Khourie
SVP National Retail Investment Group, Chris Cozby
SVP Debt and Equity Finance, Peter Gineris
SVP Capital Markets, Nicholas Matt
Managing Director Asset Services, Martin Mitchell
VP, Trent Snarr
CTO, Christopher (Chris) Holt
VP Information Technology, Rich Lantos
VP Information Technology, Mike Peeler
Director Information Technology, Bill York
Executive Director and Pan Ireland Head of Retail, Michael Harrington
Vice Chairman CB Richard Ellis Limited, John O'Bryan
CTO EMEA, Monsoor Rahaman
CEO CBRE Global Investors, Matt Khourie???
Director, Frederic V. Malek, age 75
Director, Gary L. Wilson, age 72
Director, Raymond E. (Ray) Wirta, age 68
CEO and Director, W. Brett White, age 52
Director, Laura D. Tyson, age 65
Director, Curtis F. Feeny, age 54
Director, Bradford M. Freeman, age 70
Director, Michael Kantor, age 72
Director, Jane J. Su, age 48
Auditors: KPMGLLP

LOCATIONS

HQ: CBRE Group Inc.
11150 Santa Monica Blvd. Ste. 1600, Los Angeles CA 90025
Phone: 310-405-8900 **Fax:** -13386
Web: www.dnp.co.jp/index_e.html

2011 Sales

	$ mil.	% of total
Americas	3,673	62
Europe Middle East & Africa	1,076	18
Asia/Pacific	788	13
Global investment management	290	5
Development services	76	1
Total	**5,905**	**100**

2011 Sales

	$ in mil.	% of total
US	3,492	59
UK	484	9
Other countries	1,929	32
Total	**5,905**	**100**

PRODUCTS/OPERATIONS

Selected Subsidiaries
CBRE Inc.
CBRE Capital Markets Inc.
CBRE Capital Markets of Texas LP
CBRE Global Holdings SARL
CBRE Global Investors LLC
CBRE Limited
CBRE Services Inc
Trammell Crow Company LLC

COMPETITORS

Colliers International
Cushman & Wakefield
FirstService
Grubb & Ellis
Inland Group
Jones Lang LaSalle
Lincoln Property
Mitsui Fudosan
Realogy
Studley

HISTORICAL FINANCIALS

Company Type: Public

Income Statement FYE: December 31

	REVENUE ($ mil.)	NET INCOME ($ mil.)	NET PROFIT MARGIN	EMPLOYEES
12/11	5,905	239	4.0%	34,000
12/10	5,115	200	3.9%	31,000
12/09	4,165	33	0.8%	29,000
12/08	5,128	(1,012)	—	30,000
12/07	6,034	390	6.5%	29,000
Annual Growth	(0.5%)	(11.5%)	—	4.1%

2011 Year-End Financials

Debt ratio: 49.64%
Return on equity: 20.77%
Cash ($ mil.): 1,093
Current ratio: 132.43
Long-term debt ($ mil.): 2,611
No. of shares (mil.): 327
Dividends
Yield: —
Payout: —
Market value ($ mil.): 4,992

	STOCK PRICE ($) FY Close	P/E High/Low		PER SHARE ($) Earnings	Dividends	Book Value
12/11	15.22	40	17	0.74	0.00	3.51
12/10	20.48	33	19	0.63	0.00	2.81
12/09	13.57	117	20	0.12	0.00	1.96
12/08	4.32	—	—	(4.81)	0.00	0.44
12/07	21.55	24	11	1.66	0.00	4.90
Annual Growth	(8.3%)	—	—	(18.3%)	—	(8.0%)

CBS Corp

You might say this company has a real eye for broadcasting. CBS Corporation is a leading media conglomerate with operations in television radio online content and publishing. Its portfolio is anchored by CBS Broadcasting which operates the #1 rated CBS television network along with a group of local TV stations. CBS also owns cable network Showtime and produces and distributes TV programming through CBS Television Studios and CBS Television Distribution. Other operations include CBS Radio CBS Interactive and book publisher Simon & Schuster. In addition CBS Outdoor is a leading operator of billboards and outdoor advertising. Chairman Sumner Redstone controls CBS Corporation through National Amusements.

Operations

CBS continues to draw the largest number of TV viewers among broadcast networks with hit crime shows CSI and NCIS and comedies such as Big Bang Theory. Newer hits include The Good Wife and The Mentalist. CBS also makes significant investments in sports programming through broadcasting agreements with the National Football League and the NCAA among other organizations.

In addition to its flagship network CBS Corporation owns a 50% stake in The CW Network with joint venture partner Warner Bros. Entertainment (a unit of Time Warner). The broadcast outlet launched in 2006 and has found its niche appealing mostly to young adults with such shows as Gossip Girl Smallville and America's Next Top Model. CBS also owns about 10 local affiliates of The CW; newspaper publisher Tribune Co. owns the bulk of the affiliate network.

CBS Corporation has only a small portfolio of cable networks meaning it does not generate much money from cable and satellite TV subscribers. (Carriage fees from cable system operators has been a lucrative source of revenue for some rivals such as Time Warner Disney and NBCUniversal.) Showtime is the crown jewel of the company's cable holdings.

The company also has a significant presence online with such leading websites as CNET (technology news and reviews) GameSpot (video game information) and Last.fm (social networking for music fans). Its CBS Interactive focuses on selling advertising across its vast collection of properties.

Strategy

Like rival media companies including Walt Disney and News Corporation CBS Corporation focuses on the integration of its content production and distribution businesses in order to generate multiple streams of revenue. A television show created by CBS Television Studios for example can be broadcast by the CBS network and later syndicated to local stations and cable outlets. Programming can also be released to consumers on DVD by CBS Home Entertainment and turned into licensed apparel and other retail goods by its CBS Consumer Products division. CBS Corporation also uses its multiple outlets on TV radio and online to cross-promote its vast array of media properties.

One common bond among the company's various properties is its focus on advertising supported media. Commercial ads on television radio and online along with outdoor advertising account for more than 60% of CBS Corporation's sales. But like other ad supported media the company struggled through the recession and was forced to cut expenses in order to shore up the bottom line. Those efforts did include some layoffs. Particularly hard hit by the downturn CBS Radio disposed of about 10 under-performing radio stations during 2009.

The company's publishing business is also looking to digital media in order to turn itself around. Like other publishers Simon & Schuster is struggling to manage the long slow decline in consumer book purchasing by focusing on cutting operating and production costs. Part of that effort has meant investing in new technologies to sell books to users of electronic readers such as Amazon's Kindle and the iPad from Apple. It also sells manuscripts through social publishing site Scribd.

While still chasing market leader Home Box Office the company's Showtime has made significant inroads with the help of such original series programming as Dexter and Weeds. CBS is also expanding its use of online video and other digital distribution channels for its television content.

Company Background

CBS was once part of the Viacom conglomeration of TV cable and film companies but in late 2005 the media behemoth split into two separate publicly traded companies: The "new" Viacom and CBS Corporation. Viacom took over the film and cable assets including Paramount Pictures and MTV Networks while CBS took on the primarily advertising-supported media assets (television radio and Internet operations). Les Moonves formerly the head of the CBS network was appointed to lead CBS Corporation.

While the "old" Viacom possessed an impressive array of blue-chip media assets its volatile movie studio tended to overshadow the better performing parts of the company namely its cable and broadcast television operations. The decision was made therefore to split up the company in the hope that shareholders would value the parts more than the whole.

HISTORY

The company that would eventually become CBS Corporation began as Viacom in 1970. It was the result of numerous mergers and acquisitions dating back nearly 90 years combining everything from a movie studio to a company that made car bumpers. CBS launched Viacom after the FCC ruled that TV networks could not own cable systems and TV stations in the same market. Viacom took over CBS's program syndication division and bought TV and radio stations in the late 1970s and early 1980s. In 1978 it co-founded pay-TV network Showtime. Viacom became full owner in 1982 and combined Showtime with The Movie Channel the following year to form Showtime Networks. Viacom also began producing TV series and bought MTV Networks in 1986.

After a bidding war with renowned financier Carl Icahn and a Viacom management group Sumner Redstone's National Amusements bought 83% of Viacom in 1987. Viacom bought King's Entertainment (theme parks) shortly thereafter and followed that with two mega-deals in 1994: it bought Paramount Communications for about $10 billion (which included Simon & Schuster) and Blockbuster for $8.4 billion (which included Spelling Entertainment). The next year along with Chris-Craft Viacom launched UPN (United Paramount Network) the fifth commercial-broadcast TV network in the US.

Chiseling away at a mountain of debt Viacom dumped its radio stations and sold its share in USA Networks (now named IAC/InterActiveCorp) to Universal for $1.7 billion in 1997. In 1998 it sold the reference and education publishing divisions of Simon & Schuster to Pearson for $4.6 billion and unloaded the unprofitable Blockbuster Music chain to Wherehouse Entertainment for $115 million.

Viacom created an Internet division (MTV Networks Online) in 1999 to house its MTV VH1 and Nickelodeon Web sites (later decentralized into The MTVi Group and Nickelodeon Online). Later that year it sold 18% of Blockbuster in an IPO and sold 10% of MTVi to TCI Music (later Liberty Digital) in exchange for the SonicNet websites.

Viacom bought Chris-Craft's 50%-stake in the struggling UPN Network for a paltry $5 million in 2000 by exercising a buy-sell clause in the contract. BHC Communications (Chris-Craft's 80%-owned subsidiary that actually owned the stake in UPN) filed suit to block Viacom's merger with CBS claiming that it violated a non-compete clause in the contract but the New York Supreme Court ruled in Viacom's favor. Its $45 billion merger with CBS went through (reuniting two companies split apart by the government 30 years ago) and Viacom was given one year to sell UPN. However a federal law prohibiting ownership of more than one TV network was overturned in 2001 allowing Viacom to keep the network.

Later that year Viacom's victory over Chris-Craft turned to sour grapes when News Corp. agreed to buy Chris-Craft. The deal could have forced UPN to fold if News Corp. had turned Chris-Craft's large-market UPN stations into FOX affiliates (a new pact later signed with Chris-Craft keeps UPN as the stations' network).

In 2001 Viacom bought the rest of Infinity Broadcasting that it didn't already own as well as Black Entertainment Television (the media company targeting African-Americans) for $3 billion. It also folded MTVi back into parent MTV Networks. Other cost cutting measures in 2002 included combining the business operations of UPN and CBS and placing Simon & Schuster under the same division as its film and TV production holdings.

Two years later Viacom finally sold its majority stake in Blockbuster which never really fit in with Viacom's other media properties. The media firm also didn't want to deal with the new challenges facing Blockbuster such as stiff competition from video on demand services the cheap DVD market and mail order video rental company Netflix.

In a move designed to simplify the firm's operations and re-focus the company on its core assets in late 2005 Viacom split into two separately traded firms –one called CBS Corporation consisting of traditional television and radio broadcasting operations and headed by former co-COO Les Moonves; and the other called the "new" Viacom made up of cable television and film operations and headed by former co-COO Tom Freston. (Freston resigned in 2006.) Redstone retained his title as chairman of both firms as well as his majority control.

Shortly after the split CBS Corp. sold Paramount Parks to Cedar Fair for $1.2 billion. A newly formed network called The CW a combination of UPN and The WB debuted in 2006. The following TV season the CBS network fell from first place in the ratings for the first time in six years. CBS Corp. expanded its online publishing operations in 2008 with the $1.8 billion acquisition of CNET Networks.

In 2011 production on the eighth season of its hit comedy Two and a Half Men ceased as a result of the erratic behavior of actor Charlie Sheen. CBS fired Sheen and has put the show on hiatus for an undetermined period of time.

EXECUTIVES

President and CEO Simon & Schuster, Carolyn K. Reidy, age 63
EVP Planning Policy and Government Affairs, Martin D. Franks, age 61, $702,692 total compensation
President CEO and Director, Leslie (Les) Moonves, age 62, $3,513,462 total compensation
Executive Chairman, Sumner M. Redstone, age 88, $1,003,846 total compensation
Vice Chairman, Shari E. Redstone, age 58
Chairman and CEO CBS Outdoor, Wally C. Kelly, age 56
President and CEO CBS Radio, Daniel R. (Dan) Mason
EVP and General Counsel, Louis J. Briskman, age 63, $1,305,000 total compensation
EVP and Chief Communications Officer, Gil Schwartz, age 60
SVP Communications CBS Television, Chris Ender
EVP Human Resources and Administration, Anthony G. Ambrosio, age 51
Chairman CBS Sports, Sean McManus, age 57
President CBS Interactive, James (Jim) Lanzone
Chairman and CEO Showtime Networks, Matthew C. (Matt) Blank
President CBS Entertainment, Nina Tassler
President CBS Studios International, Armando Nu?ez Jr.
SVP Communications, Dana McClintock
SEVP CBS Primetime, Kelly Kahl
President and CEO CBS Films, Amy Baer
Chief Research Officer; President CBS Vision, David F. (Dave) Poltrack
President Entertainment The CW, Mark Pedowitz
EVP and General Manager CBS Consumer Products, Liz Kalodner
CFO Interactive, Mary M. Hentges
EVP Investor Relations, Adam Townsend
SVP Strategic Development, Dan Harrison
CFO CBS Films, Reid Sullivan
President CBS Television Studios, David Stapf
EVP Worldwide Marketing CBS Films, Debbie Miller
President CBS Television Distribution, John Nogawski
SVP Corporate Licensing and Distribution; President Distribution CBS Television Distribution, Scott Koondel
EVP CBS Sports; President CBS College Sports Network, David Berson, age 39
EVP and CFO, Joseph R. Ianniello, age 44, $1,123,462 total compensation
SVP Deputy General Counsel and Secretary, Angeline C. Straka, age 66
SVP and General Tax Counsel, Richard M. Jones, age 46
SVP Strategic Development, Alexander J. (Zander) Lurie, age 38
EVP Alternative Programming CBS Entertainment, Jennifer (Jen) Bresnan
CEO Outdoor International, Antonio Alonso
VP Production CBS Films, Mark Ross
EVP and General Counsel CBS Films, Rik Toulon
COO CBS Films, Wolfgang Hammer
Chief Financial and Administrative Officer CBS News, Thomas S. (Tom) Shilen Jr., age 53
President CBS Television Stations, Peter Dunn
CTO, Doug Rousso
SVP Controller and Chief Accounting Officer, Lawrence (Larry) Liding, age 43
VP International Communications, Luke Fredberg
Director, Bruce S. Gordon, age 66
President CEO and Director, Leslie (Les) Moonves, age 62
Director, Gary L. Countryman, age 72
Vice Chairman, Shari E. Redstone, age 58
Director, Charles K. (Chad) Gifford, age 69
Director, Frederic V. (Fred) Salerno, age 68
Director, Douglas P. (Doug) Morris, age 74
Director, Joseph A. Califano Jr., age 80
Director, Linda M. Griego, age 64
Director, William S. Cohen, age 71
Director, David R. Andelman, age 72
Director, Leonard Goldberg, age 78
Director, Arnold Kopelson, age 77
Auditors: PricewaterhouseCoopersLLP

LOCATIONS

HQ: CBS Corporation
51 W. 52nd St., New York NY 10019-6188
Phone: 212-975-4321 **Fax:** 212-975-4516
Web: www.cbscorporation.com

2009 Sales

	$ mil.	% of total
US	11,154	86
International	1,860	14
Total	**13,014**	**100**

PRODUCTS/OPERATIONS

2010 Sales

	$ mil.	% of total
Advertising	9,152	65
Affiliate fees & subscriptions	1,597	11
Total	**14,059**	**100**

2010 Sales

Entertainment	7,390	52
Outdoor advertising	1,819	13
Publishing	790	5
Total	**14,059**	**100**

Selected Operations

Entertainment
- CBS Films (motion picture production)
- CBS Interactive (online content)
  - BNET
  - CBS.com
  - CBSSports.com
  - CNET
  - GameSpot
  - TV.com
- CBS Studios International (international program syndication)
- CBS Television Distribution (domestic programming syndication)
- CBS Television Network (broadcast television network)
  - CBS Entertainment
  - CBS News
  - CBS Sports
- CBS Television Studios (television production)
- The CW Network (50% broadcast television network)

Local broadcasting
- CBS Radio
- CBS Television Stations

Outdoor advertising
- CBS Outdoor

Cable networks
- CBS College Sports Network
- Showtime (pay-TV service)

Publishing
- Simon & Schuster

COMPETITORS

AOL
Citadel Broadcasting
Clear Channel
Cumulus Media
Disney
JCDecaux
Lamar Advertising
NBCUniversal
News Corp.
Random House
SIRIUS XM
Sony Pictures Entertainment
Time Warner
Yahoo!

HISTORICAL FINANCIALS

Company Type: Public

Income Statement

FYE: December 31

	REVENUE ($ mil.)	NET INCOME ($ mil.)	NET PROFIT MARGIN	EMPLOYEES
12/11	14,245	1,305	9.2%	20,915
12/10	14,059	724	5.2%	25,380
12/09	13,014	226	1.7%	25,580
12/08	13,950	(11,673)	—	25,920
12/07	14,072	1,247	8.9%	23,970
Annual Growth	0.3%	1.1%	—	(3.4%)

2011 Year-End Financials

Debt ratio: 22.83%
Return on equity: 13.17%
Cash ($ mil.): 660
Current ratio: 140.94
Long-term debt ($ mil.): 5,958
No. of shares (mil.): 651
Dividends
Yield: —
Payout: 18.23%
Market value ($ mil.): 17,668

	STOCK PRICE ($) FY Close	P/E High/Low		PER SHARE ($) Earnings	Dividends	Book Value
12/11	27.14	15	10	1.92	0.00	15.22
12/10	19.05	18	12	1.04	0.20	14.44
12/09	14.05	42	9	0.33	0.20	13.37
12/08	8.19	—	—	(17.43)	1.06	12.82
12/07	27.25	20	15	1.73	0.94	31.96
Annual Growth	(0.1%)	—	—	2.6%	—	(16.9%)

CC Media Holdings Inc

CC Media Holdings has channels for eyes and ears alike. The firm is the parent company of radio giant Clear Channel Communications and Clear Channel's advertising firm Clear Channel Outdoor Holdings. Operating more than 860 stations Clear Channel is the #1 radio company in the US reaching more than 239 million listeners. Clear Channel Outdoor Holdings which has a US operations as well as a presence in more than 30 countries sells advertising space on billboards public transportation buildings and other outdoor environments. The company is majority owned by private equity firms Bain Capital and Thomas H. Lee Partners.

Operations

The company is organized through three divisions: media and entertainment (including Clear Channel Communications) Americas outdoor advertising (125000 display structures throughout the US) and international outdoor advertising (630000 displays across 30 countries). CC Media also owns Katz Media Group a full-service media representation business. Katz Media is part of the company's media and entertainment holdings.

About half of CC Media's revenue comes from media and entertainment. The division also includes Premiere Networks a national radio network that produces distributes or represents some 90 syndicated radio programs including those from Rush Limbaugh Ryan Seacrest and Delilah. Premiere Network serves nearly 5800 radio station affiliates. In addition its Total Traffic Network delivers real-time traffic information via navigation systems radio and television broadcast media and wireless and Internet-based services.

Geographic Reach

The company does business throughout North and South America Europe and the Asia/Pacific region. Its media and entertainment executive operations are located in San Antonio and New York City. The headquarters of Americas outdoor is in Phoenix and the headquarters of International outdoor is in London.

Financial Analysis

Revenue increased 5% during fiscal year 2011 compared to 2010. Revenue from media and entertainment grew thanks to the addition of a complementary traffic operation it gained through the acquisition of the traffic business of Westwood One (now Dial Global). Revenue growth in outdoor advertising was achieved through an increase in bulletin airport and other displays as well as outdoor furniture such as bus shelters and benches.

Its concentration on one source of revenue though left CC Media vulnerable as the recession led to weakness in advertising and repeated years of losses. However while the company has been hurt by a challenging economy its net loss narrowed to $302.09 million down from a $479.08 million loss in 2010. It owes the smaller loss to cost saving initiatives and an increase in revenues.

Strategy

CC Media's growth strategy includes investing in digital platforms. It is developing the next generation of iHeartRadio an integrated digital radio platform in part through its 2011 acquisition of a cloud-based music technology business. The company is also working on the ongoing deployment of more digital outdoor displays. Outdoor Holdings installed 242 digital billboards in 2011 for a total of 857 across 37 US markets.

Mergers & Acquisitions

In 2011 the company acquired the Metro Traffic division of Dial Global (then called Westwood One). It made the deal to expand its Total Traffic Network business. Before the deal closed Metro Networks had approximately 1500 affiliates across the US while Total Traffic served more than 100 metro areas worldwide.

EXECUTIVES

Vice Chairman, Randall T. Mays, age 46
Chairman, Mark P. Mays, age 48
Chairman and CEO Clear Channel Media and Entertainment, John E. Hogan
CEO and Director, Robert W. (Bob) Pittman, age 58
EVP General Counsel and Secretary, Robert H. (Rob) Walls Jr., age 51
EVP and CFO, Thomas W. (Tom) Casey, age 49
CEO Clear Channel Outdoor Holdings Inc., William Eccleshare, age 55
SVP Chief Accounting Officer and Assistant Secretary, Scott D. Hamilton
Director, Scott M. Sperling, age 54
Vice Chairman, Randall T. Mays, age 46
Director, Richard J. Bressler, age 54
CEO and Director, Robert W. (Bob) Pittman, age 58
Director, Ian K. Loring, age 48
Director, Charles A. Brizius, age 43
Director, Blair E. Hendrix, age 46
Director, Steven W. (Steve) Barnes, age 51
Director, John P. (JC) Connaughton, age 46
Director, David C. Abrams, age 51
Director, Irving L. Azoff, age 64
Director, Jonathon S. Jacobson, age 50
Auditors: Ernst&YoungLLP

LOCATIONS

HQ: CC Media Holdings Inc.
200 E. Basse Rd., San Antonio TX 78209
Phone: 210-822-2828 **Fax:** 210-822-2299
Web: www.ccmediaholdings.com

PRODUCTS/OPERATIONS

2011 Sales

	$ mil.	% of total
Media and Entertainment	2,986	48
Internationl Outdoor Advertising	1,667	27
Americas Outdoor Advertising	1,336	21
Other	234	4
Adjustments	(63.9)	
Total	**6,161**	**100**

Selected Products & Operations

Clear Channel Media and Entertainment
- iHeartRadio
- Katz Media Group
- Premiere Radio Networks
- Total Traffic Network

Clear Channel Outdoor
- Billboards (bulletins and posters)
- Digital signs
- Street furniture displays
- Transit displays

COMPETITORS

CBS Corp
Citadel Broadcasting
Cumulus Media
JCDecaux
Lamar Advertising
Radio One Inc.

HISTORICAL FINANCIALS

Company Type: Public

Income Statement FYE: December 31

	REVENUE ($ mil.)	NET INCOME ($ mil.)	NET PROFIT MARGIN	EMPLOYEES
12/11	6,161	(302)	—	21,200
12/10	5,865	(479)	—	20,283
12/09	5,551	(4,034)	—	19,295
12/08	2,736	(5,042)	—	0
Annual Growth	31.1%	—	—	—

2011 Year-End Financials

Debt ratio: 122.16%
Return on equity: 987650001000000.00%
Cash ($ mil.): 1,228
Current ratio: 208.91
Long-term debt ($ mil.): 19,938
No. of shares (mil.): 83
Dividends
Yield: —
Payout: —
Market value ($ mil.): 365

	STOCK PRICE ($) FY Close	P/E High/Low	PER SHARE ($) Earnings	Dividends	Book Value
12/11	4.39	— —	(3.70)	0.00	(96.20)
12/10	9.00	— —	(5.94)	0.00	(92.55)
12/09	3.10	— —	(49.71)	0.00	(88.16)
12/08	2.26	— —	(62.06)	0.00	(40.21)
Annual Growth	24.8%	— —	—	—	—

Celanese Corp (DE)

Celanese Corporation gets a lot of good ink about its acetates. The company's primary operations include the manufacture of building block chemicals like acetic acid and vinyl acetate monomers. Those chemicals are used in everything from inks and paints to agricultural products and chewing gum. Canadian subsidiary Acetex the majority of whose sales come from Europe is the world's largest acetyls manufacturer. Other products include acetate tow (in cigarette filters); industrial specialties like ethylene vinyl aceta; and engineered plastics. The bulk of sales come from the US and Germany.

Operations

Celanese operates through four business segments: Advanced Engineered Materials Consumer Specialties Industrial Specialties and Acetyl Intermediates. The company is one of the world's largest producers of acetyl products as well as a top global producer of engineered polymers.

Geographic Reach

In addition to manufacturing sites in the US it also has properties plants and equipment in Belgium China Canada Germany Mexico and Singapore.

Financial Analysis

Celanese continued its recovery from the recession of 2008-09 with a 14% increase in revenues in 2011 due primarily to higher volumes and increased sales prices across most of its business segments. The largest gains were in its Industrial Specialties unit (up 18%) Advanced Engineered Materials unit (up 17%) and its Acetyl Intermediates segment (up 15%). Net income grew by 61% in 2011 as increased revenues outpaced a more modest growth in operating expenses.

Strategy

Celanese's strategy is to grow the company through expansion into emerging regions particularly China; to offer innovation through developing new products and applications; increase its productivity through energy reduction business process improvements and manufacturing optimization; and boost its portfolio by growing its business through both acquisitions or internal growth.

In 2012 the company teamed up with Indonesia's Pertamina forming a joint venture to develop fuel ethanol projects in that country.

To grow its emulsion polymers business in 2011 the company acquired two product lines Vinac and Flexbond from Ashland. The acquisition is expected to speed up growth of the company's emulsion polymers operations throughout the Americas —especially in the adhesives textiles coatings and paper segments.

Celanese subsidiary Ticona Engineering Polymers acquired two product lines Zenite liquid crystal polymer and Thermx polycyclohexylene-dimethylene terephthalate from DuPont Performance Polymers division in 2010. The units expanded Celanese's offerings in the electrical and electronics application segments of the global polymers market.

Ownership

In 2012 Capital Research Global Investors owned about 11% of Celanese with several other investment firms owning a smaller stakes.

Company Background

Celanese Corporation was created in 2004 by the Blackstone Group which had acquired a majority share in Celanese AG turned it private and then flipped it in a 2005 public offering. Blackstone finally divested its remaining holdings in Celanese in 2007.

EXECUTIVES

Chairman and CEO, Mark C. Rohr, age 60
Chairman President and CEO, David N. (Dave) Weidman, age 56, $934,615 total compensation
SVP and CFO, Steven M. (Steve) Sterin, age 40, $447,115 total compensation
COO, Douglas M. (Doug) Madden, age 59, $505,769 total compensation
SVP Corporate Affairs, Mark Oberle, age 46
Media Contact Asia, Pheobe Li
Media Contact Europe, Jens Kurth
VP Investor Relations, Jon Puckett
SVP Business Strategy Development and Procurement, Jay C. Townsend, age 53, $308,231 total compensation
SVP Finance, Christopher W. Jensen, age 45
Media Contact, Linda Beheler
SVP General Counsel and Corporate Secretary, Gjon N. Nivica Jr., age 47, $330,769 total compensation
SVP Human Resources, Jacquelyn K. Wolf, age 51
Chief Marketing Officer, Peter Holmes
Director, Daniel S. Sanders, age 72
Director, Martin G. (Marty) McGuinn, age 68
Director, Mark C. Rohr, age 60
Director, Farah M. Walters, age 67
Director, James E. (Jim) Barlett, age 68
Director, Jay V. Ihlenfeld, age 60
Director, Paul H. O'Neill, age 76
Director, John K. Wulff, age 63
Director, David F. Hoffmeister, age 57
Auditors: KPMGLLP

LOCATIONS

HQ: Celanese Corporation
222 W. Las Colinas Blvd. Ste. 900N, Dallas TX 75039
Phone: 972-443-4000 **Fax:** 972-443-8555
Web: www.celanese.com

2011 Sales

	$ mil.	% of total
Germany	2,328	34
Singapore	722	11
China	667	10
Canada	323	5
Other countries	249	4

PRODUCTS/OPERATIONS

2011 Sales

Acetyl Intermediates	3,551	49
Industrial Specialties	1,223	17
Other products	1	-
Adjustments	(471)	-

Selected Products

Acetyl Intermediates
- Acetate esters
- Acetic acid
- Acetic anhydride
- Carboxylic acids
- Methanol
- Vinyl acetate monomer (VAM)

Industrial Specialties
- Emulsions

Consumer Specialties
- Acetate tow
- Sunett sweetener

Advanced Engineered Materials
- Polyacetal products (POM)
- Polyphenylene sulfide (Forton)
- UHMW-PE (GUR)

Selected Brand Names

AOPlus
BuyTiconaDirect
Celanex
Celcon
Celstran
Celvolit
Clarifoil
Compel
Erkol
GUR
Hostaform

Impet
Mowilith
Nutrinova
Riteflex
Sunett
Thermx
Vandar
Vectra
Vinamul

COMPETITORS

Asahi Kasei
BASF SE
Daicel Chemical
Dow Chemical
DSM
DuPont
Eastman Chemical
LANXESS
Methanex
Momentive
NutraSweet
Rhodia
SABIC Innovative Plastics
Solvay

HISTORICAL FINANCIALS

Company Type: Public

Income Statement

FYE: December 31

	REVENUE ($ mil.)	NET INCOME ($ mil.)	NET PROFIT MARGIN	EMPLOYEES
12/11	6,763	607	9.0%	7,600
12/10	5,918	377	6.4%	7,250
12/09	5,082	488	9.6%	7,400
12/08	6,823	282	4.1%	8,350
12/07	6,444	426	6.6%	8,400
Annual Growth	1.2%	9.3%	—	(2.5%)

2011 Year-End Financials

Debt ratio: 35.42%
Return on equity: 45.26%
Cash ($ mil.): 682
Current ratio: 195.16
Long-term debt ($ mil.): 2,873
No. of shares (mil.): 156
Dividends
Yield: —
Payout: 5.76%
Market value ($ mil.): 6,927

	STOCK PRICE ($) FY Close	P/E High/Low		PER SHARE ($) Earnings	Dividends	Book Value
12/11	44.27	15	8	3.82	0.00	8.57
12/10	41.17	17	10	2.38	0.18	5.95
12/09	32.10	10	2	3.11	0.16	4.04
12/08	12.43	27	4	1.73	0.16	1.27
12/07	42.32	16	9	2.49	0.16	6.98
Annual Growth	1.1%	—	—	11.3%	—	5.3%

Celgene Corp.

Celgene lines up cells and genes to help create good health. The drug development company's lead product is Revlimid which is approved in the US Europe and other select markets as a treatment for multiple myeloma (bone marrow cancer). Revlimid also is used to treat a blood disorder called myelodysplastic syndrome (MDS). The company's second-biggest seller is another treatment for MDS called Vidaza; the drug is also approved to treat leukemia in Europe. Other products include Thalomid used to treat patients newly diagnosed with multiple myeloma as well as breast cancer treatment Abraxane and lymphoma drug Istodax. The firm has other drugs in development that combat inflammatory diseases and cancer.

Geographic Reach

The US is the company's largest market accounting for about 60% of revenues with Europe accounting for most of the rest of sales. However Celgene is working to expand its global presence; for instance both Revlimid and Vidaza were launched in Japan during 2010.

In addition to global sales and service locations Celgene operates manufacturing plants in the US and Switzerland that meet a majority of its needs though some of the firm's products are made by third-party manufacturers.

Operations

Revlimid is by far the company's biggest seller making up some two-thirds of Celgene's annual sales. Its other top selling products —Vidaza Thalomid Abraxane and Istodax —make up most of its remaining revenues. Outside of blood cancers and diseases Celgene receives royalties on sales of ADHD drugs Focalin Focalin XR and Ritalin LA which are licensed to and sold by global drugmaker Novartis. The company also makes a small amount of revenues from its Cellular Therapeutics subsidiary which is is researching stem cell therapies for diseases such as cancer and multiple sclerosis and its Lifebank USA unit which operates a blood bank in which parents may choose to store their newborn's cord and placenta stem cells as a way to combat possible blood diseases the child might contract later.

Sales and Marketing

Celgene sells its products in more than 65 countries through a global direct sales force as well as via independent representatives in select markets. Products are distributed to hospitals pharmacies and wholesalers though Revlimid and Thalomid must be handled under special risk-management programs (due to blood clot risks associated with the drugs).

Financial Analysis

The company's strategy of making select acquisitions finding new uses for proven sellers and performing enough R&D to keep its pipeline well-stocked seems to be paying off. It has achieved rapidly climbing revenues and profits in recent years as its product offerings grew including a 34% revenue increase (to $4.8 billion) and a 50% net income jump (to $1.3 billion) in 2011 due to increased sales of Revlamid Abraxane and Istodax. Vidaza also experienced higher sales though that trend could be reversed if a generic competitor successfully enters the US market in the near future. Thalomid sales have decreased in recent years as Revlamid and other competing therapies become the preferred treatments for multiple myeloma.

Strategy

Though Celgene has a little breathing room before it loses market exclusivity on most of its products the firm is still working avidly to avoid the dips in revenue that go hand-in-hand with patent losses by adding or developing new drugs and pipeline candidates through internal development collaborations and acquisitions. Vidaza began facing generic competition in the US in 2011; Celgene's other major drug patents aren't set to expire for several years.

Many of the firm's internal programs are focused on getting its marketed drugs approved for other indications. For instance Revlimid is in clinical trials to treat a variety of ailments including various forms of non-Hodgkin's lymphoma and chronic lymphatic leukemia as well as to treat newly diagnosed multiple myeloma patients. The company is looking to gain US approval for Vidaza to treat acute myeloid leukemia (AML); it is already used for AML indications in Europe. Other candidates target additional hematological cancers solid tumors anemia and inflammatory conditions.

Mergers and Acquisitions

The company added Abraxane to its commercial product offerings when it acquired Abraxis BioScience in 2010 for roughly $3 billion in cash and stock. Abraxane is an injectable cancer drug approved for the treatment of breast cancer; it is also being tested to treat skin lung pancreatic and other cancers. If Abraxane is approved for other uses the value of the deal could rise to $3.5 billion through milestone payments to former Abraxis shareholders.

Celgene also acquired Gloucester Pharmaceuticals in 2010 for $340 million to obtain its recently approved cancer drug Istodax. The drug was approved for cutaneous T-cell lymphoma in 2010 and peripheral T-cell lymphoma in 2011; it is also under development for other forms of non-Hodgkin's lymphoma.

In 2012 the company moved to build its position as a leader in the treatment of hematologic cancers by acquiring privately held Avila Therapeutics. Through the deal Celgene gained Avila's lead lymphoma candidate AVL-292 and its proprietary Avilomics development platform for $350 million in cash as well as up to $575 million in potential milestone payments if the acquired development programs are successful.

Celgene was founded in 1986 as a spinoff entity; it was formerly part of Celanese Corporation.

EXECUTIVES

Chairman International; Senior Advisor to the Chairman and CEO, Aart Brouwer, age 72, $462,963 total compensation
Chairman President and CEO, Robert J. (Bob) Hugin, age 57, $770,000 total compensation
EVP and CFO, Jacqualyn A. (Jackie) Fouse, age 50
EVP and COO, Perry Karsen, age 57
SVP Global Regulatory Affairs Pharmacovigilance and Corporate Quality Assurance and Compliance, Graham Burton, age 72, $470,833 total compensation
VP Global Communications, Brian P. Gill
General Counsel and Corporate Secretary, Thomas M. Moriarty, age 48
VP Investor Relations, Patrick E. Flanigan
Director External Affairs, Kevin Loth
VP Information Technology, Steve Lerner
Director Investor Relations, Tim Smith
EVP and Chief Commercial Officer, Mark Alles
Director, Michael D. (Mike) Casey, age 66
Director, Ernest Mario, age 73
Director, Carrie S. Cox, age 54
Director, Gilla Kaplan, age 65
Director, Michael A. Friedman, age 68
Director, James J. (Jim) Loughlin, age 69
Director, Rodman L. Drake, age 69
Auditors: KPMGLLP

LOCATIONS

HQ: Celgene Corporation
86 Morris Ave., Summit NJ 07901
Phone: 908-673-9000 **Fax:** 908-673-9001
Web: www.celgene.com

2012 Sales

US	3,169	58
Other regions	426	8

PRODUCTS/OPERATIONS

2012 Sales

Products		
Vidaza	823	15

Abraxane	426	8
Thalomid	302	6
Istodax	50	1
Royalties	110	2
Total	**5,506**	**100**

Selected Products

Approved
- Abraxane (breast cancer treatment)
- Istodax (cancer treatment gained through Gloucester buy)
- Revlimid (multiple myeloma myelodysplastic syndromes)
- Pomalyst (multiple myeloma)
- Thalomid (complications from leprosy multiple myeloma)
- Vidaza (myelodysplastic syndromes)

Selected Acquisitions

2010

Abraxis BioScience ($3.5 billion in cash stock and milestone payments; breast cancer drug Abraxane and development programs)

Gloucester Pharmaceuticals ($340 million lymphoma drug Istodax and development programs)

2012

Avila Therapeutics ($925 in cash and milestone payments AVL-292 lymphoma candidate and development programs)

COMPETITORS

Abbott Labs
Amgen
Astex Pharmaceuticals
AstraZeneca
Biogen Idec
Bristol-Myers Squibb
Cell Therapeutics
Eisai
Eli Lilly
Johnson & Johnson
Merck
Millennium: The Takeda Oncology Company
Novartis
Onyx Pharmaceuticals
Pfizer
Roche Holding
Sanofi
Shire

HISTORICAL FINANCIALS

Company Type: Public

Income Statement

FYE: December 31

	REVENUE ($ mil.)	NET INCOME ($ mil.)	NET PROFIT MARGIN	EMPLOYEES
12/11	4,842	1,318	27.2%	4,460
12/10	3,625	880	24.3%	4,182
12/09	2,689	776	28.9%	2,813
12/08	2,254	(1,533)	—	2,441
12/07	1,405	226	16.1%	1,685
Annual Growth	36.2%	55.3%	—	27.6%

2011 Year-End Financials

Debt ratio: 18.01%
Return on equity: 23.91%
Cash ($ mil.): 1,859
Current ratio: 282.68
Long-term debt ($ mil.): 1,275

No. of shares (mil.): 437
Dividends
Yield: —
Payout: —
Market value ($ mil.): 29,574

	STOCK PRICE ($) FY Close	P/E High	P/E Low	PER SHARE ($) Earnings	Dividends	Book Value
12/11	67.60	24	17	2.85	0.00	12.60
12/10	59.14	34	26	1.88	0.00	12.72
12/09	55.68	34	22	1.66	0.00	9.57
12/08	55.28	—	—	(3.46)	0.00	7.60
12/07	46.21	127	80	0.54	0.00	7.06
Annual Growth	10.0%	—	—	51.6%	—	15.6%

Centene Corp

Centene is sensitive to the needs of individuals and families enrolled in government-assisted health programs. The company provides managed care and related services in more than a dozen states under names such as Managed Health Services (Wisconsin and Indiana) Superior HealthPlan (Texas) and Buckeye Community Health Plan (Ohio). Centene provides services to some 1.8 million low-income elderly and disabled people receiving Medicaid Supplemental Security Income and state Children's Health Insurance Program (CHIP) benefits. Centene also offers specialty services in areas such as behavioral health (through its Cenpatico unit) vision benefits (OptiCare) and pharmacy benefits management (US Script).

Geographic Reach

Centene's health plans provide services through a network of more than 30000 primary care physicians 95000 specialists and 1250 hospitals in 12 states: Arizona Florida Georgia Illinois Indiana Kentucky Massachusetts Mississippi Ohio South Carolina Texas and Wisconsin.

Operations

Centene's Medicaid managed care contracts account for three-fourths of revenues. Its largest contracts are with the states of Texas (26% of sales) Georgia (13%) and Ohio (10%). In other areas of operations the company has expanded its specialty services to include telehealth advisory (NurseWise) and disease and wellness management (Nurtur). In addition Centene's Celtic Insurance subsidiary specializes in providing low-cost consumer-directed insurance policies to uninsured customers nationwide and its Bridgeway Health Solutions provides long-term care policies in select territories.

Financial Analysis

Centene's revenues rose 20% in 2011 to some $5.3 billion and net income rose 17% to $111 million building on a steady growth rate over the last decade. The healthy financial performance in 2011 was attributed to increased Medicaid and specialty service contracts that boosted enrollment levels.

Strategy

Centene's primary growth strategies are to enter new markets and expand in existing markets via acquisitions and by gaining new contracts with state Medicaid agencies. In 2011 it entered the Kentucky Mississippi and Illinois Medicaid markets; additional new contracts brought the firm into new areas of Texas in 2011 and 2012 as well. In addition the company was granted a contract to begin providing Medicaid services in Kansas at the start of 2013. Centene is benefitting from the growing number of mandated managed care plans in states that are looking to control Medicaid spending.

In addition to geographic expansion the company looks to grow its membership by adding new services in its existing state markets such as small business health plans and low-income individual plans. It also evaluates opportunities to grow in new fields such as health-related information technology and non-Medicaid health plans. Centene also occasionally divests operations in smaller service areas to focus on its core growth regions.

EXECUTIVES

SVP Specialty Business Unit, Jason M. Harrold, age 42, $328,077 total compensation
Chairman President and CEO, Michael F. Neidorff, age 69, $1,000,000 total compensation
EVP and Chief Administrative Officer, Carol E. Goldman, age 54, $400,000 total compensation
SVP Medical Affairs, Robert C. Packman
EVP Corporate Development, Jesse N. Hunter, age 36, $425,000 total compensation
SVP New Business Integration and Development, Karen A. Bedell, age 52
EVP; Chairman and CEO Celtic Group, Frederick J. Manning, age 64
EVP CFO and Treasurer, William N. Scheffel, age 58, $595,000 total compensation
SVP Finance and Investor Relations, Edmund E. (Ed) Kroll Jr., age 52
SVP Corporate Secretary and General Counsel, Keith H. Williamson, age 59
SVP and Chief Medical Officer, Mary V. Mason, age 43
SVP Health Policy, Holly Benson
EVP Health Plans, Mark W. Eggert, age 50, $570,000 total compensation
SVP Controller and Chief Accounting Officer, Jeffrey A Schwaneke, age 36
EVP and CIO, Donald G. Imholz, age 59
VP and Chief Marketing Officer, David Minifie
VP Media and Community Affairs, Deanne Lane
Director, Tommy G. Thompson, age 70
Director, Pamela A. (Pam) Joseph, age 53
Director, David L. Steward, age 60
Director, Frederick H. (Fred) Eppinger, age 53
Director, Robert K. Ditmore, age 77
Director, John R. Roberts, age 70
Director, Richard A. (Dick) Gephardt, age 70
Auditors: KPMGLLP

LOCATIONS

HQ: Centene Corporation
7700 Forsyth Blvd., St. Louis MO 63105
Phone: 314-725-4477 **Fax:** 314-558-2428
Web: www.centene.com

2011 Membership

Managed care (at-risk) members	Members	% of total
Texas	503,800	28
Georgia	298,200	16
Indiana	206,900	11
Florida	198,300	11
Kentucky	180,700	10
Ohio	159,900	9
South Carolina	82,900	5
Wisconsin	78,000	4
Massaschusetts	35,700	2
Mississippi	31,600	2
Arizona	23,700	1
Illinois	16,300	1
Other members	4,900	-
Total	**1,820,900**	**100**

PRODUCTS/OPERATIONS

2011 Sales

Medicaid Managed Care	4,515	73
Other	159	3
Adjustments	(818.8)	-
Total	**5,340**	**100**

Selected Acquisitions

2011

CaseNet LLC (majority stake; care management software)

2010

Carolina Crescent Health Plan (South Carolina; 40000 Medicaid members)

Citrus Health Care (Florida; 54000 Medicaid and long-term health members)

NovaSys Health (Arkansas; third party administration of self-funded health plans)

Selected Brands

Absolute Total Care (South Carolina)

Bridgeway Health Solutions (long-term care insurance)
Buckeye Community Health Plan (Ohio)
CeltiCare Health Plan (Celtic Insurance consumer directed plans)
Cenpatico (behavioral health)
Home State (Missouri)
IlliniCare Health Plan (Illinois)
Kentucky Spirit Health Plan
Louisiana Healthcare Connections (joint venture with area hospitals)
Magnolia Health Plan (Mississippi)
Managed Health Services (Wisconsin and Indiana)
NovaSys Health (Arkansas)
NurseWise (telehealth advisory)
Nurtur (wellness management)
OptiCare (vision benefits)
Peach State Health Plan (Georgia)
Sunflower State Health Plan (Kansas)
Sunshine State Health Plan (Florida)
Superior HealthPlan (Texas)
US Script (pharmacy benefits management)

COMPETITORS

Aetna
AMERIGROUP
Blue Cross and Blue Shield of South Carolina
Blue Cross and Blue Shield of Texas
CIGNA
Coventry Health Care
Health Net
Humana
Kaiser Foundation Health Plan
Molina Healthcare
Schaller Anderson Inc
Scott & White Health Plan
Security Health Plan of Wisconsin
UCare Minnesota
UnitedHealth Group
WellCare Health Plans
WellPoint

HISTORICAL FINANCIALS

Company Type: Public

Income Statement FYE: December 31

	REVENUE ($ mil.)	NET INCOME ($ mil.)	NET PROFIT MARGIN	EMPLOYEES
12/11	5,340	111	2.1%	5,300
12/10	4,448	94	2.1%	4,200
12/09	4,102	83	2.0%	3,900
12/08	3,364	83	2.5%	3,600
12/07	2,919	73	2.5%	3,100
Annual Growth	16.3%	10.9%	—	14.3%

2011 Year-End Financials

Debt ratio: 16.05%
Return on equity: 11.89%
Cash ($ mil.): 573
Current ratio: 112.22
Long-term debt ($ mil.): 348
No. of shares (mil.): 50
Dividends
Yield: —
Payout: —
Market value ($ mil.): 2,014

	STOCK PRICE ($) FY Close	P/E High/Low		PER SHARE ($) Earnings	Dividends	Book Value
12/11	39.59	18	11	2.12	0.00	18.39
12/10	25.34	13	9	1.88	0.00	16.00
12/09	21.17	11	8	1.89	0.00	13.92
12/08	19.71	15	7	1.88	0.00	11.66
12/07	27.44	16	11	1.64	0.00	9.51
Annual Growth	9.6%	—	—	6.6%	—	17.9%

Centerline Holding Co

Through its subsidiary Centerline Capital Centerline Holding provides real estate financial and asset management services for investors owners and developers of affordable housing and multifamily projects. Centerline primarily invests in tax-exempt municipal bonds issued to finance such properties. Over the years Centerline Capital has raised more than $10 billion to finance affordable housing. Centerline's mortgage banking unit writes and underwrites loans on behalf of Fannie Mae Freddie Mac and other entities. Centerline Holding has some $9 billion in assets under management.

The company also manages a joint venture fund Centerline Urban Capital which has some $180 million of committed equity. The fund focuses on urban multifamily housing; CalPers is the majority investor.

The financial crisis significantly impacted Centerline Holding as credit markets dried up and real estate values fell (especially commercial properties). The company has responded by improving its balance sheet and cash flows. In 2010 Centerline Holding underwent a restructuring in which Island Capital Group a firm controlled by real estate investor Andrew Farkas acquired an approximately 40% stake in the company. As part of the deal which also involved Centerline Holding's debtors and preferred shareholders the company received an infusion of equity eliminated debt and transferred some of its operations to affiliates of Island Capital.

As a result Centerline has more room to expand lending capacity and the company plans to grow its assets under management. In 2010 it expanded its mortgage banking group and opened new small loan offices in Atlanta New York and Chicago. Its affordable housing division closed a new $119 million fund used to manage affordable housing projects. Centerline also plans to raise additional funds.

EXECUTIVES

Head Commercial Real Estate/Agency Lending Products, William T. Hyman
Managing Director Human Resources and Operations Centerline Captial Group, Katherine B. (Kelly) Schnur, age 47
Executive Managing Director; Head Portfolio Management Group Centerline Commercial Real Estate Loan Portfolio, Paul G. Smyth, age 49, $295,385 total compensation
President CFO COO and Managing Trustee, Robert L. (Rob) Levy, age 45, $30,375 total compensation
Executive Managing Director and Head Affordable Housing Group; CEO Centerline Financial, Andrew J. Weil, age 40, $373,846 total compensation
Managing Trustee, Robert A. Meister, age 70
Managing Trustee, Thomas W. White, age 74
Managing Trustee, Jerome Y. Halperin, age 81
Managing Trustee, Robert L. Loverd, age 70
Auditors: Deloitte&ToucheLLP

LOCATIONS

HQ: Centerline Holding Company
625 Madison Ave., New York NY 10022-1801
Phone: 212-317-5700 **Fax:** 212-751-3550
Web: www.centerline.com

PRODUCTS/OPERATIONS

2010 Sales

	$ mil.	% of total
Consolidated partnershi		
Rental income	106	49
Interest income	1	-
Other	4	2
Interest income	44	20
Fee income	33	15
Other	29	14
Total	**219**	**100**

COMPETITORS

Arbor Commercial
Bank of America
iStar Financial Inc
MuniMae
PB Capital
PNC ARCS
Residential Capital
WNC & Associates

HISTORICAL FINANCIALS

Company Type: Public

Income Statement FYE: December 31

	ASSETS ($ mil.)	NET INCOME ($ mil.)	INCOME AS % OF ASSETS	EMPLOYEES
12/11	4,673	67	1.5%	240
12/10	5,005	(24)	—	206
12/09	6,003	(455)	—	400
12/08	7,382	(232)	—	375
12/07	9,491	(60)	—	500
Annual Growth	(16.2%)	—	—	(16.8%)

2011 Year-End Financials

Debt ratio: 21.05%
Return on equity: 31.32%
Cash ($ mil.): 95
Current ratio: —
Long-term debt ($ mil.): 983
No. of shares (mil.): 349
Dividends
Yield: —
Payout: —
Market value ($ mil.): 70

	STOCK PRICE ($) FY Close	P/E High/Low		PER SHARE ($) Earnings	Dividends	Book Value
12/11	0.20	—	—	0.19	0.00	0.62
12/10	0.20	—	—	(0.00)	0.00	0.50
12/09	0.20	—	—	(8.93)	0.00	(15.72)
12/08	0.20	—	—	(5.18)	0.65	(8.25)
12/07	7.62	—	—	(1.19)	1.26	14.16
Annual Growth	(59.7%)	—	—	—	—	(54.3%)

CenterPoint Energy Resources Corp.

LOCATIONS

HQ: CenterPoint Energy Resources Corp.
1111 Louisiana, Houston, TX 77002
Phone: 713 207-1111
Web: www.centerpointenergy.com

HISTORICAL FINANCIALS

Company Type:

Income Statement FYE: December 31

	REVENUE ($ mil.)	NET INCOME ($ mil.)	NET PROFIT MARGIN	EMPLOYEES
12/11	6,102	316	5.2%	4,701
12/10	6,569	300	4.6%	4,725
12/09	6,257	230	3.7%	4,678
12/08	9,395	343	3.7%	4,643
12/07	7,776	287	3.7%	4,609
Annual Growth	(5.9%)	2.4%	—	0.5%

2011 Year-End Financials

Debt ratio: 27.89%
Return on equity: 7.73%
Cash ($ mil.): 1
Current ratio: 99.16
Long-term debt ($ mil.): 2,919
No. of shares (mil.): 0
Dividends
Yield: —
Payout: —
Market value ($ mil.): —

CenterPoint Energy, Inc

CenterPoint Energy pivots around its core operations which include power and gas distribution utilities and natural gas pipeline gathering and marketing operations. CenterPoint Energy's regulated utilities distribute natural gas to 3.3 million customers in six US states and electricity to more than 2 million customers on the Texas Gulf Coast. The company's main stomping ground is Texas where it has regulated power distribution operations through subsidiary CenterPoint Energy Houston Electric. CenterPoint Energy operates more than 48230 miles of power distribution lines 8000 miles of interstate gas pipeline and 3800 miles of gas gathering pipeline. It also provides natural gas field services.

HISTORY

CenterPoint Energy's earliest predecessor Houston Electric Lighting and Power was formed in 1882 by a group including Emanuel Raphael cashier at Houston Savings Bank and Mayor William Baker. In 1901 General Electric's financial arm United Electric Securities Company took control of the utility which became Houston Lighting & Power (HL&P). United Electric sold HL&P five years later; by 1922 HL&P ended up in the arms of National Power & Light Company (NP&L) a subsidiary of Electric Bond & Share (a public utility holding company that had been spun off by General Electric).

In 1942 NP&L was forced to sell HL&P in order to comply with the 1935 Public Utility Holding Company Act. As the oil industry boomed in Houston after WWII so did HL&P.

HL&P became the managing partner in a venture to build a nuclear plant on the Texas Gulf Coast in 1973. Construction on the South Texas Project with partners Central Power and Light and the cities of Austin and San Antonio began in 1975. In 1976 Houston Industries (HI) was formed as the holding company for HL&P.

By 1980 the nuke was four years behind schedule and over budget. HL&P and its partners sued construction firm Brown & Root in 1982 and received a $700 million settlement in 1985. (The City of Austin also sued HL&P for damages but lost.) The nuke was finally brought online in 1988 with the final cost estimated at $5.8 billion.

Meanwhile HI diversified into cable TV in 1986 by creating Enrcom (later Paragon Communications) through a venture with Time Inc. Two years later it bought the US cable interests of Canada's Rogers Communications. HI left the cable business in 1995 selling out to Time Warner.

Developing Latin fever HI joined a consortium that bought 51% of Argentinean electric company EDELAP in 1992. (However in 1998 HI sold its stake to AES.) On a roll HI acquired 90% of Argentina's electric utility EDESE (1995); joined a consortium that won a controlling stake in Light a Brazilian electric utility (1996); bought a stake in Colombian electric utility EPSA (1997); and bought interests in three electric utilities in El Salvador (1998). It also won a permit to develop and operate a natural gas system in Mexico (1998).

Back in the US HI acquired gas dealer NorAm for $2.5 billion in 1997. The next year it bought five generating plants in California from Edison International and laid plans to build merchant plants in Arizona (near Phoenix) Illinois Nevada (near Las Vegas in partnership with Sempra Energy) and Rhode Island. Overseas HI finished a power plant in India in 1998. It also bought a 65% interest in Colombian electric utilities Electricaribe and Electrocosta; EPSA bought about 55% of CET in Colombia and Light bought about 75% of Metropolitana (S?o Paulo Brazil).

In 1999 HI became Reliant Energy and HL&P became Reliant Energy HL&P. That year the company bought a 52% stake in Dutch power generation firm UNA; it bought the remaining 48% the next year. Also in 2000 Reliant Energy paid Sithe Energies (now a part of Dynegy) $2.1 billion for 21 power plants in the mid-Atlantic states. It sold its operations in Brazil Colombia and El Salvador that year and transferred all of its nonregulated operations to subsidiary Reliant Resources. Reliant Energy also announced plans to spin off Reliant Resources that year.

Reliant Energy netted about $1.7 billion in 2001 from the sale to the public of nearly 20% of Reliant Resources. Later that year Reliant Resources announced that it would acquire US independent power producer Orion Power Holdings in a $4.7 billion deal; the deal was completed in 2002. Deregulation took effect in Texas that year and Reliant Energy transferred its retail power supply business to Reliant Resources.

As the finances of wholesale energy companies came under scrutiny in 2002 the SEC issued a formal investigation into "round-trip" energy trades completed by Reliant Resources. These activities artificially inflated the company's trading volumes and led it to restate its 1999 2000 and 2001 financial results; it also reduced its energy marketing and trading workforce by about 35%.

Reliant Energy announced plans in 2001 to form a new holding company (CenterPoint Energy) for itself and Reliant Resources; it completed the name change in 2002.

CenterPoint Energy changed its name in 2002 in preparation for the spin-off of its 83% stake in Reliant Resources (now GenOn Energy) a global independent power producer and energy marketer; the spinoff was completed later that year. (Reliant Resources changed its name to Reliant Energy in 2004.) CenterPoint Energy transferred its nonregulated Texas retail power supply business to Reliant Resources before spinning off the unit.

As part of its corporate reorganization and in response to Texas' electricity deregulation (which took effect in 2002) CenterPoint Energy has separated its Texas power generation and distribution operations and will work toward exiting the electric generation business. The company spun off 19% of its Texas Genco unit to shareholders in 2003. CenterPoint Energy sold Texas Genco to GC Power Acquisition (owned by investment firms The Blackstone Group Hellman & Friedman Kohlberg Kravis Roberts and Texas Pacific Group) for $3.65 billion following the buyback of Texas Genco's publicly held shares.

The company has also divested all of its international assets including its Latin American utility interests. To further its focus on core operations CenterPoint Energy has sold its Energy Management Services division to Entergy.

In 2005 CenterPoint Energy sold its majority stake in Texas Genco (now NRG Texas) which owns power plants with 14000 MW of generating capacity.

CenterPoint Energy Gas Transmission opened the 172-mile Carthage-to-Perryville pipeline in 2007 enabling the delivery of 1 billion cu. ft. of natural gas a day to pipelines serving end users in the Midwest Northeast and Southeast.

In 2008 the company expanded its presence in Indiana with the acquisition of Nordic Energy Services' commercial gas accounts.

CenterPoint Energy Houston's power infrastructure was badly affected by Hurricane Ike in 2008 which caused about $30 million worth of property damage.

EXECUTIVES

President CEO and Director, David M. McClanahan, age 62, $1,060,000 total compensation
EVP; Group President Corporate and Energy Services, Thomas R. (Tom) Standish, age 62, $457,000 total compensation
Chairman, Milton Carroll, age 62
EVP General Counsel and Corporate Secretary, Scott E. Rozzell, age 62, $475,000 total compensation
EVP and CFO, Gary L. Whitlock, age 62, $505,000 total compensation
Division President CenterPoint Energy Services, Wayne D. Stinnett Jr., age 61
SVP; Group President Pipelines and Field Services, C. Gregory (Greg) Harper, age 47, $340,000 total compensation
SVP; Division President Energy Services, Joseph B. McGoldrick, age 58
SVP and Chief Accounting Officer, Walter L. Fitzgerald, age 54
Media Contact Corporate and Financial Information, Floyd J. LeBlanc, age 51
Media Contact Corporate and Financial Information and Electric Natural Gas Pipelines and Field Services Operations, Leticia Lowe
VP Policy and Government Affairs, Clarence H. (Bud) Albright Jr.
Media Contact Electric Natural Gas Pipelines and Field Services Operations, Alicia Dixon
SVP Strategic Planning and Business Development, Jim M. Dumler
Media Contact Electric Natural Gas Pipelines and Field Services Operations, Rebecca Virden
VP Gas Operations Louisiana and Mississippi, Walter Bryant
SVP Gas Operations and Engineering, Rick Zapalac
VP Gas Operations Minnesota, Tal Centers
Division VP Information Technology and CIO, Patricia F. (Pat) Graham, age 60
VP Information Technology and CIO, Gary Hayes
SVP; Division President Gas Distribution Operations, Tracy Bridge
EVP and COO, Scott M. Prochazka, age 46
President CEO and Director, David M. McClanahan, age 62

Director, Michael P. Johnson, age 64
Director, Donald R. Campbell, age 71
Director, Sherman M. Wolff, age 71
Director, Derrill Cody, age 73
Director, O. Holcombe Crosswell, age 71
Director, Thomas F. Madison, age 76
Director, R. A. (Al) Walker, age 55
Director, Susan O. Rheney, age 52
Director, Janiece M. Longoria, age 59
Director, Peter S. Wareing, age 60
Director, Robert T. O'Connell, age 73
Auditors: Deloitte&ToucheLLP

LOCATIONS

HQ: CenterPoint Energy, Inc
1111 Louisiana Street, Houston, TX 77002
Phone: 713 207-1111
Web: www.centerpointenergy.com

PRODUCTS/OPERATIONS

2010 Sales

	$ mil.	% of total
Natural gas distribution	3,199	37
Competitive natural gas sales & services	2,617	30
Electric transmission & distribution	2,205	25
Interstate pipelines	464	5
Field services	289	3
Other	11	-
Total	**8,785**	**100**

COMPETITORS

AEP
AEP Texas Central
AEP Texas North
Ameren
Avista
Cleco
CMS Energy
Constellation Energy Group
Dominion Resources
Duke Energy
El Paso Corporation
Energy Future
Entergy
Exelon
Koch Industries Inc.
Mississippi Power
OGE Energy
ONEOK
Progress Energy
Southern Company
Southwestern Electric Power
Southwestern Energy
Williams Companies
Xcel Energy

HISTORICAL FINANCIALS

Company Type: Public

Income Statement — FYE: December 31

	REVENUE ($ mil.)	NET INCOME ($ mil.)	NET PROFIT MARGIN	EMPLOYEES
12/11	8,450	1,357	16.1%	8,827
12/10	8,785	442	5.0%	8,843
12/09	8,281	372	4.5%	8,810
12/08	11,322	447	3.9%	8,801
12/07	9,623	399	4.1%	8,568
Annual Growth	(3.2%)	35.8%	—	0.7%

2011 Year-End Financials

Debt ratio: 42.33%
Return on equity: 32.14%
Cash ($ mil.): 220
Current ratio: 90.13
Long-term debt ($ mil.): 8,641
No. of shares (mil.): 426
Dividends
Yield: —
Payout: 24.92%
Market value ($ mil.): 8,558

	STOCK PRICE ($) FY Close	P/E High	P/E Low	PER SHARE ($) Earnings	Dividends	Book Value
12/11	20.09	7	5	3.17	0.00	9.91
12/10	15.72	16	12	1.07	0.78	7.53
12/09	14.51	15	9	1.01	0.76	6.75
12/08	12.62	13	7	1.30	0.73	5.89
12/07	17.13	16	12	1.17	0.68	5.60
Annual Growth	4.1%	—	—	28.3%	—	15.3%

Central Pacific Financial Corp

When in the Central Pacific do as the islanders do. This may include doing business with Central Pacific Financial the holding company for Central Pacific Bank. The bank operates about 35 branch locations and 120 ATMs throughout the Hawaiian Islands. Targeting individuals and local businesses the bank provides such standard retail banking products as checking and savings accounts money market accounts and CDs. It maintains a diverse loan portfolio: Commercial real estate loans make up about a third while residential mortgages and construction loans are about a quarter each. The bank also writes business and consumer loans.

Central Pacific has been faced with some tough coconuts during the global economic recession that began in 2008. To reduce exposure to credit risk and operate as a smaller bank it reduced its commercial real estate and construction loan portfolios and ceased originating new commercial real estate and construction loans in 2009. The bank also closed its loan offices in California to concentrate lending in Hawaii.

Central Pacific suffered more than $500 million in losses from 2008 to 2010 as its non-performing assets ballooned. In 2011 investment firms The Carlyle Group and Anchorage Advisors stepped in to provide Central Pacific with an infusion of $325 million. The deal netted the investors nearly 23% of the company each.

Though the company's revenues were down in 2011 Central Pacific returned to profitability reporting net income of more than $36 million as general economic conditions in Hawaii exhibited signs of improvement. Better credit quality and a reduction in costs related to nonperforming assets drove the company's results.

EXECUTIVES

EVP and Chief Administrative Officer Central Pacific Financial and Central Pacific Bank, Agnes Catherine Ngo, age 52
Chairman Central Pacific Financial and Central Pacific Bank, John C. Dean, age 64
SVP Corporate Communications and Chief Marketing Officer Central Pacific Bank, Wayne H. Kirihara
President and CEO Central Pacific HomeLoans, Blenn A. Fujimoto, age 53, $285,167 total compensation
Vice Chair and COO, Denis K. Isono, age 61, $235,000 total compensation
SVP and Treasurer, David Morimoto
SVP and Corporate Secretary, Glenn K.C. Ching
EVP and CIO Central Pacific Bank, Glen Blackmon, age 57
Investor Relations, Hollie Amano
EVP and Director Human Resources Central Pacific Bank, Karen K. Street
EVP and CFO, Lawrence D. (Larry) Rodriguez, age 67
EVP and Chief Credit Officer, Raymond W. (Bill) Wilson, age 54
Director, Ronald K. (Ron) Migita, age 70
Director, Earl E. Fry, age 53
Director, Mike K. Sayama, age 57
Director, Colbert M. Matsumoto, age 59
Director, Dwight L. Yoshimura, age 57
Director, Richard J. Blangiardi, age 65
Director, Maurice H. Yamasato, age 69
Director, Paul J. Kosasa, age 54
Director, Christine H. H. Camp, age 45
Director, Jeannie B. Hedberg, age 68
Director, Crystal K. Rose, age 54
Auditors: KPMGLLP

LOCATIONS

HQ: Central Pacific Financial Corp.
220 S. King St., Honolulu HI 96813
Phone: 808-544-0500 Fax: 808-531-2875
Web: www.centralpacificbank.com/

PRODUCTS/OPERATIONS

2011 Sales

	$ mil.	% of total
Interest		
Loans & leases including fees	107	58
Taxable investment securities	27	15
Other	1	1
Noninterest		
Service charges on deposit accounts	10	5
Net gains on sales of residential loans	8	4
Other service charges & fees	17	9
Other	14	8
Total	**186**	**100**

COMPETITORS

American Savings Bank
BancWest
Bank of Hawaii
First Hawaiian Bank
Hawaiian Electric Industries
Mitsubishi UFJ Financial Group
Territorial Bancorp

HISTORICAL FINANCIALS

Company Type: Public

Income Statement — FYE: December 31

	ASSETS ($ mil.)	NET INCOME ($ mil.)	INCOME AS % OF ASSETS	EMPLOYEES
12/11	4,132	36	0.9%	935
12/10	3,938	(250)	—	921
12/09	4,869	(313)	—	1,030
12/08	5,432	(138)	—	1,065
12/07	5,680	5	0.1%	1,085
Annual Growth	(7.6%)	58.4%	—	(3.7%)

2011 Year-End Financials

Debt ratio: 3.83%
Return on equity: 8.01%
Cash ($ mil.): 257
Current ratio: —
Long-term debt ($ mil.): 158
No. of shares (mil.): 41
Dividends
Yield: —
Payout: —
Market value ($ mil.): 539

	STOCK PRICE ($) FY Close	P/E High	P/E Low	PER SHARE ($) Earnings	Dividends	Book Value
12/11	12.92	10	0	3.31	0.00	10.93
12/10	1.53	—	—	(171.13)	0.00	43.26
12/09	1.31	—	—	(220.60)	0.00	221.55
12/08	10.04	—	—	(96.60)	0.00	366.34
12/07	18.46	11	5	3.80	0.00	469.04
Annual Growth	(8.5%)	—	—	(3.4%)	—	(60.9%)

Century Bancorp, Inc.

Century Bancorp is the holding company for Century Bank and Trust which serves Boston and surrounding parts of northeastern Massachusetts from more than 20 branches. The bank offers standard deposit products including checking savings and money market accounts; CDs; and IRAs. Nearly half of the company's loan portfolio is devoted to commercial real estate. The bank also writes residential mortgages home equity loans construction and land development loans business loans and personal loans. It offers brokerage services through an agreement with third-party provider LPL Financial. Founder and chairman Marshall Sloane controls Century Bancorp.

Century Bank also provides cash management short-term financing and transaction processing services to municipalities in Massachusetts and Rhode Island. It offers automated lockbox collection services to its municipal customers as well as commercial clients. The bank also continues to open new branches in its traditional market area in metropolitan Boston.

Century Bancorp reported its highest earnings in more than four decades in 2010. Growth continued the following year with a 2% increase in revenues (to $16.7 million) and a 23% increase in profits (to $16.7 million). The company attributed its results in part to its centralized loan approval process and strict underwriting standards. It believes its reputation for fiscal conservatism also helps it attract high-quality deposits from government agencies trust fiduciaries and other banks. Also contributing to the bank's growth was an increase in net interest income as its asset portfolio grew 12% to $2.7 billion.

EXECUTIVES

Chairman Century Bank, Marshall M. Sloane, age 85, $283,101 total compensation
EVP Retail Cash Management Operations and Marketing Century Bank and Trust, Paul A. Evangelista, age 48, $276,706 total compensation
EVP and Head of Lending Century Bank and Trust, David B. Woonton, age 56, $275,706 total compensation
SVP Century Bank and Trust, Yasmine D. Whipple
Co-President and Co-CEO Century Bancorp; Co-President and Co-CEO Century Bank and Trust Company, Barry R. Sloane, age 57, $442,412 total compensation
CFO and Treasurer, William P. Hornby, age 45, $225,008 total compensation
SVP Century Bank and Trust, Gerald S. Algere
SVP Century Bank and Trust, Janice A. Brandano
SVP Century Bank and Trust, James M. Flynn Jr.
SVP Century Bank and Trust, Anthony C. LaRosa
VP Century Bank and Trust, Robert A. Bennett
SVP Century Bank and Trust, Bradford J. Buckley
Clerk; VP Century Bank and Trust, Rosalie A. Cunio
SVP Century Bank and Trust, Timothy L. Glynn
VP Century Bank and Trust, T. Daniel Kausel
First VP Century Bank and Trust, Shipley C. Mason
SVP Century Bank and Trust, Deborah R. Rush
SVP Century Bank and Trust, Kenneth A. Samuelian
VP Century Bank and Trust, Janice D. Taylor
SVP Century Bank and Trust, William J. Gambon Jr.
SVP Century Bank and Trust, Nancy Lindstrom
VP Century Bank and Trust, Karen M. Martin
VP Century Bank and Trust, David J. Waryas
SVP Century Bank and Trust, Jason J. Melius Jr.
EVP and Head of Institutional Services Century Bank and Trust, Brian J. Feeney, age 51, $210,008 total compensation
SVP Century Bank and Trust, Richard L. Billig
SVP Century Bank and Trust, Peter R. Castiglia
VP Century Bank and Trust, Gracine Copithorne
VP Century Bank and Trust, Barbara J. Cunningham
First VP Century Bank and Trust, Susan B. Delahunt
VP Century Bank and Trust, Sandra R. Edey
VP Century Bank and Trust, Judith A. Fallon
First VP Century Bank and Trust, Phillip A. Gallagher
VP Century Bank and Trust, Howard N. Gold
VP Century Bank and Trust, Nancy M. Marsh
VP Century Bank and Trust, Carl M. Mattos
VP Century Bank and Trust, Andrew J. Santos Jr.
VP Century Bank and Trust, Michael D. Ballard
VP Century Bank and Trust, Gerald Bovardi
VP Century Bank and Trust, Thomas E. Piemontese
SVP Century Bank and Trust, Linda Sloane Kay, $150,006 total compensation
Co-President and Co-CEO Century Bancorp; Co-President and Co-CEO Century Bank and Trust Company, Jonathan G. Sloane, age 53, $442,412 total compensation
Assistant Clerk, Paula A. Grimaldi
VP Century Bank and Trust, Roger F. Ballou
VP Century Bank and Trust, Jean P. Belcher-Scarpa
VP Century Bank and Trust, Pasqualina Buttiri
VP Century Bank and Trust, Toni M. Chardo
VP Century Bank and Trust, Michele English
VP Century Bank and Trust, Lisa Gosling
VP Century Bank and Trust, F. Omar Hazoury
VP Century Bank and Trust, Kathleen A. Kelly
VP Century Bank and Trust, Michael F. Long
VP Century Bank and Trust, Cornelius C. Prioleau
VP Century Bank and Trust, Bernice A. Shuman
VP Century Bank and Trust, Tuesday N. Thomas
Director, Stephanie Sonnabend, age 59
Director, Jon Westling, age 69
Director, Roger S. Berkowitz, age 59
Director, Fraser Lemley, age 71
Director, Joseph J. Senna, age 72
Co-President and Co-CEO Century Bancorp; Co-President and Co-CEO Century Bank and Trust Company, Barry R. Sloane, age 57
Director, George F. Swansburg, age 69
Director; VP Business Development Century Bank and Trust, Linda Sloane Kay, age 50
Director, Jackie Jenkins-Scott, age 62
Co-President and Co-CEO Century Bancorp; Co-President and Co-CEO Century Bank and Trust Company, Jonathan G. Sloane, age 53
Director, Jospeh P Mercurio, age 63
Auditors: KPMGLLP

LOCATIONS

HQ: Century Bancorp Inc.
400 Mystic Ave., Medford MA 02155-6316
Phone: 781-391-4000 **Fax:** 781-393-4071
Web: www.century-bank.com

PRODUCTS/OPERATIONS

2011 Sales

	$ mil.	% of total
Interest		
Loans	48	51
Securities	28	31
Other	1	1
Noninterest		
Service charges on deposit accounts	7	8
Lockbox fees	2	3
Net gains on sales of securities	1	2
Other	3	4
Total	**94**	**100**

COMPETITORS

Boston Private
Brookline Bancorp
Cambridge Financial
Capital Crossing
Central Bancorp
Eastern Bank
Middlesex Savings
Peoples Federal Bancshares Inc.
RBS Citizens Financial Group
Sovereign Bank

HISTORICAL FINANCIALS

Company Type: Public

Income Statement FYE: December 31

	ASSETS ($ mil.)	NET INCOME ($ mil.)	INCOME AS % OF ASSETS	EMPLOYEES
12/11	2,743	16	0.6%	405
12/10	2,441	13	0.6%	380
12/09	2,254	10	0.5%	369
12/08	1,801	9	0.5%	380
12/07	1,680	7	0.5%	373
Annual Growth	13.0%	20.7%	—	2.1%

2011 Year-End Financials

Debt ratio: 10.22%
Return on equity: 10.39%
Cash ($ mil.): 207
Current ratio: —
Long-term debt ($ mil.): 280
No. of shares (mil.): 5
Dividends
Yield: —
Payout: 15.95%
Market value ($ mil.): 157

	STOCK PRICE ($) FY Close	P/E High/Low		PER SHARE ($) Earnings	Dividends	Book Value
12/11	28.24	10	7	3.01	0.00	28.98
12/10	26.79	11	7	2.45	0.48	26.18
12/09	22.03	14	5	1.84	0.48	24.00
12/08	15.75	14	7	1.63	0.48	21.76
12/07	20.17	20	14	1.42	0.48	21.43
Annual Growth	8.8%	—	—	20.7%	—	7.8%

CenturyLink, Inc.

CenturyLink would like to be your communications hook-up for more than the next 100 years. Historically a regional wireline local and long-distance telephone provider it's connecting with the times by transforming into a broadband and network services provider for residential business and government clients. The company is the third-largest US telecom company by total access lines and is the incumbent local carrier in 37 states though three-quarters of its lines are in just a dozen mostly in the West and Midwest. Additionally it provides wireless service through Verizon and paid television service through its own Prism TV (in selected markets) with satellite provider DIRECTV.

As part of its transformation in 2011 CenturyLink started categorizing its products and services into legacy services (traditional phone still its largest at about 50% of sales) and strategic services (data and network connection about 40%). Its strategic services include private line broadband hosting video Internet telephony (VoIP) multi-protocol line switching (MPLS) and wireless services. The remaining 10% of sales comes mostly from data integration services such as network management and construction and equipment installation and maintenance.

CenturyLink has grown significantly through acquisitions in the past few years. The company made two major purchases in 2011 beginning with Minnesota's largest telephone company Qwest Communications in an all-stock deal valued at more than $10 billion. The acquisition was primarily what propelled CenturyLink revenues to more than double in 2011 though the related costs took a bite out of net income which fell 40%. The acquisition made it the nation's third-largest telco in total access lines bolstering its position against national industry leaders AT&T and Verizon and gave it an operational advantage over smaller regional players.

Turning its focus to enterprise communications CenturyLink paid $2.5 billion in cash and stock to acquire data and network hosting services provider SAVVIS. The company assumed $700 million of debt carried by SAVVIS as part of the deal but paid off nearly $550 million by the time the deal was closed. The acquisition helps CenturyLink expand and diversify its enterprise business as traditional residential phone struggles to stay viable as the world goes more mobile. SAVVIS will continue to operate as its own brand; however CenturyLink anticipates strong cross-selling opportunities to its business customers for managed hosting and cloud services.

After these acquisitions the company which had reported its operations as one segment divided the business into four segments: regional markets (residential customers and small midsized and regional businesses) business markets (government and large enterprise) wholesale markets (other communications providers) and Savvis (hosting and network services to global commercial customers). Legacy and regional operations still account for the most sales making up about half of all revenue.

The 2009 acquisition of Embarq a Kansas-based local phone company caused CenturyLink revenues to jump more than 40% the next year. Embarq's 6 million customers in 18 states gave CenturyLink greater access to metropolitan and suburban markets but it also put the company up against stiffer competition from other carriers. CenturyLink paid $11.6 billion in stock and debt for Embarq. The combined company changed its name from CenturyTel to CenturyLink in late 2010 to better reflect its role as a provider of data and wholesale network services for other carriers in addition to its residential business.

While acquisitions boosted CenturyLink revenues the company's own legacy service revenues fell more than 5% as its share of the combined company's total access lines dropped from nearly 6.5 million to about 6 million. That erosion is being felt across the industry as wireline phone services are being replaced with mobile and other more modern alternatives. CenturyLink forecasted a similar percentage of wireline departures in 2012. Aggressive marketing of its strategic services and data integration services will be central to combating the continuing legacy services decline.

CenturyLink has taken on a lot of debt to support its acquisitive streak. In addition the company is upgrading its network to support its Prism digital television service currently only available to about 5% of its territories. Prism's current territories are LaCrosse Wisconsin; Columbia and Jefferson City Missouri; Orlando Tallahassee and southwest Florida; Las Vegas; and central North Carolina. More TV customers mean more opportunities to offer high-margin bundled service such as phone Internet and TV.

While its traditional business as a phone service provider is dedicated to the US CenturyLink is listening to business services customers on where to invest in data center capacity. At this point the biggest need is in Singapore.

HISTORY

CenturyLink began as CenturyTel in 1930 when Marie and William Clarke Williams bought the Oak Ridge Telephone Company in Oak Ridge Louisiana. In 1946 they gave the 75-line company as a wedding present to their son Clarke who launched a course of growth by acquisition buying the Marion Louisiana telephone exchange in 1950 (Clarke Williams remained active in the company until his death in 2002). The company was renamed Century Telephone Enterprises in 1971; it went public in 1978.

Century bought local-exchange and cellular networks building regional clusters. States targeted during the early to mid-1990s included Louisiana Michigan Mississippi Ohio Tennessee and Texas. Century's biggest purchase came in 1997: It bought Pacific Telecom Inc. (PTI) from electric utility PacifiCorp for $2.2 billion. Century gained operations in 12 western and midwestern states and in Alaska more than doubling its telephone customer base.

Also in 1997 Century merged its Metro Access Networks (MAN) subsidiary into Brooks Fiber and became Brooks' largest shareholder. Brooks' shares rose when WorldCom agreed to buy it and Century sold 85% of its interest in Brooks.

The company rolled out the CenturyTel brand name in 1998 and bought Ameritech's local-exchange and directory operations in 21 Wisconsin communities. To help pay for the acquisition the carrier sold its Alaska operations in 1999 to Alaska Communications Systems Holdings a firm headed by former PTI executives. It also bought the Montana ISP DigiSys.

CenturyTel purchased nearly 500000 access lines from GTE (which later became Verizon) in Arkansas Missouri and Wisconsin in 2000 and the next year sold its PCS licenses to Leap Wireless International.

ALLTEL offered to buy CenturyTel in 2001 for $6.1 billion in cash and stock and $3.3 billion in assumed debt. ALLTEL announced the offer to the public after being told by CenturyTel that the company was not for sale. CenturyTel subsequently sued ALLTEL for releasing information about the company's plans. Tensions eased however and in 2002 the two companies reached the agreement that sent CenturyTel's wireless operations which served more than 800000 customers in six states to ALLTEL. The $1.6 billion cash deal enabled the company to expand its fixed-line business including the acquisition that year of 675000 switched phone lines in Alabama and Missouri from Verizon Communications for about $2.2 billion.

In 2003 CenturyTel acquired the regional fiber-optic business of bankrupt wholesale transport services provider Digital Teleport in a deal valued at $38 million. It also acquired fiber transport assets in Arkansas Missouri and Illinois from Level 3 Communications in a deal valued at about $16 million.

The company further expanded its network operations with the 2005 acquisition of the fiber-optic network and customer base of KMC Telecom's operations in Monroe and Shreveport Louisiana as well as metro fiber networks in 16 additional markets for $75 million in cash.

In 2007 CenturyTel purchased Madison River Communications for $830 million. The acquisition added more than 160000 rural access lines to its books and gave the company ownership of an additional 2400 miles of fiber network. Looking ahead to new opportunities outside the wireline segment CenturyLink paid about $150 million to the FCC in 2008 for wireless spectrum licenses that became available for commercial use the next year.

To reflect its transformation from a telco to a broadband and network services provider the company changed its name from CenturyTel to CenturyLink in 2010.

EXECUTIVES

SVP Operations Support and Controller, David D. Cole, age 54, $424,853 total compensation
EVP CFO and Assistant Secretary, R. Stewart Ewing Jr., age 60, $588,237 total compensation
Vice Chairman, Harvey P. Perry, age 67, $358,116 total compensation
President CEO and Director, Glen F. Post III, age 59, $1,009,440 total compensation
CEO Savvis Operations and President Enterprise Markets Groups, James E. (Jim) Ousley, age 66
EVP and COO, Karen A. Puckett, age 51, $654,023 total compensation
Chairman, William A. (Bill) Owens, age 71
SVP Public Policy and Government Relations, R. Steven (Steve) Davis
VP Investor Relations, Tony Davis
EVP Corporate Strategy and Development, Stephanie G. Comfort
EVP General Counsel and Secretary, Stacey W. Goff, age 46, $414,037 total compensation
President Wholesale Operations, William E. (Bill) Cheek, age 56
EVP Information Technology Services, Girish K. Varma
Manager External Communications, Debra D. Peterson
Region President South Central Region, Kenneth Wyatt
Region President Mid-Atlantic Region, Todd C. Schafer
Region President Northeast Region, Duane Ring
Region President Southern Region, Dana Chase
Region President Western Region, Terry E. Beeler
Corporate Leader Integration and Process Improvement, Les Meredith
EVP Network Services, Dennis G. Huber, age 52
SVP and CIO, Bill Bradley
VP Government Relations, John Jones
Manager Operations South Dakota, Steve Kolbeck
President Business Markets Group, Christopher K. (Chris) Ancell
Vice Chairman, Harvey P. Perry, age 67
President CEO and Director, Glen F. Post III, age 59
Director, Fred R. Nichols, age 65
Director, W. Bruce Hanks, age 57
Director, Peter C. Brown, age 54
Director, Laurie A. Siegel, age 64
Director, Richard A. (Dick) Gephardt, age 70
Director, Gregory J. McCray, age 49
Auditors: KPMGLLP

LOCATIONS

HQ: CenturyLink Inc.
100 CenturyLink Dr., Monroe LA 71201
Phone: 318-388-9000 **Fax:** 415-636-9820
Web: www.schwab.com

PRODUCTS/OPERATIONS

2011 Sales by Segment

	$ mil.	% of total
% of total		
Regional		51
Wholesale		21

Business	19
Savvis	3
Other	6
Total	**100**

2011 Sales by Category

	$ mil.	% of total
Legacy services	7,680	50
Strategic services	6,254	41
Data integration	537	3
Other	880	6
Total	**15,351**	**100**

COMPETITORS

AT&T
Cavalier Telephone
Comcast
Cox Communications
DISH Network
Equinix
FairPoint Communications Inc.
Farmers Telecommunications
Frontier Communications
Level 3 Communications
Nsight
NTELOS
Sprint Nextel
Telephone & Data Systems
Time Warner Cable
Verizon
XO Holdings

HISTORICAL FINANCIALS

Company Type: Public

Income Statement FYE: December 31

	REVENUE ($ mil.)	NET INCOME ($ mil.)	NET PROFIT MARGIN	EMPLOYEES
12/11	15,351	573	3.7%	49,200
12/10	7,041	947	13.5%	20,300
12/09	4,974	647	13.0%	6,700
12/08	2,599	365	14.1%	6,500
12/07	2,656	418	15.8%	6,600
Annual Growth	55.0%	8.2%	—	65.2%

2011 Year-End Financials

Debt ratio: 38.90%
Return on equity: 2.75%
Cash ($ mil.): 128
Current ratio: 87.66
Long-term debt ($ mil.): 21,356
No. of shares (mil.): 618
Dividends
Yield: —
Payout: 271.03%
Market value ($ mil.): 23,009

	STOCK PRICE ($) FY Close	P/E High/Low		PER SHARE ($) Earnings	Dividends	Book Value
12/11	37.20	44	30	1.07	0.00	33.67
12/10	46.17	15	11	3.13	2.90	31.62
12/09	36.21	11	7	3.23	2.80	31.62
12/08	27.33	12	6	3.56	2.17	31.54
12/07	41.46	13	11	3.72	0.26	31.42
Annual Growth	(2.7%)	—	—	(26.8%)	—	1.7%

CF Industries Holdings Inc

The folks at CF Industries make a lot of fertilizer and they like to spread it around. The international agricultural firm manufactures and markets nitrogen- and phosphate-based fertilizers (including diammonium phosphate or DAP); it is North America's top producer of nitrogen-based fertilizers and #2 in the world. Its ownership of fertilizer producer Terra Industries helps it keep its dominant position. CF Industries' nitrogen products include ammonia granular urea and UAN (urea ammonium nitrate) solutions and its primary phosphate products are DAP and MAP (monoammonium phosphate). The company supplies approximately 20% of the nitrogen and 15% of the phosphate used by US farmers.

Geographic Reach

Through its CF Industries Inc. subsidiary the company operates seven nitrogen fertilizer manufacturing complexes in the central US region and Canada; phosphate mining and production operations in Florida; and a network of fertilizer distribution terminals and warehouses located primarily in major grain-producing states across the Midwest. It also holds 50% of KEYTRADE AG a Switzerland-based global fertilizer trading company as well as 50% of joint ventures in Trinidad and Tobago and the UK.

Financial Analysis

In 2011 CF Industries reported a revenue increase of 54% largely due to higher nitrogen and phosphate fertilizer prices and sales volumes and the impact of its acquisition of Terra Industries.

Nitrogen segment net sales increased by 57% in 2011 due to a rise in average nitrogen fertilizer selling prices of $385 per ton as a result of an increase in planted acres and tighter supplies due to stronger demand and global supply constraints. The Phosphate segment's sales increased by 40% due to higher phosphate fertilizer selling prices and sales volumes resulting from supply constraints in the international market and strong domestic demand.

CF Industries' net income spiked by 300% thanks to higher revenues and a decrease in operating expenses. Restructuring and integration costs dropped $17.2 million as integration activities associated with the acquisition of Terra declined substantially. Interest expenses were also significantly down in 2011.

Strategy

The company is expanding its position as a leading global marketer producer and supplier of high-quality low-cost fertilizer products and services through acquisitions.

In mid-2012 CF Industries announced it would purchase about 34% of Canadian Fertilizer Limited (CFL) for C$915 million. CFL owns and operates Canada's largest nitrogen fertilizer production complex with a production capacity of approximately 425000 gross tons of ammonia and 275000 tons of urea per year. Natural resources conglomerate Glencore is buying Canadian grain company Viterra which currently owns the 34% of CFL. To placate Canadian regulators Glencore is selling certain Viterra assets.

In 2010 CF Industries acquired major fertilizer producer Terra Industries positioning itself as a nitrogen bellwether in the global fertilizer industry and the top nitrogen and phosphate fertilizer manufacturer in North America.

The company's business model also sees it increasing sales to nonaffiliated customers such as ConAgra. Prior to its 2005 IPO it sold most of its products through its original regional coop members' sales outlets. In 2011 GROWMARK and CHS were still its largest customers along with joint venture KEYTRADE and Gavilon Fertilizer.

Company Background

CF Industries was organized in 1946 as Central Farmers Fertilizer Company. The company changed its structure from a cooperative to a holding company when it began to trade publicly in 2005. It had been owned by eight regional agricultural co-ops including Land O'Lakes GROWMARK and CHS. Following the IPO the co-ops' stakes were largely reduced.

EXECUTIVES

Chairman President and CEO, Stephen R. Wilson, age 64, $900,000 total compensation
senior Vice President Sales and Market Development, Bert A. Frost, age 47, $312,500 total compensation
VP Public Affairs, Rosemary L. O'Brien
VP Manufacturing Integration, Richard S. Sanders Jr., age 54
senior Vice President Chief Financial Officer, Dennis Kelleher
Senior Vice President General Counsel Secretary, Douglas C. (Doug) Barnard, age 53, $350,000 total compensation
SVP Supply Chain, Philipp P. (Phil) Koch, age 60, $285,000 total compensation
Vice President Donaldsonville Operations, Louis M. (Lou) Frey III
VP Phosphate Operations; General Manager Plant City Phosphate Complex, Herschel E. Morris
VP Environmental Health and Safety and Engineering, Russell A. Holowachuk
Senior Director Investor Relations and Corporate Communications, Terrell (Terry) Huch
VP and Corporate Controller, Richard A. Hoker, age 47
Senior Vice President Human Resources, Wendy S. Jablow Spertus, age 49
VP Treasurer and Assistant Secretary, Randall W. (Randy) Selgrad
SVP Manufacturing and Distribution, W. Anthony (Tony) Will, age 46, $325,000 total compensation
VP Corporate Planning, Christopher D. (Chris) Bohn
VP Corporate Development, Lynn F. White, age 59
Director Business Development, Rick Sompel
Director Agribusiness Analysis, Douglas A. (Doug) Hoadley
Senior Vice President Human Resources, Wendy Spertus
Director, Robert G. (Rob) Kuhbach, age 65
Director, Edward A. (Ed) Schmitt, age 65
Director, Robert C. (Bob) Arzbaecher, age 52
Director, David R. Harvey, age 72
Director, Stephen J. (Steve) Hagge, age 60
Director, Stephen A. (Steve) Furbacher, age 64
Director, John D. Johnson, age 63
Director, Wallace W. (Wally) Creek, age 73
Director, William (Bill) Davisson, age 64
Auditors: KPMGLLP

LOCATIONS

HQ: CF Industries Holdings Inc.
4 Parkway N. Ste. 400, Deerfield IL 60015
Phone: 847-405-2400 **Fax:** 847-405-2711
Web: www.cfindustries.com

2011 Sales

US	5,175	85
Other countries	429	7

PRODUCTS/OPERATIONS

2011 Sales

	$ mil.	% of total
Nitrogen	5,012	82
Phosphate	1,085	18
Total	**6,097**	**100**

Selected Products

Anhydrous ammonia
Diammonium phosphate (DAP)
Granular urea
Monoammonium phosphate (MAP)
Urea ammonium nitrate (UAN)

COMPETITORS

Agrium
BASF SE
Cargill
JR Simplot
Koch Industries Inc.
LSB Industries
Mosaic Company
Potash Corp
Transammonia

HISTORICAL FINANCIALS

Company Type: Public

Income Statement

FYE: December 31

	REVENUE ($ mil.)	NET INCOME ($ mil.)	NET PROFIT MARGIN	EMPLOYEES
12/11	6,097	1,539	25.2%	2,500
12/10	3,965	349	8.8%	2,500
12/09	2,608	365	14.0%	1,600
12/08	3,921	684	17.5%	1,600
12/07	2,756	372	13.5%	1,500
Annual Growth	22.0%	42.6%	—	13.6%

2011 Year-End Financials

Debt ratio: 18.03%
Return on equity: 33.85%
Cash ($ mil.): 1,207
Current ratio: 174.42
Long-term debt ($ mil.): 1,617
No. of shares (mil.): 65
Dividends
Yield: —
Payout: 4.55%
Market value ($ mil.): 9,485

	STOCK PRICE ($) FY Close	P/E High/Low		PER SHARE ($) Earnings	Dividends	Book Value
12/11	144.98	9	5	21.98	0.00	69.50
12/10	135.15	25	11	5.34	0.40	56.83
12/09	90.78	13	6	7.42	0.40	35.60
12/08	49.16	14	3	12.15	0.40	27.65
12/07	110.06	17	4	6.57	0.08	21.10
Annual Growth	7.1%	—	—	35.2%	—	34.7%

Charter Communications Inc

Charter Communications navigates the waters of US cable services. The cable system operator has about 5 million mostly-residential subscribers in 25 states making it one of the top national cable companies behind Comcast Time Warner Cable and Cox Communications. Besides its some 4.3 million video customers (about 80% opting for the digital service) Charter also has about 3.7 million broadband Internet subscribers and about 2 million computer telephony users. The company also derives revenue from the sale of local advertising on such cable networks as MTV CNN and ESPN. Charter Communications which skirted bankruptcy for years began and completed a reorganization under Chapter 11 protection in 2009.

Strategy As it wrestles with all of its challenges Charter continues to pursue a strategy popular with its competitors providing voice Internet access and other data services as a complete package. Similar to the results of rival cable companies it has seen rises in telephone Internet and enterprise customers while video subscribers have dwindled among both residential and business clients. It does however continue to see upticks in the move to digital video services. Video revenues dipped 2% for 2011 while every other category saw a bump: Internet ramped up 6% telephone dialed up 4% and enterprise clients expanded 18%. Again following suit with the industry its average monthly revenue per video customer has risen over the past two years and by about the same amount as its industry mates roughly $20 going from $114 in 2009 to $136 for 2011. Among the investments eating away at those revenues was the deployment of a network upgrade to the DOCSIS 3.0 high-speed data capability standard to keep up with the competition. Charter put the technology in place for more than 90% of homes it has passed allowing Internet speeds up to 100 megabits per second. That deployment will help as it continues to pursue enterprise clients. Charter serves mostly small and medium-sized businesses (less than 200 employees) but it also targets large companies and offers its commercial services wholesale to carriers. As part of Charter's effort to improve efficiency by divesting operations in non-strategic locations the company sold certain of its cable systems to Cobridge Communications an affiliate of The Gores Group in 2010. The cable systems were located in Alabama Arkansas Georgia Louisiana Missouri Ohio and Texas. (Charter no longer operates in Arkansas and Ohio.) The company went on to acquire broadband cable assets in Alabama and Georgia in 2011 from Windjammer Communications (adding about 17000 subscribers) and a broadband system serving nearly that number in Missouri from US Cable of Coastal Texas.

Ownership AP Charter Holdings owns about 33% of the company while Oaktree Opportunities Investments holds 17%. Company Background Driven by dreams of creating a "wired world" chairman Paul Allen (a co-founder of Microsoft) reportedly poured more than $12 billion into Charter since 1998 and the billionaire saw most of that investment evaporate. After expanding through the purchase of a slew of small-town cable assets that needed extensive infrastructure upgrades Charter experienced ongoing subscriber losses financial losses and a debt load in excess of $20 billion. Faced with legal opposition from some of its lenders the company's bankruptcy reorganization plan eliminated about $8 billion of debt reduced annual interest expenses by about $830 million and left Allen controlling about one-third of the company a stake which has fallen to less than 10%.

HISTORY

Crown Media bought St. Louis-based Cencom Cable in 1992. Rather than relocate to Crown's Dallas home Cencom CEO Howard Wood joined with fellow executives Barry Babcock and Jerry Kent to form Charter Communications as a cable acquisition and management company in St. Louis. With an investment from Crown owned by Hallmark Cards the trio partnered with LEB Communications in 1994 to manage Charter's growth. And grow it did.

In 1994 Charter paid about $900 million for a majority stake in Crown. Charter spent $3 billion on 15 cable acquisitions in its first four years. It had more than 1 million subscribers by early 1997 and began offering high-speed cable Internet access and paging services in some of its markets.

Charter went into acquisition overdrive in 1998 when Microsoft co-founder Paul Allen took control with his $4.5 billion investment. The deal closely followed Allen's $2.8 billion takeover of Dallas-based Marcus Cable; Marcus was merged with Charter. The combined company based in St. Louis with Kent as CEO was the #7 US cable business with 2.5 million subscribers. Also that year the company teamed up with Wink and WorldGate to offer TV Internet services with set-top boxes.

Before the ink was dry on the merger papers Allen was at it again. The company's 1999 acquisitions included Falcon Communications (1 million cable subscribers) and Fanch Cablevision (more than 500000); it also bought cable systems from Helicon InterMedia Partners Avalon Cable Inter-Link Communications Renaissance Media and Rifkin. Charter said it would spend $3.5 billion upgrading its systems over three years after raising that amount in a major junk bond sale. Months later the company raised $3.2 billion in its IPO.

In 2000 Charter completed its purchase of Bresnan Communications (700000 subscribers) and bought a system from Cablevision to form a major cluster in Michigan Minnesota and Wisconsin. The next year the company gained 554000 subscribers by swapping noncore cable systems and $1.8 billion in cash to AT&T Broadband in exchange for systems serving the St. Louis area parts of Alabama and the Reno area of Nevada and California.

Also in 2001 Kent resigned from the company and its board of directors and was replaced as CEO by former Liberty Media executive Carl Vogel. Vogel stayed on the job until 2005 at which point he also retired. Former AOL executive Neil Smit replaced Vogel later that year. Several other executive departures followed and a subsequent securities investigation led to convictions against former COO Dave Barford (sentenced to one year in prison) and former CFO Kent Kalkwarf (14 months in prison).

The company in 2006 sold nearly $900 million in assets including systems in Illinois and Kentucky to New Wave Communications and systems in West Virginia and Virginia to Cebridge Connections. Shedding more assets Charter also sold cable TV systems serving nearly 70000 customers in the western US to subsidiaries of Orange Broadband Holding Company.

EXECUTIVES

Interim CTO, Christopher J. (Chris) Bowick, age 53
COO, John R. Bickham, age 60
President CEO and Director, Thomas M. (Tom) Rutledge, age 58
Chairman, Eric L. Zinterhofer, age 40
EVP Technology; President Commercial Services, Donald F. (Don) Detampel Jr., age 56
SVP and CTO, Jay A. Rolls
President CEO and Director, Michael J. (Mike) Lovett, age 50, $757,178 total compensation
President Charter Media, James M. (Jim) Heneghan, age 53
SVP General Counsel and Secretary, Richard R. Dykhouse, age 48
SVP Finance Controller and Chief Accounting Officer, Kevin D. Howard, age 42
SVP Customer Experience, John A. Birrer
President Operations, Steven E. Apodaca, age 45
EVP and CFO, Christopher L. (Chris) Winfrey, age 36
SVP Product and Strategy, Rich DiGeronimo
Communications and Media Relations, Anita Lamont
Communications and Media Relations, John R. Miller
VP Web Technology Customer Experience, Marti Moore
VP Investor Relations, Robin Gutzler
EVP and Chief Marketing Officer, Jonathan Hargis
EVP and Chief Administrative Officer, Robert E. Quicksilver, age 57
Director, Bruce A. Karsh, age 56
Director, Robert Cohn, age 62

President CEO and Director, Thomas M. (Tom) Rutledge, age 58
Director, W. Lance Conn, age 43
Director, David C. Merritt, age 57
Director, Stan Parker, age 36
President CEO and Director, Michael J. (Mike) Lovett, age 50
Director, Craig A. Jacobson, age 59
Director, Edgar Lee, age 35
Director, Darren Glatt, age 35
Director, John D. Markley Jr., age 46
Auditors: KPMGLLP

LOCATIONS

HQ: Charter Communications Inc.
12405 Powerscourt Dr. Ste. 100, St. Louis MO 63131-3660
Phone: 314-965-0555 **Fax:** 314-965-9745
Web: www.charter.com

PRODUCTS/OPERATIONS

2011 Sales

	$ mil.	% of total
Video	3,602	50
High-speed Internet	1,706	24
Telephone	858	12
Commercial	583	8
Advertising sales	292	4
Other	163	2
Total	**7,204**	**100**

COMPETITORS

Apple Inc.
AT&T
Bright House Networks
Cablevision Systems
Clearwire
Comcast
Cox Communications
DIRECTV
DISH Network
EarthLink
Frontier Communications
Hulu
Insight Communications
LodgeNet
Mediacom Communications
Netflix
RCN Corporation
Skype
Sprint Nextel
Suddenlink Communications
T-Mobile USA
Time Warner Cable
United Online
Verizon
Vonage
YouTube

HISTORICAL FINANCIALS

Company Type: Public

Income Statement

FYE: December 31

	REVENUE ($ mil.)	NET INCOME ($ mil.)	NET PROFIT MARGIN	EMPLOYEES
12/11	7,204	(369)	—	16,000
12/10	7,059	(237)	—	16,600
12/09*	572	2	0.3%	16,700
11/09	6,183	11,364	183.8%	0
12/08	6,479	(2,451)	—	16,600
Annual Growth	2.7%	—	—	(0.9%)

*Fiscal year change

2011 Year-End Financials

Debt ratio: 82.38%
Return on equity: (-90.22)%
Cash ($ mil.): 29
Current ratio: 32.09
Long-term debt ($ mil.): 12,856
No. of shares (mil.): 100
Dividends
Yield: —
Payout: —
Market value ($ mil.): 5,726

	STOCK PRICE ($) FY Close	P/E High/Low	PER SHARE ($) Earnings	Dividends	Book Value
12/11	56.94	— —	(3.39)	0.00	4.07
12/10	38.94	— —	(2.09)	0.00	12.90
12/09*	35.50	17251725	0.02	0.00	16.69
Annual Growth	26.6%	— —	—	—	(50.6%)

*Fiscal year change

Chemical Financial Corp.

Chemical Financial has banking down to a science. It's the holding company for Chemical Bank which serves individuals and businesses in the lower peninsula of Michigan through more than 180 branches. The bank provides standard services such as checking and savings accounts CDs and IRAs credit and debit cards and loans and mortgages. Its wealth management division has some $2 billion of assets under custody. The company also offers trust services title insurance and employee benefits. Subsidiary Chemical Financial Advisors provides financial planning mutual funds life insurance annuities and retail brokerage services through an agreement with PrimeVest.

Chemical Financial bought holding company O.A.K. Financial and its Byron Bank subsidiary for some $84 million in stock in 2010. The deal added more than a dozen bank branches in western Michigan where the company is looking for further growth. The purchase of O.A.K. added to Chemical Financial's assets and revenue as well and contributed to a 131% increase in net income in 2010.

In late 2012 the company acquired 21 branches in northeastern Michigan and Battle Creek from Independent Bank. That more than $8-million transaction further expands Chemical Bank's presence geographically. Additional acquisitions including FDIC-assisted takeovers of failed banks are possible.

The company has remained profitable despite Michigan being one of the states hardest hit by the recession. The bank which derives most of its revenue from interest and fees on loans is helped by its diverse portfolio which is more or less evenly distributed between commercial real estate business residential real estate and consumer and home equity loans. Chemical Financial's net income was up another 86% in 2011 as the company booked fewer provisions for loan losses amid an improving economic environment.

EXECUTIVES

Chairman President and CEO Chemical Financial and Chemical Bank, David B. Ramaker, age 56, $419,450 total compensation
EVP CFO and Treasurer, Lori A. Gwizdala, age 53, $254,650 total compensation
EVP and Senior Credit Officer Chemical Bank, James E. Tomczyk, age 59, $225,504 total compensation
EVP Community Banking and Secretary, Thomas W. Kohn, age 57, $247,724 total compensation
EVP and Director Bank Operations Chemical Bank, Kenneth W. Johnson, age 49, $211,060 total compensation
EVP and Chief Risk Management Officer Chemical Bank, Dominic Monastiere, age 64
EVP and Senior Trust Officer Chemical Bank, John E. Kessler, age 43
Executive Vice President; Chief Risk Management Officer, Leonardo Amat
Executive Vice President & Regional President; South, Lynn Kerber
Executive Vice President; General Counsel; Secretary, William Collins
Director, William S. Stavropoulos, age 72
Director, Aloysius J. Oliver, age 71
Director, Gary E. Anderson, age 66
Director, James B. (Jim) Meyer, age 65
Director, J. Daniel Bernson, age 70
Director, James A. Currie, age 53
Director, Terence F. Moore, age 68
Director, Nancy Bowman, age 60
Director, Thomas T. Huff, age 69
Director, Grace O. Shearer, age 64
Director, Michael T. Laethem, age 53
Director, Larry D. Stauffer, age 66
Director, Franklin C. Wheatlake, age 64
Director, James R. (Jim) Fitterling
Auditors: KPMGLLP

LOCATIONS

HQ: Chemical Financial Corporation
235 E. Main St., Midland MI 48640
Phone: 989-839-5350 **Fax:** 989-839-5255
Web: www.chemicalbankmi.com

PRODUCTS/OPERATIONS

2011 Sales

	$ mil.	% of total
Interest		
Loans including fees	197	76
Investment securities	15	6
Other	2	1
Noninterest		
Service charges on deposit accounts	18	7
Wealth management revenue	11	4
Other customer service charges & fees	10	4
Other	4	2
Total	**259**	**100**

COMPETITORS

1st Source Corporation
Bank of America
Citizens Republic Bancorp
Comerica
Fifth Third
Firstbank
Flagstar Bancorp
Huntington Bancshares
Independent Bank (MI)
Mercantile Bank

HISTORICAL FINANCIALS

Company Type: Public

Income Statement

FYE: December 31

	ASSETS ($ mil.)	NET INCOME ($ mil.)	INCOME AS % OF ASSETS	EMPLOYEES
12/11	5,339	43	0.8%	1,700
12/10	5,246	23	0.4%	1,608
12/09	4,250	10	0.2%	1,427
12/08	3,874	19	0.5%	1,416
12/07	3,754	39	1.0%	1,368
Annual Growth	9.2%	2.5%	—	5.6%

2011 Year-End Financials

Debt ratio: 0.81%
Return on equity: 7.53%
Cash ($ mil.): 381
Current ratio: —
Long-term debt ($ mil.): 43
No. of shares (mil.): 27
Dividends
Yield: —
Payout: 50.96%
Market value ($ mil.): 585

	STOCK PRICE ($) FY Close	P/E High/Low		PER SHARE ($) Earnings	Dividends	Book Value
12/11	21.32	15	9	1.57	0.00	20.82
12/10	22.15	28	21	0.88	0.80	20.41
12/09	23.58	67	37	0.42	1.18	19.85
12/08	27.88	42	24	0.83	1.18	20.58
12/07	23.79	21	13	1.60	1.14	21.35
Annual Growth	(2.7%)	—	—	(0.5%)	—	(0.6%)

Chesapeake Energy Corp.

Chesapeake Energy (named after the childhood Chesapeake Bay haunts of a founder) builds oil and natural gas reserves through the acquisition and development of oil and gas assets across the US. In 2011 the company's Southern region (including the Barnett Bossier and Haynesville shale plays) accounted for more 46% of company's estimated proved reserves of 18.8 trillion cu. ft. of natural gas equivalent. Chesapeake also has assets in Appalachia the Mid-Continent the Permian Basin and the Rockies. In 2011 the company had more than 45700 producing oil and natural gas wells that produced 3.5 billion cu. ft. of natural gas equivalent per day the bulk of which was natural gas.

Operations

Chesapeake is a leading producer of natural gas and a top 15 producer of oil and natural gas liquids. The company has vertically integrated many of its operations and owns major marketing compression midstream and oilfield services businesses. Through its Nomac Drilling unit the company saves costs by operating its own equipment. In 2011 the company was operating more than 130 drilling rigs (39 owned and 93 leased.)

Geographic Reach

The company has natural gas resources in the Haynesville and Bossier Shales in northwestern Louisiana and East Texas; the Marcellus Shale in the northern Appalachian Basin of West Virginia and Pennsylvania; the Barnett Shale in the Fort Worth Basin of north-central Texas; and the Pearsall Shale in South Texas. In addition it has built leading positions in the liquids-rich resource plays of the Eagle Ford Shale in South Texas; the Utica Shale in Ohio and Pennsylvania; the Granite Wash Cleveland Tonkawa and Mississippi Lime plays in the Anadarko Basin in western Oklahoma and the Texas Panhandle; the Bone Spring Avalon Wolfcamp and Wolfberry plays in the Permian and Delaware Basins in West Texas and southern New Mexico; and the Niobrara Shale in the Powder River Basin in Wyoming.

Financial Analysis

The company saw its 2011 revenues increase by 24%. It also took advantage of higher-priced crude to increase the production of oil. These efforts plus continued growth in its natural gas production segment helped Chesapeake to report a 15% increase in oil and gas production over 2010 allowing it post a robust growth in revenues in 2011.

Higher operating expenses led by an increase in marketing gathering and compression expenses (up 33% over 2010) and natural gas and oil depreciation depletion and amortization costs (up 17%) cut into 2011 net income which decreased by 1.8% compared to 2010.

Strategy

As part of its strategy to reduce costs by having more ownership of the rigs it uses to drill its wells in 2011 the company acquired Bronco Drilling (which owns 22 rigs) for $339 million. Chesapeake integrated Bronco's assets into its Nomac Drilling subsidiary.

To get better financial returns in 2012 the company spun off oilfield service industry affiliate Chesapeake Oilfield Services Inc. Hurt by continuing low natural gas prices that year the company sold its midstream assets in 2012 and 2013 for $4.9 billion in three separate deals. As part of this move in 2012 the company sold its limited partner units and its general partner interests in Chesapeake Midstream Partners to Global Infrastructure Partners for $2 billion. That year the company also sold about $6.9 billion of its Permian basin properties in order to pay down debt. It also sold Total E&P USA a $2.3 million 25% joint venture stake in its Utica Shale (Ohio) assets.

With natural gas prices remaining low Chesapeake in 2011 shifted its focus to exploiting gas fields with high liquids content (such as the Eagle Ford in Texas the Utica Shale and the Niobara Shale in Wyoming) allowing the company to produce high-priced natural gas liquids (NGLs). Looking to raise cash for future investments in 2011 Chesapeake sold all of its Fayetteville Shale assets to BHP Billiton unit BHP Billiton Petroleum for about $4.7 billion. It also announced plans to sell its stakes in Frac Tech Holdings and Chaparral Energy.

In 2011 it sold a 33% stake in its shale play in south Texas to CNOOC for $1.1 billion and agreed to a similar CNOOC deal for Chesapeake's assets in northeast Colorado and Southeast Wyoming.

Ownership

In 2012 Southeast Asset Management Inc. held 13.5% of Chesapeake Energy.

HISTORY

Aubrey McClendon (who grew up near Maryland's Chesapeake Bay) and Tom Ward had been non-operating partners in about 600 wells in Oklahoma before forming their own company in 1989 to develop new fields in Texas and Oklahoma during the 1990s. The firm went public in 1993. In 1995 the company acquired oil and gas acreage in Louisiana as well as Princeton Natural Gas an Oklahoma City-based gas marketing firm.

Oil finds in Louisiana and strong production from its Texas and Oklahoma wells helped lift Chesapeake's sales in 1996. That year it acquired Amerada Hess' (later renamed Hess) half of their joint operations in two Oklahoma fields. In 1997 chairman McClendon and president Ward acquired control of Chesapeake.

The company's success was based on its "growth through the drillbit" strategy –developing new wells. But after a 1997 loss Chesapeake modified its strategy and sought to grow by acquiring other companies. That year it bought energy company AnSon Production. Chesapeake subsequently bought oil and gas explorer-producer Hugoton Energy and energy company DLB Oil & Gas.

In 1998 the company acquired a 40% stake in Canadian oil producer Ranger Oil and paid Occidental Petroleum $105 million for natural gas reserves in the Texas Panhandle. Chesapeake then began to transform itself from a hotshot driller to an acquirer of natural gas properties almost tripling its proved reserves. The company suffered a huge loss that year in part from the acquisitions and continuing lower gas prices.

With gas prices soaring again the company continued its buying spree into 2000 when it agreed to buy midcontinent natural gas producer Gothic Energy for $345 million in stock and assumed debt. The deal closed in 2001. The company also sold its Canadian assets that year in order to focus on its core US properties.

In 2002 Chesapeake acquired oil and gas producer Canaan Energy for about $118 million. Later that year the company announced plans to sell or trade its Permian Basin assets.

Chesapeake acquired in 2003 a 25% stake in Pioneer Drilling (which it subsequently sold). In 2004 the company acquired Barnett Shale assets from Hallwood Energy for $292 million. That year it also bought privately owned Concho Resources for $420 million. The next year the company acquired privately held BRG Petroleum which held assets of more than 450 wells with proved reserves of more than 275 billion cu. ft. of natural gas for $325 million.

In 2005 Chesapeake acquired 20% of Gastar Exploration (reduced to 15% by 2007). That year in a major move the company acquired Columbia Natural Resources for $2.2 billion.

In 2007 Chesapeake began drilling at the Dallas/Fort Worth Airport which sits above the productive Barnett Shale formation.

Facing a deepening economic valley as commodity prices began to slump in 2008 the company moved to cut the costs of exploiting its shale assets by selling some of these properties to joint venture partners. In this regard Chesapeake sold 90000 net acres of natural gas assets in the Arkoma Basin Woodford Shale play for $1.7 billion to BP. It subsequently sold a 25% stake in its Fayetteville Shale assets in Arkansas to BP for $1.9 billion. And in early 2010 it also sold 25% of Barnett Shale properties to TOTAL forming a $2.25 billion joint venture with that company.

Accelerating its strategy to become a more vertically integrated company in 2009 Chesapeake formed Chesapeake Midstream Partners a joint venture with Global Infrastructure Partners to operate natural gas midstream assets.

EXECUTIVES

SVP Accounting Chief Accounting Officer and Controller, Michael A. Johnson, age 46, $340,000 total compensation

SVP Drilling, Stephen W. Miller, age 55

SVP Oilfield Services; CEO Chesapeake Oilfield Services, Jerry L. Winchester, age 53

SVP Corporate Development and Government Relations, Thomas S. (Tom) Price Jr., age 60

SVP Human and Corporate Resources, Martha A. Burger, age 59, $637,500 total compensation

SVP Land and Legal and General Counsel, Henry J. Hood, age 51

EVP Operations and Geosciences and COO, Steven C. (Steve) Dixon, age 53, $860,000 total compensation

Chairman and CEO, Aubrey K. McClendon, age 52, $975,000 total compensation

EVP Acquisitions and Divestitures, Douglas J. Jacobson, age 58, $800,000 total compensation

VP Urban Development Barnett Shale, Julie Wilson

SVP Secretary and Treasurer, Jennifer M. Grigsby, age 43
SVP Energy Marketing, James C. Johnson, age 54
SVP Information Technology and CIO, Cathlyn L. (Cathy) Tompkins, age 50
EVP and CFO, Domenic J. Dell'Osso, age 36
SVP Natural Gas Projects; CEO Chesapeake Midstream Partners, J. Michael (Mike) Stice, age 53
SVP Production, Jeffrey A. Fisher, age 52
SVP Investor Relations and Research, Jeffrey L. (Jeff) Mobley, age 43
SVP Geoscience, John M. Kapchinske, age 59
Director Media Relations, Jim Gipson
VP Corporate Development, Kevin McCotter
Senior Director Corporate Development and Government Affairs, Danny Games
Senior Director Corporate Development and Government Affairs, Matt Sheppard
Director Corporate Development and Government Relations, John Dill
Sr. Director - Corporate Development & Government Affairs, Adam Haynes
Vice President Chief Financial Officer, Domenic J. DellOsso
Independent Non-Executive Chairman of the Board, Archie Dunham
Senior Vice President - Legal and General Counsel, James Webb
Director, Richard K. (Dick) Davidson, age 70
Director, Merrill A. (Pete) Miller Jr., age 61
Director, V. Burns Hargis, age 66
Director, Louis A. Simpson, age 75
Director, Charles T. Maxwell, age 80
Director, Frank Keating, age 68
Director, Donald L. (Don) Nickles, age 63
Director, Kathleen Eisbrenner, age 52
Independent Director, Bob Alexander
Independent Director, Brad Martin
Independent Director, Frederic Poses
Independent Director, Vincent Intrieri
Auditors: PricewaterhouseCoopersLLP

LOCATIONS

HQ: Chesapeake Energy Corp.
6100 North Western Avenue, Oklahoma City, OK 73118
Phone: 405 848-8000 **Fax:** 405 483-0573
Web: www.chk.com

PRODUCTS/OPERATIONS

2011 Sales

	$ mil.	% of total
Exploration & production	6,024	52
Marketing gathering & compression	5,090	44
Service operations	521	4
Total	**11,635**	**100**

COMPETITORS

Adams Resources
Anadarko Petroleum
Apache
Ashland Inc.
Bonanza Creek
BP
Brigham Exploration
Chevron
ConocoPhillips
Exxon Mobil
Forest Oil
Koch Industries Inc.
Noble Energy
Occidental Petroleum
OGE Energy
Par Petroleum
Patterson-UTI Energy
Pioneer Natural Resources
Plains Exploration
Pride International
SandRidge Energy
Southwestern Energy
Unit Corporation

HISTORICAL FINANCIALS

Company Type: Public

Income Statement FYE: December 31

	REVENUE ($ mil.)	NET INCOME ($ mil.)	NET PROFIT MARGIN	EMPLOYEES
12/11	11,635	1,742	15.0%	12,600
12/10	9,366	1,774	18.9%	10,000
12/09	7,702	(5,830)	—	8,200
12/08	11,629	723	6.2%	7,600
12/07	7,800	1,451	18.6%	6,200
Annual Growth	10.5%	4.7%	—	19.4%

2011 Year-End Financials

Debt ratio: 25.87%
Return on equity: 10.48%
Cash ($ mil.): 351
Current ratio: 44.86
Long-term debt ($ mil.): 10,824
No. of shares (mil.): 659
Dividends
Yield: —
Payout: 10.78%
Market value ($ mil.): 14,697

	STOCK PRICE ($) FY Close	P/E High	P/E Low	PER SHARE ($) Earnings	Dividends	Book Value
12/11	22.29	14	9	2.32	0.00	25.21
12/10	25.91	11	8	2.51	0.30	23.34
12/09	25.88	—	—	(9.57)	0.30	17.67
12/08	16.17	60	10	1.14	0.29	26.84
12/07	39.20	15	10	2.62	0.26	23.73
Annual Growth	(13.2%)	—	—	(3.0%)	—	1.5%

Chevron Corporation

Chevron has earned its stripes as the #2 integrated oil company in the US behind Exxon Mobil. It has proved reserves of 11.2 billion barrels of oil equivalent and a daily production of 2.7 million barrels of oil equivalent and it also owns interests in chemicals mining pipeline and power production businesses. The company which is restructuring its refinery and retail businesses to cut costs owns or has stakes in 8170 gas stations in the US that operate under the Chevron and Texaco brands. Outside the US it owns or has stakes in 9660 gas stations. Chevron also owns 50% of chemicals concern Chevron Phillips Chemical. In a major move in 2011 Chevron acquired Atlas Energy in a $4.3 billion deal.

HISTORY

Thirty years after the California gold rush a small firm began digging for a new product –oil. The crude came from wildcatter Frederick Taylor's well located north of Los Angeles. In 1879 Taylor and other oilmen formed Pacific Coast Oil attracting the attention of John D. Rockefeller's Standard Oil. The two competed fiercely until Standard took over Pacific Coast in 1900.

When Standard Oil was broken up in 1911 its West Coast operations became the stand-alone Standard Oil Company (California) which was nicknamed Socal and sold Chevron-brand products. After winning drilling concessions in Bahrain and Saudi Arabia in the 1930s Socal summoned Texaco to help and they formed Caltex (California-Texas Oil Company) as equal partners. In 1948 Socony (later Mobil) and Jersey Standard (later Exxon) bought 40% of Caltex's Saudi operations and the Saudi arm became Aramco (Arabian American Oil Company).

Socal exploration pushed into Louisiana and the Gulf of Mexico in the 1940s. In 1961 it bought Standard Oil Company of Kentucky (Kyso). The 1970s brought setbacks: Caltex holdings were nationalized during the OPEC-spawned upheaval and the Saudi Arabian government claimed Aramco in 1980.

In 1984 Socal was renamed Chevron and doubled its reserves with its $13 billion purchase of Gulf Corp. which had origins in the 1901 Spindletop gusher in Texas. Gulf became an oil power by developing Kuwaiti concessions but was hobbled when those assets were nationalized in 1975. After Gulf was rocked by disclosures that it had an illegal political slush fund Socal stepped in. The deal loaded the new company with debt and it cut 20000 jobs and sold billions in assets.

Chevron bought Tenneco's Gulf of Mexico properties in 1988 and in 1992 swapped fields valued at $1.1 billion for 15.7 million shares of Chevron stock owned by Pennzoil. It also moved into the North Sea in 1994.

In the 1990s Chevron gave its retailing units a tune-up. It allied with McDonald's (1995) to combine burger stands and gas stations in 12 western states. In addition the company sold 450 UK gas stations and a refinery to Shell (1997). Meanwhile Chevron sold its natural gas operation in 1996 for a stake in Houston-based NGC (later Dynegy; sold in 2007) and it signed an onshore exploration contract in China the next year.

Poor economic conditions in Asia and slumping oil prices in 1998 forced Chevron to shed some US holdings including California properties. Looking for growth overseas in 1999 it bought Rutherford-Moran Oil increasing its interests in Thailand and Petrolera Argentina San Jorge Argentina's #3 oil company.

Chevron trimmed about 10% of its workforce in 1999 and 2000 in an effort to cut costs. As the rest of the industry consolidated Chevron discussed merging with Texaco but the talks collapsed in 1999. Later that year CEO Ken Derr retired and vice chairman Dave O'Reilly replaced him.

In 2000 Chevron formed a joint venture with Phillips Petroleum (later ConocoPhillips) that combined the companies' chemicals businesses as Chevron Phillips Chemical. That year talks with Texaco were revived and Chevron agreed to acquire its Caltex partner for about $35 billion in stock and about $8 billion in assumed debt. The deal completed in 2001 formed ChevronTexaco.

Part of the 2001 deal to acquire Texaco required Chevron to sell exclusive rights to the Texaco brand for a period of three years. A division of Royal Dutch Shell owned rights to the Texaco brand until 2004 and changed the name of the service stations to Shell. Once Chevron regained the rights to the Texaco name it revitalized the brand name by adding about 400 Texaco stations in the western US.

In 2002 ChevronTexaco divested its stakes in US downstream joint ventures Equilon (to Shell) and Motiva (to Shell and Saudi Aramco). It also sold part of a Gulf of Mexico pipeline and two natural gas plants in Louisiana to Duke Energy and its 12.5% stake in a natural gas liquids fractionator to Enterprise Products Partners. In 2004 ChevronTexaco sold 150 US natural gas and oil properties to XTO Energy for $912 million. The company changed its name to Chevron Corporation in 2005.

Chevron acquired Unocal in 2005 for more than $16 billion boosting its proved reserves by about 15%. Equally attractive to Chevron was the strategic position of Unocal's operations; at a time when industries are trying to get a foothold in China the reserves in Southeast Asia could easily be transported not only there but also to a surging India as well. Unocal's other operations easily supplied the US (from the Gulf of Mexico) and Europe (Caspian Sea) with gas and oil. Chevron bought a 5% stake in Indian refiner Reliance Petroleum for about $300 million in 2006. That year a company-led group of exploration firms announced a new successful oil strike in the Gulf of Mexico.

The company has also been growing its natural gas assets. In 2008 it announced plans to construct a $3.1 billion natural gas project in the Gulf of Thailand. The project will have the capacity to meet 14% of Thailand's natural gas needs.

Ultrapar acquired Chevron's Texaco-branded fuel distribution business in Brazil for $720 million in 2008 and the next year Chevron sold its Nigerian fuel marketing business.

A leading producer of viscous heavy oil in 2010 a Chevron-led consortium was awarded the rights to 40% of a heavy oil project in Venezuela's Orinoco Oil Belt.

In 2010 in the wake of the BP oil rig disaster in the Gulf of Mexico Chevron announced it was forming a $1 billion joint venture with Exxon Mobil Royal Dutch Shell and ConocoPhillips to create a rapid-response system capable of capturing and containing up to 100000 barrels of oil from an oil spill in water depths of 10000 feet.

Looking to develop a deepwater area unaffected by US regulations in 2010 the company acquired a 70% stake in three concessions in Liberia in West Africa. Other deepwater exploration asset acquisitions that year included purchases in China and the Turkish Black Sea.

EXECUTIVES

Chairman and CEO, John S. Watson, age 56, $946,042 total compensation
Corporate Secretary and Chief Governance Officer, Lydia I. Beebe, age 59
Chief Procurement Officer, Leo G. Lonergan
EVP Technology and Services, John E. Bethancourt, age 61
Vice Chairman; EVP Global Upstream and Gas, George L. Kirkland, age 61, $946,042 total compensation
VP and CFO, Patricia E. (Pat) Yarrington, age 56, $707,708 total compensation
EVP Downstream and Chemicals, Michael K. (Mike) Wirth, age 51
President Chevron Shipping, Michael L. (Mike) Carthew
VP and Treasurer, Paul V. Bennett, age 58
VP Production, Guy C. Hollingsworth, age 58
VP Human Resources Medical and Security, Joe W. Laymon, age 60
VP and CTO, John W. McDonald, age 60
President Chevron Pipe Line, Randy Curry, age 50
EVP Policy and Planning, Rhonda I. Zygocki, age 55
Corporate VP; President Chevron Gas and Midstream, John D. Gass, age 59
EVP Technology and Services, James R. (Jim) Blackwell, age 53
President International Products, Mark A. Nelson
Corporate VP and Comptroller, Matthew J. (Matt) Foehr, age 54
President Americas Products, Dale Walsh
Manager Supplier Diversity and Local Content, Ron Rodrigues
General Manager Public Affairs, David A. (Dave) Samson
President Chevron Asia Pacific Exploration and Production, Melody Meyer, age 54
Vice Chairman and Assistant Treasurer Insurance, James D. (Jim) Lyness
VP Business Development, Jay R. Pryor, age 55
VP Strategic Planning, Charles A. (Chuck) Taylor, age 54
President Chevron Energy Technology, Paul K. Siegele, age 52
CEO Catchlight Energy, Michael H. (Mike) Burnside
CIO; President Chevron Information Technology, Louis V. (Louie) Ehrlich
VP and General Counsel, R. Hewitt (Hew) Pate, age 50
Managing Director Australia, Roy Krzywosinski
President Chevron Global Manufacturing, Gary Yesavage
CIO Chevron Global Upstream, Randy Krotowski
General Manager Investor Relations, Jeanette Ourado
General Manager Pascagoula, Tom Kovar
President Chevron Canada, Jeffrey K. Lehrmann
General Tax Counsel, C.N. (Sandy) Macfarlane
Regional Manager UC IT North Americas Region, William (Bill) Braun
VP Policy Government and Public Policy, Stephen W. (Steve) Green, age 54
VP Health Environment and Safety, Wesley E. (Wes) Lohec, age 52
President Chevron Eurasia Europe and Middle East Exploration and Production, James (Jay) Johnson, age 52
General Manager IT Transformation Program, Willy George
Manager Technology Communications, Diane Padurean
CIO Chevron Global Supply and Trading, Debbie Ly
Policy Government and Public Affairs (PGPA) Advisor, Alexander (Alex) Yelland
General Manager and CIO Technical Computing Chevron Energy Technology Company, Jim Green
Director, John G. Stumpf, age 58
Director, Charles R. (Dick) Shoemate, age 72
Director, Robert J. Eaton, age 72
Director, Carl Ware, age 68
Director, Kevin W. Sharer, age 64
Director, Donald B. Rice, age 72
Vice Chairman; EVP Global Upstream and Gas, George L. Kirkland, age 61
Director, Ronald D. (Ron) Sugar, age 64
Director, Enrique (Rick) Hernandez Jr., age 56
Director, Robert E. Denham, age 67
Director, Linnet F. Deily, age 67
Director, Charles T. (Chuck) Hagel, age 65
Auditors: PricewaterhouseCoopersLLP

LOCATIONS

HQ: Chevron Corporation
6001 Bollinger Canyon Rd., San Ramon CA 94583-2324
Phone: 925-842-1000 **Fax:** 978-368-0236
Web: www.nypro.com

2011 Sales

	$ mil.	% of total
US	120,414	40
Adjustments	(45073)	-

PRODUCTS/OPERATIONS

2011 Sales

	$ mil.	% of total
Downstream	214,299	72
Adjustments	(45073)	-

COMPETITORS

Anadarko Petroleum
Koch Industries Inc.
BP
ConocoPhillips
Devon Energy
Eni
Exxon Mobil
Hess Corporation
Imperial Oil
PEMEX
PETROBRAS
Petroleos de Venezuela
Repsol
Royal Dutch Shell
TOTAL

HISTORICAL FINANCIALS

Company Type: Public

Income Statement FYE: December 31

	REVENUE ($ mil.)	NET INCOME ($ mil.)	NET PROFIT MARGIN	EMPLOYEES
12/11	253,706	26,895	10.6%	61,000
12/10	204,928	19,024	9.3%	62,000
12/09	171,636	10,483	6.1%	64,000
12/08	273,005	23,931	8.8%	67,000
12/07	220,904	18,688	8.5%	65,000
Annual Growth	3.5%	9.5%	—	(1.6%)

2011 Year-End Financials

Debt ratio: 4.85%
Return on equity: 22.16%
Cash ($ mil.): 15,864
Current ratio: 158.43
Long-term debt ($ mil.): 9,812
No. of shares (mil.): 1,981
Dividends
Yield: —
Payout: 22.99%
Market value ($ mil.): 210,796

	STOCK PRICE ($) FY Close	P/E High/Low		PER SHARE ($) Earnings	Dividends	Book Value
12/11	106.40	8	7	13.44	0.00	61.27
12/10	91.25	10	7	9.48	2.84	52.34
12/09	76.99	15	11	5.24	2.66	45.78
12/08	73.97	9	5	11.67	2.53	43.23
12/07	93.33	11	8	8.77	2.26	36.88
Annual Growth	3.3%	—	—	11.3%	—	13.5%

CHS Inc

CHS goes with the grain. One of the US's leading publicly traded cooperative marketers of grain oilseed and energy resources it represents farmers ranchers and co-ops from the Great Lakes to Pacific Northwest and from the Canadian border to Texas. CHS trades grain and sells farm supplies through its stores to members. It processes soybeans for use in food and animal feeds and grinds wheat into flour. Through joint ventures and various business segments the company sells soybean oil and crop nutrient products and markets grain. CHS also provides insurance financial and risk-management services and operates petroleum refineries and sells Cenex branded fuels lubricants and other energy products.

HISTORY

To help farmers through the Great Depression the Farmers Union Terminal Association (a grain marketing association formed in 1926) created the Farmers Union Grain Terminal Association (GTA) in 1938. With loans from the Farmers Union Central Exchange (later known as CENEX) and the Farm Credit Association the organization operated a grain elevator in St. Paul Minnesota. By 1939 GTA had 250 grain-producing associations as members.

GTA leased terminals in Minneapolis and Washington and built others in Wisconsin and Montana in the early 1940s. It then took over a Minnesota flour mill and created Amber Milling. GTA also began managing farming insurance provider Terminal Agency. In 1958 the association bought 57 elevators and feed plants from the McCabe Company.

Adding to its operations in 1960 GTA bought the Honeymead soybean plant. The next year the co-op acquired Minnesota Linseed Oil. In 1977 it acquired Jewett & Sherman (later Holsum Foods) which helped transform the company into a provider of jams jellies salad dressings and syrups.

In 1983 GTA combined with North Pacific Grain Growers a Pacific Northwest co-op incorporated in 1929 to form Harvest States Cooperatives. Harvest States grew in the early and mid-1990s by acquiring salad dressing makers Albert's Foods Great American Foods and Saffola Quality Foods; soup stock producer Private Brands; and margarine and dressings manufacturer and distributor Gregg Foods.

The company started a joint venture to operate the Ag States Agency agricultural insurance company in 1995. The next year the co-op's Holsum Foods division and Mitsui & Co.'s edible oils unit Wilsey Foods merged to form Ventura Foods a distributor of margarines oils spreads and other food products.

Harvest States merged in 1998 with Minnesota-based CENEX a 16-state agricultural supply co-op that had been founded in 1931 as Farmers Union Central Exchange. (Among CENEX's major operations was a farm inputs services marketing and processing joint venture with dairy cooperative Land O'Lakes formed in 1987.) CENEX CEO Noel Estenson took the helm of the resulting co-op Cenex Harvest States Cooperatives which soon formed a petroleum joint venture called Country Energy with Farmland Industries.

CHS members rejected a proposed merger with Farmland Industries in 1999. Also that year Cenex/Land O'Lakes Agronomy (it became Agriliance in 2000 when Farmland Industries joined the joint venture) bought Terra Industries' $1.7 billion distribution business (400 farm supply stores seed and chemical distribution operations partial ownership of two chemical plants).

CHS bought the wholesale propane marketing operations of Williams Companies in 2000 and the co-op paid $14 million for tortilla and tortilla chip maker Sparta Foods. Additionally Estenson retired that year and company president John Johnson took over as CEO. CHS launched an agricultural e-commerce site (Rooster.com) in conjunction with Cargill and DuPont in 2000. The site was shut down the next year however because of a lack of funds. Also in 2001 the cooperative became the full owner of Country Energy by purchasing Farmland Industries' share.

In 2002 CHS acquired Agway's Grandin North Dakota-based sunflower business and formed a wheat-milling joint venture (Horizon Milling) with Cargill. In 2003 the company changed its name from Cenex Harvest States Cooperatives to CHS Inc. and began trading on the NASDAQ. It used the proceeds from the stock offering to repay its short-term debts.

In 2004 CHS purchased all of bankrupt Farmland Industries' ownership of Agriliance thus giving CHS a 50% ownership of Agriliance (with Land O'Lakes owning the other 50%). With an eye to this growing energy sector CHS acquired a 28% ownership of ethanol producer and marketer US BioEnergy Corporation in 2005. Also that year it sold off its Mexican foods business and sold 81% of its 20% ownership of crop-nutrient manufacturer CF Industries in an initial public offering.

CHS and Land O'Lakes realigned the businesses of their 50-50 joint venture Agriliance in 2007 with CHS acquiring its crop-nutrients wholesale-products business and Land O'Lakes acquiring the crop-protection products business. Canadian ag cooperative La Coop federee purchased Agriliance's retail agronomy operation the following year. Adding to its lubricants offerings in 2007 the company acquired two Minnesota companies: Nor-Lakes Services Midwest and The Farm-Oyl Company. In 2008 it sold off all its remaining shares of CF.

Recognizing the growing demand for soy-based food products and in turn to increase shareholder value the company in 2008 acquired Legacy Foods maker of Ultra Soy and TSP brands of textured soybean products for use by both human food and pet food manufacturers. Legacy's operations are overseen by CHS's oilseed processing division.

On the energy front CHS became the sole owner of Provista Renewable Fuels Marketing in 2008 by purchasing US BioEnergy's 50% interest in the biofuels maker. (VeraSun Energy bought out US BioEnergy later that year.

In 2009 CHS acquired Winona River & Rail including 90000 tons of dry-fertilizer storage capacity a dedicated river dock and a 65-car railroad track capacity. The acquisition of the Minnesota operations bolstered the company's storage capacity and rail access in the midwestern and upper Mississippi River regions. Later that year it formed a joint venture with Russia's farm operation Agrico Group (called ACG) in order to manage the export and worldwide marketing of its wheat and feed grains. In turn it gave CHS access to the Russian grain market and improved its ability to serve its global customers.

Also in 2009 CHS formed another of its joint ventures this time at home. It joined with Nebraska's Central Valley Ag Cooperative (CVA) to form Advanced Energy Fuels to provide customers with an industry-leading fuel delivery system.

EXECUTIVES

EVP and COO Energy and Foods, Jay D. Debertin, age 52, $450,000 total compensation
SVP Refining Pipelines and Terminals, James S. (Jim) Loving
EVP Corporate Services, Patrick (Pat) Kluempke, age 64, $339,500 total compensation
EVP and COO Ag Business, Mark Palmquist, age 55, $588,000 total compensation
President and CEO, Carl M. Casale, age 51
VP Information Technology, Beth Nordin
SVP and General Counsel, Lisa Zell, age 43
Chairman, Jerry Hasnedl, age 66
General Manager and CEO CHS Europe, Claudio Scarrozza
Second Vice Chairman, Dennis Carlson, age 51
Director Corporate Communications, Lani Jordan
EVP and CFO, David (Dave) Kastelic, age 56
General Manager Protein Food Group, Michael Considine
VP Propane, Darin Hunoff
Market Access Manager, John R. Gray
SVP Grain Marketing, Rick Browne
Manager Sales Nebraska Region Feed Operations, Jerome Irlmeier
Manager Sales Pacific Northwest Region Feed Operations, Bruce Kollmann
VP Governmental Affairs, Bob Looney
Director Governmental Affairs, Jim Bareksten
SVP Energy Sales, Kevin L. Williams
Manager Marketing Brand Product, Doug Dorfman
Manager Refined Fuel Supply, Mike Derickson
VP Crop Nutrients, Cheryl Schmura
First Vice Chairman, Daniel (Dan) Schurr, age 47
VP Marketing and Supply Operations Energy Raw Material, Robert Zimmerman
SVP Oilseed Processing, Dennis Wendland
Corporate Business Continuity Planning Coordinator, Stacy Tietjen
Director Crop Nutrients Product Management and Business Development, Tim Chrislip
VP Corporate Citizenship; President CHS Foundation, William J. Nelson
Federal Affairs Specialist, Karla Farnsworth
President and CEO Ventura Foods, Christopher (Chris) Furman
VP Corporate Compliance, Josh Blaisdell
VP Insurance Risk Management, Brad Wiggins
Manager Quality Assurance Oilseed Processing, Mark Gulden
VP and COO European Grains Operations, David Christofore
SVP Business Solutions, Lynden E. Johnson, age 51
VP Accounting and Corporate Controller, Theresa Egan, age 47
VP Business Solutions Consulting and Market Development, Lynn Foth
Director, Donald (Don) Anthony, age 62
Director, Bruce Anderson, age 60
Director, Curt Eischens, age 60
Director, Richard Owen, age 58
Second Vice Chairman, Dennis Carlson, age 51
Director, Randy Knecht, age 62
Director, David Bielenberg, age 61
Director, Michael Mulcahey, age 64
Director, Steve Fritel, age 57
Director, David Kayser, age 54
Director, Steve Riegel, age 60
First Vice Chairman, Daniel (Dan) Schurr, age 47
Director, Greg Kruger, age 52
Auditors: PricewaterhouseCoopersLLP

LOCATIONS

HQ: CHS Inc
5500 Cenex Drive, Inver Grove Heights, MN 55077
Phone: 651 355-6000
Web: www.chsinc.com

PRODUCTS/OPERATIONS

2010 Sales

	$ mil.	% of total
AG Business	15,678	61
Energy	8,799	35
Processing	1,061	4
Corporate & Other	44	-
Adjustments	(316.7)	-
Total	**25,267**	**100**

Selected Operations

Ag business
- Grain exporter
- Grain merchandising in Argentina
- Grain merchandising in Europe
- Grain merchandising in Spain
- Grain procurement and merchandising in Russia
- Grain procurement and merchandising in Ukraine
- Retail distribution of agronomy products
- Soybean procurement in Brazil

Corporate and Other
- Finance company
- Insurance agency
- Insurance brokerage
- Risk management products broker

Energy
- Crude oil transportation
- Finished product transportation
- Petroleum refining

Processing

Food manufacturing and distribution
Wheat milling in Canada
Wheat milling in US

Selected Subsidiaries

Ag Business
- ACG Trade SA (Russia 50%)
- Agriliance LLC (50%)
- CHSINC Iberica SL (Spain)
- CHS de Argentina
- CHS do Brasil Ltda
- CHS Europe SA (Switzerland)
- CHS Ukraine LLC
- CHS Vostok LLC (Russia)
- TEMPCO LLC (50%)
- United Harvest LLC (50%)

Corporate and other
- Ag States Agency Inc.
- Cofina Financial LLC
- Country Hedging Inc.
- Impact Risk Solutions LLC

Energy
- Cenex Pipeline LLC
- Front Range Pipeline LLC
- National Cooperative Refinery Association (NCRA 74.5%)

Processing
- Horizon Milling LLC (24%)
- Horizon Milling General Partnership (Canada 24%)
- Ventura Foods LLC (50%)

COMPETITORS

ACH Food Companies
ADM
Ag Processing Inc.
Agrium
AmeriGas Partners
Andersons
Bartlett and Company
BP
Bunge Limited
C.F. Sauer
Cargill
CGC
CITGO
Columbia Grain
ConAgra
ConocoPhillips
Dakota Growers
ExxonMobil Chemical
Ferrellgas Partners
Flint Hills
GROWMARK
JR Simplot
Koch Industries Inc.
Land O' Lakes Purina Feed
Louis Dreyfus Group
Marathon Petroleum
Marzetti
Mondelez International
Mosaic Company
Nestle
Riceland Foods
Ridley Inc.
Scoular
Shell Oil Products
Smucker
U.S. Venture
Unilever NV
US Soy
Valero Energy
Western Petroleum
Whole Harvest Foods
Wilbur-Ellis

HISTORICAL FINANCIALS

Company Type: Public

Income Statement

FYE: August 31

	REVENUE ($ mil.)	NET INCOME ($ mil.)	NET PROFIT MARGIN	EMPLOYEES
08/12	40,599	1,260	3.1%	10,216
08/11	36,915	961	2.6%	9,562
08/10	25,267	502	2.0%	8,812
08/09	25,729	381	1.5%	8,802
08/08	32,167	803	2.5%	8,123
Annual Growth	6.0%	11.9%	—	5.9%

2012 Year-End Financials

Debt ratio: 16.72%—
Return on equity: 28.29%
Cash ($ mil.): 1,452
Current ratio: 143.18
Long-term debt ($ mil.): 1,332
Dividends
Yield: 6.31%
Payout: —
Market value ($ mil.): —

	STOCK PRICE ($) FY Close	P/E High/Low	PER SHARE ($) Earnings	Dividends	Book Value
08/12	31.69	— —	(0.00)	2.00	(0.00)
08/11	28.20	— —	(0.00)	2.00	(0.00)
08/10	28.26	— —	(0.00)	2.00	(0.00)
08/09	27.29	— —	(0.00)	2.00	(0.00)
08/08	25.65	— —	(0.00)	0.00	(0.00)
Annual Growth	5.4%	— —	—	—	—

Chubb Corp.

Here's the skinny on Chubb: The insurer is best known for comprehensive personal homeowners insurance for the demographic that owns yachts (the company insures those too). Chubb also offers commercial property/casualty insurance including multiple peril property and marine and workers' compensation. Its specialty insurance arm offers professional liability policies for executives across a spectrum of industries and also provides construction and commercial surety bonds. Chubb distributes its products through 8500 independent agents and brokers in 120 offices across the US and in more than 25 countries. The company began in 1882 when Thomas Chubb and his son began writing marine insurance in New York City.

Although the US accounts for more than 70% of Chubb's direct business developing its presence in foreign markets through organic growth is an element of the company's strategy. As a result its international operations have grown faster than its US operations.

Chubb's commercial arm prefers to target small and midsized public and privately held companies and has reduced the number of larger public companies in its customer list. In 2012 the company partnered with chief executive organization Vistage International to provide personal and commercial risk management and insurance information and products to its members (private company CEOs).

While much of the insurance industry was in spasm during the economic crisis of 2008 and 2009 Chubb only experienced a mild ache as its conservative investments temporarily lost some of their value. Its revenues have remained flat since the recession due in part to reduced earned premiums. When real estate loses some of its value it costs less to insure and premium income softens accordingly.

Another drag on the company's recent revenues have been the heavy catastrophe losses in 2010 and 2011. Natural catastrophes including earthquakes wildfires tornadoes windstorms and Hurricane Irene cost the property/casualty insurance industry more than $100 billion in 2011. Chubb's share of that was over $1 billion in losses from natural catastrophes.

HISTORY

Thomas C. Chubb and his son Percy formed Chubb & Son in New York in 1882 to underwrite cargo and ship insurance. The company soon became the US manager for Sea Insurance Co. of England and co-founded New York Marine Underwriters (NYMU). In 1901 NYMU became Chubb's chief property/casualty affiliate Federal Insurance Co.

Chubb expanded in the 1920s opening a Chicago office (1923) and just before the 1929 crash organizing Associated Aviation Underwriters. Growth slowed during the Depression but Chubb recovered enough by 1939 to buy Vigilant Insurance Co.

The company bought Colonial Life in 1959 and Pacific Indemnity in 1967. That year Chubb Corporation was formed as a holding company with Chubb & Son designated the manager of the property/casualty insurance businesses. A 1969 takeover attempt by First National City Corp. (predecessor of Citigroup) was foiled by federal regulators.

Chubb acquired Bellemead Development in 1970 to expand its real estate portfolio. Following a strategy of offering specialized insurance Chubb in the 1970s launched insurance packages for the entertainment industry including films and Broadway shows. After the Tylenol poisonings of 1982 Chubb developed insurance against product tampering (which it no longer offers). During the 1980s Chubb focused on specialized property/casualty insurance lines; in 1985 it retreated from medical malpractice insurance.

The company combined three subsidiaries into Chubb Life Insurance Co. of America in 1991. The next year Chubb subsidiary Pacific Indemnity settled a suit over Fibreboard Corporation's asbestos liability (Fibreboard was later bought by Owens Corning); the company ultimately paid some $675 million in asbestos-related settlements.

Financial difficulties at Lloyd's of London caused that market to rethink and subsequently relax its rules about doing business with corporate insurance companies. Chubb took advantage of the opportunity and opened an office at Lloyd's in 1993. The next year Chubb's acquisitions included the personal lines business of Alexander & Alexander (now part of Aon Corporation).

Since the 1880s Chubb had maintained an alliance with UK-based Royal & Sun Alliance Insurance Group and its predecessors. Royal & Sun Alliance owned about 5% of Chubb and Chubb held about 3% of Royal & Sun Alliance. In 1993 the US insurer formed a new joint venture with the British company with the purpose of extending to the UK Chubb's insurance products targeting the affluent. But in 1996 a major client of Royal & Sun Alliance Insurance Group defected and Chubb ended the agreement.

To focus on the property/casualty market Chubb in 1997 sold its life and health insurance operations to Jefferson Pilot and parts of its Bellemead real estate business to Paine Webber and Morgan Stanley Dean Witter. (Chubb blamed the real estate market for its lower 1996 earnings.) The next year the commercial lines market tanked and was followed by a drop in Chubb's earnings.

With losses dragging down its otherwise profitable property/casualty segment Chubb vowed to get tough –raising rates and getting out of unprofitable businesses. It also forged ahead with its overseas plans buying Venezuelan insurer Italseguros Internacional and creating Chubb Re to offer international reinsurance. In 1999 Chubb bought corporate officer insurer Executive Risk (now with a Chubb prefix) to beef up its executive protection and financial services lines. The next year UK aviation insurer British Aviation Group bought Chubb's Associated Aviation Underwriters.

Severely affected by terrorist strikes on September 11 2001 and the collapse of Enron Chubb paid out almost $900 million in claims. In 2002 Chubb took a $700 million charge related to asbestos and toxic waste.

While other insurers were busily adding financial services to their offerings Chubb went the other way. In 2003 it shuttered its Chubb Financial Solutions unit and put the existing business into run-off. To continue pruning it noncore operations in 2004 the company sold its post-secondary educational subsidiary The Chubb Institute.

EXECUTIVES

SVP and Financial News Media Contact, Glenn A. Montgomery
VP, Thomas J. Swartz III
Chairman President and CEO Chubb Corporation; Chairman and CEO Chubb and Son, John D. Finnegan, age 63, $1,275,000 total compensation
VP, Marc R. Hachey
EVP; President Commercial and Specialty Lines Chubb and Son, Paul J. Krump, age 52, $560,000 total compensation
SVP, Daniel J. Conway
SVP, Frederick W. Gaertner
VP, Marylu Korkuch
EVP Chubb & Son; COO Chubb Specialty Insurance, Robert C. Cox, age 54
EVP; Chief Human Resources Officer Chubb & Son, Sunita Holzer
EVP and Co-Chief Investment Officer, Robert M. Witkoff
EVP General Counsel and Chief Ethics Officer, Maureen A. Brundage, age 55
EVP; President Personal Lines and Claims, Dino E. Robusto, age 54, $470,000 total compensation
VP Corporate Counsel and Secretary, W. Andrew Macan
VP and Treasurer, Douglas A. Nordstrom
Manager Public Relations, Mark Schussel
SVP, Paul R. Geyer
VP, Stephen A. Fuller
SVP, Steven M. Versaggi
VP IT Chubb & Son, Owen E. Williams
EVP; Chief Global Field Officer and Chief Administrative Officer Chubb and Son, Harold L. Morrison Jr., age 55, $490,000 total compensation
EVP and Co-Chief Investment Officer, Ned I. Gerstman
Manager Public Relations Chubb Europe, Simon Johnston
SVP and Financial News Media Contact, Mark E. Greenberg
SVP and Chief Accounting Officer, John J. Kennedy, age 56
EVP and CFO, Richard G. Spiro, age 48, $750,000 total compensation
SVP and Chief Actuary Chubb & Son, W. Brian Barnes, age 49
EVP Chubb & Son; COO Chubb Commercial Insurance, Steven R. Pozzi, age 55
SVP Chubb and Son, Stuart A. Spencer
EVP; Global CIO Chubb & Son, James P. Knight
Public Relations Specialist Chubb Commercial Insurance and Chubb Specialty Insurance, Jodi Dorman
Public Relations Specialist Chubb Personal Insurance, David Hilgen
VP, Thomas J. Ganter
VP, Thomas J. Walsh Jr.
Chairman President and CEO Chubb Insurance Company Canada; SVP Chubb and Son, Ellen J. Moore
President and CEO Chubb Insurance Company Europe SE; SVP Chubb and Son; VP Federal Insurance Company, Michael J. Casella
VP Chubb and Son, Kenneth T. Goldstein
VP Chubb and Son, Frank F. Goudsmit
VP and Manager Worldwide Cyber Security Liability, Tracey Vispoli
SVP Chubb & Son, Kathleen S. Ellis
SVP Federal Insurance Company, Andre Dallaire
Chief Innovation Officer, Jon Bidwell
VP Chubb & Son, Christie S. Alderman
EVP Chubb and Son; COO Chubb Personal Insurance, Kathleen M. Tierney
EVP and Worldwide Claim Officer Chubb & Son, Mark Korsgaard
EVP and Western U.S. Territory Field Officer, Gary C. Petrosino
EVP and Eastern U.S. Territory Field Officer, Gerard Butler
EVP and International Field Operations Officer, Christopher J. Giles
SVP and Manager Program Business Chubb Custom Market, Franklin Sanders
Chief Architect CIO Organization, Patrick Sullivan
Director, Zoe Baird, age 58
Director, Martin G. (Marty) McGuinn, age 68
Director, James M. (Jim) Zimmerman, age 67
Director, Daniel E. Somers, age 63
Director, Lawrence M. Small, age 69
Director, Lawrence W. (Larry) Kellner, age 53
Director, Alfred W. (Al) Zollar, age 56
Director, James I. Cash Jr., age 63
Director, Shelia P. Burke, age 59
Director, Jess S?derberg, age 66
Auditors: Ernst&YoungLLP

LOCATIONS

HQ: Chubb Corp.
15 Mountain View Road, Warren, NJ 07059
Phone: 908 903-2000 **Fax:** 908 903-2003
Web: www.chubb.com

PRODUCTS/OPERATIONS

2011 Premiums Earned

Commercial insurance	42	
Specialty insurance	24	
Total	**0**	**100**

Selected Subsidiaries

Chubb Atlantic Indemnity Ltd. (Bermuda)
DHC Corporation
Chubb do Brasil Companhia de Seguros (99% Brazil)
Federal Insurance Company
Executive Risk Indemnity Inc.Executive Risk Specialty Insurance Company
Great Northern Insurance Company
Pacific Indemnity CompanyNorthwestern Pacific Indemnity CompanyTexas Pacific Indemnity Company
Vigilant Insurance Company

COMPETITORS

AIG
Allstate
Arch Capital
AXA
Berkshire Hathaway
CNA Financial
Liberty Mutual
OneBeacon
The Hartford
Travelers Companies
W. R. Berkley
XL Group plc

HISTORICAL FINANCIALS

Company Type: Public

Income Statement FYE: December 31

	ASSETS ($ mil.)	NET INCOME ($ mil.)	INCOME AS % OF ASSETS	EMPLOYEES
12/11	50,865	1,678	3.3%	10,100
12/10	50,249	2,174	4.3%	10,100
12/09	50,449	2,183	4.3%	10,200
12/08	48,429	1,804	3.7%	10,400
12/07	50,574	2,807	5.6%	10,600
Annual Growth	0.1%	(12.1%)	—	(1.2%)

2011 Year-End Financials

Debt ratio: 7.03%
Return on equity: 10.77%
Cash ($ mil.): 58
Current ratio: —
Long-term debt ($ mil.): 3,575
No. of shares (mil.): 272
Dividends
Yield: —
Payout: 27.08%
Market value ($ mil.): 18,860

	STOCK PRICE ($) FY Close	P/E High/Low		PER SHARE ($) Earnings	Dividends	Book Value
12/11	69.22	12	10	5.76	0.00	57.16
12/10	59.64	9	7	6.76	1.48	52.24
12/09	49.18	9	6	6.18	1.40	47.09
12/08	51.00	13	8	4.92	1.32	38.13
12/07	54.58	8	7	7.01	1.16	38.56
Annual Growth	6.1%	—	—	(4.8%)	—	10.3%

Cigna Corp

LOCATIONS

HQ: Cigna Corp
900 Cottage Grove Road, Bloomfield, CT 06002
Phone: 860 226-6000 **Fax:** 860 226-6741
Web: www.cigna.com

HISTORICAL FINANCIALS

Company Type:

Income Statement FYE: December 31

	ASSETS ($ mil.)	NET INCOME ($ mil.)	INCOME AS % OF ASSETS	EMPLOYEES
12/11	51,047	1,327	2.6%	31,400
12/10	45,682	1,345	2.9%	30,600
12/09	43,013	1,302	3.0%	29,300
12/08	41,406	292	0.7%	30,300
12/07	40,065	1,115	2.8%	26,600
Annual Growth	6.2%	4.4%	—	4.2%

2011 Year-End Financials

Debt ratio: 9.78%
Return on equity: 15.90%
Cash ($ mil.): 4,690
Current ratio: —
Long-term debt ($ mil.): 4,994
No. of shares (mil.): 285
Dividends
Yield: —
Payout: 0.83%
Market value ($ mil.): 11,992

	STOCK PRICE ($) FY Close	P/E High/Low		PER SHARE ($) Earnings	Dividends	Book Value
12/11	42.00	11	7	4.84	0.00	29.22
12/10	36.66	8	6	4.89	0.04	24.44
12/09	35.27	8	3	4.73	0.04	19.75
12/08	16.85	53	8	1.05	0.07	13.25
12/07	53.73	43	11	3.87	0.04	16.98
Annual Growth	(6.0%)	—	—	5.8%	—	14.5%

Cincinnati Financial Corp.

Cincinnati Financial Corporation (CFC) serves up a whole menu of insurance –plain and simple or with extras if you like. The company's flagship Cincinnati Insurance (operating through three property/casualty subsidiaries) sells commercial property liability excess and surplus auto bond and fire insurance; personal lines include homeowners auto and liability products. Subsidiary Cincinnati Life sells life disability income and annuities. The company's CFC Investment subsidiary provides commercial financing leasing and real estate services to its independent insurance agents.

CFC markets its policies in 39 states through more than 1200 independent agencies. The company writes more than 20% of its business in Ohio and is strong in Illinois Indiana and Pennsylvania. Its commercial lines segment targets primarily small to midsized businesses. CFC has tied its growth to expanding the territories it markets in and increasing the number of new agencies with which it strikes new relationships. Following that strategy since 2008 it has moved into Colorado Connecticut Oregon Texas and Wyoming.

The company maintains a force of some 1200 field associates who provide local service to the distributing independent agencies and policy holders. Its claims management system employs a team of field claims associates and a special investigations unit assigned to detect fraud.

New products are another means to growth for the company. In 2008 it created The Cincinnati Specialty Underwriters Insurance Company to offer excess and surplus lines of coverage. It then created a brokerage CSU Producer Resources to distribute the excess and surplus products to its existing network of independent agents.

The founding Schiff family including brothers John and Thomas Schiff who serve as directors owns about 14% of CFC.

HISTORY

Jack Schiff spent three years with the Travelers Company before he joined the Navy in WWII. He returned to Cincinnati to start his own independent insurance agency in 1946 and was joined by his younger brother Robert; both were Ohio State graduates whose affection for the Buckeyes led them in later years to close company banquets with the school fight song. The brothers incorporated Cincinnati Insurance with $200000 from investors.

Under Harry Turner the company's first president the company offered property/casualty insurance to small businesses and homeowners through its network of agents. By 1956 the company had spread into neighboring Kentucky and Indiana. During the next decade Cincinnati Insurance expanded its products and network adding auto burglary and commercial all-risk lines and enlisting agents throughout the Midwest.

In 1963 Turner took the chairman's seat and Jack Schiff became president introducing a more aggressive leadership style. In 1969 the company reorganized and went public forming Cincinnati Financial Corporation as a holding company for the insurance operation. CFC used the money to pay off debts and buy new businesses forming two subsidiaries: CFC Investment Company in 1970 to deal in commercial real estate and financing; and Queen City Indemnity (later named The Cincinnati Casualty Company) in 1972 to offer direct-bill personal policies.

By 1973 operations included The Life Insurance Company of Cincinnati Queen City Indemnity and fellow Cincinnati giant Inter-Ocean Insurance Company. That year Jack Schiff added CEO to his title.

CFC continued to grow throughout the 1970s with a new emphasis on independent investments. In 1982 Cincinnati Financial veteran Robert Morgan became president and CEO. The company's conservative roots and investment base helped it shake off the early-1980s recession and a string of natural disasters that left many other insurers dangling in the wind.

Also during the 1980s the company started to shift its focus from personal to commercial lines. In 1988 it reorganized its life insurance subsidiaries under the Cincinnati Life banner and formed The Cincinnati Indemnity Company to offer workers' compensation and personal insurance. In 1998 a string of storms (reminiscent of others earlier in the decade) dampened the company's earnings.

In 1999 Jack Schiff Jr. succeeded Morgan as president and CEO. The next year 96-year-old Harry Turner died. After a 1999 decision by the Ohio Supreme Court that increased exposure on auto policies CFC set up $110 million in reserves for uninsured motorists claims that year and the following year; the decision was overturned in 2003.

Jack Schiff Jr. stepped down as CEO in 2008 (but remained as chairman) and was replaced by Kenneth Stecher. In 2011 Steven Johnson was named CEO of CFC; he was promoted from his previous roles of CFO secretary and treasurer. Kenneth Stecher then became chairman.

For many years CFC held more than 10% of Fifth Third Bancorp and prior to the economic meltdown it accounted for more than 25% of the company's stock holdings. During the meltdown bank stock grew less reliable prompting CFC to sell half of its holdings in Fifth Third for more than $450 million in 2008. As the general market sank CFC offloaded the rest for $67 million in 2009.

EXECUTIVES

Chairman Cincinnati Financial and Cincinnati Insurance, Kenneth W. (Ken) Stecher, age 65, $810,000 total compensation
VP Personnel Cincinnati Insurance, Greg Ziegler
SVP Operations Cincinnati Insurance, Timothy L. Timmel, age 63, $379,196 total compensation
President CEO and Director, Steven J. Johnston, age 52, $432,000 total compensation
EVP Cincinnati Insurance, Jacob F. Scherer Jr., age 59, $492,721 total compensation
President and COO Cincinnati Life Insurance, David H. Popplewell, age 68, $376,750 total compensation
VP Assistant Secretary Assistant Treasurer and Principal Accounting Officer; SVP Cincinnati Insurance, Eric N. Mathews, age 56
SVP and CTO Cincinnati Insurance, Craig W. Forrester, age 53
SVP Corporate Communications Cincinnati Insurance, Joan O. Shevchik, age 61
SVP and CIO Cincinnati Insurance Company, John S. Kellington, age 50
SVP Cincinnati Insurance; President Cincinnati Casualty, Thomas A. Joseph, age 56, $462,115 total compensation
SVP Excess and Surplus Lines Cincinnati Insurance, Donald J. Doyle Jr.
SVP Chief Investment Officer Assistant Secretary and Assistant Treasurer, Martin F. Hollenbeck
SVP Commercial Lines Cincinnati Insurance, Charles P. Stoneburner II, age 59
SVP and Chief Claims Officer Cincinnati Insurance, Martin J. Mullen, age 56
Assistant VP Investor Relations Cincinnati Insurance, Dennis E. McDaniel
Assistant VP Shareholder Services Cincinnati Insurance, Jerry L. Litton
SVP and Chief Risk Officer Cincinnati Insurance, Teresa C. Cracas
SVP General Counsel and Corporate Secretary Cincinnati Financial and Cincinnati Insurance, Lisa A. Love, age 52
SVP CFO and Treasurer Cincinnati Financial and Cincinnati Insurance, Michael J. (Mike) Sewell
Director, John J. Schiff Jr., age 68
President CEO and Director, Steven J. Johnston, age 52
Director, William F. Bahl, age 60
Director, Kenneth C. Lichtendahl, age 63
Director, Thomas R. Schiff, age 64
Director, Larry R. Webb, age 56
Director, Gretchen W. Price, age 57
Director, W. Rodney McMullen, age 51
Director, E. Anthony (Tony) Woods, age 71
Director, Douglas S. Skidmore, age 49
Director, John F. Steele Jr., age 58
Director, Gregory T. Bier, age 65
Director, Linda W. Clement-Holmes, age 50
Auditors: Deloitte&ToucheLLP

LOCATIONS

HQ: Cincinnati Financial Corporation
6200 S. Gilmore Rd., Fairfield OH 45014-5141
Phone: 513-870-2000 **Fax:** 513-870-2911
Web: www.cinfin.com

PRODUCTS/OPERATIONS

2010 Revenues

	$ mil.	% of total
Property/casualty insurance		
Commercial	2,156	57
Personal	723	19
Life Insurance	159	5
Excess & surplus insurance	49	1
Investment income	677	18
Other income	8	-
Total	**3,772**	**100**

Selected Subsidiaries

CFC Investment Company
CSU Producer Resources Inc.
The Cincinnati Insurance Company
The Cincinnati Casualty Company
The Cincinnati Indemnity Company
The Cincinnati Life Insurance Company
The Cincinnati Specialty Underwriters Insurance Company

COMPETITORS

Allied Group
American Financial Group
CNA Financial
Erie Indemnity
Farmers Group
Great American Insurance Company
Indiana Insurance
Ohio Casualty
OneBeacon
Progressive Corporation
Selective Insurance
The Hartford
Travelers Companies
Westfield Group
Zurich American

HISTORICAL FINANCIALS

Company Type: Public

Income Statement FYE: December 31

	ASSETS ($ mil.)	NET INCOME ($ mil.)	INCOME AS % OF ASSETS	EMPLOYEES
12/11	15,668	166	1.1%	4,067
12/10	15,095	377	2.5%	4,060
12/09	14,440	432	3.0%	4,170
12/08	13,369	429	3.2%	4,179
12/07	16,637	855	5.1%	4,087
Annual Growth	(1.5%)	(33.6%)	—	(0.1%)

2011 Year-End Financials

Debt ratio: 5.90%
Return on equity: 3.28%
Cash ($ mil.): 438
Current ratio: —
Long-term debt ($ mil.): 925
No. of shares (mil.): 162
Dividends
Yield: —
Payout: 157.35%
Market value ($ mil.): 4,935

	STOCK PRICE ($) FY Close	P/E High/Low		PER SHARE ($) Earnings	Dividends	Book Value
12/11	30.46	34	24	1.02	0.00	31.20
12/10	31.69	14	11	2.31	1.59	31.06
12/09	26.24	11	7	2.65	1.57	29.38
12/08	29.07	15	7	2.62	1.56	25.81
12/07	39.54	10	7	4.97	1.42	35.72
Annual Growth	(6.3%)	—	—	(32.7%)	—	(3.3%)

Cintas Corporation

If Cintas had its way you'd never agonize over what to wear to work. The #1 uniform supplier in the US boasts 900000 clients (McDonald's Royal Caribbean) and some 5 million people wear its garb each day. Cintas –which sells leases and rents uniforms –operates more than 430 facilities across the US and Canada; it leases about half of them. Besides offering shirts jackets slacks and footwear the company provides clean-room apparel and flame-resistant clothing. Other products offered by Cintas include uniform cleaning first-aid and safety products clean-room supplies and document handling and storage. CEO Scott Farmer owns about 14% of the company. His father Richard founded the company in 1968.

Uniform rentals generate about 70% of Cintas' sales. The balance of its revenue is logged from uniform sales and its array of other products and services. Although it is the leading renter of corporate uniforms the company still sees growth potential in this area of its business.

The company was busy in 2011 building its business across the board. Cintas acquired 27 business in 2011 vs. seven in 2010. It has been active in building its non-uniform operations especially its document services unit which saw a dozen newly purchased companies added to the segment in 2011.

The US recession and accompanying job losses had pushed Cintas to reel in discretionary spending and reduce inventories. Despite the effects of the turbulent marketplace Cintas has been recognized as a top company being named among the nation's "Most Admired Companies" by Fortune magazine. Report on Business magazine also ranked it among Canada's best employers. For the curious Cintas employees must wear a Cintas uniform or business suit to work.

New York-based First Eagle Investment Management owns another 12% of Cintas.

HISTORY

In 1929 onetime animal trainer boxer and blacksmith Richard "Doc" Farmer started a business of salvaging old rags cleaning them and then selling them to factories. Farmer later began renting the rags to his customers. He would pick up the dirty rags clean them and return them to the factory. By 1936 the Acme Overall & Rag Laundry had established itself in Cincinnati with plans to convert an old bathhouse into a laundry. Farmer along with his adopted son Herschell suffered a setback from flood damage in 1937 but the family rebuilt and continued to grow the business.

Doc Farmer died in 1952 and Herschell assumed command of the company. Five years later Herschell turned the reins over to his 23-year-old son Richard who immediately moved Acme into the uniform rental market and the company blossomed. Throughout the 1960s the company grew enormously aided by Richard's innovative leadership. (Acme was the first to use a polyester-cotton blend that lasted twice as long as normal cotton work uniforms.) Through a holding company Richard established a string of uniform plants in the Midwest starting with a factory in Cleveland in 1968. Four years later the company changed its name to Cintas.

At this time the company began tapping into the new corporate identity market pushing the idea that uniforms convey a sense of professionalism and present a cleaner safer image. The company began to custom-design the uniforms adding logos and distinctive colors. This aspect of the business compelled Cintas to expand to help accommodate its national clients; by 1972 the company had offices throughout Ohio and in Chicago Detroit and Washington DC. By 1975 Cintas was operating in 13 states.

The company went public in 1983. For the rest of the 1980s Cintas rode the wave of consolidation in the uniform rental industry making a slew of acquisitions. The company also expanded from its blue-collar base into the service industry and began to supply uniforms to hotels restaurants and banks. By the early 1990s Cintas was a presence in most major US cities and its share of the US market had climbed to about 10%. Farmer turned over the title of CEO to president Robert Kohlhepp in 1995. That year the company acquired Cadet Uniform Services a Toronto uniform rental business for $41 million.

Scott Farmer Richard's 38-year-old son was named president and COO in 1997. That year Cintas made a number of acquisitions including Micron-Clean Uniform Service and Canadian firms Act One Uniform Rentals and DW King Services. The company also moved into the first aid supplies industry with its purchase of American First Aid and added clean-room garments to its expanding list of uniform rentals. In 1998 Cintas acquired uniform rental company Apparelmaster as well as Chicago-based Uniforms To You a $150 million design and manufacturing company. In an effort to expand its corporate uniform business the company acquired rival Unitog in 1999 for about $460 million.

As part of the integration of Unitog in 2000 Cintas closed several of Unitog's uniform rental operations distribution centers and manufacturing plants. The company also established first aid supplies and safety equipment unit Xpect. In 2002 Cintas purchased Omni Services marking its largest acquisition to date.

Cintas purchased more than 10 document management businesses and three first-aid and fire protection businesses in fiscal 2009.

EXECUTIVES

President and COO, J. Phillip Holloman, age 56, $530,000 total compensation
CEO and Director, Scott D. Farmer, age 53, $725,000 total compensation
SVP Finance and CFO, William C. Gale, age 56, $442,000 total compensation
Chairman, Robert J. (Bob) Kohlhepp, age 68, $300,000 total compensation
VP and CIO, G. Thomas (Tom) Thornley
VP Secretary and General Counsel, Thomas E. Frooman, age 44, $407,500 total compensation
VP Human Resources, Michael A. Womack
SVP Facility Services, Michael L. Thompson, age 45, $310,000 total compensation
Senor Manager Corporate Communications, Heather Maley
SVP Global Supply Chain and Corporate Six Sigma, Dave Wheeler
VP and Treasurer, J. Michael (Mike) Hansen
Director, James J. Johnson, age 65
Director, Ronald W. (Ron) Tysoe, age 59
CEO and Director, Scott D. Farmer, age 53
Director, Joyce Hergenhan, age 69
Director, Gerald V. Dirvin, age 74
Director, David C. Phillips, age 74
Director, Gerald S. Adolph, age 58
Director, Joseph M. (Joe) Scaminace, age 59
Auditors: Ernst&YoungLLP

LOCATIONS

HQ: Cintas Corporation
6800 Cintas Blvd., Cincinnati OH 45040
Phone: 513-459-1200 **Fax:** 513-573-4130
Web: www.cintas.com

PRODUCTS/OPERATIONS

2011 Sales

	$ mil.	% of total
Rental uniforms & ancillary products	2,692	71
Uniform direct sales	419	11
First aid safety & fire protection services	377	10
Document management services	321	8
Total	**3,810**	**100**

Selected Products and Services

Clean-room supplies
Document shredding and storage
Entrance mats
Fender covers
Fire protection
First aid and safety products and services
Linen products
Mops
Restroom supplies
Towels
Uniform cleaning
Uniform rental and sales

COMPETITORS

Alsco
Angelica Corporation
ARAMARK
G&K Services
Iron Mountain Inc
NCH
Superior Uniform Group
UniFirst

HISTORICAL FINANCIALS

Company Type: Public

Income Statement FYE: May 31

	REVENUE ($ mil.)	NET INCOME ($ mil.)	NET PROFIT MARGIN	EMPLOYEES
05/12	4,102	297	7.3%	30,000
05/11	3,810	246	6.5%	30,000
05/10	3,547	215	6.1%	30,000
05/09	3,774	226	6.0%	31,000
05/08	3,937	335	8.5%	34,000
Annual Growth	1.0%	(2.9%)	—	(3.1%)

2012 Year-End Financials

Debt ratio: 30.88%
Return on equity: 13.91%
Cash ($ mil.): 339
Current ratio: 229.78
Long-term debt ($ mil.): 1,059

No. of shares (mil.): 126
Dividends
Yield: 1.46%
Payout: 23.79%
Market value ($ mil.): 4,669

	STOCK PRICE ($) FY Close	P/E High/Low		PER SHARE ($) Earnings	Dividends	Book Value
05/12	36.90	18	12	2.27	0.54	16.91
05/11	32.85	19	14	1.68	0.97	16.74
05/10	26.00	22	15	1.40	0.00	16.58
05/09	23.29	22	12	1.48	0.00	15.49
05/08	29.52	19	13	2.15	0.00	14.67
Annual Growth	5.7%	—	—	1.4%	—	3.6%

Cisco Systems, Inc.

Cisco Systems routes packets and routs competitors with equal efficiency. Dominating the market for Internet protocol-based networking equipment the company provides routers and switches used to direct data voice and video traffic. Other products include remote access servers IP telephony equipment optical networking components Internet conferencing systems set-top boxes and network service and security systems. The company sells its products primarily to large enterprises and telecommunications service providers but it also markets products designed for small businesses and consumers such as routers modems and home network management software. Cisco gets nearly 60% of its sales from the Americas.

HISTORY

Cisco Systems was founded by Stanford University husband-and-wife team Leonard Bosack and Sandra Lerner and three colleagues in 1984. Bosack developed technology to link his computer lab's network with his wife's network in the graduate business school. Anticipating a market for networking devices Bosack and Lerner mortgaged their house bought a used mainframe put it in their garage and got friends and relatives to work for deferred pay. They sold their first network router in 1986. Originally targeting universities the aerospace industry and the government the company in 1988 expanded its marketing to include large corporations. Short of cash Cisco turned to venture capitalist Donald Valentine of Sequoia Capital who bought a controlling stake and became chairman. He hired John Morgridge of laptop maker GRiD Systems as president and CEO.

Cisco whose products had a proven track record had a head start as the market for network routers opened up in the late 1980s. Sales leapt from $1.5 million in 1987 to $28 million in 1989.

The company went public in 1990. That year Morgridge fired Lerner with whom he had clashed and Bosack quit. The couple sold their stock for about $200 million giving most to favorite causes including animal charities and a Harvard professor looking for extraterrestrials.

With competition increasing Cisco began expanding through acquisitions. Purchases included networking company Crescendo Communications (1993) and Ethernet switch maker Kalpana (1994). Cisco also surpassed the $1 billion revenue mark in 1994. In 1995 EVP John Chambers succeeded Morgridge as president and CEO; Morgridge became chairman (and Valentine vice chairman).

Cisco entered the service provider market in 1996 when it introduced a line of customer premises equipment (CPE) products. The following year the company broke into the FORTUNE 500.

Cisco acquired several niche players in 1998 such as Precept Software (video transmission software) and American Internet Corporation (software for set-top boxes and cable modems). That year Cisco's market capitalization passed the $100 billion milestone a landmark accomplishment for a company its age.

In 1999 Cisco launched a new business line aimed at bringing high-speed Internet access to the consumer market. In its largest acquisition to date Cisco bought Cerent (fiber-optic network equipment) for $7 billion.

The company continued its acquisitive ways in 2000 snatching up more than 20 companies including wireless network equipment maker Aironet. With a market capitalization exceeding $500 billion Cisco also enjoyed a turn as the world's most valuable company that year.

The company's heavy investment in Internet protocol-based telecommunications equipment proved costly when an industry-wide downturn slowed spending among telecom service providers in 2001. Chambers guided Cisco through significant rebuilding measures including job cuts and a reorganization that aligned its operations around core technologies rather than customer segments.

Entering yet another market Cisco acquired storage networking switch maker Andiamo Systems in 2002 (the deal closed in 2004). Key acquisitions over the next few years included home networking specialist Linksys (2003) conferencing systems provider Latitude Communications (2004) and router developer Procket Networks (2004). The acquisition of Procket Networks bolstered Cisco's internal router development. In 2004 the company introduced the CRS-1 a new router designed to compete with high-end offerings from challengers such as Juniper Networks. Featuring an overhauled version of Cisco's Internetwork Operating System (IOS) the CRS-1 resulted from four years of development and an investment of $500 million. Cisco purchased wireless networking vendor Airespace in 2005. The acquisition provided Cisco with wireless LAN equipment for the enterprise and government sectors.

The company's acquisition of cable set-top box leader Scientific-Atlanta for approximately $6.9 billion also counted among its most ambitious moves. That deal which closed in 2006 was the second-largest purchase in its history. (Cisco had paid $7 billion for optical networking equipment maker Cerent in 1999.) Cisco had long been an advocate of the convergence of technology behind data voice and television networks and the acquisition of Scientific-Atlanta made it one of the leading providers of the set-top boxes that cable service providers use to deliver advanced features such as movies-on-demand.

Cisco spent more than $1 billion over three years to expand its operations in India and in 2007 it unveiled a $16 billion expansion plan for China including investments in manufacturing education programs and venture capital. Among its most significant purchases the company acquired WebEx Communications (renamed Cisco WebEx) a leading provider of Internet conferencing systems for approximately $3.2 billion in 2007. It also bought network security specialist IronPort Systems (renamed Cisco IronPort Systems) for around $830 million that year.

Cisco purchased Pure Networks a developer of management software for home networks in 2008. It also acquired e-mail and calendar software maker PostPath that year.

In 2009 Cisco acquired Starent Networks for about $2.9 billion in cash. Starent specialized in systems and software for wireless networks helping satisfy global demand for more mobile access to the Internet. The company became Cisco's Mobile Internet Technology Group led by Starent CEO Ashraf Dahod and part of Cisco's Service Provider Business. Looking to build its consumer-oriented business the company also bought camcorder maker Pure Digital Technologies in 2009. (Cisco decided to shut down the Flip video camcorder product line acquired in the Pure Digital acquisition as part of a business realignment in 2011.)

Cisco unveiled a new line of hardware called the Unified Computing System in 2009. Designed to simplify the computing and networking resources in data centers the product line –which included blade servers –placed Cisco in direct competition with traditional partners such as Hewlett-Packard and IBM.

EXECUTIVES

SVP Office of the President, Howard S. Charney
Chairman and CEO, John T. Chambers, age 63, $375,000 total compensation
EVP and Chief Development Officer Global Engineering, Pankaj S. Patel
SVP Human Resources, Brian (Skip) Schipper
EVP and CFO, Frank Calderoni, age 55, $581,250 total compensation
SVP Global Government Solutions and Corporate Security Programs, Bradford J. (Brad) Boston, age 58
President and COO, Gary B. Moore
SVP Strategy and Planning Worldwide Operations, Inder Sidhu, age 52
SVP and General Manager Service Provider Video Technology Group, Enrique Rodriguez
SVP Customer Value Chain Management, Angel L. Mendez
President Development and Sales, Robert (Rob) Lloyd, $516,250 total compensation
SVP Cisco Services European Markets, Nick Earle
EVP Operations Processes and Systems, Randy Pond, age 58, $743,750 total compensation
CTO; SVP Engineering, Padmasree Warrior, age 52
SVP and General Manager Ethernet Switching Technology Group, Robert (Rob) Soderbery
SVP Wireless Security and Routing Technology Group, Brett D. Galloway
EVP Emerging Solutions and Chief Globalization Officer, Wim Elfrink, age 60, $816,658 total compensation
SVP General Counsel and Secretary, Mark Chandler, age 56

SVP TelePresence Emerging Technologies and Consumer Business, Marthin De Beer
SVP and Global Lead Internet Business Solutions Group, Gary Bridge
SVP Worldwide Channels, Keith Goodwin
President European Markets, Chris Dedicoat
SVP and General Manager Security Technology Group, Richard W. Palmer Jr.
President Emerging Markets Theatre, Paul Mountford
SVP Worldwide Sales, Chuck Robbins
SVP Development Strategy and Operations, Kathryn M. (Kathy) Hill
SVP Emerging (Markets) East, Duncan Mitchell, age 48
SVP Worldwide Channels Go-to-Market Group, Edison Peres
SVP Research and Advanced Development, Gregory (Greg) Akers
SVP, Carlos Dominguez, age 53
SVP Technical Services, Joe Pinto
SVP, Donald R. (Don) Proctor
SVP Small Business Technology Group (SBTG), Ian Pennell
President Asia Pacific and Japan Theaters, Edzard J.C. Overbeek
SVP Research and Advanced Development, Joel Bion
SVP and CTO Datacenter Switching and Security Technology Group, Thomas (Tom) Edsall
President and CEO Greater China Theater, Owen Chan
SVP U.S. Public Sector Theater, Bruce Klein
SVP Government Affairs and Chief Marketing Officer, Blair Christie
SVP Network Software and Systems Technology Group, Ben Fathi
CIO; SVP IT and Cloud & Systems Management Technology Group, Rebecca J. Jacoby
SVP and Chief Strategy Officer, Ned Hooper
SVP U.S. Service Provider Sales and Global Service Provider Market Segment, Nicholas A. (Nick) Adamo
SVP and General Manager Data Center Switching and Services Group, John F. McCool
SVP Cisco Services United States and Canada, George O'Meara
SVP U.S. and Canada Partner Organization, Jim Sherriff
SVP Sports and Entertainment Solutions Group, David K. Holland
SVP Voice Technology Group (VTG), Barry O'Sullivan
SVP Corporate Affairs, Tae Yoo
President Cisco Capital, Kristine A. (Kris) Snow, age 52
SVP and General Manager Connected Energy, Laura K. Ipsen, age 47
SVP Global Sales Operations, Bill LePage
SVP Corporate Marketing, Marilyn Mersereau
VP Silicon Switching Technology, Mark Papermaster, age 50
SVP Network Management Technology Division, Jesper Andersen
SVP Global and Transformational Partnerships, Wendy Bahr
SVP Enterprise Systems and Operations, Manny Rivelo, age 47
VP Corporate Controller and Principal Accounting Officer, Prat Bhatt, age 45
SVP Cisco Services Asia-Pacific Japan and Emerging Markets, Bob Singleton
CTO Cloud Computing, Lew Tucker
SVP Global Strategy and Operations, Karl Meulema
SVP; General Manager and Chief Architect Service Provider Business, Kelly Ahuja
SVP Enterprise and Mid-Market Marketing, William A. (Bill) Brownell
IT Architect, Sidney Morgan
VP Internet Business Service Group, Scott Puopoly
VP IT Network and Data Services, John Manville
VP Server Access and Virtualization Group, Jackie Ross
VP Communication and Collaboration IT, Sheila Jordan
SVP and General Manager Services Routing Technology Group, Praveen Akkiraju
Assistant Secretary, Evan Sloves
CEO Server Access and Virtualization Technology Group, David Yen
General Manager Taiwan, Frank Wu
Director, Michael D. Capellas, age 57
Director, Marc Benioff, age 47
Director, M. Michele Burns, age 53
Director, Brian L. Halla, age 65
Director, Carol A. Bartz, age 63
Director, Larry R. Carter, age 69
Director, John L. Hennessy, age 59
Director, Jerry Yang, age 43
Director, Richard M. (Dick) Kovacevich, age 68
Director, Arun Sarin, age 57
Director, Steven M. West, age 56
Director, Roderick C. (Rod) McGeary, age 62
Director, Kristina M. Johnson, age 52
Auditors: PricewaterhouseCoopersLLP

LOCATIONS

HQ: Cisco Systems Inc.
170 W. Tasman Dr., San Jose CA 95134-1706
Phone: 408-526-4000 **Fax:** 408-526-4100
Web: www.cisco.com

2012 Sales

	$ mil.	% of total
Americas	26,501	58
EMEA	12,075	26
Asia-Pacific Japan & China	7,485	16
Total	**46,061**	**100**

PRODUCTS/OPERATIONS

2012 Sales

	$ mil.	% of total
Product		
Switches	14,531	32
New products	12,343	27
Routers	8,425	18
Other	1,027	2
Service	9,735	21
Total	**46,061**	**100**

Selected Products

Access servers
Blade servers
Cable modems
Cables and cords
Content delivery devices
Customer contact software
Digital video recorders
Ethernet concentrators hubs and transceivers
Interfaces and adapters
Network management software
Networked applications software
Optical platforms
Power supplies
Routers
Security components
Switches
Telephony access systems
Television set-top boxes
Video networking
Virtual private network (VPN) systems
Voice integration applications
Wireless networking

Selected Acquisitions

2013
Intucell ($475 million; Israel; mobile network optimization)
2012
Cariden Technologies Inc. ($141 million; Sunnyvale CA; network planning design and traffic management tools for telecommunications service providers)
Cloupia ($125 million; Santa Clara CA; infrastructure management software)
Meraki ($1.2 billion; San Francisco; cloud networking)
2011
Inlet Technologies (digital media processing technology for video streaming applications)
newScale (hosted service catalog and self-service portal software)
Pari Networks (security risk and policy compliance software)
AXIOSS (ordering and fulfillment automation)
Versly (Microsoft Office collaboration software)
2010
LineSider Technologies (network management software)
ExtendMedia (digital content management software)
Arch Rock (IP-based wireless network technology for smart-grid applications)
CoreOptics (high-speed data transmission chips and optical network transponders)
TANDBERG (videoconferencing equipment)
2009
Starent Networks Corporation (networking equipment for wireless carriers)
Tidal Software (application management and automation)
Pure Digital Technology (camcorders)
Richards-Zeta Building Intelligence (IP network middleware)
2008
Jabber (messaging software)
Pure Networks (home networking management software)
DiviTech (digital video networking software)
Nuova Systems (data center switches)
2007
Securent (security software)
Navini Networks (WiMax equipment)
Latigent (Web-based business intelligence software for call centers)
Cognio (wireless spectrum analysis)
BroadWare Technologies (video networking and storage systems)
IronPort Systems (e-mail security software and network security appliances)
WebEx Communications (Web conferencing systems)
Five Across (social networking software)
Tivella (2007 digital signage software and systems)l

COMPETITORS

Alcatel-Lucent
ARRIS
Aruba Networks
Avaya
Belden
Brocade Communications
CA Inc.
Check Point Software
Ciena
Citrix Systems
D-Link
Dell
ECI Telecom
Enterasys
Ericsson
Extreme Networks
F5 Networks
Fortinet
Harris Corp.
Hewlett-Packard
Huawei Technologies
IBM
Juniper Networks
LogMeIn
Meru Networks
Microsoft
Motorola Mobility
MRV Communications
NETGEAR
Nokia Siemens Networks
Pace
Polycom
Riverbed Technology
Symantec
Technicolor
Tellabs
ZTE

HISTORICAL FINANCIALS

Company Type: Public

Income Statement FYE: July 28

	REVENUE ($ mil.)	NET INCOME ($ mil.)	NET PROFIT MARGIN	EMPLOYEES
07/12	46,061	8,041	17.5%	66,639
07/11	43,218	6,490	15.0%	71,825
07/10	40,040	7,767	19.4%	70,700
07/09	36,117	6,134	17.0%	65,550
07/08	39,540	8,052	20.4%	66,129
Annual Growth	3.9%	(0.0%)	—	0.2%

2012 Year-End Financials

Debt ratio: 17.79%—
Return on equity: 15.68%
Cash ($ mil.): 9,799
Current ratio: 349.29
Long-term debt ($ mil.): 16,297

Dividends
Yield: —
Payout: 18.79%
Market value ($ mil.): —

	STOCK PRICE ($) FY Close	P/E High/Low		PER SHARE ($) Earnings	Dividends	Book Value
07/12	15.69	14	9	1.49	0.00	9.68
07/11	15.97	21	13	1.17	0.00	8.69
07/10	23.07	20	15	1.33	0.00	7.83
07/09	21.88	24	13	1.05	0.00	6.68
07/08	22.43	25	16	1.31	0.00	5.83
Annual Growth	(8.5%)	—	—	3.3%	—	13.5%

CIT Group, Inc.

If you haven't heard of CIT Group then you're O-U-T of the proverbial loop. On the big-business landscape for about a century CIT is a commercial bank holding company that offers lending leasing debt restructuring equipment financing and advisory services to small- and mid-sized businesses in such industries as energy health care retail communications manufacturing IT services and sports. The company also operates CIT Bank in Utah; the bank also offers commercial financing and leasing as well as online deposit products such as CDs. CIT has more than $45 billion in assets and serves clients in more than 30 countries around the world.

HISTORY

Henry Ittleson founded CIT Group as Commercial Credit and Investment Trust in St. Louis in 1908. Initially financing horse-drawn carriages it moved to New York in 1915 as Commercial Investment Trust (CIT) to participate in one of the milestones of modern consumer debt: Its auto financing program launched in collaboration with Studebaker was the first of its kind.

CIT diversified into industrial financing during the 1920s and went public in 1924 on the NYSE. Cars remained a strong focus though: When Ford Motor Co. ran into difficulties in 1933 it sold financing division Universal Credit Corp. to CIT. CIT continued to expand into industrial financing incorporating its industrial business as CIT Financial Corp. in 1942.

During the post-WWII boom CIT began financing manufactured home sales and offering small loans. In 1964 it consolidated factoring operations into Meinhard-Commercial Corp. By the end of the 1960s the firm started to retreat from auto financing focusing instead on industrial leasing factoring and equipment financing.

In 1980 RCA bought CIT seeking to buy financing to develop its other businesses. RCA found the debt from the purchase unwieldy however and sold CIT to Manufacturers Hanover Bank (Manny Hanny) in 1984. The bank bought CIT to expand outside its home state of New York: Though it could not open banks out of state Manny Hanny could still offer financial services through CIT which became The CIT Group in 1986.

Manny Hanny executives tried to bring aggressive management to staid top-heavy CIT. The company sold its Inventory Finance division in 1987 divested the consumer loan business in 1988 and consolidated the Meinhard-Commercial and Manufacturers Hanover factoring units in 1989. By then Manny Hanny was cash-strapped over losses incurred from foreign loans so it sold a 60% stake in CIT to The Dai-Ichi Kangyo Bank of Japan.

CIT gave Dai-Ichi entree into US financial services and it began expanding CIT's range of services again including equity investment (1990) credit finance (from its purchase of Fidelcor Business Credit in 1991) and venture capital (1992). CIT also reentered the consumer loan market (including home equity lending) with a new Consumer Finance group (1992).

In 1995 Chemical Bank (Manny Hanny's successor; now part of JPMorgan Chase) sold an additional 20% share to Dai-Ichi bumping the Japanese bank's holdings to 80% and arranging to sell its remaining shares to Dai-Ichi. In 1997 instead of Dai-Ichi buying the rest of Chase's shares CIT bought them and spun them off to the public. In 1998 Dai-Ichi reduced its stake.

In 1999 CIT bought Newcourt Credit Group North America's #2 equipment finance and leasing firm; it also bought Heller Financial's commercial services unit. In 2000 the firm worked on integrating Newcourt and sold its Hong Kong consumer finance unit.

Tyco International bought CIT in 2001 renaming the new subsidiary Tyco Capital. Under Tyco's umbrella it sold its manufactured home loan portfolio to Lehman Brothers and recreational vehicle portfolio to Salomon Smith Barney in an effort to exit noncore businesses. Tyco however expanded too far too fast and the next year announced an about-face on its financial services subsidiary deciding to spin off the division and return it to its CIT identity.

Jeff Peek took the reins of the company from longtime chairman and CEO Al Gamper in 2004.

CIT Group's Student Loan Xpress unit was one of several companies in the student-lending industry that came under investigation for business practices in 2007. It discontinued its private student loans that year and in 2008 it stopped originating government-guaranteed student loans.

Amid losses the company also exited the consumer finance business to focus on commercial lending. In 2008 it sold its home loan unit to Lone Star Funds and its manufactured housing portfolio to Vanderbilt Mortgage and Finance. The previous year it sold its construction lending unit to Wells Fargo and its 30% stake in Dell Financial Services to Dell.

CIT was hit hard in the economic recession which nearly shut down the credit markets. The company struggled to stay afloat as liquidity levels sank (a situation exacerbated as nervous customers drew on their credit lines). It exited money-losing businesses sold units and secured $3 billion from company bondholders including PIMCO and Oaktree Capital. The company also converted to a bank holding company enabling it to access government bailout funds. Still struggling CIT filed for Chapter 11 in November 2009. The restructuring lasted six weeks and helped the company eliminate more than $10 billion in debt. None of CIT's operating subsidiaries were included in the bankruptcy.

Jeffrey Peek who oversaw CIT's untimely expansion activities stepped down as CEO in early 2010. He was succeeded by John Thain who has also led Merrill Lynch and New York Stock Exchange. No stranger to turning ailing companies around Thain is credited with bringing the NYSE into the modern era with electronic trading. He also merged NYSE with Euronext establishing the first trans-Atlantic exchange.

EXECUTIVES

EVP General Counsel and Secretary, Robert J. (Bob) Ingato, age 51, $406,731 total compensation
EVP and Treasurer, Glenn A. Votek
Chairman and CEO, John A. Thain, age 56
Managing Director CIT Corporate Finance, Robert (Bob) Bielinski
President, Nelson J. Chai, age 47
EVP and Head Communications and Government Relations, Margaret D. Tutwiler, age 61
Corporate Communications Director, C. Curtis (Curt) Ritter
EVP Banking, Raymond J. (Ray) Quinlan, age 59
President Trade Finance, John F. Daly, age 63
EVP and Director Investor Relations, Kenneth A. (Ken) Brause
President Transportation Finance, C. Jeffrey (Jeff) Knittel, age 53, $388,462 total compensation
EVP and Chief Administrative Oficer, Andrew T. Brandman, age 42
Global President CIT Vendor Finance, Ron G. Arrington, age 50, $347,635 total compensation
EVP and CIO, Stacey Goodman
SVP and Chief Regulatory Officer, Jeff Bardos
President CIT Canada, J. Daryl MacLellan
VP Trade Finance, Ann-Margret Crater
EVP CIT Aerospace, Anthony (Tony) Diaz
President CIT Rail, George D. Cashman
EVP Corporate Services & Procurement; President Insurance Services, Paul G. Petrylak
President Small Business Lending CIT Bank, Christine L. (Chris) Reilly
EVP Internal Audit, Michael E. Roemer, age 50
Director Marketing CIT Bank, Gia Porto-Lenza
VP and Director Brand Marketing and Communications Corporate Finance, Daniel Infanti
President CIT Vendor Finance Latin America, Fernando Luis Fiore
Managing Director and Group Head CIT Leveraged Finance Transportation, Christopher D. (Chris) Cantwell
President CIT Healthcare, Steven N. (Steve) Warden, age 56
Managing Director CIT Vendor Finance Asia, Adrian Pang
VP and Director Marketing CIT Vendor Finance, Debbie Haeringer
VP and Director Marketing and Customer Integration CIT Vendor Finance, Paul Carmedelle
Managing Director CIT Healthcare, Wesley Smith
Managing Director CIT Communications Media and Entertainment, Wade Layton
Managing Director CIT Communications Media and Entertainment Communications, Tom Westdyk
Managing Director Gaming and Leisure, Steve Reedy
Co-President CIT Corporate Finance, Peter (Pete) Connolly, age 46

Managing Director CIT Healthcare Long-Term Care and Real Estate, Kathryn Burton Gray
Co-Head Corporate Finance, James L. (Jim) Hudak
Senior Managing Director and Group Head CIT Commercial Finance Europe, Graham Randell
President CIT Commercial & Industrial; Managing Director & Industry Group Head Retail, Burt Feinberg
SVP and International Manager CIT Commercial Services, Peter Mulroy
EVP and Chief Sales Officer CIT Commercial Services, Jonathan A. (Jon) Lucas
Sales and Marketing Effectiveness Leader Europe, Rachael Woods
Manager Brand Marketing and Communications Transportation Finance, Abby Cohn
EVP and Chief Risk Officer, Lisa K. Polsky, age 55
EVP and Chief Credit Officer, Robert C. Rowe, age 51
EVP and CFO, Scott T. Parker, age 45
SVP and Corporate Controller, Carol Hayles, age 51
EVP and Global Head Human Resources, Lisa D. Zonino
COO and Interim Managing Director CIT Vendor Finance Europe, Nicholas M. (Nick) Small
Managing Director CIT Energy, Michael (Mike) Lorusso
EVP and Chief Auditor, Robert (Bob) Hart
Managing Director CIT Canada, Blake Macaskill
Director, Peter J. Tobin, age 68
Director, Marianne Miller Parrs, age 68
Director, Seymour (Sy) Sternberg, age 68
Director, David M. Moffett, age 60
Director, Michael J. Embler, age 48
Director, Gerald (Jerry) Rosenfeld, age 65
Director, Laura S. Unger, age 51
Director, Vice Adm. John R. Ryan, age 66
Director, William M. (Bill) Freeman, age 59
Director, R. Brad Oates, age 58
Auditors: PricewaterhouseCoopersLLP

LOCATIONS

HQ: CIT Group Inc.
11 W. 42nd. St., New York NY 10036
Phone: 212-461-5200 **Fax:** 682-605-0500
Web: www.getthere.com

2011 Sales

	$ mil.	% of total
US	3,047	63
Europe	899	18
Rest of the world	908	19
Total	**4,855**	**100**

PRODUCTS/OPERATIONS

2011 Sales

	$ mil.	% of total
Interest		
Loans including fees		
US	1,613	33
Other countries	585	12
Investments	34	1
Noninterest		
Rental income on operating leases	1,665	34
Other	956	20
Total	**4,855**	**100**

Selected Subsidiaries

Aireal Technologies of Harrisburg LLC
ATMOR Properties Inc.
Capita Colombia Holdings Corp.
Education Lending Services Inc.
Education Loan Servicing Corporation
The Equipment Insurance Company
Flex Holdings LLC
Flugzeug Limited (Ireland)
Imaginarium LLC
North Romeo Storage Corporation
Waste to Energy II LLC
Wellington Capital Corporation (Barbados)

COMPETITORS

Ally Financial
Citigroup
Deutsche Bank
GE Capital
ILFC
JPMorgan Chase
ORIX

HISTORICAL FINANCIALS

Company Type: Public

Income Statement

FYE: December 31

	ASSETS ($ mil.)	NET INCOME ($ mil.)	INCOME AS % OF ASSETS	EMPLOYEES
12/11	45,235	31	0.1%	3,526
12/10	50,958	521	1.0%	3,778
12/09	60,029	183	0.3%	4,293
12/08	80,448	(2,799)	—	4,995
12/07	90,248	(81)	—	6,700
Annual Growth	(15.9%)	—	—	(14.8%)

2011 Year-End Financials

Debt ratio: 58.11%
Return on equity: 0.36%
Cash ($ mil.): 7,435
Current ratio: —
Long-term debt ($ mil.): 26,288
No. of shares (mil.): 200
Dividends
Yield: —
Payout: —
Market value ($ mil.): 6,997

	STOCK PRICE ($) FY Close	P/E High/Low	PER SHARE ($) Earnings	Dividends	Book Value
12/11	34.87	377224	0.13	0.00	44.30
12/10	47.10	18 11	2.58	0.00	44.48
12/09	27.61	— —	(0.01)	0.00	41.99
Annual Growth	12.4%	— —	—	—	2.7%

Citigroup Inc

This is the Citi. One of the largest financial services firms known to man Citigroup (also known as Citi) has some 200 million customer accounts and does business in more than 160 countries. It offers deposits and loans (mainly through Citibank) investment banking brokerage wealth management and other financial services. Few other banks can equal Citigroup's global reach: In addition to Citibank it owns stakes in several international regional banks and has more than 50 million Citi-branded credit cards in circulation. However Citi has been selling dozens of underperforming and noncore businesses in the aftermath of the financial crisis in order to refocus on its original mission –traditional banking.

HISTORY

Empire builder Sanford "Sandy" Weill who helped build brokerage firm Shearson Loeb Rhoades sold the company to American Express (AmEx) in 1981. Forced out of AmEx in 1985 Weill bounced back in 1986 buying Control Data's Commercial Credit unit.

Primerica caught Weill's eye next. Its predecessor American Can was founded in 1901 as a New Jersey canning company; it eventually expanded into the paper and retail industries before turning to financial services in 1986. The firm was renamed Primerica in 1987 and bought brokerage Smith Barney Harris Upham & Co.

Weill's Commercial Credit bought Primerica in 1988. In 1993 Primerica bought Shearson from AmEx as well as Travelers taking its name and logo.

Weill set about trimming Travelers. He sold life subsidiaries and bought Aetna's property/casualty business in 1995. In 1996 he consolidated all property/casualty operations to form Travelers Property Casualty and took it public. The next year Travelers bought investment bank Salomon Brothers and formed Salomon Smith Barney Holdings (now Citigroup Global Markets).

Weill sold Citicorp chairman and CEO John Reed on the idea of a merger in 1998 in advance of the Gramm-Leach-Bliley act which deregulated the financial services industry in the US. By the time the merger went through a slowed US economy and foreign-market turmoil brought significant losses to both sides. The renamed Citigroup consolidated in 1998 and 1999 laying off more than 10000 employees. So many executives (including co-chairmen and co-CEOs Weill and Reed) were paired through "co" titling that the company was dubbed "the ark."

In 1999 Citigroup moved deeper into subprime lending. Also that year former Treasury Secretary Robert Rubin joined Citigroup as a co-chairman.

In 2000 Reed retired and the company bought the investment banking business of British firm Schroders. Citigroup also bought subprime lender Associates First Capital (now part of CitiFinancial) for approximately $27 billion to expand its consumer product lines and its international presence. The deal however also brought Citigroup federal scrutiny regarding perceived predatory lending tactics. In 2001 the company bought New York-based European American Bank from ABN AMRO and purchased Grupo Financiero Banamex one of Mexico's biggest banks.

The company parlayed the $4 billion it netted from the 2002 spinoff of 20% of Travelers Property Casualty (it distributed most of the remaining stock to Citigroup shareholders) into a $5.8 billion purchase of California-based Golden State Bancorp the parent of the then-third-largest thrift in the US Cal Fed.

Also that year Citigroup paid some $215 million to settle federal allegations that Associates First Capital made customers unwittingly purchase credit insurance by automatically billing for the service. The agreement was one of the largest consumer-protection settlements ever.

The company also became embroiled in the Enron mess as regulators scrutinized short-term loans that Citigroup floated to the energy trader and were possibly used by Enron in transactions with offshore entities to mask debt and inflate cash flow figures. Citigroup neither confirmed nor denied allegations that it helped fudge Enron's books but in 2003 remitted more than $100 million earmarked to pay victims who lost money because of Enron's malfeasance.

A landmark ruling by the SEC in 2003 implied that Citigroup issued favorable stock ratings to companies in exchange for investment banking contracts (predictably the company neither confirmed nor denied the allegations). Also as part of the ruling erstwhile star analyst Jack Grubman agreed to pay some $15 million in fines for his overly rosy stock reports and accepted a lifetime ban from working in the securities industry. Citigroup forked over $400 million in fines the largest portion of a total of some $1.4 billion levied against 10 brokerage firms regarding conflicts of interest between analysts and investment bankers.

Amid the investigations Citigroup separated its stock-picking and corporate advisory businesses creating a retail brokerage and equity research unit called Smith Barney. In the SEC's 2003 ruling such a "Chinese Wall" between bankers and analysts was later made mandatory at all firms. Still Citigroup raked in net profits of nearly $18 billion (on revenues in excess of $94 billion) in 2003 one of the largest-ever yearly takes in US corporate history.

In 2004 the company —while admitting no wrongdoing —paid $2.65 billion to investors who were burned when WorldCom went bankrupt amid an accounting scandal. (Citigroup was one of the lead underwriters of WorldCom stocks and bonds.) The settlement was one of the largest ever for alleged securities fraud and compelled Citigroup to set aside an additional $5 billion to cover legal fees for this case and others involving Enron and spinning. The company eventually paid $2 billion in mid-2005 to investors who lost money on publicly traded Enron stocks and bonds again settling the matter while denying it broke any laws. Enron shareholders had argued that Citigroup helped Enron to set up offshore companies and shady partnerships to exaggerate the energy trader's cash flow.

In Japan where Citigroup is one of the leading foreign banks regulators pulled the plug on the company's private banking operations in 2004 after determining that Citigroup misled customers regarding the sale of certain structured bonds. The closures led to the forced resignation of three top executives in the company's asset management and private banking units about a month later.

Citigroup sold The Travelers Life and Annuity Company (now MetLife Life and Annuity Company of Connecticut) plus most of its international insurance business to MetLife in 2005. Later that year a convoluted deal with Legg Mason netted Citigroup that company's retail brokerage and capital markets business (and $1.5 billion of Legg Mason stock) in exchange for most of Citigroup's asset management and mutual fund division; Citigroup concurrently sold Legg Mason's capital markets operations to Stifel Financial.

Seeking growth internationally Citigroup was part of a consortium that acquired a controlling stake in Guangdong Development Bank in 2006. Also that year the company opened more than 800 bank branches and consumer finance offices outside the US.

Weill ended years of speculation in 2003 by anointing corporate and investment bank head Chuck Prince as his successor. Weill retired as chairman in 2006 and Prince assumed that title as well. Prince resigned in 2007 as Citigroup dealt with losses on mortgage-related securities and other investments.

Prince was succeeded by Vikram Pandit a Morgan Stanley veteran who came to Citigroup when it acquired hedge fund and private equity manager Old Lane Partners in 2007. Pandit was at Citigroup only a few months before he was named CEO but during that time he oversaw the company's alternative investments and led its institutional clients group. The following year Citigroup disbanded Old Lane and wound up its flagship fund.

Citigroup further expanded its fund services operations via its 2007 acquisition of BISYS. As part of the deal the company sold BISYS' insurance services division to investment firm J.C. Flowers & Co.

Also that year it picked up remnants of the subprime mortgage collapse when it acquired ACC Capital Holding's wholesale mortgage origination operations as well as the servicing rights to some $5 billion in home loans. It also bought ABN AMRO Mortgage Group and shelled out more than $1 billion to buy Egg one of the largest online-only banks in the world from Prudential plc. The deal boosted its UK consumer operations by adding some 3 million customers.

The company sold its trademark red umbrella logo back to insurance firm Travelers which began using the symbol nearly 150 years before. Citigroup acquired the iconic logo when it bought the insurance company in 1993 and held onto it after it spun off Travelers in 2002. But the company ultimately decided that customers associated the umbrella with insurance and sold it in 2007.

In order to shore up its balance sheet Citigroup sold some 5% of itself to the Abu Dhabi Investment Authority a Middle Eastern sovereign fund for $7.5 billion in 2007. It later raised more than $12 billion by selling preferred shares to investors including a Singapore government-owned investment fund former CEO Sandy Weill and Saudi investor Prince Al-Walid bin Talal who owns roughly 5% stake of Citigroup.

Citigroup bought a majority stake in one of Japan's largest brokerages Nikko Cordial in 2007. It acquired the remaining shares of Nikko Cordial in early 2008 and merged it with Citigroup Japan Holdings to form Nikko Citi Holdings.

In 2008 Citigroup sold several of its commercial finance lines to GE Capital. It sold its German consumer banking business to French bank Groupe Credit Mutuel.

As the global credit crisis mounted in 2008 the US government injected some $700 billion into the nation's banking industry including $45 billion investment in Citigroup. It further stepped in to aid the faltering bank by backing more than $300 in loans and securities to boost confidence in the bank and protect its investments. In exchange the government took a 34% stake in Citigroup. The company received approval to pay the funds back in 2009 and the government began reducing its ownership.

EXECUTIVES

CEO Global Consumer Banking, Manuel Medina-Mora, age 62, $546,966 total compensation
Chairman, Richard D. (Dick) Parsons, age 64
CEO Citibank N.A., Eugene M. (Gene) McQuade, age 63
Head Global Digital Merchant Acquiring, Deborah D. (Debby) McWhinney, age 56
CEO and Director, Vikram S. Pandit, age 55, $125,001 total compensation
Head Human Resources, Paul D. McKinnon, age 59
General Counsel and Secretary, Michael S. Helfer, age 66
Chairman Institutional Clients Group, Edward J. (Ned) Kelly III, age 58, $270,834 total compensation
President and COO, John P. Havens, age 55, $500,000 total compensation
Vice Chairman, Lewis B. (Lew) Kaden, age 69, $500,000 total compensation
Vice Chairman, Stephen R. Volk, age 76, $500,000 total compensation
Chairman Citigroup Private Bank, Deepak Sharma
Vice Chairman Citicorp, Hamid Biglari
EVP Citi Financial Regulation Reform, Zion Shohet
CEO North America, William J. (Bill) Mills, age 56
CEO Global Enterprise Payments, Paul Galant, age 44
CEO Securities and Banking, James A. (Jim) Forese, age 49, $225,000 total compensation
Chief Risk Officer Commercial Bank, Suneel Bakhshi
CEO, Michael L. Corbat, age 52
Head Global Markets Institutional Clients Group, Paco Ybarra
CEO Consumer Finance Citi Holdings, George Awad
CFO, John C. Gerspach, age 58, $416,667 total compensation
COO U.S Consumer and Commercial Banking, William (Will) Howle III
CEO Banamex, Enrique Zorrilla Fullaondo
Chairman Asia Pacific, Shengman Zhang, age 55
CEO Asia Pacific Banking, Shirish Apte, age 59
CEO Asia Pacific, Stephen Bird, age 45
CEO Citigroup Mexico, Javier Arrigunaga
CEO Global Transaction Services, Francesco Vanni d'Archirafi
Chief Administrative Officer Chief Operations and Technology Officer, Don Callahan, age 55
Chief Brand Officer, Dermot J. M. Boden
Chief Risk Officer, Brian Leach, age 52
Head Mobile Initiatives, Omar Khan
EVP Global Public Affairs, Edward Skyler, age 38
Vice Chairman Global Banking, Peter R. Orszag, age 43
CEO Citi Holdings, Mark Mason
Head EMEA Markets Institutional Clients Group, James C. Cowles
President and CEO Citi Foundation and Director Corporate Citizenship, Pamela P. (Pam) Flaherty
Head Global Banking Citi India, Ravi Kapoor
Global Director Citi Microfinance, Robert A. (Bob) Annibale
Head Wealth Management Asia Pacific, Paul Hodes
Head Investor Services Hedge Fund Services, Steve Pitkin
Global Head Hedge Fund Services, Mike Sleightholme
CEO Citi Cards, Jud Linville
President U.S. Consumer and Commercial Banking, Cecelia (Cece) Stewart
Managing Director European Leverage Finance, David Bugge
EVP Global Government Affairs, Candida (Candi) Wolff
Managing Director Institutional Clients Group, Michael Eckhart
Vice Chairman Banking Europe the Middle East and Africa, Stuart Popham
Head Investment Banking Southeast Asian, Tracey Woon
Managing Director Southeast Asia Industrials; Co-head Energy Global Banking Asia, Abhay Pande
Co-head Energy Global Banking Asia, Jason Johnson
Managing Director China Investment Banking, Kenneth Leung
CIO Global Consumer Technology, Mark Torkos
CEO Citigroup Latin America, Francisco Aristeguieta
Controller and Chief Accounting Officer, Jeffrey R. Walsh, age 54
Director, Alain J. P. Belda, age 68
Director, Lawrence R. (Larry) Ricciardi, age 71
Director, Robert L. (Bob) Ryan, age 67
Director, Judith (Judy) Rodin, age 67
Director, Timothy C. (Tim) Collins, age 55
CEO and Director, Vikram S. Pandit, age 55
Director, Michael E. O'Neill, age 65
Director, William S. (Bill) Thompson Jr., age 66
Director, Robert L. (Bob) Joss, age 71
Director, Anthony M. (Tony) Santomero, age 66
Director, Diana Lancaster Taylor, age 57
Director, Ernesto Zedillo, age 60
Auditors: KPMGLLP

LOCATIONS

HQ: Citigroup Inc.
399 Park Ave., New York NY 10022
Phone: 212-559-1000 **Fax:** 315-366-3709
Web: www.oneidabank.com

PRODUCTS/OPERATIONS

2011 Sales

	$ mil.	% of total
Interest		
Loans including fees	50,281	48
Investments including dividends	8,320	8
Trading account assets	8,186	8
Federal funds sold & securities purchased under resale agreements	3,631	3
Deposits with banks	1,750	2
Other	513	-
Noninterest		
Commissions & fees	12,850	12
Principal transactions	7,234	7
Administration & other fiduciary fees	3,995	4
Insurance premiums	2,647	3
Realized gains on sales of investments	1,997	2
Other	3,437	3
Adjustments	(2254)	-
Total	**102,587**	**100**

2011 Assets

	$ mil.	% of total
Cash & equivalents	460,334	25
Brokerage receivables	27,777	1
Trading accounts	291,734	15
Investments	293,413	16
Net loans	617,127	33
Other	183,493	10
Total	**1,873,878**	**100**

COMPETITORS

American Express
Bank of America
Bank of New York Mellon
Barclays
Capital One
Deutsche Bank
FMR
GE
Goldman Sachs
HSBC
JPMorgan Chase
Mizuho Financial
U.S. Bancorp
UBS
USAA
Wells Fargo

HISTORICAL FINANCIALS

Company Type: Public

Income Statement

FYE: December 31

	ASSETS ($ mil.)	NET INCOME ($ mil.)	INCOME AS % OF ASSETS	EMPLOYEES
12/11	1,873,878	11,067	0.6%	266,000
12/10	1,913,902	10,602	0.6%	260,000
12/09	1,856,646	(1,606)	—	269,000
12/08	1,938,470	(27,684)	—	326,900
12/07	2,187,631	3,617	0.2%	387,000
Annual Growth	(3.8%)	32.3%	—	(8.9%)

2011 Year-End Financials

Debt ratio: 17.26%—
Return on equity: 6.22%
Cash ($ mil.): 184,485
Current ratio: —
Long-term debt ($ mil.): 323,505

Dividends
Yield: —
Payout: 0.83%
Market value ($ mil.): —

	STOCK PRICE ($) FY Close	P/E High	P/E Low	PER SHARE ($) Earnings	Dividends	Book Value
12/11	26.31	12	1	3.63	0.00	60.81
12/10	4.73	1	1	3.50	0.00	56.26
12/09	3.31	—	—	(8.00)	0.00	53.61
12/08	6.71	—	—	(55.90)	0.00	259.87
12/07	29.44	8	4	7.20	0.00	227.44
Annual Growth	(2.8%)	—	—	(15.7%)	—	(28.1%)

Citizens Republic Bancorp, Inc

Attention Citizens of the Republic! Citizens Republic Bancorp is the holding company for Citizens Bank which operates about 220 branches in Michigan Wisconsin and northern Ohio. The bank offers retail and commercial services including deposit accounts credit cards loans mortgages and investments. It also performs specialty banking services such as asset-based lending and financing to specialty health care providers. The bank's wealth management offerings include employee benefits plans and personal and institutional trust services. FirstMerit is buying Citizens Republic Bancorp for some $912 million.

Commercial loans including real estate construction and industrial loans make up more than half of Citizen Reoublic Bancorp's portfolio; consumer loans are about a third. More than 70% of the company's revenue and loan portfolio originate from its primary market of Michigan which was hit especially hard during the economic downturn that began in 2007.

Citizens Republic Bancorp suffered more than $1 billion in losses from 2008 to 2010 largely due to loan loss expenses. During that time the company focused on improving credit quality and weeding out problem assets. Though revenues were down (from nearly $580 million to some $503 million) it returned to profitability in 2011 when its amount of nonperforming loans fell below $100 million for the first time since 2007. The company is working on rebuilding its loan portfolio particularly in indirect marine and RV lending and financing to assisted living and skilled nursing care providers.

To raise capital Citizens sold its F&M Bank-Iowa subsidiary to Great Western Bank a unit of National Australia Bank in 2010. The $50 million deal included the sale of about a dozen branches in the Des Moines Iowa area.

Formerly Citizens Banking Company Citizens Republic Bancorp adopted its current moniker following its 2006 purchase of rival Republic Bancorp for more than $1 billion.

EXECUTIVES

EVP Secretary and General Counsel, Thomas W. Gallagher, age 59, $248,464 total compensation
CFO Wealth Management and Director Investor Relations, Kristine D. Brenner
Chairman, James L. (Jim) Wolohan, age 60
EVP Commercial Banking, Clinton A. (Clint) Sampson, age 66, $280,385 total compensation
EVP and Corporate Risk Officer, Stephen V. Figliuolo, age 55
EVP and Director Core Banking, Judith L. Klawinski, age 51, $246,535 total compensation
President CEO and Director, Cathleen H. (Cathy) Nash, age 49, $587,238 total compensation
EVP and Director Human Resources, Susan P. Brockett, age 62
EVP and Director Wealth Management; President Citizens Bank Wealth Management, Peter W. Ronan, age 67
EVP and General Auditor, Louise N. O'Connell, age 52
EVP and Chief Credit Officer, Mark W. Widawski, age 54
President Southeast Michigan, Clarissa Chartier
SVP and Treasurer, Brian D.J. Boike, age 35
SVP and Controller, Joseph C. Czopek, age 54
EVP and CFO, Lisa T. McNeely
EVP CIO and Director Operations, Gerald D. Bettens, age 52
Director, George J. Butvilas, age 66
Director, Robert S. Cubbin, age 54
Director, Richard J. Dolinski, age 71
Director, Stephen J. Lazaroff, age 58
Director, Gary J. Hurand, age 65
Director, Dennis J. Ibold, age 63
Director, Kendall B. Williams, age 59
Director, Benjamin W. Laird, age 62
Director, Lizabeth A. Ardisana, age 60
President CEO and Director, Cathleen H. (Cathy) Nash, age 49
Auditors: Ernst&YoungLLP

LOCATIONS

HQ: Citizens Republic Bancorp, Inc
328 S. Saginaw St., Flint, MI 48502
Phone: 810 766-7500
Web: www.citizensbanking.com

PRODUCTS/OPERATIONS

2011 Sales

	$ mil.	% of total
Interest		
Loans including fees	312	62
Investment securities	90	18
Other	5	1
Noninterest		
Service charges on deposit accounts	39	8
Trust fees	15	3
Bankcard fees	9	2
Mortgage & other loan income	9	2
ATM network user fees	7	1
Brokerage & investment fees	5	1
Other	9	2
Total	**503**	**100**

COMPETITORS

Anchor BanCorp
Associated Banc-Corp
Bank of America
Chemical Financial
Comerica
Fifth Third
Flagstar Bancorp
Huntington Bancshares
Independent Bank (MI)
JPMorgan Chase
KeyCorp
TCF Financial
U.S. Bancorp
Wells Fargo

HISTORICAL FINANCIALS

Company Type: Public

Income Statement FYE: December 31

	ASSETS ($ mil.)	NET INCOME ($ mil.)	INCOME AS % OF ASSETS	EMPLOYEES
12/11	9,462	6	0.1%	1,977
12/10	9,965	(292)	—	2,026
12/09	11,931	(514)	—	2,125
12/08	13,086	(393)	—	2,232
12/07	13,505	100	0.7%	2,501
Annual Growth	(8.5%)	(49.3%)	—	(5.7%)

2011 Year-End Financials

Debt ratio: 9.03%
Return on equity: 0.65%
Cash ($ mil.): 153
Current ratio: —
Long-term debt ($ mil.): 854
No. of shares (mil.): 40
Dividends
Yield: —
Payout: —
Market value ($ mil.): 457

	STOCK PRICE ($) FY Close	P/E High	P/E Low	PER SHARE ($) Earnings	Dividends	Book Value
12/11	11.40	—	—	(0.41)	0.00	25.46
12/10	0.62	—	—	(8.00)	0.00	25.47
12/09	0.69	—	—	(27.50)	0.00	33.75
12/08	2.98	—	—	(43.00)	0.00	127.09
12/07	14.51	2	1	13.30	0.00	208.38
Annual Growth	(5.9%)	—	—	—	—	(40.9%)

City Holding Co.

Take Me Home Country Roads may be the (unofficial) state song of West Virginia but City Holding hopes all roads lead to its City National Bank of West Virginia subsidiary which operates some 70 branches in the Mountaineer State and in neighboring areas of southern Ohio eastern Kentucky and northern Virginia. Serving consumers and regional businesses the bank offers standard deposit products loans credit cards insurance trust and investment services. Residential mortgages and home equity loans constitute more than half of City Holding's loan portfolio. The company entered a new market through the 2012 acquisition of Virginia Savings Bank which has five branches in the northern part of that state.

The acquisition was a healthy one not one of the many deals that have transpired where financial companies assume deposits and branches of troubled of failed banks in FDIC-assisted purchases. In a similar deal City Holding plans to buy Community Financial Corporation holding company of the 11-branch Community Bank in Virginia.

In addition to residential mortgages City Holding writes commercial industrial commercial mortgage and installment consumer loans.

The company's net income rose some 4% to $40.7 million in 2011 versus the $39 million it netted the year before. Its loan portfolio also grew that year prior to the Virginia Savings acquisition and the company's portfolio of nonperforming assets declined. Service fees have slipped though as the company deals with lower consumer spending and regulatory changes regarding overdraft charges. This loss was slightly offset by stronger performance in trust investment management and insurance operations.

EXECUTIVES

EVP Retail Banking Marketing and Human Resources, Craig G. Stilwell, age 56, $222,292 total compensation
President CEO and Director; President and CEO City National Bank, Charles R. (Skip) Hageboeck, age 49, $379,792 total compensation
Investor Relations Contact, Victoria Evans-Faw
EVP Commercial Banking City Holding Company and City National Bank, John A. DeRito, age 62, $189,167 total compensation
SVP and CFO City Holding Company and City National Bank, David L. Bumgarner, age 47, $166,354 total compensation
SVP and Chief Legal Counsel City Holding Company and City National Bank, John W. Alderman III, age 47, $172,771 total compensation
SVP Branch Banking City Holding Company & City National Bank, Michael T. Quinlan Jr.
Director, Philip L. McLaughlin, age 71
Director, David W. Hambrick, age 70
President CEO and Director; President and CEO City National Bank, Charles R. (Skip) Hageboeck, age 49
Director, Tracy W. Hylton II, age 63
Director, C. Dallas Kayser, age 60
Director, Oshel B. Craigo, age 74
Director, Sharon H. Rowe, age 61
Director, William H. File III, age 64
Director, James L. Rossi, age 57
Director, Mary E. Hooten Williams, age 50
Director, Jay C. Goldman, age 68
Director, Robert D. Fisher, age 59
Director, Hugh R. Clonch, age 72
Director, John Elliot, age 66
Auditors: Ernst&YoungLLP

LOCATIONS

HQ: City Holding Company
25 Gatewater Rd., Cross Lanes WV 25313
Phone: 304-769-1100 **Fax:** 304-769-1111
Web: www.cityholding.com

PRODUCTS/OPERATIONS

2011 Sales

	$ mil.	% of total
Interest		
Loans including fees	93	56
Investment securities & other	19	12
Noninterest		
Service charges	38	23
Insurance commissions	5	3
Other	10	6
Total	**167**	**100**

COMPETITORS

1st West Virginia Bancorp
BB&T
Fifth Third
First Community Bancshares
Huntington Bancshares
Ohio Valley Banc
Premier Financial Bancorp
United Bankshares
WesBanco

HISTORICAL FINANCIALS

Company Type: Public

Income Statement FYE: December 31

	ASSETS ($ mil.)	NET INCOME ($ mil.)	INCOME AS % OF ASSETS	EMPLOYEES
12/11	2,777	40	1.5%	795
12/10	2,637	38	1.5%	805
12/09	2,622	42	1.6%	809
12/08	2,582	28	1.1%	827
12/07	2,482	51	2.1%	811
Annual Growth	2.8%	(5.5%)	—	(0.5%)

2011 Year-End Financials

Debt ratio: 0.59%
Return on equity: 13.07%
Cash ($ mil.): 146
Current ratio: —
Long-term debt ($ mil.): 16
No. of shares (mil.): 14
Dividends
Yield: —
Payout: 50.94%
Market value ($ mil.): 501

	STOCK PRICE ($) FY Close	P/E High	P/E Low	PER SHARE ($) Earnings	Dividends	Book Value
12/11	33.89	14	10	2.67	0.00	21.05
12/10	36.23	15	11	2.47	1.36	20.31
12/09	32.31	13	8	2.68	1.36	19.37
12/08	34.78	27	17	1.74	1.33	17.58
12/07	33.84	14	10	3.01	1.21	18.14
Annual Growth	0.0%	—	—	(3.0%)	—	3.8%

City National Corp. (Beverly Hills, CA)

For celebrity sightings forget the Hollywood Homes Tour and camp out at City National Bank. The flagship subsidiary of City National Corporation has been known as "Bank to the Stars" since opening in Beverly Hills in 1954. The bank has since grown to some 80 branches in Southern California the San Francisco Bay area and Nevada as well as New York City Nashville and Atlanta. It focuses on personal and business banking investment management and trust services. The bank provides customized service tailoring its offerings to meet the needs of its high-powered clientele. Its target market includes small to midsized businesses entrepreneurs professionals and affluent individuals in urban markets.

Commercial loans make up more than a third of the bank's lending portfolio followed by residential and commercial real estate mortgages. Loans to the entertainment industry make up the largest segment of its commercial loan book.

Despite recent troubles in the banking industry and the economy in general City National has managed to turn a profit for 19 consecutive years thanks in part to a business model that is focused on serving a targeted customer base. It also has a conservative approach to managing its loan portfolio. The company limits its exposure to commercial real estate and construction and has relatively few loans to homebuilders. As a result of its strict approach the company has not been as hard-hit hard by non-performing loans as some of its peers. City National's net income was up in 2010 and 2011 as the company reported fewer provisions for loan losses and higher net interest income. It expects to continue to grow as the economy improves.

City National has used an acquisition strategy to build both its banking and its wealth management operations and to push the company beyond its California home. On the banking side the company first entered the Nevada market with the 2007 purchase of Business Bank. It expanded in the state with the FDIC-assisted acquisitions of two failed banks in 2010 and 2011 that included loss-sharing agreements with the regulator.

City National had already made two similar deals in California acquiring the failed Imperial Capital Bank including its nine branches in 2009. The following year it acquired another failed bank 1st Pacific Bank adding six branches in the San Diego area. In a more conventional transaction City National acquired a branch from Westamerica Bank in San Jose in 2009 which was made to expand services in Silicon Valley. City National has since bought two more bank branches in San Jose.

City National opened its second branch in New York City in 2010. The Manhattan location focuses on serving lawyers accountants business managers entrepreneurs investors and other business people in New York.

City National also is growing its private banking business and has snapped up more than a half-dozen wealth management firms and is still on the prowl. The company's wealth management division which includes Boston-based Independence Investments and Convergent Capital Management in Chicago offers brokerage services retirement plans and manages the CNI Charter family of mutual funds. The division oversees about $60 billion in client assets. In 2012 City National acquired Rochdale Investment Management a $4.8 billion New York investment firm that manages assets for rich clients.

City National also is making investments in technology. In 2010 the company made a small but strategic acquisition of Los-Angeles-based accounting software firm Datafaction. The addition expanded the bank's cash management services for business customers. In 2012 the company bought First American Equipment Finace which leases technology and office equipment.

HISTORY

In 1953 a group of investors led by Columbia Pictures board member Alfred Hart and Ben Maltz founded a little neighborhood bank. Jack Benny and George Jessel hosted the opening. In the 1960s Maltz's son-in-law real estate developer Bram Goldsmith became its largest customer. When illness caused Hart to quit Goldsmith bought him out and took over.

The bank which formed holding company City National Corporation in 1968 moved beyond Los Angeles County in 1979 financing the 1980s commercial real estate boom in Southern California. When the market crashed City National was left with a glut of nonperforming assets. Losses began in 1991 and the company was put under regulatory supervision the next year. City National sold most of its nonperforming loans in 1993. The bank returned to profitability the following year boosting fee income and diversifying its loan portfolio with residential mortgages.

In 1995 Goldsmith's son Russell became CEO. He began buying banks to build share in the Los Angeles area and scooped up disgruntled clients and employees soured by such mega mergers as Wells Fargo and First Interstate. Purchases included First Los Angeles Bank (1996) Ventura County National Bancorp (1997) Harbor Bancorp (1998) and American Pacific State Bank (1999). In 2000 the bank looked north and bought The Pacific Bank in San Francisco. Later that year it purchased asset manager Reed Conner & Birdwell.

In 2002 the company acquired Oakland California-based Civic BanCorp and opened its first office in New York City. The following year it bought Chicago-based asset manager Convergence Capital Management. City National built upon that business in 2007 when it bought the wealth management operations of Lydian which were rebranded Convergence Wealth Advisors.

City National continued to grow its wealth management business in 2009 with the acquisition of a majority interest in Lee Munder Capital Group a Boston-based investment firm that managed assets for corporations pensions endowments and affluent households. It was merged with another of City National's asset managers in Boston Independence Investments.

EXECUTIVES

EVP and Manager Treasury Services Division City National Bank, James R. Daley, age 66
President CEO and Director; Chairman and CEO City National Bank, Russell D. Goldsmith, age 62, $978,528 total compensation
Chairman, Bram Goldsmith, age 88, $350,000 total compensation
EVP and CFO City National Corporation and City National Bank, Christopher J. (Chris) Carey, age 57, $470,000 total compensation
EVP and Chief Credit Officer City National Bank, Christopher J. (Chris) Warmuth, age 57, $485,000 total compensation
EVP and CIO City National Bank, John J. Beale
EVP Northern California Region, Robert H. (Bob) Brant
EVP Core Banking Division and Regional Executive Orange County City National Bank, Kevin P. Dunigan
EVP Secretary and General Counsel City National Corporation and City National Bank, Michael B. Cahill, age 58, $400,000 total compensation
EVP and Senior Risk Management Officer City National Corporation and City National Bank, John Pedersen
EVP and Chief Credit Officer City National Bank, Brian Fitzmaurice, age 51, $312,500 total compensation
EVP and Manager Real Estate Division City National Bank, Mark J. Forbes
EVP Private Client Services Los Angeles City National Bank, Gwen T. Miller
SVP and Chief Accounting Officer City National Corporation and City National Bank, Olga Tsokova, age 38
EVP Wealth Management Services City National Bank, Richard Gershen, $348,333 total compensation
Director, Kenneth L. (Ken) Coleman, age 69
President CEO and Director; Chairman and CEO City National Bank, Russell D. Goldsmith, age 62
Director, Robert H. (Bob) Tuttle, age 68
EVP and Chief Credit Officer City National Bank, Christopher J. (Chris) Warmuth, age 57
Director, Bruce Rosenblum, age 53
Director, Ronald L. (Ron) Olson, age 70
Director, Richard L. Bloch, age 82
Director, Kenneth Ziffren, age 71
Director, Peter M. Thomas, age 62
Director, Ashok (Ash) Israni, age 64
Auditors: KPMGLLP

LOCATIONS

HQ: City National Corporation
City National Plaza 555 S. Flower St., Los Angeles CA 90071
Phone: 213-673-7700 **Fax:** 302-994-3086
Web: www.acornfactor.com

PRODUCTS/OPERATIONS

2011 Sales

	$ mil.	% of total
Interest		
Loans & leases	681	57
Securities	159	13
Other	1	-
Noninterest		
Trust & investment fees	140	12
Cash management & deposit transaction charges	44	4
International services	36	3
Brokerage & mutual fund fees	20	2
Gain on disposal of assets	20	2
Other	79	7
Total	**1,185**	**100**

COMPETITORS

1st Century Bank
Allen & Company
Bank of America
Bank of the West
Cathay General Bancorp
Citigroup
Comerica
JPMorgan Chase
NCAL Bancorp
SVB Financial
UnionBanCal
Wells Fargo

HISTORICAL FINANCIALS

Company Type: Public

Income Statement FYE: December 31

	ASSETS ($ mil.)	NET INCOME ($ mil.)	INCOME AS % OF ASSETS	EMPLOYEES
12/11	23,666	172	0.7%	3,256
12/10	21,353	131	0.6%	3,178
12/09	21,078	51	0.2%	3,017
12/08	16,455	104	0.6%	2,989
12/07	15,889	222	1.4%	2,914
Annual Growth	10.5%	(6.2%)	—	2.8%

2011 Year-End Financials

Debt ratio: 2.95%
Return on equity: 8.04%
Cash ($ mil.): 244
Current ratio: —
Long-term debt ($ mil.): 697
No. of shares (mil.): 52
Dividends
Yield: —
Payout: 24.92%
Market value ($ mil.): 2,319

	STOCK PRICE ($) FY Close	P/E High/Low		PER SHARE ($) Earnings	Dividends	Book Value
12/11	44.18	19	11	3.21	0.00	40.85
12/10	61.36	27	19	2.36	0.40	37.51
12/09	45.60	97	46	0.50	0.55	38.54
12/08	48.70	31	16	2.11	1.92	42.10
12/07	59.55	17	13	4.52	1.84	34.32
Annual Growth	(7.2%)	—	—	(8.2%)	—	4.5%

Cliffs Natural Resources, Inc.

Cliffs Natural Resources' favorite period in history? The Iron Age hands down. The company produces iron ore pellets a key component of steelmaking and owns or holds stakes in six iron ore properties that represent almost half of North America's iron ore production. Cliffs' operations including Northshore Mining and Empire Iron produce more than 38 million tons of iron ore pellets annually. The company sells its ore primarily in North America but also in Europe and China. The company owns Australian iron properties that supply the Asia/Pacific region. It also has a growing number of iron ore interests in Latin America.

Financial Analysis

After retrenching from a dismal 2009 Cliffs came on strong in 2010 doubling its revenues (up more than 99%) while quadrupling its net income (up 399%). Sales increases were due to significant improvement in customer demand for iron ore pellets as well as metallurgical and thermal coal. Demand was up across all markets but particularly strong in China. The surge in net income was due in part to a successful shift from long-term contracts to a short-term pricing policy and significantly higher operating income.

ArcelorMittal USA accounts for almost one-third of the total sales of Cliffs' North American iron ore pellets with Essar Steel Algoma and Severstal North America in for about 20% each. Although the bulk of sales are made in North America sales in Asia –particularly in China and Japan –have grown to 25% of the company's overall business.

Strategy

Cliffs' strategy is to achieve scale and presence in the mining industry and to concentrate its focus on the world's largest and fastest growing steel markets. Its mining properties are strategically located to serve the growing iron ore markets in the US China and Brazil.

In 2010 Cliffs pursued its strategy of increasing its scale and presence through several acquisitions. It raised its minority stake in iron ore producer Wabush Mines to full ownership in 2010 buying out partners U.S. Steel Canada and Dofasco. Around that same time Cliffs bought Freewest Resources for about $225 million. Also that year Cliffs acquired 51% of a joint venture with Mariana Resources to explore iron oxide-copper-gold deposits in north-central Chile.

Through a subsidiary Cliffs acquired Spider Resources in 2010 to gain control of the "Big Daddy" chromite project in Northern Ontario. The company also acquired the metallurgical and thermal coal-mining operations of West Virginia-based INR Energy LLC for $757 million.

The Freewest Wabush Mariana Spider and INR acquisitions allowed Cliffs to increase production capacity and add additional reserves to its iron ore and coal businesses gain additional access to the seaborne iron ore markets serving Europe and Asia and diversify its market base.

In 2011 Cliffs acquired Consolidated Thompson Iron Mines Limited for about $5 billion. Cliffs wants the raw materials from Consolidated Thompson's operations to bolster its exports to China and other global customers with the goal of diversifying its customer base beyond North America.

Also in 2011 Australian subsidiary Australia Coal agreed to sell its 45% stake in the Sonoma joint venture coal mine in Queensland to QCoal Sonoma for A$141 million ($142.60 million). The company wants to use the proceeds for projects where Cliffs has operational control.

HISTORY

Samuel Mashers founded the Cleveland Iron Mining Co. in 1846 just five years after the discovery of iron ore in Michigan's Upper Peninsula. To compete in a consolidating market the company merged with Iron Cliffs Mining in 1891 to form Cleveland-Cliffs. The company offset risks by forming joint ventures with steel companies to own and operate mines. It survived the Depression by selling all its steel and timber operations. The demands of WWII prompted Cleveland-Cliffs to invest in iron mines outside the US –in Canada Chile Colombia Peru and Venezuela (cut back after WWII to Canada and Australia).

In the 1960s the company rebuffed a takeover bid by Detroit Steel and in the 1970s it diversified again acquiring copper shale oil timber and uranium assets. However Cleveland-Cliffs stumbled financially and sold all its businesses not related to iron ore. The revival of the steel industry in the late 1980s and 1990s lifted Cleveland-Cliff's sales but the financial struggles of its major customers forced losses on the company.

In 1994 the company bought Cypress Ajax Mineral's Minnesota iron mine (Northshore). In 1996 Cleveland-Cliffs closed its exhausted Australian operations. That year the company formed a joint venture with LTV and Lurgi (of Germany) to make reduced-iron briquettes in Trinidad and Tobago.

Faced with a tide of steel imports from Asia Brazil and Russia the company curtailed production and deferred plans to supply steel minimills with the iron ore pellets needed to produce iron in electric furnaces –the company's planned start-up of its ferrous metallics plant in Trinidad was delayed in 2000 due to mechanical problems. During late 2000 two of Cleveland-Cliffs' mine partners –LTV and Wheeling-Pittsburgh –filed for bankruptcy protection. Cleveland-Cliffs was able to up its stake in the Empire Iron mine previously co-owned with Wheeling-Pittsburgh to 35%.

Later that year Canada-based Algoma Steel co-owner with Cleveland-Cliffs of the Tilden mine filed for bankruptcy. Also in 2001 Cleveland-Cliffs began production at its ferrous metallics plant in Trinidad; that plant was idled later in the year. In late 2001 the company along with ALLETE subsidiary Minnesota Power acquired the iron ore mining and processing facilities of LTV Steel Mining Co. including a rail line and dock facility on Lake Superior. In 2001 Cleveland-Cliffs increased its stake in the Tilden mine to 85%.

In late 2001 the Empire Iron mine was temporarily closed and its operations restructured. The mine reopened in 2002; Cleveland-Cliffs took a $52.7 million charge related to the closure. The following year the company increased its stake in the Empire Iron mine to 79%. In 2003 United Taconite (70% owned by Cleveland-Cliffs) was formed to hold the mining operations it purchased from bankrupt Eveleth Mines.

EXECUTIVES

EVP Legal Government Affairs and Sustainability and Chief Legal Officer; President Cliffs China, P. Kelly Tompkins, age 55
EVP Global Metallics, William A. Brake Jr., age 51, $400,475 total compensation
EVP; President Global Operations, Laurie Brlas, age 54, $406,265 total compensation
SVP Global Business Development, Clifford T. Smith, age 52
SVP Global Ferroalloys, William C. (Bill) Boor, age 46
EVP; President Global Commercial, Donald J. Gallagher, age 59, $412,055 total compensation
Chairman President and CEO, Joseph A. Carrabba, age 59, $750,500 total compensation
SVP North American Coal, Duke D. Vetor, age 53
VP Investor Relations and Corporate Communications, Steven R. (Steve) Baisden
SVP and CFO, Terrance M. Paradie, age 44
SVP Corporate Strategy and Communications and Chief Strategy Officer, Steven M. Raguz, age 44
CIO, Ronald K. (Ron) Aderhold, age 49
SVP Global Iron Ore and Metallic Sales, Terence R. Mee, age 42
EVP; President Global Operations, Duncan P. Price, age 56
VP Global Coat and Alternative Energy Sales, William J. (Bill) McFadden, age 47
VP and Senior Project Director Canadian Chromite Operations, David (Dave) Anthony, age 56
SVP Operations North American Iron Ore, David B. Blake, age 43
SVP Human Resources and Chief Human Resource Officer, James R. Michaud, age 56
VP Global Marketing, William Hart
VP Asia/Pacific Iron Ore, Colin Williams
Director, Richard K. Riederer, age 68
Director, Janice K. Henry, age 61
Director, Roger Phillips, age 72
Director, Francis R. (Frank) McAllister, age 69
Director, Susan M. Cunningham, age 56
Director, Alan Schwartz, age 72
Director, Andres R. Gluski, age 54
Director, Barry J. Eldridge, age 66
Director, Susan M. Green, age 52
Auditors: Deloitte&ToucheLLP

LOCATIONS

HQ: Cliffs Natural Resources Inc.
200 Public Sq., Cleveland OH 44114
Phone: 216-694-5700 **Fax:** 216-694-4880
Web: www.cliffsnaturalresources.com

2011 Sales

US Iron Ore	3,509	52
Eastern Canadian Iron Ore	1,178	17
North American Coal	512	8
Total	**6,794**	**100**

2011 Sales

US	2,774	41
Canada	914	13
Other countries	522	8
Total	**6,794**	**100**

PRODUCTS/OPERATIONS

Selected Operations

Michigan (Marquette Range)
- Empire Iron Mining Partnership (79%)
- Tilden Mine (85%)

Minnesota (Mesabi Range)
- Hibbing Taconite Company (23%)
- Northshore Mining Company
- United Taconite

Canada
- Wabush Mines (Newfoundland/Quebec)

COMPETITORS

Alpha Natural Resources
International Briquettes

Baffinland Iron Mines
BHP Billiton
CONSOL Energy
Dofasco
Ferrexpo
Great Northern Iron Ore
Peabody Energy
Rio Tinto Limited
United States Steel
Vale

HISTORICAL FINANCIALS

Company Type: Public

Income Statement FYE: December 31

	REVENUE ($ mil.)	NET INCOME ($ mil.)	NET PROFIT MARGIN	EMPLOYEES
12/11	6,794	1,619	23.8%	7,404
12/10	4,682	1,019	21.8%	6,567
12/09	2,342	205	8.8%	5,404
12/08	3,609	515	14.3%	5,711
12/07	2,275	270	11.9%	5,298
Annual Growth	31.5%	56.5%	—	8.7%

2011 Year-End Financials

Debt ratio: 25.33%
Return on equity: 27.99%
Cash ($ mil.): 521
Current ratio: 119.92
Long-term debt ($ mil.): 3,608
No. of shares (mil.): 142
Dividends
Yield: —
Payout: 7.32%
Market value ($ mil.): 8,855

	STOCK PRICE ($) FY Close	P/E High/Low		PER SHARE ($) Earnings	Dividends	Book Value
12/11	62.35	9	4	11.48	0.00	40.73
12/10	78.01	11	5	7.49	0.51	28.39
12/09	46.09	29	7	1.64	0.26	19.41
12/08	25.61	38	3	4.76	0.35	15.42
12/07	100.80	33	15	2.57	0.25	14.56
Annual Growth	(11.3%)	—	—	45.4%	—	29.3%

Clorox Co.

Bleach is the cornerstone of Clorox. The company's namesake household cleaning products are world leaders but the Clorox business reaches far beyond bleach. While it makes laundry and cleaning items (Formula 409 Pine-Sol Green Works) its vast product portfolio extends into dressings/sauces (Hidden Valley KC Masterpiece) plastic wrap and containers (Glad) cat litters (Fresh Step Scoop Away) and infection control products (HealthLink Aplicare Soy Vay). Other items include filtration systems (Brita in North America) charcoal briquettes (Kingsford Match Light) and natural personal-care items (Burt's Bees). Clorox makes products in about two dozen countries and sells them in more than 100 countries.

HISTORY

Known first as the Electro-Alkaline Company The Clorox Company was founded in 1913 by five Oakland California investors who put up $100 apiece to make bleach using water from salt ponds around San Francisco Bay. The next year the company registered the brand name Clorox (the name combines the bleach's two main ingredients chlorine and sodium hydroxide). At first the company sold only industrial-strength bleach but in 1916 it formulated a household solution.

With the establishment of a Philadelphia distributor in 1921 Clorox began national expansion. The company went public in 1928 and built plants in Illinois and New Jersey in the 1930s; it opened nine more US plants in the 1940s and 1950s. In 1957 Procter & Gamble (P&G) bought Clorox. The Federal Trade Commission raised antitrust questions and litigation ensued over the next decade. P&G was ordered to divest Clorox and in 1969 Clorox again became an independent company.

Following its split with P&G the firm added household consumer goods and foods acquiring the brands Liquid-Plumr (drain opener 1969) Formula 409 (spray cleaner 1970) Litter Green (cat litter 1971) and Hidden Valley (salad dressings 1972). Clorox entered the specialty food products business by purchasing Grocery Store Products (Kitchen Bouquet 1971) and Kingsford (charcoal briquettes 1973).

Henkel a large West German maker of cleansers and detergents purchased 15% of Clorox's stock in 1974 as part of an agreement to share research. Beginning in 1977 Clorox sold off subsidiaries and brands such as Country Kitchen Foods (1979) to focus on household goods.

During the 1980s Clorox launched a variety of new products including Match Light (instant-lighting charcoal 1980) Tilex (mildew remover 1981) and Fresh Step (cat litter 1984). Clorox began marketing Brita water filtration systems in the US in 1988 (adding Canada in 1995). In 1990 it paid $465 million for American Cyanamid's household products group including Pine-Sol cleaner and Combat insecticide. (It sold Combat and Soft Scrub to Henkel in 2004.)

Clorox left the laundry detergent business in 1991 (begun in 1988) after it was battered by heavyweights P&G and Unilever. Household products VP Craig Sullivan became CEO the next year (stepping down in December 2003). In 1993 Clorox dumped its frozen food and bottled water operations. It began marketing its liquid bleach in Hungary through a Henkel subsidiary in 1994 and also bought S.O.S soap pads from Miles Inc.

A string of acquisitions brought the company into new markets as it built on existing brands. Clorox bought Black Flag and Lestoil in 1996 and car care product manufacturer Armor All in 1997. With its 1999 purchase of First Brands –for about $2 billion in stock and debt –Clorox added four more brands of cat litter and diversified into plastic products (Glad).

Despite adding 115 new products in 2000 the company said it would put more emphasis on core brands going forward; it pushed its struggling Glad brand with more trade promotions and coupons.

Clorox in January 2001 announced a joint venture with Bombril Brazil's leading name in steel wool to form Detergentes Bombril; however Clorox canceled the agreement in April 2001 claiming that various conditions of the deal had not been met. A year later Clorox further distanced itself from the Brazilian market selling its SBP insecticides business to Reckitt Benckiser. In 2002 Clorox announced that due to the difficult economic environment in the region it was selling its Brazil business.

In 2003 it jumpstarted a joint venture with Procter & Gamble to take advantage of P&G's manufacturing acumen to improve its Glad products. P&G received a 10% stake in Glad. Clorox also sold its Jonny Cat Litter business to Oil-Dri Corporation of America and Black Flag operations in 2003.

In January 2004 Robert Matschullat the company's nonexecutive chairman replaced Sullivan upon his retirement. Matschullat stepped down as chairman and became a director in January 2005; he passed the title to Jerry Johnston. Matschullat reclaimed the titles of chairman and CEO on an interim basis when Johnston suffered a heart attack and retired in 2006. Former Coca-Cola executive Donald Knauss was named chairman and CEO in late 2006; Matschullat remained a director.

Chemical giant Henkel once owned nearly 30% of Clorox but Clorox bought it back in 2004 through an asset swap valued at $2.8 billion. The transaction involved Henkel's purchase of Clorox's 20% stake in Henkel Iberica a joint venture between the two firms operating in Portugal and Spain. Henkel also bought Clorox's stake in a pesticide company.

In late 2004 though P&G boosted its share in the joint venture (with $133 million) from 10% to 20% which is the maximum it can invest according to the agreement.

In 2010 Clorox began to explore strategic alternatives for its $300-million-in-sales car-care brands (Armor All STP) culminating in their sale to private equity firm Avista Capital Partners for $780 million.

EXECUTIVES

EVP Strategy and Growth Partnerships and Away From Home, Frank A. Tataseo, age 56, $492,500 total compensation
Chairman and CEO, Donald R. (Don) Knauss, age 61, $1,075,000 total compensation
EVP and COO, Lawrence S. (Larry) Peiros, age 56, $638,750 total compensation
SVP and Chief Innovation Officer, Wayne L. Delker, age 58
SVP and General Manager Specialty Division, George C. Roeth, age 51
SVP and General Counsel, Laura Stein, age 50, $440,000 total compensation
SVP Human Resources and Corporate Affairs, Jacqueline P. (Jackie) Kane, age 60
VP Investor Relations, Steve Austenfeld
Corporate and Financial Media Inquiries, Dan Staublin
SVP and Chief Customer Officer, Grant J. LaMontagne, age 56
SVP Cleaning Division and Canada, Benno Dorer, age 48
CIO, Ralph Loura
SVP and CFO, Stephen M. (Steve) Robb
SVP and Chief Marketing Officer, Thomas P. (Tom) Britanik, age 54
SVP and Chief Product Supply Officer, James Foster, age 49
Manager Investor Relations, Li-Mei Johnson
Assistant Manager Investor Relations, Steve Way
VP Corporate Secretary and Associate General Counsel, Angela C. Hilt
VP and General Manager International, Michael Costello
Director, Carolyn M. Ticknor, age 64
Director, George J. Harad, age 67
Director, Edward A. (Ed) Mueller, age 64
Director, Pamela A. Thomas-Graham, age 48
Director, Tully M. Friedman, age 70
Director, Daniel Boggan Jr., age 66
Director, Gary G. Michael, age 71
Director, Robert W. Matschullat, age 64
Director, Jan L. Murley, age 60
Director, Richard H. Carmona, age 62
Auditors: Ernst&Young

LOCATIONS

HQ: The Clorox Company
1221 Broadway, Oakland CA 94612-1888
Phone: 510-271-7000 **Fax:** 510-832-1463
Web: www.thecloroxcompany.com

2012 Sales

% of total	
North	78
International	22
Total	**100**

PRODUCTS/OPERATIONS

2012 Sales

	$ mil.	% of total
Cleaning	1,692	31
Household	1,676	31
International	1,199	22
Lifestyle	901	16
Total	**5,468**	**100**

Selected Food-Related Products

Brita
Glad
Glad Press ' n Seal
GladWare
Hidden Valley
K.C. Masterpiece

Selected Household & Professional Cleaning Products

Aplicare
Clorox
Clorox 2
Clorox Clean-Up
Clorox Disinfecting Wipes
Clorox Dispatch
Clorox FreshCare
Clorox Healthcare
Clorox Oxi Magic
Clorox ReadyMop
Clorox Toilet Bowl Cleaner
Formula 409
Formula 409 Carpet Cleaner
Green Works
Handi-Wipes
HealthLink
Lestoil
Liquid-Plumr
Pine-Sol
S.O.S
Stain Out
Tilex
ToiletWand
Tuffy
Ultra Clorox Bleach

Selected International Products

Agua Jane (bleach Uruguay)
Ant Rid (insecticides)
Arela (waxes)
Astra (disposable gloves)
Bluebell (cleaners)
Chux (cleaning tools)
Clorisol (bleach)
Clorox Gentle (color-safe bleach)
Glad (containers)
Glad-Lock (resealable bags)
Guard (shoe polish)
Gumption (cleaners)
Home Mat (insecticides)
Home Keeper (insecticides)
Javex (bleach Canada)
Mono (aluminum foil)
Nevex (bleach Venezuela)
OSO (aluminum foil)
Prestone (coolant)
Selton (insecticides)
S.O.S (cleaners)
Super Globo (bleach)
XLO (sponges)
Yuhanrox (bleach)

Selected Specialty Products

BBQ Bag
Burt' s Bees
EverClean
EverFresh
Fresh Step
Fresh Step Scoop
Kingsford
Match Light
Rain Dance
Scoop Away
Son of a Gun!
Tuff Stuff

COMPETITORS

Alticor
Blistex
Bonne Bell
CalCedar
Campbell Soup
Church & Dwight
Colgate-Palmolive
ConAgra
Del Monte Foods
Diversey
Dow Chemical
Dr. Bronner' s
Estee Lauder
Forever Living
Kiehl' s
Kiss My Face
McBride plc
Mondelez International
Natural Health Trends
Nature' s Sunshine
Newman' s Own
Oil-Dri
Pactiv
Procter & Gamble
Reckitt Benckiser
S.C. Johnson
Seventh Generation
The Dial Corporation
Unilever

HISTORICAL FINANCIALS

Company Type: Public

Income Statement

FYE: June 30

	REVENUE ($ mil.)	NET INCOME ($ mil.)	NET PROFIT MARGIN	EMPLOYEES
06/12	5,468	541	9.9%	8,400
06/11	5,231	557	10.6%	8,100
06/10	5,534	603	10.9%	8,300
06/09	5,450	537	9.9%	8,300
06/08	5,273	461	8.7%	8,300
Annual Growth	0.9%	4.1%	—	0.3%

2012 Year-End Financials

Debt ratio: 62.48%
Return on equity: 987650001000000.00%
Cash ($ mil.): 267
Current ratio: 66.76
Long-term debt ($ mil.): 1,571
No. of shares (mil.): 129
Dividends
Yield: —
Payout: 58.68%
Market value ($ mil.): 9,388

	STOCK PRICE ($) FY Close	P/E High/Low	PER SHARE ($) Earnings	Dividends	Book Value
06/12	72.46	18 15	4.09	0.00	(1.04)
06/11	67.44	18 15	4.02	2.20	(0.66)
06/10	62.16	15 13	4.24	2.00	0.60
06/09	55.83	17 12	3.81	1.84	(1.26)
06/08	52.20	20 16	3.24	1.60	(2.68)
Annual Growth	8.5%	— —	6.0%	—	—

CMS Energy Corp

Michigan consumers rely on CMS Energy. The energy holding company's utility Consumers Energy has a generating capacity of 6130 MW (primarily fossil-fueled) and distributes electricity and natural gas to 3.5 million customers (more than 6 million end users) in Michigan. CMS Enterprises operates the non-utility businesses of CMS Energy and is an operator of independent power generating plants; its independent power plants (coal- gas- and biomass-fired) have a capacity of more than 1034 MW and are primarily located in Michigan but also in North Carolina. Subsidiary EnerBank USA provides unsecured home improvement payment option programs for homeowners.

HISTORY

In the late 1880s W. A. Foote and Samuel Jarvis formed hydroelectric company Jackson Electrical Light Works in Jackson Michigan. After building plants in other Michigan towns Foote formed utility holding company Consumers Power. In 1910 the firm merged with Michigan Light to create Commonwealth Power Railway and Light (CPR&L) and began building a statewide transmission system.

Foote died in 1915 and after nine years of acquisitions successor Bernard Cobb sold the rail systems and split CPR&L into Commonwealth Power (CP) and Electric Railway Securities. In 1928 Cobb bought Southeastern Power & Light (SP&L) and merged CP with Penn-Ohio Edison to form Allied Power & Light. Commonwealth and Southern (C&S) was then created as the parent of Allied and SP&L.

In 1932 future GOP presidential nominee Wendell Willkie took the helm and became a national political figure by opposing the Public Utility Holding Company Act of 1935 which began 60 years of regulated monopolies. Consumers Power was divested from C&S after WWII.

Consumers brought a nuclear plant on line in 1962 and the next year began buying Michigan oil and gas fields. In 1967 it formed NOMECO (now CMS Oil and Gas) to guide its oil and gas efforts.

The completion of the Palisades nuke in 1971 began a 13-year run of chronic problems and lengthy shutdowns. Cost overruns and an environmental lawsuit killed the firm's third nuke (Midland) in 1984 –after $4.1 billion was spent.

A rate hike and new CEO William McCormick set the firm on a new path in 1985. McCormick formed a subsidiary to develop and invest in independent power projects in 1986 and created holding company CMS (short for "Consumers") Energy the next year. CMS Gas Transmission was formed in 1989.

Midland Cogeneration Venture (CMS Energy and six partners) completed converting Midland to a natural gas-fueled cogeneration plant in 1990 and CMS Energy wrote off $657 million from its losses at the former nuke. It regained profitability in 1993.

McCormick split the utilities into electric and gas divisions in 1995 and also issued stock for its gas utility and transmission businesses Consumers Gas Group. The next year CMS Energy formed an energy marketing arm.

In 1996 and 1997 CMS Energy invested in power plants in Morocco and Australia and bought a stake in a Brazilian electric utility. The next year it began developing a gas-fired plant in Ghana and won a bid to build a plant in India. CMS Energy also bought gas gathering and processing firms Continental Natural Gas and Heritage Gas Services in 1998.

Michigan's public service commission (PSC) issued utility restructuring orders in 1997 and 1998 but in 1999 the state Supreme Court ruled that the PSC lacked restructuring authority. Facing less-favorable proposed legislation CMS Energy and DTE Energy moved to implement competition per the PSC's guidelines.

CMS Energy bought Panhandle Eastern Pipe Line from Duke Energy for $2.2 billion in 1999. It also grabbed a 77% stake in another Brazilian utility and began building its Powder River Basin gas pipeline. In 2000 the company partnered with Marathon Ashland Petroleum (now Marathon Petroleum) and TEPPCO to operate a pipeline transporting refined petroleum from the US Gulf Coast to Illinois. Later that year CMS Energy announced plans for an IPO for its CMS Oil and Gas unit; however the IPO was withdrawn in 2001.

CMS Energy agreed in 2001 to sell Consumers' high-voltage electric transmission assets to independent transmission operator Trans-Elect for about $290 million; the deal which was the first of its kind in the US was completed in 2002. That year the company sold its Equatorial Guinea (West Africa) oil and gas assets to Marathon Oil for about $1 billion. Also that year McCormick stepped down amid controversy over "round trip" power trades that artificially inflated the company's sales and trading volume; CMS Energy later announced that it would restate its 2000 and 2001 financial results to eliminate the effects of the trades.

Later in 2002 the company exited the exploration and production business. It sold CMS Oil and Gas' North American and African assets to private French energy firm Perenco for $167 million and it sold the unit's Colombian properties to Spanish energy firm Compa?ia Espa?ola de Petroleos (Cepsa) for $65 million. CMS Energy sold its CMS Panhandle companies which together operated an 11000-mile pipeline system to Southern Union for $1.8 billion in 2003.

CMS Energy's nonregulated operations grew to account for more than half of sales in 2001 and 2002; however as the wholesale power marketing industry has experienced a downturn the company has refocused on its regulated energy distribution operations. The company has exited the speculative wholesale energy-trading business which was conducted through its CMS Energy Resource Management (formerly CMS Marketing Services and Trading) unit; it has sold its wholesale natural gas trading book to Sempra Energy and has sold its electricity trading book to Constellation Energy Commodities Group (formerly Constellation Power Source).

EXECUTIVES

Chairman, David W. Joos, age 59, $1,085,000 total compensation
VP Investor Relations and Treasurer, Laura L. Mountcastle
EVP and CFO CMS Energy and Consumers Energy, Thomas J. (Tom) Webb, age 59, $665,000 total compensation
SVP Governmental and Public Affairs and Chief Compliance Officer, David G. Mengebier, age 54
VP and Chief Tax Counsel, Theodore J. Vogel
VP Controller and Chief Accounting Officer, Glenn P. Barba, age 46
President CEO and Director, John G. Russell, age 54, $545,000 total compensation
SVP and General Counsel, James E. Brunner, age 59, $410,000 total compensation
Director News and Information, Jeff Holyfield
Director Public Information, Dan Bishop
SVP Human Resources and Shared Services, John M. Butler, age 47, $317,000 total compensation
VP and Corporate Secretary, Catherine M. Reynolds
VP and CIO, Mamatha Chamarthi
Director, Stephen E. Ewing, age 68
Director, Kenneth L. Way, age 72
Director, John B. Yasinsky, age 72
Director, Michael T. Monahan, age 73
Director, Jon E. Barfield, age 60
Director, Philip R. Lochner Jr., age 69
Director, Richard M. (Dick) Gabrys, age 70
President CEO and Director, John G. Russell, age 54
Director, Merribel S. Ayres, age 60
Auditors: PricewaterhouseCoopersLLP

LOCATIONS

HQ: CMS Energy Corporation
1 Energy Plaza, Jackson MI 49201
Phone: 517-788-0550 **Fax:** 517-788-1859
Web: www.cmsenergy.com

PRODUCTS/OPERATIONS

2011 Sales

	$ mil.	% of total
Electric utility	3,913	60
Enterprises	204	3
Total	**6,503**	**100**

Selected Subsidiaries

Consumers Energy Company (electric and gas utility)
CMS Capital
EnerBank USA (banking services)
CMS Enterprises Company (nonutility holding company)

COMPETITORS

AEP
AES
Alliant Energy
Calpine
CenterPoint Energy
Con Edison
DTE
Duke Energy
Dynegy
Edison International
Integrys Energy Group
NextEra Energy
ONEOK
SEMCO ENERGY
Sempra Energy
Tractebel Engineering
Wisconsin Energy
Xcel Energy

HISTORICAL FINANCIALS

Company Type: Public

Income Statement FYE: December 31

	REVENUE ($ mil.)	NET INCOME ($ mil.)	NET PROFIT MARGIN	EMPLOYEES
12/11	6,503	415	6.4%	7,727
12/10	6,432	340	5.3%	7,822
12/09	6,205	229	3.7%	8,039
12/08	6,821	300	4.4%	7,970
12/07	6,464	(215)	—	7,898
Annual Growth	0.2%	—	—	(0.5%)

2011 Year-End Financials

Debt ratio: 44.15%
Return on equity: 13.71%
Cash ($ mil.): 161
Current ratio: 109.71
Long-term debt ($ mil.): 6,207
No. of shares (mil.): 254
Dividends
Yield: —
Payout: 53.16%
Market value ($ mil.): 5,611

	STOCK PRICE ($) FY Close	P/E High/Low		PER SHARE ($) Earnings	Dividends	Book Value
12/11	22.08	13	10	1.58	0.00	11.92
12/10	18.60	14	10	1.28	0.66	11.19
12/09	15.66	17	11	0.91	0.50	12.47
12/08	10.11	13	7	1.23	0.36	12.15
12/07	17.38	—	—	(1.02)	0.20	10.77
Annual Growth	6.2%	—	—	—	—	2.6%

CNA Financial Corp.

CNA Financial provides cross-continental coverage. The company is an umbrella organization for a wide range of insurance providers including Continental Casualty and Continental Insurance. It primarily provides commercial policies such as workers' compensation auto and general liability. CNA also sells specialty insurance including professional liability (doctors lawyers and architects) and vehicle warranty service contracts. The firm offers commercial surety bonds (through CNA Surety) risk management claims administration and information services. Its products are sold by independent agents and brokers in the US and through partners abroad. Holding company Loews owns 90% of CNA.

Operations

The company has pared back its operations to strictly commercial property/casualty policies over the years. Most of its non-core insurance products are in run-off including a few remaining life annuity and pension products as well as accident and health insurance.

Financial Analysis

CNA's revenue fell 3% in 2011 vs. 2010 while net income dropped 11% over the same period. While net written premiums for CNA Specialty CNA Commercial and the non-core Life & Group all increased primarily driven by new business net income fell on investment losses. The year-over-year decline in net income resulted from lower operating income and decreased net realized investment gains. The decline in revenue and profits in 2011 followed two years of gains on the heels of steep decline in 2008.

Like most large insurers CNA has been pinched hard by investment losses and catastrophe losses in recent years. However unlike other insurance companies it has the comfort of being held by a good old-fashioned conglomerate with a solid parent backing it up.

Strategy

In 2011 CNA expanded its specialty operations by purchasing the 39% of CNA Surety it did not already own for some $463 million. As a wholly-owned subsidiary CNA Surety gained stability and capital resources. The company had first made a bid of about $380 million in 2010 to buy up the rest of CNA Surety but CNA Surety held out for CNA's higher successful offer. Later in the year CNA sold its half-ownership in Hawaii's largest property/casualty insurance firm First Insurance Company of Hawaii to its partner Tokio Marine & Nichido Fire Insurance Co. a unit of Tokio Marine Holdings. In 2012 CNA acquired Hardy Underwriting Bermuda Limited for approximately #143 million ($227 million). The purchase expanded its specialized underwriting capabilities on a global basis.

CNA is also focused on strengthening its core commercial operations through both enhanced customer retention efforts and new customer additions. It has divided its customers into two groups with its business segment covering small accounts and its commercial segment serving midsized to large accounts.

HISTORY

When merchant Henry Bowen could not find the type of fire insurance he wanted he began Continental Insurance. Bowen assembled a group of investors and started with about $500000 in capital.

In 1882 Continental Insurance added marine and tornado insurance. Seven years later Francis Moore became president; he was developer of the Universal Mercantile Schedule a system of assessing fire hazards in buildings.

About the time Continental Insurance was writing the book on fire insurance several midwestern investors were having trouble assessing risk in their own insurance field –disability. In 1897 this group founded Continental Casualty in Hammond Indiana. In the early years its primary clients were railroads. Continental Casualty eventually merged with other companies in the field and by 1905 had branch offices in nine states and Hawaii and was writing business in 41 states and territories.

Both Continentals added new insurance lines in 1911: Continental Insurance went into personal auto and Continental Casualty formed subsidiary Continental Assurance to sell life insurance. By 1915 Continental Insurance had four primary companies; spurred by growing prewar patriotism they were called the America Fore Group. Both Continentals rose to the challenges presented by the World Wars and the Depression; they entered the 1950s ready for new growth.

In the 1960s the companies began to diversify. Continental Insurance added interests in Diners Club and Capital Financial Services; in 1968 it formed holding company Continental Corp. Meanwhile Continental Assurance (which had formed its own holding company CNA Financial) went even farther afield adding mutual fund consumer finance nursing home and residential construction companies.

By the early 1970s CNA was on the ropes because of the recession and setbacks in the housing business. In 1974 Robert and Laurence Tisch bought most of the company and cut costs ruthlessly. Continental had its own problems in the 1970s including an Iranian joint venture that got caught up in the revolution.

Both companies suffered losses arising from Hurricane Andrew in 1992 but CNA which did its housecleaning in the 1970s was better able to deal with the blow than Continental which entered the 1990s in need of restructuring.

Rising interest rates in 1994 hurt Continental whose merger with CNA in 1995 made CNA one of the US's top 10 insurance companies. CNA consolidated the two operations cutting about 5000 jobs.

CNA bought Western National Warranty in 1995 followed by managed care provider CoreSource the next year. In 1997 the company spun off its surety business in a deal with Capsure Holdings and formed CNA Surety. Taking advantage of outsourcing trends CNA created CNA UniSource (payroll and human resources services) and bought its payroll servicer Interlogic Systems the next year.

CNA pursued a global strategy buying majority interests in an Argentine workers' compensation carrier and a British marine insurer but with 1998 sales flat and earnings down the tube the company did more slashing than accumulating. It cut 2400 jobs and exited such lines as agriculture and entertainment insurance.

The company exited the personal insurance business to focus on the commercial market: It transferred its personal insurance lines including its auto and homeowners coverage to Allstate in 1999. Then in 2000 CNA sold its life reinsurance operations to a subsidiary of Munich Re.

As part of a restructuring effort (the company reshuffled itself into three major segments: property/casualty life and group) CNA fired some 10% of its workforce in 2001. In 2002 CNA paid out more than $450 million in claims related to the attacks on the World Trade Center.

CNA Financial restated its earnings in 2002 after being questioned by the SEC over the accounting treatment of investment losses.

Freeing up some much needed capital CNA sold its group benefits business to The Hartford in 2003 for some $530 million. To better focus on its remaining property & casualty lines the company sold its individual life insurance segment to Swiss Re Life & Health in 2004.

EXECUTIVES

EVP General Counsel and Secretary, Jonathan D. (Jon) Kantor, age 56, $800,000 total compensation
Chairman and CEO, Thomas F. (Tom) Motamed, age 63, $1,000,000 total compensation
Chief Underwriting Officer Commercial Insurance, John A. Beckman
EVP and Chief Administration Officer, Thomas (Tom) Pontarelli, age 62, $658,333 total compensation
President and COO Canada, Gary J. Owcar
President and COO CNA Specialty, Peter W. Wilson, age 52, $650,000 total compensation
EVP and CFO, D. Craig Mense, age 60, $800,000 total compensation
Central Zone Officer, Gregory M. (Greg) Vezzosi
Southeastern Zone Officer, James R. (Rob) Huber
President and COO Commercial Lines, Robert A. (Bob) Lindemann, age 58
EVP Worldwide Property and Casualty Claim, George R. Fay, age 63
Western Zone Officer, Steve Stonehouse
EVP and Chief Actuary, Larry A. Haefner, $367,628 total compensation
Northern Zone Officer, Steve Wachtel
CEO Europe, John Hennessy
SVP and CIO, Ray Oral
President Worldwide Field Operations, Timothy J. (Tim) Szerlong, age 59
Northeastern Zone Officer, Jim Romanelli
SVP and Chief Risk Officer, Mark Verheyen
SVP Human Resources, Debbie Nutley
SVP Worldwide Operations, Katie Cunning
SVP Corporate Communications, Sarah Pang
Director, Andrew H. Tisch, age 62
Director, Joseph Rosenberg, age 78
Director, Prof Marvin Zonis, age 75
Director, Paul J. Liska, age 56
Director, Jose O. Montemayor, age 61
Auditors: Deloitte&ToucheLLP

LOCATIONS

HQ: CNA Financial Corporation
333 S. Wabash, Chicago IL 60604
Phone: 312-822-5000 **Fax:** 312-822-6419
Web: www.cna.com

PRODUCTS/OPERATIONS

2011 Sales

	$ mil.	% of total
CNA Commercial		
Commercial insurance	2,681	30
Small business insurance	581	7
International	537	6
CNA Select Risk	272	3
CNA Specialty		
Professional & management	2,541	28
Surety	472	5
Warranty & alternative risks	289	3
International	210	2
Life & Group	1,334	15
Corporate & other	33	-
Adjustments	(3)	-
Total	**8,947**	**100**

COMPETITORS

ACMAT
AIG
American Financial Group
Aspen Insurance
Assurant
Berkshire Hathaway
Chubb Corp
Cincinnati Financial
Everest Re
Liberty Mutual
Nationwide
Old Republic
State Farm
The Hartford
Travelers Companies
United Fire
W. R. Berkley
White Mountains Insurance Group
Zurich Financial Services

HISTORICAL FINANCIALS

Company Type: Public

Income Statement FYE: December 31

	ASSETS ($ mil.)	NET INCOME ($ mil.)	INCOME AS % OF ASSETS	EMPLOYEES
12/11	55,179	614	1.1%	7,600
12/10	55,331	690	1.2%	8,000
12/09	55,298	419	0.8%	8,900
12/08	51,688	(299)	—	9,000
12/07	56,732	851	1.5%	9,400
Annual Growth	(0.7%)	(7.8%)	—	(5.2%)

2011 Year-End Financials

Debt ratio: 4.58%
Return on equity: 5.31%
Cash ($ mil.): 75
Current ratio: —
Long-term debt ($ mil.): 2,525
No. of shares (mil.): 269
Dividends
Yield: —
Payout: 17.54%
Market value ($ mil.): 7,203

	STOCK PRICE ($) FY Close	P/E High/Low	PER SHARE ($) Earnings	Dividends	Book Value
12/11	26.75	14 9	2.28	0.00	42.92
12/10	27.05	13 10	2.28	0.00	40.70
12/09	24.00	24 6	1.10	0.00	39.62
12/08	16.44	— —	(1.18)	0.45	25.56
12/07	33.72	17 10	3.13	0.35	37.36
Annual Growth	(5.6%)	— —	(7.6%)	—	3.5%

CNO Financial Group Inc

Have a modest but stable income? Graying at the temples? CNO Financial Group finds that especially attractive and has life insurance and related products targeted toward you and 4 million other customers. The holding company's primary units include Bankers Life & Casualty which provides Medicare supplement life annuities and long-term care insurance sold through its own agents; Colonial Penn which offers life insurance to consumers through direct selling; and Washington National which offers specified disease insurance accident insurance life insurance and annuities through its business and independent agents and worksite marketing. CNO Financial operates nationwide.

Financial Analysis

CNO Financial Group's 2011 sales increased by just 1% vs. 2010 while net income was up 34%. Indeed the firm's sales have been relatively flat for the past several years. Bankers Life which accounts for more than 50% of the company's premiums has outperformed Washington National and Colonial Penn in terms of income growth in recent years.

Strategy

CNO's target customer is less affluent but determined to hang on to what they've earned. Assorted supplemental health insurance products account for over half of the company's collected premiums. Medicare supplement products account for half of the premiums collected for its health products with long-term care products accounting for 40%. Less than 10% of collected premiums are from a segment that consists of closed blocks of life insurance products that are no longer sold but are maintained in "run-off".

CNO's target market seniors is often overlooked by all kinds of marketers. However it's one of the fastest-growing demographic groups in the nation and a potential source of growth for the insurance firm.

Company Background

In 2010 the company changed its name from Conseco to CNO Financial Group to reflect a broader identity. (The firm also sought to distance itself from historical financial instabilities associated with the Conseco brand.) The name change came after several years' worth of management efforts to conserve capital reduce complexity and debt and sequester or divest less profitable operations.

HISTORY

The company evolved from Security National an Indiana insurance company formed in 1979 by Stephen Hilbert. The former encyclopedia salesman and Aetna executive believed most insurance companies were bloated and the industry itself overcrowded as well as ripe for consolidation by a smart lean organization.

In 1982 it began a growth-by-acquisition strategy with the purchase of Executive Income Life Insurance (renamed Security National Life Insurance). The next year it bought Consolidated National Life Insurance and renamed the expanded company Conseco.

The firm went public in 1985 using the proceeds to fund an acquisitions spree that included Lincoln American Life Insurance Lincoln Income Life (sold 1990) Bankers National Life Insurance Western National Life Insurance (sold 1994) and National Fidelity Life Insurance.

In 1990 the company formed Conseco Capital Partners (with General Electric and Bankers Trust) to finance acquisitions without seeming to burden the parent company with debt. This device financed the purchase of Great American Reserve and the 1991 acquisition of Beneficial Standard Life. The former Conseco bought Bankers Life Insurance in 1992 then sold 67% of it the next year. Also in 1993 the company formed the Private Capital Group to invest in noninsurance companies.

In 1994 the company tried to acquire the much larger Kemper Corp. but shied away from the debt load that the $2.6 billion deal would have entailed. The aborted deal cost $36 million in bank and accounting fees and spelled the end of the company's relationship with Merrill Lynch which had underwritten the company's IPO when a Merrill Lynch analyst downgraded its stock after the fiasco.

Meanwhile Private Capital's success led the company to form Conseco Global Investments. Other investments included stakes in racetrack and riverboat gambling operations in Indiana.

In 1996 and 1997 the firm absorbed eight life health property/casualty and specialty insurance companies and raised its interest in American Life Holdings to 100%.

Itching to move beyond insurance in 1998 the company bought Green Tree Financial the US's #1 mobile home financier. Charges of Green Tree's own fuzzy accounting practices helped torpedo the company's quest for a federal thrift charter. But the troubles had just begun. The mobile home finance industry took a dive as customers refinanced at lower rates and prepayments slammed Green Tree Financial reducing Conseco's earnings.

The company tried to recoup in 1999 by launching an ad campaign portraying the company as the "Wal-Mart of financial services." It also continued the acquisition spree. But Green Tree Financial (renamed Conseco Finance that year) couldn't stanch the flow of red ink: Buyers grew wary of the quality of the finance unit's loan securities and changes in accounting methods cost the parent company a $350 million charge against earnings for 1999.

In 2002 due to its financial woes Gary Wendt stepped down as CEO the NYSE suspended trading in the company and its stock was moved to the OTC. The company also filed for Chapter 11 protection in 2002. As part of the reorganization agreement it agreed to sell Conseco Finance. The company's insurance operations were not subject to the Chapter 11 agreement.

In 2003 it finally unloaded the Conseco Finance unit to CFN Investment Holdings LLC an investor group and General Electric Co.'s consumer finance unit for $1 billion. The company emerged from bankruptcy in September 2003.

The company agreed to pay a fine of $6.3 million in 2008 after an investigation determined that its long-term care insurance business Conseco Senior Health had wrongly denied claims and mishandled complaints and that some sales and marketing practices at Banker's Life did not comply with industry standards. To put what it could in the past in late 2008 the firm spun off its closed block of long-term care insurance. The new entity was named Senior Health Insurance Company of Pennsylvania and consisted entirely of policies in run-off.

After leading the firm through five years of troubles and triumphs in 2011 James Prieur retired as CEO and was replaced by CFO Ed Bonach.

EXECUTIVES

EVP and CFO, Frederick J. (Fred) Crawford
EVP COO and CTO, Bruce K. Baude
SVP and Chief Accounting Officer, John R. Kline, age 55
Chairman, Neal C. Schneider, age 68
President 40|86 Advisors, Eric R. Johnson, age 52, $500,000 total compensation
CEO and Director, Edward J. (Ed) Bonach, age 58, $472,500 total compensation
EVP Human Resources, Susan L. (Sue) Menzel, age 47
President Washington National, Steven M. (Steve) Stecher, age 52, $412,000 total compensation
SVP Corporate Communications, Anthony B. (Tony) Zehnder, age 62
COO, Scott R. Perry, age 49, $441,324 total compensation
EVP Product Development; President Other CNO Business, Christopher J. (Chris) Nickele, age 55
SVP Government Relations, William (Bill) Fritts
SVP and Chief Compliance Officer, W. Mark Johnson
VP Internal Audit, Thomas R. (Tom) Kaehr
SVP Financial Planning & Analysis, Thomas D. Barta
SVP and Corporate Actuary, Timothy J. (Tim) Tongson
VP Enterprise Risk Management, Tricia L. Borcherding, age 36
VP Investor Relations, Scott L. Galovic
EVP and General Counsel, Matthew J. (Matt) Zimpfer, age 44
VP Asset-Liability Management, Christopher J. Foote, age 54
VP Bankers Life and Casualty Valuation, Jerome J. Lynch, age 55
Director, Michael T. Tokarz, age 62
Director, Donna A. James, age 54
Director, Frederick J. (Fred) Sievert, age 64
Director, David K. Zwiener, age 57
Director, Robert C. (Bob) Greving, age 60
Director, Debra J. Perry, age 61
Director, R. Keith Long, age 63
Director, John G. Turner, age 73
CEO and Director, Edward J. (Ed) Bonach, age 58
Director, Charles W. Murphy, age 51
Auditors: PricewaterhouseCoopersLLP

LOCATIONS

HQ: CNO Financial Group Inc.
11825 N. Pennsylvania St., Carmel IN 46032
Phone: 317-817-6100 **Fax:** 317-817-2847
Web: www.cnoinc.com

PRODUCTS/OPERATIONS

2011 Premiums Collected

Supplemental health	54
Life	18

2011 Premiums Collected

% of total	
Bankers	58
Washington	19
Colonial	6
Other CNO	16
Investment	1
Total	**100**

COMPETITORS

Aetna
Aflac
American General
Lincoln Financial Group
MassMutual
MetLife
Monumental Life
Mutual of Omaha
Northwestern Mutual
Protective Life
Prudential
Securian Financial
Torchmark
Unum Group

HISTORICAL FINANCIALS

Company Type: Public

Income Statement FYE: December 31

	ASSETS ($ mil.)	NET INCOME ($ mil.)	INCOME AS % OF ASSETS	EMPLOYEES
12/11	33,332	382	1.1%	3,800
12/10	31,899	284	0.9%	3,680
12/09	30,343	85	0.3%	3,500
12/08	28,769	(1,126)	—	3,700
12/07	33,514	(179)	—	3,950
Annual Growth	(0.1%)	—	—	(1.0%)

2011 Year-End Financials

Debt ratio: 9.16%
Return on equity: 7.60%
Cash ($ mil.): 510
Current ratio: —
Long-term debt ($ mil.): 3,054
No. of shares (mil.): 241
Dividends
Yield: —
Payout: —
Market value ($ mil.): 1,523

	STOCK PRICE ($) FY Close	P/E High/Low		PER SHARE ($) Earnings	Dividends	Book Value
12/11	6.31	5	3	1.31	0.00	20.86
12/10	6.78	6	4	0.99	0.00	17.23
12/09	5.00	15	1	0.45	0.00	14.09
12/08	5.18	—	—	(6.10)	0.00	8.76
12/07	12.56	—	—	(1.12)	0.00	22.94
Annual Growth	(15.8%)	—	—	—	—	(2.3%)

Coach, Inc.

Coach is riding in style thanks to the company's leather items and some savvy licensing deals. The company designs and makes (mostly through third parties) high-end leather goods and accessories including handbags wallets and luggage. Coach founded in 1941 also licenses its name for watches eyewear fragrances scarves and footwear. The luxury brand sells its wares through about 1000 department and outlet stores (in the US and more than 20 other countries) catalogs and its website. Macy's Nordstrom Saks and others carry Coach items. It also runs more than 830 retail and factory outlet stores in North America Japan and China (including Hong Kong and Macau).

Operations

Coach operates its business through a direct-to-consumer segment and an indirect segment. Its direct-to-consumer operation which generates 89% of 2012 sales gives the company controlled access to customers through the internet and through Coach-operated stores in North America Japan Hong Kong Macau mainland China Taiwan and Singapore. The indirect segment comprising the retailer's wholesale operation accounted for 11% of sales. Before the company became a retailer with its own stable of stores Coach wholesaled its products to US department stores. The segment also includes the Coach International business which brought in 4% of the 11% segment sales.

Strategy

Despite facing an economic downturn Coach has been banking on its upscale clientele in the US Japan and elsewhere to invest in its products. The company's looking to boost its global distribution efforts mostly in North America China and Europe while also improving store sales. It's also implementing several initiatives. Coach is prudently expanding its retail presence in North America in an effort to generate higher sales revenue. The company has been scaling back its once-aggressive expansion by halving its new US store openings — from about 40 per year to 15 in 2011. In 2012 it opened about 10 net new retail stores reaching further into developing areas for revenue potential. It also opened some 25 new factory outlets. Coach believes that ultimately there is a market to support up to 500 Coach stores in the US and 30 in Canada. In 2013 Coach anticipates opening 10 net new retail stores and 18 factory outlets. It's focusing on a Men's initiative in North America and Asia to attract more males by opening new full-price and factory locations with in-shop stores and by broadening its product assortment to include more men's items. Coach's partnership with retail real estate company Simon Property Group has allowed Coach to get its foot in the door at some swanky digs where upscale customers spend more freely. The leather-goods maker has a presence in Simon's Forum Shops at Caesars Palace in Las Vegas and Roosevelt Field on Long Island. These two properties represent some of Coach's highest-volume retail operations. It's working with Simon Property Group and retail regional mall developer General Growth Properties to add new Coach retail shops and expand existing ones.

Geographic Reach

The leather goods maker has been looking at global markets to diversify and offset previous sales declines in North America. To that end Coach made plans to open 15 stores in the UK by 2013 as part of its push to penetrate the European luxury goods market. The company already has an exclusive arrangement with Printemps the French department store chain and in Spain with El Corte Ingles. It is also eyeing Germany Italy Brazil and India. In Asia Coach sees China as one of its largest opportunity and is adding 30 new locations in the country in 2013. Its Japanese business is where the company counts on its trendy target audience. Coach anticipates an ultimate market penetration of up to 180 stores.

Mergers & Acquisitions

To give it more control over the operations it has established overseas Coach has been buying out its distribution partners in recent years. In 2011 Coach acquired its domestic retail business in Singapore from former distributor Valiram Group giving it seven locations in the country. It took control of its retail locations in Taiwan too through its 2012 purchase of the retail business of Tasa Meng a distributor with 27 stores.

Financial Analysis

Revenue has grown for the past five years at Coach. Sales from the retailer's direct-to-consumer segment have helped to pump up profits. Coach's 2012 revenue increased by more than 14% with net income rising 18% in 2012 vs. 2011. The handbag maker attributes the accolades to a 16% bump in direct-to-consumer net sales spurred by its company-operated stores located in North America and China. Driven by an 8% increase in net revenue from its Coach International wholesale business the company's indirect segment logged a nearly 4% increase in sales dragged down slightly by a 1% decline in US wholesale net revenue. Sales from new and expanded stores boosted Coach's bottom line in 2012 as well in North America (13% increase) and Japan (12% increase).

Sales & Marketing

The company's creative marketing visual merchandising and public relations teams maintain the Coach image. Coach leverages its consumer and market research capabilities to assess consumer attitudes and trends. As part of Coach's direct marketing strategy it taps a growing database of some 22 million active households in North America and 6.6 million active households in Japan. To spur purchases and build brand awareness the company communicates with customers through some 1.2 billion emails and millions of catalogs worldwide. It's looking to boost e-commerce sales through its digital strategy coach.com global e-commerce sites and programs third-party flash sites marketing sites and social networking. Coach boasts 22 marketing websites in 23 countries.

EXECUTIVES

Chairman and CEO, Lew Frankfort, age 66, $1,214,100 total compensation
President Executive Creative Director, Reed Krakoff, age 48, $2,500,000 total compensation
President and COO, Jerry Stritzke, age 52, $900,000 total compensation
President Retail Division North America, Michael (Mike) Tucci, age 51, $850,000 total compensation
EVP Human Resources, Sarah Dunn, age 52
SVP Investor Relations and Corporate Communications, Andrea Shaw Resnick
President Japan, Daniel DiCicco
President International Group, Victor Luis
SVP and CIO, Thomas E. Britt
VP Information Systems, Serge Minassian
President and CEO Asia, Andre Cohen
EVP General Counsel and Secretary, Todd Kahn, age 48
President and CEO China, Jonathan Seliger
SVP Global Web and Digital Media, David Duplantis
EVP CFO and Chief Accounting Officer, Jane H. Nielsen, age 48
Director, Susan J. Kropf, age 64
Director, Gary W. Loveman, age 51
Director, Ivan M. Menezes, age 51
Director, Michael E. Murphy, age 75
Director, Irene R. Miller, age 59
Director, Jide J. Zeitlin, age 48
Director, Stephanie Tilenius, age 43
Auditors: Deloitte&ToucheLLP

LOCATIONS

HQ: Coach Inc.
516 W. 34th St., New York NY 10001-1394
Phone: 212-594-1850 **Fax:** 212-594-1682
Web: www.coach.com

2012 Stores

	No.
US	492
Japan	180
China including Hong Kong &	130
Canada	31
Total	**833**

2012 Sales

	% of total
US	68
Japan	18
Other	14
Total	**100**

PRODUCTS/OPERATIONS

2012 Sales

% of total	
Men's & Women's	65
Accessories	28
All other	7
Total	**100**

2012 Sales

% of total	
Direct-to-consumer	89
Indirect	11
Total	**100**

Selected Products

Accessories
Footwear
Fragrance
Handbags
Jewelry
Sunglasses
Travel bags
Watches

COMPETITORS

Cole Haan
Dooney & Bourke
Etienne Aigner Group
Fifth & Pacific
Gucci
Hermes
Kenneth Cole
LVMH
michael kors
Michael Kors Holdings
Mulberry Group
Prada

J. Crew
Jones Group
Juicy Couture
kate spade
Ralph Lauren
Samsonite
Tiffany & Co.

HISTORICAL FINANCIALS

Company Type: Public

Income Statement FYE: June 30

	REVENUE ($ mil.)	NET INCOME ($ mil.)	NET PROFIT MARGIN	EMPLOYEES
06/12*	4,763	1,038	21.8%	18,000
07/11	4,158	880	21.2%	15,000
07/10	3,607	734	20.4%	13,000
06/09	3,230	623	19.3%	12,000
06/08	3,180	783	24.6%	12,000
Annual Growth	10.6%	7.3%	—	10.7%

*Fiscal year change

2012 Year-End Financials

Debt ratio: 0.75%
Return on equity: 52.13%
Cash ($ mil.): 917
Current ratio: 251.27
Long-term debt ($ mil.): 0
No. of shares (mil.): 285
Dividends
Yield: —
Payout: 27.62%
Market value ($ mil.): 16,674

	STOCK PRICE ($) FY Close	P/E High/Low		PER SHARE ($) Earnings	Dividends	Book Value
06/12*	58.48	22	13	3.53	0.00	6.99
07/11	65.99	22	11	2.92	0.00	5.59
07/10	35.77	19	10	2.33	0.00	5.07
06/09	26.93	16	6	1.91	0.00	5.33
06/08	29.29	23	11	2.17	0.00	4.50
Annual Growth	18.9%	—	—	12.9%	—	11.6%

*Fiscal year change

CoBiz Financial Inc

CoBiz Financial is reaching new heights in the Rockies and in the Valley of the Sun. It's the holding company for CoBiz Bank which operates as Colorado Business Bank and Arizona Business Bank. The former operates more than 10 branches in the Denver Boulder and Vail areas; the latter has about a half-dozen branches in and around Phoenix. CoBiz's locations operate as separate community banks each with a local president who has decision-making authority. The company offers investment banking services through subsidiary Green Manning & Bunch insurance through CoBiz Insurance and wealth management through CoBiz Investment Management CoBiz Trust and Financial Designs.

Residential and commercial real estate mortgages make up approximately half of CoBiz's loan portfolio; business loans are more than a third. The company had been growing its portfolio of commercial real estate and operating loans but as with many of its peers during the economic downturn its loan volume slowed and asset quality deteriorated. CoBiz reported losses in 2009 and 2010 but returned to profitability in 2011 as its net income exceeded $28 million. The company experienced growth across its four main segments –commercial banking investment banking wealth management and insurance –as both the economic environment and the company's credit quality improved.

CoBiz courts professionals high-net-worth individuals and families small and midsized business clients as the company believes that it is able to provide more personalized services than its larger competitors while offering more sophisticated products than smaller banks. It looks to extend its relationships with customers often requiring borrowers to procure other products and services from the bank such as deposit accounts or treasury management. Other initiatives include growing its wealth management operations and other fee-based activities opening new branches and acquiring other financial institutions throughout the West.

EXECUTIVES

President and COO Arizona Business Bank Phoenix, Kevin G. Quinn
President Colorado Business Bank West, Andrew L. (Andy) Bacon
President Colorado Business Bank Littleton, Darrell J. Schulte
EVP and CFO, Lyne B. Andrich, age 45, $275,000 total compensation
EVP and COO, Richard J. Dalton, age 55, $275,000 total compensation
President Colorado Business Bank Denver, Virginia K. Berkeley
EVP; CEO Colorado Business Bank and Arizona Business Bank, Jonathan C. Lorenz, age 60, $380,000 total compensation
Chairman and CEO, Steven Bangert, age 55, $522,500 total compensation
Co-President and Managing Director Green Manning & Bunch Investment Banking, Scott H. Maierhofer
CEO Financial Designs, J. David (Dave) Hunter
EVP and Chief Credit Officer, Robert B. Ostertag, age 51, $215,000 total compensation
Market President Colorado Business Bank, Scott Page
President and COO Alexander Capital, Scott Farrar
President Colorado Business Bank Northwest, Valorie Simpson
President Arizona Business Bank Camelback, Richard (Rick) Baker
President and Senior Managing Director Green Manning & Bunch Investment Banking, Warren R. Henson Jr.
1st VP and Controller, Troy R. Dumlao
President CoBiz Insurance, Paul Boehm
Commercial Lines Account Manager Insurance, Amy Bartelson
Staff Auditor, Karim Martin
Finance Manager, David Mayhew
IT Applications System Analyst, John Strong
President and Senior Portfolio Manager Wagner Investments, Judith B. Wagner
Market President Arizona Business Bank, Bruce T. (Toby) Day
Director, Mary K. Rhinehart, age 53
Director, Morgan Gust, age 64
Director, Douglas L. Polson, age 70
Director, Timothy J. Travis, age 67
Director, Michael B. Burgamy, age 66
Director, Harold F. Mosanko, age 72
Director, Noel N. Rothman, age 82
Director, Thomas M. Longust, age 70
Director, Evan Makovsky, age 67
Director, Mary M. White, age 60
Director, Mary Beth Vitale, age 58
Auditors: Deloitte&ToucheLLP

LOCATIONS

HQ: CoBiz Financial Incorporated
821 17th St., Denver CO 80202
Phone: 303-293-2265 **Fax:** 314-342-7799
Web: www.peabodyenergy.com

PRODUCTS/OPERATIONS

2011 Sales

	$ mil.	% of total
Interest		
Loans including fees	88	60
Taxable securities	22	15
Other	0	-
Noninterest		
Insurance	13	9
Investment banking	7	5
Investment advisory & trust	5	4
Service charges	5	3
Other	5	4
Total	**147**	**100**

COMPETITORS

Bank of America
Compass Bancshares
FirstBank Holding Company
KeyCorp
U.S. Bancorp
Vectra Bank
Wells Fargo

HISTORICAL FINANCIALS

Company Type: Public

Income Statement FYE: December 31

	ASSETS ($ mil.)	NET INCOME ($ mil.)	INCOME AS % OF ASSETS	EMPLOYEES
12/11	2,423	33	1.4%	546
12/10	2,395	(22)	—	558
12/09	2,466	(83)	—	564
12/08	2,684	1	0.0%	554
12/07	2,391	23	1.0%	507
Annual Growth	0.3%	9.8%	—	1.9%

2011 Year-End Financials

Debt ratio: 3.84%
Return on equity: 15.20%
Cash ($ mil.): 59
Current ratio: —
Long-term debt ($ mil.): 93
No. of shares (mil.): 37
Dividends
Yield: —
Payout: 5.26%
Market value ($ mil.): 214

	STOCK PRICE ($) FY Close	P/E High/Low		PER SHARE ($) Earnings	Dividends	Book Value
12/11	5.77	9	6	0.76	0.00	5.93
12/10	6.08	—	—	(0.72)	0.04	5.47
12/09	4.75	—	—	(2.98)	0.10	6.28
12/08	9.74	313	107	0.05	0.28	10.79
12/07	14.87	22	14	0.96	0.26	8.23
Annual Growth	(21.1%)	—	—	(5.7%)	—	(7.9%)

Coca-Cola Co (The)

Coke is it –it being the #1 nonalcoholic beverage company in the world. The Coca-Cola Company is home to 15 billion dollar brands including four of the top five soft drinks: Coca-Cola Diet Coke Fanta and Sprite. Other top brands include Minute Maid Powerade and vitaminwater. All told it owns or licenses and markets more than 500 beverage brands mainly sparkling drinks but also waters juice drinks energy and sports drinks and ready-to-drink teas and coffees. With the world's largest beverage distribution system The Coca-Cola Company reaches consumers in more than 200 countries. About 40% of its revenue is generated in the US.

HISTORY

Atlanta pharmacist John Pemberton invented Coke in 1886. His bookkeeper Frank Robinson named the product after two ingredients coca leaves (later cleaned of narcotics) and kola nuts. By 1891 druggist Asa Candler had bought The Coca-Cola Company and within four years the soda-fountain drink was available in all states; it was in Canada and Mexico by 1898.

Candler sold most US bottling rights in 1899 to Benjamin Thomas and John Whitehead of Chattanooga Tennessee for $1. The two designed a regional franchise bottling system that created more than 1000 bottlers within 20 years. In 1916 Candler retired to become Atlanta's mayor; his family sold the company to Atlanta banker Ernest Woodruff for $25 million in 1919. Coca-Cola went public that year.

The firm expanded overseas and introduced the slogans "The Pause that Refreshes" (1929) and "It's the Real Thing" (1941). To keep WWII soldiers in Cokes at a nickel a pop the government built 64 overseas bottling plants. Coca-Cola bought Minute Maid in 1960 and began launching new drinks —Fanta (1960) Sprite (1960) TAB (1963) and Diet Coke (1982).

In 1981 Roberto Goizueta became chairman. Four years later with Coke slipping in market share the firm changed its formula and introduced New Coke which consumers soundly rejected (thus Coca-Cola Classic was born). In 1986 it consolidated the US bottling operations it owned into Coca-Cola Enterprises and sold 51% of the new company to the public. Goizueta also engineered the company's purchase of Columbia Pictures in 1982. (Columbia earned Coke a $1 billion profit when it sold the studio to Sony in 1989.)

In 1995 it bought Barq's root beer. Goizueta died of lung cancer in 1997; while he was at the helm the firm's value rose from $4 billion to $145 billion. Douglas Ivester the architect of Coca-Cola's restructured bottling operations succeeded him. An agreement to buy about 30 Cadbury Schweppes beverage brands —including Canada Dry Dr Pepper and Schweppes —outside the US and France was scaled down because of antitrust concerns. Completed in 1999 the deal also excluded Canada much of continental Europe and Mexico. (Cadbury in 2008 spun off its beverage division which became Dr Pepper Snapple Group.)

A battered Ivester resigned in 2000; president and COO Douglas Daft was named chairman and CEO. Coca-Cola began its largest cutbacks ever slashing nearly 5000 jobs and later agreed to pay nearly $193 million to settle a race-discrimination suit filed by African-American workers.

To fortify its portfolio in the fast-growing noncarbonated drinks segment Coca-Cola acquired Mad River Traders (teas juices sodas) and Odwalla (juices and smoothies) in 2001. The company also bought a 35% interest (San Miguel Corporation owned the rest) in bottler Coca-Cola Philippines from Coca-Cola Amatil. (In 2005 Coke bought the remaining percentage of the Philippine bottler.) The company announced the creation of a huge beverage and snack distribution joint venture with Procter & Gamble but the multibillion-dollar operation fell apart before it could begin. Coca-Cola also announced that it would invest $150 million to build bottling facilities in China.

In 2002 Coca-Cola introduced Vanilla Coke its biggest new product launch since the disastrous New Coke debacle. The company also secured distribution rights to Danone's Evian brand in North America and paid about $128 million when it formed a joint venture (CCDA Waters LLC) with Danone to produce market and distribute Danone's bottled water in the North America (including Dannon and Sparkletts brands under license). Also in 2002 Steven Heyer president and COO of Coca-Cola Ventures and Coca-Cola Latin America was named Coca-Cola's new president and COO. (The company's former president Jack Stahl had left after a reorganization in 2001.)

As part of the restructuring initiated by Daft in 2000 another 1000 employees (half in Atlanta) were laid off in 2003 after the company decided to combine several business units under the Coca-Cola North America umbrella. The company laid off 2800 employees worldwide in 2003.

Those layoffs led one former employee to sue claiming the soft drink maker improperly accounted for funds discriminated against minorities and in 2000 rigged test marketing of frozen Coca-Cola at a Virginia Burger King. Coca-Cola said it does not violate general accounting principles and does not discriminate. However the company said it had already disciplined employees involved in the Burger King tests and Coke executive Thomas Moore who led the fountain drinks division responsible for the questionable tests resigned. Coke also agreed to pay Burger King as much as $21 million to settle the matter. Coke said in 2003 it would reduce its revenue by $9 million to make up for accounting errors from the fountain drinks division that managed the troubled tests. Coke later settled its dispute with the former employee who first raised concerns about Coke's conduct agreeing to pay $500000 in severance and legal costs.

Later in 2003 trouble broke out for the company overseas. Claims surfaced in India that both Coke and Pepsi bottled in that country contain traces of DDT malathion and other pesticides that exceed government limits. Both Coke and Pepsi denied the reports in a joint press conference. Government labs cleared the colas saying the drinks were safe but not before both soft drink companies saw sales dip by as much as 50% in a two-week period.

Trying to boost the younger consumer's interest in its flagship cola Coca-Cola launched new marketing and ad campaigns in 2003. Efforts included changing graphics on Coke bottles and cans back to a more traditional look. However Coca-Cola took the opposite tactic to spur interest in Sprite unveiling Sprite Remix a tropical-flavored version of the soft drink. Minute Maid unveiled Minute Maid Premium Heart Wise which claims to lower cholesterol as long as people consistently drink two glasses a day.

Coca-Cola rolled out a lime version of its Diet Coke in 2004. (The non-diet version came out in 2005.) The flavor joined diet cherry lemon and vanilla. In making the announcement Coca-Cola said it also had reformulated its lemon flavor so that it tastes "lighter." Also in 2004 Coke opened an online music store in the UK called MyCokemusic.com. A month later Coke began selling its Dasani bottled water in the UK and 19 other countries. Later in 2004 the company recalled Dasani water in Europe because of elevated levels of bromate. In addition Daft retired as Coca-Cola's chairman and CEO in 2004 and former Coca-Cola HBC CEO E. Neville Isdell replaced him.

Responding to the growing awareness by consumers of health problems associated with obesity and inactive lifestyles in 2004 Coca-Cola created The Beverage Institute for Health & Wellness a beverage research and educational operation which the company hopes will lead to the creation of more healthful beverage products.

Having introduced Minute Maid products in Russia in 2004 Coke furthered its juice presence in the country with the 2005 purchase of Russian juice maker Multon. Coke bought the company in conjunction with Coca-Cola Hellenic Bottling Co. Later that year Coke began test marketing a Mountain Dew-like drink named Vault in Alabama North Carolina and Tennessee. (Surge a previous Mountain Dew competitor tried by Coke failed in testing.) In 2005 the company announced the phasing out of Vanilla Coke and introduction of Black Cherry Coke.

In 2005 Coke bought Danone's 49% stake in their North American bottled-water venture for about $100 million. The joint venture never turned a profit during its three-year run but Coke hopes full ownership of the Dannon and Sparkletts brands will prove profitable. Coke still shares North American import and marketing rights of Danone's premier water brand Evian which although the world's top-selling bottled water has seen declining in US sales.

The company's rivalry with PepsiCo goes beyond soda to juice products (Coca-Cola's Minute Maid vs. PepsiCo's Tropicana) bottled water (Dasani vs. Aquafina) and other noncarbonated products. Feeling pressure to stay competitive with these faster selling beverages Coca-Cola introduced an energy drink Full Throttle in 2005.

Also in 2005 Coke also announced a revamping of its global marketing team announcing the retirement of Sandy Allen president of its European division. In an effort to expand its international product offerings later that same year it acquired Brazilian juice maker Sucos Mais for some $48 million.

New drinks introduced in 2006 included Vault (a Mountain Dew knock-off). That year Blak a coffee-flavored Coke (with half the calories and twice the caffeine of a regular Coke that was in development for two years) was first test-marketed in France and subsequently introduced in the US. (The pricey soda —$1.99 for an 8-ounce bottle — was discontinued in the US in 2007 due to poor sales.)

Boosting its drinks in the reduced-calorie category in 2006 the company introduced a so-called "calorie-burning" drink called Enviga a green-tea-based drink. It is marketed through a joint venture with Nestle . (The joint venture called Beverage Partners Worldwide primarily focuses on black tea drinks.)

The company also launched a new line of premium coffee and tea beverages called Far Coast in 2006. The drinks were launched in Canada along with Far Coast concept stores where consumers can taste test the flavors. The company expanded its reach into coffee further with a deal with coffeehouse chain Caribou Coffee. Coca-Cola and Caribou created a new line of ready-to-drink iced coffee beverages.

Bowing to the public's growing concern about childhood obesity in 2006 Coke along with Pepsi Cadbury Schweppes (whose beverage operations later became Dr Pepper Snapple Group) and the American Beverage Association agreed to sell only water unsweetened juice and low-fat milks to public elementary and middle schools in the US. As for high schools the agreement calls for no sugary sodas to be sold and one-half of the offered drinks to be water diet sodas lemonade or iced tea. The agreement was facilitated by former president Bill Clinton.

Saying that it had lost market share to Apple's iTunes Music Store Coke announced the 2006 shut-down of its UK music-download site Mycokemusic. That year Coke also joined with Coca-Cola FEMSA to buy top Brazilian juice maker Jugos del Valle for $440 million. Still concentrating on Brazil the next year coke bought Brazil's bottled tea and beverage maker Leao Junior. The purchase added more than 60 new products to Coke's Brazilian portfolio.

The purchase of the maker of smartwater and vitaminwater Energy Brands (also known as Glaceau) saw Coke forking over some $4 billion in cash in 2007. Energy Brands became a separate operating unit of Coca-Cola North America. Another addition to its non-cola offerings took place in 2007 when the company acquired Fuze Beverage an alternative juice and tea producer for about $250 million. Forming a joint venture with Coca-Cola FEMSA that year Coke acquired of the soft drink assets of Colombia's Agua Brisa bottled water from SABMiller. Coke also purchased the San Miguel Corporation's 63% share of Coca-Cola Bottlers Philippines for $590 million. The 2007 purchase made Coke the sole owner of the Philippine bottler.

In February 2008 the company acquired a 40% stake in the tea and organic beverage company Honest Tea. Coke in 2009 bought a minority stake of UK smoothie maker Innocent and upped its share to 58% in early 2010.

In 2009 the company began removing the word "Classic" from its prominent place on its flagship US cola products saying that the reason for the word's being had disappeared. "Classic" was added during the 1980s when the company having changed the formula for its cola sought to win back the public which had soundly rejected the "New Coke." (New Coke was subsequently distributed sparingly by the company and in 2004 quietly dropped.) Although "Classic" is no longer as prominent on the company's cola products it appears as the phrase "Coke Classic original formula" in a less conspicuous place on product packaging.

In 2010 it bought out the North American bottling and distribution business of Coca-Cola Enterprises (CCE). The deal was valued at $12 billion (including nearly $9 billion in debt).

A federal judge in 2011 dismissed a lawsuit filed against Coca-Cola by the great-grandchildren of the Barq's root beer founder. The plaintiffs claimed to have an ownership stake in the company that Coca-Cola had purchased in 1995.

EXECUTIVES

EVP and CFO, Gary P. Fayard, age 59, $741,600 total compensation
VP and Chief Internal Audit, Connie D. McDaniel
VP Strategic Security and Aviation, James A. Hush
President North American Business Integration, Brian P. Kelley
President and CEO Coca-Cola Bottlers Philippines Inc. (CCBPI), William W. (Bill) Schultz, age 51
President and CEO Coca-Cola Refreshments, Steven A. (Steve) Cahillane, age 46
SVP and Corporate Treasurer, David M. Taggart
SVP Global Customer Channel Leadership, Bonnie P. Wurzbacher
EVP and Chief Marketing and Commercial Officer, Joseph V. (Joe) Tripodi, age 56
VP Supply Chain, Rick Frazier
EVP and Chief Administrative Officer, Alexander B. (Alex) Cummings Jr., age 55, $700,000 total compensation
VP Science, Eddie R. Hays
Director Diplomatic Relations, Janet A. Howard
VP and Director Flavor Ingredient Supply, Mary M. G. Riddle
SVP Global Public Affairs and Communications, Clyde C. Tuggle, age 49
EVP; President Bottling Investments and Supply Chain, Irial Finan, age 54, $787,500 total compensation
VP Corporate Social Responsibility, John C. Reid, age 59
President Latin Center Business Unit, John Murphy
President Fundacion Juan Manuel Sainz de Vicuna, Jose Nu?ez-Cervera
VP Corporate Supply Chain, Frederick P. Yochum
President and General Manager Sparkling Beverages Coca-Cola North America, Katie J. Bayne, age 45
President The 7-11 Group and Commercial Execution, R. Eric McCarthey, age 56
President Coca-Cola North America, J. Alexander M. (Sandy) Douglas Jr., age 50
President Greater China and Korea Business Unit, Douglas A. Jackson
Chairman Coca-Cola China, Steve K. W. Chan
Deputy Group President Pacific Group, Paul K. Etchells
Chairman Japanese Business Unit, Masahiko Uotani
VP and CIO, Edmund R. (Ed) Steinike, age 54
President Iberian Business Unit, Marcos de Quinto
President Eurasia and Africa Group, Ahmet C. Bozer, age 51
President Pacific Group, Glenn G. Jordan S., age 55
President Mexico Business Unit, Brian J. Smith
Associate General Counsel Litigation, Michael G. McQueeney
President Europe Group, Dominique Reiniche, age 56
VP and Director Mergers and Acquisitions, Marie D. Quintero-Johnson
VP Public Affairs Strategic Projects, Barclay T. Resler
President Japan Business Unit, Dan Sayre
President Northwest Europe and Nordics Business Unit, James R. Quincey, age 47
SVP Global Business and Technology Services, Harry L. Anderson, age 49
VP and Chief Sustainability Officer, Beatriz R. (Bea) Perez, age 42
Group Director Corporate External Affairs, Lisa Manley
Director Group Marketing Pacific, John Hackett
President South Africa Business Unit, William (Bill) Egbe
President North and West Africa Business Unit, Curtis A. (Curt) Ferguson
Associate General Counsel and Secretary, Carol Crofoot Hayes
Assistant Corporate Secretary, Fiona K. Payne
President India and South West Asia Business Unit, Atul Singh
Global Director Women's Economic Empowerment, Charlotte Oades
Chairman and CEO, Muhtar Kent, age 59, $1,200,000 total compensation
Group Director Marketing, Katherine Twells
SVP Global Community Connections; Chairperson The Coca-Cola Foundation, Ingrid Saunders Jones, age 66
Group Director Loyalty CRM and Measurement, Doug Rollins
Director Sports and Entertainment Marketing, Chip York
Manager BU Strategic Marketing, Tim Goudie
Manager Customer Agreement Team, Stacey Davis
SVP Sparkling Sports Energy Water, Santiago Blanco
Group Director Public Affairs and Communications, Lee Winfield
VP; President Global Business Services, Ann T. Taylor
VP and Controller, Kathy N. Waller, age 54
SVP and Chief Customer and Commercial Officer, Jerry S. Wilson, age 57
Managing Director, Ulrik Nehammer
Director Marketing and Olympics, Sanjay Guha
Director Global Channel, Jim Gulley
President Beverage Partners Worldwide, Beatrice Guillaume-Grabisch, age 47
VP and Chief Scientific and Regulatory Officer, Rhona Applebaum
President Central and Southern Europe Business Unit, Michael Holm Johansen
President South Latin Business Unit, Francisco Crespo Benitez
President ASEAN Business Unit, Manuel Arroyo
President East and Central Africa Business Unit, Nathan Kalumbu
President Brazil Business Unit, Xiemar Zarazua
CEO Hindustan Coca-Cola Beverages (India), Thirumalai Krishnakumar
President Latin America Group, Jose O. Reyes Lagunes, age 60, $617,871 total compensation
Director Community Affairs, Carlos Pagoaga
President Southern Eurasia Business Unit, Selcuk Erden
Group Advisor, Ahmet Burak
CEO Coca-Cola China Industries Ltd. China Bottling Investments Group, Martin Jansen, age 53
CEO Coca-Cola Erfrischungsgetranke Germany Bottling Investments Group, Damian Gammell
Regional Director Nordics Middle East and Africa Bottling Investments Group, John M. Guarino
Regional Director South Asia and Latin America Bottling Investments Group, R. Steve Buffington
President Germany Business Unit, Hendrik Steckhan
SVP Integrated Marketing Communications and Capabilities, Wendy Clark
Group Chief Executive Coca-Cola Hellenic Bottling Company S.A., Dimitris Lois, age 51
VP Global Design, David Butler
SBP Global Business Services, Nalin Garg
Director Operations, Dirk Veryser
Marketing Director G and I BU Marketing, Roel Annega
VP; President The McDonald's Division, Javier C. Goizueta
VP and Chief Strategy Officer, John M. Farrell
VP and Investor Relations Officer, Jackson Kelly
President Middle East and Southern Eurasia Group Business Unit, Iain McLaughlin
President Russia Ukraine and Belarus Business Unit, Zoran A. Vucinic
President Turkey Business Unit, Galya Frayman Molinas
Region Director Japan & Latin America Bottling Investments Group, Paul Mulligan
Director Transformational Productivity, Jane Ann Westpheling
Director Regulatory and Environmental, Scott Vitters
Global Director Finance Transformation, Jeremy Faa
SVP and Chief People Officer, Ceree Eberly, age 49
Managing Director Nigeria, Islay Rhind
President Central & Southern Europe Business Unit, Nilolaos (Nikos) Koumettis

Director Operations France, Veronique Bourez, age 48
Director General Bulgaria, Nikos Kalaitzidakis
VP Global Connections, Ivan Pollard
VP and Corporate Treasurer, Christopher P. (Chris) Nolan
VP and Chief Quality Safety and Sustainable Operations Officer, Carletta Ooton
Director Group Communications Finance, Kenth Kaerhoeg
SVP and CTO, Guy Wollaert, age 52
VP Sustainability Strategy and Communication, Abby Rodgers
VP Environment and Water, Jeff Seabright
SVP and General Counsel, Bernhard Goepelt, age 49
Global Research and Development Officer, Nancy W. Quan
President South Pacific Business Unit, Bruno Filipi
Director, Peter V. (Pete) Ueberroth, age 74
Director, Herbert A. (Herb) Allen II, age 72
Director, Jacob Wallenberg, age 56
Director, Barry Diller, age 70
Director, James D. Robinson III, age 76
Director, Ronald W. (Ron) Allen, age 70
Director, Donald F. McHenry, age 75
Director, Sam Nunn, age 73
Director, James B. Williams, age 78
Director, Howard G. Buffett, age 58
Director, Donald R. (Don) Keough, age 85
Director, Maria Elena (Mel) Lagomasino, age 62
Director, Evan G. Greenberg, age 57
Director, Alexis M. Herman, age 64
Auditors: Ernst&YoungLLP

LOCATIONS

HQ: The Coca-Cola Company
1 Coca-Cola Plaza, Atlanta GA 30313-2499
Phone: 404-676-2121 **Fax:** 214-689-5886
Web: www.commercialmetals.com

2011 Sales

	$ mil.	% of total
US	18,699	40
Other countries	27,843	60
Total	**46,542**	**100**

PRODUCTS/OPERATIONS

2011 Sales

	$ mil.	% of total
Beverage concentrates fountain syrups & finished		82
Bottling		18
Total		**100**

2011 Sales

	% of total
Finished product	61
Concentrate	39
Total	**100**

Selected Brands

Sparkling Beverages
- Core sparkling
  - Barq's
  - Coca-Cola
  - Coca-Cola Zero/Coke Zero
  - Diet Coke/Coca-Cola Light
  - Fanta
  - Fresca
  - Inca Kola
  - Lift
  - Schweppes
  - Sprite
  - Thums Up
- Energy drinks
  - Burn
  - Nos
  - Real Gold

Still Beverages
- Coffee & teas
  - Ayataka teas
  - Dogadan teas
  - Georgia coffees
  - Le?o/Matte Le?o teas
  - Nestea teas
  - Sokenbicha teas
- Juices and juice drinks
  - Cappy
  - Del Valle
  - Dobriy
  - Hi-C
  - Minute Maid
  - Minute Maid Pulpy
  - Simply
- Other still beverages
  - glaceau vitaminwater
  - Fuze
- Sports drinks
  - Aquarius
  - Powerade
- Waters
  - Bonaqua/Bonaqa
  - Ciel
  - Dasani
  - Ice Dew
  - Kinley

Selected Anchor Bottlers

Coca-Cola Amatil Limited (29%; Australia Fiji Indonesia New Zealand and Papua New Guinea)
Coca-Cola FEMSA S.A.B. de C.V. (29%; parts of Argentina Brazil Colombia Costa Rica Guatemala Mexico Nicaragua Panama and Venezuela)
Coca-Cola Hellenic Bottling Company S.A. (23%; Armenia Austria Belarus Bosnia-Herzegovina Bulgaria Croatia Cyprus the Czech Republic Estonia Greece Hungary Italy Latvia Lithuania Macedonia Moldova Montenegro Nigeria Northern Ireland Poland Republic of Ir

Selected Subsidiaries

Atlantic Manufacturing
Caribbean Refrescos Inc.
CCDA Waters LLC
Coca-Cola China Industries Ltd.
Coca-Cola Refreshments USA Inc.
Energy Brands Inc.
Hindustan Coca-Cola Beverages Private Limited
Odwalla Inc.

COMPETITORS

American Beverage
Aquaterra Corporation
Bazi
Britvic
Chiquita Brands
Clearly Canadian
Clement Pappas
Cott
Cranberries Limited
Danone
Del Monte Foods
Dole Food
Dr Pepper Snapple Group
Faygo
Fiji Water
Florida' s Natural
Fresh Del Monte Produce
Freshco
Gatorade
Great Western Juice
Hawaiian Springs
Hornell Brewing
Impulse Energy USA
IZZE
Jamba
Jones Soda
Kirin Holdings Company
Lassonde
Leading Brands
Monarch Beverage (GA)
Mondelez International
Monster Beverage
Mountain Valley
Naked Juice
National Beverage
National Grape Cooperative
Naumes
Nestle
Ocean Spray
Old Orchard
PepsiCo
Pernod Ricard
Red Bull
Silver Springs
South Beach Beverage
Southern Gardens Citrus
Sun-Rype
Sunny Delight
Suntory Holdings
Tree Top
Unilever
Welch' s
Wet Planet Beverages

HISTORICAL FINANCIALS

Company Type: Public

Income Statement

FYE: December 31

	REVENUE ($ mil.)	NET INCOME ($ mil.)	NET PROFIT MARGIN	EMPLOYEES
12/11	46,542	8,572	18.4%	146,200
12/10	35,119	11,809	33.6%	139,600
12/09	30,990	6,824	22.0%	92,800
12/08	31,944	5,807	18.2%	92,400
12/07	28,857	5,981	20.7%	90,500
Annual Growth	12.7%	9.4%	—	12.7%

2011 Year-End Financials

Debt ratio: 35.72%—
Return on equity: 27.10%
Cash ($ mil.): 12,803
Current ratio: 105.00
Long-term debt ($ mil.): 13,656
Dividends
Yield: —
Payout: 50.95%
Market value ($ mil.): —

	STOCK PRICE ($) FY Close	P/E High/Low		PER SHARE ($) Earnings	Dividends	Book Value
12/11	69.97	38	33	1.85	0.00	6.99
12/10	65.77	26	20	2.53	0.88	6.76
12/09	57.00	40	26	1.47	0.82	5.38
12/08	45.27	52	33	1.25	0.76	4.43
12/07	61.37	49	35	1.29	0.68	4.69
Annual Growth	3.3%	—	—	9.4%	—	10.5%

Coca-Cola Enterprises Inc

Scientists at The Coca-Cola Company (TCCC) concoct the secret syrup but it's up to Coca-Cola Enterprises (CCE) to do the heavy lifting. CCE buys it combines it with other ingredients then bottles and distributes Coke products in Western Europe. The world's third-largest Coca-Cola bottler by volume CCE bottles and distributes energy drinks such as glaceau's vitaminwater and Monster brands sports drinks still and sparkling waters (Dr Pepper Snapple's Schweppes Abbey Well) juices and coffees and teas. The company's European reach includes distribution in Belgium France the Netherlands Norway Sweden and the UK. All told CCE operates more than 15 production and 30 distribution facilities in Europe.

Geographic Reach

Coca-Cola Enterprises (CCE) serves about 170 million consumers in eight European countries. The UK is CCE's largest market accounting for about a third of total sales. France is next with 29% followed by Belgium (16%). The Nordic countries and Luxembourg and Monaco account for the remainder.

Financial Analysis

CCE's sales increased by more than 23% in 2011 vs. the prior year while net income was up 20% over the same period. Cash flow increased by $446 million in 2011 vs. 2010. The double-digit sales jump resulted from the acquisition of bottling operations in Norway and Sweden (acquired in late 2010) and favorable currency exchange rates. Also growth in demand for CCE's energy drinks and waters spurred sales. The European bottler sold approximately 12 billion bottles and cans in 2011 and sales topped $8.3 billion. The five top selling brands by volume were Coca-Cola Diet Coke/Coca-Cola light Coca-Cola Zero Fanta and Capri-Sun.

Strategy

In addition to delivering beverages CCE's long-term goals include delivering 6% annual revenue growth 6% to 8% operating income growth and high single-digit diluted EPS growth. In its first full year of operation CCE exceeded these goals despite economic difficulties in western Europe. (Indeed CCE is faring better than its larger sister companyCoca-Cola Hellenic which is leaving Greece for Switzerland and relisting on the London Stock Exchange.) To spur sales CCE is relying on new product launches (including POWERade Energy in the UK Monster in Sweden) and packaging innovations such as contour bottles. Also CCE is transitioning from the production and sale of refillable bottles to the production and sale of recyclable non-refillables. In 2012 the company looked to the London Olympics to spur sales.

Company Background

CCE was formed when its predecessor company also called Coca-Cola Enterprises Inc. merged with The Coca-Cola Company (TCCC) in fall 2010 and separated its European operations. As part of the $12 billion transformation CCE was established as a new company to focus on the western European Coke business. CCE's international business further expanded with the takeover of TCCC's bottling operations in Norway and Sweden soon after. CCE remains at the original Coca-Cola Enterprises headquarters in Atlanta. Although it took over its predecessor's NYSE ticker the original shareholders were issued new stock and $10 a share. CCE also has the option to buy TCCC's roughly 80% holding in its German bottling operations in the future.

EXECUTIVES

SVP and General Counsel, John R. Parker Jr., age 60
EVP and CFO, William W. (Bill) Douglas III
Chairman and CEO, John F. Brock
SVP and CIO, Esat Sezer, age 50
SVP Public Affairs and Communications, Laura Brightwell
VP Controller and Chief Accounting Officer, Suzanne D. Patterson, age 50
EVP; President European Group, Hubert Patricot, age 52
Auditors: Ernst&YoungLLP

LOCATIONS

HQ: Coca-Cola Enterprises Inc
2500 Windy Ridge Parkway, Atlanta, GA 30339
Phone: 678 260-3000
Web: www.cokecce.com

2011 Unit Sales

	% of total
UK	34
France	29
Belgium	16
Netherlands	9
Norway	7
Sweden	5
Total	**100**

PRODUCTS/OPERATIONS

2011 Brand Sales

	% of total
Coca-Cola	69
Sparkling flavors &	18
Juices isotonics &	10
Water	3
Total	**100**

COMPETITORS

AG Barr
Britvic
Cott
Danone
Fraser & Neave
Mondelez International
Nestle
Nichols plc
Ocean Spray
Orchard House Foods
PepsiCo
Red Bull
Snapple

HISTORICAL FINANCIALS

Company Type: Public

Income Statement

FYE: December 31

	REVENUE ($ mil.)	NET INCOME ($ mil.)	NET PROFIT MARGIN	EMPLOYEES
12/11	8,284	749	9.0%	13,250
12/10	6,714	624	9.3%	13,500
12/09	6,517	576	8.8%	0
12/08	6,619	514	7.8%	0
12/07	6,246	524	8.4%	0
Annual Growth	7.3%	9.3%	—	—

2011 Year-End Financials

Debt ratio: 33.12%
Return on equity: 25.84%
Cash ($ mil.): 684
Current ratio: 145.35
Long-term debt ($ mil.): 2,996
No. of shares (mil.): 304
Dividends
Yield: —
Payout: 22.27%
Market value ($ mil.): 7,862

	STOCK PRICE ($) FY Close	P/E High/Low		PER SHARE ($) Earnings	Dividends	Book Value
12/11	25.78	13	10	2.29	0.00	9.51
12/10	25.03	14	12	1.83	0.12	9.45
Annual Growth	3.0%	—	—	25.1%	—	0.6%

Cognizant Technology Solutions Corp.

Cognizant Technology Solutions remains mindful of the state of your technology. Cognizant provides application maintenance services business intelligence data warehousing software and systems development and integration and re-engineering services for legacy systems. Its customers are primarily corporations from the Forbes Global 2000. Most of Cognizant's software development centers and employees are located in India although it has other development and delivery facilities around the world. Cognizant serves more than 780 clients in the financial services health care manufacturing media retail and technology industries. The company generates about 80% of its revenues in North America.

Cognizant's top five customers account for more than 16% of revenues and the top 10 generate nearly 28%. Those percentages are down from 2010 when they were at 18% and 30% respectively. That's the direction the company wants them to go as it means the loss of any one of them would have less of a detrimental impact on sales. Business in Europe (excluding the UK) was up 28% while UK sales rose 25%. With economic worries harassing the region Cognizant expects growth to there to slow though the company still considers it a key growth region for the long haul.

Other regions the company is bullish on for long-term growth are the Middle East and Asia/Pacific especially Japan India Australia and Singapore. In 2012 Cognizant opened a new 30000 sq. ft. development center in Singapore and the company cites an independent report that pegs expected IT software and services growth in India to come in at 15% for 2012.

Much of the company's growth has been the result of increasing demand for offshore IT software and services and business process outsourcing as the market place grows more confident in the effectiveness and security of such services. Cognizant has also managed to capitalize on its customer relationships by successfully cross-selling. Additionally despite the general concerns in Europe spending on IT projects has risen.

Cognizant has tried to differentiate itself in a crowded IT services market by tailoring its services to specific industries targeting four key areas –financial services; health care; manufacturing retail and logistics; and technology and media and information services. Customers in the financial services industry account for the largest portion of revenues about 40% of sales followed by health care (one-quarter); manufacturing retail and logistics (one-fifth); and communications high tech and information media and entertainment services (less than 15%).

The company also offers a mix of on-site and near-shore and offshore service. Unlike competitors that provide no on-site assistance Cognizant typically locates technical and account management teams at its customers' locations with development work handled at dedicated development centers offshore. Those locations are in the US Canada Argentina Hungary China India and the Philippines. This boosts Cognizant's bottom line by taking advantage of cheaper labor costs while maintaining a close connection with its customers.

While many tech companies struggled through the global economic downturn Cognizant has continued to grow revenues profits and headcount over the years. The company has more than 40 IT development centers across India alone and in 2011 it announced plans to invest more than $500 million through 2014 to build an additional 8 million sq. ft. of office space for more than 55000 developers. About 80% of the company's employees are based in the Asia/Pacific region while less than 5% work in Europe mostly in the UK. Cognizant hired some 25000 people worldwide in 2010 bringing its total workforce to more than 100000 and has since grown its team to nearly 140000.

The company continues to focus on providing capabilities in customer relationship management enterprise resource planning data warehousing and business intelligence software testing infrastructure management and vertically-oriented business and knowledge process outsourcing. Cognizant's biggest growth drivers have been infrastructure management and business and knowledge process outsourcing.

Cognizant sees the industry as fragmented and offering opportunities for acquisitions. In 2011 Cognizant acquired CoreLogic Global Services Private Limited (CoreLogic India) a subsidiary of California-based CoreLogic for about $50 million in cash. The deal expands Cognizant's operations in India particularly in the areas of software development analytical modeling back-office services and technology support. CoreLogic India has offices in Bangalore Hyderabad and Mangalore. Later that year it picked up SAP-focused retail consultant and software developer Zaffera to improve its retail industry expertise in SAP offerings covering areas such as business analytics and point-of-sale integration.

In May 2010 it bought The PIPC Group a London-based management consulting firm which helped expand its geographic footprint in Australia New Zealand and the UK. It also bought Paris-based Galileo Performance a provider of IT testing services a couple of months later. In 2009 it bought the assets of Pepperweed Advisors the IT consulting services division of Pepperweed Consulting. It also acquired UBS India Service Centre Private Limited which expanded its offerings in business process outsourcing and knowledge process outsourcing for the financial services industry. Cognizant follows its global customer expansion with build outs of its sales and marketing offices and presses on in North America Europe Latin America Asia and the Middle East.

Cognizant Technology Solutions began as an in-house technology center for Dun & Bradstreet in 1994 and was spun off from D&B in 1996. Two years later Cognizant reorganized and spun off its market research operations into two public companies IMS Health and Nielsen Media Research in order to focus on IT services.

EXECUTIVES

President and Managing Director Global Delivery, Ramakrishnan (Chandra) Chandrasekaran, age 54, $340,000 total compensation
CEO, Francisco (Frank) D'Souza, age 43, $518,400 total compensation
President, Gordon J. Coburn, age 48, $466,560 total compensation
Vice Chairman, Lakshmi Narayanan, age 59, $95,554 total compensation
Chairman, John E. Klein, age 70
SVP Global Head Technology Practice, Kaushik Bhaumik
SVP and Head Customer Solutions Practice, Peter Grambs
SVP CIO and Head of Innovation, Sukumar Rajagopal
SVP Data Warehousing Business Intelligence and Performance Management, Veeraraghavan (Veera) Narayanaswamy
Group Chief Executive Industries & Markets, Rajeev Mehta, age 45, $372,000 total compensation
EVP Strategy and Marketing, Malcolm Frank
SVP General Counsel and Secretary, Steven Schwartz, age 44, $340,000 total compensation
SVP Advanced Solutions Group, Allen Shaheen
VP Investor Relations and Treasury, David Nelson
Group Chief Executive Technology & Operations, Chandra Sekaran
SVP and Chief People Officer, Shankar Srinivasan
CFO, Karen McLoughlin
Director, Thomas M. (Tom) Wendel, age 75
Director, Robert E. Weissman, age 71
Director, Robert W. (Bob) Howe, age 65
CEO, Francisco (Frank) D'Souza, age 43
Vice Chairman, Lakshmi Narayanan, age 59
Director, John N. Fox Jr., age 69
Director, Michael Patsalos-Fox
Director, Leo S. Mackay Jr., age 51
Director, Maureen Breakiron-Evans, age 58
Auditors: PricewaterhouseCoopersLLP

LOCATIONS

HQ: Cognizant Technology Solutions Corporation
Glenpointe Centre West 500 Frank W. Burr Blvd., Teaneck NJ 07666
Phone: 201-801-0233 **Fax:** 201-801-0243
Web: www.cognizant.com

2011 Sales

	$ mil.	% of total
North America	4,803	78
Europe		
UK	698	11
Other	398	7
Other	220	4
Total	6,121	100

PRODUCTS/OPERATIONS

2011 Sales

	$ mil.	% of total
Financial services	2,518	41
Health care	1,622	26
Manufacturing retail & logistics	1,197	20
Other	783	13
Total	6,121	100

Selected Services

Application design development integration and re-engineering
- Complex custom systems development
- Customer relationship management (CRM)
- Data warehousing/Business intelligence (BI)
- Enterprise resource planning (ERP)
- Software testing services

IT consulting and technology services
- Business and knowledge process consulting
- IT strategy consulting
- Program management consulting
- Technology consulting

Outsourcing services
- Application maintenance
- Business and knowledge process outsourcing
- Cloud
- CRM and ERP maintenance
- Custom application maintenance
- IT infrastructure outsourcing
- Mobility

Selected Acquisitions

CoreLogic Global Services (2011 business processing services)
Galileo Performance (2010 IT testing)
The PIPC Group (2010 management consulting)
UBS India Service Centre (2009 financial-services outsourcing)
Pepperweed Advisors (2009 IT consulting)
Active Intelligence (2009 systems integration)
Strategic Vision Consulting (2008 media and entertainment consulting)
MarketRx (2007 life-sciences analytics)
AimNet Solutions (2006 infrastructure management)

COMPETITORS

3i Infotech
Accenture
Capgemini
Computer Sciences Corp.
HCL Technologies
HP Enterprise Services
IBM Global Services
Infosys
ITC Infotech India
Mastek
MindTree
MphasiS
Ness Technologies
Patni Computer Systems
Satyam
Tata Consultancy
Wipro
Zensar Technologies

HISTORICAL FINANCIALS

Company Type: Public

Income Statement FYE: December 31

	REVENUE ($ mil.)	NET INCOME ($ mil.)	NET PROFIT MARGIN	EMPLOYEES
12/11	6,121	883	14.4%	137,700
12/10	4,592	733	16.0%	104,000
12/09	3,278	534	16.3%	78,400
12/08	2,816	430	15.3%	61,700
12/07	2,135	350	16.4%	55,400
Annual Growth	30.1%	26.0%	—	25.6%

2011 Year-End Financials

Debt ratio: —
Return on equity: 22.35%
Cash ($ mil.): 1,310
Current ratio: 337.73
Long-term debt ($ mil.): —
No. of shares (mil.): 303
Dividends
Yield: —
Payout: —
Market value ($ mil.): 19,493

	STOCK PRICE ($) FY Close	P/E High	P/E Low	PER SHARE ($) Earnings	Dividends	Book Value
12/11	64.31	28	19	2.85	0.00	13.04
12/10	73.29	30	18	2.37	0.00	11.79
12/09	45.33	25	10	1.78	0.00	8.93
12/08	18.06	25	10	1.44	0.00	6.74
12/07	33.94	78	24	1.15	0.00	5.10
Annual Growth	17.3%	—	—	25.5%	—	26.5%

Colgate-Palmolive Co.

Colgate-Palmolive takes a bite out of grime. The company is a top global maker and marketer of toothpaste and soap and cleaning products. Colgate-Palmolive also offers pet nutrition products through subsidiary Hill's Pet Nutrition which makes Science Diet and Prescription Diet pet foods. Many of its oral care products fall under the Colgate brand and include toothbrushes mouthwash and dental floss. Its Tom's of Maine unit covers the natural toothpaste niche. Personal and home care items include Ajax brand household cleaner Palmolive dishwashing liquid Softsoap shower gel and Speed Stick deodorant. The company has operations in 70-plus countries and sells its products in more than 200 countries.

HISTORY

William Colgate founded The Colgate Company in Manhattan in 1806 to produce soap candles and starch. Colgate died in 1857 and the company was passed to his son Samuel who renamed it Colgate and Company. In 1873 the company introduced toothpaste in jars and in 1896 it began selling Colgate Dental Cream in tubes. By 1906 Colgate was making 160 kinds of soap 625 perfumes and 2000 other products. The company went public in 1908.

In 1898 Milwaukee's B. J. Johnson Soap Company (founded 1864) introduced Palmolive a soap made of palm and olive oils rather than smelly animal fats. It became so popular that the firm changed its name to The Palmolive Company in 1916. Ten years later Palmolive merged with Peet Brothers a Kansas City-based soap maker founded in 1872. Palmolive-Peet merged with Colgate in 1928 forming Colgate-Palmolive-Peet (shortened to Colgate-Palmolive in 1953). The stock market crash of 1929 prevented a planned merger of the company with Hershey and Kraft.

During the 1930s the firm purchased French and German soap makers and opened branches in Europe. Colgate-Palmolive-Peet introduced Fab detergent and Ajax cleanser in 1947 and the brands soon became top sellers in Europe. The company expanded to Asia in the 1950s and by 1961 foreign sales were 52% of the total.

Colgate-Palmolive introduced a host of products in the 1960s and 1970s including Palmolive dishwashing liquid (1966) Ultra Brite toothpaste (1968) and Irish Spring soap (1972). During the same time the company diversified by buying approximately 70 other businesses including Kendall hospital and industrial supplies (1972) Helena Rubinstein cosmetics (1973) Ram Golf (1974) and Riviana Foods and Hill's Pet Products (1976). The strategy had mixed results and most of these acquisitions were sold in the 1980s.

Reuben Mark became CEO of Colgate-Palmolive in 1984. The company bought 50% of Southeast Asia's leading toothpaste Darkie in 1985; it changed its name to Darlie in 1989 following protests of its minstrel-in-blackface trademark. Both Palmolive automatic dishwasher detergent and Colgate Tartar Control toothpaste were introduced in 1986. That year Colgate-Palmolive purchased the liquid soap lines of Minnetonka the most popular of which is Softsoap. In 1992 the company bought Mennen maker of Speed Stick (the leading US deodorant).

Increasing its share of the oral care market in Latin America to 79% in 1995 Colgate-Palmolive acquired Brazilian company Kolynos (from Wyeth for $1 billion) and 94% of Argentina's Odol Saic. The company also bought Ciba-Geigy's oral hygiene business in India increasing its share of that toothpaste market. At home however sales and earnings in key segments were dismal so in 1995 Colgate-Palmolive began a restructuring that included cutting more than 8% of its employees and closing or reconfiguring 24 factories in two years.

The company introduced a record 602 products in 1996 and continued to expand its operations in countries with emerging economies. In 1997 Colgate-Palmolive took the lead in the US toothpaste market for the first time in 35 years (displacing P&G).

In 1999 the company sold the rights to Baby Magic (shampoos lotions oils) in the US Canada and Puerto Rico to Playtex Products retaining the rights in all other countries. Two years later the company sold its heavy-duty laundry detergent business in Mexico (primarily the Viva brand) to Henkel one of Europe's leading detergent producers.

In 2002 Colgate-Palmolive introduced a teeth-whitening gel Simply White to compete with rival P&G's Crest Whitestrips. The company saw success that year when its Hill's Pet Nutrition subsidiary launched new specialty foods for cats and dogs; one of its dog foods reportedly slows brain aging in canines.

In late 2004 Colgate-Palmolive implemented a four-year restructuring plan. Its three primary objectives were to increase profit reallocate resources to promising growth areas and leverage global market efficiencies. It implemented the plan by reducing its global workforce by some 12% closing about 25 of its 78 factories and focusing on core units. Colgate-Palmolive also built new state-of-the-art plants to produce toothpaste in the US and Poland. The company believed that its savings estimated at $500 million altogether would allow it to fund investments in its key businesses as well as provide for new product development.

By selling its North American laundry detergent brands in 2005 Colgate-Palmolive began focusing on the high-margin pearly whites (with bite) of its portfolio —oral care and pet care. The company's purchase of natural oral-care products maker Tom's of Maine in 2006 marked its effort to target the natural niche. It bought some 84% of the firm for about $100 million.

Chairman and CEO Reuben Mark handed over the title of CEO to then-president and COO Ian Cook in July 2007 and the title of chairman to Cook in January 2009; Mark retired at the end of 2008.

Colgate-Palmolive in early 2010 sold off its Code 10 brand which boasted about a 10% market share. Indian consumer goods maker Marico acquired the Malaysian hair-styling name; the move was intended to allow Colgate-Palmolive to focus on its oral personal and pet care businesses.

EXECUTIVES

CFO, Dennis J. Hickey, age 63
Vice Chairman, Michael J. Tangney, age 67, $824,533 total compensation
Chairman President and CEO, Ian M. Cook, age 59, $1,150,000 total compensation
Chief Legal Officer and Secretary, Andrew D. Hendry, age 64, $677,000 total compensation
VP; General Manager Professional Oral Care, Sheila A. Hopkins, age 56
VP Hill's Pet Nutrition, Richard J. Wienckowski
VP Global Human Resources, Julie A. Zerbe
CEO Tom's of Maine, Tom O'Brien
President Global Customer Development, Antonio Caro
VP Global Sustainability and Social Responsibility, Ronald T. Martin, age 63
VP Global Advertising and Digital, Jack J. Haber
COO Emerging Markets, Franck J. Moison, age 58, $641,667 total compensation
VP and Chief Ethics and Compliance Officer, Gregory P. (Greg) Woodson, age 60
COO Global Innovation and Growth and Europe, Fabian T. Garcia, age 52, $736,867 total compensation
SVP Office of the Chairman, John J. (Jack) Huston, age 57
SVP Investor Relations, Delia H. (Bina) Thompson, age 62
President Commercial Business Analytics, Suzan F. Harrison
VP; General Manager Colgate-South Pacific, Chris E. Pedersen
VP; General Manager Colgate-Brazil, Ricardo (Ricky) Ramos
VP Hill's Pet Nutrition, Don Buchner
VP Global Oral Care, N. Jay Jayaraman
President Colgate-Canada, Scott W. Jeffery Jr.
VP Global Finance, Malcolm Jones
President Colgate-Greater Asia, Derrick E.M. Samuel, age 55
VP; General Manager Colgate-Mexico, James C. Shoultz
VP Hill's Pet Nutrition, Joy D. Klemencic
VP Global Supply Chain, Michael A. (Mike) Corbo
President Colgate-Europe, Alexandre (Alec) de Guillenchmidt, age 66
SVP Global Human Resources, Daniel B. Marsili, age 51
VP Global Design and Packaging, Robert W. (Bob) Dietz
VP; General Manager Global Toothbrush Division, Panagiotis Tsourapas
VP Global Consumer Insights, James S. Figura
VP Global Shopper Marketing, Stephen J. Fogarty
President Colgate-Africa and Middle East, Richard Mener
President Colgate-North America and Global Sustainability, Noel R. Wallace
VP Colgate-US, James A. Napolitano
VP Finance and Strategic Planning Latin America, Francis M. Williamson
VP Colgate-France, Jean-Marc Navez
VP Colgate-Greater Asia, John Guiney
VP Hill's Pet Nutrition, Debra Nichols
VP; General Manager Colgate-West Andean Region/Latin America, Luis Gutierrez
VP Colgate-Europe, Roland Heincke
VP Treasury, Hans L. Pohlschroeder
VP Global Legal, Andrea Bernard
VP; General Manager Hawley and Hazel Taiwan, Louis Ruggiere
VP Hill's Pet Nutrition, Al Horning
VP Global Advertising, Jeff Salguero
VP; General Manager GABA International, Peter Brons-Poulsen
VP Global Finance, Philip (Phil) Shotts
President Global Oral Care Consumer Insights and Advertising, Nigel B. Burton
VP Global Oral Care, Marsha Butler
President Colgate-Latin America, P. Justin Skala, age 52
VP Global Design and Packaging, Joan Pierce
VP Global Research and Development, Robert C. Pierce
VP Audit, Jay Cassidy
VP Global Human Resources, Martin J. Collins
VP Colgate-U.S., Michael Sload
VP Taxation, Hector I. Erezuma, age 67
VP Global Research and Development, Leo Laitem
VP Colgate-Greater Asia, Chester P.W. Fong
VP Global Legal, Beth McQuillan
VP; General Manager Global Personal Care, Maria Fernanda Mejia
VP Global Oral Care, Anthony R. Volpe
VP; General Manager Colgate-Central American Region, Peggy Gerichter
VP Global Supply Chain, Josue M. Munoz
VP Global Research and Development, David K. Wilcox
VP; Division General Counsel Colgate-Europe, Peter Graylin
VP and CIO, Thomas W. (Tom) Greene, age 45
VP and Deputy General Counsel Operations and South Pacific, Rosemary Nelson, age 64
VP Global Finance, Joseph M. Bertolini
VP; Division General Counsel Colgate-Latin America, Mauricio Boscan
VP Colgate-US, Stephen J. Conboy
VP; General Manager Colgate-Southern Africa, Bradley Farr
VP Corporate Communications, Jan Guifarro
VP Global Design and Packaging, William H. (Bill) Lunderman
VP Global Legal, Ellen Park
VP Global Research and Development and Supply Chain, Brent Peterson
VP; General Manager Colgate-Caribbean Region, Bernal Saborio
VP; General Manager Colgate-UK and Ireland, Scott Sherwood
VP Global Supply Chain, Rick Spann
President and CEO Hill's Pet Nutrition, Neil Thompson
VP Hill's Pet Nutrition, Scott Smith
VP Global Toothbrush Division, Neil Stout
VP Hill's Pet Nutrition, Wayne Carter
VP Colgate-Europe, Louis Mancinelli
VP Global Information Technology, Michael (Mike) Crowe

VP; General Manager Colgate-South Asia Region, Mukul Deoras
VP Global Research and Development, William (Bill) DeVizio
VP Colgate-North America, Catherine Dillane
VP; General Manager Colgate-Southern Cone/Latin America, Jean-Luc Fischer
VP Global Human Resources, Laura Flavin
VP Colgate-Latin America, Diana Geofroy
VP; General Manager Colgate-Central European Region, Wojciech Krol
VP; General Manager Colgate-France, Andrea Lagioia
VP Colgate-Europe, Cesar Melo
VP Global Research and Development, Andrea Motyka
VP; General Manager Hill's Pet Nutrition-Europe, Francisco Munoz Ramirez
VP Global Research and Development, Terrell Partee
VP Deputy General Counsel and Assistant Secretary, Katherine Hargrove Ramundo
VP Global Research and Development, Mary Beth Robles
VP Global Research and Development, Andreas Somers
VP Global Supply Chain, Linda Topping
VP and CTO, Patricia Verduin, age 52
VP; General Manager Global Home Care, Juan Pablo Zamorano
VP Global Supply Chain, Manuel Arrese
VP Global Information Technology, James (Jim) Capraro
VP Global Legal, Nina Huffman, age 58
VP International Tax, Scott Cain
VP Global Research and Development, Constantina Christopoulou
VP and Corporate Controller, Victoria L. Dolan, age 52
VP Ethics and Compliance, Bob Holland
VP Global Research and Development, Raj Kohli
President Hill's Pet Nutrition U.S., Kostas Kontopanos
VP; General Manager Colgate-Iberia, John Kooyman
VP Colgate-Greater Asia, Kim Seng Lim
VP Hill's Pet Nutrition, Diane Loiselle
VP; General Manager Colgate-Nordic Group, Massimo Poli
VP Global Finance, Robert (Bob) Russo
VP Colgate-North America, Paul Trueax
VP; General Manager Colgate-Philippines, Lucie Claire Vincent
VP; General Manager Colgate-China, Lefteris Vitalis
VP; General Manager Colgate-Venezuela, Ruben Young
VP Colgate-Africa/Middle East, Robert Tatera
VP Colgate-Europe, Alain Semeneri
VP; General Manager Colgate-Italy, Vinod Nambiar
VP Professional Marketing, Moira Loten
VP Colgate-Africa and Middle East, Traci Hughes-Velez
VP Colgate-Europe, Julian Gutierrez
VP; General Manager Colgate-Global Export, Burc Cankat
VP Global Research and Development, Daniel Bagley
VP Global Information Technology, Marianne DeLorenzo
VP; General Manager Colgate-U.S., Philip Durocher
VP Global Legal, Nadine Flynn
VP Colgate-Greater Asia, Raymond Ho
VP Colgate-Latin America, Pablo Mascolo
VP Global Information Technology, Paul McGarry
VP Global Media, Nadine Karp McHugh
VP Global Toothbrush Division, Tom Mintel
VP Global Supply Chain, Pascal Montilus
VP Hill's Pet Nutrition, Ed Oblon
VP and Corporate Treasurer, Elaine C. Paik, age 47
VP Global Marketing, Spencer Pingel
VP Hill's Pet Nutrition, Ann Tracy
VP; Division General Counsel Colgate-Greater Asia, Jerome Webb
VP; Division General Counsel Colgate-North America, Cliff Wilkins
VP Colgate-Latin American, Alberico Zenzola
Director, Stephen I. (Steve) Sadove, age 61
Director, J. Pedro Reinhard, age 66
Director, Richard J. Kogan, age 70
Director, John T. Cahill, age 55
Director, Ellen M. Hancock, age 68
Director, Delano E. Lewis, age 73
Director, Joseph (Joe) Jimenez Jr., age 52
Director, Helene D. Gayle, age 56
Auditors: PricewaterhouseCoopersLLP

LOCATIONS

HQ: Colgate-Palmolive Co.
300 Park Avenue, New York, NY 10022
Phone: 212 310-2000 **Fax:** 212 310-3284
Web: www.colgate.com

2011 Sales

	$ mil.	% of total
Oral personal & home care		
Latin America	4,778	28
Europe/South Pacific	3,508	21
Greater Asia/Africa	3,281	20
North America	2,995	18
Pet nutrition	2,172	13
Total	**16,734**	**100**

PRODUCTS/OPERATIONS

2011 Sales

	$ mil.	% of total
Oral personal & home care	14,562	87
Pet nutrition	2,172	13
Total	**16,734**	**100**

Selected Brands

Home Care
- Ajax
- Fabuloso
- Murphy
- Palmolive
- Suavitel

Oral Care
- Colgate

Personal Care
- Afta
- Irish Spring
- Sanex
- Skin Bracer
- Softsoap
- Speed Stick

Pet Nutrition
- Prescription Diet
- Science Diet

COMPETITORS

Amden
Avon
Church & Dwight
Clorox
Dr. Fresh
GlaxoSmithKline
Hain Celestial
Henkel
Johnson & Johnson
Kiss My Face
L' Oreal USA
Mars Petcare
McBride plc
Nestle
Nu Skin
Philips Oral
Procter & Gamble
Reckitt Benckiser
S.C. Johnson
Sun Products
Unilever

HISTORICAL FINANCIALS

Company Type: Public

Income Statement FYE: December 31

	REVENUE ($ mil.)	NET INCOME ($ mil.)	NET PROFIT MARGIN	EMPLOYEES
12/11	16,734	2,431	14.5%	38,600
12/10	15,564	2,203	14.2%	39,200
12/09	15,327	2,291	14.9%	38,100
12/08	15,329	1,957	12.8%	36,600
12/07	13,789	1,737	12.6%	36,000
Annual Growth	5.0%	8.8%	—	1.8%

2011 Year-End Financials

Debt ratio: 37.80%
Return on equity: 102.36%
Cash ($ mil.): 878
Current ratio: 118.46
Long-term debt ($ mil.): 4,430
No. of shares (mil.): 480
Dividends
Yield: —
Payout: 45.95%
Market value ($ mil.): 44,349

	STOCK PRICE ($) FY Close	P/E High	P/E Low	PER SHARE ($) Earnings	Dividends	Book Value
12/11	92.39	19	15	4.94	0.00	4.95
12/10	80.37	19	17	4.31	2.03	5.41
12/09	82.15	19	12	4.37	1.72	6.31
12/08	68.54	21	14	3.66	1.56	3.83
12/07	77.96	24	19	3.20	1.40	4.49
Annual Growth	4.3%	—	—	11.5%	—	2.5%

Columbia Banking System, Inc.

Columbia Banking System is the holding company for Columbia State Bank (also known as Columbia Bank). The bank has about 100 branches in Washington from Puget Sound to the timber country in the southwestern part of the state as well as in northern Oregon where it also operates as Bank of Astoria. Targeting retail and business customers the bank offers standard retail services such as checking and savings accounts CDs IRAs credit cards loans and mortgages. Commercial business and real estate loans make up more than 80% of the company's loan portfolio. Columbia agreed in late 2012 to acquire West Coast Bancorp which operates nearly 60 bank branches in Oregon and Washington.

The bank's Columbia Private Banking division offers customized financial services for businesses and affluent families. Subsidiary CB Financial Services provides investment products through a pact with third-party provider PrimeVest.

Columbia Banking System has taken advantage of the rash of bank failures in recent years. It added more than 30 branches in 2010 when it acquired most of the deposits and assets of failed banks Columbia River Bank and American Marine Bank a week apart. In similar transactions the following year it acquired most of the operations of the failed institutions Summit Bank First Heritage Bank and Bank of Whitman. Those deals added more than a dozen branches in Washington.

The acquisitions most of which included loss-sharing agreements with the FDIC helped Columbia Banking System return to profitability in 2010 and contributed to a more than 40% increase in net income the following year (from nearly $26 million to $48 million).

EXECUTIVES

EVP and CFO Columbia Banking System and Columbia Bank, Gary R. Schminkey, age 54, $236,000 total compensation
President CEO and Director; President and CEO Columbia Bank, Melanie J. Dressel, age 59, $420,000 total compensation
Chairman, William T. Weyerhaeuser, age 68, $25,000 total compensation
SVP and Regional Manager Retail Administration Columbia Bank, Avery Johnson
SVP Commercial Lending Columbia Bank, Trent Jonas
SVP Commercial Lending Columbia Bank, Dwight Phillips
SVP Commercial Lending Columbia Bank, Ernie Smith
EVP and COO, Mark W. Nelson, age 60, $235,001 total compensation
VP Corporate Communications and Investor and Community Relations Columbia Bank, JoAnne Coy
SVP and Program Manager CB Financial Services Columbia Bank, Dean A. McSweeney
EVP and Director Human Resources, Kent L. Roberts, age 60, $180,000 total compensation
SVP and General Auditor Columbia Bank, Susan (Sue) Leonard
EVP and Chief Credit Officer, Andrew L. (Andy) McDonald, age 52, $195,001 total compensation
VP and Privacy Officer Columbia Bank, Ron Baker
SVP and Manager Operations Columbia Bank, Julie Tollkuehn
SVP and Manager Merchant Card Services Columbia Bank, Diane Wasalino
SVP and Manager Loan Operations Columbia Bank, Ben Shandrow
SVP and Regional Manager Retail Administration Columbia Bank, Wayne Mannie
SVP and Regional Manager Retail Administration Columbia Bank, Dan Patjens
EVP and CFO, Clint Stein
SVP and Manager Builder Banking Columbia Bank, Kevin Conklin
Business Development Officer Columbia Bank, Matt Ralston
SVP and Manager Cash Management Columbia Bank, Janice Phillips
SVP Commercial Lending Columbia Bank, Chris Gruenfeld
SVP Commercial Lending Columbia Bank, Nina Maurer
SVP Community Financial Resources SBA Loans Columbia Bank, Craig Chance
Secretary, Cathleen L. Dent
SVP and CIO Columbia Bank, Eric Eid
President CEO and Director; President and CEO Columbia Bank, Melanie J. Dressel, age 59
Director, John P. Folsom, age 67
Director, Thomas M. Hulbert, age 65
Director, Thomas L. Matson Sr., age 74
Director, Donald H. Rodman, age 73
Director, James M. Will, age 65
Director, Daniel C. (Dan) Regis, age 72
Director, Frederick M. (Fred) Goldberg, age 72
Auditors: Deloitte&ToucheLLP

LOCATIONS

HQ: Columbia Banking System Inc.
1301 A St. Ste. 800, Tacoma WA 98402
Phone: 253-305-1900 **Fax:** 253-305-0317
Web: www.columbiabank.com

PRODUCTS/OPERATIONS

2011 Sales

	$ mil.	% of total
Interest		
Loans	218	75
Securities	32	11
Other	0	-
Noninterest		
Service charges & other fees	26	9
Merchant services fees	7	3
Change in FDIC loss-sharing asset	(49.5)	-
Other	6	2
Total	**242**	**100**

COMPETITORS

Bank of America
Banner Corp
BECU
Heritage Financial
HomeStreet
JPMorgan Chase
KeyCorp
Sterling Financial (WA)
U.S. Bancorp
Washington Federal
Wells Fargo

HISTORICAL FINANCIALS

Company Type: Public

Income Statement FYE: December 31

	ASSETS ($ mil.)	NET INCOME ($ mil.)	INCOME AS % OF ASSETS	EMPLOYEES
12/11	4,785	48	1.0%	1,256
12/10	4,256	30	0.7%	1,092
12/09	3,200	(3)	—	715
12/08	3,097	5	0.2%	735
12/07	3,178	32	1.0%	775
Annual Growth	10.8%	10.4%	—	12.8%

2011 Year-End Financials

Debt ratio: 2.49%
Return on equity: 6.33%
Cash ($ mil.): 294
Current ratio: —
Long-term debt ($ mil.): 119
No. of shares (mil.): 39
Dividends
Yield: —
Payout: 22.31%
Market value ($ mil.): 761

	STOCK PRICE ($) FY Close	P/E High	P/E Low	PER SHARE ($) Earnings	Dividends	Book Value
12/11	19.27	18	11	1.21	0.00	19.22
12/10	21.06	34	22	0.72	0.04	17.97
12/09	16.18	—	—	(0.38)	0.07	18.78
12/08	11.93	96	26	0.31	0.58	22.88
12/07	29.73	19	13	1.91	0.66	19.03
Annual Growth	(10.3%)	—	—	(10.8%)	—	0.2%

Comcast Corp

Commerce plus broadcasting equals Comcast. The company's core cable division is the largest pay-TV provider in the US (ahead of satellite provider DIRECTV and direct competitor Time Warner Cable) with more than 22 million video subscribers. Comcast derives the bulk of its revenue from its cable services offered in 39 states and the District of Columbia. It has about 18 million broadband Internet subscribers while its XFINITY computer telephony service has more than 9 million customers. Comcast also has cable programming interests such as E! G4 and The Golf Channel and sells time to advertisers. In 2011 the company formed a joint venture with General Electric that gave it a 51% interest in NBCUniversal (NBCU).

HISTORY

In 1963 Ralph Roberts Daniel Aaron and Julian Brodsky bought American Cable Systems in Tupelo Mississippi. The company soon expanded throughout the state. In 1969 the company got a new name: Comcast combining "communications" and "broadcast." Two years later Comcast acquired franchises in western Pennsylvania and when it went public in 1972 it moved to Philadelphia.

Comcast bought up local operations nationwide through the early 1980s and gained its first foreign cable franchise in 1983 in London (it sold its affiliate there to NTL —now Virgin Media —in 1998). It took a 26% stake in the large Group W Cable in 1986. Roberts also lent financial support that year to a fledgling home-shopping channel called QVC —for "quality value and convenience."

A big step into telecommunications came in 1988 when Comcast bought American Cellular Network with Delaware and New Jersey franchises. Two years later Roberts' son Brian —who had trained as a cable installer during a summer away from college —became Comcast's president.

In 1992 Comcast bought Metromedia's Philadelphia-area cellular operations and began investing in fiber-optic and wireless phone companies. By then the company was a major QVC shareholder. With an eye toward Comcast's programming needs Brian persuaded FOX network head Barry Diller to become QVC's chairman. But when Diller tried to use QVC to take over CBS Comcast bought control of QVC in 1994 to quash the bid which went against cross-ownership bans. To pay for QVC Comcast had to sell its 20% stake in cable firm Heritage Communications in 1995. Diller left the company to oversee for a time InterActiveCorp parent of QVC's archrival HSN). Also in 1995 Comcast funded former Disney executive Richard Frank to launch the C3 (Comcast Content and Communication) programming company.

Comcast TCI and Cox sold Teleport their local phone venture to AT&T in 1998 but Comcast turned around and bought long-distance service provider GlobalCom (now Comcast Telecommunications). That year Sprint Spectrum —Comcast's PCS venture with Sprint Cox and the former TCI —was rolled into Sprint PCS under Sprint's management.

Comcast sold its cellular operations to SBC Communications for $1.7 billion in 1999. The company also agreed to acquire rival MediaOne in 1999 but soon after the $54 billion deal was struck AT&T weighed in with a $58 billion offer. Comcast dropped its bid for MediaOne when AT&T offered to sell Comcast 2 million cable subscribers. More than a million of those subscribers came from Pennsylvania cable operator Lenfest Communications which Comcast bought in 2000 from AT&T and the Lenfest family in a $7 billion deal. Also that year Comcast took full ownership of Jones Intercable in which it already had a controlling interest.

In 2001 Comcast completed a systems swap with Adelphia Communications and completed the $2.75 billion purchase of systems in six states from AT&T. Also that year Comcast offered to buy the rest of AT&T's cable operations for $44.5 billion in stock and $13.5 billion in assumed debt. AT&T's board rejected the offer but left the door open for another bid. That December after it had heard proposals from Time Warner and Cox AT&T agreed to sell its cable unit to Comcast for

$47 billion in stock and $25 billion in assumed debt. C. Michael Armstrong came from AT&T to Comcast and was named chairman. Challenged with the task of absorbing AT&T Broadband's assets Comcast struggled to meet its numbers. About 18 months after the AT&T Broadband deal Comcast had reduced its headcount by 10000 people.

Also in 2001 Comcast sold its 57% stake in QVC to Liberty Media for about $7.7 billion. Prior to the sale the online retailer had been responsible for bringing in a third of Comcast's sales.

When Armstrong stepped down as chairman in 2004 president and CEO Brian Roberts was named successor. The same year Comcast made an offer to buy The Walt Disney Company but withdrew it after getting a chilly reception. The following year the company joined a consortium that bought film studio MGM.

Comcast acquired TechTV for about $300 million which it merged with its video game-centric G4 network. Comcast's majority-owned subsidiary G4 Media operates the new network now called G4 - Video Game Television. Other Comcast interests include a two-thirds stake in Comcast Spectacor a venture that owns the Flyers the 76ers and arena management firm Global Spectrum among others.

Even though Comcast's 2004 bid for The Walt Disney Company didn't work out the two companies have forged a sizeable distribution deal that brought Disney-owned content to Comcast's broadband Internet subscribers. In 2006 Comcast bought Disney's nearly 40% stake in E! Entertainment Television in a deal valued at nearly $1.25 billion (Comcast already owned 60%). The deal included a multiyear distribution agreement that allows Comcast to offer Disney programming through its video-on-demand service.

Comcast had owned a 21% stake in rival Time Warner Cable (TWC) which made for strange bedfellows but the companies managed to unwind their relationship in mid-2006. The two rivals purchased all of troubled Adelphia Communications' cable television assets. Adelphia shareholders received about $9 billion from TWC and $3.5 billion in cash from Comcast which also contributed its TWC stake to the deal. Comcast no longer owns any part of TWC.

In 2006 the company expanded broadband cable operations through the acquisition of Susquehanna Communications which has operations primarily in Maine Mississippi New York and Pennsylvania (Comcast previously held a 30% stake in the company). Operating as SusCom the firm has 230000 basic cable subscribers along with 86000 broadband Internet customers and had recently introduced cable-based phone services.

In 2007 the company purchased Patriot Media & Communications a small New Jersey cable operator for about $483 million. Also that year in a bid to boost its video entertainment holdings Comcast purchased movie tickets Web site Fandango. Meanwhile the company expanded its stable of regional sports channels with the purchase of two networks from Cablevision Systems. The $570 million deal included a 60% stake in FSN Bay Area and gave Comcast full ownership of FSN New England which became part of Comcast SportsNet.

Comcast made an investment in its cable TV subscription business with the 2008 purchase of Insight Midwest for about $1.3 billion. The deal added about 700000 subscribers in Illinois and Indiana. Other purchases included the acquisition of additional interest in cable channel Comcast SportsNet Bay Area and of the remaining interest in Los Angeles-based cable and satellite channel G4 that it did not already own.

In 2010 MGM filed for Chapter 11 bankruptcy protection. The prepackaged plan of reorganization wiped out the ownership interests of the consortium (which included Comcast) that bought the film studio in 2005.

EXECUTIVES

EVP; President and CEO NBC Universal, Stephen B. (Steve) Burke, age 53, $2,329,543 total compensation
Chairman President and CEO, Brian L. Roberts, age 52, $2,908,483 total compensation
Chairman Emeritus, Ralph J. Roberts, age 92, $332,846 total compensation
SVP Customer Care Comcast Cable Central Division, Kimberly C. Edmunds
SVP Chief Accounting Officer and Controller, Lawrence J. Salva, age 55
SVP Investor Relations, Marlene S. Dooner
EVP, David L. Cohen, age 57, $1,389,455 total compensation
SVP General Counsel and Secretary, Arthur R. Block, age 56, $846,036 total compensation
SVP Strategic Planning, Mark A. Coblitz
SVP Corporate Development, Robert S. Pick, age 55
SVP; President Comcast Interactive Media, Amy L. Banse
VP Administration, Karen Dougherty Buchholz
VP Financial Operations, Joseph F. DiTrolio
SVP and Treasurer, William E. (Bill) Dordelman
EVP; President Comcast Cable Communications, Neil Smit, age 52
VP Financial Reporting, Leonard J. Gatti
CFO, Michael J. Angelakis, age 47, $1,747,157 total compensation
Chief Communications Officer, D'Arcy F. Rudnay
VP Integrated Talent Management, Beth Arnholt
VP Community Investment; EVP Comcast Foundation, Charisse R. Lillie, age 60
Senior Director Corporate Communications Customer Care and Network & Operations, Jenni Moyer
VP Public Relations Comcast-Spectacor, Ike Richman
VP Corporate Development, Gregg M. Goldstein
VP and Senior Deputy General Counsel, Marc A. Rockford
VP Government Communications, Sena Fitzmaurice
Director Corporate Communications - Video Communications, Ellen Mellody
SVP Federal Government Affairs, Melissa Maxfield
SVP Regulatory and State Legislative Affairs, Kathryn A. (Kathy) Zachem
SVP Strategic and Financial Planning, Robert S. Victor
VP Corporate Communications, Jennifer Khoury Newcomb
SVP Taxation, Kristine A. Dankenbrink
Director Corporate Communications Digital Communications, Kate Noel
Director Corporate Communications Customer Care and Network and Operations, Jorge Alberni
Senior Director Corporate Communications - Video Communications, Alana Davis
Senior Director Corporate Communications - Online and Voice Services, Charlie Douglas
Senior Director Corporate Communications - Financal & Diversity Communications, John Demming
Director Communications Comcast Spotlight - Advertising Sales, Chris Ellis
SVP Internal Audit, Cynthia K. Hook
President Comcast/NBCUniversal, Kyle E. McSlarrow
Vice President Chief Compliance Officer, Jennifer J. Heller
VP Corporate Development, Joseph P. McGinley
VP Federal Tax, Kevin P. O'Connor
Executive Director Corporate Communications Consumer Communications, Peter Dobrow
Senior Manager Corporate Communications - Online & Voice Services, Jamila Patton
Executive Director Corporate Communications Production & Internal Communications, Kirsten Siegel
Exective Director External Affairs, Johnnie Giles
EVP and General Manager Data and Communications Comcast Cable, Catherine (Cathy) Avgiris
SVP Small- and Mid-Sized Business Operations Comcast Business Services, Tracy Pitcher
Vice President, Lynn R. Charytan
Vice President Federal Tax, Kevin P. OConnor
Vice President Administration Comcast Corporation, Karen Buchholz
Vice President Global Public Policy, Rebecca Arbogast
Vice President Corporate Communications, Jennifer Newcomb
Director, Gerald L. Hassell, age 60
Director, Edward D. (Ed) Breen Jr., age 56
Chairman President and CEO, Brian L. Roberts, age 52
Chairman Emeritus, Ralph J. Roberts, age 92
Director, Judith (Judy) Rodin, age 67
Director, Jeffrey A. (Jeff) Honickman, age 55
Director, Kenneth J. (Ken) Bacon, age 57
Director, Joseph J. Collins, age 67
Director, Sheldon M. Bonovitz, age 74
Director, J. Michael Cook, age 69
Director, S. Decker Anstrom, age 61
Director, Eduardo G. Mestre, age 63
Independent Director, Johnathan Rodgers
Auditors: Deloitte&ToucheLLP

LOCATIONS

HQ: Comcast Corporation
1 Comcast Center, Philadelphia PA 19103-2838
Phone: 215-286-1700 **Fax:** 773-866-3095
Web: www.cchgroup.com

PRODUCTS/OPERATIONS

2011 Sales

	$ mil.	% of total
Cable Communicat		
Residential		
Video	19,625	34
High-speed internet	8,735	15
Voice	3,503	6
Advertising	2,005	3
Business services	1,791	3
Other	1,567	3
NBCUniversal		
Cable networks		
Distribution	4,210	7
Advertising	3,189	6
Other	709	1
Broadcast television		
Advertising	3,941	7
Content licensing	1,509	3
Other	485	1
Filmed entertainm		
Home entertainment	1,559	3
Content licensing	1,234	2
Theatrical	983	2
Other	463	1
Theme parks	1,874	3
Headquarters other and eliminations	(896)	-
Adjustments	(644)	-
Total	**55,842**	**100**

Cable Networks
Bravo
Chiller
Cloo (formerly Sleuth)
CNBC

CNBC World
E!
G4
Golf Channel
MSNBC
NBC Sports Network (formerly VERSUS)
Oxygen
Style
Syfy
Universal HD
USA Network

COMPETITORS

AT&T	ITC^DeltaCom
Blockbuster	Liberty Interactive
Cablevision Systems	Netflix
Charter Communications	News Corp.
Cox Communications	RCN Corporation
DIRECTV	Time Warner Cable
DISH Network	ValueVision Media
Disney	Verizon
EarthLink	Viacom
Insight Communications	Xanadoo

HISTORICAL FINANCIALS

Company Type: Public

Income Statement FYE: December 31

	REVENUE ($ mil.)	NET INCOME ($ mil.)	NET PROFIT MARGIN	EMPLOYEES
12/11	55,842	4,160	7.4%	126,000
12/10	37,937	3,635	9.6%	102,000
12/09	35,756	3,638	10.2%	107,000
12/08	34,256	2,547	7.4%	100,000
12/07	30,895	2,587	8.4%	100,000
Annual Growth	15.9%	12.6%	—	5.9%

2011 Year-End Financials

Debt ratio: 24.91%—
Return on equity: 8.80%
Cash ($ mil.): 1,620
Current ratio: 64.75
Long-term debt ($ mil.): 37,942
Dividends
Yield: —
Payout: 36.30%
Market value ($ mil.): —

	STOCK PRICE ($) FY Close	P/E High/Low	PER SHARE ($) Earnings	Dividends	Book Value
12/11	23.71	18 13	1.50	0.00	17.47
12/10	21.97	17 12	1.29	0.38	15.97
12/09	16.86	14 9	1.26	0.27	15.06
12/08	16.88	26 15	0.86	0.19	14.04
12/07	18.26	54 21	0.83	0.00	13.73
Annual Growth	6.7%	— —	15.9%	—	6.2%

Comerica, Inc.

If you have a cosigner Comerica will be your copilot. The holding company owns Comerica Bank which has more than 500 branches in about a dozen states across the US; Arizona California Florida Michigan and Texas are its primary markets. The company is organized into three main segments. The Business Bank division is the largest offering loans deposits and capital markets products to middle-market large corporate and government clients. The Retail Bank serves small businesses and consumers while the Wealth and Institutional Management arm provides private banking investment management financial advisory investment banking brokerage insurance and retirement services.

In 2011 the company acquired Sterling Bancshares to strengthen its franchise in Texas. The deal which carried a price tag in excess of $1 billion added nearly 60 branches mainly in the Dallas/Fort-Worth Houston and San Antonio metropolitan areas. Comerica is also growing by opening about 10 new bank branches a year.

The bank has long been a leading commercial lender in the US and more than half of the company's assets are wrapped up in commercial real estate and operating loans. However as its core small and mid-market clientele suffered during the economic downturn so did Comerica which saw both its revenue and income decline in 2008 and 2009. Its revenue was down in 2010 too but the company returned to profitability that year thanks in part to fewer charged-off loans. Comerica's net income increased again in 2011 as credit quality continued to improve.

The company's growth initiatives include increasing its lending to the energy technology life sciences and mortgage banking sectors. The company hopes to leverage its established business banking relationships to cross-sell more financial products. It is also introducing new retail banking technology and courting higher-net-worth clients in its wealth management segment.

HISTORY

Comerica traces its history to 1849 when Michigan governor Epaphroditus Ransom tapped Elon Farnsworth to found the Detroit Savings Fund Institute. At that time Detroit was a major transit point for shipping between Lakes Huron and Erie as well as between the US and Canada. The bank grew with the town and in 1871 became Detroit Savings Bank.

By 1899 Detroit was one of the top 10 US manufacturing centers and thanks to a group of local tinkerers and mechanics that included Henry Ford was on the brink of even greater growth. Detroit Savings grew also fueled by the deposits of workers whom Ford paid up to $5 a day. Detroit Savings was not however the beneficiary of significant business with the auto makers; for corporate banking they turned first to eastern banks and then to large local banks in which they had an interest.

Detroit boomed during the 1920s as America went car-crazy but after the 1929 crash Detroiters defaulted on mortgages by the thousands. By 1933 Michigan's banks were in such disarray that the governor shut them down three weeks prior to the federal bank holiday. Detroit Savings was one of only four Detroit banks to reopen. None of the major banks associated with auto companies survived.

A few months later Manufacturers National Bank backed by a group of investors that included Edsel Ford (Henry's son) was founded. Although its start was rocky Manufacturers National was on firm footing by 1936; around the same time Detroit Savings Bank renamed itself the Detroit Bank to appeal to a more commercial clientele.

WWII and the postwar boom put Detroit back in gear. In the 1950s and 1960s both banks thrived. In the 1970s statewide branching was permitted and both banks formed holding companies (DETROITBANK Corp. and Manufacturers National Corp.) and expanded throughout Michigan. As they grew they added services; when Detroit's economy was hit by the oil shocks of the 1970s these diversifications helped them through the lean years.

DETROITBANK opened a trust operation in Florida in 1982 to maintain its relationship with retired customers and renamed itself Comerica to be less area-specific. Manufacturers National also began operating in Florida (1983) and made acquisitions in the Chicago area (1987). Comerica went farther afield buying banks in Texas (1988) and California (1991).

Following the national consolidation trend in 1992 Comerica and Manufacturers National merged (retaining the Comerica name) but did not fully integrate until 1994 when the new entity began making more acquisitions. To increase sales and develop its consumer business the company reorganized in 1996. It sold its Illinois bank and its Michigan customs brokerage business and acquired Fairlane Associates to expand its property/casualty insurance line.

As part of its strategy to have operations in all three NAFTA countries Comerica opened a bank in Mexico in 1997 and one in Canada in 1998. That year it dropped $66 million for the naming rights to the Detroit Tigers' baseball stadium which opened as Comerica Park in 2000. It also started a Web-based payment system for its international trade business.

To fortify its business lending operations in California Comerica bought Imperial Bancorp in 2001. At the beginning of 2002 chairman Eugene Miller handed the CEO reins to Ralph Babb who had been CFO. Later that year Babb became chairman as well.

In 2009 Comerica sold its institutional retirement plan recordkeeping operations which served some 250 retirement plans to Wells Fargo. The company did not consider the business as part of its core operations.

EXECUTIVES

EVP National Business Finance, Ronald P. Marcinelli
EVP; President Comerica Bank Western Market, J. Michael Fulton, age 62, $390,000 total compensation
Chairman President and CEO Comerica Incorporated and Comerica Bank, Ralph W. Babb Jr., age 63, $985,000 total compensation
EVP Governance Regulatory Relations and Legal Affairs and Corporate Secretary Comerica Incorporated and Comerica Bank, Jon W. Bilstrom, age 66
SVP; President and CEO Comerica Securities and Comerica Insurance, Ross E. Rogers, age 63
EVP and CFO Comerica Incorporated and Comerica Bank, Elizabeth S. Acton, age 60, $512,500 total compensation
EVP Finance Comerica Incorporated and Comerica Bank, Robert D. (Bob) McDermott, age 54
EVP and Director National Retail Bank Comerica Incorporated and Comerica Bank, Dana A. Drago, age 54
President World Asset Management Comerica Bank, Todd B. Johnson
SVP Anti-Money Laundering Fraud Prevention and Investigative Services, Susan R. Joseph
Vice Chairman Comerica Incorporated and The Business Bank Comerica Bank, Lars C. Anderson, age 51
EVP and Chief Credit Officer Comerica Incorporated and Comerica Bank, John M. Killian, age 59
SVP Asset Quality Review, Edward T. Gwilt
EVP; President Michigan Market Comerica Bank, Thomas D. Ogden, age 63
EVP Corporate Planning Development and Risk Management and Interim Treasurer; EVP Comerica Bank, Michael H. Michalak, age 54

President Comerica Bank Florida, Randy B. Nobles
SVP Business Affairs, Linda D. Forte
SVP and Chief Economist, Dana Johnson, age 62
Managing Director and Principal Officer Canada, John H. Tan
National Director Small Business Banking, Margaret M. (Peggy) Bradshaw
SVP Corporate Marketing and Corporate Communications, Jim H. Weber
EVP and CIO, Paul R. Obermeyer
EVP and General Auditor Comerica Incorporated and Comerica Bank, David E. Duprey, age 54
SVP; Detroit Regional Manager Wealth and Institutional Management, Eileen M. Ashley
SVP Corporate Credit Policy, Curt Brown
SVP; Manager Comerica Bank Central and West Michigan Banking Centers, Robert C. Hollander
SVP and Regional Manager Western Wayne Southeast Michigan Comerica Bank, Eddie J. Gates
First VP and Regional Manager Southfield Northwest Southeast Michigan Comerica Bank, Elizabeth J. Correa
VP; National Director Platform Sales Comerica Securities, John F. Mollo
EVP Middle Market Midwest Comerica Bank, David B. (Dave) Marvin
VP Hispanic Business Affairs, Monica Martinez
SVP and Director National Sales and Marketing Wealth & Institutional Management, Michael C. Wison
Group Business Manager Private Fiduciary Services, Robert Sajdak
VP and Regional Sales Manager Financial Institutions Group Comerica Bank, Jay Barker
Managing Director Corporate Investment Banking, Anthony Caudle
SVP Comerica Bank Mexico, Josef Koberl
VP Corproate Communications, Wayne J. Mielke
SVP; Retail Market Manager Comerica Florida, Charles H. Tashjian
SVP Corporate Sustainability Program, Richard J. Plewa
EVP Middle Market Banking Northern California, Judy Love
Vice Chairman The Retail Bank and Wealth and Institutional Management, Curtis C. Farmer, age 49, $430,769 total compensation
SVP and Manager Executive Administration and National Communications Director, Wendy Walker
SVP and Regional Manager Retail Operations Arizona Comerica Bank, Bridget Cooney
EVP and Chief Credit Officer Arizona and California Credit Operations Comerica Bank, Peter Guilfoile
Financial Manager Florida Market Palm Beach Gardens Branch Comerica Bank, Anthony J. Losh
President Comerica Asset Management Group, David Skolnik
SVP and Chief Accounting Officer Comerica Incorporated and Comerica Bank, Muneera S. Carr, age 43
EVP Middle Market Banking Comerica Bank, Michael Ritchie
EVP and Chief Human Resources Officer Comerica Incorporated and Comerica Bank, Megan D. Burkhart, age 40
EVP; President Comerica Bank Texas Market, J. Patrick (Pat) Faubion, age 58
SVP and Chief Marketing Strategist Comerica Asset Management Group, Dennis A. Johnson
Investor Relations, Darlene Persons
Investor Relations, Tracy Fralick
Market President and Manager Small Business Banking Arizona, Craig Doyle
EVP Treasury Management Services Comerica Bank, Bridgit Chayt
Vice Chairman and Chief Financial Officer, Karen L. Parkhill, age 46
Executive Vice President - Finance, David Parks
Director, T. Kevin DeNicola, age 58
Director, Roger A. Cregg, age 55
Director, Robert S. Taubman, age 58
Director, Alfred A. Piergallini, age 65
Director, Richard G. (Rick) Lindner, age 57
Director, James F. (Jim) Cordes, age 71
Vice Chairman Comerica Incorporated and The Business Bank Comerica Bank, Lars C. Anderson, age 51
Director, Jacqueline P. (Jackie) Kane, age 60
Director, Reginald M. (Reggie) Turner Jr., age 52
Director, Nina G. Vaca, age 40
Independent Director, Ximena Humrichouse
Auditors: Ernst&YoungLLP

LOCATIONS

HQ: Comerica, Inc.
Comerica Bank Tower, 1717 Main Street, MC 6404, Dallas, TX 75201
Phone: 214 462-6831
Web: www.comerica.com

Selected Markets

Arizona
California
Colorado
Florida
Illinois
Michigan
Nevada
Ohio
Texas
Washington

PRODUCTS/OPERATIONS

2011 Sales

	$ mil.	% of total
Interest		
Loans including fees	1,564	60
Investment securities	233	9
Short-term investments	12	-
Noninterest		
Service charges on deposit accounts	208	8
Fiduciary income	151	6
Commercial lending fees	87	3
Letter of credit fees	73	3
Card fees	58	2
Foreign exchange	40	2
Other	175	7
Total	**2,601**	**100**

Selected Subsidiaries

Comerica Bank
Comerica Bank & Trust National Association
Comerica Capital Advisors Incorporated
Comerica Equities Incorporated
Comerica Financial Incorporated
Comerica Holdings Incorporated
Comerica Insurance Group Inc.
Comerica Insurance Services Inc.
Comerica International Corporation
Comerica Investment Services Inc.
Comerica Investments LLC
Comerica Leasing Corporation
Comerica Merchant Services Inc.
Comerica Securities Inc.
Wilson Kemp & Associates Inc.
World Asset Management Inc.

COMPETITORS

Bank of America
Citigroup
Cullen/Frost Bankers
Fifth Third
SunTrust
SVB Financial
TCF Financial
U.S. Bancorp
Huntington Bancshares
JPMorgan Chase
UnionBanCal
Wells Fargo

HISTORICAL FINANCIALS

Company Type: Public

Income Statement

FYE: December 31

	ASSETS ($ mil.)	NET INCOME ($ mil.)	INCOME AS % OF ASSETS	EMPLOYEES
12/11	61,008	393	0.6%	9,757
12/10	53,667	277	0.5%	9,365
12/09	59,249	17	0.0%	9,720
12/08	67,548	213	0.3%	10,639
12/07	62,331	686	1.1%	11,337
Annual Growth	(0.5%)	(13.0%)	—	(3.7%)

2011 Year-End Financials

Debt ratio: 8.10%
Return on equity: 5.72%
Cash ($ mil.): 3,556
Current ratio: —
Long-term debt ($ mil.): 4,944
No. of shares (mil.): 197
Dividends
Yield: —
Payout: 19.14%
Market value ($ mil.): 5,091

	STOCK PRICE ($) FY Close	P/E High	P/E Low	PER SHARE ($) Earnings	Dividends	Book Value
12/11	25.80	21	10	2.09	0.00	34.80
12/10	42.24	50	33	0.88	0.25	32.81
12/09	29.57	—	—	(0.79)	0.20	46.49
12/08	19.85	34	13	1.29	2.31	47.52
12/07	43.53	14	9	4.43	2.56	34.12
Annual Growth	(12.3%)	—	—	(17.1%)	—	0.5%

Commerce Bancshares, Inc.

C'mon to Commerce Bancshares if you're looking for the company that owns Commerce Bank which operates more than 350 locations in Missouri Kansas Illinois Oklahoma and Colorado. The bank focuses on retail and commercial banking services such as deposit accounts mortgages loans and credit cards. Commerce Bank also has a wealth management division that offers asset management trust private banking brokerage and estate planning services and manages proprietary mutual funds. In addition the company has subsidiaries devoted to insurance leasing and private equity investments.

Commerce Bancshares' loan portfolio is approximately split between business loans such commercial mortgages and operating loans and consumer loans like residential mortgages and home equity installment credit card and student loans. A majority of the bank's loans are made in the St. Louis and Kansas City markets. The company believes its presence in the Midwest has helped it to maintain relatively lower levels of loan losses compared to banks in other parts of the country. Reductions in provisions for loan losses contributed to increases in earnings in 2010 and 2011 (two of the most profitable years in the bank's history) and the company expects its credit quality to continue to improve.

Commerce Bancshares has traditionally entered new markets via acquisitions. In 2007 it moved into Oklahoma with the purchase of South Tulsa Financial and entered the Denver market with the acquisition of Colorado Commerce Bank. The company now considers those two cities to be core markets along with Kansas City and St. Louis. Commerce Bancshares has identified other metropolitan areas including Cincinnati and Nashville Tennessee for possible expansion.

EXECUTIVES

SVP; Director Operations and Information Services, Robert J. Rauscher, age 54
SVP; Director Community Bank Administration, Michael J. Petrie, age 55
EVP and CFO, Charles G. (Chuck) Kim, age 51, $345,023 total compensation
EVP Commercial Line of Business; President and COO Commerce Bank Kansas City Region, Kevin G. Barth, age 51, $345,023 total compensation
Controller, Jeffery D. Aberdeen, age 58
EVP Chief Credit Officer and Risk Manager, Robert C. Matthews Jr., age 64
Vice Chairman; Chairman and CEO Commerce Bank St. Louis, Seth M. Leadbeater, age 61, $345,023 total compensation
Vice Chairman; Vice Chairman Commerce Bank, Jonathan M. Kemper, age 58, $437,524 total compensation
Executive Vice President, Sara E. Foster, age 51
Chairman President and CEO; Chairman President and CEO Commerce Bank, David W. Kemper, age 61, $848,548 total compensation
EVP Trust Line of Business; President The Commerce Trust Company, V. Raymond (Ray) Stranghoener, age 60, $235,900 total compensation
Executive Vice President of Commerce Bancshares Inc & Commerce Bank; Chief Credit Officer, Daniel D. Callahan
Chief Operating Officer, John K. Handy
Auditor, B. Lynn Tankesley
VP Secretary and General Counsel, James L. Swarts
Vice President and Senior Financial Planner, Jason Imlay
Director, Earl H. (Trace) Devanny III, age 59
Director, W. Thomas Grant II, age 61
Vice Chairman; Chairman and CEO Commerce Bank St. Louis, Seth M. Leadbeater, age 61
Vice Chairman; Vice Chairman Commerce Bank, Jonathan M. Kemper, age 58
Director, Andrew C. (Andy) Taylor, age 64
Director, Todd R. Schnuck, age 53
Director, Benjamin F. Rassieur III, age 57
Director, Terry O. Meek, age 68
Director, John R. Capps, age 61
Director, James B. Hebenstreit, age 65
Director, Kimberly G. Walker, age 53
Director, Dan Simons, age 50
Auditors: KPMGLLP

LOCATIONS

HQ: Commerce Bancshares, Inc.
1000 Walnut, Kansas City, MO 64106
Phone: 816 234-2000 **Fax:** 816 234-2369
Web: www.commercebank.com

PRODUCTS/OPERATIONS

2011 Sales

	$ mil.	% of total
Interest		
Loans including fees	463	42
Investment securities	219	20
Other	15	1
Noninterest		
Bank card transaction fees	157	14
Trust fees	88	8
Deposit account charges & other fees	82	8
Bond trading	19	2
Investment securities gains net	10	1
Consumer brokerage services	10	1
Other	35	3
Total	**1,101**	**100**

Selected Subsidiaries

Capital for Business Inc.
CBI-Kansas Inc.
CFB Partners LLC
CFB Venture Fund L.P.
Clayton Financial Corp.
Clayton Holdings LLC
Clayton Realty Corp.
Commerce Bank National Association
Commerce Brokerage Services Inc.
Commerce Insurance Services Inc.
Commerce Investment Advisors Inc.
Commerce Mortgage Corp.
Illinois Financial LLC
Illinois Realty LLC
Tower Redevelopment Corporation

COMPETITORS

Bank of America
Bank of the West
BOK Financial
Capitol Federal Financial
Dickinson Financial
First Banks
First National of Nebraska
Great Western Bancorporation
INTRUST
U.S. Bancorp
UMB Financial
Wells Fargo

HISTORICAL FINANCIALS

Company Type: Public

Income Statement FYE: December 31

	ASSETS ($ mil.)	NET INCOME ($ mil.)	INCOME AS % OF ASSETS	EMPLOYEES
12/11	20,649	256	1.2%	4,860
12/10	18,502	221	1.2%	5,005
12/09	18,120	169	0.9%	5,239
12/08	17,532	188	1.1%	5,340
12/07	16,204	206	1.3%	5,190
Annual Growth	6.2%	5.5%	—	(1.6%)

2011 Year-End Financials

Debt ratio: 0.54%
Return on equity: 11.83%
Cash ($ mil.): 523
Current ratio: —
Long-term debt ($ mil.): 111
No. of shares (mil.): 93
Dividends
Yield: —
Payout: 32.62%
Market value ($ mil.): 3,565

	STOCK PRICE ($) FY Close	P/E High/Low	PER SHARE ($) Earnings	Dividends	Book Value
12/11	38.12	16 13	2.69	0.00	23.16
12/10	39.73	19 15	2.29	0.85	21.15
12/09	38.72	25 16	1.79	0.83	19.59
12/08	43.95	26 18	2.04	0.82	17.09
12/07	44.86	23 19	2.21	0.78	16.65
Annual Growth	(4.0%)	— —	5.0%	—	8.6%

Commercial Metals Co.

Man of Steel wanted: Commercial Metals (CMC) manufactures recycles and sells enough steel and metal to test even Superman. CMC operates via five segments: Americas Recycling its metal processing plants in the US Southwest shreds and pulverizes scrap for sale to steel mills. Americas Mills turn out reinforcing bar flats rounds fence post and other shapes. A fabrication arm shapes produces and treats steel bar and angles. International business (rolling and finishing mills recycling and fabrication plants) churn out reinforcing bar and mesh. CMC markets and distributes steel and copper products worldwide to construction energy and transportation markets; the US accounts for more than half of sales.

HISTORY

Russian immigrant Moses Feldman moved to Dallas in 1914 and founded scrap metal company American Iron & Metal the next year. In the 1920s Feldman suffered a heart attack and his son Jake helped out with the business. Low metal prices hurt the company during the Depression. In 1932 Jake formed a two-man brokerage firm Commercial Metals Company (CMC) which was combined as a partnership with his father's scrap metal operations. Moses Feldman died in 1937. CMC was incorporated in 1946 and began buying related businesses during the 1950s.

CMC was listed on the American Stock Exchange in 1960. It soon expanded geographically buying a stake in Texas steelmaker Structural Metals (1963). In 1965 it formed Commercial Metals Europa (the Netherlands) its first overseas subsidiary and Commonwealth Metal (New York). By 1966 CMC was one of the world's top three scrap metal companies. It bought copper tube manufacturer Howell Metals (Virginia) in 1968 the remainder of Structural Metals and major stakes in seven affiliated businesses. Over 10 years CMC opened trading offices around the world. Business continued to grow throughout the 1970s. The company added a small minimill in Arkansas (1971) and certain assets of General Export Iron and Metal in Texas (1976).

CMC began trading on the New York Stock Exchange in 1982. The next year the company bought Connors Steel (Alabama) its third minimill. By the end of 1984 CMC was operating 20 metal recycling plants from Texas to Florida.

The company modernized its minimills in the 1990s. CMC acquired small scrap-metal operations and Shepler's a concrete-related products business in 1994. Also that year CEO Stanley Rabin completed the $50 million purchase of Owen Steel (a South Carolina minimill) which expanded CMC's reach into the Mid-Atlantic and Southeast. The company wrapped up a $30 million capital improvement program at its Alabama minimill in 1995 –just in time to ride a strong steel market to record profits.

Although a correction in the steel and metals industry depressed prices in 1996 CMC achieved record sales and profits that fiscal year. However both dipped the next year with lower steel and scrap prices widely attributed to an influx of foreign imports. CMC strengthened its vertical integration in 1997 by acquiring Allegheny Heat Treating (heat treatment services to steel mills) and two auto salvage plants in Florida.

During 1998 CMC moved into the Midwest buying a metals recycling company in Missouri. It boosted global operations by purchasing a metals trading firm in Australia and entering a joint venture with Trinec a Czech Republic steel mill to sell steel products in Germany. The next year CMC completed construction of a rolling mill in South Carolina and renovations at an Alabama plant; both were expected to reduce production-related costs and increase efficiency to help counter slumping steel prices.

In 2000 CMC picked up three rebar fabricators –two in California (Fontana Steel and C&M Steel) and one in Florida (Suncoast Steel).

In late 2001 the company acquired Florida-based Allform a maker of concrete-related forms and supplies. The following year Commercial Metals started manufacturing its corrosion-resistant stainless steel-clad products in its facilities in South Carolina.

Marvin Selig founder and chairman of the company's steel group retired in 2002 after working for more than 50 years in the steel industry.

In 2003 CMC purchased a 71% stake in Poland-based Huta Zawiercie S.A. for approximately $50 million. CMC purchased the assets of J. L. Davidson Company a rebar fabricating operation based in California in 2004.

In 2006 the company acquired Tucson-based concrete products supplier Brost Forming Supply Inc. and almost all of the assets of Yonack Iron & Metal Co. and Metallic Resources Inc. Later that year the company bought Cherokee Supply a provider of tools and supplies for the construction oilfield and industrial sectors. The acquisition became part of CMC Construction Services division and operated under the CMC Cherokee name. Quick on the heels of the Cherokee deal came CMC's purchase of Concrete Formtek Services a renter of concrete forming and shoring equipment. Concrete Formtek Services was renamed CMC Formtek and became part of CMC Construction Services.

In 2007 CMC completed a slew of acquisitions too. CMC bought Concrete Equipment Supply which sells and rents concrete forming equipment. The business now operates as CMC Conesco. The deal was preceded by two acquisitions completed in one day: Economy Steel of Las Vegas renamed CMC Economy Steel and merged with Americas Fabrication and Distribution division and steel pipe maker Valjaonia Cijevi Sisak of Croatia renamed CMC Sisak. The latter purchase opened the door to customers in southeastern Europe a promising growth market.

Earlier in 2007 CMC bought Bouras Industries Inc. The $146 million transaction included four of Bouras' operating subsidiaries: United Steel Deck (steel decking) New Columbia Joist (steel joists) ABA Trucking Corporation (delivery services for United Steel Deck and New Columbia Joist) and Nicholas J. Bouras Inc. (sales marketing and engineering for the other three subsidiaries). The assets of Bouras Industries operated as CMC Joist and Deck part of CMC's Americas Fabrication and Distribution division. CMC agreed to sell its steel-joist manufacturing operations to Steel Dynamics in the fall of 2010.

In 2008 CMC reorganized its operations under two divisions CMC Americas and CMC International. Also that same year CMC acquired a group of companies –ABC Coating Company (of Texas and Colorado) Banner Rebar Toltec Steel Services and Rebar Trucking. The deal also scored a 50% stake in both ABC Coating of North Carolina and ABC Coating of Tennessee. All joined the CMC Americas Fabrication segment creating one of the largest fabricators of reinforcing bar as well as manufacturers of steel fence posts in the US.

EXECUTIVES

President CMC Cometals, Eliezer Skornicki
Chairman and CEO, Murray R. McClean, age 63, $654,231 total compensation
VP and Treasurer, Louis A. Federle, age 63
SVP and CFO, Barbara R. Smith, age 52
Director Public Relations, Debbie L. Okle
EVP and Division Manager Howell Metal, James K. Forkovitch
Director Marketing Strategy CMC Recycling, Robert J. Melendi
VP and Director Internal Audit, Manny Rosenfeld
President and CEO, Joseph (Joe) Alvarado, age 59
EVP; President CMC International, Hanns Zoellner, age 63, $443,302 total compensation
VP CMC Recycling, Brian Halloran
VP and Director Internal Audit, Leon K. Rusch, age 61
VP and Treasurer, Carey J. Dubois, age 52
President CMC Europe, Ludovit Gajdos
SVP Business Development and Business Processes, Devesh Sharma
SVP Human Resources and Organizational Development, James (Jim) Alleman
SVP Law Government Affairs and Global Compliance; General Counsel and Corporate Secretary, Ann J. Bruder
SVP; President CMC Americas, Tracy L. Porter
VP and CIO, Tracy Nolan
SVP and President CMC International, John C. Elmore
VP and Controller, Adam Hickey
Director, Richard B. (Rick) Kelson, age 65
Director, Robert R. Womack, age 74
Director, Rhys J. Best, age 65
Director, Anthony A. (Tony) Massaro, age 67
Director, Sarah E. Raiss, age 54
Director, Robert D. Neary, age 78
Director, Harold L. Adams, age 72
Director, J. David Smith, age 62
Director, Robert L. Guido, age 65
Auditors: Deloitte&ToucheLLP

LOCATIONS

HQ: Commercial Metals Co.
6565 N. MacArthur Blvd., Irving, TX 75039
Phone: 214 689-4300 **Fax:** 214 689-5886
Web: www.cmc.com

2012 Sales

US	4,674	60
Asia	1,018	13
Other regions	203	2

PRODUCTS/OPERATIONS

2012 Sales

Steel products	4,700	60
Nonferrous scrap	765	10
Construction materials	177	2
Other	101	1

Selected Services

Fabrication
Marketing and Distribution
Metals Recycling
Mill Products
Services
Heat Treating
Structural Engineering

COMPETITORS

AK Steel Holding Corporation
BHP Billiton
Blue Tee
Connell LP
David J. Joseph
Gerdau Ameristeel
Indel
Keywell
Metals USA
Mueller Industries
Roanoke Bar Division
Ryerson
Schnitzer Steel
Severstal North America
Simec
Steel Dynamics
Tube City IMS
United States Steel
Universal Forest Products
Nucor
OmniSource
Quanex Building Products
Worthington Industries

HISTORICAL FINANCIALS

Company Type: Public

Income Statement FYE: August 31

	REVENUE ($ mil.)	NET INCOME ($ mil.)	NET PROFIT MARGIN	EMPLOYEES
08/12	7,828	207	2.7%	9,860
08/11	7,918	(129)	—	11,422
08/10	6,306	(205)	—	11,558
08/09	6,793	20	0.3%	13,586
08/08	10,427	231	2.2%	15,276
Annual Growth	(6.9%)	(2.7%)	—	(10.4%)

2012 Year-End Financials

Debt ratio: 34.46%
Return on equity: 16.65%
Cash ($ mil.): 262
Current ratio: 248.56
Long-term debt ($ mil.): 1,157
No. of shares (mil.): 116
Dividends
Yield: 3.77%
Payout: 26.97%
Market value ($ mil.): 1,482

	STOCK PRICE ($) FY Close	P/E High	P/E Low	PER SHARE ($) Earnings	Dividends	Book Value
08/12	12.74	9	5	1.78	0.48	10.71
08/11	11.75	—	—	(1.13)	0.48	10.04
08/10	13.02	—	—	(1.81)	0.48	10.94
08/09	16.93	129	33	0.18	0.48	13.59
08/08	26.03	20	12	1.97	0.00	14.40
Annual Growth	(16.4%)	—	—	(2.5%)	—	(7.1%)

Community Bank System, Inc.

Community Bank System is right up front about what it is. The holding company owns Community Bank which operates about 180 branches across nearly 30 counties in upstate New York and five counties in northeastern Pennsylvania where it operates as First Liberty Bank and Trust. Focusing on small underserved towns the bank offers standard products and services such as checking and savings accounts certificates of deposit and loans and mortgages to consumer business and government clients. The bank's loan portfolio is divided more or less equally among business loans residential mortgages and consumer loans.

Community Bank System also owns subsidiaries that offer employee benefits administration (Benefit Plan Administrative Services) wealth management and brokerage (Community Investment Services) institutional and individual investment advisory (Nottingham Advisors) and insurance (CBNA Insurance Agency).

The company has grown mostly through acquisitions of smaller banks or branches in non-urban areas. The latest was its mid-2012 purchase of about 20 locations in upstate New York from HSBC. The deal which was made to satisfy antitrust concerns regarding First Niagara's purchase of 195 branches in New York from HSBC strengthens Community Bank Systems' geographic footprint. The company bought bank holding company The Wilber Corporation in 2011 adding about 20 locations in the Catskills Mountains region of central New York.

Community Bank System has also expanded its trust and benefits administration business through acquisitions including firms outside the bank's traditional market area in cities such as Houston Philadelphia and Pittsburgh. In 2011 it bought retirement plan administrator CAI Benefits which has offices in New York and Northern New Jersey.

Community Bank System enjoyed upticks in profitability in 2010 and 2011 (53% and 16% respectively) thanks to several factors including higher electronic banking revenue more favorable interest rate spreads and an increase in fees from benefit trust administration and consulting.

EXECUTIVES

Chairman, David C. Patterson, age 70
EVP and CFO, Scott A. Kingsley, age 47, $309,915 total compensation
President CEO and Director; President and CEO Community Bank, Mark E. Tryniski, age 51, $441,002 total compensation
EVP and Chief Banking Officer, Brian D. Donahue, age 56, $255,024 total compensation
SVP and Special Projects Director, Timothy J. (Tim) Baker, age 60
SVP and CTO, J. Michael Wilson, age 41
SVP and Chief Credit Officer, J. David Clark, age 58, $198,387 total compensation
SVP and Sales and Marketing Director, Harold M. (Harry) Wentworth, age 47
SVP and Chief Human Resources Director, Bernadette R. Barber, age 50
SVP and Chief Investment Officer, Joseph J. Lemchak, age 50
Executive Vice President and President - Pennsylvania Banking, Robert P. Matley, age 60
SVP and Retail Banking Administrator, Richard M. (Dick) Heidrick, age 53
SVP and Senior Commercial Lending Officer Northern New York, Nicholas S. (Nick) Russell, age 44
SVP and Chief Credit Administrator, Stephen G. Hardy, age 57
SVP and Retail Banking Manager, Claire F. LaGarry, age 62
EVP and General Counsel, George J. Getman, $294,231 total compensation
SVP and Chief Risk Officer, Paul J. Ward
Director, James A. (Jim) Gabriel, age 64
Director, Nicholas A. DiCerbo, age 65
Director, Paul M. Cantwell Jr., age 70
President CEO and Director; President and CEO Community Bank, Mark E. Tryniski, age 51
Director, Sally A. Steele, age 56
Director, Brian R. Ace, age 57
Director, James W. Gibson Jr.
Director, James A. Wilson
Independent Director, Alfred Whittet
Independent Director, Brian Wright
Independent Director, John Parente
Independent Director, John Whipple
Independent Director, Mark Bolus
Independent Director, Neil Fesette
Auditors: PricewaterhouseCoopersLLP

LOCATIONS

HQ: Community Bank System Inc.
5790 Widewaters Pkwy., DeWitt NY 13214-1883
Phone: 315-445-2282 **Fax:** 315-445-2997
Web: www.communitybankna.com

PRODUCTS/OPERATIONS

2011 Sales

	$ mil.	% of total
Interest		
Loans including fees	193	54
Taxable investments	55	15
Nontaxable investments	22	6
Noninterest		
Deposit service fees	42	12
Benefit trust administration consulting & actuarial fees	31	9
Wealth management	10	3
Other	4	1
Total	**360**	**100**

Selected Subsidiaries & Affiliates

Benefit Plans Administrative Services Inc.
Benefit Plans Administrative Services LLC
Brilie Corporation
CBNA Insurance Agency Inc.
CBNA Preferred Funding Corp.
CBNA Treasury Management Corporation
Community Bank N.A. (also dba First Liberty Bank & Trust)
Community Investment Services Inc.
First of Jermyn Realty Company
First Liberty Service Corporation
Flex Corporation
Hand Benefit & Trust Company
Hand Securities Inc.
Harbridge Consulting Group LLP
Nottingham Advisors Inc.
Town & Country Agency LLC
Western Catskill Realty Inc.

COMPETITORS

Alliance Financial
Arrow Financial
Bank of America
Canandaigua National
Chemung Financial
Elmira Savings Bank
Financial Institutions
First Niagara Financial
HSBC USA
JPMorgan Chase
KeyCorp
M&T Bank
NBT Bancorp
RBS Citizens Financial Group

HISTORICAL FINANCIALS

Company Type: Public

Income Statement FYE: December 31

	ASSETS ($ mil.)	NET INCOME ($ mil.)	INCOME AS % OF ASSETS	EMPLOYEES
12/11	6,488	73	1.1%	2,030
12/10	5,444	63	1.2%	1,627
12/09	5,402	41	0.8%	1,595
12/08	5,174	45	0.9%	1,615
12/07	4,697	42	0.9%	1,453
Annual Growth	8.4%	14.3%	—	8.7%

2011 Year-End Financials

Debt ratio: 12.80%
Return on equity: 9.44%
Cash ($ mil.): 324
Current ratio: —
Long-term debt ($ mil.): 830
No. of shares (mil.): 36
Dividends
Yield: —
Payout: 49.75%
Market value ($ mil.): 1,028

	STOCK PRICE ($) FY Close	P/E High	P/E Low	PER SHARE ($) Earnings	Dividends	Book Value
12/11	27.80	14	11	2.01	0.00	20.94
12/10	27.77	15	9	1.89	0.94	18.23
12/09	19.31	19	11	1.26	0.88	17.25
12/08	24.39	20	12	1.49	0.86	16.69
12/07	19.87	17	12	1.42	0.82	16.16
Annual Growth	8.8%	—	—	9.1%	—	6.7%

Community Health Systems, Inc.

Community Health Systems (CHS) isn't much of a city dweller. The hospital operator prefers small-town America owning or leasing about 140 hospitals mostly in rural areas or small cities in about 30 states. Its hospitals (which house roughly 20000 beds) typically act as the sole or primary acute health care provider in a service area and offer a variety of medical surgical and emergency services (though a handful are specialty centers). The hospitals generally have ancillary facilities including doctors' offices surgery centers and diagnostic imaging facilities as well as home health and hospice agencies. CHS' Quorum Health Resources subsidiary provides management services to non-affiliated hospitals.

Sales & Marketing

CHS receives about 40% of its revenues from Medicare and Medicaid reimbursements for patient services. Another 50% comes from commercial insurance companies with which it has managed care contracts and the rest is attributed to self-pay patients.

Financial Analysis

As it has expanded its network of facilities over the years CHS' revenues have likewise risen. The company reported a 5% increase in sales in 2011 to some $13.6 billion. It attributes its financial health to its targeted acquisitions strategy (focusing on urban markets) and its successful cost-control and facility integration efforts as well as improved returns from rate reimbursement and procurement programs. Profits have also steadily risen over the firm's history; however CHS experienced a 28% decrease in net income in 2011 as the company restructured some of its debt obligations and took goodwill impairment charges on some divested assets.

Strategy

You don't become one of the largest for-profit hospital operators in the nation without a pretty aggressive acquisition strategy and CHS certainly has that. CHS' modus operandi is to target hospitals in non-urban locations poised for growth. Because such areas have fewer people they generally have fewer hospitals which means less competition (both for patients and for managed care contracts). CHS typically purchases a number of small community hospitals each year though it also sometimes conducts larger acquisitions of hospital operating groups.

In addition to adding new hospitals and clinics CHS looks to grow revenue and profitability at its existing facilities. Its strategy focuses on recruiting primary care doctors and specialists; expanding services; investing in technology and facility improvements; and controlling costs through among other things centralizing some business operations. For instance CHS tries to trim supply costs through its membership in group purchasing organization HealthTrust which negotiates price agreements with suppliers on behalf of its members. CHS also adds complex services to its line-up including orthopedics cardiovascular services and urology thereby making its facilities more attractive to potential physicians and patients.

The firm expects its earnings to increase in coming years thanks to an aging population. It also hopes to benefit from reform measures that aim to increase the number of insured patients in the US which could cut down on self-pay patients and reduce the amount of bad debt its hospitals carry.

In addition the company sometimes divests facilities it deems as not core to its strategy. For instance in 2011 it sold two Oklahoma facilities SouthCrest Hospital and Claremore Regional Hospital to Ardent Health Services' Hillcrest HealthCare System unit for an undisclosed price. It also sold a Texas hospital Cleveland Regional Medical Center that year to New Directions Health Systems.

Mergers & Acquisitions

While the company's efforts to acquire rival hospital operator Tenet backfired in 2011 CHS completed several smaller purchases that year including the acquisition of the Mercy Health Partners Scranton operations in Pennsylvania from Catholic Health Partners. Several of the company's recent acquisitions have extended its small-community acquisition philosophy into the fringe or exurbs of attractive metropolitan markets such as the 2012 purchase of MetroSouth Medical Center in the southwestern suburbs of Chicago. Also in 2012 CHS added community hospitals and other health centers in northeastern Pennsylvania (including Moses Taylor Hospital) and in southeastern Pennsylvania (including Memorial Hospital).

HISTORY

Community Health Systems (CHS) was founded in 1985.

In 1996 it was acquired by investment firm Forstmann Little & Co. in a leveraged buyout transaction worth some $1.1 billion. It also moved its headquarters from Houston to Nashville Tennessee that year.

CHS once again became a public entity through an IPO in 2000. It engaged is engaged in a flurry of acquisition activity of small regional hospitals each year following its IPO.

However CHS limited its purchases somewhat after plunking down $7 billion in 2007 to acquire Triad Hospitals (and its more than 50 hospitals). After conducting integration efforts at the former Triad hospitals CHS fully resumed its acquisition activity when it purchased five hospitals during 2010 including the Marion Regional Hospital in South Carolina the Forum Health (later ValleyCare) hospitals in Ohio and the Bluefield Hospital in West Virginia.

Buoyed by those purchases CHS launched a campaign to acquire fellow hospital operator and rival Tenet in late 2010 in a deal worth some $7.3 billion in cash stock and debt. However after much back and forth between the firms –including lawsuits and hostile tender offers –CHS halted its acquisition attempts the following year due to a lack of response from Tenet's shareholders and board members.

The company continued its smaller purchases in 2011 including the acquisition of Tomball Regional Medical Center (TRMC) located near Houston.

EXECUTIVES

EVP CFO and Director, W. Larry Cash, age 63, $700,000 total compensation
Chairman President and CEO, Wayne T. Smith, age 66, $1,300,000 total compensation
President Division I Operations, David L. Miller, age 63, $550,000 total compensation
President Division II Operations, Michael T. Portacci, age 53, $450,000 total compensation
SVP Operations, Martin G. (Marty) Schweinhart, age 56
SVP Chief Accounting Officer and Corporate Controller, T. Mark Buford, age 58
EVP Secretary and General Counsel, Rachel A. Seifert, age 52
VP Administration, Robert A. (Bob) Horrar
SVP and CIO, J. Gary Seay
VP Finance and Treasurer, James W. Doucette
SVP Acquisitions and Development, Kenneth D. Hawkins
President Division III Operations, Martin D. (Marty) Smith, age 44
SVP and Chief Medical Officer, Barbara R. Paul, age 55
SVP Revenue Management, Larry M. Carlton
President Home Care Division, Kathie G. Thomas
President Division V Operations, Thomas D. (Tom) Miller, age 54, $550,000 total compensation
VP and Chief Purchasing Officer, Tim G. Marlette
VP Finance Division IV Operations, Brad Cash
SVP and Chief Quality Officer, Lynn T. Simon
Director, H. Mitchell Watson Jr., age 74
EVP CFO and Director, W. Larry Cash, age 63
Director, John A. Fry, age 51
Director, Julia B. North, age 65
Director, John A. Clerico, age 70
Director, William N. Jennings, age 68
Director, James S. Ely III, age 54
Auditors: Deloitte&ToucheLLP

LOCATIONS

HQ: Community Health Systems Inc.
4000 Meridian Blvd., Franklin TN 37067
Phone: 615-465-7000 **Fax:** 201-748-6088
Web: www.wiley.com

Selected Facilities

Alabama
- Cherokee Medical Center (Centre)
- Crestwood Medical Center (Huntsville)
- Dekalb Regional Medical Center (Fort Payne)
- Flowers Hospital (Dothan)
- Gadsden Regional Medical Center (Gadsden)
- L.V. Stabler Memorial Hospital (Greenville)
- Medical Center Enterprise (Enterprise)
- South Baldwin Regional Medical Center (Foley)
- Trinity Medical Center (Birmingham)

Alaska
- Mat-Su Regional Medical Center (Palmer)

Arizona
- Northwest Medical Center (Tucson)
- Northwest Medical Center Oro Valley (Oro Valley)
- Payson Regional Medical Center (Payson)
- Western Arizona Regional Medical Center (Bullhead City)

Arkansas
- Forrest City Medical Center (Forrest City)
- Harris Hospital (Newport)
- Helena Regional Medical Center (Helena)
- Medical Center of South Arkansas (El Dorado)
- Northwest Medical Center Bentonville (Bentonville)
- Northwest Medical Center Springdale (Springdale)
- Siloam Springs Memorial Hospital (Siloam Springs)
- Willow Creek Women' s Hospital (Johnson)

California
- Barstow Community Hospital (Barstow)
- Fallbrook Hospital (Fallbrook)
- Watsonville Community Hospital (Watsonville)

Florida
- Lake Wales Medical Center (Lake Wales)
- North Okaloosa Medical Center (Crestview)

Georgia
- Fannin Regional Hospital (Blue Ridge)
- Trinity Hospital of Augusta (Augusta)

Illinois
- Crossroads Community Hospital (Mt. Vernon)
- Galesburg Cottage Hospital (Galesburg)
- Gateway Regional Medical Center (Granite City)
- Heartland Regional Medical Center (Marion)
- MetroSouth Medical Center (Blue Island)
- Red Bud Regional Hospital (Red Bud)
- Union County Hospital (Anna)
- Vista Medical Center East/West (Waukegan)

Indiana
- Bluffton Regional Medical Center (Bluffton)
- Dupont Hospital (Fort Wayne)
- Dukes Memorial Hospital (Peru)
- Kosciusko Community Hospital (Warsaw)
- Lutheran Hospital of Indiana (Fort Wayne)
- Lutheran Musculoskeletal Center (Fort Wayne)
- Porter Hospital (Valparaiso)
- St. Joseph Hospital (Fort Wayne)

Kentucky
- Kentucky River Medical Center (Jackson)
- Parkway Regional Hospital (Fulton)
- Three Rivers Medical Center (Louisa)

Louisiana
- Byrd Regional Hospital (Leesville)
- Northern Louisiana Medical Center (Ruston)
- Women and Children' s Hospital (Lake Charles)

Mississippi
- River Region Health System (Vicksburg)
- Wesley Medical Center (Hattiesburg)

Missouri
- Moberly Regional Medical Center (Moberly)
- Northeast Regional Medical Center (Kirksville)

Nevada
- Mesa View Regional Hospital (Mesquite)

New Jersey
- Memorial Hospital of Salem County (Salem)

New Mexico
- Alta Vista Regional Hospital (Las Vegas)
- Carlsbad Medical Center (Carlsbad)
- Eastern New Mexico Medical Center (Roswell)
- Lea Regional Medical Center (Hobbs)
- Mimbres Memorial Hospital (Deming)
- MountainView Regional Medical Center (Las Cruces)

North Carolina
- Martin General Hospital (Williamston)

Ohio
- Affinity Medical Center (Massillon)
- ValleyCare Health System
  - Northside Medical Center (Youngstown)
  - Trumball Memorial Hospital (Warren)
  - Hillside Rehabilitation Hospital (Warren)

Oklahoma
- Claremore Regional Hospital
- Deaconess Hospital (Oklahoma City)
- Ponca City Medical Center (Ponca City)
- SouthCrest Hospital (Tulsa)
- Woodward Regional Hospital

Oregon
- McKenzie-Willamette Medical Center (Springfield)

Pennsylvania
- Berwick Hospital (Berwick)
- Brandywine Hospital (Coatesville)
- Chestnut Hill Hospital (Philadelphia)
- Easton Hospital (Easton)
- First Hospital Wyoming Valley (Wilkes-Barre)
- Jennersville Regional Hospital (West Grove)
- Lock Haven Hospital (Lock Haven)
- Phoenixville Hospital (Phoenixville)
- Memorial Hospital (York)
- Moses Taylor Health System
  - Mid-Valley Hospital (Peckville)
  - Moses Taylor Hospital (Scranton)
- Pottstown Memorial Medical Center (Pottstown)
- Regional Hospital of Scranton (Scranton formerly Mercy Hospital of Scranton)
- Special Care Hospital (Nanticoke formerly Mercy Special Care Hospital)
- Sunbury Community Hospital (Sunbury)
- Tyler Memorial Hospital (Tunkhannock formerly Mercy Tyler Hospital)
- Wyoming Valley Health Care System (Wilkes-Barre)

South Carolina
- Carolinas Hospital System (Florence)
- Chesterfield General Hospital (Cheraw)
- Marion Regional Hospital (Mullins)
- Marlboro Park Hospital (Bennettsville)
- Mary Black Healthcare (Spartanburg)
- Springs Memorial Hospital (Lancaster)

Tennessee
- Heritage Medical Center (Shelbyville)
- Dyersburg Regional Medical Center (Dyersburg)
- Gateway Medical Center (Clarksville)
- Haywood Park Community Hospital (Brownsville)
- Henderson County Community Hospital (Lexington)
- Lakeway Regional Hospital (Morristown)
- McKenzie Regional Hospital (McKenzie)

McNairy Regional Hospital (Selmer)
Regional Hospital Of Jackson (Jackson)
Sky Ridge Medical Center (Cleveland)
Volunteer Community Hospital (Martin)
Texas
Abilene Regional Medical Center (Abilene)
Big Bend Regional Medical Center (Alpine)
Brownwood Regional Medical Center (Brownwood)
Cedar Park Regional Medical Center (Cedar Park)
Cleveland Regional Medical Center (Cleveland)
College Station Medical Center (College Station)
DeTar Hospital Navarro (Victoria)
DeTar Hospital North (Victoria)
Hill Regional Hospital (Hillsboro)
Lake Granbury Medical Center (Granbury)
Laredo Medical Center (Laredo)
Longview Regional Medical Center (Longview)
Navarro Regional Hospital (Corsicana)
San Angelo Community Medical Center (San Angelo)
Scenic Mountain Medical Center (Big Spring)
South Texas Regional Medical Center (Jourdanton)
Tomball Regional Medical Center (Tomball)
Weatherford Regional Medical Center (Weatherford)
Woodland Heights Medical Center (Lufkin)
Utah
Mountain West Medical Center (Tooele)
Virginia
Southampton Memorial Hospital (Franklin)
Southern Virginia Regional Medical Center (Emporia)
Southside Regional Medical Center (Petersburg)
West Virginia
Bluefield Regional Medical Center (Bluefield)
Greenbrier Valley Medical Center (Ronceverte)
Plateau Medical Center (Oak Hill)
Wyoming
Evanston Regional Hospital (Evanston)

PRODUCTS/OPERATIONS

2011 Sales

	$ mil.	% of total
Managed care & other third-party payors	51	
Self-pay	12	
Total	**0**	**100**

Selected Acquisitions

2012
- Memorial Health Systems (York Pennsylvania; 100-bed Memorial Hospital Surgical Center of York ancillary facilities)
- MetroSouth Medical Center (southwest of Chicago; 410 bed hospital and 10 community health centers)
- Moses Taylor Health System ($162 million; Scranton Pennsylvania; 215-bed Moses Taylor Hospital and 25-bed Mid-Valley Hospital)

2011
- Mercy Health Partners Scranton ($160 million plus $70 million commitment for upgrade investments; Scranton Pennsylvania; 200-bed Mercy Hospital of Scranton 50-bed Mercy Tyler Hospital 65-bed Mercy Special Care Hospital and multiple clinics)
- Tomball Regional Medical Center ($225 million; near Houston; 360-bed acute care hospital)

2010
- Bluefield Regional Medical Center ($43 million; Bluefield West Virginia; 240 beds)
- Forum Health ($120 million; Youngstown Ohio; 360-bed Northside Medical Center 310-bed Trumball Memorial Hospital and 70-bed Hillside Rehabilitation Hospital)
- Marion Regional Healthcare System ($28 million; Marion South Carolina 125-bed Marion Regional Hospital and related nursing home)

COMPETITORS

Adventist Health
Adventist Health System Sunbelt Healthcare
Ascension Health
Banner Health
Baylor Health
Carolinas HealthCare System
Catholic Health East
Catholic Health Initiatives
Catholic Health Partners
CHRISTUS Health
Dignity Health
HCA
Health Management Associates
HealthSouth
Kaiser Permanente
LifePoint Hospitals
Mercy Health
SSM Health Care
SunLink Health Systems
Sutter Health
Tenet Healthcare
Texas Health Resources
Trinity Health (Novi)
Universal Health Services
University Health Services
Vanguard Health Systems
WellStar Health System

HISTORICAL FINANCIALS

Company Type: Public

Income Statement

FYE: December 31

	REVENUE ($ mil.)	NET INCOME ($ mil.)	NET PROFIT MARGIN	EMPLOYEES
12/11	13,626	201	1.5%	88,000
12/10	12,986	279	2.2%	87,000
12/09	12,107	243	2.0%	79,214
12/08	10,840	218	2.0%	81,334
12/07	7,127	30	0.4%	82,200
Annual Growth	17.6%	60.7%	—	1.7%

2011 Year-End Financials

Debt ratio: 58.17%
Return on equity: 8.43%
Cash ($ mil.): 129
Current ratio: 148.92
Long-term debt ($ mil.): 8,782
No. of shares (mil.): 90
Dividends
Yield: —
Payout: —
Market value ($ mil.): 1,580

	STOCK PRICE ($) FY Close	P/E High/Low		PER SHARE ($) Earnings	Dividends	Book Value
12/11	17.45	19	7	2.23	0.00	26.47
12/10	37.37	14	9	3.01	0.00	23.63
12/09	35.60	14	5	2.66	0.00	20.97
12/08	14.58	17	5	2.32	0.00	18.28
12/07	36.86	135	87	0.32	0.00	17.89
Annual Growth	(17.1%)	—	—	62.5%	—	10.3%

Community Trust Bancorp, Inc.

Community Trust Bancorp is the holding company for Community Trust Bank one of the largest banks based in Kentucky. It operates about 80 branches throughout the state as well as in northeastern Tennessee and southern West Virginia. The bank offers standard services to area businesses and individuals including checking and savings accounts credit cards and CDs. Loans secured by commercial properties and other real estate account for about two-thirds of the bank's portfolio which also includes business consumer and construction loans. Subsidiary Community Trust and Investment Company provides trust estate retirement brokerage and insurance services through five offices in Kentucky and Tennessee.

In 2010 Community Trust Bancorp bought LaFollette First National Corporation the holding company for First National Bank of LaFollette for some $16 million. The acquisition gave the company its first four bank branches and first trust office in Tennessee. Community Trust is considering additional acquisitions of smaller competitors. It also grows by opening new branches.

Although the key coal and natural gas industries in Community Trust's market have been hampered by the economic downturn and unemployment in the region remains elevated the company was able to grow its earnings in 2010. Fewer loan charge-offs improved interest rate margins and the LaFollette acquisition helped its results.

Loan demand continued to be weak but Community Trust kept the earnings momentum going into 2011 which was the second-most profitable year in the company's history. Its net income rose more than 17% as its decreased its provisions for loan losses and other economic indicators improved.

EXECUTIVES

Chairman President and CEO; Chairman Community Trust Bank, Jean R. Hale, age 65, $452,077 total compensation
EVP and Treasurer; EVP and Controller Community Trust Bank, Kevin J. Stumbo, age 51, $177,807 total compensation
EVP and Secretary; President CEO and Director Community Trust Bank, Mark A. Gooch, age 53, $333,231 total compensation
EVP; EVP and Chief Credit Officer Community Trust Bank, James J. (Jim) Gartner, age 70
EVP; EVP Operations Community Trust Bank, James B. (Jim) Draughn, age 52, $191,250 total compensation
President Pikeville Market Community Trust Bank, Lucian (Ricky) Meade
EVP; EVP and South Central Region President Community Trust Bank, Ricky D. Sparkman, age 49
EVP; EVP and Eastern Region President Community Trust Bank, Richard W. (Rick) Newsom, age 57
EVP; President Central Kentucky Region, Larry W. Jones, age 65, $151,802 total compensation
EVP; President and CEO Community Trust and Investment, Tracy E. Little, age 71, $162,000 total compensation
EVP; EVP and Chief Internal Audit and Risk Officer Community Trust Bank, Steven E. Jameson, age 55
President Flemingsburg Market Community Trust Bank, Trippy Clark
President Summersville Market Community Trust Bank, Ellis (Bucky) Frame
President Hazard Market Community Trust Bank, Janice Brafford-King
President Winchester Market Community Trust Bank, David Wills
President Advantage Valley Market Community Trust Bank, Lloyd A. Burner
President Danville Market Community Trust Bank, Dave Maynard
President Middlesboro Market Community Trust Bank, Timothy Helton
President Whitesburg Market Community Trust Bank, Reed Caudill
President Floyd/Knott County Market Community Trust Bank, David Tackett
President Mt. Vernon Market Community Trust Bank, Michael Blount
President Versailles Market Community Trust Bank, Rodney L. Mitchell

President Mt. Sterling Market Community Trust Bank, William McKenna
President Williamsburg Market Community Trust Bank, Holbert Hodges
President Tug Valley Market Community Trust Bank, Duanne Thompson
President Richmond Market Community Trust Bank, Tim Houck
EVP; President North East Region, Andrew Jones
Owner President, Earl Johnson
Executive Vice President, Andy Waters
Owner President, Krishna M. Malempati
Director, Charles J. Baird, age 62
Director, Nick A. Cooley, age 78
Director, M. Lynn Parrish, age 62
Director, James E. McGhee II, age 54
Independent Director, Anthony Charles
Independent Director, Anthony St.Charles
Auditors: BKDLLP

LOCATIONS

HQ: Community Trust Bancorp Inc.
346 N. Mayo Trail, Pikeville KY 41501
Phone: 606-432-1414 **Fax:** 606-437-3366
Web: www.ctbi.com

PRODUCTS/OPERATIONS

2011 Sales

	$ mil.	% of total
Interest		
Loans including fees	144	71
Securities	11	6
Other	2	1
Noninterest		
Service charges on deposit accounts	25	13
Trust income	6	3
Loan-related fees	2	1
Other	9	5
Total	**202**	**100**

COMPETITORS

BB&T
Farmers Capital Bank
Fifth Third
Home Federal
Premier Financial Bancorp
Republic Bancorp
U.S. Bancorp

HISTORICAL FINANCIALS

Company Type: Public

Income Statement FYE: December 31

	ASSETS ($ mil.)	NET INCOME ($ mil.)	INCOME AS % OF ASSETS	EMPLOYEES
12/11	3,591	38	1.1%	1,015
12/10	3,355	33	1.0%	1,041
12/09	3,086	25	0.8%	982
12/08	2,954	23	0.8%	986
12/07	2,902	36	1.3%	1,011
Annual Growth	5.5%	1.5%	—	0.1%

2011 Year-End Financials

Debt ratio: 2.31%
Return on equity: 10.58%
Cash ($ mil.): 235
Current ratio: —
Long-term debt ($ mil.): 82
No. of shares (mil.): 15
Dividends
Yield: —
Payout: 48.62%
Market value ($ mil.): 454

	STOCK PRICE ($) FY Close	P/E High/Low		PER SHARE ($) Earnings	Dividends	Book Value
12/11	29.42	12	9	2.53	0.00	23.78
12/10	28.96	15	10	2.16	1.21	22.16
12/09	24.45	22	14	1.65	1.20	21.17
12/08	36.75	26	16	1.52	1.17	20.46
12/07	27.53	17	11	2.38	1.10	20.03
Annual Growth	1.7%	—	—	1.5%	—	4.4%

Computer Sciences Corp.

Computer Sciences Corporation (CSC) is one of the world's leading providers of systems integration and other information technology services. The company services include application development data center management communications and networking development IT systems management and business consulting. It also provides business process outsourcing (BPO) services in such areas as billing and payment processing customer relationship management (CRM) and human resources. A major government and defense contractor CSC generates more than one-third of its revenues from US federal agencies through its public sector division; more than 60% of total company sales are made in the US. It has clients in 90 countries.

The company's government contracts have included such projects as helping the Federal Aviation Administration upgrade and modernize its air traffic control systems and supporting multiple US Navy programs. CSC's long history of serving the US government (dating back to 1961) gives it an advantage over many competitors when bidding on contracts. The company serves a broad range of government clients including most branches of the military as well as the Department of Homeland Security.

CSC divides its business into three main service lines: managed services sector (MSS) North American public sector (NPS) and business solutions and services (BS&S). MSS which primarily handles large-scale outsourcing contracts accounts for over 40% of CSC's revenues. NPS its federal government business is responsible more than one-third. The remaining approximately 20% of sales come from BS&S which provides industry-specific consulting and outsourcing services for clients in sectors such as chemicals aerospace financial services manufacturing and telecommunications.

CSC has benefited from an increased interest in outsourcing from the private sector resulting in multi-year contracts with corporations in a number of industries. Key contract wins in 2012 included a five-year deal with the U.S. Naval Air Warfare Center Training Systems Division to design develop produce test and support training systems. The contract is worth up to $2 billion. The previous year CSC won a 10-year $900 million deal with an undisclosed global commercial products manufacturer; a seven-year $348 million deal to provide IT systems outsourcing to Tryg a leading insurance provider in Europe's Nordic region; and a three-year $291 million agreement to provide a wide range of IT services to the US Citizenship and Immigration Services agency.

CSC's other clients have included hospital system Ascension Health transportation giant Bombardier diversified manufacturer Textron and defense contractor Raytheon.

CSC saw its revenue dip slightly in 2012 with all three key segments turning in lower sales but its profit plummeted about 550%. Income suffered mainly due to significantly higher costs of services such as changes to a contract with the UK National Health Service that resulted in write-offs of about $1.2 billion and a goodwill impairment charge of $2.7 billion. The company also noted difficulties managing operational costs and executing some MSS contracts as well as weakened demand from US federal and European clients.

Of the dismal fiscal results CSC CEO Mike Lawrie said that the company is working to turn itself around by enacting remediation plans for under-performing contracts revising compensation plans to reward performance looking for operational efficiencies and restructuring with an eye toward cost-cutting and a focus on specialized software and technology services. To that end in late 2012 CSC announced plans to sell its credit services business to Equifax for $1 billion and to sell its Italian consulting and systems integration business to IT services firm Dedagroup. It also made plans to divest its Australian IT staffing unit for $73.5 million.

On the acquisition front CSC in 2011 bought Philadelphia-based AppLabs a provider of software testing and quality management services to improve its application testing abilities. The ApLabs business complemented CSC's efforts to better serve the financial services manufacturing chemical energy IT and consumer products industries in particular.

The company also made two purchases to boost its health care business that year. It acquired health care imaging software company Image Solutions to expand its presence in the life sciences sector and it paid about $188 million for Australia-based iSOFT Group a developer of software used to manage patient and other medical data.

CSC has identified Latin America as a key geography for pursuing international growth and in 2011 the company acquired S?o Paulo-based IT services partner VIXIA Consultoria e Tecnologia to boost its presence in the region. VIXIA focused on providing enterprise software business consulting and systems integration services primarily to the insurance providers and other financial services industy.

In 2012 the company acquired 42Six Solutions which makes software for big data processing and analytics. Its customers include the US Department of Defense.

HISTORY

Computer Sciences Corporation (CSC) was founded in Los Angeles in 1959 by Fletcher Jones and Roy Nutt to write software for manufacturers such as Honeywell. In 1963 CSC became the first software company to go public. Three years later it signed a $5.5 million contract to support NASA's computation laboratory. Annual sales had climbed to just over $53 million by 1968.

In 1969 CSC agreed to merge with Western Union but the deal ultimately fell through. When Jones died in a plane crash in 1972 William Hoover a former NASA executive who had come aboard eight years earlier became chairman and CEO. Under Hoover CSC began transforming itself into a systems integrator. In 1986 when federal contracts still accounted for 70% of sales the company started diversifying into the commercial sector.

CSC signed a 10-year $3 billion contract in 1991 with defense supplier General Dynamics. In 1995 Hoover after more than three decades with CSC stepped down as CEO (remaining chairman until 1997); he was succeeded by president and COO Van Honeycutt. Also that year CSC bought Germany's largest independent computer services company Ploenzke. In 1996 CSC acquired insurance services provider Continuum Company for $1.5 billion.

In 1998 CSC found itself on the other side of the bargaining table with a $9.8 billion hostile takeover bid from software giant Computer Associates (now CA). After weeks of contentious battle CA withdrew its bid. That same year the IRS chose CSC to head the PRIME Alliance team that includes IBM Lucent and Unisys in a multibillion-dollar project to update the agency's computer system.

That year CSC continued its acquisition spree buying consulting firms in Europe including Informatica Group (Italy) KMPG Peat Marwick (France) Pergamon (Germany) and SYS-AID (the Netherlands). In 1999 CSC inked an 11-year $1 billion deal to manage the back-office functions of energy trading giant Enron's energy services unit. Also in 1999 the company acquired information technology company Nichols Research.

CSC in 2000 boosted its expertise in financial software and services with the cash acquisition of Mynd Corporation (formerly Policy Management Systems) for an estimated $570 million. Also that year CSC signed two large outsourcing contracts —a seven-year $3 billion deal with telecom equipment maker Nortel Networks that arranged for Nortel to transfer 2000 employees to CSC and a $1 billion outsourcing and application development agreement with AT&T.

The company continued to make large deals in 2001 including contracts with the National Security Agency (NSA) and BAE SYSTEMS. The next year saw more of the same: CSC was contracted to operate a central data exchange for the US Environmental Protection Agency and to collaborate on missile defense systems engineering for the US Army. CSC acquired Defense Department services contractor DynCorp for about $900 million in 2003 doubling the size of its federal services division. (The company sold off various DynCorp units two years later recouping about $850 million. It sold the remainder in 2010 for $1.5 billion to Cerberus Capital Management which took DynCorp private.)

Also in 2003 it won a 10-year $2.4 billion contract to provide a new network and voice data mobile and Internet services to the UK's Royal Mail. In Asia CSC acquired the 27% of subsidiary CSA Holdings it didn't already own.

CSC acquired Datatrac Information Services a prime contractor for the US Department of Homeland Security and other federal agencies in 2006.

President and COO Michael Laphen assumed the CEO's chair in 2007 inheriting the position from Honeycutt. Laphen also became chairman that year.

The company bought Covansys for about $1.3 billion in 2007. Covansys specialized in outsourcing services in such industries as financial services health care manufacturing retail and technology. The next year it acquired First Consulting Group an IT services firm focused on the health care sector for $352 million.

These acquisitions were part of a strategy to expand its offshore capabilities. Covansys operated primarily from development centers in India First Consulting added operations in India and Vietnam and Image Solutions added offices in China Germany South Korea and the UK. The purchases were also in line with CSC's focus on industry-specific offerings for select sectors including chemicals consumer products energy financial services government health care manufacturing and technology.

EXECUTIVES

VP Investor Relations, Bryan Brady
VP and CFO, Michael J. Mancuso, age 69, $585,000 total compensation
EVP Global Sales and Marketing, Peter A. Allen, age 50
Chairman, Rodney F. Chase, age 68
EVP and General Counsel, William L. (Bill) Deckelman Jr., age 55, $494,000 total compensation
EVP and General Manager Global Industries, James D. (Jim) Cook
EVP and General Manager Global Business Services and Regions, Thomas E. (Tom) Hogan, age 52
VP and Controller, Donald G. DeBuck, age 54, $333,192 total compensation
EVP and CFO, Paul N. Saleh, age 55
President Global Applications, Vivek Chopra
VP Business Development Manufacturing, Anthony C. (Tony) Patti
VP and Account Executive Managed Services Sector Americas Outsourcing Group, John Biggs
President International, Guy Hains
EVP and Chief Human Resources Officer, Sunita Holzer
President Global Business Solutions Europe Middle East and Africa (EMEA) Central Region Group, Gerhard Fercho, age 58
EVP and General Manager North American Public Sector, David W. (Dave) Zolet
VP and CIO, David McCue
President Business Development Global Sales and Marketing, Tony Keyes
VP and Treasurer, Thomas R. Irvin, age 63, $244,850 total compensation
President Global Business Solutions Europe Middle East and Africa (EMEA) South and West Region Group, Claude Czechowski
President North American Public Sector, James W. (Jim) Sheaffer
VP Deputy General Counsel and Assistant Secretary, M. Louise (Lou) Turilli, age 61
VP Corporate Development and Strategy, Randy E. Phillips, age 53, $416,000 total compensation
President Banking and Credit Services, John D. Dickson
President Managed Services Sector, Russ Owen
VP and General Manager North American Public Sector Intelligence Division, Harold C. (Hal) Smith
VP Account Management and Operations Asia, Andrew Anker
VP Human Resources, Denise M. Peppard, age 55
VP and Associate General Counsel, Gawie M. Nienaber, age 54
VP and CTO, John Glowacki
VP and Global Operations Executive, Frank Heitmann
VP Strategic Development Technology and Consumer Group, James J. (JJ) Foster
VP Chemical Energy and Natural Resources Group BSS, Robert (Bob) Welch
Director Investor Relations, Stephen Virostek
EVP and General Manager Global Infrastructure Services, Gary M. Budzinski
CIO, Doug S. Tracy, age 51
Director Media Relations, Chris Grandis
President Global Managed Services Business Development Americas Outsourcing Group, Walter A. Howell
VP Consulting Solutions and Client Development and CTO Financial Services Group, Brian Wallace
Manager Communications, Ashley Murray
President CEO and Director, J. Michael (Mike) Lawrie
Director, Thomas H. (Tom) Patrick, age 67
Director, Irving W. Bailey II, age 70
Director, Stephen L. Baum, age 70
Director, David J. (Dave) Barram, age 67
Director, Erik Brynjolfsson, age 50
Director, Chong S. Park, age 63
President CEO and Director, J. Michael (Mike) Lawrie
Auditors: Deloitte&ToucheLLP

LOCATIONS

HQ: Computer Sciences Corp.
3170 Fairview Park Drive, Falls Church, VA 22042
Phone: 703 876-1000
Web: www.csc.com

2012 Sales

	% of total
US	61
Europe	
UK	10
Other	16
Other	13
Total	**100**

PRODUCTS/OPERATIONS

2012 Sales

	% of total
Managed services	42
North America public	36
Business solutions &	23
Adjustments (1)	
Total	**100**

2012 Public Sector Sales

	% of total
Department of	68
Civil	28
Other	4
Total	**100**

Selected Service Areas

Application outsourcing
Business process outsourcing
Customer relationship management
Data hosting
Enterprise application integration
Knowledge management
Management consulting
Risk management
Security
Supply chain management

COMPETITORS

Accenture
ADP
Affiliated Computer Services
Atos
Booz Allen
CACI International
Capgemini
CIBER
Cognizant Tech Solutions
Computacenter
Convergys
Deloitte Consulting
Dimension Data
General Dynamics Information Technology
Getronics
HCL Technologies

Honeywell International
HP Enterprise Group
HP Enterprise Services
IBM Global Services
Infosys
Keane
Lockheed Martin Information Systems
Logica
ManTech
Northrop Grumman
Northrop Grumman Info Systems
Raytheon IIS
SAIC
Satyam
Siemens AG
SRA International
Tata Consultancy
Tech Mahindra
Unisys
Wipro
Wipro Technologies

HISTORICAL FINANCIALS

Company Type: Public

Income Statement FYE: March 30

	REVENUE ($ mil.)	NET INCOME ($ mil.)	NET PROFIT MARGIN	EMPLOYEES
03/12*	15,877	(4,242)	—	98,000
04/11	16,042	740	4.6%	91,000
04/10	16,128	817	5.1%	94,000
04/09	16,739	1,115	6.7%	92,000
03/08	16,499	544	3.3%	89,000
Annual Growth	(1.0%)	—	—	2.4%

*Fiscal year change

2012 Year-End Financials

Debt ratio: 24.49%
Return on equity: (-152.64)%
Cash ($ mil.): 1,093
Current ratio: 107.65
Long-term debt ($ mil.): 1,486
No. of shares (mil.): 155
Dividends
Yield: 2.67%
Payout: —
Market value ($ mil.): 4,647

	STOCK PRICE ($) FY Close	P/E High	P/E Low	PER SHARE ($) Earnings	Dividends	Book Value
03/12*	29.94	—	—	(27.37)	0.80	17.91
04/11	49.38	12	8	4.73	0.70	48.58
04/10	54.25	11	7	5.28	0.00	41.87
04/09	40.15	7	3	7.31	0.00	36.37
03/08	40.80	19	12	3.20	0.00	36.14
Annual Growth	(7.4%)	—	—	—	—	(16.1%)

*Fiscal year change

Con-Way Inc

Con-way (no relation to Twit-ty) provides trucking and logistics services. Con-way Freight the company's less-than-truckload (LTL) unit provides regional inter-regional and transcontinental service throughout North America. (LTL carriers consolidate loads from multiple shippers into a single truckload.) Con-way Freight operates a fleet of about 9200 tractors and some 26400 trailers. Con-way offers full truckload transportation services through its Con-way Truckload subsidiary which maintains a fleet of about 2700 tractors and more than 8000 trailers. Con-way's Menlo Worldwide Logistics unit provides contract logistics freight brokerage warehousing and supply chain management services.

HISTORY

What is now Con-way got its start in 1929 when Leland James co-owner of a bus company in Portland Oregon founded Consolidated Truck Lines to serve in the Pacific Northwest. Operations extended to San Francisco and Idaho by 1934 and to North Dakota by 1936. It adopted the name Consolidated Freightways (CF) in 1939.

James formed Freightways Manufacturing that year making CF the only trucking company to design and build its own trucks (Freightliners). In the 1940s CF extended service to Chicago Minneapolis and Los Angeles.

CF went public in 1951 and moved to Menlo Park California in 1956. It continued to buy companies (52 between 1955 and 1960) and extended its reach throughout the US and Canada. When an attempt to coordinate intermodal services with railroads and shipping lines failed in 1960 William White became president and exited intermodal operations to focus on less-than-truckload (LTL) shipping.

In 1966 CF formed CF AirFreight to offer air cargo services in the US. Three years later it bought Pacific Far East Lines a San Francisco shipping line (now a part of Con-Way).

CF sold Freightways Manufacturing to Daimler-Benz in 1981 and started the Con-Way carriers its regional trucking businesses in 1983 after the US trucking industry was deregulated. In the 1980s Con-Way moved back into intermodal rail truck and ocean shipping.

The company bought Emery Air Freight in 1989 and combined it with CF AirFreight to form Emery Worldwide. Founded in 1946 Emery Air Freight had expanded across the US and overseas first by using extra cargo space on scheduled airline flights then by chartering aircraft. Later operating its own air fleet Emery began having troubles in the 1980s including difficulties in integrating its 1987 acquisition Purolator Courier. A 1988 takeover attempt by former FedEx president Arthur Bass further plagued Emery; fending off the takeover resulted in losses of about $100 million in 1989. That year Emery brought CF a deal with the US Postal Service (USPS) to handle its next-day express mail.

Amid the beginning of a three-year profit slump CF formed Menlo Logistics in 1990 to provide its customers with a range of third-party logistics services. A Teamsters' strike in 1994 that halted union carriers nationwide boosted demand for Con-Way's services as customers sought nonunion carriers to move their shipments. The next year Con-Way opened 40 service centers and bought another 3300 tractors and trailers.

In 1996 CF spun off most of its long-haul transportation businesses (including CF MotorFreight Canadian Freightways and Milne & Craighead) and renamed the resulting entity Consolidated Freightways. CF then changed its own name to CNF Transportation.

CNF Transportation received a five-year $1.7 billion contract from the United States Postal Service (USPS) in 1997 to sort and transport two-day priority mail in the eastern US. The next year Menlo won contracts from six companies including Intel and IBM which were expected to generate more than $1 billion by 2003.

In 2000 CNF Transportation shortened its name to CNF and began renegotiating its money-losing second-day priority mail contract with USPS. (FedEx eventually got the job.) That year CNF formed Vector SCM a supply chain management and logistics joint venture with General Motors. In 2001 CNF's Con-Way Transportation established Con-Way Air Express an airfreight forwarder that serves the US and Puerto Rico.

Emery grounded its aircraft fleet in 2001 because of maintenance problems discovered by Federal Aviation Administration (FAA) inspectors. The company hired other carriers in order to continue its airfreight services. In a settlement with the FAA Emery agreed to pay a $1 million civil fine.

To emphasize its focus on logistics CNF combined the operations of Emery Worldwide Menlo Logistics and Vector SCM into a new company Menlo Worldwide effective in January 2002. In 2004 CNF sold its freight forwarding unit Menlo Worldwide Forwarding (formerly known as Emery Forwarding) and its subsidiary Menlo Worldwide Expedite to rival UPS for $150 million plus the assumption of $110 million in debt. The move was an opportunity to strengthen CNF's balance sheet and exit a low-margin business.

As part of an effort to focus on its operating businesses CNF renamed itself Con-way in 2006. In conjunction with the name change the businesses of the former Con-Way Transportation Services were split between Con-way Freight and Con-way Transportation LLC (later renamed Con-way Truckload Services). Con-way shut down its Con-way Forwarding subsidiary which specialized in domestic airfreight forwarding and sold its expedited freight transportation business to Panther Expedited Services. That same year the Vector SCM joint venture was unwound when GM exercised its option to buy out partner Menlo Worldwide for about $85 million.

The company's truckload business expanded dramatically in 2007 when Con-way paid $750 million for CFI. The acquisition also reshuffled Con-way's business mix. The operations of Con-way Truckload Services were combined into those of CFI which then changed its name to Con-way Truckload in January 2008. Also in 2007 the company acquired Singapore-based Cougar Logistics and Shanghai-based Chic Logistics.

Con-way Freight and Netherlands-based TNT Express N.V. (split from PostNL N.V. in mid-2011) entered into an alliance in 2009 offering intercontinental service. In 2010 the companies expanded that offering to include road pick-up and delivery of heavy shipments in the US and Europe connected by air service.

EXECUTIVES

EVP; President Menlo Worldwide, Robert L. (Bob) Bianco Jr., age 47, $411,962 total compensation
SVP Human Resources, Leslie P. Lundberg, age 54
VP Corporate Development, J. Craig Boretz
Chairman, W. Keith Kennedy Jr., age 68, $233,669 total compensation
EVP and CFO, Stephen L. (Steve) Bruffett, age 47, $394,167 total compensation
VP Investor Relations, Patrick J. (Pat) Fossenier
EVP General Counsel and Secretary, Stephen K. (Steve) Krull, age 47
SVP and Corporate Controller, Kevin S. Coel, age 53
VP Government Relations and Public Affairs, C. Randal (Randy) Mullett
President CEO and Director, Douglas W. Stotlar, age 51, $644,493 total compensation
VP Organizational and Culture Development, Julia P. (Pat) Jannausch
VP and Deputy General Counsel, Gary S. Cullen
VP Internal Audit, Maureen Maag
Director Corporate Communications, Gary N. Frantz

VP Procurement, Mitchell E. (Mitch) Plaat
President Road Systems, Lynn C. Reinbolt
EVP; President Con-way Freight Inc., W. Gregory (Greg) Lehmkuhl
EVP; President Con-way Truckload, Herbert J. (Herb) Schmidt, age 56, $402,827 total compensation
VP Sales and Marketing Menlo Worldwide, Robert W. Bassett
SVP Finance and Treasurer, Michael J. Morris, age 44
Director, Michael J. Murray, age 67
Director, William R. (Bill) Corbin, age 71
Director, Robert Jaunich II, age 72
Director, John C. (Jack) Pope, age 63
Director, Peter W. Stott, age 67
Director, William J. Schroeder, age 67
Director, John J. (Jack) Anton, age 69
President CEO and Director, Douglas W. Stotlar, age 51
Director, Prof Chelsea C. (Chip) White III, age 66
Director, Edith R. Perez, age 57
Auditors: KPMGLLP

LOCATIONS

HQ: Con-Way Inc
2211 Old Earhart Road, Suite 100, Ann Arbor, MI 48105
Phone: 734 994-6600
Web: www.con-way.com

2011 Sales

	$ mil.	% of total
US	4,966	94
Canada	111	2
Other countries	213	4
Total	**5,290**	**100**

PRODUCTS/OPERATIONS

2011 Sales

	$ mil.	% of total
Freight	3,247	59
Logistics	1,589	29
Truckload	615	12
Other	47	-
Inter-segment revenue eliminations	(208)	-
Total	**5,290**	**100**

Selected Services

Con-way Freight (LTL transportation services)
- Local
- Regional
- Transcontinental

Con-Way Truckload
Menlo Worldwide Logistics
- Distribution
- Logistics
- Supply chain solutions
- Transportation management
- Warehousing

COMPETITORS

APL Logistics
Arkansas Best
C.H. Robinson Worldwide
Central Freight Lines
CEVA Logistics
DHL
Estes Express
Expeditors
FedEx Freight
J.B. Hunt
Landstar System
Old Dominion Freight
Pacer Transportation Solutions
Panalpina Inc.
Ryder System
Saia
Schneider National
Swift Transportation
Transplace
UPS
UTi Worldwide
Werner Enterprises
YRC Worldwide

HISTORICAL FINANCIALS

Company Type: Public

Income Statement FYE: December 31

	REVENUE ($ mil.)	NET INCOME ($ mil.)	NET PROFIT MARGIN	EMPLOYEES
12/11	5,289	88	1.7%	27,800
12/10	4,952	3	0.1%	27,900
12/09	4,269	(107)	—	27,400
12/08	5,036	73	1.5%	26,600
12/07	4,387	152	3.5%	27,100
Annual Growth	4.8%	(12.8%)	—	0.6%

2011 Year-End Financials

Debt ratio: 26.09%
Return on equity: 11.65%
Cash ($ mil.): 438
Current ratio: 164.54
Long-term debt ($ mil.): 770
No. of shares (mil.): 55
Dividends
Yield: —
Payout: 25.48%
Market value ($ mil.): 1,621

	STOCK PRICE ($) FY Close	P/E High/Low	PER SHARE ($) Earnings	Dividends	Book Value
12/11	29.16	26 13	1.57	0.00	13.66
12/10	36.57	501328	0.07	0.40	14.94
12/09	34.91	— —	(2.33)	0.40	13.95
12/08	26.60	37 14	1.40	0.40	13.64
12/07	41.54	18 12	3.04	0.40	20.11
Annual Growth	(8.5%)	— —	(15.2%)	—	(9.2%)

ConAgra Foods, Inc.

ConAgra Foods fills the refrigerators freezers and pantries of most households. The company produces name-brand packaged and frozen foods. Sold in retail outlets of all kind ConAgra's cornucopia of America's best-known brands includes Banquet Chef Boyardee Egg Beaters Healthy Choice Hunt's Marie Callender Orville Redenbacher's PAM Peter Pan Slim Jim and Van Camp's. It is also one of the larger manufacturers of potato and vegetable products and seasoning and grain ingredients for the US foodservice food manufacturing and industrial markets. Restructuring ConAgra has sold off its agricultural meat and commodity products and noncore brands to focus on branded and value-added packaged foods.

HISTORY

Alva Kinney founded Nebraska Consolidated Mills in 1919 by combining the operations of four Nebraska grain mills. It did not expand outside Nebraska until it opened a mill and feed processing plant in Alabama in 1942.

Consolidated Mills developed Duncan Hines cake mix in the 1950s. But Duncan Hines failed to raise a large enough market share and the company sold it to Procter & Gamble in 1956. Consolidated Mills used the proceeds to expand opening a flour and feed mill in Puerto Rico the next year. In the 1960s while competitors were moving into prepared foods the firm expanded into animal feeds and poultry processing. By 1970 it had poultry processing plants in Alabama Georgia and Louisiana. In 1971 the company changed its name to ConAgra (Latin for "in partnership with the land"). During the 1970s it expanded into the fertilizer catfish and pet accessory businesses.

Poorly performing subsidiaries and commodity speculation caused ConAgra severe financial problems until 1974 when Mike Harper a former Pillsbury executive took over. Harper trimmed properties to reduce debt and had the company back on its feet by 1976. ConAgra stayed focused on the commodities side of the business but was thus tied to volatile price cycles. In 1978 it bought United Agri Products (agricultural chemicals).

ConAgra moved into consumer food products in the 1980s. It bought Banquet (frozen food 1980) and within six years had introduced almost 90 new products under that label. Other purchases included Singleton Seafood (1981) Armour Food Company (meats dairy products frozen food; 1983) and RJR Nabisco's frozen food business (1986). ConAgra became a major player in the red meat market with the 1987 purchases of E.A. Miller (boxed beef) Monfort (beef and lamb) and Swift Independent Packing.

Confident it had found the right path ConAgra continued with acquisitions of consumer food makers including Beatrice Foods (Orville Redenbacher's popcorn Hunt's tomato products) in 1991. In 1997 the company agreed to pay $8.3 million to settle federal charges of wire fraud and watering down grain. That year ConAgra named vice chairman and president Bruce Rohde as CEO; he became chairman in 1998. Also in 1998 the company bought GoodMark Foods maker of Slim Jim and Nabisco's Egg Beaters and table spread unit(Parkay). ConAgra bought Holly Ridge Foods (pastries) in 1999 and announced a major restructuring.

ConAgra bought Emerge an agricultural and land-use information software provider from Litton Industries in 2000. It also acquired Seaboard's poultry division and refrigerated meat alternatives maker Lightlife (Tofu pups Smart Dogs) before buying major brand holder International Home Foods from HM Capital Partners (known as Hicks Muse Tate & Furst at the time) for about $2.9 billion. The company then became ConAgra Foods.

During 2001 the company drew SEC attention and was forced to restate earnings for the previous three years due to accounting no-no's in its United Agri Products division.

In 2002 the USDA forced ConAgra to recall 19 million pounds of ground beef because of possible E. coli contamination making it the second-largest food recall in US history. (The largest recall occurred in 1997 when Hudson Foods later purchased by Tyson Foods withdrew 35 million pounds of beef.) Later in 2002 ConAgra sold its fresh beef and pork processing business –one of the largest in the US –to Booth Creek Management and HM Capital Partners and it was renamed Swift & Company Swift & Company. (Swift was acquired by Brazilian beef giant JBS in 2007.)

In 2003 the company began supplying packaged meat products for grilling to George Foreman Foods which sells them via its Web site. That year it sold its Bumble Bee canned seafood business to members of Bumble Bee management and private investment firm Centre Partners Management and its blue cheese brands (Treasure Cave Nauvoo) to Canada's Saputo Inc. for undisclosed prices. It also sold its chicken processing business to Pilgrim's Pride for a stock and cash deal worth about $550 million in 2003.

Also in 2003 ConAgra agreed to pay $1.5 million in cash and job offers to settle an EEOC lawsuit charging bias against disabled workers at the company's California-based Gilroy Foods plant. The agreement involves the largest disability settlement in the agriculture industry. The dispute dated back to 1999 when Gilroy Foods then owned by Basic Vegetable Products (ConAgra bought the facility in 2000) after a strike failed to recall disabled workers who were on leaves of absence due to illness or pregnancy or who had a history of illness or injury.

In keeping with its strategy to focus on its branded and value-added food business in 2003 ConAgra sold United Agri Products to Apollo Management for stock and securities. The deal was worth about $600 million. In 2004 it sold its minority interest in the beef and pork processing operations of Swift Foods to HM Capital Partners. The deal was worth $194 million. ConAgra also sold Swift's feedlot operations to Smithfield Foods for an undisclosed amount.

ConAgra sold its turkey hatchery and breeding business to Ag Forte in 2004. It sold its Canadian and US crop inputs businesses and its Spanish feed and Portuguese poultry businesses that year as well. In addition it sold Casa de Oro Foods (the US's third-largest tortilla maker) to the Plaza Belmont Fund II. Also that year ConAgra introduced Golden Cuisine a line of frozen meals designed for seniors. The company began manufacturing and supplying Golden Cuisine to Meals On Wheels which distributes the meals which are formulated for seniors to the homebound elderly. That year ConAgra also introduced a high-fiber flour called Ultragrain that has the taste and texture of refined flour but the nutrition of whole grain.

In 2005 ConAgra sold its remaining 15 million shares of Pilgrim's Pride to that company for about $480 million. That year CEO Bruce Rhode retired. His replacement was former chairman and CEO of PepsiCo Beverages and Foods North America Gary Rodkin who began a company-wide restructuring. The company reorganized its business structure from three channels to two: Foodservice was merged with Food Ingredients and became ConAgra Foods Commercial; the ConAgra Retail channel remained the same.

ConAgra agreed to pay a $14 million shareholder settlement in 2005 regarding a lawsuit claiming fictitious sales and mis-reported earnings at its former subsidiary United Agri Products.

In a move to demonstrate its commitment to the humane treatment of animals in 2006 ConAgra urged its poultry suppliers to consider slaughtering chickens in a more humane manner called controlled-atmosphere killing. The process which ConAgra has only suggested to its suppliers is approved by the People for the Ethical Treatment of Animals.

Rodkin continued the company redo focusing on portfolio trimming when in early 2006 he announced plans to sell a large part of ConAgra's refrigerated-meats business. The brands involved in the sale include some of the company's best-known: Armour Butterball and Eckrich. (The Brown 'N Serve Healthy Choice Hebrew National Pemmican and Slim Jim brands were not included in the portfolio reduction.) It sold its Cook's ham business to Smithfield Foods for $260 million that year.

Not long after that it agreed to sell of the rest of its refrigerated meats business that it had for sale to Smithfield as well. The deal which became final in October 2006 cost Smithfield $571 million in cash. That same month it sold its Butterball Turkey unit to Carolina Turkeys for $325 million. (Carolina subsequently changed its company name to Butterball LLC.)

Divesting almost faster than one can keep track of one day after the Butterball deal was completed ConAgra sold its MaMa Rosa's Pizza operations to investment firm the Plaza Belmont Management Group. (MaMa Rosa's is refrigerated —not frozen pizza —and competes in a different market than other pizzas albeit frozen powerhouses such as Di Giorno Tombstone or Tony's.)

In another move to improve long-term operating performance ConAgra announced its intention to sell off its seafood and domestic and imported cheese businesses. To that end the company sold its surimi business including the Louis Kemp brand to Trident Seafoods and its Singleton Seafood and Meridian Seafood to Singleton Fisheries. It sold its specialty and imported cheese operation Swissrose International to investment company Fairmount Food Group. Late in 2006 the company sold its oat-milling business to investment companies Sequel Holdings and Falcon Investment Advisors.

The company added to its Lamb Weston branded potato products with the 2008 acquisition of Watts Brothers. With operations in Washington and Oregon Watts is a vegetable-processing company that has annual sales of some $100 million. It has retail foodservice and industrial customers throughout the US as well as in Mexico Japan China and other Far East countries. The deal also included Watts' organic dairy fertilizer cold storage packaging and agricultural farming businesses.

In early 2007 salmonella was found in some of the company's Peter Pan and Great Value (a Wal-Mart product) brands of peanut butter forcing a nationwide recall of the peanut butter bearing the product code involved. Salmonella food poisoning was linked to some 600 people in 47 states. No deaths related to the peanut better were confirmed. The recall eventually included products made as far back as October 2004. ConAgra shut down the Sylvester Georgia plant that was involved in the outbreak and reopened it in Auguts 2007 having spent $15 million on renovation which included repairing the roof installing new equipment and creating a manufacturing process that better separated raw materials from the finished peanut butter.

Just two months later the company voluntarily stopped production at the Missouri plant that makes its Banquet and generic brands of frozen turkey and chicken pot pies after learning that the were linked to some 140 cases of salmonella in 30 states. ConAgra did not recall the pies but offered mail-in refunds and store returns. The USDA began an investigation and advised consumers not to eat the pies.

As part of its strategy to add to its brand-name offerings in 2007 ConAgra acquired Alexia Foods a maker of natural frozen potatoes appetizers and artisan breads for about $50 million in cash. Later that year the company paid a penalty of $45 million in the wake of SEC charges that alleged the company had misreported its profits for the fiscal years 1999 2000 and 2001.

The company acquired Lincoln Snacks Company in 2007. Lincoln's well-known brands such as Fiddle Faddle and Poppycock extended ConAgra's name-brand lineup which is in line with company strategy. That year it also announced the removal of the chemicals from its microwave popcorn products that are suspected of causing lung ailments in popcorn-plant workers.

ConAgra sold its trading and merchandising operations (ConAgra Trade Group) in 2008 to a group of investors that included the Ospraie Special Opportunities Fund for $2.8 billion. The sale was part of the company's long-term strategy to exit the commodities business and concentrate on its consumer food products. Saying it couldn't give the brand the attention it needs in 2008 the company sold its Knott's Berry Farm jam and jelly business to J. M. Smucker.

In a tragedy that made the evening news three ConAgra workers were killed and some 40 were injured in an explosion and fire at a company Slim Jim manufacturing plant in Garner North Carolina in June 2009. It was later determined that the blast was caused by a natural-gas leak. ConAgra partnered with the United Way forming the Garner Plant Fund that raised money to assist the victims and their families. The company also continued to pay workers salaries while the plant remained closed for investigation. ConAgra was fined $106000 by the government in 2010 and the plant was eventually closed.

In 2011 ConAgra Foods made an unsolicited takeover bid to buy Ralcorp Holdings a leading maker of private-label snack foods cereals and condiments. After proffering an initial bid of $82 per share ConAgra ultimately offered $94 (valuing Ralcorp at more than $5 billion). However Ralcorp spurned all bids saying they were not in the best interests of shareholders.

In May 2012 the company completed the acquisition of Odom's Tennessee Pride the #2 producer of frozen breakfast sandwiches in the US.

EXECUTIVES

President CEO and Director, Gary M. Rodkin, age 60, $1,000,000 total compensation

Chairman, Steven F. (Steve) Goldstone, age 66

President Consumer Foods, Andre J. Hawaux, age 52, $600,000 total compensation

EVP and Chief Administrative Officer, Brian L. Keck, age 59

VP Corporate Affairs; President ConAgra Foods Foundation, Chris Kircher

VP Investor Relations, Christopher W. (Chris) Klinefelter, age 45

President Sales, Douglas A. (Doug) Knudsen, age 57

EVP General Counsel and Corporate Secretary, Colleen Batcheler, age 38, $402,692 total compensation

EVP and CFO, John F. Gehring, age 51, $450,000 total compensation

VP Government Affairs, Brent A. Baglien

VP Corporate Real Estate and Facilities, James D. Doyle

EVP and Chief Marketing Officer, Joan K. Chow, age 50

VP and General Manager Spicetec Flavors and Seasoning, Mark A. Duffy, age 50

President Consumer Foods Snacks and International, David A. Palfenier

EVP Research Quality and Innovation, Albert D. (Al) Bolles, age 54

VP Finance and Corporate Controller, J. Mark Warner, age 46

President Commercial Foods, Paul Maass

VP Communication and External Relations, Teresa Paulsen

SVP Human Resources, Nicole B. Theophilus, age 42

VP Environment Health and Safety, James Lime

SVP Sales and Supply Chain ConAgra Foods Lamb Weston, Mark Hayden

VP Sustainability, Gail Tavill

Director Communication and External Relations, Stephanie K. Childs

VP Human Resources Supply Chain, Jodi Taylor

VP Operations, Mike Tracy

VP Internal Audit, Allen J. Cooper, age 48

VP Human Resources Talent Management, Tim Jones

VP Marketing and New Ventures ConAgra Foods Canada, Pina Sciarra

VP and General Manager Retail Products Lamb Weston, Mauro Pennella
Contact Corporate Programs Grocery Refrigerated, Stephanie Moritz
Contact Frozen and Snacks, Regina DeMars
EVP and Chief Strategy Officer, Andrew Ross
President CEO and Director, Gary M. Rodkin, age 60
Director, Mogens C. Bay, age 63
Director, Stephen G. Butler, age 64
Director, Kenneth E. (Ken) Stinson, age 69
Director, Richard H. Lenny, age 60
Director, Andrew J. (Andy) Schindler, age 68
Director, William G. (Jerry) Jurgensen, age 61
Director, Joie A. Gregor, age 62
Director, Rajive Johri, age 62
Director, Ruth Ann Marshall, age 58
Auditors: KPMGLLP

LOCATIONS

HQ: ConAgra Foods, Inc.
One ConAgra Drive, Omaha, NE 68102-5001
Phone: 402 240-4000
Web: www.conagrafoods.com

PRODUCTS/OPERATIONS

2012 Sales

	$ mil.	% of total
Consumer foods	8,376	63
Commercial foods	4,885	37
Total	**13,262**	**100**

Selected Brands

Commercial foods
- ConAgra Mills
- Lamb Weston
- Spicetec Flavors & Seasonings

Consumer foods
- Act II
- Alexia
- Banquet
- Bertolli
- Blue Bonnet
- Chef Boyardee
- DAVID Seeds
- Egg Beaters
- Healthy Choice
- Hebrew National
- Hunt' s
- Marie Callender' s
- Odom' s Tennessee Pride
- Orville Redenbacher' s
- PAM
- Peter Pan
- P.F. Chang' s
- Reddi-wip
- Slim Jim
- Snack Pack
- Swiss Miss
- Van Camp' s
- Wesson

COMPETITORS

American Pop Corn
B&G Foods
Bush Brothers
Campbell Soup
Clorox
Del Monte Foods
Eden Foods
Frito-Lay
General Mills
Gilster-Mary Lee
Goya
H. J. Heinz Limited
Hain Celestial
Hanover Foods
Heinz
Manischewitz Company
McCain Foods
McIlhenny
MOM Brands
Mondelez International
Monterey Gourmet Foods
Mott' s
Nestle
Newman' s Own
Nutrisystem
Pinnacle Foods
Ralcorp
Sara Lee North American Retail
Schwan' s
Hormel
Inventure foods
J-OIL MILLS
Jenny Craig
JR Simplot
Kellogg
Link Snacks
Seneca Foods
Slim-Fast
smart balance
Smucker
Snappy Popcorn
Weaver Popcorn Company

HISTORICAL FINANCIALS

Company Type: Public

Income Statement FYE: May 27

	REVENUE ($ mil.)	NET INCOME ($ mil.)	NET PROFIT MARGIN	EMPLOYEES
05/12	13,262	467	3.5%	26,100
05/11	12,303	817	6.6%	23,200
05/10	12,079	725	6.0%	24,400
05/09	12,731	978	7.7%	25,600
05/08	11,605	930	8.0%	25,000
Annual Growth	3.4%	(15.8%)	—	1.1%

2012 Year-End Financials

Debt ratio: 25.67%
Return on equity: 10.54%
Cash ($ mil.): 103
Current ratio: 144.65
Long-term debt ($ mil.): 2,858
No. of shares (mil.): 407
Dividends
Yield: —
Payout: 84.82%
Market value ($ mil.): 10,292

	STOCK PRICE ($) FY Close	P/E High	P/E Low	PER SHARE ($) Earnings	Dividends	Book Value
05/12	25.25	24	20	1.12	0.00	10.89
05/11	25.04	13	11	1.88	0.00	11.45
05/10	24.18	16	11	1.62	0.00	11.13
05/09	18.59	11	6	2.15	0.00	10.69
05/08	23.38	14	11	1.90	0.00	11.02
Annual Growth	1.9%	—	—	(12.4%)	—	(0.3%)

ConocoPhillips

Proudly combining two venerable oil industry names ConocoPhillips is the world's largest independent exploration and production company based on reserves and oil production. The company explores for oil and gas in more than 30 countries and has proved reserves of 8.4 billion barrels of oil equivalent. It produced about 1.6 million barrels per day in 2011. In 2012 ConocoPhillips spun off its refining and marketing unit as Phillips 66. Prior to that event the then-integrated company had a refining capacity of more than 2.2 million barrels per day. The company also had 8300 retail outlets in the US under the 76 Conoco and Phillips 66 brands and at 1700 owned or dealer-owned gas stations in Europe.

HISTORY

The roots of ConocoPhillips go back more than a century and run deep into the history of the US oil industry.

Isaac Elder Blake an Easterner who had lost everything on a bad investment came to Ogden Utah and founded Continental Oil & Transportation (CO&T) in 1875. In 1885 CO&T merged with Standard Oil's operations in the Rockies and was reincorporated in Colorado as Continental Oil. Continental tightened its grip on the Rocky Mountain area and by 1906 had taken over 98% of the western market. Its monopoly ended in 1911 when the US Supreme Court ordered Standard to divest several holdings: Continental was one of 34 independent oil companies created in 1913.

Seeing opportunity in autos Continental built a gas station in 1914. Two years later it got into oil production when it bought United Oil and by 1924 it had become fully integrated by merging with Mutual Oil which owned production refining and distribution assets. Continental's biggest merger came in 1929 when it merged with Marland Oil of Oklahoma.

Continental diversified in the 1960s acquiring American Agricultural Chemicals in 1963 and Consolidation Coal (Consol) in 1966. Restructuring in the 1970s into Conoco Chemical Consol and two petroleum divisions the company ramped up oil exploration and entered ventures to develop uranium. In 1979 it changed its name to Conoco.

In the late 1970s Conoco began joint ventures with chemical titan DuPont. The companies worked together well and in 1981 Conoco was acquired by DuPont to forestall hostile takeover attempts by Mobil and Seagram. DuPont sold off $1.5 billion of Conoco's assets and absorbed Conoco Chemical. In 1998 however DuPont spun off Conoco in what was the US's largest-ever IPO at the time (DuPont had completely divested its 70% stake by the next year).

Conoco expanded its natural gas reserves in 2001 by buying Gulf Canada Resources for $4.3 billion in cash and $2 billion in assumed debt. Also that year Conoco agreed to merge with Phillips Petroleum.

The story of Phillips Petroleum begins with Frank Phillips a prosperous Iowa barber who married a banker's daughter in 1897 and began selling bonds. When a missionary who worked with Native Americans in Oklahoma regaled him with stories about the oil patch Phillips migrated to Bartlesville Oklahoma and established Anchor Oil in 1903.

Anchor's first two wells were dry but the next one –the Anna Anderson No. 1 –was the first of a string of 81 successful wells. Phillips and his brother L. E. doubling as bankers in Bartlesville transformed Anchor into Phillips Petroleum in 1917.

With continued success on Native American lands in Oklahoma Phillips moved into refining and marketing. In 1927 the company opened its first gas station in Wichita Kansas. Frank Phillips retired after WWII and died in 1950.

During the 1980s Phillips became a target of takeover attempts. To fend off bids from corporate raiders T. Boone Pickens (1984) and Carl Icahn (1985) Phillips repurchased stock and ran its debt up to $9 billion. It then cut 8300 jobs and sold billions of dollars' worth of assets; strong petrochemicals earnings kept it afloat.

As part of an industry trend to share costs of less-profitable operations Phillips and Conoco flirted with the idea of merging their marketing and refining operations in 1996 but the talks failed. Discussions between Phillips and Ultramar Diamond Shamrock about merging the companies' North American oil refining and marketing operations broke down in 1999.

James Mulva took over as CEO in 1999 and Phillips decided to shift its focus to its upstream operations. The company combined its natural gas gathering and processing operations with those of Duke Energy in 2000 and received a minority stake in a new company Duke Energy Field Services. Also that year Phillips acquired ARCO's Alaska assets for $7 billion and merged its chemicals division with that of Chevron (later ChevronTexaco and still later Chevron once again).

In 2001 however Phillips elected to expand its refining and marketing operations rather than spin them off and the company bought Tosco for about $7.3 billion in stock and $2 billion in assumed debt. Big as it was the Tosco deal was eclipsed the next year by the merger of Phillips and Conoco.

In 2003 as part of its plan to exit the retail business the company sold its Circle K gas station chain to Alimentation Couche-Tard for $812 million.

In 2006 to boost its reserves base ConocoPhllips acquired Burlington Resources for about $36 billion.

In 2007 under nationalization pressure from President Hugo Chavez ConocoPhillips exited Venezuela.

In 2008 ConocoPhillips acquired a 50% stake in TransCanada's Keystone Oil Pipeline which plans to construct a 2148?mile crude oil pipeline originating in Hardisty Alberta with delivery points at Wood River and Patoka Illinois and Cushing Oklahoma. That year in a move to further expand its energy sources the company and Origin Energy in an $8 billion deal formed an Australasian natural gas business focused on coal bed methane production and liquefied natural gas processing and sales.

A decade of expansion and acquisitions left the company exposed to heavy costs. A slumping economy and the underperformance of its LUKOIL and Burlington Resources investments prompted the company to post a record loss for the fourth quarter of 2008. The largest impairment charge it took in Q4 was a $25.4 billion write-down of the goodwill value (the difference between the purchase price and the book value of tangible assets) for exploration and production assets mainly relating to the $36 billion purchase of Burlington Resources. ConocoPhillips was also forced to reduce the value of its stake in LUKOIL by $7.3 billion and lower the book value of two refineries by $537 million. The global economic slump hurt the bottom line in 2009 as well.

EXECUTIVES

SVP Corporate Shared Services, Rand C. Berney, age 56, $445,333 total compensation
SVP and Chief Administrative Officer, Eugene L. (Gene) Batchelder, age 65
Chairman President and CEO, James J. (Jim) Mulva, age 65, $1,500,000 total compensation
VP Human Resources, Sheila B. Feldman, age 57
SVP Legal General Counsel and Corporate Secretary, Janet Langford Kelly, age 54
SVP Finance and CFO, Jeffrey W. (Jeff) Sheets, age 54
VP Investor Relations and Communications, Ellen R. DeSanctis
President United Kingdom and Africa, Paul C. Warwick
SVP Exploration and Production Americas, Greg C. Garland, age 54
VP Human Resources, Carin S. Knickel
General Tax Officer, Ben J. Clayton
SVP Government Affairs, Red Cavaney
SVP Refining Marketing Transportation and Commercial, W. C. W. (Willie) Chiang, age 52
Chairman and CEO, Ryan M. Lance, age 49, $649,508 total compensation
President Global Trading, Christopher W. Conway
President Global Refining, Larry M. Ziemba
President Transportation, Deborah G. (Debbie) Adams
President Canada, Joseph P. (Joe) Marushack
Tax Administration Officer, Keith A. Kliewer
VP and Treasurer, Frances M. Vallejo
VP Corporate Affairs, Clayton C. Reasor
SVP Project Development and Procurement, Luc J. Messier
EVP Business Development and Commercial, Donald E. (Don) Wallette Jr., age 53
President Global Gas and Power, William L. Bullock
VP and Controller, Glenda M. Schwarz, age 46
President Global Supply, John W. Wright
SVP Exploration and Business Development, Larry E. Archibald
President Americas, Donald G. (Don) Hrap
President Strategy Integration and Specialty Businesses, Rex W. Bennett
VP Health Safety and Environment, Robert A. (Rob) Herman, age 53
Manager Corporate Security, Jim Snyder
Director Executive Services and Shareholder Events, Audrey Gage
EVP Exploration and Production, Matt Fox
President Qatar, Erec S. Isaacson
President Alaska, Trond-Erik Johansen
Media Contact, Nancy E. Turner
EVP Technology and Projects, Alan J. (Al) Hirshberg
Interim SVP Technology, Merl R. Lindstrom
VP Communications and Public Affairs, Ann M. Oglesby
President Russia and Caspian, Kerr A. Johnston
President Norway, Steinar Vaage
President Global Marketing, Andrew E. Viens
VP Investor Relations, Clayton Russell
Media Relations, John Roper
Director, Robert A. Niblock, age 49
Director, Ruth R. Harkin, age 65
Director, Bobby S. Shackouls, age 59
Director, Harold W. (Terry) McGraw III, age 63
Director, James E. (Jim) Copeland Jr., age 67
Director, Richard H. (Dick) Auchinleck, age 59
Director, Kenneth M. (Ken) Duberstein, age 67
Director, Victoria J. Tschinkel, age 64
Director, Kathryn C. Turner, age 63
Director, William K. Reilly, age 70
Director, William E. Wade Jr., age 68
Director, Richard L. Armitage, age 66
Director, Harald Norvik, age 64
Auditors: Ernst&YoungLLP

LOCATIONS

HQ: ConocoPhillips
600 N. Dairy Ashford, Houston TX 77079
Phone: 281-293-1000 **Fax:** -3622
Web: www.sonata-software.com

2011 Sales

	% of total
US	65
UK	15
Canada	3
Australia	1
Norway	1
Other	15
Total	**100**

PRODUCTS/OPERATIONS

2011 Sales

	$ mil.	% of total
Refining marketing & transportation	186,502	76
Exploration & production	49,453	20
Midstream	8,729	4
Emerging businesses	95	-
Chemicals	11	-
Adjustments	6,436	-
Total	**251,226**	**100**

COMPETITORS

BHP Billiton
BP
Chevron
Eni
Exxon Mobil
Hess Corporation
Marathon Oil
Occidental Petroleum
Royal Dutch Shell
TOTAL

HISTORICAL FINANCIALS

Company Type: Public

Income Statement FYE: December 31

	REVENUE ($ mil.)	NET INCOME ($ mil.)	NET PROFIT MARGIN	EMPLOYEES
12/11	251,226	12,436	5.0%	29,800
12/10	198,655	11,358	5.7%	29,700
12/09	152,840	4,858	3.2%	30,000
12/08	246,182	(16,998)	—	33,800
12/07	194,495	11,891	6.1%	32,600
Annual Growth	6.6%	1.1%	—	(2.2%)

2011 Year-End Financials

Debt ratio: 14.76%
Return on equity: 19.07%
Cash ($ mil.): 5,780
Current ratio: 107.66
Long-term debt ($ mil.): 21,610
No. of shares (mil.): 1,285
Dividends
Yield: —
Payout: 29.43%
Market value ($ mil.): 93,687

	STOCK PRICE ($) FY Close	P/E High/Low		PER SHARE ($) Earnings	Dividends	Book Value
12/11	72.87	9	7	8.97	0.00	50.73
12/10	68.10	9	6	7.62	2.15	46.72
12/09	51.07	17	11	3.24	1.91	40.96
12/08	51.80	—	—	(11.16)	1.88	36.27
12/07	88.30	12	8	7.22	1.64	55.14
Annual Growth	(4.7%)	—	—	5.6%	—	(2.1%)

CONSOL Energy Inc

Consolation prizes don't interest CONSOL Energy. CONSOL is one of the US's largest coal mining companies along with Peabody Energy and Arch Coal. The company has some 4.5 billion tons of proved reserves mainly in northern and central Appalachia and the Illinois Basin and produces about 59 million tons of coal annually. CONSOL primarily mines high BTU coal which burns cleaner than lower grades. Customers include electric utilities and steel mills. CONSOL delivers coal using its own railroad cars export terminals and fleet of towboats and barges. The company also engages in natural gas exploration and production; its proved reserves total 1.9 trillion cu. ft.

Operations

In addition to its coal and gas businesses CONSOL distributes mining and industrial supplies through its Fairmont Supply unit. About 40% of Fairmont's business is with its parent company. CONSOL also operates a distribution business and runs about 25 towboats and 700 barges.

In 2012 CONSOL which treats more than 36 billion galllons of water annually decided to form a water division to market its water resources as well as its water treatment and management services. It is targeting gas producers in the Marcellus Shale fairway in need of fresh water and acid mine drainage sources. CONSOL also acquired a minority stake in Pennsylvania-based Epiphany Solar

Water Systems to develop solar-powered water purification systems.

Strategy

Aware that most planned power plants will be gas-fired CONSOL has diversified its energy holdings by acquiring additional natural gas reserves.

The company also sold its nonproducing Northern Powder River Basin assets for $170 million in cash to Cloud Peak Energy in 2012. CONSOL will retain an 8% production royalty interest on about 200 million tons of permitted fee coal. The Northern Powder River Basin assets consist of properties that had been jointly owned by Chevron U.S.A. and additional properties in Sheridan Wyoming. Along with gains from other asset divestitures CONSOL has earned $224 million that it plans to use toward growth and maintenance projects in 2012.

In 2010 the company acquired Dominion Resources' Appalachian exploration and production assets for about $3.5 billion. The acquisiton doubles CONSOL's natural gas reserves to 3 million cu. ft. Also in 2010 as a logical follow-up on the Dominion Resources deal CONSOL acquired the remaining shares in CNX Gas that it did not already own (for about $965 million) in order to consolidate its natural gas holdings.

To raise cash to pay down debt in 2011 CONSOL agreed to sell a 50% stake in a joint venture with Noble Energy to develop 663350 Marcellus Shale acres in Pennsylvania and West Virginia. Noble Energy agreed to pay CONSOL $3.4 billion for its 50% stake. Later in 2011 Hess Corporation agreed to pay up to $593 million for joint exploration and development rights to CONSOL's nearly 200000 Utica Shale acres in Ohio.

HISTORY

When Consolidation Coal was formed in Maryland in 1864 coal was just beginning to replace wood as the world's top industrial energy source. In the 1880s Consolidation Coal like other large coal companies began operations in the Appalachia region of the US. During the 1920s the company built the Kentucky mining city of Van Lear. (Country music superstar Loretta Lynn's father worked as a Consolidation Coal miner nearby.) In 1945 Consolidation Coal merged with Pittsburgh Coal and the next year the combined company took over Hanna Coal.

In 1966 Continental Oil founded in 1875 and later renamed Conoco bought Consolidation Coal. Two years later 78 workers were killed in a Consolidation Coal mine explosion. Also in 1968 a federal jury found the United Mine Workers (UMW) and the company guilty of conspiring to put Kentucky's South East Coal out of business. In 1971 the UMW and Consolidation Coal paid South East almost $9 million in damages court costs and interest. Consolidation Coal became part of DuPont when that company bought Conoco in 1981.

Ten years later the mining unit of German conglomerate RWE Rheinbraun bought 50% of Consolidation Coal (later increased to 74%) from DuPont. That year Consolidation Coal and Conoco formed the Pocahontas Gas Partnership to recover coalbed methane gas.

A restructuring in 1992 created CONSOL Energy as a holding company for more than 60 subsidiaries including principal operating subsidiary Consolidation Coal. The next year the UMW initiated a strike against CONSOL which was using more and more nonunion workers in its mines. CONSOL opened its ash disposal facility the next year and began developing ways to reuse its plant waste and by-products.

From 1994 to 1997 the company reduced its workforce by 20% and closed six of its mining complexes. By 1997 about one-third of CONSOL's coal came from nonunion mines. In 1998 the company filed to go public and bought Rochester & Pittsburgh Coal.

CONSOL completed its IPO in 1999. The depressed coal market halved CONSOL's sales that year and the company scaled back production at some of its smaller high-cost mines in Pennsylvania and West Virginia. During the winter of 2000 and in early 2001 coal prices improved by 36% and natural gas prices skyrocketed as cold temperatures and an energy crisis in California increased demand for energy sources. Despite the improvement in coal prices the company continued to shut down high-cost mines.

In 2001 CONSOL acquired Conoco's half of the Pocahontas Gas joint venture. It also bought Windsor Coal Southern Ohio Coal and Central Ohio Coal from American Electric Power. In addition CONSOL bought 50% of the Glennies Creek Mine its first Australian property.

That year CONSOL contracted with Allegheny Energy Supply (an affiliate of largest customer Allegheny Energy) to build an 88MW electric generating plant in Virginia to be fueled by coalbed methane gas produced by CONSOL.

CONSOL in 2003 sold its Canadian operations (Cardinal River and Line Creek Mines) to Fording. The next year CONSOL sold its Glennies Creek mine interest thus exiting Australia.

Also in 2004 RWE severed ties with CONSOL by selling its remaining 19% stake in the company.

The next year CONSOL created a new subsidiary CNX Gas to handle the company's gas operations. It then sold a minority stake in CNX Gas to a group of institutional investors in a private transaction and in 2006 CNX Gas went public with CONSOL retaining an 82% stake.

EXECUTIVES

Chairman and CEO; Chairman and CEO CNX Gas, J. Brett Harvey, age 61, $1,038,462 total compensation

Vice Chairman, John L. Whitmire, age 71

EVP and CFO CONSOL Energy and CNX Gas, William J. Lyons, age 63, $525,342 total compensation

EVP Energy Sales and Transportation Services CONSOL Energy and CNX Gas; President CONSOL Energy Sales, Robert F. Pusateri, age 61

EVP Corporate Affairs Chief Legal Officer and Secretary CONSOL Energy and CNX Gas Corporation, P. Jerome Richey, age 62, $414,258 total compensation

President, Nicholas J. Deluliis, age 43, $621,077 total compensation

EVP Business Advancement and Support Services CONSOL Energy and CNX Gas, Robert P. King, age 59, $373,662 total compensation

VP Finance, David Khani

Director, Patricia A. Hammick, age 65

Director, Philip W. Baxter, age 63

Vice Chairman, John L. Whitmire, age 71

Director, John T. Mills, age 64

Director, Joseph T. (Joe) Williams, age 74

Director, William P. Powell, age 56

Director, James E. Altmeyer Sr., age 73

Director, Raj K. Gupta, age 69

Director, David C. Hardesty Jr., age 66

Director, William E. Davis, age 69

Auditors: Ernst&YoungLLP

LOCATIONS

HQ: CONSOL Energy Inc.
CNX Center 1000 CONSOL Energy Dr., Canonsburg PA 15317-6506
Phone: 724-485-4000 **Fax:** 212-207-5499
Web: www.continentalgrain.com

2011 Sales

	% of total
US	85
Europe	8
South	7
Total	**100**

PRODUCTS/OPERATIONS

2011 Sales

	$ mil.	% of total
Coal and gas	5,660	93
Freight	231	4
Gas royalty interests	66	1
Purchased gas	4	-
Other income	153	2
Total	**6,117**	**100**

COMPETITORS

Alliance Resource
Alpha Natural Resources
Arch Coal
Devon Energy
EQT Corporation
Nippon Coke & Engineering
Peabody Energy
Penn Virginia
RAG AG
Rio Tinto Limited
SM Energy
Westmoreland Coal

HISTORICAL FINANCIALS

Company Type: Public

Income Statement FYE: December 31

	REVENUE ($ mil.)	NET INCOME ($ mil.)	NET PROFIT MARGIN	EMPLOYEES
12/11	6,117	632	10.3%	9,157
12/10	5,236	346	6.6%	8,630
12/09	4,621	539	11.7%	8,012
12/08	4,652	442	9.5%	8,176
12/07	3,762	267	7.1%	7,728
Annual Growth	12.9%	24.0%	—	4.3%

2011 Year-End Financials

Debt ratio: 25.53%
Return on equity: 17.52%
Cash ($ mil.): 375
Current ratio: 136.70
Long-term debt ($ mil.): 3,177
No. of shares (mil.): 227
Dividends
Yield: —
Payout: 15.40%
Market value ($ mil.): 8,333

	STOCK PRICE ($) FY Close	P/E High	P/E Low	PER SHARE ($) Earnings	Dividends	Book Value
12/11	36.70	20	11	2.76	0.00	15.90
12/10	48.74	35	19	1.60	0.40	13.02
12/09	49.80	18	8	2.95	0.40	9.86
12/08	28.58	48	8	2.40	0.40	8.10
12/07	71.52	50	20	1.45	0.31	6.66
Annual Growth	(15.4%)	—	—	17.5%	—	24.3%

Consolidated Edison Co. of New York, Inc.

LOCATIONS

HQ: Consolidated Edison Co. of New York, Inc.
4 Irving Place, New York, NY 10003
Phone: 212 460-4600
Web: www.coned.com

HISTORICAL FINANCIALS

Company Type:

Income Statement FYE: December 31

	REVENUE ($ mil.)	NET INCOME ($ mil.)	NET PROFIT MARGIN	EMPLOYEES
12/11	10,484	989	9.4%	13,605
12/10	10,573	904	8.6%	0
12/09	10,036	792	7.9%	0
Annual Growth	2.2%	11.7%	—	—

2011 Year-End Financials

Debt ratio: 27.68%
Return on equity: 9.48%
Cash ($ mil.): 372
Current ratio: 104.35
Long-term debt ($ mil.): 9,222
No. of shares (mil.): 235
Dividends
Yield: —
Payout: 69.63%
Market value ($ mil.): 24,526

	STOCK PRICE ($) FY Close	P/E High/Low	PER SHARE ($) Earnings	Dividends	Book Value
12/11	104.15	— —	(0.00)	0.00	44.30
12/10	92.25	— —	(0.00)	5.00	43.04
12/09	88.86	— —	(0.00)	5.00	(0.00)
Annual Growth	8.3%	— —	—	—	—

Consolidated Edison, Inc.

Utility holding company Consolidated Edison (Con Edison) is the night light for the city that never sleeps. Con Edison's main subsidiary Consolidated Edison Company of New York distributes electricity to 3.3 million residential and business customers in New York City; it also delivers natural gas to about 1.1 million customers. Subsidiary Orange and Rockland Utilities serves more than 430000 electric and gas customers in three Northeast states. Con Edison's nonutility operations include retail and wholesale energy marketing independent power production and infrastructure project development.

Geographic Reach

The company's utility operations serve customers in New Jersey New York and Pennsylvania.

Operations

Competitive energy businesses include subsidiary Consolidated Edison Solutions which markets power and gas to retail customers and provides energy procurement and management services and Consolidated Edison Energy which markets and trades wholesale energy. Subsidiary Consolidated Edison Development has interests in power generation facilities.

Financial Analysis

Con Edison reported a 3% dip in revenues in 2011 primarily due to lower demand and lower gas prices. Its steam business was the only segment to see an increase in revenues thanks to it securing five new commercial New York City customers that year. Lower purchased power costs (led by weaker natural gas commodity prices) enabled the company to post a 6% jump in net income for the year. Higher electric rates and increased power demand helped to lift the company's revenues in 2010 overcoming the drop in gas revenues (as lower gas commodity prices in 2009 were passed on to customers). The increase in overall revenues and a gain on the sales of power plants help to boost net income in 2010.

Strategy

The company seeks to balance growing its competitive operations (with an emphasis on green energy) with improving its regulated infrastructure assets.

Promoting green power sources in 2011 Con Edison held stakes in solar energy projects (in New Jersey and Massachusetts) with a collective capacity of 28 MW. It also has proposed to develop 25 MW of solar energy resources in New York City by 2015. The solar power generated in the New York project would annually offset about 16000 tons of carbon dioxide.

HISTORY

Several professionals led by Timothy Dewey formed The New York Gas Light Company in 1823 to illuminate part of Manhattan. In 1884 five other gas companies joined New York Gas Light to form the Consolidated Gas Company of New York.

Thomas Edison's incandescent lamp came on the scene in 1879 and The Edison Electric Illuminating Company of New York was formed in 1880 to build the world's first commercial electric power station (Pearl Street) financed by a group led by J.P. Morgan. Edison supervised the project and in 1882 New York became the first major city with electric lighting.

Realizing electricity would replace gas Consolidated Gas acquired electric companies including Anthony Brady's New York Gas and Electric Light Heat and Power Company (1900) which joined Edison's Illuminating Company in 1901 to form the New York Edison Company. More than 170 purchases followed including that of the New York Steam Company (1930) a cheap source of steam for electric turbines.

The Public Utility Holding Company Act of 1935 ushered in the era of regulated regional monopolies. The next year New York Edison combined its holdings to form the Consolidated Edison Company of New York (Con Ed).

Con Ed opened its first nuclear station in 1962. By then Con Ed had a reputation for inefficiency and poor service and shareholders were angry about its slow growth and low earnings. Environmentalists joined the grousers in 1963 when Con Ed began constructing a pumped-storage plant in Cornwall near the Hudson River. Charles Luce a former undersecretary with the Department of Interior was recruited to rescue Con Ed in 1967. He added power plants and beefed up customer service.

In the 1970s inflation and the energy crisis drove up oil prices (Con Ed's main fuel source) and in 1974 Luce withheld dividends for the first time since 1885. He persuaded the New York State Power Authority to buy two unfinished power plants saving Con Ed $200 million. In 1980 Luce ended the Cornwall controversy and donated the land for park use. He retired in 1982.

The utility started buying power from various suppliers and in 1984 began a two-year price freeze a boon to rate-hike-weary New Yorkers. The New York State Public Service Commission didn't approve another rate increase until 1992.

In 1997 Con Ed government officials consumer groups and other energy firms outlined the company's deregulation plan which included the formation of the Consolidated Edison Inc. holding company (known as Con Edison) and a power marketing unit in 1998. The next year Con Edison sold New York City generating facilities to KeySpan Northern States Power and Orion Power for a total of $1.65 billion.

Also in 1999 Con Edison bought Orange and Rockland Utilities for $790 million to increase its New York base and expand into New Jersey and Pennsylvania. In an effort to push into New England the company that year agreed to buy Northeast Utilities (NU) for $3.3 billion in cash and stock and $3.9 billion in assumed debt. But the deal broke down in 2001. NU accused Con Edison of improperly trying to renegotiate terms while Con Edison accused NU of concealing information about unfavorable power supply contracts.

Con Edison's Indian Point Unit 2 nuclear plant was shut down temporarily in 2000 after a radioactive steam leak; later that year it agreed to sell Indian Point Units 1 and 2 to Entergy for $502 million. The sale was completed in 2001. That year Con Edison also incurred an estimated $400 million in costs related to emergency response and asset damage from the September 11 terrorist attacks on New York City.

After evaluating strategic alternatives for its telecommunications business due to losses at the unit in 2006 the company sold its Con Edison Communications unit (now RCN Business Solutions) to RCN Corporation for $32 million.

In 2008 in order to raise cash to pay down debt and reinvest in its core businesses the company's Consolidated Edison Development unit sold its merchant generation portfolio (1706 MW of fossil-fueled power generation projects) to investment group North American Energy Alliance LLC for $1.5 billion. The move also allowed Consolidated Edison Development to reorient its operations toward developing wholesale renewable power natural gas and transmission infrastructure in the US primarily in the Northeast.

EXECUTIVES

President and CEO Orange and Rockland Utilities, William G. Longhi, age 58, $409,000 total compensation

SVP Public Affairs Consolidated Edison Company of New York, Frances A. Resheske, age 51

SVP Enterprise Shared Services Consolidated Edison Company of New York, Luther Tai, age 63, $382,550 total compensation

Chairman President and CEO; Chairman CEO and Trustee Consolidated Edison of New York, Kevin Burke, age 61, $1,107,200 total compensation

Director Investor Relations, Jan C. Childress

SVP Business Shared Services Consolidated Edison Company of New York, JoAnn F. Ryan, age 54

VO and Corporate Secretary; Secretary Consolidated Edison Company of New York, Carole Sobin

SVP and CFO Con Edison and CECONY, Robert N. Hoglund, age 50, $584,200 total compensation
President Consolidated Edison of New York, Craig S. Ivey, age 49
VP Strategic Planning, Gurudatta D. Nadkarni, age 46
VP and Controller Con Edison and Consolidated Edison Company of New York; CFO and Controller Orange and Rockland Utilities, Robert Muccilo, age 56
VP and Treasurer Consolidated Edison and Consolidated Edison Company of New York, Scott L. Sanders, age 48
General Counsel Consolidated Edison and Consolidated Edison Company of New York, Elizabeth D. Moore, age 57
Director, L. Frederick Sutherland, age 60
Director, Vincent A. Calarco, age 69
Director, Ellen V. Futter, age 62
Director, George Campbell Jr., age 66
Director, Gordon J. Davis, age 70
Director, Sally Hernandez, age 59
Director, John F. Hennessy III, age 56
Director, Michael W. Ranger, age 53
Director, Michael J. Del Giudice, age 69
Director, John F. Killian, age 57
Director, Eugene R. McGrath, age 70
Auditors: PricewaterhouseCoopersLLP

LOCATIONS

HQ: Consolidated Edison Inc.
4 Irving Place, New York NY 10003
Phone: 212-460-4600 **Fax:** 734-757-1153
Web: www.con-way.com

PRODUCTS/OPERATIONS

2011 Sales

	$ mil.	% of total
Electricity	8,918	69
Gas	1,735	14
Steam	683	5
Other	1,602	12
Total	**12,938**	**100**

Selected Subsidiaries

Consolidated Edison Company of New York Inc. (utility)
Consolidated Edison Development Inc. (investments in power generation projects)
Consolidated Edison Energy Inc. (wholesale energy marketing and trading)
Consolidated Edison Solutions Inc. (retail energy marketing and services)
Orange and Rockland Utilities Inc. (utility)

COMPETITORS

Accent Energy
AEP
CH Energy
CMS Energy
Delmarva Power
Duke Energy
Enbridge
Green Mountain Energy
Iberdrola USA
National Fuel Gas
National Grid USA
New York Power Authority
Northeast Utilities
NSTAR
PPL Corporation
Public Service Enterprise Group
South Jersey Industries
USPowerGen
Viridis Energy Inc

HISTORICAL FINANCIALS

Company Type: Public

Income Statement

FYE: December 31

	REVENUE ($ mil.)	NET INCOME ($ mil.)	NET PROFIT MARGIN	EMPLOYEES
12/11	12,938	1,062	8.2%	13,605
12/10	13,325	1,003	7.5%	15,180
12/09	13,032	879	6.7%	15,541
12/08	13,583	1,196	8.8%	15,628
12/07	13,120	929	7.1%	15,214
Annual Growth	(0.3%)	3.4%	—	(2.8%)

2011 Year-End Financials

Debt ratio: 27.22%
Return on equity: 9.12%
Cash ($ mil.): 648
Current ratio: 121.79
Long-term debt ($ mil.): 10,145
No. of shares (mil.): 292
Dividends
Yield: —
Payout: 67.23%
Market value ($ mil.): 18,168

	STOCK PRICE ($) FY Close	P/E High/Low		PER SHARE ($) Earnings	Dividends	Book Value
12/11	62.03	17	14	3.57	0.00	39.77
12/10	49.57	15	12	3.47	2.38	38.66
12/09	45.43	15	10	3.14	2.36	37.21
12/08	38.93	11	9	4.37	2.34	36.21
12/07	48.85	15	13	3.47	2.32	34.15
Annual Growth	6.2%	—	—	0.7%	—	3.9%

Consumers Energy Co.

Consumers Energy Company makes sure that the energy consumers in Michigan have the power to crank up their heaters and the gas to fire up their stoves. The company's operating area includes all 68 counties of Michigan's lower peninsula. All told Consumers Energy has a generating capacity of 6130 MW (primarily fossil-fueled) and distributes electricity to 1.8 million customers and natural gas to 1.7 million customers. Included in the utility's arsenal of power production is electricity generated from fossil-fueled nuclear and hydroelectric power plants. Consumers Energy is a subsidiary and primary operating unit of CMS Energy.

The company is being guided by its "Balanced Energy Initiative" a comprehensive 20 year plan (introduced in 2007). The plan calls for the utility to develop new power plants increase the efficiency of its operations and expand its renewable energy projects.

As part of its commitment to reduce greenhouse gas emissions in 2010 Consumers Energy acquired access to about 60000 acres for the development of Lake Winds Energy Park in Mason County Michigan which is scheduled to begin operating in 2012. Cross Winds Energy Park in Tuscola and Huron counties is scheduled to come on stream in two phases in 2015 and 2017. (Earlier the company spent $10 million purchasing 440 General Motors gasoline-electric hybrid vehicles as part of its ongoing vehicle fleet replacement process). It also announced plans to begin installing smart meters (advance meters that allow customer to have better control over their energy use) across its system in 2012.

As part of its balanced energy initiative in 2009 the company received regulatory permission to develop a long-planned 830 MW coal-fired plant in return for agreeing to retire 630-958 MW of existing coal-fired plant capacity.

To improve its bottom line and the efficiency of its operations and in an effort to stem the tide of commercial and residential customers jumping ship for other electricity providers Consumers Energy is looking at options to reform its rate structures.

After a difficult 2009 due to the global recession crimping demand the company reported a jump in operting revenues and income in 2010 thanks primarily to a rate increase and surcharges.

Consumers Energy veteran David Joos served briefly as president and CEO of parent company CMS Energy in 2010 but retired in May to take the role of non-executive chairman. John G. Russell was named CMS president and CEO. Russell previously was president and CEO of Consumers Energy.

EXECUTIVES

Chairman, David W. Joos, age 59
VP Investor Relations and Treasurer, Laura L. Mountcastle
EVP and CFO, Thomas J. (Tom) Webb, age 59
SVP Government and Public Affairs and Chief Compliance Officer, David G. Mengebier, age 54
SVP Energy Supply, William E. (Bill) Garrity, age 63
VP and Chief Tax Counsel, Theodore J. Vogel
VP Controller and Chief Accounting Officer, Glenn P. Barba, age 46
VP Smart Grid, Susan C. Swan
President and CEO, John G. Russell, age 54
SVP and General Counsel, James E. Brunner, age 59
VP and Deputy General Counsel Utility Law and Regulation, Jon R. Robinson
Director News and Information, Jeff Holyfield
Director Public Information, Dan Bishop
SVP Distribution and Customer Operations, Daniel J. (Dan) Malone
SVP Human Resources and Shared Services, John M. Butler, age 47
VP and Secretary, Catherine M. Reynolds
SVP Electric Generation, Jackson L. (Jack) Hanson
VP Generation Construction, James P. Pomaranski
VP Rates and Regulation, Ronn J. Rasmussen
VP Generation Operations, Richard J. Ford
VP and CIO, Mamatha Chamarthi
VP Energy Supply Operations, Timothy J. Sparks
VP Energy Delivery, Garrick J. Rochow
Manager Combustion Turbine, Stephen T. Wawro
VP Customer Operations, Patti Poppe
VP Generation Engineering and Services, Dennis Dobbs
VP Energy Operations, Michele Kirkland
Director, Stephen E. Ewing, age 68
Director, Kenneth L. Way, age 72
Director, John B. Yasinsky, age 72
Director, Michael T. Monahan, age 73
Director, Jon E. Barfield, age 60
Director, Philip R. Lochner Jr., age 69
Director, Richard M. (Dick) Gabrys, age 70
President and CEO, John G. Russell, age 54
Director, Merribel S. Ayres, age 60
Auditors: Ernst&YoungLLP

LOCATIONS

HQ: Consumers Energy Company
1 Energy Plaza, Jackson MI 49201
Phone: 517-788-0550 **Fax:** 800-363-4806
Web: www.consumersenergy.com

PRODUCTS/OPERATIONS

2011 Sales

	$ mil.	% of total
Electric	3,913	63
Gas	2,340	37
Total	**6,253**	**100**

COMPETITORS

Detroit Edison
Indiana Michigan Power
Integrys Energy Group
MichCon
SEMCO ENERGY
We Energies
Xcel Energy

HISTORICAL FINANCIALS

Company Type: Subsidiary

Income Statement FYE: December 31

	REVENUE ($ mil.)	NET INCOME ($ mil.)	NET PROFIT MARGIN	EMPLOYEES
12/11	6,253	467	7.5%	7,435
12/10	6,156	434	7.1%	7,522
12/09	5,963	293	4.9%	7,755
12/08	6,421	364	5.7%	7,697
12/07	6,064	312	5.1%	7,614
Annual Growth	0.8%	10.6%	—	(0.6%)

2011 Year-End Financials

Debt ratio: 28.84%
Return on equity: 10.63%
Cash ($ mil.): 85
Current ratio: 146.59
Long-term debt ($ mil.): 4,154
No. of shares (mil.): 84
Dividends
Yield: —
Payout: 80.43%
Market value ($ mil.): 7,691

	STOCK PRICE ($) FY Close	P/E High/Low	PER SHARE ($) Earnings	Dividends	Book Value
12/11	91.45	— —	(0.00)	0.00	52.25
12/10	80.01	— —	(0.00)	0.00	49.70
12/09	78.35	— —	(0.00)	0.00	45.87
12/08	67.50	— —	(0.00)	0.00	44.57
12/07	82.55	— —	(0.00)	4.16	43.88
Annual Growth	2.6%	— —	—	—	4.5%

Core Mark Holding Co Inc

Smokes and snacks are at the center of Core-Mark Holding's cosmos. The company distributes packaged consumables (including cigarettes and other tobacco products candy snacks grocery items perishables nonalcoholic beverages and health and beauty aids) to about 29000 convenience stores; mass merchandisers; supermarkets; and drug liquor and specialty retailers. Cigarettes and other tobacco products are its top sellers generating more than three-quarters of net sales. Through about two dozen distribution facilities Core-Mark serves customers in all 50 US states and five Canadian provinces. Its 10 biggest clients (which include Couche-Tard and Valero) contribute about a third of sales.

Operations

Core-Mark supplies its customers from a network of more than 25 distribution centers in the US and Canada. It also operates dedicated facilities for its largest customers Couche-Tard and Valero in Phoenix and San Antonio respectively.

Geographic Reach

Its Core-Mark Canada business contributes 15% of the company's total sales.

Financial Analysis

Core-Mark's sales increased nearly 12% in 2011 vs. 2010 while net income was up 48% over the same period. The run up in sales was driven by its entry into two new markets through the 2011 purchase of Forrest City Grocery a wholesaler with customers in Arkansas Mississippi Tennessee and surrounding states and the establishment of a new operating division in Tampa Florida. Increased sales in the company's food/non-food category also contributed to top-line growth.

Strategy

In an effort to grow market share and extend its geographic reach Core-Mark has been active on the acquisition front. Most recently the company agreed to buy North Carolina-based J.T. Davenport & Sons a distributor to the convenience store industry in eight states for about $45 million. In 2011 Core-Mark purchased family-owned Forrest City Grocery a wholesaler with customers in Arkansas Mississippi Tennessee and surrounding states for about $66 million. The strategic purchase filled a gap in Core-Mark's service area. (Forrest City Grocery became a wholly-owned indirect subsidiary of Core-Mark.) A core element of Core-Mark's corporate strategy is to expand its presence east of the Mississippi. To that end in mid-2010 it purchased the assets of Finkle Distributors whose customer base included New York Pennsylvania and other surrounding states for $43 million. The deal added Finkle's customer accounts and inventory and it complemented Core-Mark's acquisition of Auburn Merchandise Distributors (2008) which served customers in Connecticut Maine Massachusetts New Hampshire and Rhode Island.

Core-Mark hopes to offset the decline in cigarette smoking by gaining a larger share of the shrinking market and growing its non-cigarette categories like fresh foods. To grow food sales Core-Marked has expanded its "Fresh and Local" food program to more than 87000 stores. The program offers freshly made sandwiches salads baked goods fruits vegetables and dairy items. In the second half of 2010 Core-Mark began distributing Jamba Juice's "Grab 'n Go" line of fresh deli wraps salads and sandwiches bolstering its fresh offering to convenience stores. (Core-Mark also supplies coffee and coffee brewing equipment and other food-to-go programs to its customers.) As consumers increase their purchases of fresh food and dairy products at convenience stores Core-Mark has focused on offering customers more fresh merchandise which has the added benefit of returning higher margins. To keep perishables fresh on the way to market the company has upgraded its refrigerated capacity and invested in chilling docks and other systems designed to deliver fresh goods quickly.

Ownership

Advisory Research Inc. owns nearly 13% of Core-Mark's shares.

Company Background

The company's roots reach back to 1888 when it was known as Glaser Bros. a family-run candy and tobacco distribution business in San Francisco.

EXECUTIVES

President CEO and Director, J. Michael (Mike) Walsh, age 64, $482,891 total compensation
VP and Chief Accounting Officer, Christopher M. (Chris) Miller, age 51
Chairman, Randolph I. Thornton, age 66
Director Investor Relations, Milton Gray Draper
SVP US Distribution West, Christopher L. Walsh, age 47, $247,336 total compensation
SVP Corporate Development, Scott E. McPherson, age 42, $226,346 total compensation
SVP Resources, Thomas B. Perkins, age 53, $246,923 total compensation
SVP and CFO, Stacy Loretz-Congdon, age 52, $281,600 total compensation
SVP US Distribution (East), Christopher M. (Chris) Murray, age 46, $205,838 total compensation
President Core-Mark Canada, Eric Rolheiser
VP Marketing, Christopher K. Hobson
Director, Gary F. Colter, age 66
President CEO and Director, J. Michael (Mike) Walsh, age 64
Director, L. William (Bill) Krause, age 69
Director, Stuart W. Booth, age 61
Director, Robert A. (Rob) Allen, age 62
Director, Harvey L. Tepner, age 55
Auditors: Deloitte&ToucheLLP

LOCATIONS

HQ: Core-Mark Holding Company Inc.
395 Oyster Point Blvd. Ste. 415, South San Francisco CA 94080
Phone: 650-589-9445 **Fax:** 650-952-4284
Web: www.coremark.com

2011 Sales

	$ mil.	% of total
US	6,865	85
Canada	1,220	15
Adjustments	28	
Total	**8,114**	**100**

PRODUCTS/OPERATIONS

2011 Sales

	$ mil.	% of total
Cigarettes	5,710	70
Food	995	12
Tobacco products (excluding cigarettes)	607	8
Candy	459	6
Health beauty & general	237	3
Non-alcoholic beverages	100	1
Equipment & other	2	
Total	**8,114**	**100**

COMPETITORS

800-JR Cigar
AMCON Distributing
Associated Food
C&S Wholesale
Coca-Cola
Eby-Brown
Frito-Lay
GSC Enterprises
H. T. Hackney
Hostess Brands
McLane
Nash-Finch
Roundy' s
Southern Wine & Spirits
Stephenson Wholesale Company
SUPERVALU
Unified Grocers
Wal-Mart

HISTORICAL FINANCIALS

Company Type: Public

Income Statement FYE: December 31

	REVENUE ($ mil.)	NET INCOME ($ mil.)	NET PROFIT MARGIN	EMPLOYEES
12/11	8,114	26	0.3%	4,852
12/10	7,266	17	0.2%	4,399
12/09	6,531	47	0.7%	4,267
12/08	6,044	17	0.3%	4,181
12/07	5,560	24	0.4%	4,035
Annual Growth	9.9%	2.1%	—	4.7%

2011 Year-End Financials

Debt ratio: 7.25%
Return on equity: 6.98%
Cash ($ mil.): 15
Current ratio: 189.32
Long-term debt ($ mil.): 63
No. of shares (mil.): 11
Dividends
Yield: —
Payout: 7.62%
Market value ($ mil.): 449

	STOCK PRICE ($) FY Close	P/E High/Low	PER SHARE ($) Earnings	Dividends	Book Value
12/11	39.60	17 13	2.23	0.00	33.10
12/10	35.59	23 16	1.55	0.00	32.62
12/09	32.96	7 3	4.35	0.00	31.43
12/08	21.52	18 9	1.64	0.00	25.46
12/07	28.72	16 11	2.15	0.00	25.51
Annual Growth	8.4%	— —	0.9%	—	6.7%

Corning, Inc.

Corning is building a foundation out of glass. Once known for its kitchenware and lab products the company manufactures glass substrates primarily for LCD displays. It also makes optical fiber and cable and other telecommunications equipment substrates and filters for automotive emissions control products glass and optical materials for a wide range of industries and labware and equipment. More than half of Corning's sales (and all of its display segment customers including AU Optronics and Sharp Electronics each around 10% of total sales) come from the Asia/Pacific region including nearly a quarter from Taiwan. Corning has about 80 manufacturing and processing facilities across more than a dozen countries.

HISTORY

Amory Houghton started Houghton Glass in Massachusetts in 1851 and moved it to Corning New York in 1868. By 1876 the company renamed Corning Glass Works was making several types of technical and pharmaceutical glass. In 1880 it supplied the glass for Thomas Edison's first lightbulb. Other early developments included the red-yellow-green traffic light system and borosilicate glass (which can withstand sudden temperature changes) for Pyrex oven and laboratory ware.

Joint ventures have been crucial to Corning's success. Early ones included Pittsburgh Corning (with Pittsburgh Plate Glass 1937 glass construction blocks) Owens-Corning (with Owens-Illinois 1938 fiberglass) and Dow Corning (with Dow Chemical 1943 silicones).

By 1945 the company's laboratories had made it the undisputed leader in the manufacture of specialty glass. Applications for its glass technology included the first mass-produced television tubes freezer-to-oven ceramic cookware (Pyroceram Corning Ware) and car headlights.

After WWII Corning emphasized consumer product sales and expanded globally. In the 1970s the company pioneered the development of optical fiber and auto emission technology (now two of its principal products).

Seeing maturing markets for such established products as lightbulbs and television tubes Corning began buying higher-growth laboratory services companies —MetPath in 1982 Hazleton in 1987 Enseco in 1989 and G.H. Besse-laar in 1989. Vice chairman James Houghton the great-great-grandson of Corning's founder was named chairman and CEO in 1983.

Corning established international joint ventures with Siemens Mitsubishi and Samsung. In 1988 the company bought Revere Ware (cookware). The next year Corning dropped Glass Works from its name.

In 1994 Corning and Siecor (joint venture with Siemens) acquired several fiber and cable businesses from Northern Telecom (now Nortel Networks) expanding the company's presence in Canada.

Joint venture Dow Corning under assault from thousands of women seeking damages because of leaking breast implants entered Chapter 11 bankruptcy protection in 1995 (and exited it in 2004). The massive losses incurred by Dow Corning due to litigation and a downturn in Corning's lab products sales prompted the company to recast itself. Corning began selling off its well-known consumer brands and putting greater emphasis on its high-tech optical and display products through acquisitions and R&D.

Company veteran Roger Ackerman was named chairman and CEO in 1996 replacing Houghton. He moved quickly to transform the company from a disjointed conglomerate to a high-tech optics manufacturer. That year the company spun off its laboratory testing division to shareholders creating Covance and Quest Diagnostics.

After deals to sell a stake in Corning Consumer Products to AEA Investors fell through in 1997 Corning sold a majority stake in the housewares unit to KKR the next year. In 1999 Corning bought UK-based BICC Group's telecom cable business.

In 2000 Corning made more than $5 billion worth of acquisitions to expand its optical fiber and hardware business. It bought Siemens' optical cable and hardware operations and the remaining 50% of the companies' Siecor joint venture. Corning acquired Oak Industries (optical components) for $1.8 billion and NetOptix (optical filters) for $2.15 billion and purchased the 67% of microelectromechanical systems specialist IntelliSense it didn't already own. Continuing its spending spree the company bought part of Pirelli's fiber-optic telecom components business for about $3.6 billion; it also acquired Cisco's 10% stake in the business.

In 2001 Ackerman retired as chairman and CEO of the company. COO John Loose was named CEO and Houghton was again appointed chairman.

In the early 21st century Corning suffered from slowing sales of telecommunications products but a realignment of its businesses allowed the company to regain its financial footing. That year the company moved to expand the segment through its acquisition of Optimum Manufacturing Corporation which makes precision machined components for the aerospace communications medical military and scientific markets.

Slowing demand prompted Corning to lay off about 25% of its staff shut down plants and discontinue its glass tubing operations that year. Houghton returned to the position of chief executive after Loose retired in 2002. That year the company made more layoffs closed plants and sold several noncore operations; it also bought rival Lucent's fiber-optic and cable facilities in China where demand was relatively strong. The following year Corning sold its photonic components business to Avanex (now part of Oclaro). In 2004 it sold its quartz crystal frequency-control products business.

Corning president Wendell Weeks succeeded Houghton as CEO in 2005. Houghton remained chairman and retired again in 2006 becoming non-executive chairman. Houghton became chairman emeritus in 2007 and remained on the board as a director. Weeks was elected chairman of the board.

Corning set plans in 2006 to build an LCD glass substrate finishing plant in Beijing the first to be constructed on the Chinese mainland. The facility was completed and opened in 2008.

Through all of the changes in Corning's business model and strategic priorities the company kept Steuben Glass as a subsidiary for 90 years. The fine-glass firm was named for Steuben County New York where Steuben maintained its design studio and glassworks. In 2007 Corning put the business up for sale after a decade of financial losses at Steuben Glass. The parent company in 2008 sold Steuben Glass to Schottenstein Stores; it kept an equity stake of nearly 20% in the fine-glass firm.

In 2007 it committed $795 million over five years to build a glass manufacturing plant at Sharp's new LCD production complex in Sakai Japan. Sharp began making large glass panels for LCD TVs at the Sakai plant in 2009. The company then started making Gen 10 LCD glass substrate sizes for Sharp with its EAGLE XG glass-making process at the new plant.

The company continued to focus on emerging technologies. Gorilla Glass a damage-resistant cover glass was introduced in 2008 for use in mobile phones notebook computers and for touch-screen technologies. The company's Green Laser technology rivals light-emitting diodes (LEDs) by offering improved images on mobile devices. It began developing better silicon on glass (SiOG) technology which adds pure crystalline silicon uniformly to computer chips and devices. The company also began work on a filter that would remove mercury released at coal-fired power plants. Other innovations include the Gen 10 (10th generation) LCD glass ClearCurve optical fiber and DuraTrap emissions-control solutions.

In 2008 Corning created its fifth operating segment Specialty Materials which includes semiconductors and optical sensors for aerospace and defense. To expand the segment the company acquired Optimum Manufacturing Corporation which made precision machined components for the aerospace communications medical military and scientific markets.

In 2009 the company acquired California-based Axygen BioScience a manufacturer and distributor of laboratory research plastic ware and bench-top equipment. Corning purchased the company and its subsidiaries from American Capital for about $400 million. Axygen BioScience was integrated into its Life Sciences segment and boosted Corning's portfolio of life sciences products. The acquisition also widened the door to promising global opportunities which will be channeled through Axygen's two manufacturing locations in Asia.

EXECUTIVES

Chairman President and CEO, Wendell P. Weeks, age 52, $1,030,000 total compensation
Vice Chairman and CFO, James B. Flaws, age 63, $821,000 total compensation
SVP and General Counsel, Vincent P. Hatton, age 61
EVP and Chief Administrative Officer, Kirk P. Gregg, age 52, $578,000 total compensation
Chairman and President Corning Display Technologies Taiwan, Alan T. Eusden
SVP Worldwide Government Affairs, Timothy J. Regan
SVP and Treasurer, Mark S. Rogus, age 52
EVP and CTO, Joseph A. (Joe) Miller Jr., age 69, $610,000 total compensation
VP Secretary and Assistant General Counsel, Denise A. Hauselt
SVP Global Compensation and Benefits, John P. MacMahon
EVP Strategy and Corporate Development, Lawrence D. (Larry) McRae, age 53
SVP and Director New Business Development, Mark A. Newhouse
SVP and General Manager Specialty Materials, James R. Steiner
Media Contacts Environmental Technologies, Pamela W. Porter
SVP and General Manager Corning Optical Fiber, Martin J. Curran
SVP Wireless Networks and New Business Development Corning Cable Systems; CEO Corning MobileAccess, Michael D. (Mike) Genovese
SVP Asia Pacific and Emerging Markets Corning Cable Systems, John R. Sicotte
President and CEO Corning Cable Systems, Clark S. Kinlin
VP and Global Business Director Corning Environmental Technologies, Thomas Appelt
President Corning Japan K.K., Akihisa Mitsuhashi
President Corning Glass Technologies, James P. Clappin, age 55
General Manager Greater China, Eric S. Musser, age 52
VP and General Manager Corning Life Sciences, Richard Eglen, age 55
SVP Manufacturing and Performance Excellence and Procurement and Transportation, Donald A. McCabe Jr.
VP and General Manager Advanced Optics Specialty Materials, Curt Weinstein
EVP and CTO, David L. Morse, age 59
SVP and General Manager Corning Environmental Technologies, Mark A. Beck, age 46
SVP Science and Technology, Charles R. Craig
VP Global Commercial Development, Vivian L. Gernand
SVP Photovoltaic and Touch Programs, Marc S. Giroux
General Manager and President Corning East Asia, Clifford L. Hund
VP and General Intellectual Property Counsel, Mark W. Lauroesch
SVP Corporate Product and Process Development, Jean-Pierre Mazeau
SVP Human Resources, Christine M. Pambianchi, age 44
Corporate Communications, Daniel F. Collins
SVP and Director Photovoltaic Glass Technologies, Gary S. Calabrese, age 55
VP Deputy General Counsel and Chief Compliance Officer, Jack H. Cleland
VP Business Services, Michael W. Donnelly
VP Investor Relations, Kenneth C. Sofio
Corporate Communications, Kelli C. Hopp-Michlosky
Media Contact Japan, Akihiko Miyatani
Media Contact Korea, Sonia Jung
Media Contact China, Holly Hu
Media Contact Corning Cable Systems, Debbie Richart
Media Contact Optical Fiber, Monica L. Sofio
Media Contact Specialty Materials, Anna Giambrone
Media Contact Life Sciences, Dana D. Moss
VP and Manager Manufacturing Environmental Technologies, Wilfred M. (Mills) Kenan Jr.
VP and Director Inorganic and Broad-Based Technologies, Madapusi K. Badrinarayan
Managing Director Cable Systems EMEA, Gilbert C. Chorosz
President and General Manager Corning Display Technologies, Lisa Ferrero
President and CEO Corning Gilbert, Steven W. Karaffa
VP Global Commercial Operations Corning Gilbert, J. David Johnson
Director Commercial Technology Life Sciences, Jeffrey L. Mooney
Director Commercial Technology Gorilla Glass Specialty Materials, Paul Tompkins
Division VP and Business Manager Technical Materials Specialty Materials, Mark A. Matthews
Division VP and General Manager Corning Life Sciences, Lydia Kenton Walsh
Division VP and Director Advanced Life Sciences, Ronald L. Verkleeren
Director Sales and Engineering Gorilla? Glass Specialty Materials, James Hollis
Director Marketing and Commercial Operations Gorilla? Glass, David R. Velasquez
Media Contact Display Technologies, John O'Hare
Media Contact Taiwan, Shao-Kang Lee
Business Controller Corning Gilbert, Denis Hubert
SVP and Operations Chief of Staff, Jeffrey Evenson
Vice Chairman and CFO, James B. Flaws, age 63
Director, Glenn F. Tilton, age 64
Director, Mark S. Wrighton, age 62
Director, Gordon Gund, age 72
Director, Kurt M. Landgraf, age 65
Director, John Seely Brown, age 71
Director, Hansel E. Tookes II, age 64
Director, William D. (Bill) Smithburg, age 74
Director, Deborah D. Rieman, age 62
Director, H. Onno (Onno) Ruding, age 72
Director, Robert F. Cummings Jr., age 62
Auditors: PricewaterhouseCoopersLLP

LOCATIONS

HQ: Corning Incorporated
1 Riverfront Plaza, Corning NY 14831-0001
Phone: 607-974-9000 **Fax:** 607-974-8091
Web: www.corning.com

2012 Sales

	$ mil.	% of total
Asia/Pacific		
China	2,103	26
Taiwan	1,708	22
Japan	751	9
South Korea	94	1
Other	243	3
North America		
US	1,859	23
Canada	246	3
Mexico	24	-
Europe		
Germany	264	3
UK	134	2
France	57	1
Other	274	4
Latin America		
Brazil	29	-
Other	33	-
Other regions	193	3
Total	8,012	100

PRODUCTS/OPERATIONS

2012 Sales

	$ mil.	% of total
Display technologies	2,909	36
Telecommunications	2,130	27
Specialty materials	1,346	17
Environmental technologies	964	12
Life sciences	657	8
Other	6	-
Total	8,012	100

Selected Products

Display technologies
- Liquid crystal displays (LCD)
- Organic light-emitting diode (OLED) displays

Telecommunications
- Optical fiber and cable
- Optical networking components

Environmental technologies
- Industrial and stationary emissions products
- Mobile emissions and automotive catalytic converter products

Life sciences
- Genomics and laboratory equipment

Other
- Polarized glass
- Semiconductor materials

COMPETITORS

3M
Alcatel-Lucent
Amphenol
Asahi Glass
Becton Dickinson
Belden
Carl-Zeiss-Stiftung
CommScope
Dai Nippon Printing
DENSO
Draka Holding
Fujikura Ltd.
Furukawa Electric
General Cable
Gerresheimer Glass
Heraeus Holding
Hoya Corp.
IBIDEN
JDS Uniphase
NGK INSULATORS
Nikon
Nippon Electric Glass
Nippon Sheet Glass
Nortel Networks
Oerlikon
Prysmian
Saint-Gobain
SCHOTT
Shin-Etsu Chemical
Sumitomo Electric
Superior Essex
SWCC SHOWA
TE Connectivity
Thermo Fisher Scientific
Thomas & Betts
Toppan Printing

HISTORICAL FINANCIALS

Company Type: Public

Income Statement

FYE: December 31

	REVENUE ($ mil.)	NET INCOME ($ mil.)	NET PROFIT MARGIN	EMPLOYEES
12/11	7,890	2,805	35.6%	28,800
12/10	6,632	3,558	53.6%	26,200
12/09	5,395	2,008	37.2%	23,500
12/08	5,948	5,257	88.4%	27,000
12/07	5,860	2,150	36.7%	28,000
Annual Growth	7.7%	6.9%	—	0.7%

2011 Year-End Financials

Debt ratio: 8.59%
Return on equity: 13.31%
Cash ($ mil.): 4,661
Current ratio: 413.78
Long-term debt ($ mil.): 2,364
No. of shares (mil.): 1,515
Dividends
Yield: —
Payout: 12.71%
Market value ($ mil.): 19,665

	STOCK PRICE ($) FY Close	P/E High/Low		PER SHARE ($) Earnings	Dividends	Book Value
12/11	12.98	13	7	1.77	0.00	13.91
12/10	19.32	9	7	2.25	0.20	12.41
12/09	19.31	15	7	1.28	0.20	10.01
12/08	9.53	8	2	3.32	0.20	8.68
12/07	23.99	20	13	1.34	0.10	6.06
Annual Growth	(14.2%)	—	—	7.2%	—	23.1%

Costco Wholesale Corp

Wal-Mart isn't the biggest in "every" business. Costco Wholesale is the largest wholesale club operator in the US (ahead of Wal-Mart's SAM'S CLUB). The company operates more than 600 membership warehouse stores serving some 67 million cardholders in 40 US states and Australia Canada Japan Mexico Puerto Rico South Korea Taiwan and the UK primarily under the Costco Wholesale name. Stores offer discount prices on an average of about 4000 products (many in bulk packaging) ranging from alcoholic beverages and appliances to fresh food pharmaceuticals and tires. Certain club memberships also offer products and services such as car and home insurance mortgage and real estate services and travel packages.

Geographic Reach

Costco Wholesale rings up the majority (72%) of its sales in the US. The company's 80-plus stores in Canada account for 16% of sales with other countries including Mexico Japan Australia and the UK contributing the rest. Costco operates in Taiwan and Korea through majority-owned subsidiaries.

Operations

Costco's retail operation numbered 608 warehouse stores in eight countries at the end of fiscal 2012 (ends August). Serving the retail stores is Costco Wholesale Industries a division of the company that operates manufacturing businesses including special food packaging optical labs meat processing and jewelry distribution. To shop at Costco customers must be members –a policy the company believes reinforces customer loyalty and provides a steady source of fee revenue (2% of fiscal 2012 sales). Three types of annual memberships are available: Business ($50 each); Gold Star ($50 for individuals and their spouses): and Executive ($100 allows members to purchase products and services including insurance mortgage services and long-distance phone service at reduced rates). Costco also operates the e-commerce site costco.com.

Financial Analysis

After a blip during the recent deep recession when Costco's historically steadily-rising sales dipped by 1.5% the warehouse club operator has returned to growth mode. In fiscal 2012 sales grew by more than 11% vs. the prior year to top $99 billion. Performance was driven by a 7% gain in same-store sales at the company's warehouse stores and higher gasoline prices among other factors. Net income increased nearly 17% over the same period. Revenue from membership fees increased 11% in fiscal 2012 vs. the prior year primarily due to new member sign-ups at warehouse stores open for more than a year and the impact of raising annual membership fees.

In fiscal 2011 sales increased by about 14% vs. the previous year while net income grew by 12%. Costco's sales performance benefitted from the addition of 20 net new warehouse clubs in 2011 and a 10% increase in sales at locations open at least one year. Membership fees increased by more than 10% as the company sold more higher-fee Executive Memberships and enlisted more members. The strong performance in 2011 followed a good 2010 when sales grew by about 9%.

Strategy

Facing competition from discounters including Target that don't charge a membership fee as well as from archrival SAM'S CLUB Costco has been busy expanding and retrofitting its warehouses (which average about 143000 sq. ft.) to accommodate fresh food sections and other ancillary units such as gas stations optical departments pharmacies and food courts. Costco's foray into grocery sales is encouraging. Food and sundries accounted for about 55% of total sales in fiscal 2012 making Costco the third-largest seller of groceries in the US behind Wal-Mart Supercenters and Kroger. Costco has expanded its premium private-label Kirkland Signature line of some 330 items (about 15% of sales) to 500 products. It also plans to grow its e-commerce business Costco.com which offers products not found in its stores and add more than a dozen new warehouse stores by the end of calendar year 2012. Despite intense competition in the warehouse club arena Costco boasts nearly a 90% renewal rate in North America and 86% worldwide. On the international front the retailer is looking to take advantage of rising consumer demand in developing markets especially in Asia. Key markets include Japan Korea and Taiwan. Also the company opened its first location in Australia in mid-2009 and now has three clubs there. Closer to home Costco bought its joint venture partner's Controladora Comercial Mexicana 50% stake in Costco Mexico for $789 million in 2012.

HISTORY

From 1954 to 1974 retailer Sol Price built his Fed-Mart discount chain into a $300 million behemoth selling general merchandise to government employees. Price sold the company to Hugo Mann in 1975 and the next year with son Robert Rick Libenson and Giles Bateman opened the first Price Club warehouse in San Diego to sell in volume to small businesses at steep discounts.

Posting a large loss its first year prompted Price Club's decision to expand membership to include government utility and hospital employees as well as credit union members. In 1978 it opened a second store in Phoenix. With the help of his father Sol's other son Laurence began a chain of tire-mounting stores (located adjacent to Price Club outlets on land leased from the company and using tires sold by the Price Clubs).

The company went public in 1980 with four stores in California and Arizona. Price Club moved into the eastern US with its 1984 opening of a store in Virginia and continued to expand including a joint venture with Canadian retailer Steinberg in 1986 to operate stores in Canada; the first Canadian warehouse opened that year in Montreal.

Two years later Price Club acquired A. M. Lewis (grocery distributor Southern California and Arizona) and the next year it opened two Price Club Furnishings offering discounted home and office furniture.

Price Club bought out Steinberg's interest in the Canadian locations in 1990 and added stores on the East Coast and in California Colorado and British Columbia. However competition in the East from ensconced rivals such as SAM'S CLUB and PACE forced the closure of two stores two years later. A 50-50 joint venture with retailer Controladora Comercial Mexicana led to the opening of two Price Clubs in Mexico City one each in 1992 and 1993.

Price Club merged with Costco Wholesale in 1993. Founded in 1983 by Jeffrey Brotman and James Sinegal (a former EVP of Price Company) Costco Wholesale went public in 1985 and expanded into Canada.

In 1993 Price/Costco opened its first warehouse outside the Americas in a London suburb. Merger costs led to a loss the following year and Price/Costco spun off its commercial real estate operations as well as certain international operations as Price Enterprises (now Price Legacy). In 1995 the company launched its Kirkland Signature brand of private-label merchandise. Two years later the company changed its corporate name to Costco Companies.

Costco began online sales and struck a deal to buy two stores in South Korea in 1998 and opened its first store in Japan in 1999. Under industrywide pressure over the way members-only chains record fees Costco took a $118 million charge for fiscal 1999 to change accounting practices. That year the company made yet another name change to Costco Wholesale (emphasizing its core warehouse operations).

In 2000 the company purchased private retailer Littlewoods' 20% stake in Costco UK increasing Costco's ownership to 80%. Costco began expanding into the Midwest in 2001 as part of plans to open 40 new clubs a year including ones in China.

During fiscal 2002 Costco opened 29 new warehouse clubs. In December 2002 the retailer opened its first home store –called Costco Home –in Kirkland Washington stocked with mostly high-end furniture. A second Costco Home store opened in Tempe Arizona in December 2004.

Costco increased its equity interest in Costco Wholesale UK in October 2003 to 100% when it purchased Carrefour Nederland's 20% stake.

In 2006 Costco began offering more than 200 generic prescription medicines (100 count) for $10 or less. The following year Costco.com logged sales in excess of $1 billion.

In July 2009 Costco shuttered its two Costco Home stores which were located in Washington and Arizona. The retailer cited the weak economy and market for home furnishings and the fact that the concept didn't fit with its expansion plans for their closure. In August the company opened its first warehouse club in Australia.

CEO Jim Sinegal stepped down in 2012 after more than 20 years at the helm. Sinegal who together with chairman Jeffrey Brotman founded Costco in 1983 handed the reins to Craig Jelinek a 28-year veteran and former president and COO of the company.

EXECUTIVES

SVP and General Manager Southeast Region, Roger A. Campbell

EVP Construction Distribution and Traffic, Thomas K. Walker, age 72

SVP Pharmacy, Charles V. Burnett

SVP Merchandising Foods and Sundries, Timothy L. Rose

SVP and Corporate Controller, David S. Petterson

EVP and CIO, Paul G. Moulton, age 61

SVP Administration and Chief Legal Officer, Joel Benoliel

SVP Human Resources and Risk Management, John Matthews
SVP Administration Global Operations, Franz E. Lazarus
EVP and COO Eastern and Canadian Divisions, Joseph P. (Joe) Portera, age 60, $550,002 total compensation
President CEO and Director, W. Craig Jelinek, age 60, $603,849 total compensation
EVP COO Southwest and Mexico Divisions, Dennis R. Zook, age 63, $545,288 total compensation
EVP CFO and Director, Richard A. Galanti, age 55, $600,000 total compensation
Chairman, Jeffrey H. (Jeff) Brotman, age 70, $350,000 total compensation
SVP Special Projects, Donald E. (Don) Burdick
SVP Costco Wholesale Industries and Business Development, Richard C. Chavez
EVP International Operations, James P. (Jim) Murphy
EVP and COO Northern and Midwest Division, John D. McKay, age 55
SVP and General Manager Northeast Region, Jeffrey R. Long
SVP and General Manager Bay Area Region, Dennis A. Hoover
SVP Merchandising Non-Foods, Dennis E. Knapp
SVP and General Manager Midwest Region, John B. Gaherty
SVP and General Manager Mexico, Jaime Gonzalez
SVP and General Manager Los Angeles Region, Bruce A. Greenwood
SVP and General Manager San Diego Region, Robert D. Hicok
EVP and COO Merchandising, Douglas W. (Doug) Schutt, age 53
SVP E-Commerce and Publishing, Ginnie M. Roeglin
SVP Operations Depots, John D. Thelan
SVP and Country Manager Canada, Louise Wendling
VP Membership Marketing Services and Costco Travel, Paul Latham
VP Operations Bay Area Region, Drew Sakuma
VP and General Merchandise Manager Service Deli and Food Court, Alan Bubitz
VP Corporate Purchasing and Business Centers, Patrick Callans
VP and Country Manager Taiwan, Richard Chang
VP Pharmacy, Victor A. Curtis
VP and General Merchandise Manager Corporate Non-Foods, Richard Delie
VP and General Merchandise Manager Corporate Non-Foods, Timothy K. Farmer
VP Real Estate Development West, Jack S. Frank
VP and General Merchandise Manager Corporate Non-Foods, Cynthia Glaser
VP and General Merchandise Manager Corporate Foods, Nancy Griese
VP and Merchandise Accounting Controller, Joseph Grachek III
VP and Financial Accounting Controller, Daniel M. Hines
VP and General Merchandise Manager Imports, Mitzi Hu
VP Administration and Community Giving, Arthur D. Jackson Jr.
VP and Corporate Treasurer, Harold E. Kaplan
VP and General Merchandise Manager Corporate Non-Foods, James (Jim) Klauer
VP Business Centers, Phil Lind
SVP Merchandising Fresh Foods, Jeffrey Lyons
VP Operations Bakery and Food Court, Susan McConnaha
VP Real Estate Development, John Minola
SVP Construction, Ali Moayeri
VP Financial Planning and Investor Relations, Robert E. (Bob) Nelson
VP Legal and General Counsel, Richard J. Olin
VP and Country Manager UK, Stephen (Steve) Pappas
VP Information Systems, James W. Rutherford
VP International, Michael Sinegal
VP and General Merchandise Manager International, Kimberley L. Suchomel
VP Construction, Keith H. Thompson
VP and General Merchandise Manager Corporate Non-Foods, Jack Weisbly
VP Operations Fresh Meat Produce and Service Deli, Charlie A. Winters
VP and General Merchandise Manager Corporare Non-Foods, Michael (Mike) Parrott
VP Operations Bay Area Region, Jeffrey Abadir
VP and General Merchandise Manager Foods and Sundries Western Canada Region, Sandi A. Babins
VP Operations Bay Area Region, John Booth
SVP Merchandising Non-Foods and E-commerce Canadian Division, Andree Brien
VP and General Merchandise Manager Foods Northwest Region, Debbie Cain
VP Operations Southeast Region, Gerard Dempsey
VP and General Merchandise Manager Foods Los Angeles Region, John T. Eagan
VP Operations Los Angeles Region, Frank Farcone
VP and General Merchandise Manager Hardlines Canadian Division, Murray Fleming
VP and General Merchandise Manager Non-Foods Northwest Region, Gary Giacomi
VP and General Merchandise Manager Hardlines Canadian Division, Isaac Hamaoui
VP and General Merchandise Manager Foods Midwest Region, William (Bill) Hanson
VP and General Merchandise Manager Foods Southeast Region, Doris Harley
VP Operations Northwest Region, David Harruff
VP Human Resources Finance and Information Systems Canadian Division, Ross Hunt
VP and General Merchandise Manager Corporate Foods, Gary Kotzen
VP Operations Northeast Region, Robert Leuck
VP and General Merchandise Manager Ancillaries Canadian Division, Gerry Liben
VP and General Merchandise Manager Merchandising Mexico, Steve Mantanona
VP and General Merchandise Manager Foods Bay Area Region, Tracy Mauldin-Avery
VP Operations Los Angeles Region, Mark Maushund
VP and General Merchandise Manager Foods and Sundries Eastern Canada Region, Pietro Nenci
VP and General Merchandise Manager Non-Foods Western Canada Region, David R. G. Nickel
VP Operations San Diego Region, Mario Omoss
VP Operations Los Angeles Region, Shawn Parks
VP E-Commerce Operations, Michael (Mike) Pollard
VP Operations Southeast Region, Steve Powers
VP Operations Northeast Region, Paul Pulver
VP Operations Southeast Region, Aldyn Royes
VP Operations Northeast Region, Yoram Rubanenko
VP and General Merchandise Manager Fresh-Foods Canadian Division, Janet Shanks
VP Operations Eastern Canada Region, David Skinner
VP Operations Eastern Canada Region, Gary Swindells
VP Operations Western Canada Region, Scott Tyler
SVP and General Manager Northwest Region, Ronald M. (Ron) Vachris
VP and General Merchandise Manager Softlines Canadian Division, Azmina Virani
VP Operations Texas Region, Richard Webb
SVP and General Manager Western Canada Region, Russell D. (Russ) Miller
SVP and General Manager Eastern Canada Region, Pierre Riel
VP and General Merchandise Manager Foods San Diego Region, Deborah Calhoun
VP US Gasoline Car Wash and Photo, Jeff Cole
VP and CFO Mexico, Mauricio Talayero
VP Operations Mexico, Adrian Thummler
VP Operations San Diego Region, Bryan Blank
VP and Country Manager Korea, Preston Draper
VP and Country Manager Australia, Patrick Noone
VP and Country Manager Japan, Ken Theriault
VP Operations Northeast Region, Rich Wilcox
VP and General Merchandise Manager Corporate Non-Foods, Shannon West
VP and General Merchandise Manager Foods Northeast Region, James (Jim) Stafford
VP Operations Depots, Sarah Mogk
Associate General Counsel and Chief Compliance Officer, John Sullivan
VP Operations Pharmacy, Richard Stephens
VP and General Merchandise Manager Corporate Produce and Fresh Meat, Frank Padilla
VP E-commerce Merchandising, Court Newberry
VP Real Estate Development, David Messner
VP Real Estate Eastern Division, Jeff Ishida
VP Operations Northwest Region, James Hayes
VP Information Systems, Timothy Haser
VP Operations Bay Area Region, Darby Greek
VP Marketing Canada, Lorelle Gilpin
VP Operations Southeast Region, Julie Cruz
VP Operations San Diego Region, Mike Casebier
VP Operations Northwest Region, Christopher Bolves
Director, Jeffrey S. (Jeff) Raikes, age 54
Director, Hamilton E. (Tony) James, age 61
Director, Charles T. (Charlie) Munger, age 88
President CEO and Director, W. Craig Jelinek, age 60
EVP CFO and Director, Richard A. Galanti, age 55
Director, James D. (Jim) Sinegal, age 76
Director, William H. (Bill Sr.) Gates Sr., age 86
Director, Daniel J. (Dan) Evans, age 87
Director, Susan L. Decker, age 49
Director, Benjamin S. Carson Sr., age 60
Director, Jill S. Ruckelshaus, age 75
Director, John W. Meisenbach, age 75
Director, Richard M. Libenson, age 70
Auditors: KPMGLLP

LOCATIONS

HQ: Costco Wholesale Corporation
999 Lake Dr., Issaquah WA 98027
Phone: 425-313-8100 **Fax:** 702-679-5595
Web: www.primadonna.com

2012 Locations

	No.
US & Puerto	439
Canada	82
Mexico	32
UK	22
Japan	13
Taiwan	9
South	8
Australia	3
Total	**608**

2012 Sales

	$ mil.	% of total
US	71,776	72
Canada	15,717	16
Other international	11,644	12
Total	**99,137**	**100**

PRODUCTS/OPERATIONS

2012 Sales

	% of total
Sundries (including candy snacks beverages cleaning products &	22
Food (dry & institutionally	21
Hardlines (including major appliances electronics & office & auto	16
Fresh food (meat bakery deli &	13
Softlines (including apparel housewares media home furnishings &	10
Other (including pharmacy optical photo & gas	18
Total	**100**

2012 Sales

	$ mil.	% of total
Sales	97,062	98
Membership fees	2,075	2
Total	**99,137**	**100**

Selected Products and Services

Alcoholic beverages
Apparel
Appliances
Automotive insurance products (tires batteries)
Automobile sales
Baby products
Books
Cameras film and photofinishing
Candy
Caskets
CDs
Checks and form printing
Cleaning and institutional supplies
Collectibles
Computer hardware and software
Computer training services
Copying and printing services
Credit card processing
DVDs
Electronics
Eye exams
Flooring
Floral arrangements
Fresh foods (bakery deli meats produce seafood)
Furniture
Gasoline
Gifts
Glasses and contact lenses
Groceries and institutionally packaged foods
Hardware
Health and beauty aids
Hearing aids
Home insurance
Housewares
Insurance (automobile small-business health home)
Jewelry
Lighting supplies
Mortgage service
Office equipment and supplies
Outdoor living products
Payroll processing
Pet supplies
Pharmaceuticals
Plumbing supplies
Real estate services
Snack foods
Soft drinks
Sporting goods
Tobacco
Tools
Toys
Travel packages and other travel services
Video games and systems
Private Label
Kirkland Signature

COMPETITORS

1-800 CONTACTS
ALDI
Amazon.com
Army and Air Force Exchange
Kohl' s
Kroger
Lowe' s
Mattress Firm
Office Depot
Aurora Wholesalers
AutoZone
Barnes & Noble
Best Buy
Big Lots
BJ' s Wholesale Club
CVS Caremark
Dollar General
Family Dollar Stores
Home Depot
Kmart
PETCO
PetSmart
Safeway
Staples
Target Corporation
Toys ' ' R' ' Us
Trader Joe' s
Wal-Mart
Walgreen
Whole Foods

HISTORICAL FINANCIALS

Company Type: Public

Income Statement

FYE: September 2

	REVENUE ($ mil.)	NET INCOME ($ mil.)	NET PROFIT MARGIN	EMPLOYEES
09/12*	99,137	1,709	1.7%	174,000
08/11	88,915	1,462	1.6%	164,000
08/10	77,946	1,303	1.7%	147,000
08/09	71,422	1,086	1.5%	142,000
08/08	72,483	1,282	1.8%	137,000
Annual Growth	8.1%	7.4%	—	6.2%

*Fiscal year change

2012 Year-End Financials

Debt ratio: 5.09%
Return on equity: 13.83%
Cash ($ mil.): 3,528
Current ratio: 110.33
Long-term debt ($ mil.): 1,381
No. of shares (mil.): 432
Dividends
Yield: —
Payout: 26.48%
Market value ($ mil.): 42,314

	STOCK PRICE ($) FY Close	P/E High/Low		PER SHARE ($) Earnings	Dividends	Book Value
09/12*	97.87	25	20	3.89	0.00	28.59
08/11	77.21	25	17	3.30	0.00	27.64
08/10	56.19	21	17	2.92	0.00	24.98
08/09	51.77	28	15	2.47	0.00	22.98
08/08	67.06	25	19	2.89	0.00	21.25
Annual Growth	9.9%	—	—	7.7%	—	7.7%

*Fiscal year change

Covanta Holding Corp

Covanta Holding has seen the light: Waste can be converted into power. Led by Covanta Energy the company is a leader in the waste-to-energy market. Covanta Holding owns or operates more than 60 energy generation facilities (primarily in the US) that use municipal solid waste and biomass as well as fossil fuels and hydroelectric sources to generate power. It processes about 20 million tons of solid waste per year and provides electricity to some 1 million homes. Related businesses include landfills ashfills transfer stations and metals recycling.

Operations

The company operates and/or has ownership positions in 46 energy-from-waste facilities primarily in North America and 15 additional energy generation facilities including other renewable energy production facilities in North America (wood biomass and hydroelectric). It also operates a waste management infrastructure that is complementary to its core energy-from-waste business.

Financial Analysis

In 2011 Covanta reported a revenue increase of 4% primarily due to increased recycled metals revenues from higher pricing higher volume and improved quality of metal as a result of its processing facility increased waste and service revenues driven by service fee contract escalations higher tip fee pricing and stronger construction revenues related to the Honolulu expansion and Durham-York energy-from-waste projects. However this was offset by lower electricity sales from biomass facilities a cut in debt service pass-through revenue resulting from project debt repayments and lower energy pricing at energy-from-waste facilities.

Covanta's net income increased by 220% in 2011 thanks to higher revenues increased income from continuing operations and a decrease in losses on extinguishment of debt. Other factors included a drop in non-cash convertible debt related expense due to lower amortization of the debt discount for debentures and the net changes to the valuation of the derivatives associated with the cash convertible senior notes.

Except for the revenue slump in 2009 as the result of the recession the company has seen an upward trend in revenues from 2007 to 2011.

Strategy

Covanta seeks to become one of the world's leading energy-from-waste producers and has been busy over the past few years in working to achieve that goal by constructing and expanding its facilities which it operates on behalf of its client communities.

In 2012 Covanta bought the Delaware Valley Resource Recovery Facility in Chester Pennsylvania from GE Energy Financial Services for $94 million.

In 2011 the company completed the expansion of the H-POWER Energy-from-Waste facility owned by the City and County of Honolulu. Covanta. The expansion added a third boiler which increases the facility's capacity by 900 tons of municipal solid waste per day bringing the facility's total daily capacity to 3000 tons. The expansion also helps the facility to produce approximately 90 MW of renewable energy about 8% of Oahu's total power needs

In 2010 Covanta planned to sell some of its noncore assets and reinvest the proceeds in assets that it believes will create the greatest value. It decided to sell its stakes in its fossil fuel independent power production (IPP) facilities in Bangladesh India and the Philippines. It sold one of its facilities in India that year and in 2011 it sold its stake in a coal-fired power plant in the Philippines to project partner Electricity Generating PCL for $215 million.

Ownership

In 2012 Covanta chairman Samuel Zell held 11% of the company through his SZ Investments unit.

EXECUTIVES

Chairman, Samuel (Sam) Zell, age 70, $87,949 total compensation

VP and Chief Accounting Officer, Thomas E. (Tom) Bucks, age 55, $220,000 total compensation

President CEO and Director, Anthony J. (Tony) Orlando, age 52, $726,923 total compensation

EVP General Counsel and Secretary, Timothy J. Simpson, age 53, $321,923 total compensation

EVP and CTO, John M. Klett, age 65, $359,820 total compensation

EVP and CFO, Sanjiv Khattri, age 47

EVP and COO, Seth Myones, age 54, $321,923 total compensation

SVP and Chief Sustainability Officer, Paul Gilman

VP Investor Relations, Alan Katz
SVP and Chief Human Resources Officer, Maj. Michael A. Wright
VP and CIO Covanta Energy, Stuart Kippelman
VP and Regional Head of IPP Projects Asia Pacific, Jim Willey
UK Managing Director, Malcolm Chilton
Director, David M. Barse, age 49
President CEO and Director, Anthony J. (Tony) Orlando, age 52
Director, Peter C. B. Bynoe, age 61
Director, Robert S. Silberman, age 54
Director, Joseph M. Holsten, age 59
Director, Linda J. Fisher, age 59
Director, Ronald J. Broglio, age 71
Director, Jean Smith, age 56
Director, William C. (Bill) Pate, age 48
Auditors: Ernst&YoungLLP

LOCATIONS

HQ: Covanta Holding Corporation
445 South St., Morristown NJ 07960
Phone: 862-345-5000 **Fax:** 212-381-3950
Web: www.pvh.com

2011 Sales

	$ mil.	% of total
US	1,592	96
Other countries	58	4
Total	**1,650**	**100**

PRODUCTS/OPERATIONS

2011 Sales

	$ mil.	% of total
Waste & service	1,080	65
Other	152	12

COMPETITORS

AEP
Atmos Energy
Energy Future
NRG Energy
Panda Energy
Veolia Environmental Services
Vista International Technologies
Waste Management

HISTORICAL FINANCIALS

Company Type: Public

Income Statement FYE: December 31

	ASSETS ($ mil.)	NET INCOME ($ mil.)	INCOME AS % OF ASSETS	EMPLOYEES
12/11	4,385	219	5.0%	3,700
12/10	4,676	61	1.3%	4,100
12/09	4,934	101	2.1%	4,100
12/08	4,279	139	3.3%	3,700
12/07	4,368	130	3.0%	3,500
Annual Growth	0.1%	13.8%	—	1.4%

2011 Year-End Financials

Debt ratio: 49.40%
Return on equity: 20.22%
Cash ($ mil.): 232
Current ratio: —
Long-term debt ($ mil.): 2,166
No. of shares (mil.): 136
Dividends
Yield: —
Payout: 19.48%
Market value ($ mil.): 1,862

	STOCK PRICE ($) FY Close	P/E High/Low		PER SHARE ($) Earnings	Dividends	Book Value
12/11	13.69	11	8	1.54	0.00	7.96
12/10	17.19	49	36	0.40	1.50	7.52
12/09	18.09	34	20	0.66	0.00	8.93
12/08	21.96	33	19	0.90	0.00	7.47
12/07	27.66	33	25	0.85	0.00	6.67
Annual Growth	(16.1%)	—	—	16.0%	—	4.5%

Coventry Health Care Inc.

Coventry Health Care offers health care coverage. Through local health plans the firm provides health care plans to millions of members in 27 markets primarily in the Midwest Mid-Atlantic and Southeast. It offers commercial risk health plans (HMO PPO and point-of-service plans) to employer groups and individuals as well as Medicare Advantage and Medicaid products prescription drug coverage and other coverage directly to individuals. The company administers a bit of workers' compensation and provides services such as bill review and case management to insurers and employers. Coventry also administers network rental and pharmacy benefit programs. Aetna has agreed to acquire Coventry.

Aetna and Coventry have agreed on a deal that between cash and Aetna's assumption of Coventry's debt will amount to $7.3 billion. Aetna will wind up with a larger Medicaid business and be poised to offer more to local consumer insurance exchanges.

Operations

Coventry's local health plans operate under such names as Altius OmniCare and of course Coventry.

Sales & Marketing

Coventry's plans are offered mostly in small and midsized towns rather than big cities. Coventry also targets smaller employers and individuals and markets its products through direct sales representatives. Its Medicaid products are marketed through state authorities while its Medicare products are promoted to individuals and groups through direct mail and brokers.

Financial Analysis

The loss of income from dropping its PFFS product line combined with an industry-wide drop in managed care premiums caused Coventry to take a hit in revenue in 2010 of about 16% compared to the previous year. It resumed growth in 2011 with a 5% increase in revenue due in part to the purchase of Mercy Health Plans which brought a large group of Medicaid patients. However during 2011 the company's Medicare Part D revenues sank when it lost members that would otherwise have been automatically assigned to its programs.

Strategy

Itself the product of an acquisition Coventry prefers to grow its range and reach through a steady rate of acquisitions. Among its targets have been workers' compensation businesses and group health plans formerly owned by health care systems.

The company also adds new products: To reverse a trend of declining enrollment in Part D programs in 2012 the company created a new Medicare Part D plan with preferred pharmacy providers intended to attract more members to its programs.

While the company has placed a great deal of its future growth upon government health plans in 2009 Coventry chose to shed its Medicaid and pharmacy benefits administration business First Health Services. Coventry sold the subsidiary to Magellan Health Services for some $110 million. That same year Coventry decided to stop offering Medicare Advantage Private-Fee-for-Service (PFFS) plans instead choosing to focus on the more cost-effective Medicare Advantage offerings.

Mergers & Acquisitions

An example: in 2012 Coventry purchased Family Health Partners a Medicaid health plan that The Children's Mercy Hospital in Kansas City had operated. The deal helped the company grow its presence in Kansas Kentucky and Missouri and included a long-term partnership whereby Children's Mercy will provide physician and hospital services to Coventry members.

A similar deal was struck in 2010 when the company purchased Mercy Health Plans from Sisters of Mercy Health System to expand its presence in Arkansas and Missouri. In that deal Coventry bulked up its operations in Missouri and surrounding areas including northwest Arkansas and entered into a long-term relationship with that health system. Mercy Health Plans was absorbed into the Coventry organization the following year; most of its operations are now contained within the Coventry Health Care of Missouri division.

Company Background

Coventry Health Care was created in 1998 when Coventry Corporation acquired Principal Financial Group's health care unit thus doubling in size.

EXECUTIVES

EVP, Harvey C. DeMovick Jr., age 65, $522,308 total compensation
Chairman and CEO, Allen F. Wise, age 69, $584,243 total compensation
SVP and Corporate Controller, John J. Ruhlmann, age 49
SVP Corporate Finance, Drew Asher
SVP and Chief Human Resources Officer, Patrisha L. Davis, age 56
EVP and General Counsel, Thomas C. Zielinski, age 60, $575,000 total compensation
EVP Government Programs, Timothy E. Nolan
EVP, Kevin P. Conlin, age 53
EVP CFO and Treasurer, Randy Parker Giles
EVP Commercial Business, Michael D. Bahr, age 53
President and CEO Coventry Health Care Workers Compensation, David W. Young, age 47
Director, Michael A. Stocker, age 70
Director, Lawrence N. (Larry) Kugelman, age 69
Director, Joel Ackerman, age 47
Director, Elizabeth E. Tallet, age 62
Director, Rodman W. Moorhead III, age 68
Director, L. Dale Crandall, age 70
Director, Timothy T. (Tim) Weglicki, age 60
Director, Joseph R. Swedish, age 60
Director, Daniel N. Mendelson, age 47
Auditors: Ernst&YoungLLP

LOCATIONS

HQ: Coventry Health Care Inc.
6720-B Rockledge Dr. Ste. 700, Bethesda MD 20817
Phone: 301-581-0600 **Fax:** 713-209-8996
Web: www.cooperindustries.com

PRODUCTS/OPERATIONS

2011 Revenues

	$ mil.	% of total
Health plans & medical services		
Commercial risk	6,009	49
Medicare Advantage	2,382	19
Medicaid risk	1,381	11
Commercial management services	302	3
Specialized managed care		
Medicare Part D	1,226	10
Other premiums & management services	201	2
Workers' compensation	783	6
Other eliminations	(101.7)	-
Total	**12,186**	**100**

Selected Health Plan Names
Altius Health Plans
Carelink Health Plans
Coventry Health Care
Coventry Health and Life
HealthAmerica
HealthAssurance
HealthCare USA
Mercy Health Plans
OmniCare
Preferred Health Systems
Southern Health
WellPath

COMPETITORS

Aetna
Affiliated Computer Services
AMERIGROUP
Blue Cross
Centene
CIGNA
CorVel
Delta Dental Plans
Health Net
HealthMarkets
Highmark
Humana
Kaiser Foundation Health Plan
Molina Healthcare
UnitedHealth Group
WellCare Health Plans
WellPoint

HISTORICAL FINANCIALS

Company Type: Public

Income Statement FYE: December 31

	REVENUE ($ mil.)	NET INCOME ($ mil.)	NET PROFIT MARGIN	EMPLOYEES
12/11	12,186	543	4.5%	14,400
12/10	11,587	438	3.8%	14,000
12/09	13,903	242	1.7%	14,400
12/08	11,913	381	3.2%	15,800
12/07	9,879	626	6.3%	15,000
Annual Growth	5.4%	(3.5%)	—	(1.0%)

2011 Year-End Financials

Debt ratio: 20.63%
Return on equity: 12.04%
Cash ($ mil.): 1,579
Current ratio: 126.25
Long-term debt ($ mil.): 1,584
No. of shares (mil.): 141
Dividends
Yield: —
Payout: —
Market value ($ mil.): 4,287

	STOCK PRICE ($) FY Close	P/E High/Low		PER SHARE ($) Earnings	Dividends	Book Value
12/11	30.37	10	7	3.70	0.00	31.95
12/10	26.40	9	6	2.97	0.00	28.10
12/09	24.29	15	5	1.64	0.00	25.09
12/08	14.88	24	4	2.54	0.00	23.14
12/07	59.25	15	12	3.98	0.00	21.35
Annual Growth	(15.4%)	—	—	(1.8%)	—	10.6%

Credit Suisse (USA) Inc

Credit Suisse (USA) is one of the top US investment banks offering advisory services on mergers and acquisitions raising capital securities underwriting and trading research and analytics and risk management products. Clients include corporations governments institutional investors such as hedge funds and private individuals. The company provides asset management services through Credit Suisse Private Equity; while Credit Suisse Private Banking USA offers wealth services to the rich throughout the country. Credit Suisse (USA) is a wholly owned subsidiary of Swiss banking powerhouse Credit Suisse Group and part of Credit Suisse Americas which includes North and South America and the Caribbean.

Credit Suisse divides its operations into four regions: Switzerland; Europe Middle East and Africa; Asia/Pacific; and the Americas. The group has been working towards its strategy of establishing a single bank with all divisions operating together to serve clients. In the US the company is focused on improving its market share in its major product areas. It also is looking to expand its private banking and asset management capabilities.

HISTORY

In 1959 shortly after graduating from Harvard Business School Dick Jenrette and partners Bill Donaldson and Dan Lufkin founded Donaldson Lufkin & Jenrette (DLJ). Their first product indepth institutional equities research was new to Wall Street. After earning a strong reputation in equities research and trading DLJ in 1970 became the first New York Stock Exchange (NYSE) member firm to go public.

In the 1970s the deregulation of commissions and lower profits from research prompted DLJ to diversify. The firm absorbed losses in proprietary trading and exited that business. DLJ found itself undercapitalized and in search of a suitor. In 1985 when The Equitable Companies (now AXA Financial) bought DLJ Jenrette was promoted to a top position in Equitable. John Chalsty became CEO of DLJ in 1986.

Under Equitable's wing DLJ expanded into niche markets such as junk (high-yield) bonds merchant banking and mortgage-backed securities. DLJ's cautious business approach left it largely unscathed by the 1987 stock market crash; as more swashbuckling firms laid off staff members DLJ scooped them up. In 1989 the firm launched PC Financial Network (which later became DLJdirect). When junk-bond king Michael Milken's Drexel Burnham Lambert finance group crumbled in 1991 DLJ snapped up several Drexel employees along with cheap junk bonds that later recovered their value. By 1993 DLJ was the #1 junk-bond underwriter in the country. In 1995 it hired Latin American markets experts cast out by other firms after the Mexican peso crash.

In the early 1990s debt-laden Equitable looked for a way to raise capital. AXA came to the rescue with a cash infusion that gave it control of Equitable after the latter's 1992 IPO. Equitable then sold 20% of DLJ in a 1995 IPO. Jenrette retired as chairman of both Equitable and DLJ in 1996 and Chalsty became chairman of DLJ.

In 1996 the firm worked on major mergers and acquisitions for such companies as GM Hughes (now DIRECTV) and Tenet Healthcare; it was lead manager on stock offerings by Host Marriott (now Host Hotels & Resorts and Trump Hotels & Casino Resorts (now Trump Entertainment Resorts) among others. That year DLJ was also lead manager on the first NYSE-listed IPOs by Russian and German companies (the chickens came home to roost in 1998 when the Russian economy imploded).

Also in 1996 DLJ opened Latin American offices to expand into those emerging markets. A year later it bought UK-based Phoenix Group (advisory and asset management services) and London Global Securities (securities lending). In 1998 the Banking Group made investments totaling more than $1 billion in an eclectic collection of companies (from industrial equipment to publishing). DLJ president Joe Roby took over as CEO from Chalsty who remained chairman.

DLJ and Sumitomo Bank (now Sumitomo Mitsui Financial Group) in 1998 launched an Internet brokerage in Japan; it also opened an international equities business in London. The next year DLJ issued a tracking stock for DLJdirect (which became Harrisdirect) and partnered with Charles Schwab Fidelity Investments and Spear Leeds & Kellogg (now Goldman Sachs Execution & Clearing) to sell Nasdaq stocks online. Its status as the top junk bond issuer was shaken in 2000 when AmeriServe Food Distribution filed for bankruptcy four months after DLJ issued its bonds. Later that year Credit Suisse Group subsidiary Credit Suisse First Boston bought the firm and changed its name to Credit Suisse First Boston (USA); Chalsty retired as chairman in conjunction with the acquisition succeeded by Roby.

Reacting to concerns of bias the company in 2001 followed rival Merrill Lynch's lead and banned its analysts from owning stock in companies they cover. The company also purchased all of the outstanding tracking stock in CSFBdirect and then sold the company to Bank of Montreal.

In 2003 former Credit Suisse First Boston star banker Frank Quattrone was was charged with "spinning" or making sure that his clients got first dibs on lucrative IPO shares of the companies CSFB brought public during the dot-com boom. After three trials Quattrone was acquitted of all charges in 2006. The company changed its name that year to Credit Suisse (USA).

Then in 2007 a Credit Suisse (USA) banker was accused of insider trading for tipping off a Pakistani banker about the Energy Future Holdings buyout.

EXECUTIVES

CEO, Robert S. (Rob) Shafir, age 54
CEO Investment Bank, Eric Varvel, age 49
Managing Director and Treasurer, Peter J. Feeney
Managing Director Investment Banking and Co-Head Retail, David Frank
CFO and Accounting Officer, Paul O'Keefe
Managing Director and General Counsel, D. Neil Radey, age 57
Director Capital Market, Sharon O'Connor
Managing Director Knowledge Process Strategy Investment Banking, Vineet Nagrani
Head Private Banking, Peter Skoglund
Managing Director and Board Member, Michael Ryan
Head of Corporate Communications Private Banking Americas, David Walker
COO and Head Finance, Thomas Sipp
Head Human Resources, Ketty Russeva
Head Strategy and Product Development, Alastair J. Cairns
Managing Director Private Banking (New York Office), Matt Gorman
Managing Director Private Banking (Boston Office), Stephen Dunne
Managing Director Private Banking (Chicago Office), David A. McGranaham
Board Member, Paul Calello, age 51
Board Member, Anthony DeChellis
Auditors: KPMGAG

LOCATIONS

HQ: Credit Suisse (USA) Inc.
11 Madison Ave., New York NY 10010-3629
Phone: 212-325-2000 **Fax:** 212-325-6665
Web: www.credit-suisse.com/us/en

PRODUCTS/OPERATIONS

COMPETITORS

Brown Brothers Harriman
Citigroup Global Markets
Citigroup Private Bank
Deutsche Banc Alex. Brown
Goldman Sachs
JPMorgan Chase
Lazard
Merrill Lynch
Morgan Stanley
Oppenheimer Holdings
Piper Jaffray
UBS Investment Bank

HISTORICAL FINANCIALS

Company Type: Subsidiary

Income Statement FYE: December 31

	REVENUE ($ mil.)	NET INCOME ($ mil.)	NET PROFIT MARGIN	EMPLOYEES
12/05	6,738	(272)	—	0
12/04	7,025	127	1.8%	10,899
12/03	6,341	787	12.4%	9,344
12/02	4,993	1,329	26.6%	8,706
Annual Growth	10.5%	—	—	—

2005 Year-End Financials

Debt ratio: 23.50%
Return on equity: (-1.51)%
Cash ($ mil.): 92,786
Current ratio: 37.09
Long-term debt ($ mil.): 42,564
No. of shares (mil.): 0
Dividends
Yield: —
Payout: —
Market value ($ mil.): 0

	STOCK PRICE ($) FY Close	P/E High/Low	PER SHARE ($) Earnings	Dividends	Book Value
12/05	116.25	— —	(0.00)	0.00	16,410,000
12/04	114.81	— —	(0.00)	0.00	10,919,090
12/03	104.13	— —	(0.00)	0.00	10,058,181
12/02	104.13	— —	(0.00)	0.00	8,563,636
Annual Growth	3.7%	— —	—	—	24.2%

Crown Holdings Inc

Crown Holdings wants to pop a top on profits. The company is a leading global manufacturer of consumer packaging; steel and aluminum food and beverage cans and related packaging are Crown's primary lines. Its portfolio includes aerosol cans and various metal vacuum closures marketed under brands Liftoff SuperEnd and Easylift as well as specialty packaging such as novelty containers and industrial cans. Crown also supplies can-making equipment and parts. Its roster of customers includes Coca-Cola Cadberry Schweppes Heinz Nestle SC Johnson Unilever and Procter & Gamble which owns Gillette another customer. Crown operates 135 plants in 41 countries with 72% of net sales coming from outside the US.

HISTORY

Formed as Crown Cork & Seal Co. (CC&S) of Baltimore in 1892 the company was consolidated into its present form in 1927 when it merged with New Process Cork and New York Patents. The next year CC&S expanded overseas and formed Crown Cork International. In 1936 CC&S acquired Acme Can and benefited from the movement at the time from home canning to processed canning. A decade later the company launched its new product in 1946 –the first aerosol can.

By 1957 CC&S was in trouble with heavy debt. Teetering on the brink of bankruptcy the company hired John Connelly as president. Connelly immediately stopped can production (sending stockpiled inventory to customers) discontinued unprofitable product lines and reduced costs (25% of employees were laid off in less than two years). He then directed CC&S to take advantage of new uses for aerosol cans (insecticides hair spray and bathroom cleaning supplies) and to expand overseas. CC&S obtained "pioneer rights" between 1955 and 1960 from foreign countries that granted the company first crack at new closure and can businesses.

The introduction of the pull-tab pop-top in 1963 hit the can business like a geyser. Connelly embraced pull tabs but he rejected getting into the production of two-piece aluminum cans (first introduced in the mid-1970s) focusing instead on existing technology for three-piece cans. He also resisted the diversification trend then popular in the can-making industry which later led to the declining performances of competitors Continental Can and American Can.

In 1970 CC&S moved into the printing end of the industry. It gained the ability to imprint color lithography on bottle caps and cans after buying R. Hoe.

Connelly kept CC&S debt-free through most of the 1980s using cash flow to buy back about half of CC&S's stock. In 1989 he picked Bill Avery to succeed him. With Connelly's blessing Avery started a buying spree that included the purchase of the plants of Continental Can. Connelly died in 1990. Acquisitions continued throughout the 1990s. CC&S's purchases included CONSTAR International the #1 maker of polyethylene terephthalate (PET) plastic containers (1992) can maker Van Dorn (1993) and the can-manufacturing unit of Tri Valley Growers (1994). California's Northridge earthquake in 1994 ruined the company's plant in Van Nuys.

CC&S bought French packaging company CarnaudMetalbox in 1996. The purchase united CC&S's efficient operations and strong presence in North America with the French company's state-of-the-art manufacturing technology and international marketing experience. In addition CC&S acquired Polish packaging company Fabryka Opakowan Blaszanyck. That year strikes over contract disputes halted production at eight of the company's plants.

In 1997 CC&S bought a 96% stake in Golden Aluminum from ACX Technologies but returned the aluminum recycler in 1999 at a cost of $10 million. Dropping sales and foreign currency fluctuations in 1998 forced the company to close seven factories and cut 7% of its workforce. CC&S closed additional factories in 1999 and sold its composite can (paper cans with metal or plastic ends) business. That year the company increased its foreign presence with the purchase of two can manufacturers in Spain and Greece.

CC&S entered into a joint venture with Tempra Technology in 2000 to make and market a self-refrigerating can. The same year Avery announced his retirement; president and COO John Conway succeeded him as CEO in 2001. The company's debt reduction plans called for major asset sales. To reduce debt and move closer to profitability CC&S sold three product divisions that year; in 2002 it sold its fragrance pump unit to Rexam PLC for about $107 million. Also in 2002 the company sold its Europe-based pharmaceutical packaging business. Later that year CC&S spun off its PET bottle subsidiary Constar International in an IPO offering.

The company completed a refinancing plan in 2003 and formed a new public holding company Crown Holdings Inc.; the CC&S name was retained for the company's operating subsidiary. In 2005 the company sold its plastics closures business to PAI Partners for about $750 million and exited entirely from plastics operations in North America and Europe. The years 2007 and 2008 marked the company's exodus from its Indonesia operations a Canadian food can plant and a beverage can and crown plant. Simultaneously new facilities were also opened in 2008 in Africa Cambodia and the Middle East.

Responding to a dent in net income in 2008 coupled with approximately $2.8 billion in debt the company shored up its bottom line and boosted cash flow from operations in 2009 over 2008 by restructuring its business. Crown's facilities also recalibrated during 2009 with investments in capital amounting to $180 million to build new and existing production capacity. It plowed in some $22 million to buy a business in Vietnam and $12 million to boost capacity in a Brazilian beverage can plant picked up in 2008 for $44 million. A new $32 million production line at its plant in Spain was installed in 2008. That investment was fueled by Crown's hope that it would double its production capacity to about 2 billion cans per year.

EXECUTIVES

EVP and CFO, Timothy J. Donahue, age 49, $505,000 total compensation
Chairman President and CEO, John W. Conway, age 66, $1,075,000 total compensation
President Americas Division, Raymond L. McGowan Jr., age 60, $505,000 total compensation
SVP Finance, Thomas A. Kelly, age 52
VP Corporate Affairs and Public Relations, Michael F. Dunleavy
SVP General Counsel and Secretary, William T. Gallagher
VP Planning and Development, Torsten J. Kreider
EVP Corporate Technology and Regulatory Affairs, Daniel A. Abramowicz
VP Corporate Risk Management, Karen E. Berigan
EVP European Division, Christopher C. Homfray, age 54, $494,343 total compensation
VP and Corporate Controller, Kevin C. Clothier, age 43
President Asia Pacific, Jozef Salaerts, age 57, $315,000 total compensation
VP and Treasurer, Michael B. Burns
President CROWN Beverage Packing North America CROWN Europe, Gerard H (Jerry) Gifford, age 57
Director, William S. (Bill) Urkiel, age 66
Director, Jim L. Turner, age 66
Director, Arnold W. Donald, age 57
Director, James H. (Jim) Miller, age 63
Director, Jenne K. Britell, age 69
Director, Thomas A. Ralph, age 71
Director, Hugues du Rouret, age 73
Director, Hans J. Loliger, age 69
Director, Josef M. Mueller
Director, William G. Little, age 69
Auditors: PricewaterhouseCoopersLLP

LOCATIONS

HQ: Crown Holdings Inc.
1 Crown Way, Philadelphia PA 19154-4599
Phone: 215-698-5100 **Fax:** 812-377-3334
Web: www.cummins.com

2010 Sales

	$ mil.	% of total
US	2,248	28
UK	740	9
France	624	8
Other regions	4,329	55
Total	**7,941**	**100**

PRODUCTS/OPERATIONS

2010 Sales

	$ mil.	% of total
Metal beverage cans & ends	4,065	51
Metal food cans & ends	2,479	31
Other metal packaging	1,299	16
Plastics packaging	31	1
Other products	67	1
Total	**7,941**	**100**

2010 Sales by Segment

	$ mil.	% of total
Americas beverage	2,097	27
European food	1,841	23
European beverage	1,524	19
North America food	897	11
European specialty packaging	395	5
Non-reportable segments	1,187	15
Total	**7,941**	**100**

Selected Products

Metal packaging
- Aerosol cans
- Beverage cans
- Closures and caps
- Crowns
- Ends
- Food cans

Plastics packaging
Specialty packaging (unusual containers)
- Vacuum closures

Other products
- Can making equipment and spares

Selected Markets

Food and beverage
Health and beauty
Household
Industrial

COMPETITORS

Alcoa
Amcor
AptarGroup
Ball Corp.
Berry Plastics
BWAY
Calmar
Metal Container Corporation
Owens-Illinois
Rexam
Silgan
Sonoco Products
Tetra Laval

HISTORICAL FINANCIALS

Company Type: Public

Income Statement FYE: December 31

	REVENUE ($ mil.)	NET INCOME ($ mil.)	NET PROFIT MARGIN	EMPLOYEES
12/11	8,644	282	3.3%	20,700
12/10	7,941	324	4.1%	20,500
12/09	7,938	334	4.2%	20,510
12/08	8,305	226	2.7%	21,300
12/07	7,727	528	6.8%	21,819
Annual Growth	2.8%	(14.5%)	—	(1.3%)

2011 Year-End Financials

Debt ratio: 51.43%
Return on equity: 987650001000000.00%
Cash ($ mil.): 342
Current ratio: 113.92
Long-term debt ($ mil.): 3,337
No. of shares (mil.): 148
Dividends
Yield: —
Payout: —
Market value ($ mil.): 4,985

	STOCK PRICE ($) FY Close	P/E High/Low		PER SHARE ($) Earnings	Dividends	Book Value
12/11	33.58	22	16	1.83	0.00	(3.19)
12/10	33.38	17	11	2.00	0.00	(0.62)
12/09	25.58	14	9	2.06	0.00	(0.04)
12/08	19.20	21	10	1.39	0.00	(1.99)
12/07	25.65	8	6	3.19	0.00	0.09
Annual Growth	7.0%	—	—	(13.0%)	—	—

CSX Corp.

CSX banks on the railway as the right way to make money. Its main subsidiary CSX Transportation (CSXT) operates a major rail system of some 21000 route miles in the eastern US. The freight carrier links 23 states 70 ports the District of Columbia and two Canadian provinces. Freight hauled by the company includes a wide variety of merchandise (food chemicals and consumer goods) coal and automotive products. CSX also transports via intermodal containers and trailers (Intermodal freight hauling uses multiple modes of transportation). CSX's rail segment also includes units that operate motor vehicle distribution centers and bulk cargo terminals.

HISTORY

CSX Corporation was formed in 1980 when Chessie System and Seaboard Coast Line (SCL) merged in an effort to improve the efficiency of their railroads.

Chessie's oldest railroad the Baltimore & Ohio (B&O) was chartered in 1827 to help Baltimore compete against New York and Philadelphia for freight traffic. By the late 1800s the railroad served Chicago Cincinnati New York City St. Louis and Washington DC. Chesapeake & Ohio (C&O) acquired it in 1962.

C&O originated in Virginia with the Louisa Railroad in 1836. It gained access to Chicago Cincinnati and Washington DC and by the mid-1900s was a major coal carrier. After B&O and C&O acquired joint control of Baltimore-based Western Maryland Railway (1967) the three railroads became subsidiaries of newly formed Chessie System (1973).

One of SCL's two predecessors Seaboard Air Line Railroad (SAL) grew out of Virginia's Portsmouth & Roanoke Rail Road of 1832. SCL's other predecessor Atlantic Coast Line Railroad (ACL) took shape between 1869 and 1893 as William Walters acquired several southern railroads. In 1902 ACL bought the Plant System (railroads in Georgia Florida and other southern states) and the Louisville & Nashville (a north-south line connecting New Orleans and Chicago) giving ACL the basic form it was to retain until 1967 when it merged with SAL to form SCL.

After CSX inherited the Chessie System and SCL it bought Texas Gas Resources (gas pipeline 1983) American Commercial Lines (Texas Gas' river barge subsidiary 1984) and Sea-Land Corporation (ocean container shipping 1986). To improve its market value CSX sold most of its oil and gas properties its communications holdings (Lightnet begun in 1983) and most of its resort properties (Rockresorts) in 1988 and 1989. American Commercial Lines acquired Valley Line in 1992.

Sea-Land struck a deal with Danish shipping company Maersk Line in 1996 to share vessels and terminals. That year CSX entered a takeover battle with rival Norfolk Southern for Conrail. Conrail decided to split its assets between the two; CSX paid $4.3 billion for 42%. (The division took place in 1999.)

CSX combined the American Commercial Lines barge business with the barge business of Vectra Group in 1998.

In 1999 CSX sold Grand Teton Lodge to Vail Resorts for $50 million. Also that year CSX divided Sea-Land into three businesses: international terminal operations (which became CSX World Terminals) domestic container shipping (CSX Lines) and global container shipping. The international shipping business was sold to Denmark's A.P. M?ller (parent of Maersk Line) for $800 million.

Rail service disruptions stemming from the integration of Conrail assets were exacerbated by damage from Hurricane Floyd in 1999. The next year a federal audit found defects in CSX track. Service problems related to the Conrail takeover continued and the company's rail unit underwent a management shake-up.

Looking to pay down debt CSX later in 2000 sold its CTI Logistx unit to TNT Post Group for $650 million. The next year CSX formed a new unit Transflo to provide intermodal services for bulk cargo.

In 2002 CSX established a CSXT office in Europe to focus on international freight and to create partnerships with European freight forwarders and ocean carriers.

CSX sold a controlling stake in its ocean container shipping unit to investment firm Carlyle Group in 2003. The former CSX Lines took the name Horizon Lines. In 2004 Carlyle sold its stake in Horizon Lines to another investment firm Castle Harlan. The next year CSX sold its CSX World Terminals to Dubai Ports International (later DP World) for $1.14 billion.

In 2004 the two companies reorganized Conrail so that each railroad directly owned the Conrail assets that it operates. (Conrail continued to operate switching facilities and terminals used by both Norfolk Southern and CSX.)

Some investors were displeased by the company's performance in 2008. The London-based hedge fund Children's Investment Fund Management (TCI) which was founded by Christopher Hohn and private investment firm 3G Capital leader of a group that owns about 9% of CSX staged a proxy fight and sought to elect a slate of four directors to the company's board. Two directors from the group's slate were seated in July and two more joined the board in September after a legal dispute was resolved. In 2009 TCI sold all of its CSX shares.

Also in 2009 CSX Real Property sold The Greenbrier Resort which it had owned since 1910 to investor James Justice for a little over $20 million. The purchase came two months after the historic resort in West Virginia filed for Chapter 11 bankruptcy. The Greenbrier's bankruptcy case was dismissed by a federal judge in May 2009.

To recover from the global financial train wreck of 2009 (the company's revenues were down 20% year-over-year) CSX adjusted its workforce to coincide with decreased orders; it also concentrated on boosting efficiency and safety as well as improving customer services and the rate of on-time performance.

EXECUTIVES

EVP Law and Public Affairs General Counsel and Corporate Secretary, Ellen M. Fitzsimmons, age 51, $500,000 total compensation
VP Strategic Planning, Lester M. Passa, age 58
VP Federal Regulation and General Counsel, Peter J. Shudtz, age 64
EVP Sales and Marketing and Chief Commercial Officer, Clarence W. Gooden, age 59, $550,000 total compensation
Chairman President and CEO, Michael J. Ward, age 61, $1,100,000 total compensation
VP Tax and Treasurer, David A. Boor, age 58
VP Capital Markets and Investor Relations, David H. Baggs, age 52
VP and Controller, Carolyn T. Sizemore, age 49
President CSX Real Property, Stephen A. Crosby, age 57
VP Finance, Dean M. Piacente, age 49
EVP; COO CSX Transportation Inc., Oscar Munoz, age 54, $650,000 total compensation
General Counsel Business and Corporate Governance, Nathan Goldman
VP Corporate Communications, Vance Meyer
SVP and Chief Administrative Officer, Lisa A. Mancini, age 52
President CSX Technology Inc., Frank A. Lonegro
SVP and Chief Human Resources Officer, Diana Sorfleet
VP Network Operations, Mike Smith
VP Strategic Infrastructure Initiatives, Louis E. Renjel
Director Corporate Communications Jacksonville FL, Gary Sease
VP Public Safety and Environment, Skip Elliott
Director Federal Affairs, Garrick Francis
General Counsel Tax and Insurance, David Bowling
Director Corporate Communications Philadelphia PA, Robert Sullivan
VP Intermodal, William (Bill) Clement
Investor Relations and Treasury, Kathryn Sharpe
EVP and CFO, Fredrik Eliasson
VP Emerging Markets, Derrick Smith
Director, David M. Ratcliffe, age 63
Director, Donald J. Shepard, age 65
Director, John D. McPherson, age 65
Director, Edward J. (Ned) Kelly III, age 58
Director, Gilbert H. Lamphere, age 59
Director, Steven T. (Steve) Halverson, age 57
Director, Donna M. Alvarado, age 63
Director, Timothy T. (Tim) O'Toole, age 56
Director, Pamela L. (Pam) Carter, age 62
Director, John B. Breaux, age 67
Director, Alexandre (Alex) Behring, age 45
Independent Director, J. Watts
Director, Steven Whisler
Independent Director, Timothy OToole
Auditors: Ernst&YoungLLP

LOCATIONS

HQ: CSX Corporation
500 Water St. 15th Fl., Jacksonville FL 32202
Phone: 904-359-3200 **Fax:** 574-293-6146
Web: www.ctscorp.com

PRODUCTS/OPERATIONS

2011 Sales

	% of total
Rail merchandis	
Industrial	
Chemicals	14
Automotive	8
Metals	5
Agricultural	
Agricultural	9
Phosphates &	4
Food &	2
Housing constructi	
Emerging	6
Forest	6
Coal	32
Intermodal	12
Other	2
Total	**100**

Selected Services

Container/trailer shipping
Freight shipping by rail
Intermodal transportation
Logistics
Property/real estate (buying/leasing property for commercial or rail)
Salvage sales (distressed cargo sales)

COMPETITORS

APL Logistics
Burlington Northern Santa Fe
Canadian National Railway
Canadian Pacific Railway
Hub Group
J.B. Hunt
Norfolk Southern
Pacer International
Schneider National
Union Pacific
Washington Companies

HISTORICAL FINANCIALS

Company Type: Public

Income Statement FYE: December 30

	REVENUE ($ mil.)	NET INCOME ($ mil.)	NET PROFIT MARGIN	EMPLOYEES
12/11	11,743	1,822	15.5%	31,344
12/10	10,636	1,563	14.7%	29,916
12/09	9,041	1,152	12.7%	30,000
12/08	11,255	1,365	12.1%	34,363
12/07	10,030	1,336	13.3%	35,443
Annual Growth	4.0%	8.1%	—	(3.0%)

2011 Year-End Financials

Debt ratio: 31.35%
Return on equity: 21.55%
Cash ($ mil.): 783
Current ratio: 109.23
Long-term debt ($ mil.): 8,734
No. of shares (mil.): 1,049
Dividends
Yield: 2.12%
Payout: 26.75%
Market value ($ mil.): 22,095

	STOCK PRICE ($) FY Close	P/E High/Low		PER SHARE ($) Earnings	Dividends	Book Value
12/11	21.06	48	11	1.67	0.45	8.06
12/10	64.61	47	31	1.35	0.33	7.82
12/09	50.40	51	21	0.97	0.00	7.49
12/08	31.50	61	27	1.11	0.26	6.87
12/07	44.27	49	33	1.00	0.18	7.10
Annual Growth	(17.0%)	—	—	13.7%	25.7%	3.2%

Cullen/Frost Bankers, Inc.

One of the largest independent bank holding companies based in Texas Cullen/Frost Bankers owns Frost National Bank and other financial subsidiaries through a second-tier holding company The New Galveston Company. The community-oriented bank serves individuals and local businesses as well as clients in neighboring parts of Mexico through more than 100 branches in Texas metropolitan areas. It offers commercial and consumer deposit products and loans trust and investment management services mutual funds insurance brokerage and leasing. Subsidiaries include Frost Insurance Agency Frost Brokerage Services Frost Investment Advisors and investment banking arm Frost Securities.

Business loans including commercial and industrial loans construction loans and commercial mortgages make up more than 85% of Frost Bank's loan portfolio. The company serves a variety of industries including energy manufacturing services retail telecommunications healthcare military and transportation. Thanks to the high concentration of commercial loans and the fact that Texas wasn't been hit as hard as other Sun Belt states Cullen/Frost remained relatively unscathed by the nationwide mortgage meltdown. (It also claims it was the first bank in the US to turn down funds from the government's Troubled Asset Relief Program or TARP in late 2008.) The company experienced upticks in net income in 2010 and 2011 thanks in part to more interest from earning assets such as loans and securities and fewer provisions for loan losses.

Cullen/Frost has built its insurance business through acquisitions in recent years; since 2009 it has bought agencies in Dallas Houston San Antonio and San Marcos that provide group employee benefit plans. The company continues to seek out acquisition opportunities while it also looks for ways to expand and diversify within its existing markets. To reduce its reliance on interest rate spreads Cullen/Frost wants to grow its income from fees such as insurance commissions trust investment fees and service charges on deposit accounts.

EXECUTIVES

Chairman and CEO; Chairman and CEO Frost Bank, Richard W. (Dick) Evans Jr., age 65, $800,000 total compensation
Group EVP and CFO, Phillip D. Green, age 57, $425,000 total compensation
Director; President Frost Bank, Patrick B. (Pat) Frost, age 52, $362,000 total compensation
EVP Corporate Counsel and Secretary, Stan McCormick
EVP Frost Brokerage Services Frost Bank, Karen Banks
President and Chief Business Banking Officer Frost Bank, David W. (Dave) Beck Jr., age 61, $375,000 total compensation
President Statewide Functions Frost Bank, Paul H. Bracher, age 55, $375,000 total compensation
Group EVP Chief Credit Officer and Chief Risk Officer Frost Bank, William L. (Bill) Perotti, age 54
Group EVP and Executive Trust Officer Frost Bank, Richard Kardys, age 65, $375,000 total compensation
EVP Shareholder Communications, Greg Parker
Media Relations, Renee Sabel
Group EVP Internet Financial Services Frost Bank, Robert A. (Bobby) Berman, age 49
Group EVP Consumer Banking Frost Bank, Paul J. Olivier, age 59
Group EVP Human Resources Frost Bank, Emily A. Skillman, age 67
Director, Karen E. Jennings, age 61
Director, Charles W. Matthews Jr., age 67

Director, Royce S. Caldwell, age 73
Director, Carlos E. Alvarez, age 61
Director; President Frost Bank, Patrick B. (Pat) Frost, age 52
Director, Ruben M. Escobedo, age 74
Director, Horace Wilkins Jr., age 61
Director, Richard M. Kleberg III, age 69
Director, R. Denny Alexander, age 66
Director, Ida Clement Steen, age 59
Director, Crawford H. Edwards, age 53
Director, David J. Haemisegger, age 58
Auditors: Ernst&YoungLLP

LOCATIONS

HQ: Cullen/Frost Bankers Inc.
100 W. Houston St., San Antonio TX 78205
Phone: 210-220-4011 **Fax:** 210-220-4325
Web: www.frostbank.com

PRODUCTS/OPERATIONS

2011 Sales

	$ mil	% of total
Interest		
Loans including fees	397	43
Securities	218	24
Other	6	1
Noninterest		
Service charges on deposit accounts	94	10
Trust fees	73	8
Insurance commissions & fees	35	4
Other charges commissions & fees	34	4
Other	53	6
Total	**913**	**100**

Selected Subsidiaries

Frost 1031 Exchange LLC (real estate services)
Frost Brokerage Services Inc. (securities brokerage)
Frost Insurance Agency Inc. (insurance brokerage)
Frost Investment Advisors LLC (mutual funds)
The Frost National Bank
Frost Premium Finance Corporation (property/casualty insurance financing)
Frost Securities Inc. (private equity and advisory services to middle-market firms)
The New Galveston Company Inc. (second-tier holding company)

COMPETITORS

Bank of America
Broadway Bancshares
Capital One
Comerica
Compass Bancshares
Extraco
First Financial Bankshares
International Bancshares
JPMorgan Chase
Lone Star Bank
PlainsCapital
Prosperity Bancshares
Texas Capital Bancshares
Wells Fargo
Woodforest Financial

HISTORICAL FINANCIALS

Company Type: Public

Income Statement FYE: December 31

	ASSETS ($ mil.)	NET INCOME ($ mil.)	INCOME AS % OF ASSETS	EMPLOYEES
12/11	20,317	217	1.1%	3,848
12/10	17,617	208	1.2%	3,777
12/09	16,288	179	1.1%	3,834
12/08	15,034	207	1.4%	3,892
12/07	13,485	212	1.6%	3,781
Annual Growth	10.8%	0.6%	—	0.4%

2011 Year-End Financials

Debt ratio: 1.10%
Return on equity: 9.53%
Cash ($ mil.): 2,888
Current ratio: —
Long-term debt ($ mil.): 223
No. of shares (mil.): 61
Dividends
Yield: —
Payout: 51.69%
Market value ($ mil.): 3,241

	STOCK PRICE ($) FY Close	P/E High/Low		PER SHARE ($) Earnings	Dividends	Book Value
12/11	52.91	18	12	3.54	0.00	37.27
12/10	61.12	18	15	3.44	1.78	33.85
12/09	50.00	18	12	3.00	1.71	31.55
12/08	50.68	18	13	3.50	1.66	29.68
12/07	50.66	16	13	3.55	1.54	25.18
Annual Growth	1.1%	—	—	(0.1%)	—	10.3%

Cummins, Inc.

If it's comin' around the mountain it could have a Cummins' engine powering it. The company makes about half of its revenues from its Engine segment which makes diesel and natural gas powered engines for the heavy and mid-duty truck RV automotive and industrial markets along with marine rail mining and construction. Its other complementary business segments include Components (filtration products and fuel systems); Power Generation (vehicle and residential generators); and Distribution (product distributors and servicing). Major customers include OEMs Chrysler Daimler Ford Komatsu PACCAR and Volvo. About two-thirds of Cummins' sales are from outside the US.

HISTORY

Chauffeur Clessie Cummins believed that Rudolph Diesel's cumbersome and smoky engine could be improved for use in transportation. Borrowing money and work space from his employer –Columbus Indiana banker W. G. Irwin –Cummins founded Cummins Engine in 1919. Irwin invested more than $2.5 million and in the mid-1920s Cummins produced a mobile diesel engine. Truck manufacturers were reluctant to switch from gas to diesel so Cummins used publicity stunts (such as racing in the Indianapolis 500) to advertise his engine.

The company was profitable by 1937 the year Irwin's grandnephew J. Irwin Miller took over. During WWII the Cummins engine was used in cargo trucks. Sales jumped from $20 million in 1946 to more than $100 million by 1956. That year Cummins started its first overseas plant in Scotland and bought Atlas Crankshafts in 1958. By 1967 it had 50% of the diesel engine market.

Cummins diversified in 1970 by acquiring the K2 Ski Company (fiberglass skis) and Coot Industries (all-terrain vehicles) but sold them by 1976. It added turbochargers in 1973 with its acquisition of Holset Engineering. (Founded in 1948 and named for founders W.C. Holmes and Louis Croset Holset became a subsidiary of BHD Engineering Limited Group in 1952; it first was acquired by Hanson Trust in 1973 and later that year by Cummins. Holset changed its name to Cummins Turbo Technologies in 2006.) In the early 1980s Cummins introduced a line of midrange engines developed in a joint venture with J.I. Case (then a subsidiary of Tenneco; now a part of Fiat-controlled CNH Global). To remain competitive Cummins cut costs by 22% doubled productivity in its US and UK plants and spent $1.8 billion to retool its factories.

Having twice repelled unwelcome foreign suitors in 1989 Cummins sold 27% of its stock to Ford Tenneco and Kubota for $250 million in 1990. The move raised cash and protected Cummins from future takeover bids.

In 1993 Cummins established engine-making joint ventures with Tata Engineering & Locomotive India's largest heavy vehicle maker and Komatsu a leading Japanese construction equipment maker. Also in 1993 Cummins introduced a natural-gas engine for school buses and formed a joint venture to produce turbochargers in India. The company began Cummins Wartsila a joint venture with engineering company Wartsila NSD to develop high-speed diesel and natural gas engines in France and the UK in 1995. It also began restructuring that year selling plants and laying off workers.

Continuing its strategy of teaming with other manufacturers Cummins agreed in 1996 to make small and midsize diesel engines with Fiat's Iveco and New Holland (now CNH Global) subsidiaries. In 1997 subsidiary Cadec Systems signed a license to develop and sell Montreal-based Canadian Marconi's (now BAE SYSTEMS CANADA) fleet-tracking system which uses satellites and computers. Cummins bought diesel exhaust and air filtration company Nelson Industries for $490 million in early 1998. The company also agreed without admission of guilt to pay a $25 million fine and contribute $35 million to environmental programs after the EPA accused Cummins of cheating on emissions tests.

Cummins sold its Atlas Crankshaft subsidiary in 1999 to ThyssenKrupp's automotive subsidiary. Chairman and CEO James Henderson retired at the end of 1999 and was succeeded by Theodore Solso.

Early in 2001 the company announced that it had signed a long-term deal to supply PACCAR (Peterbilt and Kenworth trucks) with heavy-duty ISX Signature N14 ISM and ISL engines. Cummins also formed a joint venture with Westport Innovations (Cummins Westport Inc.) for the building of low-emission natural gas engines. Later in 2001 the company shortened its name to Cummins Inc. The following year Cummins and Mercury Marine formed a joint venture Cummins MerCruiser Diesel Marine LLC to provide diesel engines to the recreational and commercial marine markets.

In 2003 Cummins and Westport Innovations strengthened their joint venture ties by signing a technology partnership agreement that made it easier for the two companies to develop and share alternative fuel technologies.

Over the next few years the company expanded its geographic presence to increase its global market share. In mid-2008 the company and China-based vehicle manufacturer Beiqi Foton entered into a 50/50 joint venture known as Beijing Foton Cummins Engine Co. to manufacture diesel engines for Beiqi Foton's Aumark light-duty trucks as well as other vehicle models; production at the Beijing plant commenced in mid-2009. The following year Cummins and Beiqi Foton made an additional capital injection into the partnership ultimately investing about CNY 844 million (over $123 million) each.

In 2010 Tata Motors signaled its intent to sell off a 24% stake in its 50/50 joint venture with Cummins' engine subsidiary to Cummins for INR 5 billion (about $112.6 million). It accumulated four overseas distribution partnerships most notably with Komatsu America which offered Cummins' a full slate of products and services. In tandem with the joint ventures Cummins planted purchasing offices around the world. These offices are driving sales and service relationships with local manufacturers.

The economic meltdown of 2009 however forced double-digit declines in sales across all Cummins business segments collectively a 25% decrease. Joint ventures both manufacturing and distribution entities worldwide fared no better slipping 15% in operating results. The company shored up its bottom line by trimming costs including headcount and manufacturing capacity as well as recalibrating inventories by 25% and capital expenditures by more than 40%. Cummins also cut the salaries of its officers by 10% in 2009. These choices were hard in light of the company's consecutive record-beating sales growth experienced in 2005 through 2008.

Cummins spent $150 million and $116 million on research and development in 2009 and 2008 respectively. With the lion share of that work completed the company spent only $38 million on compliance technologies in 2010. Cummins was also not saddled with heavy restructuring charges in 2010 that it incurred the prior two years due to reducing its global workforce by almost 5% and shuttering a number of facilities.

EXECUTIVES

EVP Corporate Responsibility; CEO Cummins Foundation, Jean S. Blackwell, age 57, $355,682 total compensation
VP Community Relations, Mark R. Gerstle, age 56
VP and CTO, John C. Wall, age 60
Chairman and CEO, N. Thomas (Tom) Linebarger, age 49, $678,125 total compensation
Chief Administrative Officer, Marya M. Rose, age 49
VP; Group VP China and Russia, Steven M. (Steve) Chapman, age 58, $362,500 total compensation
VP Government Relations, Steve May
VP; President Engine Business, Richard J. (Rich) Freeland, age 54, $461,125 total compensation
VP and General Manager High-Horsepower Engine Business Engine Business, Mark Levett
VP; President Cummins Turbo Technologies, Jim Lyons
VP Quality Heavy Duty Business Engine Business, Bob Weimer
VP; President Power Generation, Livingston L. (Tony) Satterthwaite, age 52
VP and Controller Engine Business, Karen Battin
VP and Chief Investment Officer, Richard E. Harris, age 59
VP and Corporate Controller, Marsha L. Hunt, age 48
VP; President Distribution Business, Pamela L. (Pam) Carter, age 62
VP High Horsepower Engineering Engine Business, Jim Trueblood
Executive Director Corporate Communications, Mark D. Land
Executive Director International Distribution, Ricardo Patron
Manager Communications Cummins MerCruiser Diesel Marine, Ted Varner
VP; President Components Group; Managing Director India ABO; Chairman and Managing Director Cummins India Ltd., Anant Talaulicar, age 50
VP and General Counsel, Sharon R. Barner, age 54
Director Marketing Communications Cummins Engine Business, Carol Lavengood
VP; President Cummins Fuel Systems, Ray J. Amlung, age 54
VP; Head of Cummins Emission Solutions, Srikanth Padmanabhan, age 47
VP; President Cummins Filtration, Jihad (Joseph) Saoud
VP and CFO, Patrick J. (Pat) Ward, age 48, $361,667 total compensation
VP MidRange Engineering, Jeff Weikert, age 59
VP Heavy Duty Engineering, Steve Charlton, age 60
Executive Director Chrysler Business Engine Business, Tracy Embree
Executive Director Global Parts Logistics, Norbert Nusterer
Global Head ERP Program Distribution Business, Dev Iyer
VP Truck and Bus OEM Business, Lori Thompson
VP North and Central American Distribution, Lori Cobb
Director Investor Relations, Dean Cantrell
Manager Public Relations Cummins MerCruiser Diesel, Clay Gaillard
Manager Communications Marine, Rachel Bridges
Manager Global Marketing Communication Cummins Power Generation, Flavio A. C. Mello
Manager Global Diversity Communications, Blair Claflin
Director Corporate Communications, Janet Williams
Executive Director Cummins Mining Business, John Malina
Executive Director Cummins Off-Highway Business, Hugh Foden
President Engine Business, Jim Kelly
VP MidRange Engine Business, David Crompton
VP Research and Technology, Wayne Eckerle
VP Corporate Strategy and Business Development, Thad Ewald
VP Cummins Latin America Engine Business, Louis Pasquotto
VP Global Supply Chain, Lisa Yoder
VP Human Resources, Jill E. Cook, age 48
Director, Carl Ware, age 68
Director, William I. (Will) Miller, age 55
Director, Georgia R. Nelson, age 62
Director, Alexis M. Herman, age 64
Director, Stephen B. Dobbs, age 56
Director, Robert K. Herdman, age 63
Director, Robert J. (Bob) Bernhard, age 59
Director, Franklin R. Chang-Diaz, age 62
Auditors: PricewaterhouseCoopersLLP

LOCATIONS

HQ: Cummins, Inc.
500 Jackson Street, Box 3005, Columbus, IN 47202-3005
Phone: 812 377-5000 **Fax:** 812 377-4937
Web: www.cummins.com

2011 Sales

	$ mil.	% of total
US	7,354	41
Brazil	1,286	7
UK	727	4
Mexico	631	3
Total	**18,048**	**100**

PRODUCTS/OPERATIONS

2011 Sales

	$ mil.	% of total
Engines	11,307	52
Components	4,063	18
Distribution	3,044	14
Adjustments	(3864)	-
Total	**18,048**	**100**

Selected Products

Components business
- Emission solutions
- Filtration (heavy-duty air fuel hydraulic and lube filtration and chemicals)
- Fuel systems (new fuel systems remanufactured electronic control modules)
- Turbo technologies (turbochargers)

Emissions solutions
Engine business
- Bus engines
- Heavy- and medium-duty truck engines
- Industrial engines for construction mining agricultural rail and marine equipment
- Light commercial vehicle engines
- Marine diesels (recreational and commercial)

Filtration business
- Air system
- Cooling system (crankcase ventilation)
- Diesel emission additives
- Fuel system (hydraulic)
- Lube system (transmission)

Fuel systems
- CELECT electronically controlled unit injection system
- Common rail pump
- Extreme pressure injection system
- High Pressure Injection (HPI) system
- Remanufactured products

Power generation business
- Diesel and alternative-fuel electrical generator sets (PowerCommand Onan Newage AVK SEG G-Drive)

Turbo technologies Holset (medium and heavy-duty diesel engines)

COMPETITORS

BorgWarner
Briggs & Stratton Power Products
Caterpillar
China Yuchai
CLARCOR
DENSO
Detroit Diesel
DEUTZ
Donaldson Company
Eaton
Emerson Electric
Fiat
Hino Motors
Honeywell International
Illinois Tool Works
Ingersoll-Rand
Isuzu
Kohler
Mack Trucks
MAN
Mitsubishi Heavy Industries
Navistar International
Parker-Hannifin
Regal Beloit
Robert Bosch
Tenneco
Textron
Tognum
UD Trucks
Volvo
W.W. Grainger
Weichai Power

HISTORICAL FINANCIALS

Company Type: Public

Income Statement FYE: December 31

	REVENUE ($ mil.)	NET INCOME ($ mil.)	NET PROFIT MARGIN	EMPLOYEES
12/11	18,048	1,848	10.2%	43,900
12/10	13,226	1,040	7.9%	39,200
12/09	10,800	428	4.0%	34,900
12/08	14,342	755	5.3%	39,800
12/07	13,048	739	5.7%	37,800
Annual Growth	8.4%	25.8%	—	3.8%

2011 Year-End Financials

Debt ratio: 5.88%
Return on equity: 33.65%
Cash ($ mil.): 1,484
Current ratio: 193.90
Long-term debt ($ mil.): 658
No. of shares (mil.): 192
Dividends
Yield: —
Payout: 13.87%
Market value ($ mil.): 16,900

	STOCK PRICE ($) FY Close	P/E High/Low		PER SHARE ($) Earnings	Dividends	Book Value
12/11	88.02	13	8	9.55	0.00	28.60
12/10	110.01	21	9	5.28	0.88	23.61
12/09	45.86	23	9	2.16	0.70	18.74
12/08	26.73	33	5	3.84	0.60	16.05
12/07	127.37	40	20	3.70	0.43	16.86
Annual Growth	(8.8%)	—	—	26.8%	—	14.1%

CVB Financial Corp.

CVB Financial is into the California Vibe Baby. The holding company's Citizens Business Bank offers community banking services to primarily small and midsized businesses but also to consumers through 40-plus branches and five commercial banking centers in nine central and southern California counties including Los Angeles and Orange counties. Its deposit products include checking money market and savings accounts as well as CDs. Commercial real estate loans account for about two-thirds of the bank's loan portfolio which is rounded out by business consumer and construction loans; residential mortgages; dairy and livestock loans; and municipal lease financing.

Operations

In addition to its 42 Business Financial Centers located in the Inland Empire Los Angeles County Orange County and the Central Valley areas CVB operates five Commercial Banking Centers (CBCs) four of which opened in 2008 and the fifth in 2009. The CBCs operate primarily as sales offices and focus on business clients professionals and high-net-worth individuals.

Citizens Business Bank provides auto and equipment leasing and brokers mortgage loans through its Citizens Financial Services Division; CitizensTrust offers trust and investment services.

Financial Analysis

Still struggling with the aftershocks of the deep recession and housing crisis CVB's revenue fell 19% in 2011 vs. 2010 while net income increased by nearly 30% over the same period. The decline was due to decreased revenue from interest and operating incomes.

Strategy

In 2009 CVB Financial healthier than most California banks acquired the failed San Joaquin Bank after the FDIC took it over. The deal added five branches banking centers in the Bakersfield area. CVB Financial continues to seek out acquisitions of other banking trust and investment companies in California.

The company which remained profitable throughout the economic downturn credits its success in part to its strict loan underwriting standards. It hopes to continue growing its loan portfolio and trust and service fee income. The bank targets family-owned or other privately held businesses with annual revenues of up to $200 million with the goal of maintaining its client relationships for decades.

Ownership

Chairman George Borba who led the founding of Citizens Business Bank owns about 11% of CVB Financial through a family trust.

EXECUTIVES

EVP and CFO; EVP and CFO Citizens Business Bank, Edward J. (Ed) Biebrich Jr., age 68, $282,308 total compensation
Vice Chairman, D. Linn Wiley, age 73, $554,231 total compensation
SVP Real Estate Banking Group, Mark C. Richardson
Chairman, George A. Borba, age 79
Vice Chairman, Ronald O. Kruse, age 73
SVP Bakersfield Business Financial Center & McFarland Business Financial Center, John H. Tait
SVP and Director Marketing, Nancy A. Sinclair
President CEO and Director CVB Financial and Citizens Business Bank, Christopher D. (Chris) Myers, age 49, $546,923 total compensation
SVP and Director Human Resources Citizens Business Bank, David M. Krebs
Sales Support Group Citizens Business Bank, Vince L. Gottuso
SVP and Regional Manager San Gabriel Valley, James E. Mead
VP International Services Citizens Business Bank, Frank Maslowski
Corporate Secretary, Myrna DiSanto
EVP and Citizens Trust Manager, Christopher A. Walters, age 48, $234,616 total compensation
EVP and Chief Risk Officer Citizens Business Bank, Yamynn DeAngelis
EVP and CIO Information Technology Division, Elsa I. Zavala
EVP Dairy and Livestock Industries Group Citizens Business Bank, Larry Zivelonghi
SVP Commercial Banking Centers, Ted Dondanville
SVP and Regional Manager Citizens Business Bank, Michael B. Mulcahy
Regional Manager Citizens Business Bank, Paul R. Russ
EVP Sales Citizens Business Bank, David A. Brager
SVP and Orange County Regional Manager, Michael J. Helmuth
Vice Chairman, D. Linn Wiley, age 73
Director, San E. Vaccaro, age 79
Vice Chairman, Ronald O. Kruse, age 73
Director, John A. Borba, age 84
Director, James C. Seley, age 70
President CEO and Director CVB Financial and Citizens Business Bank, Christopher D. (Chris) Myers, age 49
Director, Robert M. (Bob) Jacoby, age 70
Auditors: KPMGLLP

LOCATIONS

HQ: CVB Financial Corp.
701 N. Haven Ave. Ste. 350, Ontario CA 91764
Phone: 909-980-4030 **Fax:** 909-481-2131
Web: www.cbbank.com

Selected Branch Locations

Fresno County
Kern County
Los Angeles County
Madera County
Orange County
Riverside County
San Bernardino County
Tulare County

PRODUCTS/OPERATIONS

2011 Sales

	$ mil.	% of total
Interest		
Loans including fees	207	68
Investment securities	61	20
Other	1	-
Noninterest		
Service charges on deposit accounts	15	5
Trust & investment services	8	3
BOLI income	3	1
Bankcard services	3	1
Other	3	1
Total	**303**	**100**

COMPETITORS

Bank of America
Bank of the West
City National
Comerica
JPMorgan Chase
Popular Inc.
Provident Financial Holdings
U.S. Bancorp
UnionBanCal
Wells Fargo

HISTORICAL FINANCIALS

Company Type: Public

Income Statement FYE: December 31

	ASSETS ($ mil.)	NET INCOME ($ mil.)	INCOME AS % OF ASSETS	EMPLOYEES
12/11	6,482	81	1.3%	811
12/10	6,436	62	1.0%	819
12/09	6,739	65	1.0%	825
12/08	6,649	63	0.9%	776
12/07	6,293	60	1.0%	773
Annual Growth	0.7%	7.8%	—	1.2%

2011 Year-End Financials

Debt ratio: 8.70%
Return on equity: 11.43%
Cash ($ mil.): 405
Current ratio: —
Long-term debt ($ mil.): 563
No. of shares (mil.): 104
Dividends
Yield: —
Payout: 33.12%
Market value ($ mil.): 1,048

	STOCK PRICE ($) FY Close	P/E High/Low		PER SHARE ($) Earnings	Dividends	Book Value
12/11	10.03	13	10	0.77	0.00	6.84
12/10	8.67	19	11	0.59	0.34	6.07
12/09	8.64	21	9	0.56	0.34	6.01
12/08	11.90	20	10	0.75	0.34	7.38
12/07	10.34	19	13	0.72	0.34	5.11
Annual Growth	(0.8%)	—	—	1.7%	—	7.6%

CVR Energy Inc

CVR Energy's CV says that it puts its energy into oil refining and the production of petroleum products. It operates a 115000 barrels-per-day-throughput-capacity oil refinery in Coffeyville Kansas and a 70000 barrels-per day refinery in Oklahoma and a crude oil gathering system in Kansas and Oklahoma. CVR Energy Coffeyville refinery has 1.2 million barrels of storage tanks and it also has 2.7 million barrels of leased storage capacity in Cushing Oklahoma. It has asphalt and refined fuels storage and terminalling plants in Phillipsburg Kansas. The company through subsidiaries controls CVR Partners LP (a producer of ammonia and urea ammonium nitrate fertilizers) and serves as its general partner.

Geographic Reach

CVR Energy markets its petroleum products in the Midcontinent and Rocky Mountain regions where end users are in medium or close proximity to its oil refinery and pipelines.

Sales & Marketing

Customers include other refiners convenience store chains railroads and farm cooperatives. In 2010 the largest customer (QuikTrip) accounted for 14% of CVR Energy's total petroleum product sales.

Financial Analysis

To improve shareholder return in 2012 the company announced plans to spin off its refining assets as CVR Refining.

CVR Energy reported improved overall revenues in 2010 thanks to robust oil prices and an increase in demand for petroleum products and despite a dip in nitrogen sales due to lower prices and a temporary plant shutdown. However higher product costs led to a decline in net income.

CVR Energy saw its revenues slump in 2009 as the global recession hammered commodity prices. However those same low prices meant lower fuel costs for the company enabling it to post an improvement in operating income for the year.

Strategy

To raise cash and to focus on its core petroleum business in 2011 the spun off its CVR Partners unit (formed in 2007 to operate its nitrogen fertilizer business). Most nitrogen fertilizer producers use more expensive natural gas. CVR Partners operates the only nitrogen fertilizer plant in North America that uses coke gasification (superheating using low cost petroleum coke to generate the hydrogen used in fertilizer production). About 85% of the company's nitrogen products are for agricultural use.

Seeking to expand its refining base in 2011 the company acquired Denver-based independent Gary-Williams Energy and its Wynnewood Oklahoma refinery for $525 million. The refinery has the capacity to produce 70000 barrels per day of crude oil. With the acquisition CVR Energy bumped up its processing capacity to 185000 barrels per day.

Ownership

CVR Energy is controlled by Coffeyville Acquisitions a partnership of GS Capital Partners the private equity arm of Goldman Sachs and the private equity investment firm Kelso & Company.

In 2012 investor Carl Icahn (and 80.5% owner) made a $2.6 billion bid to acquire CVR Energy claiming that it could be sold to a larger oil company for up to $7 billion. The board of directors unanimously urged stockholders to rejected the offer.

Company Background

The company traces its roots to the National Refining Company which in 1906 built a refinery in Coffeyville. The completed refinery was the second largest in the US at the time.

EXECUTIVES

COO, Stanley A. Riemann, age 61, $415,000 total compensation
VP Investor Relations, Stirling D. Pack Jr., age 56
CFO and Treasurer, Frank A. Pici, age 56
Chairman President and CEO, John J. (Jack) Lipinski, age 61, $800,000 total compensation
VP Corporate Communications, Steven M. (Steve) Eames
EVP and General Manager Fertilizer, Kevan A. Vick, age 57, $225,000 total compensation
SVP General Counsel and Secretary, Edmund S. Gross, age 61, $315,000 total compensation
EVP Refining Operations, Robert W. Haugen, age 54, $275,000 total compensation
EVP Crude Oil Acquisition and Petroleum Marketing, Wyatt E. Jernigan, age 60, $225,000 total compensation
Chief Financial Officer, Susan M. Ball, age 49
EVP Strategy, Daniel J. Daly Jr., age 66, $220,000 total compensation
VP Environmental Health and Safety, Christopher G. Swanberg, age 54
VP and CIO, Michael T. (Mike) Brooks, age 42
Senior Vice President of Refined Products and Risk Management, Michael R. Puddy
Director Corporate Affairs, Angie Dasbach
VP Human Resources, Harry S. Nichols Jr.
CFO and Treasurer, Edward A. (Ed) Morgan, age 42, $171,346 total compensation
SVP Refined Products and Risk Management, Mike Puddy
CFO and Treasurer, Susan M. Bell
Chief Executive Officer, Byron Kelley
Chief Financial Officer, Tim Rens
Vice President - Human Resources, Carl Findley
Chairman of the Board, Carl Icahn
Director, George E. Matelich, age 55
Director, Mark E. Tomkins, age 57
Director, Joseph E. Sparano, age 64
Director, Steve A. Nordaker, age 65
Director, C. Scott Hobbs, age 58
Director, Scott L. Lebovitz, age 36
Director, Stanley de J. Osborne, age 41
Director, John K. Rowan, age 32
Independent Director, Bob Alexander
Chairman of the Board, Carl Icahn
Independent Director, Glenn Zander
Independent Director, James Strock
Independent Director, Stephen Mongillo
Auditors: KPMGLLP

LOCATIONS

HQ: CVR Energy Inc.
2277 Plaza Dr. Ste. 500, Sugar Land TX 77479
Phone: 281-207-3200 **Fax:** 646-502-4778
Web: www.answers.com

PRODUCTS/OPERATIONS

2010 Sales

	$ mil.	% of total
Petroleum	3,903	96
Nitrogen fertilizer	180	4
Adjustments	(4.5)	
Total	**4,079**	**100**

COMPETITORS

Agrium
CF Industries
ConocoPhillips
HollyFrontier
Koch Industries Inc.
National Cooperative Refinery Association
Sinclair Oil
Valero Energy

HISTORICAL FINANCIALS

Company Type: Public

Income Statement FYE: December 31

	REVENUE ($ mil.)	NET INCOME ($ mil.)	NET PROFIT MARGIN	EMPLOYEES
12/11	5,029	345	6.9%	764
12/10	4,079	14	0.4%	695
12/09	3,136	69	2.2%	474
12/08	5,016	163	3.3%	654
12/07	2,966	(56)	—	428
Annual Growth	14.1%	—	—	15.6%

2011 Year-End Financials

Debt ratio: 27.69%
Return on equity: 30.03%
Cash ($ mil.): 388
Current ratio: 230.92
Long-term debt ($ mil.): 853
No. of shares (mil.): 86
Dividends
Yield: —
Payout: —
Market value ($ mil.): 1,626

	STOCK PRICE ($) FY Close	P/E High/Low		PER SHARE ($) Earnings	Dividends	Book Value
12/11	18.73	7	4	3.94	0.00	13.27
12/10	15.18	90	40	0.16	0.00	7.98
12/09	6.86	17	4	0.80	0.00	7.57
12/08	4.00	16	1	1.90	0.00	6.72
12/07	24.94	—	—	(0.00)	0.00	5.15
Annual Growth	(6.9%)	—	—	—	—	26.7%

CVS Caremark Corporation

Size matters to CVS Caremark (formerly CVS) the nation's #2 drugstore chain and a leading pharmacy benefits manager with more than 60 million plan members. With more than 7300 retail and specialty drugstores under the CVS and Longs Drug banners it trails archrival Walgreen by about 600 stores. CVS has grown rapidly through a string of acquisitions that included the Eckerd and Longs Drug Stores chains. Also CVS now owns prescription benefits management (PBM) company Caremark Rx. Caremark Rx was combined with CVS's PBM and specialty pharmacy unit PharmaCare Management Services to form Caremark Pharmacy Services. Its MinuteClinic retail health network has more than 600 locations inside CVS drugstores.

HISTORY

Brothers Stanley and Sid Goldstein who ran health and beauty products distributor Mark Steven branched out into retail in 1963 when they opened up their first Consumer Value Store in Lowell Massachusetts with partner Ralph Hoagland.

The chain grew rapidly amassing 17 stores by the end of 1964 (the year the CVS name was first used) and 40 by 1969. That year the Goldsteins sold the chain to Melville Shoe to finance further expansion.

Melville had been founded in 1892 by shoe supplier Frank Melville. Melville's son Ward grew the company creating the Thom McAn shoe store chain and later buying its supplier. By 1969 Melville had opened shoe shops in Kmart stores (through its Meldisco unit) launched one apparel chain (Chess King sold in 1993) and purchased another (Foxwood Stores renamed Foxmoor and sold in 1985).

In 1972 CVS bought the 84-store Clinton Drug and Discount a Rochester New York-based chain. Two years later when sales hit $100 million CVS had 232 stores –only 45 of which had pharmacies. The company bought New Jersey-based Mack Drug (36 stores) in 1977. By 1981 CVS had more than 400 stores.

CVS's sales hit $1 billion in 1985 as it continued to add pharmacies to many of its older stores.

In 1987 Stanley's success was recognized companywide when he was named chairman and CEO of CVS's parent company which by then had been renamed Melville.

CVS bought the 490-store Peoples Drug Stores chain from Imasco in 1990 giving it locations in Maryland Pennsylvania Virginia West Virginia and Washington DC. CVS created PharmaCare Management Services in 1994 to take advantage of the growing market for pharmacy services and managed-care drug programs. Pharmacist Tom Ryan was named CEO that year.

With CVS outperforming Melville's other operations in 1995 Melville decided to concentrate on the drugstore chain. By that time Melville's holdings had grown to include discount department store chain Marshalls and furniture chain This End Up both sold in 1995; footwear chain Footaction spun off as part of Footstar in 1996 along with Meldisco; the Linens 'n Things chain spun off in 1996; the Kay-Bee Toys chain sold in 1996; and Bob's Stores (apparel and footwear) sold in 1997.

Melville was renamed CVS in late 1996. Amid major consolidation in the drugstore industry in 1997 CVS –then with about 1425 stores –paid $3.7 billion for Revco D.S. which had nearly 2600 stores in 17 states mainly in the Midwest and Southeast. The next year the company bought Arbor Drugs (200 stores in Michigan later converted to the CVS banner) for nearly $1.5 billion.

CVS opened about 180 new stores and relocated nearly 200 in 1998 as it shifted from strip malls to freestanding stores. (It also closed nearly 160 stores.) Stanley retired as chairman in 1999 and was succeeded by Ryan.

In 1999 the company bought online drugstore pioneer Soma.com renamed CVS.com. It also launched the CVS ProCare pharmacy to serve customers in need of complex drug therapies. A year later CVS bought Stadtlander Pharmacy of Pittsburgh from Bergen Brunswig (now AmerisourceBergen) for $124 million.

In early 2001 Wolverine Equities paid $288 million for 96 stores which CVS said it would continue to operate. In 2001 CVS opened 43 stores in new markets including Miami and Fort Lauderdale Florida; Las Vegas; and Dallas Houston and Fort Worth Texas. As part of a strategic restructuring begun in 2001 CVS closed more than 200 stores and moved others from strip malls to freestanding locations.

In July 2002 CVS was among the winning bidders for the remaining assets of bankrupt rival Phar-Mor. CVS acquired the majority of Phar-Mor's prescription lists. In October CVS named KB Toys as the exclusive toy supplier to its drugstores. CVS opened 266 new stores in 2002 and another 150 new stores in 2003.

In April 2003 specialty pharmacy division CVS ProCare changed its name to PharmaCare Specialty Pharmacy.

With those store closings behind it the drugstore chain began opening stores in Minneapolis the 10th-largest drugstore market in the US in 2004. CVS opened about 10 stores in the Los Angeles area in 2004 marking the drugstore chain's return to Southern California after a 12-year absence. CVS is also targeting other high-traffic markets including Chicago Florida Las Vegas Phoenix and Texas for expansion.

In July 2004 CVS completed the acquisition of 1260 Eckerd stores Eckerd Health Services (which included Eckerd's $1 billion mail order and pharmacy benefits management businesses) and three distribution centers from J. C. Penney Company for $2.15 billion. The acquisition of the Eckerd stores (622 in Florida) gave CVS more stores than archrival Walgreen. CVS completed the conversion of Eckerd stores in Alabama Arizona Colorado Florida Kansas Louisiana Mississippi Missouri New Mexico Oklahoma and Texas to its own banner within about a year.

In June 2005 CVS agreed to pay $110 million to settle a shareholders' lawsuit filed in 2001 that alleged the company had made misleading statements to artificially raise its stock price and violated accounting practices. CVS denied the charges and said the settlement was "purely a business decision."

In June 2006 CVS completed the acquisition of some 700 stand-alone Sav-On and Osco drugstores from Albertson's. CVS was part of a consortium that bought the nation's #2 supermarket chain and split it up amongst themselves. The transaction gave CVS access to Southern California and key Midwest markets. In September the company purchased the retail-based health clinic operator MinuteClinic for an undisclosed amount. The acquisition allowed CVS to provide in-store care to its customers for minor ailments.

In March 2007 CVS changed its name to CVS Caremark Corporation following its acquisition of the pharmacy benefits manager Caremark RX after months of bidding between CVS and Express Scripts. Ultimately CVS paid about $26.5 billion for Caremark. In November CEO Ryan added the chairman's title to his job description following the retirement of Mac Crawford.

In October 2008 CVS Caremark acquired Longs Drug Stores for about $2.9 billion. Longs Drug operates 521 pharmacies in California Hawaii Nevada and Arizona. The purchase included Long's Rx America subsidiary a pharmacy benefits management service to more than 8 million members. Also in 2008 the company opened about 190 new retail pharmacies.

In 2008 CVS settled a lawsuit regarding drug-switching allegations for $36.7 million. The company had been accused of switching Medicaid customers to a more expensive capsule form of Zantac from a tablet form; CVS denied the allegations.

In June 2009 CVS agreed to pay almost $1 million to settle allegations stemming from the sale of expired OTC medications infant formula and dairy products.

CVS Caremark in early 2011 won a contract to administer Aetna's retail pharmacy network. CVS Caremark is managing both purchasing and prescription filling for Aetna's mail-order and specialty pharmacy operations. Prior to his retirement in May 2011 Ryan assumed the title of non-executive chairman in March when Larry Merlo took over as president and CEO of CVS.

EXECUTIVES

EVP and Chief Legal Officer, Douglas A. Sgarro, age 52, $570,000 total compensation
President CEO and Director, Larry J. Merlo, age 56, $800,000 total compensation
SVP Investor Relations, Nancy R. Christal
SVP and General Counsel, Sara J. Finley, age 51
EVP; President CVS/pharmacy, Mark S. Cosby, age 53
VP and General Manager Accordant Health Services, Thomas J. Frosheiser
EVP and Chief Health Care Strategy and Marketing Officer, Helena B. Foulkes, age 47
CIO, Stephen J. Gold, age 53
Manager Corporate Communications, Mike DeAngelis
EVP Merchandising Supply Chain Advertising and Marketing, Mike Bloom
EVP; President Caremark Pharmacy Services, Per G. H. Lofberg, age 64
SVP Corporate Communications, Eileen Howard-Dunn
SVP and Chief Human Resources Officer, Lisa Bisaccia, age 55
SVP and CIO, Stuart M. McGuigan, age 53
EVP and Chief Medical Officer, Troyen A. Brennan, age 57, $575,000 total compensation
SVP and Treasurer, Carol A. DeNale
EVP Internal Operations Real Estate Retail Field Organizations and Pharmacy Operations, Scott Baker
EVP; COO Pharmacy Benefit Management Division, Jonathan C. Roberts, age 56
EVP and CFO, David M. (Dave) Denton, age 47
Chief Medical Officer MinuteClinic, Nancy J. Gagliano
VP Corporate Communications, Carolyn Castel
SVP and Associate Chief Medical Officer; President MinuteClinic, Andrew J. (Andy) Sussman
Senior Manager Public Relations, Erin Pensa
SVP Controller and Chief Accounting Officer, Laird K. Daniels, age 43
Senior Director Investor Relations, Michael P. McGuire
Manager Public Relations, Joanne Dwyer
SVP Merchandising CVS/pharmacy, Judith Strauss Sansone
Chief Marketing Officer CVS/pharmacy, Robert Price
Director, Richard J. (Dick) Swift, age 67
President CEO and Director, Larry J. Merlo, age 56
Director, Kristen E. Gibney Williams, age 63
Director, C. A. Lance Piccolo, age 71
Director, Terrence Murray, age 72
Director, Anne M. Finucane, age 58
Director, Jean-Pierre (JP) Millon, age 61
Director, Tony L. White, age 65
Auditors: Ernst&YoungLLP

LOCATIONS

HQ: CVS Caremark Corporation
1 CVS Dr., Woonsocket RI 02895
Phone: 401-765-1500 **Fax:** 401-762-9227
Web: www.cvs.com

2011 Stores

	No.
California	833
Florida	718
Texas	538
New	457
Pennsylvania	396
Massachusetts	345
Ohio	316
Georgia	312
North	306
Indiana	294
Illinois	268
New	266
Virginia	262
Michigan	244
South	195
Maryland	169
Alabama	150
Connecticut	140
Arizona	133
Tennessee	129
Louisiana	100
Nevada	85
Kentucky	59
Rhode	59
District of	58
Missouri	54
West	50
Hawaii	49
Minnesota	49
Mississippi	45
Oklahoma	45
New	36
Wisconsin	35

Kansas	32
Maine	22
Montana	14
Nebraska	13
Puerto	13
Iowa	12
New	12
North	6
Delaware	5
Vermont	3
Total	**7,327**

PRODUCTS/OPERATIONS

2011 Retail Sales

	% of total
Prescription	68
Over-the-counter & personal	11
Beauty/cosmetics	5
General merchandise &	16
Total	**100**

2011 Sales

	$ mil.	% of total
Retail pharmacy	59	50
Pharmacy services	58	50
Adjustments	(11.4)	-
Total	**107**	**100**

2011 Stores

	No.
Retail	7,327
Specialty	31
Onsite	30
Specialty Mail	12
Total	**7,400**

COMPETITORS

A&P
Aetna
Ahold U.S.A.
BioScrip
CIGNA
Costco Wholesale
drugstore.com
Express Scripts
H-E-B
Kerr Drug
Kmart
Kroger
Medicine Shoppe
OptumRx
Rite Aid
Target Corporation
UnitedHealth Group
Wal-Mart
Walgreen
WellPoint

HISTORICAL FINANCIALS

Company Type: Public

Income Statement FYE: December 31

	REVENUE ($ mil.)	NET INCOME ($ mil.)	NET PROFIT MARGIN	EMPLOYEES
12/11	107,100	3,461	3.2%	280,000
12/10	96,413	3,427	3.6%	280,000
12/09	98,729	3,696	3.7%	295,000
12/08	87,471	3,212	3.7%	305,000
12/07	76,329	2,637	3.5%	200,000
Annual Growth	8.8%	7.0%	—	8.8%

2011 Year-End Financials

Debt ratio: 15.52%
Return on equity: 9.10%
Cash ($ mil.): 1,413
Current ratio: 155.52
Long-term debt ($ mil.): 9,208
No. of shares (mil.): 1,298
Dividends
Yield: —
Payout: 19.46%
Market value ($ mil.): 52,932

	STOCK PRICE ($) FY Close	P/E High/Low		PER SHARE ($) Earnings	Dividends	Book Value
12/11	40.78	16	12	2.57	0.00	29.32
12/10	34.77	15	11	2.49	0.35	27.66
12/09	32.21	15	9	2.55	0.31	25.71
12/08	28.74	20	11	2.18	0.26	24.03
12/07	40.00	21	16	1.92	0.00	21.80
Annual Growth	0.5%	—	—	7.6%	—	7.7%

Dana Holding Corp

When it comes to building cars it starts with the parts and Dana makes the parts that carmakers use to piece together new vehicles. In addition to its core offerings which include driveline products (axles driveshafts transmissions) it provides power technologies (sealing thermal-management products) and service parts. It makes products for vehicles in the light medium/heavy (commercial) and off-highway markets. The company's products carry brand names that include Spicer Victor Reinz and Long. Dana also supplies companies that make commercial and off-highway vehicles such as Deere Navistar PACCAR and Sandvik. Customers outside the US account for about 56% of sales.

HISTORY

Clarence Spicer developed a universal joint and a driveshaft for autos while studying at Cornell University. Leaving Cornell in 1904 he patented his designs founded Spicer Manufacturing in Plainfield New Jersey and marketed the product himself.

The business ran into financial trouble in 1913 and the following year New York attorney Charles Dana joined the firm advancing Spicer money to refinance. Acquisitions after WWI strengthened Spicer's position in the growing truck industry. The business moved to Toledo Ohio in 1929 to be nearer the emerging Detroit automotive Mecca. In 1946 the company was renamed in honor of Dana who became chairman two years later. Sales topped $150 million in the 1950s.

The company entered the replacement parts market in 1963 and Charles Dana retired that year. Continuing to expand its offerings Dana acquired the Weatherhead Company (hoses fittings and couplings; 1977) and later branched into financial services. In 1989 Dana introduced a nine-speed heavy-duty truck transmission (developed jointly with truckmaker Navistar) the first all-new design of its type in over 25 years.

Dana sold its mortgage banking business and some other financial services in 1992. It bought Delta Automotive and Krizman both leading makers and distributors of automotive aftermarket parts. The next year Dana acquired the Reinz Group a German gasket maker with worldwide operations. Purchases in 1994 included Sige (axles Italy) Stieber Heidelberg (industrial components Germany) Tece (auto parts distribution the Netherlands) and Tremec (transmissions Mexico).

Acquisitions in 1995 and 1996 included a number of rubber and plastics makers. The company bought Clark-Hurth Components (drivetrains) and the piston ring and cylinder liner operations of SPX Corporation in 1997; it also increased its shares in Wix Filtron (filtration products Poland).

Dana sold some of its businesses in 1997 as well. These included its sheet-rubber and conveyor-belt business to Coltec Industries its European warehouse distribution operations to Partco Group and its Spicer clutch business to Eaton.

In 1998 Dana bought Eaton's heavy-axle and brake business and then paid $3.9 billion for Echlin. Dana then cut 3500 jobs and closed 15 plants mostly former Echlin facilities. It paid $430 million in 1998 for the bearings washers and camshafts businesses of Federal-Mogul (auto parts).

In 2000 Dana sold Gresen's hydraulic business to Parker Hannifin and Warner Electric's industrial products business to Colfax. The company also sold a truck-cab parts unit two cold-forming plants its Sierra marine aftermarket line and its Truckline distribution centers in Australia. Anticipating a slowdown in North American car production Dana closed five plants downsized three and terminated 1280 employees.

On the buying side Dana acquired the auto axle manufacturing and stamping operations of Invensys (UK) in 2000. Also that year president and CEO Joseph Magliochetti a 33-year Dana veteran became chairman. Late in 2000 the company announced it would cut 3000 production jobs.

Dana sold its Chelsea Products Division (power take-offs) in 2001 to Parker Hannifin. Later in the year Dana announced 10000 more job cuts through plant closings and consolidations. Near the end of 2001 Dana announced plans to sell its Dana Commercial Credit leasing business and to consolidate its engine and fluid businesses into a single unit; the restructuring of these divisions was completed by 2002.

In 2002 Dana sold the first piece of Dana Commercial Credit for $69 million. The division then completed the sale of certain real estate holdings for $150 million. Also in 2002 the company sold Tekonsha Engineering Company (aftermarket electric brake controls) Theodore Bargman Company (exterior lighting electrical accessories and locks and latches) and American Electronic Components (sensors switches and relays) to leveraged buyout firm The Riverside Company. The following month Dana sold its FTE brake and clutch actuation systems operations to HgCapital a European private equity finance company. In 2003 Dana sold a significant portion of the Engine Management operations of its Automotive Aftermarket Group to Standard Motor Products for $121 million. ArvinMeritor offered in 2003 to acquire Dana for $15 per share or about $2.2 billion. The deal fell apart after Dana's board of directors rejected ArvinMeritor's sweetened deal of $2.67 billion. Within weeks of fending off ArvinMeritor Dana announced it planned to sell all of its aftermarket parts businesses. The deal was completed in 2004. The following year Dana and Dongfeng Motor formed 50/50 joint venture Dongfeng Dana Axle Co. Ltd. for the manufacture of commercial vehicle axles in China.

As hard times hit the North American automotive market in 2005 Dana announced it would cut more costs by laying off workers selling non-core operations closing plants and moving more of its manufacturing base to Mexico. Dana filed for Chapter 11 bankruptcy in 2006. As the year wound to a close Dana found a buyer for its engine hard parts division earlier targeted for divestiture. MAHLE International agreed to buy the engine hard parts business for about $157 million. The sale was completed in 2007. Also that same year Dana divested its trailer axle manufacturing business. The operations were purchased by Hendrickson USA for about $31 million. Later in 2007 Dana sold certain noncore hose and tube operations to Turkish concern Orhan Holding for about $85 million.

Throughout 2007 and 2008 Dana continued to unload product lines; divested operations included its trailer axle engine hard parts fluid products hose and tubing and pump businesses. Dana emerged from Chapter 11 in 2008. It was restricted by the financial covenants of its exit financing restraints that could impede the company during the credit crisis. In late 2008 Dana amended some covenants in its exit facility.

During 2008 the company reduced its workforce by 6000 people a 17% cutback in employment. In 2009 the company slashed another 5000 jobs and announced that there would be additional workforce reductions in 2010. Dana closed more than 25 facilities since 2007.

Dana restructured its operations to streamline business. The company divested its Structural Products business to Metalsa in 2010.

EXECUTIVES

Treasurer, Ralph A. Than, age 51
Chairman, Keith E. Wandell, age 62
President and CEO, Roger J. Wood, age 49
Chief Accounting Officer, Rodney R. Filcek, age 59
EVP and CFO, William G. Quigley III, age 50
SVP Global Operations, Ernesto Gonzalez-Beltran, age 49
Chief Strategy Officer, Jacqueline A. Dedo, age 50
VP and Chief Accounting Officer, Richard J. Dyer, age 56
VP and Operations Controller, Kevin B. Biddle, age 57
VP Global Engineering and Business Development Sealing and Thermal Product Groups, Ralf Goettel, age 45, $444,106 total compensation
President Asia Pacific Operations, Ken J. Cao
EVP; President On-Highway Driveline Technologies, Mark E. Wallace, age 45, $390,384 total compensation
SVP General Counsel and Secretary, Marc S. Levin, age 57
Chief Purchasing Officer, Eric W. Schwarz, age 47
Chief Technical and Quality Officer, George T. Constand, age 53
President Off-Highway Technologies, Aziz S. Aghili
VP and CIO, Doug S. Tracy, age 51
President South American Operations, Harro Burmann
Media Relations Contact, Chuck Hartlage
Senior Director Investor Relations, Lillian Etzkorn
Chief Administrative Officer, Jeffrey Bowen
President Power Technologies, Dwayne Matthews
Director, Richard F. Wallman, age 61
Director, Joseph C. (Joe) Muscari, age 65
Director, Mark T. Gallogly, age 55
Director, Mark A. Schulz, age 59
Director, Terrence J. (Terry) Keating, age 62
Auditors: PricewaterhouseCoopersLLP

LOCATIONS

HQ: Dana Holding Corporation
3939 Technology Dr., Maumee OH 43537
Phone: 419-887-3000 **Fax:** 202-828-0860
Web: www.danaher.com

2010 Sales

	$ mil.	% of total
North America		
US	2,675	44
Other countries	285	5
Europe		
Italy	517	8
Germany	360	6
Other countries	702	11
South America		
Brazil	535	9
Other countries	304	5
Asia/Pacific	731	12
Total	**6,109**	**100**

PRODUCTS/OPERATIONS

2010 Sales

	$ mil.	% of total
Light vehicle driveline	2,516	41
Commercial vehicle	1,344	22
Off-highway	1,131	19
Power technologies	927	15
Structures	188	3
Other	3	-
Total	**6,109**	**100**

Selected Products

Automotive (light vehicle driveline)
- Axles (front and rear)
- Differentials
- Driveshafts
- Modular assemblies
- Side rails
- Torque couplings

Commercial vehicle (medium-heavy)
- Axles
- Driveshafts
- Steering shafts
- Suspension and tire management systems

Off-highway
- Axles
- Driveshafts
- Electronic controls
- Torque converters
- Transaxles
- Transmissions

Power technologies
- Cooling and heat transfer
- Cover modules
- Engine sealing systems
- Heat shields
- Gaskets

Structures (for light and medium/heavy)
- Cradles
- Frames
- Side rails

COMPETITORS

AISIN World Corp.
American Axle & Manufacturing
AxleTech International
Boler
BorgWarner
Carraro
Chrysler
DENSO
ElringKlinger
Federal-Mogul
Freudenberg-NOK
GKN
Hitachi Automotive Systems Americas
Magna International
Mahle International
Mark IV
Martinrea International
Meritor
Metaldyne
Modine Manufacturing
Tower International
Valeo
Visteon
Wanxiang
ZF Friedrichshafen

HISTORICAL FINANCIALS

Company Type: Public

Income Statement

FYE: December 31

	REVENUE ($ mil.)	NET INCOME ($ mil.)	NET PROFIT MARGIN	EMPLOYEES
12/11	7,592	219	2.9%	24,500
12/10	6,109	10	0.2%	22,500
12/09	5,228	(431)	—	24,000
12/08*	7,344	(691)	—	29,000
01/08	751	709	94.4%	0
Annual Growth	78.3%	(25.4%)	—	—

*Fiscal year change

2011 Year-End Financials

Debt ratio: 17.00%
Return on equity: 12.61%
Cash ($ mil.): 931
Current ratio: 204.22
Long-term debt ($ mil.): 831
No. of shares (mil.): 147
Dividends
Yield: —
Payout: —
Market value ($ mil.): 1,790

	STOCK PRICE ($) FY Close	P/E High/Low		PER SHARE ($) Earnings	Dividends	Book Value
12/11	12.15	15	8	1.02	0.00	11.79
12/10	17.21	—	—	(0.16)	0.00	11.69
12/09	10.84	—	—	(4.19)	0.00	12.04
12/08*	0.74	—	—	(7.20)	0.00	20.13
Annual Growth	154.2%	—	—	—	—	(16.3%)

*Fiscal year change

Danaher Corp.

Danaher Corporation makes the products that help doctors discern dissect and digest data. The company operates through five segments: Life Sciences & Diagnostics (research/clinical tools); Test & Measurement (electronic measurement instruments); Industrial Technologies (product identification motion control equipment and sensors); Environmental (turbine pumps and air/water analysis and treatment equipment); and Dental (orthodontic bracket systems and lab products). Its 50/50 joint venture with Cooper Industries –Apex Tool Group –makes power and mechanics' hand tools and wireless technologies. Danaher serves customers in more than 125 countries but it generates around 40% of its revenues in the US.

HISTORY

Danaher (from the Celtic word dana meaning "swift flowing") is named for a fishing stream off the Flathead River in Montana. The term is also an appropriate description of the spotlight-averse Rales brothers. The two have proven to be fishers not only of trout but also of companies buying underperforming companies with strong market shares and recognizable brand names. Once dubbed "raiders in short pants" by "Forbes" Steven and Mitchell Rales began making acquisitions in their 20s. In 1981 they bought their father's 50% stake in Master Shield a maker of vinyl building products. The brothers bought tire manufacturer Mohawk Rubber the following year. In 1983 they acquired control of publicly traded DMG a distressed Florida real-estate firm; the next year they sold DMG's real estate holdings and folded Mohawk and Master Shield into the company which they renamed Danaher.

Danaher then began taking over low-profile industrial firms that weren't living up to their growth potential. Backed by junk bonds from Michael Milken it purchased 12 more companies within two years. Among these early acquisitions were makers of tools (Jacobs Matco Tools) controls (Partlow Qualitrol Veeder-Root) precision components (Allen maker of the namesake hexagonal wrench) and plastics (A.L. Hyde). With its purchases Danaher proceeded to cut costs and pay down debt by unloading underperforming assets.

The Rales brothers' takeover efforts weren't always successful. They lost out to Warren Buffett when they tried to buy Scott Fetzer (encyclopedias vacuum cleaners) in 1985 and INTERCO (furniture shoes apparel) in 1988. They did however make off with $75 million for their troubles and INTERCO was driven into dismantlement and bankruptcy in the process.

In 1989 Danaher bought Easco Hand Tools the main maker of tools for Sears Roebuck and Co.'s Craftsman line. (Members of the Rales family already controlled Easco Hand Tools; a private partnership they controlled had bought the company from its parent in 1985 and taken it public in 1987.) The deal established the tool division as Danaher's largest and two years later Sears selected Danaher as the sole manufacturer of Craftsman mechanics' hand tools.

The brothers hired Black & Decker (now Stanley Black & Decker) power tools executive George Sherman as president and CEO in 1990. Between 1991 and 1995 Danaher grew through purchases such as Delta Consolidated Industries and Armstrong Brothers Tool. The firm improved its international distribution channels by adding West Instruments (UK 1993) and Hengstler (Germany 1994).

Focusing on tools and controls Danaher sold its automotive components business in 1995. After a lengthy battle the company bought test maker and controls firm Acme-Cleveland in 1996.

Danaher's 1997 purchases included Current Technology and GEMS Sensors. Danaher made its two largest purchases to date in 1998 when it bought Pacific Scientific (motion controls and safety equipment) for $460 million and Fluke (electronic tools) for $625 million.

Boosting its motion-control operations in 2000 Danaher bought Kollmorgen for about $240 million and American Precision Industries for $185 million. In 2001 Lawrence Culp formerly the company's COO was named president and CEO. Later that year Danaher made a $5.5 billion offer for Cooper Industries (electric products and tools). Cooper rejected the offer and announced that it was exploring other options. Further talks with Cooper followed but Danaher lost interest when Cooper became embroiled in asbestos lawsuits.

The following year Danaher completed the divestiture of API Heat Transfer. Also in 2002 Danaher bought Thomson Industries (motion control products) Gilbarco (which does business as Gilbarco Veeder-Root; retail automation and environmental products) and Videojet Technologies (product identification equipment). The next year it expanded its product identification business by acquiring Willett (rigid and flexible packaging labeling) and Accu-Sort Systems (bar code scanners and vision technology).

In 2004 the company entered the dental business by acquiring Gendex the dental imaging product manufacturer from Dentsply International; it also purchased KaVo. To further grow this segment the company acquired Sybron Dental Specialties in 2006 and PaloDEx Group in 2009.

Danaher's DH-Denmark subsidiary created its Acute Care segment by acquiring Radiometer a Denmark-based company that makes blood gas analyzers in the latter part of 2004. That year Danaher also acquired a product line of telecom tool and test systems from Harris Corporation. Helen Nova Scotia Unlimited Danaher's Canada-based subsidiary acquired a 94% stake in Trojan Technologies a company that makes UV lights for disinfecting water.

The summer of 2005 brought along the acquisition of German optical systems maker Leica Microsystems for about $550 million. Soon after the close of the deal Danaher sold Leica's semiconductor equipment business which had totaled sales of about $120 million as part of a regulatory agreement. It then tried to acquire Leica Geosystems a company independent of Leica Microsystems for just under $1 billion. Danaher was in competition with Sweden's Hexagon for Leica Geosystems however and lost out.

The company acquired Tektronix in 2007 and incorporated it into its Professional Instrumentation (now Test & Measurement) division. Tektronix brought general-purpose test products such as oscilloscopes and data analyzers as well as network management systems and network diagnostic equipment and services for fixed and mobile telecommunications to Danaher's product portfolio. Other strategic acquisitions for this segment included ChemTreat (industrial water treatment) for which Danaher paid a cash purchase price of $425 million; performance management company Visual Networks; and Autotank.

Danaher augmented its customer base in early 2010 by purchasing Genetix Group for approximately $82 million. Genetix carried a portfolio of genetic screening and analysis systems reagents and related supplies demanded by scientists and clinicians in developing pharmaceuticals and clinical diagnostics. For $580 million it also snapped up MDS Analytical Technologies (drug discovery and life sciences research instruments) and Keithley Instruments (for $300 million) a provider of electronic instruments and systems used by electronics manufacturers and educational institutions later that year.

To build on its product identification portfolio Danaher acquired X-Rite a provider of color-science products that include spectrophotometers and colorimeters for about $625 million in 2012.

EXECUTIVES

EVP and CFO, Daniel L. Comas, age 48, $535,031 total compensation
President CEO and Director, H. Lawrence (Larry) Culp Jr., age 49, $953,958 total compensation
SVP Finance and Tax, James H. Ditkoff, age 65, $275,000 total compensation
Chairman, Steven M. Rales, age 61
SVP Corporate Development, Daniel A. Raskas, age 45
EVP, Thomas P. Joyce Jr., age 51, $480,156 total compensation
EVP, James A. (Jim) Lico, age 46, $480,156 total compensation
SVP and Chief Accounting Officer, Robert S. Lutz, age 54
SVP and General Counsel, Jonathan P. Graham, age 51
EVP, William K. (Dan) Daniel II, age 47, $480,156 total compensation
President CEO and Director, H. Lawrence (Larry) Culp Jr., age 49
Director, Mitchell P. Rales, age 55
Director, Donald J. Ehrlich, age 74
Director, Walter G. Lohr Jr., age 68
Director, John T. Schwieters, age 72
Director, Elias A. Zerhouni, age 60
Director, Linda P. Hefner
Auditors: Ernst&YoungLLP

LOCATIONS

HQ: Danaher Corp.
2200 Pennsylvania Avenue, N.W., Suite 800W, Washington, DC 20037-1701
Phone: 202 828-0850 **Fax:** 202 828-0860
Web: www.danaher.com

2011 Sales

	$ mil.	% of total
US	6,787	42
China	1,133	7
Other countries	6,171	38

PRODUCTS/OPERATIONS

2011 Sales by Segment

	$ mil.	% of total
Life sciences & diagnostics	4,627	29
Test & measurement	3,390	21
Industrial technologies	3,121	19
Environmental	2,939	18
Dental	2,011	13
Total	**16,090**	**100**

2011 Sales by Product Group

	$ mil.	% of total
Medical & dental products	6,653	41
Analytical & physical instrumentation	5,920	37
Product identification	1,162	7
Defense	162	1
Total	**16,090**	**100**

Selected Mergers & Acquisitions

FY2012
- X-Rite Incorporated ($625 million; Grand Rapids Michigan; provider of color-science products that include spectrophotometers and colorimeter)
- IRIS International Inc. ($338 million; Chatsworth California; automated in-vitro diagnostic systems maker)

FY2011
- EskoArtwork ($470 million; Belgium; printing and packaging software provider)
- Beckman Coulter Inc. ($5.8 billion; Brea California; diagnostic testing systems and supplies)

FY2010
- Genetix Group PLC ($82 million; UK; cell imaging and screening systems maker)
- Keithley Instruments Inc. ($300 million; Solon Ohio; digital multimeters semiconductor parametric test and device characterization systems signal analyzers and generators)

Selected Products

Color measurement
- Color formulation (ColorMail)
- Colorimeters (color accuracy testing)
- Densitometers (optical and photographic density measurement)
- Ink formulations software
- Paint matching systems
- Sensitometers (photographic exposure control)

Dental
- Digital imaging
- Implant systems
- Impression bonding and restorative materials
- Infection control products
- Orthodontic brackets and lab products

Environmental
- Analytical instruments
- Fuel dispensers
- Monitoring and leak detection systems
- Submersible turbine pumps
- Ultraviolet disinfection systems
- Vapor recovery equipment
- Water treatment systems

Industrial Technologies
- Aerospace and defense
  - Electrical power generation systems
  - Electronic security systems
  - Smoke detection and fire suppression
  - Submarine periscopes and related sensors
- Motion
  - Controls
  - Drives
  - Mechanical components (linear bearings clutches/brakes and linear actuators)
  - Standard and custom motors
- Product identification equipment
- Sensors and controls
  - Monitoring and control instruments (temperature position quantity level flow and time)

Life Sciences & Diagnostics

Acute care
Blood gas and immunochemistry instruments (Radiometer brand)
Life sciences instrumentation
Compound microscopes
Laser scanning
Pathology diagnostics
Chemical and immuno-staining instruments
Slide coverslipping
Tissue embedding
Test and Measurement
Video test measurement and monitoring products
Tools and Components
Mechanics hand tools

COMPETITORS

ABB
Bosch Rexroth Corp.
Datamax-O' Neil
Eaton
Emerson Electric
GE
Goodrich Corp.
Greenlee Textron
Hitachi
Johnson & Johnson Medical
Johnson Controls
Labfacility
Makita
Mettler-Toledo
Parker-Hannifin
PerkinElmer
Rockwell Automation
Schneider Electric
Siemens Water Technologies
Snap-on
SPX
Stanley Black and Decker
Thales Air Defence
Thermo Fisher Scientific
Wayne

HISTORICAL FINANCIALS

Company Type: Public

Income Statement FYE: December 31

	REVENUE ($ mil.)	NET INCOME ($ mil.)	NET PROFIT MARGIN	EMPLOYEES
12/11	16,090	2,172	13.5%	59,000
12/10	13,202	1,793	13.6%	48,200
12/09	11,184	1,151	10.3%	46,600
12/08	12,697	1,317	10.4%	50,300
12/07	11,025	1,369	12.4%	50,000
Annual Growth	9.9%	12.2%	—	4.2%

2011 Year-End Financials

Debt ratio: 17.71%
Return on equity: 12.85%
Cash ($ mil.): 537
Current ratio: 150.34
Long-term debt ($ mil.): 5,206
No. of shares (mil.): 687
Dividends
Yield: —
Payout: 2.89%
Market value ($ mil.): 32,351

	STOCK PRICE ($) FY Close	P/E High/Low		PER SHARE ($) Earnings	Dividends	Book Value
12/11	47.04	17	13	3.11	0.00	24.58
12/10	47.17	32	13	2.64	0.08	20.89
12/09	75.20	42	27	1.73	0.07	18.02
12/08	56.61	42	24	1.98	0.06	15.40
12/07	87.74	40	32	2.10	0.06	14.29
Annual Growth	(14.4%)	—	—	10.3%	—	14.5%

Darden Restaurants, Inc.

This company has cornered not one but two dining markets: seafood and "Hospitaliano." Darden Restaurants is the #1 casual-dining operator (in terms of revenue) with about 1900 restaurants in the US and Canada. Its flagship chains include seafood-segment leader Red Lobster and top Italian-themed concept Olive Garden. Both chains cater to families by offering mid-priced menu items themed interiors and primarily suburban locations. Darden also operates the LongHorn Steakhouse chain with about 370 outlets. Other dining concepts include The Capital Grille (upscale steakhouse) Bahama Breeze (Caribbean food and drinks) and Seasons 52 (casual grill and wine bar).

Operations

Being at the forefront of the casual dining industry Darden's flagship brands have come to epitomize the chain restaurant experience. Both Red Lobster (about 675 locations) and Olive Garden (roughly 750 locations) dominate the landscape of suburban America.

Strategy

Red Lobster and Olive Garden offer a version of seafood and Italian cuisine designed for mass appeal and affordability. Darden spends heavily on research and development in order to roll out a succession of new menu items that are heavily promoted through television advertising. The chains also utilize discount pricing and special offers to win business against the competition including Applebee's Chili's (operated by Brinker International) and Outback Steakhouse (OSI Restaurant Partners).

Darden has built its dining empire without the aid of franchising a strategy that allows the company the highest degree of control for maintaining food and service quality. The major downside is the cost of operating and maintaining all those restaurants. The company is constantly focused on improving margins by negotiating lower prices for food and other ingredients and by adjusting its workforce to reduce labor costs.

The recession of recent years has posed serious challenges for most casual dining operators but Darden's chains fared better than some of the company's competitors thanks to intense customer loyalty. The company did restructure its corporate office in mid-2012 eliminating about 40 positions in departments such as finance human resources supply chain and building services.

Geographic Reach

Darden is looking outside of the US for growth including plans to develop Olive Garden and LongHorn Steakhouse locations in Puerto Rico. A Red Lobster opened in Dubai in July 2011. Most of the company's international growth emphasis has been on its Olive Garden and LongHorn Steakhouse chains. However Darden has been remodeling many of its domestic Olive Garden and LongHorn Steakhouse units in lieu of adding new locations.

HISTORY

Nineteen-year-old Bill Darden entered the restaurant business in the late 1930s with a 25-seat luncheonette called the Green Frog in Waycross Georgia. The restaurant which featured the slogan "Service with a Hop" was a hit and his career was born. During the 1950s he owned a variety of restaurants including several Howard Johnson's Bonanza and Kentucky Fried Chicken outlets.

Darden teamed with a group of investors in 1963 to buy an Orlando Florida restaurant Gary's Duck Inn. The restaurant became the prototype for Darden's idea for a moderately priced sit-down seafood chain. He decided to name the new chain Red Lobster a takeoff on the old Green Frog.

The first Red Lobster opened in Lakeland Florida in 1968 with Joe Lee who had worked in one of Darden's other restaurants as its manager. It was such a success that within a month the restaurant had to be expanded. In 1970 when there were three Red Lobsters in operation and two under construction in Central Florida Betty Crocker's boss General Mills bought the chain — keeping Darden on to run it.

Red Lobster was not General Mills' first foray into the restaurant business. The company opened Betty Crocker Tree House Restaurant in 1968 and acquired a fish-and-chips chain and a barbeque chain. But Red Lobster would be its first success. Rather than franchise the Red Lobster name General Mills chose to develop the chain on its own. Lee was named president of Red Lobster in 1975 and Darden became chairman of General Mills Restaurants.

While General Mills continued to expand Red Lobster it also sought another restaurant idea to complement the seafood chain. Among concepts tried and discarded were a steak house and Mexican and health-food restaurants. In 1980 the company decided on Italian. After two years of marketing questionnaires and recipe tests General Mills opened a prototype Olive Garden in Orlando featuring moderately priced Italian food. General Mills began to add outlets in the mid-1980s and Olive Garden became another success story of the casual-dining industry.

After testing a new Chinese restaurant concept General Mills opened its first China Coast in Orlando in 1990. The chain grew rapidly with more than 45 units opening in a single year. The Olive Garden drive began to cool off in 1993: Same-store sales slid as competitors added Italian items to their menus. The next year Olive Garden increased its advertising budget introduced new menu items and began testing new formats including smaller cafes for malls.

General Mills decided to spin off the restaurant business as a public company in 1995 and focus on consumer foods. The restaurants were renamed Darden Restaurants in honor of Bill Darden (who had died in 1994 the same year that Joe Lee was appointed CEO). That year the company abandoned its China Coast chain.

Darden Restaurants tried again in 1997 with Bahama Breeze opening a test restaurant in Orlando. Red Lobster's sales flagged in 1997 but the company initiated a turnaround in 1998 in part by revamping Red Lobster's menu. An ill-conceived all-you-can-eat offer at Red Lobster cost Darden in profits (and led to the ousting of chain president Edna Morris after just 18 months). The company dipped into the barbecue sauce in 1999 and opened its inaugural Smokey Bones in Orlando.

The following year Darden Restaurants began expanding its Smokey Bones concept nationally. In late 2001 Japanese noodle-shop operator Reins International agreed to buy Darden's 34 Red Lobster franchises in Japan for about $4.8 million. Dick Rivera who had been president of the Red Lobster chain since 1997 was named company president and COO in 2002. (He resigned from the company in early 2004.)

With financial results lagging at its Bahama Breeze chain Darden slowed growth of the concept and expanded its operating hours to include lunch business. The company also promoted former development VP Laurie Burns to lead Bahama Breeze after the unexpected resignation of Gary Heckel in 2002. Clarence Otis Jr. was appointed CEO in 2004 succeeding Joe Lee; the following year Otis added chairman to his title.

The company expanded into the steakhouse market in 2007 with its $1.4 billion (including debt) acquisition of RARE Hospitality. The following year Darden sold its unprofitable Smokey Bones Barbeque & Grill chain to an affiliate of Sun Capital Partners for about $80 million.

EXECUTIVES

SVP Purchasing and Supply Chain Innovation, Bill Herzig
SVP and Chief Supply Chain Officer, Barry B. Moullet, age 54
SVP Human Resources LongHorn Steakhouse, Thomas W. (Tom) Gathers, age 56
President Specialty Restaurant Group, Eugene I. (Gene) Lee Jr., age 51, $514,600 total compensation
Chairman and CEO, Clarence Otis Jr., age 56, $946,800 total compensation
SVP Total Rewards and HR Shared Services, Danielle Kirgan
President Bahama Breeze, Laurie B. Burns, age 50
SVP Business Development, Kim A. Lopdrup, age 54, $522,885 total compensation
President LongHorn Steakhouse, David C. (Dave) George, age 56
SVP and Corporate Controller, Valerie K. (Val) Collins, age 53
President COO and Director, Andrew H. (Drew) Madsen, age 56, $767,800 total compensation
SVP and Treasurer, Bill White
SVP Human Resources Olive Garden, Theresa Willings
EVP Operations Bahama Breeze, John Wilkerson
SVP Group Human Resources, Ronald (Ron) Bojalad
SVP Finance Specialty Restaurant Group, Jill Golder
SVP and Chief Restaurant Operations Officer, Valerie Insignares
SVP Human Resources Specialty Restaurant Group, Paula Manchester
EVP Marketing Red Lobster, Salli Setta
VP Investor Relations, Matthew Stroud
VP Consumer Insights, Glad Markunas
SVP Government and Community Affairs, Robert (Bob) McAdam, age 54
SVP Marketing Bahama Breeze, Chip Brown
VP HR Information Systems, Patrick (Pat) Harrigan
President Red Lobster, David T. (Dave) Pickens, age 57, $517,500 total compensation
Director Media and Communications Bahama Breeze, Mike Bernstein
EVP Marketing Olive Garden, Terry Stanley, age 51
SVP; President Olive Garden, John Caron
Director Culinary Development Olive Garden, Marie Grimm
SVP and Chief Marketing Officer, James (J. J.) Buettgen, age 52
SVP and CFO, C. Bradford (Brad) Richmond, age 53, $424,000 total compensation
SVP Concept Development, John Hatton
VP Total Quality, Anna Hooper
President Seasons 52, Stephen Judge
SVP General Counsel Chief Legal Officer and Secretary, Teresa M. Sebastian
VP Government Relations, Gerald R. (Chip) Kunde II
SVP Finance and Controller Red Lobster, Bill Lambert
VP Operations The Capital Grille, Brian Foye
VP Development Red Lobster, Briggs Sellers
SVP and Chief Human Resources Officer, Daisy Ng, age 54
VP Accounting and Corporate Planning, Dan Williams
SVP Finance, Dave Lothrop
EVP Operations Red Lobster, Doug Green
VP Division General Counsel, Horace Dawson
SVP Supply Management and Purchasing, Jim Lawrence
VP Beef Purchasing, Jeff Spotz
VP Corporate Strategic Insights, Joel Aach
EVP Marketing LongHorn Steakhouse, John Fadool
President The Capital Grille, John Martin
VP Information Technology, Jordan Lomas
VP Finance Olive Garden, Renato Barbon
SVP Finance LongHorn Steakhouse, Rick Cardenas
VP Seafood Purchasing, Roger Bing
VP Human Resources, Samir Gupte
SVP and Chief Development Officer, Suk Singh
VP Marketing The Capital Grille, Evelyn Moore
VP Consumer Insights Olive Garden, Margaret Olson-Cox
SVP and CIO, Patti Reilly White
Manager Media and Communications Red Lobster, Erica Jaeger
Director Sustainability, Ian Olson
Director Media Relations and External Communications, Rich Jeffers
Manager Media and Communications Olive Garden, Heidi Schauer
SVP Human Resources Red Lobster, Diane Psaras
VP Culinary and Beverage Olive Garden, Timothy (Tim) Blaise
VP Development Olive Garden, William (Bill) DeMuth
Manager Federal Government Relations, T. J. Birkel
EVP Operations Olive Garden, Dan Kiernan
Director Corporate Security, Don Slaughter
Director, David H. Hughes, age 68
Director, Charles A. Ledsinger Jr., age 62
Director, Odie C. Donald, age 62
Director, Connie Mack III, age 71
Director, Michael D. Rose, age 68
Director, Leonard L. Berry, age 69
Director, Maria A. Sastre, age 57
President COO and Director, Andrew H. (Drew) Madsen, age 56
Director, William M. Lewis Jr., age 56
Director, Victoria D. Harker, age 47
Director, Christopher J. (CJ) Fraleigh, age 48
Auditors: KPMGLLP

LOCATIONS

HQ: Darden Restaurants Inc.
1000 Darden Center Dr., Orlando FL 32837
Phone: 407-245-4000 **Fax:** 407-245-5389
Web: www.dardenrestaurants.com

PRODUCTS/OPERATIONS

COMPETITORS

Bob Evans
Brinker
Carlson Restaurants
Cheesecake Factory
Cracker Barrel
Denny' s
DineEquity
Hooters
Landry' s
OSI Restaurant Partners
Perkins & Marie Callender' s
Ruby Tuesday

HISTORICAL FINANCIALS

Company Type: Public

Income Statement FYE: May 27

	REVENUE ($ mil.)	NET INCOME ($ mil.)	NET PROFIT MARGIN	EMPLOYEES
05/12	7,998	475	5.9%	180,000
05/11	7,500	476	6.4%	178,380
05/10	7,113	404	5.7%	174,079
05/09	7,217	372	5.2%	178,692
05/08	6,626	377	5.7%	179,000
Annual Growth	4.8%	6.0%	—	0.1%

2012 Year-End Financials

Debt ratio: 35.68%
Return on equity: 25.81%
Cash ($ mil.): 70
Current ratio: 42.70
Long-term debt ($ mil.): 1,508
No. of shares (mil.): 129
Dividends
Yield: —
Payout: 48.18%
Market value ($ mil.): 6,845

	STOCK PRICE ($) FY Close	P/E High	P/E Low	PER SHARE ($) Earnings	Dividends	Book Value
05/12	53.06	15	11	3.57	0.00	14.28
05/11	50.92	15	11	3.39	0.00	14.38
05/10	42.90	17	10	2.84	0.00	13.47
05/09	36.17	15	5	2.65	0.00	11.53
05/08	31.74	18	8	2.60	0.00	10.03
Annual Growth	13.7%	—	—	8.2%	—	9.2%

DaVita HealthCare Partners Inc

DaVita HealthCare Partners (formerly DaVita) gives life in the form of dialysis treatments to patients suffering from end-stage renal disease (chronic kidney failure). Through its DaVita division the company is one of the country's largest providers of dialysis operating or providing administrative services to more than 1900 outpatient dialysis centers across the US. The firm also offers home-based dialysis services as well as inpatient dialysis in some 900 hospitals. The firm operates two clinical laboratories that specialize in routine testing of dialysis patients and serve the company's network of clinics. Subsidiary HealthCare Partners operates primary care clinics and physician practices in several states.

The company changed its legal name from DaVita to DaVita HealthCare Partners in late 2012 after it completed its acquisition of private medical group management firm HealthCare Partners. The purchase was conducted through a merger transaction worth some $4.4 billion; following the deal HealthCare Partners began operating as a subsidiary of DaVita HealthCare Partners while the dialysis division continues to operate under the DaVita name. The two companies both count California and Florida as key markets and DaVita HealthCare Partners plans to use HealthCare Partners' integrated care model to help it offer a wider range of healthcare services.

Geographic Reach

California Florida and Texas are home to about 30% of all DaVita dialysis centers though the firm has locations in more than 40 US states. Nearly all of the company's outpatient dialysis centers are either wholly owned or majority-owned by DaVita. Some 30 centers are owned by third parties which pay DaVita for administrative services. The company has also established a presence in select international markets including China Germany India and the Middle East.

The HealthCare Partners unit operates and manages medical groups and physician practice networks in California Florida Nevada and New Mexico.

Operations

Dialysis and lab services accounted for more than 90% of the company's revenues in 2011 (prior to the HealthCare Partners acquisition). DaVita and its main competitor Fresenius Medical Care together control more than 60% of the US dialysis clinic market. While the two companies each hold roughly a third of the market Fresenius also actually manufactures dialysis supplies and DaVita is a customer. Home infusion of medications and nutritionals to patients with chronic or acute conditions is provided by the HomeChoice Partners subsidiary.

Almost 90% of the company's dialysis patients are covered by government-based health plans including Medicare Medicaid and the VA making DaVita particularly vulnerable to changes in government reimbursement rates (which are regularly under threat of being lowered by state and federal governments facing budget pressures). The balance of the income comes from commercial insurance payers.

A portion of DaVita's dialysis and lab-related revenues comes from administering specialty pharmaceuticals to patients receiving dialysis. The pharmaceuticals include vitamin D iron supplements and EPO –a genetically engineered protein that stimulates the production of red blood cells. EPO is used during dialysis to treat anemia (a common complication). Amgen is the only company manufacturing EPO and in 2011 to buffer against price fluctuations or shortages DaVita struck a multiyear agreement with Amgen to secure its supply of EPO at discounted pricing.

In addition to dialysis services DaVita also offers other services related to kidney disease including specialty pharmacy services and the operation of chronic kidney disease management programs for employers and health plans. DaVita's Nephrology Partners business provides practice management and administrative services to physicians groups and its DaVita Clinical Research business conducts research trials with dialysis patients.

Strategy

Historically DaVita has grown its network of facilities through acquisition of outpatient dialysis centers. In 2011 for example the company accumulated about 200 more centers around the US through a series of purchases. The company has also been looking to branch out into new areas of health care including medical practice management a mission it accomplished through the 2012 purchase of HealthCare Partners.

Mergers and Acquisitions

DaVita significantly widened its domestic network of dialysis centers when it acquired regional dialysis chain DSI Renal for $690 million in 2011. To secure approval for the deal from the FTC DaVita agreed to divest 30 clinics but overall the acquisition added more than 100 dialysis centers to its holdings.

While its international operations are still a tiny fraction of its total business the company is involved in a long-term strategy to expand into overseas markets for growth through acquisitions and partnerships. In the Asia/Pacific region DaVita entered the Malaysian market in late 2012 by acquiring a dialysis center near Kuala Lumpur and opening two new joint venture centers there. Earlier that year it announced plans to enter China through a new joint venture to provide dialysis services with Chinese biotech company 3SBio. Also in 2012 it shored up its presence in India by acquiring a controlling interest in NephroLife.

Elsewhere around the world DaVita entered Germany with the 2011 purchase of DV Care. It also expanded into the Middle East through the acquisition of a majority stake in Lehbi Care a leading Riyadh-based kidney care company with three clinics.

HISTORY

Hospital chain National Medical Enterprises (NME now Tenet) formed Medical Ambulatory Care in 1979 to run its in-hospital dialysis centers. The unit bought other centers in NME's markets. In 1994 the subsidiary's management backed by a Donaldson Lufkin & Jenrette –now Credit Suisse First Boston (USA) –investment fund bought the dialysis business and renamed it Total Renal Care (TRC).

To become a leader in its consolidating field TRC began buying other centers and soon added clinical laboratory and dialysis-related pharmacy services and home dialysis programs. It went public in 1995.

The next year the firm added 66 facilities 32 from its acquisition of Caremark International's dialysis business. In 1997 TRC expanded abroad buying UK-based Open Access Sonography (vein care) and partnering with UK-based Priory Hospitals Group.

In 1998 TRC bought Renal Treatment Centers nearly doubling its size. But the acquisition costs caused a loss that year and sparked shareholder lawsuits (settled in 2000) over alleged misleading statements. The firm also became embroiled in a reimbursement dispute with Florida's Medicare program. Problems continued into 1999 as the company struggled to meld operations. The company took a charge to cover a billing shortfall and chairman and CEO Victor Chaltiel and COO/CFO John King resigned. New management began improving billing procedures and took other cost-cutting measures.

The company changed its name in 2000 to DaVita an Italian phrase loosely translated as "he/she gives life." It also sold its international operations to competitor Fresenius.

In 2005 the company acquired Gambro's US dialysis operations for about $3 billion adding some 565 dialysis clinics to its operations. To meet FTC requirements for the deal DaVita sold about 70 clinics to RenalAmerica a company founded by former Gambro Healthcare executive Michael Klein.

In 2007 DaVita expanded its health care offerings by acquiring a majority stake in HomeChoice Partners a provider of home infusion services. The company added about 80 new centers through acquisitions in 2009.

EXECUTIVES

CIO, Thomas H. (Tom) Murphy
Co-Chairman and CEO, Kent J. Thiry, age 56, $1,090,385 total compensation
VP Clinical Integrated Services, Stephen D. McMurray, age 64
VP, LeAnne M. Zumwalt, age 53
Co-Chairman of the Board, Robert Margolis
Interim Chief Financial Officer; Chief Accounting Officer, James K. (Jim) Hilger, age 49
VP Communications, Bill Myers
SVP and Chief Development Officer, Thomas O. (Tom) Usilton Jr., age 60, $515,380 total compensation
COO, Dennis L. Kogod, age 52, $628,855 total compensation
President, Javier J. Rodriguez, age 41, $571,143 total compensation
Chief Medical Officer, Allen R. Nissenson, age 65
CFO, Luis A. Borgen, age 42
VP Recruiting and HRIS, Tony Blake
Chief People Officer, Laura A. Mildenberger, age 53
SVP and Chief Compliance Officer, David T. Shapiro, age 42
Director Online Marketing, Jason Walker
VP Research, Mahesh Krishnan
VP General Counsel and Secretary, Kim M. Rivera, age 43
EVP Rocky Mountain Region, Scott Drake
VP Clinical Affairs Home Therapies, John Moran
VP Investor Relations, Jim Gustafson
CIO, Anthony Gabriel
Executive Director Bridge of Life, Lori Vaclavik
Director, Charles G. (Chuck) Berg, age 54
Director, Paul J. Diaz, age 50
Director, Peter T. Grauer, age 66
Director, William L. Roper, age 63
Director, Roger J. Valine, age 63
Co-Chairman, Robert Margolis
Director, John Davidson, age 57
Director, Pamela M. Arway, age 58
Director, Carol Anthony, age 56
Auditors: KPMGLLP

LOCATIONS

HQ: DaVita HealthCare Partners Inc.
2000 16th St., Denver CO 80202
Phone: 303-405-2100 **Fax:** 740-549-6100
Web: www.greif.com

PRODUCTS/OPERATIONS

2011 Revenues by Payer

Government-based programs	
Medicaid	5
Commercial	34

2011 Dialysis Revenues

Outpatient hemodialysis centers	81
Hospital inpatient hemodialysis	5

Selected Operations

Astro Hobby West Mt. Renal Care Limited Partnership
Austin Dialysis Centers L.P.
Beverly Hills Dialysis Partnership
Brighton Dialysis Center LLC
Capital Dialysis Partnership
Carroll County Dialysis Facility L.P.
Central Carolina Dialysis Centers LLC
Chicago Heights Dialysis LLC
Continental Dialysis Center Inc.
Dallas-Fort Worth Nephrology L.P.
Dialysis of Des Moines LLC
Dialysis Specialists of Dallas Inc.
Downriver Centers Inc.
Downtown Houston Dialysis Center L.P.
Durango Dialysis Center LLC
DVA Healthcare of Maryland Inc.
East End Dialysis Center Inc.
Elberton Dialysis Facility Inc.
Empire State DC Inc.
Greenwood Dialysis LLC
Hawaiian Gardens Dialysis LLC
HealthCare Partners LLC
HuntingtonPark Dialysis LLC
Indian River Dialysis Center LLC
Jedburg Dialysis LLC
Kidney Centers of Michigan L.L.C.

Lincoln Park Dialysis Services Inc.
Mason-Dixon Dialysis Facilities Inc.
Middlesex Dialysis Center LLC
Natomas Dialysis
Nephrolife Care (India) Pte. Ltd.
North Colorado Springs Dialysis LLC
Open Access Lifeline LLC
Palomar Dialysis LLC
Physicians Choice Dialysis of Alabama LLC
Physicians Dialysis of Houstin LLP
Renal Life Link Inc.
Renal Treatment Centers Inc.
RMS Lifeline Inc.
Rocky Mountain Dialysis Services LLC
Shining Star Dialysis Inc.
Soledad Dialysis Center LLC
Summit Dialysis Center L.P.
Tortugas Dialysis LLC
Total Renal Care Inc.
Total Renal Laboratories Inc.
Total Renal Research Inc.
TRC West Inc.
Tulsa Dialysis Center LLC
Upper Valley Dialysis L.P.

COMPETITORS

Apria Healthcare
Critical Care Systems International
Dialysis Clinic Inc
FMCNA
Fresenius Medical Care
Gentiva
LabCorp
Lincare Holdings
Quest Diagnostics
U.S. Renal Care

HISTORICAL FINANCIALS

Company Type: Public

Income Statement FYE: December 31

	REVENUE ($ mil.)	NET INCOME ($ mil.)	NET PROFIT MARGIN	EMPLOYEES
12/11	6,982	478	6.8%	41,000
12/10	6,447	405	6.3%	36,500
12/09	6,108	422	6.9%	34,000
12/08	5,660	374	6.6%	32,500
12/07	5,264	381	7.3%	31,000
Annual Growth	7.3%	5.8%	—	7.2%

2011 Year-End Financials

Debt ratio: 50.66%
Return on equity: 22.33%
Cash ($ mil.): 393
Current ratio: 197.86
Long-term debt ($ mil.): 4,417
No. of shares (mil.): 93
Dividends
Yield: —
Payout: —
Market value ($ mil.): 7,099

	STOCK PRICE ($) FY Close	P/E High/Low		PER SHARE ($) Earnings	Dividends	Book Value
12/11	75.81	18	12	4.96	0.00	22.86
12/10	69.49	19	14	3.94	0.00	20.61
12/09	58.74	15	10	4.06	0.00	20.72
12/08	49.57	17	12	3.53	0.00	18.82
12/07	56.35	18	14	3.55	0.00	16.17
Annual Growth	7.7%	—	—	8.7%	—	9.0%

Dean Foods Co.

Dean Foods the nation's largest milk bottler has ridden a white wave of dairy industry consolidation. The dairy giant has and continues to grow through acquisitions. Its retail and food service dairy products are sold under more than 50 national regional and private-label brands including Borden Pet Country Fresh and Meadow Gold. In addition the company manufactures coffee creamers (International Delight) dips ice cream butter cottage cheese and specialty dairy products (lactose-free and organic milk soy coconut and almond milks and flavored milks). Dean owns and operates a number of smaller dairy companies including Horizon Organic Berkeley Farms and Garelick Farms.

HISTORY

Investment banker Gregg Engles formed a holding company in 1988 with other investors including dairy industry veteran Cletes Beshears to buy the Reddy Ice unit of Dallas-based Southland (operator of the 7-Eleven chain). The company also bought Circle K's Sparkle Ice and combined it with Reddy Ice. By 1990 it had acquired about 15 ice plants.

The company changed its name to Suiza Foods when it bought Suiza Dairy in 1993 for $99 million. The Puerto Rican dairy was formed in 1942 by Hector Nevares Sr. and named for the Spanish word for "Switzerland." By 1993 it was Puerto Rico's largest dairy controlling about 60% of the island's milk market.

Suiza Foods bought Florida's Velda Farms manufacturer and distributor of milk and dairy products in 1994. The company went public in 1996 the same year it bought Swiss Dairy (dairy products California and Nevada) and Garrido y Compa?ia (coffee products Puerto Rico).

The company became one of the largest players in the North American dairy industry through its acquisitions in 1997. It paid $960 million for Morningstar (Lactaid brand lactose-free milk Second Nature brand egg substitute) which –like Suiza Foods itself –was a Dallas-based company formed in 1988 through a Southland divestiture. The company entered the Midwest with its $98 million purchase of Country Fresh and the Northeast with the Bernon family's Massachusetts-based group of dairy and packaging companies including Garelick Farms and Franklin Plastics (packaging).

Suiza Foods strengthened its presence in the southeastern US in 1998 with its $287 million acquisition of Land-O-Sun Dairies operator of 13 fluid-dairy and ice-cream processing facilities. Also that year Suiza Foods purchased Continental Can (plastic packaging) for about $345 million and sold Reddy Ice to Packaged Ice for $172 million.

After settling an antitrust lawsuit brought by the US Department of Justice in 1999 Suiza Foods bought dairy processors in Colorado Ohio and Virginia. That year Suiza Foods combined its US packaging operations with Reid Plastics to form Consolidated Containers retaining about 40% of the new company.

In 2001 Suiza Foods announced it had agreed to purchase rival Dean Foods for $1.5 billion and the assumption of $1 billion worth of debt. Dean Foods had begun as Dean Evaporated Milk founded in 1925 by Sam Dean a Chicago evaporated-milk broker. By the mid-1930s it had moved into the fresh milk industry. The company went public in 1961 and was renamed Dean Foods in 1963.

Suiza Foods completed the acquisition and took on the Dean Foods name later in 2001. The new Dean Foods bought out Dairy Farmers of America's interest in Suiza Dairy and merged it with the "old" Dean's fluid-dairy operations to create its internal division Dean Dairy Group.

Along with the purchase of "old" Dean came a 36% ownership of soy milk maker WhiteWave and in 2002 Dean Foods purchased the remaining 64% for approximately $189 million. By the end of the year Dean had sold off some smaller businesses (boiled peanuts and contract hauling) and its Puerto Rico operations for $119 million in cash.

During 2003 Dean purchased Michigan milk processor Melody Farms sold off its frozen non-dairy topping and creamer business to Rich Products and renamed its Morningstar Foods division Dean Branded Products Group. With an eye on adding organic milk Dean purchased 13% of Horizon Organic in 2003 and acquired the remainder of the company in 2004. Dean then purchased Michael Foods' dairy products unit Kohler Mix Specialties including three plants that produce mixes for ice cream and frozen yogurt soy milk and coffee creamers; it also acquired Cremora brand non-dairy creamer from Eagle Family Foods.

By 2004 sales of canned and aseptic sports drinks meal supplement drinks and weight-loss beverages had weakened to the point where the company predicted a loss up to $4.6 million from its largest customers and Dean decided to drop that part of its business. Expanding in the southeast Dean purchased Milk Products of Alabama. In California the company bought Ross Swiss Dairies. Overseas Dean acquired Tiger Foods a dairy processing firm located in Spain.

The next year the company sold Dean's Dips and Marie's Dressings to Ventura Foods. The company spun also off its specialty foods group to its shareholders as TreeHouse Foods in 2005. TreeHouse makes private-label products such as pickles and non-dairy powdered coffee creamers and various regional brands; it also gained several former Dean Foods brands including Mocha Mix non-dairy creamers and Second Nature egg substitute. The next year sold its Iberian operations (Spain and Portugal) to Portuguese dairy Lactogal Productos Alimentares.

Dean began a concerted marketing campaign in 2006 touting its hormone-free milk sold under the Schepps brand as an alternative to organic milk which is more expensive. Continuing its modus operandi of growth by purchasing regional dairies in 2007 Dean acquired Friendship Dairies for about $130 million. That year it also added to its capacity with the purchase of manufacturing facilities from Wells' Dairy and SUPERVALU for a combined outlay of some $50 million.

To expand its holdings in the dairy-replacement sector the company acquired the Alpro soy beverage and food operations of Belgium's Vandemoortele for E325 million ($450 million) in 2009.

At the beginning of 2010 Dean Foods reconfigured its business. The company combined its Fresh Dairy Direct and Morningstar businesses to form Fresh Dairy Direct-Morningstar and paired its WhiteWave business with Alpro (acquired in 2009) to form WhiteWave-Alpro. In July 2010 Dean sold Rachel's Dairy Limited (UK) business to France's Lactalis. (Dean acquired Rachel's when it bought its parent company Horizon Organic.)

Dean Foods sold its Mountain High yogurt business to General Mills in early 2011 and its private-label yogurt business to Schreiber Foods soon after.

EXECUTIVES

SVP Business Optimization, Rick Fehr, age 60, $420,000 total compensation
President Garelick Farms, Alan J. Bernon, age 57, $440,000 total compensation
Chairman and CEO, Gregg L. Engles, age 54, $1,133,333 total compensation
SVP and CIO, Barbara D. Carlini, age 52

President Morningstar Foods, Kevin C. Yost, age 46
VP Investor Relations, Barry Sievert
President WhiteWave Foods Company, Blaine E. McPeak, age 46
EVP and Chief Strategy and Transformation Officer, Gregory A. (Greg) McKelvey, age 38
EVP Human Resources, Thomas N. Zanetich, age 61
President Fresh Dairy Direct and Chief Supply Chain Officer, Gregg A. Tanner, age 56, $548,333 total compensation
EVP and CFO, Shaun P. Mara, age 47
SVP Innovation, Debra B. (Debbie) Carosella, age 55
EVP General Counsel and Corporate Secretary, Steven J. Kemps, age 48
VP Corporate Communications, Marguerite Copel
General Manager Berkeley Farms, Nicholas G. (Nick) Kelble
Chief Marketing Officer, Rick Zuroweste
EVP Research and Development, Kelly Duffin-Maxwell, age 47
Chief Commercial Officer, Christopher (Chris) Sliva, age 49
CEO Alpro, Bernard P. J. Deryckere, age 54
President Horizon Organic Dairy, Mike Ferry
Director, John R. Muse, age 61
Director, Jim L. Turner, age 66
Director, V. Janet Hill, age 64
Director, Joseph S. Hardin Jr., age 67
Director, Tom C. Davis, age 64
Director, Stephen L. Green, age 61
Director, J. Wayne Mailloux, age 63
Auditors: Deloitte&ToucheLLP

LOCATIONS

HQ: Dean Foods Company
2711 N. Haskell Ave. Ste. 3400, Dallas TX 75204
Phone: 214-303-3400 **Fax:** 214-303-3499
Web: www.deanfoods.com

PRODUCTS/OPERATIONS

2011 Sales

	$ mil.	% of total
Fresh Dairy Direct	9,596	74
WhiteWave-Alpro	2,109	16
Morningstar	1,348	10
Total	**13,055**	**100**

2011 Fresh Dairy Direct Sales

	% of total
Private-label	53
Company	47
Total	**100**

2011 Fresh Dairy Direct Sales

	% of total
Fluid dairy	
Fresh	74
Ice	9
Other	2
Cultured	4
Other	5
Fresh	3
Other	3
Total	**100**

Selected Brands

Alpro (Europe)
Alta Dena
Berkeley Farms
Borden (licensed)
Brown Cow
Brown' s Dairy
Dean' s
Garelick Farms
Hershey' s (licensed)
Horizon Organic
Knudsen (licensed)
LAND O' LAKES (licensed)
Oak Farms
Over the Moon
Pet (licensed)
Provamel (Europe)
Silk
Tuscan
WhiteWave

Selected Products

Bottled waters
Eggnog
Eggs
Cottage cheese
Half-and-half
Ice cream
Juice
Milk
Pudding
Sour cream
Soymilk
Whipping cream

COMPETITORS

Associated Milk Producers
Aurora Organic Dairy
Ben & Jerry' s
Blue Bell
Brewster Dairy
California Dairies Inc.
ConAgra
Crystal Farms Refrigerated Distribution Company
Dairy Farmers of America
Danone
Darigold Inc.
Dreyer' s
Foster Dairy Farms
Friendly' s Ice Cream
Galaxy Nutritional Foods
Grupo LALA
Hain Celestial
Hiland Dairy
HP Hood
Lactalis
Lifeway Foods
Maryland & Virginia Milk Producers
Mondelez International
National Dairy
Nestle USA
Northwest Dairy
Organic Valley
Prairie Farms Dairy
Quality Chekd
Rockview Dairies
Stonyfield Farm
Tillamook County Creamery Association
Vitasoy International

HISTORICAL FINANCIALS

Company Type: Public

Income Statement

FYE: December 31

	REVENUE ($ mil.)	NET INCOME ($ mil.)	NET PROFIT MARGIN	EMPLOYEES	STOCK PRICE ($) FY Close	P/E High/Low	PER SHARE ($) Earnings	Dividends	Book Value
12/11	13,055	(1,575)	—	24,066	11.20	— —	(8.59)	0.00	(0.56)
12/10	12,122	91	0.8%	25,780	8.84	37 15	0.50	0.00	8.23
12/09	11,158	240	2.2%	27,157	18.04	16 11	1.38	0.00	7.48
12/08	12,454	183	1.5%	25,820	17.97	24 9	1.20	0.00	3.62
12/07	11,821	131	1.1%	25,585	25.86	48 24	0.96	15.00	0.39
Annual Growth	2.5%	—	—	(1.5%)	(18.9%)	— —	—	—	—

2011 Year-End Financials

Debt ratio: 65.44%
Return on equity: 987650001000000.00%
Cash ($ mil.): 114
Current ratio: 114.76
Long-term debt ($ mil.): 3,563
No. of shares (mil.): 183
Dividends
Yield: —
Payout: —
Market value ($ mil.): 2,058

Deere & Co.

Deere & Co. is interested in seeing its customers go to seed and grow. The company one of the world's largest makers of farm equipment is also a major producer of construction forestry and commercial and residential lawn care equipment. Deere operates through three business segments: the agriculture and turf and construction and forestry segments make up its equipment operations; a credit segment provides financial services. Deere famous for its "Nothing Runs Like A Deere" marketing sells John Deere and other brands through retail dealer networks and also makes products for outlets Home Depot and Lowes. It has manufacturing and sales facilities worldwide; North America represents about 60% of sales.

HISTORY

Vermont-born John Deere moved to Grand Detour Illinois in 1836 and set up a blacksmith shop. Deere and other pioneers had trouble with the rich black soil of the Midwest sticking to iron plows designed for sandy eastern soils so in 1837 Deere used a circular steel saw blade to create a self-scouring plow that moved so quickly it was nicknamed the "whistling plow." He sold only three in 1838 but by 1842 he was making 25 a week.

Deere moved his enterprise to Moline in 1847. His son Charles joined the company in 1853 beginning a tradition of family management. (All five Deere presidents before 1982 were related by blood or marriage.) Charles set up an independent dealership distribution system and added wagons buggies and corn planters to the product line.

Under Charles' son-in-law William Butterworth (president 1907-1928) Deere bought agricultural equipment companies and developed harvesters and tractors with internal combustion engines. Butterworth's nephew Charles Wiman became president in 1928. He extended credit to farmers during the Depression and won customer loyalty. In 1931 Deere opened its first non-US plant in Canada.

William Hewitt Wiman's son-in-law became CEO in 1955. Deere passed International Harvester in 1958 to become the #1 US maker of farm equipment; by 1963 it led the world. Deere expanded into Argentina France Mexico and Spain and it used research and joint ventures abroad (Yanmar small tractors 1977; Hitachi excavators 1983) to diversify.

Robert Hanson became the first non-family CEO in 1982. He poured $2 billion into research and development during the 1980s. Despite an industry-wide sales slump resulting in losses totaling $328 million in 1986 and 1987 Deere was the only major agricultural equipment maker to change neither ownership nor close factories during the 1980s. Instead Deere cut its workforce 44% and improved efficiency.

In 1989 Deere introduced its largest (at the time) new product offering —the 9000 series of combines. Deere also acquired Funk Manufacturing (powertrain components) that year and Hans Becherer succeeded Hanson as CEO.

During the 1990s Deere expanded its lawn care equipment business mainly in Europe. In 1991 it bought a majority stake in Sabo-Maschinenfabrik (commercial lawn mowers Germany) and in 1993 it gained distribution rights to Zetor tractors and Brno diesel engines (Czech Republic) for marketing in Latin America and Asia.

After spending most of the early 1990s in the doldrums because of recession and weak farm prices Deere rebounded. By 1994 it had replaced its tractor line with all-new models and bought Homelite (handheld outdoor power equipment) from Textron.

Deere signed a deal to sell combines in Ukraine (1996) and it formed a joint venture in 1997 to make combines in China. Fading demand for agricultural equipment at home and jeopardized sales contracts from failing economies in Asia Brazil and former Soviet states caused layoffs of about 2400 workers in 1998 and production cutbacks in 1998 and 1999. Late in 1999 Deere sold its property/casualty insurance operations to Sentry Insurance. Also late in 1999 Deere and Credit Suisse First Boston and affiliated investment entities formed joint venture Nortrax as a vehicle for consolidating developing and managing Deere's construction and forestry equipment dealers. Deere took a minority stake of 41% in the venture.

In 2000 Deere purchased regional parts distributor Sunbelt Outdoor Products and Metso's Timberjack forestry-equipment business for about $600 million. President and COO Robert Lane succeeded Becherer as chairman and CEO. Deere bought McGinnis Farms —the US's largest horticultural products distributor —in 2001.

That year it cut production due to soft demand. Late in 2001 Deere said it would add to its previously announced job cuts bringing the total to about 3000 jobs. Job cuts came from the company's November sale of its Homelite consumer products division (which lost about $70 million in 2000) to Hong Kong-based TechTronics Industries Co. and the consolidation of Deere's construction-forestry division. Deere also acquired Richton International Corporation; that deal included Richton's landscape irrigation-equipment distributor Century Supply (#1 in the US) and Richton Technology Group (hardware software and systems support services). Deere then formed John Deere Landscapes to distribute its growing line of irrigation and other landscaping products.

In 2002 Deere dissolved its hay farm and forage equipment joint venture Alloway Industries with Woods Equipment Company. The following year Deere sold its stake in Sunstate Equipment a construction and forestry equipment rental company for around $30 million. Late in 2003 Deere bought an additional 42% of joint venture Nortrax from Credit Suisse First Boston and its affiliated partners for about $112 million. The deal brought Deere's stake in Nortrax to 83%.

The company bought all of the outstanding shares of Nortrax from Credit Suisse First Boston and its affiliated partners in 2004. The move made Nortrax a wholly owned subsidiary of Deere. That year the company began development along with iRobot (maker of the Roomba vacuum cleaner) of a battlefield vehicle for use as a scout based on its Gator light-utility vehicle platform for the US Army. The R-Gator was released in 2008.

Deere sold John Deere Health Care (now named UnitedHealthcare Services Company of the River Valley Inc.) in 2006 to UnitedHealth Group for half a billion dollars. Later that year Deere purchased Roberts Irrigation Products a maker of micro and drip irrigation equipment used in the agricultural nursery and greenhouse markets.

In 2007 the company added to its barn-full of turf lawn and landscape products when it bought LESCO Inc. The addition of LESCO roughly doubled the number of store locations for Deere's John Deere Landscapes division with the addition of 345 stores and 114 Stores-on-Wheels. The 2005 acquisition of United Green Mark a maker of irrigation and landscaping products gave the John Deere Landscapes division 52 additional dealerships in the western US.

Looking to address demand for small tractors in a key global market later in 2007 Deere acquired Ningbo Benye Tractor & Automobile Manufacture based in southern China. Deere had been involved in the Chinese market for decades but this deal gave Deere a low-horsepower tractor manufacturing presence in the Chinese market. While Ningbo Benye Tractor got most of its sales from China it exported its 20-50hp tractors to other countries. The business was renamed John Deere Ningbo Agricultural Machinery.

Deere invested in two acquisitions in 2008 that expand its John Deere Water Technologies business. It bought Plastro Irrigation Systems Israel's leading maker of irrigation system components. Plastro also provides consultation design planning and installation of irrigation systems. The deal followed Deere's move to scoop up T-Systems International which makes a variety of products for the agricultural nursery landscape and greenhouse markets. T-Systems' operational infrastructure is particularly valuable; it has established manufacturing facilities in Australia France and the US as well as a pipeline to a range of desirable agricultural markets.

In late 2008 the company signed an agreement with Ashok Leyland to make backhoes and four-wheel-drive loaders in India one of the largest markets for backhoes in the world. As part of the joint venture agreement Deere is building a manufacturing facility there. Ashok Leyland maintains an extensive dealer network that encompasses India and about 20 additional countries.

Spying cotton equipment opportunities in Israel the company bought some of Israel-based BHC Manufacturing's assets and customer connections in spring 2010. Deere scooped up the company's cotton picker repair parts manufacturing operation along with its cotton picker row unit business which caters to OEMs.

In late 2010 Deere sold off its wind energy business (now Exelon Wind) to power generation giant Exelon. The deal which included 36 projects in eight states garnered approximately $900 million. In early 2011 Deere shed certain assets of its Agri Services too to Constellation Software. The division provided information management software for agribusiness.

EXECUTIVES

President Agriculture and Turf Division-North America Asia Australia Sub-Saharan and South Africa and Global Tractor and Turf Products, David C. Everitt, age 59, $624,820 total compensation

Chairman and CEO, Samuel R. (Sam) Allen, age 58, $795,965 total compensation

VP Public Affairs Worldwide, Charles R. Stamp Jr.

VP Corporate Communications and Global Brand Management, Frances B. Emerson

SVP and General Counsel, James R. Jenkins, age 66, $546,225 total compensation

SVP Global Marketing Services Agriculture and Turf, Douglas C. DeVries

VP Pension Fund and Investments, Dennis R. (Denny) Schwartz

VP and Treasurer, Marie Z. Ziegler, age 54

President Agriculture & Turf Division Americas Australia and the Global Harvesting and Turf Platforms, James M. Field, age 48, $492,321 total compensation

SVP John Deere Power Systems Worldwide Parts Services Advanced Technology and Engineering and Global Supply Management and Logistics, Jean Gilles, age 54

SVP Human Resources Communications Public Affairs and Labor Relations, Max A. Guinn

President Worldwide Construction and Forestry Division, Michael J. Mack Jr., age 55, $543,367 total compensation

President John Deere Landscapes, David P. (Dave) Werning

President Worldwide Financial Services Division, James A. Israel, age 55, $460,863 total compensation

SVP International Lending Worldwide Financial Services Division, Stephen Pullin

SVP Credit and Operations U.S. and Canada, Lawrence W. Sidwell

VP and Deputy General Counsel International, James H. Becht

VP Labor Relations, Kenneth C. (Ken) Huhn

SVP Sale and Marketing U.S. and Canada, Daniel C. McCabe

VP Taxes, Thomas K. Jarrett

VP Global Platform Hay and Forage Agriculture and Turf, William F. Norton

VP Internal Audit, Gary L. Medd

VP and Chief Compliance Officer, Linda E. Newborn

SVP Intelligent Solutions Group and CIO, Barry W. Schaffter

VP Global Platform Corp Care Agriculture and Turf, Eric P. Hansotia

SVP Renewable Energy Deere & Company, Martin L. Wilkinson

VP TCI and Deliver Customer Value, Bharat S. Vedak, age 64

SVP Engineering and Manufacturing Worldwide Construction and Foresty, Randal A. (Randy) Sergesketter

Director Global Public Relations, Ken Golden

VP Advanced Technology and Engineering, Klaus G. Hoehn

VP Corporate Strategy and Business Development, James A. Davlin, age 48

VP Strategic Partnerships Worldwide Construction & Forestry, Douglas M. Gage

SVP Global Platform Tractor Agriculture and Turf, Bernard E. Haas

President Agriculture and Turf Division Europe Asia Africa and the Global Tractor Platform, Mark von Pentz, age 48

VP Worldwide Supply Management and Logistics, Thomas E. Knoll

VP Worldwide Parts Service, Gail E. Leese

SVP Sales and Marketing Worldwide Construction & Forestry, Domenic G. Ruccolo

VP Sales and Marketing Latin America Agriculture and Turf, Aaron L. Wetzel

VP Sales and Marketing Europe CIS North Africa and Middle East Agriculture and Turf, Christoph Wigger

VP Sales Europe North Africa Near and Middle East Agriculture and Turf, Stefan von Stegmann

VP and Comptroller, John J. Dalhoff

Corporate Secretary and Associate General Counsel, Gregory R. Noe
Marine Marketing Manager John Deere Power Systems, Dave Flaherty
Group Manager Worldwide Military Affairs, Mark Bodwell
VP and Deputy General Counsel North America, Michael A. Harring
SVP and CFO, Rajesh (Raj) Kalathur
VP Sales and Marketing United States Canada Australia and New Zealand Agriculture and Turf, John D. Lagemann
President Agricultural Solutions and CIO, John C. May
VP Global Platform Services Agriculture and Turf, Patrick Pinkston
VP Global Supply Management Agriculture and Turf, James (Jim) Schrempf
Manager Marketing Communications John Deere Power Systems, Tom Withers
Director Corporate Affairs John Deere South America, Alfredo Miguel Neto
Manager Public Relations John Deere Russia, Maria Maleyeva
Public Affairs John Deere India, Sidharth Mande
Manager Public Relations Worldwide Agriculture and Turf Equipment Europe Northern Africa and Near and Middle East, Oliver Neumann
Director Corporate Affairs John Deere China, Nina Wang
Communications Manager Worldwide Agriculture and Turf Equipment Australia and New Zealand, Craig Pretorius
Manager Communications John Deere Financial Services, Angela Gallagher
Manager Marketing Communication Events and Promotions Worldwide Construction and Forestry Equipment, Audrey Hecht
Manager Media Relations Worldwide Agriculture and Turf Equipment, Barry Nelson
SVP and General Counsel, Mary K. W. Jones
Director, Thomas H. (Tom) Patrick, age 67
Director, Charles O. (Chad) Holliday Jr., age 65
Director, David B. Speer, age 60
Director, Vance D. Coffman, age 67
Director, Clayton M. (Clay) Jones, age 62
Director, Joachim Milberg, age 68
Director, Aulana L. Peters, age 70
Director, Crandall C. Bowles, age 65
Director, Prof Dipak C. Jain, age 54
Director, Richard B. (Dick) Myers, age 70
Auditors: Deloitte&ToucheLLP

LOCATIONS

HQ: Deere & Co.
One John Deere Place, Moline, IL 61265
Phone: 309 765-8000 Fax: 309 765-9929
Web: www.johndeere.com

2011 Sales

	$ mil.	% of total
US & Canada	19,214	60
Rest of the world	12,799	40
Total	32,013	100

PRODUCTS/OPERATIONS

2011 Sales

	$ mil.	% of total
Agriculture & turf net sales	24,094	75
Construction & forestry net sales	5,372	17
Financial services	2,163	7
Other	384	1
Total	32,013	100

Selected Products and Services

Agricultural and turf equipment
- Balers
- Combines
- Cotton harvesting equipment
- Golf course equipment
- Harvesters
- Hay and forage equipment
- Irrigation
- Landscape and nursery
- Loaders
- Mowers (commercial riding lawn equipment and walk-behind mowers)
- Planting and seeding equipment
- Power products (outdoor)
- Sprayers
- Tillage
- Tractors (large medium and utility)
- Utility vehicles

Construction and forestry equipment
- Articulated dump trucks
- Backhoe loaders
- Crawler dozers
- Crawler loaders
- Excavators
- Landscape loaders
- Log skidders and loaders
- Material handling equipment
- Motor graders
- Skid-steer loaders

Credit
- Leasing
- Retail and wholesale financing

Power systems
- Diesel and natural gas engines (marine industrial mining)
- Powertrain components
- Transmissions

COMPETITORS

AGCO
Buhler Industries
Caterpillar
CNH Global
Great Plains Manufacturing
Honda
Komatsu
Kubota
Mahindra
Navistar International
Terex
Toro Company
Uzel Makina Sanayi
Valmont Industries
Volvo
Woods Equipment

HISTORICAL FINANCIALS

Company Type: Public

Income Statement

FYE: October 31

	REVENUE ($ mil.)	NET INCOME ($ mil.)	NET PROFIT MARGIN	EMPLOYEES
10/12	36,157	3,064	8.5%	66,900
10/11	32,012	2,799	8.7%	61,300
10/10	26,004	1,865	7.2%	55,700
10/09	23,112	873	3.8%	51,300
10/08	28,437	2,052	7.2%	56,700
Annual Growth	6.2%	10.5%	—	4.2%

2012 Year-End Financials

Debt ratio: 57.62%
Return on equity: 44.79%
Cash ($ mil.): 4,652
Current ratio: 88.74
Long-term debt ($ mil.): 22,453
No. of shares (mil.): 387
Dividends
Yield: 2.10%
Payout: 23.46%
Market value ($ mil.): 33,134

	STOCK PRICE ($) FY Close	P/E High	P/E Low	PER SHARE ($) Earnings	Dividends	Book Value
10/12	85.44	12	9	7.63	1.79	17.64
10/11	75.90	15	9	6.63	1.52	16.75
10/10	76.80	18	11	4.35	0.00	14.90
10/09	45.55	23	12	2.06	0.00	11.39
10/08	38.56	37	6	4.70	1.06	15.47
Annual Growth	22.0%	—	—	12.9%	14.0%	3.3%

Delek US Holdings Inc

Delek US Holdings takes a delectable approach to the petroleum business –with a tasty balance of refining fuel marketing and retail operations. The company a subsidiary of Israeli-based conglomerate Delek Group operates a 60000 barrels-per-day refinery in Tyler Texas. Delek US Holdings' marketing segment sells refined products on a wholesale basis in west Texas through company-owned and third-party operated terminals. In 2012 refinery customer Exxon Mobil accounted for about 12% of the company's total sales. On the retail side its MAPCO Express unit operates more than 410 convenience store/gas stations under MAPCO Express East Coast Discount Food Mart and other names in 10 southern US states.

The company's fuel distribution business supplies 57 dealer-operated retail locations

Delek US Holdings operates Lion Oil Company which owns a 80000 barrels-per-day refinery in El Dorado Arkansas as well as other pipeline and product assets. To grow its refinery operations in 2011 the company bought Ergon's 54% stake in Lion Oil boosting its ownership of that company to 88%. Later that year it boosted its holdings in Lion Oil to 100%.

To generate cash in 2012 the company filed to spin off wholly-owned crude oil and refined products logistics and marketing subsidiary Delek Logistics Partners LP.

Delek US has historically grown by pursuing acquisitions to strengthen its retail business (six gas station/convenience store chain acquisitions between its founding in 2001 and 2007) and its refinery assets. In 2010 the company sought to expand its refinery base through the acquisition of Shell Canada's Montreal East refinery but the deal fell through.

The company is pursuing a retrofitting program to physically improve and upgrade the appearance of its convenience stores and gas stations in order to boost market share. It initiated a "raze and rebuild" program and upgraded some 22 Tennessee locations in 2009. It plans to pursue this program in other markets where it has strong brand recognition. Facing tough competition in the Virginia retail market the company has sold most of its gas stations in that state.

In 2009 Delek US Holdings reported a 43% slump in revenues caused by a combination of the global recession (producing low commodity prices and suppressing oil and gas demand) and a refinery shutdown (caused by a fire) which cut production volumes.

With higher oil prices and the Tyler refinery operating for the entire year (following a 2009 fire) in 2010 the company reported a 43% spike in revenues. However higher operating costs and impairment charges cut into the company's operating profits that year.

In 2011 Delek Group owned 73% of the company.

EXECUTIVES

EVP and CFO, Mark B. Cox, age 53, $73,846 total compensation
Chief Marketing Officer MAPCO Express, Bill Reilly
EVP; President and COO Delek Refining, Frederec C. Green, age 47, $222,692 total compensation
VP Sales and Merchandising MAPCO Express, Tony Miller

President CEO and Director, Ezra Uzi Yemin, age 43, $486,000 total compensation
VP, Andrew L. (Andy) Schwarcz, age 44
SVP; EVP and COO MAPCO Express, Harry P. (Pete) Daily, age 63
EVP, Assaf Ginzburg, age 37, $213,077 total compensation
General Counsel and Secretary, Kent B. Thomas, age 43
VP and Chief Accounting Officer, Joane Walker
VP Trading and Supply Delek Refining, J. Charles Williams
VP and Treasurer, Greg Intemann
President MAPCO Express and VP and COO Delek Marketing and Supply, Igal Zamir, age 46, $121,000 total compensation
VP Regulatory and Environmental Affairs Delek Refining, Michael Norman
Israel Media Relations Contact, Moshe Gal
Director and Head Investor Relations and Communications, Noel R. Ryan II
Director, Philip L. Maslowe, age 65
Director, Charles H. Leonard, age 63
President CEO and Director, Ezra Uzi Yemin, age 43
Director, Gabriel Last, age 65
Director, Shlomo Zohar, age 61
Director, Carlos E. Jorda, age 62
Director, Aharon Kacherginski, age 74
Auditors: Ernst&Young

LOCATIONS

HQ: Delek US Holdings Inc.
7102 Commerce Way, Brentwood TN 37027
Phone: 615-771-6701 **Fax:** 615-224-1185
Web: www.delekus.com

PRODUCTS/OPERATIONS

2011 Sales

	$ mil.	% of total
Refining	4,634	64
Retail	1,859	26
Marketing	704	10
Other	0	-
Total	**7,198**	**100**

COMPETITORS

7-Eleven
Chevron
CITGO
ConocoPhillips
Costco Wholesale
Cumberland Farms
Exxon Mobil
Gate Petroleum
Motiva Enterprises
Murphy Oil
Publix
Racetrac Petroleum
The Pantry
Wal-Mart
Winn-Dixie

HISTORICAL FINANCIALS

Company Type: Public

Income Statement FYE: December 31

	REVENUE ($ mil.)	NET INCOME ($ mil.)	NET PROFIT MARGIN	EMPLOYEES
12/11	7,198	158	2.2%	3,801
12/10	3,755	(79)	—	3,395
12/09	2,666	0	0.0%	3,578
12/08	4,615	26	0.6%	3,692
12/07	4,097	96	2.4%	3,708
Annual Growth	15.1%	13.2%	—	0.6%

2011 Year-End Financials

Debt ratio: 19.39%
Return on equity: 24.23%
Cash ($ mil.): 225
Current ratio: 105.62
Long-term debt ($ mil.): 358
No. of shares (mil.): 58
Dividends
Yield: —
Payout: 11.87%
Market value ($ mil.): 662

	STOCK PRICE ($) FY Close	P/E High/Low		PER SHARE ($) Earnings	Dividends	Book Value
12/11	11.41	6	2	2.78	0.00	11.26
12/10	7.28	—	—	(1.47)	0.15	8.15
12/09	6.81	1190529		0.01	0.15	9.89
12/08	5.29	40	8	0.49	0.15	9.94
12/07	20.23	16	8	1.82	0.55	9.55
Annual Growth	(13.3%)	—	—	11.2%	—	4.2%

Dell Inc

Dell's name rings from the desktop to the data center. The world's #3 supplier of PCs (behind #1 HP and China-based #2 Lenovo) the company provides a broad range of technology products for the consumer education enterprise and government sectors. In addition to its line of desktop and notebook PCs Dell offers network servers data storage systems printers Ethernet switches and peripherals such as displays and projectors. It also markets third-party software and hardware. The company's services unit provides asset recovery financing infrastructure consulting support systems integration and training as well as hosted IT services. Dell generates more than half of its revenue outside of the US.

HISTORY

At age 13 Michael Dell was already a successful businessman. From his parents' home in Houston Dell ran a mail-order stamp trading business that within a few months grossed more than $2000. At 16 he sold newspaper subscriptions and at 17 bought his first BMW. When Dell enrolled at the University of Texas in 1983 he was thoroughly bitten by the entrepreneurial bug.

Dell started college as a pre-med student but found time to establish a business selling random-access memory (RAM) chips and disk drives for IBM PCs. Dell bought products at cost from IBM dealers who were required at the time to order from IBM large monthly quotas of PCs which frequently exceeded demand. Dell resold his stock through newspapers and computer magazines at 10%-15% below retail.

By 1984 Dell's dorm room computer components business was grossing about $80000 a month –enough to persuade him to drop out of college. Soon he started making and selling IBM clones under the brand name PC's (sic) Limited. Dell sold his machines directly to consumers rather than through retail outlets as most manufacturers did. By eliminating the retail markup Dell could sell PCs at about 40% of the price of an IBM PC.

The company was plagued by management changes during the mid-1980s. Renamed Dell Computer it added international sales offices in 1987. In 1988 the company started selling to larger customers including government agencies. That year Dell went public.

The company tripped in 1990 reporting a 64% drop in profits. Sales were growing –but so were costs mostly because of efforts to design a PC using proprietary components and reduced instruction set computer (RISC) chips. Also the company's warehouses were oversupplied. Within a year Dell turned itself around by cutting inventories and introducing new products.

Dell entered the retail arena by letting retailer Soft Warehouse (later CompUSA) in 1990 and office supply chain Staples in 1991 sell its PCs at mail-order prices. Also that year Dell opened a plant in Ireland.

In 1992 Xerox agreed to sell Dell machines in Latin America. Dell opened subsidiaries in Japan and Australia the next year. The computer maker abandoned retail stores in 1994 to refocus on its mail-order origins. It also retooled its troubled notebook computer line and introduced servers.

The company started selling PCs through its website in 1996. The next year Dell entered the market for workstations and strengthened its consumer business by separating it from its small-business unit and launching a leasing program for consumers. In 1998 the company stepped up manufacturing in the Americas and Europe and added a production and customer facility in China.

Dell began selling a $999 PC in 1999. (Dell phased out the WebPC line after just seven months due to slow sales.) That year the company made its first acquisition –storage area network equipment maker ConvergeNet –and opened a plant in Brazil. In 2000 Dell broadened its high-end network servers and Internet-related services offerings and formed a division for its storage operations.

Faced with slumping PC sales in 2001 the company eliminated 1700 jobs –about 4% of its workforce. Later that year it expanded its storage offerings when it agreed to resell systems from EMC. Looking to grow its services unit Dell acquired Microsoft software support specialist Plural in 2002.

The following year the company shortened its name to simply Dell Inc. Dell himself stepped down as CEO in 2004. Company president Kevin Rollins Dell's hand-picked successor filled the position; Dell remained chairman of the company.

The company diversified its PC offerings in 2005 with the launch of XPS a line of high-end desktop and notebook PCs for gamers and others willing to pay premium prices for top performance. The following year Dell acquired high-performance PC specialist Alienware.

In 2006 the company added search giant Google to its list of server customers. Also that year Dell responded to customer demand and rolled out select computers with chips from AMD. In 2007 the company began offering a version of Linux as an option on some of its consumer PCs.

That year Rollins resigned as CEO and as a member of the board of directors and Dell reassumed the top role. Rollins' resignation came as the company struggled with a number of difficult issues most notably disappointing earnings and an SEC investigation into its finances. (Dell restated several years of financial results after an audit revealed accounting irregularities.) Immediately following the shakeup Dell announced streamlining measures including a reduction in managers and the elimination of 2006 bonuses. The workforce was cut by 10% over the next year.

The company began selling through retail stores in 2007. It also acquired a number of software businesses. Dell purchased ASAP Software a volume software acquisition and deployment specialist for $340 million in 2007. It also bought ZING Systems a developer of software used in portable music devices. Other acquisitions that year included SilverBack Technologies a developer of network asset management software and Everdream a provider of remote desktop management software and services.

Also in 2007 Dell moved to take full ownership of Dell Financial Services a technology-leasing joint venture it formed with CIT Group in 1997; Dell paid $306 million for CIT's 30% stake.

The company closed its Austin Texas-based desktop PC manufacturing facility in 2008. It also shuttered customer care centers in Canada.

Also in 2008 the company acquired MessageOne a provider of email management and archiving services for $155 million in cash. MessageOne which was founded by Michael Dell's brother Adam was integrated into Dell's global service organization.

In 2009 Dell acquired Perot Systems for about $3.9 billion in cash. The transaction allowed the company to deliver a broader range of IT services particularly to clients in the US and to sell more computers to Perot clients. The company made its move a year after PC archrival Hewlett-Packard (HP) acquired the much larger Electronic Data Systems (EDS) the outsourcing services pioneer founded by Ross Perot Sr. The deals underscored the growing importance of the IT services industry to computer manufacturers as IBM Global Services and EDS (renamed HP Enterprise Services) grew to join the leading providers of technical services in the world. Dell formed a new organization Dell Services following the purchase of Perot Systems.

In 2011 Dell bought Internet security software developer Force10 Networks which specializes in applications for data centers. Its 2010 acquisition of Boomi added hosted cloud integration technology to Dell's cloud computing expansion efforts. (Such cloud integration technology allows for easy data transfer between cloud-based and on-premise applications with no software or coding required.)

Also that year the company boosted its software-as-a-service (SaaS) offerings buying SecureWorks a provider of remote security monitoring and management services.

EXECUTIVES

President Public and Large Enterprise, Paul D. Bell, age 51, $594,231 total compensation
Chairman and CEO, Michael S. Dell, age 47, $950,000 total compensation
SVP Dell.com, Ronald V. (Ron) Rose, age 61
EVP Applications and Business Process Outsourcing Dell Services; Chairman India, Suresh Vaswani, age 52
President Software Group, John A. Swainson
Vice Chairman and President Global Operations and End User Computing Solutions, Jeffrey W. (Jeff) Clarke, age 49
SVP General Counsel and Secretary, Lawrence P. (Larry) Tu, age 57
President Dell Services, Stephen F. (Steve) Schuckenbrock, age 51, $678,365 total compensation
SVP and CFO, Brian T. Gladden, age 47, $700,000 total compensation
VP IT Strategy Technology and Governance Office, Rhonda Gass
President Enterprise Solutions, Bradley R. (Brad) Anderson, age 52
VP Finance; President Dell Financial Services, Don Berman
VP and General Manager Major Accounts Education State and Local Government, John Mullen
President and Chief Commercial Officer, Stephen J. (Steve) Felice, age 54, $585,000 total compensation
Global VP Consumer Small and Medium Business Marketing, Paul-Henri Ferrand
VP Corporate Finance, Thomas W. Sweet, age 52
VP Global Communications, Kelly McGinnis
VP Sales and Marketing Global Consumer Business, Michael Tatelman
VP Small and Medium Business Dell Americas, Erik Dithmer
Assistant Secretary, Janet B. Wright
Senior Manager Global Recycling Services, Mike Watson
General Manager Data Center Solutions, Roy Guillen
Investor Relations, Robert Williams
Senior Manager Dell Precision Workstations, Greg Weir
Director Dell Product Group, Brett McAnally
VP Dell Healthcare and Life Sciences, Jamie Coffin
VP Platform Marketing, Sally Stevens
Director General Procurement and Global Supplier Diversity, Jens Gruenkemeier
VP and General Manager Original Equipment Manufacturers, Rick Froehlich
VP Government Services Unit Dell Perot Systems, Lee Carrick
SVP Human Resources, Steve H. Price, age 48
SVP Corporate Strategy, David L. (Dave) Johnson, age 58
SVP and Chief Marketing Officer, Karen H. Quintos, age 54
Director and CTO Communications, Liam Quinn
Business Information Executive Dell Services, Angela Yochem
Global CIO, Adriana Karaboutis
Director, Donald J. (Don) Carty Jr., age 65
Director, James W. (Jim) Breyer, age 51
Director, Alex J. Mandl, age 68
Director, Shantanu Narayen, age 50
Director, H. Ross Perot Jr., age 53
Vice Chairman and President Global Operations and End User Computing Solutions, Jeffrey W. (Jeff) Clarke, age 49
Director, William H. (Bill) Gray III, age 70
Director, Klaus S. Luft, age 71
Director, Thomas W. Luce III, age 71
Director, Gerard J. Kleisterlee, age 66
Director, Kenneth M. (Ken) Duberstein, age 68
Director, Laura Conigliaro, age 66
Auditors: PricewaterhouseCoopersLLP

LOCATIONS

HQ: Dell Inc.
1 Dell Way, Round Rock TX 78682
Phone: 512-338-4400 **Fax:** 678-281-2019
Web: www.ebix.com

2012 Sales

	$ mil.	% of total
US	30,404	49
Other countries	31,667	51
Total	**62,071**	**100**

PRODUCTS/OPERATIONS

2012 Sales

	$ mil.	% of total
Client		
Mobility	19,104	31
Desktop PCs	14,144	23
Enterprise products		
Servers & networking	8,336	13
Storage	1,943	3
Enterprise services	8,322	13
Software & peripherals	10,222	17
Total	**62,071**	**100**

2012 Sales by Market

	$ mil.	% of total
Large enterprise	18,457	30
Public	16,548	27
Small & medium business	15,166	24
Consumer	11,900	19
Total	**62,071**	**100**

Selected Products

Computers
- Desktop (Alienware Dimension OptiPlex Studio Vostro XPS)
- Notebook (Adamo Inspiron Latitude Vostro XPS)

Enterprise systems
- Network servers (PowerEdge)
- Storage (EqualLogic PowerVault)
- Workstations (Precision)

Ethernet switches (PowerConnect)
Point-of-sale systems
Printers
- Inkjet multifunction
- Laser

Projectors
Refurbished systems
Smartphones (Mini 3)
Third-party peripherals and software

Selected Acquisitions

2012
- Credant Technologies Inc. (undisclosed price; Addison TX; data protection products)
- Gale Technologies (infrastructure automation software)

COMPETITORS

Acer
Apple Inc.
ASUSTeK
BenQ
Brother Industries
Canon
CDW
Cisco Systems
EMC
Enterasys
Epson
Extreme Networks
Fujitsu Technology Solutions
HCL Infosystems
Hewlett-Packard
Hitachi
IBM
Insight Enterprises
Lenovo
Microsoft
NEC
Panasonic Corp
Positivo Informatica
Sony
Symantec
Tatung
Toshiba
Unisys

HISTORICAL FINANCIALS

Company Type: Public

Income Statement

FYE: February 3

	REVENUE ($ mil.)	NET INCOME ($ mil.)	NET PROFIT MARGIN	EMPLOYEES
02/12*	62,071	3,492	5.6%	109,400
01/11	61,494	2,635	4.3%	103,300
01/10	52,902	1,433	2.7%	96,000
01/09	61,101	2,478	4.1%	78,900
02/08	61,133	2,947	4.8%	88,200
Annual Growth	0.4%	4.3%	—	5.5%

*Fiscal year change

2012 Year-End Financials

Debt ratio: 20.78%
Return on equity: 39.16%
Cash ($ mil.): 13,852
Current ratio: 133.85
Long-term debt ($ mil.): 6,387
No. of shares (mil.): 1,761
Dividends
Yield: —
Payout: —
Market value ($ mil.): 31,099

	STOCK PRICE ($)	P/E		PER SHARE ($)		
	FY Close	High/Low		Earnings	Dividends	Book Value
02/12*	17.66	9	7	1.88	0.00	5.06
01/11	13.15	13	9	1.35	0.00	4.05
01/10	12.90	23	11	0.73	0.00	2.88
01/09	9.50	21	7	1.25	0.00	2.20
02/08	20.35	23	15	1.31	0.00	1.86
Annual Growth	(3.5%)	—	—	9.5%	—	28.4%

*Fiscal year change

Delta Air Lines, Inc. (DE)

Just as a delta is a symbol for change in math Delta Air Lines symbolizes the changing mathematics of the airline industry. Delta became one of the world's largest airlines by traffic after its $2.8 billion acquisition of Northwest Airlines in 2008. Through its regional carriers (including subsidiary Comair) the company serves about 350 destinations in more than 60 countries and it operates a mainline fleet of 700-plus aircraft as well as maintenance repair and overhaul (MRO) and cargo operations. Delta is a founding member of the SkyTeam marketing and code-sharing alliance (airlines extend their networks by selling tickets on one another's flights) which includes carriers Air France KLM and Alitalia.

HISTORY

Delta Air Lines was founded in Macon Georgia in 1924 as the world's first crop-dusting service Huff-Daland Dusters to combat boll weevil infestation of cotton fields. It moved to Monroe Louisiana in 1925. In 1928 field manager C. E. Woolman and two partners bought the service and renamed it Delta Air Service after the Mississippi Delta region it served.

In 1929 Delta pioneered passenger service from Dallas to Jackson Mississippi. Flying mail without a government subsidy Delta finally got a US Postal Service contract in 1934 to fly from Fort Worth to Charleston via Atlanta. Delta relocated to Atlanta in 1941. Woolman became president in 1945 and managed the airline until he died in 1966.

Delta added more flights including a direct route from Chicago to New Orleans with its 1952 purchase of Chicago and Southern Airlines. The carrier offered its first transcontinental flight in 1961. In 1972 the airline bought Northeast Airlines and added service to New England and Canada; it offered service to the UK in 1978 the year that the US airline industry was deregulated.

In 1982 Delta's employees pledged $30 million to buy a Boeing 767 jet christened "The Spirit of Delta" as a token of appreciation. In fiscal 1983 the company succumbed to the weak US economy and posted its first loss ever; it quickly became profitable again in 1985. It bought Los Angeles-based Western Air Lines in 1986.

Delta began service to Asia in 1987 the year that longtime employee Ronald Allen became CEO. In 1990 Delta joined TWA and Northwest to form Worldspan a computer reservation service.

Despite a slump in 1990 earnings in 1991 Delta bought gates planes and Canadian routes from Eastern as well as Pan Am's New York-Boston shuttle European routes and Frankfurt hub. The purchases elevated Delta from a domestic player to a top international carrier but they also contributed to a $2 billion loss between 1991 and 1994.

Allen began a cost-reduction plan in 1994 that cut many routes and 15000 jobs over the next three years. However it also drove down employee morale and Delta's customer service reputation. The airline discontinued unprofitable international routes in 1995 and introduced no-frills Delta Express in 1996.

Allen was let go in 1997 and replaced by Leo Mullin a former electric utility chief. That year Delta's unprofitable eight-year-old code-sharing agreement with Singapore Airlines was dissolved and the carrier began a Latin American expansion drive.

Delta held takeover talks with Continental in 1998 but Continental joined with Northwest instead. On the rebound Delta signed a marketing accord with United (owned by United Continental formerly UAL) under which the carriers joined their frequent-flier programs.

Spurred by the threat of emerging global alliances Oneworld and Star Delta announced in 1999 that it would create a competing alliance with Air France and Aeromexico. SkyTeam which also included Korean Air Lines was launched in 2000. The realignment led Delta to end code-sharing deals with Swissair Group Sabena and Austrian Airlines that year. At home Delta bought regional carriers Atlantic Southeast Airlines and Comair.

In the wake of the September 11 2001 terrorist attacks on New York and Washington DC and the resulting reduction in air travel Delta cut back its flight schedule and reduced its workforce by about 15% (about 13000 employees).

To streamline operations further the airline sold its 40% stake in reservation system Worldspan in 2003. That year CEO Leo Mullin resigned and was replaced by Gerald Grinstein a Delta director. Delta launched a budget carrier named Song in 2003 to compete with other low-fare carriers like Southwest and JetBlue. (Song failed to thrive on its own however and in 2006 the carrier's operations were folded back into those of Delta.) Also in 2003 the federal government approved the largest code-share agreement among US airlines which included Delta Continental and Northwest.

Delta cut costs significantly during 2005 in an effort to avoid bankruptcy. In a last-ditch bid to raise cash the company sold its Atlantic Southeast Airlines unit to SkyWest for $425 million in September 2005. Days later however the combination of high fuel prices and a string of losses from operations dating back to 2001 finally forced Delta to file for Chapter 11 protection. To keep flying Delta secured a $2 billion financing package from its creditors chiefly GE Commercial Finance (now GE Capital). At the end of 2005 Delta's fleet stood at about 650 aircraft —down nearly 200 planes from the year before.

A milestone in Delta's journey back to solvency was reached in May 2006 when the company's pilots voted to accept a contract with changes in pay benefits and work rules designed to save Delta about $280 million a year. The deal which included the termination of the pilots' pension plan averted a threatened strike that Delta said would have put the company out of business.

In the midst of Delta's restructuring US Airways offered in November 2006 to pay about $8 billion —half in cash and half in stock —for the carrier. After the buyout proposal was rejected by Delta's board US Airways upped its bid to about $10 billion in January 2007 in hopes of persuading Delta's creditors to back a deal. The creditors failed to bite however and US Airways withdrew its offer. Delta exited Chapter 11 in April 2007 as an independent company. Richard Anderson the former CEO of Northwest Airlines succeeded Grinstein as Delta's CEO in September 2007.

Delta gained ground after emerging from Chapter 11 but an unprecedented surge in fuel prices in 2008 followed by a severe drop in travel demand caused the carrier to renew its efforts to control costs. Delta and other airlines lost millions of dollars on fuel hedging in 2008 and into 2009. (Fuel hedging is when airlines lock in a pre-determined price for future jet fuel purchases.) In 2008 Delta offered buyout packages to about 30000 of the company's 55000 employees and about 4000 accepted —twice the number the company expected. The carrier also slashed international capacity by 15% and domestic capacity by 10%.

The year 2008 also recorded a groundbreaking event in the airline industry when Delta acquired Northwest Airlines. The acquisition was first announced in April 2008 but the deal faced several hurdles throughout the year including a review by antitrust regulators and initial opposition from Northwest's unionized pilots who unlike those at Delta were unable to reach an agreement on a contract to fly for the combined company before the Delta-Northwest deal was completed. Several weeks after the acquisition was announced a deal was finally struck and both sets of pilots were given raises and an equity stake in the combined company. Anderson then steered the company through one of the airline industry's biggest mergers when Delta finally acquired Northwest Airlines for $2.8 billion in October 2008. The acquisition sent shockwaves throughout the industry and made Delta the #1 airline in the world by traffic. Delta finished its consolidation of Northwest Airlines in early 2010.

EXECUTIVES

CEO and Director, Richard H. Anderson, age 56, $600,000 total compensation

Vice Chairman, Roy J. Bostock, age 71

Chairman, Daniel A. (Dan) Carp, age 63

EVP & COO, Stephen E. (Steve) Gorman, age 57, $450,000 total compensation

EVP Human Resources and Labor Relations, Michael H. (Mike) Campbell, age 63, $387,500 total compensation

SVP and Chief Communications Officer, John E. (Ned) Walker, age 60

President and Director, Edward H. (Ed) Bastian, age 54, $500,000 total compensation

EVP Network Planning Revenue Management and Marketing, Glen W. Hauenstein, age 51, $400,000 total compensation

SVP Government Affairs, Andrea Fischer Newman

SVP Corporate Strategy and Real Estate, Holden Shannon

SVP and CFO, Paul A. Jacobson

SVP and CIO, Theresa Wise

Director Cargo Sales & Service. Europe Middle East Africa and India, Danita Waterfall-Brizzi

SVP and General Counsel, Richard B. (Ben) Hirst, age 67

SVP and Chief Cargo Officer, Neel Shah, age 42

Managing Director Global Sales Delta Cargo, Ray Curtis

Managing Director Global Cargo Operations Delta Cargo, Greg Mays

Director Finance and Business Planning Delta Cargo, Vishant Bhatia
Director Greater China and South Asian Pacific Delta Cargo, Francis Lui
Director Revenue Management Network Planning and Alliances, Cesar Marti Garro
Regional Director Cargo Sales, Abimael Ortiz
General Manager Marketing Customer Service and eCommerce Delta Cargo, David P. (Dave) Paule
General Manager Postal Affairs, Nick Whalen
SVP Financial Planning & Analysis and Investor Relations, Gary Chase
SVP Finance and Controller, Mike Randolfi
VP and Treasurer, Ken Morge
Director, Paula R. Reynolds, age 54
CEO and Director, Richard H. Anderson, age 56
Vice Chairman, Roy J. Bostock, age 71
Director, John S. Brinzo, age 69
Director, David R. Goode, age 70
Director, Mickey P. Foret, age 66
Director, Kenneth B. (Ken) Woodrow, age 67
President and Director, Edward H. (Ed) Bastian, age 54
Director, John M. Engler, age 62
Director, Shirley Franklin
Director, Kenneth C. Rogers, age 50
Auditors: Ernst&YoungLLP

LOCATIONS

HQ: Delta Air Lines Inc.
1030 Delta Blvd., Atlanta GA 30320-6001
Phone: 404-715-2600 **Fax:** 404-715-5042
Web: www.delta.com

2011 Sales

	$ mil.	% of total
Domestic	22,649	64
Atlantic	6,499	19
Pacific	3,943	11
Latin America	2,024	6
Total	**35,115**	**100**

PRODUCTS/OPERATIONS

2011 Sales

	$ mil.	% of total
Passenger		
Mainline	23,864	68
Regional carriers	6,393	18
Cargo	1,027	3
Other	3,831	11
Total	**35,115**	**100**

COMPETITORS

Air Canada
AirTran Airways
AMR Corp.
British Airways
Cathay Pacific
Japan Airlines
JetBlue
Lufthansa
Qantas
SAS
Singapore Airlines
Southwest Airlines
United Continental
US Airways
Virgin Atlantic Airways

HISTORICAL FINANCIALS

Company Type: Public

Income Statement FYE: December 31

	REVENUE ($ mil.)	NET INCOME ($ mil.)	NET PROFIT MARGIN	EMPLOYEES
12/11	35,115	854	2.4%	78,392
12/10	31,755	593	1.9%	79,684
12/09	28,063	(1,237)	—	81,106
12/08	22,697	(8,922)	—	84,306
12/07	13,358	314	2.4%	55,044
Annual Growth	27.3%	28.4%	—	9.2%

2011 Year-End Financials

Debt ratio: 31.70%
Return on equity: 98765000100000.00%
Cash ($ mil.): 2,657
Current ratio: 60.85
Long-term debt ($ mil.): 11,847
No. of shares (mil.): 845
Dividends
Yield: —
Payout: —
Market value ($ mil.): 6,838

	STOCK PRICE ($) FY Close	P/E High	P/E Low	PER SHARE ($) Earnings	Dividends	Book Value
12/11	8.09	13	6	1.01	0.00	(1.65)
12/10	12.60	21	14	0.70	0.00	1.08
12/09	11.38	—	—	(1.50)	0.00	0.31
12/08	11.46	—	—	(19.08)	0.00	1.26
12/07	14.89	28	18	0.79	0.00	34.31
Annual Growth	(14.1%)	—	—	6.3%	—	—

Detroit Edison Co.

Ford Motors is not the only powerhouse operating in Detroit Detroit Edison is another. The utility generates and distributes electricity to 2.1 million customers in Michigan. The company a unit of regional power player DTE Energy has almost 11000 MW of generating capacity from its interests in fossil-fueled nuclear and hydroelectric power plants. It operates more than 45890 circuit miles of distribution lines and owns and operates more than 670 distribution substations. Detroit Edison also sells excess power to wholesale customers and provides coal transportation services.

The largest electric utility in Michigan Detroit Edison has a 1 million utility poles across its 7600-sq. ml. service area.

The utility operates nine fossil fuel-(coal and oil) fired generating plants and one nuclear power plant (which accounts for 30% of Michigan's nuclear power output). It also co-owns a hydroelectric pumped storage plant with Consumers Energy. Coal and gas accounted for 73% of Detroit Edison's total power output in 2010.

To meet the state requirements for reducing carbon emissions in 2009 the company announced plans to add 1200 MW of renewable power by 2015 half through contracts with third-parties and the remainder through its own renewable energy projects (primarily wind farms). In 2011 the company was working on developing a 200 MW wind farm.

In 2010 the company began operating a 60-kW solar energy plant in Scio Township in Washtenaw County the first installation to produce power for the grid under Detroit Edison's SolarCurrents program. Its 270 solar panels include 60 that track the sun's movement.

In 2009 the company reported lower revenues as the global recession hammered commodity prices and weakened demand for power especially from industrial customers. However lower costs allowed Detroit Edison to post improved operating margins for the year. In 2010 the recovering economy prompted increased power demand especially from residential and industrial customers. This and higher electric rates and wholesale prices helped to lift Detroit Edison's revenues and income that year.

EXECUTIVES

EVP CFO and Director, David E. Meador, age 55
VP Corporate Secretary and Director, Susan M. Beale
Chairman, Anthony F. Earley Jr., age 63
SVP Customer Service, Joyce V. Hayes-Giles
VP and General Counsel, Thomas A. Hughes, age 69
President and COO, Steven E. Kurmas, age 56
VP Controller and Chief Accounting Officer, Peter Oleksiak
Corporate Secretary and Director, Sandra K. (Sandy) Ennis, age 55
SVP and General Counsel, Bruce Peterson
Director Investor Relations, Lisa Muschong
VP and Treasurer, N.A. Khouri
Director, Bruce D. Peterson
EVP CFO and Director, David E. Meador, age 55
Corporate Secretary and Director, Sandra K. (Sandy) Ennis, age 55
Director, Bruce D. Peterson
Auditors: Deloitte&ToucheLLP

LOCATIONS

HQ: The Detroit Edison Company
1 Energy Plaza, Detroit MI 48226-1279
Phone: 313-235-4000 **Fax:** 313-235-8055
Web: my.dteenergy.com

PRODUCTS/OPERATIONS

2011 Sales

	$ mil.	% of total
Residential	2,182	43
Commercial	1,704	33
Industrial	692	13
Interconnection sales	118	2
Other	456	9
Total	**5,152**	**100**

COMPETITORS

Consumers Energy
Indiana Michigan Power
Integrys Energy Group
ITC Holdings Corp.
SEMCO ENERGY
We Energies
Xcel Energy

HISTORICAL FINANCIALS

Company Type: Subsidiary

Income Statement FYE: December 31

	REVENUE ($ mil.)	NET INCOME ($ mil.)	NET PROFIT MARGIN	EMPLOYEES
12/11	5,152	437	8.5%	4,800
12/10	4,993	441	8.8%	4,700
12/09	4,714	376	8.0%	4,864
12/08	4,874	331	6.8%	4,682
12/07	4,900	317	6.5%	4,674
Annual Growth	1.3%	8.4%	—	0.7%

2011 Year-End Financials

Debt ratio: 28.94%	No. of shares (mil.): 138
Return on equity: 10.57%	Dividends
Cash ($ mil.): 13	Yield: —
Current ratio: 128.19	Payout: 70.02%
Long-term debt ($ mil.): 4,593	Market value ($ mil.): —

Devon Energy Corp.

Independent oil and gas producer Devon Energy puts its energy into oil and gas fields far from England's southwestern coast in North America. It focuses on exploration and production assets in Oklahoma Texas Wyoming and western Canada. In 2011 Devon Energy reported proved reserves of 3 billion barrels of oil equivalent (58% natural gas) and more than 19900 net acres of assets. It also drilled almost 2500 gross wells. Devon Energy produces about 2.5 billion cu. ft. of natural gas a day (more than 3% of all the gas consumed in North America). The company is the largest producer and lease holder in the Barnett Shale (Texas) and is looking to replicate its success there to other unconventional plays.

Geographic Reach

Once active in major oil patches worldwide such as Azerbaijan Brazil and China in the mid-2000s the company decided to focus on safer and increasingly productive unconventional onshore exploration opportunities (shales and oil sands) in North America. As a result Devon Energy has sold all of its international assets.

Financial Analysis

Devon Energy posted a major improvement in revenues in 2010 thanks to higher commodity prices and an increase in production. In 2011 buoyed by record level reserves high oil prices and an increased demand for oil and gas products the company posted a further 15% growth in revenues. Net income only rose by 3% however as higher operating depreciation deletion and amortization costs and an increase in deferred income tax expense trimmed income growth.

Boosting its financial resources in 2012 Devon Energy secured a commitment from Sinopec International Petroleum Exploration & Production for the Chinese company to invest $2.2 billion in exchange for one-third of Devon's interest in five new joint venture plays in the Tuscaloosa Marine Shale Niobrara Mississippian Ohio Utica Shale and the Michigan Basin.

That year it also closed a similar $1.4 billion joint venture deal with Sumitomo Corp. to develop 650000 net acres in the Cline Shale and the Midland-Wolfcamp Shale in West Texas.

Strategy

In 2010 it sold most of its remaining international assets to BP for $7 billion. As part of this deal BP sold undeveloped oil sand leases in Canada to Devon Energy for $500 million and formed a joint venture with the company to exploit them. The company also sold its Panyu field offshore China to China National Offshore Oil for $515 million.

Consolidating its North American assets to just its onshore properties In 2010 Devon Energy sold its stakes in the Cascade Jack and St. Malo fields in the Gulf of Mexico (about 200 million barrels of estimated recoverable reserves) to AP Moller-Maersk's oil unit for $1.3 billion. It also sold its remaining Gulf of Mexico shelf assets to Apache for $1 billion.

HISTORY

Larry Nichols (a lawyer who clerked for US Supreme Court Chief Justice Earl Warren) and his father John founded Devon Energy in 1969. John Nichols was a partner in predecessor company Blackwood and Nichols an oil partnership formed in 1946.

In 1981 the company bought a small stake in the Northeast Blanco Unit of New Mexico's San Juan Basin. To raise capital Devon formed the limited partnership Devon Resource Investors and took it public in 1985. In 1988 Devon consolidated all of its units into a single publicly traded company.

The firm increased its stake in Northeast Blanco in 1988 and again in 1989 ending up with about 25%. By 1990 Devon had drilled more than 100 wells in the area and had proved reserves of 58 billion cu. ft. of natural gas.

During the 1990s the company launched a major expansion program using a two-pronged strategy: acquiring producing properties and drilling wells in proven fields. In 1990 it bought an 88% interest in six Texas wells; two years later Devon snapped up the US properties of Hondo Oil & Gas. After its 1994 purchase of Alta Energy which operated in New Mexico Oklahoma Texas and Wyoming Devon had proved reserves of more than 500 billion cu. ft. of gas.

Between 1992 and 1997 the company also drilled some 840 successful wells. Buoyed by new seismic techniques that raise the odds of finding oil Devon devoted more resources to pioneering fields in regions where it already had expertise.

Continuing its buying spree Devon bought Kerr-McGee's onshore assets in 1997. Two years later it bought Alberta Canada-based Northstar for $775 million creating a company with holdings divided almost evenly between oil and gas.

Also in 1999 Devon grabbed its biggest prize when it purchased PennzEnergy of Houston in a $2.3 billion stock-and-debt deal that analysts called a bargain. PennzEnergy spun off from Pennzoil in 1998 dates back to the Texas oil boom after WWII. In addition to new US holdings the deal gave Devon a number of international oil and gas assets in such places as Azerbaijan Brazil Egypt Qatar and Venezuela.

On a roll Devon in 2000 bought Santa Fe Snyder for $2.35 billion in stock and $1 billion in assumed debt. The deal increased Devon's proved reserves by nearly 400 million barrels of oil equivalent.

In 2001 the company agreed to a major deal to supply Indonesian natural gas to Singapore. It also made an unsuccessful bid for rival Barrett Resources that was trumped by a bid from Williams Companies. Undaunted that year Devon acquired Anderson Exploration for $3.4 billion in cash and $1.2 billion in assumed debt. It also purchased Mitchell Energy & Development for $3.1 billion in cash and stock and $400 million in assumed debt.

As part of its strategy to refocus on core operations in 2002 the company sold its Indonesian assets to PetroChina for $262 million. By mid-year the company had raised about $1.2 billion through the disposition of oil properties worldwide.

Over this decade Devon Energy bought its way into the big leagues as a North American producer through a series of multibillion-dollar acquisitions of oil and gas producers including Ocean Energy in 2003 for $3.5 billion and US-based Chief Holdings LLC in 2006 for $2.2 billion.

In 2007 Devon began to divest all of its assets in West Africa. It sold its oil and gas business in Egypt to Dana Petroleum for $375 million and its Gabon assets for $206 million. In 2008 it sold its oil and gas business in Cote d'Ivoire to Afren plc for $205 million and in Equatorial Guinea (to that country's national oil company GE Petrol) for $2.2 billion.

EXECUTIVES

President CEO and Director, John Richels, age 61, $1,150,000 total compensation
EVP Marketing Midstream and Supply Chain, Darryl G. Smette, age 64, $610,000 total compensation
SVP Accounting, Danny J. Heatly, age 56, $339,900 total compensation
Chairman, J. Larry Nichols, age 69, $1,400,000 total compensation
EVP Human Resources, Frank W. Rudolph, age 55
EVP Administration, R. Alan Marcum, age 45
SVP Exploration, William A. (Bill) Van Wie, age 66
SVP Investor Relations, Vincent W. White, age 54
SVP Western Divisioin, Don D. DeCarlo, age 55
VP Corporate Governance and Secretary, Carla D. Brockman, age 53
EVP Exploration and Production, David A. (Dave) Hager, age 55, $504,952 total compensation
SVP Canadian Division; President Devon Canada, Christopher R. (Chris) Seasons, age 51
EVP and CFO, Jeffrey A. (Jeff) Agosta, age 44
SVP Mid-Continent Division, Bradley A. Foster, age 54
SVP Exploration and Production Strategic Services, Anthony D. (Tony) Vaughn, age 54
Senior Manager Investor Relations, Shea Snyder
EVP and General Counsel, Lyndon C. Taylor, age 53
VP Tax, Gina E. Sewell, age 50
VP Exploration, Joseph P. Ash, age 54
VP Planning and Business Development, William D. Fulton, age 54
SVP Southern Division, Gregory T. Kelleher, age 57
EVP Public Affairs, William F. (Bill) Whitsitt
VP and Controller, Gregg L. Henson, age 45
Manager Investor Relations, Scott Coody
VP Business Technology, Ben Williams
Investor Relations Coordinator, Malaina Vivona
SVP Exploration and Production Technical Support, Jeffrey L. (Jeff) Ritenour, age 38
Manager Media Relations, Chip Minty
President CEO and Director, John Richels, age 61
Director, Duane C. Radtke, age 64
Director, Robert A. Mosbacher Jr., age 60
Director, Robert H. Henry, age 59
Auditors: KPMGLLP

LOCATIONS

HQ: Devon Energy Corporation
20 N. Broadway, Oklahoma City OK 73102-8260
Phone: 405-235-3611 **Fax:** 405-552-4550
Web: www.devonenergy.com

2011 Sales

	$ mil.	% of total
US	8,358	73
Canada	3,096	27
Total	**11,454**	**100**

PRODUCTS/OPERATIONS

2011 Sales

	$ mil.	% of total
Oil gas & natural gas liquids	8,315	72
Marketing & midstream	2,258	20
Oil gas & natural gas liquids derivatives	881	8
Total	**11,454**	**100**

COMPETITORS

Abraxas Petroleum
Apache
Bonanza Creek
BP
Cabot Oil & Gas
Chesapeake Energy
Chevron
ConocoPhillips
Encana
EOG
Exxon Mobil
Forest Oil
Hess Corporation
Imperial Oil
JKX
Jones Energy
Marathon Oil
Occidental Petroleum
PETROBRAS
Petroleos de Venezuela
Royal Dutch Shell
Swift Energy
TOTAL
Williams Companies
XTO Energy

HISTORICAL FINANCIALS

Company Type: Public

Income Statement FYE: December 31

	REVENUE ($ mil.)	NET INCOME ($ mil.)	NET PROFIT MARGIN	EMPLOYEES
12/11	11,454	4,704	41.1%	5,200
12/10	9,940	4,550	45.8%	5,000
12/09	8,015	(2,479)	—	5,400
12/08	15,211	(2,148)	—	5,500
12/07	11,362	3,606	31.7%	5,000
Annual Growth	0.2%	6.9%	—	1.0%

2011 Year-End Financials

Debt ratio: 23.79%
Return on equity: 21.95%
Cash ($ mil.): 5,555
Current ratio: 138.10
Long-term debt ($ mil.): 5,969
No. of shares (mil.): 403
Dividends
Yield: –
Payout: 5.96%
Market value ($ mil.): 25,029

	STOCK PRICE ($) FY Close	P/E High	P/E Low	PER SHARE ($) Earnings	Dividends	Book Value
12/11	62.00	8	5	11.25	0.00	53.08
12/10	78.51	8	6	10.31	0.64	44.62
12/09	73.50	—	—	(5.58)	0.64	34.86
12/08	65.71	—	—	(4.85)	0.64	38.45
12/07	88.91	12	8	8.00	0.56	49.54
Annual Growth	(8.6%)	—	—	8.9%	—	1.7%

Dick's Sporting Goods, Inc

See Dick's shoppers run putt dunk drive dribble –and buy. Fast-growing Dick's Sporting Goods operates about 480 stores in 40-plus states. The stores contain on average five smaller shops ("stores within a store") featuring sporting goods apparel and footwear for leisure pursuits ranging from football golf and cycling to hunting and camping. In addition to brands such as NIKE and adidas Dick's carries Ativa Walter Hagen and others exclusive to the firm. The company also operates 80 Golf Galaxy stores in 30 states. Dick's and Golf Galaxy both sell their products online. Dick's was founded in 1948 when Dick Stack father of company chairman and CEO Edward Stack opened a bait and tackle store.

Ownership

Stack controls the company through his ownership of about 66% of the voting shares. Subsidiaries of investment firm Baron Capital Group own about 10% of the company's common stock.

Financial Analysis

The sporting goods chain saw its fiscal 2012 (ends January) sales increase 7% vs. the prior year to about $5.2 billion. Net income increased nearly 45% over the same period. The company credited a 2% gain in same-store sales and a growing network of stores for the gains.

Strategy

Dick's has expanded in recent years through a strategy of acquisitions and organic growth. Within the past five years Dick's has grown from 294 stores at the end of fiscal 2007 (ends January) to about 560 stores at the end of fiscal 2012. The company continues to add stores (40 new Dick's locations are planned in fiscal 2013) and has set an ultimate target of at least 900 Dick's locations nationwide focusing its expansion on east of the Mississippi River in large markets. Dick's stores are the company's growth engine. Indeed it added more than 35 Dick's stores in fiscal 2012 and no Golf Galaxy locations. (The previous year the company shuttered a dozen underperforming Golf Galaxy stores primarily due to the locations being inadequate or too expensive to maintain.) After the disposition of the underperforming golf stores in fiscal 2012 Golf Galaxy posted about a 4% increase in same-store sales vs. a less than 1% increase for Dick's locations.

Geographic Reach

The company operates about 480 stores under the Dick's Sporting Goods banner in more than 40 states. It also operates 80 Golf Galaxy stores in 30 states. Believing that the sporting goods retailing market can bear at least 900 Dick's locations nationwide the company is focused on expanding its retail footprint east of the Mississippi River in Atlanta Chicago and the corridor between New York and Washington DC.

Mergers & Acquisitions

Golf Galaxy became part of the sporting goods retailer's portfolio in 2007. Dick's acquired the specialty golf retailer for about $225 million. The acquisition tightened the gap between it and top sporting goods retailer The Sports Authority and gave it a leg up in other areas particularly because Golf Galaxy is recognized in the industry as a customer-focused thriving company.

EXECUTIVES

Chairman and CEO, Edward W. (Ed) Stack, age 57, $700,000 total compensation
Director Investor Relations, Anne-Marie Megela
EVP Finance & Administration and CFO, Timothy E. (Tim) Kullman, age 56, $504,615 total compensation
Vice Chairman, William J. (Bill) Colombo, age 56, $649,038 total compensation
President and COO, Joseph H. (Joe) Schmidt, age 52, $675,000 total compensation
SVP and CIO, Matthew J. (Matt) Lynch
SVP Strategic Planning and Analysis and Treasury Services, Lee Belitsky
SVP and Chief Marketing Officer, Lauren Hobart, age 43
SVP General Counsel and Secretary, David I. Mosse, age 38
SVP Human Resources, Kathryn (Kathy) Sutter, age 49, $333,846 total compensation
SVP Real Estate, David G. Stanchak
SVP Chief Accounting Officer and Controller, Joseph R. Oliver, age 52
EVP Global Merchandising, John Duken, age 51
Director, Larry D. Stone, age 60
Director, Emanuel (Manny) Chirico, age 54
Director, David I. Fuente, age 66
Director, Jacqualyn A. (Jackie) Fouse, age 50
Vice Chairman, William J. (Bill) Colombo, age 56
Director, Walter Rossi, age 69
Director, Lawrence J. Schorr, age 58
Auditors: Deloitte&ToucheLLP

LOCATIONS

HQ: Dick' s Sporting Goods Inc.
345 Court St., Coraopolis PA 15108
Phone: 724-273-3400 **Fax:** 724-227-1902
Web: www.dickssportinggoods.com

PRODUCTS/OPERATIONS

2012 Sales

	$ mil.	% of total
Hardlines	2,726	52
Apparel	1,504	29
Footwear	982	19
Total	**5,212**	**100**

2012 Stores

	No.
Dick's	480
Golf	81
Total	**561**

Selected Categories

Archery
Backpacking
Baseball
Basketball
Boating
Bowling
Camping
Cycling
Exercise
Fishing
Football
Golf
Hockey (ice and roller)
Hunting
In-line skating
Lacrosse
Optics/telescopes
Paintball
Racquetball/squash
Running
Skateboarding
Snow sports
Soccer
Tennis
Volleyball
Water sports

COMPETITORS

Academy Sports
Big 5
Cabela' s
Costco Wholesale
Dunham' s
Eastern Mountain Sports
Edwin Watts Golf
Finish Line
Foot Locker
Gander Mountain
Golfsmith
Hibbett Sports
J. C. Penney
Kmart
L.L. Bean
Modell' s
Olympia Sports
REI
Sears
Sports Authority
Target Corporation
Wal-Mart
Winmark

HISTORICAL FINANCIALS

Company Type: Public

Income Statement FYE: January 28

	REVENUE ($ mil.)	NET INCOME ($ mil.)	NET PROFIT MARGIN	EMPLOYEES
01/12	5,211	263	5.1%	28,400
01/11	4,871	182	3.7%	26,700
01/10	4,412	135	3.1%	25,200
01/09*	4,130	(35)	—	27,600
02/08	3,888	155	4.0%	26,400
Annual Growth	7.6%	14.2%	—	1.8%

*Fiscal year change

2012 Year-End Financials

Debt ratio: 5.31%
Return on equity: 16.16%
Cash ($ mil.): 734
Current ratio: 198.73
Long-term debt ($ mil.): 151

No. of shares (mil.): 121
Dividends
Yield: —
Payout: 23.81%
Market value ($ mil.): 4,994

	STOCK PRICE ($) FY Close	P/E High/Low		PER SHARE ($) Earnings	Dividends	Book Value
01/12	41.16	19	14	2.10	0.00	13.46
01/11	35.80	24	14	1.50	0.00	11.48
01/10	22.37	22	9	1.15	0.00	9.44
01/09*	11.01	—	—	(0.31)	0.00	7.97
02/08	32.93	50	18	1.33	0.00	7.99
Annual Growth	5.7%	—	—	12.1%	—	13.9%

*Fiscal year change

Dillard's Inc.

Tradition is trying to catch up with the times at Dillard's. Sandwiched between retail giant Macy's and discount chains such as Kohl's Dillard's is rethinking its strategy and trimming its store count. The department store chain operates about 300 locations (down from 330 in 2005) in about 30 states covering the Sunbelt and the central US. Its stores cater to middle- and upper-middle-income women selling name-brand and private-label merchandise with a focus on apparel and home furnishings. Women's apparel and accessories account for more than 35% sales. Founded in 1938 by William Dillard family members through the W. D. Company control nearly all of the company's voting shares and run the company.

Operations

Beyond department stores Dillard's owns CDI Contractors a Little Rock Arkansas-based construction firm that was started to build and remodel its stores. CDI which accounts for only about 1% of Dillard's total sales saw its sales decline by 31% in fiscal 2012. New under Dillard's umbrella is Arkansas-based Acumen Brands (acquired in 2012) the operator of a dozen online retailers including scrubschopper.com (medical uniforms) and countryoutfitter.com (western wear). Dillard's hopes to use Acumen's acumen to improve its namesake e-commerce site and the dozen operated by Acumen. Dillard's owns more than three-quarters of its stores as well as most its distribution centers.

Financial Analysis

Dillard's posted a nearly 3% gain in retail sales in fiscal 2012 (ends January) vs. the prior year while same-store sales climbed 4% their strongest gain in years. Sales of shoes and cosmetics posted significant sales gains while apparel posted more modest gains and the home and furniture category declined. In terms of profit growth Dillard's had an excellent year with net income up about 158%. The uptick in retail sales followed an essentially flat comparison in fiscal 2011 and several lean years during the deep recession. Still the $6.4 billion in total sales rung up in fiscal 2012 was well below the $7.8 billion Dillard's took in in fiscal 2007. Indeed in fiscal 2002 the department store chain enjoyed sales in excess of $8 billion.

Strategy

Along with the decline in sales the company's store count has slipped as it shutters underperforming locations including the last of its 16 home and furniture stores. Indeed the schedule of store closings has accelerated in recent years as Dillard's tries to reduce operating expenses in a recessionary environment. After reducing its store count by an additional four locations in fiscal 2012 the company has no plans to open any new locations in the coming year. To reverse falling sales the department store chain has moved "up market" positioning itself above Macy's and Belk and below high-end chains such as Nordstrom and Bloomingdale's. To attract more customers Dillard's is focusing on adding more fashion much like J. C. Penney has done in recent years. The firm's new direction is inspired on the success of specialty stores with their edited displays or merchandise in boutique-like settings rather than an endless sea of apparel racks. New stores are smaller (averaging 170000 sq. ft.) and located in open-air lifestyle centers rather than enclosed malls. Dillard's which is averse to marking down merchandise but has been forced to discount by its lower-end competitors hopes its move up market will stop the markdowns.

Ownership

Dillard's Inc. Retirement Trust owns about 25% of the company's common stock.

HISTORY

At age 12 William Dillard began working in his father's general store in Mineral Springs Arkansas. After he graduated from Columbia University in 1937 the third-generation retailer spent seven months in the Sears Roebuck manager training program in Tulsa Oklahoma.

With $8000 borrowed from his father William opened his first department store in Nashville Arkansas in 1938. Service was one of the most important things he had to offer he said and he insisted on quality —he personally inspected every item and would settle for nothing but the best. William sold the store in 1948 to finance a partnership in Wooten's Department Store in Texarkana Arkansas; he bought out Wooten and established Dillard's the next year.

Throughout the 1950s and 1960s the company became a strong regional retailer developing its strategy of buying well-established downtown stores in small cities; acquisitions in those years included Mayer & Schmidt (Tyler Texas; 1956) and Joseph Pfeifer (Little Rock Arkansas; 1963). Dillard's moved its headquarters to Little Rock after buying Pfeifer. When it went public in 1969 it had 15 stores in three states.

During the early 1960s the company began computerizing operations to streamline inventory and information management. In 1970 Dillard's added computerized cash registers which gave management hourly sales figures.

The chain continued acquiring outlets (more than 130 over the next three decades including stores owned by Stix Baer & Fuller Macy's Joske's and Maison Blanche). In a 1988 joint venture with Edward J. DeBartolo Dillard's bought a 50% interest in the 12 Higbee's stores in Ohio (buying the other 50% in 1992 shortly after Higbee's bought five former Horne's stores in Ohio).

In 1991 Vendamerica (subsidiary of Vendex International and the only major nonfamily holder of the company's stock) sold its 8.9 million shares of Class A stock (25% of the class) in an underwritten public offering.

Dillard's purchase of 12 Diamond stores from Dayton Hudson in 1994 gave it a small-event ticket-sales chain in the Southwest which it renamed Dillard's Box Office. A lawsuit filed by the FTC against Dillard's that year claiming the company made it unreasonably difficult for its credit card holders to remove unauthorized charges from their bills was dismissed the following year.

Dillard's continued to grow; it opened 11 new stores in 1995 and 16 more in 1996 (entering Georgia and Colorado). The next year it opened 12 new stores and acquired 20 making its way into Virginia California and Wyoming.

William retired in 1998 and William Dillard II took over the CEO position while brother Alex became president. The company then paid $3.1 billion for Mercantile Stores which operated 106 apparel and home design stores in the South and Midwest. To avoid redundancy in certain regions Dillard's sold 26 of those stores and exchanged seven others for new Dillard's stores. The assimilation of Mercantile brought distribution problems that cut into earnings for fiscal 1999. In late 2000 with a slumping stock price and declining sales Dillard's said it would de-emphasize its concentration on name-brand merchandise and offer deep discounts on branded items already in stock. Despite these efforts sales and earnings continued to slide in 2001.

Founder and patriarch William Dillard (the company's guiding force) died in February 2002. Son William II became chairman of the company which has been family-controlled for half a century. Dillard's opened four new stores and closed nine in 2002. Sales declined 3% versus the previous year.

In 2003 Dillard's shuttered 10 stores and opened five new store locations.

In November 2004 Dillard's completed the sale of Dillard National Bank the retailer's credit card portfolio to GE Consumer Finance for about $1.1 billion (plus debt). Dillard's had said it would use the proceeds to reduce debt repurchase stock and to achieve general corporate purposes.

In the spring of 2005 Dillard's shuttered the last of 16 home and furniture stores acquired when the department store chain acquired Mercantile Stores Co. in 1998. Hurricanes Katrina Rita and Wilma took a toll on Dillard's in 2005 interrupting business in about 60 of the company's stores at various times.

In August 2008 Dillard's purchased the 50% stake in the Arkansas-based construction firm CDI Contractors that it didn't already own for about $9.8 million. CDI is a general contactor that also builds stores for Dillard's. In November Dillard's announced 500 job cuts including about 60 at headquarters.

Amid falling sales and rising investor discontent Dillard's bowed to pressure from hedge funds Barington Capital Group and Clinton Group and appointed four new directors in April 2008 to avoid a proxy fight.

In February 2012 Dillard's acquired Acumen Brands an e-commerce company located in Fayetteville Arkansas.

EXECUTIVES

VP, Burt Squires, age 62
VP, Robin Sanderford, age 65
VP and General Counsel, Paul J. Schroeder Jr., age 64
VP, Randal L. Hankins, age 57
EVP and Director, Drue Matheny, age 65, $580,000 total compensation
VP Merchandising, Joseph P. Brennan
VP, Kent Burnett, age 67
SVP CFO and Director, James I. Freeman, age 62, $610,000 total compensation
EVP and Director, Mike Dillard, age 60, $610,000 total compensation
President and Director, Alex Dillard, age 62, $720,000 total compensation
Chairman and CEO, William (Bill) Dillard II, age 67, $810,000 total compensation
Manager General Merchandise, Bob Thompson
Director Investor Relations, Julie J. Bull
VP, Steven K. Nelson, age 54
VP Merchandising Merchandising Product Development, William T. Dillard III
VP, Denise Mahaffy
VP, James W. Cherry Jr.
VP, Michael E. Price
VP, Sidney A. Sanders
Manager General Merchandise, Anthony Menzie
VP, Christine Rowell
Regional VP Mechandising; President Regional Merchandising, David Terry, age 63
Regional VP Stores, Keith White
VP, Julie A. Taylor, age 60
Manager General Merchandise, Mark Killingsworth
Regional VP Stores, Ronald Wiggins
Regional VP Stores, W. R. Appleby II
Regional VP Stores, Tom Bolin
Regional VP Stores, Mark Gastman
Regional VP Stores, Marva Harrell
Regional VP Stores, Gene D. Heil
Regional VP Stores, William H. Hite
Regional VP Stores, Dan W. Jensen
VP Merchandising Merchandising Product Development, Lloyd Keith Tidmore
Manager General Merchandise, Sandra Steinberg
VP Merchandising Merchandising Product Development, James D. Stockman
VP Merchandising Merchandising Product Development, Mike McNiff
VP Product Development, Les Chandler
VP Merchandising Merchandising Product Development, Neil Christensen
VP Merchandising Product Development, Gianni Duarte
VP Merchandising Merchandising Product Development, Christine A. Ferrari
VP Merchandising Merchandising Product Development, Terry Smith
VP Product Development, Kay White
VP Merchandising Merchandising Product Development, Richard Moore
VP, Phillip R. Watts
VP, Sherrill E. Wise
VP, Richard B. Willey
VP Stores, Kent Wiley, age 61
Regional VP Stores, Mike Litchford
Manager General Merchandise, Lisa M. Roby
Regional VP Stores, Debra Dumas
Regional VP Stores, Brant Musgrave
Regional VP Stores, Zeina T. Nassar
VP, Tony Bolte
VP, Chris Johnson
Regional VP Stores, Michael J. Hubbell
VP Product Development, Gary M. Borofsky
CIO, Woodrow Chin
EVP and Director, Drue Matheny, age 65
SVP CFO and Director, James I. Freeman, age 62
EVP and Director, Mike Dillard, age 60
President and Director, Alex Dillard, age 62
Director, R. Brad Martin, age 60
Director, Peter R. Johnson, age 64
Director, Nick White, age 67
Director, H. Lee Hastings, age 57
Auditors: KPMGLLP

LOCATIONS

HQ: Dillard' s Inc.
1600 Cantrell Rd., Little Rock AR 72201
Phone: 501-376-5200 **Fax:** 501-399-7831
Web: www.dillards.com

2012 Stores

	No.
Texas	60
Florida	42
Arizona	17
North	16
Ohio	15
Louisiana	14
Georgia	12
Alabama	10
Oklahoma	10
Missouri	10
Tennessee	10
Arkansas	8
Colorado	8
South	8
Kansas	7
Virginia	7
Kentucky	6
Mississippi	6
New	6
Utah	6
Iowa	5
Nevada	4
California	3
Illinois	3
Indiana	3
Nebraska	3
Idaho	2
Montana	2
Wyoming	1
Total	**304**

PRODUCTS/OPERATIONS

2012 Sales

	% of total
Women's apparel &	37
Men's apparel &	17
Shoes	16
Cosmetics	15
Juniors' & children's	8
Home &	6
Construction	1
Total	**100**

COMPETITORS

Abercrombie & Fitch
American Eagle Outfitters
Ann Taylor
Bed Bath & Beyond
Belk
Bon-Ton Stores
Brown Shoe
Burlington Coat Factory
Eddie Bauer LLC
Foot Locker
J. C. Penney
J. Crew
Kohl' s
Lands' End
Macy' s
Mattress Firm
Men' s Wearhouse
Neiman Marcus
Nordstrom
Saks
Sears
Stein Mart
Talbots
Target Corporation
The Gap
TJX Companies
Tuesday Morning Corporation
Von Maur
Walgreen

HISTORICAL FINANCIALS

Company Type: Public

Income Statement

FYE: January 28

	REVENUE ($ mil.)	NET INCOME ($ mil.)	NET PROFIT MARGIN	EMPLOYEES
01/12	6,399	463	7.2%	38,900
01/11	6,253	179	2.9%	38,900
01/10	6,226	68	1.1%	41,300
01/09*	6,988	(241)	—	49,900
02/08	7,370	53	0.7%	49,938
Annual Growth	(3.5%)	71.4%	—	(6.1%)

*Fiscal year change

2012 Year-End Financials

Debt ratio: 20.97%
Return on equity: 22.61%
Cash ($ mil.): 224
Current ratio: 182.88
Long-term debt ($ mil.): 823
No. of shares (mil.): 49
Dividends
Yield: —
Payout: 2.23%
Market value ($ mil.): 2,281

	STOCK PRICE ($) FY Close	P/E High	P/E Low	PER SHARE ($) Earnings	Dividends	Book Value
01/12	46.14	7	4	8.52	0.00	41.50
01/11	40.21	16	6	2.67	0.00	34.79
01/10	16.56	22	3	0.93	0.00	31.21
01/09*	4.35	—	—	(3.25)	0.00	30.65
02/08	20.56	58	22	0.68	0.00	33.45
Annual Growth	22.4%	—	—	88.1%	—	5.5%

*Fiscal year change

Dime Community Bancshares, Inc

Dime Community Bancshares is in a New York state of mind. It is the holding company for The Dime Savings Bank of Williamsburgh which operates more than 25 branches in Brooklyn Queens and the Bronx as well as Nassau County on Long Island. Founded in 1864 it provides standard products and services including checking savings retirement money market and club accounts accounts. Multifamily residential and commercial real estate loans comprise most of the bank's lending activities. Subsidiary Dime Insurance Agency (formerly Havemeyer Investments) offers life policies fixed annuities and wealth management services.

Multifamily residential real estate loans account for some three-quarters of Dime Savings' loan portfolio; most of these are secured by properties in Brooklyn Queens and Manhattan. The community-oriented bank believes that multifamily residential and mixed-use loans in the New York City area produce higher yields than securities with similar maturities. Beginning in 2008 it implemented a plan to restrict growth in order to maintain sufficient capital to protect against potential loan losses. Investments in rent-regulated multifamily dwellings coupled with the bank's conservative strategy helped to shield it from the recession.

The moves paid off as economic conditions showed signs of improvement. In 2010 Dime Community Bancshares reported a nearly 60% increase in net income compared to the previous year. Earnings were up almost 15% from that figure in 2011 representing the company's second-highest annual level ever. Reductions in loan loss provisions and improved interest rate spreads helped the company's bottom line.

Employees own more than 10% of Dime Community Bancshares.

EXECUTIVES

EVP and Chief Investment Officer Dime Community Bancorp and Dime Savings Bank, Timothy B. King, age 53, $257,920 total compensation
President COO and Director Dime Community Bancorp and Dime Savings Bank, Michael P. Devine, age 65, $541,000 total compensation
First EVP CFO and Director Dime Community Bancorp and Dime Savings Bank, Kenneth J. Mahon, age 61, $388,000 total compensation
Chairman and CEO Dime Community Bancorp and Dime Savings Bank, Vincent F. Palagiano, age 71, $686,000 total compensation
EVP and Chief Retail Officer Dime Community Bancshares and Dime Savings Bank, Terence J. Mitchell, age 59
EVP and Chief Accounting Officer Dime Community Bancshares and Dime Savings Bank, Michael Pucella, age 58, $219,000 total compensation
Secretary, Lance J. Bennett
EVP and Chief Lending Officer Dime Community Bancorp and Dime Savings Bank, Daniel J. Harris, age 55, $290,000 total compensation
President COO and Director Dime Community Bancorp and Dime Savings Bank, Michael P. Devine, age 65
First EVP CFO and Director Dime Community Bancorp and Dime Savings Bank, Kenneth J. Mahon, age 61
Director, Anthony Bergamo, age 65
Director, George L. Clark Jr., age 71
Director, Steven D. Cohn, age 63
Director, John J. Flynn, age 75
Director, Patrick E. Curtin, age 66
Director, Fred P. Fehrenbach, age 75
Director, Joseph J. Perry, age 45
Director, Omer S. J. (Jack) Williams, age 71
Auditors: CroweHorwathLLP

LOCATIONS

HQ: Dime Community Bancshares Inc.
209 Havemeyer St., Brooklyn NY 11211
Phone: 718-782-6200 **Fax:** 718-486-7535
Web: www.dimewill.com

PRODUCTS/OPERATIONS

2011 Sales

	$ mil.	% of total
Interest		
Loans secured by real estate	200	92
Mortgage-backed securities	5	2
Other	4	2
Noninterest		
Service charges & other fees	3	2
Bank-owned life insurance	1	1
Other	2	1
Total	**217**	**100**

COMPETITORS

Astoria Financial
Carver Bancorp
Citigroup
First of Long Island
Flushing Financial
HSBC
JPMorgan Chase
Valley National Bancorp

HISTORICAL FINANCIALS

Company Type: Public

Income Statement FYE: December 31

	ASSETS ($ mil.)	NET INCOME ($ mil.)	INCOME AS % OF ASSETS	EMPLOYEES
12/11	4,021	47	1.2%	435
12/10	4,040	41	1.0%	442
12/09	3,952	26	0.7%	433
12/08	4,055	28	0.7%	453
12/07	3,501	22	0.6%	414
Annual Growth	3.5%	20.5%	—	1.2%

2011 Year-End Financials

Debt ratio: 23.37%
Return on equity: 13.10%
Cash ($ mil.): 43
Current ratio: —
Long-term debt ($ mil.): 939
No. of shares (mil.): 35
Dividends
Yield: —
Payout: 40.00%
Market value ($ mil.): 442

	STOCK PRICE ($) FY Close	P/E High	P/E Low	PER SHARE ($) Earnings	Dividends	Book Value
12/11	12.60	11	7	1.40	0.00	10.28
12/10	14.59	12	9	1.24	0.56	9.50
12/09	11.73	17	9	0.79	0.56	8.57
12/08	13.30	24	13	0.85	0.56	8.10
12/07	12.77	24	16	0.67	0.56	7.93
Annual Growth	(0.3%)	—	—	20.2%	—	6.7%

DIRECTV

DIRECTV takes television straight to the masses. The company operates the largest direct-to-home (DTH) digital TV service in the US ahead of #2 DISH Network and in direct competition with cable providers Comcast (#1 overall in the pay-TV market) and Time Warner. In addition to its roughly 20 million US customers the company counts about another 12 million subscribers in Latin America under the DIRECTV and SKY brands. Services include HD 3D and video-on-demand (VOD) programming. Phone companies such as Verizon and AT&T bundle the company's video services with their own traditional voice digital telephone and Internet packages.

HISTORY

The DIRECTV Group's roots go back to 1932 when Hughes Aircraft was founded to build experimental airplanes for Howard Hughes who set a number of world airspeed records with the company's H-1 racer. During WWII the company began building a mammoth flying boat to serve as a troop carrier but the "Spruce Goose" wasn't completed until 1947 when Hughes piloted it for its only flight (to silence critics who claimed it couldn't fly).

After WWII the company began moving into the growing defense electronics field. In 1953 it underwent a major shake-up when about 80 of its top engineers walked out dissatisfied with Howard Hughes who was becoming distant and difficult.

The US Air Force threatened to cancel the company's contracts because of Hughes' erratic behavior so he transferred the company's assets to the Howard Hughes Medical Institute (with himself as its sole trustee) and hired former Bendix Aviation executive Lawrence Hyland to run the company. Hyland rebuilt its research staff and the institute produced the first beam of coherent laser light (1960) and placed the first communications satellite into geosynchronous orbit (1963). The Hughes-built Surveyor landed on the moon in 1966.

When Hughes died in 1976 a board of trustees was created to oversee the institute. In 1984 the Department of Defense canceled several missile contracts and the firm found it difficult to fund R&D.

The next year the institute sold Hughes Aircraft to General Motors for $5.2 billion. GM teamed its Delco Electronics auto parts unit with Hughes to form GM Hughes Electronics (GMHE). GMHE acquired General Dynamics' missile business in 1992 and installed former IBM executive Michael Armstrong as CEO. He cut personnel by 25% and refocused the company on commercial electronics.

In 1995 GMHE became Hughes Electronics and launched its DIRECTV satellite service. That year the company strengthened its defense business by acquiring CAE-Link (training and technical services) and Magnavox Electronic Systems (warfare and communications systems). Hughes bought a majority stake in satellite communications provider PanAmSat in 1996 (PanAmSat was acquired in 2006 by Intelsat).

In 1997 GM sold its defense electronics unit to Raytheon and merged Delco Electronics into GM subsidiary Delphi Automotive Systems (now Delphi Holdings). Armstrong left Hughes to head AT&T and was replaced by Michael Smith whose brother John Smith was then GM's CEO.

In 1998 the company boosted its stake in PanAmSat to 81% (which it later sold in 2004). The investment and sluggish sales led to a drop in profits for 1998. Hughes also took a public relations hit that year when several of its satellites failed and temporarily halted most US pager activity.

To gain customers and expand its broadcast channel offerings Hughes in 1999 bought United States Satellite Broadcasting and the satellite business of rival PRIMESTAR and folded the businesses into DIRECTV. Also that year Hughes began building its SPACEWAY broadband satellite network through its subsidiary Hughes Network Systems.

In 2000 Hughes sold its satellite manufacturing market to Boeing in an effort to focus on its faster-growing communications services businesses. GM also issued a tracking stock for Hughes but retained ownership of all the company's assets. That same year GM announced that it would try to sell Hughes.

Hughes bought Telocity (renamed DIRECTV Broadband) an ISP that used DSL technology for about $177 million in 2001. Later that year Michael Smith retired abruptly amid reports of disputes over the sale of the company. GM's Harry Pearce took over as chairman of Hughes and Jack Shaw was named CEO.

As negotiations to sell Hughes to Rupert Murdoch's News Corp. continued in 2001 EchoStar made an unsolicited bid to buy Hughes for more than $30 billion. After more negotiations News Corp. dropped out of the bidding and GM reached a $25.8 billion deal with EchoStar.

Despite news reports in 2002 that the Justice Department and the FCC were set to block the company's sale to EchoStar Hughes announced that it was confident the deal would win regulatory approval by the end of the year; however the companies terminated their merger agreement in December 2002.

Instead GM sold its 19.8% interest in Hughes Electronics to News Corp. in 2003. News Corp. acquired another 14.2% from common stockholders amounting to a 34% stake in Hughes Electronics which it quickly transferred to its Fox Entertainment Group.

DIRECTV Latin America filed for Chapter 11 bankruptcy in 2003 and exited the following year. The parent company subsequently reorganized its Latin American operations through several transactions between the DIRECTV Group and News Corp. in order to consolidate DIRECTV and Sky Latin America geographically.

In 2004 Hughes Electronics changed its name to The DIRECTV Group declaring its focus and commitment to the DIRECTV brand and DTH satellite business. The company restructured its business segments throughout that year and the next and sold all operations and investment holdings not considered core to the DTH business line. This included the sale of its 80% stake in satellite network operator PanAmSat to a group of private equity firms (KKR The Carlyle Group and Providence Equity Partners) for about $2.6 billion.

Electronics manufacturer THOMSON purchased HNS' set-top box assets in a 2004 deal and electronics manufacturing services provider Flextronics acquired HNS' 55% ownership stake in Hughes Software Systems later renamed Aricent for about $226 million. DIRECTV also sold its holdings in XM Satellite Radio (now part of SIRIUS XM Radio) in 2004.

DIRECTV had a less-than-harmonious relationship over the years with affiliate Pegasus Communications (which later became Xanadoo). Pegasus was licensed to provide DIRECTV-branded satellite service to about 1 million rural customers in the US. The conflict centered around contract disputes some of which wrapped up in 2004 but by DIRECTV had altered or ended the exclusive distribution agreements by the middle of that year and some Pegasus subsidiaries filed for bankruptcy protection. DIRECTV ultimately acquired Pegasus' satellite assets in a deal valued at $938 million.

In 2005 DIRECTV sold 50% of HNS a provider of satellite equipment and services to SkyTerra (now LightSquared) in a cash and stock deal worth about $250 million (HNS was at one point valued at $1.3 billion). SkyTerra acquired the remaining 50% stake in 2006 through Apollo Management the Purchase New York-based private equity firm that controlled SkyTerra at the time.

After selling a majority stake in its Mexico-based operations and making acquisitions in Brazil and other areas DIRECTV restructured its Latin American unit in 2007 to include PanAmericana Sky Brazil and Sky Mexico. The segment came fully under DIRECTV's ownership in 2007 when it purchased Darlene Investment's 14% stake.

Looking to expand its control of the installation and home service network for its products DIRECTV acquired service provider 180 Connect in 2008. In a related deal UniTek USA a provider of communications management and support services bought 180 Connect's cable TV services unit; UniTek transferred satellite TV installation businesses in select markets to DIRECTV in exchange. DIRECTV moved that year to entice new customers and pull in additional revenue from existing subscribers with the launch of its DIRECTV-on-Demand video service and the expansion of its international programming options.

Also that year Liberty Media exchanged its 16% stake in News Corp. for that company's 41% share held through Fox Entertainment Group of DIRECTV. Liberty Media increased its stake in a subsequent share purchase that year giving it ownership of 53% of DIRECTV shares but control of only 48% of its voting rights.

In a deal orchestrated by former chairman John Malone The DIRECTV Group merged with Liberty Entertainment Inc. (LEI) in a series of transactions to form DIRECTV in 2009. To facilitate the merger LEI was created by the spin off of assets from Liberty Media late that year; its holdings included a 57% stake in the DIRECTV Group as well as three networks affiliated with FOX Sports Net online game developer FUN Technologies and a 65% share of Game Show Network. The deal included about $120 million in cash and about $2 billion in debt held by LEI. The company subsequently became known simply as DIRECTV. Costs related to the transaction contributed to a dip in DIRECTV's profits for the year. In 2010 Malone swapped his preferred shares in DIRECTV for common stock bringing his voting interest down to 3% from 24%. Post-merger LEI doesn't have any ownership stake in DIRECTV.

EXECUTIVES

Chairman President and CEO, Michael D. (Mike) White, age 61
EVP and General Counsel, Larry D. Hunter, age 61, $774,753 total compensation
EVP and Chief Human Resources Officer, Joseph A. (Joe) Bosch, age 54
EVP CFO and Treasurer, Patrick T. (Pat) Doyle, age 56, $500,032 total compensation
EVP and CIO, Michael R. (Mike) Benson
SVP Customer Care, Ellen Filipiak
EVP and CTO, Romulo C. Pontual, age 52, $749,567 total compensation
EVP; President DIRECTV Latin America; President New Enterprises, Bruce B. Churchill, age 54, $1,136,188 total compensation
SVP Financial Planning and Investor Relations, Jonathan M. (Jon) Rubin
EVP Operations, Michael W. (Mike) Palkovic, age 54, $879,753 total compensation
SVP Controller and Chief Accounting Officer, John F. Murphy, age 43
SVP and Treasurer, J. William Little, age 43
Senior Vice President; Treasurer, Fazal Merchant
Director, David B. Dillon, age 61
Director, Peter A. Lund, age 71
Director, Charles R. Lee, age 72
Director, Samuel A. (Sam) DiPiazza Jr., age 62
Director, Neil R. Austrian, age 72
Director, Lorrie M. Norrington, age 52
Director, Nancy S. Newcomb, age 68
Director, Ralph F. Boyd Jr., age 55
Independent Director, Dixon Doll
Auditors: Deloitte&ToucheLLP

LOCATIONS

HQ: DIRECTV
2230 E. Imperial Hwy., El Segundo CA 90245
Phone: 310-964-5000 **Fax:** 310-535-5225
Web: www.directv.com

PRODUCTS/OPERATIONS

2011 Sales

	$ mil.	% of total
$ in mil. % of total		
DIRECTV US	21,872	80
DIRECTV Latin America	5,096	19
Sports networks eliminations & other	258	1
Total	**27,226**	**100**

COMPETITORS

Amazon.com
Apple Inc.
AT&T
Bright House Networks
Cablevision Systems
Charter Communications
Comcast
Cox Communications
DISH Network
Empresas Cablevision
Hulu
Insight Communications
Net Servicos de Comunicac?o
Netflix
RCN Corporation
Sprint Nextel
Telefonica
Telmex
Time Warner Cable
Verizon
YouTube

HISTORICAL FINANCIALS

Company Type: Public

Income Statement FYE: December 31

	REVENUE ($ mil.)	NET INCOME ($ mil.)	NET PROFIT MARGIN	EMPLOYEES
12/11	27,226	2,609	9.6%	26,800
12/10	24,102	2,198	9.1%	25,100
12/09	21,565	942	4.4%	23,300
12/08	19,693	1,521	7.7%	19,600
12/07	17,246	1,451	8.4%	12,300
Annual Growth	12.1%	15.8%	—	21.5%

2011 Year-End Financials

Debt ratio: 73.08%
Return on equity: 987650001000000.00%
Cash ($ mil.): 873
Current ratio: 89.42
Long-term debt ($ mil.): 13,464
No. of shares (mil.): 691
Dividends
Yield: —
Payout: —
Market value ($ mil.): 29,560

	STOCK PRICE ($) FY Close	P/E High/Low	PER SHARE ($) Earnings	Dividends	Book Value
12/11	42.76	15 11	3.47	0.00	(4.49)
12/10	39.93	19 13	2.30	0.00	(0.24)
12/09	33.35	35 20	0.95	0.00	3.12
12/08	22.91	21 13	1.37	0.00	4.74
12/07	23.12	22 17	1.21	0.00	5.49
Annual Growth	16.6%	— —	30.1%	—	—

Discover Financial Services

Seems cardholders aren't the only ones getting paid to discover. Discover Financial Services is best known for issuing Discover-brand credit cards which are used by more than 25 million members. The company's cards which include several levels of business and consumer accounts repay cardholders a percentage of the purchase price each time they use their cards. Discover also licenses Diners Club credit cards which are accepted in more than 185 countries. But there's more to this business than just plastic. The company also offers direct banking services issues student and personal loans and runs the PULSE Network ATM system.

Discover reported record net income in 2011 buoyed by higher volume in its card and ATM operations growth in its student and personal loan portfolios and historically low loan delinquencies and charge-offs. The company did encounter a setback however when it made a move to grow its banking business by arranging to buy more than $1 billion of deposits from Allstate Bank. That deal fell through after Discover was unable to get regulatory approval to complete the transaction. In a separate deal the company in 2012 bought Home Loan Center the mortgage origination operations of Tree.com for nearly $56 million.

Meanwhile Discover has also been busy building its international business. The company has reciprocity alliances with card issuers in countries such as Canada China France Germany Japan South Korea and the UK to increase its cards' acceptance in those markets and to provide cardholders in those countries to gain global payment acceptance through Discover's network. In 2012 Discover issued its first cards outside the US (in Ecuador) and entered into an alliance with National Payments Corporation to increase network acceptance in India.

Discover boosted its lending operations in 2010 with its $600 million purchase of Citibank's 80% stake in Student Loan Corporation. It also acquired a $4.2 billion portfolio of private student loans from Citibank. The company later divested its portfolio of federal student loans after the government overhauled its lending program and became the sole provider of government-backed student loans in 2010. The following year Discover bought another $2.5 billion in student loans from Citibank. The company plans to ramp up its student and personal lending.

In response to federal legislation meant to protect consumers from unfair billing practices (the Credit Card Accountability Responsibility and Disclosure or CARD Act) Discover Financial increased annual percentage rates and converted many accounts from fixed to adjustable rates. It has also added to its number of partnerships with retailers and restaurants to enhance its customer rewards programs to encourage card usage.

Morgan Stanley spun off Discover Financial Services in 2007. A similar move had been announced in 2005 but Morgan Stanley pulled the plug on that earlier attempt amid market turmoil. In 2008 Discover settled antitrust litigation with its chief rivals for some $2.75 billion. In the suit the company had claimed that Visa and MasterCard had illegally barred their member financial institutions from issuing Discover cards.

To gain access to federal funds made available through the Troubled Asset Relief Program (TARP) Discover Financial converted to a bank holding company in 2009. It received $1.2 billion from the program which it repaid the following year.

EXECUTIVES

Chairman and CEO, David W. Nelms, age 51, $1,000,000 total compensation
President and COO, Roger C. Hochschild, age 47, $725,000 total compensation
EVP CFO and Chief Accounting Officer, R. Mark Graf, age 47
VP and Assistant General Counsel, Simon Halfin
EVP and President Payment Services, Diane E. Offereins, age 54, $625,000 total compensation
EVP and President Consumer Banking and Operations, Carlos Minetti, age 49, $625,000 total compensation
EVP and President US Cards, Harit Talwar, age 51
EVP General Counsel and Secretary, Kathryn McNamara Corley, age 51
Media Director, Jennifer Murillo
President Discover Bank, Christina Favilla
VP Global Business Development, Joe Hurley
SVP Marketing, Gloria Colgan, age 48
VP Retail Partner Marketing, Dana Traci
Director Public Relations and Community Affairs, Leslie Sutton
EVP and Chief Credit Risk Officer, James V. Panzarino, age 59
VP Portfolio Marketing, Sarah Alter
VP Assistant General Counsel Banking and Securitization, D. Christopher Greene
SVP and CIO, Glenn Schneider, age 50
VP Customer Service and Engagement Strategy, Steve Mendelson
SVP Discover Student Loans, Steve Olszewski
VP Acquisitions, Kelly Tufts
SVP Brand and Product Management, Julie Loeger
Director, Robert M. Devlin, age 70
Director, Lawrence A. (Larry) Weinbach, age 72
Director, Richard H. Lenny, age 60
Director, Mary K. Bush, age 63
Director, E. Follin Smith, age 52
Director, Cynthia A. Glassman, age 64
Director, Thomas G. (Tom) Maheras, age 49
Director, Jeffrey S. Aronin, age 44
Director, Michael H. Moskow, age 75
Director, Gregory C. (Greg) Case, age 49
Auditors: Deloitte&ToucheLLP

LOCATIONS

HQ: Discover Financial Services
2500 Lake Cook Rd., Riverwoods IL 60015
Phone: 224-405-0900 **Fax:** 224-405-4993
Web: www.discoverfinancial.com

PRODUCTS/OPERATIONS

2011 Sales

	$ mil.	% of total
Interest		
Credit card loans	5,654	66
Other loans	618	7
Other	72	1
Noninterest		
Net discount & interchange revenue	1,083	13
Fee products	428	5
Loan fees	338	4
Transaction processing	180	2
Other	174	2
Total	**8,550**	**100**

2011 Sales by Segment

	$ mil.	% of total
Direct Banking	8,252	97
Payment Services	297	3
Total	**8,550**	**100**

COMPETITORS

Ally Financial
American Express
Bank of America
Capital One
Citigroup
First Data
JPMorgan Chase
MasterCard
Sallie Mae
Visa Inc
Wells Fargo

HISTORICAL FINANCIALS

Company Type: Public

Income Statement FYE: November 30

	ASSETS ($ mil.)	NET INCOME ($ mil.)	INCOME AS % OF ASSETS	EMPLOYEES
11/11	68,783	2,226	3.2%	11,650
11/10	60,784	764	1.3%	10,300
11/09	46,020	1,276	2.8%	10,500
11/08	39,892	927	2.3%	11,900
11/07	37,376	588	1.6%	12,800
Annual Growth	16.5%	39.5%	—	(2.3%)

2011 Year-End Financials

Debt ratio: 26.59%
Return on equity: 27.02%
Cash ($ mil.): 2,849
Current ratio: —
Long-term debt ($ mil.): 18,287
No. of shares (mil.): 528
Dividends
Yield: 0.84%
Payout: 4.93%
Market value ($ mil.): 12,597

	STOCK PRICE ($) FY Close	P/E High	P/E Low	PER SHARE ($) Earnings	Dividends	Book Value
11/11	23.82	7	4	4.06	0.20	15.59
11/10	18.28	16	10	1.22	0.08	11.85
11/09	15.46	7	2	2.39	0.12	15.54
11/08	10.23	10	3	1.92	0.00	12.32
11/07	17.37	26	13	1.23	0.06	11.72
Annual Growth	8.2%	—	—	34.8%	35.1%	7.4%

Discovery Communications, Inc.

Discovery Communications allows viewers to go on safari without ever having to leave their couch. It is the world's #1 non-fiction media company with more than 150 worldwide cable TV networks including Discovery Channel Animal Planet and The Learning Channel (TLC). Among its US joint venture networks are The Oprah Winfrey Network (OWN) The Hub and 3net (the first 24-hour 3D network). Discovery Communications reaches more than 1.8 billion subscribers in more than 200 countries. In addition the company offers educational products and services to school; a diverse set of digital media services; and online content through Discovery.com and AnimalPlanet.com.

HISTORY

John Hendricks a history graduate who wanted to expand the presence of educational programming on TV founded Cable Educational Network in 1982. Three years later he introduced the Discovery Channel. Devoted entirely to documentaries and nature shows the channel premiered in 156000 US homes. After dodging bankruptcy (it had $5000 cash and $1 million in debt to the BBC) within a year the Discovery Channel had 7 million subscribers and a host of new investors including Cox Communications and TCI (later AT&T Broadband). It expanded its programming from 12 hours to 18 hours a day in 1987.

Discovery continued to attract subscribers reaching more than 32 million by 1988. The next year it launched Discovery Channel Europe to more than 200000 homes in the UK and Scandinavia. The company began selling home videos in 1990 and entered the Israeli market. The following year Discovery Communications Inc. (DCI) was formed to house the company's operations and it bought The Learning Channel (TLC founded 1980). The company revamped TLC's programming and in 1992 introduced a daily six-hour commercial-free block of children's programs. The next year it introduced its first CD-ROM title "In the Company of Whales" based on the Discovery Channel documentary.

DCI increased its focus on international expansion in 1994 moving into Asia Latin America the Middle East North Africa Portugal and Spain. The next year the company introduced its website and began selling company merchandise such as CD-ROMs and videos. DCI solidified its move into the retail sector in 1996 with the acquisition of The Nature Company and Scientific Revolution chains (renamed Discovery Channel Store). Also that year it launched its third major cable channel Animal Planet.

The company continued expanding internationally throughout the mid-1990s establishing operations in Australia Canada India New Zealand and South Korea (1995); Africa Brazil Germany and Italy (1996); and Japan and Turkey (1997). DCI also added to its stable of cable channels with the purchase of 70% of the Travel Channel from Paxson Communications (later ION Media Networks) in 1997. (It acquired the remaining 30% interest in 1999.) The company's 1997 original production "Titanic: Anatomy of a Disaster" attracted 3.2 million US households setting a network ratings record.

The following year DCI and the BBC launched Animal Planet in Asia through a joint venture and agreed to market and distribute new cable channel BBC America. It also bought CBS's Eye on People renaming the channel Discovery People (DCI shut the channel down in 2000). DCI spent $330 million launching its new health and fitness channel Discovery Health in 1999 and formed partnerships with high-speed online service Road Runner (to provide interactive information and services to Road Runner customers) and Rosenbluth Travel (to provide vacation packages based on DCI programming).

DCI reorganized its Internet activities into one unit called Discovery.com in 2000 with plans to eventually take it public. Later that year the Discovery Channel set back-to-back records with the two highest-rated documentaries ever on cable "Raising the Mammoth" (10.1 million people) and "Walking With Dinosaurs" (10.7 million people). In 2001 the company cut about 50 jobs as part of a restructuring. Later that year Discovery Communications struck a three-year deal to lease time from NBC on Saturday mornings (paying $6 million per season) to show its Discovery Kids programs.

In 2002 the company launched a 24-hour high-definition television network called Discovery HD Theater. Two years later founder John Hendricks relinquished his CEO duties (he remained chairman). President Judy McHale replaced him.

DCI started off 2005 by rebranding its aviation-themed Discovery Wings channel as the Military Channel. Later that year former majority owner Liberty Media placed its stake in DCI into a new company called Discovery Holding which it then spun off to Liberty shareholders.

Early in 2007 former NBC Universal Cable executive David Zaslav was named CEO replacing McHale. DCI later bought out 25%-partner Cox Communications in exchange for $1.3 billion in cash along with such assets as the Travel Channel and Antenna Audio. It also began shuttering its chain of Discovery Channel Stores as part of a cost-cutting effort.

Joint venture partners Discovery Holding and Advance/Newhouse (an affiliate of Advance Publications) combined their stakes in Discovery Communications in 2008 spinning off DCI as a public company.

Over the next few years DCI worked diligently to launch new networks targeting a diverse selection of audience segments. In 2010 it rolled out The Hub a channel targeting kids ages 2-11. Another 50/50 joint venture with toy maker Hasbro The Hub offers programming based on many of Hasbro's popular brands including G.I. Joe Scrabble Tonka and Transformers.

In early 2011 the company helped launch OWN talk show host Oprah Winfrey's new network and 3net one of the first networks dedicated to providing 3D programming 24 hours a day.

EXECUTIVES

EVP Programming TLC, Steve Cheskin
President and CEO Hasbro-Discovery Communications Joint Venture, Margaret A. Loesch, age 64
Chairman, John S. Hendricks, age 60, $1,000,000 total compensation
President CEO and Director, David M. Zaslav, age 52, $2,000,000 total compensation
President and General Manager Planet Green and FitTV, Laura Michalchyshyn
President and CEO Discovery Networks International, Mark G. Hollinger, age 53, $1,000,000 total compensation
EVP Ad Sales Discovery Networks US, Evan Sternschein
CEO OWN; The Oprah Winfrey Network, Christina Norman
CFO The Oprah Winfrey Network (OWN), Brent Willman
EVP and COO Discovery Channel and Science Channel, Wonya Y. Lucas
President Advertising Sales, Joseph (Joe) Abruzzese
EVP and General Manager Advertising Sales Discovery Networks US, Scott McGraw
SVP National Advertising Sales Discovery Networks US, Ben Price
SVP Marketing Resources New York, Beth Rockwood
SEVP and COO, Peter Liguori, age 52
President and General Manager Investigation Discovery and Military Channel, Henry S. Schleiff, age 63
EVP and Head International Business Operations Discovery Networks International, John Honeycutt
SVP Strategic Planning Investigation Discovery, Ed Hersh
President and General Manager Discovery Channel, W. Clark Bunting
Chief Digital Officer, Jean-Briac (JB) Perrette
SEVP and CFO, Andrew C. (Andy) Warren, age 45
SVP Programming Hasbro-Discovery Communications Joint Venture, Donna Ebbs
EVP and Managing Director Discovery Networks Europe the Middle East and Africa, Arthur Bastings
President Global Distribution; CEO Discovery Education, Bill Goodwyn
EVP Media Technology Production and Operations, Glenn Oakley
SVP Communications Discovery and Science Channels, Elizabeth Hillman
SVP Business Affairs and Programming Legal, Barbara Bellini
EVP and Chief Content Officer Discovery Networks International, Luis Silberwasser
Marketing and Branding Officer Discovery Channel, James Hitchcock
Chief Communications Officer and SEVP Corporate Marketing and Affairs, David C. Leavy
VP Global Benefits, Anthony (Tony) Amato
VP Sales Midwest Region, Pepe Miller
VP Digital Advertising Sales Eastern Region, Brent Spitzer
EVP Production and Chief Science Editor National Geographic Channel, Steve Burns
President and General Manager Discovery Studios, Carole Tomko
Group President Discovery and TLC Networks, Eileen O'Neill
SVP Strategy and Digital Media Discovery Networks International, Catherine Mullen
SVP Discovery Solutions, Jocelyn Egan
VP Advertising Sales Western Region, Michael Weber
VP Advertising Sales Midwest Region, Scott Kohn
VP Advertising Sales Discovery.com, Andrew Snyder
SVP Advertising Sales Eastern Region TLC, John Barry
SVP Advertising Sales Eastern Region Discovery Science Military, Scott Felenstein
VP Advertising Sales Southeast Region, Fred Norris
VP Advertising Sales East Central Region, Joe Paglino
President and CEO Sony Discovery Communications and IMAX 3D Television Network, Tom Cosgrove
SVP and General Manager Emerging Markets Discovery Networks EMEA, Caleb Weinstein
President Animal Planet and Science Networks, Marjorie Kaplan
Chief Development Officer General Counsel and Secretary, Bruce L. Campbell, age 45, $890,385 total compensation
SVP Production and Development Planet Green, Jeff Hasler
EVP Human Resources, Amy Girdwood
Network CFO Discovery Channel and The Science Channel, Kristen Welch
CFO Discovery Networks International, Doug Baker
SVP Digital Media Operations, Douglas Craig
VP Programming TLC, Brent Zacky
SVP Media Engineering, Bart Palmer
EVP Business Affairs, Clara Kim
EVP and Managing Director Discovery Networks Asia/Pacific, Tom Keaveny
SVP Communications TLC, Laurie Goldberg
VP Interactive Media Discovery Channel, Iain Langridge
SVP Strategic Marketing TLC, Tom Carr
EVP; General Manager Science Channel, Deborah (Debbie) Myers
VP Commercial and Digital Media Discovery Networks International, Alden Mitchell
VP Production Discovery Channel, Liz Brach
EVP and Managing Director Discovery Networks Latin America/U.S. Hispanic, Enrique R. (Henry) Martinez
SVP Advertising Sales Animal Planet and Discovery Kids, Sharon O'Sullivan
SVP Integrated Advertising Sales Marketing Discovery Communications U.S., Ian Parmiter
SVP Digital Media Distribution, Rebecca Glashow
SVP Interactive Technology, Kevin Loftis
Senior Science Editor, Paul Gasek
Chief Marketing Officer Discovery Education and Domestic Distribution, Lori McFarling
SEVP Human Resources, Adria Alpert-Romm, age 57
VP Programming and Business Operations, Darcy Tomlin
Research Director Discovery Networks Europe Middle East and Africa, Christian Kurz
VP Domestic Distribution, Greg Yavello
VP Operations Discovery Networks Latin America and U.S. Hispanic, Jackie Tejada
VP Programming The Oprah Winfrey Network (OWN), Timothy Kuryak
VP Programming The Oprah Winfrey Network (OWN), Jill Dickerson
SVP Research, Steve McGowan

VP Production Discovery Emerging Networks, Sara Kozak
SVP Discovery Enterprises International, Nicolas Bonard
Managing Director and EVP Discovery Networks UK Discovery Networks International, Dee Forbes
SVP Commercial Development UK and EMEA, Chris Shaw
VP Marketing Planet Green, Laura Giacalone
SVP Marketing Planet Green, Rob Jacobson
CFO Discovery Communications-Hasbro Joint Venture, Dan Pimentel
SVP Ad Sales Discovery Communications-Hasbro Joint Venture, Brooke Goldstein
SVP Consumer Insights and Research Discovery Communications-Hasbro Joint Venture, Lorrie Copeland
VP Digital Media Distribution, Todd Zander
Managing Director Antenna Audio, Steven Sidel
EVP Digital Advertising Sales, Kathy Kayse
Director Publicity, Juliet Farrell
Manager Corporate Communications, Bonnary Lek
VP Corporate Communications, Tammy Shea
SVP Creative Marketing TLC, Amy Winter
VP Strategy and Mergers & Acquisitions Discovery Networks, Mark Smith
SVP Programming Discovery Channel, Kevin Bennett
EVP and Chief Accounting Officer, Thomas R. Colan, age 57
SVP National Ad Sales Pricing and Planning, Robert (Bob) Voltaggio
SVP Direct Response Advertising Sales, Maria Kennedy
COO and Interim General Manager TLC, Edward Sabin
EVP Global Tax, Todd Davis
Director, John C. Malone, age 71
President CEO and Director, David M. Zaslav, age 52
Director, Paul A. Gould, age 66
Director, Steven A. Miron, age 46
Director, Robert J. (Bob) Miron, age 75
Director, M. La Voy Robison, age 77
Director, J. David Wargo, age 58
Director, Robert R. Beck, age 72
Director, Robert R. Bennett, age 54
Director, Lawrence S. (Larry) Kramer, age 62
Auditors: PricewaterhouseCoopersLLP

LOCATIONS

HQ: Discovery Communications, Inc.
One Discovery Place, Silver Spring, MD 20910
Phone: 240 662-2000
Web: www.corporate.discovery.com

2011 Sales

US	2,784	66
Total	**4,235**	**100**

PRODUCTS/OPERATIONS

2011 Sales

	$ mil.	% of total
Distribution	2,070	51
Other	313	4

2011 Sales

US networks	2,619	62
Education & other	162	4
Total	**4,235**	**100**

Selected Operations

Cable channels
- Animal Planet
- Discovery Channel
- Discovery Kids
- FitTV
- HD Theater
- Investigation Discovery
- Military Channel
- Planet Green
- Science Channel
- TLC (The Learning Channel)

Commerce and education
- Discovery Education
- DiscoveryStore.com

COMPETITORS

A&E Networks
AMC Networks
CBS Corp
Disney
E! Entertainment Television
NBCUniversal
PBS
Scripps Networks
Turner Broadcasting
Viacom

HISTORICAL FINANCIALS

Company Type: Public

Income Statement FYE: December 31

	REVENUE ($ mil.)	NET INCOME ($ mil.)	NET PROFIT MARGIN	EMPLOYEES
12/11	4,235	1,132	26.7%	4,600
12/10	3,773	653	17.3%	4,200
12/09	3,516	560	15.9%	4,400
12/08	3,443	317	9.2%	4,000
12/07	707	(68)	—	0
Annual Growth	56.4%	—	—	—

2011 Year-End Financials

Debt ratio: 35.63%
Return on equity: 17.37%
Cash ($ mil.): 1,048
Current ratio: 325.87
Long-term debt ($ mil.): 4,219
No. of shares (mil.): 261
Dividends
Yield: —
Payout: —
Market value ($ mil.): 10,693

	STOCK PRICE ($) FY Close	P/E High/Low		PER SHARE ($) Earnings	Dividends	Book Value
12/11	40.97	16	12	2.82	0.00	24.97
12/10	41.70	29	18	1.52	0.00	21.92
12/09	30.67	25	10	1.30	0.00	21.86
12/08	14.16	17	10	0.98	0.00	19.63
Annual Growth	42.5%	—	—	42.2%	—	8.4%

Dish Network Corp

DISH Network serves up fare intended to whet everyone's appetite for televised entertainment. The #2 provider of satellite-based pay-TV in the US (behind DIRECTV) the company serves about 14 million subscribers which includes business clients in such industries as hospitality restaurant and retail. Programming includes premium movies SIRIUS radio on-demand video service augmented by its Blockbuster assets regional and specialty sports local and international channels and pay-per-view in addition to basic video programming. It offers bundled voice and Internet services through partnerships with voice and data communications providers. Co-founder and chairman Charlie Ergen controls about 90% of the company.

HISTORY

Charlie Ergen a former financial analyst for Frito-Lay founded a Denver company called Echosphere a retailer of large-dish C-band satellite TV equipment with his wife Cantey and James DeFranco in 1980. Echosphere evolved into a national manufacturer and distributor which in 1987 began its move toward the new direct broadcast satellite (DBS) delivery system. It filed for a DBS license and set up subsidiary EchoStar Communications Corporation to build launch and operate DBS satellites. In 1992 the FCC granted the company an orbital slot.

By 1994 Echosphere was the US's largest distributor of conventional home satellite equipment but the future clearly rested with DBS and EchoStar. A 1995 reorganization renamed the firm EchoStar Communications; the Echosphere distributor business became a subsidiary. EchoStar also created the DISH (Digital Sky Highway) Network brand aiming for an easier-to-remember name than its rivals' "DSS" and "USSB."

The company launched the EchoStar I satellite in 1995 followed a year later by EchoStar II. Commencing DISH Network service in 1996 EchoStar competed against other DBS providers including DIRECTV to win 350000 subscribers by year's end.

In 1997 Rupert Murdoch scrubbed a deal that called for News Corp. to buy half of EchoStar for $1 billion; Ergen sued for $5 billion in damages. EchoStar also went public in 1997 and reached the 1-million-customer mark.

The next year EchoStar tangled again with Murdoch winning FCC approval to access programming from FX Networks (owned by News Corp. and the former TCI now AT&T's cable unit) despite FX Networks' claims that it was locked up in exclusive programming agreements with cable companies. That issue and the 1997 lawsuit were put to rest in 1999 when News Corp. and MCI WorldCom (now WorldCom) traded DBS assets including an orbital slot for a combined 15% stake in EchoStar.

That year EchoStar and DIRECTV joined forces to successfully lobby for federal legislation allowing local TV signals to be delivered by satellites nationwide. The company entered the Internet business providing WebTV Internet access via satellite to customers through an agreement with US software giant Microsoft. EchoStar also bought Media4 (now EchoStar Data Networks) which specializes in providing Internet and data transmission over satellite networks.

In 2000 the company reached an agreement to distribute two-way broadband Internet access using technology developed by the Israel-based Gilat Satellite Networks and Microsoft in a joint venture called StarBand Communications. In addition EchoStar paid $50 million for a 13% stake in startup WildBlue Communications which had planned to launch two geostationary satellites used to offer the two-way data services. EchoStar later backed out of those alliances.

When Hughes Electronics at that time the parent of DIRECTV was put up for sale in 2001 EchoStar expressed interest. After months of negotiations EchoStar appeared to have given up but instead made an unsolicited offer. Hughes' parent General Motors agreed to sell the company to EchoStar after News Corp. dropped out of the bidding. Regulators rejected the deal in 2002 and the companies abandoned their merger plans (To help in the effort to purchase DIRECTV Vivendi Universal had acquired a 10% stake in EchoStar in a $1.5 billion deal that included a distribution alliance but it sold the stake back to EchoStar after the merger failed).

As part of its attempt to compete with regional cable companies that have the capability to provide regional TV channels DISH Network began offering local channels to towns in California Idaho Maryland Montana North Carolina South Carolina Virginia and Wisconsin in 2003. The next year EchoStar announced it had made local channels available in markets in all 50 states.

In 2007 the company initiated a reorganization that resulted in the spinoff of its broadcast satellite receiver antennae and commercial satellite businesses as EchoStar Corporation. The remaining direct satellite subscription service operations became known as DISH Network Corporation.

Also that year DISH bought video technology-maker Sling Media for $380 million in order to strengthen its technology development operations.

In a 2008 federal appeals court decision a previous patent infringement ruling brought against DISH Network by digital video recorder maker TiVo was upheld. The company was ordered to pay millions in damages for violating a software patent held by TiVo that enables viewers to watch one program while recording others. The court agreed to rehear the case at the request of DISH; in the end DISH settled by paying $500 million to TiVo in exchange for TiVo granting it some patent rights.

Making things tougher a distribution agreement with AT&T that brought in about 17% of DISH's annual gross subscriber additions in 2008 expired in 2009 and contributed to a dip in revenue for the year. Rubbing salt in the wound AT&T subsequently entered into a deal with DIRECTV. The loss of this sales channel made it more difficult for DISH in one very crucial objective: adding new subscribers. It drew in a scant 33000 net new subscribers in 2010 compared to 422000 net new subscribers in 2009.

EXECUTIVES

EVP and COO, Bernard L. (Bernie) Han, age 48, $451,923 total compensation
President CEO and Director, Joseph P. Clayton, age 62
EVP Special Advisor to the CEO and Director, James (Jim) DeFranco, age 59, $371,154 total compensation
Chairman, Charles W. (Charlie) Ergen, age 59, $623,078 total compensation
EVP Corporate Development, Thomas A. (Tom) Cullen, age 52
EVP Advanced Technologies, Roger J. Lynch, age 49
EVP and CFO, Robert E. Olson, age 53, $200,769 total compensation
President Blockbuster, Michael Kelly, age 50, $305,674 total compensation
EVP and Chief Human Resources Officer, Stephen W. Wood, age 53
EVP DNS and Service Operations, W. Erik Carlson, age 42
EVP General Counsel and Secretary, R. Stanton Dodge, age 44, $296,155 total compensation
SVP Programming, David (Dave) Shull
VP Advanced Advertising Solutions, Caroline Horner
Director Product Management, Vivek Khemka
SVP and Chief Marketing Officer, James G. Moorhead
President CEO and Director, Joseph P. Clayton, age 62
Director and Senior Advisor, David K. Moskowitz, age 53
EVP Special Advisor to the CEO and Director, James (Jim) DeFranco, age 59
Director, Gary S. Howard, age 61
Director and Senior Advisor, Carl E. Vogel, age 54
Director, Steven R. Goodbarn, age 54
Director, Cantey (Candy) Ergen, age 56
Director, Tom A. Ortolf, age 61
Auditors: KPMGLLP

LOCATIONS

HQ: DISH Network Corporation
9601 S. Meridian Blvd., Englewood CO 80112
Phone: 303-723-1000 **Fax:** 303-723-1999
Web: www.dishnetwork.com

PRODUCTS/OPERATIONS

2011 Sales

	$ mil.	% of total
Subscriber-related revenue	12,976	92
Equipment sales & other	1,035	8
Equipment sales services - EchoStar	36	-
Total	**14,048**	**100**

2011 Sales

	$ mil.	% of total
DISH	13,078	93
Blockbuster	974	7
Other	(4.5)	-
Total	**14,048**	**100**

COMPETITORS

AMC Networks
AT&T
Cablevision Systems
Charter Communications
Comcast
Cox Communications
DIRECTV
Grande Communications
Hulu
Insight Communications
Netflix
RCN Corporation
Time Warner Cable
Verizon
Xanadoo

HISTORICAL FINANCIALS

Company Type: Public

Income Statement FYE: December 31

	REVENUE ($ mil.)	NET INCOME ($ mil.)	NET PROFIT MARGIN	EMPLOYEES
12/11	14,048	1,515	10.8%	34,000
12/10	12,640	984	7.8%	22,000
12/09	11,664	635	5.4%	24,500
12/08	11,617	902	7.8%	26,000
12/07	11,090	756	6.8%	23,000
Annual Growth	6.1%	19.0%	—	10.3%

2011 Year-End Financials

Debt ratio: 65.33%
Return on equity: 987650001000000.00%
Cash ($ mil.): 609
Current ratio: 116.37
Long-term debt ($ mil.): 7,458
No. of shares (mil.): 447
Dividends
Yield: —
Payout: 59.00%
Market value ($ mil.): 12,732

	STOCK PRICE ($) FY Close	P/E High	P/E Low	PER SHARE ($) Earnings	Dividends	Book Value
12/11	28.48	9	6	3.39	0.00	(0.94)
12/10	19.66	10	8	2.20	0.00	(2.56)
12/09	20.77	16	6	1.42	2.00	(4.68)
12/08	11.09	19	4	1.98	0.00	(4.36)
12/07	37.72	30	22	1.68	0.00	1.43
Annual Growth	(6.8%)	—	—	19.2%	—	—

Disney (Walt) Co. (The)

The monarch of this magic kingdom is no man but a mouse —Mickey Mouse. The Walt Disney Company is the world's largest media conglomerate with assets encompassing movies television publishing and theme parks. Its Disney/ABC Television Group includes the ABC television network and 10 broadcast stations as well as a portfolio of cable networks including ABC Family Disney Channel and ESPN (80%-owned). Walt Disney Studios produces films through imprints Walt Disney Pictures Disney Animation and Pixar and its Marvel Entertainment is a top comic book publisher and film producer. In addition Walt Disney Parks and Resorts operates the company's popular theme parks including Walt Disney World and Disneyland.

HISTORY

After getting started as an illustrator in Kansas City Walt Disney and his brother Roy started Disney Brothers Studio in Hollywood California in 1923. Walt directed the first Mickey Mouse cartoon "Plane Crazy" in 1928 (the third "Steamboat Willie" was the first cartoon with a soundtrack). The studio produced its first animated feature film "Snow White and the Seven Dwarfs" in 1937. Walt Disney Productions went public in 1940 and later produced classics such as "Fantasia" and "Pinocchio." The Disneyland theme park opened in 1955.

Roy Disney became chairman after Walt died of lung cancer in 1966. Disney World opened in Florida in 1971 the year Roy died. His son Roy E. became the company's principal individual shareholder. Walt's son-in-law Ron Miller became president in 1980. Two years later Epcot Center opened in Florida. In 1984 the Bass family of Texas in alliance with Roy E. bought a controlling interest in the company. New CEO Michael Eisner (from Paramount) and president Frank Wells (from Warner Bros.) ushered in an era of innovation prosperity and high executive salaries.

The company later launched The Disney Channel and opened new theme parks including Tokyo Disneyland (1984) and Disney-MGM Studios (1989; eventually renamed Hollywood Studios). In 1986 the company changed its name to The Walt Disney Company. The Disney Store retail chain debuted in 1987. Disneyland Paris (originally Euro Disney) opened in 1992. The following year Disney expanded its movie studio with the purchase of independent film company Miramax the brainchild of producers Bob and Harvey Weinstein.

Following Wells' death in a helicopter crash in 1994 boardroom infighting led to the acrimonious departure of studio head Jeffrey Katzenberg. (He was awarded $250 million in compensation in 1999.) The next year Eisner appointed Hollywood agent Michael Ovitz as president. (Ovitz left after 16 months with a severance package of more than $100 million.) Disney bought Capital Cities/ABC (now ABC Inc.) for $19 billion in 1996 and two years later it bought Web services firm Starwave from Microsoft co-founder Paul Allen. It later acquired 43% of Internet search engine Infoseek for $70 million and together they launched the GO Network in 1999. Disney bought the remaining 57% of Infoseek later that year and formed GO.com (later Disney Online) which began trading as a separate tracking stock.

In early 2000 ABC chairman Robert Iger was named Disney's president and COO. Later that year Time Warner Cable briefly suspended ABC broadcasts during a dispute over re-broadcasting rights drawing the ire of some 3.5 million cable customers. (The FCC later ruled that Time Warner violated rules against dropping a station from cable systems during sweeps periods.)

The company expanded its theme parks in Anaheim in 2001 opening Downtown Disney and Disney's California Adventure. It also announced a further restructuring of its Internet business including closing the GO.com search site and converting its Internet tracking stock back into Disney common stock. That year Disney formed a joint venture with Wenner Media (US Weekly LLC) and took a 50% stake in entertainment magazine US Weekly (sold in 2006). Later Disney bought Fox Family Channel which it renamed ABC Family from News Corporation and Haim Saban for $2.9 billion in cash and assumption of $2.3 billion in debt.

In 2003 Disney began its exit from the sports world by selling the Anaheim Angels. (The company had acquired a 25% stake in the baseball team in 1995 and purchased the remaining interest four years later.) At Disney's annual shareholder meeting in 2004 about 45% of stock owners voted to not re-elect the embattled Eisner to the board. In response Disney directors stripped Eisner of the chairman title and named director and former US senator George Mitchell to that position.

Disney sold its under-performing chain of Disney Store retail outlets to The Children's Place in 2004. Amid all the strife the company boosted its children's entertainment properties by purchasing the Muppet and Bear in the Big Blue House characters along with their film and television libraries from The Jim Henson Company.

Several big executive shakeups occurred at Walt Disney in late 2005. Eisner finally passed the CEO torch after more than 20 years to former COO Iger. That same year Disney Parks opened Hong Kong Disneyland the company's biggest foray into the world's most populated country. In addition the Weinstein brothers left Miramax to form The Weinstein Company ending two of the most successful tenures of the independent film movement. (Disney ceased the operations of Miramax in a cost-cutting move in 2010 and announced plans to sell the Miramax label later that year.)

In mid-2006 Walt Disney completed a crucial acquisition –the $7.4 billion purchase of Pixar Animation. Disney almost lost Pixar as a production partner in the animation house's blockbuster films but Iger successfully dodged the bullet. Disney Studios' release of Pirates of the Caribbean: Dead Man's Chest that year topped box office records when it brought in $132 million during its opening weekend. The mark was broken by the third installment of the series Pirates of the Caribbean: At World's End which took in $156 million when it was released the next year. Also in 2007 Disney spun off ABC's radio broadcasting operations to Citadel Broadcasting for $2.7 billion in cash and stock.

Disney re-acquired the Disney Store chain in 2008 from Hoop Holdings a subsidiary of retailer The Children's Place in an effort to save the stores from closing. Hoop Holdings had filed bankruptcy that year citing continued losses and rising debt. (The Children's Place was not involved in the bankruptcy filing.) Also in 2008 the company reorganized its digital holdings with the formation of Disney Interactive Media Group. The following year the company purchased a 30% stake in video streaming website Hulu.

Roy E. died in late 2009 at age 79. Also that year Disney acquired Marvel Entertainment bringing Spider-Man Iron Man and other comic book characters into the Magic Kingdom. The deal was worth a whopping $4 billion and changed the course of its movie-making strategy reducing the number of films the studio releases each year while significantly ramping up production of costly big-budget franchises.

In attempts to cut costs Disney Studios in 2010 sold its venerable Miramax production unit (producer of films as Pulp Fiction and Shakespeare in Love) in 2010 to a group of investors (including Ron Tutor private equity firm Colony Capital and Qatar Holdings) for some $663 million. Also that year the company spent $563.2 million to acquire Playdom a popular social game company on Facebook in order to boost its DIMG holdings. Meanwhile Pixar's Toy Story 3 was the top grossing summer release in 2010.

Jobs who stepped down as CEO of Apple in 2011 for medical reasons and died of pancreatic cancer later that year had been Disney's largest individual stockholder with a 7% stake he acquired when the company purchased Pixar. (Jobs had bought Pixar from Lucasfilm in 1986.) Upon his death his Disney shares were converted to the Steven P. Jobs Trust led by his widow Laurene Powell Jobs.

Disney's 2012 box office bomb John Carter lost some $200 million and is reported to be one of the biggest money-losing films of all time.

EXECUTIVES

EVP and Chief Communications Officer, Zenia Mucha
SEVP General Counsel and Secretary, Alan N. Braverman, age 63, $1,120,769 total compensation
Chairman Walt Disney Parks and Resorts, Thomas O. (Tom) Staggs, age 51, $1,274,038 total compensation
Chairman Disney Consumer Products Worldwide, Andrew P. (Andy) Mooney
SEVP and CFO, James A. (Jay) Rasulo, age 55
President CEO and Director, Robert A. (Bob) Iger, age 59, $2,038,462 total compensation
EVP Corporate Finance Corporate Real Estate Sourcing and Alliances and Treasurer, Christine M. McCarthy, age 56, $588,606 total compensation
SVP Planning and Control, Brent A. Woodford
Co-Chairman Disney Media Networks; President ESPN and ABC Sports, George W. Bodenheimer, age 54
Co-Chairman Disney Media Networks; President Disney/ABC Television, Anne M. Sweeney
Co-President Disney Interactive Media Group; General Manager Playdom, John F. Pleasants, age 46
Chairman, John E. Pepper Jr., age 73
Chairman The Walt Disney Studios, Rich Ross, age 51
Chairman Walt Disney International, Andy Bird, age 48
EVP Creative Advertising, Frank Chiocchi
SVP Global Security, Ronald L. Iden
EVP Corporate Strategy and Business Development, Kevin A. Mayer, age 49, $713,269 total compensation
Co-President Disney Interactive Media Group, James A. (Jimmy) Pitaro
EVP and Chief Human Resources Officer, Jayne Parker, age 50
SVP Affiliate Sales and Marketing, Chris Brush
VP Digital Video Distribution, Christen Harris
Director, Susan E. Arnold, age 58
Director, John E. Bryson, age 68
President CEO and Director, Robert A. (Bob) Iger, age 59
Director, John S. Chen, age 56
Director, Orin C. Smith, age 68
Director, Fred H. Langhammer, age 68
Director, Aylwin B. Lewis, age 58
Director, Judith L. Estrin, age 57
Director, Robert W. Matschullat, age 64
Director, Monica C. Lozano, age 55
Director, Sheryl K. Sandberg, age 42
Auditors: PricewaterhouseCoopersLLP

LOCATIONS

HQ: The Walt Disney Company
500 S. Buena Vista St., Burbank CA 91521-9722
Phone: 818-560-1000 **Fax:** 818-560-1930
Web: disney.go.com

2011 Sales

	$ mil.	% of total
US & Canada	30,848	75
Europe	6,455	16
Asia/Pacific	2,517	6
Latin America & other regions	1,073	3
Total	**40,893**	**100**

PRODUCTS/OPERATIONS

2011 Sales

	$ mil.	% of total
Media networks	18,714	46
Parks & resorts	11,797	29
Studio entertainment	6,351	16
Consumer products	3,049	7
Interactive media	982	2
Total	**40,893**	**100**

Selected Operations

Consumer products
- Disney Publishing Worldwide
- Disney Stores (retail outlets)

Interactive media
- Disney Interactive Studios (video games)
  - Club Penguin (social networking for children)
- Disney Online
  - Disney.com
  - DisneyFamily.com

Media networks
- A&E Television Networks (42%)
  - A&E
  - Bio (The Biography Channel)
  - The History Channel
  - History International
  - Lifetime
  - Lifetime Movie Network
  - Lifetime Real Women
  - The Military History Channel
- ABC Family Channel
- ABC Television Network
- Disney Channel
- ESPN (80%)
  - ESPN2
  - ESPN Classic
  - ESPNEWS
- JETIX Europe
- SOAPnet
- Television broadcast stations
  - KABC (Los Angeles)
  - KFSN (Fresno CA)
  - KGO (San Francisco)
  - KTRK (Houston)
  - WABC (New York City)
  - WJRT (Flint MI)
  - WLS (Chicago)
  - WPVI (Philadelphia)
  - WTVD (Raleigh-Durham NC)
  - WTVG (Toledo OH)
- Toon Disney

Studio entertainment
- Dimension
- Disney Music Group (music production and distribution)
- Disney Theatrical Group (live entertainment events)
- Marvel Entertainment
- Pixar

Touchstone Pictures
Walt Disney Pictures
Theme parks and resorts
Adventures by Disney (vacation packages)
Disney Cruise Line
Euro Disney (40%)
Disney Village
Disneyland Paris
The Walt Disney Studios Park (Marne-La-Vallee France)
Disneyland Resort (Anaheim CA)
Disneyland
Disney's California Adventure
Hong Kong Disneyland (47%)
Tokyo Disney Resort (owned and operated by Oriental Land Co.; Disney earns royalties)
Tokyo Disneyland
Tokyo DisneySea
Walt Disney Imagineering (planning and development)
Walt Disney World Resort (Orlando FL)
Disney Vacation Club
Disney's Animal Kingdom
Disney's Hollywood Studios
Disney's Wide World of Sports
Downtown Disney
Epcot
Magic Kingdom

Selected ABC Shows

20/20
Cougar Town
Dancing With the Stars
Desperate Housewives
Extreme Makeover: Home Edition
Grey' s Anatomy
Modern Family
Private Practice

Selected Film Releases

Alice in Wonderland
Apocalypto
The Avengers
Cars (Pixar)
The Chronicles of Narnia: Prince Caspian
The Chronicles of Narnia: The Lion The Witch and The Wardrobe
Cinderella Man
Dan in Real Life
Finding Nemo (Pixar)
High School Musical
The Hitchhiker' s Guide to the Galaxy
The Incredibles (Pixar)
Kill Bill: Vol 1
Kill Bill: Vol 2
National Treasure
National Treasure: Book of Secrets
No Country for Old Men
Pirates of the Caribbean: At World' s End
Pirates of the Caribbean: The Curse of the Black Pearl
Pirates of the Caribbean: Dead Man' s Chest
The Queen
There Will Be Blood
Toy Story (Pixar)
Toy Story 2 (Pixar)
Toy Story 3 (Pixar)
Under the Tuscan Sun
Up (Pixar)
The Village
WALL-E (Pixar)

COMPETITORS

AOL
CBS Corp
Discovery Communications
DreamWorks Animation
Liberty Interactive
Lucasfilm
MGM
NBCUniversal
News Corp.
SeaWorld Parks
Six Flags
Sony Pictures Entertainment
Time Warner
Viacom
Yahoo!

HISTORICAL FINANCIALS

Company Type: Public

Income Statement

FYE: September 29

	REVENUE ($ mil.)	NET INCOME ($ mil.)	NET PROFIT MARGIN	EMPLOYEES
09/12*	42,278	5,682	13.4%	166,000
10/11	40,893	4,807	11.8%	156,000
10/10	38,063	3,963	10.4%	149,000
10/09	36,149	3,307	9.1%	144,000
09/08	37,843	4,427	11.7%	150,000
Annual Growth	2.8%	6.4%	—	2.6%

*Fiscal year change

2012 Year-End Financials

Debt ratio: 19.49%
Return on equity: 14.29%
Cash ($ mil.): 3,387
Current ratio: 106.99
Long-term debt ($ mil.): 10,981
No. of shares (mil.): 1,780
Dividends
Yield: —
Payout: 19.17%
Market value ($ mil.): 93,058

	STOCK PRICE ($) FY Close	P/E High/Low		PER SHARE ($) Earnings	Dividends	Book Value
09/12*	52.28	17	9	3.13	0.00	22.34
10/11	30.16	17	12	2.52	0.00	21.21
10/10	33.34	18	13	2.03	0.00	19.78
10/09	27.21	17	9	1.76	0.00	18.55
09/08	32.75	15	12	2.28	0.00	17.73
Annual Growth	12.4%	—	—	8.2%	—	5.9%

*Fiscal year change

Dole Food Co., Inc.

With a history rooted in pineapple plantations Dole Foods has become the world's largest producer of fresh fruit and vegetables. Recognized by its Dole label on bananas pineapples and tropical produce the company boasts some 200 food products that are sourced grown processed marketed and distributed in 90-plus countries. Items are produced by Dole or its associated producers and marketed under Dole and other brand names to supermarkets mass merchandisers wholesalers and foodservice operators. Dole also markets a line of packaged cut fruit salads canned and frozen fruit and juices. The company was founded in 1851 when James Dole founded a pineapple growing and canning company in Hawaii.

Operations

Dole's operations today are multinational spanning 117000 acres of farms and other holdings including thousands of acres of farmland in Hawaii and peach orchards in California. Worldwide the company owns more than 1 million sq. ft. of vegetable processing facilities. Its packaged food operations encompass nearly double that in square foot manufacturing space. Dole also operates the largest dedicated refrigerated containerized fleet in the world.

Sales & Marketing

The company contends with few Goliaths (primarily Chiquita Brands and Fresh Del Monte Produce) making the entire business –from growing to processing –highly competitive.

Strategy

Not surprisingly Dole leads the market in many of the sectors and regions its serves. In North America it holds the #1 market position in bananas cauliflower celery iceberg lettuce and packaged fruit products. Producing roughly 150 million boxes of bananas each year the company dominates the US with a third of the market; in Japan it boasts slightly under a third. Dole produces more than 32 million boxes of pineapple trailing only Fresh Del Monte Produce in that segment. Dole fends off rivals by both exploiting its capabilities to deliver produce at a lower cost and focusing on a high-growth value-added segments. Specifically consumer preferences for convenient tasty pre-cut fresh and frozen fruits and vegetables are outstripping demand for bulk fresh produce. Indeed Dole has managed to increase the percentage of its value-added product sales offering bagged vegetables and salads ready-to-eat salads and individual fruit servings packaged in plastic cups and bowls. To this end in fall 2011 the company acquired SunnyRidge Farm Inc. one of the premium fresh blueberry companies in the US.

Geographic Reach

With more than 1 million sq. ft. of vegetable processing plants worldwide Dole is always looking for ways to keep costs down. Going forward Dole is restructuring its fresh fruit segment in Europe Latin America and Asia. It aims to cut costs by better matching fruit supply with forecast demand. Some $21.3 million in restructuring charges taken in 2010 are anticipated to result in $37 million in savings in early fiscal 2011. Most of the savings are based on lower production costs particularly labor increased farm productivity along with slashed distribution and selling and general administrative costs.

Financial Analysis

Dole is squeezed by volatile prices for commodities energy and labor coupled with swings in consumer demand. Following a 30% tumble in earnings in 2009 from 2008 Dole posted a loss in 2010 –its third in five years –on relatively flat year-over-year sales. Results were impacted a higher benefit from asset sales and hedging gains in 2009 versus 2010. The company's bottom line also took a hit from extremely low operating earnings attributable to fresh fruit segment (hurt by lower banana production worldwide). The damage was mitigated by a rise in its fresh vegetables and packaged foods segments which have room for higher pricing and a stronger mix of products. In light of its equity Dole's debt is also unfavorable –more than $1.4 billion. The company's ability to keep up with its obligations moreover is limited by reduced cash generated from operations compared to 2009.

Divestitures

To cut debt further Dole announced it was selling its worldwide packaged foods and Asia Fresh Produce businesses to ITOCHU for around $1.7 billion in cash. The two businesses accounted for some $2.5 billion in revenues. The sale to ITOCHU is expected to close in late 2012.

Ownership

The company's direction in large part is driven by David Murdock. Murdock who has served as chairman of the company since 1985 owns about 58% of the company. He controls interests in real estate and other businesses as well through holding company Castle & Cooke. The self-made billionaire is known for his activities funding nutritional and medical research.

HISTORY

James Dole embarked on an unlikely career in a faraway land when he graduated from Harvard College in 1899 and sailed to Hawaii. He bought 61 acres of farmland for $4000 in 1900 and the next year organized the Hawaiian Pineapple Company announcing that the island's pineapples would eventually be in every US grocery store.

Others had tried and failed to sell fresh fruit to the mainland. Dole decided he would succeed by canning pineapples. He built his first cannery in 1903 and introduced a national magazine advertising campaign in 1908 designed to make consumers associate Hawaii with pineapples (then considered exotic fruits).

In 1922 Dole expanded his production by buying the island of Lanai where he set up a pineapple plantation. He financed the purchase by selling a third interest in Hawaiian Pineapple to Waialua Agricultural Company which was part of Castle & Cooke (C&C). Samuel Castle and Amos Cooke missionaries to Hawaii formed C&C in 1851 to manage their church's failing depository which supplied outlying mission posts with staple goods. In 1858 they entered the sugar business and within 10 years served as agents for several Hawaiian sugar plantations and the ships that carried their cargoes.

C&C gained control of Hawaiian Pineapple in 1932 when it acquired an additional 21% interest in the business. The company began using the Dole name on packaging the next year. Dole became chairman of the board of the reorganized company in 1935 but pursued other business interests until he retired in 1948.

Hawaiian Pineapple was run separately until C&C bought the remainder in 1961. The company started pineapple and banana farms in the Philippines in 1963 to supply markets in East Asia. C&C began importing bananas when it purchased 55% of Standard Fruit of New Orleans in 1964. (It purchased the remainder four years later.)

Heavily in debt and limping from two hostile takeover attempts C&C agreed in 1985 to merge with Flexi-Van a container leasing company. The merger brought with it needed capital Flexi-Van owner David Murdock (who became C&C's CEO) and a fleet of ships to transport produce. Murdock began trimming back leaving C&C with its fruit and real estate operations. He then decided to end all pineapple operations on Lanai to concentrate on tourist properties. (The company took a $168 million write-off on them in 1995 when it spun off its real estate and resort operations as Castle & Cooke.)

C&C became Dole Food in 1991. The company expanded at home and internationally adding SAMICA (dried fruits and nuts Europe 1992) Dromedary (dates US 1994) Chiquita's New Zealand produce operations (1995) and SABA Trading (60% produce importing and distribution Sweden 1998; Dole acquired 100% of SABA in 2005).

In 1995 Dole sold its juice business to Seagram's Tropicana Products division keeping its pineapple juices and licensing the Dole name to Seagram. (PepsiCo bought Tropicana in 1998.) Dole entered the fresh-flower trade in 1998 by acquiring four major growers and marketers. It is now the world's largest producer of freshly cut flowers.

A worldwide banana glut Hurricane Mitch and severe freezes in California hit the company hard in late 1998. The next year Dole launched cost-cutting measures which by early 2000 had ripened into better earnings. Nonetheless cutbacks and disposals continued throughout 2001.

In 2002 Murdock made a cash and debt takeover bid for the company worth about $2.5 billion. However at least one minority shareholder was dissatisfied with the offer and filed a proposal calling for Murdock's resignation. After his offer was rejected Murdock raised his bid and the company agreed to the buyout the following year.

When Maui Land & Pineapple decided to sell off its Costa Rican subsidiary Dole scooped it up in late 2003 paying $15.3 million for the pineapple-growing and marketing business. (Maui Land & Pineapple exited the pineapple business in 2009.)

In 2004 the company acquired frozen fruit manufacturer J.R. Wood Inc. which it renamed Dole Packaged Frozen Foods Inc. It also acquired fresh berry producer Coastal Berry Company (now Dole Berry Company) in 2004 making Dole a top North American strawberry producer.

In 2006 Dole paid almost $42 million in cash to Jamaica Producers Group for the remaining 65% that it did not already own of Jamaica Producers' subsidiary JP Fruit Distributors.

Over time Dole has also divested some of its holdings in an effort to pay down debt including the sale of its fresh-cut flowers business and some real estate holdings. In 2009 the company went public in order to further repay its debt. The initial public offering of 36 million shares of Dole common stock was priced at $12.50 per share. The IPO raised $446 million and netted $415 million.

Adding blueberries to the fruit salad Dole acquired SunnyRidge Farm Inc. one of the top fresh blueberry companies in the US in October 2011.

EXECUTIVES

President CEO and Director, David A. DeLorenzo, age 64, $1,200,000 total compensation
Chairman, David H. Murdock, age 88, $951,538 total compensation
EVP General Counsel and Corporate Secretary, C. Michael Carter, age 69, $601,538 total compensation
VP Chief Accounting Officer and Controller, Yoon J. Hugh
SVP Dole Nutrition Institute, Jennifer Grossman
EVP and CFO, Joseph S. Tesoriero, age 58, $500,000 total compensation
VP Worldwide Corporate Responsibility and Sustainability, Sylvain Cuperlier
VP Marketing and Communications, Marty Ordman
General Manager Dolefil, Kevin Davis
VP and Managing Director Dolefil, Simon Denye
President North American Tropical and Fresh Fruit Division, Mike Cavallero
President Dole Latin America, Jonathan Bass
President CEO and Director, David A. DeLorenzo, age 64
Director, Dennis M. (Denny) Weinberg, age 59
Director, Elaine L. Chao, age 59
Director, Sherry Lansing, age 66
Director, Andrew J. Conrad, age 48
Director, Justin M. Murdock, age 39
Auditors: Deloitte&ToucheLLP

LOCATIONS

HQ: Dole Food Company Inc.
1 Dole Dr., Westlake Village CA 91362
Phone: 818-879-6600 **Fax:** 818-879-6615
Web: www.dole.com

2010 Sales

	$ mil.	% of total
North America		
US	2,853	41
Canada	344	5
Europe		
Germany	481	7
Sweden	469	7
UK	71	1
Other	740	11
Japan	745	11
Other	1,185	17
Total	**6,892**	**100**

PRODUCTS/OPERATIONS

2010 Sales

	$ mil.	% of total
Fresh fruit	4,715	69
Packaged foods	1,121	16
Fresh vegetables	1,055	15
Other	.6	—
Total	**6,892**	**100**

Selected Products by Business Segment

Fresh fruit
- Bananas
- Dole Chile (export)
  - Apples
  - Grapes
  - Kiwifruit
  - Pears
  - Stone fruitPeachesPlums
- European ripening and distribution
  - DOLE branded fresh produce
  - Non-DOLE branded fresh produce
- Fresh pineapples
  - DOLE TROPICAL GOLD (sweet yellow)
  - Other varieties

Fresh vegetables
- Fresh-packed vegetables
  - Artichokes
  - Asparagus
  - Broccoli
  - Brussels sprouts
  - Carrots
  - Cauliflower
  - Celery
  - Fresh fruitStrawberriesRaspberries
  - Green onions
  - LettuceButterIcebergRed and green leafRomaine
  - Radishes
  - Snow peas
- Value-added vegetables
  - Fresh-cut vegetables
  - Salads

Packaged foods
- Canned
  - Fruit juice concentrate
  - Pineapple
  - Pineapple juice
- Frozen fruit
- Fruit
  - Jars
  - Plastic cups
  - Pouches
- Fruit parfaits
- Healthy snack foods

Selected Subsidiaries

Agrondustrial Pinas del Bosque S.A. (Costa Rica)
Bananapuerto Puerto Bananero S.A. (Ecuador)
Bananera La Paz S.A. (Costa Rica)
Bud Antle Inc.
Coastal Berry Company LLC
Dole Chile S.A.
Dole Comercializacion S.A. (Spain)
Dole Dried Fruit and Nut Company a California general partnership
Dole Foods of Canada Ltd.
Dole Fresh Fruit Company
Dole Fresh Fruit Europe OHG (Germany)
Dole Fresh Fruit International Limited (Bermuda)
Dole Italia s.p.a.
Dole Japan Ltd.
Dole Korea Limited
Dole Packaged Foods Europe (France)
Dole Packaged Foods LLC
Dole Philippines Inc.
Dole South Africa (Pty) Ltd.
Dole Thailand Limited (64%)
Dole U.K. Limited
Saba Fresh Cuts AB (Sweden)
Shanghai Dole Food Company Ltd. (China)
Standard Fruit Company (Bermuda) Ltd.
Standard Fruit Company de Costa Rica S.A.
Standard Fruit De Honduras S.A.
Union de Bananeros Ecuatorianos S.A. (Ecuador)

COMPETITORS

A. Duda & Sons
Bonduelle
Calavo Growers
Chiquita Brands
Del Monte Foods
Fresh Del Monte Produce
Fresh Kist Produce
Fyffes
National Grape Cooperative
Ocean Mist Farms
Ocean Spray
Ready Pac
Seneca Foods
Sunkist
Sunsweet Growers
Tanimura & Antle
Taylor Fresh Foods
The Nunes Company
Tropicana
Worldwide Fruit

HISTORICAL FINANCIALS

Company Type: Public

Income Statement FYE: December 31

	REVENUE ($ mil.)	NET INCOME ($ mil.)	NET PROFIT MARGIN	EMPLOYEES
12/11*	7,223	38	0.5%	71,100
01/11	6,892	(34)	—	74,300
01/10	6,778	84	1.2%	75,600
01/09	7,619	121	1.6%	75,800
12/07	6,820	(57)	—	0
Annual Growth	1.4%	—	—	—

*Fiscal year change

2011 Year-End Financials

Debt ratio: 38.68%
Return on equity: 4.84%
Cash ($ mil.): 122
Current ratio: 167.57
Long-term debt ($ mil.): 1,641
No. of shares (mil.): 88
Dividends
Yield: —
Payout: —
Market value ($ mil.): 769

	STOCK PRICE ($) FY Close	P/E High/Low		PER SHARE ($) Earnings	Dividends	Book Value
12/11*	8.65	34	18	0.44	0.00	8.91
01/11	13.51	—	—	(0.39)	0.00	8.94
01/10	12.41	9	8	1.43	0.00	9.51
Annual Growth	(16.5%)	—	—	(44.5%)	—	(3.2%)

*Fiscal year change

Dollar General Corp

Dollar General's at ease with living off the crumbs of Wal-Mart. The fast-growing retailer commands a chain of more than 10000 discount stores in about 40 states primarily in the southern and eastern US the Midwest and the Southwest. (In 2011 Dollar General entered three new states its first since 2006.) Offering mostly basic household products such as cleaning supplies and health and beauty aids it also peddles seasonal items apparel and increasingly food. Dollar General typically targets low- middle- and fixed-income shoppers. The company's no-frills stores are located in small towns that are off the radar of giant discounters. Some 25% of its merchandise is priced at $1 or less.

HISTORY

J. L. Turner was 11 when his father was killed during the 1890s in a Saturday night wrestling match. This forced J. L. to drop out of school and work on the family farm which was weighted by a mortgage. By his 20s J. L. who never learned to read well was running an area general store. Experiencing some success he branched out and purchased two stores of his own. They failed but J. L. rebounded going to work for a wholesaler. With the onset of the Depression J. L. found he could buy out the inventories of failing merchants for next to nothing using short-term bank loans that were quickly repaid.

In 1939 J. L. was joined by his son Cal. The two each put up $5000 to start a new Scottsville Kentucky-based dry goods wholesaling operation called not surprisingly J.L. Turner & Son. It was not until 1945 when the company experienced a glut of women's underwear that it expanded into retail. J.L. Turner & Son sold off the dainties in their first store located in Albany Kentucky. Within a decade the company was operating 35 stores. In 1956 J.L. Turner & Son introduced its first experimental Dollar General Store –all items priced less than a dollar –in Springfield Kentucky. Like the company's first stores the dollar store concept would grow: Dollar General Stores numbered 255 a decade later.

Cal Jr. J. L.'s 25-year-old grandson joined the family business in 1965 and became a director in 1966. The company changed its name to Dollar General and went public two years later. In 1977 Cal Jr. was named president and CEO. That year Dollar General acquired Arkansas-based United Dollar Stores.

The early 1980s saw Dollar General continue its acquisition-powered growth. The company bought INTERCO's 280-store P.N. Hirsch chain and the 203-store Eagle Family Discount chain in 1983 and 1985 respectively. To cope with expanded distribution demands Dollar General opened an additional distribution center in Homerville Georgia in 1986 to help out the original Scottsville facility. The acquisitions led by Cal Jr.'s brother Steve ended up costing the company dearly; Dollar General's 1987 stock price dropped nearly 85%. The next year they also cost Steve his job: He was forced out by the company's new chairman Cal Jr. In addition to ousting Steve Cal Jr. replaced more than half of Dollar General's executives in 1988. The retailer began moving toward everyday low pricing (a la Wal-Mart) in the late 1980s.

Growth from then on was powered by internal expansion. In 1990 the company operated nearly 1400 stores; by 1995 it had more than 2000. To accommodate the growth Dollar General built a third distribution center in Ardmore Oklahoma in 1995 and another in South Boston Virginia in 1997. Cal Jr.'s CEO heir-apparent former Circle K COO Bruce Krysiak joined the company as president that January only to resign in December a casualty of differing corporate visions.

Dollar General opted to stop advertising in 1998. Cal Turner Sr. died in 2000. The company's stock fell 31% in April 2001 after it announced that earnings over the past three years would be cut by 4% because of accounting irregularities. (In January 2002 the company restated net income for the three prior fiscal years by $199.2 million thereby ending the investigation into accounting problems.)

While continuing to focus on small towns and neighborhoods Dollar General has expanded beyond the Southeast and Midwest opening its first stores in New York and New Jersey in 2001.

Cal Jr. stepped down in 2002 after 15 years at the helm of Dollar General amid a Securities and Exchange Commission investigation into accounting irregularities at the company launched in 2001. (Later the company restated its earnings for 1998 through 2000 saying it had overbooked earnings by about $100 million.) President and COO Donald Shaffer was named acting CEO in November 2002. In April 2003 former Reebok Brand president and CEO David Perdue joined Dollar General as its new chief executive. Perdue was elected chairman of the company in June 2003 when Turner stepped down. Overall in 2003 Dollar General opened 673 new stores including two Dollar General Market stores.

In October 2004 president and COO Lawrence Jackson resigned to join Wal-Mart. Perdue temporarily took over Jackson's responsibilities. Overall in 2004 the company opened more than 700 locations and expanded into Arizona New Mexico and Wisconsin.

In April 2005 the company settled a Securities and Exchange Commission investigation into the circumstances that resulted in a $100 million earnings restatement for the years 1998 through 2000 with payment of a $10 million civil penalty.

To support its growth Dollar General opened a new distribution center in South Boston (its ninth) in 2006 and one in Union County South Carolina in mid-2005. Also in 2006 the retailer expanded its warehouse in Ardmore Oklahoma.

In July 2007 Dollar General was taken private by Kohlberg Kravis & Roberts GS Capital Partners (an affiliate of Goldman Sachs) and Citi Private Equity an investment arm of Citigroup in a deal valued at $7.3 billion. Concurrently the stock was delisted from the New York Stock Exchange and CEO David Perdue resigned. President and COO David Bere was named interim chief executive. In a bid to improve profitability the chain shuttered about 400 stores in 2007. In January 2008 Richard Dreiling formerly of drugstore chain Duane Reade and supermarket operator Safeway was named CEO of the company.

In November 2009 the company went public with an offering valued at $716 million. The fast-growing chain opened its 9000th store in late July 2010.

In 2011 the company entered three new markets: Connecticut Nevada and New Hampshire and launched an e-commerce site. In early 2012 it added California to the list of states in which it does business. In March it opened its 10000th store.

EXECUTIVES

EVP and CFO, David M. Tehle, age 56, $626,884 total compensation
Chairman and CEO, Richard W. (Rick) Dreiling, age 59, $1,100,876 total compensation
Treasurer, Wade L. Smith
SVP Real Estate and Store Development, Gayle Aertker
EVP and General Counsel, Susan S. Lanigan, age 50, $341,680 total compensation
SVP and Controller, Anita C. Elliott, age 47
EVP Store Operations, Gregory A. (Greg) Sparks
EVP; Division President and Chief Merchandising Officer, Todd J. Vasos, age 50, $595,023 total compensation
VP Human Resources, Jeffrey R. (Jeff) Rice, age 45
Corporate Secretary and Chief Compliance Officer, Christine Connolly
Senior Director Corporate Communications, Tawn Earnest
VP and Division Manager Store Operations, Thomas A. (Tom) Drugan
VP Process Improvement, Roderick J. (Rod) West
VP Internal Audit, Spencer Ferebee
VP Merchandise Planning Allocation & Replenishment, Timothey G. Money
SVP and General Merchandise Manager Consumables, James W. (Jim) Thorpe

VP Division Merchandise Manager Seasonal Toys and Auto and Sundries, Bryan Wheeler
EVP and Chief People Officer, Robert D. (Bob) Ravener, age 53
VP and Division Manager Store Operations, Karen Sensabaugh
EVP Global Supply Chain, John W. Flanigan, age 61
VP and Division Manager Store Operations, Jeffery C. Owen
VP and Division Merchandise Manager HBA Cleaning and Paper, Michael J. Wilkins
VP Investor Relations and Public Relations, Mary Winn Gordon
Manager Media Relations, Emily Weiss
SVP Merchandising Strategy and Operations, Michael W. Buxton
SVP and General Merchandise Manager Apparel and Home and Seasonal, Jeffrey A. Elliott
SVP Finance and Strategy, John W. Feray
VP Information Technology Operations and Architecture, Robert A. Aflatooni
VP Transportation, Joseph L. Bandlow Jr.
VP and Division Manager Store Operations, David (Dave) Barker
VP Store Operations, William C. Bass
VP and Division Manager Store Operations, Steven H. Brimner
VP Government Affairs, Stephen J. Brophy
VP Real Estate, Timothy E. Dearman
VP Shrink and Loss Prevention, Steven R. Deckard
VP and Division Merchandise Manager Apparel, Lynn C. Derry
VP and Divisional Merchandise Manager Food Pet Perishables and Market Stores, Lawrence J. Gatta
VP Distribution Centers, Michael J. Kindy
VP Financial Planning and Analysis, Clayton E. Klutts
VP Real Estate, Stephen B. Krumholz
VP Lease Administration, Maurice A. Laliberte
VP Talent Management and Rewards, Lawrence P. LeBlanc
VP Consumer Brands, Terry C. Lee
VP Distribution Centers, Stephen A. McCormick
VP Tax, James L. Miller
VP Construction, Daniel J. Nieser
VP and Division Merchandise Manager Home, Gerald W. Reinhardt
VP and Assistant General Counsel General Business and Assistant Secretary, Robert R. Stephenson
VP Marketing, David L. Stewart
VP and Assistant General Counsel, Rhonda M. Taylor
VP Pricing and Merchandising Data Optimization, Emily C. Taylor
VP and Division Manager Store Operations, Vince R. Volz
Director, Warren F. Bryant, age 66
Director, David B. (Dave) Rickard, age 65
Director, William C. (Bill) Rhodes III, age 47
Director, Michael M. Calbert, age 49
Director, Adrian M. Jones, age 48
Director, Raj K. Agrawal, age 39
Auditors: Ernst&YoungLLP

LOCATIONS

HQ: Dollar General Corporation
100 Mission Ridge, Goodlettsville TN 37072
Phone: 615-855-4000 **Fax:** 214-559-0301

2012 Stores

	No.
Texas	1,109
North	559
Georgia	569
Florida	555
Alabama	540
Ohio	527
Tennessee	525
Pennsylvania	432
Louisiana	409
South	400
Kentucky	381
Indiana	379
Illinois	371
Missouri	364
Mississippi	336
Oklahoma	312
Michigan	288
Arkansas	287
Virginia	280
New	258
Kansas	181
Iowa	175
West	166
Wisconsin	99
Nebraska	80
Maryland	76
Arizona	65
New	59
New	56
Delaware	30
Colorado	28
Minnesota	16
Vermont	15
South	11
Utah	8
Nevada	7
California	5
Connecticut	2
New	1
Total	**9,961**

PRODUCTS/OPERATIONS

2012 Sales

	$ mil.	% of total
Consumables	10,833	73
Seasonal	2,051	14
Home products	1,005	7
Apparel	917	6
Total	**14,807**	**100**

Selected Merchandise

Basic apparel
Cleaning supplies
Dairy products
Frozen foods
Health and beauty aids
Housewares
Packaged foods
Seasonal goods
Stationery

COMPETITORS

99 Cents Only
Big Lots
Costco Wholesale
CVS Caremark
Dollar Tree
Family Dollar Stores
Fred' s
Kmart
Rite Aid
Target Corporation
TJX Companies
Variety Wholesalers
Wal-Mart
Walgreen

HISTORICAL FINANCIALS

Company Type: Public

Income Statement FYE: February 3

	REVENUE ($ mil.)	NET INCOME ($ mil.)	NET PROFIT MARGIN	EMPLOYEES
02/12*	14,807	766	5.2%	90,000
01/11	13,035	627	4.8%	85,900
01/10	11,796	339	2.9%	79,800
01/09	10,457	108	1.0%	72,500
02/08	5,571	(4)	—	71,500
Annual Growth	27.7%	—	—	5.9%

*Fiscal year change

2012 Year-End Financials

Debt ratio: 27.03%
Return on equity: 16.40%
Cash ($ mil.): 126
Current ratio: 150.68
Long-term debt ($ mil.): 2,617
No. of shares (mil.): 338
Dividends
Yield: —
Payout: —
Market value ($ mil.): 14,179

	STOCK PRICE ($) FY Close	P/E High/Low		PER SHARE ($) Earnings	Dividends	Book Value
02/12*	41.94	19	12	2.22	0.00	13.83
01/11	28.40	18	12	1.82	0.00	11.90
01/10	23.49	23	21	1.04	0.00	10.01
Annual Growth	33.6%	—	—	46.1%	—	17.5%

*Fiscal year change

Dollar Tree, Inc.

Dollars may not grow on trees but Dollar Tree stores work hard to bring in the green. The company operates more than 4200 Dollar Tree Deal$ and Dollar Bills discount stores in 48 US states and the District of Columbia and about 100 Dollar Tree (formerly Dollar Giant) stores in Canada. Stores carry a mix of housewares toys seasonal items food health and beauty aids gifts and books –most priced at $1 or less. About 40% of merchandise is imported primarily from China. The stores are located in high-traffic strip centers anchored by mass merchandisers supermarkets malls and in small towns. Founded in 1986 as Dollar Tree Stores the company later changed its name to Dollar Tree Inc.

Operations

In addition to its retail stores Dollar Tree has an e-commerce site –dollartreedirect.com –which allows customers to purchase large quantities of items from its stores. The company's nationwide retail network is supplied by nine distribution centers.

Geographic Reach

While the company does not break out sales for its Canadian subsidiary. it operates about 100 locations across Alberta British Columbia Manitoba Ontario and Saskatchewan.

Financial Analysis

Dollar Tree along with other dollar store operators has thrived in recent years as the recession turned more and more shoppers into bargain hunters. Apparently those thrifty buying habits stuck as the chain continues to thrive with the economy on the mend. In fiscal 2012 (ends January) the company's sales increased nearly 13% and net income rose by about 23% vs. the prior year. Indeed. Dollar Tree has logged double-digit sales growth for the past three years and net sales per store increased to $1.6 million in 2012 from $1.3 million in fiscal 2009.

Strategy

The fast-growing chain has added more than 900 stores since 2008 both through acquisitions and opening new locations. Dollar Tree entered Canada with the purchase of Dollar Giant in 2010. The deal valued at C$52 million (US$51 million) added 85 Dollar Giant stores to its operations. Since then Dollar Giant has grown to number 100-plus stores in five provinces. Indeed Dollar Tree isn't the only US deep-discount retailer looking to grow in Canada. Rival Big Lots purchased the Calgary-based 85-store Liquidation World chain in 2011 and mass-merchandiser Target is poised to enter the market. Originally a purveyor of primarily seasonal items and gifts Dollar Tree added everyday merchandise such as food water and household and health and beauty items to its mix of products. Indeed sales of consumable products including food have increased in recent years to reach 51% of sales. To capitalize on the move by discount stores to fill basic needs the chain has freezers and coolers in about 2200 stores. Other dollar store operators notably Dollar General have also been aggressively adding food to boost sales. Also in a bid to increase sales Dollar Tree has begun opening larger stores (approx. 10000-15000 sq. ft.). Looking for a way to extend beyond its "everything's a dollar" concept Dollar Tree took the opportunity to test-market a new pricing strategy with its Deal$ banner. Following Dollar Tree's 2006 purchase of the 138-store chain from grocer and wholesaler SUPERVALU the discounter rolled out new above-$1 prices at some of the stores. Dollar Tree has since adopted the alternative pricing across its Deal$ network of stores which sell items for $1 or less as well as items for more than $1.

Ownership

Financial services conglomerate FMR owns about 11% of Dollar Tree.

EXECUTIVES

CFO, Kevin S. Wampler, age 49, $425,000 total compensation
COO, Gary M. Philbin, age 55, $500,000 total compensation
President CEO and Director, Bob Sasser, age 60, $850,000 total compensation
Chief People Officer, James E. Fothergill
Chairman, Macon F. Brock Jr., age 69, $400,000 total compensation
SVP Deal$ Stores, Allan Goldman
Chief Logistics Officer, Stephen W. (Steve) White, age 57, $325,000 total compensation
CIO, Raymond K. Hamilton
Chief Merchandising Officer, Robert H. (Bob) Rudman, age 61, $425,000 total compensation
General Counsel and Corporate Secretary, James A. Gorry
VP and Controller, Kathleen E. (Katy) Mallas, $171,724 total compensation
VP Investor Relations, Timothy J. (Tim) Reid
VP Governance and Corporate Counsel, Shawnta Totten
Director, Thomas E. Whiddon, age 59
Director, Conrad M. Hall, age 68
Director, Arnold S. Barron, age 65
President CEO and Director, Bob Sasser, age 60
Chairman Emeritus, J. Douglas Perry, age 64
Director, H. Ray Compton, age 69
Director, Lemuel E. Lewis, age 65
Director, Thomas A. Saunders III, age 74
Director, Mary Anne Citrino, age 53
Director, Carl P. Zeithaml, age 62
Auditors: KPMGLLP

LOCATIONS

HQ: Dollar Tree Inc.
500 Volvo Pkwy., Chesapeake VA 23320
Phone: 757-321-5000 **Fax:** 757-321-5111
Web: www.dollartree.com

2012 US Stores

	No.
California	363
Florida	306
Texas	268
Pennsylvania	230
New	187
Illinois	177
North	169
Ohio	168
Georgia	167
Michigan	164
Virginia	141
Tennessee	109
Indiana	96
New	96
Maryland	94
Alabama	91
Missouri	86
Washington	83
Massachusetts	82
Wisconsin	82
Arizona	80
Oregon	80
South	80
Kentucky	73
Colorado	71
Minnesota	70
Louisiana	68
Mississippi	54
Oklahoma	52
Arkansas	46
Connecticut	43
Utah	39
Iowa	34
West	33
Kansas	32
Nevada	31
New	31
New	29
Delaware	24
Idaho	23
Maine	22
Rhode	19
Nebraska	16
Wyoming	12
Montana	9
South	9
North	6
Vermont	6
District of	1
Total	**4,252**

2012 Canadian Stores

	No.
Ontario	40
British	39
Alberta	16
Saskatchewan	3
Manitoba	1
Total	**99**

PRODUCTS/OPERATIONS

2012 Sales

	% of total
Consumables	51
Variety	45
Seasonal	4
Total	**100**

Store Names
Deal$
Dollar Bills
Dollar Tree
Dollar Deal$

Selected Products

Books
Candy
Cards
Food
Gifts
Health and beauty care products
Housewares
Party goods
Personal accessories
Seasonal goods
Stationery
Toys

COMPETITORS

99 Cents Only
ALDI
Big Lots
Pamida Stores
Rite Aid
Salvation Army
CVS Caremark
Dollar General
Family Dollar Stores
Fred' s
Goodwill Industries
Grocery Outlet
Kmart
Save-A-Lot Food Stores
Savers Inc.
Target Corporation
Wal-Mart
Walgreen
Winn-Dixie

HISTORICAL FINANCIALS

Company Type: Public

Income Statement

FYE: January 28

	REVENUE ($ mil.)	NET INCOME ($ mil.)	NET PROFIT MARGIN	EMPLOYEES
01/12	6,630	488	7.4%	72,770
01/11	5,882	397	6.8%	63,860
01/10	5,231	320	6.1%	54,480
01/09*	4,644	229	4.9%	45,840
02/08	4,242	201	4.7%	42,600
Annual Growth	11.8%	24.8%	—	14.3%

*Fiscal year change

2012 Year-End Financials

Debt ratio: 11.40%
Return on equity: 36.32%
Cash ($ mil.): 288
Current ratio: 208.16
Long-term debt ($ mil.): 250
No. of shares (mil.): 231
Dividends
Yield: —
Payout: —
Market value ($ mil.): 19,566

	STOCK PRICE ($) FY Close	P/E High/Low		PER SHARE ($) Earnings	Dividends	Book Value
01/12	84.64	42	24	2.02	0.00	5.82
01/11	50.99	41	26	1.55	0.00	5.91
01/10	49.52	43	28	1.19	0.00	5.44
01/09*	42.71	52	29	0.84	0.00	4.60
02/08	27.79	65	30	0.70	0.00	3.67
Annual Growth	32.1%	—	—	30.3%	—	12.2%

*Fiscal year change

Dominion Resources Inc

And darkness shall have no dominion as long as Dominion Resources powers lights across the territory it serves. Dominion is one of the top energy players in the US. Dominion Generation (its largest revenue generator) manages regulated and non-regulated power plants (28200 MW of capacity). Through its Dominion Virginia Power unit the company transmits and distributes electricity across 56800 miles of electric distribution lines to 2.4 million customers and natural gas to 1.7 million customers in five states. Subsidiary Dominion Energy trades and markets energy oversees 11000 miles of natural gas transmission pipelines and operates underground gas storage facilities (947 billion cu. ft. of capacity.)

HISTORY

In 1781 the Virginia General Assembly established a group of trustees including George Washington and James Madison to promote navigation on the Appomattox River. The group (named the Appomattox Trustees) formed the Upper Appomattox Company in 1795 to secure its water rights. The company eventually began operating hydroelectric plants on the river and by 1888 it had added a steam-powered plant to its portfolio.

The Virginia Railway and Power Company (VR&P) led by Frank Jay Gould purchased the Upper Appomattox Company (which had changed its name) in 1909. The next year the firm acquired several electric and gas utilities as well as some electric streetcar lines.

In 1925 New York engineering company Stone & Webster acquired VR&P. The company became known as Virginia Electric and Power Company (Virginia Power) and was placed under Engineers Public Service (EPS) a new holding company. Virginia Power purchased several North Carolina utilities following its acquisition.

During the 1930s the Depression (and the popularity of the automobile) led the company to exit the trolley business. The Public Utility Holding Company Act of 1935 (repealed in 2005) which ushered in an era of regulated utility monopolies forced EPS to divest all of its operations except Virginia Power. However the utility soon merged with the Virginia Public Service Company thus doubling its service territory.

The company added new power plants to keep up with growing customer demand in the 1950s. Always an innovator it also built an extra-high-voltage transmission system the first in the world.

In the 1970s Virginia Power's first nuclear plants became operational. By 1980 however the firm was near bankruptcy. That year William Berry who had completed a 23-year rise through the ranks to become president canceled two other nuclear units. He also became an early supporter of competition in the electric utility industry. In 1983 he formed Dominion Resources as a parent company for Virginia Power and halted nearly all plant construction. Two additional subsidiaries were soon formed: Dominion Capital in 1985 and Dominion Energy in 1987.

In 1990 the year Thomas Capps took over as CEO Dominion sold its natural gas distribution business and in 1995 Dominion Energy began developing natural gas reserves through joint ventures and by purchasing three natural gas exploration and production companies.

The company acquired UK utility East Midlands Electricity in 1997. However after it was hit by a hefty windfall tax by the newly elected Labour Party and its hopes for mergers with other UK utilities were dashed it sold East Midlands to PowerGen just 18 months after acquiring it.

In 1999 Dominion prepared for energy deregulation through reorganization. It separated its electricity generation activities from its transmission and distribution operations. In 2000 Dominion bought Consolidated Natural Gas (CNG) for $9 billion making it one of the largest fully integrated gas and electric power companies in the US; it then sold CNG's Virginia Natural Gas to AGL Resources and the two firms' combined Latin American assets to Duke Energy.

Virginia Power moved to head off state and federal lawsuits in 2000 by agreeing to spend $1.2 billion over 12 years to reduce pollution from coal-fired plants. The company also agreed to pay $1.3 billion for Northeast Utilities' Millstone nuclear power complex that year (the deal closed in 2001). Also in 2000 Dominion changed its brand name from Dominion Resources to just Dominion and re-branded several of its subsidiaries as well.

In 2001 Dominion bought exploration and production company Louis Dreyfus Natural Gas for about $1.8 billion in cash and stock and $500 million in assumed debt; the acquisition added 1.8 trillion cu. ft. of natural gas equivalent to Dominion's proved reserves. The company also sold the assets of its financial services unit Dominion Capital that year.

The following year Dominion purchased a 500-MW Chicago power plant from US power producer Mirant (now GenOn Energy)for $182 million and it purchased the Cove Point LNG (liquefied natural gas) import facility from The Williams Companies for $217 million.

Dominion began to prepare for power deregulation implemented in most of its service territories by expanding its nonregulated electric operations. The company also divested its non-US operations to focus on its businesses in the Northeast Mid-Atlantic and Midwest. In 2004 it sold its telecom business to private firm Elantic Networks. The firm completed the acquisition of three fossil-fueled plants (2800 MW) from USGen New England a subsidiary of National Energy & Gas Transmission for $656 million in 2005. That was the same year Dominion purchased the 550-MW Kewaunee nuclear plant from WPS Resources subsidiary Wisconsin Public Service and Alliant Energy subsidiary Wisconsin Power & Light for $220 million.

At the end of 2006 Dominion Exploration & Production had proved reserves of 6.5 trillion cu. ft. of natural gas equivalent. The next year Dominion began to dismantle the unit selling its offshore operations in the Gulf of Mexico to Eni; its assets in Alabama Michigan and Texas to Loews Corp.; its Mid-Continent operations to Linn Energy; and operations in the Rocky Mountain and Gulf Coast regions to XTO Energy. Dominion Resources pocketed almost $14 billion from the sales.

EXECUTIVES

VP Executive Communications, William C. (Bill) Hall Jr.
EVP; CEO Dominion Virginia Power, Paul D. Koonce, age 52, $495,883 total compensation
Chairman President and CEO; Chairman and CEO Virginia Power, Thomas F. Farrell II, age 58, $1,200,000 total compensation
SVP Tax and Treasurer, G. Scott Hetzer, age 55
SVP and CIO Dominion Resources Services, Margaret E. (Lyn) McDermid
SVP and Chief Administrative Officer; President and Chief Administrative Officer Dominion Resources Services, Steven A. Rogers, age 50
SVP Financial Management Dominion Generation, Fred G. Wood III
EVP and CFO Dominion Resources and Virginia Power, Mark F. McGettrick, age 54, $648,250 total compensation
CEO Dominion Generation, David A. Christian, age 57, $551,550 total compensation
President and Chief Nuclear Officer Dominion Nuclear, David A. Heacock, age 54
CEO Dominion Energy; President Dominion Transmission, Gary L. Sypolt, age 58
SVP Alternative Energy Solutions Dominion Resources Services, Mary C. Doswell, age 53
SVP State Electric Regulation Dominion Resources Services, Thomas P. (Tom) Wohlfarth, age 51
SVP Dominion Resources Services, M. Stuart Bolton Jr., age 58
Director Media Relations East Ohio Gas, Tracy A. Oliver
SVP Dominion Transmission, Paul E. Ruppert
Director Advertising and Creative Services, Hunter Applewhite
Director Media Relations Dominion Energy Solutions, Daniel E. (Dan) Donovan
Director Media Relations Dominion Generation, Jim Norvelle
Media Relations Nuclear-Powered Electric Generation at North Anna and Surry Power Stations Dominion Generation, Richard Zuercher
Director Media Relations Dominion Virginia Power and Dominion North Carolina Power, David B. Botkins
Community Affairs and Broadcasting Liaison The Piedmont and Shenandoah Valley Dominion Virginia Power and Dominion North Carolina Power, Daisy Pridgen
Manager Media and Community Relations Dominion Virginia Power/Dominion North Carolina Power, Le-Ha Anderson
Manager Media and Community Relations Dominion Hope, Charles (Chuck) Penn
SVP Law Public Policy and Environment Dominion Resources Dominion Resources Services and Virginia Power, Robert M. (Bob) Blue, age 44
SVP and General Manager Dominion East Ohio, Anne E. Bomar
SVP Business Development and Generation Construction Dominion Generation, Diane G. Leopold
Senior Communications Specialist Dominion Cove Point LNG Facility, Karl R. Neddenien
Managing Director Corporate Communications, Chet Wade
Media Relations Nuclear-Powered Electric Generation Dominion Generation, Mark Kanz
Senior Communications Specialist East Ohio Gas, Neil J. Durbin
Senior Communications Specialist East Ohio Gas, Jeff Zidonis
VP General Counsel and Secretary, Carter M. Reid, age 43
SVP Regulatory Affairs Dominion Resources Services, James K. Martin, age 47
VP Accounting and Controller, Ashwini Sawhney, age 62
Senior Communications Specialist Executive Communications and Editorial Services, Ryan Frazier
SVP Fossil and Hydro Dominion Generation, J. David Rives
SVP Producer Services Dominion Resources Services, Charles E. Roberts
Director, George A. Davidson Jr., age 73
Director, Robert S. Jepson Jr., age 69
Director, Robert H. (Rob) Spilman Jr., age 55
Director, Michael E. (Mike) Szymanczyk, age 63
Director, William P. Barr, age 61
Director, Frank S. Royal, age 72
Director, John W. Harris, age 64
Director, Margaret A. McKenna, age 66
Director, David A. Wollard, age 74
Director, Peter W. Brown, age 69
Director, Mark J. Kington, age 52
Director, Helen E. Dragas, age 50
Auditors: Deloitte&ToucheLLP

LOCATIONS

HQ: Dominion Resources Inc.
120 Tredegar St., Richmond VA 23219
Phone: 804-819-2000 **Fax:** 804-819-2233
Web: www.dom.com

PRODUCTS/OPERATIONS

2011 Sales

	$ mil.	% of total
Dominion Generation	7,320	56
Dominion Energy	2,044	16
Adjustments	1,298	-

Selected Subsidiaries and Business Units

Dominion Generation Corporation (power plant management)
Dominion Energy (energy marketing gas and power transmission)
  Dominion Transmission Inc. (natural gas pipelines)
Dominion Virginia Power
  Consolidated Natural Gas
    Dominion East Ohio (or The East Ohio Gas Company gas distribution)
    Dominion Hope (or Hope Gas Inc. West Virginia gas distribution)
    Dominion North Carolina Power (or Virginia Electric and Power Company electricity distribution)
  Dominion Retail Inc. (retail energy marketing)
  Virginia Electric and Power Company (electricity distribution)

COMPETITORS

AEP	Exelon
CenterPoint Energy	Koch Industries Inc.
Duke Energy	NiSource
El Paso Corporation	Piedmont Natural Gas
Entergy	

HISTORICAL FINANCIALS

Company Type: Public

Income Statement FYE: December 31

	REVENUE ($ mil.)	NET INCOME ($ mil.)	NET PROFIT MARGIN	EMPLOYEES
12/11	14,379	1,408	9.8%	15,800
12/10	15,197	2,808	18.5%	15,800
12/09	15,131	1,287	8.5%	17,900
12/08	16,290	1,834	11.3%	18,000
12/07	15,674	2,539	16.2%	17,000
Annual Growth	(2.1%)	(13.7%)	—	(1.8%)

2011 Year-End Financials

Debt ratio: 42.11%
Return on equity: 12.03%
Cash ($ mil.): 102
Current ratio: 77.99
Long-term debt ($ mil.): 17,394
No. of shares (mil.): 570
Dividends
  Yield: —
  Payout: 80.41%
Market value ($ mil.): 30,256

	STOCK PRICE ($) FY Close	P/E High	P/E Low	PER SHARE ($) Earnings	Dividends	Book Value
12/11	53.08	22	17	2.45	0.00	20.53
12/10	42.72	9	8	4.76	1.83	21.09
12/09	38.92	18	13	2.17	1.75	19.10
12/08	35.84	15	11	3.16	1.58	17.73
12/07	47.45	24	12	3.88	1.46	16.75
Annual Growth	2.8%	—	—	(10.9%)	—	5.2%

Domtar Corp

Leaving a paper trail is Domtar's business; the company is North America's #1 uncoated freesheet paper manufacturer and marketer. Some 85% of its sales are from paper comprising office commercial printing and publishing and converting and specialty papers. The lines include offset printing paper photocopying paper as well as fine and imaging (security) papers. Its top paper freesheet (coated and uncoated) is used for a range of printed materials with demanding image and press requirements such as food packaging medical and industrial applications. The company's Distribution segment buys stores and sells paper products made by Domtar and other manufacturers.

Financial Analysis

Despite posting overall positive gains in 2010 Domtar suffered decreases in both its profit and revenue levels for 2011. Net sales dipped by 4% from $5.9 billion to $5.6 billion while profits declined by roughly 40% from $605 million to $365 million. Domtar has felt the painful effects as more customers cut back on paper and switch to new forms of digital communication. Upward momentum has also been offset by its Distribution business (formerly known as Paper Merchants) which has experienced reduced consumer consumption due to the accelerating adoption of electronic document storage. For a third consecutive year this segment's sales dropped modestly in 2011.

Strategy

In order to adjust its cost structure Domtar has been disposing of several underperforming operations. The paper maker in mid-2011 sold its Prince Albert Saskatchewan pulp mill to Netherlands-based Paper Excellence Canada Holdings for $200 million. The year before Domtar axed its wood processing business selling it to EACOM Timber Corporation for roughly $120 million. The cash sale (plus certain capital adjustments) to EACOM reflected the economic downturn and industry-wide sagging demand for wood-related products in the US and Canada.

Domtar intends to broaden its product offerings through business acquisitions and alliances. In mid-2012 it obtained EAM Corporation a maker of laminated absorbent cores used in hygiene adult incontinence baby diapers and medical packaging products. Domtar bought EAM for $61 million and the deal broadened its adult incontinence product portfolio and added to its newly created Personal Care business segment.

Domtar formed this new segment earlier when it bought Attends Healthcare a manufacturer and supplier of incontinence products for $315 million from KPS Capital Partners in late 2011. Attends has a 775000-sq.-ft. plant and distribution center in North Carolina. A few months later Domtar bought Attends' European operations for E180 million ($235 million). In Europe Attends has a 374000-sq.-ft. plant in Sweden as well as distribution centers in Germany Scotland and Sweden.

EXECUTIVES

SVP Human Resources, Melissa H. Anderson, age 47
Chairman, Harold H. MacKay, age 71
SVP Corporate Development, Patrick Loulou, age 43
SVP Law and Corporate Affairs and General Counsel, Zygmunt Jablonski, age 58
SVP and CFO, Daniel Buron, age 48, $374,395 total compensation
SVP Sales and Marketing, Richard L. Thomas, age 58, $373,846 total compensation
VP Corporate Law and Secretary, Razvan L. Theodoru
VP Communications and Investor Relations, Pascal Bosse
Group SVP Pulp and Paper Manufacturing, Michael Edwards, age 64, $384,231 total compensation
SVP Forest Products, Jean-Francois Merette, age 45
President CEO and Director, John D. Williams, age 57, $792,836 total compensation
SVP Distribution, Mark Ushpol, age 48
Director, William C. Stivers, age 73
Director, Michael R. (Mick) Onustock, age 72
Director, Brian M. Levitt, age 65
Director, Louis P. Gignac, age 61
Director, Robert J. (Bob) Steacy, age 62
Director, Denis A. Turcotte, age 50
Director, Pamela B. (Pam) Strobel, age 59
Director, W. Henson Moore, age 72
Director, Jack C. Bingleman, age 69
Director, Richard Tan, age 56
President CEO and Director, John D. Williams, age 57
Auditors: PricewaterhouseCoopersLLP

LOCATIONS

HQ: Domtar Corporation
395 de Maisonneuve Blvd. West, Montreal Quebec H3A 1L6 Canada
Phone: 514-848-5555 **Fax:** 514-848-6878
Web: www.domtar.com

2011 Sales

	$ mil.	% of total
US	4,200	75
China	229	4
Other countries	427	8

PRODUCTS/OPERATIONS

2011 Sales

Pulp & paper	4,953	85
Personal care	71	1
Total	**5,612**	**100**

Selected Products and Brands

Paper
  Business and office papers
  Commercial printing papers
  Converting papers
  Digital printing papers
  EarthChoice papers
  Publishing papers
  Specialty papers
Pulp
  Ashdown hardwood
  Ashdown softwood
  Dryden softwood
  Espanola aspen
  Espanola birch
  Espanola maple
  Espanola softwood
  Hawesville hardwood
  Kamloops chinook
  Kamloops tyee
  Marlboro softwood
  Plymouth fluff
  Windsor wet lap

COMPETITORS

Blandin Paper	NewPage
Boise Cascade	RockTenn CP
Boise Inc.	Sappi
Canfor	Tembec
Cascades Inc.	USG
Georgia-Pacific	Wausau Paper
International Paper	West Fraser Timber
Neenah Paper	

HISTORICAL FINANCIALS

Company Type: Public

Income Statement FYE: December 31

	REVENUE ($ mil.)	NET INCOME ($ mil.)	NET PROFIT MARGIN	EMPLOYEES
12/11	5,612	365	6.5%	8,700
12/10	5,850	605	10.3%	8,500
12/09	5,465	310	5.7%	10,000
12/08	6,394	(573)	—	11,000
12/07	5,947	70	1.2%	13,000
Annual Growth	(1.4%)	51.1%	—	(9.6%)

2011 Year-End Financials

Debt ratio: 14.45%
Return on equity: 12.28%
Cash ($ mil.): 444
Current ratio: 270.11
Long-term debt ($ mil.): 837
No. of shares (mil.): 36
Dividends
Yield: —
Payout: 14.32%
Market value ($ mil.): 2,889

	STOCK PRICE ($) FY Close	P/E High/Low		PER SHARE ($) Earnings	Dividends	Book Value
12/11	79.96	11	7	9.08	0.00	82.26
12/10	75.92	6	3	14.00	0.75	76.91
12/09	55.41	8	0	7.18	0.00	63.29
12/08	1.67	—	—	(13.32)	0.00	51.99
12/07	7.70	6	4	1.80	0.00	81.42
Annual Growth	79.5%	—	—	49.9%	—	0.3%

Donnelley (R.R.) & Sons Co.

If you can read it R.R. Donnelley & Sons can print it. A leading full-service printing company R.R. Donnelley produces magazines catalogs and books as well as advertising material business forms financial reports and telephone directories. The company offers graphics and prepress services in conjunction with printing. In addition it provides logistics distribution and business process outsourcing services related to getting printed material to its audience. Along with publishers R.R. Donnelley's customers include companies in the advertising financial services healthcare retail and technology industries. The company does business mainly in the US but also in Europe Asia and Latin America.

HISTORY

In 1864 Canadian Richard Robert Donnelley joined Chicago publishers Edward Goodman and Leroy Church to form what eventually would become Lakeside Publishing and Printing. The company's building and presses were destroyed in the 1871 Chicago fire but soon were rebuilt.

By 1890 Richard Donnelley's son Thomas was leading the company which was incorporated as R.R. Donnelley & Sons. The company spun off its phone directory publishing subsidiary the Chicago Directory Company in 1916. (Renamed the Reuben H. Donnelley Corporation after another of Richard Donnelley's sons the business was acquired by Dun & Bradstreet –now D&B –in 1961 which spun it off as R.H. Donnelley now Dex One in 1998.)

R.R. Donnelley began printing "Time" in 1928 and "LIFE" in 1936. The company endured limits on commercial printing and paper shortages during WWII. It went public in 1956. Thomas Donnelley's son Gaylord steered the company from 1964 until 1975 when Charles Lake the first CEO who was not a member of the Donnelley family replaced him.

During the 1980s R.R. Donnelley developed the Selectronic process which allowed magazine publishers to tailor content and ads to different geographic audiences. The company acquired Metromail the largest US mailing list business in 1987. John Walter became CEO in 1988. R.R. Donnelley's South Side Chicago plant its oldest was shuttered in 1993 when Sears stopped publishing its catalogs.

R.R. Donnelley merged its software operations with Corporate Software to form Stream International (technical support software licensing and fulfillment) in 1995. That year Donnelley expanded internationally into Chile China India and Poland.

In 1996 Donnelley took both its Donnelley Enterprise Solutions subsidiary (IT services) and its Metromail subsidiary public retaining about 43% and 38% of each company respectively. Controversy erupted that year when it was revealed that Metromail had sold personal information in its customer database and through contracting had given prison inmates access to its database. In the wake of these revelations Walter resigned in 1996. Former Emerson Electric executive William Davis was appointed CEO in 1997.

Davis restructured the company reorganized Stream's operations and integrated digital printing into R.R. Donnelley's other operations. He also pushed the company to jettison underperforming units. In 1998 the company sold its interests in Metromail and Donnelley Enterprise Solutions.

Sharpening its focus in commercial printing R.R. Donnelley continued divesting in 1999 selling most of its stake in Stream International (which was later acquired by Solectron) and its stakes in software distributor Corporate Software & Technology and manufacturing and fulfillment firm Modus Media International. The company's Internet unit also unveiled ePublish a turnkey system enabling magazine publishers to publish on the Web.

In early 2000 the company doubled the size of its logistics unit when it bought business-to-home parcel mailer CTC Distribution Direct. It also expanded its digital services through the purchase of premedia services firm Iridio. In 2001 the company announced closures of a handful of plants as part of a streamlining effort. It also cut about 1700 jobs.

The company sold off its investments in two more companies MultiMedia Live and Global Directory Services in 2003. That same year it acquired distribution service provider Momentum Logistics and in 2004 it bought business forms and label printer Moore Wallace for about $2.8 billion. Moore Wallace CEO Mark Angelson took over leadership of the combined company. In its continuing efforts to divest itself of noncore assets R.R. Donnelley sold off its package logistics business including CTC Distribution Direct in 2004; it retained its print logistics and distribution businesses.

In 2005 R.R. Donnelley sold Peak Technologies a former Moore Wallace company that integrated and resold automated data capture and identification systems to Platinum Equity. R.R. Donnelley also acquired a number of regional printers in the US in 2005. It also bought The Astron Group a UK-based provider of outsourced document and information management services for $990 million. In 2006 the company acquired business process outsourcing company OfficeTiger for $250 million.

In 2007 Angelson retired in and CFO Thomas Quinlan replaced him as president and CEO. Also that year the firm acquired the business forms company Cardinal Brands for $130 million as well as rival Banta for $1.3 billion gaining printing operations in the US Europe and Asia and a supply chain management business that serves technology companies. Later in 2007 R.R. Donnelley completed the acquisition of magazine and catalog printer Perry Judd's Holdings for $176 million and textbook printer Von Hoffman for $413 million.

The following year it bought newspaper inserts printer Pro Line Printing in Irving Texas for about $120 million. Acquisitions in 2009 included Prospectus Central which provides electronic delivery of investment prospectuses and the assets of Santiago Chile-based PROSA a Web-based printing company.

Also in 2009 the company offered about $1.5 billion to take over the operations of rival printer Quebecor World which had filed for bankruptcy in 2008. Quebecor World rejected the bid however saying it was on track to emerge from bankruptcy protection by late summer. The following year R.R. Donnelley was able to buy Bowne & Co. a New York-based financial documents printer for about $480 million and Nimblefish Technologies a provider of software and services for managing direct marketing campaigns.

In 2011 R.R. Donnelley acquired LibreDigital a provider of digital distribution services. The following year it acquired Edgar Online a distributor of SEC documents.

EXECUTIVES

President CEO and Director, Thomas J. (Tom) Quinlan III, age 49, $1,000,000 total compensation
Chairman, Stephen M. Wolf, age 70
EVP General Counsel Corporate Secretary and Chief Compliance Officer, Suzanne S. (Sue) Bettman, age 47, $400,000 total compensation
Group President, Daniel L. (Dan) Knotts, age 47, $550,000 total compensation
VP Product Management and Innovation Digital Solutions Group, Roe J. McFarlane
COO, John R. Paloian, age 53, $700,000 total compensation
EVP and CFO, Daniel N. (Dan) Leib, age 45
SVP Controller and Chief Accounting Officer, Andrew B. Coxhead, age 43
EVP Communications, Doug Fitzgerald
VP Investor Relations, Dave Gardella
Director, Lee A. Chaden, age 70
President CEO and Director, Thomas J. (Tom) Quinlan III, age 49
Director, Judith H. Hamilton, age 67
Director, Michael T. Riordan, age 61
Director, John C. (Jack) Pope, age 63
Director, Thomas S. (Tom) Johnson, age 71
Director, Oliver R. Sockwell, age 68
Director, Susan M. Ivey, age 53
Auditors: Deloitte&ToucheLLP

LOCATIONS

HQ: R.R. Donnelley & Sons Company
111 S. Wacker Dr., Chicago IL 60606-4301
Phone: 312-326-8000 **Fax:** 312-326-7156
Web: www.rrdonnelley.com

2011 Sales

	$ mil.	% of total
US	8,073	76
Europe	1,067	10
Asia	668	6
Other regions	802	8
Total	**10,611**	**100**

PRODUCTS/OPERATIONS

2011 Sales

	$ mil.	% of total
US print & related services		
Magazines catalogs & retail inserts	1,903	18
Books & directories	1,292	12
Variable print	1,250	12
Financial print	907	9
Forms & labels	789	7
Logistics	688	6

Commercial	639	6
Office products & premedia	374	4
International	2,764	26
Total	**10,611**	**100**

Selected Operations

US print and related services
- Book (consumer religious educational and specialty and telecommunications)
- Direct mail (content creation database management printing personalization finishing and distribution in North America)
- Directories (yellow and white pages)
- Logistics (consolidation and delivery of printed products; expedited distribution of time-sensitive and secure material; print-on-demand warehousing and fulfillment services)
- Magazine catalog and retail inserts
- Short-run commercial print (annual reports marketing brochures catalog and marketing inserts pharmaceutical inserts and other marketing retail point-of-sale and promotional materials and technical publications)

International
- Business process outsourcing
- Global Turnkey Solutions (product configuration customized kitting and order fulfillment)

COMPETITORS

Accenture
Arandell
Capgemini
Cenveo
Consolidated Graphics
Courier Corporation
Dai Nippon Printing
Deluxe Corporation
EBSCO
Harte-Hanks
IBM Global Services
Infosys
M & F Worldwide
Merrill
Penn Lithographics
Quad/Graphics
St Ives
St. Joseph Communications
Taylor Corporation
Toppan Printing
Transcontinental Inc.
Valassis
Vertis Inc

HISTORICAL FINANCIALS

Company Type: Public

Income Statement

FYE: December 31

	REVENUE ($ mil.)	NET INCOME ($ mil.)	NET PROFIT MARGIN	EMPLOYEES
12/11	10,611	(122)	—	58,000
12/10	10,018	221	2.2%	58,700
12/09	9,857	(27)	—	56,800
12/08	11,581	(189)	—	62,000
12/07	11,587	(48)	—	65,000
Annual Growth	(2.2%)	—	—	(2.8%)

2011 Year-End Financials

Debt ratio: 44.20%
Return on equity: (-11.76)%
Cash ($ mil.): 449
Current ratio: 139.76
Long-term debt ($ mil.): 3,416
No. of shares (mil.): 178
Dividends
Yield: —
Payout: —
Market value ($ mil.): 2,576

	STOCK PRICE ($) FY Close	P/E High/Low	PER SHARE ($) Earnings	Dividends	Book Value
12/11	14.43	— —	(0.63)	0.00	5.84
12/10	17.47	22 14	1.06	1.04	10.77
12/09	22.27	— —	(0.13)	1.04	10.37
12/08	13.58	— —	(0.90)	1.04	11.27
12/07	37.74	— —	(0.22)	1.04	18.10
Annual Growth	(21.4%)	— —	—	—	(24.6%)

Dover Corp

The "D" in Dover could stand for diversity. Dover manages more than 30 companies that make equipment ranging from car wash systems to aerospace components. Dover operates in four segments: engineered systems (fluid systems and refrigeration systems); energy (extraction and handling of oil and gas); printing & identification (printing coding and testing for consumer goods food pharmaceuticals alternative energy electronics and other markets); and communication technologies (such products as electromechanical components for communications life sciences and other markets). Dover traces its historical roots back to 1955.

HISTORY

George Ohrstrom a New York stockbroker formed Dover in 1955 and took it public that year. Originally headquartered in Washington DC Dover consisted of four companies: C. Lee Cook (compressor seals and piston rings) Peerless (space-venting heaters) Rotary Lift (automotive lifts) and W.C. Norris (components for oil wells). In 1958 Dover made the first of many acquisitions and entered the elevator industry by buying Shepard Warner Elevator.

Dover continued to diversify throughout the 1960s. Acquisitions included OPW (gas pump nozzles) in 1961 and De-Sta-Co (industrial clamps and valves) the next year. OPW head Thomas Sutton became Dover's president in 1964 and the company moved its headquarters to New York City. Dover acquired Groen Manufacturing (food industry products) in 1967 and Ronningen-Petter (filter-strainer units) the following year.

During the 1970s Dover expanded beyond its core industries (building materials industrial components and equipment). In 1975 it acquired Dieterich Standard a maker of liquid-measurement instruments. Dieterich Standard's president Gary Roubos became Dover's president and COO in 1977 and its CEO in 1981. The company sold Peerless in 1977 and acquired electronics assembly equipment manufacturer Universal Instruments in 1979.

Electronics became an increasingly important part of Dover's business during the 1980s. The company bought K&L Microwave a maker of microwave filters used in satellites and cable TV equipment (1983) Dielectric Laboratories (microwave filter parts 1985) and NURAD (microwave antennas 1986). Between 1985 and 1990 Dover bought some 25 companies including Weldcraft Products (welding equipment 1985) Wolfe Frostop (salad bars 1987) Weaver Corp. (automotive lifts 1987) General Elevator (1988) Texas Hydraulics (1988) Security Elevator (1990) and Marathon Equipment (waste-handling equipment 1990).

The corporation spun off its DOVatron circuit board assembly subsidiary to shareholders in 1993 after finding that DOVatron was competing with important Dover customers. That year Dover acquired The Heil Company (garbage trucks).

President/COO Thomas Reece succeeded Roubos as CEO in 1994. Dover purchased 10 companies that year including Hill Phoenix (commercial refrigeration cases) and Koolrad Design & Manufacturing (radiators for transformers). In 1995 it bought France-based Imaje (ink-jet printers and specialty inks) for $200 million. It was the largest purchase in the company's history at the time.

The following year Dover bought Everett Charles Technologies a maker of electronic testing equipment. In 1997 the corporation and its subsidiaries purchased 17 companies including Vitronics Soltec (soldering equipment for circuit board assembly). The next year the company sold its Dover elevator unit —a popular brand but a management headache —to German steel giant Thyssen (now ThyssenKrupp) for $1.1 billion.

Dover continued its acquisitive ways in 1999 and 2000 picking up 18 and 23 companies respectively. Notable were Alphasem which makes semiconductor manufacturing equipment and Graphics Microsystems which took Dover into the pressroom equipment market. Dover picked up Triton Systems a maker of ATMs in 2000. The following year Dover acquired Kurz-Kasch a US-based electromagnetic manufacturer with customers in the automotive market.

The company's prodigious acquisition rate (it completed more than 70 between 1998 and 2002) gradually declined. Only one stand-alone company was purchased in 2002 (there were five add-ons however) and eight were sold in 2001 and 2002. The divestitures brought in about $400 million.

The seemingly interminable manufacturing recession continued to hurt Dover in 2002 especially its technology division. Its circuit board assembly and test equipment business a star performer before the economic downturn turned in about $50 million in losses for that year. Dover looked to Asia and China in particular as its best hope for near-term growth for its beleaguered telecommunications and electronic assembly businesses; Dover subsidiary Universal Instruments christened a major manufacturing plant in China early in 2003.

In mid-2003 VP Ronald Hoffman who also served as president and CEO of Dover Resources was promoted to president and COO of the parent company. Hoffman took over as CEO at the outset of 2005 becoming only the fifth chief executive of Dover Corp.

Early in 2005 Dover augmented its division structure from four market segments to six striving to position the company into a model for future growth while also implanting a more efficient management structure. The Dover Systems segment specialized in the manufacture of cooking equipment refrigeration systems fire suppression systems and packaging technology; Dover Electronics manufactured microwave components electromechanical switches and cash-dispensing machines.

The Electronics segment was busy in the latter half of 2005 making a small acquisition of Colder Products (a maker of couplings for flexible tubing). It picked up Knowles Electronics later in the year for $750 million. Knowles made components for hearing aids and microphones for high-end cell phones.

Following that the company sold Dover Diversified's Tranter a manufacturer of heat transfer products to the Swedish equipment maker Alfa Laval for $150 million. It marked the second disposal of a Diversified subsidiary. Early in 2005 the segment sold its Hydratight Sweeney unit (now just Hydratight) to Actuant for $93 million.

Among the divestitures in 2006 were Alphasem Hover-Davis Universal Instruments and Vitronics Soltec from the Circuit Assembly and Test Group and Mark Andy from the Product Identification Group. Alphasem was acquired by Kulicke & Soffa Industries while buyout firm Francisco Partners purchased Hover-Davis Universal Instruments and Vitronics Soltec. Mark Andy went to a management buyout with financial backing from Morgenthaler.

Also in 2006 Dover acquired Paladin Brands Holding a manufacturer of attachments and tools for heavy and light mobile construction equipment. Paladin's products were also employed with mobile equipment used in demolition forestry material handling and recycling among other applications. Dover bought the company from Norwest Equity Partners.

The company sold Kurz-Kasch to Monomoy Capital Partners a private equity firm in early 2007. It also discontinued its Graphics Microsystems business as part of the 2007 realignment. Graphics Microsystems (which makes pressroom automation equipment) was sold for $33 million in cash to Advanced Vision Technology Ltd. of Israel. It also agreed to sell Triton Systems a manufacturer of ATMs to a subsidiary of Hyosung Corp.

From 2004 through 2007 the company made 32 acquisitions valued in total at about $3 billion. Twenty-two businesses were marked for sale between 2005 and 2007 with 20 of those sold by the end of 2007 for a total of nearly $700 million. In late 2007 Dover combined two product identification companies in its Engineered Systems segment Imaje and Markem into one unit Markem.Image.

Dover sold its semiconductor test handler business Rasco to fellow test equipment maker Cohu for $80 million cash in 2008. That same year Robert Livingston was named CEO and elected to the board. Livingston succeeded Ronald Hoffman who retired. Prior to assuming the lead position Livingston was president and CEO of Dover's Engineered Systems segment.

Between 2007 and 2009 Dover acquired 11 add-on businesses (at a cost of $377 million). The company focused on target areas such as product identification energy and fluid solutions refrigeration equipment and electronic communication components in 2009. Along these lines it completed six acquisitions that year. Its subsidiary Hill Phoenix's purchase of Barker Company Limited (refrigerated non-refrigerated and hot display cases) expanded its engineered products offerings. This followed the Hill Phoenix purchase of Tyler Refrigeration formerly a unit of Carrier Commercial Refrigeration which brought added energy-saving and compression technology. Subsidiary Waukesha Bearings acquired Inpro/Seal Company adding bearing isolators to Waukesha's line of hydrodynamic bearings for the power generation and oil and gas industries. Another subsidiary Datamax-O'Neil bought the data systems division (portable printers) of Extech Instruments a subsidiary of FLIR Systems. The acquisition supplemented Datamax-O'Neil's thermal printing technologies.

EXECUTIVES

Chairman, Robert W. Cremin, age 71
SVP General Counsel and Secretary, Joseph W. Schmidt, age 65
SVP Human Resources, Jay L. Kloosterboer, age 51
President and CEO Dover Communication Technologies, Jeffrey S. (Jeff) Niew, age 45
VP and Controller, Raymond T. McKay Jr., age 58
President and CEO Dover Energy, William W. (Bill) Spurgeon, age 53, $601,250 total compensation
President CEO and Director, Robert A. (Bob) Livingston, age 58, $783,750 total compensation
EVP Dover Energy, Sivasankaran (Soma) Somasundaram, age 46
SVP and CFO, Brad M. Cerepak, age 53, $268,052 total compensation
VP Investor Relations, Paul E. Goldberg, age 48
President and CEO Dover Engineered Systems, Thomas W. (Tom) Giacomini, age 46, $513,125 total compensation
President and CEO Dover Printing & Identification, John F. Hartner, age 49
Director of Communications, Adrian W. Sakowicz
EVP Dover Engineered Systems, James H. Moyle, age 59
SVP Corporate Development, Stephen R. Sellhausen, age 53
President Asia, Michael-Yuepeng Zhang, age 48
VP Tax, Kevin P. Buchanan, age 56
EVP Dover Engineered Systems, C. Anderson Fincher, age 41
VP and Treasurer, Brian P. Moore, age 41
SVP Global Sourcing, Niclas Ytterdahl, age 47
Director, Bernard G. Rethore, age 70
Director, Peter T. Francis, age 59
Director, Jean-Pierre M. Ergas, age 72
Director, David H. Benson, age 74
Director, Kristiane C. Graham, age 54
Director, Richard K. Lochridge, age 68
Director, Michael B. Stubbs, age 63
Director, Mary A. Winston, age 50
President CEO and Director, Robert A. (Bob) Livingston, age 58
Director, Stephen M. Todd, age 63
Director, Stephen K. Wagner, age 65
Auditors: PricewaterhouseCoopersLLP

LOCATIONS

HQ: Dover Corporation
3005 Highland Pkwy. Suite 200, Downers Grove IL 60515
Phone: 630-541-1540 **Fax:** 630-743-2671
Web: www.dovercorporation.com

2011 Sales

	$ mil.	% of total
Americas		
US	4,037	51
Other Americas	788	10
Asia	1,502	19
Europe	1,348	17
Other	272	3
Total	**7,950**	**100**

PRODUCTS/OPERATIONS

2011 Sales

	$ mil.	% of total
Engineered systems	3,100	39
Energy	1,900	24
Printing & identification	1,592	20
Communication technologies	1,360	17
Intra-segment eliminations	(4.4)	-
Total	**7,950**	**100**

Selected Companies

Communication Technologies
Colder Products
Ceramic & Microwave Products
Knowles
Sargent Aerospace & Defense
Vectron International
Energy
  Cook Compression
  Norris Production Solutions
  OPW
  TWG Power
  US Synthetic
  Waukesha Bearings
Engineered Systems
  Belvac Production Machinery
  Hill PHOENIX
  SWEP
  Tipper Tie
  Unified Brands
Printing & Identification
Datamax O' Neil
DEK
Everett Charles Technologies
Markem Imaje
Multitest
OK International

COMPETITORS

Carlisle Companies
Cookson Group
Cooper Industries
Crane Co.
Gardner Denver
IDEX
Ingersoll-Rand
Kaydon
KEMET
KSB AG
Mark IV
Middleby
Navistar
Oshkosh Truck
Paul Mueller
Sequa
Smith Bits
Snap-on
Swagelok
Tatung
Thermador Groupe
Wastequip
Weatherford International
Weston EU

HISTORICAL FINANCIALS

Company Type: Public

Income Statement FYE: December 31

	REVENUE ($ mil.)	NET INCOME ($ mil.)	NET PROFIT MARGIN	EMPLOYEES
12/11	7,950	895	11.3%	34,000
12/10	7,132	700	9.8%	32,000
12/09	5,775	356	6.2%	29,300
12/08	7,568	590	7.8%	32,300
12/07	7,226	661	9.1%	33,400
Annual Growth	2.4%	7.9%	—	0.4%

2011 Year-End Financials

Debt ratio: 23.02%
Return on equity: 18.16%
Cash ($ mil.): 1,206
Current ratio: 282.39
Long-term debt ($ mil.): 2,186
No. of shares (mil.): 183
Dividends
Yield: —
Payout: 24.89%
Market value ($ mil.): 10,657

	STOCK PRICE ($) FY Close	P/E High/Low		PER SHARE ($) Earnings	Dividends	Book Value
12/11	58.05	14	9	4.74	0.00	26.86
12/10	58.45	16	11	3.70	1.07	24.27
12/09	41.61	22	12	1.91	1.02	21.85
12/08	32.92	17	8	3.12	0.90	20.39
12/07	46.09	17	14	3.26	0.77	20.34
Annual Growth	5.9%	—	—	9.8%	—	7.2%

Dow Chemical Co.

The Tao of Dow Chemical lies within its integrated production of plastics chemicals hydrocarbons and agrochemicals. The largest chemical company in the US and #2 worldwide behind BASF Dow also makes performance plastics (engineering plastics polyurethanes and materials) for Dow Automotive. It uses chlorine-based and hydrocarbon-based raw materials to make 5000 finished chemical products at 197 sites in 36 countries. The maker of Styrofoam insulation also is the world's #1 producer of chlorine and caustic soda and a top maker of ethylene dichloride and vinyl chloride monomer (used in making alumina pulp and paper soaps and in construction). Dow also owns 50% of silicone products maker Dow Corning.

HISTORY

Herbert Dow founded Dow Chemical in 1897 after developing a process to extract bromides and chlorides from underground brine deposits around Midland Michigan. Its first product was chlorine bleach. Dow eventually overcame British and German monopolies on bleach bromides and other chemicals.

In the mid-1920s Dow rejected a takeover by DuPont. By 1930 the year of Herbert Dow's death sales had reached $15 million. Dow started building new plants around the country in the late 1930s.

Dow research yielded new plastics in the 1940s such as Saran Wrap the company's initial major consumer product. In 1952 Dow built a plant in Japan (Asahi-Dow) its first subsidiary outside North America. Plastics represented 32% of sales by 1957 compared with 2% in 1940. Strong sales of plastics and silicone products propelled the company into the top ranks of US firms. Dow entered the pharmaceutical field with the 1960 purchase of Allied Labs.

Dow suffered earnings drops from 1981 to 1983 from falling chemical prices. To limit the cyclical effect of chemicals on profits the company expanded its interests in pharmaceuticals and consumer goods. In 1989 it merged its pharmaceutical division with Marion Labs to create Marion Merrell Dow (it sold its 71% stake to Hoechst in 1995). Also in 1989 it formed DowElanco a joint venture with Eli Lilly to produce agricultural chemicals.

Following allegations that it had put a breast implant on the market without proper testing Dow Corning (a joint venture with glassmaker Corning Inc.) the #1 producer of silicone breast implants stopped making the devices in 1992. In 1995 a federal judge ordered Dow to pay a Nevada woman $14 million in damages –the first breast-implant verdict against the company as a sole defendant. Facing thousands of pending cases Dow Corning filed for bankruptcy protection. (In 1998 Dow Corning agreed to pay $3.2 billion to settle most breast-implant claims.) Dow Corning finally climbed out of bankruptcy in 2004.

Dow entered the polypropylene and polyethylene terephthalate markets with the 1996 purchase of INCA International a subsidiary of Italy's Enichem. It also bought a stake in seed developer Mycogen.

The company sold its 80% of Destec Energy in 1997 and bought Eli Lilly's 40% stake in DowElanco (renamed Dow AgroSciences 1998). That year Dow bought South Africa's Sentrachem (crop-protection products) but regulators made Dow sell part of it to Akzo Nobel.

In 1998 Dow sold its DowBrands unit –maker of bathroom cleaner (Dow) plastic bags (Ziploc) and plastic wrap (Saran Wrap) –to S.C. Johnson & Son. It also paid $322 million for the rest of Mycogen which became part of Dow AgroSciences.

The company paid $600 million in 1999 to purchase ANGUS Chemical (specialty chemicals) from TransCanada PipeLines. Dow also announced it planned to buy rival Union Carbide for $9.3 billion; it completed the acquisition early in 2001 after agreeing to divest some polyethylene assets to satisfy regulatory concerns.

In 2000 Dow acquired Flexible Products Company (polyurethane foam) and General Latex Chemical Corporation (rigid polyurethane foam). That year Michael Parker succeeded William Stavropoulos as president and CEO (Stavropoulos remained as chairman).

Dow acquired Rohm and Haas' agricultural chemicals (fungicides insecticides herbicides) business for $1 billion in 2001. That year it also acquired Celotex Corporation's rigid-foam insulation business and UK fine and specialty chemicals firm Ascot Plc.

A weakened economy high raw material costs and falling prices took a toll on Dow's sales and profits around the turn of the century. As a result of costs related to the Union Carbide takeover – such as the $830 million charge related to Union Carbide's exposure to asbestos claims –and the sputtering economy Dow recorded its first annual loss in nearly 10 years in 2001 then reported another loss in 2002. Parker was let go and William Stavropoulos returned to his post as both chairman and CEO. Stavropoulos went to work cutting jobs and closing plants in an effort to cut at least $1 billion in costs and make the company cash-flow positive in 2003.

From 2002 to 2004 the company cut nearly 7000 jobs or better than 13% of its entire workforce. By 2004 those moves coupled with a rebounding chemicals market had made Dow profitable again. Stavropoulos felt comfortable enough to relinquish the chief executive title and gave it to president and COO Andrew Liveris.

In the latter half of the decade the company began to switch its focus to more downstream products like performance plastics and systems. It acquired Bayer company Wolff Walsrode in 2007 and then more grandly specialty chemicals company Rohm and Haas in 2009.

Dow did take on significant debt during the Rohm and Haas transaction and as part of negotiations to close the deal Rohm and Haas sold salt-producing subsidiary Morton International to German company K+S. Dow also sold Rohm and Haas's powder coatings business to Akzo Nobel.

In 2010 Dow sold its Trinseo SA (then called Styron) unit to private investment group Bain Capital for $1.6 billion. Trinseo is a world leader in the production of plastics latex and rubber. Dow also sold its half of the Americas Styrenics joint venture with Chevron Phillips Chemical as part of the Trinseo deal.

That year Dow also formed a 50-50 joint venture with Mitsui to build a world-scale chlor-alkali plant at Dow's Freeport Texas manufacturing complex. The venture makes chlorine for feedstocks to supply Dow's downstream performance operations. Mitsui's share of the chlorine produced is converted to ethylene dichloride used primarily to make vinyl chloride monomer (VCM). VCM in turn is used to make polymers used in plastics and a range of both synthetic and natural materials.

Dow sold its polypropylene business to Brazil's Braskem in 2011 for $323 million. The deal involved two manufacturing plants in the US (Freeport and Seadrift Texas) and two in Germany (Wesseling and Schkopau) with a total annual polypropylene production capacity of 2.3 billion pounds.

To produce a new chlorocarbon for next-generation climate-friendly refrigerants Dow agreed to form a joint venture with Occidental Chemical Corporation in 2011. Known as HCC-1230xa the chlorocarbon will be used to produce the refrigerant known as HFO-1234yf which has low global-warming potential and zero ozone depletion potential. It will initially be used in air-conditioning systems in autos.

In 2011 Dow also formed an Advanced Electrolyte Technologies joint venture with Ube Industries to make electrolytes for lithium-ion batteries in energy storage applications.

Dow formed another joint venture in 2011 this time with Mitsui & Co. to develop biopolymers or organic plastics in Brazil. The 50-50 operation will use Dow's sugar cane production to develop biofuels and packaging materials offering a "green alternative" and replacement product for the flexible packaging hygiene and medical markets.

EXECUTIVES

EVP Business Services Chief Sustainability Officer and CIO, David E. (Dave) Kepler II, age 59, $511,128 total compensation

Corporate VP and Treasurer, Fernando Ruiz, age 56

EVP Ventures New Business Development and Licensing and CTO, William F. (Bill) Banholzer, age 55, $733,200 total compensation

Chairman President and CEO, Andrew N. Liveris, age 57, $1,650,000 total compensation

EVP; President Dow Europe Middle East and Africa; Chairman Dow Europe, Geoffery E. (Geoff) Merszei, age 60, $861,396 total compensation

EVP; President Manufacturing and Engineering, Carol Williams

EVP; President and CEO Dow Advanced Materials, Jerome A. Peribere

SVP; Chairman Sadara Project Office, James D. (Jim) McIlvenny, age 54

EVP Law and Government Affairs General Counsel and Corporate Secretary, Charles J. Kalil, age 60, $390,074 total compensation

Director Office of the Corporate Secretary Assistant Secretary and Senior Managing Counsel Securities Law, W. Michael McGuire

EVP and Chief Commercial Officer, Heinz Haller, age 57, $739,442 total compensation

EVP and CFO, William H. (Bill) Weideman, age 57, $390,074 total compensation

Chief Tax Officer and Assistant Secretary, William L. Curry

Media Contact Europe, Sue Breach

EVP Human Resources Corporate Affairs and Aviation, Gregory M. Freiwald, age 58

Corporate Auditor, Greg Grocholski

Assistant Secretary, Amy Wilson

VP and Controller, Ronald C. (Ron) Edmonds

Media Contact Latin America, Fern?o Silveira

EVP; President Feedstocks and Energy and Corporate Development, James R. (Jim) Fitterling

SVP; President Performance Plastics, Howard Ungerleider

Corporate Media Relations, Greg Baldwin

Financial Communications and Investor Relations Contact, Rebecca Bentley

Press Contact North America, Tracie Copeland

Press Contact Middle East and Africa, Mira Meghdessian

Press Contact Asia Pacific, Emily Zhang

EVP; President Performance Materials, Joe E. Harlan, age 52

Director, John B. Hess, age 58

Director, Arnold A. Allemang, age 69

Director, Ruth G. Shaw, age 64

Director, Jeff M. Fettig, age 54

Director, Dennis H. Reilley, age 59

Director, James M. (Jim) Ringler, age 66

Director, Jacqueline K. Barton, age 59

Director, Paul G. Stern, age 74

Director, James A. Bell, age 63

Director, Barbara Hackman Franklin, age 72

Director, Paul Polman, age 55

Director, Jennifer M. Granholm, age 53

Auditors: Deloitte&ToucheLLP

LOCATIONS

HQ: The Dow Chemical Company
2030 Dow Center, Midland MI 48674
Phone: 989-636-1000 **Fax:** 989-636-1830
Web: www.dow.com

2011 Sales

	$ mil.	% of total
Europe Middle East Africa	20,840	35
Other regions	19,771	33

PRODUCTS/OPERATIONS

2011 Sales

	$ mil.	% of total
Performance Plastics	16,257	27
Feedstocks & Energy	11,302	19
Coatings & Infrastructure	7,200	12
Agricultural Sciences	5,655	9
Electronic & Functional Materials	4,599	8
Corporate Services	325	1

Selected Products

Basic Plastics
- Polyethylene (resins including HDPE LDPE and LLDPE grades and catalysts and process technology)
- Polypropylene (resins and performance polymers)
- Styrenics (resins and styrenic alloys)

Performance Products
- Engineering plastics (thermoplastic resins and elastomers advanced resins and crystalline polymers)
- Emulsion polymers (synthetic latex)
- Epoxy products and intermediates (acetone acrylic monomers epoxy resins glycerine and phenol)
- Polyurethanes (Great Stuff foam sealant dispersions carpet backings polyurethane gloves roof adhesives and fiberboard products)

Performance Systems
- Dow Automotive (resins engineering plastic materials fluids adhesives sealants acoustical systems)
- Industrial chemicals (biocides surfactants and deicing fluids)
- Oxide derivatives (glycol ethers and amines)
- Specialty polymers (acrylic acid/acrylic esters epoxides dispersants vinyl resins specialty monomers)
- Wire and cable compounds (flame-retardant compounds wire and cable insulation compounds)

Health and Agricultural Sciences
- Fumigants
- Fungicides
- Herbicides
- Insecticides

Hydrocarbons and Energy
- Benzene
- Butadiene
- Butylene
- Cumene
- Ethylene
- Propylene
- Styrene

Coatings and Infrastructure
- Adhesives and Functional Polymers
- Dow Building and Construction
  - Fabricated products (plastic film Styrofoam and Weathermate house wrap)
- Dow Coating Materials

Electronic and Specialty Materials
- Electronic Materials
  - Antireflective coatings
  - CMP slurries
  - Immersion photoresists
- Specialty Materials
  - Ion-exchange resins
  - Nitroparaffins and nitroparaffin-based specialty chemicals
  - Printing ink distillates
  - Scale inhibitors
  - UCAR emulsion systems (water-based emulsions)
  - Water-soluble resins

Basic Chemicals
- Caustic soda
- Chlorine
- Ethylene glycol
- Ethylene oxide
- Vinyl chloride monomer

Other
- Property and casualty insurance (Liana Limited)

COMPETITORS

Akzo Nobel
BASF SE
Bayer AG
Chevron Phillips Chemical
DuPont
Eastman Chemical
ExxonMobil Chemical
FMC
Formosa Plastics
INEOS
Koch Industries Inc.
LANXESS
Lucite
Mitsui Chemicals
Monsanto Company
Occidental Chemical
Olin Chlor Alkali
PPG Industries
SABIC
Shell Chemicals
Syngenta
Taminco Acquisition

HISTORICAL FINANCIALS

Company Type: Public

Income Statement

FYE: December 31

	REVENUE ($ mil.)	NET INCOME ($ mil.)	NET PROFIT MARGIN	EMPLOYEES
12/11	59,985	2,742	4.6%	51,705
12/10	53,674	2,310	4.3%	49,505
12/09	44,875	648	1.4%	52,195
12/08	57,514	579	1.0%	46,102
12/07	53,513	2,887	5.4%	45,856
Annual Growth	2.9%	(1.3%)	—	3.0%

2011 Year-End Financials

Debt ratio: 31.07%
Return on equity: 12.31%
Cash ($ mil.): 5,444
Current ratio: 171.79
Long-term debt ($ mil.): 18,310
No. of shares (mil.): 1,184
Dividends
Yield: —
Payout: 43.90%
Market value ($ mil.): 34,068

	STOCK PRICE ($) FY Close	P/E High/Low		PER SHARE ($) Earnings	Dividends	Book Value
12/11	28.76	20	10	2.05	0.00	18.81
12/10	34.14	20	13	1.72	0.60	18.71
12/09	27.63	92	20	0.32	0.60	17.87
12/08	15.09	69	25	0.62	1.68	15.16
12/07	39.42	16	13	2.99	1.64	21.68
Annual Growth	(7.6%)	—	—	(9.0%)	—	(3.5%)

Dr Pepper Snapple Group Inc

In this case it's a snap decision about what doctor to choose. Dr Pepper Snapple Group (DPS) is the bottler and distributor of Dr Pepper soda and Snapple drinks. Serving Canada Mexico and the US the company offers a vast portfolio of non-alcoholic beverages including flavored carbonated soft drinks and non-carbonated soft drinks along with ready-to-drink non-carbonated teas juices juice drinks and mixers. Among its brands are Dr Pepper and Snapple of course along with A&W Root Beer Hawaiian Punch Mott's and Schweppes. It has some cult favorites as well including Vernors Squirt and Royal Crown Cola. DPS is the #3 soda business in North America after #1 Coke and #2 Pepsi.

Operations

The company primarily serves bottlers (including quick-serve restaurants for syrups) and distributors as well as retailers. Wal-Mart is DPS's largest customer accounting for approximately 14% of its 2011 sales. Other customers include Kroger SUPERVALU Safeway Target McDonald's Yum! Brands Sonic Corp. Subway Restaurants and 7-Eleven. DPS competes head-to-head with Coke and Pepsi in the battle for North American customers. In addition to its flavored carbonated sodas DPS makes Venom Energy (an energy drink designed to compete with Pepsi's Gatorade) Coke's PowerAde and a growing list of smaller companies' energy drinks. In addition to its own brands DPS manufactures and distributes brands owned by third parties in specified licensed geographic territories. Among these brands are Country Time Lemonade and Sunkist and Welch's sodas which are licensed from Kraft Foods Sunkist Growers and Welch Foods respectively.

Geographic Reach

Headquartered in Plano Texas the company operates about 160 administrative manufacturing and distribution facilities across the US which supply customers in the US and Canada. In Mexico it has more than a dozen sites through which it serves its customers in that country.

Change in Company Type

DPS is doing well on its own. Formerly a subsidiary of Cadbury Schweppes DPS as it operates today is the result of the 2008 separation of Cadbury's beverage and confectionary businesses. DPS was spun off into a publicly traded company. The split came to fruition in part due to the urging of activist billionaire investor and then Cadbury shareholder Nelson Peltz who saw the split as a way to improve Cadbury's share price.

Financial Analysis

Sales at the soda maker rose 5% from $5.6 billion in 2010 to $5.9 billion in 2011 primarily attributable to price increases. Profit margins slipped however from 60% in 2010 to 58% in 2011 as DPS devoted more dollars to packaging materials sweeteners apple juice concentrate and other costly commodities.

Strategy

The company might be #3 in overall North American sales but it wins the gold in one category. DPS is the #1 flavored (non-cola) carbonated soft drinks (CSD) company in the US. Its market share in the US for flavored CSDs in 2011 was 21.1% an increase over the 19.7% share it had in 2008. In the CSD sector as a whole its market share for 2011 was 40%. In addition to soft drinks the company manufactures fountain syrups for its foodservice customers in Canada and the US. DPS leverages the strength of its best-selling core brands –such as Diet Dr Pepper 7UP Sunkist soda A&W and Canada Dry –to launch both new products and product extensions. Products that debuted in 2011 as part of this strategic effort include Dr Pepper TEN BlueRaspberry Crush Mott's Garden Blend and Snapple's Papaya Mango Tea and Tea Will Be Loved. The company's Dr Pepper TEN introduced in late 2011 contains blended sweeteners developed by DPS for a low-calorie version of its regular Dr Pepper. In a strategic partnership rival Coke and DPS inked a long-term deal in 2010 that made competitor Pepsi perk up. The Coke/DPS alliance involves a 20-year deal worth some $715 million. As part of the agreement Coca-Cola will distribute the Dr Pepper brand in the US and Canada Dry in the Northeast. Also the deal has Coke distributing Canada Dry C'Plus and Schweppes in Canada for DPS. The distribution deal also puts the Dr Pepper and Diet Dr Pepper names on Coca-Cola's new touch-screen dispenser. In a bid to spur already increasing sales volume of its flagship 7UP drink DPS in late 2010 launched a reformulated 7UP in the US that boasts a "crisper" lemon and lime taste thanks to technological advances. The beverage maker hopes to pit the newer 7UP version against Pepsi's Mountain Dew and Coke's Sprite. The two rival sodas have a share of 6.7% and 5.5% respectively of the US carbonated soft drink market compared to 7UP's 1% according to Beverage Digest. DPS anticipates the crisper 7UP its best-selling CSD after its namesake Dr Pepper brand will shake up this niche of the drinks industry.

EXECUTIVES

Chairman, Wayne R. Sanders, age 64
President CEO and Director, Larry D. Young, age 57, $934,616 total compensation
EVP and CFO, Martin M. (Marty) Ellen, age 58
EVP Marketing, James R. (Jim) Trebilcock, age 54
President Packaged Beverages, Rodger L. Collins, age 54, $510,000 total compensation
EVP General Counsel and Secretary, James L. (Jim) Baldwin Jr., age 51
EVP Supply Chain, Derry L. Hobson, age 61, $430,578 total compensation
President Beverage Concentrates and Latin America Beverages, James J. (Jim) Johnston Jr., age 55, $519,231 total compensation
EVP Human Resources, Lawrence N. (Larry) Solomon, age 57, $430,962 total compensation
EVP Corporate Affairs, Tina S. Barry, age 55
EVP Research and Development, David J. Thomas, age 50
SVP and CIO, Tom Farrah
Director, Jack J. Stahl, age 59
Director, John L. Adams, age 67
President CEO and Director, Larry D. Young, age 57
Director, Ronald G. (Ron) Rogers, age 64
Director, Pamela H. (Pam) Patsley, age 55
Director, Michael F. (Mike) Weinstein, age 63
Director, M. Anne Szostak, age 61
Director, Terence D. (Terry) Martin, age 69
Director, Joyce M. Roche, age 64
Auditors: Deloitte&ToucheLLP

LOCATIONS

HQ: Dr Pepper Snapple Group Inc.
5301 Legacy Dr., Plano TX 75024
Phone: 972-673-7000 **Fax:** 780-702-0647
Web: www.katzgroup.ca/

2011 Sales

	$ mil.	% of total
US	5,243	89
Other countries	660	11
Total	**5,903**	**100**

PRODUCTS/OPERATIONS

2011 Sales

	$ mil.	% of total
Packaged beverages	4,292	73
Beverage concentrates	1,193	20
Latin America beverages	418	7
Total	**5,903**	**100**

Selected Brands

7UP
A&W
Aguafiel (Mexico only)
Cadbury
Canada Dry
Clamato
Country Time (licensed)
Crush
Diet Rite
Dr Pepper
Hawaiian Punch
Holland House (licensed)
IBC
Margaritaville (licensed)
Mott' s
Mr & Mrs T
Nantucket Nectars
Orangina
Pe?afiel (Mexico only)
RC Cola
Rose' s (licensed)
Schweppes
Snapple
Squirt
Stewart' s (licensed)
Sundrop
Sunkist (licensed)
Sussex (Canada only)
Venom Energy
Vernors
Welch' s (licensed)
Yoo-Hoo

COMPETITORS

American Beverage
Austin Coca-Cola
Campbell Soup
Coca-Cola
Coca-Cola Bottling company of southern california
Coca-Cola Bottling Consolidated
Coca-Cola Bottling of Northern New England
Coca-Cola FEMSA
Coca-Cola North America
Coca-Cola Refreshments
Coca-Cola Tennessee
Coke United
Cott
Country Pure Foods
Del Monte Foods
Dole Food
Faygo
Florida' s Natural
G & J Pepsi-Cola Bottlers
Gatorade
Great Plains Coca-Cola
Great Western Juice
Hornell Brewing
IZZE
Jones Soda
Jugos del Valle
Lane Affiliated
Mondelez International
Monster Beverage
National Beverage
Nestle
Ocean Spray
Odwalla
Old Orchard
Pepsi Bottling Ventures
Pepsi-Cola Bottling Company of NY
Pepsi-Cola Bottling of Central Virginia
Pepsi-Cola of Ft. Lauderdale
PepsiCo
Philadelphia Coca-Cola
Red Bull
Reed' s
Roll Global
South Beach Beverage
Sunny Delight
Swire Coca-Cola
Tree Top
Tropicana
Wet Planet Beverages

HISTORICAL FINANCIALS

Company Type: Public

Income Statement

FYE: December 31

	REVENUE ($ mil.)	NET INCOME ($ mil.)	NET PROFIT MARGIN	EMPLOYEES
12/11	5,903	606	10.3%	19,000
12/10	5,636	528	9.4%	19,000
12/09	5,531	555	10.0%	19,000
12/08	5,710	(312)	—	20,000
12/07	5,748	497	8.6%	20,000
Annual Growth	0.7%	5.1%	—	(1.3%)

2011 Year-End Financials

Debt ratio: 29.17%
Return on equity: 26.78%
Cash ($ mil.): 701
Current ratio: 91.75
Long-term debt ($ mil.): 2,256
No. of shares (mil.): 212
Dividends
Yield: —
Payout: 44.16%
Market value ($ mil.): 8,375

	STOCK PRICE ($) FY Close	P/E High	P/E Low	PER SHARE ($) Earnings	Dividends	Book Value
12/11	39.48	15	12	2.74	0.00	10.67
12/10	35.16	18	12	2.17	0.90	10.98
12/09	28.30	14	5	2.17	0.15	12.54
12/08	16.25	—	—	(1.23)	0.00	10.28
Annual Growth	34.4%	—	—	—	—	1.2%

DTE Energy Co.

Detroit's economy may be lackluster but DTE Energy still provides a reliable spark. The holding company's main subsidiary Detroit Edison distributes electricity to some 2.1 million customers in southeastern Michigan. The utility's power plants (mainly fossil-fueled) have a generating capacity of more than 10420 MW. The company's Michigan Consolidated Gas (MichCon) unit distributes natural gas to 1.2 million customers. DTE Energy's nonregulated operations (in 26 US states) include energy marketing and trading; coal transportation and procurement; energy management services for commercial and industrial customers; independent and on-site power generation; and gas exploration production and processing.

Geographic Reach

The company operates in the Midwest the northeastern US and eastern Canada. It has utilities in Michigan and merchant generation facilities in Illinois Indiana and Michigan. Its portfolio includes non-utility energy businesses operating in 26 states (energy trading power and industrial projects coal and gas midstream and unconventional gas production).

Operations

DTE Energy has electric and gas utilities. It also has wholesale power gas and coal marketing operations.

Financial Analysis

Higher rates and increased power demand lifted DTE Energy's overall revenues in 2011 by 4% despite lower natural gas prices which caused gas utility revenues to drop by 9%. Net income was up by 13% primarily due to lower operational costs and a drop in depreciation depletion and amortization charges and lower interest expenses.

Strategy

DTE Energy is expanding its nonutility businesses (especially gas storage and pipeline projects and power and industrial projects) to broaden its revenue base. In 2012 it signed a deal with Spectra Energy and Enbridge to jointly develop the NEXUS Gas Transmission system a 250-mile long pipeline project to transport the growing supplies of Ohio Utica shale gas to markets in Michigan Ohio and Ontario.

As part of its commitment to reduce its carbon footprint to meet regulatory requirements the company is developing alternatives to coal-fired power generation and is seeking ways to conserve power. In 2011 the company was operating four biomass-fired electric generating plants with a capacity of 183 MW. In addition DTE Energy offers appliance recycling and is pursuing the adoption of advanced metering infrastructure and other technologies to improve the efficiency of its electric distribution service.

HISTORY

DTE Energy's predecessor threw its first switch in 1886 when George Peck and local investors incorporated the Edison Illuminating Company of Detroit. Neighboring utility Peninsular Electric Light was formed in 1891 and both companies bought smaller utilities until they merged in 1903 to form Detroit Edison. A subsidiary of holding company North American Co. Detroit Edison was incorporated in New York to secure financing for power plants.

Detroit's growth in the 1920s and 1930s led the utility to build plants and buy others in outlying areas. Detroit Edison acquired Michigan Electric Power which had been divested from its holding company under the Public Utility Holding Company Act of 1935 and was itself divested from North American in 1940.

The post-WWII boom prompted Detroit Edison to build more plants most of them coal-fired. In 1953 it joined a consortium of 34 companies to build Fermi 1 a nuclear plant brought on line in 1963. Still strapped for power Detroit Edison built the coal-fired Monroe plant which began service in 1970. In 1972 Fermi 1 had a partial core meltdown and was taken off line.

Detroit Edison began shipping low-sulfur Montana coal through its Wisconsin terminal in 1974 which reduced the cost of obtaining the fuel. The next year it began building another nuke Fermi 2. The nuke had cost more than $4.8 billion by the time it went on line in 1988. That year the utility began its landfill gas recovery operation (now DTE Biomass Energy).

A recession pounded automakers in the early 1990s leading to cutbacks in electricity purchases. In 1992 Congress passed the Energy Policy Act allowing wholesale power competition. In 1993 a fire shut down Fermi 2 for almost two years. Michigan's public service commission (PSC) approved retail customer-choice pilot programs for its utilities in 1994. Detroit Edison and rival Consumers Energy (now CMS Energy) took the PSC to court.

DTE Energy became Detroit Edison's holding company in 1996. The next year it formed DTE Energy Trading (to broker power) and DTE-CoEnergy (to provide energy-management services and sell power to large customers). It also formed Plug Power with Mechanical Technology to develop fuel cells that convert natural gas to power without combustion.

In 1997 and 1998 the PSC bolstered by state court decisions issued orders to restructure Michigan's utilities. The transition to retail competition began in 1998. That year DTE Energy and natural gas provider Michigan Consolidated Gas (MichCon) began collaborating on some operations including billing and meter reading. DTE and GE formed a venture to sell and install Plug Power fuel cell systems.

A higher court shot down the PSC's restructuring orders in 1999 but DTE Energy and CMS Energy decided to implement customer choice using PSC guidelines. That year the US Department of Energy selected DTE Energy to install the world's first super power-cable which could carry three times as much electricity as conventional copper. Also in 1999 DTE Energy agreed to acquire MCN Energy MichCon's parent.

In 2000 DTE Energy formed subsidiary International Transmission (ITC) to hold Detroit Edison's transmission assets; the next year ITC joined the Midwest Independent System Operator which began to manage ITC's network. It also completed its $4.3 billion purchase of MCN Energy in 2001. Full deregulation of Michigan's electricity market was completed in 2002. International Transmission was sold in 2003 to affiliates of Kohlberg Kravis Roberts and Trimaran Capital Partners for $610 million.

In 2007 it sold its Michigan Antrim Shale gas exploration and production assets to Atlas Energy Resources (which later was acquired by Chevron) for about $1.3 billion. That year due to the expiration of synthetic fuel production tax credits DTE Energy exited the synfuels business. In 2010 it sold its rail service unit (DTE Rail Services) to FreightCar America for $23 million.

EXECUTIVES

SVP Major Enterprise Projects, Ron A. May, age 60
EVP and CFO, David E. Meador, age 55, $545,000 total compensation
Chairman President and CEO, Gerard M. (Gerry) Anderson, age 54, $820,000 total compensation
VP Human Resources, Larry E. Steward, age 59
VP Regulatory Affairs, Daniel G. (Dan) Brudzynski, age 51
SVP Customer Service, Joyce V. Hayes-Giles
VP and Treasurer, Nick A. Khouri, age 54
Group President; President and COO Detroit Edison, Steven E. Kurmas, age 56, $435,000 total compensation
VP Corporate and Governmental Affairs, Frederick E. (Fred) Shell, age 60
President Midwest Energy Resources, Fred L. Shusterich, age 57
VP Marketing and Renewables, Trevor F. Lauer, age 47
SVP and General Counsel, Bruce D. Peterson, age 55, $458,000 total compensation
Group President; President and COO Michigan Consolidated Gas Company, Gerardo (Jerry) Norcia, age 49, $354,231 total compensation
SVP Gas Operations Michigan Consolidated Gas Company, Robert A. (Bob) Richard, age 51
VP Gas Sales and Supply Michigan Consolidated Gas Company, Mark W. Stiers, age 49
VP Distribution Operations Detroit Edison, Vincent G. (Vince) Dow, age 55
SVP Corporate Affairs, Paul C. Hillegonds, age 63
VP Environmental Management and Resources, Skiles Boyd, age 56
VP Corporate Communications, Sandra K. (Sandy) Ennis, age 55
SVP and Chief Nuclear Officer, Jack M. Davis, age 64
VP and Chief Tax Officer, JoAnn Chavez, age 47
EVP DTE Energy Resources; President DTE Energy Services, David Ruud
President DTE Coal Services, Matt T. Paul, age 42
VP Strategy & Corporate Development; President - DTE Energy Ventures, Knut Simonsen, age 48
President DTE Biomass Energy, Mark Cousino, age 47
Corporate Secretary and Chief of Staff, Lisa Muschong
VP Controller and Investor Relations, Peter B. Oleksiak, age 45
President DTE Gas Storage and DTE Pipeline, Peter Cianci, age 44
President DTE Energy Trading, Steven (Steve) Mabry, age 50
VP Fossil Generation Detroit Edison, Paul Fessler, age 59
President DTE Gas Resources, Steven H. Prelipp, age 45
General Auditor, James Tompkins, age 56
Director, Lillian Bauder, age 72
Director, Ruth G. Shaw, age 64
Director, Eugene A. (Gene) Miller, age 74
Director, James H. (Jim) Vandenberghe, age 62
Director, David A. Brandon, age 60
Director, Maj. Gen. Josue (Joe) Robles Jr., age 66
Director, Frank M. Hennessey, age 74
Director, Charles W. Pryor Jr., age 67
Director, Allan D. Gilmour, age 77
Director, John E. Lobbia, age 70
Director, W. Frank Fountain Jr., age 67
Director, Gail J. McGovern, age 60
Director, Mark A. Murray, age 57
Auditors: PricewaterhouseCoopersLLP

LOCATIONS

HQ: DTE Energy Company
1 Energy Plaza, Detroit MI 48226
Phone: 313-235-4000 **Fax:** 313-235-8055
Web: www.dteenergy.com

PRODUCTS/OPERATIONS

2011 Sales

	$ mil.	% of total
Electric utility	5,154	56
Gas utility	1,505	17
Non-utility operations		
Energy trading	1,276	14
Power & industrial products	1,129	12
Gas storage & pipeline	91	1
Unconventional gas production	39	
Adjustments	(297)	-
Total	**8,897**	**100**

COMPETITORS

AEP
CMS Energy
CMS Enterprises
Dairyland Power
DPL
Duke Energy
Dynegy
Exelon Energy
Integrys Energy Group
Nicor Gas
Peabody Energy
PG&E Corporation
SEMCO ENERGY
Southern Company
Wisconsin Energy
Xcel Energy

HISTORICAL FINANCIALS

Company Type: Public

Income Statement FYE: December 31

	REVENUE ($ mil.)	NET INCOME ($ mil.)	NET PROFIT MARGIN	EMPLOYEES
12/11	8,897	711	8.0%	9,800
12/10	8,557	630	7.4%	9,800
12/09	8,014	532	6.6%	10,244
12/08	9,329	546	5.9%	10,471
12/07	8,506	971	11.4%	10,262
Annual Growth	1.1%	(7.5%)	—	(1.1%)

2011 Year-End Financials

Debt ratio: 31.27%
Return on equity: 10.14%
Cash ($ mil.): 68
Current ratio: 121.61
Long-term debt ($ mil.): 7,187

No. of shares (mil.): 169
Dividends
Yield: —
Payout: 55.56%
Market value ($ mil.): 9,216

	STOCK PRICE ($) FY Close	P/E High/Low		PER SHARE ($) Earnings	Dividends	Book Value
12/11	54.45	13	11	4.18	0.00	41.41
12/10	45.32	13	11	3.74	2.18	39.67
12/09	43.59	14	7	3.24	2.12	37.96
12/08	35.67	13	9	3.36	2.12	36.77
12/07	43.96	9	8	5.70	2.12	35.86
Annual Growth	5.5%	—	—	(7.5%)	—	3.7%

Du Pont (E.I.) de Nemours & Co

E. I. du Pont de Nemours (also known simply as DuPont) wants to coat your car feed your crops and decrease your dependence on fossil fuels. A top US chemical maker (along with Dow and ExxonMobil Chemicals) the company consists of 14 businesses that are divided into nine segments each of which serves a diverse set of markets. Using its expertise in science-based development it offers products materials and services that are applied in everything from agriculture apparel and construction to electronics nutrition and safety. DuPont operates worldwide with most of its sales coming from outside of the US.

HISTORY

Eleuthere Irenee du Pont de Nemours fled to America in 1800 after the French Revolution. Two years later he founded a gunpowder plant in Delaware. Within a decade the DuPont plant was the largest of its kind in the US. After Irenee's death in 1834 his sons Alfred and Henry took over. DuPont added dynamite and nitroglycerine in 1880 guncotton in 1892 and smokeless powder in 1894.

In 1902 three du Pont cousins bought DuPont. By 1906 the company controlled most of the US explosives market but a 1912 antitrust decision forced it to sell part of the powder business. WWI profits were used to diversify into paints plastics and dyes.

DuPont acquired an interest in General Motors in 1917; the stake increased to 37% by 1922 (the company surrendered its stake in 1962 due to antitrust regulations). In the 1920s the firm bought and improved French cellophane technology and began producing rayon. DuPont's inventions include neoprene synthetic rubber (1931) Lucite (1937) nylon (1938) Teflon (1938) and Dacron. The last du Pont to head the company resigned as chairman in 1972. DuPont got into the energy business by acquiring Conoco for $7.6 billion in 1981.

In 1991 DuPont and Merck created DuPont Merck Pharmaceutical to focus on non-US markets. After record earnings in 1994 DuPont spent $8.8 billion the next year to buy back shares of the corporation from Seagram. In 1997 DuPont purchased Protein Technologies International (soy proteins) from Ralston Purina and Imperial Chemical's polyester-resins and intermediates operations (1997) and polyester-film business (1998).

DuPont president Chad Holliday became CEO in early 1998. That year DuPont purchased a 20% stake in Pioneer Hi-Bred International (corn seed) for $1.7 billion and Merck's 50% stake in DuPont Merck Pharmaceutical for $2.6 billion. DuPont's public offering of Conoco in 1998 raised $4.4 billion the largest US IPO at the time.

In 1999 DuPont bought the Herberts paints and coatings unit from Hoechst. It also bought the remaining 80% of Pioneer Hi-Bred for $7.7 billion and biotechnology research firm CombiChem for $95 million. Making a clean break with its oil business DuPont sold its remaining 70% stake in Conoco.

Bristol-Myers Squibb bought DuPont's pharmaceutical operations (HIV heart disease nerve disorder and cancer drugs) in late 2001 for $7.8 billion in cash. In early 2002 DuPont initiated a restructuring that included the eventual spinoff of its fibers businesses (now called INVISTA) and the reorganization of its remaining business units into five segments: Electronics & Communication Technologies Performance Materials Coatings & Color Technologies Safety & Protection and Agriculture & Nutrition.

Later that year DuPont acquired TOTAL's surface protection and fluoroadditives business to become the largest integrated fluorotelomer protectants maker in both Europe and North America. DuPont also acquired semiconductor chemicals maker ChemFirst and packaging company Liqui-Box in 2002.

Excluding the former pharmaceutical operations DuPont wasn't profitable for the first few years of the new century. Much of its losses were due to employee severance costs and the write-down of assets. In 2003 the company took a large hit from the separation of INVISTA among other costs. So despite a 12% increase in sales the company saw no real profit.

DuPont announced in late 2003 an initiative that it hoped would deliver $900 million in growth by the end of 2005. In addition to workforce cuts and product consolidation DuPont also began to shift its focus to emerging markets by which it meant Asia. The company announced a substantial shift in management in January 2004 to follow up on the initiative which included appointing a head of global sales for the first time and rearranging its leadership in Asia. The workforce cuts were announced in April; 3500 jobs were lost in 2004 mostly in the US and Western Europe.

Preparing to separate INVISTA DuPont reabsorbed DuPont Canada (which had been a separate public company) into the fold. In early 2004 the company completed the sale of INVISTA; with that DuPont was completely out of the fibers business.

In 2007 the company sold part of its fluorochemical products business to Huntsman. The unit sold provided fluoro-products for nonwovens to the textiles industry.

DuPont's Chemicals division agreed to enter a joint venture with Honeywell in 2010 to produce a new refrigerant for use in automotive air conditioning systems. The new product has 99.7% lower global warming potential than current refrigerants. DuPont and Honeywell will share financial and technological resources and will jointly design construct and operate a world-scale manufacturing facility. Also that year DuPont acquired MECS Inc. a provider of process technology specialty equipment and technical services to the sulfuric acid industry. The deal expands DuPont's clean air and clean fuel offerings to global chemical markets.

In 2010 DuPont subsidiary Pioneer Hi-Bred ended its participation in the GreenLeaf Genetics joint venture with former partner Syngenta Seeds taking full ownership. GreenLeaf develops genetic hybrid seeds for growing corn and soybeans. Pioneer Hi-Bred also acquired two agricultural firms Seed Consultants of Washington Court House Ohio and Terral Seed of Lake Providence Louisiana.

DuPont's Performance Polymers unit sold two of its product lines Zenite liquid crystal polymer and Thermx polycyclohexylene-dimethylene terephthalate to a unit of Celanese in 2010. Those units generated approximately $40 million in revenue in 2009.

EXECUTIVES

EVP and Member Office of the Chief Executive, James C. Borel, age 56
President Nutrition and Health; Chairman Solae, Craig F. Binetti, age 57
Chairman and CEO, Ellen J. Kullman, age 56, $703,685 total compensation
President Latin America, Eduardo W. Wanick, age 55
SVP Integrated Operations and Engineering, Jeffrey A. Coe, age 60
VP Operations North America, Willie C. Martin
VP Global Supply Chain Performance Polymers, Francine C. Shaw, age 57
President Performance Polymers, Diane H. Gulyas, age 55
EVP Chief Innovation Officer and Member Office of the Chief Executive, Thomas M. (Tom) Connelly Jr., age 59, $638,600 total compensation
VP Finance and Treasurer, Susan M. Stalnecker, age 59
VP Agriculture Biotechnology Pioneer Hi-Bred, John Bedbrook, age 62
President and CFO Canada, Michael J. (Mike) Oxley
President Electronics and Communications, David B. Miller, age 55
President Korea, Cheoroo Won, age 58
President Packaging and Industrial Polymers, William J. (Bill) Harvey, age 61
SVP Chief Science and Technology Officer, Douglas W. (Doug) Muzyka, age 57
SVP Corporate Strategy, David G. Bills, age 50
VP Business Process Excellence and Corporate Champion DuPont Six Sigma, Don R. Linsenmann
SVP Corporate Productivity and Business Process Simplification, Richard C. Olson, age 55
SVP General Counsel and Member Office of the Chief Executive, Thomas L. Sager, age 62
VP Sourcing and Logistics and Chief Procurement Officer, Shelley Stewart Jr., age 59
President Titanium Technologies, Boo Ching (BC) Chong, age 50
VP BioMaterials Group, John P. Ranieri
VP Government Marketing and Government Affairs, Barry M. Granger
EVP and Member Office of the Chief Executive; Head Building Innovations Protection Technologies Sustainable Solutions Electronics & Communications Chemicals & Fluoroproducts and Titanium Technologies Businesses, Mark P. Vergnano, age 53
VP Pioneer Hi-Bred - China, William S. (Bill) Niebur, age 55
EVP and CFO, Nicholas C. (Nick) Fanandakis, age 55
President Protection Technologies, Thomas G. (Tom) Powell, age 53
President Industrial Biosciences, James C. Collins Jr., age 49

VP Tax and Business Finance, Robert E. Giblin, age 59
Media Relations, Tara Stewart
VP Corporate Planning and Analyses, Linda B. West, age 53
President and CEO Capital Management, Valerie J. Sill
President East Asia, Carl J. Lukach, age 55
VP Safety Health and Environment and Chief Sustainability Officer, Linda J. Fisher, age 59
VP Sourcing and Logistics and Chief Procurement Officer, Keith J. Smith
VP Strategic Planning Pioneeer Hi-Bred, Peter C. Hemken
President Performance Coatings, John G. McCool, age 59
VP Technology Protection Technologies, Roger K. Siemionko, age 57
President K.K. Japan, Minoru Amoh
VP and Controller, Barry J. Niziolek, age 55
President Europe Middle East and Africa; President International SA Geneva, Ian Hudson
President Chemicals and Fluoroproducts, Gary W. Spitzer, age 54
President South Asia, Balvinder S. Kalsi, age 55
VP Global Operations Corporate Supply Chains, Donald D. (Don) Wirth
VP and Assistant General Counsel, Martha L. Rees
President Building Innovations, Timothy P. (Tim) McCann, age 55
VP Investor Relations, Karen A. Fletcher
President Sustainable Solutions, James R. Weigand, age 57
SVP Human Resources and Member Office of the Chief Executive, Benito Cachinero-Sanchez, age 53
President Pioneer Hi-Bred, Paul E. Schickler, age 60
VP Corporate Marketing and Sales and Chief Marketing and Sales Officer, Scott Coleman, age 48
VP Information Technology and CIO, Phuong Tram, age 57
VP General Auditor and Chief Ethics and Compliance Officer, Donna H. Grier, age 53
Chief Engineer and VP DuPont Engineering Facilities and Real Estate, Jocelyn E. Scott
CEO Solae, Torkel Rhenman
VP Human Resources, Maritza J. Poza-Grise
Chairman and President Taiwan; Sales Excellence Leader Titanium Technologies Asia Pacific, Steve Chen
VP Supply Chain Performance Coatings, K. Peter Hurd
Director Media Relations, Anthony Farina
Media Relations, Marie Beletti
VP Protection Technologies North America, William F. Weber, age 52
VP Global Technology Performance Coatings, Lewis E. Manring
VP Supply Chain DuPont Chemicals & Fluoroproducts, Janet H. Waters
VP and Assistant General Counsel, Hinton J. Lucas Jr.
VP Supply Chain Pioneer Hi-Bred Crop Protection Nutrition & Health and Applied BioSciences, John W. (Bill) Mooney
VP Regulatory and Product Stewardship, James C. Romine
Secretary and Corporate Counsel, Mary E. Bowler
President Greater China, Tony H.S. Su, age 55
VP Performance Coatings Europe Middle East and Africa, Thierry F. J. Vanlancker, age 48
President Crop Protection, Rik L. Miller, age 54
Director Global Automotive Technology, David A. Glasscock
VP Integrated Business Management, David L. Peet
Leader Media Relations, Mike Hanretta
Media Relations, Dan Turner
Global IT Planning Manager DuPont Information Technology, Vicki L. Garrison
Director, Alexander M. (Sandy) Cutler, age 60
Director, Richard H. (Dick) Brown, age 64
Director, Curtis J. Crawford, age 64
Director, Bertrand P. Collomb, age 69
Director, Lois D. Juliber, age 63
Director, William K. Reilly, age 72
Director, Robert A. Brown, age 60
Director, Eleuthere I. (There) du Pont, age 45
Director, Marillyn A. Hewson, age 58
Auditors: PricewaterhouseCoopersLLP

LOCATIONS

HQ: E. I. du Pont de Nemours and Company
1007 Market St., Wilmington DE 19898
Phone: 302-774-1000 **Fax:** 302-999-4399
Web: www.dupont.com

2011 Sales

	% of total
US &	38
Europe Middle East &	26
Asia/Pacific	23
Latin	13
Total	**100**

PRODUCTS/OPERATIONS

2011 Sales

	% of total
Agriculture	24
Performance	20
Performance	18
Performance	11
Safety &	10
Electronics &	8
Nutrition &	7
Industrial	2
Pharmaceuticals	-
Total	**100**

Selected Operations

Agriculture
- DuPont Crop Protection
- Pioneer HiBred International

Performance Chemicals
- DuPont Chemicals and Fluoroproducts
- DuPont Titanium Technologies

Performance Materials
- DuPont Packaging and Industrial Polymers
- DuPont Performance Polymers
- DuPont Teijin Films

Performance Coatings
- DuPont Performance Coatings
  - Liquid and powder coatings for vehicle manufacturers

Safety and Protection
- DuPont Advanced Fiber Systems
- DuPont Chemical Solutions Enterprise
- DuPont Nonwovens
- DuPont Safety Resources
- DuPont Surfaces

Electronic and Communication Technologies
- DuPont Displays Technologies
- DuPont Electronic Technologies
- DuPont Imaging Technologies

Nutrition and Health
- Danisco (specialty food ingredients)
- Solae (soy-based technologies)

Industrial Biosciences
- Danisco enzymes
- DuPont Sorona renewably-sourced polymer
- BioPDO propanediol

COMPETITORS

3M
Ahlstrom
Akzo Nobel
Asahi Kasei
BASF SE
Bayer AG
Cargill
Chevron Phillips Chemical
ConAgra
DIC Corporation
Dow Chemical
Eastman Chemical
Evonik Degussa
FMC
Formosa Plastics
Henkel
Honeywell International
Occidental Chemical
PPG Industries
Reliance Industries
Sherwin-Williams
Shin-Etsu Chemical
Syngenta

HISTORICAL FINANCIALS

Company Type: Public

Income Statement

FYE: December 31

	REVENUE ($ mil.)	NET INCOME ($ mil.)	NET PROFIT MARGIN	EMPLOYEES
12/11	38,719	3,474	9.0%	70,000
12/10	32,733	3,031	9.3%	60,000
12/09	27,328	1,755	6.4%	58,000
12/08	31,836	2,007	6.3%	60,000
12/07	30,653	2,988	9.7%	60,000
Annual Growth	6.0%	3.8%	—	3.9%

2011 Year-End Financials

Debt ratio: 25.89%
Return on equity: 40.43%
Cash ($ mil.): 3,586
Current ratio: 161.45
Long-term debt ($ mil.): 11,736
No. of shares (mil.): 926
Dividends
Yield: —
Payout: 44.57%
Market value ($ mil.): 42,398

	STOCK PRICE ($) FY Close	P/E High/Low		PER SHARE ($) Earnings	Dividends	Book Value
12/11	45.78	15	10	3.68	0.00	9.28
12/10	49.88	15	10	3.28	1.64	10.11
12/09	33.67	18	8	1.92	1.64	7.98
12/08	25.30	24	10	2.20	1.64	7.90
12/07	44.09	16	13	3.22	1.52	12.38
Annual Growth	0.9%	—	—	3.4%	—	(7.0%)

Duke Energy Corp

Duke Energy is a John Wayne-sized power business. The company serves electric and gas customers in the South and Midwest. Its US Franchised Electric and Gas unit operates primarily through its Duke Energy Carolinas Duke Energy Ohio Duke Energy Indiana and Duke Energy Kentucky regional businesses. The company has 58200 MW of electric generating capacity 32000 miles of transmission lines and 250200 miles of distribution lines. It also has commercial and international power assets. While it is focused on energy operations Duke also has some limited insurance real estate and telecom assets. In a major expansion in 2012 Duke acquired Progress Energy in a $32 billion deal.

HISTORY

Surgeon Gill Wylie founded Catawba Power Company in 1899; its first hydroelectric plant in South Carolina was on line by 1904. The next year Wylie and James "Buck" Duke (founder of the American Tobacco Company and Duke University's namesake) formed Southern Power Company with Wylie as president.

In 1910 Buck Duke became president of Southern Power and organized Mill-Power Supply to sell electric equipment and appliances. He also began investing in electricity-powered textile mills which prospered as a result of the electric power and continued to bring in customers. He formed the Southern Public Utility Company in 1913 to buy other Piedmont-region utilities. Wylie died in 1924 the same year the company was renamed Duke Power; Buck Duke died the next year.

Growing after WWII the company went public in 1950 and moved to the NYSE in 1961. It also formed its real estate arm Crescent Resources in the 1960s. Insulating itself from the 1970s energy crises Duke invested in coal mining and three nuclear plants the first completed in 1974.

In 1988 Duke began to develop power projects outside its home region and it also bought neighboring utility Nantahala Power and Light. The next year it formed a joint venture with Fluor's Fluor Daniel unit to provide engineering and construction services to power generators. Mill-Power Supply was sold in 1990.

By the 1990s Duke had moved into overseas markets acquiring an Argentine power station in 1992. It also tried its hand at telecommunications creating DukeNet Communications in 1994 to build fiber-optic systems and in 1996 it joined oil giant Mobil to create a power trading and marketing business. As the US power industry traveled toward deregulation Duke also sought natural gas operations. It targeted PanEnergy which owned a major pipeline system in the eastern half of the US. Duke Power bought PanEnergy in 1997 to form Duke Energy Corporation.

Seeing an opportunity in 1998 Duke formed Duke Communication Services to provide antenna sites to the fast-growing wireless communications industry. It also acquired a 52% stake in Electroquil an electric power generating company in Guayaquil Ecuador. That year it purchased a pipeline company in Australia from PG&E; it also bought three PG&E power plants to compete in California's deregulated electric utility marketplace.

Duke merged its pipeline business Duke Energy Trading and Transport with TEPPCO Partners and acquired gas processing operations from Union Pacific Resources. It sold Panhandle Eastern Pipe Line and gas-related assets in the Midwest to CMS Energy in 1999 to reduce operations in the region and made plans to build a pipeline extending from Alabama to Florida (completed in 2002).

To further enhance natural gas operations in other regions Duke bought El Paso's East Tennessee Natural Gas pipeline unit in 2000 and a 20% stake in Canadian 88 Energy; it also purchased $1.4 billion in South American generation assets including assets from Dominion Resources and the gas trading operations of Mobil (now Exxon Mobil) in the Netherlands. Also in 2000 Duke and Phillips Petroleum (now ConocoPhillips) merged their gas gathering and processing and NGL operations into Duke Energy Field Services.

In 2001 Duke announced the $8 billion acquisition of Westcoast Energy; the purchase which was completed in 2002 added more than a million natural gas customers and 6900 miles of gas pipeline in Canada. That year Duke sold its Duke Engineering & Services unit to Framatome ANP and its DukeSolutions unit to Ameresco. Duke Energy Field Services purchased Chevron's 33% stake in Discovery Producer Services which operates a Gulf of Mexico gas pipeline and nearby processing facilities.

Duke set out to sell $1.5 billion in assets in 2003 to focus on core operations. The company sold its Empire State Pipeline subsidiary to National Fuel Gas for $240 million and sold its stakes in the Alliance Pipeline Alliance Canada Marketing and the Aux Sable refinery to Enbridge and Fort Chicago Energy Partners for $245 million. Also that year Duke sold its stake in Foothills Pipe Lines to TransCanada for $181 million and it sold $300 million in renewable energy facilities to privately owned Highstar Renewable Fuels.

In 2004 the company sold an Indonesian power plant to Freeport-McMoRan in a $300 million deal and it sold its 30% interest in the Vector Pipeline to Enbridge and DTE Energy for $145 million. It also sold the assets of its merchant finance business (Duke Capital Partners) and its stake in Canadian 88 Energy (now Esprit Exploration). Following this trend in 2005 Duke Energy sold its 620-MW Grays Harbor facility (Washington) to an affiliate of Invenergy for $21 million.

In 2006 Duke sold a 50% stake in its real estate subsidiary Crescent Resources to Morgan Stanley Real Estate. That year the company bought an 825-MW power plant in Rockingham County North Carolina from Dynegy for $195 million.

In a major industry power move in 2006 the company bought energy provider Cinergy in a $9 billion stock swap. Reorganizing its business lines to focus on its US power businesses that year Duke Energy sold its commercial marketing and trading businesses to Fortis and in 2007 it spun off its natural gas transmission business as Spectra Energy. The company also exited the European energy marketing business; it also left the proprietary (third-party) energy trading business in North America (primarily made up of Duke Energy North America or DENA sold to LS Power Equity Partners for a reported $1.5 billion). Duke also wound down its energy-trading joint venture with Exxon Mobil.

In 2008 Duke moved to strengthen its alternative energy assets by buying wind energy producer Catamount Energy for about $240 million plus assumed debt. Catamount had about 500MW of renewable energy in operation.

That year as part of its refocusing on its energy businesses the company stopped reporting on its Crescent Resources unit (a joint venture with Morgan Stanley Real Estate Fund which manages land holdings and develops real estate projects).

EXECUTIVES

SVP and Chief Sustainability Officer, Roberta B. Bowman, age 57
Chairman President and CEO, James E. (Jim) Rogers, age 64
SVP and Controller, Steven K. Young, age 54
Chief Integration Officer, A. R. Mullinax, age 58
EVP; President Commercial Business, Marc E. Manly, age 60, $600,000 total compensation
EVP and Chief Legal Officer, Julia S. (Julie) Janson, age 48
SVP and Chief Procurement Officer, Ronald R. Reising, age 52
SVP Construction and Major Projects U.S. Franchised Electric and Gas, Richard W. (Rick) Haviland
SVP and Chief Communications Officer, Virginia S. (Ginny) Mackin
SVP Strategy Rates Wholesale Customers Commodities and Analytics, Paul R. Newton
EVP Regulated Utilities, Lloyd M. Yates, age 51
Group Executive and CFO, Lynn J. Good, age 52, $540,627 total compensation
SVP Federal Government and Regulatory Affairs, William F. (Bill) Tyndall
EVP; COO Regulated Utilities, B. Keith Trent, age 53, $500,004 total compensation
Group Executive Human Resources and Corporate Relations, Jennifer L. Weber, age 45
SVP and CTO, David W. Mohler
SVP Environmental Health and Safety President ? The Duke Energy Foundation, Richard T. (Stick) Williams
SVP Investor Relations and Treasurer, Stephen G. De May, age 50
SVP Power Delivery US Operations, Jim L. Stanley, age 57
SVP Audit Services and Chief Ethics and Compliance Officer, Jeffery G. Browning
President Duke Energy Indiana, Douglas F. (Doug) Esamann, age 54
Group Executive Chief Generation Officer and Chief Nuclear Officer, Dhiaa M. Jamil, age 56
President Duke Energy North Carolina, Brett C. Carter
SVP and Chief Customer Officer, Gianna M. Manes
VP Global Risk Management and Insurance and Chief Risk Officer, Swati V. Daji
SVP Wind Energy Development Duke Energy Generation Services, Tony Dorazio
President Duke Energy South Carolina, Catherine E. Heigel
SVP Commercial Transmission and Strategy Policy and Integration, Phillip C. (Phil) Grigsby
President Duke Energy Renewables, Gregory C. (Greg) Wolf
State President Florida, Alexander Glenn
Senior Vice President - Investor Relations; Treasurer, Stephen May
EVP Chief Legal Officer and Corporate Secretary, Julie S. Janson
State President Ohio and Kentucky, James P. Henning
President Midwest Commercial Generation, Chuck Whitlock
Director, John H. Forsgren, age 65
Director, Daniel R. (Dan) DiMicco, age 61
Director, James H. (Jim) Hance Jr., age 67
Director, G. Alex Bernhardt Sr., age 68
Director, Ann Maynard Gray, age 66
Director, Philip R. Sharp, age 69
Director, Michael G. Browning, age 65
Director, William (Bill) Barnet III, age 69
Director, James T. Rhodes, age 70
Director, E. James (Jim) Reinsch, age 68
Auditors: Deloitte&ToucheLLP

LOCATIONS

HQ: Duke Energy Corporation
550 South Tryon St., Charlotte NC 28202-4200
Phone: 704-594-6200 **Fax:** 704-382-3814
Web: www.duke-energy.com

2011 Sales

	$ mil.	% of total
US	13,062	90
Latin America	1,467	10
Total	**14,529**	**100**

PRODUCTS/OPERATIONS

2011 Sales

	$ mil.	% of total
Regulated electric	10,589	73
Non-regulated electric natural gas & other	3,383	23
Regulated natural gas	557	4
Total	**14,529**	**100**

COMPETITORS

AEP
AES
Avista
CenterPoint Energy
Constellation Energy Group
Dynegy
GenOnEnergy
Koch Industries Inc.
PG&E Corporation
Piedmont Natural Gas
Progress Energy
SCANA
SemGroup

El Paso Corporation	Southern Company
Energy Future	Tractebel Engineering
Entergy	TVA
Enterprise Products	Williams Companies
Exelon	

HISTORICAL FINANCIALS

Company Type: Public

Income Statement FYE: December 31

	REVENUE ($ mil.)	NET INCOME ($ mil.)	NET PROFIT MARGIN	EMPLOYEES
12/11	14,529	1,706	11.7%	18,249
12/10	14,272	1,320	9.2%	18,440
12/09	12,731	1,075	8.4%	18,680
12/08	13,207	1,362	10.3%	18,250
12/07	12,720	1,500	11.8%	17,800
Annual Growth	3.4%	3.3%	—	0.6%

2011 Year-End Financials

Debt ratio: 33.15%	No. of shares (mil.): 445
Return on equity: 7.49%	Dividends
Cash ($ mil.): 2,110	Yield: —
Current ratio: 124.46	Payout: 77.34%
Long-term debt ($ mil.): 18,679	Market value ($ mil.): 9,797

	STOCK PRICE ($) FY Close	P/E High/Low		PER SHARE ($) Earnings	Dividends	Book Value
12/11	22.00	6	4	3.84	0.00	51.13
12/10	17.81	6	5	3.00	0.00	50.84
12/09	17.21	7	5	2.49	0.00	49.85
12/08	15.01	6	4	3.21	0.00	49.50
12/07	20.17	6	5	3.54	0.00	50.39
Annual Growth	2.2%			2.1%	—	0.4%

E*TRADE Financial Corp.

E*TRADE wants you to use its services for nearly E*VERYTHING financial. A top online brokerage the company has more than 2.5 million retail account holders who can trade stock over the Internet (the majority of transactions) and by phone. E*TRADE also offers mutual funds options fixed income products exchange-traded funds and portfolio management services. For corporate clients the company performs market making trade clearing and employee stock option plan administration services. Subsidiary E*TRADE Bank offers deposits savings and credit cards online as well as at some 30 financial centers in major US cities; customers can transfer funds between their banking and brokerage accounts in real time.

E*TRADE's decision to move more strongly into banking –it aimed to triple its loan business –could not have come at a worse time as the credit crisis struck down banks and lenders around the world. The company suffered considerable losses tied to its home loan portfolio and investments in risky asset-backed securities. E*TRADE was given some needed relief in 2007 when an affiliate of hedge fund Citadel Investment Group provided it with a $2.5 billion cash pick-me-up. Citadel acquired the firm's securities portfolio at a discount and reshuffled its senior management team. The company is E*TRADE's second-largest shareholder with a nearly 10% stake plus board representation through Citadel CEO Ken Griffin; Citadel slightly reduced its stake in 2012. (Now the largest shareholder by a slim margin Fidelity also owns nearly 10% of the E*TRADE.)

The company refocused its efforts on its retail customer business and shed noncore operations. It has been hoarding reserves to counter loan losses and exited both its wholesale lending and direct lending operations. The company also shuttered its institutional brokerage business.

E*TRADE also decided to exit its international channels focusing on local trades and instead concentrate on providing cross-border trades of US securities. In 2009 and 2010 the company sold its local German Nordic and UK operations. E*TRADE currently maintains about a dozen retail brokerage websites in Europe the Middle East and the Pacific Rim in addition to the US.

All of the changes were not enough. In 2011 E*TRADE started looking to sell itself after its largest stockholder Citadel urged the company to explore its alternatives. Later that year it called off plans to find a buyer instead preferring to turn itself around. Its strategy to do so revolves around focusing on its brokerage business while continuing to mitigate credit losses in its loan portfolio.

While revenues slipped some 2% (to $2.4 billion) in 2011 the company reported positive net incomes for the first time in five years. Part of the earnings decrease was attributed to the company's dropping its trading prices as well as the elimination of all account activity fees which took place in 2010. The changes were part of the company's efforts to stay competitive as other brokerages drop their prices and to provide a more simple and transparent operating model for its customers. Additionally E*TRADE sold some $1 billion in savings accounts to Discover Financial Services in 2010 which boosted its revenues that year but comparatively impacted its earnings negatively in 2011. However the firm has been slowly cutting its loan losses as it rids itself of its troubled portfolio which helped it end 2011 in the black.

The company has been building up its financial consultant team with a focus on its most most lucrative clients. Through consultations with those customers E*TRADE has been able to improve their returns and boost its own brokerage accounts.

HISTORY

In 1982 physicist William Porter created Trade Plus an electronic brokerage service for stockbrokers; clients included Charles Schwab & Co. and Fidelity Brokerage Services. A decade later subsidiary E*TRADE Securities became CompuServe's first online securities trader.

In 1996 E*TRADE moved from the institutional side to retail when it launched its website. Christos Cotsakos (a Vietnam and FedEx veteran) became CEO and took the firm public. But there were problems: E*TRADE covered $1.7 million in customer losses and added backup systems after computer failure stymied user access. In 1997 it formed alliances with America Online and BANK ONE and ended the year with 225000 accounts.

The firm began to position itself globally in 1997 and 1998 opening sites for Australian Canadian German Israeli and Japanese customers. It offered its first IPO (Sportline USA) in 1997. Volume grew as Internet trading increased but technical glitches dogged E*TRADE. In 1999 day trading became fashionable and the company began running ads promoting prudent trading to counter criticism that online trading fosters a get-rich-quick mentality.

The company also continued to add services. In 1999 it teamed with Garage.com to offer affluent clients venture capital investments in young companies and launched online investment bank E*OFFERING with former Robertson Stephens & Co. chairman Sanford Robertson. (E*TRADE sold its stake in the bank to Wit Soundview —which later became SoundView Technology Group –the next year.) It also bought TIR Holdings which executes and settles multi-currency securities transactions.

Retail banking was a major focus in 2000. The company bought Telebanc Financial (now E*TRADE Financial) owner of Telebank an online bank with more than 100000 depositors and started E*TRADE Bank which offers retail banking products on the E*TRADE website. To provide clients with "real-world" access to their money it bought Card Capture Services an operator of more than 9000 ATMs across the US.

Continuing to expand its global reach E*TRADE bought the part of its E*TRADE UK joint venture it didn't already own; acquired Canadian firm VERSUS Technologies a provider of electronic trading services; and teamed with UBS Warburg to allow non-US investors to buy US securities without needing to trade in dollars. Later its E*Trade International Capital announced plans to offer IPOs to European investors.

In 2001 E*TRADE entered consumer lending when it bought online mortgage originator LoansDirect (now E*TRADE Mortgage). Also that year the company bought online brokerage Web Street and moved to the NYSE. In late 2002 E*TRADE Bank purchased Ganis Credit Corp. (a US-based unit of Germany's Deutsche Bank) to boost its consumer finance business.

E*TRADE purchased the online trading operations of Tradescape in mid-2002. The deal which cost E*TRADE $280 million was hashed out the previous April –just days after rival Ameritrade announced its acquisition of online brokerage Datek.

Cotsakos resigned in early 2003 days after the company issued a gloomy forecast (he also had been criticized for his 2001 pay of $80 million although he subsequently gave up about $20 million). He was replaced by company president Mitch Caplan who had been viewed as instrumental in the company's effort to integrate brokerage and banking operations.

In 2005 E*TRADE bought US-based online brokerage Harrisdirect from Bank of Montreal as well as the former J.P. Morgan Invest unit BrownCo which served experienced online traders. The acquisitions expanded its client base and helped the company to keep pace with TD Ameritrade (the result of the 2006 merger of rivals Ameritrade and TD Waterhouse).

E*TRADE built its wealth management operations in 2005 and 2006 by purchasing several money managers including Boston-area investment advisory firm Kobren Insight Management.

After E*TRADE got snared in the subprime mortgage crisis in 2007 Caplan stepped down. He was replaced in 2008 by Donald Layton a former executive with JPMorgan Chase.

Layton retired the following year. Company director Robert Druskin took over as chairman while Steven Freiberg became CEO. Freiberg was formerly a co-CEO of Citigroup's global consumer operations.

To raise additional cash it sold its Canadian operations to Scotiabank for more than $440 million in 2008. The following year it raised some $733 million in three separate stock offerings and exchanged another $1.7 billion in debt for convertible debentures.

EXECUTIVES

Chairman and Interim CEO, Frank J. Petrilli, age 61
EVP and Chief Marketing Officer, Nicholas A. (Nick) Utton, age 55, $519,231 total compensation
CEO and Director, Steven J. Freiberg, age 55
EVP and President E*TRADE Securities, Michael J. Curcio, age 50, $467,307 total compensation
EVP and COO, Gregory (Greg) Framke, age 52, $467,307 total compensation
EVP and President E*TRADE Bank, Peter Knitzer, age 53
EVP and CFO, Matthew J. Audette, age 37
EVP and Chief Risk Officer, Paul Brandow
EVP Secretary and General Counsel, Karl A. Roessner
EVP and Chief Human Resources Officer, Andrew Goodman
Director, Rodger A. Lawson, age 65
Director, Joseph M. Velli, age 53
Director, Ronald D. (Ron) Fisher, age 64
Director, Joseph L. (Joe) Sclafani, age 63
Director, Donna L. Weaver, age 68
Director, Frederick W. Kanner, age 68
Director, Rebecca (Becky) Saeger, age 56
CEO and Director, Steven J. Freiberg, age 55
Director, Kenneth C. (Ken) Griffin, age 43
Director, Michael K. Parks, age 52
Director, Stephen H. Willard, age 51
Auditors: Deloitte&ToucheLLP

LOCATIONS

HQ: E*TRADE Financial Corporation
1271 Avenue of the Americas 14th Fl., New York NY 10020
Phone: 646-521-4300 **Fax:** 801-486-5575
Web: www.fxenergy.com

PRODUCTS/OPERATIONS

2011 Sales

	$ mil.	% of total
Operating interest income		
Loans	692	29
Available-for-sale securities	421	18
Margin receivables	221	9
Held-to-maturity securities	137	6
Securities borrowed & other	60	3
Fees & service charges	130	6
Net gains on loans & securities	120	5
Other	39	2
Adjustments	(14.9)	

COMPETITORS

Charles Schwab
FMR
Morgan Stanley
Scottrade
ShareBuilder
Siebert Financial
TD Ameritrade
UBS Financial Services

HISTORICAL FINANCIALS

Company Type: Public

Income Statement FYE: December 31

	ASSETS ($ mil.)	NET INCOME ($ mil.)	INCOME AS % OF ASSETS	EMPLOYEES
12/11	47,940	156	0.3%	3,240
12/10	46,373	(28)	—	2,962
12/09	47,366	(1,297)	—	3,084
12/08	48,538	(511)	—	3,249
12/07	56,845	(1,441)	—	3,800
Annual Growth	(4.2%)	—	—	(3.9%)

2011 Year-End Financials

Debt ratio: 19.29%
Return on equity: 3.18%
Cash ($ mil.): 3,375
Current ratio: —
Long-term debt ($ mil.): 9,245
No. of shares (mil.): 285
Dividends
Yield: —
Payout: —
Market value ($ mil.): 2,272

	STOCK PRICE ($) FY Close	P/E High	P/E Low	PER SHARE ($) Earnings	Dividends	Book Value
12/11	7.96	30	13	0.54	0.00	17.27
12/10	16.00	—	—	(0.13)	0.00	18.35
12/09	1.76	—	—	(11.80)	0.00	19.80
12/08	1.15	—	—	(10.00)	0.00	45.99
12/07	3.55	—	—	(34.00)	0.00	61.38
Annual Growth	22.4%	—	—	—	—	(27.2%)

Eagle Bancorp Inc (MD)

For those nest eggs that need a little help hatching holding company Eagle Bancorp would recommend its community-oriented EagleBank subsidiary. The bank serves businesses and individuals through more than 15 branches in Washington DC and its suburbs. Deposit products include checking savings and money market accounts; certificates of deposit; and IRAs. Commercial real estate and construction real estate loans combined represent about 70% of its loan portfolio. The bank which has significant expertise as a Small Business Administration lender also writes business consumer and home equity loans. EagleBank offers insurance products through an agreement with The Meltzer Group.

The company has been focused on growing within its existing markets. After launching three new branches in 2011 it opened its 16th branch in Virginia in early 2012 and has another new branch on the way. In the past it has also expanded by buying other banks. In 2011 Eagle Bancorp planned to acquire Alliance Bankshares for some $31 million but the two firms terminated the agreement citing irreconcilable differences.

The company reported record net income for the third straight year in 2011 despite the difficult economic conditions that wrecked many banks' results. Profits increased by some 47% from 2010 to 2011. That year the company received a $56.6 million capital infusion due to its participation in the Small Business Lending Fund a recently formed Treasury program designed to encourage small business lending. To further fund its lending activities the company has been pushing such products as its money market accounts in its market.

In 2010 Eagle expanded its residential mortgage lending division in efforts to increase mortgage production volume. The expansion also helped raise the company's noninterest income by nearly half in 2011 as it sold most of the mortgages on the secondary markets rather than holding them on its books.

The company's strategy for further growth includes continuing to seek opportunities to open or acquire new banking locations while waiting out record low interest rates. Eagle's strict loan underwriting standards –it didn't write subprime residential mortgages and didn't buy securities backed by subprime mortgages –has helped it have fewer problem loans the downfall for many banks.

EXECUTIVES

Vice Chairman, Robert P. Pincus, age 65
EVP and CFO; EVP and CFO EagleBank, James H. Langmead, age 63, $243,100 total compensation
EVP; SEVP and COO EagleBank, Susan G. Riel, age 62, $243,100 total compensation
President Community Banking EagleBank, Thomas D. Murphy, age 64, $243,100 total compensation
Chairman President and CEO; Chairman and CEO EagleBank, Ronald D. (Ron) Paul, age 56, $350,000 total compensation
EVP EagleBank, Martha Foulon-Tonat, age 56, $243,100 total compensation
EVP and COO, Michael T. (Mike) Flynn, age 64, $236,080 total compensation
VP and Manager Marketing and Advertising, Janette S. Shaw
VP and Business Development Officer, Jenny A. Shtipelman
VP and Manager Business Development Sales, Deborah C. Shumaker
VP and Commercial Real Estate Loan Officer, Matthew Leydig
VP and Commercial Real Estate Loan Officer, James R. Walker
President Eagle Commercial Ventures, Richard D. Corrigan
President EagleBank Washington DC and Virginia, Barry C. Watkins
EVP and Chief Credit Officer EagleBank, Janice L. Williams, age 55
EVP and Controller, Diane M. Begg
EVP and Interim Chief Lending Officer EagleBank, Robert R. Hoffman
EVP and Senior Operating Officer, Kim Ray
SVP and Director Marketing, J. Mercedes Alvarez
SVP and Business Development Officer, Lawrence J. Bolton
SVP and Manager Branch Administration, Joseph L. Clarke
SVP and Director Customer Service, Elizabeth A. Ferrenz
SVP and Chief Risk Officer, Susan O. Kooker
SVP and Manager Information Technology, Linda M. Lacy
SVP and Consumer Loan Manager, R. Frederick Marsden
SVP and Group Leader Commercial Real Estate Lending Maryland, Thomas A. Mee
SVP and Manager Loan Administration, Joan Y. Pawloski
SVP and Chief Risk Officer, Cynthia A. Pehl
SVP and Group Leader Commercial Lending Washington DC, John B. Richardson
SVP and Manager Commercial Deposit Services, Susan J. Schumacher
SVP and Controller, Terrence D. Weber
VP and Commercial Deposit Services Officer, Maria G. Acosta
VP and Commercial Loan Real Estate Officer, Allan L. Acree
VP and Business Development Officer, Jacqueline Ames
VP and Commercial Loan Officer II, John A. Bettini
VP and Business Development Officer, Andrew S. Bridge
VP and Manager Deposit Operations, Judy L. Callaway
VP and Workout Recovery and Liquidation Officer, Michele Capone
VP and Commercial Loan Officer II, Horacio Chacon
VP and Market Manager, James R. Chittock
SVP and Branch Administration Manager, Terry Clarke

VP and Business Development Officer, Linda A. Dawkins
VP and SBA Lender, Michael L. Devito
VP and Market Manager, Juanita Douglas
VP and Credit Analyst II, P. Lucas Flynn
VP and Manager Wiire and Cash Room, Joan M. Grant
VP and Manager Loan Operations, Sharon A. Gray
VP and Manager Residential Mortgage Lending, Stephen L. Greene
VP and Commercial Loan Officer II, Timothy D. Hamilton
VP and Business Development Officer, Kai M. Hills
VP and Credit Analyst II, Jackie Ho
VP and Non-Profit Specialist, Malcolm S. Karl
VP and Branch Manager, Deborah J. Keller
VP and Commercial Loan Officer II, Scott S. Kinlaw
VP and Manager Branch Operations, Susan M. Lewis
VP and Workout Recovery and Liquidation Officer, Jodee Lichtenstein
VP and Commercial Loan Officer, K. Russel Marsh
VP and Director Compliance, Ludwell L. Miller III
VP and Commercial Loan Officer, Robin D. Powell
VP and Commercial Real Estate Loan Officer, Ryan A. Riel
VP and Commercial Loan Officer II, Kenneth S. Scales
VP and Commercial Real Estate Loan Officer, Carisa D. Stanley
VP and Credit Analyst II, Jane N. Willis
SVP Eagle Bancorp and EagleBank, Laurence E. (Larry) Bensignor
Vice Chairman, Robert P. Pincus, age 65
Director, Leonard L. Abel, age 85
Director, Neal R. Gross, age 69
Director, Dudley C. Dworken, age 62
Director, Leslie M. Alperstein, age 69
Director, Philip N. Margolius, age 72
Director, Leland M. Weinstein, age 50
Director, Harvey M. Goodman, age 56
Director, Donald R. Rogers, age 67
Director, Norman R. Pozez, age 57
Auditors: Stegman&Company

LOCATIONS

HQ: Eagle Bancorp Inc.
7815 Woodmont Ave., Bethesda MD 20814
Phone: 301-986-1800 **Fax:** 301-986-8529
Web: www.eaglebankmd.com

PRODUCTS/OPERATIONS

2011 Sales

	$ mil.	% of total
Interest		
Loans including fees	112	85
Securities	6	5
Other	0	-
Noninterest		
Gain on sale of loans	6	5
Service charges on deposits	3	2
Gain on sale of investment securities	1	1
Other	2	2
Total	**132**	**100**

Selected Subsidiaries

EagleBank
- Bethesda Leasing LLC
- Eagle Insurance Services LLC
- Fidelity Mortgage Inc.

Eagle Commercial Ventures LLC

COMPETITORS

Bank of America
BB&T
OBA Financial Services
PNC Financial
Capital One
First Mariner Bancorp
M&T Bank
Sandy Spring Bancorp
SunTrust

HISTORICAL FINANCIALS

Company Type: Public

Income Statement

FYE: December 31

	ASSETS ($ mil.)	NET INCOME ($ mil.)	INCOME AS % OF ASSETS	EMPLOYEES
12/11	2,831	24	0.9%	338
12/10	2,089	16	0.8%	292
12/09	1,805	10	0.6%	235
12/08	1,496	7	0.5%	235
12/07	846	7	0.9%	173
Annual Growth	35.2%	33.6%	—	18.2%

2011 Year-End Financials

Debt ratio: 1.74%
Return on equity: 9.21%
Cash ($ mil.): 210
Current ratio: —
Long-term debt ($ mil.): 49
No. of shares (mil.): 19
Dividends
Yield: —
Payout: —
Market value ($ mil.): 290

	STOCK PRICE ($) FY Close	P/E High	P/E Low	PER SHARE ($) Earnings	Dividends	Book Value
12/11	14.54	13	10	1.14	0.00	13.37
12/10	14.43	19	13	0.77	0.00	10.39
12/09	10.47	20	10	0.55	0.00	9.64
12/08	5.75	23	9	0.62	0.16	11.20
12/07	12.10	24	16	0.71	0.22	7.59
Annual Growth	4.7%	—	—	12.6%	—	15.2%

East West Bancorp, Inc

East West Bancorp is the holding company for East West Bank which operates more than 100 branches in California mainly in and around Los Angeles the San Francisco Bay area Orange County and Silicon Valley. The bank has more than 25 additional branches in the Atlanta Boston Houston New York and Seattle metropolitan areas as well as locations in China Hong Kong and Taiwan. Catering to the Asian-American community it provides international banking and trade financing to importers/exporters doing business in the Asia/Pacific region. East West Bank offers multilingual service in English Cantonese Mandarin Vietnamese and Spanish.

The bank also offers standard services such as personal and business loans checking and savings accounts insurance and merchant credit card processing services. Catering to the manufacturing wholesale trade and service sectors East West Bank focuses its lending activities on commercial and industrial real estate loans which account for about 60% of the company's loan portfolio. The bank also writes multifamily real estate residential mortgage construction business and consumer loans. Although East West Bancorp is highly involved in California's slumping commercial real estate market and it suffered its first yearly loss in nearly three decades in 2008 the company's strong liquidity and reserves has helped it weather the economic downturn.

East West Bancorp has expanded its market area through acquisitions. In 2009 the company acquired more than 60 branches and most of the banking operations of larger rival United Commercial Bank which had been seized by regulators. The deal gave East West Bank about 40 more California branches plus some 20 additional US locations beyond the state. Pre-tax gains from the transaction which included a loss-sharing agreement with the FDIC helped East West Bancorp return to profitability in fiscal 2009. The company kept the momentum going into 2010 as net interest margins improved.

Also in 2010 East West Bancorp made an unsolicited bid to acquire bankrupt real estate company Meruelo Maddux which owns about 50 properties in Southern California but the offer was rebuffed by both the target company and a bankruptcy court judge. East West Bancorp inherited some $27 million in loans to Meruelo Maddox as part of its takeover of United Commercial Bank and had hoped to turn convert the credit into an ownership stake in the property company.

In another 2010 deal East West Bancorp acquired the failed Washington First International Bank adding six branches in Seattle; the transaction also included a loss-sharing agreement with the FDIC.

EXECUTIVES

EVP Chief Risk Officer General Counsel and Secretary East West Bancorp and East West Bank, Douglas P. Krause, age 55, $217,005 total compensation
EVP, Donald S. Chow, age 61, $216,305 total compensation
President and COO East West Bancorp and East West Bank, Julia S. Gouw, age 52, $286,654 total compensation
Chairman and CEO East West Bancorp and East West Bank, Dominic Ng, age 53, $800,000 total compensation
EVP and Chief Credit Officer East West Bank, John Hall, age 56, $205,004 total compensation
EVP and Head North California Commercial Lending Division, William H. Fong, age 64
EVP and Director Corporate Banking East West Bank, Wellington Chen, age 52, $244,130 total compensation
EVP and Director International Trade Banking East West Bank, Kwok-Yin Cheng, age 59
Vice Chairman East West Bancorp and East West Bank, John Lee, age 80
EVP and Director Business Banking East West Bank, Andy Yen, age 54
EVP and Head International Banking East West Bank, Agatha Fung, age 52
EVP and Head Retail Banking and Technology, Karen Fukumura, age 47
EVP and CFO, Irene Oh
EVP and Director Loan Operations East West Bank, Ming Lin Chen, age 51
EVP and Director Credit Risk Management, Lawrence B. Schiff
EVP and Chief Human Resources Officer, James T. Schuler
Director, Peggy Tsiang Cherng, age 64
Vice Chairman; President and COO East West Bancorp and East West Bank, Julia S. Gouw, age 52
Director, Rudolph I. (Rudy) Estrada, age 64
Director, Herman Y. Li, age 59
Director, Jack C. Liu, age 53
Director, Keith W. Renken, age 77
Director, Paul H. Irving
Director, Iris S. Chan
Vice Chairman East West Bancorp and East West Bank, John Lee, age 80

Director, Andrew S. Kane, age 59
EVP and Director Credit Risk Management, Lawrence B. Schiff
Auditors: KPMGLLP

LOCATIONS

HQ: East West Bancorp Inc.
135 N. Los Robles Ave. 7th Fl., Pasadena CA 91101
Phone: 626-768-6000 **Fax:** 626-799-3167
Web: www.eastwestbank.com

PRODUCTS/OPERATIONS

2011 Sales

	$ mil.	% of total
Commercial lending	619	57
Retail banking	358	33
Other& adjustments	112	10
Total	**1,091**	**100**

COMPETITORS

Bank of America
Bank of East Asia
BBCN
Cathay General Bancorp
Citibank
City National
Comerica
Hanmi Financial
JPMorgan Chase
U.S. Bancorp
Wells Fargo
Wilshire Bancorp

HISTORICAL FINANCIALS

Company Type: Public

Income Statement FYE: December 31

	ASSETS ($ mil.)	NET INCOME ($ mil.)	INCOME AS % OF ASSETS	EMPLOYEES
12/11	21,968	245	1.1%	2,329
12/10	20,700	164	0.8%	2,131
12/09	20,559	76	0.4%	2,667
12/08	12,422	(49)	—	1,346
12/07	11,852	161	1.4%	1,472
Annual Growth	16.7%	11.1%	—	12.2%

2011 Year-End Financials

Debt ratio: 3.04%
Return on equity: 10.61%
Cash ($ mil.): 1,431
Current ratio: —
Long-term debt ($ mil.): 667
No. of shares (mil.): 149
Dividends
Yield: —
Payout: 10.00%
Market value ($ mil.): 2,949

	STOCK PRICE ($) FY Close	P/E High	P/E Low	PER SHARE ($) Earnings	Dividends	Book Value
12/11	19.75	15	9	1.60	0.00	15.48
12/10	19.55	23	16	0.83	0.04	14.23
12/09	15.80	49	9	0.33	0.05	20.78
12/08	15.97	—	—	(0.94)	0.40	24.33
12/07	24.23	16	9	2.60	0.40	18.56
Annual Growth	(5.0%)	—	—	(11.4%)	—	(4.4%)

Eastman Chemical Co.

Eastman Chemical can recall its past through photos —it was once part of film giant Eastman Kodak. The company is a major producer of chemicals fibers and plastics. It is one of the world's largest suppliers of acetate tow for cigarette filters. Eastman's products go into such items as food and medical packaging films and toothbrushes. In 2012 Eastman acquired US-based chemicals firm Solutia in a $4.7 billion cash-and stock deal. With the addition of Solutia Eastman becomes a top-tier specialty chemicals company. Its products include rubber materials specialty polymers (synthetic plastics) solvents adhesives plasticizers (additives to soften plastics such as PVC) and specialty fluids.

HISTORY

Eastman Chemical went public in 1994 but the company traces its roots to the 19th century. George Eastman after developing a method for dry-plate photography established the Eastman Dry Plate and Film Company in 1884 in Rochester New York (the name was changed to Eastman Kodak in 1892).

In 1886 Eastman hired scientist Henry Reichenbach to help create and manufacture new photographic chemicals. As time passed Reichenbach and the company's other scientists came up with chemicals that were either not directly related to photography or had uses in addition to photography.

Eastman bought a wood-distillation plant in Kingsport Tennessee in 1920 and formed the Tennessee Eastman Corporation to make methanol and acetone for the manufacture of photographic chemicals. The company by this time called Kodak introduced acetate yarn and Tenite a cellulose ester plastic in the early 1930s. During WWII the company formed Holston Defense to make explosives for the US armed forces.

Kodak began to vertically integrate Tennessee Eastman's operations during the 1950s acquiring A. M. Tenney Associates Tennessee Eastman's selling agent for its acetate yarn products in 1950. It also established Texas Eastman opening a plant in Longview to produce ethyl alcohol and aldehydes raw materials used in fiber and film production. At the end of 1952 Kodak created Eastman Chemical Products to sell alcohols plastics and fibers made by Tennessee Eastman and Texas Eastman. Also that year Tennessee Eastman developed cellulose acetate filter tow for use in cigarette filters. In the late 1950s the company introduced Kodel polyester fiber.

Kodak created Carolina Eastman Company in 1968 opening a plant in Columbia South Carolina to produce Kodel and other polyester products. It also created Eastman Chemicals Division to handle its chemical operations.

In the late 1970s Eastman Chemicals Division introduced polyethylene terephthalate (PET) resin used to make containers. It acquired biological and molecular instrumentation manufacturer International Biotechnologies in 1987.

Eastman Chemicals Division became Eastman Chemical Company in 1990. In 1993 it exited the polyester fiber business. When Kodak spun off Eastman Chemical in early 1994 the new company was saddled with $1.8 billion in debt.

Eastman's 1996 earnings were reduced when oversupply lowered prices for PET. Eastman opened plants in Argentina Malaysia and the Netherlands in 1998.

Eastman added to its international locations in 1999 by opening a plant in Singapore and an office in Bangkok. It also bought Lawter International (specialty chemicals for ink and coatings) with locations in Belgium China and Ireland. In 2000 the company began restructuring into two business segments (chemicals and polymers) and acquired resin and colorant maker McWhorter Technologies.

In 2001 Eastman acquired most of Hercules' resins business. In November the company announced that it had postponed plans to split into two companies (one focusing on specialty chemicals and plastics the other concentrating on polyethylene plastics and acetate fibers) until mid-2002 due to the weak economy. In early 2002 the company announced that it had cancelled those plans altogether and would operate the two as separate divisions.

The following year Eastman announced it would split off part of its coatings adhesives specialty polymers and inks (CASPI) segment. The division had been underperforming and had been hit particularly hard by the high costs of raw materials and a general overcapacity in the marketplace. Eastman sold a portion of CASPI to investment firm Apollo Management for $215 million. Businesses included in the sale were composites inks and graphic arts raw materials liquid and powder resins and textile chemicals. (Apollo called the acquired businesses Resolution Specialty Materials and then joined RSM with Resolution Performance Products and another of its chemical companies Borden Chemical to form the new Hexion Specialty Chemicals in 2005.)

It restructured its divisional alignment in 2006 in an attempt to group together related product groups and technologies. In the process Eastman disbanded its former Voridian Division.

At the end of 2007 the company decided to divest its PET facilities in the UK and the Netherlands as well as its Dutch PTA plants. Eastman sold the facilities to Indorama for about $330 million.

Chairman and CEO Brian Ferguson retired in 2009 after nearly seven years as CEO. James Rogers who had been president of the company and head of the chemicals and fibers group became his successor and Ferguson became executive chairman.

In 2009 the company joined with SK Chemicals in a joint venture to construct a cellulose acetate tow facility in Ulsan South Korea. Eastman owns 80% of the JV and operates the plant. It also bought a facility in China in 2010 in a joint venture with Mazzucchelli 1849 SPA. The previous year Eastman had expanded an acetate tow facility it owns in the UK.

Eastman Chemical acquired Genovique Specialties Corporation a global provider of benzoate plasticizers from Arsenal Capital Partners in 2010. Genovique produces benzoic acid sodium benzoate and specialty plasticizers with operations in North America Europe and Asia.

EXECUTIVES

Chairman and CEO, James P. (Jim) Rogers, age 61, $799,183 total compensation
SVP Chief Legal and Administrative Officer, Theresa K. Lee, age 60, $424,769 total compensation
SVP and CFO, Curtis E. (Curt) Espeland, age 47, $410,288 total compensation
EVP Performance Chemicals and Intermediates Fibers Engineering and Construction and Manufacturing Support, Ronald C. Lindsay, age 53, $421,164 total compensation
EVP Specialty Polymers Coatings and Adhesives and Chief Marketing Officer, Mark J. Costa, age 45, $444,077 total compensation
SVP and CTO, Gregory W. (Greg) Nelson, age 49, $311,326 total compensation
VP Controller and Chief Accounting Officer, Scott V. King, age 43
SVP Fibers and Global Supply Chain, Richard L. Johnson, age 62
Media Contact, Tracy Broadwater
SVP and Chief International Ventures Officer, Michael H.K. Chung, age 58

SVP and Chief Regional and Sustainability Officer, Godefroy A.F.E. Motte, age 53
Media Relations Contact, Susan Hickey
Investor Relations Contact, Brett Goodman
Director Information Security and Services, Karen Carman
VP and CIO, Keith Sturgill, age 49
SVP Chief Legal Officer and Corporate Secretary, David A Golden
SVP Chief Human Resources Officer, Perry Stuckey III
Director, Lewis M. (Lew) Kling, age 67
Director, Stephen R. (Steve) Demeritt, age 68
Director, Robert M. Hernandez, age 67
Director, Renee J. Hornbaker, age 59
Director, Thomas H. (Tom) McLain, age 54
Director, David W. Raisbeck, age 62
Director, Michael P. Connors, age 56
Director, Howard L. Lance, age 56
Director, Brett D. Begemann, age 51
Director, Humberto P. (Bert) Alfonso
Director, Gary E. Anderson, age 67
Director, Julie F Holder
Auditors: PricewaterhouseCoopersLLP

LOCATIONS

HQ: Eastman Chemical Company
200 S. Wilcox Dr. PO Box 431, Kingsport TN 37662
Phone: 423-229-2000 **Fax:** 215-672-8900
Web: corp.mace.com/

2011 Sales

	$ mil.	% of total
US & Canada	3,824	53
Asia/Pacific	1,681	23
Europe Middle East & Africa	1,352	19
Latin America	321	5
Total	**7,178**	**100**

PRODUCTS/OPERATIONS

2011 Sales

	$ mil.	% of total
PCI	2,860	40
Fibers	1,279	18

COMPETITORS

Akzo Nobel
BASF SE
Celanese
Clariant
DIC Corporation
Dow Chemical
DSM
DuPont
ExxonMobil Chemical
Honeywell Specialty Materials
Huntsman Corp
Rhodia
Solvay

HISTORICAL FINANCIALS

Company Type: Public

Income Statement FYE: December 31

	REVENUE ($ mil.)	NET INCOME ($ mil.)	NET PROFIT MARGIN	EMPLOYEES
12/11	7,178	696	9.7%	10,000
12/10	5,842	438	7.5%	10,000
12/09	5,047	136	2.7%	10,000
12/08	6,726	346	5.1%	10,500
12/07	6,830	300	4.4%	10,800
Annual Growth	1.3%	23.4%	—	(1.9%)

2011 Year-End Financials

Debt ratio: 25.84%
Return on equity: 37.22%
Cash ($ mil.): 777
Current ratio: 206.64
Long-term debt ($ mil.): 1,445
No. of shares (mil.): 136
Dividends
Yield: —
Payout: 20.37%
Market value ($ mil.): 5,348

	STOCK PRICE ($) FY Close	P/E High/Low		PER SHARE ($) Earnings	Dividends	Book Value
12/11	39.06	22	7	4.86	0.00	13.66
12/10	84.08	28	17	2.96	0.90	11.51
12/09	60.24	65	19	0.93	0.88	10.45
12/08	31.71	34	12	2.28	0.88	10.72
12/07	61.09	39	32	1.79	0.88	13.07
Annual Growth	(10.6%)	—	—	28.4%	—	1.1%

Eastman Kodak Co.

When Kodak made Brownies folks said "Cheese!" The Brownie camera inventor Kodak has retouched its image and is exiting the camera business. Production of digital cameras and picture frames pocket video cameras and Kodachrome color film has stopped. Kodak's future is in its brand-licensing business along with providing such products as home photo printers commercial inkjet presses and workflow software and packaging. In September 2012 Kodak reorganized into three segments: Digital Printing and Enterprise (DP&E); Graphics Entertainment and Commercial Films (GECF); and (to be sold) Personalized Imaging and Document Imaging. The move follows a decision to file for Chapter 11 bankruptcy in early 2012.

HISTORY

After developing a method for dry-plate photography George Eastman established The Eastman Dry Plate and Film Company in 1884. In 1888 it introduced its first camera a small easy-to-use device that was loaded with enough film for 100 pictures. Owners mailed the camera back to the company which returned it with the pictures and more film. The firm settled on the name Eastman Kodak in 1892 after Eastman tried many combinations of letters starting and ending with "k" which he thought was a "strong incisive sort of letter." The user-friendly Brownie camera followed in 1900. Three years later Kodak introduced a home movie camera projector and film.

Ailing and convinced that his work was done Eastman committed suicide in 1932. Kodak continued to dominate the photography industry with the introduction of color film (Kodachrome 1935) and a handheld movie camera (1951). The company established US plants to produce the chemicals plastics and fibers used in its film production.

The Instamatic introduced in 1963 became Kodak's biggest success. The camera's foolproof film cartridge eliminated the need for loading in the dark. By 1976 Kodak had sold an estimated 60 million Instamatics 50 million more cameras than all its competitors combined. Subsequent introductions included the Kodak instant camera (1976) and the unsuccessful disc camera (1982).

In the 1980s Kodak diversified into electronic publishing batteries floppy disks (Verbatim 1985 sold 1990) pharmaceuticals (Sterling Drug sold 1994) and do-it-yourself and household products (L&F Products sold 1994).

Kodak entered a joint research and development project with four Japanese photo giants (Canon Nikon Minolta and Fuji Photo Film) in 1992 to develop the Advanced Photography System. Also that year the company introduced the Photo CD a CD capable of storing photographs.

George Fisher former chairman of Motorola became Kodak's chairman and CEO in 1993. Fisher began cutting debt by selling noncore assets. Kodak spun off Eastman Chemical in 1994. Sales in 1996 included its money-losing copier sales and services business.

Kodak wrote off nearly $1.5 billion in 1997 mostly because of costs related to the layoffs. That year Kodak bought the document management operations from Wang Laboratories (now part of Getronics) and the next year it formed deals to expand its digital offerings including a collaboration with Intel and Adobe Systems allowing consumers to manipulate print and send personal photos from their PCs. Kodak acquired the medical imaging business of Imation in 1998 but it also unloaded more of its noncore operations including its 450-store Fox Photo chain.

President and COO Daniel Carp replaced Fisher as CEO in early 2000. Also that year Kodak formed a joint venture with computer giant Hewlett-Packard to develop photofinishing equipment for digital photography; extended its push into the online photo business by buying the remaining shares (it already owned 51%) of PictureVision a digital image storage service; and acquired Lumisys a maker of digital imaging systems for the medical industry.

In early 2001 Kodak announced a three-year plan to introduce camera and film vending machines in about 10000 high-traffic US locations (amusement parks zoos airports ski resorts and other tourist spots). The company also completed its acquisition of Bell & Howell's ProQuest (now Voyager Learning Center) imaging operations. In April former Avaya executive Patricia Russo was named president and COO; Carp remained chairman and CEO. Also in 2001 Kodak acquired Ofoto (rebranded in early 2005 as Kodak Imaging Network) a provider of online photo albums (EasyShare Gallery) that friends and families of registered users can view and download.

Further hits to the economy and Kodak's revenue prompted management in 2001 to eliminate regional divisions and realign the business along product lines. In December Kodak and SANYO Electric Co. announced the formation of a business venture to manufacture OLED displays for cameras PDAs and other devices. In January 2002 Russo left to rejoin Lucent Technologies; Carp assumed her responsibilities as president and COO. In May Kodak renewed a multi-year agreement that secured its position as the exclusive imaging supplier of film and related products for The Walt Disney Company.

In April 2003 former Hewlett-Packard executive Antonio Perez was named president and COO and in June Kodak closed its only single-use camera factory in the US and shifted operations overseas. A month later Kodak said it would purchase Practiceworks a dental imaging and software business. In July the company announced it would cut as many as 6000 jobs worldwide. This came after reducing as many as 2200 jobs in the US and Western Europe earlier in the year and cutting as many as 7000 jobs worldwide in 2002. In October Kodak purchased LaserPacific Media Corporation which provides post-production film editing and processing for television video and motion pictures. In November the company purchased Algotec Systems; a developer of advanced picture-archiving-and-communications systems (PACS).

In January 2004 the company completed its purchase of Scitex Digital Printing (now Kodak Versamark). The company makes commercial high-speed inkjet printers. Also in January on the heels of its announcement that it would stop selling film-based cameras in Western markets by year's end Kodak said it would also stop global production of its Advantix Advanced Photo System (APS) cameras but production of APS film would not be affected. In February Kodak Japan purchased the outstanding shares of digital camera developer Chinon Industries (it already owned about 60% of the company) and made it a wholly owned subsidiary. In September 2004 Kodak purchased the imaging business of National Semiconductor which makes metal oxide image-sensor chips for cell phones and small cameras and folded it into its Image Sensor Solutions (ISS) organization. Foveon patent-holder for an image sensor used in high-end digital cameras was not included in the acquisition. (National holds an unspecified stake in Foveon.)

Kodak sold its Remote Sensing Systems (RSS) business (including the Research Systems subsidiary) to optical imaging component maker ITT Corporation in early 2004. The RSS unit designed satellite imaging systems for the aerospace and defense industries. The sale was in line with the company's strategy to focus on digital technologies and consumer and health imaging. It also acquired the Digital Print division of Heidelberger Druckmaschinen as well as the company's 50% interest in NexPress maker of high-end digital color printing systems.

In May Kodak completed a licensing agreement for Lexar Media to make Kodak-branded memory cards. The company renamed its Commercial Printing group to the Graphic Communications group which consists of the Encad NexPress and Versamark subsidiaries as well as the management of its Kodak Polychrome Graphics. Also that month the company announced a deal with one of China's largest telecommunications companies CHINA PUTIAN involving the sale of the company's mobile phones in Kodak's some 9000 film and digital developing outlets throughout China.

In February 2005 Kodak changed the name of its Health Imaging Group to Health Group to reflect its increasing focus on health care information technology with the development of digital equipment and technology systems such as Kodak Carestream Solutions. A couple years later Kodak sold its Health Group to Onex Corporation. In March Kodak acquired Israel's OREX Computerized Radiography Ltd. for more than $50 million in cash. OREX's compact radiography systems convert medical and dental X-ray images eliminate the need for film and chemicals and produce images that can be sent digitally for remote diagnosis. In mid-2005 Kodak said that it would phase out production of black-and-white photographic paper manufactured at one of its plants in Brazil by the end of the year. The company attributed its exit from the business to a move from chemical-based photography to digital imaging and a 25% decline in demand for black-and-white paper annually. In late 2005 Kodak announced changes related to its 2004 restructuring program that included consolidating color photographic paper manufacturing for North America closing a Rochester operation that recycles waste to produce Estar polyester film base and reducing capacity for the production of consumer film products at its Xiamen China plant.

Antonio Perez who took over as president and CEO in mid-2005 added the title of chairman in January 2006 when Dan Carp retired. Also that year Kodak inked a service and support agreement with now-defunct Fischer Imaging Corporation to provide post-sale support (including repair and maintenance) for Fischer's mammography products (such as SenoScan and MammoTest) installed worldwide.

In December 2009 the company sold its organic light-emitting diode (OLED) business to LG Electronics. The technology was pioneered by Kodak in the 1970s.

In March 2011 Kodak acquired the assets of the relief plate business of Tokyo Ohka Kogyo. The business became part of Kodak's Prepress Solutions unit and will conduct business under the name of Yamanashi RPB Supply Company.

Unable to find a buyer for 10% of its patents portfolio to raise a needed $3 billion to continue operating its business Kodak in 2012 filed for bankruptcy protection.

EXECUTIVES

SVP and Chief Marketing Officer; President Consumer Digital Imaging, Pradeep Jotwani, age 57
Treasurer, William G. Love
SVP, Robert L. (Bob) Berman, age 54, $358,566 total compensation
VP; VP Worldwide Strategic Account Management and New Business Development, Michael A. Korizno
SVP; President Film Photofinishing and Entertainment Group, Brad W. Kruchten, age 51
Manager Community Affairs Global Diversity and Community Affairs, David Kassnoff
Chairman and CEO, Antonio M. Perez, age 66, $988,660 total compensation
VP; General Manager Digital Capture & Imaging Devices, John Blake
VP and CIO, Kim E. VanGelder
VP; Director Communications and Public Affairs, Gerard K. Meuchner, age 47
VP; General Manager Internet and Software Services Consumer Digital Imaging Group, Victor Cho, age 41
VP; General Manager Digital Imaging Systems & Customer Growth Graphic Communications Group, Michael L. Marsh, age 53
President, Philip J. (Phil) Faraci, age 56, $651,950 total compensation
General Counsel and Secretary, Patrick M. Sheller, age 50
SVP and CTO, Terry R. Taber, age 57
Manager Worldwide Public Relations Business to Business Group, Nancy Carr
VP; General Manager Digital Printing Solutions, Isidre Rosello
President and COO, Laura G. Quatela, age 54
VP; VP and General Manager Prepress Solutions Graphic Communications Group, Douglas J. Edwards
VP; Managing Director Americas Region, John O'Grady
VP; General Manager Business Solutions and Services, Dolores K. Kruchten
SVP, Antoinette P. (Ann) McCorvey, age 55
VP; General Manager Retail Systems Solutions Consumer Digital Imaging Group, Nicoletta A. (Nicki) Zongrone, age 53
VP and Chief Customer Officer; General Manager Worldwide Regional Operations, Gustavo Oviedo, age 59
VP; President and General Manager Entertainment Imaging Film Photofinishing and Entertainment Group, Kimberly A. (Kim) Snyder, age 49
VP, Stephen Green, age 55
VP; Managing Director Corporate Development, Jeremy R. Salesin, age 48
Chief Accounting Officer and Controller, Eric Samuels, age 44
VP; General Manager Film Capture Paper & Output Systems Film Photofinishing & Entertainment Group, Steven Decker, age 50
VP; General Manager Consumer Inkjet Systems, Susan H. Tousi
Manager Corporate Communications, Christopher (Chris) Veronda
Manager Public Relations Worldwide Public Relations Business to Consumer Group, Krista Gleason
Manager Public Relations Worldwide Public Relations Business to Consumer Group, Jacqueline Mangione
Manager Worldwide Public Relations Business to Business Group, Jack Kasperski
Manager Marketing Image Sensor Solutions, Michael (Mike) Deluca
Director Communications FPEG Industrial Films Group, Kelly Mandarano
Worldwide Marketing Communications and Public Relations Film Photofinishing and Entertainment Imaging (FPEG), Audrey Jonckheer
Director Marketing Americas, Judith Doherty
Director Communication Chief Technical Office, Bruce Graham
General Manager Unified Workflow Solutions Business Solutions and Services, Jon Bracken
General Manager Document Imaging Business Solutions and Services Group, Anthony (Tony) Barbeau
Director Channel Development United States and Canada, Don Whaley
Director and VP Business to Business Marketing, Chris Payne
VP and Director Marketing Business Solutions and Services Group, Michael Lo
Worldwide VP Customer Development Digital Printing Solutions, Eric Owen
Manager Channel Sales United States and Canada Document Imaging, Daniel T. McAtee
Director Business Development United States and Canada Document Imaging, Brian Bagan
Chief Data Steward, Syam Chodagiri
Director Pension Investments, Timothy Barrett
VP Corporate Finance and Director Investor Relations, Sandra E. (Sandy) Rowland, age 41
Assistant Director Employee Communications, Alan Brakoniecki
Director Worldwide Public Relations for Consumer and Commercial Markets Chief Marketing Office, Erin Foster
Director Customer Marketing, Gudrun Baunach
Manager Worldwide Public Relations Business to Business Group, Jonathan Ghent
VP; Managing Director Intellectual Property Transactionsv, Timothy M. Lynch
Chief Diversity and Community Affairs Officer; Director Human Resources and Commercial Segment; VP, Augustin Melendez
Director, Douglas R. (Doug) Lebda, age 41
Director, Dennis F. (Denny) Strigl, age 64
Director, William H. (Bill) Hernandez, age 62
Director, Joel Seligman, age 61
Director, Richard S. (Rick) Braddock, age 69
Director, Herald Y. Chen, age 41
Director, Timothy M. (Tim) Donahue, age 62
Director, Adam H. Clammer, age 41
Director, Delano E. Lewis, age 73
Director, Laura D' Andrea Tyson, age 63
Director, William G. (Bill) Parrett, age 65
Director, Michael Hawley, age 49
Director, Kyle P. Legg, age 60
Auditors: PricewaterhouseCoopersLLP

LOCATIONS

HQ: Eastman Kodak Co.
343 State Street, Rochester, NY 14650
Phone: 585 724-4000
Web: www.kodak.com

2011 Sales

	$ mil.	% of total
US	2,043	34
Europe Middle East & Africa	1,973	33
Asia/Pacific	1,239	20
Canada & Latin America	767	13
Total	**6,022**	**100**

PRODUCTS/OPERATIONS

2011 Sales

	$ mil.	% of total
Products	5,113	85
Licensing & royalties	781	13
Services	128	2
Total	**6,022**	**100**

2011 Sales

	$ mil.	% of total
Graphic Communications Group	2,736	45
Consumer Digital Imaging Group	1,739	29
Film Photofinishing & Entertainment Group	1,547	26
Total	**6,022**	**100**

Selected Products and Services

Commercial inkjet printing systems
Commercial printing workflow software
Consumer and professional photographic film
Digital picture frames
Document scanners
Electrophotographic equipment
Inkjet printers
Origination and print films
Photographic paper
Prepress equipment
Processing chemicals
Retail printing kiosks APEX drylab systems and related media
Wholesale photofinishing services

COMPETITORS

3M
Agfa
CASIO COMPUTER
Dell
FUJIFILM
Hewlett-Packard
Konica Minolta
Lexmark
NEC
Olympus
Panasonic Corp
Philips Electronics
Procter & Gamble
Ricoh Company
Sharp Corp.
Shutterfly
Sony
Xerox

HISTORICAL FINANCIALS

Company Type: Private

Income Statement

FYE: December 31

	REVENUE ($ mil.)	NET INCOME ($ mil.)	NET PROFIT MARGIN	EMPLOYEES
12/11	6,022	(764)	—	17,100
12/10	7,187	(687)	—	18,800
12/09	7,606	(210)	—	20,250
12/08	9,416	(442)	—	24,400
12/07	10,301	676	6.6%	26,900
Annual Growth	(12.6%)	—	—	(10.7%)

	STOCK PRICE ($) FY Close	P/E High/Low		PER SHARE ($) Earnings	Dividends	Book Value
12/11	0.65	—	—	(2.84)	0.00	(8.67)
12/10	5.36	—	—	(2.56)	0.00	(4.01)
12/09	4.22	—	—	(0.78)	0.25	(0.13)
12/08	6.58	—	—	(1.57)	0.50	3.58
12/07	21.87	13	9	2.35	0.50	10.52
Annual Growth	(58.5%)	—	—	—	—	—

2011 Year-End Financials

Debt ratio: 32.39%
Return on equity: 987650001000000.00%
Cash ($ mil.): 861
Current ratio: 125.72
Long-term debt ($ mil.): 1,363
No. of shares (mil.): 271
Dividends
Yield: —
Payout: —
Market value ($ mil.): 176

eBay Inc.

I got it on eBay has barreled its way into the lexicon of the new millennium placing a cyber-grin on the corporate face of this online auctioneer. Trading about $2000 worth of goods every second eBay offers an online forum for selling merchandise worldwide from fine antiques to the latest video games. eBay generates revenue through listing and selling fees and through advertising and boasts more than 100 million users. Its online payments assets consist of PayPal and Bill Me Later; other e-commerce platforms include StubHub and Half.com. eBay also has a mobile version of its service and owns e-commerce services provider GSI Commerce as well as a minority stake in online classifieds service craigslist.

HISTORY

cPierre Omidyar created a flea market in cyberspace when he launched online auction service Auction Web on Labor Day weekend in 1995. Making a name for itself largely through word of mouth the company incorporated in 1996 the same year it began to charge a fee to auction items online. That year it enhanced its service with Feedback Forum (buyer and seller ratings).

The company changed the name to eBay in 1997 and began promoting itself through advertising. By the middle of that year eBay was boasting nearly 800000 auctions each day and Benchmark Capital came on board as a significant financial backer.

Margaret ("Meg") Whitman a former Hasbro executive replaced Omidyar as CEO in early 1998. EBay made a blockbuster debut as a public company later that year. The company moved closer to household name status the same year by launching a national ad campaign and inking alliance deals with AOL and WebTV.

eBay showed its acquisitive streak in 1999 with purchases of Alando (online auctions in Germany) and Billpoint (person-to-person credit card technology). It also made one of its first investments in an outside company with the purchase of 6% of TradeOut.com an online seller of corporate surplus materials. The company set the jewel in its 1999 acquisition crown when it acquired upscale auction house Butterfield & Butterfield (now just Butterfields). eBay also expanded down under through a joint venture with Australia-based ecorp (formerly PBL Online). A bit of the bloom came off the rose in 1999 when online service interruptions (one "brownout" in June persisted for 22 hours) revealed a chink in eBay's armor. The company called its top 10000 users to convey its apologies and pledged to improve its website's performance.

In 2000 eBay agreed to develop person-to-person and merchant-to-person auction sites for Disney's GO Network began distributing information through wireless products and joined with banking giant Wells Fargo to offer eBay sellers the option of accepting online checks. Also that year the US Department of Justice began an investigation to determine if eBay had violated antitrust laws in its dealings with competitors. In other legal news a class-action lawsuit was filed against the company claiming that eBay was an auctioneer and therefore must authenticate the items on its site. (A trial court dismissed the case in early 2001.)

Also in 2000 the company expanded into Japan through eBay Japan with computer firm NEC acquiring 30% of the Japanese subsidiary and eBay owning the rest; it also launched Canadian and Austrian sites. In addition eBay took an equity stake in online used-car dealer AutoTrader.com and launched a co-branded used-car auction website and it acquired online trading community Half.com.

eBay strengthened its European position in 2001 through the purchase of French Internet auction firm iBazar. It also launched sites in Ireland New Zealand and Switzerland. eBay made a deal that year to provide its e-commerce capabilities to Microsoft developers and to add business-to-business auctions to its consumer operations. In addition the company began offering virtual storefronts for retailers to sell fixed-price items and purchased auctioneer of foreclosed property HomesDirect. In late 2001 eBay sold its iBazar's Brazilian subsidiary to MercadoLibre Latin America's leading auction site in exchange for a 19.5% stake (now 18%) in MercadoLibre.

Disappointed with the performance of eBay Premiere (fine art and other high-end merchandise) in 2002 the company partnered with Sotheby's in a deal that moved Sotheby's entire online business into the eBay website replacing eBay Premiere (Sotheby's later pulled out of the deal citing lagging sales). eBay also sold its traditional auction house Butterfields and shuttered its eBay Japan operations after its dismal performance in that market. In 2003 the company continued to grow through acquisitions with its purchases of EachNet (after acquiring a minority stake in the Chinese e-commerce company in 2002) FairMarket and Internet Auction.

In 2004 eBay took several steps toward diversifying its business. It expanded its international presence through acquisitions in China and India and spent heavily to establish operations there. Three years later eBay shifted its China strategy entering into a joint venture with Chinese Internet gaming firm TOM Online.

The company purchased about a 25% stake in online classifieds provider craigslist and announced plans to offer a music downloading service. Overall in 2004 more than 60% of eBay's new registered users were in the international business.

2005 was a particularly acquisitive year for eBay. That year it picked up Internet listing site Rent.com for about $415 million. Then eBay's international classifieds group Kijiji (Swahili for "village") acquired London-based Gumtree.com and Spain's LoQUo.com a community-based listings website that operates sites for several Spanish cities alongside ones for France Germany Norway Portugal and the UK. Kijiji next acquired opusforum a local classifieds website based in Germany for an undisclosed sum.

Later in 2005 eBay closed on three major deals. It acquired Shopping.com —a provider of online comparison shopping and consumer reviews with sites in France the UK and the US –for about $635 million. It also purchased PayPal VeriSign's payment gateway business for about $370 million. Also in 2005 eBay acquired start-up online telecom service provider Skype of Luxembourg for nearly $3 billion. Skype's Web-based software allowed its 220 million registered users to make phone calls over the Internet. The acquisition proved costly however. eBay took about $1.5 billion in Skype-related charges in the third quarter of 2007.

Keeping the acquisitions rolling in 2006 eBay snatched up the leading Swedish online auctioneer Tradera.com for $48 million; eBay made the purchase to strengthen its Swedish trading opportunities in the future. Later in 2006 Internet powerhouse Yahoo! and eBay entered an agreement to join forces on advertising Web searches online payments (through eBay's PayPal platform) and a co-branded toolbar. Key elements of the arrangement's design included Yahoo! providing advertisements throughout eBay's site and the integration of PayPal into Yahoo!'s e-commerce infrastructure.

eBay bought German auction management software company Via-Online in 2007. Via-Online operated sales tool Afterbuy.com and eBay made the deal to ramp up support for its Germany sellers. Looking to diversify its online marketplace operations also that year eBay acquired ticket seller StubHub for about $310 million. The company followed that up with the significant $900 million purchase of Bill Me Later in 2008.

In 2008 eBay settled its long-running patent dispute with MercExchange agreeing to buy the three MercExchange patents it had been accused of violating. MercExchange had sued eBay in 2001 claiming that eBay's "Buy It Now" option infringed on its patent technology. A federal judge ruled that eBay should pay MercExchange $30 million in damages in the case. Terms of the settlement were not disclosed.

Later in 2008 eBay announced it would end its arrangement with LiveAuctioneers.com that allowed customers to participate in live auctions hosted by other companies. eBay said ending the deal allowed it to better concentrate on growing listings in its core product.

To encourage further growth in its auctions the company reduced fees and rolled out an improved matching feature in 2008. The feature implemented a ranking system that took into account time remaining feedback scores quality of listing pictures and other criteria.

Whitman who led eBay for a decade stepped down as president and CEO of the company in 2008. She was succeeded by John Donahoe who previously led the company's highest revenue-producing unit eBay Marketplaces. Also that year eBay acquired the California-based visual media company VUVOX Network to further develop rich media capabilities in the eBay marketplace.

In a program that ran through the bulk of 2009 eBay partnered with resurrected automaker General Motors to sell new cars online. Prospective buyers could place bids for vehicles from more than 225 GM dealers in California at gm.ebay.com. The program did not move as many cars as anticipated however prompting the automaker to halt sales and shift its attention to marketing. eBay in 2009 paid about $1 billion for a majority stake (99.2%) in Gmarket a leading online marketplace in South Korea.

eBay also sold a majority of Skype in 2009. Four years after investing in the service eBay acknowledged that Skype did not complement the rest of its operations. It sold off a 70% stake in Skype to investors led by the private-equity firm Silver Lake in a deal involving $1.9 billion in cash and a $125 million note. As part of the agreement eBay retained a 30% interest in the Skype. (eBay had purchased Skype for nearly $3 billion but in 2007 it took a write-down for about half that amount.) eBay sold its share in Skype to Microsoft in 2011.

In 2010 eBay acquired popular German shopping site Brands4Friends for about $200 million. It made the deal to become a leading online fashion destination in Europe. The company continued its shopping spree in Germany the following year when it bolstered PayPal assets by acquiring the German company BillSAFE adding over 15 million accounts. The deal gave eBay purchase-on-invoice capabilities that are popular to merchants and consumers in Austria German the Netherlands and Switzerland.

eBay bought mobile software application developer Critical Path in 2010. Critical Path had worked with eBay to develop several of its applications for Apple's iPhone. The acquisition doubled the size of eBay's mobile team which is working to capitalize on the growing numbers of consumers who are shopping on their smart phones.

In its largest acquisition since purchasing Skype in 2011 eBay bought GSI Commerce a provider of such services as website development and maintenance order fulfillment and digital advertising for $2.4 billion.

In 2012 eBay sold Rent.com to PRIMEDIA.

EXECUTIVES

President eBay Global Marketplaces, Devin N. Wenig, age 45
SVP Legal Affairs General Counsel and Secretary, Michael R. Jacobson, age 57, $393,079 total compensation
Chairman, Pierre M. Omidyar, age 44
SVP Finance and CFO, Robert H. (Bob) Swan, age 51, $778,846 total compensation
President CEO and Director, John J. Donahoe, age 51, $934,615 total compensation
SVP Human Resources, Elizabeth L. (Beth) Axelrod, age 49, $480,135 total compensation
VP Mobile and Platform Business Solutions, Steve Yankovich
CTO and SVP Global Products Marketplaces, Mark T. Carges, age 50, $571,154 total compensation
President GSI, Christopher D. (Chris) Saridakis, age 43
SVP Corporate Communications, Alan Marks, age 49
VP Product Management Search, Scott Prevost
VP Technology Marketplaces, Raji Arasu
VP Social Commerce, Don Bradford
VP Global Product Management, Dane Glasgow
Senior Director Global Data Center Strategy Architecture and Operations, Dean Nelson
Chief Information Security Officer, Dave Cullinane
Director, Marc L. Andreessen, age 40
Director, Dawn G. Lepore, age 58
Director, William C. (Bill) Ford Jr., age 54
Director, Fred D. Anderson, age 68
Director, Richard T. Schlosberg III, age 67
Director, David M. Moffett, age 60
Director, Edward W. (Ned) Barnholt, age 69
Director, Scott D. Cook, age 59
President CEO and Director, John J. Donahoe, age 51
Director, Thomas J. (Tom) Tierney, age 58
Auditors: PricewaterhouseCoopersLLP

LOCATIONS

HQ: eBay Inc.
2145 Hamilton Ave., San Jose CA 95125
Phone: 408-376-7400 **Fax:** 408-516-8811
Web: www.ebay.com

2011 Sales

	$ mil.	% of total
US	5,483	47
International	6,168	53
Total	**11,651**	**100**

PRODUCTS/OPERATIONS

2011 Sales

	$ mil.	% of total
Marketplaces	6,641	57
Payments	4,412	38
GSI	590	5

Selected Operations

Marketplaces
- eBay.com
- Half.com
- Shopping.com
- StubHub

Payments
- Paypal
- Bill Me Later

GSI

Selected eBay.com Auction Categories

Antiques
Automobiles
Books
Coins and paper money
Collectibles
Computers
Electronics
Dolls and bears
DVDs and movies
Jewelry and watches
Pottery and glass
Real estate
Sports memorabilia
Toys and hobbies

Selected Mergers & Acquisitions

2011
- GSI Commerce ($2.4 billion; King of Prussia PA; e-commerce services provider)
- Zong ($240 million; San Jose CA; cell phone payments provider)

2010
- Critical Path (Portland OR; mobile software application developer)
- Brands4Friends ($200 million; Berlin; German shopping site)

COMPETITORS

AKQA
Alibaba.com
Amazon.com
Blast Radius Inc.
Buy.com
Christie' s
Collectors Universe
Convergys
Costco Wholesale
Digital River
Digitas
Enable Holdings
Etsy
First Data
Gallery of History
Google
Half Price Books
HSN
J. C. Penney
K-tel
MasterCard
Microsoft
MSN
NexTag
Office Depot
OfficeMax
OnlineAuction
Overstock.com
PriceGrabber.com
QVC
Royal Bank of Scotland
Sam' s Club
Sears
Shopzilla
Sotheby' s
Spectrum Group
Staples
Target Corporation
Tickets.com
Visa Inc
Walmart.com
Yahoo!

HISTORICAL FINANCIALS

Company Type: Public

Income Statement

FYE: December 31

	REVENUE ($ mil.)	NET INCOME ($ mil.)	NET PROFIT MARGIN	EMPLOYEES
12/11	11,651	3,229	27.7%	27,770
12/10	9,156	1,800	19.7%	17,700
12/09	8,727	2,389	27.4%	16,400
12/08	8,541	1,779	20.8%	16,200
12/07	7,672	348	4.5%	15,500
Annual Growth	11.0%	74.5%	—	15.7%

2011 Year-End Financials

Debt ratio: 7.65%
Return on equity: 18.01%
Cash ($ mil.): 4,691
Current ratio: 188.02
Long-term debt ($ mil.): 1,525

No. of shares (mil.): 1,286
Dividends
Yield: —
Payout: —
Market value ($ mil.): 39,019

	STOCK PRICE ($) FY Close	P/E High/Low		PER SHARE ($) Earnings	Dividends	Book Value
12/11	30.33	14	11	2.46	0.00	13.94
12/10	27.83	23	14	1.36	0.00	11.79
12/09	23.53	14	6	1.83	0.00	10.62
12/08	13.96	24	8	1.36	0.00	8.65
12/07	33.19	156	110	0.25	0.00	8.67
Annual Growth	(2.2%)	—	—	77.1%	—	12.6%

Ecolab, Inc.

Ecolab cleans up by cleaning up. The company offers cleaning sanitation pest-elimination and maintenance products and services to hospitality institutional and industrial customers. Its largest unit Cleaning and Sanitizing accounts for nearly half of its sales and serves hotels schools and commercial and institutional laundries. Its Kay unit provides cleaning supplies to quick-service restaurants. Other units focus on products for textile care water care health care food and beverage processing and pest control. Newly acquired unit Nalco makes chemicals used in water treatment for industrial processes. In 2012 Ecolab agreed to buy Houston-based Champion Technologies for $2.2 billion.

The acquisition of Champion Technologies and its related company Corsicana Technologies (collectively referred to as Champion Technologies) helps Ecolab to boost its technology and product strengths in North America and is very complementary to its innovative technology and services in the offshore and international energy markets. The deal is expected to yield $150 million in cost synergies by the end of 2015.

Operations

The company provides cleaning and sanitizing programs and products equipment repair and pest elimination for markets such as food service food and beverage processing healthcare government and education and textile care. Ecolab's chemicals and services are used in water treatment pollution control energy steelmaking papermaking mining and other industrial processes. It is also one of the top suppliers of chemical dishwashing products to institutions in the US.

Ecolab now splits its US Cleaning and Sanitizing segment into six operating divisions: Institutional Food & Beverage Kay Healthcare Textile Care and Vehicle Care. Its US Other Services segment consists of two units: Pest Elimination and Equipment Care.

Geographic Reach

The company's International segment includes subsidiaries that operate in 74 countries outside of the US as well as a joint venture in Venezuela. Its largest International operations which are similar to those in the US are in Europe Asia/Pacific Latin America and Canada. Smaller operations are in Africa and the Middle East.

Ecolab serves customers in more than 160 countries and territories worldwide.

Financial Analysis

The acquisition of Nalco and other companies helped Ecolab deliver a strong performance in 2011. It reported net sales of $6.8 billion up 12% over that of 2010. Driving that growth were acquisitions appropriate pricing and sales gains which offset the rise in product costs and the company's investments in the business. Sales increased in almost all units except Pest Elimination which remained flat compared to the previous year. With the acquisition of O.R. Solutions the company's Healthcare division saw a 28% hike in sales compared to 2010 primarily for hand hygiene and surgical instrument cleaning products.

The company's overall net income however dipped about 13% in 2011 to $463 million due to costs associated with the Nalco acquisition a reduced tax expense and other charges.

To keep costs in line with its continued investments Ecolab has deployed a comprehensive plan to improve efficiencies. Part of the effort includes more shared and outsourced services a centralization of business functions and a realignment of the company's supply chain. Ecolab continues to trim its global workforce and office facilities following the merger of Nalco but it expects to complete those efforts by the end of 2013.

The company began a major financial restructuring of its European operations in 2011 expecting to save about $120 million over a three-year period. The plan includes changes to the division's supply chain administrative operations and other functions as well as a 12% reduction in workforce. As a part of the restructuring it rolled out its Ecolab Business System platform a common set of business processes and systems for its European operations. The EBS platform is designed to streamline the organization improve efficiency and competitiveness and more rapidly improve the region's profitability. Ecolab is also implementing EBS in China.

Strategy

Following its acquisition of Nalco Ecolab continued restructuring and cutting costs in early 2012 including cutting back on its global workforce and streamlining its supply chain. With the merging of both companies' operations Ecolab emerged as a global leader in water hygiene and energy technologies and services. The company's global reach and expanded line of products and services will enable it to provide total water processing management to food and beverage hospitality and laundry customers worldwide.

Ecolab's strategy for growth includes investing organically in its businesses including equipment used by customers to dispense its cleaning and sanitizing products as well as in process control and monitoring equipment. The company also invests in innovation such as a new R&D facility in Shanghai China. It continues to target key acquisitions to complement its businesses and to focus on key growth areas.

Mergers & Acquisitions

In 2011 Ecolab acquired water treatment company Nalco in a $5.4 billion cash and stock deal. Ecolab is operating the Nalco business under three new segments: Water Services Paper Services and Energy Services.

In 2011 Ecolab completed its acquisition of O.R. Solutions a privately held Virginia company that makes warming and cooling systems for surgical fluids for $260 million. The business became part of the US Cleaning and Sanitizing segment.

Ecolab purchased the Cleantec business of Campbell Brothers of Brisbane Australia for $43 million in 2010. Cleantec is a developer manufacturer and marketer of cleaning and hygiene products primarily for the Australian food and beverage processing food service hospitality and commercial laundry markets.

In 2010 the company also acquired the commercial laundry division of Dober Chemical Corporation which strengthens Ecolab's US and Canadian Textile Care business. Dober Chemical has annual sales of about $37 million.

Ownership

Bill Gates and his wife own nearly 11% of Ecolab.

HISTORY

Salesman Merritt Osborn founded Economics Laboratory in 1924 as a specialty chemical maker; its first product was a rug cleaner for hotels. It added industrial and institutional cleaners and consumer detergents in the 1950s. The company went public in 1957. By 1973 it had been organized into five divisions: industrial (cleaners and specialty chemical formulas) institutional (dishwasher products sanitation formulas) consumer (dishwasher detergent and laundry aids coffee filters floor cleaners) food-processing (detergents) and international (run by future CEO Fred Lanners).

At the time household dishwasher detergent was Economics Laboratory's top seller second to Procter & Gamble in the US and #1 overseas. The company began offering services and products as packages in the early 1970s including on-premise laundry services for hotels and hospitals and sanitation and cleaning services for the food industry.

E. B. Osborn son of the founder retired in 1978 and Lanners became the company's first CEO outside the Osborn family. Sales of dishwashing detergent had fallen while the institutional cleaning business had become its primary segment quadrupling in sales between 1970 and 1980. International sales were growing rapidly. In 1979 the company bought Apollo Technologies (chemicals and pollution-control equipment) to improve its share of the industrial market.

A depressed industrial sector caused Apollo's sales to drop in early 1980. The man expected to save Apollo Richard Ashley succeeded Lanners in 1982 but died in a car crash that year. Sandy Grieve became CEO in 1983 and shut down Apollo. Meanwhile debt was up the institutional market had shrunk and the company was slipping in the dishwashing-detergent market. Grieve sold the firm's coffee-filters unit and several plants laid off employees and began new packaging processes. The company changed its name to Ecolab in 1986 and in 1987 it sold its dishwashing-detergent unit and bought lawn-service provider ChemLawn. (ChemLawn was sold in 1992.)

As 1990 neared Grieve introduced what's now known as "Circle the Customer –Circle the Globe" the aim being to become a worldwide leader in core businesses and broaden product offerings. The company concentrated on building its presence in Africa the Asia/Pacific region Latin America and the Middle East. In 1991 Ecolab also began a highly successful joint venture Henkel-Ecolab with German consumer-products company Henkel to better exploit European markets.

Ecolab acquired Kay Chemical (cleaning and sanitation products for the fast-food industry 1994) Monarch (cleaning and sanitation products for food processing 1996) Huntington Laboratories (janitorial products 1996) and Australia-based Gibson (cleaning and sanitation products 1997). In 1995 Grieve stepped down and president Allan Schuman became CEO. Adding a few more degrees to its circle of services in 1998 Ecolab bought GCS Service (commercial kitchen equipment repair).

The company further secured footholds in Asia and South America in 2000 by acquiring industrial and institutional cleaning firms Dong Woo Deterpan (South Korea) Spartan de Chile and Spartan de Argentina. At home it bought kitchen-equipment companies ARR/CRS and Southwest Sanitary Distributing. Late in 2000 Ecolab sold its Johnson dish machines unit to Endonis and announced a restructuring that was soon followed by the departure of several top executives including president and COO Bruno Deschamps.

In 2001 Ecolab purchased the 50% of Henkel-Ecolab that it didn't own from Henkel for about $435 million; the move greatly expanded the company's international business.

Schuman stepped down as CEO in 2004 (retaining the chairman's role); president Doug Baker took over and became a director in addition to his role as president and CEO. Two years later Schuman retired as chairman ending his 49-year tenure with Ecolab. The company named Baker to replace him.

In 2007 Ecolab made an acquisition to expand its operations in the health care field buying Microtek Medical Holdings which makes infection control products for health care facilities for about $275 million. The next year it paid $210 million for Ecovation a company that treats wastewater solid waste and air pollution primarily for food and beverage companies.

EXECUTIVES

CFO, Steven L. Fritze, age 57, $500,000 total compensation
President, J. Erik Fyrwald, age 52
Chairman and CEO, Douglas M. (Doug) Baker Jr., age 53, $1,000,000 total compensation
EVP; President Latin America, James H. White, age 47
EVP; President Global Corporate Initiatives, James A. Miller, age 55, $437,500 total compensation
President Global Healthcare Sector, Susan K. Nestegard, age 51
CFO, Daniel J. Schmechel, age 52
SVP and CIO, Stewart H. McCutcheon, age 54
President and COO, Thomas W. Handley, age 57, $425,000 total compensation
EVP; President Europe, Phillip J. Mason, age 61
EVP; President Global Institutional, Michael A. Hickey, age 50
EVP Human Resources, Michael L. Meyer, age 54
SVP and Corporate Controller, John J. Corkrean, age 46
EVP and CTO, Larry L. Berger, age 51
EVP; President Regions, Christophe Beck, age 44
SVP Corporate Development, Angela M. Busch
SVP and General Manager Institutional Foodservice Division, James W. Chamberlain
VP and Treasurer, Ching-Meng Chew
SVP and General Manager Institutional North America Hospitality Healthcare and Commercial Business, Tracy J. Crocker
SVP Institutional Field Sales, Derrick A. Johns
VP Tax, Judy M. McNamara
EVP and General Manager Institutional EMEA, Thomas W. Schnack
SVP Institutional Global and Corporate Accounts, Robert J. Sherwood
VP and General Manager Healthcare North America, Paul B. Chaffin
SVP; President Global Water and Process Services, Timothy Mulhere
EVP and Chief Supply Chain Officer, Gregory E. Temple
EVP General Counsel and Secretary, James J. Siefert
Director, Arthur J. Higgins, age 56
Director, Victoria J. (Vicki) Reich, age 54
Director, Richard U. (Dick) De Schutter, age 71
Director, Joel W. Johnson, age 68
Director, Jerry W. Levin, age 67
Director, Robert L. Lumpkins, age 68
Director, Beth M. Pritchard, age 65
Director, Leslie S. (Les) Biller, age 64
Director, Jerry A. Grundhofer, age 67
Director, John J. Zillmer, age 56
Director, Barbara J. Beck, age 51
Director, C. Scott O'Hara, age 52
Auditors: PricewaterhouseCoopersLLP

LOCATIONS

HQ: Ecolab, Inc.
370 Wabasha Street North, St. Paul, MN 55102
Phone: 651 293-2233
Web: www.ecolab.com

PRODUCTS/OPERATIONS

2011 Sales

	$ mil.	% of total
US		
Other Services	457	7
Currency Impact	136	2
Legacy Nalco Services	193	3
Adjustments	(29.6)	-

COMPETITORS

3M Health Care
3M Purification
Ashland Inc.
Chemed
CPAC
Diversey
GE Water and Process Technologies
Healthcare Services
ISS A/S
Medline Industries
Rollins Inc.
ServiceMaster
STERIS
UGL Services UNICCO
Unilever
Unisource
Zep Inc.

HISTORICAL FINANCIALS

Company Type: Public

Income Statement FYE: December 31

	REVENUE ($ mil.)	NET INCOME ($ mil.)	NET PROFIT MARGIN	EMPLOYEES
12/11	6,798	462	6.8%	40,200
12/10	6,089	530	8.7%	26,494
12/09	5,900	417	7.1%	25,931
12/08	6,137	448	7.3%	26,500
12/07	5,469	427	7.8%	26,050
Annual Growth	5.6%	2.0%	—	11.5%

2011 Year-End Financials

Debt ratio: 41.86%
Return on equity: 8.16%
Cash ($ mil.): 1,843
Current ratio: 170.42
Long-term debt ($ mil.): 6,613
No. of shares (mil.): 291
Dividends
Yield: —
Payout: 37.96%
Market value ($ mil.): 16,879

	STOCK PRICE ($) FY Close	P/E High	P/E Low	PER SHARE ($) Earnings	Dividends	Book Value
12/11	57.81	30	23	1.91	0.00	19.41
12/10	50.42	23	18	2.23	0.64	9.16
12/09	44.58	27	17	1.74	0.58	8.46
12/08	35.15	28	17	1.80	0.53	6.65
12/07	51.21	30	23	1.70	0.48	7.84
Annual Growth	3.1%	—	—	3.0%	—	25.4%

Edison International

Edison International has been around the world but its largest subsidiary is Southern California Edison (SCE) which distributes electricity to a population of almost 14 million people in central coastal and southern California; it is also the top purchaser of renewable energy in the US. The utility's system consists of about 12000 circuit miles of transmission lines and more than 103500 circuit miles of distribution lines. SCE also has 5574 MW of generating capacity from interests in nuclear hydroelectric and fossil-fueled power plants. Through Edison Mission Group's Edison Mission Energy unit Edison owns leases operates and sells energy and capacity (10780 MW) from power generation facilities.

Geographic Reach

Southern California Edison (SCE) is a regulated electric utility serving Southern California. After having sold plants in Asia and Europe Edison Mission Energy markets energy in the US and Turkey. The company has interests in more than 40 power plants in the US and one in Turkey (the Doga project) that give it a net physical generating capacity of about 10780 MW.

Operations

Through its subsidiaries Edison International generates and distributes electric power and invests in infrastructure and energy assets including renewable energy projects.

Financial Analysis

In 2011 rate increases and solid cost-recovery income by SCE helped to lift Edison International's overall revenues by 3% after two years of almost flat revenue growth and despite a weak wholesale market which resulted in weaker competitive energy sales. However net income dropped by more than 98% in 2011 due to higher purchased power prices increased depreciation decommissioning and amortization expenses and a jump in asset impairment costs.

Strategy

Edison International's strategy is to focus on the financially more secure US power market balancing revenues from its regulated utility with higher-margin returns from its competitive power generation business. Edison also provides consulting management and maintenance services for energy projects. It is investing in upgrading its traditional power infrastructure and expanding its portfolio of solar and wind energy projects to make the company compliant with increasingly stringent state and federal carbon emission requirements. In 2011 SCE had the capacity to deliver 3720 MW of power from renewable sources although in late 2011 it reduced its development pipeline of potential wind projects to 1300 MW in order conserve cash.

HISTORY

In 1896 a group including Elmer Peck and George Baker organized West Side Lighting to provide electricity in Los Angeles. The next year the company merged with Los Angeles Edison Electric which owned the rights to the Edison name and patents in the region and Baker became president. Edison Electric installed the first DC-power underground conduits in the Southwest.

John Barnes Miller took over the top spot in 1901. During his 31-year reign the firm bought many neighboring utilities and built several power plants. In 1909 it took the name Southern California Edison (SCE).

SCE doubled its assets by buying Southern California electric interests from rival Pacific Light & Power in 1917. However in 1912 the City of Los Angeles had decided to develop its own power distribution system and by 1922 SCE's authority in the city had ended. A 1925 earthquake and the 1928 collapse of the St. Francis Dam severely damaged SCE's facilities.

SCE built 11 fossil-fueled power stations (1948-1973) and moved into nuclear power in 1963 when it broke ground on the San Onofre plant with San Diego Gas & Electric (brought online in 1968). It finished consolidating its service territory with the 1964 purchase of California Electric Power. In the late 1970s SCE began to build solar geothermal and wind power facilities.

Edison Mission Energy (EME) was founded in 1986 to develop buy and operate power plants around the world. The next year investment arm Edison Capital was formed as well as a holding company for the entire group SCEcorp. EME began to build its portfolio in 1992 when it snagged a 51% stake in an Australian plant and bought hydroelectric facilities in Spain. In 1995 it bought UK hydroelectric company First Hydro; it also began building plants in Italy Turkey and Indonesia.

The 1994 Northridge earthquake that cut power to a million SCE customers was nothing compared to the industry's seismic shifts. In 1996 SCEcorp became the more worldly Edison International. California's electricity market opened to competition in 1998 and the utility began divesting SCE's generation assets; it sold 12 gas-fired plants. Overseas EME picked up 25% of a power plant being built in Thailand and a 50% stake in a cogeneration facility in Puerto Rico.

SCE got regulatory approval to offer telecom services in its utility territory in 1999. That year EME snapped up several plants in the Midwest from Unicom for $5 billion. Overseas it purchased two UK coal-fired plants from PowerGen (which it sold to American Electric Power in 2001 for $960 million). The next year EME CEO Edward Muller (who had held the post since 1994) abruptly resigned and Edison bought Citizens Power from the Peabody Group.

In 2000 SCE got caught in a price squeeze brought on in part by deregulation. Prices on the wholesale power market soared but the utility was unable to pass along the increase to customers because of a rate freeze. The company gained some prospect of relief in 2001 when California's governor signed legislation to allow a state agency to buy power from wholesalers under long-term contracts. In addition the California Public Utilities Commission (CPUC) approved a substantial increase in retail electricity rates and the Federal Energy Regulatory Commission approved a plan to limit wholesale energy prices during periods of severe shortage in 11 western states.

To reduce debt Edison International agreed to sell its transmission grid to the state for $2.8 billion. While the California legislature debated the agreement however the CPUC announced a settlement in which SCE would be allowed to keep its current high rates in place until its debts are paid off. The settlement which was approved in 2002 eliminated the need for the sale of the company's transmission grid.

Also in 2001 the company sold most of its Edison Enterprises businesses including home security services unit Edison Select which was sold to ADT Security Services.

In 2004 Edison International committed to taking a lead position in developing comprehensive national programs to reduce greenhouse gas emissions primarily carbon dioxide.

In 2006 SCE signed the largest wind energy deal ever completed by a US utility providing for 1500 MW of wind power from plants in the Tehachapi area of California.

EXECUTIVES

Chairman President and CEO, Theodore F. (Ted) Craver Jr., age 60, $1,054,038 total compensation
Director; President Southern California Edison, Ronald L. (Ron) Litzinger, age 52, $508,904 total compensation
SVP Corporate Communications, Janet Clayton, age 53
SVP Business Integration and CIO Southern California Edison, Mahvash Yazdi, age 60, $395,817 total compensation
EVP External Relations Southern California Edison, Stephen E. Pickett, age 61, $379,454 total compensation
SVP Human Resources, Daryl D. David, age 57
President Edison Mission Group, Pedro J. Pizarro, age 46, $396,252 total compensation
VP and CIO Edison Mission Group, Todd L. Inlander
VP Investor Relations, Scott S. Cunningham
VP and Controller, Mark C. Clarke, age 55
SVP Strategic Planning, Bertrand A. (Bert) Valdman, age 49
EVP Public Affairs, Polly L. Gault, age 58, $378,151 total compensation
EVP CFO and Treasurer, W. James (Jim) Scilacci Jr., age 56, $493,846 total compensation
SVP and CFO Southern California Edison, Linda G. Sullivan, age 48, $302,575 total compensation
VP Associate General Counsel Chief Governance Officer and Corporate Secretary; VP Associate General Counsel Chief Governance Officer and Corporate Secretary Southern California Edison, Barbara E. Mathews
VP and General Auditor; VP and General Auditor Southern California Edison, Megan E. Scott-Kakures
VP Tax, Jeffrey L. (Jeff) Barnett
EVP and General Counsel, Robert L. Adler, age 64, $527,019 total compensation
Director, Thomas C. Sutton, age 69
Director, W. Brett White, age 52
Director, Richard T. Schlosberg III, age 67
Director, Ronald L. (Ron) Olson, age 70
Director, Luis G. Nogales, age 68
Director, James M. Rosser, age 72
Director, Bradford M. Freeman, age 70
Director, Vanessa C. L. Chang, age 59
Director, France A. Cordova, age 64
Director, Jagjeet S. (Jeet) Bindra, age 64
Director, Charles B. Curtis, age 71
Auditors: PricewaterhouseCoopersLLP

LOCATIONS

HQ: Edison International
2244 Walnut Grove Ave., Rosemead CA 91770
Phone: 626-302-2222 **Fax:** 626-302-2517
Web: www.edison.com

PRODUCTS/OPERATIONS

2011 Sales

	$ mil.	% of total
Electric utility	10,574	83
Competitive power generation	2,186	17
Total	**12,760**	**100**

Selected Subsidiaries

Edison Mission Group (unregulated activities)
- Edison Mission Energy (power generation energy trading and marketing)

Southern California Edison Company (SCE electric utility)

COMPETITORS

AES
Avista
Calpine
CMS Energy
Constellation Energy Group
Dynegy
Electricite de France
Endesa S.A.
Enel
Entergy
GenOnEnergy
IBERDROLA
Los Angeles Water and Power
MidAmerican Energy
NextEra Energy
NRG Energy
NV Energy
PacifiCorp
PG&E Corporation
Portland General Electric
Sacramento Municipal Utility
Sempra Energy

HISTORICAL FINANCIALS

Company Type: Public

Income Statement

FYE: December 31

	REVENUE ($ mil.)	NET INCOME ($ mil.)	NET PROFIT MARGIN	EMPLOYEES
12/11	12,760	(37)	—	19,930
12/10	12,409	1,256	10.1%	20,117
12/09	12,361	849	6.9%	19,244
12/08	14,112	1,215	8.6%	18,291
12/07	13,113	1,098	8.4%	17,275
Annual Growth	(0.7%)	—	—	3.6%

2011 Year-End Financials

Debt ratio: 29.51%
Return on equity: (-0.37)%
Cash ($ mil.): 1,469
Current ratio: 103.13
Long-term debt ($ mil.): 13,689
No. of shares (mil.): 325
Dividends
Yield: —
Payout: 1995.24%
Market value ($ mil.): 13,489

	STOCK PRICE ($) FY Close	P/E High/Low		PER SHARE ($) Earnings	Dividends	Book Value
12/11	41.40	—	—	(0.11)	0.00	30.86
12/10	38.60	10	8	3.82	1.27	32.48
12/09	34.78	14	9	2.58	1.25	32.99
12/08	32.12	15	8	3.68	1.23	31.99
12/07	53.37	18	13	3.31	1.18	28.73
Annual Growth	(6.2%)	—	—	—	—	1.8%

Electronic Arts, Inc.

To armchair quarterbacks and couch-potato commandos Electronic Arts (EA) is their Picasso. EA is a top-three global video game publisher with popular titles such as Battlefield "Madden NFL" The Sims and Need for Speed. The company also distributes third-party titles such as Rock Band and Valve Software's Left 4 Dead and it publishes games based on other media franchises such as Harry Potter. EA develops its games for consoles from Sony Nintendo and Microsoft as well as for PCs. EA also serves mobile devices including e-readers and provides online social games including Hasbro-licensed games such as Monopoly via websites Pogo and Playfish. Most of EA's sales are divided between North America and Europe.

As EA pursues a digital approach its structure morphs along with it. The company now divides operations into various labels: EA Games (Battlefield Dead Space Medal of Honor Need for Speed) EA SPORTS (Tiger Woods Fight Night FIFA) BioWare (Mass Effect Star Wars Dragon Age) Maxis (Sims Spore) recently-acquired PopCap Games (Bejeweled Plants vs. Zombies Zuma) and social and mobile studios (EA Mobile Playfish Pogo). The company's social and mobile efforts entail free-to-play social games produced for sites such as Facebook Google Bebo MySpace as well as for Google's Android operating system and Apple's iPhone.

Whether digital or physical product revenues still drive the business but EA's digital focus also means growing service revenue (less than 20% of sales). Service revenue includes games and content that require hosting support for the essential game experience as well as recurring subscriptions.

For fiscal 2012 (ended March) EA finally turned around two consecutive years of revenue decline thanks to payoff in its digital aspirations. Digital sales climbed nearly 50% outweighing the marginal dip in publishing. Major title contributors to product revenue which rose 7% were FIFA 12 (13% of overall sales) and Battlefield 3 (11%) Madden NFL 12 and Crysis. Service revenue increase of nearly 80% was driven by BioWare's online role-playing action game Star Wars: The Old Republic microtransactions from The Sims Social and the FIFA Ultimate Team add-on service.

Although it's pressing hard to be predominantly a digital publisher EA'a largest single customers are still retailers the two biggest being GameStop (15% of sales) and Wal-Mart (now less than 10%). The company however increasingly looks to mobile and third-party e-commerce marketplaces and more so its own e-commerce platform Origin which also offers titles from other publishers such as SEGA.

Like most of its competitors EA has responded to industry struggles by culling its catalog to focus on titles that generate the most revenue. In line with its digital transformation those games are now designed to include additional online features where they used to have few or none. In 2009 EA published more than 60 titles practically devoid of online options in the packaged goods format but plans only 14 for 2013 each with an online component. Social and mobile platforms will be where it attacks with volume slating in excess of 40 titles for release.

In tandem with its strategy to offer fewer titles for consoles and PC EA also hopes to make them year-round revenue generators and taking a cue from Hollywood seeks to develop and maintain brands that can produce sequels. Its sports games for example typically are iterated on a yearly basis while others such as Battlefield and The Sims receive new installments less frequently.

HISTORY

After four years with Apple video game pioneer Trip Hawkins left in 1982 raised $5 million and founded Electronic Arts to explore the entertainment potential of PCs. The company went public in 1989 and sales exploded the next year when EA began designing games for SEGA's Genesis video game system. Hawkins stepped down as CEO in 1991 and was replaced by president Larry Probst. (Hawkins remained chairman until 1994; he left to devote time to another game company 3DO which later went bankrupt.) The company bought game developer ORIGIN Systems in 1992 and began marketing its games in Japan with partner JVC. By 1995 more than 40% of EA's sales were from outside the US. That year Sony introduced its PlayStation game system in the US.

In 1997 the company bought US publisher Maxis ("SimCity") for about $215 million. That year ORIGIN introduced "Ultima Online" an online fantasy game in which players interact with each other. In 1998 EA bought Westwood Studios for $122 million. The next year it established EA.com an Internet division to develop games for online players. It also agreed to pay America Online (now AOL) about $80 million to operate AOL's game channel.

In 2000 the company bought DreamWorks Interactive a joint venture between Microsoft and DreamWorks. It also launched EA.com's website released six titles for Sony's PlayStation 2 and agreed to develop titles for Microsoft's Xbox game system. In 2001 EA bought online gaming site pogo.com and launched "Majestic" (an interactive subscription-based game played online) only to terminate the game in 2002 because of its failure to catch on with fans.

EA was banking on the success of the Internet incarnation of its popular Sims franchise "The Sims Online" which charged players a monthly subscription fee. The game was launched in 2002; the response —including negative reviews and sluggish sales —was a letdown. In 2003 EA consolidated its money-losing online unit (EA.com) into its core operations. However the company continued to experiment with online gaming; it made some of its titles available for online play via the PlayStation 2 and Xbox systems.

John Riccitiello stepped down as president and COO in 2004 to start his own private equity business (He returned as CEO in 2007). Also that year EA moved the operations of ORIGIN Systems from Austin Texas to Redwood City California as part of a larger move toward consolidation of development in California and British Columbia.

When EA suffered a challenge to its popular Madden NFL franchise from Take-Two and SEGA (which had joined up to create a set of low-priced ESPN-branded sports titles) it fired back by procuring a five-year exclusive license to use NFL players and teams in its games as well as acquiring the exclusive rights to the ESPN trademark in 2006. Take-Two retaliated to these challenges with a two-year exclusive license to use MLB teams in its games essentially putting an end to any new versions of EA's blockbuster hit MVP Baseball during that time.

Hardcore video game fans don't just love the company's games they love the music heard in the games as well. In recognition of this EA teamed with Nettwerk Music Group in 2005 in the creation of EA Recordings a digital-only record label that distributes music from EA's games to popular digital music-downloading services such as Apple's iTunes.

In its most aggressive move to snatch up a portion of the mobile gaming market the company acquired mobile gaming leader JAMDAT Mobile in 2006 and created a new division EA Mobile. The next year it bought Mythic Entertainment an MMORPG developer and publisher. Later that year it purchased VG Holding Corp. for $775 million the owner of BioWare and Pandemic Studios. In 2008 the company offered $2 billion to purchase Take-Two Interactive publisher of the Grand Theft Auto franchise; Take-Two rejected the offer marking a pause in EA's spending spree.

In 2009 EA implemented a cost-reduction plan to narrow its product portfolio reduce its workforce by about 11% and close 10 facilities. Among the casualties was Pandemic Studios acquired a couple of years before. It's expansion efforts that year were focused on the growing market for social games as it bought social networking game company Playfish in a deal worth up to $400 million.

EXECUTIVES

CEO and Director, John S. Riccitiello, age 52, $800,000 total compensation
EVP Global Publishing, Nancy L. Smith, age 59
Chairman, Lawrence F. (Larry) Probst III, age 62, $738,462 total compensation
EVP and Chief Talent Officer, Gabrielle Toledano, age 45
President EA Games Label, Frank D. Gibeau, age 44, $545,000 total compensation
President Chief Operating Officer, Peter R. Moore, age 57, $565,000 total compensation
Interim CFO, Kenneth A. (Ken) Barker, age 45
SVP General Counsel and Corporate Secretary, Stephen G. Bene, age 48
EVP Business and Legal Affairs, Joel Linzner, age 60
Senior Director General and Administrative Playfish, Shukri Shammas
EVP Digital, Kristian Segerstr?le, age 34
VP; Chief Technical Officer Playfish, Sami Lababidi
VP Business Development and Strategic Partnerships Interactive, Sebastien de Halleux
Director Communications US, Holly Rockwood
EVP EA Play Label, Rodney (Rod) Humble, age 46
Marketing Director EA Sports, Nathan Stewart
Director Public Relations EA Sports, David Tinson
Director Communications Europe, Tiffany Steckler
CTO, Rajat Taneja
Investor Relations, Peter Ausnit
Head E-Commerce, David (Dave) DeMartini
General Manager EA Partners, Brian Neider
CIO, Mark Tonneson
Director, Vivek Paul, age 53
CEO and Director, John S. Riccitiello, age 52
Director, Geraldine B. (Gerry) Laybourne, age 65
Director, Leonard S. Coleman Jr., age 63
Director, Gregory B. (Greg) Maffei, age 50
Director, Linda J. Srere, age 56
Director, Richard A. (Rick) Simonson, age 54
Director, Jeffrey T. (Jeff) Huber, age 44
Director, Luis A. Ubi?as
Auditors: KPMGLLP

LOCATIONS

HQ: Electronic Arts, Inc.
209 Redwood Shores Parkway, Redwood City, CA 94065
Phone: 650 628-1500
Web: www.ea.com

2012 Sales

	$ mil.	% of total
North America	1,991	48
Europe	1,898	46
Asia	254	6
Total	**4,143**	**100**

PRODUCTS/OPERATIONS

2012 Sales

	$ mil.	% of total
Product		
Publishing & other	2,674	65
Digital (Wireless Internet & advertising)	518	13
Distribution	223	5
Service		
Digital (Wireless Internet & advertising)	641	15
Publishing & other	87	2
Total	**4,143**	**100**

2012 Sales

	$ mil.	% of total
Publishing & other	2,736	66
Digital (Wireless Internet & advertising)	1,227	29
Distribution	223	5
Adjustments	(43)	-
Total	**4,143**	**100**

2012 Sales

	$ mil.	% of total
Product	3,415	82
Service & other	728	18
Total	**4,143**	**100**

Selected Game Titles by Studio & Label

BioWare
- Command & Conquer
- Dragon Age
- Mass Effect
- Star Wars: The Old Republic

EA Games
- DICE (Sweden)
  - Battlefield
- Criterion (UK)
  - Burnout
  - Need for Speed
- Visceral
  - Dante's Inferno
  - Dead Space
- Various EA studios
  - Medal of Honor
- Third-party
  - Crysis (Crytek)
  - Half-Life (Valve)
  - Rock Band (Harmonix)

Maxis
- The Sims
- Spore

EA SPORTS
- FIFA
- Madden NFL
- NASCAR
- NBA Street
- NHL
- Skate 3
- SSX
- Tiger Woods PGA Tour

Selected Acquisitions

2011
- PopCap Games ($750 million; Seattle; game publisher Bejeweled Plants vs. Zombies Zuma)
- KlickNation (Sacramento; freemium RPG developer (now BioWare Sacramento))
- Firemint (Melbourne Australia; mobile games Real Racing)
- Mobile Post Production (cross-platform developer and porting)

2010
- Chillingo (UK; games publisher Angry Birds distributor)

COMPETITORS

Activision Blizzard
Atari
Big Fish Games
Capcom
DeNA
eGames
Gameloft
Glu Mobile
Konami
Lucasfilm Entertainment
Microsoft
Namco Limited
NCsoft
Nintendo
Rovio Entertainment
SEGA
Sony Online Entertainment
Square Enix
Take-Two
Tencent
THQ
Ubisoft
Valve Corporation
ZeniMax Media
Zynga

HISTORICAL FINANCIALS

Company Type: Public

Income Statement FYE: March 31

	REVENUE ($ mil.)	NET INCOME ($ mil.)	NET PROFIT MARGIN	EMPLOYEES
03/12	4,143	76	1.8%	9,200
03/11	3,589	(276)	—	7,600
03/10	3,654	(677)	—	7,800
03/09	4,212	(1,088)	—	9,100
03/08	3,665	(454)	—	9,000
Annual Growth	3.1%	—	—	0.6%

2012 Year-End Financials

Debt ratio: 9.82%
Return on equity: 3.09%
Cash ($ mil.): 1,293
Current ratio: 123.07
Long-term debt ($ mil.): 539
No. of shares (mil.): 320
Dividends
Yield: —
Payout: —
Market value ($ mil.): 5,277

	STOCK PRICE ($) FY Close	P/E High/Low	PER SHARE ($) Earnings	Dividends	Book Value
03/12	16.48	110 71	0.23	0.00	7.68
03/11	19.53	— —	(0.84)	0.00	7.71
03/10	18.66	— —	(2.08)	0.00	8.28
03/09	18.19	— —	(3.40)	0.00	9.71
03/08	49.92	— —	(1.45)	0.00	13.64
Annual Growth	(24.2%)	— —	—	—	(13.4%)

EMC Corp. (MA)

EMC has its head in the cloud. And rightly so for a company that's helping businesses build Web-based computing systems with its data storage products and services. Its hardware and software platforms enable enterprises to store manage protect and analyze massive volumes of data. EMC also offers data security products through its RSA Security business and virtualization software through majority-owned VMware. The company serves both large FORTUNE 500 organizations and smaller businesses across many industries. Banks government agencies ISPs and manufacturers are among its customers. EMC serves a global client base from facilities and partners worldwide.

HISTORY

Former Intel executive Dick Egan and his college roommate Roger Marino founded EMC in 1979. (Their initials gave the company its name.) Egan a feisty entrepreneur whose first job was shining shoes served as a Marine in Korea and later worked at MIT on the computer system for NASA's Apollo program. Egan also helped found Cambridge Memory Systems (later Cambex).

EMC was started with no business plan only the idea that Egan and Marino would be better off working for themselves. At first they sold office furniture which in short order led to contacts at technology companies and recognition of the niche market for add-on memory boards for minicomputers.

EMC grew steadily throughout the early 1980s and went public in 1986. Two years later Michael Ruettgers a former COO of high-tech publishing and research company Technical Financial Services joined the company as EVP of operations. Ruettgers spent his first year and a half at EMC dealing with a crisis that almost ruined the company: Defective disk drives in some of its products were losing customers' files. Ruettgers stepped up quality control and guided EMC through the crisis period. In 1989 he became the company's president and COO.

In the late 1980s EMC expanded into data storage developing a system that employed small hard disks rather than larger more expensive disks and tapes used in IBM mainframes. EMC then separated itself from competitors by providing systems with a large cache —a temporary storage area used for quicker data retrieval.

In 1990 EMC pioneered redundant array of independent disks (RAID) storage and eliminated nearly a dozen major product lines focusing on storage for large IBM computers in a bid to beat Big Blue by undercutting prices. The company introduced its original Symmetrix system based on the new integrated cached disk array technology that held data from a variety of computer types. Marino left the company in 1990.

Ruettgers became CEO in 1992. The next year the company acquired Epoch Systems a provider of data management software and in 1994 it bought storage products company Array Technology as well as Magna Computer a leader in tape storage technology for IBM computers. EMC also introduced its first storage product for open systems the Centriplex series and its sales passed the $1 billion mark.

EMC increased its presence in this fast-growing data switching and computer connection market with the 1995 acquisition of McDATA. The next year it launched a digital video storage and retrieval system for the TV and film industry and introduced software that let its systems work on networks instead of requiring file servers for data storage management.

In 1997 the company began managing Web sites for customers. Expanding its international service presence EMC in 1998 bought French technology services provider Groupe MCI and in 1999 opened an Internet services office in Ireland. Also that year the company moved into the market for midrange storage when it acquired data storage and server specialist Data General.

EMC bought data storage software provider SOFTWORKS in 2000. That year EMC took McDATA public; the following year it distributed its majority stake in that company to EMC shareholders. In 2001 the company's corporate ladder shifted. Joe Tucci who joined EMC in 2000 as president added CEO to his title. Ruettgers became chairman and Egan was named chairman emeritus. (Tucci succeeded Ruettgers as chairman at the end of 2005.) Later in 2001 EMC acquired performance monitoring specialist Luminate Software for approximately $50 million.

Responding to a contracting economy and a subsequent drop in sales EMC took a restructuring charge in 2001 that contributed to its first quarterly loss in 12 years. Late that year the company formed a reseller alliance with Dell Computer (now just Dell). EMC continued its software push in 2002 acquiring storage management software maker Prisa Networks for approximately $20 million in cash.

The company began a major push to expand its software offerings in 2003. It acquired LEGATO Software for $1.3 billion and Documentum for approximately $1.5 billion. The following year EMC purchased server software maker VMware for approximately $625 million and backup and recovery software developer Dantz Development for about $50 million.

EMC's acquisition tear continued over the next few years. The company acquired System Management ARTS (SMARTS) for approximately $260 million in 2005. It also acquired Rainfinity (storage virtualization software) the assets of Maranti Networks (storage network switches) and input management software maker Captiva Software. EMC's most significant purchase in 2006 was the acquisition of RSA Security for about $2.1 billion. It bought network configuration and change management specialist Voyence as well as Berkeley Data Systems the provider of an online backup and recovery service called Mozy in 2007. Also in 2007 EMC sold off 10% of VMware with an IPO.

The company acquired content management software developer Document Sciences for about $86 million in 2008 and grew its consumer-focused hardware portfolio acquiring data storage device maker Iomega for about $213 million. Those were part of a dozen acquisitions EMC made that year half of which went into its Information Infrastructure business (Information Storage and Content Management and Archiving).

The following year EMC acquired Configuresoft a developer of software that manages server configuration updates and compliance issues. Also in 2009 the company acquired Kazeon Systems a developer of e-discovery software for law firms corporations and government agencies; Kazeon became part of EMC's Content Management and Archiving Division.

In 2009 after a two-month bidding war with rival NetApp EMC won its bid to acquire Data Domain for $2.4 billion in cash trumping NetApp's $1.9 billion cash and stock offer. The company hoped to improve its disk-based backup and archiving products by leveraging Data Domain's deduplication technologies.

In 2010 EMC sold certain assets of its Ionix IT management business to VMware for about $200 million in cash. VMware purchased the FastScale Application Discovery Manager Server Configuration Manager and Service Manager products lines while EMC retained the Ionix brand and kept reseller rights to the products sold.

The same year EMC bought privately held Greenplum which specialized in storing and analyzing large amounts of data from multiple sources using its Greenplum Database open-source software. With customers that included NASDAQ OMX Group NYSE Euronext and Equifax Greenplum expanded EMC's Information Storage segment.

EMC again boosted its data storage business later in 2010 when it acquired Isilon a maker of scalable network attached storage (NAS) products for about $2.25 billion. By combining Isilon's midrange storage products with its Atmos cloud storage infrastructure software EMC hoped to accelerate its growth in easy-to-configure storage offerings for cloud computing systems and serve a broader range of customers particularly in the media and entertainment health care and oil and gas markets.

EXECUTIVES

Vice Chairman, William J. (Bill) Teuber Jr., age 60, $609,673 total compensation
EVP and General Counsel, Paul T. Dacier, age 54
Chairman President and CEO, Joseph M. (Joe) Tucci, age 65, $872,308 total compensation
Executive Chairman RSA Security Division, Arthur W. (Art) Coviello Jr., age 58
President and COO EMC Information Infrastructure Products, Patrick P. (Pat) Gelsinger, age 51, $182,308 total compensation
EVP and CFO, David I. Goulden, age 52, $523,391 total compensation
President and COO EMC Information Infrastructure and Cloud Services, Howard D. Elias, age 55, $523,391 total compensation
Chief Strategy Officer Information Infrastructure Products (IIP), Mark S. Lewis, age 49, $221,150 total compensation
EVP Customer Experience, Frank M. Hauck, age 52
EVP Office of the Chairman, Harry L. You, age 53, $523,391 total compensation
President Cloud Infrastructure Business, Harel Kodesh, age 54
SVP Global Solutions, Prasad L. Rampalli, age 57
VP Global Marketing CTO, Charles (Chuck) Hollis
EVP and Chief Marketing Officer, Jeremy Burton, age 44
Chief Security Officer RSA, Edward G. Schwartz, age 51
EVP Americas and Europe Middle East and Africa, Bill Scannell
SVP and Treasurer, Irina Simmons
SVP Finance New Ventures, Mark A. Link
President EMC Japan, Toshio Morohoshi
CTO Information Intelligence Group, Jeetu Patel
EVP Human Resources, John T. (Jack) Mollen, age 61
Chairman EMC International, Rainer Erlat
SVP and CTO, Jeffrey M. (Jeff) Nick
SVP and General Manager Data Computing Products Division (DCD), Bill Cook
President Asia/Pacific and Japan, Steven (Steve) Leonard
CIO and COO Global Centers of Excellence, Sanjay Mirchandani, age 48
Senior Director Public Relations, Michael J. Gallant
President Information Intelligence Group (IIG), Richard R. (Rick) Devenuti, age 53
Chief Accounting Officer and Chief Operating Officer Finance, Denis G. Cashman, age 51
President Backup Recovery Systems (BRS), William (B. J.) Jenkins
VP Private Cloud Infrastructure and Services, Jon Peirce
Chief Security Officer, Dave Martin
Vice Chairman, William J. (Bill) Teuber Jr., age 60
Director, Gail Deegan, age 65
Director, Edmund F. (Ted) Kelly, age 66
Director, Windle B. Priem, age 74
Director, Paul L. Sagan, age 53
Director, David N. (Dave) Strohm, age 63
Director, Michael W. (Mike) Brown, age 66
Director, John R. Egan, age 54
Director, Randolph L. (Randy) Cowen, age 61
Director, James S. DiStasio, age 64
Auditors: PricewaterhouseCoopersLLP

LOCATIONS

HQ: EMC Corporation
176 South St., Hopkinton MA 01748
Phone: 508-435-1000 **Fax:** 585-724-1089
Web: www.kodak.com

2011 Sales

	$ mil.	% of total
US	10,549	53
Europe Middle East & Africa	5,667	28
Asia Pacific	2,639	13
Latin America Mexico & Canada	1,151	6
Total	**20,007**	**100**

PRODUCTS/OPERATIONS

2011 Sales

	$ mil.	% of total
Information storage	14,714	74
VMware virtual infrastructure	3,762	19
RSA information security	828	4
Information intelligence group	702	3
Total	**20,007**	**100**

Selected Acquisitions

NetWitness (2011 security software)
Isilon (2010 network storage sevices)
Greenplum (2010 database software)
Archer Technologies (2010 risk and compliance software)
Kazeon Systems (2010 legal software)
Data Domain (2009 data storage software)
Configuresoft (2009 server configuration software)
Iomega (2008 data storage devices and media)
Conchango (2008 IT consulting)
WysDM software (2008 data protection software)
Pi (2008 online data storage software)
Infra (2008 IT service management software)
Document Sciences (2008 content management software)
Voyence (2007 network configuration software)
Berkeley Data Systems (2007 online data backup and recovery service)
Verid (2007 data security software)

COMPETITORS

CA Inc.
Citrix Systems
Dell
Fujitsu
Hewlett-Packard
Hitachi Data Systems
IBM
LSI Corp.
McAfee
Microsoft
NetApp
Oracle
Quantum Corporation
Symantec
Teradata
Western Digital
Xyratex

HISTORICAL FINANCIALS

Company Type: Public

Income Statement FYE: December 31

	REVENUE ($ mil.)	NET INCOME ($ mil.)	NET PROFIT MARGIN	EMPLOYEES
12/11	20,007	2,461	12.3%	53,600
12/10	17,015	1,900	11.2%	48,500
12/09	14,025	1,088	7.8%	43,200
12/08	14,876	1,345	9.0%	42,100
12/07	13,230	1,665	12.6%	37,700
Annual Growth	10.9%	10.3%	—	9.2%

2011 Year-End Financials

Debt ratio: 4.68%
Return on equity: 12.98%
Cash ($ mil.): 4,531
Current ratio: 111.63
Long-term debt ($ mil.): —
No. of shares (mil.): 2,048
Dividends
Yield: —
Payout: —
Market value ($ mil.): 44,133

	STOCK PRICE ($) FY Close	P/E High/Low		PER SHARE ($) Earnings	Dividends	Book Value
12/11	21.54	24	17	1.10	0.00	9.25
12/10	22.90	25	18	0.88	0.00	8.41
12/09	17.47	34	18	0.53	0.00	7.58
12/08	10.47	28	13	0.64	0.00	6.48
12/07	18.53	32	16	0.77	0.00	5.96
Annual Growth	3.8%	—	—	9.3%	—	11.6%

EMCOR Group, Inc.

Electrical and mechanical construction is at the core of EMCOR Group. One of the world's largest specialty construction firms EMCOR designs installs operates and maintains complex mechanical and electrical systems. These include systems for power generation and distribution lighting water and wastewater treatment voice and data communications fire protection plumbing and heating ventilation and air-conditioning (HVAC). EMCOR also provides facilities services including management and maintenance support. Through more than 70 subsidiaries and joint ventures the company serves a range of commercial industrial institutional and utility customers. EMCOR operates primarily in the US and UK.

More than 90% of EMCOR's revenues come from work performed in the US. The remainder is derived from the UK through EMCOR Group (UK). Of this business about 40% of revenues are related to new construction. The remainder comes from renovation or retrofit projects as well as facilities services.

Challenging economic conditions have forced EMCOR to make some adjustments as customers limit capital spending. The company aggressively cut costs early on in the economic recession (mostly through job cuts) and it continues to bid on projects that present favorable profit margins. This strategy has kept EMCOR profitable even during the downturn. Additionally the company has grown by diversifying its services and expanding geographically within the US.

EMCOR narrowed its international focus in 2011 when it sold its Canadian unit Comstock. The year prior EMCOR sold its joint venture operations in the Middle East.

The divestures allowed EMCOR to focus on its core US market. Most recently the company has built its facilities services segment as facilities have become more complex and customers' desire to outsource maintenance of its systems has increased. The company provides facilities services for some of the country's most famous buildings including the headquarters for the Secret Service FDIC and World Bank.

The company has made several recent acquisitions to expand its facilities services arm. In 2010 EMCOR strengthened its government services business by acquiring Florida-based government infrastructure company Harry Pepper & Associates. The addition allowed EMCOR to start offering diversified contracting services to federal and municipal governments. In 2011 the company acquired industrial services provider Bahnson Holdings and USM Services further expanding its facilities maintenance offerings. The following year it bought North Carolina-based industrial services contractor Southern Industrial Constructors.

The acquisitions helped boost revenues in 2011. They were up by about 16%. And for the first time in the company's history its facilities services segment earned more than $2 billion in revenues. That year EMCOR particularly experienced an increase in demand for its services in the refinery and petrochemical markets as well as in the mobile mechanical and government services industries.

Some of EMCOR's largest institutional industrial and commercial projects include water treatment plants hospitals correctional facilities research labs manufacturing plants oil refineries data centers hotels shopping malls and office buildings. Many of those projects exceed $10 million and can span several years. Clients include Microsoft the US Department of Veteran Affairs and Hard Rock Hotel & Casino in Las Vegas.

HISTORY

EMCOR's forerunner Jamaica Water Supply Co. was incorporated in 1887 to supply water to some residents of Queens and Nassau Counties in New York. In 1902 it bought Jamaica Township Water Co. and by 1906 it was generating revenue –reaching $1.6 million by 1932. Over the next 35 years the company kept pace with the population of its service area.

In 1966 the enterprise was acquired by Jamaica Water and Utilities which then bought Sea Cliff Water Co. In 1969 and 1970 it acquired Welsbach (electrical contractors) and A to Z Equipment (construction trailer suppliers); it briefly changed its name in 1974 to Welsbach Corp. before becoming Jamaica Water Properties in 1976.

Diversification proved unprofitable however and in 1977 Martin Dwyer and his son Andrew took over the management of the struggling firm. Despite posting million-dollar losses in 1979 it was profitable by 1980.

The Dwyers acquired companies in the electrical and mechanical contracting security telecommunications computer energy and environmental businesses. In 1985 Andrew Dwyer became president and the firm changed its name the next year to JWP.

Between 1986 and 1990 JWP acquired more than a dozen companies including Extel (1986) Gibson Electric (1987) Dynalectric (1988) Drake & Scull (1989) NEECO and Compumat (1990) and Comstock Canada (1990).

In 1991 JWP capped its strategy of buying up US computer systems resellers by acquiring Businessland. It then bought French microelectronics distributor SIVEA. Later that year JWP bought a 34% stake in Resource Recycling Technologies (a solid-waste recycler).

JWP's shopping spree extended the firm's reach but the company began to struggle when several sectors turned sour. A price war in the information services business and a weak construction market led to a loss of more than $600 million in 1992. That year president David Sokol resigned after questioning JWP's accounting practices. He turned over to the SEC a report that claimed inflated profits.

Cutting itself to about half its former size the company sold JWP Information Services in 1993. (JWP Information Services later became ENTEX Information Services which was acquired by Siemens in 2000.) However JWP continued to struggle and in early 1994 it filed for bankruptcy. Emerging from Chapter 11 protection in December 1994 the reorganized company took the name EMCOR. That year Frank MacInnis former CEO of electrical contractor Comstock Group stepped in to lead EMCOR.

In 1995 the SEC using Sokol's information charged several former JWP executives with accounting fraud claiming they had overstated profits to boost the value of their company stock and their bonuses. EMCOR later reached a non-monetary settlement with the SEC. The company sold Jamaica Water Supply and Sea Cliff in 1996; it also achieved profitability that year.

Focusing on external growth EMCOR acquired a number of firms in 1998 and 1999 including Marelich Mechanical Co. and Mesa Energy Systems BALCO Inc. and the Poole & Kent group of mechanical contracting companies based in Baltimore and Miami. To meet increased demands for facilities services in 2000 EMCOR consolidated the operations of three of its mechanical contractors (BALCO J.C. Higgins and Tucker Mechanical) into one company EMCOR Services which operates in New England.

That year about six years after emerging from bankruptcy EMCOR began trading on the New York Stock Exchange. In 2002 EMCOR bought 19 subsidiaries from its financially troubled rival Comfort Systems USA including its largest unit Shambaugh & Son. Later that year it expanded its facilities services operations with the acquisition of Consolidated Engineering Services (CES) an Archstone-Smith subsidiary that operated in 20 states.

EMCOR broadened its facilities services operations by acquiring the US facility management services unit of Siemens Building Technologies in 2003; in 2005 it added Fluidics Inc. a mechanical services company based in Philadelphia.

In 2007 EMCOR acquired FR X Ohmstede Acquisitions Co. a leading provider of aftermarket maintenance and repair services and replacement parts for oil refinery equipment.

The company added to its industrial services operations by acquiring South Carolina-based facilities maintenance provider MOR PPM in 2008.

In 2009 EMCOR bought LT Mechanical of North Carolina a leading plumbing and mechanical contractor. The following year it bought Pennsylvania-based engineering and facilities services firm Scalise Industries broadening its mechanical services business.

EXECUTIVES

VP Risk Management, Rex C. Thrasher

EVP and CFO, Mark A. Pompa, age 47, $450,000 total compensation

EVP Shared Services, R. Kevin Matz, age 53, $410,000 total compensation

EVP General Counsel and Corporate Secretary, Sheldon I. (Shelly) Cammaker, age 72, $475,000 total compensation

Chairman, Frank T. MacInnis, age 65, $950,000 total compensation

CEO Emcor UK, Keith Chanter, age 53

President CEO and Director, Anthony J. (Tony) Guzzi, age 47, $650,000 total compensation

Chairman EMCOR Government Services, Michael W. (Mike) Shelton

VP Marketing and Communications, Mava K. Heffler

President and CEO EMCOR Construction Services, Michael J. (Mike) Parry, age 63

VP Integrated Services, Anthony R. Triano

Treasurer, Joseph A. (Joe) Serino

VP Safety and Quality Management, David M. Copley

President EMCOR Energy Services, Arthur L. Strenkert

CEO Comstock Canada, Geoff W. Birkbeck
President EMCOR Mechanical and Facilities Services, Michael P. (Mike) Bordes
EVP and General Manager EMCOR Facilities Services, Daniel (Dan) Rodstrom
Director, Stephen W. Bershad, age 70
Director, Larry J. Bump, age 72
Director, Richard F. Hamm Jr., age 52
Director, David A. B. Brown, age 68
President CEO and Director, Anthony J. (Tony) Guzzi, age 47
Director, Jerry E. Ryan, age 69
Director, Michael T. (Tim) Yonker, age 69
Director, David H. Laidley, age 65
Auditors: Ernst&YoungLLP

LOCATIONS

HQ: EMCOR Group Inc.
301 Merritt Seven, Norwalk CT 06851-1092
Phone: 203-849-7800 **Fax:** 203-849-7900
Web: www.emcorgroup.com

PRODUCTS/OPERATIONS

2011 Sales

	$ mil.	% of total
US facilities services	2,024	36
US electrical construction & facilities services	1,155	21

Selected Operations

Mechanical and Electrical Construction
- Building plant and lighting systems
- Data communications systems
- Electrical power distribution systems
- Energy recovery
- Heating ventilation and air-conditioning (HVAC) systems
- Lighting systems
- Low-voltage systems (alarm security communications)
- Piping and plumbing systems
- Refrigeration systems
- Voice communications systems

Facilities Services
- Facilities management
- Installation and support for building systems
- Mobile maintenance and service
- Program development and management for energy systems
- Remote monitoring
- Site-based operations and maintenance
- Small modification and retrofit projects
- Technical consulting and diagnostic services

Selected Subsidiaries

Dyn Specialty Contracting Inc.
EMCOR Construction Services Inc.
EMCOR-CSI Holding Co.
EMCOR Facilities Services Inc.
EMCOR Group (UK) plc
EMCOR International Inc.
EMCOR (UK) Limited
EMCOR Mechanical/Electrical Services (East) Inc.
EMCOR (UK) Limited
FR X Ohmstede Acquisitions Co.
MES Holdings Corporation

COMPETITORS

ABM Industries
APi Group
CBRE Group
Comfort Systems USA
Dycom
Fluor
Hoffman Corporation
Honeywell International
Integrated Electrical Services
Jacobs Technology
Johnson Controls
Jones Lang LaSalle
Limbach Facility Services
MasTec
MYR Group
Quanta Services
Schneider Electric
Siemens AG
SteelFab
Trane Inc.
Tutor Perini
UGL Services UNICCO
URS

HISTORICAL FINANCIALS

Company Type: Public

Income Statement FYE: December 31

	REVENUE ($ mil.)	NET INCOME ($ mil.)	NET PROFIT MARGIN	EMPLOYEES
12/11	5,613	130	2.3%	25,000
12/10	5,121	(86)	—	24,000
12/09	5,547	160	2.9%	25,000
12/08	6,785	182	2.7%	28,000
12/07	5,927	126	2.1%	29,000
Annual Growth	(1.4%)	0.8%	—	(3.6%)

2011 Year-End Financials

Debt ratio: 5.14%
Return on equity: 10.60%
Cash ($ mil.): 511
Current ratio: 145.51
Long-term debt ($ mil.): 153
No. of shares (mil.): 66
Dividends
Yield: —
Payout: 2.62%
Market value ($ mil.): 1,781

	STOCK PRICE ($) FY Close	P/E High	P/E Low	PER SHARE ($) Earnings	Dividends	Book Value
12/11	26.81	17	9	1.91	0.00	18.58
12/10	28.98	—	—	(1.31)	0.00	17.30
12/09	26.90	11	6	2.38	0.00	18.40
12/08	22.43	12	4	2.71	0.00	15.92
12/07	23.63	38	12	1.90	0.00	13.58
Annual Growth	3.2%	—	—	0.1%	—	8.2%

Emerson Electric Co.

Ralph Waldo Emerson's adage "Make yourself necessary to somebody" holds true for Emerson Electric. The company makes a slew of electrical electromechanical and electronic products many of which are used to control gases liquids and electricity. Its InSinkErator is the largest maker of food waste disposers and hot water dispensers. Emerson pursues an aggressive acquisition strategy coupled with select divestitures in building up its global presence. The company gathers its 80 business units and divisions under five business segments. It has more than 235 manufacturing locations with about 155 outside of the US. International markets make up more than half of Emerson's sales.

HISTORY

Emerson Electric was founded in 1890 in St. Louis by brothers Alexander and Charles Meston inventors who developed uses for the alternating-current electric motor which was new at the time. The company was named after former Missouri judge and US marshal John Emerson who financed the enterprise and became its first president. Emerson's best-known product was an electric fan introduced in 1892. Between 1910 and 1920 the company helped develop the first forced-air circulating systems.

The Depression and labor problems in the 1930s brought Emerson close to bankruptcy but new products including a hermetic motor for refrigerators revived it. The company's electric motors were adapted for additional uses during WWII including powering the gun turrets in B-24 bombers.

Emerson suffered in postwar years having grown dependent on military business. Wallace Persons took over as president in 1954 and reorganized the company's commercial product line seeking to bring in customers from outside the consumer appliance market.

In the early 1960s Persons bought a number of smaller companies to produce thermostats and gas controls power transmission products and welding and cutting tools. Emerson's sales increased from $56 million in 1954 to $800 million in 1973. Persons retired in 1974 and Chuck Knight became CEO. Knight took the company into high-tech fields and expanded its hardware segment with six acquisitions between 1976 and 1986.

In 1989 Emerson expanded its electrical offerings by acquiring a 45% stake in Hong Kong-based Astec (power supplies). The company spun off its defense systems electronics and other businesses in 1990 as ESCO Electronics (now ESCO Technologies).

Emerson bought Fisher Controls International in 1992 and formed S-B Power Tool with Robert Bosch. It also acquired Buehler International (destructive testing equipment). From 1993 through 1995 Emerson expanded globally by targeting the Asia/Pacific market setting up operations in China and Eastern Europe and forming joint ventures in China and India.

Emerson and Caterpillar invested in plants in Northern Ireland in 1996 through their power-generating equipment joint venture F. G. Wilson. Bosch bought out Emerson's interest in S-B Power Tool (now Robert Bosch Tool) in 1996. Production began at Emerson's Thailand compressor plant in 1997 and its Appleton Electric division formed EGS Electrical a joint venture with General Signal (acquired by SPX 1998) to serve the electrical distribution industry. Also in 1997 Emerson bought Computational Systems which makes equipment that detects potential problems in machinery at utility and plant facilities.

In 1998 Emerson bought CBS Corporation's Westinghouse Process Control division. It also acquired PC&E to enhance its monitoring diagnostic and testing capabilities. Through Astec Emerson pushed into the telecom market by purchasing the Advanced Power Systems (power conversion) business of Northern Telecom (now Nortel Networks).

Emerson sold its F. G. Wilson stake to partner Caterpillar in 1999 in exchange for that company's Kato Engineering electric generator subsidiary. Purchases that year included Daniel Industries (measurement and flow-control equipment) and the rest of Astec.

Early in 2000 Emerson acquired the telecom products division of Jordan Industries for about $980 million and later bought European telecommunications power provider Ericsson Energy Systems from Ericsson for $725 million. Later that year the company dropped "Electric" from its everyday name to reflect its diverse product line. Also in 2000 Emerson executive David Farr replaced long-time CEO Chuck Knight.

Emerson sold its Chromalox division (electric heating and control products) to JPMorgan Partners in late 2001 for a reported $165 million. In 2002 the company's Process Management segment inked a three-year deal worth an estimated $20 million a year to provide control valves and related instrumentation to Chevron. Emerson sold its Dura-Line unit (fiber-optic conduit) the following year.

In 2004 Farr assumed the additional title of chairman when Knight retired (Knight was named to the honorary position of chairman emeritus).

Emerson acquired Metran Industrial a provider of flow products and services in Russia and Eastern Europe in 2004. Emerson also acquired the US-based outside plant and power systems businesses of Marconi (now telent) for $375 million which it combined with its Emerson Network Power business. The acquisition strengthened Emerson's presence in DC power products and services particularly with the regional Bell operating companies as well as wireless and cable firms in the North American market.

Emerson acquired process measurement and control equipment maker Solartron Mobrey from the Roxboro Group in 2005. The company renamed the unit Mobrey Measurement and integrated it into the Emerson Process Management group. The following year Emerson purchased Knurr a German manufacturer of racks and enclosures for data centers for approximately $97 million; Knurr became part of Emerson's Network Power segment which also included Liebert. In a move that further expanded its Network Power group Emerson also acquired power conversion equipment maker Artesyn Technologies. Emerson sold the wireline test systems business of Emerson Network Power to Tollgrade Communications early in 2006. It then acquired Bristol Babcock a unit of British diversified manufacturer FKI for about $120 million; the purchase added measurement and control products for the energy and utilities markets to Emerson's Process Management segment. Also in 2006 Emerson sold its Buehler materials testing business.

In 2007 the company acquired Stratos International for $83.5 million net of acquired cash. The purchase expanded the portfolios of the Emerson Network Power and Emerson Connectivity Solutions segments. Stratos made radio-frequency and microwave components as well as optical subsystems components and interconnect products for a variety of applications.

At the end of 2007 Emerson sold its Brooks Instrument subsidiary to American Industrial Partners a private equity firm for about $100 million in cash. Brooks a manufacturer of measurement and control devices for the chemical and semiconductor industries posted fiscal 2007 sales of around $90 million. The sale reflected Emerson's favoring high-growth high-return businesses that were strategic to its entire corporate portfolio. To that end the company previously sold several small businesses including Western Forge (hand tools) and its share in the Industrial Motion Control joint venture with Crane.

In early 2008 Emerson acquired the Embedded Communications Computing (ECC) business of Motorola for $350 million in cash. ECC became part of the Emerson Network Power segment. The purchase extended Emerson's product portfolio in embedded computing a niche key to telecommunications industry customers among others. The company entered the embedded computing market in 2006 through its acquisition of Artesyn Technologies.

Emerson's Process Management business segment bolstered its oil and gas recovery and flow management business with the 2009 purchase of Roxar a Norway-based maker of measurement instruments and software for offshore oil platforms.

Taking advantage of historic bargains Emerson invested about $1 billion in 2009 to strengthen its other core operations via the acquisition of several small businesses. Emerson Climate Technologies added energy-efficient controls for refrigeration and HVAC systems to its portfolio by acquiring Dixell and expanded its industrial refrigeration and gas compressor business by purchasing Vilter Manufacturing.

Emerson also invested in its Industrial Automation arm by acquiring SSB Wind Systems part of SSB Group held by Parcon Deutsche Private Equity in 2009. The German wind technology company produces electrical pitch systems and switchgears used to control the blades of a wind turbine. The deal followed another 2009 acquisition Trident Power an India-based maker of power generating alternators.

Also in 2009 Emerson acquired System Plast an Italian maker of belts and conveyer components.

In 2010 the company disposed of its Commercial and Industrial Motors and Emerson Appliance Motors & Controls (part of the Industrial Automation and Tools and Storage segments) to Nidec.

EXECUTIVES

SEVP and Director, Charles A. Peters, age 56, $546,250 total compensation
SVP and CTO, Randall D. Ledford, age 62
Chairman and CEO, David N. Farr, age 57, $1,168,750 total compensation
Vice Chairman, Walter J. Galvin, age 65, $716,250 total compensation
VP Development, Catherine I. Greany, age 55
EVP Emerson Industrial Automation, Jean-Paul L. Montupet, age 64
SVP Administration, Robert M. Cox Jr.
EVP, James J. (Jim) Lindemann, age 56
EVP Emerson Storage Solutions & Professional Tools, Patrick J. (Pat) Sly
EVP Emerson Network Power, Edward K. (Ed) Feeney, age 68
Group VP, Richard J. Schul
VP and Chief Marketing Officer, Katherine Button Bell
VP and Chief Employment Counsel, J. R. Carius
SVP and CFO, Frank J. Dellaquila, age 54
SVP, B. N. Eckhardt
VP Audit, L. A. Flavin
VP Executive Compensation, Cynthia G. Heath
VP Manufacturing, R. E. Keefe
VP Environmental Affairs and Real Estate, Harold J. Lamboley Jr.
VP Development, R.M. Levy
VP Government Affairs, R.D. McDonald
SVP Organization Planning, Paul E. McKnight
VP Tax, D. C. Moon
VP and Treasurer, D. J. Rabe
VP Financial Planning, S. C. Roemer
VP Controller and Chief Accounting Officer, Richard J. Schlueter, age 57
President and COO, Edward L. Monser, age 61, $606,250 total compensation
EVP Planning and Development, Craig W. Ashmore, age 50
President Emerson India, Pradipta Sen
Corporate Media Relations, Mark Polzin
VP Labor Relations, A. E. Lebon
President Emerson Latin America, L. A. Rodriguez
EVP Emerson Network Power, Jay L. Geldmacher, age 57
Group VP, Robert P. (Bob) Bauer
VP IT and CIO, Kathleen (Kathy) McElligott
EVP Emerson Climate Technologies, Edgar M. Purvis Jr.
VP Product Management, Craig A. Doiron
SVP Human Resources, M.G. Rohret
VP Aviation, Steven E. Von Gruben
EVP Emerson Process Management, Steven A. (Steve) Sonnenberg, age 59
VP Planning, Steve J. Pelch
EVP Secretary and General Counsel, Frank L. Steeves, age 57, $565,000 total compensation
Group VP, R.P. Kerstetter
Group VP, J-P.D. Yaouanc
VP Benefits, J.L. Bansch
VP Development, R.E. Browning
VP Tax Planning, P.G. Conrad
VP Global Logistics, G.A. Fromknecht
President Emerson Middle East and Africa, S. L. Nicholls
VP Supply Chain, Kenneth J. (Ken) Poczekaj
VP Pension Investments, Michael W. Neal
VP and Associate General Counsel, Timothy G. Westman
VP International Tax, P. C. Palsen
VP and Associate General Counsel, M. J. Keating
VP Financial Services, J.F. Kelly
VP and Associate General Counsel, D.A. Kubly
VP And Deputy General Counsel, V.A. Lazzaretti
Assistant Treasurer and Director Investor Relations, L. M. Maxeiner
VP Development, A. D. Mielcuszny
President Emerson Canada, C. F. Eagleson
President Emerson Asia/Pacific, S. Y. Bosco
Group VP, E. L. Weaver
Group VP, P. E. Sarre
Group VP, L. W. Flatt
Corporate Media Relations, Mike Slatin
Corporate Media Relations, Dave Baldridge
International - Asia/Pacific Media Relations, Dave Catanach
International - Europe Media Relations, Lucy O'Brien
Group VP, W. T. Bosway
VP Employee Relations, T.M. Volk
SEVP and Director, Charles A. Peters, age 56
Vice Chairman, Walter J. Galvin, age 65
Director, Clemens A. H. Borsig, age 64
Director, August A. Busch III, age 74
Director, Harriet Green, age 50
Director, William R. (Bill) Johnson, age 63
Director, John B. Menzer, age 60
Director, Carlos Fernandez Gonzalez, age 45
Director, Randall L. Stephenson, age 51
Director, Rozanne L. (Roz) Ridgway, age 76
Director, Adm. Joseph W. (Joe) Prueher, age 69
Director, Arthur F. Golden, age 65
Auditors: KPMGLLP

LOCATIONS

HQ: Emerson Electric Co.
8000 W. Florissant Ave., St. Louis MO 63136-8506
Phone: 314-553-2000 **Fax:** 314-553-3527
Web: www.emerson.com

2011 Sales

	$ mil.	% of total
US & Canada	10,773	45
Asia	5,636	23
Europe	5,271	22
Latin America	1,319	5
Middle East/Africa	1,223	5
Total	**24,222**	**100**

PRODUCTS/OPERATIONS

2011 Sales

	$ mil.	% of total
Process management	7,000	28
Network power	6,811	27
Industrial automation	5,294	21
Climate technologies	3,995	16
Tools & storage	1,837	8
Adjustments	(715)	-
Total	**24,222**	**100**

Selected Products & Services

Process Management
- Actuators
- Measurement and analytical instrumentation
- Software services and systems
- Regulators

Valves
Network Power
- Electrical switching equipment
- Embedded power supplies
- Integrated infrastructure monitoring & management systems
- Power conditioning & uninterruptible AC & DC power supplies
- Precision cooling systems

Industrial Automation
- Commercial & industrial motors & drives
- Electrical distribution equipment
- Fluid power & control mechanisms
- Low medium & high voltage alternators
- Materials joining products
- Power transmission & materials handling equipment
- Precision cleaning products

Climate Technologies
- Compressors
- Flow controls
- Remote monitoring services
- Temperature sensors & controls
- Thermostats

Tools & Storage
- Appliance products
- Home & commercial storage systems
- Tools for professionals & homeowners

COMPETITORS

ABB
AMETEK
Cooper Industries
Cummins
Dana Holding
Danaher
Dresser Inc.
Eaton
Endress + Hauser
GE
Hitachi
Honeywell International
Illinois Tool Works
Ingersoll-Rand
Interpump
Invensys
Johnson Controls
Kinetek
Lennox
Mark IV
McDermott
NEC
Parker-Hannifin
Power-One
Raytheon
Rexnord
Rockwell Automation
Rolls-Royce
Siemens AG
Sino-American Electronic
Snap-on
SPX
Stanley Black and Decker
TE Connectivity
Tecumseh Products
Toshiba
Trippe Manufacturing
United Technologies
Yokogawa Electric

HISTORICAL FINANCIALS

Company Type: Public

Income Statement FYE: September 30

	REVENUE ($ mil.)	NET INCOME ($ mil.)	NET PROFIT MARGIN	EMPLOYEES
09/12	24,412	1,968	8.1%	134,900
09/11	24,222	2,480	10.2%	133,200
09/10	21,039	2,164	10.3%	127,700
09/09	20,915	1,724	8.2%	129,000
09/08	24,807	2,412	9.7%	140,700
Annual Growth	(0.4%)	(5.0%)	—	(1.0%)

2012 Year-End Financials

Debt ratio: 22.22%
Return on equity: 19.12%
Cash ($ mil.): 2,367
Current ratio: 141.96
Long-term debt ($ mil.): 3,787
No. of shares (mil.): 724
Dividends
Yield: —
Payout: 59.93%
Market value ($ mil.): 34,953

	STOCK PRICE ($) FY Close	P/E High/Low		PER SHARE ($) Earnings	Dividends	Book Value
09/12	48.27	20	15	2.67	0.00	14.22
09/11	41.31	19	13	3.27	1.38	14.07
09/10	52.66	19	13	2.84	1.34	13.01
09/09	40.08	18	11	2.27	1.32	11.38
09/08	40.79	19	12	3.06	1.20	11.82
Annual Growth	4.3%	—	—	(3.4%)	—	4.7%

Employers Holdings Inc

Because workers' compensation is nothing to gamble with small business owners can turn to Employers Holdings. The Reno-based holding company provides workers' compensation services including claims management loss prevention consulting and care management to small businesses in low hazard industries including retailers and restaurants. The company provides workers' compensation through its Employer Insurance Company of Nevada (EICN) and Employers Compensation Insurance Company. Employers Holdings also operates Employers Assurance and Employers Preferred Insurance Company both of which also offer workers' compensation.

While it distributes its products through independent agents and brokers in more than 30 states and the District of Columbia more than half of its premiums come from California. It also markets its products along with ADP's payroll services in several states and with Anthem Blue Cross of California's group health insurance products in California. Employers Holdings is forging additional distribution partners in other markets.

Employers Holdings maintains a strategy of engaging in low-to-medium hazard industries in order to try to keep its losses under control. Its top types of insureds include restaurants the clerical side of physician offices automobile service or repair centers and colleges (professional employees and clerical). The company also spreads its risk around and is not dependent upon any one customer for a significant portion of its income.

Along with spreading its risk among many customers the company also grows geographically. In 2011 Employers Holdings expanded its discounted workers' compensation coverage to small businesses in four additional states through the National Federation of Independent Business (NFIB). It launched NFIB-endorsed programs in eight more states later in 2011. The NFIB is focused largely on small businesses about 97% of its members have 50 or fewer employees.

Like all workers compensation insurers Employers Holdings has been hurt by the economic recession. (As employers cut their workforces they also cut the amount of workers' comp coverage they need). The company's net income has dropped by nearly half since 2008. In response the company restructured during 2009 and 2010 by cutting its workforce consolidating its claims system and combining its four regional operating units into two. It also cozied up to its distribution partners to keep warm by offering bundled products in bulk.

In fiscal 2011 Employers Holdings' revenues increased by 10% from the previous year to $464.2 million reflecting an 11% increase in premiums earned (attributable to increased policy count) and doubled gains on investments as a result of the company's strategic rebalancing of its investment portfolio. Its net income dropped 23% however to $48.3 million or $1.29 per diluted share compared with $62.8 million or $1.51 per diluted share for 2010. This was primarily due to a 16% increases in expenses including losses and loss adjustment expenses.

HISTORY

EICN was the successor to Nevada's public workers' compensation fund. The state-run system which was deeply in debt and on the verge of collapse was officially privatized in 2000 under the guidance of CEO Douglas Dirks. In 2004 EICN reorganized into a mutual insurance company which took the name EIG Mutual Holdings and included EICN as its subsidiary.

In 2006 EIG Mutual Holdings filed its initial public offering to convert from a mutual insurance holding company to a publicly traded corporation. When the company's members approved the conversion in early 2007 the name changed to Employers Holdings Inc. Eligible members received shares of the new company; non-eligible members took home just their share of the proceeds raised.

EXECUTIVES

President CEO and Director, Douglas D. Dirks, age 53, $575,509 total compensation
EVP Chief Legal Officer General Counsel and Corporate Secretary, Lenard T. Ormsby, age 59, $320,665 total compensation
EVP Corporate and Public Affairs EICN and ECIC, Ann W. Nelson, age 51, $218,963 total compensation
EVP and Chief Administrative Officer, John P. Nelson, $210,392 total compensation
President Western Region; SVP EICN, George Tway
SVP and Chief Claims Officer EICN and ECIC, Stephen V. Festa
EVP CFO and Treasurer, William E. Yocke, age 61, $313,236 total compensation
Chairman, Robert J. Kolesar, age 68
SVP and Chief Strategy Officer EICN and ECIC, Teresa M. Shappell
SVP and Regional Manager Eastern, Timothy J. Spear, age 45
President Pacific Region; SVP ECIC, T. Hale Johnston
President Strategic Markets Region; SVP ECIC, David M. Quezada
VP and Corporate Controller and Chief Accountant EICN and ECIC, Cynthia M. Morrison
SVP and CIO, Richard P. Hallman
VP Strategy and Management Reporting, Barbara Giannini
VP Corporate Marketing, Ty Vukelich
VP Investor Relations, Vicki Erickson
Director, Michael D. (Mike) Rumbolz, age 58
President CEO and Director, Douglas D. Dirks, age 53
Director, Richard W. Blakey, age 62
Director, Valerie R. Glenn, age 57
Director, Rose E. McKinney-James, age 60
Director, Ronald F. Mosher, age 68
Director, Katherine W. Ong, age 54
Director, John P. Sande III, age 62
Auditors: Ernst&YoungLLP

LOCATIONS

HQ: Employers Holdings Inc.
10375 Professional Circle, Reno NV 89521
Phone: 775-327-2700 **Fax:** 888-527-3422
Web: www.eig.com

2011 Premiums In-force

California	56
Illinois	6
Georgia	4
Nevada	4
Other states	26

PRODUCTS/OPERATIONS

2011 Sales

Net premiums earned	363	78
Realized gains on investments & adjustment	20	5
Other income	0	-
Total	**464**	**100**

Selected Subsidiaries

AmSERV Inc.
EIG Services Inc.
Elite Insurance Services Inc.
Employers Assurance Company
Employers Compensation Insurance Company
Employers Group Inc.
Employers Insurance Company of Nevada
Employers Occupational Health Inc.
Employers Preferred Insurance Company
Pinnacle Benefits Inc.

COMPETITORS

AMERISAFE
AmTrust Financial
Baldwin & Lyons
Berkshire Hathaway
CNA Financial
Donegal
EMC Insurance
Harleysville Group
Liberty Mutual
Meadowbrook Insurance
Navigators
PMA Insurance Group
ProAssurance
Republic Indemnity
RLI
Safety Insurance
SeaBright Insurance
Selective Insurance
State Auto Financial
State Compensation Insurance Fund
The Hartford
TowerGroup
Travelers Companies
United Fire
Zenith National

HISTORICAL FINANCIALS

Company Type: Public

Income Statement

FYE: December 31

	ASSETS ($ mil.)	NET INCOME ($ mil.)	INCOME AS % OF ASSETS	EMPLOYEES
12/11	3,481	48	1.4%	651
12/10	3,480	62	1.8%	699
12/09	3,676	83	2.3%	941
12/08	3,756	101	2.7%	1,040
12/07	3,191	120	3.8%	671
Annual Growth	2.2%	(20.4%)	—	(0.8%)

2011 Year-End Financials

Debt ratio: 3.50%
Return on equity: 10.19%
Cash ($ mil.): 258
Current ratio: —
Long-term debt ($ mil.): 122
No. of shares (mil.): 33
Dividends
Yield: —
Payout: 18.60%
Market value ($ mil.): 597

	STOCK PRICE ($) FY Close	P/E High	P/E Low	PER SHARE ($) Earnings	Dividends	Book Value
12/11	18.09	16	8	1.29	0.00	14.37
12/10	17.48	12	8	1.51	0.24	12.58
12/09	15.34	9	5	1.80	0.24	11.62
12/08	16.50	10	5	2.07	0.24	9.11
12/07	16.71	11	7	2.19	0.18	7.65
Annual Growth	2.0%	—	—	(12.4%)	—	17.1%

Enbridge Energy Partners, L.P.

Head of the class in transporting petroleum around the Great Lakes is Enbridge Energy Partners which owns the 1900-mile US portion (Lakehead System) of the world's longest liquid petroleum pipeline. When combined with the Canadian segment (owned and operated by Enbridge Inc.) the pipeline system spans some 3300 miles across North America. Other midstream assets include 6200 miles of crude oil gathering and transportation lines and 30.7 million barrels of crude oil storage and terminaling capacity and 11300 miles of natural gas gathering and transportation pipelines. Enbridge's US unit Enbridge Energy Management owns a 27% stake in the company.

Financial Analysis

The global recession and resulting low commodity prices and weaker demand hurt the company's revenues and income in 2009. However the market bounced back in late 2009 and in 2010. Higher oil prices resulted in higher revenues for Enbridge Energy Partners in 2010 but net income slumped due mainly to higher operating expenses and costs related to the oil spills.

Strategy

Enbridge Energy Partners' business strategy is to focus on maintaining and expanding its core pipelines business while developing additional transportation and storage assets.

In 2009 and 2010 the company completed two big pipeline expansion projects Alberta Clipper and Southern Access. The Alberta Clipper line stretches 1000 miles from Superior to the Alberta oil sands in Canada is already underway. The crude oil pipeline provides service between Hardisty Alberta and Superior Wisconsin. Initial capacity is 450000 barrels per day eventually reaching up to 800000 barrels per day. The Southern Access project increases heavy crude oil capacity of into the Chicago region by 400000 barrels a day.

Growing its midstream assets in 2010 the company acquired the Elk City Gathering and Processing System from Atlas Pipeline Partners for $682 million. The deal which includes 800 miles of natural gas gathering pipeline and related assets expands the company's market position and existing midstream assets in the Texas Panhandle and Southwestern Oklahoma.

In 2010 the company acquired the Elk City pipeline from Atlas Pipeline Partners for $686 million. The deal boosted Enbridge Energy Partners' Anadarko assets adding 800 miles of natural gas gathering pipeline one hydrogen sulfide treating plant and three cryogenic processing plants.

In a major public relations setback in July 2010 Enbridge Energy Partners' Lakehead System pipeline sprung a leak spilling more than 1 million gallons of oil into the Kalamazoo River causing the company to close down the 190000 barrel-per-day pipeline and launch a major clean up program. In September the company reported another pipeline leak in Illinois. Both leaks were contained and the pipelines repaired.

EXECUTIVES

SVP and Director Enbridge Management; President and Director Enbridge Energy Company, Terrance L. (Terry) McGill, age 57, $341,646 total compensation
President and CEO Enbridge Inc., Patrick D. Daniel, age 65
EVP Liquids Pipelines and Director Enbridge Management and Enbridge Energy Company, Stephen J. (Steve) Wuori, age 54
Chairman, Martha O. Hesse, age 69
President Enbridge Management; SVP and Director Enbridge Energy Company, Mark A. Maki, age 47, $275,504 total compensation
VP Law and Deputy General Counsel Enbridge Management and Enbridge Energy Company, E. Chris Kaitson, age 55
VP U.S. Operations Liquids Pipelines Enbridge Management and Enbridge Energy Company, Richard L. Adams, age 47
VP Operations Liquids Pipelines Enbridge Management and Enbridge Energy Company, Leon A. Zupan, age 56
SVP Commercial and Business Development Enbridge Management and Enbridge Energy Company, Douglas V. Krenz, age 60
Secretary Enbridge Management and Enbridge Energy Company, Bruce A. Stevenson, age 56
VP Finance Enbridge Management and Enbridge Energy Company, Stephen J. Neyland, age 44
VP Commercial Activities Enbridge Management and Enbridge Energy Company, John A. Loiacono, age 49
President Enbridge Gas Distribution, Janet A. Holder
VP Regulated Engineering and Operations Enbridge Management and Enbridge Energy Company, Allan M. Schneider, age 53
VP Engineering and Operations Gathering and Processing Enbridge Management and Enbridge Energy Company, Kerry C. Puckett, age 50
VP and CIO Enbridge Inc., Brent D. Poohkay
Treasurer Enbridge Management and Enbridge Energy Company; Director Finance Enbridge, David K. Wudrick, age 48
Director Investor Relations, Douglas Montgomery
VP Natural Gas Marketing Enbridge Management and Enbridge Energy Company, Janet L. Coy, age 54
VP Integrity Enbridge Management and Enbridge Energy Company, Susan E. Miller, age 53
VP Major Projects Enbridge Management and Enbridge Energy Company, Byron C. Neiles, age 46
Controller Enbridge Management and Enbridge Energy Company, William M. Ramos, age 52
SVP and Director Enbridge Management; President and Director Enbridge Energy Company, Terrance L. (Terry) McGill, age 57
Director, Jeffrey A. Connelly, age 65
EVP Liquids Pipelines and Director Enbridge Management and Enbridge Energy Company, Stephen J. (Steve) Wuori, age 54
President Enbridge Management; SVP and Director Enbridge Energy Company, Mark A. Maki, age 47
Director, Al Monaco, age 52
Director, Dan A. Westbrook, age 59
Director, J. Herbert (Herb) England, age 65
Auditors: PricewaterhouseCoopersLLP

LOCATIONS

HQ: Enbridge Energy Partners L.P.
1100 Louisiana St. Ste. 3300, Houston TX 77002
Phone: 713-821-2000 **Fax:** 713-821-2232
Web: www.enbridgepartners.com

PRODUCTS/OPERATIONS

2010 Sales

	$ mil.	% of total
Natural gas	4,230	55

Marketing	2,334	30
Liquids	1,171	15
Total	**7,736**	**100**

COMPETITORS

Buckeye Partners
DCP Midstream Partners
Duke Energy
Dynegy
El Paso Corporation
Enron
Koch Industries Inc.
Magellan Midstream
Martin Midstream Partners
ONEOK Partners
Sunoco Logistics
TransCanada
Williams Companies

HISTORICAL FINANCIALS

Company Type: Public

Income Statement FYE: December 31

	REVENUE ($ mil.)	NET INCOME ($ mil.)	NET PROFIT MARGIN	EMPLOYEES
12/11	9,109	624	6.8%	0
12/10	7,736	(198)	—	0
12/09	5,731	316	5.5%	0
12/08	10,060	403	4.0%	0
12/07	7,282	249	3.4%	0
Annual Growth	5.8%	25.8%	—	—

2011 Year-End Financials

Debt ratio: 46.14%
Return on equity: 14.98%
Cash ($ mil.): 422
Current ratio: 90.98
Long-term debt ($ mil.): 5,146
No. of shares (mil.): 284
Dividends
Yield: —
Payout: 105.15%
Market value ($ mil.): 9,440

	STOCK PRICE ($) FY Close	P/E High/Low		PER SHARE ($) Earnings	Dividends	Book Value
12/11	33.19	34	13	1.99	0.00	14.65
12/10	62.38	—	—	(1.09)	2.02	13.56
12/09	53.69	48	22	1.12	1.98	15.83
12/08	25.50	29	13	1.82	1.94	16.28
12/07	50.54	50	40	1.23	1.86	14.16
Annual Growth	(10.0%)	—	—	12.8%	—	0.9%

Energizer Holdings, Inc.

Energizer Holdings keeps going and going...and leading the battery market in the process. Known for its pink bunny marketing icon the company was spun off in 2000 by pet food maker Nestle Purina PetCare (formerly Ralston Purina). Its popular Energizer and Eveready battery products – which include alkaline carbon zinc lithium miniature and specialty batteries –are sold in more than 165 countries. Its Energizer lithium batteries provide additional power for portable electronics. Other products include flashlights razors shaving cream moist wipes and feminine care products. Its largest customer Wal-Mart makes up about 20% of sales. Energizer gets about half of its sales from the US.

Behind the contribution of recently acquired American Safety Razor (ASR) and favorable currency exchanges Energizer's net sales in 2011 were up 9% over 2010. The company also remained profitable though it carries a lot of debt – almost $2.4 billion. Both its growth and its debt are driven in part by acquisitions. Energizer also spends large amounts on advertising and promotions as well as product development.

By segment net sales for personal care increased about 20%. The product groups in this segment that performed well were wet shave (increasing 29%) and skin care (up 9%).

Year-over-year sales for household products in 2011 were flat. The company restructured that group in 2011 which included closing its carbon zinc battery factory in the Philippines and its alkaline battery plant in Switzerland. The same year Energizer developed business in the portable electronic device market by launching new chargers and cables that meet the USB standard.

Both internal development and acquisitions have fueled Energizer's growth.

In 2010 Energizer acquired ASR for about $301 million in cash and the assumption of certain liabilities. Energizer had the winning bid in an auction of the assets of ASR which filed for bankruptcy earlier in the year. The purchase of ASR added private-label shaving razors and blades which are sold under retailer names to its Schick-Wilkinson Sword unit. The products were a strategic fit for Energizer's branded shaving products.

In 2009 the company purchased the Edge and Skintimate shaving cream business of S.C. Johnson & Son for about $275 million. The deal added products that complement the company's Schick-Wilkinson Sword shaving business.

In 2007 Energizer acquired Playtex Products for about $1.2 billion in cash adding feminine hygiene infant care diaper disposal systems sun care products moist wipes and household gloves to its portfolio. (Playtex Apparel a maker of bras is a separate company and was not part of this transaction; it is a subsidiary of Hanesbrands.) Energizer also assumed Playtex's debt putting the value of the deal at around $1.9 billion.

In 2003 Energizer purchased Schick-Wilkinson Sword the world's second-largest razor and blade maker from Pfizer for $930 million. The deal brought Schick wet shaving brands (Xtreme Silk Effects Intuition Quattro) into the fold and aligned Energizer against Gillette a leader in the wet shaving market. (Gillette lost its suit claiming that the Quattro razor is a violation of its Mach3 patent and was ordered to reimburse Energizer's court costs.) The companies also competed in the battery market as Gillette owned Duracell prior to Gillette's 2005 acquisition by Procter & Gamble (P&G). Duracell and Energizer compete in the flashlight market as well.

By combining Playtex Products with Schick-Wilkinson Sword Energizer assembled a portfolio of personal care products to better compete with the P&G behemoth. Its Banana Boat and Hawaiian Tropic brands of sunscreen and tanning lotions Wet Ones brand moist wipes and Playtex brand household gloves are among the leaders in their markets. Playtex is the second largest tampon brand in the US. Playtex Products also includes a broad line of infant care products including pacifiers bottles cups plates utensils placemats and Diaper Genie brand diaper disposal systems.

The Energizer Bunny has appeared in more than 100 TV commercials since the character was introduced in 1989.

HISTORY

thi

EXECUTIVES

CEO and Director, Ward M. Klein, age 56, $833,430 total compensation
VP Human Resources, Peter J. Conrad, age 51
Chairman, J. Patrick (Pat) Mulcahy, age 67, $650,000 total compensation
VP Global Operations, Joseph J. Tisone
VP and Treasurer, William C. Fox
VP Latin America, Robert K. Zimmermann
EVP and CFO, Daniel J. Sescleifer, age 49, $446,300 total compensation
VP Investor Relations, Jacqueline E. (Jackie) Burwitz
VP and General Counsel, Gayle G. Stratmann, age 55, $354,850 total compensation
President and CEO Energizer Personal Care, David P. Hatfield, age 51, $404,919 total compensation
VP and Controller, John J. McColgan, age 54, $449,166 total compensation
VP Global Battery Finance, Brian Hamm
VP and Secretary, Mark S. LaVigne
President and CEO Energizer Household Products, Alan Hoskins
Director, Pamela M. (Pam) Nicholson, age 52
Director, R. David (Dave) Hoover, age 67
Director, John C. Hunter III, age 64
Director, Bill G. Armstrong, age 63
CEO and Director, Ward M. Klein, age 56
Director, John E. Klein, age 66
Director, W. Patrick (Pat) McGinnis, age 64
Director, John R. Roberts, age 70
Auditors: PricewaterhouseCoopersLLP

LOCATIONS

HQ: Energizer Holdings Inc.
533 Maryville University Dr., St. Louis MO 63141
Phone: 314-985-2000 **Fax:** 314-985-2205
Web: www.energizer.com

2011 Sales

	$ mil.	% of total
US	2,341	50
Other countries	2,303	50
Total	**4,645**	**100**

PRODUCTS/OPERATIONS

2011 Sales

	$ mil.	% of total
Wet shave	1,637	36
Alkaline batteries	1,311	28
Other batteries and lighting products	884	19
Skin care	417	9
Infant care	198	4
Feminine care	195	4
Other personal care products	1	-
Total	**4,645**	**100**

Selected Brands

Batteries
- Energizer
- Energizer Max
- Eveready
- Ultimate Lithium

Personal Care
- Banana Boat
- Binky
- Diaper Genie
- Edge
- Gentle Glide
- Get on the Boat
- HandSaver
- Hawaiian Tropic
- Hydro
- Intuition
- Lady Protector
- NaturaLatch
- Natural Shape
- Playtex
- Quattro
- Schick
- Silk Effects

Sipster
Skintimate
Sunsure
VentAire
Wet Ones
Wilkinson Sword
Xtreme

COMPETITORS

BIC
BYD
Dorel Industries
DSG International Ltd
Gerber Products
GP Batteries
Johnson & Johnson
Kimberly-Clark
Mag Instrument
Merck
Panasonic Corp
Procter & Gamble
SANYO
Sony
Spectrum Brands
Ultralife
Xenonics

HISTORICAL FINANCIALS

Company Type: Public

Income Statement FYE: September 30

	REVENUE ($ mil.)	NET INCOME ($ mil.)	NET PROFIT MARGIN	EMPLOYEES
09/12	4,567	408	9.0%	14,800
09/11	4,645	261	5.6%	15,000
09/10	4,248	403	9.5%	16,700
09/09	3,999	297	7.4%	15,500
09/08	4,331	329	7.6%	16,410
Annual Growth	1.3%	5.6%	—	(2.5%)

2012 Year-End Financials

Debt ratio: 37.62%
Return on equity: 19.76%
Cash ($ mil.): 718
Current ratio: 192.93
Long-term debt ($ mil.): 2,138
No. of shares (mil.): 61
Dividends
Yield: —
Payout: 6.43%
Market value ($ mil.): 4,590

	STOCK PRICE ($) FY Close	P/E High/Low		PER SHARE ($) Earnings	Dividends	Book Value
09/12	74.61	13	10	6.22	0.00	33.64
09/11	66.44	22	17	3.72	0.00	31.33
09/10	67.23	12	9	5.72	0.00	29.84
09/09	66.34	17	6	4.72	0.00	25.35
09/08	80.55	21	12	5.59	0.00	17.12
Annual Growth	(1.9%)	—	—	2.7%	—	18.4%

Energy Future Holdings Corp

Energy Future Holdings (formerly TXU) has seen the future and it works –powered by electricity. The company is the largest nonregulated retail electric provider in Texas (TXU Energy) with 2 million customers and through its Luminant unit it has a generating capacity of almost 15430 MW from its interests in nuclear and fossil-fueled power plants in the state. Energy Future Holdings has regulated power transmission and distribution operations through 80%-owned Oncor Electric Delivery. Oncor operates the largest regulated distribution and transmission system in Texas providing power to more than 3 million electric delivery points over more than 117000 miles of transmission and distribution lines.

HISTORY

The first North Texas electric power company was founded in Dallas in 1883. Another was built in 1885 in Fort Worth. From these and other small power plants three companies grew to serve most of the state: Texas Power & Light (TP&L incorporated in 1912) Dallas Power & Light (DP&L 1917) and Texas Electric Service (TES 1929). Texas Utilities Company called TU was formed in 1945 as a holding company for the three utilities.

In the 1940s TU began leasing large lignite coal reserves and in 1952 formed Industrial Generating to mine lignite and operate a coal-fired power plant. TU after pioneering lignite-burning technology in the 1960s opened the first of nine large lignite units in 1971. In 1974 it began building the Comanche Peak nuclear plant near Fort Worth.

DP&L TES TP&L and Industrial Generating joined in 1984 as Texas Utilities Electric (TU Electric). The mining company was renamed Texas Utilities Mining.

The Nuclear Regulatory Commission wouldn't license Comanche Peak in 1985 citing design and construction faults but finally granted the license in 1990. TU bought out its construction partners after much wrangling over multibillion-dollar cost overruns.

In 1993 TU bought Southwestern Electric Service (now TXU SESCO) another Texas electric utility. Accounting changes resulted in a loss for TU in 1995. However it did gain entry to the telecom arena buying a 20% stake in the Texas operations of wireless PCS provider PrimeCo. (The company sold the PrimeCo stake in 1999.) TU expanded its telecom holdings in 1997 when it acquired phone company Lufkin-Conroe (now part of TXU Communications).

TU headed down under in 1996 buying Australian electric company Eastern Energy (now part of TXU Electricity). It purchased gas dealer ENSERCH (now TXU Gas) which brought substantial energy services and trading assets on board including Texas' largest gas utility Lone Star Gas.

Despite a windfall tax levied by the UK's Labor Party TU bought British utility The Energy Group (now TXU Europe) for about $10 billion in 1998. TU sold Energy Group's Citizens Power a US power marketer and Peabody Coal the #1 US coal producer to the investment arm of Lehman Brothers.

In 1999 the company bought Australian state-owned natural gas distributors Westar (now TXU Networks (Gas) Pty. Ltd.) and Kinetic Energy (now TXU Pty. Ltd.). TU also joined a consortium to build undersea power lines connecting Tasmania to the Australian mainland.

Back in Texas the 1999 Legislature approved retail competition for the electric industry beginning in 2002. Also in 1999 Texas Utilities restructured its operations and began using the name TXU Corp. It officially changed its name the next year.

Also in 2000 TXU acquired Norweb Energi United Utilities' electricity and gas supply business which added some 1.8 million electricity customers and 400000 gas customers in the UK. TXU also contributed the stock of its telecommunications companies to Pinnacle One Partners in exchange for a 50% stake and about $960 million which was earmarked for TXU's debt. Other efforts to reduce debt and streamline operations included TXU's sale of its natural gas processing operations UK gas metering business and interests in a Czech utility and North Sea gas fields.

After raising its stake in Spanish utility Hidroelectrica del Cantabrico to 19% TXU sold its interest to a consortium led by Electricidade de Portugal and Spanish bank Caja de Ahorro de Asturias in 2001. That year TXU also acquired a 50% stake in Stadtwerke Kiel its first utility in Germany (where TXU Europe was already trading energy) and it agreed to sell two gas-fired power plants (2300 MW) in Texas to Exelon for $443 million (completed in 2002). TXU Europe sold two UK power stations (3000 MW) in 2001 and sold its Eastern Electricity distribution unit and its interest in joint venture 24seven in 2002.

In 2002 retail electric competition began in Texas and TXU responded by separating TXU Electric's regulated and nonregulated operations. TXU Electric's name was changed to TXU US Holdings which also took over TXU SESCO's electric operations.

TXU sold TXU Europe's retail supply and generation operations to UK utility Powergen in late 2002 due to poor market conditions. Shortly after TXU Europe filed for bankruptcy protection and TXU wrote off its investment in the unit. The following year TXU sold the northeastern US gas marketing operations of TXU Energy to UGI. In 2004 TXU Australia was sold to Singapore Power for $1.9 billion in cash and $1.7 billion in assumed debt.

Continuing with its effort to reduce debt and focus on core utility businesses TXU sold subsidiary TXU Communications to private telecom firm Consolidated Communications for $527 million and its TXU Fuel (gas transportation) unit to Energy Transfer Partners for approximately $500 million.

The company sold TXU Gas to Atmos Energy for $1.9 billion in 2004; the transaction included the company's gas transportation and storage assets. It has also agreed to sell its Oncor Utility Solutions unit to utility consulting firm UMS Group. Due to market conditions the firm has retired or temporarily shut down some of its power plants in Texas; the company is also considering the sale of its nuclear power generation assets. As a result of its narrowed focus the company has restructured its operations and reorganized its management.

The company announced plans to form a wholesale energy marketing joint venture with Credit Suisse First Boston in 2004; however the two firms later decided not to pursue the venture. Energy Future Holdings also outsourced its information technology functions to Capgemini Energy LP a unit of Capgemini.

In 2006 the company teamed up with InfrastruX Group to form the InfrastruX Energy Services joint venture in a 10-year $8.7 billion agreement to provide for utility infrastructure and management services.

In 2007 TXU was acquired in a $45 billion leveraged buyout by an investor group led by Goldman Sachs Kohlberg Kravis Roberts and Texas Pacific Group and became Energy Future Holdings. To help raise capital in 2008 Energy Future Holdings sold a 20% stake in Oncor to an investor group led by Borealis Infrastructure Management for $1.2 billion.

EXECUTIVES

Chairman, Donald L. (Don) Evans, age 65
Chairman and CEO Oncor, Robert S. (Bob) Shapard, age 56
Advisory Chairman, James A. (Jim) Baker III, age 82

Chairman Emeritus, Thomas L. (Tom) Baker, age 62, $536,242 total compensation
SVP and CFO Oncor, David M. Davis, age 54
President CEO and Director, John F. Young, age 55
SVP and Chief Nuclear Officer Luminant, Rafael Flores
SVP and Chief Customer Officer Oncor, Brenda L. Jackson, age 61
CIO TXU Energy, Kevin Chase
EVP Mergers Acquisition and Strategy; Chief Commercial Officer Luminant, Mac A. McFarland, age 42
Chairman and CEO TXU Energy, James A. (Jim) Burke, age 43, $342,712 total compensation
CEO Luminant, David A. Campbell, age 43, $382,000 total compensation
SVP Asset Management and Engineering Oncor, James A. (Jim) Greer, age 51
VP Public Affairs TXU Energy, Brian Tulloh
General Counsel Luminant, Bill Moore
SVP and CIO, Linda P. Jojo, age 46
COO TXU Energy, Scott A. Hudson
CEO Luminant Construction, Charles R. (Chuck) Enze, age 58
SVP and CFO TXU Energy, David Faranetta
VP Innovation TXU Energy, John Geary
VP Residential Markets TXU Energy, David Hennekes
Chief People Officer Human Resources TXU Energy, Nancy Perry
SVP Human Resources Oncor, Debra L. (Debbi) Elmer, age 55
Media Contact, Lisa B. Singleton
SVP and COO Oncor, Charles W Jenkins III, age 61
SVP Distribution Oncor, Brenda J. Pulis, age 53
SVP Public Affairs Luminant, Phil Wilson
SVP Human Resources, Carrie Kirby
SVP External Affairs Oncor, Don J. Clevenger, age 41
EVP and CFO, Paul M. Keglevic, age 58
VP and General Counsel TXU Energy, Cecily S. Gooch
Media Contact Oncor, Megan Wright
SVP Finance Operations and IT TXU Energy, Michael Carter
VP Government Affairs TXU Energy, Carl S. Richie Jr.
Media Contact Luminant, Ashley Barrie
EVP Human Resources, Richard Landy
EVP Public Policy and External Affairs, Joel Kaplan
VP Customer Care TXU Energy, Don Smith
Chief Marketing Officer TXU Energy, Michael Grasso
Chief Fossil Officer Luminant, Mike Williams
Director Investor Relations, Rima Hyder
SVP General Counsel and Secretary Oncor, E. Allen Nye Jr.
SVP and General Counsel, Stacey Dore
SVP Public Policy and External Affairs, John O'Brien
Director, David Bonderman, age 69
Advisory Chairman, James A. (Jim) Baker III, age 82
Director, Kneeland C. Youngblood, age 56
Chairman Emeritus, Thomas L. (Tom) Baker, age 62
Director, Kenneth A. Pontarelli
President CEO and Director, John F. Young, age 55
Director, James R. Huffines, age 61
Director, Lyndon L. Olson Jr., age 65
Director, Michael G. MacDougall, age 41
Director, William K. Reilly, age 72
Director, Frederick M. Goltz, age 41
Director, Scott Lebovitz, age 36
Director, Jeffrey Liaw, age 35
Director, Marc S. Lipschultz, age 43
Director, Jonathan D. Smidt, age 39
Director, Arcilia C. Acosta, age 46
Director, Thomas D. Ferguson
Auditors: Deloitte&ToucheLLP

LOCATIONS

HQ: Energy Future Holdings Corp.
1601 Bryan St., Dallas TX 75201-3411
Phone: 214-812-4600 **Fax:** 401-457-2220
Web: www.textron.com

PRODUCTS/OPERATIONS

2011 Sales

	$ mil.	% of total
Retail electricit		
Residential	3,377	48
Small business	896	13
Large business & other	997	14
Wholesale electricity	1,482	21
Other	288	4
Total	**7,040**	**100**

COMPETITORS

AEP
AEP Texas Central
AEP Texas North
AES
Atmos Energy
Brazos Electric
Calpine
CenterPoint Energy
Direct Energy
Duke Energy
El Paso Electric
Entergy
First Choice Power
GenOnEnergy
Gexa Energy
Green Mountain Energy
NextEra Energy
NRG Energy
ONEOK
Southwestern Electric Power
Texas Gas Transmission

HISTORICAL FINANCIALS

Company Type: Private

Income Statement FYE: December 31

	REVENUE ($ mil.)	NET INCOME ($ mil.)	NET PROFIT MARGIN	EMPLOYEES
12/11	7,040	(1,913)	—	9,300
12/10	8,235	(2,812)	—	9,200
12/09	9,546	344	3.6%	9,030
12/08	11,364	(9,838)	—	8,150
12/07	502	(1,360)	—	7,600
Annual Growth	93.5%	—	—	5.2%

2011 Year-End Financials

Debt ratio: 82.76%
Return on equity: 987650001000000.00%
Cash ($ mil.): 826
Current ratio: 94.46
Long-term debt ($ mil.): 35,657
No. of shares (mil.): 1,679
Dividends
Yield: —
Payout: —
Market value ($ mil.): —

Energy Transfer Equity L P

Energy Transfer Equity transfers some of its equity in order to get more out of its midstream energy assets. The company gets most of its revenues by acting as the general partner of Energy Transfer Partners which sells about 570 million gallons of propane a year to more than 1 million customers from 440 service centers in 40 states. In 2012 the company bought diversified gas player Southern Union for $9.4 billion (including $3.7 billion in debt). The deal which made Energy Transfer Equity one of the largest natural gas infrastructure companies in the US was upped from $7.9 billion to thwart a counter offer by The Williams Companies.

Operations

Through its Energy Transfer Partners GP unit Energy Transfer Equity owns a 2% general partnership stake in Energy Transfer Partners and about 26% of common stock. Energy Transfer Equity is managed by general partner LE GP LLC.

Energy Transfer Partners operates as a conglomerator in the fragmented pipeline and propane industries. It has more than 44000 miles of natural gas pipelines (up from 17570 miles before the acquisition) and 30.7 billion cu. ft. per day of natural gas transportation capacity.

Financial Analysis

The improving economy plus higher commodity prices and greater demand meant that both Energy Transfer Partners reported stronger revenues and in 2010.

Strategy

In 2010 Energy Transfer Equity acquired the general partner stake of Regency Energy Partners and sold a 49.9% stake in its Midcontinent Express Pipeline to that company. The move was seen as a way for the company to diversify its general partner operations with the aim of getting a better return for shareholders. Regency Energy Partners focuses on the gathering processing marketing and transportation of natural gas and natural gas liquids (NGLs) in Arkansas Kansas Louisiana and Texas.

Company Background

Energy Transfer Equity was formed in 2002 as La Grange Energy a Texas limited partnership. In early 2005 it changed its name to Energy Transfer Company. In August 2005 it converted from a Texas limited partnership to a Delaware limited partnership and became Energy Transfer Equity.

Energy Transfer Partners was formerly controlled by AGL Resources Atmos Energy Piedmont Natural Gas and TECO Energy; the utilities sold their interests to La Grange Energy in 2004.

EXECUTIVES

President Heritage Propane, William G. (Bill) Powers Jr., age 58, $407,692 total compensation
Chairman and CEO, Kelcy L. Warren, age 56, $2,289 total compensation
Chief Administrative and Compliance Officer, Jerry J. Langdon, age 60, $356,058 total compensation
President CFO and Director, John W. McReynolds, age 61, $406,923 total compensation
President Midstream, Richard Cargile
VP General Counsel and Secretary, Thomas P. Mason, age 55, $420,240 total compensation
CFO Energy Transfer Partners, Martin Salinas Jr., age 40, $350,000 total compensation
President Midstream Operations, Mike Howard
President and COO Energy Transfer Partners L.P., Marshall S. (Mackie) McCrea III
Investor Relations, Brent Ratliff
VP and CIO, Paul Grone
Chief Compliance Officer, Greg Brazaitis
Director, Paul E. Glaske, age 78
Director, Ted Collins Jr., age 73
Director, K. Rick Turner, age 53
Director, Bill W. Byrne, age 82
Director, John D. Harkey Jr., age 51
Director, Ray C. Davis, age 70
Director, David R. Albin, age 52

President CFO and Director, John W. McReynolds, age 61
Director, Michael K. Grimm
Director, Marshall S. McCrea III
Auditors: GrantThorntonLLP

LOCATIONS

HQ: Energy Transfer Equity L.P.
3738 Oak Lawn Ave., Dallas TX 75219
Phone: 214-981-0700 **Fax:** 214-981-0703
Web: www.energytransfer.com

PRODUCTS/OPERATIONS

2011 Sales

	$ mil.	% of total
Investment in Energy Transfer Partners	6,812	83
Investment in Regency Energy Partners	1,425	17
Adjustments	2	-
Total	**8,240**	**100**

COMPETITORS

AmeriGas Partners
Atmos Energy
Crestwood Midstream Partners LP
DCP Midstream Partners
Enbridge
Ferrellgas Partners
Star Gas Partners
Suburban Propane

HISTORICAL FINANCIALS

Company Type: Public

Income Statement FYE: December 31

	REVENUE ($ mil.)	NET INCOME ($ mil.)	NET PROFIT MARGIN	EMPLOYEES
12/11	8,240	309	3.8%	2,477
12/10	6,598	192	2.9%	6,229
12/09	5,417	442	8.2%	5,581
12/08	9,293	375	4.0%	5,430
12/07	2,349	92	3.9%	0
Annual Growth	36.9%	35.2%	—	—

2011 Year-End Financials

Debt ratio: 54.42%
Return on equity: 435.47%
Cash ($ mil.): 126
Current ratio: 79.04
Long-term debt ($ mil.): 10,946
No. of shares (mil.): 222
Dividends
Yield: —
Payout: 170.29%
Market value ($ mil.): 9,048

	STOCK PRICE ($) FY Close	P/E High	P/E Low	PER SHARE ($) Earnings	Dividends	Book Value
12/11	40.58	33	23	1.38	0.00	0.56
12/10	39.07	47	33	0.86	2.16	0.86
12/09	30.58	16	8	1.98	2.11	(0.00)
12/08	16.21	21	8	1.68	1.95	(0.37)
12/07	35.23	105	74	0.41	1.46	(0.07)
Annual Growth	3.6%	—	—	35.4%	—	—

Energy Transfer Partners L P

Energy Transfer Partners transfers energy (in the form of natural gas natural gas liquids (NGLs) across the US. The company operates more than 7700 miles of intrastate natural gas gathering and transmission pipelines and about 2875 miles of interstate pipelines and related storage assets. Energy Transfer Partners also operates 7000 miles of gas gathering pipelines three gas processing plants and almost 30 gas treating facilities. In 2012 in a major expansion of its crude oil transportation terminalling and logistics operations and its NGLs and refined products businesses the company acquired Sunoco for $5.3 billion.

The deal expands Energy Transfer Partners' portfolio of transportation storage and logistics of crude oil natural gas and refined petrochemical product assets deepens its profile as an integrated and diversified energy provider and gives it a much broader geographic footprint.

Earlier in 2012 to raise cash to invest in its natural gas operations the company sold its propane business (570 million gallons of propane a year to more than 1 million customers through 440 retail outlets in 40 states) to AmeriGas for $2.9 billion.

A conglomerator in the fragmented pipeline and propane industries Energy Transfer Partners had expanded through acquisitions from the likes of the former TXU Custer Gas Service Devon Energy and Titan Energy Partners. The company expects to continue to make natural gas businesses (such as the purchases of Transwestern Pipeline and Canyon Gathering System both in 2007) the focus of its acquisition strategy although it also makes complementary propane company purchases as well. (The Transwestern Pipeline purchase marked Energy Transfer Partners' entry into the interstate gas pipeline business). In 2008 Energy Transfer Partners acquired about 20 propane businesses for $96.4 million.

In 2010 it announced plans to expand its gathering and treating assets in the Haynesville Shale area in Louisiana and East Texas by buying a 120-mile gas gathering system from Tristate Midstream L.P. It also began work on increasing the capacity of the Tiger Pipeline (an interstate gas pipeline also serving the Haynesville Shale area) from 2 billion cu. ft. per day to 2.6 billion cu. ft. per day.

A rebounding economy helped to drive up commodity prices and demand in 2010 resulting in a jump in revenues across the company's various segments. However increased costs did cause its overall income to drop from the previous year when low gas prices helped to limit expenses.

In 2011 in a major move to add an NGL platform with storage transportation and fractionation capabilities Energy Transfer Partners and Regency Energy Partners formed a joint venture which purchased LDH Energy Asset Holdings from Louis Dreyfus Highbridge Energy for $1.9 billion.

Energy Transfer Equity controls about 26% of the company. Energy Transfer Partners was formerly controlled by AGL Resources Atmos Energy Piedmont Natural Gas and TECO Energy; the utilities sold their interests to Energy Transfer Equity in 2004.

EXECUTIVES

President Propane Division, William G. (Bill) Powers Jr., age 58, $407,692 total compensation
Chairman and CEO, Kelcy L. Warren, age 56, $2,289 total compensation
Chief Administrative and Compliance Officer, Jerry J. Langdon, age 60, $356,058 total compensation
Director; President and CFO Energy Transfer Equity, John W. McReynolds, age 61
VP General Counsel and Secretary, Thomas P. Mason, age 55, $420,240 total compensation
CFO, Martin Salinas Jr., age 40, $350,000 total compensation
SVP Interstate Pipeline Division, Lee Hanse
Investor Relations, Brent Ratliff
Media Relations Contact, Vicki Granado
President Midstream, J. Michael (Mike) Howard, age 38
President Midstream Operations, Mike Howard
President COO and Director, Marshall S. (Mackie) McCrea III, $500,000 total compensation
SVP and COO Propane Division, R. Paul Grady
VP Intertate Pipeline Division, Luke Fletcher
SVP Commercial Operations Central Intrastate Transportation, Tim Dahlstrom
VP Louisiana Business Development, Mac Stallcup
Media Relations Contact, Meredith Hargrove
Director, Paul E. Glaske, age 78
Director, Ted Collins Jr., age 73
Director, K. Rick Turner, age 53
Director, Bill W. Byrne, age 82
Director, John D. Harkey Jr., age 52
Director, Ray C. Davis, age 70
Director, David R. Albin, age 52
Director; President and CFO Energy Transfer Equity, John W. McReynolds, age 61
Director, Michael K. Grimm
President COO and Director, Marshall S. (Mackie) McCrea III
Auditors: GrantThorntonLLP

LOCATIONS

HQ: Energy Transfer Partners L.P.
3738 Oak Lawn Ave., Dallas TX 75219
Phone: 214-981-0700 **Fax:** 214-981-0703
Web: www.energytransfer.com

PRODUCTS/OPERATIONS

2010 Sales

	$ mil.	% of total
Intrastate transportation & storage	3,290	39
Midstream	3,169	38
Retail propane	1,419	17
Interstate transportation	292	3
Other	287	3
Adjustments	(2574.8)	-
Total	**5,884**	**100**

COMPETITORS

Atmos Energy
DCP Midstream Partners
Dynegy
El Paso Corporation
Enbridge
OGE Energy
Williams Companies
XTO Energy

HISTORICAL FINANCIALS

Company Type: Public

Income Statement FYE: December 31

	REVENUE ($ mil.)	NET INCOME ($ mil.)	NET PROFIT MARGIN	EMPLOYEES
12/11	6,850	668	9.8%	1,946
12/10	5,884	617	10.5%	5,433
12/09	5,417	791	14.6%	5,581
12/08	9,293	866	9.3%	5,430
12/07	2,349	261	11.1%	0
Annual Growth	30.7%	26.4%	—	—

2011 Year-End Financials

Debt ratio: 50.34%
Return on equity: 11.69%
Cash ($ mil.): 106
Current ratio: 80.46
Long-term debt ($ mil.): 7,388
No. of shares (mil.): 225
Dividends
Yield: —
Payout: 325.00%
Market value ($ mil.): 10,338

STOCK PRICE ($) FY Close		P/E High/Low		PER SHARE ($) Earnings	Dividends	Book Value
12/11	45.85	50	36	1.10	0.00	25.38
12/10	51.82	43	36	1.19	3.58	24.55
12/09	44.97	19	13	2.53	3.58	25.66
12/08	34.01	14	7	3.74	3.78	24.61
12/07	53.88	52	39	1.22	3.19	23.79
Annual Growth	(4.0%)	—	—	(2.6%)	—	1.6%

Entergy Corp.

If Entergy had an Entergizer bunny for a mascot it would stay fully charged (with a safe radioactive glow). The integrated utility holding company's subsidiaries distribute electricity to 2.8 million customers in four southern states (Arkansas Louisiana Mississippi and Texas) and provide natural gas to 191000 customers in Louisiana. Entergy operates more than 15500 miles of high-voltage transmission lines and 1550 transmission substations. In addition the company has interests in regulated and nonregulated power plants in North America that have a combined generating capacity of about 30000 MW. An advocate of nuclear power Entergy is one of the largest nuclear power generators in the US.

Financial Analysis

In 2011 the company reported a 2% drop in revenues mainly due to regulatory changes in charges (which led to a drop in utility income from residential users) as well as a lower prices for power sales by its competitive businesses. However it did post an almost 8% growth in net income in 2011 thanks to lower operating expenses lower interest expenses and lower income taxes.

Strategy

The company has increased its generating capacity (to support its utilities and its marketing and trading operations) through domestic nuclear plant acquisitions. In 2007 Entergy acquired Consumers Energy's 798 MW Palisades Nuclear Plant in Michigan for $380 million.

Entergy has also been focused on new plant construction. In 2007 it received one of the first early site permits in the US from the US Nuclear Regulatory Commission for a possible new nuclear unit at the Grand Gulf site in Mississippi. It was also the first company to submit (in 2008) two combined Construction and Operating Licenses for new nuclear plants at two different sites –at Grand Gulf and at River Bend Station near St. Francisville Louisiana. However the Japanese nuclear accident in 2011 forced the US nuclear industry to pause and take stock of its existing plants and future development plans.

To generate shareholder return Entergy has pursued a spinoff of its non-utility nuclear businesses from its regulated utility nuclear segment. However it received a major setback in 2010 when the New York Public Service Commission rejected the plan concerned at the debt load of the proposed new company.

Mergers & Acquisitions

Growing its traditional wholesale power portfolio in 2011 Entergy bought a 583-MW power plant located in Johnston Rhode Island from a unit of NextEra Energy for about $346 million. It also bought Unit 2 of the Acadia Energy Center a 580 MW generating plant in Louisiana from an independent power producer for $300 million.

In a move to raise cash and to focus on its core utility and power generation businesses in 2011 the company agreed to merge its electric transmission business into ITC Holdings to create a leading transmission enterprise with more than 30000 miles of lines.

HISTORY

Arkansas Power & Light (AP&L founded in 1913) consolidated operations with three other Arkansas utilities in 1926. Also that year New Orleans Public Service Inc. (NOPSI founded in 1922) merged with two other Big Easy electric companies. Louisiana Power & Light (LP&L) and Mississippi Power & Light (MP&L) were both formed in 1927 also through consolidation of regional utilities.

AP&L LP&L MP&L NOPSI and other utilities were combined into a Maine holding company Electric Power and Light which was dissolved in 1949. A new holding company Middle South Utilities emerged that year to take over the four utilities' assets.

In 1971 the company bought Arkansas-Missouri Power. In 1974 it brought its first nuclear plant on line and formed Middle South Energy (now System Energy Resources) to develop two more nuclear facilities Grand Gulf 1 and 2. Unfortunately Grand Gulf 1 was completed behind schedule and about 400% over budget. When Middle South tried to pass on the costs to customers controversy ensued. Construction of Grand Gulf 2 was halted and the CFO Edwin Lupberger took charge in 1985. Two years later nuke-related losses took the company to the brink of bankruptcy.

The company moved to settle the disputes by absorbing a $900 million loss on Grand Gulf 2 in 1989. To distance itself from the controversy Middle South changed its name to Entergy. In 1991 NOPSI settled with the City of New Orleans over Grand Gulf 1 costs.

That year Entergy anticipating deregulation branched out into nonregulated industries and looked abroad for growth opportunities. In 1993 a consortium including Entergy acquired a 51% interest in Edesur a Buenos Aires electric utility. In 1995 Entergy agreed to buy a 20% stake in a power plant under construction in India but the state government soon halted the project accusing the participating US companies of exploiting India.

Entergy completed its acquisition of CitiPower an Australian electric distributor in 1996 and the next year it bought the UK's London Electricity.

But diversification had drained funds. Lupberger resigned in 1998 and a new management team began selling noncore businesses such as CitiPower and London Electricity. It contracted out construction on two UK power plants to be owned by Entergy and moved into Eastern Europe through a joint venture with Bulgaria's National Electricity Company. NYMEX began trading electricity futures in 1998 using Entergy and Cinergy as contract-delivery points.

In 1999 Wayne Leonard Cinergy's former CFO stepped in as Entergy's CEO. The company bought the Pilgrim nuclear reactor in Massachusetts its first plant outside its utility territory from BEC Energy (now NSTAR); it also contracted to operate the Nine Mile Point nuclear plants in New York. Entergy sold its security monitoring business and its interest in a telecom joint venture to partner Adelphia Business Solutions.

Entergy continued its push into the Northeast by buying two nuclear plants –Indian Point 3 and James Fitzpatrick –from the New York Power Authority for $967 million in 2000 and it announced that it would purchase Indian Point 1 and 2 from Consolidated Edison (completed in 2001). In 2001 the company agreed to buy the Vermont Yankee nuclear plant from a group of New England utilities; the deal was completed in 2002 for $180 million.

Entergy agreed to merge with FPL Group in 2000 but the deal was called off the next year. The company also moved to expand through joint ventures. In 2000 Entergy and The Shaw Group a piping systems fabricator formed Entergy-Shaw which designs and builds power plants. Entergy announced an agreement with Framatome to create a nuclear operations company and in 2001 Entergy and Koch Industries formed an energy marketing and trading joint venture.

In 2002 Entergy sold its power plant interests in Argentina Chile and Peru to Southern Cone Power for $136 million. It also sold interests in projects in Spain and the UK.

Entergy and Koch Industries exited their Entergy-Koch's joint venture in 2004 through the sale of the unit's marketing operations to Merrill Lynch for an undisclosed amount and the sale of its gas transportation and storage assets to TGT Pipeline a subsidiary of Loews for approximately $1.1 billion.

As a result of Hurricane Katrina in August 2005 more than 1 million of Entergy's customers in Mississippi and Louisiana lost power; not all have been able to return to their homes. Lost customers and extensive storm damage led to Entergy New Orleans filing for Chapter 11 bankruptcy in September 2005; it emerged from bankruptcy in 2007.

EXECUTIVES

President and CEO Entergy Arkansas, Hugh T. McDonald, age 53, $319,286 total compensation

Chairman and CEO, J. Wayne Leonard, age 61, $1,341,174 total compensation

EVP Human Resources and Administration, E. Renae Conley, age 54, $403,096 total compensation

President Wholesale Commodity, Richard J. (Rick) Smith, age 60, $669,807 total compensation

EVP and COO, Mark T. Savoff, age 55, $570,115 total compensation

President CEO and Chief Nuclear Officer Entergy Nuclear, John T. Herron, age 58

Group President Utility Operations, Gary J. Taylor, age 58, $591,924 total compensation

Executive Secretary Investor Relations, Maureen Tedrow

EVP and CFO, Leo P. Denault, age 52, $654,231 total compensation

VP Investor Relations, Paula Waters

EVP and Chief Adminstrative Officer, Roderick K. (Rod) West, age 43, $300,474 total compensation

VP Corporate Communications, Toni Beck

President and CEO Entergy Mississippi, Haley R. Fisackerly, $248,346 total compensation

Director Transmission and Distribution Operations Entergy Texas, Shawn Corkran, age 44

President and CEO Entergy Texas, Joe Domino

President and CEO Entergy Louisiana and Entergy Gulf States Louisiana, Bill Mohl

VP System Planning and Operations, Andrew Marsh

President and CEO Entergy New Orleans, Charles Rice

VP Utility Strategy, Mike Twomey

SVP Federal Policy Regulatory and Government Affairs, Kimberly Despeaux

Director Investor Relations, Anne Kulakowski
Manager Investor Relations, Kristen Labat
VP Federal Governmental Affairs, Daniel Turton
SVP and General Counsel, Marcus V Brown
Director Government Affairs, Jody R Montelaro
Group President Utility Operations, Theo Bunting
President and CEO Entergy Texas Inc., Sallie Rainer
Director, Stuart L. Levenick, age 59
Director, Donald C. (Don) Hintz, age 68
Director, Maureen Scannell Bateman, age 68
Director, William A. Percy II, age 72
Director, W. Frank Blount, age 72
Director, James R. Nichols, age 73
Director, Alexis M. Herman, age 64
Director, Steven V. Wilkinson, age 70
Director, Gary W. Edwards, age 70
Director, W. J. (Billy) Tauzin, age 67
Director, Stewart C. Myers, age 71
Auditors: Deloitte&ToucheLLP

LOCATIONS

HQ: Entergy Corp.
639 Loyola Avenue, New Orleans, LA 70113
Phone: 504 576-4000 **Fax:** 504 576-4428
Web: www.entergy.com

PRODUCTS/OPERATIONS

2011 Sales

	$ mil.	% of total
Electric	8,673	77
Competitive businesses	2,389	21
Natural gas	165	2
Total	**11,229**	**100**

Selected Subsidiaries

Entergy Arkansas Inc. (electric utility)
Entergy Gulf States Inc. (electric and gas utility)
Entergy Louisiana LLC. (electric utility)
Entergy Mississippi Inc. (electric utility)
Entergy New Orleans Inc. (electric and gas utility)
Entergy Nuclear Inc. (nuclear plant operation)
Entergy Operations Inc. (plant management and maintenance for Entergy utilities)
Entergy Services Inc. (management services for Entergy utilities)
System Energy Resources Inc. (plant management and supply to Entergy utilities)
System Fuels Inc. (fuel storage and delivery to Entergy utilities)

COMPETITORS

AEP
AES
Atmos Energy
Avista
Brazos Electric
CenterPoint Energy
Cleco
Constellation Energy Group
Dominion Resources
Duke Energy
Edison International
El Paso Electric
Energy Future
Exelon
GenOnEnergy
MidAmerican Energy
NextEra Energy
OGE Energy
Peabody Energy
PG&E Corporation
Progress Energy
Sempra Energy
Southern Company
TVA
Williams Companies
Xcel Energy

HISTORICAL FINANCIALS

Company Type: Public

Income Statement FYE: December 31

	REVENUE ($ mil.)	NET INCOME ($ mil.)	NET PROFIT MARGIN	EMPLOYEES
12/11	11,229	1,367	12.2%	14,682
12/10	11,487	1,270	11.1%	15,000
12/09	10,745	1,251	11.6%	15,181
12/08	13,093	1,220	9.3%	14,669
12/07	11,484	1,134	9.9%	14,322
Annual Growth	(0.6%)	4.8%	—	0.6%

2011 Year-End Financials

Debt ratio: 30.17%
Return on equity: 14.80%
Cash ($ mil.): 694
Current ratio: 73.18
Long-term debt ($ mil.): 10,082
No. of shares (mil.): 176
Dividends
Yield: —
Payout: 43.97%
Market value ($ mil.): 12,883

	STOCK PRICE ($) FY Close	P/E High/Low		PER SHARE ($) Earnings	Dividends	Book Value
12/11	73.05	10	8	7.55	0.00	52.40
12/10	70.83	13	10	6.66	3.24	49.27
12/09	81.84	13	9	6.30	3.00	47.19
12/08	83.13	20	11	6.20	3.00	43.71
12/07	119.52	22	16	5.60	2.58	42.33
Annual Growth	(11.6%)	—	—	7.8%	—	5.5%

Enterprise Financial Services Corp

Enterprise Financial Services wants you to boldly bank where many have banked before. It's the holding company for Enterprise Bank & Trust which primarily targets closely held businesses and their owners but also serves individuals in the St. Louis Kansas City and Phoenix metropolitan areas. Through more than 20 branches Enterprise Bank & Trust offers standard products such as checking savings and money market accounts and CDs. Loans to businesses including commercial mortgages and operating loans make up most of the company's lending activities. The bank also originates consumer construction and residential mortgage loans. Bank subsidiary Enterprise Trust offers wealth management services.

Wealth management is a strategic area of emphasis for Enterprise Financial Services. Enterprise Trust targets business owners wealthy individuals and institutional investors providing financial planning business succession planning and related services. The unit also invests in Missouri state tax credits from funds for affordable housing development which it then sells to clients and others. Although wealth management revenues slipped in the turbulent economy the company remains dedicated to the segment and the non-interest fees it brings.

Enterprise Bank & Trust operates about a dozen offices in the Kansas City area and about five locations in each of the St. Louis and Phoenix markets. Wealth management arm Enterprise Trust has an office in the St. Louis area and one within a Kansas-area banking branch.

Enterprise Financial's earnings have been improving since 2009 when the company lost $48 million. In 2011 revenues climbed 15% to $161.4 million while profits more than doubled to $25.4 million. Much of that growth came from the company's banking operations and loan portfolio which has expanded in the wake of a series of failed bank acquisitions. Wealth management revenues and profits especially related to the sale of state tax credits also increased in 2011 helping Enterprise diversify and lessen its dependency on its bank income.

Arizona remains a focus for growth for Enterprise. Since 2009 Enterprise Financial has acquired the Arizona operations of three failed institutions in FDIC-assisted transactions: Valley Capital Bank Home National Bank and Legacy Bank. It also opened a couple of branches and a loan production office there. Phoenix's economy took a severe hit in the economic downturn but Enterprise Financial sees long-term potential in the market. Enterprise is also growing at home: In 2011 it bought a single branch in St. Louis from BankLiberty.

In a restructuring move Enterprise Financial Services sold life insurance arm Millennium Brokerage in 2010 five years after investing in the company. The company took a $1.6 million pretax loss on the sale. However Enterprise has been very successful in raising capital. In 2011 the company sold $35 million in company stock through a public offering. The sale helped boost the bank's capital position. That money will be used to support growth.

Also that year the bank assumed the assets of another failed bank this time in its home state of Kansas. Enterprise Bank & Trust took over the assets (including six branches) of The First National Bank of Olathe in an FDIC-assisted deal. The acquisition helped strengthen Enterprise's presence in Kansas City which has an attractive private company market.

EXECUTIVES

President CEO and Director, Peter F. Benoist, age 64, $406,368 total compensation
Chairman Kansas City Region Enterprise Bank & Trust, Jack L. Sutherland, $284,347 total compensation
EVP and CFO, Frank H. Sanfilippo, age 49, $202,333 total compensation
Chairman, James J. (Jim) Murphy Jr., age 68
EVP; Chairman CEO and Chief Credit Officer Enterprise Bank & Trust, Stephen P. (Steve) Marsh, age 57, $275,000 total compensation
President and CEO Enterprise Trust, Paul L. Vogel, $96,000 total compensation
SVP Support Center Operations, Joseph (Joe) Feld
SVP Human Resources, Mark Murtha
President Kansas City Region Enterprise Bank & Trust, Linda M. Hanson, age 51, $250,000 total compensation
President Kansas City North Region Enterprise Bank & Trust, Angela Wasson-Hunt
VP and Corporate Secretary, Karen Sher
President and CEO Clayco Banc Corporation, Jeffrey (Jeff) Kiefer
SVP Marketing Enterprise Bank & Trust, Jerry Mueller
Director, John M. Tracy
Director, Sandra A. Van Trease, age 51
Director, William H. (Bill) Downey, age 67
Director, Lewis A. Levey, age 70
Director, Brenda D. Newberry, age 58
President CEO and Director, Peter F. Benoist, age 64

Director, Michael A. (Mike) DeCola, age 58
Director, John S. Eulich, age 61
Director, Robert E. Guest Jr., age 57
Director, Birch M. Mullins, age 68
Director, Henry D. Warshaw, age 58
Auditors: Deloitte&ToucheLLP

LOCATIONS

HQ: Enterprise Financial Services Corp
150 N. Meramec Ave., Clayton MO 63105
Phone: 314-725-5500 **Fax:** 314-812-4025
Web: www.enterprisebank.com

PRODUCTS/OPERATIONS

2011 Sales

	$ mil.	% of total
Interest		
Loans including fees	130	79
Securities	11	7
Other	0	1
Noninterest		
Wealth management	6	4
Service charges on deposit accounts	5	3
Gain on state tax credits net	3	2
Other service charges and fee income	1	1
Other	4	3
Adjustments	(3.5)	-
Total	**161**	**100**

Selected Acquisitions

2011
Legacy Bank (Scottsdale AZ; community bank)
The First National Bank of Olathe (Olathe KS; community bank)
BankLiberty (Liberty MO; single branch)
2010
Home National Bank (AZ operations; community bank)
2009
Valley Capital Bank (Mesa AZ; community bank)

COMPETITORS

Bank of America
BOK Financial
Commerce Bancshares
First Clover Leaf Financial
Midwest BankCentre
Pulaski Financial
U.S. Bancorp
Wells Fargo

HISTORICAL FINANCIALS

Company Type: Public

Income Statement FYE: December 31

	ASSETS ($ mil.)	NET INCOME ($ mil.)	INCOME AS % OF ASSETS	EMPLOYEES
12/11	3,377	25	0.8%	450
12/10	2,805	9	0.3%	331
12/09	2,365	(47)	—	308
12/08	2,270	4	0.2%	348
12/07	1,999	17	0.9%	364
Annual Growth	14.0%	9.7%	—	5.4%

2011 Year-End Financials

Debt ratio: 5.54%
Return on equity: 10.61%
Cash ($ mil.): 188
Current ratio: —
Long-term debt ($ mil.): 187
No. of shares (mil.): 17
Dividends
Yield: —
Payout: 15.67%
Market value ($ mil.): 263

	STOCK PRICE ($) FY Close	P/E High/Low		PER SHARE ($) Earnings	Dividends	Book Value
12/11	14.80	12	8	1.34	0.00	13.48
12/10	10.46	25	17	0.45	0.21	12.31
12/09	7.71	—	—	(3.92)	0.21	12.72
12/08	15.24	72	33	0.34	0.21	17.01
12/07	23.81	22	14	1.40	0.21	13.96
Annual Growth	(11.2%)	—	—	(1.1%)	—	(0.9%)

Enterprise Products Partners L.P.

Both enterprising and productive Enterprise Products Partners is the #1 player in the North American natural gas natural gas liquids (NGL) and crude oil industries with a range of processing transportation and storage services. Operations include natural gas processing NGL fractionation petrochemical services and crude oil transportation including 50200 miles of pipelines 27 billion cu. ft. of natural gas storage and 192 million barrels of NGL refined products and crude oil storage capacity. It also has about 20 NGL fractionators and some 120 barges and 60 tow boats. The hub of Enterprise Products Partners' business is Houston's Mont Belvieu refinery complex.

Financial Analyis

In 2010 the company owned the general partner of Duncan Energy Partners and 58% of its stock. To boost market share in 2011 it bought 100% of Duncan Energy Partners for $2.4 billion.

The company reported robust sales growth in 2010 thanks to its expanded activities and higher commodity prices.

To raise cash and to focus on its core marine business in 2011 Enterprise sold its bunker fuel transportation business (including 21 tank barges and 15 towboats) to Kirby Corp. for $53.2 million. It also sold its Mississippi natural gas storage facilities to a Boardwalk Pipeline Partners' joint venture for $550 million.

Strategy

Enterprise's strategy is focused on building and managing an integrated network of midstream energy assets (including salt domes and fractionation and natural gas processing plants) to take advantage of growing US market demand for natural gas NGLs crude oil and refined products. In a major expansion move in 2009 the company acquired rival TEPPCO Partners L.P. in a $26 billion all-stock deal which boosted its pipelines and oil refined products and NGL storage capacity. The TEPPCO Partners purchase made the company the largest publicly traded energy partnership in the US. The expanded company's assets include 60 liquid storage terminals 25 natural gas storage facilities 17 fractionation facilities and six offshore hub platforms.

The company is investing heavily in serving shale plays especially the Eagle Ford in South Texas and is building midstream facilities to serve the surge in natural gas production. In 2010 it opened a fourth NGL fractionator at its Mont Belvieu facility to process Eagle Ford hydrocarbons and a fifth in 2012.

That year Enterprise joined Enbridge Energy Partners and Anadarko Petroleum in advancing development of the Texas Express Pipeline by the companies' joint venture. The 20-inch diameter pipeline will extend about 580 miles from Skellytown Texas to the Mont Belvieu NGL fractionation complex. The pipeline also provides access to other producers in several regions: West Texas the Rocky Mountains southern Oklahoma and the Mid-continent area. The pipeline which secured 15-year contracts from several shippers is expected to begin service in 2013.

In 2010 in a move to increase its footprint in the lucrative Haynesville/Bossier Shale play Enterprise acquired two natural gas gathering and treating systems in northwest Louisiana and East Texas from M2 Midstream LLC for $1.2 billion.

That year the company acquired Enterprise GP Holdings which controlled the general partner of Enterprise Products Partners. The $8 billion deal is aimed at reducing long-term capital costs and simplifying the business structure of Enterprise Products Partners.

Ownership

Chairman Dan Duncan controls a 40% stake in Enterprise.

EXECUTIVES

EVP CFO and Vice Chairman, W. Randall Fowler, age 55, $190,781 total compensation
SVP Natural Gas Services and Marketing Group, Christopher R. (Chris) Skoog, age 48
EVP Chief Legal Officer Secretary and Director; President and CEO Enterprise Products Company, Richard H. Bachmann, age 59
EVP Chief Commercial Officer and Director; COO Enterprise Products GP LLC, A. J. (Jim) Teague, age 66, $558,333 total compensation
President CEO and Director; Vice Chairman Enterprise Products Company, Michael A. Creel, age 59, $563,200 total compensation
SVP Engineering, Leonard W. Mallett, age 53
SVP Controller and Principal Accounting Officer, Michael J. Knesek, age 57
VP Investor Relations, John R. (Randy) Burkhalter
EVP, William (Bill) Ordemann, age 52, $242,500 total compensation
SVP, James M. Collingsworth, $260,000 total compensation
SVP Enterprise General Partner, James A. (Jim) Cisarik, $225,500 total compensation
SVP Supply and Marketing, Lynn L. Bourdon III
Director, Edwin E. Smith, age 80
SVP Crude Oil and Offshore, Mark Hurley
Director Public Relations, Rick Rainey
SVP Enterprise General Partner, Terry L. Hurlburt
SVP and Treasurer, Bryan F. Bulawa, age 42
SVP Asset Optimization, Rudy Nix
SVP Enterprise Products GP, Thomas M. Zulim, age 54
SVP General Counsel and Assistant Secretary, Stephanie C. Hildebrandt
Director, Charles E. McMahen, age 72
EVP Chief Legal Officer Secretary and Director; President and CEO Enterprise Products Company, Richard H. Bachmann, age 59
EVP Chief Commercial Officer and Director; COO Enterprise Products GP LLC, A. J. (Jim) Teague, age 66
President CEO and Director; Vice Chairman Enterprise Products Company, Michael A. Creel, age 59
Director, E. William Barnett, age 79
Director, Thurmon M. Andress, age 78
Director, Richard S. Snell, age 69
Director, Edwin E. Smith, age 80

Director, Rex Ross, age 68
Director, Larry J. Casey, age 79
Director, Randa D. Williams, age 50
Auditors: Deloitte&ToucheLLP

LOCATIONS

HQ: Enterprise Products Partners L.P.
1100 Louisiana Street, 10th Floor, Houston, TX 77002
Phone: 713 381-6500
Web: www.epplp.com

PRODUCTS/OPERATIONS

2010 Sales

	$ mil.	% of total
NGL pipelines & services	24,412	52
Onshore crude oil pipelines & services	11,722	25
Petrochemical services	5,836	12
Onshore natural gas pipelines & services	4,602	10
Offshore pipeline & services	314	1
Adjustments	(13148)	-
Total	**33,739**	**100**

Selected Subsidiaries

Baton Rouge Fractionators LLC (32%)
Baton Rouge Propylene Concentrator LLC (30%)
Belle Rose NGL Pipeline LLC (42%)
Belvieu Environmental Fuels LLC (99%)
K/D/S Promix LLC (50%)
Mid-America Pipeline Company LLC
Seminole Pipeline Company (90%)
Tri-States NGL Pipeline LLC (50%)
WILPRISE Pipeline Company LLC (75%)

COMPETITORS

Crestwood Midstream Partners LP
Duke Energy
Dynegy
Equistar Chemicals
Exxon Mobil
Huntsman International
Occidental Petroleum
Spectra Energy
Williams Companies

HISTORICAL FINANCIALS

Company Type: Public

Income Statement FYE: December 31

	REVENUE ($ mil.)	NET INCOME ($ mil.)	NET PROFIT MARGIN	EMPLOYEES
12/11	44,313	2,088	4.7%	0
12/10	33,739	320	1.0%	0
12/09	25,510	1,030	4.0%	0
12/08	21,905	954	4.4%	0
12/07	16,950	533	3.1%	0
Annual Growth	27.2%	40.6%	—	—

2011 Year-End Financials

Debt ratio: 42.58%
Return on equity: 17.24%
Cash ($ mil.): 19
Current ratio: 81.65
Long-term debt ($ mil.): 14,029
No. of shares (mil.): 886
Dividends
Yield: —
Payout: 101.05%
Market value ($ mil.): 41,099

	STOCK PRICE ($) FY Close	P/E High	P/E Low	PER SHARE ($) Earnings	Dividends	Book Value
12/11	46.38	19	15	2.38	0.00	13.67
12/10	41.61	38	26	1.15	2.29	13.41
12/09	31.41	19	10	1.73	2.17	15.58
12/08	20.73	18	9	1.85	2.05	13.78
12/07	31.88	35	29	0.96	1.92	14.09
Annual Growth	9.8%	—	—	25.5%	—	(0.8%)

EOG Resources, Inc.

EOG Resources' geography is determined by where it can locate primary energy resources –natural gas natural gas liquids and oil. The independent oil and gas company is engaged in exploring for natural gas and crude oil and developing producing and marketing those resources. In 2011 EOG's total estimated net proved reserves were 2.05 billion barrels of oil equivalent of which 517 million barrels were crude oil and condensate reserves 228 million barrels were natural gas liquids reserves and 7851 billion cubic feet (or 1.3 billion barrels of oil equivalent) were natural gas reserves.

Geographic Reach

EOG Resources is developing major shale plays in North America –the Eagle Ford Shale and Barnett Shale in Texas and the Bakken Formation in North Dakota. EOG also has operations in Canada offshore Trinidad the UK North Sea and East Irish Sea the China Sichuan Basin and the Neuquen Basin of Argentina.

Financial Analysis

In 2011 EOG's revenue increased by 66% thanks to a 92% rise in crude oil and condensate revenues primarily due to an increase in wellhead crude oil and condensate deliveries as a result of stronger production in Texas and Colorado; a 69% increase in natural gas liquids revenue due to a jump in natural gas liquids deliveries and a higher average price as a result of increased volumes in the Fort Worth Basin Barnett Shale the Eagle Ford Shale and the Rocky Mountain area; and a more than 132% increase in gathering processing and marketing revenues due to a surge in crude oil marketing activities.

Net income spiked by 579% in 2011 thanks to strong revenue growth and a decrease in exploration costs due to lower geological and geophysical expenditures in the US.

Strategy

EOG's strategy is to focus on organic growth of its North American shale plays and through strategic acquisitions of properties in North America and internationally.

EOG announced significant oil finds in Texas North Dakota and Colorado in 2011 and targeted double-digit growth in its organic production through 2012. In 2011 EOG was the largest oil producer in the Eagle Ford shale play in Texas where its net production was 30200 barrels per day of crude oil and condensate 3900 barrels per day of natural gas liquids and 21 million cubic feet per day of natural gas.

Expanding its energy portfolio in 2010 EOG Resources Canada acquired Galveston LNG for $210 million giving it a 24.5% stake in Pacific Trail Pipelines Limited Partnership and a 49% share of Kitimat LNG a planned liquefied natural gas export terminal in British Columbia.

Moving into a new exploration area in 2010 EOG acquired rights from ConocoPhillips in a Petroleum Contract covering the Chuanzhong Block exploration area in China's Sichuan Basin. In 2011 the company held 131000 net acres in China.

HISTORY

In 1987 Enron formed Enron Oil & Gas from its existing InterNorth and Houston Natural Gas operations to concentrate on exploration for oil and natural gas and their production. Enron maintained full ownership until 1989 when it spun off 16% of Enron Oil & Gas to the public raising about $200 million. Later offerings reduced its holdings to just over 50%.

Enron Oil & Gas in 1992 was awarded a 95% working interest in three fields off Trinidad that previously had been held by government-owned companies. Two years later the company assumed the operations of three drilling blocks off Bombay (including the Tapti field) as well as a 30% interest in them. Natural gas prices fell in the winter of 1994 causing Enron Oil & Gas to focus its 1995 drilling on crude oil exploitation and the enhancement of its natural gas reserves. Natural gas prices rebounded in 1996. That year Enron Oil & Gas was awarded a 90% interest in an offshore area of Venezuela. In 1997 the company inked a 30-year production contract with China. The company made a major discovery of natural gas in offshore Trinidad in 1998. That year Mark Papa succeeded Forrest Hoglund as CEO (Papa became chairman in 1999).

In 1999 Enron traded most of its remaining stake in Enron Oil & Gas to the company in exchange for Enron Oil & Gas' operations and assets in India and China. Consequently the company changed its name from Enron Oil & Gas to EOG Resources.

The next year EOG won contracts to develop properties in Canada's Northwest Territories. It also moved into the Appalachian Basin in 2000 through the acquisition of Somerset Oil & Gas. Buoyed by a strong performance that year the company increased its capital spending on North American exploration by more than 30% and in 2001 it bought Energy Search a small natural gas exploration and production company that operated in the Appalachian Basin.

EXECUTIVES

SVP and General Counsel, Frederick J. (Rick) Plaeger II, age 58
President, William R. Thomas, age 59
COO, Gary L. Thomas, age 62, $602,481 total compensation
VP Audit, Kevin S. Hanzel
VP and CIO, Sandeep Bhakhri
Chairman and CEO, Mark G. Papa, age 65, $976,154 total compensation
VP Human Resources and Administration, Patricia L. Edwards
VP Accounting, Ann D. Janssen
VP and CFO, Timothy K. Driggers, age 50, $346,154 total compensation
EVP and General Manager Denver, Kurt D. Doerr
EVP and General Manager San Antonio, Robert K. Garrison, age 59, $361,488 total compensation
VP and General Manager International; President EOG Resources International, Lindell L. Looger
VP Tax, Richard A. Ott
VP Investor Relations, Maire A. Baldwin
VP and General Manager Pittsburgh, Gary L. Smith
VP and Treasurer, Helen Y. Lim
Controller Operations Accounting, Joseph C. Landry
VP and General Manager Oklahoma City, Tony C. Maranto
VP and General Manager Corpus Christi, Kenneth E. Dunn
VP Marketing and Regulatory Affairs, Marc R. Eschenburg
EVP Operations, Lloyd W. Helms Jr.
VP and General Manager Midstream, Raymond L. Ingle
Corporate Secretary, Michael P. Donaldson
VP Drilling, Robert C. Smith
VP and General Manager Midland, Gary L. Pitts

Managing Director EOG Resources Trinidad, Sammy G. Pickering
VP and General Manager Tyler, Ernest J. LaFlure
General Manager EOG Resources United Kingdom, David J. Griffiths
VP and General Manager Fort Worth North, David W. Trice
VP and General Manager Forth Worth South, J. Pat Woods
Controller Land Administration, James C. Fletcher
Controller International Accounting, John H. Haskins
Controller Compliance and Controls, Janet B. Johnson
Controller Financial Reporting, Gary Y. Peng
Controller Financial Planning, Robert L. West
Director Investor Relations, Elizabeth M. Ivers
Manager Engineering and Acquisitions, Jill Miller
Chief Landman, Steve Wentworth
Director Business Development and New Ventures, Sherry Reese
Division Acquisitions Coordinator West Texas/Permian Basin, Rick Morton
Division Land Manager South Texas/Gulf of Mexico, Brad Blackwood
Division Land Manager East Texas/Gulf Coast, Randall Davis
Division Land Manager South North and Central Texas/Barnett Shale, David Frye
Division Land Manager Rocky Mountains/California, J. Michael Schween
Division Land Manager Mid-Continent, Bryan E. Hennigan
Manager Land EOG Resources Canada, Rob Weeks
VP and General Manager Canada, Colleen A. Marples
Director, Frank G. Wisner, age 74
Director, James C. (Jim) Day, age 69
Director, Charles R. Crisp, age 65
Director, George A. Alcorn, age 80
Director, H. Leighton Steward, age 77
Auditors: Deloitte&ToucheLLP

LOCATIONS

HQ: EOG Resources Inc.
1111 Bagby Sky Lobby 2, Houston TX 77002
Phone: 713-651-7000 **Fax:** 713-651-6995
Web: www.eogresources.com

2011 Sales

	$ mil.	% of total
US	9,065	90
Trinidad	555	5
Canada	477	5
Other countries	28	-
Total	**10,126**	**100**

PRODUCTS/OPERATIONS

2011 Sales

	$ mil.	% of total
Crude oil & condensate	3,838	38
Natural gas	2,240	22
Gathering processing & marketing	2,115	21
Natural gas liquids	779	8
Gains on Mark-to-Market commodity derivatives	626	6
Gains on asset dispositions	492	5
Other	33	-
Total	**10,126**	**100**

COMPETITORS

Adams Resources
Anadarko Petroleum
Apache
BP
Cabot Oil & Gas
Chevron
Murphy Oil
Occidental Petroleum
Pioneer Natural Resources
Royal Dutch Shell
Sonde Resources Corp.
El Paso Corporation
Exxon Mobil
Talisman Energy

HISTORICAL FINANCIALS

Company Type: Public

Income Statement FYE: December 31

	REVENUE ($ mil.)	NET INCOME ($ mil.)	NET PROFIT MARGIN	EMPLOYEES
12/11	10,126	1,091	10.8%	2,550
12/10	6,099	160	2.6%	2,290
12/09	4,786	546	11.4%	2,100
12/08	7,127	2,436	34.2%	2,100
12/07	4,190	1,089	26.0%	1,800
Annual Growth	24.7%	0.0%	—	9.1%

2011 Year-End Financials

Debt ratio: 20.17%
Return on equity: 8.63%
Cash ($ mil.): 615
Current ratio: 129.01
Long-term debt ($ mil.): 5,009
No. of shares (mil.): 269
Dividends
Yield: —
Payout: 15.49%
Market value ($ mil.): 26,501

	STOCK PRICE ($) FY Close	P/E High/Low		PER SHARE ($) Earnings	Dividends	Book Value
12/11	98.51	29	16	4.10	0.00	46.99
12/10	91.41	178	135	0.63	0.61	40.27
12/09	97.30	46	21	2.17	0.57	39.59
12/08	66.58	15	6	9.72	0.47	36.11
12/07	89.25	20	13	4.37	0.33	28.35
Annual Growth	2.5%	—	—	(1.6%)	—	13.5%

Erie Indemnity Co.

Erie Indemnity may be near a lake but it prefers pools. Founded in 1925 as an auto insurer it now provides management services that relate to the sales underwriting and issuance of policies of one customer: Erie Insurance Exchange. The Exchange is a reciprocal insurance exchange that pools the underwriting of several property/casualty insurance firms. It offers property/casualty insurance through almost 2100 agencies and 9500 independent agents with a reach that extends to about a dozen states east of the Mississippi River. Erie Indemnity charges a management fee of 25% of all premiums written or assumed by the Exchange. It is the only publicly traded part of the Erie Insurance Group.

Erie Indemnity's structure and relationship to other parts of the larger Erie Insurance Group are complex to say the least. The company operated as a property/casualty insurer through its wholly-owned subsidiaries Erie Insurance Co. Erie NY and EI P&C throughout 2010. At year-end however Erie Indemnity sold all of its outstanding capital stock and voting shares of these subsidiaries to the Exchange. As a result now all of its former property/casualty insurance operations are owned by the Exchange and Erie Indemnity serves as the management company. The sale of the subsidiaries did not affect its pooling agreement. The company also sold its approximate 22% ownership in Erie Family Life to the Exchange which became its full parent.

In 2011 Erie Indemnity's earned premiums made up more than 85% of its revenues. Of that 98% were derived from its property and casualty lines insurance business. The property and casualty group operates in 11 midwestern mid-Atlantic and southeastern states and the District of Columbia. Its largest markets are Pennsylvania Maryland and Virginia which together made up 63% of the direct written premium in 2011.

The company's overall revenue remained fairly flat in 2011 dropping a percentage point from 2010 to $4.8 billion. Its net losses for the year were $4 million compared to net gains of $313 million in 2010 mainly due to significant valuation gains on its common stock portfolio that year.

Erie Indemnity plan for growth includes increasing its property and casualty group premiums and improving its competitive position in the marketplace by expanding the size of its agency force and increasing market penetration in its existing territories. Susan Hirt Hagen a director and daughter of founder H. O. Hirt along with her niece Elizabeth Hirt Vorsheck who is also a director control the company through three family trusts. Hagen's husband Thomas (chairman of the company) and their son Jonathan (director) are contingent beneficiaries of the family trusts.

EXECUTIVES

EVP Insurance Operations, Michael S. (Mike) Zavasky, age 59, $325,000 total compensation
SVP Chief Investment Officer and Treasurer, Douglas F. Ziegler, age 61, $359,042 total compensation
Regional VP West, Timothy G. NeCastro
SVP Actuarial, Eugene C. Connell
EVP General Counsel and Secretary, James J. Tanous, age 64, $375,000 total compensation
SVP Commercial Operations, Eric D. Root
EVP and CFO, Marcia A. Dall, age 48, $289,231 total compensation
EVP and CIO, Robert C. (Bob) Ingram III
VP and Manager Marketing Communications, Karen Kraus Phillips
Chairman, Thomas B. Hagen, age 76
SVP and Division Officer Marketing, Lorianne Feltz-Upperman
EVP Services, George D. (Chip) Dufala, age 40
SVP Corporate Services, Cheryl A. Ferrie
President CEO and Director, Terrence W. Cavanaugh, age 58, $700,000 total compensation
SVP Agency Operations, Louis F. Colaizzo
EVP Sales and Marketing, John F. Kearns, age 52
SVP Information Technology and CIO, Eric A. Miller
SVP Claims, Matthew W. Myers
SVP Personal Line Underwriting, Douglas E. Smith
SVP Law and Goverment Affairs and Deputy General Counsel, Gary D. Veshecco
SVP Field Claims Operations, Christopher J. Zimmer
Regional VP East, Timothy G. Maher
Assistant VP and Manager Marketing Services, Karen Rugare
SVP and Controller, Gregory J. Gutting
SVP Human Resources, Christina Marsh
Director, Richard L. Stover, age 69
Director, J. Ralph Borneman Jr., age 73
Director, Susan Hirt Hagen, age 76
Director, Claude C. Lilly III, age 65
Director, Robert C. Wilburn, age 68
Director, Martin P. Sheffield, age 62
Director, C. Scott Hartz, age 66
Director, Jonathan Hirt Hagen, age 49
Director, Thomas W. Palmer, age 64
Director, Lucian L. Morrison, age 75
Director, Elizabeth A. Vorsheck, age 56

President CEO and Director, Terrence W. Cavanaugh, age 58
Auditors: Ernst&YoungLLP

LOCATIONS

HQ: Erie Indemnity Co.
100 Erie Insurance Place, Erie, PA 16530
Phone: 814 870-2000
Web: www.erieinsurance.com

PRODUCTS/OPERATIONS

2011 Revenues

	$ mil.	% of total
Premiums earned	4,214	87
Investment income	433	9
Realized investment losses	(4)	-
Impairment losses recognized in earnings	(2)	-
Equity in earnings of limited partnerships	149	3
Other income	34	1
Total	**4,824**	**100**

2011 Premiums Earned

	$ mil.	% of total
Property & casualty insurance	4,149	98
Life insurance	67	2
Adjustments	(2)	-
Total	**4,214**	**100**

2011 Property and Casualty Written Premiums

	% of total
Private passenger	47
Homeowners	22
Commercial	12
Commercial	7
Workers'	7
Other	5
Total	**100**

COMPETITORS

ACE USA
Alleghany Corporation
Gallagher
Marsh & McLennan
Navigators
Old Republic
PMA Companies
Transatlantic Holdings
Travelers Companies

HISTORICAL FINANCIALS

Company Type: Public

Income Statement FYE: December 31

	ASSETS ($ mil.)	NET INCOME ($ mil.)	INCOME AS % OF ASSETS	EMPLOYEES
12/11	14,348	169	1.2%	4,300
12/10	14,344	162	1.1%	4,200
12/09	2,666	108	4.1%	4,200
12/08	2,613	69	2.6%	4,200
12/07	2,878	212	7.4%	4,100
Annual Growth	49.4%	(5.6%)	—	1.2%

2011 Year-End Financials

Debt ratio: —
Return on equity: 21.64%
Cash ($ mil.): 185
Current ratio: —
Long-term debt ($ mil.): —
No. of shares (mil.): 47
Dividends
Yield: —
Payout: 66.88%
Market value ($ mil.): 3,741

	STOCK PRICE ($) FY Close	P/E High/Low		PER SHARE ($) Earnings	Dividends	Book Value
12/11	78.16	23	18	3.08	0.00	16.32
12/10	65.47	21	12	2.85	1.92	18.22
12/09	39.02	19	14	1.89	1.83	17.61
12/08	37.63	42	24	1.19	1.77	15.44
12/07	51.89	16	13	3.43	1.60	19.71
Annual Growth	10.8%	—	—	(2.7%)	—	(4.6%)

Exelis Inc.

Exelis excels when it comes to high-tech modern weaponry. The company offers products for integrated electronic warfare sensing and surveillance air traffic management information and cyber security and networked communications. It also deals in composite aerostructures logistics and technical services. Most of its business comes from the US government particularly the Department of Defense (about 70% of sales) the FAA and NASA. It also serves commercial clients; and about 10% of sales comes from international customers. Formerly the defense and information solutions unit of ITT Corp. Exelis was spun off in 2011 as a publicly-traded company.

Exelis' largest segment (about 60% of revenues) provides products for what is known as C4ISR (Command Control Communications Computers Intelligence Surveillance and Reconnaissance). That business represents more than half of sales. Exelis' other segment –information and technical services (I&TS) –accounts for the remaining revenue.

C4ISR products include electronic systems (communications and force protection) geospatial systems (night vision and intelligence surveillance and reconnaissance) information systems communications imaging and image-processing radar and sonar systems and space systems. Contracts won in this space have included satellite imagers for DigitalGlobe's and GeoEye's Enhanced View.

I&TS provides systems integration network design and development cyber intelligence advanced engineering logistics space launch and range-support services for the US military and other government agencies. Recent contracts include one with the US Air Force to provide self-encrypting solid state computer hard drives which will be engineered at Exelis' Tempe Arizona facility and manufactured in Fort Wayne Indiana.

Exelis revenues only dipped 1% in 2011 but the $5.8 billion in sales marks a continuing pesky decline from its 2008 height of nearly $6.1 billion. C4ISR intake fell by more than 20% which couldn't be fully recovered by the more than 30% gain in I&TS business. C4ISR backed off due to maturity in its CREW 2.1 offering which is now expected mainly to produce maintenance income as well as weak demand for single channel ground and airborne radio system (SINCGARS) special purpose jammer products and electronic warfare systems on special operations aircraft. Increased revenue related to its Enhanced View contract work helped balance out the decreases from this segment.

I&TS growth continued to benefit from US military involvement in the Middle East and Afghanistan as well as from demand in its space communication and network services offerings and technology and systems engineering bridge program. On the decline were global maintenance and supply services and its data and analysis center for software contract both of which were essentially completed by the end of 2010 and were replaced by growth-producing options.

With fierce competition for contracts Exelis and its competitors sometimes team up to increase their chances of success. In 2012 the company and industry powerhouses BAE Systems and L-3 formed a joint venture to try to lock on to more business with the US Air Force.

Looking ahead Exelis is pursuing adjacent markets to use its military technology in health care. In 2011 the company signed a long-term supply agreement with Novocure to adapt its piezoelectric ceramic technology for brain cancer treatments. Products for the deal will be made at its Salt Lake City facility which has undergone expansion to also begin manufacturing new aircraft body composite materials.

As part of Exelis' strategy it remains committed to its business with the military and other DoD branches. The company is planning however for the possibility of related budget cuts over the next decade. To protect its top line Exelis is making an extra effort to serve agencies that offer more predictable demand like the FAA. In addition to broadening its non-DoD client base it also looks to international growth targeting allied countries with ongoing defense needs or air traffic infrastructure modernization in high growth regions such as Asia/Pacific Brazil India and the Middle East.

EXECUTIVES

Chairman, Ralph F. Hake, age 63
Director, Steven R. Loranger, age 60
SVP Chief Legal Officer and Corporate Secretary, Ann D. Davidson, age 60
EVP and President Electronic Systems, Christopher C. Bernhardt
SVP and CFO, Peter J. Milligan
SVP and Chief Human Resources Officer, A. John Procopio
VP Operations, Vincent Thomas
EVP and President Geospatial Systems, Christopher D. Young
EVP and President Information Systems, Michael (Mike) Wilson
President CEO and Director, David F. Melcher
VP and Chief Communications Officer, David J. Albritton
SVP and Chief Strategy and Corporate Development Officer, John Shephard
EVP and President Mission Systems, Kenneth W. (Ken) Hunzeker
VP Government Relations, Robert E. (Bob) Durbin
Vice President International Government Relations, Chris Tucker
Communications Manager, John Dench
Director Global External Affairs, Anne Eisele
Director, Patrick J. Moore, age 58
Director, Christina A. Gold, age 64
Director, R. David Yost
Director, Steven R. Loranger, age 60
Director, John J. Hamre, age 61
Director, Herman E. Bulls, age 56
Director, Paul J. Kern, age 66
Director, Mark L. Reuss, age 48
President CEO and Director, David F. Melcher
Independent Director, Billie Williamson
Auditors: Deloitte&ToucheLLP

LOCATIONS

HQ: Exelis Inc.
1650 Tysons Boulevard, Suite 1700, McLean, VA 22102
Phone: 703 790-6300
Web: www.exelisinc.com

2011 Sales

	$ mil.	% of total
$ of total % of total		
US	5,305	91
International	534	9
Total	**5,839**	**100**

PRODUCTS/OPERATIONS

2011 Sales

	$ mil.	% of total
C4ISR electronics & systems	3,022	52
Information & technical services	2,817	48
Total	**5,839**	**100**

2011 Sales by Customer

	% of total
Dept. of Defense & intelligence	69
FAA NASA other US government & US	22
International	9
Total	**100**

Selected Product Categories

C4ISR
- Airborne remote sensing systems
- Climate and environmental monitoring
- Counter RCIED electronic warfare (CREW)
- Defense surveillance and mobile radar systems
- GPS payload receiver and control systems
- Integrated optical systems
- Mine sensing and neutralization
- Networked communications
- Piezoelectrics (electric charge produced by mechanical stress)
- Sensors and microelectronics
- Sonar and acoustic systems
- Test and support systems
- Weapons suspension and release systems

Information & Technical Services
- Air traffic management
- Base operations support
- C3 (command control and communications) systems
- Logistics support
- Quick reaction capabilities
- Security and support
- Vehicle and equipment

Selected Customers

US Government
- FAA
- Department of Homeland Security
- Military
  - Army
  - Navy
  - Air Force
  - Marines
- NASA
- Small Business Administration

Civil
- Embry-Riddle Aeronautical University
- Metropolitan Washington Airports Authority
- Philadelphia International Airport

Selected Acquisitions

2012
- Space Computer Corporation (Los Angeles; hidden or obscured object detection through real-time signal processing systems software and algorithms)
- Kilovolts (high-voltage power supply maker serving the medical scientific pharmaceutical and food safety sectors)

2010
- SRA International' s airport operations solutions (AOS) group ($235 million; web-based airport operation management services in North America)

COMPETITORS

BAE SYSTEMS
Ball Aerospace
Boeing
DynCorp International
EADS
Finmeccanica
Fluor
General Dynamics
Globecomm
Harris Corp.
Honeywell Aerospace
Honeywell Technology Solutions
KBR
L-3 Communications
Lockheed Martin
Northrop Grumman
Raytheon
Rockwell Collins
SAIC
Sanmina
Sierra Nevada Corp
Thales
Ultra Electronics

HISTORICAL FINANCIALS

Company Type: Public

Income Statement FYE: December 31

	REVENUE ($ mil.)	NET INCOME ($ mil.)	NET PROFIT MARGIN	EMPLOYEES
12/11	5,839	326	5.6%	20,500
12/10	5,891	587	10.0%	20,400
12/09	6,061	469	7.7%	0
12/08	6,072	421	6.9%	0
Annual Growth	(1.3%)	(8.2%)	—	—

2011 Year-End Financials

Debt ratio: 12.73%
Return on equity: 36.51%
Cash ($ mil.): 116
Current ratio: 131.00
Long-term debt ($ mil.): 649
No. of shares (mil.): 184
Dividends
Yield: —
Payout: 5.90%
Market value ($ mil.): 1,672

	STOCK PRICE ($) FY Close	P/E High/Low	PER SHARE ($) Earnings	Dividends	Book Value
12/11	9.05	7 5	1.75	0.00	4.83
Annual Growth	—	— —	—	—	—

Exelon Corp.

The City of Brotherly Love meets the Windy City and The Greatest City in America in utility and power generating holding company Exelon. The company distributes electricity and gas to 6.6 million customers in Maryland northern Illinois and southeastern Pennsylvania through subsidiaries Baltimore Gas and Electric Commonwealth Edison (ComEd) and PECO Energy. Subsidiary Exelon Generation holds the company's power assets of 35000 MW (19000 MW of which is nuclear). Exelon Power Team is a top wholesale energy marketer and Exelon Energy markets retail power and offers other energy-related services. In a major move in 2012 the company bought Constellation Energy in a $7.9 billion stock deal.

Strategy

The acquisition part of an industry-wide consolidation trend gives Exelon access to Constellation Energy's major retail operations in Maryland enabling it to grow its retail profile. (The regulated retail markets with their more predictable revenues tend to do well during times when wholesale markets are down.) Exelon plans to consolidate its power marketing business and Constellation's retail and wholesale business under the Constellation brand and be based in Baltimore. The deal makes Exelon the #1 power generator in the US and the #2 residential electric and gas distributor.

The US Department of Justice required Exelon and Constellation to divest three electricity generating plants in Maryland to proceed with the merger. It contended that combining the companies' assets would potentially enable the merged firm to raise wholesale electricity prices and reduce output.

As part of a portfolio repositioning strategy in 2012 the company sold its stakes in five California power plants (a total of 70 MW of generating capacity) to Japan-based IHI Corporation.

To meet stricter environmental regulations the company has been bulking up its non-fossil fuel generating assets. Growing its cleaner-burning plant fleet in Texas in 2011 the company bought Wolf Hollow a 720 MW combined-cycle natural gas-fired power plant in north Texas from Sequent Wolf Hollow for $305 million.

Expanding its green energy assets that year the company also agreed to acquire Antelope Valley Solar Ranch One from First Solar. The 230-MW solar power project is under development in northern Los Angeles County. The $1.4 billion investment complements Constellation Energy's solar power holdings and marks Exelon's first move into the California merchant power market.

In 2010 in a bid to grow its renewable energy segment and lower its carbon emissions the company acquired wind power developer John Deere Renewables for about $860 million. The deal added 735 MW of operating wind power capacity (and 230 MW under development) to Exelon's generation assets.

The green energy power sources complement the core of Exelon's long term energy expansion plan the development and maintenance of nuclear generating capacity. However the Fukushima nuclear plant disaster in early 2011 placed Exelon's nuclear power expansion plans under serious scrutiny from regulators and investors.

Financial Analysis

Higher prices and demand lifted revenues in 2011 despite a drop in PECO Energy's revenues due in part to the ending (in late-2010) of its competitive transition charges structure (a levy to help electric utilities pay down stranded costs resulting from the transition from regulated to deregulated markets). In 2011 higher expenses also brought down Exelon's net income.

The company reported improved operating revenues in 2010 thanks to a rebounding economy and an increase in power demand. However lower margins realized on market and affiliate power sales (due to unfavorable market conditions) and lower mark-to-market gains on hedging activities along with higher nuclear fuel costs dragged down Exelon's net income for the year.

HISTORY

Thomas Dolan and local investors formed the Brush Electric Light Company of Philadelphia in 1881 to provide street and commercial lighting. Competitors sprang up and in 1885 Brush merged with the United States Electric Lighting Company of Pennsylvania to form a secret "electric trust" or holding company. Dolan became president in 1886 and bought four other utilities.

In 1895 Martin Maloney formed Pennsylvania Heat Light and Power to consolidate the city's electric companies. By the next year it had acquired among other businesses Columbia Electric Light Philadelphia Edison and the electric trust. In 1899 a new firm National Electric challenged Maloney by acquiring neighboring rival Southern Electric Light. Before retiring Maloney negotiated the merger of the two firms forming Philadelphia Electric in 1902.

Demand rose rapidly into the 1920s fueled in part by the company's promotion of electric appliances. In 1928 the year after it completed the Conowingo Hydroelectric Station Philadelphia Electric was absorbed by the much larger United Gas Improvement. United Gas avoided large layoffs during the Depression but passage of the Public Utility Holding Company Act (PUHCA) in 1935 sounded its death knell. (PUHCA was repealed in 2005.) In 1943 the SEC forced United Gas to divest Philadelphia Electric.

Philadelphia Electric built several plants in the 1950s and 1960s in response to a postwar electricity boom. A small experimental nuclear reactor was completed at Peach Bottom Pennsylvania in 1967 and in 1974 the company placed two nuclear units in service at the plant. The Salem (New Jersey) nuke (Unit 1) followed in 1977. The company relied on these plants during the OPEC oil crisis. Another one Limerick Unit 1 began operations in 1986 and Unit 2 went on line in 1990 but the Peach Bottom plant was shut down from 1989 to 1991 because of management problems (later resolved).

The company began reorganizing in 1993 and changed its name the next year to PECO Energy Company. It also sold Maryland retail subsidiary Conowingo Power retaining the hydroelectric plant. In 1995 rival PP&L rejected PECO's acquisition bid citing PECO's nuclear liabilities.

A year later PECO teamed with AT&T Wireless to offer PCS in Philadelphia (service was launched in 1997). EnergyOne a national venture formed in 1997 by PECO UtiliCorp United (now Aquila) and AT&T offered consumers a package of power phone and Internet services on one bill. However the slow deregulation process caused the venture to fail.

PECO also joined with British Energy in 1997 to form AmerGen hoping to buy nukes at rock-bottom prices from utilities eager to unload them. AmerGen purchased three nuclear facilities in 1999 and 2000: Unit 1 of the Three Mile Island (Pennsylvania) facility; a plant in Clinton Illinois; and an Oyster Creek (New Jersey) location.

In 1999 PECO announced plans to acquire Chicago's Unicom the parent company of Commonwealth Edison (ComEd). After the deal was completed in 2000 the combined company took the name Exelon and established its headquarters in Chicago.

Pennsylvania's utility markets were fully deregulated in 2000. To expand its power generation business Exelon that year bought 49.9% of Sithe Energies for $682 million. In 2001 Exelon agreed to buy two gas-fired power plants (2300 MW) in Texas from TXU for $443 million; the deal was completed in 2002.

Also in 2002 Exelon purchased Sithe Energies' stakes in six New England power plants with 2000 MW of capacity (plus 2400 MW under construction) for $543 million plus the assumption of $1.15 billion in debt. The company also sold its Philadelphia PCS venture interest to former partner AT&T Wireless Services (now part of AT&T Mobility). Sithe Energies was sold to Dynegy in 2005 for $135 million.

To focus on core utility operations the company sold its infrastructure construction business InfraSource and its facility and infrastructure management business Exelon Solutions. Exelon then completed the sale of its interest in telecommunications joint venture PECO TelCove which provides voice and data services to its partner TelCove and sold its district heating and cooling division (Thermal Chicago).

In 2008 in a move to expand its geographic reach Exelon made a $6.2 billion bid to buy NRG Energy. Though the offer to buy NRG met with resistance Exelon had kept up its pursuit of the company. Toward the end of 2008 it announced an exchange offer for NRG's shares. By the expiration date of the offer early the next year it had acquired just more than 50% of those shares. In addition to announcing another extension of the offer Exelon said it hoped NRG's Board would allow it to do due diligence and begin negotiations for an acquisition. But an NRG proxy vote rejection in 2009 led Exelon to terminate its offer.

EXECUTIVES

Chairman and CEO Commonwealth Edison, Frank M. Clark Jr., age 66, $546,692 total compensation
President CEO and Director, Christopher M. (Chris) Crane, age 53, $821,154 total compensation
Executive Chairman, Mayo A. Shattuck III, age 57
EVP Legislative and External Affairs Commonwealth Edison, John T. Hooker, age 63
EVP and Chief Administrative and Diversity Officer; President Exelon Business Services, Ruth Ann M. Gillis, age 58
COO Exelon Transmission Company, Ronald J. (Ron) DeGregorio
President and Chief Nuclear Officer Exelon Nuclear, Michael J. Pacilio, age 51
EVP and CFO, Jonathan W. (Jack) Thayer, age 40
VP and Controller, Duane M. DesParte, age 48
President and CEO Commonwealth Edison, Anne R. Pramaggiore, age 53
EVP and Chief Commercial Officer; President and CEO Constellation, Kenneth W. (Ken) Cornew, age 46
Manager Investor Relations, Marybeth Flater
Senior Manager Communications, Judy Rader
SVP and General Counsel, Darryl M. Bradford, age 56
SVP and CFO PECO Energy, Phillip S. Barnett, age 48
SEVP and Chief Strategy Officer, William A. (Bill) Von Hoene Jr., age 58
VP and Assistant Corporate Controller; Chief Accounting Officer Generation, Matthew R. Galvanoni, age 39
COO Exelon Generation, Charles G. (Chip) Pardee, age 52
EVP; President and CEO PECO Energy, Craig L. Adams, age 59
SVP Human Resources, Calvin G. Butler Jr., age 42
VP Corporate Financial Planning and Analysis, Karie Anderson
VP Regulatory Affairs and General Counsel PECO Energy, Paul R. Bonney, age 53
SVP Customer Operations Commonwealth Edison, Fidel Marquez Jr., age 50
SVP CFO and Treasurer Commonwealth Edison, Joseph R. (Joe) Trpik Jr., age 42
VP and Controller PECO Energy, Jorge A. Acevedo, age 40
VP Comptroller Accountant and Controller Commonwealth Edison, Kevin J. Waden, age 40
VP Governmental and External Affairs PECO Energy, Romulo L. (Romy) Diaz Jr., age 65
Associate General Counsel, Anthony (Tony) Gay
VP Treasury Operations and Assistant Treasurer, JaCee M. Burnes, age 41
SVP Federal Government Affairs and Public Policy, David C. Brown
SVP Federal Regulatory Affairs and Public Policy, Joseph Dominguez, age 48
VP Wholesale Market Development, Steve Naumann
VP and Director Federal Regulatory Affairs and Policy, Karen Hill
SVP Communications and Public Policy Exelon and State Government Affairs Exelon Generation, James Firth
VP Investor Relations, Stacie Frank
VP Corporate Strategy and Exelon 2020, Christopher Gould
SEVP; President and CEO Exelon Utilities, Denis P. O?Brien, age 51
EVP Operations Commonwealth Edison, Terence R. Donnelly, age 51
Director Nuclear Communications Exelon Nuclear & Exelon Nuclear Partners, Marshall Murphy
Director Power Communications Exelon Generation Power and Power Team, Valencia McClure
Manager Corporate Planning, Paul Mountain
COO and SVP Exelon Nuclear, Susan Landahl
VP Federal Regulatory Affairs and Policy, Kathleen Barron
SVP Generation; President Exelon Power, Sunil (Sonny) Garg, age 45
VP Federal Government Affairs, Mary Streett
SVP Compensation and Benefits, Victor Fonseca
SVP Labor Relations, John Samolis
VP Talent Management and Organizational Effectiveness, Michael Campbell
VP Cyber and Physical Security, Ellen Caya
VP Commercial Operations Group, Susan Weiss
VP Braidwood Generating Station, Dan Enright
SVP Exelon Nuclear Partners, Amir Shahkarami
SVP Distribution Operations Commonwealth Edison, Anthony J. Tyler, age 47
President CEO and Director, Christopher M. (Chris) Crane, age 53
Director, John A. Canning Jr., age 67
Director, Nicholas DeBenedictis, age 66
Director, William C. (Bill) Richardson, age 71
Director, Sue L. Gin, age 70
Director, Rosemarie B. Greco, age 65
Director, Donald (Don) Thompson, age 48
Director, John W. Rogers Jr., age 53
Director, M. Walter D'Alessio, age 78
Director, Stephen D. (Steve) Steinour, age 53
Director, Thomas J. (Tom) Ridge, age 66
Director, Nelson A. Diaz, age 64
Director, Adm. Richard W. Mies, age 67
Director, Paul L. Joskow, age 64
Auditors: PricewaterhouseCoopersLLP

LOCATIONS

HQ: Exelon Corp.
10 South Dearborn Street, P.O. Box 805379, Chicago, IL 60680-5379
Phone: 312 394-7398
Web: www.exeloncorp.com

PRODUCTS/OPERATIONS

2011 Sales

	$ mil.	% of total
Generation	10,308	49
PECO	3,720	18
Adjustments	(1990)	-

Selected Operating Units Subsidiaries and Affiliates

Exelon Energy Delivery
Baltimore Gas and Electric (BGE electric and gas utility)
- Commonwealth Edison Company (ComEd electric utility)
- PECO Energy Company (PECO electric and gas utility)

Exelon Generation Company LLC
- Exelon Power
  - Exelon Hydro
  - Exelon Solar
  - Exelon Wind
- Exelon Power Team
  - Exelon Energy (nonregulated retail power sales)
  - Exelon Nuclear (nuclear power generation)

Exelon Transmission Company

COMPETITORS

AES
Alliant Energy
Ameren
American Transmission
CenterPoint Energy
Delmarva Power
Dynegy
Entergy
FirstEnergy
GenOnEnergy
Green Mountain Energy
Integrys Energy Group

Dominion Resources	NextEra Energy
Duke Energy	Nicor Gas
Duquesne Light Holdings	PPL Corporation
	UGI

HISTORICAL FINANCIALS

Company Type: Public

Income Statement FYE: December 31

	REVENUE ($ mil.)	NET INCOME ($ mil.)	NET PROFIT MARGIN	EMPLOYEES
12/11	18,924	2,495	13.2%	19,267
12/10	18,644	2,563	13.7%	19,214
12/09	17,318	2,707	15.6%	19,329
12/08	18,859	2,737	14.5%	19,610
12/07	18,916	2,736	14.5%	17,800
Annual Growth	0.0%	(2.3%)	—	2.0%

2011 Year-End Financials

Debt ratio: 24.33%
Return on equity: 17.24%
Cash ($ mil.): 1,016
Current ratio: 110.02
Long-term debt ($ mil.): 12,189
No. of shares (mil.): 663
Dividends
Yield: —
Payout: 56.00%
Market value ($ mil.): 28,770

	STOCK PRICE ($) FY Close	P/E High	P/E Low	PER SHARE ($) Earnings	Dividends	Book Value
12/11	43.37	12	11	3.75	0.00	21.82
12/10	41.64	13	10	3.87	2.10	20.62
12/09	48.87	14	10	4.09	2.10	19.29
12/08	55.61	22	11	4.13	2.03	16.92
12/07	81.64	21	14	4.05	1.76	15.47
Annual Growth	(14.6%)	—	—	(1.9%)	—	9.0%

Exelon Generation Co LLC

You've heard of Generation X well Exelon Generation Company is a member of Generation P as in power. The company a subsidiary of Exelon Corporation is one of the largest electric wholesale and retail power generation companies in the US. In 2010 Exelon Generation had a generation capacity of 25620 MW (primarily nuclear but also fossil-fired and hydroelectric and renewable power). Exelon Corporation also controls another 6140 MW through long-term contracts. Exelon Power oversees a fleet of more than 100 fossil- and renewable-fueled plants in Illinois Maryland Massachusetts Pennsylvania and Texas.

A third unit Exelon Power Team sells electricity produced at Exelon Generation's plants through long and short term contracts.

The company's Exelon Energy unit is engaged in the retail marketing of natural gas (in Illinois Michigan and Ohio) and electricity (in Illinois and Michigan) to commercial and industrial clients.

In 2010 to grow its renewable energy unit the company acquired wind power developer John Deere Renewables for about $860 million. The purchase adds 735 MW of operating wind power capacity to its generation capacity.

In a major move to grow its retail operations in 2011 parent Exelon Corporation agreed to buy Constellation Energy in a $7.9 billion stock deal. The purchase of Constellation Energy (which gets 17% of its power from nuclear plants) also helps the company boost its nuclear-generated power plant assets.

The rebounding economy and favorable capacity pricing in the Midwest and Mid-Atlantic regions helped to lift the Exelon Generation's revenues in 2010.

Growing its cleaner-burning plant fleet in Texas in 2011 Exelon Corporation bought the 720 MW capacity Wolf Hollow plant in north Texas from Sequent Wolf Hollow for $305 million.

Exelon Nuclear operates the largest nuclear fleet in the US (10 stations with 17 nuclear units) and has about 20% of the industry's total capacity. Exelon Generation has submitted an application to the Nuclear Regulatory Commission to build a new nuclear generating facility in Texas. The company hasn't made the decision to build the facility but wanted to get a start on the potentially onerous process. The last license to result in the construction of a new nuclear facility in the US was granted in 1973. However the Fukushima nuclear plant disaster in early 2011 placed nuclear power expansion plans under serious scrutiny from regulators.

EXECUTIVES

President, Christopher M. (Chris) Crane, age 53, $821,154 total compensation
Chairman, John W. Rowe, age 66, $1,468,077 total compensation
President Power Team, Kenneth W. (Ken) Cornew, age 46
Chief Accounting Officer, Matthew R. Galvanoni, age 39
COO, Charles G. (Chip) Pardee, age 52
SVP Operations Support Nuclear, Christopher H. Mudrick
President Exelon Power, Sunil (Sonny) Garg, age 45
Auditors: PricewaterhouseCoopersLLP

LOCATIONS

HQ: Exelon Generation Company LLC
300 Exelon Way, Kennett Square PA 19348
Phone: 610-765-5959 **Fax:** 418-523-4205
Web: www.wantedtech.com

PRODUCTS/OPERATIONS

2010 Generating Resources

	MW	% of total
Owned generation assets		
Nuclear	17,047	55
Fossil	6,189	19
Hydroelectric/renewable	2,383	7
Long-term contracts	6,139	19
Total	**31,758**	**100**

COMPETITORS

AES	Duke Energy
AMP	NextEra Energy
Buckeye Power	Wolverine Power Supply
CMS Energy	

HISTORICAL FINANCIALS

Company Type: Subsidiary

Income Statement FYE: December 31

	REVENUE ($ mil.)	NET INCOME ($ mil.)	NET PROFIT MARGIN	EMPLOYEES
12/11	10,308	1,771	17.2%	9,586
12/10	10,025	1,972	19.7%	9,595
12/09	9,703	2,122	21.9%	9,616
12/08	10,754	2,278	21.2%	9,540
12/07	10,749	2,029	18.9%	8,000
Annual Growth	(1.0%)	(3.3%)	—	4.6%

2011 Year-End Financials

Debt ratio: 13.41%—
Return on equity: 20.35%
Cash ($ mil.): 496
Current ratio: 149.44
Long-term debt ($ mil.): 3,674
Dividends
Yield: —
Payout: —
Market value ($ mil.): —

Expeditors International of Washington, Inc.

Need your goods moved expeditiously? Freight forwarder Expeditors International of Washington can help. As a freight forwarder the company purchases air and ocean cargo space on a volume basis and resells that space to its customers at lower rates than they could obtain directly from the carriers. The company also acts as a customs broker for air and ocean freight shipped by its customers and offers supply chain management services. Expeditors operates from more than 400 facilities in about 60 countries. More than half of the company's sales come from Asia. Customers include global businesses engaged in retailing/wholesaling electronics and manufacturing.

Expeditors' airfreight services segment 47% of revenue represents airlines as an agent in addition to providing freight consolidation for shippers. The consolidation of airfreight owned by several shippers is a valuable service because increasing the weight of an air shipment decreases its cost per pound/kilo or cubic inch/centimeter. Besides shipping on scheduled flights the company sometimes charters aircraft for the delivery of backlogs. By not purchasing its own aircraft the company avoids the costs of large capital expenditures and operating costs.

Ocean freight & ocean services 31% of revenue operates as what is known as a non-vessel operating common carrier which is a contractor with ocean shipping lines for a set amount of containers. Expeditors also obtains less-than container load freight to fill containers. The segment additionally provides such order management services as document management and SKU visibility. Similar to the strategy of the airfreight services segment the ocean freight segment does not own its own vessels.

Customs brokerage & other services 22% of revenue aids in the movement of shipments across borders by providing such services as adding up duties and taxes and arranging inspections. Beyond the border entry the segment provides additional services including warehousing product distribution and time-definite transportation. Expeditors provides these services not only for its own shipping customers but also for businesses that have not hired the company as a forwarder a class of client that accounts for a significant portion of the segment's revenue.

Net revenue for the company as a whole inched up 3% in 2011 vs. 2010. Net revenue for the airfreight services segment rose 9% in 2011 compared with 2010 thanks in part to an uptick in net revenue per kilo as a result of excess carrier capacity mainly in Asia. Ocean freight & ocean services' net revenue increased 13% in 2011 vs. 2010 on the back of more demand in North America Asia/Pacific and Europe. The ocean freight consolidation sub-segment of ocean freight & ocean services was pushed up 12% in 2011 vs. 2010 by an increase in net revenue per container as a result of excess carrier capacity similarly to that enjoyed by the airfreight services segment. In 2011 compared with 2010 customs brokerage & other services was lifted 14% by more market share and a growth in domestic time definite freight volumes.

In its rapid development Expeditors has favored internal growth over expansion by acquisition (though it has also selectively made some strategic acquisitions) and the company continues to open new offices and to invest in its information technology infrastructure. By eschewing acquisitions as its main form of growth the company has been able to develop a common hardware platform that lets the entire company use the same accounting and transportation software.

HISTORY

After leaving the freight forwarding company that became Circle International (later acquired by EGL) Peter Rose used $55000 in seed money to start his own company Expeditors International of Washington in 1979. Two years later Rose met with several fellow shipping veterans to implement their idea of combining freight forwarding and customs clearing services.

Expeditors soon had people beating a path to its door. It grew quickly to become a leading importer of goods made in Asia. Expeditors added export services in 1982 and went public in 1984. The next year it added ocean freight services to its offerings and in 1986 it entered the European market. As the 1980s ended the company had offices in 42 countries. Expeditors expanded into the Middle East in 1991 and despite the economic doldrums of the early 1990s opened 14 offices in 1992.

Expeditors also diversified with services such as long-term customs brokerage contracts and distribution. In 1997 it added truck and rail border brokerage services for the US Mexico and Canada. Expeditors continued to expand rapidly: In 1997 it added 22 offices and in 1999 opened still more including five in Turkey and others in Greece Lebanon and the UK.

EXECUTIVES

SVP and Corporate Controller, Charles J. Lynch, age 51
President Global Sales and Marketing, Timothy C. Barber, age 52
President Europe Africa Near/Middle East and Indian Subcontinent, Rommel C. Saber, age 54, $100,000 total compensation
Director; President Asia Pacific, James L. K. Wang, age 64, $100,000 total compensation
President COO and Director, R. Jordan Gates, age 56, $100,000 total compensation
Chairman and CEO, Peter J. Rose, age 68, $110,000 total compensation
President The Americas, Robert L. Villanueva, age 59, $100,000 total compensation
EVP North America, Eugene K. Alger, age 51
EVP North America, Philip M. Coughlin, age 51
SVP and CFO, Bradley S. (Brad) Powell, age 51, $100,000 total compensation
VP Global Distribution Services, Richard P. (Rick) Ballantyne
Regional VP Northwest Region North America, Roger A. Idiart, age 58
EVP Global Customs, Rosanne Esposito, age 60
SVP Ocean Services, Daniel R. Wall, age 43
VP Research and Development, Bret C. Backman
VP Training and Personnel Development, Samuel R. Bokor
VP Global Business Processes, Deanna L. Wilson
SVP South East Asia, Andrew Goh
EVP and CIO, Jeffrey S. Musser, age 46
VP Global Ocean Services, Scott M. Kelly
VP Americas Sales and Marketing, Carol Kijac
SVP Asia Pacific, David Hsieh
SVP South Pacific Indo China and Philippines, Paul L. Arthur
Regional VP Northeast Region North America, Joseph P. Coogan
Regional VP Southwest Region North America, Karl C. Francisco
Regional VP Canada, J. Ross Hurst
SVP Global Transcon Services, William A. Romberger III
Regional VP Midwest Region North America, Richard H. Rostan
SVP Air Cargo, Jose A. Ubeda
SVP Continental Europe, Kurt Meister
Regional VP United Kingdom Ireland and South Africa, Barry L. Baron
Regional VP East Mediterranean and North Africa, Tony Helayel
Regional VP Gulf States Pakistan India and Nepal, David Macpherson
Regional VP Southern Border and Mexico, Bruce J. Krebs
Regional VP Latin America, Guillermo Ayerbe
SVP General Counsel and Secretary, Amy J. Tangeman, age 43
VP and Treasurer, Rebecca A. Cates
Regional VP Southeast Region North America, Brian R. Carrabes
Regional VP North Central Region North America, Todd A. Hinkle
VP Air Cargo The Americas, Sean M. Francisco
SVP Account Management, Steven J. Grimmer
VP Security Health and Safety, Todd R.N. Brown
VP Information Services, Christopher J. McClincy
VP Risk Management and Insurance, Aaron Howes
Regional VP South Central Region North America, John A. Kerner
Regional VP Mid-Atlantic Region North America, Craig Wilwerding
Director; President Asia Pacific, James L. K. Wang, age 64
President COO and Director, R. Jordan Gates, age 56
Director, Michael J. Malone, age 67
Director, Dan P. Kourkoumelis, age 61
Director, John W. Meisenbach, age 75
Director, Mark A. Emmert, age 59
Director, Robert R. Wright, age 52
Auditors: KPMGLLP

LOCATIONS

HQ: Expeditors International of Washington Inc.
1015 3rd Ave. 12th Fl., Seattle WA 98104
Phone: 206-674-3400 **Fax:** 212-421-7442
Web: www.reis.com

2011 Sales

	$ mil.	% of total
Asia/Pacific	3,144	51
North America		
US	1,540	25
Other North America	189	3
Europe & Africa	891	15
Middle East & India	302	5
Latin America	82	1
Total	**6,150**	**100**

PRODUCTS/OPERATIONS

2011 Sales

	$ mil.	% of total
Airfreight services	2,893	47
Ocean freight & ocean services	1,878	31
Customs brokerage & other services	1,378	22
Total	**6,150**	**100**

Selected Products and Services

Air consolidation
Air forwarding
Cargo insurance
Customs
Distribution management
Ocean shipment
Purchase order management

COMPETITORS

APL Logistics
C.H. Robinson Worldwide
CEVA Logistics
DHL
FedEx Trade Networks
Kintetsu World Express
Kuehne + Nagel International
Mitsui-Soko
Nippon Express
NYK Line
Panalpina
Schenker
Sino-Global
Sinotrans
UPS Supply Chain Solutions
UTi Worldwide
Yamato Holdings

HISTORICAL FINANCIALS

Company Type: Public

Income Statement

FYE: December 31

	REVENUE ($ mil.)	NET INCOME ($ mil.)	NET PROFIT MARGIN	EMPLOYEES
12/11	6,150	385	6.3%	13,590
12/10	5,967	344	5.8%	12,880
12/09	4,092	240	5.9%	12,010
12/08	5,633	301	5.3%	12,580
12/07	5,235	269	5.1%	12,310
Annual Growth	4.1%	9.4%	—	2.5%

2011 Year-End Financials

Debt ratio: —
Return on equity: 19.25%
Cash ($ mil.): 1,294
Current ratio: 287.24
Long-term debt ($ mil.): —
No. of shares (mil.): 212
Dividends
Yield: —
Payout: 27.93%
Market value ($ mil.): 8,684

	STOCK PRICE ($) FY Close	P/E High	P/E Low	PER SHARE ($) Earnings	Dividends	Book Value
12/11	40.96	30	22	1.79	0.00	9.45
12/10	54.60	35	20	1.59	0.40	8.21
12/09	34.77	33	21	1.11	0.38	7.33
12/08	33.27	35	19	1.37	0.32	6.45
12/07	44.68	42	32	1.21	0.28	5.76
Annual Growth	(2.1%)	—	—	10.3%	—	13.2%

Express Scripts Holdings Co

Express Scripts Holding knows that its customers like their medicine delivered quickly. The company administers the prescription drug benefits of millions of health plan members in the US and Canada. Members have access to a network of about 64000 retail pharmacies as well as the company's own mail-order pharmacies. On behalf of its insurer clients Express Scripts processes claims for about 1.4 billion prescriptions per year designs drug benefit plans and offers such services as specialty drug delivery disease management programs and consumer drug data analysis. The firm merged with rival PBM Medco Health Solutions in 2012 creating the largest pharmacy benefits management (PBM) company in North America.

Following the merger transaction through which Express Scripts acquired Medco for some $29 billion the two companies were combined under a new holding company structure based at Express Script's existing headquarters in St. Louis. The combined organization named Express Scripts Holding lays claim to a one-third share of the US PBM market. Though the deal faced some opposition over competitive concerns Express Scripts and Medco believe that their merger will ultimately help lower prescription drug costs by boosting consumer advocacy programs and increasing operational efficiencies through a broader network and service offering. Post-merger integration efforts aim to enhance efficiencies in areas including supply chain management mail-order services specialty pharmaceutical distribution and fraud and abuse control.

Express Scripts' clients include HMOs and other health insurers self-insured businesses and union benefit plans throughout North America. The company and the industry have grown rapidly as the PBMs strive to save money for their customers by negotiating good deals for prescription drugs with networks of retail pharmacies as well as by encouraging the use of cheaper generic drugs and home-delivered medications. Express Scripts also works to save clients' money by offering disease and medication management programs to help members avoid un-necessary medical expenses.

The PBM industry has also undergone rapid consolidation a factor that has allowed Express Scripts to grow its sales and profits exponentially in recent years. For instance Express Scripts doubled its PBM revenues in 2010 thanks to its 2009 acquisition of another PBM NextRx and the Medco acquisition is expected to cause a jump in Express Scripts finances in 2012 and beyond as well. Revenues increased by about 3% in 2011 to some $46 billion largely due to increases in the home delivery specialty pharma and emerging market businesses (offsetting a slight drop in PBM claims volumes that year). Net income has also been on the rise jumping some 8% in 2011 to about $1.3 billion. In addition to business unit and merger growth Express Scripts' bottom line has benefited from lower drug purchasing costs stemming from increased generic usage by consumers.

Express Scripts had historically expanded its PBM operations through smaller purchases. It has also grown through organic measures such as the addition of new customer contracts as well as the extension of existing contracts to add new services. In addition Express Scripts occasionally establishes new operating centers. For instance it opened a new pharmacy fulfillment center in St. Louis in 2010 to support its growing home delivery business which is experiencing increased demand from clients and patients seeking to cut costs on traditional maintenance medications through the use of mail-order services.

Another element of Express Scripts' PBM business that is experiencing higher consumer demand is specialty pharmacy subsidiary CuraScript. Through its primary operating unit CuraScript Specialty Pharmacy (or CuraScript SP) the subsidiary provides home distribution of specialty prescriptions (primarily injectable biotech drugs that require special packaging and handling); the unit also delivers to doctors' offices and other health care providers.

While its PBM operations account for the lion's share of Express Script's revenues the company has also been looking to expand into new high-growth fields of managed care through its emerging markets segment. It has added such services as group purchasing for doctors and clinics (through CuraScript Specialty Distribution or CuraScript SD) and third-party administration of consumer-driven health plans (ConnectYourCare). The company is shuffling some of the emerging market operations however; it moved its FreedomFP fertility drug distribution unit over to the PBM segment in 2011 and in 2012 it began exploring strategic options for the ConnectYourCare business.

Express Script has also divested some operations that it determined were not core to its growth initiatives. In late 2010 the company spun off its Rx Outreach business which provides access to prescription drugs for low income and uninsured patients. Following the spinoff Rx Outreach applied for federal recognition as a not-for-profit organization. Also in 2010 Express Scripts sold its Phoenix Marketing Group business which provided outsourced distribution and verification services to pharmaceutical manufacturers.

HISTORY

In 1986 St. Louis-based drugstore chain Medicare-Glaser and HMO Sanus joined forces to create Express Scripts which would manage the HMO's prescription program. Express Scripts began managing third-party programs in 1988 and later developed other operations: mail-order prescription infusion therapy and vision services. New York Life bought Sanus and picked up the rest of Express Scripts in 1989 when Medicare-Glaser went into bankruptcy.

In 1992 Express Scripts went public. The next year the company formed subsidiary Practice Patterns Science to begin profiling providers and tracking treatment outcomes.

In the late 1990s the company continued to expand adding customers in Canada (1996) and building operations –with varying success. A 1996 expansion of its eye care management services was abandoned in 1998. Express Scripts has traditionally grown through big-ticket contracts such as its 1997 pact with RightCHOICE Managed Care and through acquisitions. For example it boosted its PBM operations with its 1998 acquisition of Columbia/HCA's (now HCA) ValueRx unit and its 1999 purchase of SmithKline Beecham's Diversified Pharmaceutical Services (DPS); however it lost DPS's largest customer when United Healthcare began moving its more than 8 million enrollees to Merck-Medco in 2000.

The company suffered another setback in 2000 when it wrote down its 20% interest in online pharmacy PlanetRx. It had bought into the company in 1999 when dot-coms were soaring transferring its own Internet pharmacy operations (YourPharmacy.com) into the fledgling company. In 2001 Express Scripts joined rivals AdvancePCS and Merck-Medco (now Medco Health Solutions) to form RxHub to create technology to allow physicians to file prescriptions electronically.

In 2001 the firm began a bit of an acquisition spree. That year it bought Phoenix Marketing Group one of the biggest prescription drug sample fulfillment companies in the US. National Prescription Administrators a top private pharmacy benefits management company in the US joined the family in 2002. Express Scripts expanded its specialty pharmacy capabilities with the purchases of CuraScript a leading specialty pharmacy in 2004 and biopharmaceutical pharmacy and distributor Priority Healthcare in 2005.

In 2007 Express Scripts acquired ConnectYourCare a third-party administrator of consumer-directed health plans which link a high-deductible plan with tax-sheltered savings accounts. The company expanded again in 2008 by purchasing the pharmacy services division of Medical Services Company for $251 million. The acquired business specialized in managing pharmacy benefits for workers' compensation insurers.

To focus on its core distribution operations the company divested its CuraScript Infusion Pharmacy business which operated infusion therapy centers in six states to Walgreen's Option Care subsidiary in 2008.

In 2009 the company expanded its contract with the US Department of Defense adding a number of services beyond its existing management of the pharmacy network of the TRICARE military health care program. The contract now includes home delivery specialty pharmacy claims management and other integrated offerings.

The company grew substantially at the end of 2009 with the acquisition of NextRx the PBM business of Blue Cross Blue Shield (BCBS) licensee WellPoint for about $4.7 billion. As part of the acquisition the company gained a 10-year contract to provide PBM services to WellPoint the nation's largest health insurer. The purchase launched Express Scripts closer to its top two rivals (Medco and Caremark Pharmacy Services) by increasing its claims processing load from 500 million to more than 750 million prescriptions per year. It also enhanced the company's online generic drug and mail delivery service offerings. Revenues from Express Scripts' PBM division jumped from $23 billion in 2009 to $43 billion in 2010 primarily due to the NextRx acquisition.

Through a 2012 $29 billion merger transaction with rival PBM Medco Express Scripts became the largest PBM in the US. Following the transaction the company changed its name to Express Scripts Holding.

EXECUTIVES

Chairman and CEO, George Paz, age 56, $971,692 total compensation

EVP and COO, Patrick (Pat) McNamee, age 52, $490,412 total compensation

EVP Sales and Marketing, Edward (Ed) Ignaczak, age 46, $460,123 total compensation

EVP and CFO, Jeffrey L. (Jeff) Hall, age 45, $507,846 total compensation

VP Investor Relations, David Myers

SVP Marketing and Chief Marketing Officer, Larry Zarin, age 57

EVP General Counsel and Secretary, Keith J. Ebling, age 43, $408,677 total compensation
SVP and Chief Medical Officer, Steven (Steve) Miller
SVP and Chief Human Resources Officer, Sara Wade
VP Government Affairs, Robert (Rob) Lively
VP and Deputy General Counsel, Martin P. Akins
SVP and CIO, Gary Wimberly
Director, Gary G. Benanav, age 66
Director, Nicholas J. (Nick) LaHowchic, age 64
Director, Thomas P. Mac Mahon, age 65
Director, Seymour (Sy) Sternberg, age 68
Director, Frank Mergenthaler, age 51
Director, Woodrow A. Myers Jr., age 58
Director, John O. Parker Jr., age 67
Director, Maura C. Breen, age 56
Director, Samuel K. Skinner, age 73
Auditors: PricewaterhouseCoopersLLP

LOCATIONS

HQ: Express Scripts Holding Co.
1 Express Way, St. Louis MO 63121
Phone: 314-996-0900 **Fax:** 952-893-0704
Web: www.uhs.com

PRODUCTS/OPERATIONS

2011 Sales

	$ mil.	% of total
Pharmacy Benefits Management (PBM)		
PBM products		
Network	30,007	65
Home delivery & specialty	14,547	31
PBM services	273	1
Emerging Markets (EM)		
EM products	1,279	3
EM services	21	-
Total	**46,128**	**100**

Selected Products and Services

Pharmacy Benefits Management (PBM)
- Benefit design consultation
- Biopharma management
- Compliance management programs for members
- Drug formulary management
- Drug utilization review
- Electronic claims processing
- Fertility drug distribution (specialty handling/packaging Freedom FP)
- Group purchasing organization administration
- Home delivery pharmacy services
- Information analysis services
- Patient care contacts and information
- Personalized medicine
- Rebate programs
- Retail drug card programs
- Retail network pharmacy management
- Specialty pharmacy services (CuraScript)

Emerging Markets (EM)
- Drug distribution and group purchasing to clinics and doctors (CuraScript SD)
- Third-party administration of consumer-directed health plans (ConnectYourCare)

COMPETITORS

Aetna
Argus
BioScrip
Caremark Pharmacy Services
Catalyst Health Solutions
Catamaran
CIGNA
First Health Group
HealthTrans
Humana
MedImpact
NationsHealth
Omnicare
OptumRx
PharMerica
Prime Therapeutics
Rite Aid
Wal-Mart
Walgreen

HISTORICAL FINANCIALS

Company Type: Public

Income Statement FYE: December 31

	REVENUE ($ mil.)	NET INCOME ($ mil.)	NET PROFIT MARGIN	EMPLOYEES
12/11	46,128	1,275	2.8%	13,120
12/10	44,973	1,181	2.6%	13,170
12/09	24,748	827	3.3%	14,270
12/08	21,978	776	3.5%	10,820
12/07	18,273	567	3.1%	11,820
Annual Growth	26.0%	22.4%	—	2.6%

2011 Year-End Financials

Debt ratio: 51.75%
Return on equity: 51.57%
Cash ($ mil.): 5,620
Current ratio: 147.63
Long-term debt ($ mil.): 7,076
No. of shares (mil.): 484
Dividends
Yield: —
Payout: —
Market value ($ mil.): 21,656

	STOCK PRICE ($) FY Close	P/E High	P/E Low	PER SHARE ($) Earnings	Dividends	Book Value
12/11	44.69	24	14	2.53	0.00	5.11
12/10	54.05	48	19	2.17	0.00	6.83
12/09	86.42	57	28	1.56	0.00	6.46
12/08	54.98	50	31	1.54	0.00	2.18
12/07	73.00	94	45	1.08	0.00	1.38
Annual Growth	(11.5%)	—	—	23.7%	—	38.7%

Exxon Mobil Corp.

It's not necessarily the oil standard but Exxon Mobil is the world's largest integrated oil company (ahead of Royal Dutch Shell and BP). Exxon Mobil engages in oil and gas exploration production supply transportation and marketing worldwide. In 2011 it reported proved reserves of 24.9 billion barrels of oil equivalent including its major holdings in oil sands through Imperial Oil. Exxon Mobil's 36 refineries in 20 countries have a throughput capacity of more than 6.2 million barrels per day. The company supplies refined products to more than 25000 gas stations in 100 countries. Exxon Mobil is also a major petrochemical producer.

HISTORY

Exxon's 1999 acquisition of Mobil reunited two descendants of John D. Rockefeller's Standard Oil Company. Rockefeller a commodity trader started his first oil refinery in 1863 in Cleveland. Realizing that the price of oil at the well would shrink with each new strike Rockefeller chose to monopolize oil refining and transportation. In 1870 he formed Standard Oil and in 1882 he created the Standard Oil Trust which allowed him to set up new ostensibly independent companies including the Standard Oil Company of New Jersey (Jersey Standard); Rochester New York-based Vacuum Oil; and Standard Oil of New York (nicknamed Socony).

Initially capitalized at $70 million the Standard Oil Trust controlled 90% of the petroleum industry. In 1911 after two decades of political and legal wrangling the Supreme Court broke up the trust into 34 companies the largest of which was Jersey Standard.

Walter Teagle who became president of Jersey Standard in 1917 secretly bought half of Humble Oil of Texas (1919) and expanded operations into South America. In 1928 Jersey Standard joined in the Red Line Agreement which reserved most Middle East oil for a few companies. Teagle resigned in 1942 after the company was criticized for a prewar research pact with German chemical giant I.G. Farben.

The 1948 purchase of a 40% stake in Arabian American Oil Company combined with a 7% share of Iranian production bought in 1954 made Jersey Standard the world's #1 oil company at that time.

Meanwhile Vacuum Oil and Socony reunited in 1931 as Socony-Vacuum and the company adopted the Flying Red Horse (Pegasus —representing speed and power) as a trademark. The fast-growing diversifying company changed its name to Socony Mobil Oil in 1955 and became Mobil in 1976.

Other US companies still using the Standard Oil name objected to Jersey Standard's marketing in their territories as Esso (derived from the initials for Standard Oil). To end the confusion in 1972 Jersey Standard became Exxon a name change that cost $100 million.

Nationalization of oil assets by producing countries reduced Exxon's access to oil during the 1970s. Though it increased exploration that decade and the next Exxon's reserves shrank.

Oil tanker "Exxon Valdez" spilled some 11 million gallons of oil into Alaska's Prince William Sound in 1989. Exxon spent billions on the cleanup and in 1994 a federal jury in Alaska ordered the company to pay $5.3 billion in punitive damages to fishermen and others affected by the spill. (Exxon appealed and in 2001 the jury award was reduced to $2.5 billion and in 2008 to $507.5 million).

With the oil industry consolidating Exxon merged its worldwide oil and fuel additives business with that of Royal Dutch/Shell in 1996. The next year under FTC pressure Exxon agreed to run ads refuting claims that its premium gas enabled car engines to run more efficiently. Another PR disaster followed in 1998 when CEO Lee Raymond upset environmentalists by publicly questioning the global warming theory.

Still Exxon was unstoppable. It acquired Mobil for $81 billion in 1999; the new company had Raymond at the helm and Mobil's Lucio Noto as vice chairman. (Noto retired in 2001.) To get the deal done Exxon Mobil had to divest $4 billion in assets. It agreed to end its European gasoline and lubricants joint venture with BP and to sell more than 2400 gas stations in the US.

In 2000 Exxon Mobil sold 1740 East Coast gas stations to Tosco for $860 million. It sold a California refinery and 340 gas stations to Valero Energy for about $1 billion.

More than a decade after the "Exxon Valdez" wreaked environmental havoc off the shores of Alaska Exxon Mobil attempted to atone in 2001 by joining the California Fuel Cell Partnership a group studying possible alternatives to and supplements for gasoline in fuel-burning engines. That year Exxon Mobil also announced that it was proceeding with a $12 billion project (with Japanese Indian and Russian partners) to develop oil fields in the Russian Far East.

In 2002 Exxon Mobil sold its 50% stake in a Colombian coal mine as part of its strategy to divest coal assets in order to focus on its core businesses. That year the company sold its Chilean copper mining subsidiary (Disputada de Las Condes) to mineral giant Anglo American for $1.3 billion. Exxon Mobil sold its 3.7% stake in China Petroleum & Chemical Corp. (Sinopec) in early 2005. Later that year the company was ordered to pay $1.3 billion to about 10000 gas station owners for overcharges dating back to 1983; the average amount for each station owner was about $130000.

Shortages caused by Hurricane Katrina prompted Exxon Mobil to receive a 6 million barrel of crude oil loan primarily from the US Strategic Petroleum Reserve and increase gasoline production at its Baton Rouge facility.

Exiting the low-margin retail gasoline business in order to focus on its other operations in 2008 the company began to sell to distributors its remaining 820 company-owned US gas stations and another 1400 outlets operated by dealers.

In 2009 the company signed up to partner with TransCanada to jointly develop the $26 billion Alaska Pipeline Project. A long-term project if and when built the pipeline will deliver natural gas from Alaska's North Slope to US markets.

EXECUTIVES

SVP Treasurer and Principal Financial Officer, Donald D. (Don) Humphreys, age 64, $1,010,000 total compensation
VP and Controller, Patrick T. (Pat) Mulva, age 60
SVP, Michael J. (Mike) Dolan, age 58, $845,000 total compensation
Chairman and CEO, Rex W. Tillerson, age 59, $2,057,000 total compensation
VP Human Resources, Lucille J. Cavanaugh
VP Public and Government Affairs, Kenneth P. (Ken) Cohen
SVP, Andrew P. (Andy) Swiger, age 55
SVP, Mark W. Albers, age 55
VP; President ExxonMobil Chemical, Stephen D. (Steve) Pryor, age 62, $940,000 total compensation
VP and General Tax Counsel, James M. Spellings, age 50
VP Environmental Policy and Planning, Sherri K. Stuewer
President ExxonMobil Research and Engineering Company, T.J. Wojnar
VP; President ExxonMobil Fuels Lubricants & Specialties Marketing Company, Allan J. Kelly, age 54
VP; President ExxonMobil Refining and Supply Company, Sherman J. Glass Jr., age 64
President ExxonMobil Development Company, Neil W. Duffin, age 55
VP; President ExxonMobil Production Company, Richard M. (Rich) Kruger, age 52
VP Washington Office, Theresa M. Fariello
VP Investor Relations and Secretary, David S. Rosenthal, age 55
VP Corporate Strategic Planning, William M. (Bill) Colton, age 58
VP; President ExxonMobil Gas and Power Marketing, Thomas R. (Tom) Walters, age 57
VP; President ExxonMobil Exploration, Steve M. Greenlee, age 54
VP; President ExxonMobil Upstream Ventures, Robert S. Franklin, age 54
VP and General Counsel, S. Jack Balagia, age 60
General Manager Public and Government Affairs; President Exxon Mobil Foundation, Suzanne M. McCarron
President XTO Energy, Jack P. Williams Jr., age 48
President ExxonMobil Upstream Research, Sara N. Ortwein
VP and Treasurer, Robert N. Schleckser, age 55
VP Safety Security Health and Environment, J.J. Woodbury
President ExxonMobil Global Services Company, B.W. Milton
Director, Kenneth C. (Ken) Frazier, age 57
Director, Larry R. Faulkner, age 67
Director, Peter Brabeck-Letmathe, age 68
Director, Samuel J. (Sam) Palmisano, age 61
Director, William W. George, age 69
Director, Steven S. (Steve) Reinemund, age 64
Director, Edward E. (Ed) Whitacre Jr., age 70
Director, Marilyn Carlson Nelson, age 72
Director, Jay S. Fishman, age 59
Director, Michael J. Boskin, age 66
Auditors: PricewaterhouseCoopersLLP

LOCATIONS

HQ: Exxon Mobil Corporation
5959 Las Colinas Blvd., Irving TX 75039-2298
Phone: 972-444-1000 **Fax:** 972-444-1350
Web: www.exxon.mobil.com

2011 Sales

	% of total
US	32
UK	8
Canada	7
Japan	7
Belgium	6
France	4
Germany	4
Italy	3
Singapore	3
Other	26
Total	**100**

PRODUCTS/OPERATIONS

2011 Sales

	% of total
Downstream	81
Upstream	10
Chemicals	9
Total	**100**

Selected Acquisitions

2013
Celtic Exploration Ltd. ($2.5 billion; Calgary; oil and gas exploration and production in Alberta)
2011
Phillips Resources and TWP Inc. ($1.7 billion; Pittsburgh PA; Marcellus Shale gas producers)
2010
Ellora Energy Inc. ($695 million; Boulder CO; oil and gas producer in Haynesville shales in Texas and Louisiana)
XTO Energy Inc. ($41 billion; Fort Worth TX; unconventional natural gas production in the US)

COMPETITORS

7-Eleven
Ashland Inc.
BHP Billiton
BP
Chevron
ConocoPhillips
Costco Wholesale
Dow Chemical
DuPont
Eastman Chemical
Eni
Hess Corporation
Huntsman International
JX Holdings
Koch Industries Inc.
Marathon Oil
Norsk Hydro ASA
Occidental Petroleum
PEMEX
PETROBRAS
Petroleos de Venezuela
Racetrac Petroleum
Repsol
Royal Dutch Shell
Saudi Aramco
Sunoco
TOTAL
Valero Energy

HISTORICAL FINANCIALS

Company Type: Public

Income Statement FYE: December 31

	REVENUE ($ mil.)	NET INCOME ($ mil.)	NET PROFIT MARGIN	EMPLOYEES
12/11	486,429	41,060	8.4%	82,100
12/10	383,221	30,460	7.9%	83,600
12/09	310,586	19,280	6.2%	80,700
12/08	477,359	45,220	9.5%	104,700
12/07	404,552	40,610	10.0%	107,100
Annual Growth	4.7%	0.3%	—	(6.4%)

2011 Year-End Financials

Debt ratio: 5.15%—
Return on equity: 26.59%
Cash ($ mil.): 13,068
Current ratio: 94.14
Long-term debt ($ mil.): 9,322
Dividends
Yield: —
Payout: 21.97%
Market value ($ mil.): —

	STOCK PRICE ($) FY Close	P/E High	P/E Low	PER SHARE ($) Earnings	Dividends	Book Value
12/11	84.76	10	8	8.42	0.00	32.61
12/10	73.12	12	9	6.22	1.74	29.49
12/09	68.19	20	16	3.98	1.66	23.39
12/08	79.83	11	7	8.69	1.55	22.70
12/07	93.69	13	9	7.28	1.37	22.62
Annual Growth	(2.5%)	—	—	3.7%	—	9.6%

F.N.B. Corp.

F.N.B. Corporation is the holding company for First National Bank of Pennsylvania which serves consumers and small to midsized businesses though more than 260 bank branches in Pennsylvania and northeastern Ohio. The company also has more than 50 consumer finance offices operating as Regency Finance in those states as well as Tennessee and Kentucky. In addition to community banking and consumer finance F.N.B. also has segments devoted to insurance and wealth management. It also offers leasing and merchant banking services. F.N.B. strengthened its presence in the Pittsburgh metropolitan area in 2012 through the some $130 million acquisition of Parkvale Financial which operated nearly 50 bank branches.

F.N.B. has agreed to acquire Annapolis Bancorp the parent company of BankAnnapolis in an all-stock transaction valued at about $51 million. The deal is expected to close in April 2013.

F.N.B. which moved its headquarters from Pennsylvania to Florida in 2001 spun off First National Bankshares of Florida at the start of 2004 and returned to the Pittsburgh area. F.N.B. still operates two loan offices in Florida but these primarily manage the company's legacy loan portfolio there.

The bank is again rooted firmly in the Keystone State and bordering markets. After returning it expanded via several acquisitions prior to the Parkvale deal including bank holding companies NSD Bancorp Slippery Rock Financial North East Bancshares Omega Financial and Iron and Glass Bancorp. In 2011 F.N.B. expanded in northeastern Pennsylvania through the acquisition of Comm Bancorp. The deal valued at some $70 million brought in 15 branches.

F.N.B has remained profitable since the credit crisis and broader economic turmoil took hold in 2007 and its revenues and net income increased each of the last two years. The company did experience elevated levels of charge-offs and nonperforming loans mainly due to restructured home loans in Pennsylvania and its real estate portfolio in Florida but those numbers stabilized during 2011. Commercial loans including mortgages account for more than half of the company's loan portfolio.

EXECUTIVES

President and CEO First National Trust and FNB Investment Advisors, Kim Craig
Corporate Controller SVP and Principal Accounting Officer, Timothy G. Rubritz, age 58
President and CEO; Chairman and CEO First National Bank of Pennsylvania and FNB Capital, Stephen J. (Steve) Gurgovits, age 68, $660,000 total compensation
Chairman, William B. Campbell, age 73
Corporate Secretary; SVP and Secretary First National Bank, David B. Mogle, age 62, $171,312 total compensation
Chief Legal Officer; SVP First National Bank, James G. Orie, age 53, $165,000 total compensation
CFO and Controller, Vincent J. Calabrese, age 49, $208,032 total compensation
Vice Chairman and COO, Brian F. Lilly, age 53, $323,136 total compensation
EVP and Senior Commercial Lending Officer First National Bank of Pennsylvania, Frank Krieder
EVP and Chief Credit Officer First National Bank of Pennsylvania, Gary Guerrieri, age 51
Treasurer; SVP and Treasurer First National Bank, Scott D. Free, age 48
SVP and CFO Regency Finance, Mark D. Lozzi
VP and Relationship Manager Western Region Personal Client Services Group First National Trust, Amy C. Atkinson
VP and Financial Advisor Sales Group First National Trust, Jeffrey T. Baker
SVP and Senior Relationship Manager Relationship Management & Sales Development FNB Investment Advisors, Samuel A. Piccioni
VP and Client Services Officer Eastern Region Personal Client Services Group First National Trust, Sharon G. Coleman
VP and Manager Client Accounting and IT Client Accounting Group First National Trust, Linda J. Blough
VP and Client Services Officer Institutional Client Services Group First National Trust, Adele E. Necastro
President and CEO Regency Finance Company, Robert D. Carter
President; CEO First National Bank, Vincent J. (Vince) Delie Jr., age 47, $279,996 total compensation
EVP and Chief Marketing Officer First National Bank of Pennsylvania, Susan B. Bergen-Painter, age 42
EVP Retail Banking First National Bank of Pennsylvania, Jonathan W. Roberts
EVP Tampa Bay Region First National Bank of Pennslyvania, Dale Dignum
Media Relations, Kathryn Lima
Shareholder Relations, Jennifer DeFazio
EVP First National Bank of Pennsylvania, Louice C. Lowrey, age 58, $190,008 total compensation
EVP Small Business Lending First National Bank of Pennsylvania, Peter J. Asimakopoulos
EVP Florida First National Bank of Pennsylvania, Jody Hudgins
Regional President Capital Region First National Bank of Pennsylvania, Lloyd Lamm
SVP Human Resources First National Bank of Pennsylvania, Bob Perrin
SVP and Director Retail Operation First National Bank of Pennsylvania, Bob Rimbey
President First National Bank, John C. Williams Jr.
Regional President Northwest Region First National Bank of Pennsylvania, Tom Wedzik
SVP Corporate Strategies Coordinator and Group Manager Private Banking First National Bank of Pennsylvania, David B. Yates
VP and Manager Client Services Western Region Personal Client Services Group First National Trust, Samuel L. Haines
VP and Manager Client Services Eastern Region Personal Client Services Group First National Trust, James T. Hnatkovich
VP and Manager Client Services Capital Region First National Trust, Karen Kenderline
Vice President & Client Services Manager Capital Region First National Trust, Kimberly Arthur Tressler
Vice President & Financial Advisor Sales Group First National Trust, Charles G. Driscoll
SVP and CIO Investment Strategy Group FNB Investment Advisors, Jeffrey W. Wagner
Vice President and Senior Portfolio Manager Portfolio Management Group FNB Investment Advisors, John C. Ayre
President and CEO First National Insurance Agency, James Morrell
SVP First National Insurance Agency, Randall Butz
SVP First National Insurance Agency, James Pudlewski
VP FNB Capital, Matthew T. (Matt) Harnett
Director, Dawne S. Hickton, age 54
Director, D. Stephen Martz, age 69
Director, Robert B. Goldstein, age 71
Director, Stanton R. (Stan) Sheetz, age 56
Director, Earl K. Wahl Jr., age 71
Director, Henry M. Ekker, age 73
Director, William J. Strimbu, age 51
Director, John W. Rose, age 62
Director, David J. Malone, age 57
Vice Chairman and COO, Brian F. Lilly, age 53
Auditors: Ernst&YoungLLP

LOCATIONS

HQ: F.N.B. Corporation
1 F.N.B. Blvd., Hermitage PA 16148
Phone: 724-981-6000 **Fax:** 724-983-4873
Web: www.fnbcorporation.com

PRODUCTS/OPERATIONS

2011 Sales by Segment

	$ mil.	% of total
Community banking	439	86
Consumer finance	36	7
Wealth management	23	5
Insurance	12	2
Other	(0.1)	-
Total	**511**	**100**

2011 Sales

	$ mil.	% of total
Interest		
Loans including fees	341	67
Securities including dividends	49	10
Other	0	-
Noninterest		
Service charges	61	12
Insurance commissions & fees	15	3
Trust services	14	3
Securities commissions & fees	7	1
Other	20	4
Total	**511**	**100**

Selected Subsidiaries
F.N.B. Capital Corporation (merchant banking)
First National Bank of Pennsylvania
  Bank Capital Services LLC (also dba F.N.B. Commercial Leasing)
  First National Trust Company
    F.N.B. Investment Advisors
    First National Investment Services Company
First National Insurance Agency LLC
Regency Finance Company
  Citizens Financial Services Inc.
  F.N.B. Consumer Discount Company
  Finance and Mortgage Acceptance Corporation

COMPETITORS

Dollar Bank
Fifth Third
First Commonwealth Financial
First Niagara Financial
Fulton Financial
Huntington Bancshares
M&T Bank
Northwest Bancshares
PNC Financial
RBS Citizens Financial Group
S&T Bancorp
Sovereign Bank
Susquehanna Bancshares
United Community Financial

HISTORICAL FINANCIALS

Company Type: Public

Income Statement

FYE: December 31

	ASSETS ($ mil.)	NET INCOME ($ mil.)	INCOME AS % OF ASSETS	EMPLOYEES
12/11	9,786	87	0.9%	3,015
12/10	8,959	74	0.8%	2,718
12/09	8,709	41	0.5%	2,525
12/08	8,364	35	0.4%	2,497
12/07	6,088	69	1.1%	1,893
Annual Growth	12.6%	5.7%	—	12.3%

2011 Year-End Financials

Debt ratio: 2.98%
Return on equity: 7.19%
Cash ($ mil.): 208
Current ratio: —
Long-term debt ($ mil.): 291
No. of shares (mil.): 127
Dividends
  Yield: —
  Payout: 68.57%
Market value ($ mil.): 1,439

	STOCK PRICE ($) FY Close	P/E High/Low		PER SHARE ($) Earnings	Dividends	Book Value
12/11	11.31	16	12	0.70	0.00	9.51
12/10	9.82	15	10	0.65	0.48	9.29
12/09	6.79	42	17	0.32	0.48	9.14
12/08	13.20	40	22	0.44	0.96	10.32
12/07	14.70	16	12	1.15	0.95	8.99
Annual Growth	(6.3%)	—	—	(11.7%)	—	1.4%

Family Dollar Stores, Inc.

Penny-pinching single moms are drawn to Family Dollar. The nation's #2 dollar store (behind Dollar General) targets forty-something women shopping for a family earning less than $40000 a year. It operates more than 7475 stores across some 45 states and Washington DC. Consumables (food health and beauty aids and household items) account for more than two-thirds of sales; stores also sell apparel shoes and linens. Family Dollar runs small neighborhood stores near its low- and middle-income customers in rural and urban areas. Most merchandise costs less than $10. Family Dollar was founded in 1959 by the father of CEO Howard Levine.

Sales & Marketing

Family Dollar Stores spent $19.6 million on advertising in fiscal 2012 (ends August) up from $17.1 million in 2011.

Financial Analysis

The retailer's fiscal 2012 (ends August) sales increased 9% vs. the prior year to $9.3 billion. Net income also was up more than 8% over the same period. Same-store sales increased nearly 5% as more low-income and also middle-income families frequented its stores and spent more per visit. Indeed Family Dollar's sales have nearly doubled over the past nine years. While the chain and its rivals have clearly benefitted from the economic pain of many working families Family Dollar has seen competition for those dollars increase.

Strategy

After shunning a hostile advance in 2011 Family Dollar reaffirmed its own strategic growth plans. The retailer believes that its shareholders are best served through new store openings and remodeling existing locations. Indeed retail expansion has hastened since the height of the recession. Family Dollar accelerated the pace of new store openings in fiscal 2012 (ends August) adding more than 400 locations including 44 stores in California (its first in the Golden State). Going forward the fast-growing chain plans to open 500 new stores in fiscal 2013.

In the face of increased competition from mass discounters such as Wal-Mart the company has also increased purchases of lower-margin consumables and avoided higher-priced merchandise. Its food assortment includes milk and other perishables as well as more quick-prep and ready-to-eat products. In a move designed to broaden its grocery offering including refrigerated and frozen food Family Dollar in spring 2012 formed a strategic partnership with grocery distributor McLane. Family Dollar has shifted to an "everyday low price" strategy as opposed to short-lived promotional advertising while increasing the number of brand-name goods it carries. Also after learning that smokers make more shopping trips per year the company added tobacco products to its offering in fiscal 2012 with the intent of capturing both tobacco sales and spill over to other merchandise categories.

HISTORY

Leon Levine came from a retailing family. His father who founded The Hub a general store-style department store in Rockingham North Carolina in 1908 died when Levine was 13. Leon and his older brother Al helped their mother run the store. (Al went on to found the Pic 'n Pay self-service shoe stores in 1957.) In 1959 when he was 25 Levine (with his cousin Bernie) opened his own store in Charlotte with nothing priced over a dollar targeting low- and middle-income families. The concept of low prices and small neighborhood stores was immediately popular and Levine began adding stores. By 1970 when he took Family Dollar Stores public it had 100 stores in five states. That year Levine brought his cousin Lewis into the business.

Family Dollar's profits plummeted in the mid-1970s as the chain's low-income customers hit by recession cut back on spending —even though all merchandise was priced at $3 or less. Such pricing made for tight margins so the company dropped the policy. Family Dollar also improved inventory controls to make operations more efficient and began moving into other states. Sales picked up topping $100 million in 1977 and the next year the firm bought the 40-store Top Dollar chain from Sav-A-Stop.

As the 1980s began Family Dollar had nearly 400 stores in eight southern states; rapidly expanding it was adding more than 100 stores a year. But in an effort to boost margins the company had lost its pricing edge to a new threat — Wal-Mart's truckload prices and quick domination of the southern discount retailing market.

After Family Dollar sales were flat in 1986 and dropped 10% in 1987 Levine finally took action. He found his prices were sometimes as much as 10% higher than Wal-Mart's and his stores were often insufficiently stocked with advertised products. He lowered prices declaring that Family Dollar would not be undersold and again instituted new inventory controls. But the action had not come quickly enough argued president and COO Lewis who left the company in 1987. (He was also upset over a huge salary disparity: Leon —noted for being a hard bargainer with suppliers —was making $1.8 million a year compared to Lewis' $260000.) Leon's son Howard who joined the firm in 1981 also left; he returned to the fold in 1996 and became CEO in 1998.

Family Dollar picked up momentum in the 1990s. It implemented a major renovation of stores and phased out low-margin items such as motor oil and tools in favor of such high-margin items as toys and electronics. The company also accelerated its growth plans opening stores in a number of new markets and setting up a second distribution center in Arkansas in 1994 to support its westward expansion. Also that year Family Dollar began offering everyday low prices and scaled back its sales promotions.

The pace of expansion was steady during the late 1990s as the company opened hundreds of new stores and more distribution centers and closed underperforming locations. Family Dollar added 165 stores in fiscal 1996 186 in fiscal 1997 250 in fiscal 1998 and 366 in fiscal 1999 (its largest single-year increase in stores). It continued adding stores in 2000 and 2001 (although the rate of growth began slowing) and it began emphasizing food household products and gift and seasonal items rather than clothing.

Family Dollar increased its presence in urban areas by locating 40% of the 475 stores added in 2002 in cities. Historically about 25% of its stores have been placed in urban markets.

Founder Leon Levine retired in January 2003 43 years after starting the company. His son Howard (CEO) succeeded him as chairman. In 2003 Family Dollar Stores opened its seventh distribution center and 475 new stores including its first outlets in Wyoming and North Dakota. In 2004 the chain opened an additional 500 outlets increasing its store count by about 10%.

In April 2006 an Alabama jury found Family Dollar guilty of violating the Federal Labor Standards Act by misclassifying hourly employees as salaried managers to avoid paying overtime. As a result the company was fined $16.6 million. Also that year Family Dollar opened a new Northeast regional distribution center in Rome New York bringing the total to nine centers.

To attract more low-income customers Family Dollar began accepting food stamps in 2008.

In 2009 the chain celebrated 50 years in business and added more than 80 new shops bringing its store count to more than 6600 locations. In August 2011 it opened its 7000th store.

EXECUTIVES

EVP Supply Chain, Charles S. Gibson Jr., age 51, $404,094 total compensation
SVP Hardlines, John J. Scanlon, age 61
SVP Real Estate and Facilities, Keith M. Gehl, age 51
Chairman and CEO, Howard R. Levine, age 53, $998,464 total compensation
SVP Real Estate Development, Thomas M. (Tom) Nash
SVP Finance, Kenneth T. (Ken) Smith, age 50, $299,347 total compensation
SVP Information Technology and CIO, Joshua R. (Josh) Jewett, age 41
VP Merchandising and General Merchandise Manager, Donna Barker
EVP and Chief Merchandising Officer, Paul G. White, age 55
EVP Store Operations, Barry W. Sullivan, age 48
Vice Chairman Strategy and Chief Administrative Officer, Dorlisa K. Flur, $406,502 total compensation
SVP Space Management and Inventory Optimization, Bryan P. Causey
SVP Chief Marketing Officer, Jocelyn Wong
VP Finance, David R. Styka, age 49
SVP Human Resources, Bryan E. Venberg, age 44
VP Human Resources, Jacob J. (Jake) Modla
SVP General Counsel and Secretary, James C. (Jim) Snyder Jr., age 48
SVP Customer Marketing, Don Hamblen
SVP Global Sourcing, Kevin Boyanowski
EVP and CFO, Mary A Winston
Manager Public Relations, Joshua Braverman
VP and Treasurer, Steven E. Burt
VP Loss Prevention, Christopher (Chris) Nielsen
President and COO, Michael K. Bloom
SVP Food, Trey Johnson
Public Relations Manager, Bryn Winburn
SVP Merchandising, Holly Shaskey-Platek
SVP Food, Tammy L. DeBoer
Director, Glenn A. Eisenberg, age 50
Director, George R. Mahoney Jr., age 70
Director, Dale C. Pond, age 66
Director, Sharon Allred Decker, age 55
Director, Pamela L. Davies, age 55
Director, Harvey Morgan, age 70
Director, Mark R. Bernstein, age 82
Director, James G. Martin, age 76
Director, Edward P. Garden, age 49
Director, Edward C. Dolby, age 67
Auditors: PricewaterhouseCoopersLLP

LOCATIONS

HQ: Family Dollar Stores Inc.
10401 Monroe Rd., Matthews NC 28105
Phone: 704-847-6961 **Fax:** 641-782-4844
Web: www.fansteel.com

2012 Stores

	No.
Texas	946
Florida	518
Ohio	451
North	401
Michigan	387
Georgia	358
New	315
Pennsylvania	290
Louisiana	274
Tennessee	235
Virginia	234
Illinois	231
South	212
Indiana	205
Kentucky	200
Alabama	159
Arizona	145
Mississippi	143
Wisconsin	136

Oklahoma	132
Colorado	124
West	120
New	108
Arkansas	107
Massachusetts	107
New	103
Maryland	100
Missouri	99
Minnesota	69
Utah	62
Connecticut	56
Maine	54
Kansas	46
California	44
Nevada	38
Idaho	36
Iowa	36
New	33
Nebraska	32
Rhode	26
South	25
Wyoming	24
Delaware	23
North	16
Vermont	12
District of	3
Total	**7,475**

PRODUCTS/OPERATIONS

2012 Sales

	% of total
Consumables	69
Home	11
Seasonal &	11
Apparel &	9
Total	**100**

2012 Sales

	% of total
Nationally advertised	56
Family Dollar	25
Other	19
Total	**100**

Selected Products

Hardlines
- Automotive supplies
- Candy snacks and other foods
- Electronics
- Gifts
- Hardware
- Health and beauty aids
- Household chemical products
- Household paper products
- Housewares
- Seasonal goods
- Stationery and school supplies
- Toys

Soft goods
- Apparel (men' s women' s children' s and infants')
- Domestics (blankets sheets and towels)
- Shoes

COMPETITORS

7-Eleven
ALCO Stores
Big Lots
BJ' s Wholesale Club
Costco Wholesale
CVS Caremark
Dollar General
Dollar Tree
Food Lion
Fred' s
J. C. Penney
Kmart
Kroger
Meijer
Old Navy
Rite Aid
Sears
Shopko Stores
Simply Amazing
SUPERVALU
Target Corporation
The Pantry
Toys ' ' R' ' Us
Variety Wholesalers
Wal-Mart
Walgreen

HISTORICAL FINANCIALS

Company Type: Public

Income Statement FYE: August 25

	REVENUE ($ mil.)	NET INCOME ($ mil.)	NET PROFIT MARGIN	EMPLOYEES
08/12	9,331	422	4.5%	55,000
08/11	8,547	388	4.5%	52,000
08/10	7,866	358	4.6%	50,000
08/09	7,400	291	3.9%	47,000
08/08	6,983	233	3.3%	44,000
Annual Growth	7.5%	16.0%	—	5.7%

2012 Year-End Financials

Debt ratio: 16.23%
Return on equity: 32.54%
Cash ($ mil.): 92
Current ratio: 165.92
Long-term debt ($ mil.): 516
No. of shares (mil.): 115
Dividends
Yield: —
Payout: 21.79%
Market value ($ mil.): 7,193

	STOCK PRICE ($) FY Close	P/E High/Low		PER SHARE ($) Earnings	Dividends	Book Value
08/12	62.35	20	13	3.58	0.00	11.25
08/11	47.55	18	13	3.12	0.00	9.26
08/10	43.34	17	10	2.62	0.00	10.90
08/09	30.68	17	11	2.07	0.00	10.38
08/08	24.92	18	10	1.66	0.00	8.98
Annual Growth	25.8%	—	—	21.2%	—	5.8%

Fannie Mae

The Federal National Mortgage Association or Fannie Mae has helped more than 50 million low- to middle-income families realize the American Dream. Like its brother Freddie Mac the government-supported enterprise (GSE) provides liquidity in the mortgage market by buying mortgages from lenders and packaging them for resale transferring risk from lenders and allowing them to offer mortgages to those who may not otherwise qualify. It owns or guarantees about $3.1 trillion in home loans or more than a quarter of all outstanding mortgages in the US. Due to losses caused largely by the subprime mortgage crisis the government seized both Fannie and Freddie in 2008. It plans to wind the GSEs down over time.

HISTORY

In 1938 President Franklin Roosevelt created Fannie Mae as part of the government-owned Reconstruction Finance Corporation; its mandate was to buy FHA (Federal Housing Administration) loans. Fannie Mae began buying VA (Veterans Administration) mortgages in 1948. It was rechartered as a public-private mixed-ownership corporation in 1954.

The Housing Act of 1968 divided the corporation into the Government National Mortgage Association (Ginnie Mae which retained explicit government backing) and Fannie Mae which went public (with only an implicit US guarantee). Fannie Mae retained its treasury backstop authority whereby the secretary of the treasury can purchase up to $2.24 billion of the company's obligations.

The company introduced uniform conventional loan mortgage documents in 1970 began to buy conventional mortgages in 1972 and started buying condo and planned-unit development mortgages in 1974. By 1976 it was buying more conventional loans than FHA and VA loans.

As interest rates rose in the 1970s Fannie Mae's profits declined and by 1981 it was losing more than $1 million a day. Then it began offering mortgage-backed securities (MBSs) –popular as an investment product because of their implicit guarantee from the government. By 1982 the company funded 14% of US home mortgages.

Fannie Mae began borrowing money overseas and buying conventional multifamily and co-op housing loans in 1984. The next year it tightened credit rules and began issuing securities aimed at foreign investors such as yen-denominated securities. Fannie Mae issued its first real estate mortgage investment conduit (REMIC) securities (shares in mortgage pools of specific maturities and risk classes) and introduced a program to allow small lenders to pool loans with other lenders to create MBSs in 1987.

After CEO David Maxwell's 1991 retirement with a reported $29 million pension package Fannie Mae's powerful Washington lobby squelched calls to limit executive salaries. Other attempts to make the company more competitive with private concerns were more successful. In 1992 Fannie Mae's capital requirements were raised; a new mandate also required the organization to lend greater support to inner-city buyers. A new client/server computer system helped the company handle the deluge of new and refinanced loans that came in 1993 (Fannie Mae had struggled to improve its information systems in the 1980s pouring more than $100 million into a mainframe system that was obsolete before it went online).

In 1997 Fannie Mae officially adopted its longtime nickname. The next year Fannie Mae named White House budget chief Franklin Raines to succeed CEO James Johnson.

Fannie Mae is no stranger to bad news or bad press. In 1999 the Department of Housing and Urban Development began investigating charges that the company's automated underwriting systems were racially biased. The next year the agency released a study that found it to be negligent in promoting homeownership in low-income neighborhoods. In response Fannie Mae eased credit requirements in an effort to boost minority homeownership (1999) and announced plans to loan some $2 trillion to minority and low-income homebuyers (2000). This move however invoked criticism that the company was exposing itself to increased risk from buyers more likely to default.

Following the lead of rival Freddie Mac in 2000 Fannie Mae offered securities for sale over the Internet. In 2002 it tightened standards for mortgage refinance cash-out loans it would buy as mortgage defaults rose (even as home sales and mortgage refinancings were helping prop up the sagging US economy).

In response to those who thought it was in bed with the federal government Fannie Mae kicked off the covers and put one foot on the floor. In 2003 it fulfilled a voluntary commitment to register its common stock with the SEC and came permanently under that organization's disclosure and oversight requirements.

But the move did not stop controversy from swirling around the lender. Chairman and CEO Franklin Raines CFO Timothy Howard and auditor KPMG were ousted in December 2004 after the SEC determined Fannie Mae had violated accounting rules. The inquiry was prompted by accusations Fannie Mae had manipulated earnings; earnings from 2001 through 2003 were restated and those from 2004 and 2005 were each released more than a year late.

In 2006 federal regulators hit the firm with a whopping $400 million fine. Investigators claimed that its former executives willfully overstated earnings by more than $10 billion –and then tried to impede an investigation into the discrepancies –in order to reap performance bonuses. Chairman Stephen Ashley and CEO Daniel Mudd who'd been brought in to replace Franklin Raines in late 2004 were brought to task by the Senate Banking Committee in regard to accounting misdeeds.

Though the Justice Department eventually dropped criminal charges against the firm Fannie Mae agreed to major changes in its accounting internal controls and management practices. It additionally agreed to appoint an independent chief risk officer as well as an organizational review overseen by a compliance committee. Meanwhile the lender suspended its home construction loan program –worth about $10 billion –while it got its financial house in order.

Fannie suffered huge losses in 2007 and 2008 as a result of the subprime mortgage crisis which saw a tremendouse increase in loan defaults. The government stepped in loans and in 2008 seized both Fannie and Freddie. It also shuffled their management teams: Fannie CEO Mudd was replaced by Herbert Allison former TIAA-CREF. Allison was later tapped by the Obama administration to run the Treasury Department's financial recovery program. Former COO Michael Williams was named CEO in 2009.

The Federal Housing Finance Agency (FHFA) was created in 2008 to oversee both Fannie and Freddie as well as the 12 Federal Home Loan Banks. The FHFA was granted more authority than its predecessor agencies the Federal Housing Finance Board and the Office of Federal Housing Enterprise Oversight.

EXECUTIVES

EVP and Operating Plan Program Executive, Linda K. Knight, age 62
Chairman, Philip A. (Phil) Laskawy, age 71
EVP Multifamily, Kenneth J. (Ken) Bacon, age 57, $550,800 total compensation
President CEO and Director, Michael J. (Mike) Williams, age 54, $860,523 total compensation
EVP Operations and Technology, Edward G. (Ed) Watson, age 50
EVP Credit Portfolio Management, Terence W. (Terry) Edwards, age 56
President CEO and Director, Timothy J. (Tim) Mayopoulos, age 52, $439,346 total compensation
EVP and CFO, Susan R. McFarland, age 51
SVP Multifamily Mortgage Business, Jeffery R. Hayward, age 56
EVP Captial Markets, David C. Benson, age 52, $519,231 total compensation
EVP and Chief Credit Officer, Michael A. (Mike) Shaw, age 64
SVP and Chief Compliance and Ethics Officer, Nancy J. Jardini
Director Media and External Relations, Amy Bonitatibus
EVP and Chief Risk Officer, Kenneth J. (Ken) Phelan, age 52
EVP Single-Family Mortgage Business, Karen R. Pallotta, age 48
SVP and Chief Audit Executive, Patricia E. Black
SVP and Chief Communications Officer Communications and Marketing Services, Kelli Parsons
VP Corporate Communications, Maureen Davenport
VP Business Management and Client Services, Lisa Giesler
VP Business Marketing and Communications, Meg Simeone
SVP; Head of Underwriting and Pricing, Andrew J. Bon Salle, age 46
EVP and Chief Risk Officer, John R. Nichols, age 49
SVP; Head of Customer Engagement, Zachary Oppenheimer, age 52
Director, David H. Sidwell, age 58
Director, W. Thomas Forrester, age 63
President CEO and Director, Michael J. (Mike) Williams, age 54
Director, Dennis R. (Denny) Beresford, age 73
Director, Brenda J. Gaines, age 62
Director, Frederick B. (Bart) Harvey III, age 62
President CEO and Director, Timothy J. (Tim) Mayopoulos, age 52
Director, Charlynn Goins, age 69
Director, Egbert L. J. Perry, age 56
Director, Jonathan Plutzik, age 57
Auditors: Deloitte&ToucheLLP

LOCATIONS

HQ: Fannie Mae
3900 Wisconsin Avenue, NW, Washington, DC 20016
Phone: 202 752-7000
Web: www.fanniemae.com

PRODUCTS/OPERATIONS

2011 Sales

	$ mil.	% of total
Interest		
Mortgage loans		
Of consolidated trusts	123,633	86
Of Fannie Mae	14,829	10
Available-for-sale securities	3,277	2
Trading securities	1,087	1
Other	117	-
Noninterest		
Net investment gains	506	
Fees & other income	1,163	1
Adjustments	(7161)	-
Total	**137,451**	**100**

COMPETITORS

FHLB Atlanta

HISTORICAL FINANCIALS

Company Type: Public

Income Statement FYE: December 31

	ASSETS ($ mil.)	NET INCOME ($ mil.)	INCOME AS % OF ASSETS	EMPLOYEES
12/11	3,211,484	(16,855)	—	7,000
12/10	3,221,972	(14,014)	—	7,300
12/09	869,141	(71,969)	—	6,000
12/08	912,404	(58,707)	—	5,800
12/07	882,547	(2,050)	—	5,700
Annual Growth	38.1%	—	—	5.3%

2011 Year-End Financials

Debt ratio: 99.33%
Return on equity: 987650001000000.00%
Cash ($ mil.): 17,539
Current ratio: —
Long-term debt ($ mil.): 3,189,872
No. of shares (mil.): 1,157
Dividends
Yield: —
Payout: —
Market value ($ mil.): 232

	STOCK PRICE ($) FY Close	P/E High/Low	PER SHARE ($) Earnings	Dividends	Book Value
12/11	0.20	— —	(4.61)	0.00	(3.99)
12/10	0.30	— —	(3.81)	0.00	(2.32)
12/09	1.18	— —	(13.11)	0.00	(13.81)
12/08	0.76	— —	(24.04)	0.75	(14.11)
12/07	39.98	— —	(2.63)	2.04	45.18
Annual Growth	(73.4%)	— —	—	—	—

FBL Financial Group, Inc.

Insurance holding company FBL Financial Group (FBL) is the parent of Farm Bureau Life Insurance Company. Through its subsidiary the firm sells life insurance annuities and investment products to farmers ranchers and agricultural businesses. Farm Bureau Life sells insurance and annuities through an exclusive network of about 2000 agents across some 15 states in the Midwest and West. The company markets its products through an affiliation with the American Farm Bureau Federation. FBL also manages for a fee two Farm Bureau-affiliated property/casualty insurance companies. The Iowa Farm Bureau Federation owns close to 65% of the company. FBL Financial Group sold its EquiTrust Life business in 2011.

After deciding to focus on its Farm Bureau Life business FBL Financial sold its EquiTrust Life subsidiary (its largest transaction to date) which offered annuity products through more than 14500 independent agents across the US. Financial services firm Guggenheim Partners paid some $470 million for EquiTrust Life at the close of 2011. Before agreeing to sell the business FBL had already worked to reduce risk and diversify EquiTrust Life –it first halted new sales of variable annuities and then introduced new life insurance products in 2010. The sale strengthened its capital position and enabled FBL to reduce its overall risk retire $225 million of debt and repurchase more than 4 million of the company's shares for $136.5 million.

The two Farm Bureau-affiliated property/casualty insurers that FBL manages are Farm Bureau Property & Casualty and Western Agricultural Insurance. The two affiliates underwrite auto crop and other property/casualty policies for individuals and groups in the midwestern and western US.

FBL has expanded its territory over the years through acquisitions while traditionally keeping an eye out for other consolidation opportunities. However unstable conditions in the US financial markets in 2008 and 2009 caused the company to focus on strengthening its capital operations restoring its financial ratings and reducing risk in its businesses. Like many insurance companies FBL suffered from losses on investments in mortgage and asset-backed securities during those years.

With the sell-off of its EquiTrust operations FBL's net revenues of $618 million in 2011 declined by 44% from the $1 billion it achieved in 2010 although seperately its Farm Bureau Life reported record sales. The company's net income of $31.3 million dropped 74% from 2010's $120.6

million. Because of the company's renewed focus and new prospects for growth within its niche Farm Bureau customer base it is not dampened by the results particularly since fluctuations in the industry are a given (due to a range of variables from interest rates and competition to ratings and economic conditions among other factors). The company was in fact named as one of FORTUNE magazine's "100 Fastest-Growing Companies" for 2011. It ranked 39th on the list for earnings-per-share growth (over the past three years) and 83rd overall.

Strategically FBL expands its penetration in both the life and property/casualty markets by encouraging existing policyholders to purchase other insurance products through the agents they already know. Its cross-selling technique has led the industry as a whole. Additionally FBL depends on the talent of the agents it engages and its overall ability to provide products that meet changing needs as well as superior customer service and market knowledge.

EXECUTIVES

EVP Farm Bureau Life, JoAnn W. Rumelhart, age 58, $287,426 total compensation
VP Human Resources, Mark Mincks
CEO, James P. (Jim) Brannen, age 49, $416,250 total compensation
Vice Chairman, Jerry L. Chicoine, age 69
VP Information Technology, Douglas W. Gumm, age 57
EVP Marketing and Distribution, Kevin R. Slawin
Chairman, Craig A. Lang, age 60
Chairman, Craig D. Hill, age 56
CEO and Director, James E. (Jim) Hohmann, age 56
VP Investor Relations, Kathleen Till Stange
VP Strategy and Business Development, David T. Sebastian, age 59
EVP Farm Bureau Life, Richard J. (Rich) Kypta, age 59, $381,063 total compensation
CFO and Treasurer, Donald J. (Don) Seibel, age 48
Media, Nancy Doll
EVP and Chief Investment Officer, Charles T. Happel, age 50
VP General Counsel and Secretary, David A. McNeill
Chief Actuary, Russell J. (Russ) Wiltgen
VP EquiTrust, Tom May
Director, Roger K. Brooks, age 74
Vice Chairman, Jerry L. Chicoine, age 69
Director, John E. Walker, age 73
Director, Edward W. (Ed) Mehrer Jr., age 73
Director, Keith R. Olsen, age 67
Director, Craig D. Hill, age 56
Director, Tim H. Gill, age 59
Director, Robert H. Hanson, age 70
Director, Paul E. Larson, age 59
Director, Steve L. Baccus, age 62
CEO and Director, James E. (Jim) Hohmann, age 56
Director, Kevin G. Rogers, age 51
Director, Dennis J. Presnall
Director, Scott E. VanderWal
Auditors: Ernst&YoungLLP

LOCATIONS

HQ: FBL Financial Group Inc.
5400 University Ave., West Des Moines IA 50266-5997
Phone: 515-225-5400 **Fax:** 425-401-0971
Web: www.4shs.com

Selected Areas of Operation

Farm Bureau Life Insurance Company
Multi-line (life and property/casualty
Arizona
Iowa
Kansas
Minnesota
Nebraska
New Mexico
South Dakota
Utah
Life only
Idaho
Montana
North Dakota
Oklahoma
Wisconsin
Wyoming
Farm Bureau Property & Casualty Insurance Company and Western Agricultural Insurance Company
Arizona
Iowa
Kansas
Minnesota
Nebraska
New Mexico
South Dakota
Utah

PRODUCTS/OPERATIONS

2011 Revenues

	$ mil.	% of total
Life Insurance	353	56
Losses on investments	(8.3)	
Total	**618**	**100**

Selected Subsidiaries

Insurance

Farm Bureau Life Insurance Company
Noninsurance
5400 Holdings L.L.C.
FBL Assigned Benefit Company
FBL Financial Group Capital Trust
FBL Financial Group Capital Trust II
FBL Financial Services Inc.
FBL Investment Management Services Inc.
FBL Leasing Services Inc.
FBL Marketing Services L.L.C.

COMPETITORS

AIG
Allstate
American Equity Investment Life Holding Company
American Farmers & Ranchers Mutual Insurance Co.
COUNTRY Financial
Farm Family Holdings
Farmers & Merchants Investment
Great American Financial Resources
MetLife
Midland National Life
Nationwide
Nationwide Agribusiness
Prudential
State Farm
Thrivent Investment Management

HISTORICAL FINANCIALS

Company Type: Public

Income Statement FYE: December 31

	ASSETS ($ mil.)	NET INCOME ($ mil.)	INCOME AS % OF ASSETS	EMPLOYEES
12/11	8,225	31	0.4%	1,570
12/10	15,334	120	0.8%	1,679
12/09	14,259	69	0.5%	1,714
12/08	14,060	(18)	—	1,866
12/07	14,002	86	0.6%	1,818
Annual Growth	(12.5%)	(22.4%)	—	(3.6%)

2011 Year-End Financials

Debt ratio: 1.79%
Return on equity: 2.45%
Cash ($ mil.): 296
Current ratio: —
Long-term debt ($ mil.): 146
No. of shares (mil.): 30
Dividends
Yield: —
Payout: 28.75%
Market value ($ mil.): 1,043

	STOCK PRICE ($) FY Close	P/E High	P/E Low	PER SHARE ($) Earnings	Dividends	Book Value
12/11	34.02	35	25	1.00	0.00	41.70
12/10	28.67	7	4	3.92	0.25	37.05
12/09	18.52	10	1	2.31	0.31	28.59
12/08	15.45	—	—	(0.61)	0.50	8.56
12/07	34.53	15	11	2.84	0.48	30.08
Annual Growth	(0.4%)	—	—	(23.0%)	—	8.5%

Federal Agricultural Mortgage Corp.

Farmer Mac (Federal Agricultural Mortgage Corporation) is Fannie Mae and Freddie Mac's country cousin. Like its city-slicker kin it provides liquidity in its markets (agricultural real estate and rural housing mortgages) by buying loans from lenders and then securitizing the loans into Farmer Mac Guaranteed Securities. Farmer Mac buys both conventional loans and those guaranteed by the US Department of Agriculture. About 40% of Farmer Mac's outstanding loans are secured by real estate in the southwestern US; the Northwest and the Upper Midwest account for nearly 20% apiece. More than 40% of its loans are for crops some 25% for livestock facilities and about another 20% for permanent plantings.

In 2007 the company was affected by the credit crisis that afflicted most loan buyers but not because of subprime loans; rising interest rates caused a $40 million loss in its derivatives and other trading assets. In 2008 several lenders in the Farm Credit System as well as Zions First National Bank invested $65 million into Farmer Mac to help alleviate its investment losses. Long-time CEO Henry Edelman was replaced by Michael Gerber the head of Farm Credit of Western New York.

The US Congress created Farmer Mac in 1987 at a time when agricultural lending had slowed due to defaults; the Farm Credit Administration oversees Farmer Mac. Zions First National Bank is Farmer Mac's largest stockholder controlling more than 20% the firm; AgribBank FCB controls 13%.

EXECUTIVES

EVP Agricultural Finance and COO, Tom D. Stenson, age 61, $346,716 total compensation
VP General Counsel and Secretary, Jerome G. Oslick, age 65, $278,554 total compensation
Chairman, Lowell L. Junkins, age 68
VP CFO and Treasurer, Timothy L. (Tim) Buzby, age 43, $253,591 total compensation
VP Corporate Relations, Mary K. Waters, age 53
President CEO and Director, Michael A. Gerber, age 53, $131,712 total compensation
Director, Dennis L. Brack, age 59
Director, Paul A. DeBriyn, age 57
Director, Mitchell A. Johnson, age 70
Director, John D. Raines Jr., age 68

Director, Dennis A. Everson, age 61
Director, Julia Bartling, age 53
Director, Glen O. Klippenstein, age 74
Director, Ernest M. Hodges, age 64
Director, James R. Engebretsen
Director, Brian P. Jackson, age 55
Director, Brian J. O'Keane, age 44
Director, Clark Maxwell, age 41
President CEO and Director, Michael A. Gerber, age 53
Director, Sarah L. Faivre-Davis
Director, Myles Watts
Auditors: Deloitte&ToucheLLP

LOCATIONS

HQ: Federal Agricultural Mortgage Corporation
1133 21st St. NW Ste. 600, Washington DC 20036
Phone: 202-872-7700 **Fax:** 202-872-7713
Web: www.farmermac.com

PRODUCTS/OPERATIONS

2007 Sales

	$ mil.	% of total
Interest		
Investments & cash equivalents	174	54
Farmer Mac Guaranteed Securities	77	24
Loans	45	14
Noninterest		
Guarantee & commitment fees	25	8
Losses on financial derivatives & trading assets	(40.3)	-
Other	1	-
Total	**324**	**100**

Selected Programs

Farmer Mac I (purchase of loans not guaranteed by any US agency)
Farmer Mac II (purchase of loans guaranteed by US Department of Agriculture)

COMPETITORS

AgFirst
AgriBank
AgStar
Bank of America
Citigroup
Fannie Mae
Farm Credit Services of Mid-America
Freddie Mac

HISTORICAL FINANCIALS

Company Type: Public

Income Statement

FYE: December 31

	ASSETS ($ mil.)	NET INCOME ($ mil.)	INCOME AS % OF ASSETS	EMPLOYEES
12/11	11,883	16	0.1%	62
12/10	9,479	31	0.3%	58
12/09	6,138	99	1.6%	53
12/08	5,107	(150)	—	43
12/07	4,977	6	0.1%	42
Annual Growth	24.3%	25.8%	—	10.2%

2011 Year-End Financials

Debt ratio: 85.77%
Return on equity: 5.33%
Cash ($ mil.): 817
Current ratio: —
Long-term debt ($ mil.): 10,192
No. of shares (mil.): 10
Dividends
Yield: —
Payout: 15.63%
Market value ($ mil.): 187

	STOCK PRICE ($) FY Close	P/E High/Low		PER SHARE ($) Earnings	Dividends	Book Value
12/11	18.02	17	11	1.28	0.00	30.19
12/10	16.32	11	3	2.08	0.20	23.05
12/09	7.01	1	0	8.04	0.20	33.56
12/08	3.50	—	—	(15.40)	0.40	15.75
12/07	26.32	83	57	0.42	0.40	22.60
Annual Growth	(9.0%)	—	—	32.1%	—	7.5%

Federal Home Loan Bank New York

Federal Home Loan Bank of New York (FHLBNY) provides funds for residential mortgages and community development to more than 330 member banks savings and loans credit unions and life insurance companies in New York New Jersey Puerto Rico and the US Virgin Islands. One of a dozen Federal Home Loan Banks (FHLBs) in the US it is cooperatively owned by its member institutions and supervised by the Federal Housing Finance Agency. FHLBNY like the others in the system is privately capitalized; it receives no taxpayer funding. The bank instead raises funds mainly by issuing debt instruments in the capital markets.

FHLBNY is a secured lender that requires collateral for its advances which are typically used by members to underwrite residential mortgages or to invest in US Treasury and agency securities mortgage-backed securities and other real estate-related assets. The bank has remained consistently profitable by keeping very low overhead and investing in relatively low-risk loans and securities. Loan demand (along with corresponding revenue and net income) declined in 2010 however as member institutions grew their deposit bases giving them a bigger pool of money to lend.

Credit unions are a possible area of growth for FHLBNY. The bank has identified more than 50 credit unions and banks that are not members but are eligible. To be under consideration an institution must have more than $50 million in assets ($100 million for banks) be an established wholesale lender maintain a high deposit-to-loan ratio and have management that has done business with an FHLB in the past.

EXECUTIVES

Vice Chairman, Jose R. Gonzalez, age 57
Chairman, Michael M. (Mike) Horn, age 72
President and CEO, Alfred A. DelliBovi, age 66, $649,494 total compensation
Director Compliance, Steve S. Christatos
SVP and Head Member Services, Paul B. Heroux, age 53, $300,980 total compensation
SVP and Head Asset Liability Management, Craig E. Reynolds, age 63, $270,443 total compensation
SVP and CFO, Patrick A. Morgan, age 71, $319,154 total compensation
SVP and Chief Risk Officer, Peter S. Leung Jr., age 57, $423,294 total compensation
VP and Director Collateral Operations, Michael A. Volpe
SVP and Head Strategy and Business Development, Kevin M. Neylan, age 54, $310,415 total compensation
VP, Backer Ali
SVP and Director Bank Relations, Eric P. Amig, age 53
VP, Edwin Artuz
VP and Director Credit and Correspondent Services, James Bernard
VP, Sean Borde
VP and Director Acquired Member Assets, Thomas J. Doyle
VP, John Edelen
VP, Paul Friend
VP, G. Robert Fusco
VP Director Community Investment and Community Investment Officer, Joseph Gallo
SVP and Head Marketing and Sales, Adam Goldstein, age 38
Director Credit Policy, Susan Isquith
VP Sales and Calling Officer, Maureen Kalena
Director Operations Risk, Rebecca Logan
VP, Walter Moran
VP Sales and Calling Officer, Alfred O'Connell
VP, Agnes Olah
VP Funds Transfer and Deposit Services, Aida Polanco
VP Sales and Calling Officer, Facundo (Frank) Saenz de Viteri
VP, Grace Sit
VP and Director Funding and Derivatives, Louis Solimine
VP, Barbara Sperrazza
VP, John Surre
Director Risk Analytics, M. Hampton Tunis
VP, Barbara Way
VP and Community Investment Operations Officer, Edwin Bird
VP Sales and Manager Sales, James Feeney
VP and Director Investment Portfolio, Diahann Rothstein
VP and Senior Trader Analyst, Phil Scott
VP and Director Marketing Communications, Candice Soldano
Internet Services Specialist Funds Transfer and Deposit Services, Shirley Hemphill
VP and Director Loan Review Analysis, Cynthia Palladino
VP and Collateral Valuations, Bryan Gallagher
SVP and Chief Audit Officer, Stephen Angelo
Director, Joseph R. Ficalora, age 65
Director, James W. (Jim) Fulmer, age 60
Director, George Strayton, age 68
Director, Ronald E. Hermance Jr., age 64
Director, John R. Buran, age 62
Director, Joseph J. (Joe) Melone, age 80
Vice Chairman, Jose R. Gonzalez, age 57
Director, C. Cathleen (Cathi) Raffaeli, age 55
Director, Thomas M. O'Brien, age 61
Director, Anne Evans Estabrook, age 67
Director, Katherine J. Liseno, age 67
Director, Kevin J. Lynch, age 65
Director, Richard S. Mroz, age 50
Director, Rev Edwin C. Reed, age 58
Director, Jay M. Ford, age 62
Director, DeForest B. Soaries Jr., age 60
Vice Chairman, Jose R. Gonzalez, age 57
Chairman, Michael M. (Mike) Horn, age 72
President and CEO, Alfred A. DelliBovi, age 66, $649,494 total compensation
Director Compliance, Steve S. Christatos
SVP and Head Member Services, Paul B. Heroux, age 53, $300,980 total compensation
SVP and Head Asset Liability Management, Craig E. Reynolds, age 63, $270,443 total compensation
SVP and CFO, Patrick A. Morgan, age 71, $319,154 total compensation

SVP and Chief Risk Officer, Peter S. Leung Jr., age 57, $423,294 total compensation
VP and Director Collateral Operations, Michael A. Volpe
SVP and Head Strategy and Business Development, Kevin M. Neylan, age 54, $310,415 total compensation
VP, Backer Ali
SVP and Director Bank Relations, Eric P. Amig, age 53
VP, Edwin Artuz
VP and Director Credit and Correspondent Services, James Bernard
VP, Sean Borde
VP and Director Acquired Member Assets, Thomas J. Doyle
VP, John Edelen
VP, Paul Friend
VP, G. Robert Fusco
VP Director Community Investment and Community Investment Officer, Joseph Gallo
SVP and Head Marketing and Sales, Adam Goldstein, age 38
Director Credit Policy, Susan Isquith
VP Sales and Calling Officer, Maureen Kalena
Director Operations Risk, Rebecca Logan
VP, Walter Moran
VP Sales and Calling Officer, Alfred O'Connell
VP, Agnes Olah
VP Funds Transfer and Deposit Services, Aida Polanco
VP Sales and Calling Officer, Facundo (Frank) Saenz de Viteri
VP, Grace Sit
VP and Director Funding and Derivatives, Louis Solimine
VP, Barbara Sperrazza
VP, John Surre
Director Risk Analytics, M. Hampton Tunis
VP, Barbara Way
VP and Community Investment Operations Officer, Edwin Bird
VP Sales and Manager Sales, James Feeney
VP and Director Investment Portfolio, Diahann Rothstein
VP and Senior Trader Analyst, Phil Scott
VP and Director Marketing Communications, Candice Soldano
Internet Services Specialist Funds Transfer and Deposit Services, Shirley Hemphill
VP and Director Loan Review Analysis, Cynthia Palladino
VP and Collateral Valuations, Bryan Gallagher
SVP and Chief Audit Officer, Stephen Angelo
Director, Joseph R. Ficalora, age 65
Director, James W. (Jim) Fulmer, age 60
Director, George Strayton, age 68
Director, Ronald E. Hermance Jr., age 64
Director, John R. Buran, age 62
Director, Joseph J. (Joe) Melone, age 80
Vice Chairman, Jose R. Gonzalez, age 57
Director, C. Cathleen (Cathi) Raffaeli, age 55
Director, Thomas M. O'Brien, age 61
Director, Anne Evans Estabrook, age 67
Director, Katherine J. Liseno, age 67
Director, Kevin J. Lynch, age 65
Director, Richard S. Mroz, age 50
Director, Rev Edwin C. Reed, age 58
Director, Jay M. Ford, age 62
Director, DeForest B. Soaries Jr., age 60
Auditors: PricewaterhouseCoopersLLP

LOCATIONS

HQ: Federal Home Loan Bank of New York
101 Park Ave., New York NY 10178-0599
Phone: 212-681-6000 **Fax:** 212-441-6890
Web: www.fhlbny.com

PRODUCTS/OPERATIONS

2010 Sales

	$ mil.	% of total
Interest		
Advances	614	56
Long-term securities	352	32
Mortgage loans held for portfolio	65	6
Available-for-sale securities	31	3
Other	14	1
Noninterest	16	2
Total	**1,095**	**100**

HISTORICAL FINANCIALS

Company Type: Private - Member-Owned Banking Authority

Income Statement FYE: December 31

	ASSETS ($ mil.)	NET INCOME ($ mil.)	INCOME AS % OF ASSETS	EMPLOYEES
12/11	97,662	244	0.3%	276
12/10	100,212	275	0.3%	271
12/09	114,460	570	0.5%	264
12/08	137,539	259	0.2%	251
12/07	109,682	323	0.3%	246
Annual Growth	(2.9%)	(6.7%)	—	2.9%

2011 Year-End Financials

Debt ratio: 69.05%
Return on equity: 4.85%
Cash ($ mil.): 10,877
Current ratio: —
Long-term debt ($ mil.): 67,440
No. of shares (mil.): 44
Dividends
Yield: —
Payout: 86.08%
Market value ($ mil.): —

Federal Home Loan Bank Of San Francisco

The city by the bay is the home to the Federal Home Loan Bank of San Francisco one of a dozen regional banks in the Federal Home Loan Bank System chartered by Congress in 1932 to provide credit to residential mortgage lenders. The government-sponsored enterprise is privately owned by its members which include some 400 commercial banks credit unions industrial loan companies savings and loans insurance companies and housing associates headquartered in Arizona California and Nevada. The bank links members to worldwide capital markets which provide them with low-cost funding. Members then pass these advances along to their customers in the form of affordable home mortgage and economic development loans.

FHLB San Francisco and its counterparts around the country are governed by the Federal Housing Finance Agency which recently gave eligible community development financial institutions approval to become FHLB members. In addition to providing its member institutions with advances the bank also acquires residential mortgage-backed securities (RMBS) from its members.

Although FHLB San Francisco has remained profitable through the economic downturn it has been dealing with the ill effects of the crash which has severely impacted the states of Arizona California and Nevada in particular. In 2011 the bank's revenues fell 35% to $1.1 billion while net income fell 46% to $216 million. Demand for loans remains low in the stagnant economy and FHLB San Francisco's interest earnings fell 20% that year. Additionally the value of its RMBS portfolio has declined in the downturn.

EXECUTIVES

Chairman, Timothy R. Chrisman, age 65
Vice Chairman, John F. Luikart, age 62
President and CEO, Dean Schultz, age 65, $725,000 total compensation
SVP and Chief Capital Markets Officer, Steven T. Honda, age 60, $330,000 total compensation
EVP and COO, Lisa B. MacMillen, age 52, $466,500 total compensation
SVP Financial Services and Community Investment, Stephen P. Traynor, age 55, $282,800 total compensation
SVP and Chief Risk Officer, David H. Martens, age 59, $345,230 total compensation
SVP Controller and Operations Officer, Vera Maytum, age 62
SVP and CFO, Kenneth C. Miller, age 59, $345,000 total compensation
SVP External and Legislative Affairs, Lawrence H. Parks, age 50, $394,823 total compensation
SVP General Counsel and Corporate Secretary, Suzanne Titus-Johnson, age 54
SVP and Chief Corporate Securities Counsel, Kevin A. Gong, age 52
SVP Mortgage Finance Sales and Product Development, Patricia M. Remch, age 59
VP Corporate Communications, Amy Stewart
VP Marketing, Cynthia Lopez
SVP and Director Human Resources, Gregory P. Fontenot, age 53
SVP and Director Internal Audit, Mark J. Watson, age 50
SVP Credit and Collateral Risk Management, Robert M. (Rob) Shovlowsky, age 53
SVP and CIO, Elena Andreadakis, age 50
Director, Craig G. Blunden, age 64
Vice Chairman, John F. Luikart, age 62
Director, John F. Robinson, age 64
Director, Douglas H. (Tad) Lowrey, age 59
Director, W. Douglas (Doug) Hile, age 59
Director, Kenneth A. (Ken) Vecchione, age 57
Director, J. Benson Porter, age 46
Director, Paul R. Ackerman, age 50
Director, David A. Funk, age 68
Director, Scott C. Syphax, age 48
Director, Melinda Guzman, age 48
Director, John T. Wasley, age 50
Director, Kevin G. Murray, age 51
Director, Reginald Chen, age 51
Director, Robert F. Nielsen, age 65
Chairman, Timothy R. Chrisman, age 65
Vice Chairman, John F. Luikart, age 62
President and CEO, Dean Schultz, age 65, $725,000 total compensation
SVP and Chief Capital Markets Officer, Steven T. Honda, age 60, $330,000 total compensation
EVP and COO, Lisa B. MacMillen, age 52, $466,500 total compensation
SVP Financial Services and Community Investment, Stephen P. Traynor, age 55, $282,800 total compensation
SVP and Chief Risk Officer, David H. Martens, age 59, $345,230 total compensation
SVP Controller and Operations Officer, Vera Maytum, age 62
SVP and CFO, Kenneth C. Miller, age 59, $345,000 total compensation
SVP External and Legislative Affairs, Lawrence H. Parks, age 50, $394,823 total compensation
SVP General Counsel and Corporate Secretary, Suzanne Titus-Johnson, age 54

SVP and Chief Corporate Securities Counsel, Kevin A. Gong, age 52
SVP Mortgage Finance Sales and Product Development, Patricia M. Remch, age 59
VP Corporate Communications, Amy Stewart
VP Marketing, Cynthia Lopez
SVP and Director Human Resources, Gregory P. Fontenot, age 53
SVP and Director Internal Audit, Mark J. Watson, age 50
SVP Credit and Collateral Risk Management, Robert M. (Rob) Shovlowsky, age 53
SVP and CIO, Elena Andreadakis, age 50
Director, Craig G. Blunden, age 64
Vice Chairman, John F. Luikart, age 62
Director, John F. Robinson, age 64
Director, Douglas H. (Tad) Lowrey, age 59
Director, W. Douglas (Doug) Hile, age 59
Director, Kenneth A. (Ken) Vecchione, age 57
Director, J. Benson Porter, age 46
Director, Paul R. Ackerman, age 50
Director, David A. Funk, age 68
Director, Scott C. Syphax, age 48
Director, Melinda Guzman, age 48
Director, John T. Wasley, age 50
Director, Kevin G. Murray, age 51
Director, Reginald Chen, age 51
Director, Robert F. Nielsen, age 65
Auditors: PricewaterhouseCoopersLLP

LOCATIONS

HQ: Federal Home Loan Bank of San Francisco
600 California St., San Francisco CA 94108
Phone: 415-616-1000 **Fax:** 415-616-2626
Web: www.fhlbsf.com

PRODUCTS/OPERATIONS

2011 Sales

	$ mil.	% of total
Interest		
Advances	692	38
Held-to-maturity securities	679	37
Available-for-sale securities	238	13
Mortgage loans held for portfolio	113	6
Other	64	3
Noninterest	55	3
Adjustments	(700)	-
Total	**1,141**	**100**

HISTORICAL FINANCIALS

Company Type: Private - Member-Owned Banking Authority

Income Statement FYE: December 31

	ASSETS ($ mil.)	NET INCOME ($ mil.)	INCOME AS % OF ASSETS	EMPLOYEES
12/11	113,552	216	0.2%	274
12/10	152,423	399	0.3%	304
12/09	192,862	515	0.3%	311
12/08	321,244	461	0.1%	284
12/07	322,999	652	0.2%	270
Annual Growth	(23.0%)	(24.1%)	—	0.4%

2011 Year-End Financials

Debt ratio: 90.27%
Return on equity: 4.59%
Cash ($ mil.): 3,494
Current ratio: —
Long-term debt ($ mil.): 102,502
No. of shares (mil.): 48
Dividends
Yield: —
Payout: 10.19%
Market value ($ mil.): —

Federal Reserve Bank of Atlanta, Dist. No. 6

One of 12 regional banks in the Federal Reserve System the Federal Reserve Bank of Atlanta oversees Fed member banks and thrifts and their holding companies throughout the Southeast including Alabama Florida Georgia and parts of Louisiana Mississippi and Tennessee. It conducts examinations and investigations of member institutions distributes cash issues savings bonds and Treasury securities and assists the Fed in setting monetary policy such as interest rates. The bank also processes checks and acts as a clearinghouse for payments between banks. Fed Reserve Banks are independent arms within the government and return earnings (gleaned mostly from investments in government bonds) to the US Treasury.

The Federal Reserve Bank of Atlanta has six branch offices in Birmingham Jacksonville Miami Nashville and New Orleans. It represents the Sixth District within the Federal Reserve System.

The Federal Reserve Bank of Atlanta was established by an act of Congress in 1913.

EXECUTIVES

President and CEO, Dennis P. Lockhart, age 63
Chair, Carol B. Tome, age 55
VP Consumer Compliance and Complaints, Juan C. Sanchez
First VP and COO, Patrick K. (Pat) Barron
SVP Corporate Services, Anne M. DeBeer
SVP Corporate Services, Christopher G. Brown
SVP Supervision and Regulation, William B. Estes III
EVP Retail Payments Risk Forum, Richard R. (Rich) Oliver
SVP Check Operations and Automation, Donald E. Nelson
SVP and General Counsel, Richard A. Jones
SVP and General Auditor, Lois C. Bethaume
VP Risk Management and Analysis, Cynthia C. Goodwin
SVP Cash Function, Robert J. Musso
SVP Strategic Planning, James M. McKee
VP Human Resources, Mary M. Mandel
VP Public Affairs, Bobbie H. McCrackin
SVP District Operations and Administrative Services, Leah Davenport
Assistant VP Miami, Paul Graham
VP Large and Regional Bank Supervision, David E. Tatum
First VP and COO, Marie C. Gooding
VP Minority and Women Inclusion and Chief Diversity Officer, Joan M. Buchanan
VP Check Operations and Automation, Robert A. Love
VP International Examinations and Foreign Banking Organizations Wealth Management and Bank Secrecy Act, Robert M. Schenk
VP Consumer Affairs, J. Stephen Foley
VP Administrative Support, Suzanna J. Costello
SVP Corporate Engagement, Andre T. Anderson
EVP and Director of Research, David E. Altig
Assistant Vice President and Director Forum for Retail Payments Risk Management, Clifford S. Stanford
Deputy Chair, Thomas I. Barkin
Director, Rudy E. Schupp, age 61
Director, Lee M. Thomas, age 67
Director, James M. (Jim) Wells III, age 65
Director, Teri G. Fontenot
Director, James H. McKillop III
Director, Renee L. Glover
Deputy Chair, Thomas I. Barkin
Auditors: Deloitte&ToucheLLP

LOCATIONS

HQ: Federal Reserve Bank of Atlanta
1000 Peachtree St. NE, Atlanta GA 30309-4470
Phone: 404-498-8500 **Fax:** 613-254-6398
Web: www.firstair.ca

HISTORICAL FINANCIALS

Company Type: Private - Member-Owned Banking Authority

Income Statement FYE: December 31

	REVENUE ($ mil.)	NET INCOME ($ mil.)	NET PROFIT MARGIN	EMPLOYEES
12/11	7,222	6,498	90.0%	0
12/10	8,205	7,440	90.7%	0
12/09	6,222	5,374	86.4%	0
12/08	4,344	3,316	76.3%	0
12/07	4,604	3,413	74.1%	0
Annual Growth	11.9%	17.5%	—	—

2011 Year-End Financials

Debt ratio: 54.92%
Return on equity: 211.25%
Cash ($ mil.): 201,229
Current ratio: 428.46
Long-term debt ($ mil.): 116,694
No. of shares (mil.): 30
Dividends
Yield: —
Payout: —
Market value ($ mil.): —

Federal Reserve Bank of Chicago, Dist. No. 7

The Federal Reserve Bank of Chicago regulates banks and bank holding companies in northern Illinois northern Indiana southern Wisconsin the Lower Peninsula of Michigan and all of Iowa. It supervises more than 850 bank holding companies and state member banks distributes money issues savings bonds and Treasury securities and assists the Fed in setting monetary policy. The bank also processes checks and acts as a clearinghouse for payments between banks. Like the 11 other regional banks in the Federal Reserve System the Federal Reserve Bank of Chicago returns its profits (earned largely from investments in government and federal agency securities) to the US Treasury.

Charles Evans is president and CEO of the Federal Reserve Bank of Chicago. He took office September 2007.

EXECUTIVES

Chair, William C. Foote, age 61
First VP and COO and Product Director Customer Relations and Support Office, Gordon Werkema
President and CEO, Charles L. (Charlie) Evans, age 54
SVP and General Counsel, Elizabeth A. Knospe
SVP Supervision and Regulation, James W. (Jim) Nelson, age 52
SVP and Manager Detroit Branch, Robert G. (Bob) Wiley

EVP Supervision and Regulation, Catharine (Cathy) Lemieux
SVP and General Auditor, Margaret K. (Peg) Koenigs
SVP and Associate Director Financial Markets, David A. Marshall, age 61
SVP and Senior Research Advisor, Spencer D. Krane, age 56
EVP and Director Research, Daniel G. Sullivan
EVP Customer Relations and Support Office, Ellen J. Bromagen
SVP Customer Relations Support, Sean Rodriguez
SVP CFO and Director Office of Minority and Women Inclusion, Valerie J. Van Meter
SVP Risk Specialist Division, Carl R. Tannenbaum, age 52
SVP Supervision and Regulation, Steven M. Durfey, age 48
Director, Jeffrey A. (Jeff) Joerres, age 53
Director Detroit, Lou Anna K. Simon
Director Detroit, Brian C. Walker, age 50
Director Detroit, Michael M. Magee Jr., age 56
Director, Frederick H. (Rick) Waddell, age 58
Director, Terry Mazany
Director Detroit, Mark T. Gaffney, age 57
Director, Mark C. Hewitt
Director, Stephen J. (Steve) Goodenow
Director Detroit, Sheilah P. Clay
Auditors: Deloitte&ToucheLLP

LOCATIONS

HQ: Federal Reserve Bank of Chicago
230 S. LaSalle St., Chicago IL 60604-1413
Phone: 312-322-5322 **Fax:** 312-322-5091
Web: www.chicagofed.org

PRODUCTS/OPERATIONS

HISTORICAL FINANCIALS

Company Type: Private - Member-Owned Banking Authority

Income Statement FYE: December 31

	REVENUE ($ mil.)	NET INCOME ($ mil.)	NET PROFIT MARGIN	EMPLOYEES
12/11	5,586	5,026	90.0%	0
12/10	6,541	6,068	92.8%	0
12/09	5,112	4,690	91.7%	0
12/08	3,237	2,792	86.3%	0
12/07	3,752	3,208	85.5%	0
Annual Growth	10.5%	11.9%	—	—

2011 Year-End Financials

Debt ratio: 46.07%
Return on equity: 350.00%
Cash ($ mil.): 20
Current ratio: 196.57
Long-term debt ($ mil.): 76,931

No. of shares (mil.): 14
Dividends
Yield: —
Payout: —
Market value ($ mil.): —

Federal Reserve Bank of New York, Dist. No. 2

The Federal Reserve Bank of New York is the largest in the Federal Reserve System to oversee US bank activities. It issues currency clears money transfers and lends to banks in its district. In addition to the duties it shares with 11 other regional Federal Reserve Banks the New York Fed trades US government securities to regulate the money supply intervenes on foreign exchange markets and stores monetary gold for foreign central banks and governments. The New York Fed's district is relatively small (made up of New York Puerto Rico the US Virgin Islands northern New Jersey and Fairfield County Connecticut) but the bank is the largest in the Federal Reserve System in assets and volume of transactions.

Secured in a vault 80 feet below street level in the New York Fed's Manhattan headquarters is billions of dollars worth of gold –some 25% to 30% of the world's official monetary gold reserves. The vault rests on Manhattan Island's bedrock considered to be one of the few foundations adequate enough to support the weight of the vault and its contents.

The New York Fed has assumed a prominent role during the credit crisis which began in 2007. The bank's assets have more than tripled as it has expanded its lending to depository institutions and has increased its liquidity swaps with foreign central banks. The New York Fed also facilitated JPMorgan Chase's takeover of failed investment bank Bear Stearns and has provided financial support to troubled financial services giants AIG and Citigroup.

In 2009 president and CEO Timothy Geithner left New York Fed to succeed Henry Paulson as the US Treasury secretary. His role as president and CEO was filled by William Dudley.

EXECUTIVES

Chairman, Lee C. Bollinger, age 65
EVP; Head Emerging Markets and International Affairs Group, Terrence J. Checki
EVP and General Counsel, Thomas C. Baxter Jr.
EVP Financial Services Group, Carl W. Turnipseed
First VP and COO, Christine M. Cumming
Assistant VP Corporate Staff, Joseph J. Marraccino
VP and Medical Director Compensation and Benefits Health & Wellness, Gerald L. Stagg
VP Human Resources, Evelyn E. Kender
SVP Technology Engineering and Computing Services, Sean G. Mahon
SVP and Chief of Staff Financial Institution Supervision Group, James R. Hennessy
EVP; Head Financial Institution Supervision Group, Sarah J. Dahlgren
SVP Risk and Policy Financial Institution Supervision, Arthur G. Angulo
SVP Group Operations Financial Institution Supervision, Homer C. Hill III
SVP Talent Management and Administration Technology Services, Elaine D. Mauriello
SVP Regional and Community Outreach, Kausar Hamdani
SVP Financial Market Infrastructure Financial Institution Supervision, JeanMarie Davis
SVP Payments Policy Credit and Payments Risk, Lawrence M. Sweet
SVP Development Studies and Foreign Research Emerging Markets and International Affairs, John J. Clark Jr.
SVP Financial Markets and Institutions Emerging Markets and International Affairs, B. Gerard Dages
SVP International Affairs Emerging Markets and International Affairs, Michele S. Godfrey
EVP; Head Special Investments Management Group, Roseann Stichnoth
SVP Strategic Investment and Risk Assessment Office, Lola S. Judge
VP Business Process Excellence Office, Ann M. Heron
VP International Treasury Services Financial Services, Patricia (Pat) Hilt
SVP and Deputy General Counsel, Joyce M. Hansen
SVP and Deputy General Counsel Enforcement and Litigation, Thomas H. Roche
SVP and Deputy General Counsel Financial Services and Automation, Stephanie A. Heller
VP Banking Applications, Ivan J. Hurwitz
SVP and Chief Investigator Protection Department Legal Group, Nicholas L. Proto
SVP Business Technology, Michael J. Recupero
EVP Credit and Payments Risk Group, Sandra C. (Sandy) Krieger
SVP and Product Manager Wholesale Product Office, Lauren A. Hargraves
SVP Foreign Financial Institutions Financial Institution Supervision, Zahra El-Mekkaway
SVP Group Shared Services, Anne F. Baum
EVP; Co-Head Research and Statistics Group, James J. McAndrews
SVP Statistics Research and Statistics, Ken Lamar
Deputy Chair, Kathryn S. Wylde
EVP Markets Group, Brian P. Sack
EVP and General Auditor, Edward C. Smith
EVP Corporate, Edward F. Murphy
VP Internal Communication, Cheryl A. Gleason
VP Government-wide Accounting Financial Services, Donna J. Crouch
SVP Governance and Strategic Planning Technology Services, Matthew D. Larson
VP Financial Intermediation, Zenyu Wang
SVP Financial Sector Analysis Financial Institution Supervision, Kevin J. Stiroh
SVP Investment Support Office Special Investments Management, Helen E. Mucciolo
SVP Central Bank and International Account Services, Timothy J. Fogarty
SVP Equal Employment Opportunity Office, Betty S. Lau
SVP Market Operations Monitoring and Analysis, Richard P. Dzina
VP Cash and Custody Financial Services, Robert G. Kraus
SVP Cash and Custody Financial Services, David A. Duttenhofer Jr.
VP Electronic Payments Financial Services, Gail R. Armendinger
SVP Deputy General Counsel and Secretary, Michael A. Held
President and CEO, William C. Dudley, age 59
SVP and Chief Compliance and Ethics Officer, Martin C. Grant
VP Real Estate and General Services, Thomas P. Reilly
VP International Research Research and Statistics, Thomas Klitgaard
SVP Information Security Technology Services, Roy D. Thetford Jr.
EVP Technology Services, William T. Christie
SVP Complex Financial Institutions Financial Institution Supervision, Steven J. Manzari
EVP Human Resources, Susan W. Mink
EVP; Head Communications, Krishna Guha
Assistant VP Capital Markets Research and Statistics Group, Michael J. Fleming
VP Office of the Director Research and Statistics, Andrew F. Haughwout
VP Payments Policy Credit and Payments Risk Group, Marsha K. Takagi
EVP; Co-Head Research and Statistics Group, Simon M. Potter
VP Financial Risk Management Credit and Payments Risk, Adam Ashcraft
VP Group Support Function Credit and Payments Risk, Melanie L. Heintz
VP and Chief of Staff, James Bergin
VP and Chief Diversity Officer, Diane T. Ashley

VP Media Relations, Jack Gutt
Assistant VP Digital and Multimedia Communications, Dona Wong
SVP Enterprise Data Management, Betsy Irwin-McCaughey
SVP Financial Management Strategy and Vendor Management and Procurement, Christina S. Kite
SVP Financial Management, Maria Grace Ambrosio
SVP Financial Risk Management Credit and Payments Risk, Joshua Rosenberg
VP Regional and Community Banking Organizations and Consumer Compliance, Patricia T. Meadow
VP Talent Management, Louis J. Scenti Jr.
VP Application Development Technology Services, Michael Kane
SVP Program Management Office Technology Services, Kathryn K. Smith
Director, Jeffrey B. (Jeff) Kindler, age 56
Director, James S. Tisch, age 59
Director, Richard L. Carrion, age 59
Director, James (Jamie) Dimon, age 56
Director, Jeffrey R. (Jeff) Immelt, age 56
Deputy Chair, Kathryn S. Wylde
Director, Charles V. Wait
Auditors: Deloitte&ToucheLLP

LOCATIONS

HQ: Federal Reserve Bank of New York
33 Liberty St., New York NY 10045
Phone: 212-720-5000 **Fax:** 212-720-7459
Web: www.newyorkfed.org

Selected Offices

Buffalo New York
East Rutherford New Jersey
New York City
Utica New York

PRODUCTS/OPERATIONS

2009

	$ mil.	% of total
Interest		
Investments held by consolidated variable interest entities	9,820	30
US government federal agency & government-sponsored-enterprise securities	8,779	26
Loans to depository institutions	644	2
Other loans	4,447	13
Central bank liquidity swaps	568	2
Other	8,797	27
Total	**33,055**	**100**

HISTORICAL FINANCIALS

Company Type: Private - Member-Owned Banking Authority

Income Statement

FYE: December 31

	REVENUE ($ mil.)	NET INCOME ($ mil.)	NET PROFIT MARGIN	EMPLOYEES
12/11	39,655	35,026	88.3%	0
12/10	43,290	39,761	91.8%	0
12/09	30,736	24,827	80.8%	0
12/08	17,284	14,993	86.7%	0
12/07	15,716	14,124	89.9%	0
Annual Growth	26.0%	25.5%	—	—

2011 Year-End Financials

Debt ratio: 23.12%
Return on equity: 201.83%
Cash ($ mil.): 1,258,575
Current ratio: 131.84
Long-term debt ($ mil.): 376,865
No. of shares (mil.): 173
Dividends
Yield: —
Payout: —
Market value ($ mil.): —

Federal Reserve Bank of Richmond, Dist. No. 5

One of 12 regional banks in the Federal Reserve System the Federal Reserve Bank of Richmond oversees the Fifth District's system member banks and bank holding companies in Virginia; Maryland; the Carolinas; Washington DC; and most of West Virginia from branches in Maryland North Carolina and Virginia. It conducts examinations and investigations of member institutions distributes money issues savings bonds and Treasury securities and assists the Federal Reserve System in setting monetary policy. The bank also processes checks and acts as a clearinghouse for payments between banks. Federal Reserve Banks return earnings (mostly from investments in government bonds) to the US Treasury.

The Richmond Fed employs economists scholars and research associates to conduct economic study regarding the Fifth District economy and also to support the Federal Reserve System's policymakers. It was organized in 1914 subsequent to the enactment of the Federal Reserve Act in 1913.

EXECUTIVES

Chair, Lemuel E. Lewis, age 65
Chair, Margaret E. (Lyn) McDermid
Deputy Chair, Linda D. Rabbitt, age 64
First VP and COO, Sally Green
President, Jeffrey M. (Jeff) Lacker, age 57
SVP and General Auditor, Robert E. Wetzel Jr.
SVP Human Resources, Tammy H. Cummings
SVP and General Counsel, Michelle H. Gluck, age 52
SVP Director Research and Chief Advisor to President, John A. Weinberg
SVP and CFO, Claudia N. MacSwain
Media Relations, Laura Fortunato
SVP and CTO, Roland Costa
VP and Regional Executive Richmond, Alan H. Crooker
VP, A. Linwood Gill III
VP, Howard S. Goldfine
VP, Mattison W. Harris
VP, Andreas L. Hornstein
VP, Eugene W. Johnson Jr.
VP, Malissa M. Ladd
VP, Constance B. Frudden
VP Federal Reserve Information Technology Audit, Gregory A. Johnson
Assistant VP and Secretary, Page W. Marchetti
VP Engineering Services Currency Technology Office, Andrew S. McAllister
VP Corporate Communications, Lisa T. Oliva
VP and Controller, Michael L. Wilder
SVP and Regional Executive Baltimore, David E. (Dave) Beck
SVP Supervision Regulation and Credit, Jennifer J. Burns
VP and Deputy Regional Executive Charlotte, Terry J. Wright
VP Charlotte, Lisa A. White
Deputy General Counsel, Patricia A. Lacey Nunley
Medical Director, Victor M. Brugh II
SVP Fifth District Information Technology Law Enforcement Unit and Facilities Management and Food Services, Janice E. Clatterbuck
VP Charlotte, Stacy L. Coleman
Assistant General Counsel, William R. McCorvey Jr.
VP, Edward S. Prescott
Assistant VP and Deputy Regional Executive Baltimore, Karen L. Brooks
Assistant VP Operations Law Enforcement Unit, James T. Nowlin
Assistant VP Corporate Plannings, James K. (Jim) Hayes
VP Operations and Staff Development Supervision Regulation and Credit Department, Mary S. (Meg) Johnson
SVP and Regional Executive Charlotte, Matthew A. Martin
Assistant General Counsel, Dennis P. Smith
Media Relations, Jim Strader
VP, Dennis G. McDonald
VP, Ann B. Macheras
VP, Bruce E. Grinnell
Director, Kelly S. King, age 63
Deputy Chair, Margaret E. (Lyn) McDermid
Deputy Chair, Linda D. Rabbitt, age 64
Director, Robert H. Gilliam Jr., age 66
Director, Richard J. (Rick) Morgan, age 64
Director, Patrick C. Graney III, age 58
Director, Wilbur E. Johnson
Auditors: Deloitte&ToucheLLP

LOCATIONS

HQ: Federal Reserve Bank of Richmond, Dist. No. 5
701 East Byrd Street, Richmond, VA 23219
Phone: 804 697-8000
Web: www.richmondfed.org

PRODUCTS/OPERATIONS

HISTORICAL FINANCIALS

Company Type: Private - Member-Owned Banking Authority

Income Statement

FYE: December 31

	REVENUE ($ mil.)	NET INCOME ($ mil.)	NET PROFIT MARGIN	EMPLOYEES
12/11	10,043	9,222	91.8%	0
12/10	7,178	6,241	86.9%	0
12/09	2,990	2,120	70.9%	0
12/08	4,816	4,220	87.6%	0
12/07	4,194	3,626	86.5%	2,650
Annual Growth	24.4%	26.3%	—	—

2011 Year-End Financials

Debt ratio: 24.42%
Return on equity: 82.87%
Cash ($ mil.): 312,562
Current ratio: 258.13
Long-term debt ($ mil.): 83,711
No. of shares (mil.): 111
Dividends
Yield: —
Payout: —
Market value ($ mil.): —

Federal Reserve Bank of San Francisco, Dist. No. 12

One of 12 regional banks in the Federal Reserve System the Federal Reserve Bank of San Francisco through four branch offices oversees more than 580 banks and thrifts in nine western states and American Samoa Guam and the Northern Mariana Islands - the largest of the 12 districts. It conducts examinations and investigations of member institutions distributes money issues savings bonds and Treasury securities and assists the Federal Reserve in setting monetary policy. The bank also processes checks and acts as a clearinghouse for payments between banks. Federal Reserve Banks are not-for-profit and return earnings (mostly from investments in government bonds) to the US Treasury.

EXECUTIVES

Chairman, T. Gary Rogers, age 69
Chairman, Douglas W. (Doug) Shorenstein
Deputy Chairman, Patricia E. (Pat) Yarrington, age 56
First VP and COO, John F. Moore
EVP and Branch Manager Los Angeles, Mark L. Mullinix
SVP District Business Continuity Human Resources Legal Equal Employment Opportunity Statistics Strategy and Communications, Susan A. Sutherland
VP, Scott C. Turner
EVP Banking Supervision and Regulation, Stephen M. (Steve) Hoffman Jr.
Media Relations Manager, Carol A. Eckert
Media Relations Specialist, Lily Ruiz
Group VP, Richard B. Hornsby
SVP and CIO Seattle Branch, Mark A. Gould
Group VP and General Auditor, Lee C. Dwyer
Group VP, Darren S. Post
VP and Equal Employment Officer, Beverley-Ann Hawkins
Group VP, Joy K. Hoffmann
VP, Ann Marie Kohlligian
VP, David G. Tresmontan
VP, Simon H. Kwan
VP, Mark M. Spiegel
SVP and Associate Director Research Economic Research, Glenn D. Rudebusch
VP, Randy Balducci
President and CEO, John C. Williams
Group VP, Teresa M. Curran
VP, Tracy A. Basinger
Group VP, Fred T. Furlong
VP, Barbara A. Bennett
Group VP, Reuven Glick
VP, Kenneth R. Binning
Group VP and CFO, Donald R. Lieb
Group VP and General Counsel, Sharon A. Ruth
Group VP, Clifford N. Croxall
Group VP Information and Technology Services, Deborah S. Smyth
Group VP and Deputy, David W. Walker
VP, Mary C. Daly
SVP Los Angeles Branch, Roger W. Replogle
VP, Warren C. Howard
VP Community Perspectives; Branch Manager Salt Lake City, Robin A. Rockwood
VP Regional Adjustment Site and Customer Support; Branch Manager Portland, Steven H. Walker
VP, Robert E. Kellar
Group VP, David M. Wright
VP, John G. Fernald
SVP and CIO, Gopa Kumar
VP and Secretary, Peggy L. Speck
Associate General Counsel and Principal Legal Executive Committee and Secretary, Gerald C. Tsai
VP, Stanley M. Crisp
VP, William O. Riley
VP, Kevin E. Zerbe
Director, Blake W. Nordstrom, age 51
Chairman Seattle Branch, William S. (Bill) Ayer, age 57
Director, Russell D. Goldsmith, age 62
Director, Kenneth P. (Ken) Wilcox, age 64
Deputy Chairman, Douglas W. (Doug) Shorenstein
Deputy Chairman, Patricia E. (Pat) Yarrington, age 56
Director, William D. Jones, age 56
Chairman Salt Lake City Branch, Scott L. Hymas
Chairman Los Angeles Branch, Grace Evans Cherashore
Director, Karla S. Chambers
Chairman Portland Branch, James H. Rudd
Director, Arnold T. Grisham, age 65
Director, Dann H. Bowman
Auditors: Deloitte&ToucheLLP

LOCATIONS

HQ: Federal Reserve Bank of San Francisco
101 Market St., San Francisco CA 94105
Phone: 415-974-2000 **Fax:** 415-974-3341
Web: www.frbsf.org

PRODUCTS/OPERATIONS

HISTORICAL FINANCIALS

Company Type: Private - Member-Owned Banking Authority

Income Statement FYE: December 31

	REVENUE ($ mil.)	NET INCOME ($ mil.)	NET PROFIT MARGIN	EMPLOYEES
12/11	8,863	8,071	91.1%	0
12/10	8,622	7,890	91.5%	0
12/09	5,842	5,219	89.3%	0
12/08	4,397	3,856	87.7%	0
12/07	4,862	4,251	87.4%	0
Annual Growth	16.2%	17.4%	—	—

2011 Year-End Financials

Debt ratio: 37.54%
Return on equity: 98.21%
Cash ($ mil.): 269,116
Current ratio: 252.36
Long-term debt ($ mil.): 110,003
No. of shares (mil.): 82
Dividends
Yield: —
Payout: —
Market value ($ mil.): —

Federal Reserve System

LOCATIONS

HQ: Federal Reserve System
20th Street and Constitution Avenue N.W.,
Washington, DC 20551
Phone: 202 452-3245 **Fax:** 202 728-5886
Web: www.federalreserve.gov

HISTORICAL FINANCIALS

Company Type:

Income Statement FYE: December 31

	REVENUE ($ mil.)	NET INCOME ($ mil.)	NET PROFIT MARGIN	EMPLOYEES
12/11	88,027	78,538	89.2%	0
12/10	89,816	81,689	91.0%	0
12/09	62,565	52,416	83.8%	0
Annual Growth	18.6%	22.4%	—	—

2011 Year-End Financials

Debt ratio: 35.43%—
Return on equity: 145.99%
Cash ($ mil.): 2,706,636
Current ratio: 160.67
Long-term debt ($ mil.): 1,034,052
Dividends
Yield: —
Payout: —
Market value ($ mil.): —

Federal-Mogul Corp.

For Federal-Mogul the sum of the parts is greater than the whole. The company makes components used in cars trucks and commercial vehicles as well as in energy industrial and other transportation equipment. Its products include pistons spark plugs ignition coils bearings gaskets seals and brake pads sold under brand names such as Champion Federal-Mogul Fel-Pro Glyco and Moog. Federal-Mogul has manufacturing and distribution facilities in 34 countries worldwide; customers include global automakers BMW Ford General Motors and Volkswagen. Federal-Mogul also distributes its own and other company's auto parts to aftermarket customers. About 60% of sales come from outside the US.

Geographic Reach

Federal-Mogul operates almost 175 worldwide manufacturing facilities technical and distribution centers as well as sales and administration offices. The US represents its largest market generating 37% of its total revenue; Germany is next in line representing almost 20% of sales.

Operations

In September 2012 Federal-Mogul restructured its operations into two segments in order to focus on two distinct customer sets. Its new powertrain segment makes and sells original equipment products for automotive heavy duty and industrial applications. The vehicle components segment distributes products in the global vehicle aftermarket and also serves original equipment (OE/OES) manufacturers with vehicle products like brakes chassis wipers and other vehicle components.

Financial Analysis

The company has worked to rebuild its health after a rough decade. Its total sales increased by 11% from 2010 to 2011. Sales for its powertrain energy segment increased by 24% as a result of stronger market share gains in all regions and the 2010 acquisition of piston ring supplier Daros Group. Other segments that increased its sales in 2011 included powertrain sealing and bearings (16%) and vehicle safety and protection (8%).

After earning a profit of $167 million in 2010 Federal-Mogul suffered a net loss of $83 million in 2011 as a result of a weakened US dollar and an increase in manufacturing labor and variable overhead costs associated with the higher production volume.

Strategy

Federal-Mogul is taking steps to maintain its flexibility and reduce its dependence on cars trucks and commercial vehicles by applying its core products in other areas. For example it has expanded into the aerospace (brake products for airplanes) railroad (piston rings for locomotives) and offshore and marine markets (large bore rings and seals). Its push into power generation (large bearings for windmills) included its mid-2010 acquisition of piston ring supplier Daros Group which expanded Federal-Mogul's presence in commercial engines and wind energy.

Federal-Mogul has a number of joint ventures and alliances allowing it to expand its geographic reach into emerging markets including the BRIC (Brazil Russia India China) countries as well as South Korea and Turkey. Federal-Mogul maintains a controlling interest in just over half of its almost 30 joint ventures in 13 countries. These partnerships also allow the company to lower manufacturing costs broaden its customer base and develop and extend its product lines. Federal-Mogul works closely with customers to develop products specific to their needs utilizing its research and development centers in major global auto manufacturing locations including the US Germany UK France China and Japan.

Mergers and Acquisitions

In 2012 Federal-Mogul purchased the spark plug business belonging to BorgWarner. The deal improved the company's European market share by adding new spark plug manufacturing sites located in France and Germany.

Ownership

Billionaire investor and chairman Carl Icahn owns a little more than 77% of Federal-Mogul.

HISTORY

In 1899 J. Howard Muzzy and Edward Lyon formed the Muzzy-Lyon Company and later subsidiary Mogul Metal Company. The two modified a printer's typecasting machine and developed a process for making die-cast engine bearings. Their first big order came in 1910 when Buick ordered 10000 connecting rod bearings for the Buick 10. In 1924 Mogul Metal merged with Federal Bearing and Bushing to become Federal-Mogul Corporation.

In 1941 Federal-Mogul had about 50 factories dedicated to the war effort and by 1945 sales had doubled from prewar levels. In 1955 the company acquired Bower Roller Bearing Company and changed its name to Federal-Mogul-Bower Bearings Inc. By the late 1950s it had nearly 100 distribution centers and sales had quadrupled in 10 years.

The company began investing in foreign manufacturing plants during the 1960s to safeguard against lower US car exports as more foreign cars entered the global market. It changed its name back to Federal-Mogul in 1965 and moved its headquarters from Detroit to Southfield Michigan the following year. After a recession in the mid-1970s Federal-Mogul realized that it was too dependent on the big automakers and began diversifying. It acquired the Mather Company a maker of high-performance sealing products in 1985. The next year it bought Carter Automotive (fuel pumps) and Signal-Stat (lighting and safety components).

In 1989 Dennis Gormley became CEO. He continued the diversification strategy and led the company into the automotive aftermarket. Gormley proposed a push into retail in 1992 and that year Federal-Mogul bought the aftermarket business of TRW Inc. In its effort to become the Pep Boys of the third world the company sold parts of its manufacturing business to finance its retail ventures. By 1996 it owned about 130 retail stores primarily in Latin America. The company lost money and that year Gormley resigned. His successor Dick Snell put an immediate end to the retail fiasco.

By 1998 Federal-Mogul had sold all of its retail holdings and was concentrating on providing parts for entire engine systems. That year it made two major acquisitions: Fel-Pro a domestic maker of gaskets and other sealing products for $720 million and T&N plc a British maker of bearings pistons and brake pads and Europe's largest asbestos maker during the 1980s. T&N was picked up on the cheap as its stock was depressed by looming asbestos lawsuits. The decision would prove a grave one for Federal-Mogul.

Driving further into the aftermarket Federal-Mogul paid $1.9 billion for the automotive business of Cooper Industries (Champion spark plugs windshield wipers steering and suspension parts brake parts). UK-based LucasVarity rejected Federal-Mogul's $6.4 billion buyout offer in 1999 in favor of a $7 billion offer from TRW.

In 2000 Federal-Mogul announced plans to close 22 North American replacement parts warehouses and consolidate 18 manufacturing plants in Europe and Asia. Despite the proposed cutbacks aimed at revitalizing the company CEO Richard Snell stepped down that year. Federal-Mogul director Robert Miller replaced Snell as chairman and became the interim CEO.

Early in 2001 Frank Macher a former Ford and ITT Automotive executive was named CEO. Not long after in the midst of the economic slowdown Federal-Mogul announced that it would cut its salaried workforce by almost 9%. In August the company acquired 85% of WSK Gorzyce a Polish piston maker.

After an ill-advised acquisitions bender which more than tripled the size of the company Federal-Mogul was forced into bankruptcy in 2001. The company entered Chapter 11 bankruptcy protection as a result of asbestos claims related to its acquisition of T&N plc. Following six years in bankruptcy in 2007 Federal-Mogul became the first of the leading suppliers of auto parts to emerge from Chapter 11. Competitors Dana (exited 2008) and Delphi (exited 2009) followed suit.

Federal-Mogul sold its Signal-Stat lighting business to Truck-Lite (a subsidiary of Penske) for $23 million in 2002. Early the next year the company sold its original equipment molded lighting assembly operations to Magna International for $19 million.

The company sold its large bearing operations in South Africa and Germany as well as its Dayton Ohio transmission operations in 2004. In 2005 the company named Jose Maria Alapont as CEO. Carl Icahn was appointed chairman in 2008 after acquiring an additional 50% stake in Federal-Mogul.

By the time 2008 rolled around the global financial markets were beginning to show signs of stress as the economic crisis was first rearing its ugly head. Between 2008 and 2010 the company implemented restructuring activities including a workforce reduction of more than 9% and a number of facility closures.

EXECUTIVES

VP Customer Relations Global Aftermarket, Bob Egan

President CEO and Director, Jose Maria Alapont, age 61, $1,500,000 total compensation

Chairman, Carl C. Icahn, age 76

VP and Treasurer, David A. (Dave) Bozynski, age 57

SVP Customer Satisfaction Global Engineering and Manufacturing, Rene L.F. Dalleur, age 58, $483,727 total compensation

SVP Vehicle Safety and Protection, Ramzi Y. Hermiz, age 46

VP Corporate Communications and Government Relations, Steven K. Gaut, age 50

CEO and Director, Rainer Jueckstock, age 52

SVP Powertrain Bearings and Sealings, Gerard Chochoy, age 58, $452,010 total compensation

SVP and CFO, Alan Haughie, age 48, $250,000 total compensation

SVP Business and Operations Strategy, Jean Brunol, age 59, $556,320 total compensation

SVP Sales and Marketing, William (Steve) Bowers, age 59, $400,000 total compensation

SVP Customer Satisfaction and Global Manufacturing, Eric McAlexander, age 55

SVP Global Aftermarket, James (Jay) Burkhart, age 54

SVP Global Human Resources and Organization, Pascal Goachet, age 61

SVP Global Purchasing, Markus Wermers, age 47

VP Investor Relations, David Pouliot

VP and CIO, Alston German, age 47

SVP General Counsel Chief Compliance Officer and Secretary, Brett Pynnonen, age 43

Investor Relations Representative, Kathy Fauls

Retail Shareholder Communications, Karen Shulhan

Manager Marketing Operations Aftermarket Europe, Laurence Aernouts

Director Corporate Communications, Jim Burke

Manager Europe Middle East and Africa Communications, Ursula Hellstern

VP Controller and Chief Accounting Officer, Jerome Rouquet, age 45

VP Global Aftermarket North America, Paul Johnson

CTO Powertrain Segment, Gian Maria Olivetti

President CEO and Director, Jose Maria Alapont, age 61

Director, George Feldenkreis, age 76

Director, James H. (Jim) Vandenberghe, age 62

Director, James M. (Mike) Laisure, age 60

Director, Vincent J. Intrieri, age 55

Director, Neil S. Subin, age 47

CEO and Director, Rainer Jueckstock, age 52

Director, Daniel A. (Dan) Ninivaggi, age 47

Director, David S. Schechter, age 36

Director, Samuel J. Merksamer, age 31

Auditors: Ernst&YoungLLP

LOCATIONS

HQ: Federal-Mogul Corporation
26555 Northwestern Hwy., Southfield MI 48033
Phone: 248-354-7700 **Fax:** 248-354-8950
Web: www.federalmogul.com

2011 Sales

US	2,529	37
France	520	7
Belgium/Switzerland	299	4
UK	284	4
India	251	4
Total	**6,910**	**100**

PRODUCTS/OPERATIONS

2011 Sales

Global aftermarket	2,325	34
Powertrain sealing & bearings	1,266	18
Total	**6,910**	**100**

Selected Products

Global Aftermarket
- Bearings and seals
- Camshafts
- Chassis
- Driveline
- Engine bearings
- Filters
- Friction products (brake drums linings pads and rotors)
- Fuel pumps
- Gaskets
- Ignition products
- Lighting products
- Oil pumps
- Performance additives
- Piston rings
- Pistons
- Spark plugs
- Steering and suspension products
- Timing components
- Valvetrain components
- Wipers

Powertrain Energy
- Camshafts
- Connecting rods
- Cylinder liners
- Engine pistons
- Ignition products
- Piston pins
- Piston rings
- Valve seats and guides

Powertrain Sealing and Bearings
- Aluminum engine bearings
- Bonded piston seals
- Bronze engine bearings
- Bushings and washers
- Combustion and exhaust gaskets
- Dynamic seals
- Engine and industrial bearings
- Heat shields
- Metallic filters
- Sintered engine and transmission components
- Static gaskets and seals
- Transmission components

Vehicle Safety and Protection
- Brake disc pads
- Brake linings and blocks
- Brake shoes
- Chassis parts (ball joints tie rod ends sway bar links idler arms and pitman arms)
- Dic pads (light vehicle and railway)
- Element resistant sleeving systems (protection products for wires hoses sensors and mechanical components)
- Flexible heat shields
- Fuel pumps
- Lighting (interior and exterior lighting components)
- Railway brake blocks
- Windshield wipers

Selected Brand Names

Abex (brake products)
AE (bearings piston rings pistons timing belts and kits and valves)
ANCO (wiper blades washer pumps and wiper arms)
Atlas (gaskets for diesel engines and heavy-duty equipment in Mexico)
Beral (brake linings and disc brake pads for commercial vehicles and trailers)
Carter (fuel pumps)
Champion (spark plugs filters and wiper blades)
DURON (brake products for commercial vehicles in Europe)
Fel-Pro (sealing products)
Ferodo (brake discs brake fluids brake pads and shoes motorcycle products and racing products)
FP Diesel (engine parts and gaskets for vehicles used in agricultural construction gas compression industrial marine mining and trucking sectors)
Glyco (bearings)
Goetze (piston rings and cylinder liners)
Moog (steering and suspension parts)
National (wheel end products)
Necto (brake products for vehicles in Spain)
Nural (pistons)
Payen (gaskets cylinder head bolts and oil seals)
PowerMAX (spark plug wires)
Precision (universal joints)
Raimsa (clutch-release bearings hanger bearings and kingpins for vehicles in Mexico)
Sealed Power (camshafts engine bearings oil pumps pistons piston rings timing components and valvetrain products)
Speed-Pro (high-performance engine components)
Wagner Brake Products (brake products for passenger cars and medium-duty commercial vehicles)
Wagner Lighting

COMPETITORS

Affinia Group
Aisin Seiki
Akebono Brake
American Trim
Bendix Commercial Vehicle Systems
BERU
Continental AG
Cooper-Standard Automotive
Daido Steel
Dana Holding
Delphi Automotive Systems
DENSO
Edelbrock
ElringKlinger
EnPro
Freudenberg-NOK
GE
GKN
Hastings Manufacturing
Hella
Hitachi Automotive Systems Americas
Honeywell International
Kolbenschmidt Pierburg
Linamar Corp.
Mahle International
MAN
Meritor
Miba
NGK SPARK PLUG
Nippon Piston Ring
OSRAM
Remy International
Riken Corporation
Robert Bosch
SPX
Stanadyne
Standard Motor Products
Stant Manufacturing
Sumitomo Metal Industries
Timken
Trico Products
TRW Automotive
UCI International
Universal Manufacturing
Valeo
Visteon

HISTORICAL FINANCIALS

Company Type: Public

Income Statement FYE: December 31

	REVENUE ($ mil.)	NET INCOME ($ mil.)	NET PROFIT MARGIN	EMPLOYEES
12/11	6,910	(90)	—	45,000
12/10	6,219	161	2.6%	42,700
12/09	5,330	(45)	—	39,000
12/08	6,865	(467)	—	43,000
12/07	6,913	1,412	20.4%	50,000
Annual Growth	(0.0%)	—	—	(2.6%)

2011 Year-End Financials

Debt ratio: 40.25%
Return on equity: (-9.44)%
Cash ($ mil.): 953
Current ratio: 230.70
Long-term debt ($ mil.): 2,741
No. of shares (mil.): 98
Dividends
Yield: —
Payout: —
Market value ($ mil.): 1,459

	STOCK PRICE ($) FY Close	P/E High/Low		PER SHARE ($) Earnings	Dividends	Book Value
12/11	14.75	—	—	(0.91)	0.00	9.64
12/10	20.65	13	7	1.62	0.00	12.91
12/09	17.30	—	—	(0.46)	0.00	10.34
12/08	4.23	—	—	(4.69)	0.00	9.56
12/07	29.50	2	2	15.46	0.00	21.13
Annual Growth	(15.9%)	—	—	—	—	(17.8%)

FedEx Corp

Holding company FedEx hopes its package of subsidiaries will keep delivering significant market share. Its FedEx Express unit is the world's #1 express transportation provider delivering about 3.5 million packages daily to more than 220 countries and territories from about 2000 FedEx Office shops. It maintains a fleet of about 690 aircraft and more than 50000 motor vehicles and trailers. To complement the express delivery business FedEx Ground provides small-package ground delivery in North America and less-than-truckload (LTL) carrier FedEx Freight hauls larger shipments. FedEx Office stores offer a variety of document-related and other business services and serve as retail hubs for other FedEx units.

HISTORY

From his undergraduate classes at Yale and his experience as a charter airplane pilot Fred Smith got the idea that increased automation of business processes would create the need for a reliable overnight delivery service and he presented his case in a term paper in 1965. After serving in the Marine Corps in Vietnam Smith began raising money to develop the overnight delivery idea. He founded Federal Express in 1971 with $4 million inherited from his father and $80 million from investors. Overnight and second-day delivery to two dozen US cities began in 1973.

Several factors contributed to FedEx's early success: Airlines turned their focus from parcels to passengers; United Parcel Service (UPS) union workers went on strike in 1974; and competitor REA Express went bankrupt. FedEx went public in 1978.

Spotting e-mail's threat to express delivery in the early 1980s FedEx invested heavily in satellite-based system ZapMail. However the humble fax machine blindsided FedEx and it lost over $300 million in 1986 on the short-lived service. The 1987 launch of PowerShip which processed shipments electronically was more successful.

FedEx expanded internationally in the late 1980s buying Italy's SAMIMA and three Japanese freight carriers in 1988 and Tiger International (Flying Tigers line) in 1989. That year it doubled overseas sales to become the #1 air cargo company.

In 1991 FedEx introduced EXPRESSfreighter an international air-express cargo service but suffered a setback when its loss-making European delivery service was scrapped the next year. However FedEx was back on its feet in 1995 when it created Latin American and Caribbean divisions and became the first US express carrier with direct flights to China.

FedEx jumped back into the Web in 1996 and introduced Internet-based shipping management system interNetShip. It also began selling BusinessLink a software package that helps businesses use the Internet to sell goods which are delivered by FedEx.

The 1997 UPS strike put an extra 850000 packages a day into FedEx's hands. Turning the screws on UPS FedEx bought ground carrier Caliber System in 1998 and reorganized into holding company FDX. FedEx pilots (unionized in 1993) threatened their own strike during the 1998 holiday season prompting FedEx to outsource more of its flight operations. Nevertheless the pilots ratified a five-year contract in 1999.

Focusing on the supply chain in 1999 FedEx restructured Caliber's logistics unit and formed a business-to-business logistics alliance with KPMG. The company also bought freight forwarder GeoLogistics Air Services (renamed Caribbean Transportation Services). Internationally FedEx opened its first European hub in Paris and launched a joint venture in China.

In 2000 FDX changed its name to FedEx. As part of a major rebranding effort RPS became FedEx Ground and Roberts Express became FedEx Custom Critical. Also that year the company formed FedEx Trade Networks to offer customs brokerage and trade consulting services. The new unit took in logistics provider Tower Group International which FedEx acquired from McGraw-Hill.

In a landmark deal with the United States Postal Service FedEx Express began transporting mail shipments (but not making deliveries) in 2001 and FedEx drop boxes were placed in post offices. (In 2004 FedEx won a contract to deliver international express shipments for the Postal Service.) Also that year FedEx phased out its FedEx Logistics subsidiary shifting its operations into other subsidiaries.

The company acquired less-than-truckload (LTL) carrier American Freightways in 2001 and FedEx Freight was created to operate American Freightways and Viking Freight which the company had acquired in the Caliber deal. (By 2002 both carriers were using the FedEx Freight brand name.)

FedEx which already operated service counters in more than 130 Kinko's locations gained more than 1000 additional outlets in 2004 by buying the document services and copying company. The $2.4 billion cash deal followed UPS's 2001 acquisition of Mail Boxes Etc. and its retail locations most of which have been rebranded as The UPS Store. Following suit FedEx adopted a new brand for Kinko's stores: FedEx Kinko's Office and Print Center.

The holding company expanded its ground delivery business in 2004 by acquiring Parcel Direct a unit of Quad/Graphics for about $120 million. Parcel Direct was rebranded as FedEx SmartPost.

In 2006 FedEx bought UK-based express transportation company ANC Holdings for about $240 million gaining a fleet of 2200 vehicles and a network of 80 offices. (ANC was rebranded as FedEx UK.)

To boost FedEx Freight's long-haul capabilities FedEx in 2006 paid about $790 million for LTL carrier Watkins Motor Lines and the assets of Watkins' Canadian unit Watkins Canada Express. They were renamed FedEx National LTL and FedEx Freight Canada respectively.

In 2007 FedEx Express spent about $430 million to buy out DTW Group (its joint venture partner in China) and acquire DTW Group's domestic delivery network. It also acquired PAFEX which had provided express delivery service in India under contract with FedEx since 2002 for about $30 million.

Like the rest of the industry FedEx experienced high fuel costs at the beginning of 2008 which transitioned to lower consumer demand for its express services during the end of the year. Coping with the crisis at the end of 2008 FedEx implemented a hiring freeze suspended 401K contributions and decreased pay for salaried personnel by 5%. The company shed some 10000 workers by 2009 –still only about 3% of its total workforce.

FedEx's 2010 results showed another annual revenue loss yet it experienced an increase in net income of more than 90%. This was due in part to a reduction of impairment charges from the prior year when the company bore charges of more than $1 billion for aircraft-related asset impairments and goodwill-related to acquisitions. Basically all FedEx segments lost sales except for the company's Ground segment which posted positive results of about 25% due to customers opting for lower-priced ground transportation services.

FedEx in 2010 opened several offices in Europe and the Middle East in an effort to capitalize on consumer preferences for a regional business presence.

EXECUTIVES

EVP Market Development and Corporate Communications; President and CEO FedEx Services, T. Michael Glenn, age 56, $776,372 total compensation
EVP and CFO, Alan B. Graf Jr., age 56, $842,132 total compensation
Chairman President and CEO, Frederick W. (Fred) Smith, age 68, $1,190,029 total compensation
President and CEO FedEx Express, David J. Bronczek, age 58, $879,368 total compensation
VP Human Resources, Judith H. Edge
EVP Information Services and CIO, Robert B. (Rob) Carter, age 52, $709,676 total compensation
President and CEO FedEx Ground, David F. (Dave) Rebholz, age 59, $869,090 total compensation
COO FedEx Express and President International, Michael L. Ducker, age 59
SVP; President Europe Middle East and Africa, Gerald P. (Jerry) Leary, age 59
EVP Global Sales and Solutions FedEx Services, Donald F. (Don) Colleran
President and CEO FedEx Custom Critical, Virginia C. Albanese
SVP; President Latin America, Juan N. Cento, age 60
Corporate VP and Principal Accounting Officer, John L. Merino
SVP International Marketing FedEx Services, Rajesh Subramaniam
EVP IT FedEx Services, Sherry A. Aaholm
EVP General Counsel and Secretary, Christine P. Richards, age 57, $617,640 total compensation
VP US Marketing, Karen Rogers
Director Advertising, Steve Pacheco
President and CEO FedEx Office and Print Services, Brian D. Philips, age 44
SVP European Operations, David Binks
SVP; President Asia Pacific, David L. Cunningham
President and CEO FedEx Trade Networks, Fred Schardt
SVP Corporate Marketing FedEx Services, Laurie A. Tucker, age 55
President and CEO FedEx Freight, William J. Logue, age 54
Media Contact, Jess Bunn
VP Investor Relations, Mickey Foster
SVP Global Communications and Investor Relations, William G. Margaritis
VP and Chief Economist FedEx Services, Gene Huang
President and COO FedEx TechConnect, Cary C. Pappas
President and CEO FedEx SupplyChain, Craig M. Simon
SVP; President Canada, Lisa Lisson
SVP Products and Digital Access Marketing FedEx Services, Mark J. Colombo
Director, Paul S. Walsh, age 57
Director, Gary W. Loveman, age 51
Director, John A. Edwardson, age 63
Director, Steven R. Loranger, age 60
Director, David P. Steiner, age 52
Director, Shirley Ann Jackson, age 64
Director, Prof Susan C. Schwab, age 57
Director, James L. Barksdale, age 69
Director, Joshua I. Smith, age 71
Auditors: Ernst&YoungLLP

LOCATIONS

HQ: FedEx Corporation
942 S. Shady Grove Rd., Memphis TN 38120
Phone: 901-818-7500 **Fax:** 301-998-3700
Web: www.federalrealty.com

2012 Sales

	$ in mil.	% of total
US	29,837	70
Other countries	12,843	30
Total	**42,680**	**100**

PRODUCTS/OPERATIONS

2012 Sales

FedEx Express	26,515	62
FedEx Freight	5,282	12
Adjustments	(361)	-

COMPETITORS

Allegra Network	Pitney Bowes
AlphaGraphics	PostNL
Arkansas Best	Ricoh USA
Canada Post	Ryder System
Con-way Inc.	TNT Express
DHL	UPS
Japan Post	US Postal Service
Mail Boxes Etc.	Xerox
Nippon Express	YRC Worldwide
Office Depot	

HISTORICAL FINANCIALS

Company Type: Public

Income Statement FYE: May 31

	REVENUE ($ mil.)	NET INCOME ($ mil.)	NET PROFIT MARGIN	EMPLOYEES
05/12	42,680	2,032	4.8%	149,000
05/11	39,304	1,452	3.7%	143,000
05/10	34,734	1,184	3.4%	141,000
05/09	35,497	98	0.3%	140,000
05/08	37,953	1,125	3.0%	273,700
Annual Growth	3.0%	15.9%	—	(14.1%)

2012 Year-End Financials

Debt ratio: 5.58%
Return on equity: 13.80%
Cash ($ mil.): 2,843
Current ratio: 168.52
Long-term debt ($ mil.): 1,250
No. of shares (mil.): 317
Dividends
Yield: 0.58%
Payout: 8.11%
Market value ($ mil.): 28,257

	STOCK PRICE ($) FY Close	P/E High/Low	PER SHARE ($) Earnings	Dividends	Book Value
05/12	89.14	15 10	6.41	0.52	46.46
05/11	93.64	21 15	4.57	0.48	48.01
05/10	83.49	25 13	3.76	0.00	43.98
05/09	55.43	302111	0.31	0.00	43.67
05/08	91.71	32 23	3.60	0.00	46.71
Annual Growth	(0.7%)	— —	15.5%	—	(0.1%)

Fidelity National Financial Inc

To make sure that buying a dream home doesn't become a nightmare Fidelity National Financial provides title insurance escrow home warranties and other services related to real estate transactions. It is now the biggest dog in the residential and commercial title insurance sectors (the next largest player is First American) and accounts for 35% of all title insurance policies in the US. The company operates through its four underwriters: Fidelity National Title Company Chicago Title Commonwealth Land Title and Alamo Title. It sells its products both directly and through independent agents. Fidelity National has also grown its holdings in casual restaurant chains.

Geographic Reach

Fidelity National Financial operates exclusively within the US. Naturally the biggest markets are in states with the greatest populations. California Texas and New York account for more than a third of its title insurance premiums.

Operations

Title insurance is typically one of the most stable types of insurance written. It is folded into the piles of paperwork homebuyers sign during closings with little or no fuss. Even though US home sales remain sluggish the company has stayed busy from the brisk pace of refinancing of existing mortgages.

Title insurance premiums account for more than two-thirds of Fidelity National Financial's revenues but the company also maintains a small handful of other operations completely outside of the title insurance industry. These include a 50.2% stake in auto parts manufacturer Remy International and a minority interest in Ceridian a payroll and HR services firm. It has also committed to expanding its holdings in casual dining restaurants though its 55% ownership of American Blue Ribbon Holdings.

Sales and Marketing

Fidelity National Financial maintains some 1100 retail offices to provide residential title insurance. It markets its commercial title insurance in major urban real estate markets.

Financial Analysis

While the company is basically sound Fidelity National Financial's revenues are hampered by stiffness in the residential mortgage lending market. Its revenues fell 8% to $4.8 million in 2011. The decrease mostly reflects the fact that the company has been shrinking through divestitures. Its net income has stabilized around $370 million in 2011 and 2010 following the roller coaster years of the recession.

Strategy

Fidelity National Financial is now so dominant within the title insurance industry that any attempt to grow larger there would draw the scrutiny of regulators. Instead the company is diversifying by buying up restaurant chains and transferring them to American Blue Ribbon Holdings. By mid-2012 Fidelity National Financial boasted a new restaurant segment on its financial results.

To raise a bit of cash for diversification the company sold its profitable flood insurance business to WRM America Holdings for $210 million in late 2011. It then sold all but 15% of Fidelity National Property Casualty Insurance its personal lines business to WT Holdings for some $119 million in 2012.

Mergers and Acquisitions

In late 2012 Fidelity National Financial acquired the Nashville-based J. Alexander's chain of 33 restaurants and merged it under American Blue Ribbon Holdings which also owns Ohio-based Max & Erma's and Tennessee-based O'Charley's.

Company Background

Like all title insurers Fidelity National Financial shivered when the big chill hit the real estate market in 2008. But while the company slowed it remained quick enough to take advantage of opportunities. When its ailing rival LandAmerica Financial Group filed Chapter 11 in 2008 the company bought up the choicer bits for $235 million. This purchase helped make it into the largest title insurer in the US and caught the attention of the FTC prompting the company to divest a few holdings to soothe the agency's nerves. The 2009 sale of Fidelity National Capital only brought in $50 million but took $214 million of debt off company ledgers. The 2010 sale of its 32% stake in Sedgwick Claims Management brought in some $225 million.

The current company arose in 2006 when a previous company also named Fidelity National Financial split apart its title insurance operations from its information services business. What had been Fidelity National Title Group took on its former parent's name while Fidelity National Information Services took on the former parent's remaining operations. The two companies share a history and some stray holdings but are otherwise separate.

EXECUTIVES

EVP, Alan L. (Al) Stinson, age 66, $642,000 total compensation
EVP and Chief Legal Officer, Peter T. Sadowski, age 57, $431,671 total compensation
President; CEO Fidelity National Title Group, Raymond R. (Randy) Quirk, age 65, $721,500 total compensation
Vice Chairman, Frank P. Willey, age 58
Chairman, William P. (Bill) Foley II, age 67, $585,000 total compensation
CEO, George P. Scanlon, age 53
EVP General Counsel and Corporate Secretary; EVP Chief Legal Officer and Corporate Secretary Fidelity National Information Services, Michael L. Gravelle, age 50
EVP Corporate Finance, Brent B. Bickett, age 47, $164,287 total compensation
EVP and CFO, Anthony J. (Tony) Park, age 45, $363,029 total compensation
SVP and Treasurer, Daniel K. Murphy, age 45
SVP Government Relations, Sherwood (Woody) Girion
Director, Gen. William Lyon Sr., age 88
Vice Chairman, Frank P. Willey, age 58
Director, Daniel D. (Ron) Lane, age 77
Director, Willie D. Davis, age 77
Director, Thomas M. Hagerty, age 49
Director, Cary H. Thompson, age 55
Director, Peter O. Shea Jr., age 45
Director, Douglas K. (Doug) Ammerman, age 60
Director, Richard N. Massey, age 56
Auditors: KPMGLLP

LOCATIONS

HQ: Fidelity National Financial Inc.
601 Riverside Ave., Jacksonville FL 32204
Phone: 904-854-8100 **Fax:** 904-357-1007
Web: www.fnf.com

PRODUCTS/OPERATIONS

2011 Revenues

	$ mil.	% of total
Title premiums	3,261	67
Other revenues	1,429	30
Interest & investment income	149	3
Total	**4,839**	**100**

Selected Acquisitions

2012
- Remy International Inc. (50.2%; Pendleton IN; auto parts manufacturer)
- O' Charley' s ($178 million; Nashville TN; casual dining restaurants)

2010
- Commerce Velocity (title insurance)

2008
- Lawyer' s Title Insurance (title insurance)
- Commonwealth Land Title Insurance (title insurance)
- United Capital Title Insurance (title insurance)

COMPETITORS

Allstate
American Coast Title
American Home Shield
Equity Title Company
Farmers Group
First American
Gracy Title A Stewart Company
Investors Title
Nationwide
North American Title
Old Republic
Old Republic National Title
State Farm
Stewart Information Services
The Hartford
Title Resource Group
Travelers Companies
United General Title Insurance

HISTORICAL FINANCIALS

Company Type: Public

Income Statement

FYE: December 31

	ASSETS ($ mil.)	NET INCOME ($ mil.)	INCOME AS % OF ASSETS	EMPLOYEES
12/11	7,862	369	4.7%	17,396
12/10	7,887	370	4.7%	18,200
12/09	7,934	222	2.8%	17,200
12/08	8,368	(179)	—	13,700
12/07	7,556	129	1.7%	15,500
Annual Growth	1.0%	29.9%	—	2.9%

2011 Year-End Financials

Debt ratio: 11.65%
Return on equity: 10.17%
Cash ($ mil.): 665
Current ratio: —
Long-term debt ($ mil.): 915
No. of shares (mil.): 220
Dividends
Yield: —
Payout: 28.92%
Market value ($ mil.): 3,515

	STOCK PRICE ($) FY Close	P/E High	P/E Low	PER SHARE ($) Earnings	Dividends	Book Value
12/11	15.93	10	8	1.66	0.00	16.46
12/10	13.68	10	8	1.61	0.69	15.32
12/09	13.46	23	13	0.97	0.60	14.45
12/08	17.75	—	—	(0.85)	1.05	13.06
12/07	14.61	47	22	0.59	1.20	15.23
Annual Growth	2.2%	—	—	29.5%	—	2.0%

Fidelity National Information Services Inc

At Fidelity National Information Services (FIS) the check will never get lost in the mail. FIS provides software outsourcing and IT consulting for the financial services industry. For banks and other financing entities the company's offerings address financial functions such as core processing decision and risk management and retail channel operations as well as payment services such as electronic funds transfer check and ticket processing and credit card production and activation. The company's 14000 customers aren't just the largest private financial institutions but also small businesses and government entities and are in more than 100 countries.

Operations FIS is divided into two product/service segments –payment solutions and financial solutions –and an international segment. Payment solutions is the company's largest segment at more than 40% of sales while financial solutions makes up more than 35%. International solutions which makes up the remainder of sales provides the company's services outside North America primarily in Brazil Germany and the UK. Financial Analysis In an effort to boost its presence in the banking and payments software market FIS acquired Milwaukee-based Metavante Technologies for about $3 billion in 2009. The acquisition included Metavante's NYCE Payments Network which operates a network of more than 360000 ATMs serving more than 90 million cardholders. FIS reaped the benefits of Metavante in 2010 when overall sales got back on track (after dropping to a six-year low in 2009) growing 40% while profits bounded back more than 280%. The company continued its return to form in 2011 though its largest segment grew only nominally (less than 1%). The payment solutions group eked out its growth thanks to print and mail and card personalization and electronic payment services which was almost completely neutralized by diminished item processing and retail check business. The financial solutions group grew 10% for the year driven by professional services processing and The Capital Markets Company (Capco acquired in 2010) revenues. International expanded almost 30% again partially from Capco business (in Europe) as well as through credit card increases in Brazil ATM management in India core banking business in Australia and license revenue from customers in EMEA (Europe Middle East and Africa). Foreign currency exchange rate chipped in nearly $50 million (about 20% of the growth) for the segment. Mergers & Acquisitions In order to focus on providing services to financial institutions in 2012 FIS sold its Healthcare Benefit Solutions business to equity investor Lightyear Capital in a $335 million deal. The sale included the Consumer Driven Healthcare Solutions and Health and Financial Network Solutions divisions including benefits administration benefit account processing and payment fulfillment services for consumers health care providers and payers. FIS retained its state and federal government electronic benefits transfer (EBT) business which has operations in 25 states because the company is a market leader in that business with significant geographic scale. FIS bought IT consultancy Capco from majority shareholder Symphony Technology Group to further expand its list of services for clients the financial industry. Earlier that year FIS bought Compliance Coach a provider of risk assessment software used to manage compliance with laws and regulations. The deal expanded FIS' offerings for compliance management and added about 1500 clients to its customer roster.

The company also enlisted the help of BMO Harris Bank to provide it with additional back-end customer-facing functions such as core processing mobile financial services online bill payment trust services and EFT processing. The late 2012 five-year agreement extends FIS's existing partnership with BMO Harris Bank. While FIS does the bulk of its business in North America the company continues to look overseas for growth opportunities and international business has brought in around a fifth of FIS's revenues in each of the past few years. In 2010 it expanded its presence in the Philippines with the opening of a new service facility to focus on business process outsourcing. The company made related investments in its India operations the previous year. Besides growing its top line FIS is keen on using global expansion to produce scale-driven operating efficiencies.

EXECUTIVES

President CEO and Director, Frank R. Martire, age 64
Chairman, William P. (Bill) Foley II, age 67, $557,500 total compensation
Corporate EVP; CEO Capco, Rob Heyvaert
SVP Investor Relations, Mary K. Waggoner, age 53
Corporate EVP Chief Legal Officer and Corporate Secretary, Michael L. Gravelle, age 50
Corporate EVP and COO, Gary A. Norcross, age 46, $602,500 total compensation
Corporate EVP Corporate Finance, Brent B. Bickett, age 47, $401,250 total compensation
EVP Financial Solutions, Anthony Jabbour
Corporate EVP and Chief Human Resources, Michael P. Oates, age 52
EVP International, Mark Davey
Senior Vice President; Chief Accounting Officer; Controller, James W. (Woody) Woodall, age 42
SVP Global Marketing and Communications, Marcia Danzeisen
Corporate EVP and CFO, Michael D. (Mike) Hayford
EVP Global Commercial Services, Ram Chary
EVP Business Development, James Susoreny
EVP Enterprise Strategy, Fred Brothers
Chief Marketing Officer, Ellyn Raftery
Chief Risk Officer, Greg Montana
Senior Vice President; Treasurer, Kirk Larsen
President CEO and Director, Frank R. Martire, age 64
Director, Keith W. Hughes, age 65
Director, Stephan A. (Steve) James, age 65
Director, Thomas M. Hagerty, age 49
Director, David K. Hunt, age 66
Director, James C. (Jim) Neary, age 47
Director, Richard N. Massey, age 56
Auditors: KPMGLLP

LOCATIONS

HQ: Fidelity National Information Services Inc
601 Riverside Avenue, Jacksonville, FL 32204
Phone: 904 435-6000
Web: www.fisglobal.com

PRODUCTS/OPERATIONS

2011 Sales

	$ mil.	% of total
Payment solutions	2,492	43
Financial solutions	2,076	36
International solutions	1,177	21
Corporate & other	(0.9)	-
Total	**5,745**	**100**

COMPETITORS

Accenture
ACI Worldwide
Alliance Data Systems
DST Systems
First Data
Fiserv
Global Payments
Harland Financial Solutions
Heartland Payment Systems
HP Enterprise Services
IBM
Infosys
Jack Henry
MasterCard
Misys
Open Solutions
Oracle Financial Services Software
SEI Investments
SunGard
TeleCheck
Total System Services
Visa Inc

HISTORICAL FINANCIALS

Company Type: Public

Income Statement — FYE: December 31

	REVENUE ($ mil.)	NET INCOME ($ mil.)	NET PROFIT MARGIN	EMPLOYEES
12/11	5,745	469	8.2%	33,000
12/10	5,269	404	7.7%	33,000
12/09	3,769	105	2.8%	31,000
12/08	3,446	214	6.2%	26,000
12/07	4,758	561	11.8%	31,000
Annual Growth	4.8%	(4.4%)	—	1.6%

2011 Year-End Financials

Debt ratio: 34.73%
Return on equity: 7.22%
Cash ($ mil.): 415
Current ratio: 124.19
Long-term debt ($ mil.): 4,550
No. of shares (mil.): 292
Dividends
Yield: —
Payout: 13.07%
Market value ($ mil.): 7,788

	STOCK PRICE ($) FY Close	P/E High	P/E Low	Earnings	Dividends	Book Value
12/11	26.59	22	14	1.53	0.00	22.20
12/10	27.39	26	19	1.15	0.20	21.21
12/09	23.44	57	34	0.44	0.20	22.19
12/08	16.27	39	11	1.11	0.20	18.51
12/07	41.59	20	14	2.86	0.20	19.42
Annual Growth	(10.6%)	—	—	(14.5%)	—	3.4%

Fifth Third Bancorp (Cincinnati, OH)

Fifth Third Bancorp wants to be first in the hearts and minds of its customers. The holding company operates some 1300 Fifth Third Bank branches including more than 100 Bank Mart locations open seven days a week inside supermarkets in a dozen states in the Midwest and Southeast. Its largest markets are Ohio Michigan and Florida. Fifth Third operates through four segments: branch banking (deposit accounts and loans for consumers and small businesses) commercial banking (lending leasing and syndicated and trade finance for corporate clients) consumer lending (residential mortgages home equity loans and credit cards) and investment advisors (private banking brokerage and asset management).

HISTORY

In 1863 a group of Cincinnati businessmen opened the Third National Bank inside a Masonic temple to serve the Ohio River trade. Acquiring the Bank of the Ohio Valley (founded 1858) in 1871 the firm progressed until the panic of 1907. Third National survived and in 1908 consolidated with Fifth National forming the Fifth Third National Bank of Cincinnati. The newly organized bank acquired two local banks in 1910.

A second bank consolidation in 1919 resulted in Fifth Third's affiliation with Union Savings Bank and Trust Company permitting the bank to establish branches theretofore forbidden by regulators. The company acquired the assets and offices of five more banks and thrifts that year operating them as branches.

In 1927 the bank merged its operations with the Union Trust Company forming the Fifth Third Union Trust. With its combined strength it weathered the Great Depression and acquired three more banks between 1930 and 1933. However the Depression also brought massive banking regulations to the industry limiting Fifth Third's acquisitions.

In the postwar years and during the 1950s and 1960s the bank expanded its consumer banking services offering traveler's checks. Under CEO Bill Rowe son of former CEO John Rowe the firm emphasized the convenience of its locations and increased hours of operations.

In the 1970s Fifth Third shifted its lending program's emphasis from commercial loans to consumer credit and launched its ATM and telephone banking services. Aware that the bank was technologically unprepared for the onslaught of electronic information Fifth Third expanded its data processing and information services resources forming the basis for its Midwest Payment Systems division.

The company formed Fifth Third Bancorp a holding company and began to branch within Ohio (branching had previously been limited to the home county) in 1975. Ten years later more deregulation allowed the bank to move into contiguous states. Focused on consumer banking and with cautious underwriting policies Fifth Third weathered the real estate bust and leveraged-buyout problems of the 1980s and acquired new outlets cheaply by buying several small banks as well as branches from larger banks. It acquired the American National Bank in Kentucky and moved further afield with its purchase of the Sovereign Savings Bank in Palm Harbor Florida in 1991.

The company continued to expand buying several banks and thrifts in Ohio in 1997 and 1998. In 1999 Fifth Third moved into Indiana in a big way with its purchase of CNB Bancshares then solidified its position in the state with the acquisition of Peoples Bank of Indianapolis. Fifth Third also moved into new business areas buying mortgage banker W. Lyman Case broker-dealer The Ohio Company (1998) and Cincinnati-based commercial mortgage banker Vanguard Financial (1999). The company began to offer online foreign exchange via its FX Internet Trading Web in 2000.

In 2001 Fifth Third bought money manager Maxus Investments and added some 300 bank branches with its purchase of Capital Holdings (Ohio and Michigan) and Old Kent Financial (Michigan Indiana and Illinois) its largest-ever acquisition.

Fifth Third exited the property/casualty insurance brokerage business in 2002 selling its operations to Hub International. Also that year Fifth Third arranged to enter Tennessee via its planned purchase of Franklin Financial. But the deal was stalled as industry regulators investigated Fifth Third's risk management procedures and internal controls. A moratorium on acquisitions was placed on the bank during the investigation. It was lifted in 2004 and the purchase of Franklin was completed not long afterwards. That opened the door for Fifth Third's acquisition of First National Bankshares of Florida in 2005. Two years later it continued growing with its purchase of R-G Crown Bank from R&G Financial which added some 30 branches in Florida in addition to locations in Georgia.

In 2008 the company entered the North Carolina market with its purchase of First Charter and some 60 branch offices. Other deals during this period included the purchase of 10 Atlanta-area branches from First Horizon National and the takeover of insolvent Freedom Bank in an FDIC-assisted transaction (which added another four Florida locations).

Fifth Third suffered steep loan losses in 2008 after which it began raising capital through common and preferred share offerings dividend cuts and other efforts. In 2009 the company raised some $1.8 billion when it sold 51% of its profitable ATM and credit card processing division to Advent International.

To cut costs and to simplify its operations particularly as banking regulations grew in complexity in the aftermath of the financial crisis the holding company consolidated all of its separate bank charters: It went from having 13 separate charters in 1991 to having a single Ohio charter in 2009.

Another financial services firm from the company's hometown insurer Cincinnati Financial Corporation (CFC) was once Fifth Third's largest shareholder. CFC sold its entire Fifth Third stake in 2009.

EXECUTIVES

EVP Chief Risk Officer and Secretary, Paul L. Reynolds, age 50
EVP and Chief Risk Officer, Mary E. Tuuk, age 47
SVP and Chief Marketing Officer, Larry S. Magnesen, age 54
President and CEO Fifth Third Bank Southern Indiana, John N. Daniel Jr.
Chairman Fifth Third Bank Southern Indiana, H. Lee Cooper III
President CEO and Vice Chairman, Kevin T. Kabat, age 55, $2,108,747 total compensation
President and CEO Fifth Third Bank North Carolina, Robert E. (Bob) James Jr., age 61
President and COO, Greg D. Carmichael, age 50, $1,022,349 total compensation
Chairman Fifth Third Bank Central Ohio, Donald B. Shackelford, age 77
Chairman Fifth Third Bank Tennessee, Gordon E. Inman
Chairman, William M. (Bill) Isaac, age 68
SVP and Head of Retail Banking, Raymond J. (Ray) Webb
EVP and CFO, Daniel T. (Dan) Poston, age 53, $564,638 total compensation
President and CEO Fifth Third Bank Central Kentucky, Samuel G. Barnes
SEVP, Robert A. (Bob) Sullivan, age 57, $818,242 total compensation
Chairman Fifth Third Bank Northwestern Ohio, John S. Szuch
EVP and Chief Administrative Officer, Todd F. Clossin, age 50
President and Chief Investment Officer Fifth Third Asset Management, E. Keith Wirtz
EVP and Chief Credit Officer, Bruce K. Lee, age 51
SVP Corporate Healthcare Lending, Kevin P. Lavender, age 50
EVP, Gregory L. (Greg) Kosch, age 52
Regional President; President and CEO Fifth Third Bank Tennessee, Dan W. Hogan
EVP and Regional President; President and CEO Fifth Third Bank Chicago, Terry E. Zink, age 60, $807,158 total compensation
SVP and Head of Investment Advisors, Philip R. McHugh
Regional President, Michelle L. VanDyke
SVP and Treasurer, Mahesh Sankaran, age 49
President and CEO Fifth Third Bank Northwestern Ohio, Robert W. LaClair
SVP and Director Community Affairs, Ed Owens III
President and CEO Fifth Third Bank South Florida, David A. Call, age 44
President and CEO Fifth Third Bank Tampa Bay, Brian P. Keenan
President and CEO Fifth Third Bank West Michigan, John Bultema III
SVP and Head of Retail Banking Northern Michigan, Mark Eckhoff, age 55
Director Investor Relations and Corporate Analysis, Jeff Richardson, age 47
President Fifth Third Mortgage, Robert (Bob) Lewis
SVP and Head of Business Banking Fifth Third Bank Tampa, Brian Lamb
President and CEO Fifth Third Bank Central Florida, Karen L. Dee, age 50
VP and Relationship Manager Commercial Group Fifth Third Bank Chicago, Frank Gruber
President Fifth Third Bank Central Ohio, Jordan A. Miller Jr.
EVP Employee Development, Lauris Woolford
VP and Private Banking Manager, Pamela Goetting
EVP and Auditor, Robert Shaffer
SVP Treasury Management Sales Chicago, Vanja St. Clair
Chief Fixed Income Officer Fifth Third Asset Management, Mitch Stapley
VP Corporate Communications, Debra DeCourcy
VP External Financial Reporting, Denise Meismer
VP and Managing Director Trade Finance and Correspondent Banking, Peter Mack
Assistant VP Fifth Third Bank Western Michigan, Julie Vickery
Market President Northeastern Ohio, Tom Partridge
SVP and Controller, Mark D. Hazel, age 46
SVP and Director National Treasury Management Sales, Jean Hilliard
President and CEO Fifth Third Bank Eastern Michigan, David Girodat
EVP Consumer Lending and Mortgage, Steve Alonso
SVP Commercial Banking, Jeffrey Chapman
EVP and CIO, Joseph R. Robinson
President and CEO Fifth Third Bank Central Indiana, Nancy Huber
EVP and Chief Human Resources Officer, Teresa J. Tanner, age 43
SVP and Chief Legal Officer, James R. Hubbard, age 53
SVP and Treasurer, Tayfun Tuzun, age 47
Director, Gary R. Heminger, age 58
Director, Darryl F. Allen, age 68
Director, John J. Schiff Jr., age 68
President CEO and Vice Chairman, Kevin T. Kabat, age 55

Director, Hendrik G. (Hank) Meijer, age 60
Director, James P. Hackett, age 57
Director, Marsha C. Williams, age 61
Director, Dudley S. Taft, age 71
Director, Mitchel D. Livingston, age 67
Director, Emerson L. Brumback, age 60
Director, Ulysses L. (Junior) Bridgeman Jr., age 58
Director, Jewell D. Hoover, age 63
Director, B. Evan Bayh, age 56
Auditors: Deloitte&ToucheLLP

LOCATIONS

HQ: Fifth Third Bancorp
38 Fountain Sq. Plaza Fifth Third Center, Cincinnati OH 45263
Phone: 513-579-5300 **Fax:** 910-576-5023
Web: www.firstbancorp.com

Selected Markets

Florida
Georgia
Indiana
Illinois
Kentucky
Michigan
Missouri
North Carolina
Ohio
Pennsylvania
Tennessee
West Virginia

PRODUCTS/OPERATIONS

2011 Sales

	$ mil.	% of total
Interest		
Loans & leases including fees	3,613	54
Securities & other	605	9
Noninterest		
Net mortgage banking revenue	597	9
Service charges on deposits	520	8
Investment advisory revenue	375	6
Corporate banking revenue	350	5
Card & processing revenue	308	5
Other	305	4
Total	**6,673**	**100**

Selected Subsidiaries

Fifth Third Capital Trust VII
Fifth Third Financial Corporation
Fifth Third Bank
GNB Management LLCGNB Realty LLC
Fifth Third Asset Management Inc.
Fifth Third Funding LLC
Fifth Third Holdings LLC
Fifth Third Insurance Agency Inc.
Fifth Third International CompanyFifth Third Trade Services Limited (Hong Kong)
Fifth Third Equipment Finance Company (formerly The Fifth Third Leasing Company)The Fifth Third Auto Leasing Trust
Fifth Third Mortgage CompanyFifth Third Real Estate Investment Trust Inc.
Fifth Third Real Estate Capital Markets Company
Fifth Third Securities Inc.
Old Kent Mortgage Services Inc.
Fifth Third Community Development Corporation
Fifth Third New Markets Development Co. LLC
Fifth Third Investment Company
Fountain Square Life Reinsurance Company Ltd. (Turks and Caicos Islands)
Vista Settlement Services LLC

COMPETITORS

Bank of America	JPMorgan Chase
Citigroup	KeyCorp
Comerica	Northern Trust
FirstMerit	PNC Financial
Harris	U.S. Bancorp
Huntington Bancshares	Wells Fargo

HISTORICAL FINANCIALS

Company Type: Public

Income Statement

FYE: December 31

	ASSETS ($ mil.)	NET INCOME ($ mil.)	INCOME AS % OF ASSETS	EMPLOYEES
12/11	116,967	1,297	1.1%	21,334
12/10	111,007	753	0.7%	20,838
12/09	113,380	737	0.7%	20,998
12/08	119,764	(2,113)	—	22,423
12/07	110,962	1,076	1.0%	22,678
Annual Growth	1.3%	4.8%	—	(1.5%)

2011 Year-End Financials

Debt ratio: 8.28%
Return on equity: 9.83%
Cash ($ mil.): 2,840
Current ratio: —
Long-term debt ($ mil.): 9,682
No. of shares (mil.): 919
Dividends
Yield: —
Payout: 23.73%
Market value ($ mil.): 11,700

	STOCK PRICE ($) FY Close	P/E High/Low		PER SHARE ($) Earnings	Dividends	Book Value
12/11	12.72	13	8	1.18	0.00	14.35
12/10	14.68	24	15	0.63	0.04	17.65
12/09	9.75	15	1	0.67	0.04	16.98
12/08	8.26	—	—	(3.94)	0.75	20.92
12/07	25.13	22	13	1.99	1.70	17.20
Annual Growth	(15.7%)	—	—	(12.2%)	—	(4.4%)

First Bancorp

EXECUTIVES

SVP and Controller; Controller First Bank, Lee C. McLaurin, age 49
President Montgomery Data Services, David G. Grigg, age 61, $91,000 total compensation
EVP and Chief Lending Officer; Loan Administrator First Bank, Teresa C. Nixon, age 54, $345,676 total compensation
EVP COO and Secretary First Bancorp and First Bank, Anna G. Hollers, age 61, $265,356 total compensation
EVP and CFO First Bancorp and First Bank, Eric P. Credle, age 43, $214,000 total compensation
SVP and Assistant Secretary; SVP Assistant Secretary and Investment Officer First Bank, Timothy S. Maples, age 51
EVP and Director; EVP First Bank, John F. Burns, age 64, $207,027 total compensation
Chairman, David L. Burns, age 73
EVP and Director; EVP and Director First Bank, R. Walton Brown, age 59
President CEO and Director, Jerry L. Ocheltree, age 52, $340,000 total compensation
SVP and Regional Executive First Bank, Richard E. Clayton Sr.
SVP and Regional Executive First Bank, David C. Foushee
SVP and Regional Executive First Bank, Roger S. Gentry Jr.
SVP and Regional Executive First Bank, Jimmy R. Preslar
SVP and Regional Executive First Bank, Stamey R. Taylor
SVP and Regional Executive First Bank, Charles R. Vance III
SVP and Regional Executive First Bank, Janet D. Abernethy
SVP and Regional Executive First Bank, Jimmy G. Grubbs
SVP and Regional Executive First Bank, Michael L. Hardin
SVP and Regional Executive First Bank, J. Bradford Mickle
SVP and Area Executive First Bank, H. Dean Martin
SVP and Area Executive First Bank, Robert T. Patterson
SVP and Area Executive First Bank, Frances H. Cagle
SVP and Area Executive First Bank, Joseph F. Youngblood
VP and Area Executive First Bank, Susie C. Jones
SVP and Area Executive First Bank, Glenn Batten
SVP and Area Executive First Bank, Michael W. Vinson
EVP and Regional Executive First Bank, John S. Long
SVP and Area Executive First Bank, Phillip W. Fulghum
SVP and Area Executive First Bank, Jerry M. Kinlaw
SVP and Area Executive First Bank, Frank E. Love
Director, Jack D. Briggs, age 72
EVP and Director; EVP First Bank, John F. Burns, age 64
Director, James G. Hudson Jr., age 72
Director, James C. Crawford III, age 55
Director, Dennis A. Wicker, age 59
Director, George R. Perkins Jr., age 72
Director, Thomas F. Phillips, age 66
Director, Virginia C. Thomasson, age 60
Director, A. Jordan Washburn, age 75
Director, John C. Willis, age 69
Director, Goldie H. Wallace, age 65
EVP and Director; EVP and Director First Bank, R. Walton Brown, age 59
Director, Mary Clara Capel, age 53
Director, Frederick L. Taylor II, age 42
President CEO and Director, Jerry L. Ocheltree, age 52
Director, Daniel T. Blue Jr.
Director, R. Winston Dozier
Director, Richard T. Moore
Auditors: ElliottDavisLLC

LOCATIONS

HQ: First Bancorp
1519 Ponce de Leon Avenue, Stop 23,
Phone: (787) 729 8200 **Fax:** (787) 729 8139
Web: www.firstbankpr.com

PRODUCTS/OPERATIONS

2011 Sales

	$ mil.	% of total
Interest		
Loans including fees	147	70
Investment securities	7	4
Other	0	-
Noninterest		
FDIC indemnification asset income net	20	10
Service charges on deposit accounts	12	6
Gain from acquisition	10	5
Other service charges commissions & fees	8	4
Other	3	1
Adjustments	(27.9)	-
Total	**182**	**100**

COMPETITORS

Bank of America	NewBridge Bancorp
BB&T	PNC Financial
BNC Bancorp	South Street Financial

First Citizens BancShares
FNB United
SunTrust
Wells Fargo

HISTORICAL FINANCIALS

Company Type: Public

Income Statement

FYE: December 31

	ASSETS ($ mil.)	NET INCOME ($ mil.)	INCOME AS % OF ASSETS	EMPLOYEES
12/11	13,127	(82)	—	2,490
12/10	15,593	(524)	—	2,518
12/09	19,628	(275)	—	2,713
12/08	19,491	109	0.6%	2,995
12/07	17,186	68	0.4%	3,000
Annual Growth	(6.5%)	—	—	(4.6%)

2011 Year-End Financials

Debt ratio: 4.74%
Return on equity: (-5.69)%
Cash ($ mil.): 443
Current ratio: —
Long-term debt ($ mil.): 622
No. of shares (mil.): 205
Dividends
Yield: —
Payout: —
Market value ($ mil.): 716

	STOCK PRICE ($) FY Close	P/E High/Low		PER SHARE ($) Earnings	Dividends	Book Value
12/11	3.49	3	0	2.18	0.00	7.04
12/10	0.46	—	—	(10.79)	0.00	49.66
12/09	2.30	—	—	(52.20)	0.00	259.19
12/08	11.14	1	1	11.25	0.00	250.92
12/07	7.29	3	1	4.80	0.00	230.53
Annual Growth	(16.8%)	—	—	(17.9%)	—	(58.2%)

First Bancorp (NC)

First things first: Don't confuse this First Bancorp with Virginia's First Bancorp or First BanCorp in Puerto Rico. This one is the holding company for First Bank which operates about 100 branch locations in east-central North Carolina east South Carolina and western Virginia (where it operates under the name First Bank of Virginia). In addition to offering standard commercial banking services such as deposit accounts and lending the bank offers investment products and discount brokerage services. Another subsidiary First Bank Insurance Services offers property/casualty products. First Bank focuses its lending on mortgages which account for more than half of its loan portfolio.

First Bancorp's strategy for growth includes buying banks in or near its existing market areas or banks that offer new business lines. (It entered South Carolina through its 2008 purchase of Great Pee Dee Bancorp.) In late 2011 the company arranged to purchase nearly a dozen branches in coastal portions of the Carolinas from Waccamaw Bank.

In addition to buying healthy banks the company has also been able to take advantage of the glut of bank failures by participating in FDIC-assisted transactions. Also in 2011 First Bancorp bought the assets and liabilities of The Bank of Asheville a five-branch bank in a new North Carolina market. Previously it took over the assets of the failed Cooperative Bank and its Lumina Mortgage subsidiary in a deal that added two dozen branches.

The acquisitions especially in respect to Cooperative Bank also added to First Bank's loan losses as a result of foreclosed properties assumed with the purchases. The bank's market area is slowly recovering from the effects of the recession and battered property values and it could be another couple of years before volatility in the region subsides. Overall the company has struggled with the lackluster economic recovery which has depressed loan and deposit levels. Revenues in 2011 slipped some 3% from the year before to $182 million but net income jumped 27% largely as a result of gain related to the Bank of Asheville acquisition. (Net FDIC indemnification asset income accounted for some 10% of the company's revenues that year.)

First Bancorp provided electronic data processing to external customers through its Montgomery Data Services subsidiary until 2010 when its last remaining client terminated its service agreement. The bank absorbed Montgomery's data processing operations that year.

EXECUTIVES

SVP and Controller; Controller First Bank, Lee C. McLaurin, age 49
President Montgomery Data Services, David G. Grigg, age 61, $91,000 total compensation
EVP and Chief Lending Officer; Loan Administrator First Bank, Teresa C. Nixon, age 54, $345,676 total compensation
EVP COO and Secretary First Bancorp and First Bank, Anna G. Hollers, age 61, $265,356 total compensation
EVP and CFO First Bancorp and First Bank, Eric P. Credle, age 43, $214,000 total compensation
SVP and Assistant Secretary; SVP Assistant Secretary and Investment Officer First Bank, Timothy S. Maples, age 51
EVP and Director; EVP First Bank, John F. Burns, age 64, $207,027 total compensation
Chairman, David L. Burns, age 73
EVP and Director; EVP and Director First Bank, R. Walton Brown, age 59
President CEO and Director, Jerry L. Ocheltree, age 52, $340,000 total compensation
SVP and Regional Executive First Bank, Richard E. Clayton Sr.
SVP and Regional Executive First Bank, David C. Foushee
SVP and Regional Executive First Bank, Roger S. Gentry Jr.
SVP and Regional Executive First Bank, Jimmy R. Preslar
SVP and Regional Executive First Bank, Stamey R. Taylor
SVP and Regional Executive First Bank, Charles R. Vance III
SVP and Regional Executive First Bank, Janet D. Abernethy
SVP and Regional Executive First Bank, Jimmy G. Grubbs
SVP and Regional Executive First Bank, Michael L. Hardin
SVP and Regional Executive First Bank, J. Bradford Mickle
SVP and Area Executive First Bank, H. Dean Martin
SVP and Area Executive First Bank, Robert T. Patterson
SVP and Area Executive First Bank, Frances H. Cagle
SVP and Area Executive First Bank, Joseph F. Youngblood
VP and Area Executive First Bank, Susie C. Jones
SVP and Area Executive First Bank, Glenn Batten
SVP and Area Executive First Bank, Michael W. Vinson
EVP and Regional Executive First Bank, John S. Long
SVP and Area Executive First Bank, Phillip W. Fulghum
SVP and Area Executive First Bank, Jerry M. Kinlaw
SVP and Area Executive First Bank, Frank E. Love
Director, Jack D. Briggs, age 72
EVP and Director; EVP First Bank, John F. Burns, age 64
Director, James G. Hudson Jr., age 72
Director, James C. Crawford III, age 55
Director, Dennis A. Wicker, age 59
Director, George R. Perkins Jr., age 72
Director, Thomas F. Phillips, age 66
Director, Virginia C. Thomasson, age 60
Director, A. Jordan Washburn, age 75
Director, John C. Willis, age 69
Director, Goldie H. Wallace, age 65
EVP and Director; EVP and Director First Bank, R. Walton Brown, age 59
Director, Mary Clara Capel, age 53
Director, Frederick L. Taylor II, age 42
President CEO and Director, Jerry L. Ocheltree, age 52
Director, Daniel T. Blue Jr.
Director, R. Winston Dozier
Director, Richard T. Moore
Auditors: ElliottDavisLLC

LOCATIONS

HQ: First Bancorp (NC)
341 North Main Street, Troy, NC 27371-0508
Phone: 910 576-6171
Web: www.firstbancorp.com

PRODUCTS/OPERATIONS

2011 Sales

	$ mil.	% of total
Interest		
Loans including fees	147	70
Investment securities	7	4
Other	0	-
Noninterest		
FDIC indemnification asset income net	20	10
Service charges on deposit accounts	12	6
Gain from acquisition	10	5
Other service charges commissions & fees	8	4
Other	3	1
Adjustments	(27.9)	-
Total	**182**	**100**

COMPETITORS

Bank of America
BB&T
BNC Bancorp
First Citizens BancShares
FNB United
NewBridge Bancorp
PNC Financial
South Street Financial
SunTrust
Wells Fargo

HISTORICAL FINANCIALS

Company Type: Public

Income Statement FYE: December 31

	ASSETS ($ mil.)	NET INCOME ($ mil.)	INCOME AS % OF ASSETS	EMPLOYEES
12/11	3,290	13	0.4%	849
12/10	3,278	9	0.3%	794
12/09	3,545	60	1.7%	800
12/08	2,750	22	0.8%	687
12/07	2,317	21	0.9%	655
Annual Growth	9.2%	(11.1%)	—	6.7%

2011 Year-End Financials

Debt ratio: 4.07%
Return on equity: 3.95%
Cash ($ mil.): 215
Current ratio: —
Long-term debt ($ mil.): 133
No. of shares (mil.): 16
Dividends
Yield: —
Payout: 72.73%
Market value ($ mil.): 189

	STOCK PRICE ($) FY Close	P/E High/Low		PER SHARE ($) Earnings	Dividends	Book Value
12/11	11.15	38	18	0.44	0.00	20.41
12/10	15.31	48	34	0.35	0.32	20.51
12/09	13.97	6	2	3.37	0.32	20.47
12/08	18.35	15	8	1.37	0.76	13.27
12/07	18.89	17	11	1.51	0.76	12.11
Annual Growth	(12.3%)	—	—	(26.5%)	—	13.9%

First Banks, Inc. (MO)

First Banks keeps it in the family. The holding company for First Bank it is owned by chairman James Dierberg and his family; many of the bank's branches and ATMs are located in Dierbergs Markets a Missouri-based grocery chain owned by relatives of the chairman. First Bank has about 150 branches in California Florida Illinois and Missouri with a concentration in metropolitan markets such as Los Angeles San Diego San Francisco Tampa and St. Louis. The bank offers standard services like deposits mortgages and business and consumer loans. Additional services include brokerage insurance trust and private banking as well as commercial treasury management and international trade services.

First Bank's lending activities are focused on commercial real estate and business loans which make up around 35% and 25% of its loan portfolio respectively. Residential mortgages account for more than 20%. In light of economic conditions the company hopes to reduce its reliance on business and real estate lending.

As with many of its peers First Bank has been adversely affected by the credit crisis and the resulting rise in nonperforming assets especially in its construction and commercial real estate loan portfolios. In 2008 the bank formed a subsidiary FB Holdings expressly as a way to manage nonperforming loans until they could be sold. The Dierberg family invested more than $100 million to fund the unit which is majority-owned by the bank.

The following year First Banks implemented a capital optimization plan to improve its financial performance by cutting expenses (such as reducing headcount) and making divestitures including branch sales and the sales of loans from its insurance premium financing and restaurant franchise portfolios. The moves helped First Banks to cut its losses in 2010.

In its effort to raise capital First Banks in 2010 sold some two-dozen branches in the Chicago area to FirstMerit; the deal came after First Banks sold most of its asset-based lending portfolio to the Ohio-based bank. It also sold about 10 branches in northern Illinois to First Mid-Illinois Bancshares and sold investment advisor Missouri Valley Partners to Stifel Financial.

First Banks had an agreement in place to sell its nearly 20 branches in Texas to Sterling Bancshares but the two companies backed out of the deal after it failed to receive regulatory approval by the end of 2009. First Banks eventually sold its Texas locations to Prosperity Bancshares the following year.

Before the company hit its rough patch that has seen it record losses for three consecutive years First Banks had been growing through both the acquisitions of other bank holding companies as well as by opening new branches and purchasing non-bank financial services companies. The company has made nearly 20 acquisitions since 2003 including the troubled Coast Financial Holdings in 2007 which gave First Bank an entrance into Florida. Holding company First Banks has since put the brakes on further purchases amid the difficult economic environment.

EXECUTIVES

SVP and Chief Human Resources Officer, John D. Kitson
Chairman, James F. (Jim) Dierberg, age 74
SVP Credit Administration and Director Credit Loss Recovery First Bank St. Louis, Steve H. Savio
EVP and Director Operations and Technology, Mary P. Sherrill, age 57
President CEO and Director; Chairman President and CEO First Bank, Terrance M. (Terry) McCarthy, age 57, $500,000 total compensation
President First Bank Southern Illinois, Douglas R. Distler
EVP and CFO, Lisa K. Vansickle, age 44, $214,800 total compensation
EVP and Director Retail Banking, F. Christopher McLaughlin, age 58, $245,900 total compensation
SVP Corporate Administration and Director Tax First Bank, Annette R. Carson
SVP Corporate Administration and Chief Investment Officer First Bank, Edward D. Furman
SVP Credit Administration and Director Credit Risk Assessment First Bank, J. Brett Zedialis
SVP Commercial Banking First Bank San Diego, David L. Beall
SVP Commercial Banking First Bank Central Coast California, Timothy A. Marme
President First Bank St. Louis, Joseph T. (Joe) Ambrose
SVP General Counsel and Secretary, Peter D. Wimmer
SVP Corporate Administration and Director Loan Operations First Bank, Gregory P. Wayman
Regional President Commercial Banking First Bank St. Charles, Kurt Beanblossom
SVP Commercial Banking First Bank St. Louis, Catherine T. Campbell
SVP Private Banking Commercial Banking First Bank St. Louis, Lindsay J. Gerken
SVP Commercial Real Estate First Bank St. Louis, Gregory M. Fuesting
EVP and Acting Chief Credit Officer First Banks and First Bank, Gary S. Pratte
SVP Retail Banking First Bank Metro St. Louis, Wayne H. Henson
SVP Retail Banking First Bank Southern Illinois, Kathryn S. Theen
President Association Banking First Bank, Michael J. Kennedy
SVP Retail Banking First Bank Northern California, Peter A. Goetze
EVP Commercial Real Estate and Director National Real Estate Division First Bank Southern California, Alan G. Rye
SVP Commercial Banking First Bank Inland Empire San Gabriel Valley, Kenneth D. Kross
SVP Commercial Banking First Bank Warner Center Beverly Hills, Donna K. Owen
SVP Commercial Banking First Bank Orange County and Long Beach, Richard C. Reid
EVP Credit Administration and Senior Regional Credit Officer First Bank California, Albert S. Brown
President Religious Lending First Bank, Therese M. DeGroot
SVP Retail Banking First Bank Southern California, Jane S. Lief
SVP Retail Banking First Bank Southern California, Joel E. Schwartz
SVP and Director Risk Management and Audit, Laura A. Schumacher
SVP Commercial Banking First Bank Southern Illinois, Mary R. Dix
SVP Commercial Banking First Bank Southern Illinois, David E. Hopkins
SVP Commercial Banking First Bank Walnut Creet San Jose, R. Michael Law
SVP Treasury Management Services Commercial Banking First Bank, John D. Spencer
SVP Commercial Banking First Bank Sacramento, Kingman H. Tsang
SVP Commercial Real Estate First Bank Northern California, Thomas M. Lynn
SVP Healthcare Banking First Bank St. Louis, L. Alec Blanc
SVP Small Business Banking First Bank Sacramento, Rick A. Woody
SVP Small Business Banking First Bank Midwest, Kenneth B. Eisler
SVP Small Business Banking First Bank California, T. Lee Fenn
SVP Credit Administration and Regional Credit Officer First Bank St. Louis, John A. Novatny
Retail President First Bank Florida, Anne V. Lee
SVP Retail Banking First Bank Metro St. Louis, Lisa M. Blamy
President Mortgage Banking First Bank, William A. Kusman
SVP Corporate Administration Corporate Real Estate First Bank, Jason A. Gray
SVP and Controller, Michael J. Normile
President First Bank Florida, David A. Austin
President First Bank Northern Illinois, James C. Fassino
President First Bank California, John S. Grauten
President First Bank Cincinnati, John R. Mirlisena
SVP Commercial Banking First Bank Galesburg, Mark Blackburn
SVP Commercial Banking First Bank Peoria, John M. Brown
SVP Commercial Banking First Bank San Francisco, George P. McCullagh
SVP Commercial Banking First Bank St. Louis, Patricia A. O'Herin
SVP Commercial Banking First Bank Bloomington, Michael T. Stone
SVP Credit Administration and Director Commercial Loans First Bank Southern California, Norman O. Broyer

SVP Retail Banking First Bank Southern Illinois, Julie K. Laurent
SVP Mortgage Banking First Bank, Judith A. Schmersahl
SVP Mortgage Banking First Bank, Kathy J. Alexander
Director, Allen H. Blake, age 69
Director, Douglas H. Yaeger, age 62
Director, David L. Steward, age 60
President CEO and Director; Chairman President and CEO First Bank, Terrance M. (Terry) McCarthy, age 57
Director, James A. Cooper, age 56
Auditors: KPMGLLP

LOCATIONS

HQ: First Banks Inc.
135 N. Meramec Ave., Clayton MO 63105
Phone: 314-854-4600 **Fax:** 314-592-6840
Web: www.firstbanks.com

PRODUCTS/OPERATIONS

2010 Sales

	$ mil.	% of total
Interest		
Loans including fees	281	72
Taxable investment securities	25	7
Other	6	2
Noninterest		
Service charges on deposit accounts & customer service fees	42	11
Gain on loans sold & held for sale	9	2
Loan servicing fees	8	2
Net gain on investment securities	8	2
Other	9	2
Total	**391**	**100**

Selected Subsidiaries

The San Francisco Company
First Bank
FB Holdings LLC (53%)
First Bank Business Capital Inc.
Small Business Loan Source LLC

COMPETITORS

Bank of America
Capital One
Citigroup
Comerica
Commerce Bancshares
JPMorgan Chase
Regions Financial
U.S. Bancorp
UMB Financial
Wells Fargo

HISTORICAL FINANCIALS

Company Type: Private

Income Statement FYE: December 31

	ASSETS ($ mil.)	NET INCOME ($ mil.)	INCOME AS % OF ASSETS	EMPLOYEES
12/11	6,608	(41)	—	1,171
12/10	7,378	(191)	—	1,380
12/09	10,582	(427)	—	1,890
12/08	10,783	(287)	—	2,340
12/07	10,897	57	0.5%	2,525
Annual Growth	(11.8%)	—	—	(17.5%)

2011 Year-End Financials

Debt ratio: 5.36%
Return on equity: (-24.25)%
Cash ($ mil.): 472
Current ratio: —
Long-term debt ($ mil.): 354
No. of shares (mil.): 0
Dividends
Yield: —
Payout: —
Market value ($ mil.): —

First Busey Corp.

First Busey Corporation keeps itself busy taking care of nest eggs. It's the holding company for Busey Bank which has more than 40 branches in Illinois Florida and Indiana. The bank offers standard deposit products and services; it uses funds from deposits to originate loans primarily real estate loans and mortgage. First Busey also owns nonbanking subsidiaries. Busey Wealth Management provides asset management trust brokerage and related services to individuals businesses and foundations; it has some $4 billion under management. Another subsidiary FirsTech provides retail payment processing services. Most of Busey Bank's branches are located in downstate Illinois.

Real estate loans including commercial and residential mortgages account for some three-fourths of the bank's loan portfolio. Busey Bank also writes construction commercial and consumer installment loans. Busey Trust a subsidiary of Busey Wealth Management provides brokerage services (via an arrangement with Raymond James Financial) through its Busey Investment Services division.

Busey Bank has more than 30 branches in Illinois; it has about a half-dozen locations in southwest Florida and another office in Indianapolis.

The bank suffered significant loan-related losses (more than $360 million) in 2008 and 2009. By 2010 the company was once again profitable. Although revenues fell 12% in 2011 to $192 million net income grew 29% to $30 million that year. The company's loan losses have waned somewhat in the improving economy but First Busey has also been selling the bad loans it held in its portfolio (which has in turn cut into interest earnings). Additionally the company has shied away from riskier loans such as commercial mortgages and construction loans. In 2011 the company cut its provision for loan losses from $42 million to $20 million signaling fewer net charge-offs.

The company's primary market in Illinois hasn't been as badly impacted in the economic downturn as its secondary market in Florida has been. That region has proved to be a drag on the bank as its recovery has been gradual. Following an industry trend First Busey recently consolidated its various bank charters under the Busey Bank banner to streamline and cut costs. The company's nonbanking subsidiaries performed better in the economic meltdown especially FirsTech and the wealth management operations. First Busey plans to invest significantly into the business to spur organic growth and maintain its diverse sources of revenues.

EXECUTIVES

EVP and Regional President Busey Bank, David R. Wampler
SVP Human Resources, Lisa A. Davis
Chief Risk Officer; Chief Risk Officer Busey Bank, Barbara J. Harrington, age 52, $200,000 total compensation
EVP and Senior Business Lender Busey West Region, Thomas M. Good, age 59, $175,000 total compensation
EVP and Chief Retail Officer, Susan L. Abbott
EVP Special Assets Busey Bank, Don A. Monteith
EVP Busey Bank, Donald J. Schlorff
EVP Busey Wealth Management, Curt A. Anderson
EVP Busey Wealth Management, R. Scott MacAdam
President CEO and Director; Chairman Busey Bank, Van A. Dukeman, age 53, $400,000 total compensation
EVP Busey Bank, Phillip C. (Phil) Wise
CFO; CFO Busey Bank, David B. (Dave) White, age 60, $70,833 total compensation
Chief Credit Officer; Chief Credit Officer Busey Bank; President Florida Region Busey Bank, Robert F. (Bob) Plecki Jr., age 51
CIO; CIO Busey Bank and Busey Wealth Management, Leanne C. Heacock, age 47
Chairman, Gregory B. (Greg) Lykins, age 64
President and CEO FirsTech, Howard F. Mooney II, age 47
SVP Busey Bank, Todd J. Anderson
SVP Human Resources, Carol A. Slough
EVP and President West Region Busey Bank, Daniel P. Daly
SVP First Capital Bank, Anthony Lees
SVP Busey Bank, Pamela J. Irvin
SVP Busey Wealth Management, Elizabeth B. Czys
SVP Busey Wealth Management, Gregory W. Fink
SVP Busey Wealth Management, Elizabeth A. Krchak
SVP Busey Wealth Management, Gregg McElroy
SVP Busey Wealth Management, R. Michael Murphy
SVP Busey Bank, Robert B. Fazzini
SVP Busey Bank, David W. Gillon
SVP Busey Bank, Kirk L. Harney
SVP Busey Bank, Richard A. Holiner
SVP Busey Bank, Louis S. Hensley III
SVP Busey Bank, John A. Kahle
EVP and Senior Business Lender Busey East Region, J. Rod Kirby
SVP Busey Bank, Janis R. Koller
SVP Busey Bank, Larry C. McClellan
SVP Busey Bank, Dennis R. McMillan
SVP Busey Wealth Management, Steven S. Myers
SVP Busey Bank, James D. Owens
SVP Busey Bank, Edward G. Paine
SVP Busey Bank, Mary Ann Pankau
SVP Busey Bank, Allan S. Penwell
SVP Busey Bank, Douglas E. Roesch
SVP Busey Bank, Thomas W. Scharlau
SVP Busey Bank, Michael A. Stevenson
SVP Busey Bank, David E. Strang
SVP Busey Bank, Cheryle A. Turner
SVP Busey Bank, Ronald Wesbecher
SVP Busey Bank, Thomas L. Wiggins
President and CEO Busey Wealth Management, Donna R. Greene, age 58
SVP Busey Bank, Mary M. Severino
EVP Busey Bank, Chuck Eyman
SVP Busey Bank, Leon M. Hinton
EVP Busey Bank, David Weber
SVP Busey Bank, John Holden
SVP Busey Bank, Larry Johnson
SVP Busey Bank, Michael Swearingen
SVP Busey Bank, Jeffrey Troxell
SVP Busey Bank, William Weistart
President and CEO Busey Bank, Christopher M. (Chris) Shroyer, age 46
EVP Business Banking, N. John Waddock
SVP Busey Bank, Janet Carr
SVP Busey Bank, Tracy Doubet
EVP Busey Bank, Nancy Weimer
SVP Busey Bank, Ray Pratt
SVP Busey Bank, Diana Reinhart
SVP Busey Bank, Susan Thuney
SVP Busey Wealth Management, Thomas Heinhorst
SVP Busey Wealth Management, Dean Kyburz
SVP Busey Wealth Management, Brian Waibel
SVP Residential Mortgage Banking, Gary L. Jackson
Director, Joseph M. Ambrose, age 54
Director, E. Phillips Knox, age 65
Director, V. B. Leister Jr., age 66

President CEO and Director; Chairman Busey Bank, Van A. Dukeman, age 53
Director, David L. Ikenberry, age 51
Director, August C. Meyer Jr., age 74
Director, George T. Shapland, age 81
Director, Thomas G. Sloan, age 63
Director, David J. Downey, age 70
Auditors: McGladreyLLP

LOCATIONS

HQ: First Busey Corporation
201 W. Main St., Urbana IL 61801
Phone: 217-365-4528 **Fax:** 217-365-4592
Web: www.busey.com

PRODUCTS/OPERATIONS

2011 Sales

	$ mil.	% of total
Interest		
Loans including fees	114	60
Interest & dividends on securities	18	9
Noninterest		
Trust fees	15	8
Service charges on deposit accounts	12	7
Gain on sales of loans	10	6
Other service charges & fees	5	3
Other	14	8
Total	**191**	**100**

COMPETITORS

Bank of America
CIB Marine Bancshares
Fifth Third
First Mid-Illinois Bancshares
First Midwest Bancorp
JPMorgan Chase
Mercantile Bancorp
PNC Financial
Wintrust Financial

HISTORICAL FINANCIALS

Company Type: Public

Income Statement FYE: December 31

	ASSETS ($ mil.)	NET INCOME ($ mil.)	INCOME AS % OF ASSETS	EMPLOYEES
12/11	3,402	29	0.9%	888
12/10	3,605	23	0.6%	866
12/09	3,814	(323)	—	912
12/08	4,460	(37)	—	986
12/07	4,192	31	0.8%	1,023
Annual Growth	(5.1%)	(1.3%)	—	(3.5%)

2011 Year-End Financials

Debt ratio: 2.19%
Return on equity: 7.30%
Cash ($ mil.): 315
Current ratio: —
Long-term debt ($ mil.): 74
No. of shares (mil.): 86
Dividends
Yield: —
Payout: 55.17%
Market value ($ mil.): 433

	STOCK PRICE ($) FY Close	P/E High/Low		PER SHARE ($) Earnings	Dividends	Book Value
12/11	5.00	19	14	0.29	0.00	4.72
12/10	4.70	20	13	0.27	0.16	5.31
12/09	3.89	—	—	(7.85)	0.40	4.94
12/08	18.24	—	—	(1.06)	0.80	12.67
12/07	19.86	21	17	1.13	0.77	14.54
Annual Growth	(29.2%)	—	—	(28.8%)	—	(24.5%)

First Citizens BancShares, Inc. (NC)

First Citizens BancShares knows the first thing about commercial banking. The company owns First-Citizens Bank & Trust which operates about 430 branches in nearly 20 states mainly in the southeastern and western US and urban areas scattered throughout the country. The bank provides standard services such as deposits loans mortgages and trust services in addition to processing and operational support to other banks. Subsidiary First Citizens Investor Services offers investments and discount brokerage services to bank clients. Real estate loans including commercial residential and revolving mortgages and construction and land development loans make up most of the company's loan portfolio.

First Citizens BancShares has been fortifying its presence along the West Coast by snapping up failed financial institutions. Since 2009 it has acquired most of the banking operations of Temecula Valley Bank Washington-based Venture Bank and First Regional Bank in Southern California. It also acquired the failed Florida-based bank Sun American and entered Colorado through the acquisitions of United Western Bank and Colorado Capital Bank. All were FDIC-assisted transactions and each acquired institution became branches of First-Citizens Bank. The deals added about 50 branches to the bank's network. First Citizens BancShares continues to seek out acquisitions of other seized institutions.

Though the company has been able to grow geographically thanks to the economic downturn its IronStone Bank division which focused on business customers suffered from weakened markets in Florida and Georgia. (First Citizens Bancshares merged IronStone into First-Citizens Bank in 2011 to increase efficiency and unify the company's brand.) It has remained profitable thanks in part to its acquisitions which include loss-sharing agreements with the FDIC but has had to increase its provisions for loan losses each of the last five years.

The Holding family which occupies several positions in the company's board room and executive suite controls First Citizens BancShares.

EXECUTIVES

EVP Technology and Operations First-Citizens Bank & Trust; SVP IronStone, Joseph A. Cooper Jr., age 58, $201,085 total compensation
President Citizens BancShares and First-Citizens Bank and Trust Company, Edward L. Willingham IV, age 57, $483,344 total compensation
Vice Chairman First Citizens BancShares and First-Citizens Bank & Trust; President Western Division; COO IronStone, James M. (Jay) Parker, age 69, $440,987 total compensation
Chairman and CEO First Citizens BancShares First-Citizens Bank & Trust and IronStone Bank, Frank B. Holding Jr., age 50, $749,009 total compensation
VP CFO and Treasurer; EVP CFO and Treasurer First-Citizens Bank & Trust; SVP and Treasurer IronStone, Kenneth A. Black, age 60, $369,154 total compensation
Executive Vice Chairman First Citizens BancShares and First-Citizens Bank & Trust, Frank B. Holding Sr., age 83, $995,114 total compensation
CIO First Citizens Bank, Dede F. Ramoneda
Vice Chairman; Vice Chairman EVP and Business Banking Segment Manager First-Citizens Bank & Trust; President IronStone Bank, Hope Holding Connell, age 48
EVP and Chief Human Resources Officer First-Citizens Bank & Trust, Lou J. Davis, age 59
EVP and Wealth Management Manager First-Citizens Bank & Trust; SVP IronStone, Carol B. Yochem, age 52, $542,367 total compensation
EVP and Chief Governance Officer First-Citizens Bank & Trust; SVP IronStone, Donald P. Geaslen, age 54
Secretary; Group VP Legal Services and Secretary First-Citizens Bank & Trust; VP and Secretary IronStone, James E. Creekman, age 64
EVP and Chief Credit Officer First-Citizens Bank & Trust; Group VP and Chief Credit Officer IronStone, Ricky T. Holland, age 58
Vice Chairman First Citizens BancShares and First-Citizens Bank & Trust; President Western Division; COO IronStone, James M. (Jay) Parker, age 69
Executive Vice Chairman First Citizens BancShares and First-Citizens Bank & Trust, Frank B. Holding Sr., age 83
Director, John M. Alexander Jr., age 62
Director, Carmen Holding Ames, age 43
Director, George H. Broadrick, age 88
Director, Hubert M. Craig III, age 55
Director, Lewis M. Fetterman, age 90
Director, Lucius S. Jones, age 69
Director, Lewis T. Nunnelee II, age 85
Director, David L. Ward Jr., age 76
Vice Chairman; Vice Chairman EVP and Business Banking Segment Manager First-Citizens Bank & Trust; President IronStone Bank, Hope Holding Connell, age 48
Director, Victor E. Bell III, age 55
Director, H. Lee Durham Jr., age 63
Director, Robert T. Newcomb, age 51
Director, Ralph K. Shelton, age 69
Director, Daniel Lee Heavner, age 64
Director, Robert E. Mason IV, age 53
Auditors: DixonHughesGoodmanLLP

LOCATIONS

HQ: First Citizens BancShares Inc.
4300 Six Forks Rd., Raleigh NC 27609
Phone: 919-716-7000 **Fax:** 919-716-7074
Web: www.firstcitizens.com

2011 Branches

	No.
North	273
Virginia	49
California	22
Florida	20
Georgia	15
Colorado	11
Washington	10
Texas	7
Tennessee	6
West	5
Arizona	2
New	2
Oklahoma	2
Oregon	2
Kansas	1
Maryland	1
Missouri	1
Washington	1
Total	**430**

PRODUCTS/OPERATIONS

2011 Sales

	$ mil.	% of total
Interest		
Loans & leases	967	65

Investment securities including dividends	46	3
Overnight investments	1	-
Noninterest		
Gains on acquisitions	150	10
Cardholder & merchant services	110	8
Service charges on deposit accounts	63	4
Wealth management services	55	4
Fees from processing services	30	2
Other service charges & fees	22	2
Other	31	2
Total	**1,479**	**100**

COMPETITORS

Bank of America
BB&T
Capital One
Citibank
Compass Bancshares
First Horizon
JPMorgan Chase
PNC Financial
Regions Financial
SunTrust
Synovus
United Bankshares
Wells Fargo

HISTORICAL FINANCIALS

Company Type: Public

Income Statement FYE: December 31

	ASSETS ($ mil.)	NET INCOME ($ mil.)	INCOME AS % OF ASSETS	EMPLOYEES
12/11	20,881	195	0.9%	5,077
12/10	20,806	193	0.9%	5,135
12/09	18,466	116	0.6%	5,006
12/08	16,745	91	0.5%	4,843
12/07	16,212	108	0.7%	4,781
Annual Growth	6.5%	15.8%	—	1.5%

2011 Year-End Financials

Debt ratio: 5.40%
Return on equity: 10.48%
Cash ($ mil.): 1,025
Current ratio: —
Long-term debt ($ mil.): 1,128
No. of shares (mil.): 10
Dividends
Yield: —
Payout: 6.38%
Market value ($ mil.): 1,800

	STOCK PRICE ($) FY Close	P/E High	P/E Low	PER SHARE ($) Earnings	Dividends	Book Value
12/11	174.99	11	7	18.80	0.00	180.97
12/10	189.05	11	9	18.50	1.20	166.08
12/09	164.01	15	7	11.15	1.20	149.42
12/08	152.80	21	14	8.73	1.10	138.33
12/07	145.85	21	14	10.41	1.10	138.12
Annual Growth	4.7%	—	—	15.9%	—	7.0%

First Commonwealth Financial Corp. (Indiana, PA)

First Commonwealth Financial is the holding company for First Commonwealth Bank which operates more than 110 offices in 15 central and western Pennsylvania counties. The bank offers standard products such as checking and savings accounts CDs IRAs and credit cards. Its loan book is mainly made up of commercial and industrial loans including real estate operating agricultural and construction loans. The bank also issues consumer loans such as education automobile and home equity loans. First Commonwealth Financial offers wealth management insurance financial planning retail brokerage and trust services as well. The company has total assets of $5.8 billion and deposits totaling about $4.5 billion.

Financial Analysis

The bank's revenue declined by 9% in 2011 vs. 2010 while net income fell more than 33% over the same period. First Commonwealth Financial returned to profitability in 2010 and remained profitable albeit less so in 2011. (The bank's focus on credit quality following a decline in loan demand during the deep recession have helped it return and remain profitable.)

Strategy

Over the last several decades First Commonwealth Financial has grown steadily through the acquisition of more than a dozen smaller banks and thrifts in its market area. However in recent years the company has focused more on organic growth and has expanded its franchise network by opening more than a dozen new branches in the Pittsburgh area since 2005.

EXECUTIVES

EVP and CFO, Robert E. (Bob) Rout, age 60
SVP Investments; SVP Trust and Treasury First Commonwealth Bank; SVP First Commonwealth Professional Resources, R. John Previte, age 62
SVP Secretary Treasurer and Director, David R. Tomb Jr., age 80, $268,000 total compensation
EVP Strategic Resources, Thaddeus J. (Thad) Clements, age 55
President CEO and Director, John J. Dolan, age 55, $460,000 total compensation
Chairman, David S. (Dave) Dahlmann, age 62
EVP and CIO; SVP First Commonwealth Bank, Sue A. McMurdy, age 55, $285,000 total compensation
SVP Controller and Interim Principal Financial Officer, Teresa M. Ciambotti
EVP and Chief Credit Officer First Commonwealth Bank, I. Robert (Bob) Emmerich
President First Commonwealth Bank, T. Michael (Mike) Price, age 49, $350,000 total compensation
EVP and Chief Audit Executive, Leonard V. Lombardi, age 52
SVP Secretary Treasurer and Director, David R. Tomb Jr., age 80
Director, Johnston A. Glass, age 62
President CEO and Director, John J. Dolan, age 55
Director, Robert J. Ventura, age 62
Director, Dale P. Latimer, age 81
Director, Julie A. Caponi, age 50
Director, David W. Greenfield, age 62
Director, Ray T. Charley, age 60
Director, James W. Newill, age 77
Director, Laurie Stern Singer, age 60
Director, Julia E. Trimarchi Cuccaro, age 51
Auditors: KPMGLLP

LOCATIONS

HQ: First Commonwealth Financial Corporation
22 N. 6th St., Indiana PA 15701
Phone: 724-349-7220 **Fax:** 888-711-2329
Web: www.fcbanking.com

PRODUCTS/OPERATIONS

2011 Sales

	$ mil.	% of total
Interest		
Loans including fees	197	69
Taxable investments	33	12
Other	0	-
Noninterest		
Service charges on deposit accounts	14	5
Card-related interchange income	12	4
Insurance & retail brokerage commissions	6	2
Trust income	6	2
Income from bank-owned life insurance	5	2
Other	12	4
Total	**289**	**100**

Selected Subsidiaries

First Commonwealth Bank
First Commonwealth Insurance Agency
First Commonwealth Home Mortgage LLC (49.9%)
First Commonwealth Financial Advisors Incorporated

COMPETITORS

Allegheny Valley Bancorp
AmeriServ Financial
Dollar Bank
ESB Financial
F.N.B. (PA)
Fidelity Bancorp (PA)
First Niagara Financial
Northwest Bancshares
PNC Financial
RBS Citizens Financial Group
S&T Bancorp

HISTORICAL FINANCIALS

Company Type: Public

Income Statement FYE: December 31

	ASSETS ($ mil.)	NET INCOME ($ mil.)	INCOME AS % OF ASSETS	EMPLOYEES
12/11	5,841	15	0.3%	1,506
12/10	5,812	22	0.4%	1,622
12/09	6,446	(20)	—	1,709
12/08	6,425	43	0.7%	1,693
12/07	5,883	46	0.8%	1,430
Annual Growth	(0.2%)	(24.2%)	—	1.3%

2011 Year-End Financials

Debt ratio: 3.55%
Return on equity: 2.01%
Cash ($ mil.): 78
Current ratio: —
Long-term debt ($ mil.): 207
No. of shares (mil.): 104
Dividends
Yield: —
Payout: 80.00%
Market value ($ mil.): 552

	STOCK PRICE ($) FY Close	P/E High	P/E Low	PER SHARE ($) Earnings	Dividends	Book Value
12/11	5.26	49	24	0.15	0.00	7.23
12/10	7.08	30	17	0.25	0.06	7.15
12/09	4.65	—	—	(0.24)	0.35	7.50
12/08	12.38	26	15	0.58	0.68	7.68
12/07	10.65	21	14	0.63	0.68	7.78
Annual Growth	(16.2%)	—	—	(30.1%)	—	(1.8%)

First Financial Bancorp (OH)

First Financial spreads itself thick. The holding company's flagship subsidiary First Financial Bank operates through around 160 branches in Indiana Kentucky and Ohio. Founded in 1863 the bank offers checking and savings accounts money market accounts CDs credit cards private banking wealth management and trust services. Commercial loans including real estate and construction loans make up about 70% of First Financial's total loan portfolio; the bank also offers residential mortgage and consumer loans. Another subsidiary First Financial

Capital Advisors acts as the investment advisor to the company's proprietary mutual funds The First Funds Group.

In 2009 First Financial acquired the branches and deposits of the failed Peoples Community Bancorp in an FDIC-assisted transaction adding about 20 locations in the Cincinnati area. It also purchased three Indiana branches from Irwin Financial along with a package of loans and deposits. That deal gave First Financial a larger foothold in Indiana. Irwin Financial's Irwin Union Bank and Irwin Union Bank and Trust subsidiaries later failed and were seized by regulators and First Financial Bancorp assumed all of the institutions' deposits and gained more than two dozen branches also in a FDIC-brokered deal. The transaction included restaurant franchisee lender Irwin Franchise Capital (now First Franchise Capital). The acquisitions boosted the bottom line of First Financial which remained profitable throughout the recession.

Meanwhile the company announced in 2010 that would exit the Michigan and Louisville Kentucky markets (areas it entered via the Irwin deal) in order to focus on its core markets of Indiana and southwestern Ohio. To that end it acquired 16 branches in western Ohio from Liberty Savings Bank bought 22 Indianapolis-area branches from Flagstar Bank in 2011.

EXECUTIVES

EVP and COO, C. Douglas (Doug) Lefferson, age 47, $262,404 total compensation
President CEO and Director; Chairman President and CEO First Financial Bank, Claude E. Davis, age 51, $420,000 total compensation
Chairman, Murph Knapke, age 64
VP and Controller, Elizabeth E. Fontaine, age 47
EVP and CFO, J. Franklin (Frank) Hall, age 43, $220,673 total compensation
SVP Chief Accounting Officer and Controller, Anthony M. Stollings, age 57
Market President Northwestern Indiana First Financial Bank, David S. Harvey
EVP Banking Markets, Samuel J. (Sam) Munafo, age 61, $228,461 total compensation
SVP Retail Credit and Product Management, John C. Hoying
Chairman President and CEO First Financial Insurance, Mark A. Willis
Market President North Manchester First Financial Bank, Michael R. Terrone
Market President Hartford City First Financial Bank, James M. (Jim) Weiseman
SVP Sales and Marketing, Jill L. Wyman, age 50
SVP and Chief Credit Officer, Richard S. Barbercheck, age 53
Assistant VP Investor Relations; Secretary First Financial Bancorp and First Financial Bank, Terri J. Ziepfel
Market President Butler and Warren First Financial Bank, Adrian O. Breen
Market President Southeastern Indiana First Financial Bank, Michael A. Sorrells
SVP and General Counsel, Gregory A. Gehlmann, age 50, $219,327 total compensation
Market President Cincinnati First Financial Bank, John Marrocco
Market President Northern Kentucky First Financial Bank, Thomas R. Saelinger
VP and Retail Market Manager Dayton and Middletown, Jason Newport
VP Commercial Lending Clark and Greene Counties First Financial Bank, Herb Greer
VP and Commercial Bank Manager First Financial Bank, Dan Kane
Market President Lafayette First Financial Bank, Bradley W. (Brad) Marley
Market President Celina and Van Wert First Financial Bank, George Brooks
Market President Clyde First Financial Bank, John Christman
Market President Hastings First Financial Bank, Cortney Collison
Market President Dayton and Middletown First Financial Bank, Roger Furrer
SVP and Managing Director Wealth Resource Group First Financial Bank, David C. Brooks
SVP and Chief Investment Officer First Financial Capital Advisors, Alfred Shepard
SVP and Chief Risk Officer, John Sabath
SVP and President Indiana First Financial Bank, Al Roszczyk
VP Investor Relations and Corporate Development, Kenneth Lovik
President CEO and Director; Chairman President and CEO First Financial Bank, Claude E. Davis, age 51
Director, Maribeth S. Rahe, age 63
Director, Donald M. Cisle, age 57
Director, Corinne R. Finnerty, age 55
Director, Steven C. Posey, age 61
Director, Mark A. Collar, age 59
Director, Susan L. Knust, age 58
Director, William J. Kramer, age 51
Director, Richard E. Olszewski, age 62
Director, J. Wickliffe Ach, age 63
Director, David S. Barker
Auditors: Ernst&YoungLLP

LOCATIONS

HQ: First Financial Bancorp
4000 Smith Rd. Ste. 400, Cincinnati OH 45209
Phone: 877-322-9530 **Fax:** 843-529-5883
Web: www.firstfinancialholdings.com

PRODUCTS/OPERATIONS

2011 Sales

	$ mil.	% of total
Interest		
Loans including fees	285	63
Investment securities	29	6
(Adjustment) (5.9) (1)		
Noninterest		
FDIC loss-sharing income	60	13
Accelerated discount on covered loans	20	5
Service charges on deposit accounts	19	4
Trust & wealth management fees	14	3
Bankcard income	9	2
Net gains from sales on loans	4	1
Gains of sales of investment securities	2	1
Other	11	3
Total	**451**	**100**

COMPETITORS

AMB Financial
Commercial Bancshares
Farmers National
Fifth Third
First Defiance Financial
First Franklin
LCNB
Liberty Capital
Logansport Financial
MutualFirst Financial
Peoples Community Bancorp
Peoples-Sidney
PNC Financial
Rurban Financial
U.S. Bancorp

HISTORICAL FINANCIALS

Company Type: Public

Income Statement FYE: December 31

	ASSETS ($ mil.)	NET INCOME ($ mil.)	INCOME AS % OF ASSETS	EMPLOYEES
12/11	6,671	66	1.0%	1,656
12/10	6,250	59	0.9%	1,664
12/09	6,681	246	3.7%	1,748
12/08	3,699	22	0.6%	1,127
12/07	3,369	35	1.1%	1,159
Annual Growth	18.6%	16.9%	—	9.3%

2011 Year-End Financials

Debt ratio: 1.15%
Return on equity: 9.37%
Cash ($ mil.): 525
Current ratio: —
Long-term debt ($ mil.): 76
No. of shares (mil.): 58
Dividends
Yield: —
Payout: 68.42%
Market value ($ mil.): 970

	STOCK PRICE ($) FY Close	P/E High	P/E Low	PER SHARE ($) Earnings	Dividends	Book Value
12/11	16.64	16	12	1.14	0.00	12.22
12/10	18.48	21	14	0.99	0.40	12.01
12/09	14.56	3	1	5.33	0.40	13.13
12/08	12.39	24	13	0.61	0.68	9.29
12/07	11.40	18	11	0.93	0.65	7.40
Annual Growth	9.9%	—	—	5.2%	—	13.4%

First Financial Bankshares, Inc.

Texas hold 'em? Well sort of. First Financial Bankshares is the holding company for eleven banks consolidated under the First Financial brand all of which are located in small and midsized markets in Texas. Together they have about 50 locations. The company maintains a decentralized management structure with each of the subsidiary banks having their own local leadership and decision-making authority. Its First Financial Trust & Asset Management subsidiary administers retirement and employee benefit plans in addition to providing trust services. First Financial Bankshares also owns an insurance agency.

Real estate mortgages account for approximately half of the company's loan portfolio while commercial financial and agricultural loans account for about another third. The banks also offer construction and consumer loans as well as deposit products like checking and savings accounts and CDs. Some locations offer brokerage services through arrangements with third parties.

First Financial Bankshares has grown both organically and through acquisitions. In 2010 the company bought Huntsville Texas-based Sam Houston Financial Corporation the parent of The First State Bank. The deal worth more than $22 million expanded First Financial Bankshares' footprint in East Texas. The following year The First State Bank changed its name to First Financial Bank bringing all of the company's banks under the same banner.

First Financial Bankshares continues to open new branches and seek out acquisitions of other banks in Texas with a continued focus on burgeoning smaller markets where competition is less intense than metropolitan areas. The company whose earnings have increased each year for a quarter-century has benefitted from the Texas economy which was not nearly as hard-hit by the recession as other regions and is one of the fastest-growing in the country. First Financial Bankshares has also gotten a boost by investing its capital wisely; a relatively large proportion of its revenues –more than 25% –comes from interest-earning assets such as mortgage-backed securities state and municipal bonds and government agency securities.

EXECUTIVES

Chairman President and CEO; Chairman First Financial Bank Abilene, F. Scott Dueser, age 58, $468,333 total compensation
SVP Lending, Tommy J. Barrow
SVP Human Resources First Financial Bank Abilene, Pamela (Pam) Mann
Chairman President and CEO First Financial Bank Cleburne Burleson Alvardo and Midlothian, Matt Reynolds
EVP and Senior Lending Officer, Gary S. Gragg, age 52, $177,500 total compensation
VP Investment Services, William A. (Bill) Rowe
EVP CFO Secretary and Treasurer, J. Bruce Hildebrand, age 56, $300,000 total compensation
EVP Operations, Gary L. Webb, age 54, $261,666 total compensation
Chairman President and CEO San Angelo National Bank, Michael L. (Mike) Boyd
Chairman President and CEO Hereford State Bank, Mike Mauldin
Assistant Secretary, Gaila N. Kilpatrick
Director Investor Relations and Corporate Communications, David A. (Dave) Hogan
VP Commercial Lending First Financial Bank Abilene, Daniel A. Ortiz
SVP Advertising and Marketing, Michele P. Stevens
EVP and Chief Administrative Officer; Chairman and CEO First Financial Bank Abilene, Ronald D. (Ron) Butler II
President and CEO First Financial Bank Stephenville Granbury Glen Rose and Acton, Ronald (Ron) Mullins
President and CEO First Financial Trust & Asset Management, Kirk W. Thaxton
Compliance Officer, Bob Goodner
President and CEO First Financial Bank Southlake Trophy Club Keller Bridgeport Boyd and Decatur, Mark L. Jones
SVP Training and Education, Courtney Jordan
Chairman First Financial Bank Sweetwater, J. V. Martin
President and CEO First Financial Bank Sweetwater, Kirby N. Andrews
Compliance Officer, Michelle Fagan
Chairman President and CEO First Financial Bank Eastland Ranger and Rising Star, Thomas M. (Tom) O'Neil
President and CEO First Financial Bank Weatherford Aledo Willow Park and Brock, Jay Gibbs
Chairman and CEO First Financial Bank Weatherford Aledo Willow Park and Brock, Doyle Lee
Chairman President and CEO First Financial Bank Mineral Wells, Kenneth A. (Ken) Williamson
President and CEO First Technology Services, Gary Tucker
President of First Financial Bank Abilene, Marelyn B. Shedd
EVP Lending, Marna Yerigan
Director, Joseph E. Canon, age 69
Director, Mac A. Coalson, age 72
Director, David L. Copeland, age 56
Director, Derrell E. Johnson, age 72
Director, Kade L. Matthews, age 53
Director, Dian Graves Stai, age 71
Director, Tucker S. Bridwell, age 60
Director, Johnny E. Trotter, age 60
Director, Murray Edwards, age 60
Director, Ronald (Ron) Giddiens, age 64
Auditors: Ernst&YoungLLP

LOCATIONS

HQ: First Financial Bankshares Inc.
400 Pine St., Abilene TX 79601
Phone: 325-627-7155 **Fax:** 325-627-7393
Web: www.ffin.com

PRODUCTS/OPERATIONS

2011 Sales

	$ mil.	% of total
Interest		
Loans including fees	98	47
Investment securities	60	28
Other	1	1
Noninterest		
Service charges on deposit accounts	17	8
ATM & credit card fees	13	6
Trust fees	12	6
Other	7	4
Total	**211**	**100**

Selected Subsidiaries

First Financial Bank National Association (Abilene)
First Financial Bank National Association (Cleburne)
First Financial Bank National Association (Eastland)
First Financial Bank National Association (Hereford)
First Financial Bank National Association (Huntsville)
First Financial Bank National Association (Mineral Wells)
First Financial Bank National Association (San Angelo)
First Financial Bank National Association (Southlake)
First Financial Bank National Association (Stephenville)
First Financial Bank National Association (Sweetwater)
First Financial Bank National Association (Weatherford)
First Financial Insurance Agency Inc.
First Financial Trust & Asset Management Company National Association

COMPETITORS

Bank of America
Compass Bancshares
Cullen/Frost Bankers
JPMorgan Chase
Wells Fargo
Woodforest Financial

HISTORICAL FINANCIALS

Company Type: Public

Income Statement FYE: December 31

	ASSETS ($ mil.)	NET INCOME ($ mil.)	INCOME AS % OF ASSETS	EMPLOYEES
12/11	4,120	68	1.7%	980
12/10	3,776	59	1.6%	1,000
12/09	3,279	53	1.6%	950
12/08	3,212	53	1.7%	1,000
12/07	3,070	49	1.6%	975
Annual Growth	7.6%	8.4%	—	0.1%

2011 Year-End Financials

Debt ratio: —
Return on equity: 13.44%
Cash ($ mil.): 312
Current ratio: —
Long-term debt ($ mil.): —
No. of shares (mil.): 31
Dividends
Yield: —
Payout: 43.63%
Market value ($ mil.): 1,043

	STOCK PRICE ($) FY Close	P/E High/Low		PER SHARE ($) Earnings	Dividends	Book Value
12/11	33.43	26	12	2.17	0.00	16.30
12/10	51.25	29	23	1.91	0.91	14.17
12/09	54.23	32	21	1.72	0.91	13.41
12/08	55.21	33	21	1.70	0.89	11.91
12/07	37.65	28	22	1.59	0.84	10.77
Annual Growth	(2.9%)	—	—	8.1%	—	10.9%

First Financial Corp. (IN)

Which came first the First Financial in Indiana Ohio South Carolina or Texas? Regardless this particular First Financial Corporation is the holding company for First Financial Bank which operates more than 60 branches in west-central Indiana and central Illinois. The bank offers traditional services such checking and savings accounts CDs and credit cards. It also provides trust private banking wealth management and investment services. First Financial sells personal and commercial insurance through regional agency subsidiary Forrest Sherer. Another unit Morris Plan originates indirect auto loans through some 70 dealerships in the bank's market area.

In 2011 First Financial bought Freestar Bank adding more than a dozen branches in central Illinois. It was the largest acquisition in the company's history. The bank also grows by opening new branches.

First Financial has remained profitable throughout the economic turmoil that began in earnest during 2008; not only that it has grown its net income each of the last three fiscal years including an increase of nearly 33% in 2011 when the company reported record earnings. Though the bank recorded fewer provisions for loan losses that year its amount of charged-off loans remained elevated compared to pre-recession levels. Commercial loans and mortgages account for more than half of the company's loan portfolio which also includes residential mortgage and consumer loans

With roots dating back to 1834 First Financial Bank is not only one of the oldest banks in Indiana but also the entire country. It is also one of the oldest continually operating businesses in its hometown of Terre Haute. Another local business Princeton Mining Company owns nearly 10% of First Financial Corporation.

EXECUTIVES

COO First Financial Bank, Norman D. Lowery, age 44
Vice Chairman and CEO; President and CEO First Financial Bank, Norman L. Lowery, age 65, $512,128 total compensation
VP Human Resources First Financial Bank, Karen Stinson
Chairman and President, Donald E. Smith, age 85, $614,640 total compensation
Branch Administrator First Financial Bank, Richard O. White, age 62, $157,630 total compensation

Chief Credit Officer First National Bank, Thomas S. Clary, age 59, $173,040 total compensation
Secretary and Treasurer; CFO First Financial Bank, Rodger McHargue, age 50
Director, Anton H. (Tony) George, age 52
Vice Chairman and CEO; President and CEO First Financial Bank, Norman L. Lowery, age 65
Director, B. Guille Cox Jr., age 66
Director, Gregory L. Gibson, age 49
Director, Virginia L. Smith, age 63
Director, Thomas T. Dinkel, age 61
Director, Patrick O'Leary, age 75
Director, William J. Voges, age 57
Director, W. Curtis Brighton, age 58
Director, Ronald K. Rich, age 74
Director, William R. Krieble
Auditors: CroweHorwathLLP

LOCATIONS

HQ: First Financial Corporation
1 First Financial Plaza, Terre Haute IN 47807
Phone: 812-238-6000 **Fax:** 812-238-6140
Web: www.first-online.com

PRODUCTS/OPERATIONS

2011 Sales

	$ mil.	% of total
Interest		
Loans including related fees	91	61
Securities	22	15
Other	2	1
Noninterest		
Service charges & fees on deposit accounts	9	6
Other service charges & fees	8	6
Insurance commissions	7	5
Trust & financial services	4	3
Other	4	3
Total	**149**	**100**

COMPETITORS

FFW
Fifth Third
First Midwest Bancorp
First Robinson Financial
Huntington Bancshares
JPMorgan Chase
MainSource Financial
Old National Bancorp
PNC Financial

HISTORICAL FINANCIALS

Company Type: Public

Income Statement FYE: December 31

	ASSETS ($ mil.)	NET INCOME ($ mil.)	INCOME AS % OF ASSETS	EMPLOYEES
12/11	2,954	37	1.3%	923
12/10	2,451	28	1.1%	813
12/09	2,518	22	0.9%	830
12/08	2,302	24	1.1%	766
12/07	2,231	25	1.1%	790
Annual Growth	7.3%	9.8%	—	4.0%

2011 Year-End Financials

Debt ratio: 4.96%
Return on equity: 10.72%
Cash ($ mil.): 134
Current ratio: —
Long-term debt ($ mil.): 146
No. of shares (mil.): 13
Dividends
Yield: —
Payout: 33.22%
Market value ($ mil.): 439

	STOCK PRICE ($) FY Close	P/E High/Low	PER SHARE ($) Earnings	Dividends	Book Value
12/11	33.28	12 9	2.83	0.00	26.29
12/10	35.14	17 12	2.14	0.92	24.46
12/09	30.52	25 16	1.73	0.90	23.34
12/08	40.99	26 13	1.89	0.89	21.87
12/07	28.34	18 12	1.94	0.87	21.44
Annual Growth	4.1%	— —	9.9%	—	5.2%

First Financial Holdings, Inc.

First Financial Holdings serves the Carolinas through subsidiary First Federal Savings and Loan Association of Charleston (First Federal). The bank has approximately 75 branches in North and South Carolina. First Federal offers checking and savings accounts retirement accounts and credit cards. The bank uses funds from deposits to write a variety of loans. Residential and commercial estate loans account for more than 80% of its loan portfolio. Other offerings include business mobile home and consumer loans. Other subsidiaries provide trust asset management and securities brokerage services.

First Federal has focused on maintaining a healthy balance sheet during the economic crisis as unemployment levels and mortgage defaults have risen in its market areas. The company's strategies include raising deposit levels while reducing its bad loan portfolio as well as the long-term goal of expanding its non-banking offerings to broaden revenues.

The downturn has brought some opportunities for expansion. In 2009 the bank took over the eight branches and accounts of failed North Carolina bank Cape Fear after it was shut down by the FDIC. That transaction provided First Federal entry to the North Carolina market. Later that year the company acquired retirement plan consulting and administrating firm American Pensions. In another FDIC-related transaction the company acquired certain assets and all deposits of the six-branch Plantation Federal Bank (thereby entering the Greenville market).

In 2012 First Federal acquired Liberty Savings Bank's five Hilton Head South Carolina branches. The $109.5 million deal expanded First Federal's deposit base in the Hilton Head area and added two new locations (three branches will be consolidated).

Meanwhile the company divested its insurance subsidiaries in order to focus on its core banking activities and to raise capital. It sold First Southeast Insurance Services to Hub International and Kimbrell Insurance Group to Burns & Wilcox in 2011. In another 2011 transaction First Financial sold more than $197 million in performing loans and other assets. The deal helped remove risk from the company's balance sheet.

In 2012 First Financial converted First Federal's charter to a commercial bank. The change to a bank charter was a result of new government regulations that removed any advantages to maintaining a savings and loan charter. First Financial then became a bank holding company.

EXECUTIVES

EVP Human Resources, Jerry P. Gazes
EVP and COO, Susan E. Baham, age 62, $227,326 total compensation
EVP, Charles F. Baarcke Jr., age 65, $227,326 total compensation
EVP; EVP First Federal Retail Banking Division, John L. Ott Jr., age 64, $227,326 total compensation
Director; President and Director First Federal Savings and Loan, A. Thomas Hood, age 66, $291,190 total compensation
EVP and CFO First Financial and First Federal, Blaise B. Bettendorf, age 49
SVP Investments First Federal Savings and Loan, Mark R. Adelson
SVP Marketing First Financial Holdings and First Federal Savings and Loan, R. Bruce Copeland Jr.
SVP Internal Audit First Financial Holdings and First Federal Savings and Loan, Betsy B. Lewis
EVP Insurance Services, Allison A. Rhyne
Director; President First Southeast Insurance Services and Kinghorn Insurance Services, James L. Rowe, age 69
President First Southeast Investor Services, Timothy B. Sease
SVP Planning and Development First Financial Holdings and First Federal Savings and Loan, Richard H. Stoughton
Chairman, Paula Harper Bethea, age 57
Director, Paul G. Campbell Jr., age 66
Vice Chairman, Thomas J. Johnson, age 61
Chairman First Financial Holdings and First Federal Savings and Loan, James C. Murray, age 73
President and CEO First Financial and First Federal and Director, R. Wayne Hall, age 62, $233,665 total compensation
SVP First Federal, C. Alexander Elmore Jr., age 52, $175,074 total compensation
VP Sales First Federal Savings and Loan, Karen L. Ross
SVP and Chief Risk Officer, George D. Clonts
VP Investor Relations and Corporate Secretary; Corporate Secretary First Federal Savings and Loan, Dorothy B. (DeeBee) Wright
SVP Branch Administration First Federal Savings and Loan, Robert C. Bailey
SVP Retail Lending First Federal Savings and Loan, Elton K. Carrier
SVP Lending and Loan Operations First Federal Savings and Loan, Kenneth J. Clair
SVP Loan Servicing First Federal Savings and Loan, Charles L. Clark II
SVP and Controller First Federal Savings and Loan; CFO First Southeast Investor Services, Mark G. Endres
SVP Information Technology First Federal Savings and Loan, Anthony J. Johnston IV
SVP Support Services First Federal Savings and Loan, Robert F. Snyder Jr.
VP Employment First Federal Savings and Loan, Susan Bagwell
VP and City Executive North Strand First Federal Savings and Loan, Laurence S. Bolchoz Jr.
VP Trust Services First Federal Savings and Loan; President First Southeast Fiduciary & Trust Services, Stephen D. Bowen III
VP and City Executive Summerville First Federal Savings and Loan, James G. Burgess Jr.
VP Employee Relations First Federal Savings and Loan, Lisa G. DeVeaux
VP and City Executive West Ashley First Federal Savings and Loan, William D. Hilton Jr.
VP and City Executive Hilton Head First Federal Savings and Loan, Stewart J. Hull
VP and Mortgage Sales Manager First Federal Savings and Loan, Todd C. Huss

VP and City Executive South Strand First Federal Savings and Loan, Blinda J. Hutchinson
VP and City Executive Florence First Federal Savings and Loan, James M. Ivey Jr.
VP CRA/Community Development First Federal Savings and Loan, Edward McKelvey Jr.
VP Retail Banking North Region First Federal Savings and Loan, William A. Nelson
VP Savings Administration and City Executive Charleston First Federal Savings and Loan, Harold J. Petterson
VP Secondary Marketing and Mortgage Technology First Federal Savings and Loan, Charles H. Stuart
VP and Director of Commercial Lending First Federal Savings and Loan, Andrew B. Thomas
VP and City Executive East Cooper First Federal Savings and Loan, Molly R. Thomas
VP Correspondent Lending First Federal Savings and Loan, Peter C. Wehman
VP Credit First Federal Savings and Loan, J. Eric Wooten
EVP and Chief Banking Officer, James Dale Hall
EVP and Chief Credit Officer, Joseph W. Amy
Director; President and Director First Federal Savings and Loan, A. Thomas Hood, age 66
Director; President First Southeast Insurance Services and Kinghorn Insurance Services, James L. Rowe, age 69
Chairman, Paula Harper Bethea, age 57
Director, Paul G. Campbell Jr., age 66
Vice Chairman, Thomas J. Johnson, age 61
Chairman First Financial Holdings and First Federal Savings and Loan, James C. Murray, age 73
Director First Financial and First Federal, D. Kent Sharples, age 69
President and CEO First Financial and First Federal and Director, R. Wayne Hall, age 62
Director, Henry M. Swink, age 66
Director, Ronnie M. Givens, age 69
Auditors: GrantThorntonLLP

LOCATIONS

HQ: First Financial Holdings, Inc.
2440 Mall Drive, Charleston, SC 29406
Phone: 843 529-5933 **Fax:** 843 529-5929
Web: www.firstfinancialholdings.com

PRODUCTS/OPERATIONS

2011 Sales

	$ mil.	% of total
Interest		
Loans including fees	139	67
Investments	18	9
Other	2	1
Noninterest		
Service charges on deposit accounts	26	13
Mortgage & other loan income	10	5
Trust & plan administration	4	2
Brokerage fees	2	1
Other	3	2
Adjustments	(0.9)	-
Total	**207**	**100**

Selected Subsidiaries

First Federal Savings and Loan Association of Charleston
First Reinsurance Holdings Inc.
First Southeast Reinsurance Co. Inc.
The Carolopolis Corporation
First Southeast Investor Services Inc.

COMPETITORS

Bank of America
BB&T
Fifth Third
First Citizens Bancorporation
JPMorgan Chase
Regions Financial
SCBT Financial
SunTrust
Wells Fargo

HISTORICAL FINANCIALS

Company Type: Public

Income Statement

FYE: September 30

	ASSETS ($ mil.)	NET INCOME ($ mil.)	INCOME AS % OF ASSETS	EMPLOYEES
09/11	3,206	(41)	—	876
09/10	3,323	(36)	—	1,129
09/09	3,510	29	0.8%	1,023
09/08	2,973	22	0.8%	915
09/07	2,711	25	0.9%	873
Annual Growth	4.3%	—	—	0.1%

2011 Year-End Financials

Debt ratio: 18.88%
Return on equity: (-15.34)%
Cash ($ mil.): 85
Current ratio: —
Long-term debt ($ mil.): 605
No. of shares (mil.): 16
Dividends
Yield: 4.99%
Payout: —
Market value ($ mil.): 66

	STOCK PRICE ($) FY Close	P/E High	P/E Low	PER SHARE ($) Earnings	Dividends	Book Value
09/11	4.01	—	—	(2.72)	0.20	16.25
09/10	11.14	—	—	(2.46)	0.20	19.25
09/09	15.97	11	2	2.50	0.41	22.12
09/08	26.18	17	8	1.94	1.02	15.69
09/07	31.28	19	13	2.07	0.00	15.96
Annual Growth	(40.2%)	—	—	—	—	0.5%

First Horizon National Corp

First Horizon would like to be the first bank people think of in the Volunteer State and beyond. The company operates more than 170 First Tennessee Bank branches in its home state and neighboring markets. In addition to general banking services like loans deposit accounts and credit cards the company also offers trust asset management financial advisory and investment services. Subsidiary FTN Financial performs securities sales and trading fixed-income underwriting and other investment banking services through more than 15 offices in more than a dozen states as well as Hong Kong and Tokyo.

The challenging economy and slow recovery has been problematic for First Horizon but the company has been trying to adapt by becoming leaner and more flexible.

At the start of the recession First Horizon began selling non-core assets and refocused growth closer to home. During the past few years First Horizon exited the Baltimore-Washington DC and Atlanta markets. The company also sold some 230 First Horizon Home Loan offices as well as the unit's loan origination and servicing operations outside of Tennessee to MetLife. After the sale First Horizon Financial outsourced some its mortgage origination processing and servicing operations within Tennessee to PHH Mortgage.

In 2008 the bank discontinued its specialty construction and consumer lending activities beyond Tennessee. It exited the institutional equity research business in 2010 and sold its First Horizon Insurance unit to Brown & Brown the following year. Also in 2011 First Horizon sold a subsidiary that provided administrative services for health savings accounts.

First Horizon's strategy has helped. Although revenues were down First Horizon returned to profitability in 2011 after suffering hundreds of millions of dollars of loan-related losses in prior years. By 2011 asset quality improved. Net charge-offs dropped significantly and nonperforming assets declined by 38%. Lower revenues in 2011 were due to a decline in mortgage banking capital markets and net interest income. The company's positive performance reflected its choice to focus on its core businesses of regional banking and capital markets.

As the company continues to concentrate on improving its efficiency and as economic conditions improve First Horizon may look to make acquisitions. In 2012 the company added to FTN Financial with the purchase of Las Vegas-based Main Street Capital Advisors which provides investment management and consulting services mainly to state and local municipalities.

EXECUTIVES

EVP and Chief Human Resources Officer, John M. Daniel, age 57
EVP; Chief Accounting Officer First Horizon and First Tennessee Bank, James F. (Jim) Keen, age 61
EVP Regional Banking; COO First Tennessee Bank, David T. Popwell
Chairman President and CEO, D. Bryan Jordan, age 50, $830,769 total compensation
Chairman, Michael D. Rose, age 68
President Banking, Charles G. Burkett, age 61, $756,000 total compensation
EVP Government Relations, Herbert H. (Herb) Hilliard, age 64
EVP and General Counsel, Charles T. Tuggle Jr., age 63, $493,269 total compensation
SVP Corporate Secretary and Assistant General Counsel, Clyde A. Billings Jr.
EVP Corporate Communications, Kim Cherry
EVP Corporate Banking First Tennessee Bank, Christine B. Munson
EVP and Corporate Treasurer, Thomas C. Adams Jr., age 62, $363,462 total compensation
EVP and CIO, Bruce Livesay
EVP and CFO, William C. (BJ) Losch III, age 41, $400,000 total compensation
EVP and Chief Credit Officer, Gregory D. (Greg) Jardine, age 56
EVP and Chief Risk Officer, Yousef A. Valine, age 52
President FTN Financial, Michael E. Kisber, age 52
Media Relations, Jack Bradley
Director, Vicki R. Palmer, age 58
Director, R. Brad Martin, age 60
Director, James A. (Jimmy) Haslam III, age 58
Director, William B. (Bill) Sansom, age 70
Director, Colin V. Reed, age 64
Director, Robert B. (Rob) Carter, age 52
President CEO and Director, D. Bryan Jordan, age 50
Director, Mark A. Emkes, age 59
Director, Luke Yancy III, age 62
Director, John C. Compton, age 50
Director, Vicky B. Gregg, age 57
Auditors: KPMGLLP

LOCATIONS

HQ: First Horizon National Corporation
165 Madison Ave., Memphis TN 38103
Phone: 901-523-4444 **Fax:** 925-361-9999
Web: www.epicor.com

PRODUCTS/OPERATIONS

2010 Sales

	$ mil.	% of total
Interest		
Loans including fees	654	40
Investment securities	118	7
Trading securities	43	3
Loans held for sale	15	1
Other	0	-
Noninterest		
Capital markets	355	22
Deposit transactions & cash management	134	8
Mortgage banking	90	6
Trust services & investment management	25	2
Brokerage management fees & commissions	23	1
Insurance commissions	3	-
Other	153	10
Total	**1,618**	**100**

COMPETITORS

Athens Federal Community Bank
Bank of America
BB&T
Citigroup
JPMorgan Chase
Regions Financial
SunTrust
Trustmark
Wells Fargo

HISTORICAL FINANCIALS

Company Type: Public

Income Statement FYE: December 31

	ASSETS ($ mil.)	NET INCOME ($ mil.)	INCOME AS % OF ASSETS	EMPLOYEES
12/11	24,789	131	0.5%	4,809
12/10	24,698	50	0.2%	5,487
12/09	26,068	(269)	—	5,739
12/08	31,021	(191)	—	6,266
12/07	37,015	(170)	—	10,130
Annual Growth	(9.5%)	—	—	(17.0%)

2011 Year-End Financials

Debt ratio: 10.01%
Return on equity: 5.49%
Cash ($ mil.): 837
Current ratio: —
Long-term debt ($ mil.): 2,481
No. of shares (mil.): 257
Dividends
Yield: —
Payout: 8.00%
Market value ($ mil.): 2,060

	STOCK PRICE ($) FY Close	P/E High/Low	PER SHARE ($) Earnings	Dividends	Book Value
12/11	8.00	25 11	0.50	0.00	9.28
12/10	11.78	— —	(0.25)	0.00	9.05
12/09	13.40	— —	(1.49)	0.00	13.55
12/08	10.57	— —	(1.10)	0.40	17.41
12/07	18.15	— —	(1.35)	1.80	19.24
Annual Growth	(18.5%)	— —	—	—	(16.7%)

First Interstate BancSystem, Inc.

This Treasure State bank wants to be your treasury. First Interstate BancSystem is the holding company for First Interstate Bank which has more than 70 branches in Montana western South Dakota and Wyoming. Serving area consumers businesses and municipalities the bank provides traditional services including deposit accounts wealth management and loans. Commercial loans including mortgages make up more than half of the bank's loan portfolio; residential real estate agricultural and construction loans round out its lending activities. On the wealth management side the bank has more than $3 billion in trust assets held in a fiduciary or agent capacity.

First Interstate remained profitable throughout the recession as the economy in its market area – bolstered by tourism agriculture and energy –was not hit as hard as other parts of the country. (In fact the company has reported a profit for each year for more than two decades.) It was not immune to pressures however as credit quality deteriorated and the bank suffered from loan losses. Construction loans and commercial mortgages make up the bulk of First Interstate's nonperforming loan portfolio which topped out at 6.6% of total loans in 2011. As such interest earnings slipped causing overall revenues to fall 5% that year to $385 million.

The company is eyeing opportunities for expansion including organic growth as well as growth through acquisitions.

The Scott family including brothers Thomas (chairman) James (vice chairman) and Homer (founder) controls First Interstate BancSystem which went public in 2010.

EXECUTIVES

President CEO and Director, Lyle R. Knight, age 66, $544,677 total compensation
Vice Chairman, James R. Scott, age 62
Chairman, Thomas W. Scott, age 68, $380,000 total compensation
EVP and CFO, Terrill R. Moore, age 59, $261,385 total compensation
President CEO and Director, Edward Garding, age 62, $259,385 total compensation
SVP and CIO, Kevin J. Guenthner
President First Interstate Bank Wealth Management, Julie G. Castle, age 51, $223,846 total compensation
SVP and Chief Credit Officer, Robert M. Cerkovnik
EVP and Chief Banking Officer, Michael G. Huston
Director, Martin A. White, age 70
Director, Michael J. (Mike) Sullivan, age 72
President CEO and Director, Lyle R. Knight, age 66
Director, Charles E. Hart, age 62
Vice Chairman, James R. Scott, age 62
President CEO and Director, Edward Garding, age 62
Director, David H. Crum, age 67
Director, William B. Ebzery, age 61
Director, James W. Haugh, age 74
Director, Ross E. Leckie, age 54
Director, Terry W. Payne, age 70
Director, Julie A. Scott, age 40
Director, Randall I. Scott, age 58
Director, Sandra A. Scott Suzor, age 52
Director, Charles M. Heyneman, age 51
Director, Steven J. Corning, age 59
Auditors: McGladreyLLP

LOCATIONS

HQ: First Interstate BancSystem Inc.
401 N. 31st St., Billings MT 59116-0001
Phone: 406-255-5390 **Fax:** 406-255-5160
Web: www.firstinterstatebank.com

PRODUCTS/OPERATIONS

2011 Sales

	$ mil.	% of total
Interest		
Loans including fees	245	64
Taxable investment securities	41	11
Other	5	1
Noninterest		
Origination & sale of loans	21	6
Service charges on deposit accounts	17	5
Wealth management	13	3
Other service charges commissions & fees	31	8
Other	8	2
Total	**384**	**100**

COMPETITORS

Bank of the West
Crazy Woman Creek
Eagle Bancorp
Glacier Bancorp
Great Western Bancorporation
U.S. Bancorp
Wells Fargo

HISTORICAL FINANCIALS

Company Type: Public

Income Statement FYE: December 31

	ASSETS ($ mil.)	NET INCOME ($ mil.)	INCOME AS % OF ASSETS	EMPLOYEES
12/11	7,325	44	0.6%	1,677
12/10	7,500	37	0.5%	1,723
12/09	7,137	53	0.8%	1,727
12/08	6,628	70	1.1%	0
12/07	0	68	****************%	0
Annual Growth	—	(10.2%)	—	—

2011 Year-End Financials

Debt ratio: 2.20%
Return on equity: 5.78%
Cash ($ mil.): 472
Current ratio: —
Long-term debt ($ mil.): 160
No. of shares (mil.): 42
Dividends
Yield: —
Payout: 47.66%
Market value ($ mil.): 560

	STOCK PRICE ($) FY Close	P/E High/Low	PER SHARE ($) Earnings	Dividends	Book Value
12/11	13.03	17 10	0.96	0.00	17.94
12/10	15.24	20 13	0.85	0.45	17.21
Annual Growth	(14.5%)	— —	12.9%	—	4.2%

First Merchants Corp.

First Merchants makes community banking its first priority. The company owns First Merchants Bank which operates some 80 branches in Indiana and western Ohio. Along with its Lafayette Bank and Trust and Commerce National Bank divisions the bank provides standard consumer and commercial banking services including checking and savings accounts CDs check cards and loans and mortgages. First Merchants Corporation also owns First Merchants Trust Company which provides trust and asset management services and First Merchants Insurance Services which sells personal property/casualty and employee benefit coverage.

Loans secured by commercial real estate and farmland account for the largest portion of First Merchants' loan portfolio (more than 40%) followed by residential mortgages and business loans. After setting aside more than $120 million to cover loan losses in 2009 the company returned to profitability in 2010. Higher interest margins and reduced expenses contributed to its results but mainly better loan portfolio management helped the bank to cut its provisions for loan losses by more than half. The company built upon its performance in 2011 as the economy continued to exhibit signs of rebound. First Merchants is also building its technological capabilities such as online and mobile banking.

Geographic expansion has also been a key part of the company's strategy for growth. In 2012 it acquired certain loans and core deposits of Shelby County Bank which was seized by the FDIC. The deal included four branches in Shelby County Indiana a new market for First Merchants. In 2008 the company bought Lincoln Bancorp the parent of Lincoln Bank which had about 15 offices in the Indianapolis area.

EXECUTIVES

SVP and CIO, Robert R. Connors, age 62, $200,000 total compensation
SVP and Director Human Resources, Kimberly J. (Kim) Ellington, age 52
Director; Regional President Central Region First Merchants Bank, Jerry R. Engle, age 67
EVP and CFO, Mark K. Hardwick, age 41, $250,000 total compensation
Regional President Southeast Region First Merchants Bank, Jack L. Demaree
Regional President Lafayette Bank & Trust, Tony S. Albrecht
Regional President North Central Region First Merchants Bank, Michael L. (Mike) Baker
Regional President First Merchants Bank, James A. Meinerding
Regional President Northeast Region First Merchants Bank, Robert G. (Bob) Bell
CTO, Stephan H. Fluhler
Chairman, Charles E. Schalliol, age 64
SVP Administration Services, Shawn R. Blackburn, age 58
President CEO and Director, Michael C. (Mike) Rechin, age 53, $350,000 total compensation
Secretary and Shareholder Relations Officer, Cynthia G. Holaday
Regional President Commerce National Bank, Jennifer M. Griffith
SVP and Chief Credit Officer First Merchants Bank, David W. Spade, age 59, $179,823 total compensation
EVP and Chief Banking Officer, Michael J. (Mike) Stewart, age 46, $245,000 total compensation
SVP and Chief Accounting Officer, Jami L. Bradshaw, age 49, $119,878 total compensation
SVP and Chief Risk Officer, Jeffrey B. Lorentson, age 48
President and CEO First Merchants Trust, Terri Matchett
SVP and Chief Credit Officer, John J. Martin, age 45, $161,423 total compensation
First VP and Director Investor Relations, David L. Ortega
Head Purchasing, Lisa Brothers
Head Human Resources, Kim Ellington
Director, Thomas B. Clark, age 66
Director, Roderick (Rod) English, age 60
Director, Patrick A. Sherman, age 64
Director; Regional President Central Region First Merchants Bank, Jerry R. Engle, age 67
Director, Barry J. Hudson, age 72
Director, Jean L. Wojtowicz, age 54
Director, Jo Ann M. Gora, age 66
President CEO and Director, Michael C. (Mike) Rechin, age 53
Director, Terry L. Walker, age 65
Director, William L. Hoy, age 63
Auditors: BKDLLP

LOCATIONS

HQ: First Merchants Corp.
200 East Jackson Street, Muncie, IN 47305-2814
Phone: 765 747-1500
Web: www.firstmerchants.com

PRODUCTS/OPERATIONS

2011 Sales

	$ mil.	% of total
Interest		
Loans receivable	150	65
Investment securities	29	13
Other	—	1
Noninterest		
Service charges on deposit accounts	12	5
Other customer fees	10	4
Fiduciary activities	7	3
Net gains & fees on sales of loans	7	3
Commissions	5	3
Other	6	3
Total	**230**	**100**

COMPETITORS

Ameriana Bancorp
JPMorgan Chase
MainSource Financial
MutualFirst Financial
Old National Bancorp
STAR Financial Group
U.S. Bancorp

HISTORICAL FINANCIALS

Company Type: Public

Income Statement FYE: December 31

	ASSETS ($ mil.)	NET INCOME ($ mil.)	INCOME AS % OF ASSETS	EMPLOYEES
12/11	4,173	25	0.6%	1,144
12/10	4,170	6	0.2%	1,178
12/09	4,480	(40)	—	1,207
12/08	4,784	20	0.4%	1,367
12/07	3,782	31	0.8%	1,121
Annual Growth	2.5%	(5.5%)	—	0.5%

2011 Year-End Financials

Debt ratio: 7.98%
Return on equity: 4.91%
Cash ($ mil.): 126
Current ratio: —
Long-term debt ($ mil.): 333
No. of shares (mil.): 28
Dividends
Yield: —
Payout: 11.76%
Market value ($ mil.): 242

	STOCK PRICE ($) FY Close	P/E High/Low		PER SHARE ($) Earnings	Dividends	Book Value
12/11	8.47	29	20	0.34	0.00	18.01
12/10	8.86	20	11	0.48	0.04	17.77
12/09	5.94	—	—	(2.17)	0.47	21.85
12/08	22.21	26	14	1.14	0.92	18.69
12/07	21.84	16	11	1.73	0.92	18.88
Annual Growth	(21.1%)	—	—	(33.4%)	—	(1.2%)

First Midwest Bancorp, Inc. (Naperville, IL)

There's a lot of cabbage in corn country. Just ask First Midwest Bancorp the holding company for First Midwest Bank. Through about 100 branches the bank mainly serves suburban Chicago though its market extends into central and western Illinois and neighboring portions of Iowa and Indiana. Focusing on area small to mid-sized businesses it offers deposit products loans trust services wealth management insurance and retirement plan services; it has more than $5 billion of client trust and investment assets under management. Commercial real estate loans account for more than half of the company's portfolio; commercial and industrial loans are around a third.

Illustrative of its commitment to business lending First Midwest Bank does not originate subprime residential mortgages or retail credit card loans and one- to four-family residential mortgages account for less than 5% of its portfolio. The company does have a significant amount of nonperforming residential construction loans particularly raw land loans on its books but its delinquency rates have declined since 2008.

Not coincidentially First Midwest suffered losses each year from 2008 to 2010 but returned to profitability in 2011 reporting earnings of some $25.4 million on revenues of more than $423 million as its credit quality continued to improve. It hopes to keep the momentum going by focusing on niche lending and fee-generating activities such as wealth and treasury management.

First Midwest has capitalized on the rash of bank failures that have occurred in the Chicago area amid the recessionary economy. Its relative financial soundness put it in a position to acquire three failed Illinois banks through separate FDIC-facilitated transactions in 2009 and 2010: First DuPage Bank Peotone Bank and Trust and Palos Bank and Trust. The deals which included loss-sharing agreements with the regulator added a total of nearly 10 branches. In 2012 the company acquired the deposits and loans of Waukegan Savings Bank in another FDIC-assisted deal that added two more branches to its network. First Midwest will continue to consider acquisitions of failed banks in the Chicago area.

EXECUTIVES

Chairman, Robert P. (Bob) O'Meara, age 74, $560,000 total compensation
President CEO and Director; Chairman and CEO First Midwest Bank, Michael L. Scudder, age 51, $623,077 total compensation
EVP and Director Retail Sales and Services First Midwest Bank, Janet M. Viano, age 56
EVP CIO and COO First Midwest Bank, Kent S. Belasco, age 60
EVP and Director of Strategic Planning and Execution First Midwest Bank, Stephanie R. Wise, age 44
EVP and Chief Credit Officer First Midwest Bank, Michael J. Kozak, age 60
EVP and CFO, Paul F. Clemens, age 59, $306,346 total compensation
EVP and Corporate Secretary, Cynthia A. Lance, age 43

SEVP and COO; President and Chief Operating Officer First Midwest Bank, Mark G. Sander, age 53
EVP and Director Commercial Banking First Midwest Bank, Victor P. Carapella
EVP and Treasurer, James P. Hotchkiss, age 55
EVP and Director of Wealth Management First Midwest Bank, Robert P. Diedrich
EVP and Chief Risk Officer, Kevin L. Moffitt
EVP and Director Retail Banking First Midwest Bank, Thomas M. Prame
Director, Joseph W. England, age 71
Director, Michael J. Small, age 54
Director, J. Stephen (Steve) Vanderwoude, age 68
Director, John E. (Jack) Rooney, age 69
Director, Patrick J. McDonnell, age 68
Director, Bruce S. Chelberg, age 77
Director, James Gaffney, age 69
Director, John L. Sterling, age 68
Director, Thomas M. Garvin, age 76
Director, Phupinder S. Gill, age 51
Director, Ellen A. Rudnick, age 61
President CEO and Director; Chairman and CEO First Midwest Bank, Michael L. Scudder, age 51
Director, John F. Chlebowski, age 66
Director, Barbara A. Boigegrain, age 54
Auditors: Ernst&YoungLLP

LOCATIONS

HQ: First Midwest Bancorp Inc.
1 Pierce Place Ste. 1500, Itasca IL 60143
Phone: 630-875-7450 **Fax:** 858-550-7506
Web: www.ligand.com

PRODUCTS/OPERATIONS

2011 Sales

	$ mil.	% of total
Interest		
Loans	252	59
Investment securities	36	9
Covered loans	28	7
Other	3	1
Noninterest		
Service charges on deposit accounts	37	9
Card-based fees	19	4
Waelth management fees	16	4
Other service charges commissions & fees	20	5
Other	7	2
Total	**423**	**100**

COMPETITORS

Bank of America
BankFinancial
Cummins-Allison
Fifth Third
First Busey
Harris
JPMorgan Chase
Meta Financial Group
Northern Trust
PrivateBancorp
QCR Holdings
West Suburban Bancorp
Wintrust Financial

HISTORICAL FINANCIALS

Company Type: Public

Income Statement FYE: December 31

	ASSETS ($ mil.)	NET INCOME ($ mil.)	INCOME AS % OF ASSETS	EMPLOYEES
12/11	7,973	36	0.5%	1,768
12/10	8,146	(9)	—	1,820
12/09	7,710	(25)	—	1,722
12/08	8,528	49	0.6%	1,794
12/07	8,091	80	1.0%	1,843
Annual Growth	(0.4%)	(17.8%)	—	(1.0%)

2011 Year-End Financials

Debt ratio: 4.57%
Return on equity: 3.80%
Cash ($ mil.): 641
Current ratio: —
Long-term debt ($ mil.): 364
No. of shares (mil.): 74
Dividends
Yield: —
Payout: 11.43%
Market value ($ mil.): 754

	STOCK PRICE ($) FY Close	P/E High/Low		PER SHARE ($) Earnings	Dividends	Book Value
12/11	10.13	38	20	0.35	0.00	12.93
12/10	11.52	—	—	(0.27)	0.04	15.01
12/09	10.89	—	—	(0.71)	0.04	17.18
12/08	19.97	32	14	1.00	1.16	18.68
12/07	30.60	24	18	1.62	1.20	14.94
Annual Growth	(24.1%)	—	—	(31.8%)	—	(3.5%)

First Niagara Financial Group, Inc.

A lot of water and a few barrels have gone over Niagara Falls since First Niagara Bank was founded. Tracing its roots to 1870 the flagship subsidiary of acquisitive First Niagara Financial operates about 430 branches in upstate New York Connecticut Massachusetts and Pennsylvania. The bank offers financial services like deposits loans insurance investments and wealth management. Commercial real estate loans business loans and residential mortgages account for most of the bank's loan portfolio. Subsidiary First Niagara Risk Management offers risk management employee benefits consulting and investment services while First Niagara Commercial Bank accepts municipal deposits.

First Niagara has been expanding rapidly via transformative acquisitions. In 2012 the company bought nearly 200 HSBC branches in upstate New York and Connecticut for some $1 billion. To satisfy antitrust concerns it is selling more than 35 locations included in the deal to KeyCorp and nearly 30 more to Community Bank System and Financial Institutions in separate transactions. The company is also consolidating 35 branches with nearby locations. In addition to expanding First Niagara's branch network the HSBC acquisition will boost the company's commercial business and credit card portfolio as well.

First Niagara previously entered Pennsylvania in a big way acquiring more than 50 branches from PNC Financial in 2009 and buying bank holding company Harleysville National the next year. The PNC acquisition which expanded First Niagara's operations into western Pennsylvania included locations that PNC was compelled to divest to satisfy antitrust concerns regarding its takeover of National City. The purchase of Harleysville National Bank added some 80 branches in central and eastern Pennsylvania.

First Niagara expanded its insurance business in Pennsylvania in 2010 with the acquisitions of employee benefits risk management and investment services firm Banyan Consulting and Summit Insurance Group's operations in the state. The new businesses were combined with previous acquisitions RTI Insurance Services and Three Rivers Financial Services and took the First Niagara Risk Management name.

To facilitate its expansion First Niagara Financial converted from a thrift holding company to a bank holding company and First Niagara Bank converted from a savings institution to a commercial bank in 2010 moves that gave the company more flexibility in making acquisitions.

In 2011 the company completed its $1.5 billion acquisition of NewAlliance Bancshares adding some 90 bank branches and extending its franchise into Connecticut and Massachusetts. The addition along with organic growth in First Niagara's commercial loan portfolio contributed to a nearly 25% increase in net income for the company that year.

Prior to its latest round of acquisitions First Niagara Financial had already more than doubled its size with an earlier spree of smaller deals. It had fewer than 50 branches operating under its banner at the end of 2003. That year the company acquired Finger Lakes Bancorp. It bought Troy Financial in 2004 and Hudson River Bancorp the following year. In 2008 the company bought Great Lakes Bancorp the parent of Greater Buffalo Savings Bank.

EXECUTIVES

EVP Commercial Real Estate, G. Gary Berner, age 64, $239,615 total compensation
President CEO and Director, John R. Koelmel, age 59, $691,346 total compensation
EVP Operations, Frank J. Polino, age 52, $265,750 total compensation
EVP Commercial Business; Regional President Western New York, Daniel E. Cantara III, age 52, $326,539 total compensation
Vice Chairman, David M. Zebro, age 61
Chairman, G. Thomas Bowers, age 68
Regional President Eastern New York, Thomas L. Amell
Treasurer and Chief Investment Officer, Michael W. Harrington, age 48, $344,231 total compensation
SVP and Chief Administrative Officer, Elizabeth A. (Beth) Bauman, age 51
Manager Public Relations and Corporate Communications, Leslie G. Garrity
Investor Relations, Jason Benten
Manager Investor Relations, Anthony M. Alessi
EVP and COO, Gary M. Crosby, age 58
SVP Retail Banking, Mark R. Rendulic
SVP and CIO, John Petrey
CFO, Gregory W. Norwood
Treasurer, Jeffrey J Maddigan
EVP Corporate Development, Oliver H. Sommer, age 43
EVP and Chief Risk Officer, Richard Barry
Director, Barbara S. Jeremiah, age 60
Director, Nathaniel D. (Nat) Woodson, age 68
Director, Carlton L. Highsmith, age 59
President CEO and Director, John R. Koelmel, age 59
Director, Carl A. Florio, age 63
Director, Peter B. Robinson, age 63
Director, William H. (Tony) Jones, age 69
Director, Louise Woerner, age 69
Vice Chairman, David M. Zebro, age 61
Director, George M. Philip, age 64
Director, Roxanne J. Coady, age 60
Director, Thomas E. Baker, age 68
Auditors: KPMGLLP

LOCATIONS

HQ: First Niagara Financial Group Inc.
726 Exchange St. Ste. 618, Buffalo NY 14210
Phone: 716-819-5500 **Fax:** 952-829-2743
Web: www.surmodics.com

PRODUCTS/OPERATIONS

2011 Sales

	$ mil.	% of total
Interest		
Loans & leases	704	54
Investment securities & other	360	28
Noninterest		
Banking services	92	7
Insurance commissions	65	5
Wealth management services	30	2
Mortgage banking	15	1
Lending & leasing	13	1
Other	28	2
Total	**1,310**	**100**

COMPETITORS

Capital One
Citigroup
Community Bank System
HSBC USA
JPMorgan Chase
KeyCorp
M&T Bank
NBT Bancorp
PNC Financial
RBS Citizens Financial Group
SEFCU
TD Bank USA

HISTORICAL FINANCIALS

Company Type: Public

Income Statement FYE: December 31

	ASSETS ($ mil.)	NET INCOME ($ mil.)	INCOME AS % OF ASSETS	EMPLOYEES
12/11	32,810	173	0.5%	4,827
12/10	21,083	140	0.7%	3,791
12/09	14,584	79	0.5%	3,000
12/08	9,331	88	0.9%	1,909
12/07	8,096	84	1.0%	1,824
Annual Growth	41.9%	19.9%	—	27.5%

2011 Year-End Financials

Debt ratio: 18.04%
Return on equity: 3.63%
Cash ($ mil.): 836
Current ratio: —
Long-term debt ($ mil.): 5,918
No. of shares (mil.): 351
Dividends
Yield: —
Payout: 100.00%
Market value ($ mil.): 3,036

	STOCK PRICE ($) FY Close	P/E High/Low		PER SHARE ($) Earnings	Dividends	Book Value
12/11	8.63	24	13	0.64	0.00	13.64
12/10	13.98	21	16	0.70	0.57	13.22
12/09	13.91	35	21	0.46	0.56	12.61
12/08	16.17	23	12	0.81	0.56	14.57
12/07	12.04	18	14	0.81	0.54	12.92
Annual Growth	(8.0%)	—	—	(5.7%)	—	1.4%

FirstEnergy Corp.

FirstEnergy's first goal is to generate and deliver power but its second goal is to stay profitable in a market undergoing deregulation. Its ten utilities provide electricity to six million customers in the Midwest and the Mid-Atlantic. The company's domestic power plants have a total generating capacity of more than 20000 MW most generated by coal-fired plants. Subsidiary FirstEnergy Solutions trades energy commodities in deregulated US markets and has more than 120000 accounts. FirstEnergy's other nonregulated operations include electrical and mechanical contracting and energy planning and procurement. Beefing up its generation assets in 2011 the company acquired Allegheny Energy in a $8.5 billion deal.

HISTORY

FirstEnergy came to light in 1893 as the Akron Electric Light and Power Company. After several mergers the business went bankrupt and was sold in 1899 to Akron Traction and Electric Company which became Northern Ohio Power and Light (NOP&L).

In 1930 Commonwealth and Southern (C&S) bought NOP&L and merged it with four other Ohio utility holding companies to form Ohio Edison. The new firm increased sales during the Depression by selling electric appliances.

The Public Utility Holding Company Act of 1935 (passed to rein in uncontrolled utilities) caught up with C&S in 1949 forcing it to divest Ohio Edison. Rival Ohio Public Service was also divested from its holding company and in 1950 Ohio Edison bought it.

In 1967 after two decades of expansion Ohio Edison and three other Ohio and Pennsylvania utilities formed the Central Area Power Coordination Group (CAPCO) to share new power-plant costs including the construction of the Beaver Valley nuclear plant (1970-76). Although the CAPCO partners agreed in 1980 to cancel four planned nukes in 1985 Ohio Edison took part in building the Perry Unit 1 and Beaver Valley Unit 2 nuclear plants.

The federal Energy Policy Act of 1992 allowed wholesale power competition and to satisfy new federal requirements Ohio Edison formed a six-state transmission alliance in 1996 with fellow utilities Centerior Energy Allegheny Power System and Dominion Resources' Virginia Power to coordinate their grids.

Ohio Edison paid about $1.5 billion in 1997 for Centerior Energy formed in 1986 as a holding company for Toledo Edison and Cleveland Electric. Ohio Edison and Centerior both burdened by high-cost generating plants merged to cut costs and the expanded energy concern was renamed FirstEnergy Corp.

The transmission issue arose again in 1997. FirstEnergy left the transmission-coordination alliance Midwest ISO (Independent System Operator) to start a rival Alliance with 11 utility members. However the Alliance group was later dissolved.

Looking toward deregulation FirstEnergy began buying mechanical construction contracting and energy management companies in 1997 including Roth Bros. and RPC Mechanical. In 1998 it added nine more. FirstEnergy then ventured into natural gas operations by purchasing MARBEL Energy. The company also created separate subsidiaries for its nuclear and transmission assets.

Power marketers Federal Energy Sales and the Power Co. of America couldn't deliver the juice to FirstEnergy during the summer of 1998's hottest days. FirstEnergy later sued Federal Energy for $25 million in damages. The next year it bought electricity outage insurance.

Pennsylvania began large-scale electric power competition in 1999 when Ohio lawmakers passed deregulation legislation. To comply with state regulation FirstEnergy agreed to trade power plants including Beaver Valley with DQE (now Duquesne Light Holdings). That year brought trouble when the EPA named FirstEnergy and six other utilities in a suit that charged the utility with noncompliance with the Clean Air Act.

In 2000 FirstEnergy agreed to acquire New Jersey-based electric utility GPU in an $11.9 billion deal; it became one of the largest US utilities in 2001 when it completed the acquisition which added three utilities (Jersey Central Power & Light Metropolitan Edison and Pennsylvania Electric) serving 2.1 million electricity customers.

Following the acquisition FirstEnergy agreed to sell an 80% stake in GPU's UK utility Midlands Electricity to UtiliCorp (later Aquila) in a $2 billion deal completed in 2002. It also agreed to sell four Ohio coal-fired plants (2500 MW) to NRG Energy for $1.5 billion; however the deal was later canceled. The firm also spun off GPU's Australian GasNet subsidiary to the public.

To focus on its domestic operations FirstEnergy has sold the international energy assets gained through the acquisition of GPU. It has divested its Australian utility GasNet and its UK utility Midlands Electricity and it has exited its Argentine utility business (Emdersa) and sold its stakes in Latin American European and Asian power plants. The company has also left some of its facilities services businesses and in 2004 sold its 50% stake in Great Lakes Energy Partners which explores for and produces oil and gas in the Appalachian Basin for $200 million.

The US-Canada Power System Outage Task Force which investigated the massive August 14 2003 blackout that affected eight states and a Canadian province released its interim report that November and a final report the following year. The initial report found that FirstEnergy violated four voluntary standards set by the North American Electric Reliability Council and stated that the blackout was largely caused by FirstEnergy's failure to set up proper communication and monitoring procedures for its transmission assets. The report also cited the company's failure to trim trees which caused several major transmission lines in its service territory to short-circuit during the incident.

The final report did not lay any additional blame on the utility but stated that the blackout could have been prevented if utilities had followed voluntary reliability standards. FirstEnergy paid a total of $90 million to settle federal lawsuits over its involvement in the blackout as well as other securities and derivative issues without admitting any wrongdoing. FirstEnergy faced a formal SEC investigation into financial restatements (in 2003) and an extended nuclear power plant outage (2002-04); the investigation was not related to the blackout and was an extension of an informal SEC inquiry.

To settle with the US Environmental Protection Agency FirstEnergy agreed in 2005 to pay an estimated $1.1 billion in fines and for anti-pollution devices to be installed at its coal-burning plants in Ohio and Pennsylvania.

In 2006 company acquired 34.5 MW of output from the Casselman Wind Power Project under development in Somerset County Pennsylvania.

In 2009 FirstEnergy began to reengineer units 4 and 5 at its R.E. Burger Plant in Shadyside Ohio to generate electricity primarily with biomass a move that boosted FirstEnergy's portfolio of renewable energy to more than 1100 MW including 451 MW of pumped-storage hydro and 376 MW of wind power.

EXECUTIVES

SVP Human Resources FirstEnergy Service, Lynn M. Cavalier, age 60

VP Compliance and Regulated Services, Stanley F. Szwed

VP Corporate Affairs and Community Involvement, Mary Beth Carroll
President Pennsylvania Operations, Douglas S. (Doug) Elliott, age 57
President CEO and Director FirstEnergy Corp. and FirstEnergy Service; CEO FirstEnergy Nuclear Operating Company; President and CEO Allegheny Energy Service, Anthony J. Alexander, age 60, $1,159,615 total compensation
VP Marketing Policies and E-Group FirstEnergy Solutions, Tony C. Banks, age 57
EVP and General Counsel; Chair FirstEnergy Foundation, Leila L. Vespoli, age 52, $505,538 total compensation
VP Controller and Chief Accounting Officer, Harvey L. Wagner, age 59
Assistant Treasurer, Randy Scilla
President West Virginia Operations, James R. Haney
Chairman, George M. Smart, age 66
EVP and CFO, Mark T. Clark, age 61, $533,231 total compensation
SVP External Affairs, Michael J. Dowling, age 47
SVP Governmental Affairs FirstEnergy Service, David C. Luff, age 64
President FirstEnergy Solutions, Donald R. (Donny) Schneider, age 50
Regional President The Cleveland Electric Illuminating Company, Trent A. Smith
VP Corporate Services and CIO, Bennett L. Gaines
President Ohio Operations, Dennis M. Chack
President Jersey Central Power & Light, Donald M. Lynch
SVP; President FirstEnergy Utilities, Charles E. (Chuck) Jones, age 56
VP Transmission, Bradley S. Ewing, age 51
VP Utility Operations, Mark A. Julian, age 55
Manager Investor Relations, Rey Y. Jimenez Jr.
VP and Treasurer, James F. Pearson, age 57
VP Fossil Fleet Operations, Charles D. (Charlie) Lasky, age 50
SVP Retail Sales and Marketing FirstEnergy Solutions, Arthur W. Yuan
VP Investor Relations, Ronald E. Seeholzer
Assistant Corporate Secretary, Jacqueline S. Cooper
VP Corporate Secretary and Chief Ethics Officer, Rhonda S. Ferguson
VP Legal, Robert P. Reffner
VP Integrated Business and Financial Planning, Kelley E. Mendenhall
VP Supply Chain, John W. Judge
VP Corporate Risk and Chief Risk Officer FirstEnergy Service, William D. Byrd, age 57
Financial Communications, Tricia Ingraham
VP Human Resources, Dennis L. Dabney
VP Federal Affairs and Energy Policy, Martin L. Hall
Director External Relations, Ellen Raines
President and COO FirstEnergy Nuclear Operating Company, Peter P. Sena III
VP Rates and Regulatory Affairs, William R. Ridmann
Executive Director Business Development, Gary D. Benz
Assistant Controller FirstEnergy Solutions and FirstEnergy Generation, Dena R. McKee
Assistant Controller Corporate, Kevin R. Burgess
VP Tax, James G. Garanich
President FirstEnergy Generation and Chief Nuclear Officer FirstEnergy Nuclear Operating Company (FENOC), James H. (Jim) Lash, age 61
VP Fossil Engineering and Construction, George J. Farah
Regional President Pennsylvania Electric, John E. Skory
Assistant Controller FirstEnergy Utilities, K. Jon Taylor
Regional President The Toledo Edison Company, Randall A. Frame
Regional President Ohio Edison Company, Donald A. Moul
Regional President Metropolitan Edison, David J. Karafa
Regional President West Penn Power, David W. McDonald
President Maryland Operations, James V. Fakult
Executive Director Investor Relations, Irene M. Prezelj
VP Sales FirstEnergy Solutions, Gerard J. (Jerry) Bellitt
VP Fuel and Unit Dispatch FirstEnergy Solutions, James G. Mellody
Director Asset Development and Commodity Supply Planning FirstEnergy Solutions, David W. Pinter
VP Commercial Operations Structuring and Pricing FirstEnergy Solutions, Kevin T. Warvell
VP Local Affairs and Economic Development, Joel Bailey
VP Energy Efficiency, John Dargie
VP IT Solutions, Jennifer Fischer
VP Customer Service, Ron I. Green
VP IT Operations, Ernie Maley
VP Distribution Support, Steve Strah
VP Communications, Gretchan Sekulich
Assistant Treasurer, Steve Staub
VP Nuclear Support FirstEnergy Nuclear Operating Company, Eric A. Larson
Director, Robert B. (Yank) Heisler Jr., age 63
President CEO and Director FirstEnergy Corp. and FirstEnergy Service; CEO FirstEnergy Nuclear Operating Company; President and CEO Allegheny Energy Service, Anthony J. Alexander, age 60
Director, Catherine A. Rein, age 69
Director, Michael J. (Mike) Anderson, age 60
Director, Theodore J. (Ted) Kleisner, age 67
Director, Christopher D. Pappas, age 56
Director, Carol A. Cartwright, age 70
Director, Julia L. Johnson, age 49
Director, Wes M. Taylor, age 69
Director, Paul T. Addison, age 65
Director, William T. Cottle, age 66
Director, Ernest J. Novak Jr., age 67
Director, Donald T. Misheff
Auditors: PricewaterhouseCoopersLLP

LOCATIONS

HQ: FirstEnergy Corp.
76 S. Main St., Akron OH 44308
Phone: 800-736-3402 **Fax:** 330-384-3866
Web: www.firstenergycorp.com

PRODUCTS/OPERATIONS

2011 Sales

	$ mil.	% of total
Regulated distribution	10,004	57
Competitive energy services	7,173	41
Regulated independent transmission	391	2
Adjustments	(1310)	-
Total	**16,258**	**100**

Electric Utility Subsidiari
American Transmission Systems Inc.
The Cleveland Electric Illuminating Company (The Illuminating Company)
Jersey Central Power & Light Company (JCP&L)
Metropolitan Edison Company (Met-Ed)
Ohio Edison Company
Pennsylvania Electric Company (Penelec)
Pennsylvania Power Company (Penn Power)
The Toledo Edison Company
West Penn Power Company The Potomac Edison Company Monongahela Power Company (formerly Allegheny Power)

Selected Unregulated Subsidiaries
FirstEnergy Nuclear Operating Co. (nuclear generation facilities)
FirstEnergy Properties Inc.
FirstEnergy Securities Transfer Company
FirstEnergy Service Company
FirstEnergy Solutions Corp. (retail and wholesale energy marketing and management services)
FirstEnergy Ventures Corp.
GPU Diversified Holdings LLC
GPU Nuclear Inc. (nuclear plant management and decommissioning)>?

COMPETITORS

AEP
Avista
CMS Energy
Constellation Energy Group
Delmarva Power
Dominion Resources
DPL
Duke Energy
Duquesne Light
Duquesne Light Holdings
Dynegy
EnergySolve
Exelon
Exelon Energy
Integrys Energy Group
National Fuel Gas
NiSource
Peabody Energy
Peoples Natural Gas
Pepco Holdings
PG&E Corporation
PPL Corporation
PSEG Energy Holdings
Public Service Enterprise Group
Southern Company
TVA
Vectren
WGL Holdings

HISTORICAL FINANCIALS

Company Type: Public

Income Statement FYE: December 31

	REVENUE ($ mil.)	NET INCOME ($ mil.)	NET PROFIT MARGIN	EMPLOYEES
12/11	16,258	885	5.4%	17,257
12/10	13,339	784	5.9%	13,330
12/09	12,967	1,006	7.8%	13,379
12/08	13,627	1,342	9.8%	14,968
12/07	12,802	1,309	10.2%	14,534
Annual Growth	6.2%	(9.3%)	—	4.4%

2011 Year-End Financials

Debt ratio: 36.63%
Return on equity: 6.66%
Cash ($ mil.): 202
Current ratio: 69.10
Long-term debt ($ mil.): 15,716
No. of shares (mil.): 418
Dividends
Yield: —
Payout: 99.55%
Market value ($ mil.): 18,527

	STOCK PRICE ($) FY Close	P/E High	P/E Low	PER SHARE ($) Earnings	Dividends	Book Value
12/11	44.30	21	16	2.21	0.00	31.75
12/10	37.02	18	13	2.57	2.20	28.03
12/09	46.45	16	11	3.29	2.20	28.08
12/08	48.58	19	10	4.38	2.20	27.17
12/07	72.34	18	14	4.22	2.00	29.45
Annual Growth	(11.5%)	—	—	(14.9%)	—	1.9%

FirstMerit Corp

FirstMerit Corporation is the holding company for FirstMerit Bank which provides retail and commercial banking services through more than 150 branches in Ohio and western Pennsylvania and about another 50 in the Chicago area. Serving local consumers and small to midsized businesses the bank provides standard services such as deposit accounts credit and debit cards and loans as well as wealth management and trust services. Subsidiaries offer investment and brokerage services financial planning commercial lease financing life and title insurance annuities and mortgage servicing. FirstMerit is buying Citizens Republic Bancorp for some $912 million.

The deal will strengthen FirstMerit's presence in northeastern Ohio and expand its banking franchise into Michigan and Wisconsin. The combined firm will have more than 400 branches.

FirstMerit entered the Chicago market in early 2010 by buying some two dozen branches there from First Banks after it had already acquired most of that company's asset-based lending portfolio. The bank nearly doubled its branch network in the Windy City later that year when it acquired the failed Midwest Banc in an FDIC-assisted transaction. It previously acquired the four branches of Chicago-area institution George Washington Savings Bank in a similar transaction. The acquisitions helped the company's bottom line by bringing in additional fee income and bargain purchase gains.

FirstMerit hasn't forgotten about its roots either adding deposit market share in traditional markets such as Akron Canton Cleveland and Toledo Ohio. The bank emphasizes relationship banking and local decision-making with credit authority appropriate to specific markets. It is also focused on building its wealth management services for commercial clients.

Commercial loans including real estate and operating loans account for approximately half of FirstMerit's loan portfolio which is rounded out by consumer installment loans residential mortgages home equity loans and credit card loans. Though its home state of Ohio experienced a slowdown in its predominantly manufacturing-based economy the bank remained profitable throughout the recession (and has been so for over a decade).

EXECUTIVES

President and CEO Northeat Region, Bruce M. Kephart, age 57, $233,750 total compensation
EVP Human Resources, Christopher J. (Chris) Maurer, age 62
EVP and CFO FirstMerit and FirstMerit Bank, Terrence E. Bichsel, age 62, $345,650 total compensation
EVP and CTO FirstMerit and FirstMerit Bank, Larry A. Shoff, age 55, $273,300 total compensation
President and CEO Erie (Elyria) Shores Region, William G. (Bill) Lamb, age 56
President and CEO Akron Region, Nicholas V. Browning
President and CEO Toledo Region, Donald H. (Don) Kincade
EVP and Treasurer, Mark N. DuHamel
Chairman President and CEO FirstMerit and FirstMerit Bank, Paul G. Greig, age 56, $708,509 total compensation
President and CEO Columbus Region, Sue E. Zazon
SVP and Chief Marketing Officer, Julie C. Tutkovics
EVP Wealth Management Services, Kenneth A. Dorsett, age 57, $270,475 total compensation
EVP and Chief Credit Officer, William P. (Bill) Richgels, age 61, $345,650 total compensation
EVP Risk Management General Counsel and Secretary, Judith A. (Judy) Steiner, age 49
SVP Business Banking, P. Gene Gottfried
EVP Retail Banking, N. James (Jim) Brocklehurst
President and CEO North Coast Region, Sean P. Richardson
President and CEO Central, Timothy J. (Tim) Burke Jr.
EVP Commercial Banking, David G. Goodall, $206,667 total compensation
President and CEO Chicago Region, Peter K. Gillespie
EVP and Director Commercial Solutions., Joseph V. Dolan
VP and Portfolio Manager Asset-Based Lending, Kathryn C. Ellero
President Medina Market, Eric N. Shaffer
VP and Business Development Officer Wealth Management Services, Gary Habeeb
Media Contact, Robert (Rob) Townsend
Director, Terry L. Haines, age 65
Director, Richard Colella, age 76
Director, Philip A. Lloyd II, age 65
Director, Karen S. Belden, age 69
Director, R. Cary Blair, age 72
Director, Robert W. Briggs, age 70
Director, Clifford J. Isroff, age 75
Director, John C. Blickle, age 61
Director, Gina D. France, age 53
Director, J. Michael (Mike) Hochschwender, age 51
Director, Steven H. Baer, age 62
Auditors: Ernst&YoungLLP

LOCATIONS

HQ: FirstMerit Corporation
3 Cascade Plaza 7th Fl., Akron OH 44308-1103
Phone: 330-996-6300 **Fax:** 601-208-6684
Web: www.trustmark.com

PRODUCTS/OPERATIONS

2011 Sales

	$ mil.	% of total
Interest		
Loans	438	57
Investment securities	99	13
Noninterest		
Service charges on deposits	64	8
Credit card fees	49	7
Trust department	22	3
Bank-owned life insurance	14	2
Loan sales & servicing	**14.5**	**2**
ATM & other service fees	13	2
Investment securities gains net	11	1
Investment services & insurance	8	1
Other	26	4
Total	**754**	**100**

Selected Subsidiaries

Citizens Savings Corporation of Stark County
FirstMerit Bank National Association
 FirstMerit Advisors Inc.
 FirstMerit Equipment Finance Inc.
 FirstMerit Financial Services Inc.
 FirstMerit Insurance Agency Inc.
 FirstMerit Insurance Group Inc.
 FirstMerit Mortgage Corporation
 FirstMerit Mortgage Reinsurance Company Inc.
 FirstMerit-Moss Creek Ventures LLC
 FirstMerit Securities Inc.
 FirstMerit Title Agency Ltd.
 Midwest Financial and Investment Services Inc.
FirstMerit Community Development Corporation

COMPETITORS

Fifth Third	Park National
Harris	Peoples Bancorp (OH)
Huntington Bancshares	PNC Financial
JPMorgan Chase	TFS Financial
KeyCorp	U.S. Bancorp
MB Financial	Wintrust Financial

HISTORICAL FINANCIALS

Company Type: Public

Income Statement

FYE: December 31

	ASSETS ($ mil.)	NET INCOME ($ mil.)	INCOME AS % OF ASSETS	EMPLOYEES
12/11	14,441	119	0.8%	3,177
12/10	14,136	102	0.7%	3,058
12/09	10,539	82	0.8%	2,495
12/08	11,100	119	1.1%	2,575
12/07	10,400	123	1.2%	2,775
Annual Growth	8.6%	(0.7%)	—	3.4%

2011 Year-End Financials

Debt ratio: 1.41%
Return on equity: 7.64%
Cash ($ mil.): 377
Current ratio: —
Long-term debt ($ mil.): 203
No. of shares (mil.): 109
Dividends
 Yield: —
 Payout: 58.18%
Market value ($ mil.): 1,653

	STOCK PRICE ($) FY Close	P/E High	P/E Low	PER SHARE ($) Earnings	Dividends	Book Value
12/11	15.13	18	9	1.10	0.00	14.33
12/10	19.79	24	16	1.02	0.64	13.86
12/09	20.14	24	14	0.90	0.77	12.25
12/08	20.59	18	10	1.47	1.16	11.51
12/07	20.01	16	12	1.52	1.16	11.32
Annual Growth	(6.8%)	—	—	(7.8%)	—	6.1%

Fiserv, Inc.

It's 10:30 America. Do you know where your money is? Fiserv does. The company provides financial services technology to banks thrifts credit unions and other entities. Its offerings include core processing systems electronic billing and payment systems ATM management and loan processing. It also provides licensed software consulting and other support services to round out its offerings. Fiserv serves customers of all sizes but its bread and butter has traditionally been small to midsized banks without in-house processing units. Other clients include insurance companies merchants leasing firms and government agencies. Fiserv primarily operates in the US but has offices in about 20 other countries.

The company makes about 80% of its revenues from processing and services revenue and the bulk of the rest from ancillary product sales. It serves approximately 16000 clients around the world and enjoys a very high renewal rate of 99% (exclusing clients lost because they have themselves been acquired). Banks typically stay with their service providers as the cost and work involved in changing providers is prohibitive.

Fiserv has capitalized on the increasing reliance on transaction-oriented services which demand a large data-processing capability. The company has made more than 100 acquisitions in its history to broaden its offerings and stay relevant in the changing world. Among its most notable deals was the 2007 acquisition of electronic bill payments firm CheckFree for $4.2 billion. The CheckFree acquisition was the largest in Fiserv's history and allowed the company to serve a broader market.

The company has since continued building its operations through acquisitions and new offerings. In 2010 it acquired AdviceAmerica which provides desktop technology for financial advisers. It also introduced ZashPay a peer-to-peer platform available to consumers. The following year it acquired two firms it had previously held partnerships with: credit union payments processor Credit Union On-Line and mobile banking provider Mobile Commerce. Fiserv also bought digital payments company CashEdge for some $465 million in mid-2011.

Adding CheckFree and other businesses helped Fiserv become one of the leading financial technology providers but also raised its debt levels. Company management has been repositioning the firm by selling noncore units cutting costs and reducing its debt. The careful repositioning of the group and the key role Fiserv plays for its customers have helped ease the sting of the financial crisis. The company's earnings have remained steady even through the downturn. In 2011 revenues grew some 5% to $4.3 billion from its 2010 revenues of $4.1 billion while net income slipped about 5% to $472 million (down from $496 million in 2010). The growth has been led by the company's payment segment and by revenues from acquired companies.

Despite some belt-tightening in the banking industry core processing services remain essential to Fiserv's customers and lenders rarely jump ship and switch service providers. Among the threats to Fiserv and its competitors is the ongoing consolidation among banks with record numbers of small to midsized firms failing and banks buying one another. Additionally a growing number of larger banks have been converting to in-house systems. Finally primary competitor Fidelity National Information Services has been doing some growing on its own through mergers and expansions which could potentially cut into Fiserv's 37% market share.

HISTORY

When First Bank System of Minneapolis bought Milwaukee-based Midland Bank in 1984 the head of Midland's data processing operation George Dalton bought the unit and then merged that operation with Sunshine State Systems a newly independent Florida processing company headed by Leslie Muma. Christened Fiserv the company went public in 1986. It grew by providing outsourcing services to small banks and thrifts.

In the 1990s Fiserv began targeting larger clients. But industry consolidation sometimes hurt the company as when the 12-year term of a 1995 contract with Chase Manhattan was reduced to three after Chase and Chemical Bank merged in 1996.

As banks moved into new areas Fiserv went along. In the late 1990s it acquired BHC Financial and Hanifen Imhoff Holdings (securities transaction processing). Other purchases that broadened its service list included Automated Financial Technology (credit union software) and Network Data Processing (administrative software for insurance companies). The push into software continued with 1999 purchases in the field of workers' compensation systems.

Also in 1999 Fiserv bolstered its client list by buying QuestPoint's check servicing business. It moved into retirement plan administration with the purchase of a unit from what is now SunAmerica Financial Group. In 2000 a deal to provide back-office services for American Express' online Membership Banking unit fell apart but Fiserv recovered its momentum with enhanced mortgage servicing offerings and an agreement to provide technology services to cahoot the online banking unit of the UK's Abbey National (which was acquired by Spanish group Banco Santander in 2004).

Fiserv continued its acquisitive activities in 2001 buying Benefit Planners (a leading employee benefit program administrator with operations in Europe the Middle East South America and the US) Facilities and Services Corporation (a California-based insurance software maker) NCSI (information and services targeting the flood insurance industry) and the bank processing operations of NCR Corporation. The company that year also sold its Human Resources Information Services unit to buyout firm Gores Group.

Fiserv boosted its ATM and electronic funds transfer (ETF) business with the 2002 purchase of the Consumer Network Services unit of Electronic Data Systems (now HP Enterprise Services).

The company embarked on a series of sales in the next few years. It sold its securities clearing operations to a unit of FMR in 2005. Three years later it sold most of its health business to UnitedHealth for some $480 million. The sale included Fiserv Health Plan Administration Fiserv Health Plan Management Innoviant Pharmacy Avidyn Health and other units but not WorkingRx (workers' compensation) and CareGain (technology) which remained with Fiserv.

The company also sold the bulk of its Fiserv Trust Company (also known as Fiserv Investment Support Services or Fiserv ISS) business including advisor services and institutional retirement services to TD AMERITRADE. In a separate transaction the newly formed Trust Institution Bank (headed by former Fiserv ISS management) acquired most of the company's investment administration services business.

Fiserv acquired one of the largest electronic payments firms CheckFree in 2007 boosting its capabilities in the payments landscape. In a smaller deal Fibought payment processor i_Tech from First Interstate BancSystem in 2008.

All of the acquisition activity led the company to higher debt levels which it began paying down through a combination of cost-cutting measures and divesting noncore operations. In 2008 it sold most of its health business to UnitedHealth and the bulk of Fiserv Trust Company to TD AMERITRADE. The following year it sold 51% of Fiserv Insurance Services (now StoneRiver) to investment firm Stone Point Capital for some $540 million. It also sold Loan Fulfillment Solutions a provider of mortgage-related services including settlement and title certification. As it added new operations and jettisoned others the company introduced a new marketing strategy in 2009 to unify its brands under the Fiserv banner.

EXECUTIVES

EVP and COO, Mark A. Ernst, age 53
EVP General Counsel and Secretary, Charles W. Sprague, age 62, $405,000 total compensation
Chairman, Donald F. (Don) Dillon, age 72
EVP and Group President International, Steven (Steve) Tait, age 53
President CEO and Director, Jeffery W. (Jeff) Yabuki, age 52, $840,000 total compensation
EVP CFO Treasurer and Assistant Secretary, Thomas J. Hirsch, age 48, $400,000 total compensation
EVP Corporate Development, James W. Cox, age 49
Group President Digital Payment Solutions, Rahul Gupta, age 54
EVP and Chief Marketing Officer, Donald J. (Don) MacDonald, age 50
Director Global Communications, Wade Coleman
EVP and CIO, Maryann Goebel, age 61
EVP and Group President Financial Institutions, Michael P. (Mike) Gianoni, age 51
EVP and Group President Depository Institution Services and Distribution and Sales, Thomas W. Warsop III, age 45, $400,000 total compensation
VP Communications, Judy DeRango Wicks
Assistant VP Strategic Marketing, Lori Stafford-Thomas
VP Product Management and Marketing Bank Solutions, Carol Cowan
Senior Public Relations Manager, Julie Nixon
Chief Economist, David Stiff
Head of Product Management and Strategy Global Institutional Software Solutions Investment Services, Terry Gibson
Interim President Investment Services, Cheryl Nash
Senior Public Relations Manager, Ann Cave
Public Relations Manager, Amanda S. McCracken
VP Investor Relations, Peter Holbrook
SVP Sales Investment Services, Brandon Sharrett
President Risk and Compliance, John Filby
Director, Glenn M. Renwick, age 56
Director, Kim M. Robak, age 56
Director, Carl W. Stern, age 66
Director, Peter J. (Pete) Kight, age 56
President CEO and Director, Jeffery W. (Jeff) Yabuki, age 52
Director, Doyle R. Simons, age 48
Director, Daniel P. Kearney, age 72
Director, Denis J. O'Leary, age 55
Director, Thomas C. (Tom) Wertheimer, age 71
Auditors: Deloitte&ToucheLLP

LOCATIONS

HQ: Fiserv Inc.
255 Fiserv Dr., Brookfield WI 53045
Phone: 262-879-5000 **Fax:** 904-396-2715
Web: www.patriottrans.com

PRODUCTS/OPERATIONS

2011 Sales

	$ mil.	% of total
Payments		
Processing & services	1,736	40
Products	645	15
Financial		
Processing & services	1,820	41
Products	184	4
Adjustments	(48)	
Total	**4,337**	**100**

Selected Subsidiaries

BillMatrix Corporation
CheckFree Corporation
CheckFreePay Corporation
Data-Link Systems LLC
Fiserv Automotive Solutions Inc.
Fiserv CIR Inc.
Fiserv (Europe) Limited (UK)
Information Technology Inc.
ITI of Nebraska Inc.
USERS LLC

COMPETITORS

Accenture
Banc of America Merchant Services
CGI Group
DST Systems
Fidelity National Information Services
First Data
Jack Henry
Open Solutions
SunGard
Total System Services

HISTORICAL FINANCIALS

Company Type: Public

Income Statement FYE: December 31

	REVENUE ($ mil.)	NET INCOME ($ mil.)	NET PROFIT MARGIN	EMPLOYEES
12/11	4,337	472	10.9%	20,000
12/10	4,133	496	12.0%	19,000
12/09	4,077	476	11.7%	20,000
12/08	4,739	569	12.0%	20,000
12/07	3,922	439	11.2%	25,000
Annual Growth	2.5%	1.8%	—	(5.4%)

2011 Year-End Financials

Debt ratio: 39.72%
Return on equity: 14.49%
Cash ($ mil.): 337
Current ratio: 97.98
Long-term debt ($ mil.): 3,216
No. of shares (mil.): 140
Dividends
Yield: —
Payout: —
Market value ($ mil.): 8,229

	STOCK PRICE ($) FY Close	P/E High/Low		PER SHARE ($) Earnings	Dividends	Book Value
12/11	58.74	20	15	3.28	0.00	23.25
12/10	58.56	18	14	3.27	0.00	21.98
12/09	48.48	16	10	3.06	0.00	19.75
12/08	36.37	16	8	3.49	0.00	16.64
12/07	55.49	22	18	2.60	0.00	14.94
Annual Growth	1.4%	—	—	6.0%	—	11.7%

Flagstar Bancorp, Inc.

Flagstar Bancorp is the holding company for Flagstar Bank which operates about 115 branches (including some in retail stores) in Michigan. Home loans are a major focus for Flagstar. The thrift originates purchases and services residential mortgages in all 50 states through a network of brokers and correspondents as well as nearly 30 of its own loan offices in more than a dozen states. More than three-quarters of the company's revenue (after interest expenses) is linked to residential lending but the reliance on this business hurt Flagstar during the housing bust. Expanding its commercial lending operations the firm in 2011 opened four full-service branches in Massachusetts Connecticut and Rhode Island.

Flagstar is broadening its reach beyond mortgage lending. The company is transforming its branches into full-service community banks and focusing on cross-selling an expanded suite of retail commercial and government banking services. It has also recently introduced a line of consumer loans such as credit cards and home equity lines of credit and added services for small and midsized businesses like treasury management and specialty lending. Additionally the bank formally expanded its commercial lending business into New England. While home mortgage lending remains key to Flagstar the company hopes to diversify its revenue streams so the business eventually accounts for about a third of sales.

The shift likely has something to do with the company's exposure to the miserable mortgage market. Flagstar has reported annual losses every year since 2007 since which it has lost a total of nearly $1.4 billion. Revenues fell 11% to $851 million in 2011 while losses that year totaled $182 million. Both interest and noninterest earnings declined that year as as the credit markets remained challenged. The company has been slowing its losses down though and despite reporting another quarter in the red in 2012 expects to return to profitability for the year. Flagstar has also lowered its provision for loan losses thanks to a decline in charge-offs.

To raise capital the company sold 27 bank branches in the suburbs north of Atlanta along with their deposits to PNC in 2011. The company also sold its 22 Indiana branches to First Financial Bancorp in late 2011. In addition to bringing in some cash the divestitures help Flagstar focus on its Michigan operations.

MP Thrift an affiliate of private equity firm MatlinPatterson Global Advisors assumed a controlling stake of Flagstar in 2009. Today it owns 64% of the company.

EXECUTIVES

Chairman, John D. Lewis
EVP and Chief Investment Officer Flagstar Bancorp and Flagstar Bank; President of Flagstar Capital Markets, Kirstin A. Hammond, age 46, $428,754 total compensation
Chairman President and CEO; Chairman President and CEO Flagstar Bank, Joseph P. (Joe) Campanelli, age 55, $647,883 total compensation
SVP Administration and Corporate Secretary, Mary Kay Ruedisueli
EVP and Chief Credit Officer, Daniel J. Landers
EVP Human Resources, Laura C. Anger
EVP and Head of Retail Banking Flagstar Bancorp and Flagstar Bank, Alessandro P. DiNello, age 57
EVP and Managing Director Commercial Banking, Steven J. (Steve) Issa
EVP and CFO Flagstar Bancorp and Flagstar Bank, Paul D. Borja, age 51, $464,243 total compensation
EVP and Director Corporate Services, Marshall P. Soura, age 72
Chief Legal Officer, Matthew I. Roslin, age 44, $443,269 total compensation
EVP and COO, Salvatore J. Rinaldi, age 57
EVP and Managing Director Mortgage Banking and Warehouse, Matthew A. Kerin, age 57
EVP and National Sales Manager Flagstar Bank, Greg Lutin
Manager Editorial Services Marketing Advertising and Promotions, Susan Cherry
EVP and Chief Risk Officer, Todd McGowan
EVP Home Lending, William (Bill) Robinson
President CEO and Director, Michael J. Tierney
Director, David L. Treadwell, age 57
EVP and Chief Investment Officer Flagstar Bancorp and Flagstar Bank; President of Flagstar Capital Markets, Kirstin A. Hammond, age 46
Director, James D. Coleman, age 65
Director, Mark R. Patterson, age 60
Director, James A. Ovenden, age 49
Director, Walter N. (Walt) Carter, age 61
Director, Jay J. Hansen, age 49
Director, David J. Matlin, age 50
Director, Gregory Eng, age 46
President CEO and Director, Michael J. Tierney
Independent Director, Michael J. Shonka
Auditors: BakerTillyVirchowKrauseLLP

LOCATIONS

HQ: Flagstar Bancorp Inc.
5151 Corporate Dr., Troy MI 48098-2639
Phone: 248-312-2000 **Fax:** 248-312-6704
Web: www.flagstar.com

PRODUCTS/OPERATIONS

2011 Sales

	$ mil.	% of total
Interest income		
Loans	427	41
Securities	35	3
Other	2	-
Noninterest income		
Net gain on loan sales	300	29
Loan administration	94	9
Loan fees & charges	77	8
Deposit fees & charges	29	3
Other	76	7
Adjustments	(194.1)	
Total	**850**	**100**

COMPETITORS

Bank of America
Capitol Bancorp
Citizens Republic Bancorp
Comerica
Fifth Third
Harris
Huntington Bancshares
JPMorgan Chase
KeyCorp
Northern Trust
PNC Financial

HISTORICAL FINANCIALS

Company Type: Public

Income Statement FYE: December 31

	ASSETS ($ mil.)	NET INCOME ($ mil.)	INCOME AS % OF ASSETS	EMPLOYEES
12/11	13,637	(181)	—	3,136
12/10	13,643	(374)	—	3,279
12/09	14,013	(496)	—	3,411
12/08	14,203	(275)	—	3,920
12/07	15,792	(39)	—	3,960
Annual Growth	(3.6%)	—	—	(5.7%)

2011 Year-End Financials

Debt ratio: 30.81%
Return on equity: (-16.84)%
Cash ($ mil.): 731
Current ratio: —
Long-term debt ($ mil.): 4,201
No. of shares (mil.): 55
Dividends
Yield: —
Payout: —
Market value ($ mil.): 28

	STOCK PRICE ($) FY Close	P/E High/Low		PER SHARE ($) Earnings	Dividends	Book Value
12/11	0.51	—	—	(3.60)	0.00	19.43
12/10	1.63	—	—	(24.40)	0.00	2.28
12/09	0.60	—	—	(16.20)	0.00	(0.00)
12/08	0.71	—	—	(38.20)	0.00	564.76
12/07	6.97	—	—	(64.00)	0.00	1,149.78
Annual Growth	(48.0%)	—	—	—	—	(63.9%)

Florida Power & Light Co.

Florida Power & Light (FPL) sheds extra light onto the Sunshine State. The company a subsidiary of utility holding company NextEra Energy serves some 4.6 million electricity customers in eastern and southern Florida. FPL has more than 74160 miles of transmission and distribution lines as well as interests in fossil-fueled and nuclear power plants that give it a generating capacity of about 24500 MW. Natural gas accounts for 65%

of the power it generates; nuclear 20%; and coal only 5%. FPL has 110 MW of solar generated capacity more than any other utility outside of California. FPL's Energy Marketing and Trading unit purchases and sells energy commodities to wholesale customers.

The company's 10-year strategic plan (initiated in 2012) for meeting Florida's energy needs relies on building additions to its existing generating plants while ramping up renewable energy sources in order to avoid building four medium-sized fossil-fueled power plants (called for by an earlier plan).

In 2010 the Florida Public Service Commission turned down the company's proposed 30% retail rate hike or $1.3 billion. FPL adjusted its expansion programs accordingly.

The company revived a $2 billion also revived a $2 billion plan to convert a plant in Port St. John and a plant in Riviera Beach from heavy fuel to natural gas. It also plans to get a further 490 MW of capacity from its Turkey Point and St. Lucie nuclear power plants by 2013.

Moving further to meet federal requirements for green energy production in 2010 the company commissioned the Space Coast Next Generation Solar Energy Center at the Kennedy Space Center three solar farms built in tandem with NASA to produce 10 MW of clean energy enough to serve 1100 homes. It also brought into service the 75-MW Martin Next Generation Solar Energy Center designed to power about 11000 homes. The hybrid facility connects more than 190000 solar thermal mirrors to an existing combined-cycle natural gas power plant.

FPL reported a 1% increase in overall revenues in 2011 largely due to higher revenues from its fuel cost recovery program (a fixed year long fuel charge for customers aimed at combating price volatility). Despite a 2% drop in power use by the average retail customer a rate increase higher demand during peak periods and a growth in customers helped to lift FPL's retail revenues. Net income grew by 13% in 2011 thanks to higher revenues and lower operating expenses.

Between 2011 to 2013 FPL plans to invest $9 billion to strengthen and improve its electric generation and delivery system. To help pay for these improvements in 2012 it submitted a 2.6% rate increase request with state authorities.

EXECUTIVES

Chairman, Lewis (Lew) Hay III, age 56
EVP Engineering Construction and Corporate Services, Robert L. (Bob) McGrath, age 58
EVP Power Generation Division, Antonio Rodriguez, age 69
EVP Finance and CFO, Moray P. Dewhurst, age 56
Treasurer and Assistant Secretary, Paul I. Cutler, age 52
VP Customer Service, Marlene M. Santos
EVP, Charles E. Sieving, age 39
VP Environmental Services, Randall R. (Randy) LaBauve
EVP Finance and CFO, Armando Pimentel Jr., age 49
VP and Chief Information Officer, Lakshman Charanjiva
President and CEO, Eric E. Silagy
VP Marketing and Communications, Timothy (Tim) Fitzpatrick
VP Distribution, Adalberto Alfonso
EVP Human Resources and Assistant Secretary, James W. Poppell Sr., age 61
VP Corporate and External Affairs, Pamela M. Rauch
VP and General Counsel, R. Wade Litchfield
VP Finance, Robert E. Barrett
Media Relations, Jackie Anderson
Media Relations, Sharon Bennett
Media Relations, Sarah Marmion
Media Relations, Mayco Villafana
VP Distribution, G. Keith Hardy
EVP Nuclear Division and Chief Nuclear Officer, Manoochehr K. Nazar
VP Controller and Chief Accounting Officer, Kimberly Ousdahl
Media Relations, Neil Nissan
Director Information Management Technology, Liane M. Sawyer
EVP Human Resources, Shaun J. Francis
VP and COO, Deborah H. Caplan
VP Transmission and Substation, Manuel B. Miranda
Auditors: Deloitte&ToucheLLP

LOCATIONS

HQ: Florida Power & Light Co.
700 Universe Boulevard, Juno Beach, FL 33408
Phone: 561 694-4000 **Fax:** 407 694-4620
Web: www.fpl.com

PRODUCTS/OPERATIONS

2011 Operating Revenues

	% of total
Residential	55
Commercial	39
Other	6
Total	**100**

2011 Sales

	$ mil.	% of total
Fuel cost recovery	4,416	42
Retail base	4,217	40
Other	1,980	18
Total	**10,613**	**100**

COMPETITORS

AGL Resources
Clay Electric
Florida Public Utilities
Gulf Power
JEA
Orlando Utilities Commission
Progress Energy Florida
Seminole Electric
Sumter Electric
Tampa Electric

HISTORICAL FINANCIALS

Company Type: Subsidiary

Income Statement FYE: December 31

	REVENUE ($ mil.)	NET INCOME ($ mil.)	NET PROFIT MARGIN	EMPLOYEES
12/11	10,613	1,068	10.1%	9,800
12/10	10,485	945	9.0%	10,000
12/09	11,491	831	7.2%	10,500
12/08	11,649	789	6.8%	10,700
12/07	11,622	836	7.2%	10,500
Annual Growth	(2.2%)	6.3%	—	(1.7%)

2011 Year-End Financials

Debt ratio: 24.71%
Return on equity: 9.84%
Cash ($ mil.): 36
Current ratio: 89.31
Long-term debt ($ mil.): 7,483
No. of shares (mil.): 0
Dividends
Yield: —
Payout: —
Market value ($ mil.): —

Florida Power Corp.

Sometimes the sunshine state just isn't bright enough and that's when Florida Power (doing business as Progress Energy Florida) really shines. The utility transmits and distributes electricity to 1.6 million customers and oversees 10025 MW of generating capacity from interests in 14 nuclear and coal- oil- and gas-fired power plants. Additionally Florida Power purchases about 20% of the energy it provides. The company is interconnected with 22 municipal power systems and with nine rural electric cooperative systems. Florida Power a subsidiary of holding company Duke Energy also sells wholesale power to other utilities and marketers.

The company's wholesale customers include Seminole Electric Cooperative Florida Municipal Power Agency and Tampa Electric Company the city of Gainesville and Reedy Creek Improvement District.

In 2010 Florida Power was operating 5000 miles of transmission lines and 18000 miles of overhead and 13000 miles of underground distribution cable. It also had 800 transformers.

Florida Power reported improved revenues in 2009 despite the global recession's impact which meant lower demand from non-residential end users. The increase in sales was largely due to a rate increase stemming from damages to the infrastructure from hurricane earlier in the decade.

Revenues were flat in 2010. A growth in the retail customer base and favorable weather conditions lifted retail revenues but the restructuring of a contract with a major customer led to a slump in wholesale revenues.

EXECUTIVES

VP Finance, Peter E. Toomey
VP Audit, Robert H. (Bob) Bazemore Jr., age 58
VP Human Resources, Anne M. Huffman
SVP CFO and Director, Mark F. Mulhern, age 52
VP Efficiency and Innovative Technology, Robert F. (Rob) Caldwell
President and CEO, Vincent M. (Vinny) Dolan, age 57
SVP Energy Delivery, Michael A. Lewis, age 50
VP Customer and Market Services, R. Tucker Mann
SVP Corporate Development and Improvement, Paula J. Sims, age 50
VP Chief Risk Officer and Treasurer, Thomas R. (Tom) Sullivan
VP Operational Readiness, Dale E. Young
VP Corporate Planning, Mark A. Myers
VP Transmission Operations and Planning, J. Dale Oliver
VP Distribution, Jackie Joyner
VP and Controller, Jeffrey M. (Jeff) Stone, age 50
Chairman, William D. (Bill) Johnson, age 58
VP South Central Region, Laura M. Boisvert
VP Nuclear Operations, Robert J. Duncan
VP Supply Chain, Lee T. Mazzocchi
VP South Coastal Region, Mark Wimberly
SVP and Chief Nuclear Officer Progress Energy and Florida Power, James Scarola, age 56
VP Nuclear Engineering and Services, Joseph W. (Joe) Donahue
VP Nuclear Plant Development, John Elnitsky
VP Regulated Fuels, Alexander J. (Sasha) Weintraub
VP North Coastal Region, Martha W. Barnwell
VP Crystal River Nuclear Plant, Jon A. Franke
VP North Central Region, David J. (Dave) Maxon
VP Power Generation, David W. Sorrick

EVP Progress Energy and Director, John R. McArthur, age 56
SVP CFO and Director, Mark F. Mulhern, age 52
Director, Jeffrey A. (Jeff) Corbett, age 52
Director, James (Jim) Scarola, age 56
Director, Lloyd M. Yates, age 51
Director, Robert W. Jones, age 61

LOCATIONS

HQ: Florida Power Corporation
299 1st Ave. North, St. Petersburg FL 33701
Phone: 727-820-5151 **Fax:** 727-384-7865
Web: www.progress-energy.com

PRODUCTS/OPERATIONS

2011 Sales

	% of total
Fuel & other pass-through	58
Retail	32
Wholesale	2
Miscellaneous	8
Total	**100**

COMPETITORS

AGL Resources
Florida Power & Light
Florida Public Utilities
Gulf Power
JEA
Orlando Utilities Commission
Seminole Electric
Tampa Electric

HISTORICAL FINANCIALS

Company Type: Subsidiary

Income Statement FYE: December 31

	REVENUE ($ mil.)	NET INCOME ($ mil.)	NET PROFIT MARGIN	EMPLOYEES
12/11	4,369	314	7.2%	4,000
12/10	5,254	453	8.6%	4,000
12/09	5,251	462	8.8%	4,000
12/08	4,731	385	8.1%	4,000
12/07	4,749	317	6.7%	4,000
Annual Growth	(2.1%)	(0.2%)	—	0.0%

2011 Year-End Financials

Debt ratio: 33.86%
Return on equity: 6.67%
Cash ($ mil.): 16
Current ratio: 120.90
Long-term debt ($ mil.): 4,671
No. of shares (mil.): 0
Dividends
Yield: —
Payout: 163.46%
Market value ($ mil.): 0

	STOCK PRICE ($) FY Close	P/E High/Low	PER SHARE ($) Earnings	Dividends	Book Value
12/11	93.00	— —	(0.00)	0.00	47,090,000.00
12/10	80.00	— —	(0.00)	0.00	49,240,000.00
12/09	79.00	— —	(0.00)	0.00	45,240,000.00
12/08	65.70	— —	(0.00)	0.00	34,330,000.00
12/07	85.00	— —	(0.00)	0.00	30,360,000.00
Annual Growth	2.3%	— —	—	—	11.6%

Flowserve Corp.

Flowserve is pumped about flow control equipment. After reorganizing in 2010 the company operates through three segments. The flow control division (FCD) makes valves and actuators that control the flow of liquids and gases. The flow solutions group's (FSG) engineered product division (EPD) makes pumps and mechanical seals. FSG's industrial product division (IPD) makes pre-configured engineered pumps and pump systems. Flowserve also provides services that include installation diagnostics repair and retrofitting. Flowserve's client base includes customers in the chemical oil and gas power generation and water management industries. The company operates in more than 50 countries.

Year-over-year sales in 2011 for Flowservice increased about 12% which included currency benefits of $144 million thanks to strong sales for all of the company's three reportable segments. Also contributing: two of the company's major customer segments oil and gas (accounting for 40% of sales) and the chemical industry (18% of sales) enjoyed healthy levels of capital spending in 2011.

The company's largest business segment EPD accounting for 50% of sales enjoyed a year-over-year uptick in 2011 of about 8% which includes currency benefits of $67 million. The segment's healthy sales resulted in part from increased aftermarket demand in the Americas and more demand for original equipment in Asia/Pacific.

The second largest segment FCD soared 23% which included currency benefits of about $48 million. The segment's sales were lifted by recovery of the oil and gas market and strong demand for Valbart products. FCD represents 33% of sales.

The IPD segment's 2011 year-over-year sales rose about 10% which includes currency benefits of $29 million thanks mainly to strong demand for original equipment in the Americas. For this segment the company is developing a product slated for release in 2012 and targeted for distribution in the International Standards Organization market.

In addition to making its 50+ branded products in manufacturing facilities around the world the company also operates a network of Quick Response Centers (QRC) that provide aftermarket equipment services. Since Flowserve's aftermarket parts and services business has provided a steady source of revenues and cash flows –accounting for about 41% of sales –the company will continue to expand this business through its QRC network. The company added six QRCs in 2011 increasing the count to about 120.

Organic growth acquisitions technology and innovation and joint ventures continue to fuel Flowserve's performance. In 2011 the company acquired Massachusetts-based manufacturer of centrifugal pumps Lawrence Pumps. The deal added critical solids-pumping and high temperature technologies necessary to the Flowserve petrochemical and oil and gas clients. Meanwhile the company has expanded through joint ventures in China India Japan Saudi Arabia South Korea and the United Arab Emirates.

The company believes that incorporating advanced technologies into its products will increase the appeal of its product portfolio. To that end Flowserve has been concentrating on the commercialization of new technologies and has partnered with universities and other experts through consortiums to expedite the development time for new products and services. The company spent $35 million on product development in 2011 up from more than $29 million the previous year.

HISTORY

Extending its reach in 2009 the company picked up Calder a privately owned Swiss company specializing in the design engineering and supply of energy-recovery equipment for desalination plants. The move capitalized on growing demand for global water desalination as well as conservation efforts pushing to reduce energy consumption in the desalination process.

In 2010 the company formed a joint venture with China-based SUFA Technology Industry called SUFA - Flowserve Nuclear Power Equipment (Souzhou) Co. Ltd. The JV was set up to manufacture safety valves (including main steam isolation valves which help safely shut down a nuclear reactor if the plant's steam piping ruptures) for the nuclear power industry in China. SUFA contributed 55% of the capital and Flowserve provided the remaining 45%. Flowserve had been selling valves to the civilian nuclear power generation market in China for more than 20 years.

Also in 2010 Flowserve acquired Italy-based valve manufacturer Valbart for a reported $200 million. The addition of Valbart strengthened Flowserve's position in the oil and gas equipment industry.

EXECUTIVES

Chairman, James O. Rollans, age 69
SVP and General Counsel, Ronald F. Shuff, age 59, $335,461 total compensation
SVP and Chief Administrative Officer, Mark D. Dailey, age 53, $400,824 total compensation
President CEO and Director, Mark A. Blinn, age 50, $652,139 total compensation
SVP and President Flow Solutions Group, Thomas E. (Tom) Ferguson, age 56, $465,000 total compensation
SVP and COO, Thomas L. Pajonas, age 56, $465,000 total compensation
VP Finance FSG, Paul W. Fehlman, age 48
SVP and CFO, Michael S. Taff, age 50
VP Tax, Deborah K. (Kathy) Bethune, age 53
Director Global Logistics, Rob Lewin
President Operations India, S. Gopinath
Director Investor Relations, Mike Mullin
Director Global Communications and Public Affairs, Steve Boone
VP and Corporate Secretary, Carey A. O'Connor
Director, Rick J. Mills, age 64
Director, Roger L. Fix, age 59
Director, William C. (Bill) Rusnack, age 67
Director, Charles M. (Charlie) Rampacek, age 68
Director, John R. Friedery, age 55
Director, Michael F. (Mike) Johnston, age 64
President CEO and Director, Mark A. Blinn, age 50
Director, Joseph E. (Joe) Harlan, age 53
Auditors: PricewaterhouseCoopersLLP

LOCATIONS

HQ: Flowserve Corporation
5215 N. O' Connor Blvd. Ste. 2300, Irving TX 75039
Phone: 972-443-6500 **Fax:** 972-443-6800
Web: www.flowserve.com

2011 Sales

	$ mil.	% of total
Europe Middle East & Africa	1,954	43
US	1,507	33
Asia	517	12
Other	531	12
Total	**4,510**	**100**

PRODUCTS/OPERATIONS

2011 Sales

	$ mil.	% of total
Engineered product division	2,239	50
Flow control division	1,467	33
Industrial product division	802	17
Total	**4,510**	**100**

2011 Sales

	% of total
Oil &	40
General	22
Chemical	18
Power	16
Water	4
Total	**100**

Selected Products

Actuation and instrumentation (positioners controls switches)
Energy recovery devices
Hydraulic decoking systems
Monitoring and controls
Pumps
Seals
Steam traps
Valves

Selected Brands

Aldrich
Byron Jackson
Cameron
Durco
Durametallic
Flowserve
IDP
Jeumont-Schneider
Limitorque
Pleuger
Scienco
TKL
United Centrifugal
Valtek
Western Land Roller
Wilson-Snyder
Worthington

COMPETITORS

Aalberts
Cameron Valves & Measurement
CIRCOR International
Colfax
Crane Co.
Curtiss-Wright Flow Control
Dresser Inc.
Ebara
Emerson Electric
GE
Hamilton Sundstrand
IDEX
IMI plc
ITT Corp.
John Crane
KSB AG
Metso
Robbins & Myers
Smiths Group
Strahman Valves
Sulzer
Tyco Flow Control
Weir Group

HISTORICAL FINANCIALS

Company Type: Public

Income Statement FYE: December 31

	REVENUE ($ mil.)	NET INCOME ($ mil.)	NET PROFIT MARGIN	EMPLOYEES
12/11	4,510	428	9.5%	16,000
12/10	4,032	388	9.6%	15,000
12/09	4,365	427	9.8%	15,000
12/08	4,473	442	9.9%	15,000
12/07	3,762	255	6.8%	15,000
Annual Growth	4.6%	13.8%	—	1.6%

2011 Year-End Financials

Debt ratio: 10.93%
Return on equity: 18.88%
Cash ($ mil.): 337
Current ratio: 178.76
Long-term debt ($ mil.): 451
No. of shares (mil.): 53
Dividends
Yield: —
Payout: 16.75%
Market value ($ mil.): 5,354

	STOCK PRICE ($) FY Close	P/E High	P/E Low	PER SHARE ($) Earnings	Dividends	Book Value
12/11	99.32	17	9	7.64	0.00	42.11
12/10	119.22	17	12	6.88	1.16	38.20
12/09	94.53	14	6	7.59	1.08	32.68
12/08	51.50	18	5	7.74	1.00	24.77
12/07	96.20	22	11	4.46	0.60	22.96
Annual Growth	0.8%	—	—	14.4%	—	16.4%

Fluor Corp.

From the ground up Fluor Corporation is one of the world's largest international design engineering and contracting firms. It provides engineering procurement construction maintenance (EPCM) as well as project management services for a variety of industrial sectors around the world. Its myriad portfolio includes manufacturing plants refineries pharmaceutical facilities health care buildings power plants and telecommunications and transportation infrastructure. Oil and gas industrial and infrastructure projects account for more than half of Fluor's sales. The group also provides operations and maintenance services for its projects as well as administrative and support services to the US government.

The company is structured into five primary segments by sector: oil and gas industrial and infrastructure power global services and government. A separate group Fluor Constructors International provides unionized construction and construction services in the US and Canada. Fluor's oil and gas segment provides design engineering and construction and project management services to markets including upstream oil and gas producers refiners petrochemical manufacturers and producers of specialty and fine chemicals. The unit also provides oversight of other contractors and procurement of labor equipment and materials.

Fluor's oil and gas segment has traditionally been the primary driver for growth in the company generally benefitting from increased global demand for oil. However falling oil prices and the downturn in the economy has hurt the segment especially related to its downstream operations. No longer Fluor's largest segment as of 2011 oil and gas saw its revenues slip by about half in 2010. Increased construction activities led to modest growth in 2011 but profitability declined that year.

Even still Flour continues to look for new opportunities to grow its oil and gas business. In 2011 the company made a niche acquisition when it bought Goar Allison & Associates a company that specializes in sulfur technologies for upstream gas plants and refineries.

The rapidly growing industrial and infrastructure segment —which overtook oil and gas as the largest segment in 2011 —provides design engineering procurement and construction services for pharmaceutical and biotechnology facilities commercial and institutional buildings and mining telecommunications wind power and transportation projects. The unit also participates in public/private partnerships to oversee financing and management of roadway and railway projects. One ongoing significant project is the world's largest offshore wind farm development off the coast of the UK. The project is expected to help produce 25 gigawatts of wind energy by 2020.

Fluor's government services segment another growing division offers project management services primarily to the US Departments of Energy Defense and Homeland Security. It provides environmental restoration engineering and construction and operations and maintenance services for two former nuclear weapons complexes that are now DOE cleanup sites: the Savannah River site in South Carolina and the Hanford Environmental Management Project in Richland Washington. Subsidiary Del-Jen provides military base operations and maintenance services and other logistical and infrastructure services around the world. Fluor's largest long-term job a multi-billion dollar multiyear project is its LOGCAP IV contract to provide services to the US military primarily in Afghanistan. However defense spending is expected to decline which could hurt Fluor's business in the future.

Fluor jumped into the growing outsourcing services market with its global services segment which provides operations and maintenance support temporary staffing (through TRS Staffing Solutions) and asset management. Fluor also provides construction equipment tools and fleet outsourcing for construction projects and plant sites worldwide through subsidiary American Equipment Company (AMECO).

The group's smallest segment is its power segment through which it provides EPCM and other services to the gas fueled solid fuels renewables environmental compliance nuclear and power services markets. Fluor added to the segment in 2011 with the acquisition of a majority stake in NuScale Power a designer of small modular nuclear reactors.

Overall the engineering and construction industry faces challenges with heavy competition and overcapacity. Due to its great size Fluor is well-positioned to survive in this climate as it is active in diverse sectors as well as experienced in carrying out projects in difficult locations such as the Middle East. The company also boasts a strong balance sheet which makes it ready to take advantage of strategic acquisition opportunities. Fluor's revenues grew by 12% to a record $23.4 billion in 2011 while its net income rose some 66% to $593.7 million. The growth was led by its mining and metals operations of its industrial and infrastructure segment.

HISTORY

Fluor's history began in 1890 when three Fluor brothers immigrants from Switzerland opened a Wisconsin lumber mill under the name Rudolph Fluor & Brothers. In 1912 John Simon Fluor formed a construction firm in Santa Ana California. Fluor's company soon began a relationship with Southern California Gas which led it to specialize in oil and gas construction. The company incorporated as Fluor Construction in 1924 later began making engine mufflers. In 1930 it expanded outside of California with a contract to build Texas pipelines.

After WWII Middle East oil reserves were aggressively developed by Western companies. Fluor cashed in on the stampede winning major contracts in Saudi Arabia. During the early 1960s it continued to emphasize oil and gas work establishing a contract drilling unit and in the 1970s it began work on giant energy projects.

In 1977 Fluor made its biggest purchase: Daniel International a South Carolina engineering and construction firm with more than $1 billion in annual revenues. The contracting firm founded by Charles Daniel in 1934 initially did construction work for the textile industry then later worked for the chemical pharmaceutical metal and power industries.

Flush with cash Fluor bought St. Joe Minerals in 1981. A drop in oil prices in the 1980s killed demand for the big projects that were its bread and butter. As metal prices fell St. Joe didn't help the bottom line either. John Robert Fluor the last of the founding family to head the firm died in 1984.

When David Tappan stepped in as CEO he faced a $573 million loss the first year. The white-haired son of missionaries to China Tappan –known as the Ice Man –dumped subsidiaries and halved the payroll. In 1986 he merged Daniel into Fluor's engineering unit forming Fluor Daniel.

Leslie McCraw succeeded Tappan as CEO in 1991. McCraw saw Fluor as overly conservative and three years later he began setting up offices around the world while decentralizing Fluor's structure and adding new business such as temporary staffing and equipment leasing. Fluor also shed some of its commodity companies including its lead business in 1994. In 1996 Fluor's environmental services unit merged with Groundwater Technology and was spun off as a public company Fluor Daniel GTI.

Fluor saw mixed results from its expansion. Amid fierce competition and pricing pressure Fluor Daniel began cutting its overhead in early 1997 by reorganizing and selling noncore businesses.

Ill with cancer McCraw stepped down in 1998 and Philip Carroll who had overhauled Shell Oil took over as CEO. Carroll reorganized Fluor into four business units and tagged $90 million to rebuild its internal information management systems. Fluor also unloaded its 52% stake in Fluor Daniel GTI to The IT Group for $36 million.

Fluor in 1999 cut 5000 jobs further streamlined operations and focused on growth industries such as biotechnology and telecommunications. The next year the company split its construction and coal mining operations into two separate publicly traded companies one to concentrate on engineering and construction and one on coal mining. Former Fluor subsidiary A. T. Massey Coal was spun off as Massey Energy.

Carroll his restructuring job complete announced in December 2001 that he would retire the following February. That year the company also made plans to dispose of noncore operations of the company's construction equipment and temporary staffing businesses. Alan Boeckmann who had been president and COO succeeded Carroll in 2002.

The next year Fluor acquired Del-Jen a provider of outsourced services to US military bases and to the US Department of Labor. It also picked up five specialty operations and maintenance business groups from Philip Services. And in 2003 the company decided to dissolve its Duke/Fluor Daniel joint venture.

Fluor moved its headquarters from California to Dallas in 2006. The move resulted in the elimination of about 100 jobs. That year the company also entered the health care construction market.

In 2007 the company saw growth in all of its business segments with the exception of its government contracts in part because of the conclusion of projects for FEMA and in Iraq. The following year Fluor formed Fluor Offshore Solutions which is dedicated to global oil and gas clients in the offshore market. The company's construction segment acquired two private engineering companies in Europe –Belgium's UNEC Engineering N.V. and Spain's Europea de Ingenieria y Asesoramiento –increasing Fluor's ability to support its clients from a local level.

In early 2011 Alan Boeckmann retired as CEO after nearly a decade at the helm. He was succeeded by longtime company executive David Seaton who previously led Fluor's energy and chemicals global sales and China operations among others.

EXECUTIVES

Group Executive Operations, Kirk D. Grimes, age 54, $530,026 total compensation
SVP Chief Legal Officer and Corporate Secretary, Carlos M. Hernandez, age 57
VP Corporate Affairs; President Fluor Foundation, Lee C. Tashjian
Group Executive Corporate Development and New Ventures Group, John L. Hopkins, age 58, $535,517 total compensation
SVP and CFO, Biggs C. Porter, age 58
Group President Government, Bruce A. Stanski, age 51
VP Corporate Finance and Investor Relations, Kenneth H. (Ken) Lockwood
VP and CIO, Ray F. Barnard, age 53
Newsroom Contact Energy and Chemicals Global Services and Power, Brian Mershon
President Industrial, Dwayne A. Wilson, age 53
Senior Group President Industrial and Infrastructure and Global Services, Stephen B. Dobbs, age 56, $556,213 total compensation
Group President Global Services, Garry W. Flowers, age 60
SVP Government Relations, David (Dave) Marventano
Newsroom Contact Fluor Corporate Government and Industrial and Infrastructure, Keith Stephens
Chairman and CEO, David T. Seaton, age 51, $512,520 total compensation
VP Corporate Compliance, Wendy Hallgren
President Fluor Constructors International, Richard P. (Ric) Carter
VP and Controller, Gary G. Smalley, age 53
SVP Human Resources and Administration, Glenn C. Gilkey, age 53
Group President Power, David R. (Dave) Dunning, age 60
Group President Energy and Chemicals, Peter W. B. Oosterveer
Director, Dean R. O'Hare, age 70
Director, Kent Kresa, age 74
Director, James T. (Jim) Hackett, age 58
Director, Peter K. Barker, age 63
Director, Nader H. Sultan, age 63
Director, Suzanne H. (Sue) Woolsey, age 70
Director, Adm. Joseph W. (Joe) Prueher, age 69
Director, Peter J. Fluor, age 64
Director, Rosemary T. Berkery, age 58
Director, Paulett Eberhart, age 58
Chairman and CEO, David T. Seaton, age 51
Director, Ilesanmi Adesida, age 62
Auditors: Ernst&YoungLLP

LOCATIONS

HQ: Fluor Corporation
6700 Las Colinas Blvd., Irving TX 75039
Phone: 469-398-7000 **Fax:** 469-398-7255
Web: www.fluor.com

2011 Sales

	$ mil.	% of total
US	6,959	30
Asia/Pacific	4,395	19
Canada	4,127	18
Middle East & Africa	3,339	14
Central & South America	2,822	12
Europe	1,736	7
Total	**23,381**	**100**

PRODUCTS/OPERATIONS

2011 Sales by Segment

	$ mil.	% of total
Industrial & Infrastructure	9,700	41
Oil & Gas	7,961	34
Government	3,398	15
Global Services	1,577	7
Power	743	3
Total	**23,381**	**100**

Selected Services

Construction management
Design
Engineering procurement and construction (EPC)
Operations and maintenance
Program management
Project development and finance
Project management
Staffing

Selected Industries Served

Biotechnology
Chemicals and petrochemicals
Commercial and institutional
Equipment
Gas processing
Government
Manufacturing
Mining
Oil and gas production
Petroleum refining
Pharmaceuticals
Power generation
Telecommunications
Transportation

Selected Subsidiaries

American Equipment Company Inc.
  American Construction Equipment Company Inc.
Fluor Constructors International Inc.
Fluor Enterprises Inc.
  Daniel International Corporation
  Del-Jen Inc.
  Fluor Daniel Mexico S.A.
    ICA-Fluor Daniel S. de R.L. de C.V. (49% Mexico)
Fluor Holding Company LLC
TRS Staffing Solutions Inc.

COMPETITORS

ARCADIS
Balfour Construction
Bechtel
Bilfinger Berger
Black & Veatch
Bouygues
CH2M HILL
Foster Wheeler
Hitachi
Jacobs Engineering
KBR
McDermott
Parsons Corporation
POSCO
Raytheon
Shaw Group
Technip
Tetra Tech
URS
WorleyParsons Corp.

HISTORICAL FINANCIALS

Company Type: Public

Income Statement FYE: December 31

	REVENUE ($ mil.)	NET INCOME ($ mil.)	NET PROFIT MARGIN	EMPLOYEES
12/11	23,381	593	2.5%	43,087
12/10	20,849	357	1.7%	39,329
12/09	21,990	684	3.1%	36,152
12/08	22,325	720	3.2%	42,119
12/07	16,691	533	3.2%	41,260
Annual Growth	8.8%	2.7%	—	1.1%

2011 Year-End Financials

Debt ratio: 6.44%
Return on equity: 17.49%
Cash ($ mil.): 2,161
Current ratio: 153.14
Long-term debt ($ mil.): 513

No. of shares (mil.): 168
Dividends
Yield: —
Payout: 14.71%
Market value ($ mil.): 8,491

	STOCK PRICE ($) FY Close	P/E High	P/E Low	PER SHARE ($) Earnings	Dividends	Book Value
12/11	50.25	22	13	3.40	0.00	20.09
12/10	66.26	33	21	1.98	0.50	19.82
12/09	45.04	15	8	3.75	0.50	18.48
12/08	44.87	49	7	3.93	0.50	14.71
12/07	145.72	55	25	2.93	0.40	12.82
Annual Growth	(23.4%)	—	—	3.8%	—	11.9%

Flushing Financial Corp.

Flush with cash? You could keep it at Flushing Financial Corp. (FFC). The holding company's Flushing Savings Bank operates more than 15 branches in the Brooklyn Manhattan and Queens boroughs of New York City and in nearby Nassau County. The bank offers services catering to the sizable populations of Asians and other ethnic groups in its market. Deposit products include CDs and checking savings passbook money market and NOW accounts. Mortgages secured by multifamily residential commercial and mixed-use real estate account for most of the company's loan portfolio; other offerings include single-family mortgages construction loans business loans and taxi medallion loans.

The bank has shifted its strategy from operating as a traditional thrift to a more commercial slant focusing on such offerings as business lending and cash management services as well as commercial lending. Recently formed Flushing Savings subsidiary Flushing Commercial Bank provides banking services and collects deposits from public customers throughout the New York metropolitan area. (The unit does originate loans.) In late 2012 parent FFC applied to combine Flushing Savings Bank and Flushing Commercial Bank to convert the bank from a federally-chartered savings bank to a New York State-chartered commercial bank. As a result Flushing Commercial will become a full-service commercial bank and change its name to Flushing Bank.

Flushing Savings tightened its lending practices after seeing a rise in bad loans during the financial crisis. It has also reduced the number of construction loans and commercial mortgages it originates as they typically carry a higher risk. As a result the bank has been originating and purchasing fewer loans than it did before the downturn started. However higher-yielding multifamily mortgages remain a key strategic focus for the company.

With the decline in lending Flushing's interest earnings have also declined. Lower-yielding securities investments further cut into the company's interest earnings. Costs associated with opening a branch in early 2011 contributed to an increase in operating expenses. (The bank opened another branch in early 2012.) Overall revenues fell 1% to $234.8 million in 2011 while profits fell 9% to $35.4 million.

EXECUTIVES

EVP and Chief of Real Estate Lending Flushing Financial and Flushing Savings Bank, Francis W. (Frank) Korzekwinski, age 49, $337,773 total compensation
President CEO and Director Flushing Financial and Flushing Savings Bank, John R. Buran, age 62, $735,054 total compensation
Chairman Flushing Financial and Flushing Savings Bank, John E. Roe Sr., age 78
EVP CFO and Treasurer; EVP Finance Flushing Savings Bank, David W. Fry, age 61, $316,105 total compensation
SVP and Director Retail Banking and Investment Sales, Leeann L. Tannuzzo, age 44
EVP COO and Corporate Secretary Flushing Financial and Flushing Savings Bank, Maria A. Grasso, age 47, $388,758 total compensation
SVP Residential Mixed-Use and Small Multi-Family Real Estate Lending, Jeoung (A. J.) Jin, age 45
SVP and CIO, Allen M. Brewer, age 59
SVP and Chief Investment Officer, William J. (Jeff) Weichsel, age 62
SVP and Chief Internal Auditor, Robert G. (Bob) Kiraly, age 56
SVP and Director Human Resources, Ruth E. Filiberto, age 53
SVP and Director Operations, Barbara A. Beckmann, age 53
SVP and Director Government Banking, Patricia Mezeul, age 52
SVP Commercial Real Estate Lending, Ronald Hartmann, age 56
SVP Business Banking Flushing Financial and Flushing Savings Bank, Theresa Kelly, age 50, $235,243 total compensation
SVP and Controller, Astrid Burrowes, age 47
SVP and Director Strategic Development and Delivery, Caterina dePasquale, age 44
SVP Asian Markets, Paul W. Ho, age 54
Director, Gerard P. Tully Sr., age 84
Director, Michael J. Hegarty, age 72
President CEO and Director Flushing Financial and Flushing Savings Bank, John R. Buran, age 62
Director, James D. Bennett, age 73
Director, Vincent F. Nicolosi, age 72
Director, Louis C. (Lou) Grassi, age 56
Director, Michael J. Russo, age 77
Director, John J. McCabe, age 68
Director, Donna M. O'Brien, age 56
Director, Steven J. D'Iorio, age 62
Director, Sam S. K. Han, age 58
Auditors: GrantThorntonLLP

LOCATIONS

HQ: Flushing Financial Corporation
1979 Marcus Ave. Ste. E140, Lake Success NY 11042
Phone: 718-961-5400 **Fax:** 408-735-9036
Web: www.sst.com

PRODUCTS/OPERATIONS

2011 Sales

	$ mil.	% of total
Interest		
Loans including fees	191	81
Securities & other	33	14
Noninterest		
Bank-owned life insurance	2	1
Net gain from fair value adjustments	2	1
Other	7	3
Adjustments	(1.6)	-
Total	**234**	**100**

COMPETITORS

Apple Bank for Savings
Astoria Financial
Bank of America
Bank of New York Mellon
Citigroup
Dime Community Bancshares
First of Long Island
HSBC USA
JPMorgan Chase
Korea Exchange Bank
New York Community Bancorp

HISTORICAL FINANCIALS

Company Type: Public

Income Statement FYE: December 31

	ASSETS ($ mil.)	NET INCOME ($ mil.)	INCOME AS % OF ASSETS	EMPLOYEES
12/11	4,287	35	0.8%	394
12/10	4,324	38	0.9%	379
12/09	4,143	25	0.6%	355
12/08	3,949	22	0.6%	343
12/07	3,354	20	0.6%	325
Annual Growth	6.3%	15.0%	—	4.9%

2011 Year-End Financials

Debt ratio: 11.66%
Return on equity: 8.48%
Cash ($ mil.): 55
Current ratio: —
Long-term debt ($ mil.): 499

No. of shares (mil.): 30
Dividends
Yield: —
Payout: 45.22%
Market value ($ mil.): 390

	STOCK PRICE ($) FY Close	P/E High	P/E Low	PER SHARE ($) Earnings	Dividends	Book Value
12/11	12.63	13	9	1.15	0.00	13.49
12/10	14.00	11	8	1.28	0.52	12.48
12/09	11.26	15	4	0.91	0.52	11.57
12/08	11.96	18	10	1.10	0.52	13.94
12/07	16.05	18	14	1.02	0.48	10.96
Annual Growth	(5.8%)	—	—	3.0%	—	5.3%

FMC Technologies, Inc.

FMC Technologies is named after its early years as a food machinery maker but this company's bread and butter is oil and gas equipment. FMC Technologies offers subsea drilling and production systems for the exploration and production of oil and gas. It also offers similar equipment and services for onshore oil production. In addition the company's energy infrastructure segment makes fluid control measurement marine loading separation material handling blending systems and other equipment. FMC Technologies operates 28 manufacturing centers in 16 countries.

Operations

FMC Technologies is the world's largest manufacturer of "Christmas Trees" an assembly of control valves gauges and chokes that control oil and gas flow in an underwater or subsea oil well. The trees are a crucial component of the company's subsea systems that direct the flow of oil and gas to processing stations on land or on the offshore production platforms.

Sales and Marketing

The company's largest customers in 2011 were Norwegian energy giant Statoil and French oil major TOTAL.

Financial Analysis

FMC Technologies gets most of its sales from offshore markets in the US and Norway. The company is also growing its operations in Brazil and Angola.

The company's global spread and diversified portfolio enabled it to weather the impacts of the recession especially the weaker demand for oil and gas exploration and production activities in the North America. However the effects of the recession on FMC Technologies' backlog dragged own revenues in 2010.

High oil prices and strong global demand for oil and gas exploration activity boosted sales in all three of its segments in 2011 and overall revenues by more than 23%. Despite higher sales costs and operating expenses the company reported a 6% growth in net income that year.

Strategy

In 2012 FMC Technologies formed a joint venture with Edison Chouest Offshore LLC to provide integrated vessel-based subsea services for offshore oil and gas companies globally.

In 2010 FMC Technologies won a $90 million contract to provide an industry ground breaking subsea separation and pumping system for PETROBRAS' Marlim field in offshore Brazil. The system will increase the field's production capacity by removing unwanted water from the production stream on the sea floor.

Mergers and Acquisitions

Expanding its portfolio FMC Technologies in 2012 acquired Calgary-based Pure Energy Services Ltd. for approximately $285 million. FMC acquired Pure Energy which provides frac flowback and wireline services for oilfields in North America to complement its Surface Technologies segment. The combination provides an integrated set of well site products and services which should increase value for customers.

Other key 2012 acquisitions include the purchase of Control Systems International a major supplier of control and automation systems for the oil and gas industry for an undisclosed price and the purchase of Schilling Robotics which produces remotely operated vehicles and other control systems for oil and gas subsea production.

Company Background

FMC Technologies was formed as subsidiary of FMC Corporation in 2000 and went public as an independent unit the next year. It spun off its industrial food equipment and airport systems unit into a separate company called John Bean Technologies in 2008.

EXECUTIVES

EVP, William H. (Bill) Schumann III, age 61, $589,384 total compensation
SVP General Counsel and Secretary, Jeffrey W. Carr, age 55
President, Robert L. (Bob) Potter, age 61, $436,810 total compensation
Chairman and CEO, John T. Gremp, age 60, $498,488 total compensation
SVP Global Subsea Production Systems, Tore H. Halvorsen, age 57, $451,000 total compensation
VP Administration, Mark J. Scott
VP Energy Infrastructure, Barry Glickman
SVP and CFO, Maryann T. Seaman, age 49
VP and Controller, Jay A. Nutt, age 48
VP Technology, Bradley D. Beitler
VP Global Surface Technologies, Johan F. Pfeiffer
EVP and COO, Douglas J. Pferdehirt
Treasurer, Richard Clark
Director, Thorleif Enger, age 69
Director, Thomas M. (Tom) Hamilton, age 68
Director, Joseph H. Netherland, age 65
Director, Phillip J. Burguieres, age 68
Director, James M. (Jim) Ringler, age 66
Director, Richard A. (Rich) Pattarozzi, age 68
Director, Edward J. (Ted) Mooney, age 70
Director, Claire S. Farley, age 53
Director, Mike R. Bowlin, age 69
Director, C. Maury (Maury) Devine, age 61
Director, Eleazar de Carvalho Filho, age 54
Auditors: KPMGLLP

LOCATIONS

HQ: FMC Technologies, Inc.
1803 Gears Road, Houston, TX 77067
Phone: 281 591-4000
Web: www.fmctechnologies.com

2011 Sales

	$ mil.	% of total
US	1,156	23
Brazil	541	11
Other countries	2,434	47

PRODUCTS/OPERATIONS

2011 Sales

	$ mil.	% of total
Subsea technologies	3,288	64
Surface technologies	1,310	26
Energy infrastructure	503	10
Adjustments	(3.3)	-
Total	**5,099**	**100**

COMPETITORS

Aker Solutions
Baker Hughes
Cameron International
Dril-Quip
GE Oil
John Wood Group
McDermott
National Oilwell Varco
Weatherford International

HISTORICAL FINANCIALS

Company Type: Public

Income Statement FYE: December 31

	REVENUE ($ mil.)	NET INCOME ($ mil.)	NET PROFIT MARGIN	EMPLOYEES
12/11	5,099	399	7.8%	14,200
12/10	4,125	375	9.1%	11,500
12/09	4,405	361	8.2%	10,400
12/08	4,550	361	7.9%	9,800
12/07	4,615	302	6.6%	13,000
Annual Growth	2.5%	7.2%	—	2.2%

2011 Year-End Financials

Debt ratio: 14.60%
Return on equity: 28.06%
Cash ($ mil.): 344
Current ratio: 124.86
Long-term debt ($ mil.): 36
No. of shares (mil.): 237
Dividends
Yield: —
Payout: —
Market value ($ mil.): 12,420

	STOCK PRICE ($) FY Close	P/E High/Low		PER SHARE ($) Earnings	Dividends	Book Value
12/11	52.23	58	22	1.64	0.00	5.99
12/10	88.91	58	31	1.53	0.00	5.48
12/09	57.84	40	16	1.44	0.00	4.53
12/08	23.83	57	14	1.39	0.00	2.79
12/07	56.70	82	43	1.13	0.00	3.95
Annual Growth	(2.0%)	—	—	9.8%	—	11.0%

FNB United Corp

FNB United is the holding company for CommunityONE Bank (formerly First National Bank and Trust) which has about 45 branches in North Carolina. The bank's offerings include checking savings and money market accounts CDs IRAs credit cards and trust services. It concentrates on real estate lending: Commercial mortgages account for more than 35% of the company's loan portfolio while residential mortgages and construction loans are about 25% apiece. The bank also makes business and consumer loans. Subsidiary Dover Mortgage Company originates mortgages for sale into the secondary market through about five loan production offices in its home state. FNB United merged with Bank of Granite in 2011.

The two North Carolina-based companies will ultimately combine to create a community banking group with more than 60 branches. The combined company will be called FNB United Corp. and the two banking subsidiaries (CommunityOne and Bank of Granite) will eventually merge under the CommunityOne Bank name. The consolidation is scheduled to be completed in the spring of 2012.

As part of the transaction FNB United will be under new management. Brian Simpson will serve as CEO and Bob Reid will become president.

FNB United has grown through acquisitions including United Financial (2005) and Integrity Financial (2006). The banks acquired in those acquisitions were merged into CommunityONE Bank.

EXECUTIVES

Chief Risk Officer CommunityOne Bank, Dean S. Tingey
Chief Human Resources Officer CommunityOne Bank, Deborah B. Auman
EVP CFO and Treasurer; EVP and CFO CommunityOne Bank, Mark A. Severson, age 58, $180,000 total compensation
Interim President Interim CEO and Director; Interim President and Interim CEO CommunityOne Bank, R. Larry Campbell, age 67, $180,000 total compensation
Chairman, James M. Campbell Jr., age 73
Vice Chairman, Eugene B. McLaurin II, age 55
Chief Wealth Management Officer CommunityOne Bank, Timothy C. Britt
Chief Lending Officer CommunityOne Bank, Eddie M. Causey

EVP and Chief Banking Officer CommunityOne Bank, R. Mark Hensley, age 53, $180,000 total compensation
President Dover Mortgage, Harvey W. Goldberg
Treasurer CommunityOne Bank, W. Carey Chapman Jr.
Chief Credit Officer CommunityONE Bank, David C. Lavoie
Interim President Interim CEO and Director; Interim President and Interim CEO CommunityOne Bank, R. Larry Campbell, age 67
Director, Thomas A. Jordan, age 72
Director, Darrell L. Frye, age 66
Director, J. M. Ramsay III, age 64
Director, R. Reynolds Neely Jr., age 58
Vice Chairman, Eugene B. McLaurin II, age 55
Director, Ray H. McKenney Jr., age 57
Director, Carl G. Yale, age 60
Director, Jacob F. Alexander III, age 61
Director, Hal F. (Chip) Huffman Jr., age 57
Director, Larry E. Brooks, age 71
Director, Lynn S. Lloyd, age 61
Auditors: DixonHughesGoodmanLLP

LOCATIONS

HQ: FNB United Corp.
150 South Fayetteville St., Asheboro NC 27203
Phone: 336-626-8300 **Fax:** 336-625-2452
Web: www.myyesbank.com/

PRODUCTS/OPERATIONS

2007 Sales

	$ mil.	% of total
Interest		
Loans including fees	114	78
Investment securities	10	7
Other	1	1
Noninterest		
Service charges on deposit accounts	9	6
Mortgage loan sales	4	3
Cardholder & merchant services	1	1
Trust & investment services	1	1
Other	4	3
Total	**148**	**100**

COMPETITORS

BB&T
BNC Bancorp
Capital Bank
Capitol Bancorp
Carolina Bank
First Bancorp (NC)
First Citizens BancShares
First Merchants
NewBridge Bancorp
PNC Financial
Regions Financial
Southern Community Financial
Yadkin Valley Financial Corporation

HISTORICAL FINANCIALS

Company Type: Public

Income Statement FYE: December 31

	ASSETS ($ mil.)	NET INCOME ($ mil.)	INCOME AS % OF ASSETS	EMPLOYEES
12/11	2,409	(137)	—	609
12/10	1,921	(112)	—	526
12/09	2,101	(101)	—	485
12/08	2,044	(59)	—	492
12/07	1,906	12	0.6%	526
Annual Growth	6.0%	—	—	3.7%

2011 Year-End Financials

Debt ratio: 4.78%
Return on equity: (-106.43)%
Cash ($ mil.): 553
Current ratio: —
Long-term debt ($ mil.): 115
No. of shares (mil.): 21
Dividends
Yield: —
Payout: —
Market value ($ mil.): 270

	STOCK PRICE ($)	P/E		PER SHARE ($)		
	FY Close	High/Low		Earnings	Dividends	Book Value
12/11	12.80	—	—	(22.09)	0.00	6.11
12/10	0.33	—	—	(1,017.00)	0.00	(86.91)
12/09	1.30	—	—	(916.00)	0.00	860.80
12/08	3.14	—	—	(524.00)	0.00	1,294.34
12/07	12.16	0	0	109.00	0.00	1,892.52
Annual Growth	1.3%	—	—	—	—	(76.2%)

Foot Locker, Inc.

Foot Locker leads the pack in the race to capture the biggest share of the global athletic footwear market. The company is a leading retailer of athletic shoes and apparel with more than 3350 specialty stores in 20-plus countries in North America and Europe as well as Australia and New Zealand. Its 1900-store namesake Foot Locker chain is the #1 seller of name-brand (NIKE) athletic footwear in the US. The company also operates stores under the Lady Foot Locker Kids Foot Locker Footaction Champs Sports and CCS banners. In addition to its bricks-and-mortar business Foot Locker markets sports gear through its direct-to-customer unit which consists of catalog retailer Eastbay and Footlocker.com.

HISTORY

With the idea of selling merchandise priced at no more than five cents Frank Woolworth opened the Great Five Cent Store in Utica New York in 1879; it failed. That year he moved to Lancaster Pennsylvania and created the first five-and-dime. Woolworth moved his headquarters to New York City (1886) and spent the rest of the century acquiring other dime-store chains. He later expanded to Canada (1897) England (1909) France (1922) and Germany (1927).

The 120-store chain with $10 million in sales incorporated as F.W. Woolworth & Company in 1905 with Woolworth as president. In 1912 the company merged with five rival chains and went public with 596 stores making $52 million in sales the first year. The next year paying $13.5 million in cash Woolworth finished construction of the Woolworth Building then the world's tallest building (792 feet). When he died in 1919 the chain had 1081 stores with sales of $119 million.

Woolworth became more competitive after WWII by advertising establishing revolving credit and self-service moving stores to suburbs and expanding merchandise selections. In 1962 it opened Woolco a US and Canadian discount chain.

From the 1960s through the 1980s the company grew by acquiring and expanding in the US and abroad. It picked up Kinney (shoes 1963) Richman Brothers (men's clothing 1969) Holtzman's Little Folk Shop (children's clothing 1983) Champs Sports (sporting goods 1987) and Mathers (shoes Australia 1988).

The company introduced Foot Locker the athletic shoe chain in 1974 later developing Lady Foot Locker (1982) and Kids Foot Locker (1987). In 1993 Woolworth launched an ambitious restructuring plan focusing on specialty stores (mostly apparel and shoes). It also closed 400 US stores and sold 122 Canadian Woolco stores to Wal-Mart that year. Former Macy's president Roger Farah became CEO in 1994. Farah eliminated 16 divisions and dozens of executives.

A year later the firm sold its Kids Mart/Little Folks children's wear chain. In 1996 Woolworth began a major remodeling program that included removing its venerable lunch counters. (Another alleged renovation at the Woolworth chain –the firing of older workers who were replaced by teenagers –led to an Equal Employment Opportunity Commission lawsuit against the company in 1999.) The changes failed and the next year the company closed its US Woolworth stores and bought athletic-products catalog company Eastbay.

In 1998 Woolworth changed its name to Venator Group and sold the Woolworth Building a national landmark (headquarters remained in the building). The company then shed itself of more than 1400 stores including Kinney shoes and Footquarters (both closed).

Internet site eVenator was launched in 1999 to sell Eastbay Champs and Foot Locker merchandise. Venator came out the champ in a proxy fight against investment group Greenway Partners in July 1999. Shortly thereafter Farah was replaced as CEO (he remained chairman) by president Dale Hilpert.

In 2000 Venator slashed 7% of its workforce in the US and Canada (a small part of the planned 30% cut) and closed 465 stores. COO Matt Serra became president and Hilpert became chairman when Farah resigned later that year.

In March 2001 Hilpert resigned replaced by Carter Bacot as chairman and Serra added CEO to his title. Venator later sold its Canadian Northern Group unit to investment firm York Management Services and closed its Northern Reflections stores in the US. Venator changed its name to Foot Locker in November. It also sold gift retailer San Francisco Music Box Co. and its hospitality division's fast-food franchises before the end of the year.

In early 2004 chairman Bacot become lead director and president and CEO Serra added chairman to his title.

In 2004 Foot Locker capitalizing on the Chapter 11 filing of Footstar Inc. purchased from the company 350 of its Footaction stores. The company also acquired 11 stores in Ireland from Champion Sports Group later in the same year.

The company's short-lived family footwear retail concept –called Footquarters –launched in early 2007 but was quickly discontinued due to poor performance. The locations were converted to Foot Lockers and Champs Sports outlet stores. Also in early 2007 Foot Locker made an unsolicited $1.2 billion bid for rival Genesco that was rejected by Genesco's board. Foot Locker closed about 275 mostly underperforming stores in 2007.

In 2008 the company reduced its store count by about 145 locations across its five chains in a bid to boost profitability by focusing on its most profitable locations and improving operations. In November Foot Locker acquired the CCS brand from dELia*s for about $103 million. The CCS brand includes skateboarding and snowboarding equipment apparel and footwear targeting primarily teenage boys.

J.C. Penney executive Kenneth Hicks was recruited to succeed Serra as president and CEO in August 2009. Serra who had held the CEO title since 2001 retained the chairman's title until his retirement in January 2010. At that time Hicks became chairman.

EXECUTIVES

SVP General Counsel and Secretary, Gary M. Bahler, age 60, $524,975 total compensation
EVP and CFO, Lauren B. Peters, age 50
Chairman President and CEO, Kenneth C. (Ken) Hicks, age 59, $506,349 total compensation
SVP Real Estate, Jeffrey L. Berk, age 56, $448,969 total compensation
EVP Operations Support, Robert W. McHugh, age 53, $562,500 total compensation
VP Logistics, Joseph N. (Joe) Bongiorno, age 59
SVP and CIO, Peter D. Brown, age 57
VP and Deputy General Counsel, Dennis E. Sheehan, age 54
SVP Human Resources, Laurie J. Petrucci, age 53, $468,573 total compensation
VP Human Resources, Patricia A. Peck
SVP and Chief Accounting Officer, Giovanna Cipriano, age 42
VP Global Sourcing and Team Edition, James T. Bulzis
VP Risk Management, Bernard F. Steenman
VP Treasurer and Investor Relations, John A. Maurer, age 52
EVP and Group President?Retail Stores, Richard A. (Dick) Johnson, age 54, $525,000 total compensation
President and CEO Footlocker.com/Eastbay/CCS, Dowe S. Tillema
President and CEO Champs Sports, Byron W. Milburn
President and CEO Foot Locker Europe, Lewis P. Kimble
President and CEO Foot Locker Inc. International, Ronald J. Halls, age 58, $750,000 total compensation
VP Associate General Counsel and Assistant Secretary, Sheilagh M. Clarke
VP Strategic Planning, Natalie M. Ellis
President and CEO Foot Locker/Lady Foot Locker/Kids Foot Locker/Footaction, Stephen D. Jacobs
Managing Director Foot Locker Asia/Pacific, Phillip G. Laing
Managing Director Foot Locker Canada, Nicholas Jones
Director, Alan D. Feldman, age 60
Director, Matthew M. (Matt) McKenna, age 61
Director, Dona D. Young, age 58
Chairman President and CEO, Kenneth C. (Ken) Hicks, age 59
Director, Allen I. Questrom, age 72
Director, Jarobin Gilbert Jr., age 66
Director, James E. Preston, age 78
Director, David Y. Schwartz, age 71
Director, Guillermo G. (Gil) Marmol
Auditors: KPMGLLP

LOCATIONS

HQ: Foot Locker Inc.
112 W. 34th St., New York NY 10120
Phone: 212-720-3700 **Fax:** 212-720-4397
Web: www.footlocker-inc.com

2012 Sales

	$ mil.	% of total
US	3,959	70
International	1,664	30
Total	**5,623**	**100**

2012 Foot Locker Stores

	No.
US Puerto Rico Guam & US Virgin	1,118
Europe	563
Canada	129
Australia & New	91
Total	**1,901**

PRODUCTS/OPERATIONS

2012 Stores

	No.
Foot	1,901
Champs	534
Lady Foot	331
Footaction	292
Kids Foot	289
CCS	22
Total	**3,369**

2012 Sales

	$ mil.	% of total
Athletic stores	5,110	91
Direct-to-consumer	513	9
Total	**5,623**	**100**

COMPETITORS

Academy Sports
Brown Shoe
Dick' s Sporting Goods
Dillard' s
DSW
FGL Sports
Finish Line
Genesco
Hibbett Sports
J. C. Penney
Kmart
L.L. Bean
Macy' s
Modell' s
Pacific Sunwear
Quiksilver
Sears
Shoe Carnival
shoebuy.com
Sports Authority
Target Corporation
The Gap
TJX Companies
Wal-Mart
Zappos.com

HISTORICAL FINANCIALS

Company Type: Public

Income Statement FYE: January 28

	REVENUE ($ mil.)	NET INCOME ($ mil.)	NET PROFIT MARGIN	EMPLOYEES
01/12	5,623	278	4.9%	39,077
01/11	5,049	169	3.3%	38,007
01/10	4,854	48	1.0%	38,764
01/09*	5,237	(80)	—	39,758
02/08	5,437	51	0.9%	44,407
Annual Growth	0.8%	52.8%	—	(3.1%)

*Fiscal year change

2012 Year-End Financials

Debt ratio: 4.43%
Return on equity: 13.18%
Cash ($ mil.): 851
Current ratio: 379.38
Long-term debt ($ mil.): 135
No. of shares (mil.): 151
Dividends
Yield: —
Payout: 36.67%
Market value ($ mil.): 4,009

	STOCK PRICE ($) FY Close	P/E High/Low		PER SHARE ($) Earnings	Dividends	Book Value
01/12	26.44	15	9	1.80	0.00	13.92
01/11	17.77	18	10	1.07	0.00	13.10
01/10	11.29	42	24	0.30	0.00	12.44
01/09*	7.36	—	—	(0.52)	0.00	12.42
02/08	13.94	73	30	0.33	0.00	14.70
Annual Growth	17.4%	—	—	52.8%	—	(1.4%)

*Fiscal year change

Ford Motor Co. (DE)

Ford Motor began a manufacturing revolution with mass production assembly lines in the early 20th century but today it is one of the world's largest automakers. Brands include Ford and Lincoln; Mercury ceased production in 2010. Among its models are the redesigned Ford Mustang the F-Series pickup and the fuel-efficient Focus. Finance unit Ford Motor Credit is one of the US's leading auto finance companies. Ford owns a small stake in Mazda but sold Volvo in 2010 to Zhejiang Geely Holding parent of Geely Automobile for about $1.3 billion cash and other monetary consideration. It operates about 65 plants worldwide but gets more than half of its sales from North America.

HISTORY

Henry Ford started the Ford Motor Company in 1903 in Dearborn Michigan. In 1908 Ford introduced the Model T produced on a moving assembly line that revolutionized both carmaking and manufacturing. By 1920 some 60% of all vehicles on the road were Fords.

After Ford omitted its usual dividend in 1916 stockholders sued. Ford responded by buying back all of its outstanding shares in 1919 and didn't allow outside ownership again until 1956.

Ford bought Lincoln Motor Company in 1922 and discontinued the Model T in 1927. Its replacement the Model A came in 1932. With Henry Ford's health failing his son Edsel became president that year. Despite the debut of the Mercury (1938) market share slipped behind General Motors and Chrysler. After Edsel's death in 1943 his son Henry II took over and decentralized Ford following the GM model. Henry Ford died in 1947 at the age of 83. In 1950 the carmaker recaptured second place. Ford rolled out the infamous Edsel line in 1958 and launched the Mustang in 1964.

Hurt by the oil crisis of the 1970s Ford cut its workforce and closed plants during the 1980s. It also diversified into agricultural equipment by purchasing New Holland (1986) and Versatile (1987). Ford added luxury sports cars in 1987 by buying 75% of Aston Martin (it bought the rest in 1994). The 1988 introduction of the Taurus and Sable spurred Ford to its largest share of the US car market (almost 22%) in 10 years. In 1989 it bought Associates First Capital (financial services) and Jaguar (luxury cars).

The company sold Ford Aerospace to Loral in 1990 and merged New Holland (renamed CNH Global 1999) with a Fiat subsidiary the next year.

Ford acquired Hertz in 1994 and two years later bought #3 rental agency Budget Rent a Car (sold 1997). Also in 1996 it sold a 19% stake in finance unit Associates First Capital in an IPO and increased its stake in Mazda to one-third. The next year Ford sold its heavy-duty truck unit to Daimler's Freightliner subsidiary (since renamed Daimler Trucks North America) for about $200 million and spun off 19% of Hertz in an IPO. Also in 1997 it launched automotive systems supplier Visteon (formerly Ford Automotive Products Operations) at the Frankfurt Motor Show.

Ford began building a minibus line in China in 1997 beating GM in the race to produce vehicles for the Chinese market. In 1998 Ford spun off the rest of Associates First Capital and acquired Cosworth's racing-engines unit from Audi. Ford additionally sold off its direct stake in Kia Motors but kept an indirect stake through its interest in Mazda.

Henry Ford's great-grandson William Clay Ford Jr. became chairman in 1998. Company veteran Jacques Nasser became president and CEO in early 1999.

Ford bought Volvo's carmaking operations for $6.45 billion in 1999 adding the brand to its new Premier Automotive Group (Aston Martin Jaguar and Lincoln) headed by former BMW chairman Wolfgang Reitzle. Other acquisitions included the UK's Kwik-Fit Holdings for $1.6 billion (to boost aftermarket services for new-car buyers) and Automobile Protection Corporation (APCO) a provider of extended-service contracts. (In 2007 Ford sold APCO to an affiliate fund of Stone Point Capital and APCO's management.) Ford then began buying up junkyards in the US as a new business source.

Ford GM and Daimler formed Covisint (now Compuware Covisint) a website for online transactions among suppliers and manufacturers in 2000. Ford also spun off Visteon as an independent company that year and bought BMW's Land Rover SUV operations for about $2.7 billion in a move to boost its European presence.

Ford won exclusive bidding rights in 2000 for Daewoo Motor (now named GM Daewoo Auto & Technology) South Korea's #2 carmaker (beating out GM and Daimler) as it poised to grow its market share in Asia. However in a surprise announcement Ford dropped the $6.9 billion bid to buy Daewoo after deciding that it wasn't worth the hefty price tag. Around the same time the company was embroiled in controversy when Bridgestone/Firestone recalled some 6.5 million tires many of which were used as original equipment on Ford Explorers.

In 2001 Ford recalled some 300000 cars including 1995-96 Ford Contour and Mercury Mystique sedans which posed possible fire danger linked to engine overheating problems. The company also spent about $700 million to buy the remaining 19% of Hertz that it didn't already own thus completing its full acquisition. Additionally Ford announced a 50-50 truck-building joint venture with Navistar to produce a common medium-duty chassis customized for the Ford and Navistar brands.

A 2001 study revealed that the tires Ford used on its vehicles —Firestone Wilderness AT tires — failed three times more frequently than the industry average. Ford took a $2.1 billion charge to cover the replacement of up to 13 million Firestone tires. The news led Firestone to stop doing business with Ford ending a 95-year relationship. Within days Ford inked a deal with Goodyear in which Goodyear replaced Ford owners' Firestone Wilderness AT tires with Goodyear tires and then billed Ford.

Ford announced a major management shake-up mid-year 2001. Among the changes: Nick Scheele —credited with restructuring Ford Europe and turning Jaguar around —was named head of North American operations and Martin Inglis was named to replace Henry Wallace as CFO. The company also announced the creation of an "office of the chairman and chief executive" to increase chairman William Clay Ford Jr.'s input in decision making with CEO Nasser. In August Ford announced that it would use early retirement incentives to eliminate 4500-5000 (about 10%) of its salaried employees. Not long afterwards the company combined its car and truck engineering groups. In 2001 Nasser resigned and was replaced as CEO by chairman Ford.

A week or so into 2002 Ford announced far-reaching cost-cutting measures including 35000 worldwide job cuts (22000 in North America) the closure of three North American assembly plants and the discontinuation of four vehicle models — The Ford Escort the Mercury Cougar the Mercury Villager and the Lincoln Continental.

Just three years after purchasing it in 2002 Ford sold Kwik-Fit (at a considerable loss) to London-based equity firm CVC Capital Partners for about $505 million in cash and a note to be paid after CVC obtains additional financing. Ford retained a 19% equity stake in Kwik-Fit. Later that year citing poor customer demand and little government support Ford announced it would sell its underperforming Th!nk division (the division was sold in 2004).

Ford signed a deal with the Chinese government early in 2004 to secure rights to land in Nanjing where the company planned to build a second Ford plant in China. The following year Ford took full control of its operations in India with the purchase of a nearly 16% stake from its Indian partner Mahindra & Mahindra Ltd. (Ford Motor set up its Indian subsidiary in Madras in 1995 as a 50-50 joint venture with Mahindra; Ford later raised its stake.) In mid-2004 William Clay Ford Sr. the CEO's father retired from Ford's board of directors after 55 years of service.

In order to focus on its struggling automotive operations Ford sold its Hertz car rental business in 2005 to a private equity group made up of Clayton Dubilier & Rice The Carlyle Group and Merrill Lynch Global Private Equity for $5.6 billion and the assumption of nearly $10 billion of Hertz debt.

Former Boeing executive Alan Mulally was named president and CEO of Ford in 2006. Bill Ford remained executive chairman. Mulally was credited with fixing Boeing's commercial aircraft business and was chosen for his strengths in manufacturing product development and customer satisfaction. Later in the year Ford exercised its right of first refusal agreement with BMW regarding rights to the control of the Land Rover brand. The agreement stemmed from BMW's sale of Land Rover to Ford in 2000. Ford paid about $11 million for the rights to the Land Rover nameplate.

In early 2007 Ford sold Aston Martin to a group including British race-shop owner David Richards Aston Martin racing backer John Sinders and two Kuwaiti investment firms Investment Dar and Adeem Investment Co. The sale price was $925 million although Ford retained a stake in Aston Martin valued at about $77 million.

While business in its home market of North America was rough Ford was profitable abroad in 2007. South America Europe and Asia showed a combined profit of about $2.2 billion. In 2007 Ford of Europe invested $88 million to acquire a Romanian car manufacturing plant owned by the government. Early in 2008 Ford took over the plant and invested around $1 billion in upgrades and expansions. Ford also invested some $3 billion in manufacturing facilities based in Mexico. The Fiesta a vehicle that was not made in North America since 1981 was one of the first cars produced at the Mexico plants in an attempt to compete with Honda and Nissan.

After clearing all of the antitrust and labor hurdles Ford sold Land Rover and Jaguar to India-based Tata Motors for about $2.3 billion in 2008. (Ironically one of the other firms bidding for the two car companies was One Equity Partners an entity led by former Ford CEO Jacques Nasser. It was Nasser that oversaw the creation of Ford's Premier Automotive Group which included both Jaguar and Land Rover.) Ford agreed to deposit some $600 million into the Jaguar and Land Rover pension funds.

In 2009 Visteon filed for Chapter 11 protection from creditors and one of its UK subsidiaries went into administration closing three plants as the Ford auto parts spinoff reeled from the effects of the automotive industry's severe recession-driven downturn. The supplier emerged from bankruptcy protection the following year.

In mid-2009 the US Department of Energy approved $5.9 billion in low-interest loans to Ford for converting its US plants to making cleaner more efficient engines transmissions and vehicles. As a result Ford reported it would spend $550 million to convert its Michigan Assembly Plant where Ford Expedition and Lincoln Navigator SUVs were produced into a modern facility for making its next-generation Focus small car. The new Focus rolled off the assembly line in 2010 with an all-electric version of the Focus to follow in 2011. Ford consolidated operations from its Wayne Assembly Plant as part of the project and worked with the UAW on more flexible work rules for the Michigan Assembly Plant. In addition Ford converted its Cuautitlan Assembly Plant in Mexico from SUV production to assembly of small cars commencing in 2011. The Mexican plant began building the new Fiesta subcompact in 2010.

With the automotive industry reeling from the global economic crisis companies made decisions to streamline their operations for survival. In mid-2010 Ford sold all of Volvo Car Corporation to Geely Automotive a subsidiary of China-based Zhejiang Geely Holding Group. Volvo's headquarters and manufacturing operations remain in Sweden and Belgium with Stefan Jacoby (former CEO of Volkswagen Group of America) serving as president and CEO of Volvo Cars.

At the onset of 2011 Ford's Mercury model production was discontinued.

EXECUTIVES

President CEO and Director, Alan R. Mulally, age 66, $1,400,003 total compensation

Executive Chairman, William C. (Bill) Ford Jr., age 54

CFO, Robert L. (Bob) Shanks, age 59

COO, Mark Fields, age 51, $1,300,000 total compensation

EVP; President Europe Middle East and Africa, Stephen T. Odell, age 57

Group VP Sustainability Environment and Safety Engineering, Susan M. (Sue) Cischke, age 57

Group VP Design and Chief Creative Officer, J. C. Mays, age 57

Group VP and General Counsel, David G. Leitch, age 51, $875,000 total compensation

VP Global Product Programs, Barb J. Samardzich, age 53

Group VP Global Purchasing, Thomas K. (Tony) Brown, age 55

VP Marketing Sales and Service Europe, Roelant de Waard, age 50

EVP Global Manufacturing and Labor Affairs, John Fleming, age 61, $750,000 total compensation

Group VP Quality and New Model Launch, Bennie W. Fowler II, age 55

EVP; Chairman and CEO Ford Motor Credit Company, Michael E. (Mike) Bannister, age 62, $708,700 total compensation

Group VP Government and Community Relations, Ziad S. Ojakli, age 44

EVP Global Marketing Sales and Service and Lincoln, James D. (Jim) Farley Jr., age 49, $700,000 total compensation

VP Engineering Global Product Development, Hau Thai-Tang, age 46

EVP; President Americas, Joseph R. (Joe) Hinrichs, age 45
Group VP Human Resources and Corporate Services, Felicia J. Fields, age 46
VP Research and Advanced Engineering and CTO, Paul A. Mascarenas, age 51
VP Labor Affairs, Martin J. (Marty) Mulloy
VP; President Asia Pacific, Dave Schoch, age 60
VP International Government Affairs, Stephen E. Biegun
VP Powertrain Engineering, Joseph (Joe) Bakaj, age 50
Director Global Marketing Sales and Service Operations, Elena Ford, age 45
Director Global Electrification, Nancy Gioia, age 50
Executive Director Ford Americas Design, Moray S. Callum, age 54
VP US Marketing Sales and Service, Kenneth M. (Ken) Czubay, age 63
VP North American Manufacturing, James P. Tetreault, age 56
Group VP and CIO, Nicholas J. (Nick) Smither, age 53
Chairman and CEO Ford Motor Land Development Corporation (Ford Land), Donna Inch
Secretary, Peter J. Sherry Jr.
VP Global Ford Customer Service Division, Frederiek Toney, age 56
President and CEO Ford Motor Company of Canada, Dianne Craig
VP and Controller, Stuart Rowley, age 45
VP Communications, Raymond F. (Ray) Day, age 43
VP and Treasurer, Neil M. Schloss
VP Marketing Ford Motor Canada, Dean Stoneley
Group VP Global Product Development, Raj Nair, age 47
VP Manufacturing Ford Europe, Ken Macfarlane, age 62
Director Global Performance Vehicles and Motorsport Business Development, Jost Capito, age 54
Director Advanced Product Creation and Special Vehicle Team, Hermann Salenbauch
VP Government Relations, Peter (Pete) Lawson
VP Product Development Europe, Frank Davis, age 51
CEO FordDirect Joint Venture, Stacey Coopes
Executive Director Powertrain Engineering Ford Europe, Graham Hoare
Senior Economist The Americas, Emily Kolinski Morris
Director Occupational Health and Safety, Greg Stone
President Ford Motor Company Fund and Community Services, James G. Vella Jr.
Director Sustainable Business Strategies, John Viera
Corporate Nurse, Audrey Zavodsky
VP; Chairman and CEO Ford Motor China, John Lawler
President CEO and Director, Alan R. Mulally, age 66
Director, Gerald L. (Gerry) Shaheen, age 67
Director, Anthony F. Earley Jr., age 63
Director, Richard A. Manoogian, age 75
Director, John L. Thornton, age 58
Director, Irvine O. Hockaday Jr., age 75
Director, Stephen G. Butler, age 64
Director, James H. (Jim) Hance Jr., age 67
Director, Edsel B. Ford II, age 63
Director, Ellen R. Marram, age 65
Director, Homer A. Neal, age 69
Director, Kimberly A. Casiano, age 54
Director, Richard A. (Dick) Gephardt, age 70
Auditors: PricewaterhouseCoopersLLP

LOCATIONS

HQ: Ford Motor Company
1 American Rd., Dearborn MI 48126-2798
Phone: 313-322-3000 **Fax:** 918-838-8810
Web: www.matrixservice.com

2011 Sales

	$ mil.	% of total
North America		
US	71,165	53
Canada	9,525	7
Mexico/Other	1,436	1
Europe		
UK	9,486	7
Germany	8,717	6
Italy	3,038	2
France	2,806	2
Spain	2,189	2
Russia	1,913	1
Belgium	1,288	1
Other Europe	5,843	4
Other regions	18,858	14
Total	**136,264**	**100**

PRODUCTS/OPERATIONS

2011 Sales

	$ mil.	% of total
Automotive	128,168	94
Financial services	8,096	6
Total	**136,264**	**100**

Selected Products

Cars
- Fiesta
- Focus
- Fusion
- Mustang
- Taurus

Crossovers
- Edge
- Flex

Commercial trucks
- Chassis Cab
- E-Series Cutaway
- E-Series Van
- E-Series Wagon
- F-650
- F-750
- Stripped Chassis
- Super Duty Pickup
- Transit Connect

Electric vehicles (EVs)
- Transit Connect EV

Hybrids
- Escape Hybrid
- Fusion Hybrid

Sport utility vehicles (SUVs)
- Escape
- Expedition
- Explorer

Trucks
- E-Series Wagon
- F-150
- Ranger
- Super Duty
- Transit Connect

Selected Auto Brands

Ford
Lincoln

COMPETITORS

Adam Opel
AutoNation
Bank of America
BMW
Chrysler
Citigroup
Daimler
Fiat
General Motors
Honda
Hyundai Motor
Isuzu
JPMorgan Chase
Kia Motors
Mazda
Mitsubishi Motors
Navistar International
Nissan
Renault
Saab Automobile
Suzuki Motor
Tata Motors
Toyota
Vauxhall
Volkswagen
Volvo
Volvo Car Corp.

HISTORICAL FINANCIALS

Company Type: Public

Income Statement FYE: December 31

	REVENUE ($ mil.)	NET INCOME ($ mil.)	NET PROFIT MARGIN	EMPLOYEES
12/11	136,264	20,213	14.8%	164,000
12/10	128,954	6,561	5.1%	164,000
12/09	118,308	2,717	2.3%	198,000
12/08	146,277	(14,672)	—	213,000
12/07	172,455	(2,723)	—	246,000
Annual Growth	(5.7%)	—	—	(9.6%)

2011 Year-End Financials

Debt ratio: 55.78%—
Return on equity: 134.50%
Cash ($ mil.): 17,148
Current ratio: 57.05
Long-term debt ($ mil.): 59,177
Dividends
Yield: —
Payout: 1.01%
Market value ($ mil.): —

	STOCK PRICE ($) FY Close	P/E High/Low		PER SHARE ($) Earnings	Dividends	Book Value
12/11	10.76	4	2	4.94	0.00	3.95
12/10	16.79	9	5	1.90	0.00	(0.18)
12/09	10.00	11	2	0.86	0.00	(2.32)
12/08	2.29	—	—	(6.46)	0.00	(7.22)
12/07	6.73	—	—	(1.38)	0.00	2.55
Annual Growth	12.4%	—	—	—	—	11.6%

Forest Laboratories, Inc.

Forest Laboratories doesn't just blend in with the trees. The company develops and manufactures prescription drugs to address a wide field of ailments. Its central nervous system (CNS) drugs include antidepressants Celexa and Lexapro as well as Namenda which treats Alzheimer's disease and Savella for fibromyalgia. Other products include treatments for hypertension thyroid disease respiratory ailments and pain. In addition to its branded prescription drugs Forest has limited operations in generic and over-the-counter (OTC) drug manufacturing. The company has manufacturing plants and warehouses in Ireland and the US.

Sales & Marketing

Forest markets its branded drugs directly to doctors hospitals drugstore chains managed care organizations and distributors through its own sales force in the US; it also has direct and independent sales representatives in Europe. Subsidiary Inwood Laboratories promotes the company's generic products in the US while OTC products are sold through UK and Irish subsidiaries. Meanwhile the distribution functions are mostly handled by wholesalers such as McKesson Cardinal Health and AmerisourceBergen.

Financial Analysis

Despite fierce competition from other established brands Forest has found a niche in the antidepressant market that has aided in the company's steady annual revenue growth including a 4% increase to some $4.6 billion in fiscal 2012. However Forest's future success is challenged by the loss of patent protection on some of its most popular CNS drugs including bestseller Lexapro which began facing generic competition in early 2012. Lexapro's sales accounted for 48% of the company's annual revenues in 2012 down from 55% in 2011. Though Forest expects to retain some sales of branded Lexapro as well as royalties on the authorized generic version made by Mylan it expects that the patent expiration will cause total annual revenues to decrease by more than 25% in 2013. While it has remained profitable Forest's net income in 2012 declined more than 6% to $979 million due to increased expenses to support the launch of several new products.

Strategy

Following the patent loss of Lexapro Forest is focused on increasing sales of its other bestsellers including Namenda (accounting for about 30% of sales in 2012) Bystolic and Savella. It also aims to boost market penetration on several new products including Daliresp which was launched in 2011 for treatment of chronic obstructive pulmonary disease (COPD) and Teflaro introduced in 2010 as a wide-spectrum antibiotic for antibiotic resistant infections.

To further offset losses from patent expirations the firm is working to internally develop and release more new drug candidates that it hopes will make up for any decline in sales seen from generic competition. Its pipeline includes potential drugs to treat neuropathic pain gastrointestinal disorders respiratory conditions heart arrhythmias depression and schizophrenia. Many of the company's development programs are collaborative efforts with other pharmaceutical companies including AstraZeneca and Nycomed with which it developed Daliresp.

The company has also widened its portfolio and pipeline through strategic acquisitions. In early 2011 the company expanded its antidepressant offerings by acquiring drug development firm Clinical Data in a deal worth some $1.2 billion. Clinical Data had recently received FDA approval for depression treatment Viibryd and has other antidepressants in development. Forest launched Viibryd in the US market later that year helping to offset losses from Lexapro's patent expiration. The purchase of Clinical Data which was absorbed into the Forest organization also added pipeline candidates in areas such as diagnostic imaging cardiology and oncology.

To expand its presence in Europe in late 2010 Forest acquired the rights to Colobreathe an antibiotic used to treat infection in patients with cystic fibrosis. The drug was approved by the European Union regulatory agency in 2012. Forest promptly launched Colobreathe in Ireland and the UK and is gradually extending sales into other European countries. The company also moved to expand in Latin America in late 2012 by forming a distribution agreement with moksha8 which began promoting certain Forest products through its sales and marketing network in Brazil and Mexico; Forest Labs has the option to purchase moksha8 after two years.

Ownership

Activist investor Carl Icahn who owns a minority stake in Forest has taken a more direct interest in the company since 2011. Icahn disagrees with the company's current diversification strategy and its executive leadership succession plan. After a first proxy battle failed in 2011 Icahn again nominated four directors that he hoped to have elected to Forest's board of directors in mid-2012. Forest again resisted the board takeover attempt stating that it has a promising pipeline of products and a strong leadership team and ultimately Icahn was only successful in getting one of his nominees elected to the final board.

Company Background

In 2010 the company agreed to pay some $313 million to settle allegations from the federal government that it inappropriately marketed certain antidepressants in the early 2000s. The agreement ended an investigation launched by the Department of Justice back in 2004. Forest also agreed to operate under a corporate integrity agreement for five years following the settlement.

HISTORY

Forest Laboratories began as a drug research and development firm in 1956. The company diversified into the food business but when company attorney Howard Solomon took charge in 1977 he sold the food holdings and moved from drug development to drug commercialization. It acquired drugs from other companies and improved them through its proprietary Synchron continuous-release drug-delivery technology.

In 1984 Forest bought scandal-ridden drug company O'Neal Jones & Feldman to grow its sales force. The next year it bought headache formula ESGIC (later pulled because it qualified as a new drug needing FDA approval). In 1986 it acquired Aerobid from Schering-Plough.

The company continued to grow through acquisitions buying UAD Laboratories and its analgesic Lorcet in 1989 Pharmasciences' labor-induction agent Cervidil and other drugs. Although the firm had mostly successes one of its failures was Micturin an incontinence treatment whose dangerous side effects led the company to discontinue it in 1991.

In 1998 the FDA approved antidepressant citalopram (Celexa). Celexa was to be marketed by Warner-Lambert but when that firm was acquired by Pfizer (which makes rival antidepressant Prozac) Forest Labs bought its way out of the deal and grew its own sales force. Celexa proved worthy of such effort becoming Forest Labs' biggest seller. The following year the company entered into an alliance with 3M's pharmaceutical unit to make asthma treatment Aerospan. In 2000 the company expanded its research facilities and licensed drugs to treat hypertension dementia and irritable bowel syndrome.

In 2002 the company launched hypertension drug Benicar through an alliance with Sankyo and failed to win FDA approval for alcohol dependence treatment acamprosate (licensed from Merck KGaA). In 2003 bestseller Celexa lost patent protection and the company released its next-generation antidepressant Lexapro.

The company received FDA approval and launched pain treatment Combunox in 2004. Campral (acamprosate) for alcohol abstinence was finally approved in 2005.

To bolster its biopharmaceutical research capabilities Forest Laboratories purchased private biotech firm Cerexa for about $494 million in early 2007. Cerexa brought with it a series of injectable antibiotics under development to combat bacterial infections including MRSA (methicillin-resistant Staphylococcus aureus).

The company ended a co-promotion agreement with Daiichi Sankyo in 2008 for the hypertension drug Axor to focus on sales efforts for its other commercial products. The two companies had also marketed antihypertensive drug Benicar together; Forest continued to receive royalties from the agreement but stopped actively marketing the drug.

EXECUTIVES

EVP and Chief Commercial Officer, Elaine Hochberg, age 55, $622,939 total compensation
Chairman President and CEO, Howard Solomon, age 84, $1,277,500 total compensation
SVP and Director Operations, Kevin Walsh
VP Marketing, William J. Meury
EVP Finance and Administration and CFO, Francis I. (Frank) Perier Jr., age 52, $579,250 total compensation
SVP Research and Development; President Forest Research Institute, Marco Taglietti, age 52, $527,725 total compensation
VP General Counsel and Secretary, Herschel S. Weinstein
VP and Controller, Rita Weinberger
VP Investor Relations, Frank J. Murdolo
SVP Corporate Development and Strategic Planning, David F. Solomon
VP Corporate Tax and Treasury, Ralph Kleinman
Director, William J. Candee III, age 85
Director, Lawrence S. (Larry) Olanoff, age 60
Director, Kenneth E. Goodman, age 64
Director, George S. Cohan, age 88
Director, Dan L. Goldwasser, age 72
Director, Lester B. Salans, age 76
Director, Nesli Basgoz, age 54
Director, Peter Zimetbaum, age 48
Auditors: BDOSeidmanLLP

LOCATIONS

HQ: Forest Laboratories, Inc.
909 Third Avenue, New York, NY 10022-4731
Phone: 212 421-7850 **Fax:** 212 750-9152
Web: www.frx.com

2012 Net Sales

	$ mil.	% of total
US		97
UK		2
Total	**0**	**100**

PRODUCTS/OPERATIONS

2012 Sales

	$ mil.	% of total
Net sales		
Central nervous system	3,694	81
Cardiovascular	381	8
Other drugs	316	7
Contract revenue	155	3
Interest income	20	1
Other income	17	-
Total	**4,586**	**100**

Selected Products

Central Nervous System
- Campral (alcohol dependence)
- Celexa (antidepressant)
- Lexapro (depression and anxiety)
- Namenda (Alzheimer' s disease)
- Savella (fibromyalgia)
- Viibryd (antidepressant)

Cardiovascular
- Benicar (antihypertensive royalties from Daiichi Sankyo)
- Bystolic (antihypertensive)
- Tiazac (antihypertensive)

Other drugs
- Aerobid (asthma)
- AeroChamber Plus (asthma)
- Armour Thyroid (endocrinology)

Cervidil (labor induction)
Combunox (pain)
Daliresp (respiratory)
Levothroid (endocrinology)
Lorcet (pain)
Teflaro (injectable antibiotic)
Thyrolar (endocrinology)

Selected Subsidiaries

Cerexa Inc.
Cerexa UK Ltd.
Forest Laboratories Ireland Ltd.
Forest Laboratories UK Ltd.
Forest Pharmaceuticals Inc.
Forest Tosara Ltd. (Ireland)
Inwood Laboratories Inc. (generics)
Pharmax Healthcare Ltd. (UK)

COMPETITORS

AstraZeneca
Bayer AG
Bristol-Myers Squibb
Daiichi Sankyo
Eisai Inc.
Eli Lilly
GlaxoSmithKline
Hi-Tech Pharmacal
Johnson & Johnson
Merck
Mylan Pharmaceuticals
Novartis
Par Pharmaceutical Companies
Pfizer
Ranbaxy Laboratories
Roche Holding
Sanofi
Shire
Sun Pharmaceutical
Sunovion
Teva
Valeant Pharmaceuticals
Watson Pharmaceuticals

HISTORICAL FINANCIALS

Company Type: Public

Income Statement

FYE: March 31

	REVENUE ($ mil.)	NET INCOME ($ mil.)	NET PROFIT MARGIN	EMPLOYEES
03/12	4,586	979	21.3%	5,700
03/11	4,419	1,046	23.7%	5,600
03/10	4,192	682	16.3%	5,200
03/09	3,922	767	19.6%	5,225
03/08	3,836	967	25.2%	5,211
Annual Growth	4.6%	0.3%	—	2.3%

2012 Year-End Financials

Debt ratio: —
Return on equity: 17.25%
Cash ($ mil.): 1,579
Current ratio: 385.90
Long-term debt ($ mil.): —
No. of shares (mil.): 265
Dividends
Yield: —
Payout: —
Market value ($ mil.): 9,214

	STOCK PRICE ($) FY Close	P/E High	P/E Low	PER SHARE ($) Earnings	Dividends	Book Value
03/12	34.69	11	8	3.57	0.00	21.37
03/11	32.30	10	7	3.59	0.00	19.22
03/10	31.36	14	9	2.25	0.00	16.17
03/09	21.96	16	7	2.52	0.00	13.64
03/08	40.01	18	12	3.06	0.00	11.93
Annual Growth	(3.5%)	—	—	3.9%	—	15.7%

Franklin Resources, Inc.

Franklin Resources believes a penny saved is a penny lost —if it's not wisely invested. Operating as Franklin Templeton Investments the firm manages more than 100 mutual funds that invest in international and domestic stocks; taxable and tax-exempt money market instruments; and corporate municipal and US government bonds. Franklin Resources also offers separately managed accounts closed-end funds insurance product funds and retirement and college savings plans. Its investment products are sold through more than 1600 banks securities firms and financial advisors under the Franklin Templeton Mutual Series Bissett Darby and Fiduciary banners.

In addition to its core business Franklin Resources also provides shareholder services and manages investments for high-net-worth clients and institutional investors. Retail banking private banking auto finance and trust services are offered through Franklin Templeton Bank & Trust Franklin Capital Fiduciary Trust Company International and other subsidiaries. Serving some 21 million shareholder accounts Franklin Resources and its subsidiaries have approximately $660 billion in assets under management.

A majority of Franklin Resources' assets under management is in equity and fixed-income investments though the company also offers hybrid and cash management investment strategies. It has been increasing its focus on alternative investments establishing a unit with capabilities in private equity real estate and asset allocation strategies among others. In 2010 Franklin Resources acquired a 20% stake in Pelagos Capital Management a Boston-based investment advisor that employs commodity managed futures and hedge fund replication strategies. Franklin Resources also has units that make private equity investments in emerging markets in Asia Central and South America and central and eastern Europe.

The company continues to expand its geographic reach. It does most of its business in North America but has been adding assets under management in Europe and the Asia-Pacific region. Since 2008 the company has established asset management groups or joint ventures in countries such as Brazil China Dubai India Japan and Vietnam. All told Franklin Resources has offices in some 30 countries and has clients in more than 150. The company expanded in Australia and the UK through the 2011 acquisitions of Balanced Equity Management and the fund management business of Rensburg Sheppards respectively.

Most of Franklin Resources' revenues come from investment management fees which are directly tied to its assets under management. Client inflows and assets gained from acquisitions more than offset market depreciation during fiscal 2011 and in turn its net income increased by about a third.

Descendants of founder Rupert Johnson Sr. own about a third of Franklin Resources.

HISTORY

Rupert Johnson Sr. founded Franklin Distributors (capitalizing on Benjamin Franklin's reputation for thrift) in New York in 1947; it launched its first fund Franklin Custodian in 1948. Custodian grew into five funds including conservatively managed equity and bond funds. In 1968 Johnson's son Charles (who had joined the firm in 1957) became president and CEO. The company went public in 1971 as Franklin Resources.

In 1973 Franklin bought San Mateo-based investment firm Winfield & Co. and relocated to the Golden State. The buy provided additional products including the Franklin Gold Fund (made possible by the end of the prohibition in the US against private interests owning commodity gold). With interest rate spikes in the late 1970s and early 1980s money drained from savings accounts was poured into more lucrative money market mutual funds.

The Franklin Money Fund launched in 1975 fueled the firm's tremendous asset growth in the 1980s. In 1981 the Franklin Tax-Free Income Fund (introduced in 1977) began investing solely in California municipal bonds. The fund's success led Franklin to introduce 43 tax-free income funds in later years.

In 1985 Franklin bought Pacific Union Bank and Trust (now Franklin Bank) allowing it to offer consumers such services as credit cards and to compete with financial services supermarkets such as Merrill Lynch. It also bought real estate firm Property Resources (now Franklin Properties).

The 1987 stock crash and the California real estate slump forced Franklin to focus on its funds businesses. In 1992 it bought Bahamas-based Templeton Galbraith & Hansberger the manager of Templeton Funds a major international funds business. The Templeton deal added an aggressive investment management unit to complement the conservatively managed Franklin funds.

In 1940 Sir John Templeton gained control of investment company Templeton Dobbrow and Vance (TDV). TDV launched Templeton Growth Fund in 1954. In 1969 Templeton sold his interest in TDV but continued to manage the Templeton Growth Fund. John Galbraith became president of Securities Fund Investors (SFI) the distribution company for Templeton Growth Fund in 1974. In 1977 Galbraith bought SFI from Templeton and began building the Templeton funds broker-dealer network in the US. The Templeton World Fund was formed in 1978. Templeton Investment Counsel was launched to provide investment advice in 1979. In 1986 these companies were combined to form Templeton Galbraith & Hansberger Ltd.

In 1996 Franklin bought Heine Securities previous investment adviser to Mutual Series Fund Inc. Max Heine a leading investor had established Mutual Shares Corp. in 1949. Heine Securities was formed in 1975. Following the purchase Franklin set up subsidiary Franklin Mutual Advisers as the investment adviser for Mutual Series Fund.

In 1997 the weak Asian economy hurt Templeton's international funds prompting liquidation of a Japanese stocks-based fund. Franklin cut jobs and shuffled management in 1999; the restructuring acknowledged the clash between the firm's value-investing style and investors' bull-market optimism.

In 2000 the firm gained a foothold in Canada with its purchase of Bissett & Associates Investment Management. Franklin's purchase of Fiduciary Trust the following year gave the firm greater access to institutional investors and affluent individuals.

Franklin Resources boosted its alternative investment offerings with the 2003 acquisition of Darby Overseas which focuses on private equity mezzanine and fixed-income investment products and specializes in Asian and Latin American fixed-income securities.

Chairman Charles Johnson retired from the CEO's office in 2004 turning the reins over to a new generation; his son Gregory was named CEO. Also that year Franklin Resources agreed to pay $50 million to settle market-timing allegations and reached a $20 million settlement with the SEC and an $18 million settlement with the state of California over commissions paid to brokers for mutual fund sales.

The company continued its international growth with the acquisitions of stakes in Dubai's Algebra Capital (in 2007) and Brazilian asset manager

Bradesco Templeton (in 2006) since renamed Franklin Templeton Investimentos (Brasil).

EXECUTIVES

SVP and Assistant Secretary, Leslie M. Kratter, age 67
President CEO and Director, Gregory E. (Greg) Johnson, age 51, $702,119 total compensation
EVP and COO, Jennifer M. (Jenny) Johnson Bolt, age 48, $472,500 total compensation
EVP and CFO, Kenneth A. Lewis, age 51, $472,500 total compensation
VP Human Resources International; SVP Human Resources International Franklin Templeton Companies, Donna S. Ikeda, age 56
Vice Chairman, Rupert H. Johnson Jr., age 72
Chairman, Charles B. (Charlie) Johnson, age 79, $594,330 total compensation
EVP Alternative Strategies, William Y. Yun, age 52, $472,500 total compensation
CEO and President Fiduciary Trust Company International, Henry P. Johnson
EVP Investment Management, John M. Lusk, age 54
VP Human Resources US; SVP Human Resources US Franklin Templeton Companies, Penelope S. Alexander, age 52
VP Corporate Communications and Corporate Citizenship, Holly E. Gibson Brady, age 46
EVP and General Counsel, Craig S. Tyle, age 52
EVP Global Advisory Services, Vijay C. Advani, age 51, $472,500 total compensation
SVP and Chief Administrative Officer; SVP FTDI, Norman R. (Rick) Frisbie Jr., age 45
Corporate Communications, Matt Walsh
VP Global Corporate Communications, Lisa Gallegos
Head Corporate Communications U.S., Stacey Johnston
VP and Secretary, Maria Gray, age 63
Managing Director India and CEEMEA, Vivek Kudva
President Indian Asset Management, Harshendu Bindal
Director Corporate Communications Latin America, Bill Weeks
VP Private Real Estate Franklin Templeton Real Estate Advisors, Julie Rost
Global Head and Managing Director Franklin Templeton Real Esate Advisors, Jack Foster
Investor Relations, Brian Sevilla
Media Relations Europe, Dorine Johnson
Media Relations Asia, Mae Loon
President CEO and Director, Gregory E. (Greg) Johnson, age 51
Director, Sanchayan (Chutta) Ratnathicam, age 64
Director, Charles Crocker, age 73
Director, Samuel H. Armacost, age 73
Vice Chairman, Rupert H. Johnson Jr., age 72
Director, Thomas H. (Tom) Kean, age 76
Director, Peter M. Sacerdote, age 74
Director, Anne M. Tatlock, age 72
Director, Joseph R. Hardiman, age 74
Auditors: PricewaterhouseCoopersLLP

LOCATIONS

HQ: Franklin Resources Inc.
1 Franklin Pkwy. Bldg. 970 1st Fl., San Mateo CA 94403
Phone: 650-312-2000 **Fax:** 650-312-5606
Web: www.franklinresources.com

2011 Sales

	$ mil.	% of total
North America		
US	4,589	64
Bahamas	1,041	15
Canada	344	5
Asia-Pacific	688	10
Europe Middle East & Africa	435	6
Latin America	39	-
Total	**7,140**	**100**

PRODUCTS/OPERATIONS

2011 Sales

	$ mil.	% of total
Investment management fees	4,531	63
Sales & distribution fees	2,263	32
Shareholder servicing fees	300	4
Other	44	1
Total	**7,140**	**100**

2011 Assets under Management

	% of total
Fixed-income	45
Equity	39
Hybrid	15
Cash	1
Total	**100**

COMPETITORS

AllianceBernstein
American Century
BlackRock
Capital Group
Dodge & Cox
FMR
Invesco
John Hancock Financial Services
Legg Mason
Morgan Stanley
Old Mutual (US)
PIMCO
Principal Financial
Putnam
T. Rowe Price
The Vanguard Group

HISTORICAL FINANCIALS

Company Type: Public

Income Statement FYE: September 30

	REVENUE ($ mil.)	NET INCOME ($ mil.)	NET PROFIT MARGIN	EMPLOYEES
09/12	7,101	1,931	27.2%	8,600
09/11	7,140	1,923	26.9%	8,500
09/10	5,853	1,445	24.7%	7,927
09/09	4,194	896	21.4%	7,700
09/08	6,032	1,588	26.3%	8,800
Annual Growth	4.2%	5.0%	—	(0.6%)

2012 Year-End Financials

Debt ratio: 19.25%
Return on equity: 20.99%
Cash ($ mil.): 6,051
Current ratio: 409.37
Long-term debt ($ mil.): 2,839
No. of shares (mil.): 212
Dividends
Yield: —
Payout: 34.41%
Market value ($ mil.): 26,541

	STOCK PRICE ($) FY Close	P/E High/Low		PER SHARE ($) Earnings	Dividends	Book Value
09/12	125.07	14	10	8.95	0.00	43.36
09/11	95.64	16	11	8.62	1.00	39.16
09/10	106.90	19	13	6.33	3.88	34.49
09/09	100.60	27	10	3.87	0.83	33.28
09/08	88.13	21	12	6.67	0.75	30.39
Annual Growth	9.1%	—	—	7.6%	—	9.3%

Freddie Mac

These siblings know there's no place like home. Government-sponsored enterprises (GSEs) Freddie Mac (officially Federal Home Loan Mortgage Corporation) and Fannie Mae were established to buy residential mortgages and boost the housing market. They do so by purchasing mortgages from lenders and packaging them for resale thereby mitigating risk and allowing lenders to provide mortgages to those who may not otherwise qualify. The agency also provides assistance for affordable rental housing. Together Fannie and Freddie guarantee some 70% of all new home loans in the US. Due to losses related to the subprime mortgage crisis the government seized Fannie and Freddie in 2008. It now plans to wind the GSEs down.

In 2011 the Obama Administration delivered a plan to Congress to reform the housing finance market. The plan included a recommendation to minimize Fannie's and Freddie's role in the market and ultimately wind the companies down. The future of the entities still remains unclear and they operate under significant levels of uncertainty.

Ironically the companies contributed to the financial crisis in their mission to provide housing funds to more citizens. Fannie and Freddie were unable to recover from their exposure to mortgages that had gone sour and the Federal Reserve stepped in with an initial round of loans. The bleeding didn't stop though and the government placed the companies in conservatorship which is a legal status similar to bankruptcy rather than risk the possibility they might fail. The government assumed a nearly 80% stake in the troubled companies in a $111 billion bailout (and counting with a commitment of up to $400 billion).

The companies are overseen by the Federal Housing Finance Administration (FHFA) which was created in 2008 in the aftermath of the housing bust. The FHFA has more authority than its predecessor agencies the Federal Housing Finance Board and the Office of Federal Housing Enterprise Oversight. The administration also oversees the 12 Federal Home Loan Banks.

As public scrutiny of the troubled agencies increased so did the call by many that Fannie and Freddie be dismantled or drastically restructured. In 2011 the Obama administration proposed to restructure the housing market in a plan that will reduce the government's role and eventually eliminate the GSEs.

Thus far Freddie has remained a central element in the government's efforts to make housing affordable. In 2009 it introduced the Home Affordable Modification and Freddie Mac Relief Refinance Mortgage programs which have helped hundreds of thousands of borrowers avoid foreclosure. Unfortunately defaults didn't stop and in 2011 Fannie and Freddie together owned more than 180000 foreclosed homes. (In 2012 the FHFA began selling homes in bulk as part of a program to reduce the number of foreclosure homes Fannie and Freddie own.) The government's investments in the companies are proving to be the most costly of its bailouts and are estimated to ultimately reach the $400 billion commitment level.

Under the FHFA Freddie Mac has been limited in its trading activities which the company asserts has negatively impacted its earnings. The ongoing weakness in the economy and reduced long-term interest rates further has further hurt Freddie. However the company has been inching closer to ending its fiscal years in the black. While Freddie lost $50 billion in 2008 it has improved every year and reported a loss of $5 billion in 2011. Revenues declined that year falling 10% to $88 billion (from $98 billion in 2010) as a result of limited purchasing activity and lower earnings on investments.

HISTORY

Ah the '60s –free love great tunes and a war nobody wanted to pay for with taxes. By the '70s inflation was rising and real income was starting to fall. To divert a construction industry recession Congress created a new entity to buy home mortgages and boost the flow of money into the housing market.

Fannie Mae had been buying mortgages since 1938 but focused on Federal Housing Administration (FHA) and Veterans Administration loans. In 1970 Congress created Freddie Mac and enlarged Fannie Mae's field of action to include conventional mortgages. Still rising interest rates in the 1970s were brutal to the US real estate market.

In the early 1980s dealers devised a way to securitize the company's loans –seen as somewhat frumpy investments –by packaging them into more alluring bond-like investments made even sexier by the implicit government guarantee. When three major government securities dealers collapsed in 1985 ownership of some Freddie Mac securities was in doubt and the Federal Reserve Bank of New York quickly automated registration of government securities.

In 1984 Freddie Mac issued shares to members of the Federal Home Loan Bank (the overseer of US savings and loans). By 1989 the shares had been converted to common stock and were traded on the NYSE. Freddie Mac's board expanded from three political appointees to 18 members.

Nationwide real estate defaults (rampant in the wake of the late 1980s crash) kindled concern about Freddie Mac's reserve levels and whether it might need to tap its US Treasury line of credit. In response Congress in 1992 created the Office of Federal Housing Enterprise Oversight to regulate Freddie Mac and Fannie Mae. Initial examinations sounded no alarms. A 1996 Congressional Budget Office report questioned whether the government should continue its implicit guarantees of the pair's debt securities.

In 1997 Freddie Mac officially adopted its longtime nickname. The next year it launched a system to cut loan approval time from weeks to minutes (it agreed to develop a similar version for the FHA). The streamlining was crucial to pacts in which mortgage lenders (including one of the US's largest Wells Fargo) promised to sell Freddie Mac their loan originations. In 1999 Freddie Mac hired former House Speaker Newt Gingrich as a consultant.

Freddie Mac made a major Internet push in 2000 with its first online taxable bond offering. A wired venture involving Freddie Mac Microsoft and such big lenders as Chase Manhattan (now part of JPMorgan Chase & Co.) Bank of America and Wells Fargo drew fire from small banks that said it would push them out of the online lending business.

In 2001 Freddie Mac bought Tuttle Decision Systems a loan-pricing software system provider. Critics responded that Freddie Mac overstepped its government charter with such a move.

In a move initiated by its auditor Freddie Mac re-audited its earnings from 2000 to 2003 uncovering accounting irregularities and employee misconduct. Further investigations executive oustings restructuring and numerous lawsuits followed. In late 2003 Freddie Mac announced the findings of its re-audit. The company admitted to understating earnings by $4.4 billion between 2000 and 2002 and overstating profits by $989 million in 2001 all in an attempt to smooth out results and show steady profit growth.

In 2006 the company paid a record $3.8 million fine to settle allegations by the Federal Election Commission that the company made illegal campaign contributions to members of the US House Financial Services Committee. It also agreed to pay $4.65 million to settle a lawsuit related to its employee 401(k) plan. Freddie Mac did receive good news that year though when the Department of Justice dropped criminal charges against the company for misstating earnings from 2000 to 2002.

As the subprime mortgage crisis began heating up in 2007 and 2008 Freddie Mac announced plans to stop purchasing risky subprime mortgages. However the company tried to help restore stability to the teetering mortgage market by investing in billions of dollars in new jumbo mortgages raising its loan limits to more than $700000.

Although the government stepped in with loans to help Freddie the company still struggled with subprime mortgage losses. The government seized Fannie Mae and Freddie Mac in 2008 and placed them in conservatorship. Freddie Mac's leadership was also shaken up. David Moffat resigned as CEO in 2009 and chairman John Koskinen stepped in to serve as his interim replacement. Later that year Charles Haldeman Jr. the former head of Putnam Investments was selected to lead the company.

The Federal Housing Finance Administration (FHFA) was created in 2008 to oversee Fannie and Freddie as well as the 12 Federal Home Loan Banks. The FHFA was granted more authority than its predecessor agencies the Federal Housing Finance Board and the Office of Federal Housing Enterprise Oversight.

EXECUTIVES

CEO and Director, Donald H. (Don) Layton, age 61
CEO and Director, Charles E. (Ed) Haldeman Jr., age 60
SVP Corporate Relations and Housing Outreach, Dwight P. Robinson
SVP Models Mission & Research, Edward L. Golding
CFO, Ross J. Kari, age 53
EVP and Chief Administrative Officer, Jerry Weiss, age 51
SVP Multifamily, David M. Brickman
SVP External Relations, Hollis S. McLoughlin
Chairman, Christopher S. Lynch, age 54
SVP Single Family Sourcing, Paul E. Mullings
SVP and General Auditor, Timothy Kenny
EVP Single-Family Business and Operations and Technology, Anthony (Tony) Renzi
Chief Enterprise Risk Officer, Paige Wisdom
SVP Human Resources, Keith Green
SVP and Chief Compliance Officer, Carol Wambeke
SVP Investments and Capital Markets, Devajyoti (Doc) Ghose
Director, Clayton S. Rose, age 54
Director, Laurence E. (Larry) Hirsch, age 66
CEO and Director, Donald H. (Don) Layton, age 61
CEO and Director, Charles E. (Ed) Haldeman Jr., age 60
Director, Robert R. Glauber, age 73
Director, Carolyn H. Byrd, age 63
Director, Eugene B. Shanks Jr.
Director, Linda B. Bammann
Director, Nicolas P. (Nic) Retsinas, age 65
Director, Anthony A. Williams, age 59
Auditors: PricewaterhouseCoopersLLP

LOCATIONS

HQ: Federal Home Loan Mortgage Corporation
8200 Jones Branch Dr., McLean VA 22102-3110
Phone: 703-903-2000 **Fax:** 703-903-4045
Web: www.freddiemac.com

PRODUCTS/OPERATIONS

2011 Sales

	$ mil.	% of total
Interest		
Mortgage loans	86,282	85
Investments in securities	12,791	13
Other	67	-
Noninterest		
Gains ons debt recorded at fair value	91	-
Other	2,199	2
Adjustments	(13168)	-
Total	**88,262**	**100**

COMPETITORS

FHLB Atlanta

HISTORICAL FINANCIALS

Company Type: Public

Income Statement FYE: December 31

	ASSETS ($ mil.)	NET INCOME ($ mil.)	INCOME AS % OF ASSETS	EMPLOYEES
12/11	2,147,216	(5,266)	—	4,921
12/10	2,261,780	(14,025)	—	5,309
12/09	841,784	(21,553)	—	5,408
12/08	850,963	(50,119)	—	5,012
12/07	794,368	(3,094)	—	5,396
Annual Growth	28.2%	—	—	(2.3%)

2011 Year-End Financials

Debt ratio: 99.29% | No. of shares (mil.): 649
Return on equity: 987650001000000.00% | Dividends
Cash ($ mil.): 28,442 | Yield: —
Current ratio: — | Payout: —
Long-term debt ($ mil.): 2,131,983 | Market value ($ mil.): 136

	STOCK PRICE ($) FY Close	P/E High/Low	PER SHARE ($) Earnings	Dividends	Book Value
12/11	0.21	— —	(3.63)	0.00	(0.22)
12/10	0.30	— —	(6.09)	0.00	(0.62)
12/09	1.47	— —	(7.89)	0.00	6.60
12/08	0.73	— —	(34.60)	0.75	(47.48)
12/07	34.07	— —	(5.37)	1.75	41.35
Annual Growth	(72.0%)	— —	—	—	—

Freeport-McMoRan Copper & Gold Inc.

Freeport-McMoRan Copper & Gold (FCX) digs its profits from copper and precious metal mines around the world. In 2011 FCX's proven and probable reserves totaled 119.7 billion pounds of copper 33.9 million ounces of gold and 330.3 million ounces of silver. Copper in concentrates and in refined products such as cathodes and anodes accounts for most of FCX's sales. Its 91%-owned subsidiary PT Freeport Indonesia (PT-FI) operates the vast Grasberg gold copper and silver mine in Indonesia while the government owns the other 9%. FCX is also engaged in smelting and refining via PT-FI's 25% stake in PT Smelting a copper smelter and refinery in Indonesia. FCX is the world's #2 copper company behind Codelco.

HISTORY

The Freeport Sulfur Company was formed in Texas in 1912 by Francis Pemberton banker Eric Swenson and several investors to develop a sulfur field. The next year Freeport Texas was formed as a holding company for Freeport Sulfur and other enterprises.

During the 1930s the company diversified. In 1936 Freeport pioneered a process to remove hydrocarbons from sulfur. The company joined Consolidated Coal in 1955 to establish the National Potash Company. In 1956 Freeport formed an oil and gas subsidiary Freeport Oil.

Internationally Freeport formed an Australian minerals subsidiary in 1964 and a copper-mining subsidiary in Indonesia in 1967. The company changed its name to Freeport Minerals in 1971 and merged with Utah-based McMoRan Oil & Gas (formerly McMoRan Explorations) in 1982.

McMoRan Explorations had been formed in 1969 by William McWilliams Jim Bob Moffett and Byron Rankin. In 1973 McMoRan formed an exploration and drilling alliance with Dow Chemical and signed a deal with Indonesia to mine in the remote Irian Jaya region. McMoRan went public in 1978.

Moffett became chairman and CEO of Freeport-McMoRan in 1984. The company formed Freeport-McMoRan Copper in 1987 to manage its Indonesian operations. The unit assumed the Freeport-McMoRan Copper & Gold name in 1991. Two years later Freeport-McMoRan acquired Rio Tinto Minera a copper-smelting business with operations in Spain.

To support expansion in Indonesia Freeport-McMoRan spun off its copper and gold division in 1994. In 1995 Freeport-McMoRan Copper & Gold (FCX) formed an alliance with the UK's RTZ Corporation to develop its Indonesian mineral reserves. Local riots that year closed the Grasberg Mine and FCX's political risk insurance was canceled. Despite these setbacks higher metal prices and growing sales in 1995 helped the company double its operating income.

An Indonesian tribal leader filed a $6 billion lawsuit in 1996 charging FCX with environmental human rights and social and cultural violations. The company called the suit baseless but offered to set aside 1% of its annual revenues or about $15 million to help local tribes. Tribal leaders rejected the offer and in 1997 a judge dismissed the lawsuit.

In 1997 FCX pulled out of Bre-X Minerals' Busang gold mine project which independent tests later proved to be a fraud of historic proportions. Amid widespread rioting Indonesia's embattled president Suharto was forced out of office in 1998. The new government investigated charges of cronyism involving FCX.

FCX received permission from the Indonesian government in 1999 to expand the Grasberg Mine and increase ore output up to 300000 metric tons per day. However the next year an overflow accident killed four workers in Grasberg and as a result of the accident the Indonesian government ordered FCX to reduce its production at the mine by up to 30%. Normal production at the mine resumed in early 2001.

FM Services (administrative legal and financial services) was added as a subsidiary in 2002. In 2003 FCX bought an 86% stake in PT Puncakjaya Power a supplier of power to PT-FI.

The $26 billion acquisition of Phelps Dodge in 2007 brought that company's global copper gold and molybdenum business into the fold. The deal placed FCX in a position to thrive as a global competitor in the rank just below metals and mining giants such as BHP Billiton Rio Tinto and Vale. A year later FCX sold the wire and cable business it acquired in the Phelps Dodge deal to General Cable Corporation for $735 million.

Following the acquisition –and benefiting from high copper prices and a good business climate – the company began to invest in its development projects. It was also able to retire a sizable portion of its debt much of it accumulated from the Phelps Dodge acquisition.

Political and environmental controversy in Indonesia has been a problem for FCX since its major protector former President Suharto was forced to resign in 1998 after more than 30 years in power. Sectarian violence in Indonesia where FCX is one of the largest employers also makes the company vulnerable to work stoppages. Anglo-Australian mining giant Rio Tinto is jointly involved with FCX in developing mineral properties in Indonesia's politically and environmentally sensitive Papua region. The company's Tenke Fungume copper and gold mine named Too is located in the Democratic Republic of Congo which also can be an unstable environment in which to do business. Tenke Fungume is jointly owned with Lundin Mining and the Congolese government. It began production in 2009.

Moving only peripherally into the oil and gas business FCX agreed in 2010 to make a $500 million investment in sister company McMoRan Exploration (MMR) to finance that operation's proposed acquisition of properties from Plains Exploration & Production Company. The investment and subsequent acquisition will allow MMR to expand its exploration development and production of oil and gas in the lucrative shallow water region of the Gulf of Mexico's Continental Shelf.

EXECUTIVES

EVP and Chief Administrative Officer, Michael J. Arnold, age 59, $550,000 total compensation
President Atlantic Copper; SVP FCX (Concentrates), Javier Targhetta
SVP International Relations and Federal Government Affairs, W. Russell King, $166,917 total compensation
President CEO and Director, Richard C. Adkerson, age 65, $2,500,000 total compensation
Chairman, James R. (Jim Bob) Moffett, age 73, $2,500,000 total compensation
EVP CFO and Treasurer, Kathleen L. Quirk, age 48, $650,000 total compensation
VP and Controller Financial Reporting, C. Donald Whitmire Jr.
Vice Chairman, B. M. Rankin Jr., age 82
VP Communications, William L. (Bill) Collier III
President Americas, Harry M. (Red) Conger, age 80
President Mining, Richard E. Coleman
President Climax Molybdenum, David H. (Dave) Thornton
President Freeport-McMoRan Indonesia, Mark J. Johnson, age 52, $400,000 total compensation
President Director PT Freeport Indonesia, Armando Mahler, age 56
SVP and General Counsel, L. Richards (Rick) McMillan II, age 65
President Africa, Phillip S. (Phil) Brumit
Manager Investor Relations, David Joint
Director External Communications, Eric Kinneberg
Secretary, Douglas N. Currault II
President Freeport-McMoRan Sales Company; VP FCX (Cathode and Rod), Stephen T. Higgins
Webmaster, Kathy Kelley
Director, Robert J. Allison Jr., age 73
President CEO and Director, Richard C. Adkerson, age 65
Director, Gerald J. Ford, age 68
Director, Jon C. Madonna, age 69
Director, Charles C. Krulak, age 70
Director, Dustan E. (Dusty) McCoy, age 62
Director, Robert A. Day, age 68
Director, H. Devon Graham Jr., age 77
Vice Chairman, B. M. Rankin Jr., age 82
Director, Bobby Lee Lackey, age 74
Director, Stephen H. Siegele, age 52
Auditors: Ernst&YoungLLP

LOCATIONS

HQ: Freeport-McMoRan Copper & Gold Inc.
333 N. Central Ave., Phoenix AZ 85004-2189
Phone: 602-366-8100 **Fax:** 763-542-5100
Web: www.cyberoptics.com

2011 Sales by Destination

US	7,176	34
Indonesia	2,266	11
Switzerland	1,219	6
India	878	4
Chile	741	4
Korea	561	3
Other countries	2,953	14

PRODUCTS/OPERATIONS

2011 Sales

Refined copper products	10,297	49
Gold	2,429	12
Other products	868	4

Selected Subsidiaries and Affiliates

Atlantic Copper Holding SA (smelting and refining Spain)
Chino Mines Company
Climax Molybdenum Company
FM Service Company (administrative and financial services)
Missouri Lead Smelting Company
PT Freeport Indonesia Co. (91% mining)
PT Smelting (Gresik) Co. (25% smelting Indonesia)
PT Irja Eastern Minerals Corp. (mining Indonesia)
PT Puncakjaya Power (86% supplies power to PT Freeport Indonesia)

COMPETITORS

Antofagasta
Barrick Gold
BHP Billiton
Chevron Mining
Codelco
Newmont Mining
Rio Tinto Limited
Southern Copper
Vale Limited

HISTORICAL FINANCIALS

Company Type: Public

Income Statement FYE: December 31

	REVENUE ($ mil.)	NET INCOME ($ mil.)	NET PROFIT MARGIN	EMPLOYEES
12/11	20,880	5,747	27.5%	31,800
12/10	18,982	5,544	29.2%	29,700
12/09	15,040	3,534	23.5%	28,400
12/08	17,796	(11,067)	—	29,300
12/07	16,939	2,977	17.6%	34,900
Annual Growth	5.4%	17.9%	—	(2.3%)

2011 Year-End Financials

Debt ratio: 11.03%
Return on equity: 36.74%
Cash ($ mil.): 4,822
Current ratio: 341.73
Long-term debt ($ mil.): 3,533

No. of shares (mil.): 948
Dividends
Yield: —
Payout: 31.38%
Market value ($ mil.): 34,877

	STOCK PRICE ($)	P/E		PER SHARE ($)		
	FY Close	High/Low		Earnings	Dividends	Book Value
12/11	36.79	25	6	4.78	0.00	16.50
12/10	120.09	26	12	4.57	0.95	13.23
12/09	80.29	29	7	2.93	0.69	10.60
12/08	24.44	—	—	(14.86)	0.91	7.52
12/07	102.44	29	12	3.75	1.38	23.80
Annual Growth	(22.6%)	—	—	6.3%	—	(8.8%)

Frontier Communications Corp

Serving city dwellers and country folk alike Frontier Communications provides phone Internet and satellite TV (through a partnership with DISH Network) services across 27 states. The company has more than 3 million residential and 2 million business voice subsribers. It also has 1.7 million broadband Internet customers and more than half a million satellite video subscribers. Frontier is active mostly in rural and small to mid-sized markets where it is the incumbent local-exchange carrier (ILEC). The company's top three markets in terms of subscribers are West Virginia Indiana and New York.

Residential landlines may be on the decline as more households switch to a wireless provider for their primary phone service but Frontier operates mostly in rural markets where cellular service can still be spotty. Frontier is able to remain competitive with other triple-play providers because of the TV service it offers through DISH Network. (Satellite TV operators can't offer digital phone service which puts them at a disadvantage to cable companies such as Comcast and Time Warner.

Frontier significantly expanded its footprint in 2010 when it bought 4.8 million telephone and broadband access lines in 14 states from Verizon Communications for about $8.6 billion in cash and stock. The deal roughly tripled Frontier's size and gave it a healthy boost against other rural carriers. Before it was approved the transaction met with opposition from labor unions and legislators in Illinois. Verizon which initiated the sale to meet regulatory requirements for its 2009 purchase of wireless carrier Alltel took a more than two-thirds stake in Frontier as part of the deal.

The expansion has fueled sales with the company's 2011 revenue topping $5 billion after coming in well under $4 billion the previous year. Frontier's income slipped a bit for the year however as the company contends with expenses from integrating the far-flung operations of its acquired business.

HISTORY

Frontier Communications was formed in 1935 as Citizens Utilities Company to acquire Public Utilities Consolidated Corporation a Minneapolis-based company with interests in electric gas water and telephone utilities throughout the US. From 1950 to 1970 the company bought utilities in rural and suburban areas of Arizona California Hawaii Illinois Indiana Ohio and Pennsylvania. A major acquisition was Hawaii's Kauai Electric Company in 1969. By the mid-1970s electric power brought in 40% of the company's revenues.

Leonard Tow head of Century Communications was brought on board in 1989 and elected chairman the next year remaining in that position until 2004. Expanding Citizens through more electric water and natural gas acquisitions he tripled the company's revenues in less than 10 years.

In 1993 Citizens acquired a majority stake in Electric Lightwave the first competitive local-exchange carrier (CLEC) west of the Mississippi River. Citizens started its long-distance telephone service in 1994. It also acquired 500000 local access lines in nine states from GTE quadrupling the size of its operations. By 1995 the telecom group was the fastest-growing segment of the company.

After the Telecommunications Act was passed in 1996 Citizens acquired another 110000 local access lines and cable systems with more than 7000 customers from ALLTEL and bought three Southern California cable systems with Century Communications. Citizens aggressively marketed local phone service in neighboring areas to its service territories but the company didn't see the return it expected and by 1997 had to cut its workforce and tighten cost controls. In light of the cutbacks bookkeeping troubles and 1996 threats from Vermont to revoke Citizens' license there for accounting and permit problems the board voted Tow a pay cut.

The company sold a minority stake in Electric Lightwave to the public in 1997 (Citizens reacquired the stake in 2002 and Electric Lightwave became a wholly owned subsidiary). Citizens continued its buying spree with telecom and gas firms in New York and Hawaii and a local phone company in Pennsylvania in 1998.

The next year Citizens began turning itself into a pure telecom company through a series of transactions. It agreed to pay about $2.8 billion for 900000 local phone lines owned by U S WEST and GTE. It also sold its cable TV interests and agreed to sell its water and wastewater operations (for $835 million).

Citizens bought more than 1 million local phone lines in 2001 from Global Crossing for about $3.5 billion. Later that year the company canceled its pending acquisition agreements with Qwest U S WEST's successor amid a dispute over how much revenue the local lines were producing. The terminated deals valued at $1.7 billion would have given Citizens another 540000 local lines. It later pulled out of a deal to buy an additional 63000 access lines in Arizona and California from Verizon Communications.

The company also sold part of its natural gas business for $375 million in 2001 the same year it changed its name to Citizens Communications. Although an earlier deal to sell its electric properties fell through the company completed the sale of its Kauai Electric division in 2002 for $215 million to the Kauai Island Utility Cooperative. That year it also reached an agreement to sell its Hawaiian gas division in a deal valued at $115 million and completed the following year.

In November 2002 two executives of the company's public utilities division were dismissed after an SEC investigation into $7.8 million in payments for services the company did not receive.

Citizens sold its competitive local-exchange carrier (CLEC) Electric Lightwave to Integra Telecom in mid-2006 in a deal that was valued at $247 million. The next year it acquired Commonwealth Telephone effectively expanding its access to the Pennsylvania market. Later that year the company then spent $62 million to purchase Global Valley Networks a provider of telephone and Internet services in California in a move to expand its service area in the Western US.

Frontier changed its legal name from Citizens Communication in to its brand name Frontier in 2008.

EXECUTIVES

EVP Revenue Development and Product Marketing and General Manager Marketing and New Business Operations, Melinda M. White, age 52
Chairman President and CEO, Mary Agnes (Maggie) Wilderotter, age 57, $882,308 total compensation
President Central Region, John J. Lass
Manager Communications Southeast Region U.S., Dan Page
EVP and COO, Daniel J. McCarthy, age 47, $317,826 total compensation
EVP Regulatory and Government Affairs and Chief Legal Officer, Kathleen Q. Abernathy, age 55
SVP Government and Regulatory Affairs, Steven C. (Steve) Crosby
SVP and General Manager Southeast Region West Virginia, Dana E. Waldo, age 60
EVP Commercial Sales, Peter B. (Pete) Hayes, age 54, $286,154 total compensation
General Manager Central Region Southern Ohio, Dave George
EVP and CFO, Donald R. (Don) Shassian, age 56, $429,231 total compensation
EVP Human Resources and Call Center Sales and Service, Cecilia K. McKenney, age 49, $276,616 total compensation
SVP and Treasurer, David R. Whitehouse
President Southeast Region, Ken Arndt
President Northeast Region, Ann L. Burr
Assistant VP Assistant Treasurer and Director Investor Relations, Gregory H. Lundberg
Assistant VP Corporate Communications, Brigid Smith
Manager Communications National Region U.S., Karen Miller
SVP National Region, Rhonda Lutzke
SVP and General Manager Central Region Illinois, Michael C. (Mike) Flynn
SVP and General Manager Central Region Ohio, Dave Davidson
SVP Controller and Chief Accounting Officer, Susana D'Emic, age 48
Manager Communications Pennsylvania and Central Region, Patricia Amendola
Manager Local Marketing and Community Relations New York and Pennsylvania, Stephanie Schifano
Manager Communications Midwest Region U.S., Matt Kelley
Manager Communications West Region U.S., Stephanie Beasly
SVP Deputy General Counsel and Secretary, Nancy S. Rights
Regional Director Marketing Northeast Region, Tom Grooms
Regional Director Marketing Central Region, Burgess Harrison
President Midwest Region, Don Banowetz
Manager Marketing Midwest Region, Christanne Bauer-Johnson
President West Region, Denise Baumbach
Regional Director Marketing West Region, Jack Yovanovich

General Manager Central Region Altamont Illinois, Brett Gilsinger
General Manager Central Region Greater Bloomington and Normal Illinois, Mike Nelson
General Manager Central Region Carlinville/Jacksonville Illinois, Steve Saylor
General Manager Central Region Rantoul Illinois, Michael Boebinger
General Manager Central Region Carbondale Illinois, Eric Shadley
General Manager Central Region Monmouth Illinois, Kim Sheetz-Zugmaier
General Manager Central Region Morrison Illinois, Kent Klima
General Manager Central Region DeKalb & Sycamore Illinois, Thomas Kuschman
General Manager Central Region Central/Northern WI, Ryan Curtis
General Manager Central Region Eastern Wisconsin, Frank Maydak
General Manager Central Region Southern Wisconsin, Terry Kucera
Area General Manager Central Region Minnesota, Scott Behn
General Manager Central Region Souteast Minnesota, Darrell Hansen
General Manager Central Region West Metro Minnesota, Bob Trombley
General Manager Central Region South Metro Minnesota, Holly Dahl
General Manager Central Region Northern Minnesota, Kirk Lehman
General Manager Central Region Southwestern Minnesota, Todd Van Epps
General Manager Central Region Columbus Nebraska, Dan Staack
General Manager Central Region Central Ohio, Tom Travis
General Manager Central Region Northeast Ohio, Jennifer Smith
General Manager Central Region North Central Ohio, Stephen Euton
General Manager Central Region Northwest Ohio, Dick Hutchinson
General Manager Central Region Eastern OH, Kevin Wallick
Director, James S. (Jim) Kahan, age 64
Director, Myron A. (Mike) Wick III, age 68
Director, Pamela D. A. Reeve, age 62
Director, Howard L. Schrott, age 57
Director, Peter C. B. Bynoe, age 61
Director, Leroy T. Barnes Jr., age 60
Director, Jeri B. Finard, age 52
Director, Larraine D. Segil, age 63
Director, Mark S. Shapiro, age 42
Director, Edward Fraioli, age 65
Auditors: KPMGLLP

LOCATIONS

HQ: Frontier Communications Corporation
3 High Ridge Park, Stamford CT 06905
Phone: 203-614-5600 **Fax:** 512-836-9785
Web: www.citizensinc.com

PRODUCTS/OPERATIONS

2011 Sales

	$ mil.	% of total
Local & long distance	2,451	47
Data & Internet	1,842	35
Switched access & subsidy	619	12
Other	329	6
Total	**5,243**	**100**

COMPETITORS

AT&T
Cablevision Systems
CenturyLink
Charter Communications
Comcast
Cox Communications
FairPoint Communications Inc.
Integra Telecom
Time Warner Cable
tw telecom
Verizon
Vonage
XO Holdings

HISTORICAL FINANCIALS

Company Type: Public

Income Statement FYE: December 31

	REVENUE ($ mil.)	NET INCOME ($ mil.)	NET PROFIT MARGIN	EMPLOYEES
12/11	5,243	149	2.9%	15,400
12/10	3,797	152	4.0%	14,800
12/09	2,117	120	5.7%	5,400
12/08	2,237	182	8.2%	5,671
12/07	2,288	214	9.4%	5,900
Annual Growth	23.0%	(8.6%)	—	27.1%

2011 Year-End Financials

Debt ratio: 47.53%
Return on equity: 3.36%
Cash ($ mil.): 326
Current ratio: 107.34
Long-term debt ($ mil.): 8,205
No. of shares (mil.): 995
Dividends
Yield: —
Payout: 500.00%
Market value ($ mil.): 5,125

	STOCK PRICE ($) FY Close	P/E High	P/E Low	PER SHARE ($) Earnings	Dividends	Book Value
12/11	5.15	65	32	0.15	0.00	4.48
12/10	9.73	42	31	0.23	0.88	5.23
12/09	7.81	23	14	0.38	1.00	1.05
12/08	8.74	22	12	0.57	1.00	1.67
12/07	12.73	24	19	0.65	1.00	3.05
Annual Growth	(20.2%)	—	—	(30.7%)	—	10.1%

Fulton Financial Corp. (PA)

Fulton Financial is simply full of banks. The multibank holding company owns six community banks which together operate about 270 branches in rural and suburban areas of eastern Pennsylvania Delaware Maryland New Jersey and Virginia. The banks offer standard products such as checking and savings accounts CDs IRAs and credit cards. Commercial loans and mortgages account for about two-thirds of the company's loan portfolio. Home loans are available through its Fulton Mortgage Company subsidiary. Other nonbank units include investment management and trust services provider Fulton Financial Advisors and Fulton Insurance an agency selling life insurance and related products.

Fulton Financial's subsidiary banks include Fulton Bank (its largest with about 120 branches in Pennsylvania and Delaware) The Columbia Bank FNB Bank Fulton Bank of New Jersey Lafayette Ambassador Bank and Swineford National Bank. The company had owned more than a dozen banks as recently as 2007 but consolidated some of them in the hopes of creating operating and marketing efficiencies. Maryland-based Hagerstown Trust Company and The Peoples Bank of Elkton merged into The Columbia Bank in 2009 and Delaware National Bank which had a dozen branches in the state became part of Fulton Bank the following year. In 2011 Fulton Financial merged two more banks New Jersey-based The Bank and Skylands Community Bank to form Fulton Bank of New Jersey which has some 70 branches throughout the state.

Fulton Financial has weathered the US economic turmoil by managing expenses and curtailing its construction lending amid that sector's downturn. Though revenues declined it reported a nearly 25% increase in net income (to more than $145 million) in 2011. Its results were bolstered in part by improved credit quality and interest rate spreads.

The company is focusing on organic growth by opening new branches and building market share in the communities that it serves.

EXECUTIVES

Chairman and CEO, R. Scott Smith Jr., age 65, $734,946 total compensation
SEVP and CFO, Charles J. Nugent, age 63, $478,400 total compensation
President COO and Director, E. Philip Wenger, age 54, $350,000 total compensation
SEVP Administrative Services, James E. Shreiner, age 62, $306,000 total compensation
SEVP Human Resources, Craig H. Hill, age 57
VP Corporate Communications, Laura J. Wakeley
President and CEO Lafayette Ambassador Bank, Gerald A. Nau
SEVP Community Banking; Chairman and CEO Fulton Bank, Craig A. Roda
EVP Domestic and International Cash Management, James M. Lowe
EVP Head of Retail Banking and Chief Deposit Officer, Mark E. Huntley
VP International Operations, Amy Sahm
President Fulton Financial Advisors, David M. Campbell
Director, Rufus A. Fulton Jr., age 71
Director, John M. Bond Jr., age 68
Director, John O. Shirk, age 68
Director, George W. Hodges, age 61
Director, Craig A. Dally, age 55
Director, Donald M. Bowman Jr., age 73
Director, Patrick J. Freer, age 62
Director, Donald W. Lesher Jr., age 67
Director, Jeffrey G. Albertson, age 71
Director, Gary A. Stewart, age 64
Director, Dana A. Chryst, age 52
Director, Willem Kooyker, age 69
President COO and Director, E. Philip Wenger, age 54
Director, Joe N. Ballard
Auditors: KPMGLLP

LOCATIONS

HQ: Fulton Financial Corporation
1 Penn Sq., Lancaster PA 17604-4887
Phone: 717-291-2411 **Fax:** 717-295-4792
Web: www.fult.com

PRODUCTS/OPERATIONS

2011 Sales

	$ mil.	% of total
Interest		
Loans including fees	596	68
Investment securities	95	11
Other	2	-
Noninterest		

Service charges on deposit accounts	58	7
Investment management & trust services	36	4
Mortgage banking	25	3
Other service charges & fees	47	5
Other	20	2
Total	**881**	**100**

2011 Branches

	No.
Fulton Bank	118
Fulton Bank of New	71
The Columbia Bank	40
Lafayette Ambassador Bank	23
FNB Bank	8
Swineford National Bank	7
Total	**267**

COMPETITORS

First Commonwealth Financial
Investors Bancorp
M&T Bank
Metro Bancorp
Mid Penn Bancorp
PNC Financial
Sovereign Bank
Susquehanna Bancshares
TD Bank USA

HISTORICAL FINANCIALS

Company Type: Public

Income Statement FYE: December 31

	ASSETS ($ mil.)	NET INCOME ($ mil.)	INCOME AS % OF ASSETS	EMPLOYEES
12/11	16,370	145	0.9%	3,530
12/10	16,275	128	0.8%	3,530
12/09	16,635	73	0.4%	3,560
12/08	16,185	(5)	—	3,630
12/07	15,923	152	1.0%	3,680
Annual Growth	0.7%	(1.2%)	—	(1.0%)

2011 Year-End Financials

Debt ratio: 7.31%
Return on equity: 7.31%
Cash ($ mil.): 467
Current ratio: —
Long-term debt ($ mil.): 1,196
No. of shares (mil.): 200
Dividends
Yield: —
Payout: 27.40%
Market value ($ mil.): 1,964

	STOCK PRICE ($) FY Close	P/E High	P/E Low	PER SHARE ($) Earnings	Dividends	Book Value
12/11	9.81	16	10	0.73	0.00	9.95
12/10	10.34	20	14	0.59	0.12	9.44
12/09	8.72	32	15	0.31	0.12	10.98
12/08	9.62	—	—	(0.03)	0.60	10.62
12/07	11.22	19	12	0.88	0.60	9.08
Annual Growth	(3.3%)	—	—	(4.6%)	—	2.3%

GameStop Corp

GameStop holds the top score in video game retailing. Operating under the GameStop EB Games and Micromania banners it's the largest retailer of new and used games hardware entertainment software and accessories. It boasts nearly 6700 stores in the US Europe Australia and Canada. By carrying about 4500 items including more than 3000 used video game titles a majority of GameStop's revenue is generated by sales of new and used video games and their software. The company also sells downloadable add-on content from publishers. GameStop operates several e-commerce websites offers GameStop TV in many of its locations and publishes Game Informer a video game magazine with some 7.2 million subscribers.

Strategy

Despite the gloomy selling forecast for retailers during the past few years GameStop has logged its greatest revenue increases during the recession and beyond. It's seeing the largest gains among used video game products as the company lures more frugal customers who want to stay in the game even with tighter budgets. For used items revenue rose from 23% of 2009 revenue to 28% in 2012. More consumers are turning to existing video game products rather than new due to their availability and cost-effectiveness. That bodes well for GameStop because used game products (with their higher gross margins) is the company's most profitable segment. To maintain its foothold in new and used gaming GameStop continues to target hardcore gamers as well as those niche customers who purchase games as gifts during the holidays.

Financial Analysis

Those gamers who jockey for the latest and greatest video game software still chose to shop at GameStop which brought in another 42% of its 2012 revenue from new video game software. GameStop saw slight sales declines however among its lower-margin new video game hardware product segment (21% in 2009 to 17% in 2012). The company points to lower consumer demand and price cuts on hardware consoles for the sales slips. The sales decline on new hardware wasn't detrimental to GameStop though as the products generate a high single-digit profit margin for the games chain.

Geographic Reach

GameStop operates its stores in the US Europe Australia and Canada.

Operations

GameStop has continued to expand its operations in the US and overseas but most of its recent sales growth has come from outside the US. In Europe the company has logged revenue increases that have offset sales declines in the US related to decreased demand. Boosting its store count overseas has allowed GameStop to maintain its overall store growth strategy. While expansion from 2011 to 2012 slowed to a mere net 13 stores the company has reached its current store count through several years of aggressive growth. In 2010 alone GameStop added more than 220 stores to its operations across the board (107 in the US 88 in Europe 17 in Australia and eight in Canada). Albeit this is modest growth for GameStop which opened 674 new stores in 2008 586 stores during 2007 and 421 stores in 2006. (To the uninitiated GameStop was a much smaller game in town just seven years ago. The company's purchase of rival Electronics Boutique in 2005 doubled GameStop's size.)

Mergers & Acquisitions

GameStop is also looking to the Web's game space for growth. In 2011 the company acquired Spawn Labs which develops peer-to-peer game streaming technology so that gamers can access their video games and play with others (via an Internet-connected device) even when they are away from home. Spawn Labs sells its streaming applications to game developers. The business is being integrated into GameStop's research and development unit as Spawn Labs' expertise in virtualization is key to strengthening the retailer's online gaming offerings. Also in 2011 GameStop acquired the Impulse subsidiary of software company Stardock Systems whose online distribution platform enables gamers to purchase and download games to their computers. Impulse offers more than 1100 games a number that is sure to grow with Spawn Labs on board. Prior to these deals GameStop secured a digital platform in 2010 when it acquired Kongregate a gaming site launched in 2007 for social gaming that attracts some 10 million users a month. As part of the purchase Kongregate operates as a wholly owned subsidiary of GameStop and maintains its headquarters in San Francisco.

Sales & Marketing

The company considers itself a destination location for gamers. It develops relationships with video game enthusiasts through its PowerUp Rewards loyalty program (launched in 2010) by allowing consumers to trade in used video games for store credits on future purchases.

HISTORY

NeoStar Retail Group resulted from the 1994 combination of software retailers Babbage's and Software Etc. Babbage's had been founded by James McCurry and Gary Kusin in 1983. Named for 19th-century mathematician Charles Babbage (considered the father of the computer) it went public in 1988.

Software Etc. began as a division of B. Dalton Bookseller in 1984. Bookstore chain Barnes & Noble and Dutch retailer Vendex acquired B. Dalton two years later. Software Etc. went public in 1992.

Both companies focused on mall retailing: Babbage's on game software and Software Etc. on a broader variety of PC software. Both saw growth spurred by the rising popularity of Nintendo and Sega game systems and by falling PC prices. The two merged in 1994 in an effort to stave off growing competition from big retail chains such as Best Buy and Wal-Mart. NeoStar opened 122 stores in 1995.

Amid flat sales the following year several senior executives left. Also in 1996 NeoStar lost its contract to operate software departments at 136 Barnes & Noble sites and it soon filed for Chapter 11. Late that year a group led by Barnes & Noble's head honcho Leonard Riggio purchased about 460 of NeoStar's 650 stores for $58.5 million and renamed the company Babbage's Etc. Former Software Etc. chief Dick Fontaine was named CEO.

By 1997 the company began concentrating on popular games and software and in 1999 it formed its e-commerce site GameStop.com. In late 1999 Barnes & Noble paid Riggio's group $210 million for Babbage's Etc. In June 2000 the company fortified its position and became the #1 US video game retailer with the purchase of rival game retailer Funco (about 400 stores) for $161.5 million. The company changed its name to GameStop in August 2001 and filed to go public which it accomplished in February 2002. Though public it was still under the majority control of Barnes & Noble until 2004 when GameStop bought back its shares.

GameStop bought rival Electronics Boutique in 2005 more than doubling its size from 2000 to about 4500 stores. Steven R. Morgan a former executive with Electronics Boutique became president of GameStop later that year.

A new CEO took the controls at GameStop in 2008 –its first CEO change since the company's inception in 1996. Dick Fontaine gave up the title of chief executive to Daniel DeMatteo who had served as COO since 1996 and vice chairman of the company since 2004. Also Paul Raines formerly with Home Depot joined the company as COO in September 2008. Fontaine retained the chairman's title and focused on international operations and acquisitions.

GameStop focused on international expansion in 2008 driven primarily by a pair of acquisitions. The largest of those was its $629 million purchase of video game retailer Micromania which brought with it some 330 stores in France. South of the equator GameStop acquired The Gamesman the largest independent gaming retailer in New Zealand. The deal included eight Gamesman video game stores and brought GameStop's total store count in the country to 38.

In June 2010 DeMatteo was promoted to executive chairman of the company while Raines was named CEO.

EXECUTIVES

Chairman, Daniel A. (Dan) DeMatteo, age 64, $1,246,154 total compensation
Chairman International, R. Richard (Dick) Fontaine, age 70, $1,184,615 total compensation
SVP and General Manager Digital Business, Shawn D. Freeman
President, Tony D. Bartel, age 48, $492,308 total compensation
SVP Supply Chain and Refurbishment, Bruce Kulp, age 46
CEO, J. Paul (Paul) Raines, age 48, $328,846 total compensation
EVP and CFO, Robert A. (Rob) Lloyd, age 50
VP Corporate Communications, Chris Olivera
EVP GameStop International, Michael (Mike) Mauler, age 51
Divisional VP Investor Relations, Matt Hodges
General Manager Digital Ventures, Chris Petrovic
SVP and Chief Accounting Officer, Tony W. Crawford, age 44
SVP and CIO, Jeff Donaldson
Media Relations, Beth Sharum
Chairman International, R. Richard (Dick) Fontaine, age 70
Director, Michael N. Rosen, age 71
Director, Gerald R. (Jerry) Szczepanski, age 64
Director, Stanley (Mickey) Steinberg, age 79
Director, Stephanie M. Shern, age 64
Director, Jerome L. Davis Sr., age 57
Director, Edward A. Volkwein, age 71
Director, Lawrence S. (Larry) Zilavy, age 61
Director, Steven R. (Steve) Koonin, age 54
Director, Shane Kim, age 50
Auditors: BDOUSALLP

LOCATIONS

HQ: GameStop Corp.
625 Westport Pkwy., Grapevine TX 76051
Phone: 817-424-2000 **Fax:** 817-424-2002
Web: www.gamestop.com

2012 Sales

	$ mil.	% of total
US	6,637	70
Europe	1,810	19
Australia	604	6
Canada	498	5
Total	**9,550**	**100**

2012 Stores

	No.
US	4,503
Europe	1,423
Australia	411
Canada	346
Total	**6,683**

PRODUCTS/OPERATIONS

2012 Sales

	$ mil.	% of total
New video game software	4,048	42
Used video game products	2,620	28
New video game hardware	1,611	17
Other	1,270	13
Total	**9,550**	**100**

Selected Mergers & Acquisitions

FY2011
- Spawn Labs (peer-to-peer game streaming technology developer)
- Impulse (online distribution platform)

FY2010
- Kongregate (social gaming site)

Selected Websites

www.ebgames.com.au
www.gamestop.ca
www.gamestop.co.uk
www.gamestop.com
www.gamestop.com/pcgames
www.gamestop.de
www.gamestop.es
www.gamestop.ie
www.gamestop.it
www.kongregate.com
www.micromania.fr

Selected Merchandise

Accessories
- PC entertainment accessories
- Video game accessories
- Other

Internet streaming technology & digital distribution
Online games
PC entertainment software & other software
Used video games
Video game hardware
Video game software

COMPETITORS

Amazon.com
Best Buy
Blockbuster
Buy.com
Carrefour
CompUSA
Costco Wholesale
eBay
Fry' s Electronics
GAME Group
GameFly
Kmart
RadioShack
Target Corporation
Toys ' ' R' ' Us
Wal-Mart
Zones

HISTORICAL FINANCIALS

Company Type: Public

Income Statement

FYE: January 28

	REVENUE ($ mil.)	NET INCOME ($ mil.)	NET PROFIT MARGIN	EMPLOYEES
01/12	9,550	339	3.6%	71,000
01/11	9,473	408	4.3%	68,000
01/10	9,078	377	4.2%	59,000
01/09*	8,805	398	4.5%	56,000
02/08	7,093	288	4.1%	43,000
Annual Growth	7.7%	4.2%	—	13.4%

*Fiscal year change

2012 Year-End Financials

Debt ratio: —
Return on equity: 11.17%
Cash ($ mil.): 655
Current ratio: 122.24
Long-term debt ($ mil.): —
No. of shares (mil.): 136
Dividends
Yield: —
Payout: —
Market value ($ mil.): 3,327

	STOCK PRICE ($) FY Close	P/E High	P/E Low	Earnings	Dividends	Book Value
01/12	24.32	12	8	2.41	0.00	22.24
01/11	20.98	9	6	2.65	0.00	19.84
01/10	19.77	14	9	2.25	0.00	17.16
01/09*	24.78	23	7	2.38	0.00	14.04
02/08	52.52	35	15	1.75	0.00	11.57
Annual Growth	(17.5%)	—	—	8.3%	—	17.7%

*Fiscal year change

Gannett Co Inc

Gannett satisfies news junkies with a stash of daily US papers. The company is the top newspaper publisher in the US with about 80 daily papers boasting a total circulation of about 5 million. Its flagship USA TODAY with a circulation of 1.8 million is the nation's second-largest newspaper (behind the Wall Street Journal). Other papers in Gannett's holdings include The Arizona Republic and the Detroit Free Press. The company also owns about 600 non-daily publications as well as more than 200 papers in the UK through Newsquest. In addition Gannett owns 23 television stations in about 20 markets publishes periodicals and inserts (including USA WEEKEND) and operates websites for many of its papers.

HISTORY

In 1906 Frank Gannett started a newspaper empire when he and his associates purchased a stake in New York's "Elmira Gazette." In 1923 Gannett bought out his associates' interests and formed the Gannett Company. The company's history of technical innovation dates to the 1920s when Frank Gannett invested in the development of the Teletypesetter; some of his newspapers were printing in color by 1938. The company continued to buy small and medium-sized dailies in the Northeast and by Gannett's death in 1957 it had accumulated 30 newspapers.

Gannett expanded nationally in the 1960s through acquisitions. It was not until 1966 however that it started its own paper "TODAY" (now "FLORIDA TODAY") in Cocoa Beach Florida. Gannett went public in 1967.

The company's greatest period of growth came during the 1970s and 1980s under the direction of Allen Neuharth (CEO from 1973 to 1986). Gannett captured national attention in 1979 when it merged with Phoenix-based Combined Communications Corporation (CCC) whose holdings included TV and radio stations an outdoor advertising business and pollster Louis Harris & Associates.

In 1982 Gannett started "USA TODAY" a national newspaper whose splashy format and mini-stories made it an industry novelty. Critics branded it "McPaper" but circulation passed a million copies a day by the end of 1983. (It wasn't profitable until 1993 however.)

Declines in newspaper advertising in 1990 primarily among US retailers broke the company's string of 89 consecutive quarters of positive earnings. USA TODAY-On-Demand a fax news service began in 1992. Gannett bought Multimedia Inc. a newspaper TV cable and program syndication company for about $2.3 billion in 1995.

Website "USA TODAY Online" debuted in 1995. The next year Gannett teamed up with newspaper publisher Knight Ridder and privately held media firm Landmark Communications to form Internet service provider InfiNet. In 1996 Gannett sold Louis Harris & Associates and its outdoor advertising operations and traded six radio stations to Jacor Communications for one Tampa TV station.

Gannett exited the radio industry in 1998 by selling its last five stations. It also sold its Multimedia Security Service. That year the company expanded its TV holdings through purchases of three stations in Maine and South Carolina. Gannett's integrity took a blow in 1998 when a reporter for one of its newspapers ("The Cincinnati Enquirer") illegally obtained information for a report accusing Chiquita Brands International of unscrupulous business practices. Gannett retracted the story and settled with Chiquita to the tune of about $14 million.

The company broke new ground in 1999 when Karen Jurgensen was named editor of "USA TODAY" (she was the first woman to head a national newspaper). Also that year Gannett acquired Newsquest one of the largest regional newspaper publishers in the UK. In early 2000 Gannett sold its cable operations to Cox Communications for $2.7 billion. The company also formed TV and Web venture USA Today Live to produce news stories for its TV stations. Later that year chairman John Curley passed the title of CEO to president Douglas McCorkindale (McCorkindale would become chair the next year).

Gannett also made a slew of acquisitions in 2000 including a purchase of the UK's News Communications & Media "Arizona Republic" publisher Central Newspapers and 21 newspapers from Thomson Corp. (now Thomson Reuters). The company moved its headquarters in 2001 from Arlington to McLean Virginia. Amid an industry-wide advertising recession Gannett saw its profits decline in 2001 and "USA TODAY" cut more than 5% of its staff (about 100 employees). In early 2002 Gannett sold nearly $2 billion in debt in unsecured global notes in order to use the funds to repay short-term loans. Later that year the company bought a stake in the online job site CareerBuilder.

In 2003 the company bought several Hawaiian magazines and a related website from Greg Gardiner. Later that year Gannett acquired Clipper Magazine a direct-mail ad company.

The company joined with Knight Ridder and Tribune Company in 2004 to acquire online marketing services provider CrossMedia Services. That year Gannett also purchased more than 30 newspapers and specialty publications from Brown County Publishing in Wisconsin. Jurgensen stepped down as editor of USA Today in the fallout of a scandal involving reporter Jack Kelley.

Broadcasting chief Craig Dubow took over as president and CEO in 2005. The company boosted its online marketing quotient with its 2005 purchase of Internet advertising technology firm PointRoll. In late 2005 Gannett acquired a TV station in Denver (KTVD-TV).

In 2006 McCorkindale retired and Dubow added chairman to his title. Later that year the company acquired WATL-TV in Atlanta from the Tribune Company for $180 million.

More recently Gannett has focused on acquiring interests in online businesses including shopping site ShopLocal and jobs site CareerBuilder. The company has also rolled out news applications for mobile devices.

EXECUTIVES

President CEO and Director, Gracia C. Martore, age 60, $659,615 total compensation
Chairman and CEO Newsquest, Paul Davidson, age 57, $730,000 total compensation
VP Planning and Development, Daniel S. Ehrman Jr., age 65
VP and Chief Accounting Officer, George R. Gavagan, age 65
SVP and CFO, Paul N. Saleh, age 54
Chairman, Marjorie (Marge) Magner, age 62
VP and Senior Associate General Counsel, Barbara W. Wall
VP Interim CFO and Treasurer, Michael A. Hart
VP Information Technology, Mark Morneau
SVP Human Resources, Roxanne V. Horning, age 62
SVP General Counsel and Secretary, Todd A. Mayman, age 52
VP Internal Audit, Jane Ann Wimbush
VP Corporate Communications, Robin Pence
Director Investor Relations, Jeffrey Heinz
VP Corporate Communications, Jeremy Gaines
EVP Gannett Broadcasting; President and General Manager KSDK-TV, Lynn Beall
President Gannett Digital Ventures, John A. (Jack) Williams, age 61
President of Sales, Mary Murcko
SVP and Chief Marketing Officer, Maryam Banikarim, age 43
President US Community Publishing, Robert J. (Bob) Dickey, age 54, $588,942 total compensation
President Gannett Broadcasting, David T. (Dave) Lougee, age 53, $550,000 total compensation
President and Publisher USA TODAY, David L. (Dave) Hunke, age 58, $463,141 total compensation
VP Product Gannett Digital, Mitch Gelman
President Gannett Supply, Karen R. Moreno
President and Publisher Florida Today Communications Group, Jeff Kiel, age 52
VP Taxes, Sally K. Clurman
EVP; General Manager USA TODAY, Susie Ellwood
President Detroit Media Partnership, Joyce Jenereaux, age 58
VP and Controller, Teresa (Teri) Gendron, age 43
SVP Labor Relations, William A. Behan, age 53
President and Publisher USA Today, Larry Kramer
VP Mobile Strategy and Operations Gannett Digital, Matt Jones
SVP and Chief Digital Officer, David A. Payne, age 49
VP Marketing, Debra Goetz
President and Publisher The Daily Advertiser and Daily World, Karen Lincoln
SVP and Chief Human Resources Officer, Kevin Lord
President CEO and Director, Gracia C. Martore, age 60
Director, John E. Cody, age 65
Director, Duncan M. McFarland, age 68
Director, Howard D. Elias, age 55
Director, Neal B. Shapiro, age 54
Director, Arthur H. (Art) Harper, age 56
Director, John J. Louis, age 49
Director, Scott K. McCune, age 55
Auditors: Ernst&YoungLLP

LOCATIONS

HQ: Gannett Co. Inc.
7950 Jones Branch Dr., McLean VA 22107-0910
Phone: 703-854-6000 **Fax:** 703-854-2053
Web: www.gannett.com

PRODUCTS/OPERATIONS

2011 Sales

	$ mil.	% of total
Publishing	3,832	73
Digital media	686	13

Selected Operations

Newspapers
- The Arizona Republic (Phoenix)
- Asbury Park Press (New Jersey)
- The Cincinnati Enquirer
- The Courier-Journal (Louisville KY)
- The Des Moines Register (Iowa)
- Detroit Free Press
- The Indianapolis Star
- Rochester Democrat and Chronicle (New York)
- The Tennessean (Nashville)
- USA TODAY (McLean VA)

Broadcasting
- KARE (NBC Minneapolis)
- KNAZ (NBC; Flagstaff AZ)
- KPNX (NBC Phoenix)
- KSDK (NBC St. Louis)
- KTHV (CBS; Little Rock AR)
- KTVD (MyNetworkTV Denver)
- KUSA (NBC Denver)
- KXTV (ABC; Sacramento CA)
- WATL (MyNetworkTV Atlanta)
- WBIR (NBC; Knoxville TN)
- WCSH (NBC; Portland ME)
- WFMY (CBS; Greensboro NC)
- WGRZ (NBC; Buffalo NY)
- WJXX (ABC Jacksonville)
- WKYC (NBC Cleveland)
- WLBZ (NBC; Bangor ME)
- WLTX (CBS; Columbia SC)
- WMAZ (CBS; Macon GA)
- WTLV (NBC Jacksonville)
- WTSP (CBS Tampa)
- WUSA (CBS; Washington DC)
- WXIA (NBC Atlanta)
- WZZM (ABC; Grand Rapids MI)

Other holdings and investments
- Army Times Publishing Company (newspapers)
- California Newspapers Partnership (19% community newspapers)
- Captivate Network (display advertising)
- CareerBuilder (51% online job recruitment)
- Classified Ventures (24% online content publishing)
- Clipper Magazine (direct mail advertising)
- Gannett Healthcare Group (periodical publishing)
- Gannett Media Technologies International (publishing software)
- Gannett Offset (commercial printing)
- Metromix (51% local information Web sites)
- Newsquest Media Group (newspaper publishing UK)
- Planet Discover (Internet search and advertising)
- PointRoll (digital media marketing services)
- Ponderay Newsprint (13%)
- QuadrantONE (25% online advertising)
- ShopLocal.com (online shopping portal)
- Texas-New Mexico Newspapers Partnership (41% community newspapers)
- Topix (34% online news aggregation)
- USA WEEKEND (weekly newspaper insert)

COMPETITORS

Advance Publications
CBS
E. W. Scripps
Google
Hearst Corporation
Lee Enterprises
Local TV
McClatchy Company
Media General
MediaNews
New York Times
News Corp.
Philadelphia Media
Raycom Media
Sinclair Broadcast Group
Tribune Company
Washington Post
Yahoo!

HISTORICAL FINANCIALS

Company Type: Public

Income Statement FYE: December 25

	REVENUE ($ mil.)	NET INCOME ($ mil.)	NET PROFIT MARGIN	EMPLOYEES
12/11	5,239	458	8.8%	31,000
12/10	5,438	588	10.8%	32,600
12/09	5,612	355	6.3%	35,000
12/08	6,767	(6,647)	—	41,500
12/07	7,439	1,055	14.2%	46,100
Annual Growth	(8.4%)	(18.8%)	—	(9.4%)

2011 Year-End Financials

Debt ratio: 26.61%
Return on equity: 19.71%
Cash ($ mil.): 166
Current ratio: 119.25
Long-term debt ($ mil.): 1,760

No. of shares (mil.): 237
Dividends
Yield: —
Payout: 12.70%
Market value ($ mil.): 3,212

	STOCK PRICE ($) FY Close	P/E High/Low	PER SHARE ($) Earnings	Dividends	Book Value
12/11	13.55	9 4	1.89	0.00	9.82
12/10	15.43	8 5	2.43	0.00	9.03
12/09	15.63	10 1	1.51	0.00	6.76
12/08	7.58	— —	(29.11)	0.00	4.63
12/07	38.23	14 8	4.52	0.00	39.17
Annual Growth	(22.8%)	— —	(19.6%)	—	(29.2%)

General Cable Corp. (DE)

General Cable keeps power flowing and communication going. The company designs manufactures and distributes copper aluminum and fiber optic wire and cable products that are used in electrical transmission and distribution power generation and voice and data communications. Major brands include BICC (energy cables) Carol (temporary power cables) and NextGen (data communication cables). General Cable's products are sold to commercial industrial electric utility telecom military and government retail and OEM distributor customers worldwide. The company also makes copper and aluminum rod for other wire and cable manufacturers and it integrates and installs high voltage systems on land and under water.

HISTORY

General Cable originated from some of the oldest names in the wiring business: Standard Underground Cable (founded by George Westinghouse) and Phillips Wire and Safety Cable Company both founded in the 1800s. The companies supplied wire for historic events such as Samuel Morse's first telegram between Baltimore and Washington DC in 1844 the lighting of the Statute of Liberty in 1886 and the first Chicago World's Fair in 1892.

The company's best-known brand of nonmetallic sheathed cable Romex was invented at the company's Rome New York facility in 1922. Five years later Phillips Wire and Standard Underground Cable joined to form General Cable Corporation. In 1935 the company's cables were used for power lines connecting the Hoover Dam to Los Angeles.

In the early 1980s the company was purchased by Penn Central Corporation (now known as American Premier Underwriters part of American Financial Group). Later that decade Penn Central added the Carol brand when it purchased the Carol Cable Company (1989) and bought other wiring companies. The construction industry declined in the early 1990s leaving wire inventories overstocked. In 1992 Penn Central spun off General Cable to shareholders but the Lindner family (which owned Penn Central) continued to control most of the stock. The company also made news in 1992 when it moved its corporate headquarters from Cincinnati to northern Kentucky representing a win in the battle for companies being waged between the bordering states. That year General Cable also sold its equipment-making subsidiary Marathon LeTourneau because it was not directly tied to the wire and cable business.

In 1994 Wassall a British holding company bought General Cable which had lost more than $130 million in the previous two years. (Wassall sold its interest in 1997.) Soon afterward the company hired a new CEO Stephen Rabinowitz who had been president of General Electric's electrical distribution and control unit and president of the braking-systems business of AlliedSignal (now Honeywell International). He began integrating the company's many units which previously had been run separately. He also consolidated the company's distribution sites and closed five manufacturing plants.

General Cable went public in 1997. That year it formed a joint venture with glass company Spectran Corporation (since acquired by Lucent) to create fiber-optic cable under the name General Photonics. In 1999 General Cable bought the energy cable businesses of BICC Plc for $440 million. The deal made General Cable one of the largest makers of wire and cable in the world. (The company briefly operated under the BICC General name.)

When its energy cable businesses in Europe Africa and Asia failed to perform to expectations General Cable agreed to sell some of those businesses (in the UK Italy Africa and Asia) to Italy-based Pirelli for $216 million in 2000. Fearing Pirelli's dominant position the European Commission opened an in-depth investigation of the takeover but the deal was approved and completed later that year.

In 2001 General Cable sold its Pyrotenax unit to Raychem HTS Canada (a division of Tyco International) for $60 million. The company also freed up $175 million in that same year by selling its building wire interests and exiting the cordset (indoor and outdoor extension cords) business. In early 2002 General Cable acquired the New Zealand-based data cable manufacturer Brand-Rex from Novar plc. Later that same year General Cable sold its building wire operations to Southwire Company.

The company acquired certain specialty electronics and datacom assets from Draka Comteq in 2005. It also purchased Cuernavaca Mexico-based Beru S.A. de C.V. which is an automotive aftermarket assembly and distribution enterprise.

In Europe it bought Silec in late 2005 which had been the wire and cable business of SAFRAN. The following year the company acquired French power cable maker E.C.N. Cable Group.

The company expanded into China in 2007 with the acquisition of Jiangyin Huaming Specialty Cable which makes automotive and industrial cables. Later that year it purchased German submarine cable system maker Norddeutsche Seekabelwerke (NSW) from Corning.

As part of its global expansion into energy and electrical infrastructure markets the company acquired Phelps Dodge International Corporation the cable and wire operations of Freeport-McMoRan Copper & Gold for about $740 million in October 2007. The acquisition gave General Cable a significant foothold in emerging markets including China India and parts of Africa.

The company continued to expand its geographic presence in 2008 when it partnered with the Algerian government to acquire a majority stake in Enica Biskra a cable manufacturer previously run by the state. Adding to its interest for growing business in Southeast Asia General Cable upped its stake in Phelps Dodge Philippines from 40% to 60% the same year.

In 2009 General Cable acquired cable products and systems provider Gepco International and the specialty electronic cable business of Isotec. The acquisitions expanded the company's reach in the US market as well as its global sales structure.

EXECUTIVES

EVP General Counsel and Secretary, Robert J. Siverd, age 63, $394,512 total compensation
President CEO and Director, Gregory B. Kenny, age 59, $856,731 total compensation
EVP and Managing Director Grupo General Sistemas SA, Domingo Goenaga, age 70, $389,638 total compensation
Chairman, John E. Welsh III, age 61
EVP Global Sales and Business Development, Roderick (Roddy) Macdonald, age 63, $300,000 total compensation
EVP; President and CEO General Cable North America, Gregory J. (Greg) Lampert, age 44, $327,115 total compensation
EVP CFO and Treasurer, Brian J. Robinson, age 43, $327,115 total compensation
EVP; President and CEO General Cable Rest of World and Phelps Dodge International Corporation, Mathias F. Sandoval, age 51, $363,462 total compensation
EVP; CEO and President Europe and Mediterranean Region, Emmanuel Sabonnadiere
Manager Investor Relations, Leonard R. (Len) Texter
VP Sales and Project Leadership, Thorsten Schwarz
VP Inside Sales, Victoria Steele
VP Technology, Amjad Abu-Ali
VP Administration, Zareen Khan
VP Finance, Vera Gee
VP Mergers and Acquisitions, Xavier Salas
VP Sales Management, Sophie Trinel
VP Information Technology, Rohit Nadella
VP Human Resources, Daranee Sengmuang
VP Finance and Operations Management, Angela Pugliese
VP Business Development, Manuel Guerrero
VP Engineering, Ndaba Ndabeni
Director, Craig P. Omtvedt, age 62
President CEO and Director, Gregory B. Kenny, age 59
Director, Robert L. Smialek, age 68
Director, Charles G. (Chip) McClure Jr., age 58
Director, Gregory E. Lawton, age 61
Director, Patrick M. Prevost, age 57
Auditors: Deloitte&ToucheLLP

LOCATIONS

HQ: General Cable Corporation
4 Tesseneer Dr., Highland Heights KY 41076-9753
Phone: 859-572-8000 **Fax:** 859-572-8458
Web: www.generalcable.com

2011 Sales

	$ mil.	% of total
North America	2,120	36
Europe & Mediterranean	1,735	30
Other	2,010	34
Total	**5,866**	**100**

PRODUCTS/OPERATIONS

2011 Sales by Product

	$ mil.	% of total
Electric utility	1,851	32
Electrical infrastructure	1,708	29
Construction	1,395	24
Communications	655	11
Rod mill products	256	4
Total	**5,866**	**100**

COMPETITORS

Belden
Coleman Cable
CommScope
Corning
Encore Wire
Hubbell
Kalas Manufacturing
LEONI
Nexans
Owl Wire & Cable
Quabbin Wire
Southwire
Standard Motor Products
Sumitomo Electric
Superior Essex
Volex

HISTORICAL FINANCIALS

Company Type: Public

Income Statement

FYE: December 31

	REVENUE ($ mil.)	NET INCOME ($ mil.)	NET PROFIT MARGIN	EMPLOYEES
12/11	5,866	85	1.5%	12,000
12/10	4,864	76	1.6%	11,700
12/09	4,385	116	2.7%	11,300
12/08	6,230	217	3.5%	13,000
12/07	4,614	208	4.5%	11,800
Annual Growth	6.2%	(20.1%)	—	0.4%

2011 Year-End Financials

Debt ratio: 24.00%
Return on equity: 6.09%
Cash ($ mil.): 434
Current ratio: 189.59
Long-term debt ($ mil.): 892
No. of shares (mil.): 49
Dividends
Yield: —
Payout: —
Market value ($ mil.): 1,243

	STOCK PRICE ($) FY Close	P/E High/Low		PER SHARE ($) Earnings	Dividends	Book Value
12/11	25.01	30	13	1.57	0.00	28.14
12/10	35.09	27	16	1.31	0.00	28.44
12/09	29.42	20	7	2.06	0.00	24.42
12/08	17.69	18	2	4.07	0.00	13.68
12/07	73.28	21	10	3.82	0.00	12.42
Annual Growth	(23.6%)	—	—	(19.9%)	—	22.7%

General Dynamics Corp.

Generally dynamic General Dynamics is a prime military contractor to the Pentagon (the US government accounts for about 70% of sales). The company's military operations include information systems & technology (information technology and collection as well as command control systems); marine systems (warships commercial tankers and nuclear submarines); and combat systems (battle tanks wheeled combat/tactical vehicles munitions and rockets and gun systems). Its aerospace unit which is composed of Gulfstream Aerospace and Jet Aviation designs makes and refurbishes business jets primarily for civilian customers.

HISTORY

In 1899 John Holland founded Electric Boat Company a New Jersey ship and submarine builder. The company built ships PT boats and submarines during WWII but when faced with waning postwar orders CEO John Jay Hopkins diversified with the 1947 purchase of aircraft builder Canadair. Hopkins formed General Dynamics in 1952 merging Electric Boat and Canadair and buying Consolidated Vultee Aircraft (Convair) a major producer of military and civilian aircraft in 1954.

Electric Boat launched the first nuclear submarine the "Nautilus" in the mid-1950s. In 1955 at the urging of Howard Hughes Convair began designing its first commercial jetliners. Weakened by the planes' production costs General Dynamics merged with building-materials supplier Material Service Corporation (1959). Nuclear subs became a mainstay for the company and it abandoned jetliners in 1961 after losses on the planes reached the staggering sum of $425 million.

During the 1960s General Dynamics developed the controversial F-111 fighter. Despite numerous problems the aircraft proved financially and militarily successful (F-111s participated in the 1986 US bombing raid on Libya).

In the following years the company won contracts for the US Navy's 688-class attack submarine (1971) liquefied natural gas tankers for Burmah Oil Company (1972) the Trident ballistic missile submarine (1974) and the F-16 lightweight fighter aircraft (1975). The company sold Canadair in 1976 and bought Chrysler Defense which had a contract to build the US Army's M1 tank in 1982.

The company bought Cessna Aircraft in 1986. The next year it won a contract to design and build the upper stage of the Titan IV space-launch rocket. Facing defense cuts General Dynamics sold off pieces of the company: In 1992 it sold Cessna Aircraft to Textron and sold its missile operations to Hughes Aircraft; its electronics business was sold to The Carlyle Group in 1993. The company sold its space systems business to Martin Marietta (now part of Lockheed Martin) in 1994.

The next year General Dynamics began a buying spree with the purchase of shipbuilder Bath Iron Works. In 1996 it added Teledyne's combat vehicle unit followed in 1997 by Lockheed Martin's Defense Systems and Armament Systems units and defense electronics units from Ceridian and Lucent. Also that year Nicholas Chabraja director of Ceridian and former general counsel for General Dynamics became CEO. In 1998 General Dynamics acquired National Steel and Shipbuilding to gain a major naval shipyard on the West Coast.

The company's $2 billion bid to buy rival submarine and warship maker Newport News Shipbuilding in 1999 was rejected by the Pentagon which cited monopoly concerns. To strengthen its information systems business General Dynamics bought GTE's military communications electronic systems and worldwide telecom services divisions that year. General Dynamics also bought business jet maker Gulfstream Aerospace which accounted for almost all of the company's commercial aircraft sales.

General Dynamics acquired Saco Defense Corp. a maker of small- and medium-caliber machine guns and cannon barrels in 2000 from New Colt Holding. Saco Defense became of General Dynamics Armament Systems.

In 2001 General Dynamics completed the $520 million acquisition of munitions maker Primex Technologies –now General Dynamics Ordnance and Tactical Systems. The company also paid $330 million (plus contingency payments) to acquire Galaxy Aerospace thus adding midsize aircraft to its Gulfstream lineup. Additionally General Dynamics acquired Empresa Nacional Santa Barbara de Industrias Militares of Spain and Motorola's Integrated Information Systems Group (communications and IT products) for $825 million plus the assumption of some liabilities. In late 2001 General Dynamics' bid for Newport News lost out when the Defense Department approved Northrop Grumman's rival bid and the US Department of Justice sued to stop General Dynamics' acquisition attempt on antitrust grounds. Shortly afterwards General Dynamics withdrew its bid.

General Dynamics sold its space propulsion and fire suppression operations to Aerojet-General in 2002. The next year General Dynamics acquired General Motors' armored vehicle operations (for about $1.1 billion) and Austria's Steyr Spezialfahrzeug maker of the Pandur line of wheeled armored vehicles. General Dynamics also acquired government security and intelligence specialist Veridian for about $1.5 billion in 2003.

In 2004 General Dynamics made a bid to acquire Alvis maker of the Challenger (tank) and Warrior (armored vehicle) but BAE SYSTEMS made a better offer at the last minute. Undaunted General Dynamics soon acquired TriPoint Global Communications a satellite and wireless communications company. Later in 2004 General Dynamics bought Spectrum Astro a provider of satellite and ground base integration.

General Dynamics sold its aeronautics services business which provided aeronautic testing engineering and support services in 2005 to Wyle Laboratories. Later that year General Dynamics boosted its rugged computer operations by acquiring Itronix Corporation.

The following year General Dynamics acquired the large-caliber artillery and mortar projectile operations of Chamberlain Manufacturing for an undisclosed sum. Chamberlain was a subsidiary of The Duchossois Group (formerly known as Duchossois Industries). In 2006 General Dynamics also acquired IT specialist Anteon International for $2.1 billion. Anteon specialized in IT systems for defense homeland security intelligence units and other government agencies. Anteon was combined with General Dynamics Network Systems to create a new division General Dynamics Information Technology. Also in 2006 General Dynamics sold Material Service Corporation its aggregates subsidiary to Hanson PLC for $300 million.

Early in 2007 General Dynamics acquired SNC Technologies a Canadian ammunition maker from SNC-Lavalin Group for about $275 million. The following year the Combat Systems segment purchased AxleTech International a Carlyle Group-owned manufacturer of axles and other suspension components used in military and off-road heavy vehicles.

Switzerland-based Jet Aviation Management was acquired for more than $2 billion in late 2008. Jet Aviation provides aviation services such as repairs overhauls and fixed base operations.

EXECUTIVES

VP and Treasurer, David H. Fogg, age 56
EVP Combat Systems, David K. Heebner, age 67

SVP Planning and Development, Robert W. Helm, age 60
VP; President Armament and Technical Products, Michael J. Mulligan, age 47
VP Government Relations and Communications, Kendell M. Pease, age 64
SVP Human Resources and Administration, Walter M. Oliver, age 66, $350,000 total compensation
VP; SVP Administration and General Counsel Gulfstream Aerospace, Ira P. Berman
Executive Vice President - Marine Systems group, John P. Casey, age 57
VP; President NASSCO, Frederick J. (Fred) Harris, age 65
VP; President Gulfstream Aerospace Corporation, Larry R. Flynn, age 60
VP; SVP Programs Engineering and Test Gulfstream Aerospace, Preston A. (Pres) Henne, age 62
VP International, William O. Schmieder, age 62
VP; President Ordnance and Tactical Systems, Michael S. Wilson, age 62
Chairman and CEO, Phebe N. Novakovic, age 54
Chairman and CEO, Jay L. Johnson, age 65, $1,126,250 total compensation
VP Communications General Dynamics Land Systems, Peter M. Keating
EVP Information Systems and Technology, Gerard J. (Jerry) DeMuro, age 56, $643,750 total compensation
VP; President General Dynamics C4 Systems, Christopher (Chris) Marzilli, age 52
VP; President Bath Iron Works, Jeffrey S. Geiger, age 50
VP Information Technology Strategy and CIO General Dynamics Information Technology, Spain (Woody) Hall Jr.
Director Public Affairs General Dynamics C4 Systems, Fran Jacques
VP; President Advanced Information Systems, Lewis F. Von Thaer, age 51
President Product Support Gulfstream Aerospace, Mark Burns
EVP Aerospace, Joseph T. (Joe) Lombardo, age 64
VP Marketing and Communications General Dynamics Information Technology, Mark Meudt
SVP and CFO, L. Hugh Redd, age 54, $721,250 total compensation
VP; President European Land Systems, John C. Ulrich
Director Communications Electric Boat, Robert A. Hamilton
VP; President General Dynamics Land Systems, Mark C. Roualet, age 54
Director Communications Armament and Technical Products, Karl Johnson
President American Overseas Marine, Capt. Thomas W. Merrell
VP; President General Dynamics Information Technology, S. Daniel (Dan) Johnson, age 64
SVP Group Marketing and Communications Jet Aviation, Heinz R. Aebi
VP; President Jet Aviation, Daniel G. Clare, age 53
VP Strategic Planning, M. Thomas (Tom) Davis
VP Financial Planning and Analysis, Randy M. Collins, age 55
VP Human Resources and Shared Services, Henry C. Eickelberg, age 54
Manager Communications Bath Iron Works, Jim DeMartini
General Manager General Dynamics Canada, David Ibbetson
VP Tax, Kenneth R. Hayduk, age 51
Vice President Communications, Rob Doolittle
President and Managing Director General Dynamics United Kingdom, A.D. (Sandy) Wilson
Director Marketing Services Ordnance and Tactical Systems, Laurie VanBrocklin
SVP General Counsel and Secretary, Gregory S. (Greg) Gallopoulos, age 52
VP and Controller, Jason W. Aiken, age 39
VP and Deputy General Counsel, Ernest J. Babcock
Director Communications General Dynamics Canada, Amy MacLeod
Director Communications European Land Systems, Rafael Moreno
Director Marketing and Public Relations Advanced Information Systems, Jennifer Montesano
Senior Manager International Corporate Affairs General Dynamics United Kingdom, Andrew Boyle
Director Communications NASSCO, James Gill
VPand Controller, Kimberly A. Kuryea
President of Electric Boat, Kevin Poitras
Vice President; President of General Dynamics Advanced Information Systems Inc., Lewis Thaer
Director, Nicholas D. (Nick) Chabraja, age 69
Director, William A. Osborn, age 64
Director, James S. Crown, age 58
Director, William P. Fricks, age 67
Director, Paul G. Kaminski, age 69
Director, Gen. Lester L. Lyles, age 65
Director, Sir Robert Walmsley, age 71
Director, Mary T. Barra, age 51
Independent Director, James Jones
Auditors: KPMGLLP

LOCATIONS

HQ: General Dynamics Corporation
2941 Fairview Park Dr. Ste. 100, Falls Church VA 22042-4513
Phone: 703-876-3000 **Fax:** 703-876-3125
Web: www.gendyn.com

2011 Sales

	$ mil.	% of total
North America		
US	26,401	81
Canada	806	2
Other North America	39	-
Europe		
UK	857	3
Switzerland	582	2
Spain	405	1
Other Europe	1,113	3
Asia/Pacific		
China	929	3
Other Asia/Pacific	555	2
Africa/Middle East	672	2
South America	318	1
Total	**32,677**	**100**

PRODUCTS/OPERATIONS

2011 Sales by Segment

	$ mil.	% of total
Information systems & technology	11,221	34
Combat systems	8,827	27
Marine systems	6,631	20
Aerospace	5,998	19
Corporate - -		
Total	**32,677**	**100**

2011 Sales by Customer

	% of total
US	69
US	12
International	10
International	9
Total	**100**

2011 Sales by Product

	$ mil.	% of total
Products	21,440	66
Services	11,237	34
Total	**32,677**	**100**

Selected Operations

Aerospace
- Gulfstream Aerospace
  - G150 (Midsize range of 3000 nautical miles 4 passengers)
  - G280 (Super midsize range 3600 nautical miles 4 passengers)
  - G350 (Large-cabin range of 3800 nautical miles 8 passengers)
  - G450 (Large-cabin range of 4350 nautical miles 8 passengers)
  - G500 (Large-cabin range of 5800 nautical miles 8 passengers)
  - G550 (Large-cabin range of 6750 nautical miles 8 passengers)
  - G650 (Ultra-large-cabin range of 7000 nautical miles 8 passengers)

Combat systems
- Armament & technical products
  - Advanced materials (composites)
  - Armament systems
  - AxleTech
- European land systems
  - Ammunition
  - Artillery
  - Bridge systems
  - Tracked vehicles
  - Wheeled vehicles
- Land systems
  - Abrams tank
  - MRAP combat vehicle
  - Stryker combat vehicle
- Ordnance and tactical systems
  - Artillery projectiles
  - Bomb bodies
  - Combat systems
  - Munitions
  - Mortar weapons

Information systems and technology
- Advanced information systems
- C4 Systems
- Information technology

Marine systems
- Bath Iron Works Corp.
  - Arleigh Burke (DDG 51) destroyer
  - Zumwalt (DDG 1000) destroy
- Electric Boat
  - Virginia submarine
  - Seawolf submarine
- NASSCO (ship construction and repair)

COMPETITORS

Airbus
Alliant Techsystems
BAE SYSTEMS
Boeing
Bombardier
Cisco Systems
Dassault Aviation
Day & Zimmermann
DRS Technologies
FLIR Systems
Goodrich Corp.
Harris Corp.
Herley Industries
HP Enterprise Services
ITT Corp.
L-3 Communications
Lockheed Martin
Motorola Solutions
Navistar International
Nokia
Northrop Grumman
Peugeot
Raytheon
Renco
Rockwell Collins
SAIC
Textron
United Technologies

HISTORICAL FINANCIALS

Company Type: Public

Income Statement FYE: December 31

	REVENUE ($ mil.)	NET INCOME ($ mil.)	NET PROFIT MARGIN	EMPLOYEES
12/11	32,677	2,526	7.7%	95,100
12/10	32,466	2,624	8.1%	90,000
12/09	31,981	2,394	7.5%	91,700
12/08	29,300	2,459	8.4%	92,300
12/07	27,240	2,072	7.6%	83,500
Annual Growth	4.7%	5.1%	—	3.3%

2011 Year-End Financials

Debt ratio: 11.27%
Return on equity: 19.09%
Cash ($ mil.): 2,649
Current ratio: 137.89
Long-term debt ($ mil.): 3,907

No. of shares (mil.): 356
Dividends
Yield: —
Payout: 26.64%
Market value ($ mil.): 23,671

	STOCK PRICE ($) FY Close	P/E High/Low		PER SHARE ($) Earnings	Dividends	Book Value
12/11	66.41	11	8	6.87	0.00	37.12
12/10	70.96	11	8	6.81	1.64	35.79
12/09	68.17	11	6	6.17	1.49	32.21
12/08	57.59	15	8	6.17	1.34	26.00
12/07	88.99	18	14	5.08	1.10	29.13
Annual Growth	(7.1%)	—	—	7.8%	—	6.2%

General Electric Co

From turbines to TV from household appliances to power plants General Electric (GE) is plugged in to businesses that have shaped the modern world. The company produces –take a deep breath –aircraft engines locomotives and other transportation equipment kitchen and laundry appliances lighting electric distribution and control equipment generators and turbines and medical imaging equipment. GE is also one of the US's pre-eminent financial services providers: GE Capital comprising commercial finance commercial aircraft leasing real estate and energy financial services is its largest segment. GE's other segments are Energy Aviation Healthcare Home & Business Solutions and Transportation.

Although financial services is GE's biggest segment the company's raison d'etre has traditionally been its industrial products. In response to changes in the economic markets the company has shuffled its organizational structure several times as of late. In 2011 it reorganized its former Technology Infrastructure segment into three segments: Healthcare Aviation and Transportation. It also dropped its NBC Universal segment after selling its controlling stake in NBC. (GE now owns 49% of the newly formed venture NBCUniversal.) Previously GE planned to spin off its appliance unit as a result of slow growth but those plans were put on hold due to the poor economy. The company recommitted to its appliances and lighting business by creating the Home & Business Solutions segment in 2010.

The company's financial services businesses have also taken a hit in the rocky economy. GE Capital offers commercial loans and leases consumer loans and credit cards fleet management and other services. To combat losses in the financial services unit the company is exiting underperforming or noncore businesses; it has sold numerous units (such as its credit card businesses in the UK and Ireland its consumer business in Canada its GE Money Japan unit and its trailer fleet services business in Mexico) and it continues to seek opportunities for other divestitures. To manage its debt and lending GE has also tightened its underwriting standards and increased its collections manpower. In an effort to diversify its capital business the company announced plans to buy MetLife's banking unit in 2011.

For the most part GE has tried to reduce its reliance on its riskier financial businesses and make further investments in its infrastructure and health care sectors. The company has embarked on a series of energy acquisitions helped by capital received in the NBC sale. In 2011 it spent $3.2 billion to acquire France-based Converteam a maker of automation and electrification equipment. To complement that acquisition GE announced it will build a solar panel factory in the US. The plant (the largest in the country) will make enough panels to power 80000 homes every year. It is part of GE's plan to invest more than $600 million in its solar energy segment. It's also making plans in 2013 to pilot a renewable energy power plant in Indonesia through a partnership with Perusahaan Listrik Negara. Concentrating their efforts on Sumba and other islands the pair will be using wood chips as a fuel source to provide electricity to millions of rural Indonesians.

But that was just one of several big deals the company made in 2011. GE that year bought industrial equipment manufacturer Dresser for about $3 billion; it was later folded into GE's Energy Services and Power & Water business units. GE also bought Lineage Power which makes power converters for computer data centers for some $520 million as well as waste-heat recovery systems maker Calnetix Power Solutions. The company acquired UK-based pipeline products manufacturer Wellstream for approximately $1.3 billion and then bought frame technology from Wind Tower Systems which it will use to build taller wind turbine towers that can accommodate longer blades. GE also acquired Commtest a New Zealand-based company that designs and makes systems that monitor machinery function.

The company hopes to double its oil and gas revenues by 2015 and plans to continue making investments to grow the business. In line with that strategy GE bought the Well Support operations of British energy services company John Wood Group for $2.8 billion in 2011. GE sold its security business to United Technologies Corporation (UTC) in 2010 in order to sharpen its focus on its industrial and manufacturing businesses.

On the health care front GE is partnering with Intel to develop products that will lower costs for at-home and assisted-living care. The venture will focus on chronic-disease management and independent living technologies. GE has been actively making acquisitions in this sector too. It purchased diagnostics firm Clarient for some $580 million in late 2010 and bought cellular imaging company Applied Precision the following year.

Another growth area for GE is mining. In 2012 the company acquired underground mining equipment manufacturers Industrea Limited and Fairchild International. Both companies are positioned for growth in China Australia and the US. It also created a new business unit that year Australia-based GE Mining.

And in aviation the company made a big move in late 2012 with the $4.3 billion purchase of the aviation propulsion components and systems business of Italy's Avio. The move expands GE's activities in the appealing jet propulsion segment and strengthens its global supply chain.

Overall GE is recovering from the hit it took in 2009 largely related to financial services. Its income from continuing operations grew in 2010 and 2011 with all segments showing growth other than Home & Business Solutions and its appliances business. Energy & Infrastructure led the growth primarily due to numerous acquisitions the company has made. Transportation a relatively small part of the company's business saw profitability more than double in 2011 as a result of increased equipment sales and services.

CEO Jeff Immelt is obviously not shy about making sweeping changes whether by divesting underperforming segments or investing in probable growth industries. He has emerged from the considerable shadow of his predecessor Jack Welch by diverging somewhat from Welch's slavish obsession with the bottom line and encouraging managers to innovate and take more risks. As a result GE has been growing in such areas as biotech renewable energy nanotechnology and digital technology. He built the company's traditional businesses with acquisitions including Smiths Aerospace and Vetco Gray and exited the insurance industry.

Immelt has taken a page from his former boss' playbook by pursuing growth outside the US particularly in emerging markets like India China Eastern Europe Africa and the Middle East. The company hopes to lead the push to expand US exports; GE is the among the world's largest suppliers of medical-imaging equipment jets locomotives and power generation equipment. It sells its wares in more than 100 countries and more than half of GE's revenues originate outside the US.

HISTORY

General Electric (GE) was established in 1892 in New York the result of a merger between Thomson-Houston and Edison General Electric. Charles Coffin was GE's first president and Thomas Edison who left the company in 1894 was one of the directors.

GE's financial strength (backed by the Morgan banking house) and its research focus contributed to its initial success. Early products included such Edison legacies as light bulbs elevators motors toasters and other appliances under the GE and Hotpoint labels. In the 1920s GE joined AT&T and Westinghouse in a radio broadcasting venture Radio Corporation of America (RCA) but GE sold off its RCA holdings in 1930 because of an antitrust ruling.

By 1980 GE had reached $25 billion in revenues from plastics consumer electronics nuclear reactors and jet engines. But it had become rigid and bureaucratic. Jack Welch became president in 1981 and shook up the company. He decentralized operations and adopted a strategy of pursuing only high-achieving ventures and dumping those that didn't perform. GE shed air-conditioning (1982) housewares (1984) and semiconductors (1988) and with the proceeds acquired Employers Reinsurance (1984); RCA including NBC (1986 but sold RCA in 1987); CGR medical equipment (1987); and investment banker Kidder Peabody (1990).

In the early 1990s GE grew its lighting business. It bought mutual fund wholesaler GNA in 1993 and GE Investment Management (now GE Financial Network) began selling mutual funds to the public.

GE sold scandal-plagued Kidder Peabody to Paine Webber in 1994. General Electric Capital Services (GECS) expanded its lines buying Amex Life Insurance (Aon's Union Fidelity unit) and Life Insurance Co. of Virginia in 1995 and First Colony the next year. The company sold its struggling GEnie online service in 1996 and formed an NBC and Microsoft venture the MSNBC cable news channel. In 1997 GE Engine Services bought aircraft engine maintenance firms Greenwich Air Services and UNC.

GE acquired Lockheed Martin's medical imaging unit in 1997 and added to the medical systems business with the 1998 purchase of Marquette Medical Systems. In 1998 GECS became the first foreign company to enter Japan's life insurance market when it bought assets from Toho Mutual Life Insurance and set up GE Edison Life.

In 1999 GECS bought the 53% of Montgomery Ward it didn't already own along with the retailer's direct-marketing arm as Montgomery Ward emerged from bankruptcy. (Ward declared bankruptcy again in 2000.) In 2000 it reorganized GE Information Systems to form an e-commerce unit Global eXchange Services (GXS). (GE sold 90% of GXS to buyout firm Francisco Partners in 2002.)

Later in 2000 the company announced its biggest acquisition of the Welch era. Moving in at the last minute GE trumped a rival bid from United Technologies and agreed to pay $45 billion in stock for manufacturing giant Honeywell International and to assume $3.4 billion in Honeywell debt.

Welch by then viewed as one of the best corporate leaders in the US had agreed to postpone his retirement from April 2001 until the end of that year in order to oversee the completion of the Honeywell acquisition. But European regulators concerned about the potential strength of the combined GE-Honeywell aircraft-related businesses blocked the Honeywell deal that summer. Welch then stepped down and Jeff Immelt formerly president and CEO of GE Medical Systems succeeded him in September 2001.

Immelt initially set about reshaping GE by spinning off its life and mortgage insurance businesses into a new entity Genworth Financial which went public in 2004 (completely divested in 2006). GE acquired UK-based Amersham a medical diagnostics and life sciences company since renamed GE Healthcare Medical Diagnostics.

In 2006 GE sold off most of its remaining insurance businesses including GE Insurance Solutions and Employers Reinsurance in a sale to Swiss Re. The company kept its US life reinsurance business.

Citing rising commodities costs GE sold its advanced materials unit which produced silicone quartz and ceramics products to Apollo Management and sold its GE Plastics unit (now SABIC Innovative Plastics) to SABIC for more than $11 billion in 2007. Also that year GE shut down the operations of wholesale subprime lender WMC Mortgage.

At the same time GE built some of its traditional businesses through acquisitions. In early 2007 the company's aviation division acquired aircraft systems manufacturer Smiths Aerospace from Smiths Group. GE Energy bought oil and gas production equipment supplier Vetco Gray and the US retail natural gas distribution network of Knight (then named Kinder Morgan).

In 2011 GE sold a controlling stake in NBCUniversal to Comcast. GE retained a 49% stake in the media venture.

EXECUTIVES

SVP and CFO, Keith S. Sherin, age 53, $1,500,000 total compensation
President and COO Universal Studios NBC Universal, Ron Meyer
President and CEO GE Africa, James W. (Jay) Ireland III, age 57
Chairman NBC Universal Sports and Olympics NBC Universal, Dick Ebersol
President and CEO GE Capital Real Estate, Mark W. Begor, age 53
Vice Chairman; Chairman and CEO GE Capital, Michael A. (Mike) Neal, age 58, $1,750,000 total compensation
SVP; CFO GE Technology Infrastructure, John J. Falconi
SVP; CFO GE Capital, Jeffrey S. (Jeff) Bornstein
President and CEO GE Europe & North Asia; CEO GE Germany, Ferdinando F. (Nani) Beccalli-Falco
SVP and Director GE Global Research, Mark M. Little, age 58
SVP and Chief Marketing Officer, Elizabeth J. (Beth) Comstock, age 51
SVP Corporate Business Development, Pamela Daley, age 59
SVP General Counsel and Secretary, Brackett B. Denniston III, age 64, $1,200,000 total compensation
VP and Senior Counsel Tax Policy and Planning, John M. Samuels
VP and Senior Competition Counsel, Ronald A. Stern
SVP; President and CEO GE Japan Corporation, Yoshiaki Fujimori, age 61
SVP; President and CEO GE Oil and Gas, Claudi Santiago Ponsa
Managing Director Communications and Public Affairs GE Capital, Russell Wilkerson
President and CEO GE Healthcare, John M. Dineen, age 49
Vice Chairman; President and CEO Global Growth & Operations, John G. Rice, age 55, $1,750,000 total compensation
VP Investment Management GE Capital, Joseph E. (Joe) Parsons
Chairman Commercial Aviation Services GE Capital, Henry A. Hubschman, age 64
Chairman and CEO, Jeffrey R. (Jeff) Immelt, age 56, $3,300,000 total compensation
Vice Chairman; President and CEO GE Energy, John Krenicki Jr., age 49, $1,200,000 total compensation
SVP; COO GE Capital, William H. (Bill) Cary, age 52
VP Global Marketing Communications GE Capital Real Estate, John L. Oliver, age 53
President and CEO GE Capital Americas, Daniel S. (Dan) Henson
President and CEO GE India, John L. Flannery Jr., age 50
SVP; President and CEO GE Oil & Gas, Daniel C. (Dan) Heintzelman, age 55
VP Strategic Development GE Capital, Aris Kekedjian, age 45
VP Commercial Distribution Finance GE Capital, Jeffrey (Jeff) Malehorn
President and CEO GE Capital Europe Middle East and Africa, Richard A. (Rich) Laxer
VP and Chief Diversity Officer, Deborah (Deb) Elam, age 48
VP Corporate Citizenship, Robert L. (Bob) Corcoran
VP Executive Development and Chief Learning Officer, Susan P. Peters
VP Ecomagination, Mark L. Vachon, age 53
President and CEO GE Lighting, Maryrose T. Sylvester
President and COO Universal Television Group, Jeff Gaspin
SVP; President and CEO GE Aviation, David L. Joyce, age 55
SVP and Treasurer GE and GE Capital, Kathryn A. (Kathy) Cassidy, age 57
SVP and CIO; President and CEO Home and Business Solutions, Charlene T. Begley, age 45
VP and Chief Risk Management GE Capital, James A. (Jim) Colica
Director Public Relations GE Appliances and Lighting, Kim Freeman
Manager Communications GE Home and Business Solutions, Michelle May
President and CEO GE Security, Dean S. Seavers, age 51
President and CEO China, Mark Norbom, age 54
VP and General Counsel Europe and European Regulatory Affairs, Mark Elborne
CFO Global Growth & Operations, Shane Fitzsimons, age 42
VP Mid-Market Finance GE Capital, Thomas M. (Tom) Quindlen
President Corporate Financial Services Bank Loans GE Commercial Finance, Ronald F. (Ron) Carapezzi
President and CEO GE Latin America, Edmundo M. Vallejo
EVP and CFO NBC Universal, Lynn Calpeter
SVP; President and CEO GE Power and Water, Steve Bolze, age 49
SVP Human Resources, John F. Lynch, age 60
VP Global Communications GE Capital Global Banking, Robert J. (Bob) Rendine
President and CEO Middle East and Africa, Nabil A. Habayeb, age 51
President and CEO GE Energy Financial Services GE Capital, J. Alexander (Alex) Urquhart
VP Corporate Environmental Programs, Ann Klee, age 51
VP Government Relations, Nancy P. Dorn
President and CEO Commercial Aviation Services GE Capital, Norman C. T. Liu, age 54
Manager Communications GE Transportation, Stephan Koller
VP Product Management GE Energy Power and Water, Darryl L. Wilson
President and CEO Sensing and Inspection Technology Infrastructure, Caroline A. Reda, age 49
EVP Corporate Communications NBC Universal, Allison Gollust
Medical Director Patient Safety Organization (PSO), Peter B. Angood
VP Controller and Chief Accounting Officer, Jamie S. Miller, age 43
VP International GE Capital, Mark Hutchinson, age 52
President and CEO GE Asset Management, Dmitri L. Stockton, age 47
President and CEO U.S. Consumer Retail Finance, Margaret M. Keane
VP Financial Planning & Analysis, Brian Worrell, age 40
President and CEO GE Energy Management, Daniel C. (Dan) Janki, age 44
VP Ecomagination, Steven (Steve) Fludder, age 52
VP Corporate Investor Communications, Trevor A. Schauenberg, age 43
President and CEO GE Appliances, Charles P. (Chip) Blankenship Jr., age 46
VP Healthymagination, Michael J. Barber, age 51
VP Litigation and Legal Policy, Alexander (Alex) Dimitrief
VP Communications and Public Affairs and Labor Issues, Gary Sheffer
VP and Chief Corporate Securities and Finance Counsel, Michael McAlevey, age 48
Deputy Treasurer, Dennis Sweeney
President and CEO GE Corporate Financial Services Asia; President and CEO GE Commercial Finance China, Nancy Ku, age 55
President and CEO GE Intelligent Platforms, Jody Markopoulos, age 40
SVP Global Marketing GE Capital, Vincenzo Picone
VP; CEO Eastern and Africa Growth Markets, Richard di Benedetto
General Manager Engineering and Product Development GE Transportation, Evren Eryurek
President GE Transportation China, Timothy J. (Tim) Schweikert, age 51
General Manager Global Signaling GE Transportation, Pierre Comte

VP and Senior Counsel International Government Relations and Policy, Karan Bhatia, age 44
VP and Controller Technical Center of Excellence, Walter F. Ielusic, age 50
President and CEO GE India, Tejpreet S. Chopra
President and CEO GE Capital Asia Pacific; CEO GE Australia and New Zealand, Steve Sargent, age 52
President and CEO GE Transportation, Lorenzo Simonelli, age 39
Director Communications GE Corporate India, Purnima SahniMohanty
VP and CFO GE Capital, Gregory Cameron, age 43
President and CEO Digital Energy Enterprise Solutions, Larry A. Sollecito, age 59
Senior Executive Regional Sales GE Energy Asia, Kenji Uenishi
VP Human Resources GE International, Heather X. Wang, age 49
VP Government Strategy and Sales GE International; National Executive GE France, Clara Gaymard, age 52
VP Communications GE Capital Consumer Finance, Stephen G. White
VP and Chief Engineer GE Energy Infrastructure, Ralph Kirkpatrick, age 59
SVP Subsea Product Platform GE Oil & Gas, Manuel Terranova
VP Transmission and Distribution GE Energy, Bob Gilligan
Shareowner Information and Corporate Investor Communications, Elizabeth Y. Seibert
Director Corporate Investor Communications, JoAnna H. Morris
Deputy Treasurer Fixed Income Investor Relations and Banking, Michael Bellora
Managing Director Fixed Income Investor Relations, Lisa Capodici
Director Financial Communications GE Corporate, Anne Eisele
Director Communications GE Corporate, Erik Hendrickson
Manager Public Relations and Marketing Services, Lisa Lanspery
Director Public Relations and Marketing Services GE Corporate; Marketing Brand and Advertising; and Olympic Games, Deirdre Latour
Director Executive Communications and Public Relations GE Corporate Ecomagination Environment and Government, Peter O'Toole
Global Director Digital Media GE Corporate and GE.com, Jennifer Walsh
Executive Director Communications GE Corporate International, Greg Farrett
Leader Communications Africa, Justus Waimiri
Manager Communications Argentina Chile and Peru, Cecilia Cecilia Albuixech
VP Marketing and Communications Australia and New Zealand, Emma Rugge-Price
VP Communications Canada, Kim Warburton
Manager Communications Singapore Philippines and Cambodia, Jessica Blas
Leader Corporate Communications and Public Relations Western Europe and Russia, Elma Peters
Manager Communications Middle East and Africa, Rania Rostom
Director Public Relations and Communications GE Corporate Latin America Brazil and Ecuador, Alexandre Alfredo
Director Corporate Communications Japan, Chika Miyamori
Director Public Relations GE Corporate China, Geoff Li
Manager Public Relations and Communications Central America Colombia Mexico and Venezuela, Ramon Lopez
Manager Public Relations and Communications Central and Eastern Europe and Turkey, Eszter Szabo
Manager Public Affairs Communication Germany Austria and Switzerland, Hans Schregelmann
Manager Communications Indonesia and Vietnam, Inggita Notosusanto
Manager Public Relations Korea and Southeast Asia, Bill Joh
Manager Communications Malaysia and Thailand, Jiak Woen Khor
Director Communications GE Energy, Jim Healy
Manager Media Relations GE Aviation, Rick Kennedy
Communications Leader GE Capital - Americas, Marissa Moretti
Director Communications GE Capital - Asia, Roger Pua
Communications Leader GE Capital - Europe Middle East and Africa, William Spiers
Director Global Communications GE Capital Aviation Services (GECAS), Daniel J. Whitney
Manager Communications GE Digital Energy, Donna Mirandola
Manager Marketing Communications GE Power and Water, Dan Nelson
Manager Public Relations GE Intelligent Platforms, Elli Holman
SVP Communications GE Energy Financial Services, Andrew Katell
Media Relations GE Oil and Gas, Nigel O'Connor
Manager Communication GE Sensing and Inspection Technologies, Lindsay Lindsay Theile
Manager Communications and Public Relations GE Global Research, Patrick Jarvis
President and CEO Canada, Elyse Allen, age 56
VP and Chief Marketing and Commercial Officer GE Capital Americas, Lee Cooper, age 50
President and CEO GE Lighting Solutions, Jaime A. Irick
Chief Marketing Officer GE Lighting Solutions, Brian Sroub
VP; CEO Latin America GE International, Rogerio Patrus, age 53
Executive Director Global Market Insight and Chief Economist, Marco Annunziata
VP Global Business Development Corporate Business Development Group, Robert Duffy, age 46
VP and Global Technology Director Software Sciences & Analytics GE Global Research, Bill Ruh, age 50
VP Business Development GE Energy, Ronnie S. Hawkins, age 43
VP Oil and Gas GE Energy, Prady Iyyanki, age 42
President and CEO Global Services GE Healthcare, Michael J. Swinford
General Manager American Appliances, Harry van den Boogaard
President and CEO GE Healthcare Systems, Tom Gentile
VP and Chief Risk Officer, Puneet Mahajan
Director, Andrea Jung, age 53
Director, Robert W. (Bob) Lane, age 62
Director, Ralph S. Larsen, age 73
Director, James S. Tisch, age 59
Director, James J. (Jim) Mulva, age 65
Director, Alan G. (A. G.) Lafley, age 64
Director, Roger S. Penske, age 75
Director, Douglas A. (Sandy) Warner III, age 65
Director, Ann M. Fudge, age 60
Director, Sam Nunn, age 73
Director, James I. Cash Jr., age 63
Director, Rochelle B. (Shelly) Lazarus, age 64
Director, W. Geoffrey (Geoff) Beattie, age 52
Director, Robert J. Swieringa, age 69
Director, Susan Hockfield, age 60
Auditors: KPMGLLP

LOCATIONS

HQ: General Electric Company
3135 Easton Tpke., Fairfield CT 06828-0001
Phone: 203-373-2211 **Fax:** 203-373-3131
Web: www.ge.com

2011 Sales

	% of total
Americas	
US	47
Other	9
Europe	20
Pacific	16
Middle East &	7
Other	1
Total	**100**

PRODUCTS/OPERATIONS

2011 Sales

	$ mil.	% of total
Sales of goods	66,875	45
GE Capital Services revenues from services	47,714	32
Sales of services	27,648	19
Other	5,063	4
Total	**147,300**	**100**

2011 Sales by Segment

	$ mil.	% of total
GE Capital	45,730	31
Energy Infrastructure	43,694	30
Aviation	18,859	13
Healthcare	18,083	12
Home & Business Solutions	8,465	6
Transportation	4,885	3
Corporate items & eliminations	7,584	5
Total	**147,300**	**100**

COMPETITORS

Agilent Technologies
ALSTOM
Bank of America
Capital One
Caterpillar
CBS Corp
CIGNA
Citigroup
Cooper Industries
Deutsche Bank
Electrolux
General Re
Hitachi
HSBC
ITT Corp.
Jacuzzi Brands
Johnson Controls
JPMorgan Chase
News Corp.
Panasonic Corp
Philips Electronics
Raytheon
Rockwell Automation
Rolls-Royce
Siemens AG
Sony
Textron
ThyssenKrupp
Toshiba
United Technologies
Whirlpool

HISTORICAL FINANCIALS

Company Type: Public

Income Statement FYE: December 31

	REVENUE ($ mil.)	NET INCOME ($ mil.)	NET PROFIT MARGIN	EMPLOYEES
12/11	147,300	14,151	9.6%	301,000
12/10	150,211	11,644	7.8%	287,000
12/09	156,783	11,025	7.0%	304,900
12/08	182,515	17,410	9.5%	323,000
12/07	172,738	22,208	12.9%	327,000
Annual Growth	(3.9%)	(10.7%)	—	(2.0%)

2011 Year-End Financials

Debt ratio: 53.13%—
Return on equity: 12.15%
Cash ($ mil.): 84,501
Current ratio: 65.20
Long-term debt ($ mil.): 243,459

Dividends
Yield: —
Payout: 49.59%
Market value ($ mil.): —

	STOCK PRICE ($) FY Close	P/E High/Low		PER SHARE ($) Earnings	Dividends	Book Value
12/11	17.91	17	12	1.23	0.00	11.01
12/10	18.29	18	13	1.06	0.46	11.20
12/09	15.13	17	7	1.01	0.61	11.00
12/08	16.20	22	7	1.72	1.24	9.93
12/07	37.07	19	16	2.17	1.15	11.57
Annual Growth	(16.6%)	—	—	(13.2%)	—	(1.2%)

General Mills, Inc.

General Mills gets its Kix trying to grab the biggest-bowl prize as the US's #1 breakfast cereal maker (wrangling for the top spot every year with uber-rival Kellogg). But #1 or not the company has supermarket aisles full of kid-friendly morning-meal products. Its Big G Cereals include the well-known brands Cheerios Chex and Wheaties. But breakfast isn't the last meal on the menu at General Mills. The company makes ice cream (Haagen-Dazs) canned soup (Progresso) frozen dough products (Pillsbury) and Green Giant brand veggies. General Mills which produces yogurt under the Yoplait brand bought a controlling stake in the world's second-largest yogurt maker for $1.2 billion in 2011.

HISTORY

Cadwallader Washburn built his first flour mill in 1866 in Minneapolis which eventually became the Washburn Crosby Company. After winning a gold medal for flour at an 1880 exposition the company changed the name of its best flour to Gold Medal Flour.

In 1921 advertising manager Sam Gale created fictional spokeswoman Betty Crocker so that correspondence to housewives could go out with her signature. The firm introduced Wheaties cereal in 1924. James Bell named president in 1925 consolidated the company with other US mills in 1928 to form General Mills the world's largest miller. The companies operated independently of one another with corporate headquarters coordinating advertising and merchandising.

General Mills began introducing convenience foods such as Bisquick (1931) and Cheerios (1941). During WWII it produced war goods such as ordnance equipment and developed chemical and electronics divisions.

When Edwin Rawlings became CEO in 1961 he closed half of the flour mills and divested such unprofitable lines as electronics. This cost $200 million in annual sales but freed resources for such acquisitions as Kenner Products (toys 1967) and Parker Brothers (board games 1968) which made General Mills the world's largest toy company.

During the next 20 years the company made many acquisitions including Gorton's (frozen seafood 1968) Monet (jewelry 1968) Eddie Bauer (outerwear 1971) and The Talbots (women's clothing 1973). It bought Red Lobster in 1970 and acquired the US rights to Yoplait yogurt in 1977. When the toy and fashion divisions' profits fell in 1984 they were spun off as Kenner Parker Toys and Crystal Brands (1985). Reemphasizing food in 1989 the firm sold many businesses including Eddie Bauer and Talbots.

To expand into Europe General Mills struck two important joint ventures: Cereal Partners Worldwide (with Nestle in 1989) and Snack Ventures Europe (with PepsiCo in 1992).

As part of a cereal price war in 1994 the company cut coupon promotion costs by $175 million and lowered prices on many cereals. But some retailers did not pass on the price cuts to consumers due to shortages that developed after the FDA found an unauthorized pesticide in some cereals. General Mills destroyed 55 million boxes of cereal at a cost of $140 million. Stephen Sanger became CEO in 1995. That year the company sold Gortons to Unilever and spun off its restaurant businesses as Darden Restaurants.

Focused on a food-only future in the late 1990s General Mills picked up several smaller businesses including Ralcorp Holdings' Chex snack and cereal lines and Gardetto's Bakery snack mixes as well as the North American rights to Olibra an appetite suppressant food additive made by Scotia Holdings. Entering the natural foods market in 2000 General Mills launched Sunrise organic cereal and bought organic foods producer Small Planet Foods.

Big changes came in 2001 when General Mills became the #1 cereal maker in the US overtaking Kellogg for the first time since 1906. The company then completed its $10.5 billion purchase of Pillsbury from Diageo in October 2001. A month later General Mills sold competing product lines to International Multifoods. Also that year the company launched a 50-50 joint venture with DuPont to develop soy beverages marketed under the 8th Continent brand name. While busily integrating Pillsbury in 2002 General Mills saw its income fall and watched as Kellogg regained the lead in the cereal market. In 2003 the SEC began an investigation into the company's sales and accounting practices (which it terminated in 2005 taking no action against General Mills).

In 2004 General Mills filed a universal shelf registration with the SEC the result of which is that Diageo had to register the common shares of General Mills that it owns before it could sell those shares in a public offering. Also as a result of the shelf registration two Diageo-designated members of General Mills' board (including Diageo CEO Paul Walsh) resigned as a result of a change in the two companies' stockholders agreement that terminated Diageo's right to designate two General Mills' board members. Diageo sold part of its approximate 20% stake in General Mills. General Mills in turn sold an $835 million stake to an affiliate of Lehman Brothers Holding and used $750 million to buy back the Diageo shares and $85 million to pay down debt.

Also in 2004 the company sold its US Haagen-Dazs ice cream shop franchise business to Dreyer's Grand Ice Cream. In 2005 it sold its stake in Snack Ventures Europe joint venture to PepsiCo for $750 million. That year the company introduced Yoplait Healthy Heart which contains cholesterol-lowering plant sterols.

Diageo sold two-thirds of its 20% stake in General Mills in 2005. Later that year General Mills announced the sale of Lloyd's barbecue business to Hormel Foods. In 2006 Cereal Partners Worldwide (its joint venture with Nestle) acquired the Australian breakfast cereal operations of Uncle Tobys from Burns Philp.

After more than 10 years of being ignored the Jolly Green Giant came out of retirement in 2005 as part of a multi-million dollar marketing campaign by General Mills to up its veggie sales. The next year General Mills declined to renew its licensing agreement with Archer Daniels Midland regarding the sale and marketing of Pillsbury Bakery Flour to the industrial and foodservice sectors. General Mills integrated the brand which consists of mixes and frozen bakery products into its bakery ingredients segment.

In order to develop healthier products in 2006 the company entered a supply agreement for DHA (an omega-3 fatty acid said to play a role in mental and cardiovascular health) with Martek Biosciences maker of DHA (which is already widely used in infant formula).

General Mills pulled its reduced-sugar children's cereal from the market in 2007 due to poor sales. Sweetened with SPLENDA the cereals never took off with consumers perhaps due to resistance to the sugar replacement. (Kellogg and Kraft use sugar in their reduced-sugar cereal offerings.) That year the company acquired UK chilled pastry company Saxby Bros.

Also in 2007 CEO Sanger stepped down. President and COO Ken Powell replaced him. The following year General Mills and DuPont sold their soy-milk joint venture 8th Continent to Stremicks Heritage Foods.

To better focus on its core brands and foodservice offerings the company in mid-2010 sold its Delicity chain of bakeries in Argentina to Tentissimo Group which also operates restaurants under the Tentissimo banner in the country. The deal included the Delicity brand five company-owned bakeries and franchiser rights which apply to the roughly 55 bakery locations operated by franchisees. General Mills also agreed to continue supplying dough products to the chain. It had owned Delicity since acquiring Pillsbury in 2001.

In 2008 the company sold its Pop?Secret operations to Diamond Foods for some $190 million in cash. Pop?Secret is the second-largest-selling branded popcorn in the US after Orville Redenbacher which is made by ConAgra. (ConAgra also makes Act II microwaveable popcorn.) While General Mills said it is concentrating its efforts on increasing the sales of its more lucrative core brands the high price of corn most probably also figured into the decision to jettison Pop?Secret.

General Mills made no divestures in 2009 but in 2010 the company ceased making Perfect Portions refrigerated biscuits and exited the kids' refrigerated yogurt beverage and microwave soup segments in its US retail operations; internationally it also stopped the manufacture of foodservice breadcrumbs with the sale of its Brazilian bread and pasta plant for $6 million. These product cessations were made in response to its declining financial results particularly in its international segment.

To better focus on its retail sales channels in late 2010 General Mills sold its Croissant King (acquired in 2005) and van den Bergh's (acquired in 1999) frozen bakery business in Australia to Ireland's Kerry Group. The sale includes frozen dough and pastry products sold to professional bakers.

In early 2011 General Mills completed the purchase of the Mountain High yogurt brand from Dean Foods for $84.8 million.

EXECUTIVES

SVP Wholesome Snacks, Peter J. Capell

EVP and COO US Retail, Ian R. Friendly, age 51, $520,532 total compensation
EVP Global Strategy Growth and Marketing Innovation, Y. Marc Belton, age 53
Chairman and CEO, Kendall J. (Ken) Powell, age 58, $973,042 total compensation
EVP General Counsel Chief Compliance and Risk Management Officer and Secretary, Roderick A. (Rick) Palmore, age 60
SVP; CEO Cereal Partners Worldwide, Christianne L. (Christi) Strauss
SVP; President General Mills Canada, David P. (Dave) Homer
SVP; President Bakeries and Foodservice, John T. Machuzick
EVP and COO International, Christopher D. (Chris) O'Leary, age 53, $500,248 total compensation
SVP and Chief Marketing Officer, Mark W. Addicks
SVP; President Meals, Juliana L. Chugg, age 44
SVP External Relations, Kimberly A. (Kim) Nelson
SVP; President Pillsbury USA, Ann W.H. Simonds
SVP Financial Operations, Keith A. Woodward
SVP; President Greater China, Gary Chu
EVP and CFO, Donal L. (Don) Mulligan, age 51, $486,300 total compensation
SVP Global Strategy and Growth, James H. (Jim) Murphy
VP and Controller, Richard O. (Rick) Lund, age 62
SVP Supply Chain, John R. Church, age 46
VP; President Small Planet Foods, Michele S. Meyer
VP Investor Relations, Kristen S. (Kris) Wenker
SVP; President Consumer Food Sales, Shawn P. O'Grady, age 48
VP; President Europe Middle East and Africa, Luis G. Merizalde
SVP; President Big G Cereals, Jeffrey L. Harmening
SVP Innovation Technology and Quality, Peter C. Erickson, age 51
SVP; President US Channels Sales, David E. Dudick Sr.
SVP Global Human Resources, Michael L. Davis, age 56
Media Contact, Kirstie Foster
VP; President Asia Pacific Region, Samir Behl
VP and Treasurer, Koff A. Bruce
VP; President Yoplait, Rebecca L. (Becky) O'Grady
VP; President Latin America and South Africa, Sean N. Walker
VP; President Snacks Unlimited, Jonathon J. (Jon) Nudi
VP; President Baking Products, Anton Vincent
Director, Heidi G. Miller, age 57
Director, Bradbury H. (Brad) Anderson, age 61
Director, Robert L. (Bob) Ryan, age 67
Director, Raymond V. Gilmartin, age 69
Director, R. Kerry Clark, age 58
Director, William T. (Bill) Esrey, age 70
Director, Dorothy A. Terrell, age 65
Director, Steve Odland, age 51
Director, Judith Richards Hope, age 69
Director, Michael D. Rose, age 68
Director, Hilda Ochoa-Brillembourg, age 66
Director, Paul Danos, age 68
Auditors: KPMGLLP

LOCATIONS

HQ: General Mills Inc.
1 General Mills Blvd., Minneapolis MN 55426
Phone: 763-764-7600 **Fax:** 763-764-8330
Web: www.generalmills.com

2011 Sales

	$ mil.	% of total
US	11,987	81
International	2,892	19
Total	**14,880**	**100**

PRODUCTS/OPERATIONS

2011 Sales

	$ mil.	% of total
US retail	10,163	69
International	2,875	19
Bakeries & foodservice	1,840	12
Total	**14,880**	**100**

Selected Brands

Dessert and baking mixes
- Betty Crocker
- Bisquick
- Gold Medal
- SuperMoist
- Warm Delights

Dry dinners and shelf stable and frozen vegetable products
- Bac*O' s
- Betty Crocker
- Chicken Helper
- Diablitos
- Green Giant
- Hamburger Helper
- Old El Paso
- Potato Buds
- Simply Steam
- Suddenly Salad
- Valley Selections
- Tuna Helper
- Wanchai Ferry

Frozen pizza and pizza snacks
- Jeno' s
- Party Pizza
- Pillsbury Pizza Minis
- Pillsbury Pizza Pops
- Pizza Rolls
- Totino' s

Grain fruit and savory snacks
- Bugles
- Chex Mix
- Fiber One
- Fruit By The Foot
- Fruit Roll-Ups
- Gardetto' s
- Gushers
- Larabar
- Nature Valley
- Stickerz

Ice cream and frozen desserts
- Haagen-Dazs

Organic products
- Cascadian Farm
- Muir Glen

Ready-to-eat cereals
- Basic 4
- Cheerios
- Chex
- Cinnamon Toast Crunch
- Clusters
- Cocoa Puffs
- Cookie Crisp
- Fiber One
- Golden Grahams
- Kix
- Lucky Charms
- Oatmeal Crisp
- Reese' s Puffs
- Total
- Trix
- Wheaties

Ready-to-serve soup
- Progresso

Refrigerated and frozen dough products
- Big Deluxe
- Golden Layers
- Grands!
- Jus-Rol
- La Salte?a
- Latina
- Pasta Master
- Pillsbury
- Savorings
- Toaster Scrambles
- Toaster Strudel
- V.Pearl
- Wanchai Ferry

Refrigerated yogurt
- Go-GURT
- Fiber One
- Mountain High
- Trix
- Yoplait
- Yoplait Kids
- Yoplait Whips!
- YoPlus

Selected Joint Ventures and Subsidiaries

Joint Ventures
- Cereal Partners Worldwide (CPW) (50% with Nestle)

Subsidiaries
- Bournazi Pastries S.A. (Greece)
- Gardetto' s Bakery Inc.
- Green Giant International Inc.
- Haagen-Dazs International Shoppe Company Inc.
- Kifissia Pastries S.A. (Greece)
- La Saltena S.A. (Argentina)
- Old El Paso Foods B.V. (the Netherlands)
- Pasta Master Distribution Pty Ltd
- Pet Incorporated
- The Pillsbury Company LLC
- Saxby Bros Limited (England and Wales)
- Small Planet Foods Inc.
- Yoplait USA Inc.

COMPETITORS

B&G Foods
Barbara' s Bakery
Bay State Milling
Ben & Jerry' s
Birds Eye
Blue Bell
Bob' s Red Mill Natural Foods
Campbell Soup
Carvel
Chelsea Milling
Cold Stone Creamery
ConAgra
Dairy Queen
Danone
Del Monte Foods
Dole Food
Dreyer' s
Freshens
Friendly' s Ice Cream
Frito-Lay
Gilster-Mary Lee
Hain Celestial
Hanover Foods
Heinz
Kellogg
King Arthur Flour
Lakeside Foods
Manischewitz Company
McKee Foods
MOM Brands
Mondelez International
Mrs. Fields
Nature' s Path
Nestle
Pinnacle Foods
Pro-Fac
Procter & Gamble
Ralcorp
Ralston Food
Seneca Foods
Stonyfield Farm
Unilever
Victoria Packing
YoCream

HISTORICAL FINANCIALS

Company Type: Public

Income Statement FYE: May 27

	REVENUE ($ mil.)	NET INCOME ($ mil.)	NET PROFIT MARGIN	EMPLOYEES
05/12	16,657	1,567	9.4%	35,000
05/11	14,880	1,798	12.1%	35,000
05/10	14,796	1,530	10.3%	33,000
05/09	14,691	1,304	8.9%	30,000
05/08	13,652	1,294	9.5%	29,500
Annual Growth	5.1%	4.9%	—	4.4%

2012 Year-End Financials

Debt ratio: 35.22%
Return on equity: 24.41%
Cash ($ mil.): 471
Current ratio: 96.05
Long-term debt ($ mil.): 6,161
No. of shares (mil.): 648
Dividends
Yield: —
Payout: 51.91%
Market value ($ mil.): 25,343

	STOCK PRICE ($) FY Close	P/E High/Low		PER SHARE ($) Earnings	Dividends	Book Value
05/12	39.08	17	14	2.35	0.00	9.90
05/11	39.29	27	12	2.70	0.00	9.87
05/10	71.23	32	22	2.24	0.00	8.23
05/09	51.18	36	24	1.90	0.00	7.89
05/08	61.09	32	27	1.86	0.00	9.21
Annual Growth	(10.6%)	—	—	6.0%	—	1.8%

General Motors Co.

General Motors (GM) the world's largest auto manufacturer makes cars and trucks with brands such as Buick Cadillac Chevrolet and GMC. GM also builds cars through its GM Daewoo Opel Vauxhall and Holden units. Financing activities are primarily conducted by General Motors Financial Company. Throughout its financial woes GM has received billions of dollars in loans from the Canadian and US governments negotiated concessions with labor unions and jettisoned brands. The auto giant went through a six-week period of bankruptcy protection in 2009; it issued an initial public offering and returned to the stock market in 2010.

HISTORY

In the early years of the auto industry hundreds of carmakers each produced a few models. William Durant who bought a failing Buick Motors in 1904 reasoned that manufacturers could benefit from banding together and formed the General Motors Company in Flint Michigan in 1908.

Durant bought 17 companies (including Oldsmobile Cadillac and Pontiac) by 1910 the year a bankers' syndicate forced him to step down. In 1915 he regained control when he formed a company with race car driver Louis Chevrolet. They soon formed GM Acceptance Corporation (GMAC now known as Ally Financial) and bought businesses including Frigidaire (sold in 1979) and Hyatt Roller Bearing.

With Hyatt came Alfred Sloan (president 1923-37) who built GM into a corporate colossus via a decentralized management system. Unlike Ford Motor –which offered cars in any color you liked as long as it was black –GM offered a range of models and colors; by 1927 it was the industry leader. It bought Vauxhall Motors (UK 1925) merged with Adam Opel (Germany 1929) added defense products for WWII and diversified into home appliances and locomotives.

GM expanded with the nation in the postwar boom years; the good times rolled until Japanese automakers became established in the 1970s. GM spent much of the decade trying to emulate the Japanese while making its cars meet federal pollution-control mandates. CEO Roger Smith laid off thousands of workers.

In 1984 GM formed New United Motor Manufacturing Inc. (NUMMI) with Toyota Motor to see if Toyota's manufacturing techniques would work in the US. GM also bought Electronic Data Systems (1984 now HP Enterprise Services) Hughes Aircraft (1986) and 50% of Saab Automobile (1989). GM launched the Saturn car in 1990; that year Robert Stempel became CEO. In 1992 GM made what was then the largest stock offering in US history ($2.2 billion) and Jack Smith replaced Stempel as CEO.

GM sold its National Car Rental business to an investment group led by William Lobeck in 1995 and spun off Electronic Data Systems the next year. In 1997 it sold the defense electronics business of Hughes Electronics to Raytheon and merged Hughes' auto parts business with Delphi Automotive Systems (now Delphi Corporation).

Walkouts by United Auto Workers (UAW) at two Michigan GM parts plants in 1998 forced the shutdown of virtually all of the company's North American production lines. That year GM began consolidating operations for its five major brands and agreed to build cars with Suzuki increasing its stake in the Japanese company to 10%.

In 1999 GM spun off Delphi and boosted its stake in small-truck partner Isuzu to 49%. Meanwhile subsidiary Hughes Electronics acquired Primestar's direct-to-home business for about $1.3 billion and subsidiary GMAC (today's Ally Financial) bought the commercial finance unit of the Bank of New York (now the Bank of New York Mellon) for $1.8 billion.

GM and Honda inked a deal late in 1999 for Honda to supply V6 engines and transmissions for GM while Isuzu Motors supplied Honda with diesel engines. GM also bought the rights to the Hummer brand from AM General. The next year GM acquired the 50% of Saab Automobile that it didn't already own (from Investor AB) and acquired a 20% stake in Fiat Auto (Lancia and Alfa Romeo but not Ferrari and Maserati) in exchange for a 5.6% Fiat stake in GM. GM also acquired a 20% stake in Fuji Heavy Industries (Subaru).

President Rick Wagoner replaced Smith as CEO in June 2000. Also that year GM and Fiat entered talks to acquire Daewoo Motor after Ford withdrew its bid for the South Korean carmaker and GM cut its salaried workforce by 10%.

In 2001 GM paid about $600 million to double its stake in Suzuki to 20%. In addition it submitted a bid (reportedly around $776 million) to take over Daewoo Motor. The company also announced that it would spend $340 million on a joint venture with AvtoVAZ (Russia's biggest automaker) to build 75000 SUVs a year.

As GM reportedly neared a deal that year to combine Hughes Electronics (and DIRECTV) with Rupert Murdoch's News Corp. EchoStar –the US's #2 satellite TV business –made a $32 billion all-share offer for Hughes (Echostar's offer later dropped to $26 billion after News Corp. dropped out of the bidding). The deal later fell through when it was blocked by the FCC.

Later in 2001 GM announced that it planned to discontinue the once popular Chevrolet Camaro and Pontiac Firebird models.

The following year GM took a 42% stake in South Korea's bankrupt Daewoo Motor (now named GM Daewoo Auto & Technology Company) for $251 million. GM entered the Daewoo deal with partners Suzuki (which took a 15% stake) and Shanghai Automotive Industry Corp. (with a 10% stake). The remaining 33% of the venture was held by GM Daewoo's creditors. GM later increased its stake in GM Daewoo to 49% and then again to 51%.

Meanwhile GM retooled its relationship with Isuzu Motors. Through a recapitalization GM's stake in Isuzu was reduced to 9%. Fiat sold its entire stake in GM in late 2002 to an unnamed investment bank for nearly $1.2 billion.

Early in 2003 GM completed the sale of its defense unit (armored vehicles) to General Dynamics for $1.1 billion. Later that year GM finally made a deal to unload its 20% stake in Hughes Electronics by agreeing to sell its shares to News Corp. in a transaction valued at about $3.1 billion. The deal was completed in the waning days of 2003.

The company announced in 2004 that the headquarters for its Asia/Pacific operations would move from Singapore to Shanghai. That year also marked the last model year for GM's Oldsmobile brand. The world's final Oldsmobile rolled off the assembly line in 2004 –almost 100 years after GM first bought the brand.

Later in 2004 GM wrote its first car loan in China through a joint venture with its Chinese partner Shanghai Automotive Industry Corp. and in so doing became the first Western car company to offer auto loans to Chinese consumers. GM also announced that year it would trim 12000 jobs in Europe (one-fifth of its workforce there) in hopes of saving its ailing European operations about $618 million per year.

Early in 2005 GM sold its money-losing locomotive manufacturing operations (GM Electro-Motive) to Greenbriar Equity Group LLC and Berkshire Partners for an undisclosed sum. GM also said it would invest about $69 million to double its production capacity in India. The year also saw the fruition of a "put option" deal signed with Fiat in 2000. The deal could have forced GM to purchase the remaining stake in Fiat's troubled automotive operations that it didn't already own. Instead GM paid $2 billion to make the whole mess go away. GM and Fiat dissolved their joint venture operations and went their separate ways.

GM sold its stake in Fuji Heavy Industries maker of Subaru passenger vehicles in 2005. The two companies' collaboration never bore the desired fruit and GM sold just under 9% of its 20% stake to Toyota for about $315 million. GM's remaining 11% stake was sold back to Fuji as part of Fuji's open market buyback program and through regular stock sales.

In 2006 GM's finance arm GMAC (now Ally Financial) sold a 78% equity stake in its commercial mortgage business to a private equity consortium including KKR Five Mile Capital Partners and Goldman Sachs Partners for about $9 billion. GM trimmed its stake in Suzuki from 20% to 3% about the same time and it sold its 8% stake in Isuzu to Mitsubishi Corp. ITOCHU Corp. and Mizuho Corporate Bank for $300 million.

Later that year billionaire GM investor Kirk Kerkorian (who owned about a 10% stake) suggested GM might improve its fortunes by hooking up a three-way alliance with Nissan Motor and Renault. Kerkorian's advice quickly prompted board meetings at all three companies to consider the idea. After a 90-day examination of an alliance's potential Renault and GM walked away from the table in the midst of the 2006 Paris Auto Show without a deal. (Kerkorian slowly reduced his stake that year officially ending his influence on the company.)

Also in 2006 GM sold a 51% stake in GMAC (today's Ally Financial) to a consortium of investors led by Cerberus Capital Management for $14 billion.

GM sold its Allison Transmission commercial and military business to The Carlyle Group and Onex Corp. for about $5.6 billion in 2007. GM retained an Allison plant in Baltimore to build transmissions used in the automaker's light trucks.

The company dodged a bullet in 2007 when the UAW fighting for health care for retirees ended a two-day strike –the first nationwide UAW strike against GM in more than 35 years. The two hammered out a deal creating a $50 billion independent health care trust (with GM ponying up most of the trust's funding) a move expected to stop health care-related red ink from piling up on the GM balance sheet.

For 2007 GM reported the largest annual loss in the history of the automotive industry –$38.7 billion. The loss was largely attributable to a $39 billion third-quarter charge for unused tax credits. GM's stake in GMAC (now Ally Financial) also hurt the auto giant as the lender struggled with the US mortgage crisis.

The reporting of the record loss was accompanied by a fresh round of employee buyouts. The plan offered buyouts to as many as 74000 US hourly workers.

Health care costs were a GM pain point for years with retiree health care arguably the biggest drag on GM profits. To cut costs GM early in the decade offered to finance the early retirement of thousands of unionized GM and Delphi workers. By 2006 GM reached its target of more than 20000 blue-collar workers accepting the buyouts. Ultimately about 35000 hourly employees or about one-third of GM's hourly workforce accepted the buyouts. The better-than-expected reaction to the buyout offers put GM about two years ahead of schedule for planned job cuts. In addition to hourly job cuts GM cut 7% of its white-collar positions or about 2500 jobs.

Growing increasingly desperate GM made merger overtures to Chrysler and Ford in 2008. Leaders at GM which bled cash to the tune of about $32 billion in 2008 are looking for some way to stop the massive losses. Rebuffed by Ford GM entered merger talks with Chrysler. Those talks were abandoned however as GM warned in late 2008 that it might run out of cash by the end of the year. A Chapter 11 reorganization something GM's management wanted to avoid was widely debated in public.

Among other restructuring moves in 2009 GM decided to end its 25-year association with Toyota Motor pulling out of the NUMMI joint venture. GM and Toyota were unable to reach agreement on a future product plan for the JV. The company completed a brief government-supervised bankruptcy reorganization in mid-2009 emerging from Chapter 11 as a "New GM" with fewer brands less debt and lower operating costs.

GM continued to rid itself of brands considered peripheral to its operations in 2009 and 2010. In September 2009 the company announced it would wind down its Saturn brand after a deal to sell Saturn to Penske Automotive Group fell through. Around the same time GM agreed to sell Opel/Vauxhall to Canadian auto parts maker Magna International. About two months later the GM board decided not to sell Opel after all opting instead to restructure the units citing their strategic importance to GM's global strategy. Late in 2009 GM agreed to sell HUMMER to a Chinese heavy equipment maker Sichuan Tengzhong Heavy Industrial Machinery; that deal fell through early in 2010 as Tengzhong was unable to obtain approval for the deal from the Chinese government. In February 2010 GM managed to sell its Saab Automobile subsidiary to Dutch sports car maker Swedish Automobile. Following the collapse of earlier bids for the unit the deal came as GM prepared to wind down Saab.

GM filed papers in August 2010 detailing its plans to go public again. The stock offering is one of the largest in US business history.

In late 2010 GM and SAIC Motor created Shanghai Chengxin Used Car Operation and Management a joint venture that sells used vehicles in China. The joint venture the first of its kind in China uses current Shanghai GM distributors for used car sales and service facilities across the country.

The auto company is also focused on the world's largest pool of potential drivers. GM signed a two-year deal with joint venture partner Shanghai General Motors in early 2011 to ship Cadillacs Buicks and Chevrolets to China. The agreement came on the heels of the trade and investment agreements made between Chinese President Hu Jintao and the US.

EXECUTIVES

Chairman and CEO, Daniel F. (Dan) Akerson, age 63
VP Controller and Chief Accounting Officer, Nicholas S. (Nick) Cyprus, age 59
General Auditor and Chief Risk Officer, Brian D. Thelen, age 48
VP Global Human Resources, Cynthia J. (Cindy) Brinkley, age 52
VP Global Public Policy, Robert E. (Bob) Ferguson, age 53
VP; President GM International Operations, Timothy E. (Tim) Lee, age 61
VP Global Communications, Selim Bingol, age 52
VP; President GM North America, Mark L. Reuss, age 48
Vice Chairman Corporate Strategy Business Development Global Product Planning Global Purchasing and Supply Chain, Stephen J. (Steve) Girsky, age 49
SVP Global Product Development, Mary T. Barra, age 50
VP Finance and Treasurer, James A. Davlin, age 48
VP; President South America, Jaime Ardila, age 57
SVP and General Counsel, Michael P. Millikin, age 64
Secretary, Anne T. Larin
VP; President GM Europe, Karl-Friedrich Stracke, age 55
SVP and CFO, Daniel (Dan) Ammann, age 40
Chief Tax Officer, Victoria McInnis
VP and Global Chief Marketing Officer, Joel Ewanick, age 52
VP and CTO, Jon J. Lauckner, age 54
GM Communications IT Support Media Materials and Websites, Bill Betts
VP and CIO, Randy Mott
Director, Robert D. Krebs, age 70
Director, Philip A. (Phil) Laskawy, age 71
Director, Erroll B. Davis Jr., age 67
Director, David Bonderman, age 69
Director, E. Neville Isdell, age 69
Director, Patricia F. (Pat) Russo, age 59
Director, Carol M. Stephenson, age 61
Director, Kathryn V. (Kathy) Marinello, age 55
Director, Cynthia A. Telles, age 59
Vice Chairman Corporate Strategy Business Development Global Product Planning Global Purchasing and Supply Chain, Stephen J. (Steve) Girsky, age 49
Auditors: Deloitte&ToucheLLP

LOCATIONS

HQ: General Motors Company
300 Renaissance Center, Detroit MI 48265-3000
Phone: 313-556-5000 **Fax:** 203-328-6423
Web: www.genre.com

2011 Sales

	$ mil.	% of total
North America		
US	79,868	53
Canada & Mexico	10,153	7
GM Financial		
US	1,363	1
Canada	47	-
Europe		
Germany	5,975	4
UK	4,899	3
Italy	2,429	2
France	2,343	2
Spain	1,263	1
Other European countries	8,284	6
South America		
Brazil	9,635	6
Argentina	1,723	1
Venezuela	1,472	1
Other South American countries	3,801	3
Asia		
Korea	9,087	6
Thailand	911	-
Other Asian countries	496	-
Other regions	6,527	4
Total	**150,276**	**100**

PRODUCTS/OPERATIONS

2011 Sales

	$ mil.	% of total
GMNA	90,233	56
GME	26,757	17
GMIO	24,761	15
GMSA	16,877	11
GM Financial	1,410	1
Corporate & eliminations	(9762)	-
Total	**150,276**	**100**

Selected Brands

Buick
Cadillac
Chevrolet
GMC
Holden
Isuzu
Opel
Vauxhall

Selected Operations

Adam Opel GmbH (Germany)
Ally Financial Inc. (formerly General Motors Acceptance Corp. " GMAC" 10%)
GM Automotive
GM Daewoo Auto & Technology Company

COMPETITORS

BMW
Chrysler
Daimler
Fiat
Ford Motor
Fuji Heavy Industries
Honda
Hyundai Motor
Kia Motors
Land Rover
Mazda
Mitsubishi Motors
Navistar International
Nissan
Peugeot
Renault
Suzuki Motor
Tata Motors
Toyota
Volkswagen
Volvo Car Corp.

HISTORICAL FINANCIALS

Company Type: Public

Income Statement

FYE: December 31

	REVENUE ($ mil.)	NET INCOME ($ mil.)	NET PROFIT MARGIN	EMPLOYEES
12/11	150,276	9,190	6.1%	207,000
12/10	135,592	6,172	4.6%	202,000
12/09*	57,474	(4,297)	—	209,000
07/09	47,115	109,118	231.6%	0
12/08	148,979	(30,943)	—	243,000
Annual Growth	0.2%	—	—	(3.9%)

*Fiscal year change

2011 Year-End Financials

Debt ratio: 9.22%
Return on equity: 24.11%
Cash ($ mil.): 31,647
Current ratio: 123.12
Long-term debt ($ mil.): 11,650
No. of shares (mil.): 1,564
Dividends
Yield: —
Payout: —
Market value ($ mil.): 31,717

STOCK PRICE ($) FY Close	P/E High/Low		PER SHARE ($) Earnings	Dividends	Book Value
12/11 20.27	8	4	4.58	0.00	24.36
12/10 36.86	12	11	2.89	0.00	24.12
Annual Growth (45.0%)	—	—	58.5%	—	1.0%

Genuine Parts Co.

What do spark plugs hydraulic hoses paper clips and magnet wire have in common? They're all Genuine Parts. The diversified company is the largest member and majority owner of National Automotive Parts Association (NAPA) a voluntary trade association that distributes auto parts nationwide. Genuine Parts Company (GPC) operates about 1000 NAPA Auto Parts stores in 40-plus US states. North of the border NAPA Canada runs some 690 auto parts and TRACTION stores supplied by UAP. GPC's Auto Todo unit runs four auto parts stores and four tire centers in Mexico. Other subsidiaries include auto parts distributor Balkamp industrial parts supplier Motion Industries and office products distributor S.P. Richards.

HISTORY

Genuine Parts Company (GPC) got its start in Atlanta in 1928 when Carlyle Fraser bought a small auto parts store. That year GPC had the only loss in its history. Three years earlier a group that included Fraser had founded the National Automotive Parts Association (NAPA) an organization of automotive manufacturers remanufacturers distributors and retailers.

The Depression was a boon for GPC because fewer new-car sales meant more sales of replacement parts. During the 1930s GPC's sales rose from less than $350000 to more than $3 million. One tool it developed to spur sales during the Depression was its monthly magazine "Parts Pups" which featured pretty girls and corny jokes (discontinued in the 1990s). GPC acquired auto parts rebuilder Rayloc in 1931 and established parts distributor Balkamp in 1936.

WWII boosted sales at GPC because carmakers were producing for the war effort but scarce resources limited auto parts companies to producing functional parts. GPC went public in 1948.

The postwar boom in car sales boosted GPC's sales in the 1950s and 1960s. It expanded during this period with new distribution centers across the country. GPC bought Colyear Motor Sales (NAPA's West Coast distributor) in 1965 and introduced a line of filters and batteries in 1966 that were the first parts to carry the NAPA name.

GPC moved into Canada in 1972 when it bought Corbetts a Calgary-based parts distributor. That acquisition included Oliver Industrial Supply. During the mid-1970s GPC began to broaden its distribution businesses adding S.P. Richards (office products 1975) and Motion Industries (industrial replacement parts 1976). In the late 1970s GPC acquired Bearing Specialty and Michigan Bearing as part of Motion Industries.

In 1982 the company introduced its now familiar blue-and-yellow NAPA logo. Canadian parts distributor UAP (formerly United Auto Parts) and GPC formed a joint venture UAP/NAPA in 1988 with GPC acquiring a 20% stake in UAP.

During the 1990s GPC diversified its product lines and its geographic reach. Its 1993 acquisition of Berry Bearing made the company a leading distributor of industrial parts. The next year GPC formed a joint venture with Grupo Auto Todo of Mexico.

NAPA formed an agreement in 1995 with Penske Corporation to be the exclusive supplier of auto parts to nearly 900 Penske Auto Centers. GPC purchased Horizon USA Data Supplies that year adding computer supplies to S.P. Richards' product mix.

A string of acquisitions in the late 1990s increased GPC's industrial distribution business (including Midcap Bearing Power Drives & Bearings and Amarillo Bearing).

GPC paid $200 million in 1998 for EIS a leading wholesale distributor of materials and supplies to the electrical and electronics industries. Late in 1998 after a 10-year joint venture it bought the remaining 80% of UAP it didn't already own. GPC continued to expand its auto parts distribution network in 1999 acquiring Johnson Industries an independent distributor of auto supplies for large fleets and car dealers. GPC also acquired Oklahoma City-based Brittain Brothers a NAPA distributor that serves about 190 auto supply stores in Arkansas Missouri Oklahoma and Texas.

In 2000 the company bought a 15% interest in Mitchell Repair Information (MRIC) a subsidiary of Snap-on Incorporated that provides diagnostic and repair information services. The next year Johnson Industries acquired Coach and Motors a distribution center in Detroit.

GPC acquired NAPA Hawaii which serves more than 30 independently owned NAPA stores and four company-owned ones in Hawaii and Samoa in 2003. Also that year the company sold its interest in the partnership that distributes industrial parts in Mexico Refacciones Industriales de Mexico.

President Thomas Gallagher became the company's fourth CEO in more than 75 years when he was named to the position in August 2004. Former CEO Larry Prince remained as chairman until early in 2005 when Gallagher was elected chairman; Prince remains on the board. Also during 2005 the company acquired a 25% interest in Altrom Canada Corp.

GPC subsidiary Motion Industries in mid-2006 acquired Lewis Supply Co. a provider of casters cutting tools machinery accessories and other general mill supplies. In October the company merged HorizonUSA Data Supplies previously a wholly owned subsidiary of S.P. Richards into S.P. Richards.

In early 2008 the company sold its Johnson Industries subsidiary which provided automotive supplies to fleets and new car dealers. In October GPC's S.P. Richards unit acquired ActionEmco's business assets in the midwestern US including its Grand Rapids Michigan distribution center. Also that year Motion Industries acquired Texas-based Drago Supply Company Mill Supply Corp. and Monroe Rubber and Plastic Supply.

In 2009 GPC added eight companies to its industrial and automotive operations for about $70 million and snapped up the remaining 11% interest in Balkamp that it did not already control for some $60 million making it a wholly owned subsidiary. These deals compare to a broader acquisition strategy in 2008 which added a dozen companies to all four of GPC's business segments (automotive industrial office products and electrical and electronic) for nearly $135 million.

Also in 2010 it acquired Canada's BC Bearing a distributor of bearing and power transmission components.

EXECUTIVES

SVP Finance and Corporate Secretary, Carol B. Yancey
SVP and Treasurer, Frank M. Howard
VP Planning and Acquisitions, Treg S. Brown
Vice Chairman EVP Finance and CFO, Jerry W. Nix, age 66, $505,000 total compensation
Chairman and CEO, Thomas C. (Tom) Gallagher, age 64, $875,000 total compensation
VP Finance U.S. Automotive Parts Group, Richard A. Geiger
SVP and Corporate Counsel, Scott C. Smith
Director; Chairman NAPA Canada/UAP Inc., Jean Douville, age 68
SVP Human Resources, R. Bruce Clayton, age 65, $310,000 total compensation
SVP and CIO US Automotive Parts Group, R. Craig Bierman
President and CEO Motion Industries, William J. (Bill) Stevens
VP Real Estate and Construction, Karl J. Koenig
President; President U.S. Automotive Parts Group, Paul D. Donahue, age 55, $435,000 total compensation
VP Human Resources NAPA Canada/UAP Inc., Daniel Dallaire
SVP CFO and Secretary NAPA Canada/UAP Inc., Pierre Lefebvre
EVP Operations U.S. Automotive Parts Group, Glenn M. Chambers
President Heavy Vehicle Parts Group, D. Gary Silva
VP Information Technolgy U.S. Automotive Parts Group, Jay C. Burnworth
VP Store Operations U.S. Automotive Parts Group, Mark W. Hohe
VP Operations Heavy Vehicle Parts Group, Greg A. Lancour
VP Inventory and Procurement U.S. Automotive Parts Group, Michael L. Swartz
VP Information Systems U.S. Automotive Parts Group, W. Larry Bevil
EVP U.S. Automotive Parts Group, Lee A. Maher
VP Southern Division U.S. Automotive Parts Group, Stuart A. Kambury
VP Central Division U.S. Automotive Parts Group, Grant L. Morris
VP Eastern Division U.S. Automotive Parts Group, Michael J. Kelleher
EVP Auto Parts NAPA Canada/UAP Inc., Kevin M. Chase
SVP Sales U.S. Automotive Parts Group, Daniel F. Askey
VP Western Division U.S. Automotive Parts Group, Bradley A. Shaffer
VP Southern Division American Parts Group, J. Richard Borman
VP Marketing Rayloc, Michael S. Gaffney II
EVP Balkamp Inc., Frank C. Amato
VP Finance and Treasurer Belkamp Inc., Mary F. Knudsen
President and CEO Grupo Auto Todo Mexico, Juan Lujambio
VP Finance Grupo Auto Todo Mexico, Jorge Otero
President and COO NAPA Canada/UAP Inc., Robert Hattem
President and CEO EIS, Robert W. Thomas
SVP Merchandising and Product Strategy U.S. Automotive Parts Group, Scott W. LeProhon
EVP and COO U.S. Motion Industries, M. Wayne Law
SVP Logistics and Operations EIS, William C. (Bill) Knight

SVP Technology and Process Improvement, Charles A. Chesnutt, age 52
SVP Operations and Logistics, Michael D. Orr
VP Compensation and Benefits, Phillip C. Johnson
VP Human Resources U.S. Automotive Parts Group, Nancy Vepraskas
VP Classification U.S. Automotive Parts Group, Karl E. Wolfe
VP Midwest Division American Parts Group, Kevin E. Herron
VP Atlantic Division U.S. Automotive Parts Group, M. Todd McMurtrie
VP Information Services Rayloc, Joseph Lashley
VP AutoCare Sales U.S. Automotive Parts Group, Bret A. Robyck
VP Investor Relations, Sidney G. (Sid) Jones
VP Southern Division Stores U.S. Automotive Parts Group, Cary V. Carter
VP Commercial Marketing U.S. Automotive Parts Group, John J. Hanighen IV
VP Operations Controls U.S. Automotive Parts Group, Jerry W. Biggers
VP Process Improvement - Distribution U.S. Automotive Parts Group, Michael J. Fusaro
VP NAPA Tools and Equipment Sales U.S. Automotive Parts Group, David B. Nicki
VP Organizational Development U.S. Automotive Parts Group, J. Michael Phillips
VP Marketing Strategy U.S. Automotive Parts Group, Gaylord M. Spencer
VP Major Accounts U.S. Automotive Parts Group, Dennis P. Toliver
VP Mountain Division U.S. Automotive Parts Group, Eric G. Fritsch
VP Human Resources Rayloc, Damon E. Elmore
VP Product Rayloc, David Gonzales
VP Finance Rayloc, Debbie E. Niffin
President Balkamp Inc., D. Tip Tollison
VP Finance NAPA Canada/UAP Inc., Frank Pipito
President Altrom America Altrom Import Parts Group, Scott S. Mountford
President and COO S.P. Richards, Richard T. Toppin
President Rayloc, John Mosteller
SVP Human Resources U.S. Automotive Parts Group, Todd P. Helms
VP Operations Rayloc, William J. Westerman III
SVP Electrical and Assembly EIS, Alexander Gonzalez
SVP Marketing EIS, Griffin L. Griffin
SVP Manufacturing EIS, Thomas A. Jones
SVP Finance and Secretary EIS, Matthew C. Tyser
VP and General Manager Altrom America, Geoffrey H. Watson
VP Distribution and Logistics NAPA Canada/UAP Inc., J. Duncan Pickard
SVP Marketing S. P. Richards, James F. O?Brien
VP Information Technology, Eric Sundby
Assistant VP and Corporate Controller, David Haskett
Assistant VP Internal Audit, Napoleon Rutledge
Director, Michael M. E. Johns, age 70
Vice Chairman EVP Finance and CFO, Jerry W. Nix, age 66
Director, Larry L. Prince, age 73
Director, J. Hicks Lanier, age 71
Director, Gary W. Rollins, age 67
Director, Robert C. (Robin) Loudermilk Jr., age 52
Director, John D. Johns, age 59
Director; Chairman NAPA Canada/UAP Inc., Jean Douville, age 68
Director, George C. (Jack) Guynn, age 69
Director, Mary B. Bullock, age 67
Director, Wendy B. Needham, age 59
Director, John R. Holder, age 57
Auditors: Ernst&YoungLLP

LOCATIONS

HQ: Genuine Parts Company
2999 Circle 75 Pkwy., Atlanta GA 30339
Phone: 770-953-1700 **Fax:** 770-956-2211
Web: www.genpt.com

2011 Sales

	$ mil.	% of total
US	10,791	87
Canada	1,571	12
Mexico	118	1
Adjustments	(23.0)	-
Total	**12,458**	**100**

PRODUCTS/OPERATIONS

2011 Sales

	$ mil.	% of total
Automotive	6,061	49
Industrial	4,173	33
Office products	1,689	14
Electrical & electronic materials	557	4
Adjustments	(23.0)	-
Total	**12,458**	**100**

Selected Operations

Automotive Parts Group
- Altrom Canada Corp. (distribution of import automotive parts Canada)
- Balkamp (majority-owned subsidiary; distribution of replacement parts and accessories for cars heavy-duty vehicles motorcycles and farm equipment)
- UAP Inc. (auto parts distribution Canada)

Electrical/Electronic Materials Group
- EIS Inc. (products for electrical and electronic equipment including adhesives copper foil and thermal management materials)

Industrial Parts Group
- Motion Industries (Canada) Inc.
- Motion Industries Inc.

Office Products Group
- S.P. Richards Company

COMPETITORS

Advance Auto Parts
Applied Industrial Technologies
Arrow Electronics
AutoZone
Avnet
CARQUEST
Coast Distribution
Cole Office Products
Complete Office
CSK Auto
D & H Distributing
Ford Motor
General Motors
General Parts
Gould Paper
Graybar Electric
Hahn Automotive
Ingersoll-Rand
Kaman Industrial Technologies
MSC Industrial Direct
O' Reilly Automotive
Office Depot
OfficeMax
Pep Boys
Staples
United Stationers
W.W. Grainger

HISTORICAL FINANCIALS

Company Type: Public

Income Statement

FYE: December 31

	REVENUE ($ mil.)	NET INCOME ($ mil.)	NET PROFIT MARGIN	EMPLOYEES
12/11	12,458	565	4.5%	29,800
12/10	11,207	475	4.2%	29,500
12/09	10,057	399	4.0%	29,000
12/08	11,015	475	4.3%	30,300
12/07	10,843	506	4.7%	32,000
Annual Growth	3.5%	2.8%	—	(1.8%)

2011 Year-End Financials

Debt ratio: 9.09%
Return on equity: 20.30%
Cash ($ mil.): 525
Current ratio: 252.56
Long-term debt ($ mil.): 534
No. of shares (mil.): 155
Dividends
Yield: —
Payout: 50.28%
Market value ($ mil.): 9,526

	STOCK PRICE ($) FY Close	P/E High	P/E Low	PER SHARE ($) Earnings	Dividends	Book Value
12/11	61.20	17	13	3.58	0.00	17.88
12/10	51.34	17	12	3.00	1.64	17.72
12/09	37.96	16	10	2.50	1.60	16.49
12/08	37.86	16	11	2.92	1.56	14.58
12/07	46.30	17	16	2.98	1.46	16.36
Annual Growth	7.2%	—	—	4.7%	—	2.2%

Genworth Financial Inc

What's a Genworth? Insurance and investment specialist Genworth Financial might ask what your nest egg is worth. The company specializes in life insurance and retirement investments. Internationally Genworth offers mortgage insurance and other payment protection products. In the US it is the exclusive provider of long-term care insurance to AARP members. The firm also provides private residential mortgage insurance in the US. Genworth focuses its retirement investment products including fixed annuities and mutual funds on affluent individuals. Genworth serves over 15 million customers in 25 countries; its products are sold through banks independent distributors and financial advisors.

Geographic Reach

While US operations account for about three-fourths of revenues Genworth's international operations include significant mortgage insurance businesses in Australia Canada Mexico and parts of Europe. The firm is looking to expand its mortgage insurance operations into emerging markets. The international offerings also include "lifestyle protection" products that help to cover any payments on other loans in the event of accident illness death or disability.

In 2012 the company announced plans to raise a bit of cash by spinning off a minority stake (about 40%) in its Australian mortgage insurance business through an IPO. It had previously launched a public offering of its Canadian mortgage insurance business in 2009.

Operations

Genworth's largest source of income is its US life insurance division which accounts for about 60% of annual revenues. The international mortgage division makes up about 15% of sales and international protection 10%. The smaller US mortgage insurance and wealth management divisions each account for less than 10% of sales as does the runoff segment (consisting of the divested Medicare operations).

Financial Analysis

Genworth reported a 3% increase in revenues to $10.3 billion in 2011 due to higher insurance and investment fees in the life insurance and wealth management segments as well as higher investment returns. The growth was offset by a 3% decrease in total insurance premiums (its largest revenue source) primarily within the runoff and international protection segments despite an increase in international mortgage premiums. Net income decreased 8% due to higher acquisition expenses and operating costs.

Strategy

Genworth has been streamlining its operations through asset sales during 2011 and 2012. The asset sales allow Genworth to improve its cash position and focus on its core offerings: life policies long-term care insurance mortgage insurance lifestyle protection products fixed annuities and wealth management services. It has groomed its largest segment US life to focus on term universal and universal life insurance policies while discontinuing term and whole life products.

It is specifically focused on expansion of its independent advisor offerings in the wealth management field. For instance the Genworth Financial Wealth Management unit launched a new investment portfolio risk mitigation product in 2011. Genworth is also looking to grow its mortgage businesses in developing countries.

Mergers Acquisitions & Divestitures

Despite steady growth in the sales of its Medicare supplemental products in 2011 the company sold the block of products (held by the former Continental Life Insurance Company unit) to Aetna for $290 million. The company sold its Genworth Financial Investment Services unit which provides tax and accounting financial advisory services to investment brokerage firm Cetera Financial Group in 2012. In addition in 2011 the company stopped offering mortgage insurance policies in New Zealand. It is also is planning to spin off a portion of its Australian mortgage unit.

In late 2010 Genworth expanded its asset management operations with the purchase of hedge fund and managed futures producer Altegris Capital. The purchase brought in alternative investments and $2.2 billion in assets under management.

Company Background

The company was formed in 2004 to acquire certain insurance and financial services business from General Electric (GE). GE retained a controlling stake in Genworth Financial after its stock offering but sold its remaining stake in 2006.

During the downturn in the US housing market (starting in 2008) the company faced losses in its US mortgage insurance segment. After considering divestitures Genworth instead simply yanked hard on those operations making its underwriting criteria more stringent and restricting new business. The company also conducted extensive restructuring programs including a 15% workforce reduction in 2009 and a de-risking of its investment portfolio to recover from the economic downturn. Nonetheless the company saw income and cash flow losses during those years as a result of poor returns on investments.

EXECUTIVES

Chairman, James S. (Jim) Riepe, age 69
President CEO and Director, Thomas J. (Tom) McInerney, age 56
Chairman and CEO Canada, Brian L. Hurley
SVP General Counsel and Secretary, Leon E. Roday, age 59, $568,177 total compensation
SVP and Chief Risk Officer, Michel G. Perreault, age 52
SVP Human Resources, Michael S. Laming, age 61
SVP and CIO, Scott J. McKay, age 51
EVP; President and CEO Global Mortgage Insurance, Kevin D. Schneider, age 50
President and CEO Wealth Management, Gurinder S. Ahluwalia
President Insurance Products, Thomas M. (Buck) Stinson
President Europe, Robert J. (Bob) Brannock
SVP Corporate Development, Joseph J. Pehota, age 51
EVP, Patrick B. (Pat) Kelleher, age 54, $448,561 total compensation
SVP and CFO Retirement and Protection, Amy R. Corbin, age 45
President Mortgage Insurance Australia, Ellie F. Comerford
SVP and CFO, Martin P. Klein, age 52
COO International, Jerome T. Upton, age 48
Chief Marketing Officer Wealth Management, Myra Rothfeld
SVP and Chief Investment Officer, Daniel J. (Dan) Sheehan IV
senior Vice President commercial operations, John Clifford
Director, Thomas E. Moloney, age 68
Director, James A. Parke, age 67
Director, William H. Bolinder, age 68
Director, Nancy J. Karch, age 64
Director, Risa J. Lavizzo-Mourey, age 57
Director, J. Robert (Bob) Kerrey, age 68
Director, Steven W. (Steve) Alesio, age 58
President CEO and Director, Thomas J. (Tom) McInerney, age 56
Director, Christine B. (Chris) Mead, age 56
Auditors: KPMGLLP

LOCATIONS

HQ: Genworth Financial Inc
6620 West Broad Street, Richmond, VA 23230
Phone: 804 281-6000
Web: www.genworth.com

2011 Revenues

	$ mil.	% of total
US	7,815	75
Other countries	2,529	25
Total	**10,344**	**100**

PRODUCTS/OPERATIONS

2011 Revenues

US Life	6,130	59
International mortgage	1,507	15
US Mortgage Insurance	719	7
Runoff	501	5
Wealth management	453	4
Total	**10,344**	**100**

2011 Revenues

	$ mil.	% of total
Premiums	5,705	55
Investment income	3,160	31
Insurance & investment product fees & other	1,479	14
Total	**10,344**	**100**

Selected Products and Services

Life insurance
Long-term care insurance
Mortgage insurance
Retirement solutions
Wealth management solutions

COMPETITORS

AEGON USA
AIG
Great American Financial Resources
John Hancock Financial Services
MassMutual
Medamerica Insurance
MetLife
MGIC Investment
Nationwide
New York Life
Northwestern Mutual
PMI Group
Prudential
Radian Group
The Hartford

HISTORICAL FINANCIALS

Company Type: Public

Income Statement FYE: December 31

	ASSETS ($ mil.)	NET INCOME ($ mil.)	INCOME AS % OF ASSETS	EMPLOYEES
12/11	114,302	122	0.1%	6,400
12/10	112,395	142	0.1%	6,500
12/09	108,187	(460)	—	6,000
12/08	107,389	(572)	—	6,000
12/07	114,315	1,220	1.1%	7,000
Annual Growth	(0.0%)	(43.8%)	—	(2.2%)

2011 Year-End Financials

Debt ratio: 6.98%
Return on equity: 0.74%
Cash ($ mil.): 4,488
Current ratio: —
Long-term debt ($ mil.): 7,982
No. of shares (mil.): 491
Dividends
Yield: —
Payout: —
Market value ($ mil.): 3,216

	STOCK PRICE ($) FY Close	P/E High	P/E Low	PER SHARE ($) Earnings	Dividends	Book Value
12/11	6.55	57	20	0.25	0.00	33.69
12/10	13.14	65	37	0.29	0.00	28.29
12/09	11.35	—	—	(1.02)	0.30	25.10
12/08	2.83	—	—	(1.32)	0.40	20.61
12/07	25.45	13	8	2.73	0.37	30.91
Annual Growth	(28.8%)	—	—	(45.0%)	—	2.2%

Georgia Power Co.

Bigger than a giant peach Georgia Power is the largest subsidiary of US utility holding company Southern Company. The regulated utility provides electricity to about 2.4 million residential commercial and industrial customers throughout most of Georgia. It has interests in 14 fossil-fueled 2 nuclear and 20 hydroelectric power plants that give it about 16000 MW of generating capacity. When necessary the company purchases excess power from nine small power producers. Georgia Power sells wholesale electricity to several cooperatives and municipalities in the region. The utility also offers energy efficiency surge protection and outdoor lighting products and services.

Decreased demand and lower commodity prices spurred by the global recession resulted in lower operating revenues in 2009. Favorable weather conditions spiked power demand in 2010 helping to lift both revenues and income.

To reduce carbon emissions Georgia Power is looking to increase its renewable energy portfolio via the purchase of energy from renewable generators and through investments in its own renewable generation plants. The company is also investing $43 million a year in 18 energy-efficiency programs expected to reduce power demand by 900 MW by 2013. As part of this broad initiative in 2010 it signed a long-term contract with Waste Management to produce electricity from landfill gas.

In 2008 Georgia Power signed a 20-year contract for electricity that will be generated from environmentally-friendly wood waste. Yellow Pine Energy Company LLC's biomass-fired facility will be located near Fort Gaines Georgia.

The company released an integrated resource plan in 2008 which in addition to a renewables push included building two additional nuclear power units at its power plant in Vogtle near Waynesboro Georgia (the country's first nuclear power plants in more than 30 years). In 2010 Georgia Power received a provisional agreement for loan guarantees from the Department of Energy to fund their construction and in 2012 it secured US Nuclear Regulatory Commission approval to go ahead and build these units.

To upgrade its coal plants between 1990 and 2015 Georgia Power will invest $7 billion on environmental control technologies.

EXECUTIVES

EVP Nuclear Development, Joseph A. (Buzz) Miller, age 50
EVP Customer Service and Operations, Anthony L. Wilson
EVP Customer Service Organization, Mickey A. Brown, age 64, $357,813 total compensation
President CEO and Director, W. Paul Bowers, age 55
EVP CFO and Treasurer, Ronnie R. Labrato, age 56
VP Distribution, Leslie R. Sibert, age 46
EVP External Affairs, W. Craig Barrs, age 54
SVP Metro Atlanta Region, Richard L. Holmes, age 57
SVP Customer Service and Sales, E. Lamont Houston
SVP Fossil and Hydro Generation, Douglas E. (Doug) Jones, age 53, $305,170 total compensation
SVP General Counsel Chief Compliance Officer and Corporate Secretary, Thomas P. Bishop, age 51
SVP Charitable Giving, Judy M. Anderson
VP Energy Planning and Nuclear Development, Chris Bell
SVP and Senior Production Officer, Stanley W. Connally Jr.
Director, David M. Ratcliffe, age 63
Director, Richard W. (Rick) Ussery, age 64
President CEO and Director, W. Paul Bowers, age 55
Director, William J. (Jerry) Vereen, age 71
Director, Jimmy C. Tallent, age 59
Director, Stephen S. Green, age 63
Director, Robert L. Brown Jr., age 60
Director, D. Gary Thompson, age 65
Director, Beverly D. Tatum, age 57
Auditors: Deloitte&ToucheLLP

LOCATIONS

HQ: Georgia Power Company
241 Ralph McGill Blvd. NE, Atlanta GA 30308
Phone: 404-506-6526 **Fax:** 404-506-3771
Web: www.georgiapower.com

PRODUCTS/OPERATIONS

2010 Sales

	$ mil.	% of total
Retail		
Residential	3,072	37
Commercial	3,011	36
Industrial	1,441	17
Other retail	84	1
Wholesale	433	5
Other	308	4
Total	**8,349**	**100**

2010 Fuel Mix

	% of total
Coal	67
Nuclear	21
Oil &	10
Hydro	2
Total	**100**

COMPETITORS

AGL Resources
Atmos Energy
Energen
Entergy
Flint Energies
MEAG Power
Oglethorpe Power
Progress Energy
Progress Energy Carolinas
Sawnee EMC
SCANA
South Carolina Electric & Gas
TECO Energy
Walton EMC

HISTORICAL FINANCIALS

Company Type: Subsidiary

Income Statement FYE: December 31

	REVENUE ($ mil.)	NET INCOME ($ mil.)	NET PROFIT MARGIN	EMPLOYEES
12/11	8,800	1,162	13.2%	8,310
12/10	8,349	967	11.6%	8,330
12/09	7,691	831	10.8%	8,599
12/08	8,411	920	10.9%	9,337
12/07	7,571	842	11.1%	9,270
Annual Growth	3.8%	8.4%	—	(2.7%)

2011 Year-End Financials

Debt ratio: 33.10%
Return on equity: 12.51%
Cash ($ mil.): 13
Current ratio: 81.18
Long-term debt ($ mil.): 8,018
No. of shares (mil.): 9
Dividends
Yield: —
Payout: 95.72%
Market value ($ mil.): 292

	STOCK PRICE ($) FY Close	P/E High/Low	PER SHARE ($) Earnings	Dividends	Book Value
12/11	31.49	— —	(0.00)	0.00	1,002.97
12/10	30.40	— —	(0.00)	2.05	972.52
12/09	30.54	— —	(0.00)	1.95	882.03
12/08	26.67	— —	(0.00)	0.00	771.49
Annual Growth	5.7%	— —	—	—	9.1%

Gilead Sciences, Inc.

Gilead Sciences has biotech balms for infectious diseases including hepatitis HIV and infections related to AIDS. The company's HIV franchise includes Truvada a combination of two of its other drugs Viread and Emtriva. It co-promotes another HIV treatment called Atripla in the US and Europe with Bristol-Myers Squibb (BMS). Other products on the market include AmBisome used to treat systemic fungal infections such as those that accompany AIDS or kidney disease; Vistide for AIDS-related eye infections; and hepatitis B antiviral Hepsera. Beyond HIV/AIDS Gilead also markets cardiovascular drugs Letairis and Ranexa as well as respiratory and ophthalmic medicines.

Operations

Gilead has only been expanding into areas such as cardiovascular and pulmonary diseases since 2007. As such the company's main source of revenue continues to be its antiviral franchise which contributes more than 80% of product sales and primarily consists of HIV medications.

Aside from the Atripla partnership with BMS Gilead has collaborations with other companies including Japan Tobacco which promotes HIV drugs Truvada Viread and Emtriva in Japan and with GlaxoSmithKline which markets Hepsera Viread and Volbris in select international markets. Additionally Gilead Sciences receives royalties on influenza treatment Tamiflu which it developed with Roche and on Macugen an ophthalmologic drug developed by Eyetech using Gilead's technology. In addition to distributing AmBisome in Canada and the US Astellas pays royalties on the US sales of Lexiscan which is used in stress tests for coronary artery disease.

Marketing and Sales

Gilead promotes its antiviral drugs through its own commercial infrastructure in North America some European and Asian countries and in Australia and New Zealand; products are promoted through partnerships in other regions. The company's product distribution processes are handled primarily by wholesalers.

Financials

Increased sales of antiviral products have provided healthy revenue increases for Gilead in recent years with the antiviral segment producing an 8% sales increase in 2011. Sales of Atripla and Truvada have especially shown growth with Atripla rising to above $3 billion in annual sales in 2011. The newly launched Complera/Eviplera HIV offering also boosted Gilead's revenues that year as did increased sales of AmBisome Ranexa and Letaris. Overall the company's annual revenues increased more than 5% to some $8.4 billion. Though profits had also been on a positive trajectory for several years net income decreased in 2011 by 3% to some $2.8 billion due to increased R&D expenses and acquisition costs.

One of the pitfalls of the pharma manufacturing business is patent expirations however and products such as Gilead's AIDS drug Vistride have seen declining sales as they begin to face generic competition; such patent expirations can offset growth in other areas. The company also saw a decline in royalty revenues from Tamiflu in 2011 as demand for the drug decreased due to lower pandemic flu preparation efforts. Sales of Hepsera also declined marginally in 2011 due to fierce competition from other hepatitis B drugs.

Strategy

Increasing sales of existing products in new territories (and sometime for new medical indications) is a major growth strategy for Gilead. With partner BMS the firm is especially focused on increasing international commercialization of Atripla. To stay ever-vigilant about protecting itself against patent expirations on older products the company also works to launch new or next generation drugs to keep the money coming in. The company's development programs include potential treatments for viral infections respiratory and cardiovascular ailments and cancer. Gilead also conducts R&D efforts through collaborations; for instance it has a development partnership with Japan Tobacco on new HIV drugs. As yet another way of fending off losses from patent expirations Gilead Sciences has diversified its product line through acquisitions.

Mergers and Acquisitions

The company made a bold diversification move in early 2012 when it purchased Pharmasset a development firm with a promising pipeline of hepatitis C candidates for some $11 billion. Following the purchase Pharmasset's operations were integrated into the Gilead organization.

In late 2012 Gilead struck another deal this time to purchase YM BioSciences for some $126 million. The purchase adds clinical development programs for oncology therapies in the field of hematologic cancers.

Gilead had already been keeping a steady acquisition pace to help it expand in new product areas. In 2010 and 2011 it made several smaller purchases to expand its development pipeline in areas including cancer inflammation fibrotic disease and respiratory ailment treatments.

HISTORY

Dr. Michael Riordan started Gilead Sciences in 1987 backed by venture capital firm Menlo Ventures. The name was derived from the Biblical phrase "Is there no balm in Gilead?" In 1990 Glaxo Wellcome (now GlaxoSmithKline) agreed to fund Gilead's research into code-blocking treatments for cancer. Gilead went public in 1992.

In 1994 the company formed an alliance with American Home Products' Storz Instruments (now part of Bausch & Lomb) to develop and market a topical treatment for an ophthalmic virus. Two years later Gilead joined forces with Roche to develop treatments for influenza.

Vistide was approved in the US in 1996 and in Europe in 1997. But more-effective HIV therapies brought declining demand for Vistide.

The company bounced back with Tamiflu (the fruit of its Roche partnership) which was approved in 1999. Sales were brisk during that flu season. Also that year Gilead expanded its pipeline and geographic reach with the $550 million all-stock acquisition of NeXstar Pharmaceuticals which focused on antifungals antibiotics and cancer treatments.

In 2000 Gilead sought approval for Tamiflu in Japan and Europe (it withdrew the European application after regulators there asked for more information) and also sought approval for pediatric uses for the drug which was granted. The following year it resubmitted Tamiflu for approval in Europe.

Chairman Donald Rumsfeld resigned in 2001 to become US secretary of defense and was replaced by retired Sears Roebuck executive James Denny. Perhaps the Defense connection helped: Vistide became one of the many drugs that researchers began studying as possible alternatives to vaccines should a smallpox bio-attack occur in the US.

Also in 2001 Gilead sold its oncology pipeline to OSI Pharmaceuticals to focus on infection-control products and its hepatitis B lead drug candidate. The sale was a smart move —the FDA approved Hepsera less than a year later.

To help alleviate the AIDS epidemic in 2003 the company announced plans to sell Viread at cost to all African nations and some 15 other impoverished countries striken by the disease. That year Gilead won FDA approval for another weapon to battle AIDS: antiretroviral Emtriva.

To acquire new ammo in its battle against HIV the firm bought Triangle Pharmaceuticals in 2003.

Gilead sparred with its Tamiflu partner Roche in 2005 claiming Roche had not put forth enough effort to make the antiviral a blockbuster. The two companies reached a new agreement late that year with Roche agreeing to a one-time $62.5 million payment and increased royalties.

The 2006 acquisition of Corus Pharma expanded the company's pipeline of investigational drugs outside its core area of infectious disease. Corus Pharma brought a focus on respiratory diseases adding a late-stage compound that aims to fight cystic fibrosis-related infections.

It also completed a $2.4 billion acquisition of Myogen which had development programs in the area of cardiovascular disease including Letairis. (The 2007 FDA approval of Letairis was the first big payoff from Gilead's foray into areas outside of infectious disease.)

Gilead Sciences shored up its manufacturing capabilities with a couple of acquisitions in 2006 and 2007. It bought Raylo Chemicals formerly a Canada-based subsidiary of Degussa (now Evonik Degussa); Raylo is a manufacturer of active pharmaceutical ingredients and other chemicals used in drug development. It also purchased a manufacturing plant in Ireland in 2007.

Keeping on schedule of at least one acquisition per year the company purchased Navitas Assets in 2008 to gain Cicletanine (pulmonary arterial hypertension) and then bought CV Therapeutics in 2009; the acquired business was later absorbed and its main facilities were renamed Gilead Palo Alto. That $14 billion acquisition brought in candidates in development for chronic angina (chest pain) and other cardiovascular ailments as well as cardiac imaging agents.

Smaller purchases included the 2010 acquisition of inflammatory disease (including rheumatoid arthritis) drug developer CGI Pharmaceuticals in a $120 million deal. Acquisitions in 2011 included the purchase of Arresto Biosciences for $225 million adding potential treatments for a variety of diseases including idiopathic pulmonary fibrosis and tumors and Calistoga Pharmaceuticals for $375 million (plus another $225 million in potential milestone payments) that year; the purchase added cancer and inflammatory disease candidates. In a smaller deal Gilead paid $8 million to license a drug candidate to treat respiratory synctial virus from MicroDose Therapeutx.

EXECUTIVES

EVP Research and Development and Chief Scientific Officer, Norbert W. Bischofberger, age 56, $677,923 total compensation
Chairman and CEO, John C. Martin, age 60, $1,242,095 total compensation
President and COO, John F. Milligan, age 51, $805,008 total compensation
EVP Commercial Operations, Kevin Young, age 54, $596,672 total compensation
SVP and CFO, Robin L. Washington, age 49, $527,505 total compensation
EVP Corporate and Medical Affairs, Gregg H. Alton, age 46, $493,338 total compensation
SVP Human Resources, Kristen M. Metza, age 52
Investor Relations, Andre Torres
Investor Relations, Ruey-Li Hwang
Senior Vice President - Oncology Therapeutics, Roy Baynes
Director, Per Wold-Olsen, age 64
Director, John W. Madigan, age 75
Director, Gordon E. Moore, age 83
Director, Kevin E. Lofton, age 57
Director, Nicholas G. (Nick) Moore, age 69
Director, James M. Denny, age 79
Director, Carla A. Hills, age 78
Director, Etienne F. Davignon, age 79
Director, Gayle E. Wilson, age 69
Director, John F. Cogan, age 64
Director, Richard J. (Rich) Whitley, age 66
Auditors: Ernst&YoungLLP

LOCATIONS

HQ: Gilead Sciences Inc.
333 Lakeside Dr., Foster City CA 94404
Phone: 650-574-3000 **Fax:** 650-578-9264
Web: www.gilead.com

2012 Sales

	$ mil.	% of total
US	5,592	58
Europe	3,332	34
Other countries & regions	777	8
Total	**9,702**	**100**

PRODUCTS/OPERATIONS

2012 Sales

Antiviral product sales		
Truvada	3,181	33
Complera/Eviplera	342	3
Hepsera	108	1
Stribild	57	1
Other product sales		
Ranexa	373	4
Other	126	1
Contract & other	13	-

Selected Products

Antiviral
- Atripla (HIV with Bristol-Myers Squibb)
- Complera/Eviplera (HIV)
- Emtriva (HIV)
- Hepsera (hepatitis B)
- Stribild (HIV)
- Tamiflu (flu treatment royalties from Roche)
- Truvada (fixed-dose combination of Viread and Emtriva for HIV)
- Viread (HIV chronic hepatitis B with liver disease)
- Vistide (AIDS-related cytomegalovirus retinitis)

Other products
- AmBisome (antifungal with Astellas)
- Cayston (cystic fibrosis)
- Flolan (pulmonary hypertension)
- Letairis (pulmonary arterial hypertension)
- Lexiscan/Rapiscan (cardiovascular with Astellas)
- Macugen (age-related macular degeneration royalties from Eyetech)
- Ranexa (chronic angina)

Products in development
- Aztreonam (cystic fibrosis)
- Cobicistat (HIV/AIDS)
- Elvitegravir (HIV/AIDS)
- GS-1101 (leukemia and lymphoma)
- GS-7977 (hepatitis C)
- Integrase (HIV)
- Ranolazine (cardiovascular diabetes)

Selected Acquisitions

2013
- YM BioSciences Inc. ($510 million; Mississauga Canada; oncology development programs)

2012
- Pharmasset Inc. ($11 billion; Princeton New Jersey; hepatitis C)

2011
- Arresto Biosciences Inc. ($225 million; fibrotic diseases and cancer)
- Calistoga Pharmaceuticals Inc. ($375 million plus $225 in potential milestone payments; Seattle; cancer and inflammatory diseases)

2010
- CGI Pharmaceuticals Inc. ($120 million; Branford Connecticut; serious inflammatory diseases)

2009
- CV Therapeutics Inc. ($14 billion; Palo Alto California; cardiovascular disorders)

COMPETITORS

Abbott Labs
Actelion
AstraZeneca
Bausch & Lomb
BioCryst Pharmaceuticals
Boehringer Ingelheim
Bristol-Myers Squibb
Enzon
Genentech
GlaxoSmithKline
Merck
Novartis
Pfizer
Roche Holding
Shire

HISTORICAL FINANCIALS

Company Type: Public

Income Statement FYE: December 31

	REVENUE ($ mil.)	NET INCOME ($ mil.)	NET PROFIT MARGIN	EMPLOYEES
12/11	8,385	2,803	33.4%	4,500
12/10	7,949	2,901	36.5%	4,000
12/09	7,011	2,635	37.6%	3,852
12/08	5,335	2,011	37.7%	3,441
12/07	4,230	1,615	38.2%	2,979
Annual Growth	18.7%	14.8%	—	10.9%

2011 Year-End Financials

Debt ratio: 44.82%
Return on equity: 41.60%
Cash ($ mil.): 9,883
Current ratio: 553.48
Long-term debt ($ mil.): 7,753
No. of shares (mil.): 753
Dividends
Yield: —
Payout: —
Market value ($ mil.): 30,825

	STOCK PRICE ($) FY Close	P/E High/Low		PER SHARE ($) Earnings	Dividends	Book Value
12/11	40.93	12	10	3.55	0.00	8.95
12/10	36.24	15	9	3.32	0.00	7.31
12/09	43.27	18	14	2.82	0.00	7.08
12/08	51.14	26	17	2.10	0.00	4.56
12/07	46.01	48	21	1.68	0.00	3.71
Annual Growth	(2.9%)	—	—	20.6%	—	24.6%

Glacier Bancorp, Inc.

Glacier Bancorp is on a Rocky Mountain high. The holding company owns about a dozen community bank divisions with about 100 locations in Montana Idaho Utah Washington Colorado and Wyoming. Serving individuals small to midsized businesses not-for-profits and public entities the banks offer traditional deposit products and credit cards in addition to retail brokerage and investment services through agreements with third-party providers. Its lending activities consist of commercial real estate loans (about half of the company's loan portfolio) as well as residential mortgages business loans and consumer loans.

In 2012 Glacier Bancorp consolidated its 11 bank subsidiaries under a single charter to help cut down on regulatory costs but the banks continue to operate under their own brands. The company believes that maintaining local brands and management teams with knowledge of their markets allows for more effective decision making at the community level compared to a centralized business model.

Glacier Bancorp has built its banking empire partly through acquisitions –about a dozen of them in 2000. Recent transactions have included the purchase of First National Bank & Trust in Wyoming in 2009 and the 2008 acquisition of Bank of the San Juans which marked the company's first entry into Colorado.

Glacier Bancorp hopes to capitalize on additional acquisition opportunities that it expects to arise as small banks deal with new industry regulations. The company is also banking on organic growth with the populations of the states in its market area growing faster than the national average thanks to an influx of retiring Baby Boomers and an increase in energy- and natural resource-related jobs.

An improved overall economic environment helped Glacier Bancorp to cut its provisions for loan losses in 2010 enhaning the company's profitability. Net income however was down the following year (from more than $42 million to $17.5) as the company recorded writedowns of goodwill related to losses at its Mountain West banking division and a decline in credit quality at 1st Bank.

EXECUTIVES

President CEO and Director, Michael J. (Mick) Blodnick, age 59, $346,662 total compensation
SVP Human Resources, Robin S. Roush
SVP CFO and Treasurer, Ronald J. (Ron) Copher, age 55, $209,098 total compensation
President and CEO Mountain West Bank, Jon W. Hippler, age 67, $273,800 total compensation
Chairman Glacier Bancorp and Glacier Bank, Everit A. Sliter, age 73
SVP Information Technology, Mark D. MacMillan
Chairman Mountain West Bank, Charles R. Nipp
VP Internal Audit, Jessica H. Rice
SVP Operations, Marcia L. Johnson
SVP Credit Administration, Barry L. Johnston
VP Compliance, April D. Kelso
SVP and Controller, Donald B. McCarthy
VP Information Technology, Glenn G. Nelson
SVP Internal Audit, Ryan T. Screnar
VP Information Security, Sam G. Mauch
VP Enterprise-Wide Risk Management, T. J. Frickle
EVP and Chief Administrative Officer, Don J. Chery, $209,098 total compensation
Chairman First Security Bank of Missoula, Christopher B. Swartley
Chairman First Bank of Montana, William C. Spratt
Chairman Western Security Bank, John O. Weber
Chairman 1st Bank, Gerald L. Goulding
Chairman Big Sky Western Bank, Michael R. Scholz
Chairman Valley Bank of Helena, Kenneth V. Carpenter
Chairman Bank of the San Juans, Thomas V. Melchior
Secretary, LeeAnn Wardinsky
VP Internal Audit, Douglas A. Daufel
VP and Principal Accounting Officer, Angela L. Dose
VP Internal Audit, James J. Joslin
VP Internal Audit, Debra M. McGlone
Chairman First National Bank & Trust, Richard S. Nelson
Chairman Citizens Community Bank, Diana B. Lyon
Director, Allen J. Fetscher, age 66
President CEO and Director, Michael J. (Mick) Blodnick, age 59
Director, L. Peter Larson, age 73
Director, James M. English, age 67
Director, Sherry L. Cladouhos
Director, John W. Murdoch, age 69
Director, Dallas I. Herron, age 67
Director, Craig A. Langel, age 61
Director, Douglas J. McBride, age 59
Auditors: BKDLLP

LOCATIONS

HQ: Glacier Bancorp Inc.
49 Commons Loop, Kalispell MT 59901-2679
Phone: 406-756-4200 **Fax:** 920-429-4799
Web: www.shopko.com

2011 Locations

	No.
Montana	53
Idaho	29
Wyoming	14
Utah	4
Colorado	3
Washington	3
Total	**106**

PRODUCTS/OPERATIONS

2011 Sales

	$ mil.	% of total
Interest		
Commercial loans	130	37
Investment securities	76	21
Residential real estate loans	33	9
Consumer & other loans	40	11
Noninterest		
Service charges & other fees	44	12
Gain on sale of loans	21	6
Miscellaneous loan fees & charges	3	1
Other	9	3
Total	**358**	**100**

Selected Bank Divisions

1st Bank (Wyoming)
Bank of the San Juans (Colorado)
Big Sky Western Bank (Montana)
Citizens Community Bank (Idaho)
First Bank of Montana
First National Bank & Trust (Wyoming)
First Security Bank (Montana)
Glacier Bank (Montana)
Mountain West Bank (Idaho)
Valley Bank of Helena (Montana)
Western Security Bank (Montana)

COMPETITORS

BancWest
Eagle Bancorp
First Citizens Banc Corp
First Interstate
Sterling Financial (WA)
U.S. Bancorp
Wells Fargo
Zions Bancorporation

HISTORICAL FINANCIALS

Company Type: Public

Income Statement FYE: December 31

	ASSETS ($ mil.)	NET INCOME ($ mil.)	INCOME AS % OF ASSETS	EMPLOYEES
12/11	7,187	17	0.2%	1,653
12/10	6,759	42	0.6%	1,674
12/09	6,191	34	0.6%	1,739
12/08	5,553	65	1.2%	1,662
12/07	4,817	68	1.4%	1,580
Annual Growth	10.5%	(29.0%)	—	1.1%

2011 Year-End Financials

Debt ratio: 16.62%
Return on equity: 2.06%
Cash ($ mil.): 128
Current ratio: —
Long-term debt ($ mil.): 1,194
No. of shares (mil.): 71
Dividends
Yield: —
Payout: 216.67%
Market value ($ mil.): 865

	STOCK PRICE ($) FY Close	P/E High/Low		PER SHARE ($) Earnings	Dividends	Book Value
12/11	12.03	66	38	0.24	0.00	11.82
12/10	15.11	31	21	0.61	0.52	11.66
12/09	13.72	35	21	0.56	0.52	11.13
12/08	19.02	23	12	1.19	0.52	11.04
12/07	18.74	20	14	1.28	0.49	9.85
Annual Growth	(10.5%)	—	—	(34.2%)	—	4.7%

Gleacher & Co, Inc. (DE)

Gleacher & Co. provides advisory services capital raising research and securities and brokerage services to institutional clients in the US and Europe. The investment bank's MBS/ABS & Rates arm sells and trades asset and mortgage-backed securities. Gleacher's Corporate Credit unit offers sales and trading on a range of debt securities. Another subsidiary ClearPoint Funding (acquired in 2011) engages in residential mortgage lending through the origination processing and underwriting of single and multi-family loans in 43 states. Its FA Technology Ventures subsidiary provides growth capital to technology firms. Gleacher & Company has offices in New York Illinois California Connecticut and New Jersey.

Change in Company Type

Gleacher & Co. has put itself up for sale. Following two years of losses the struggling investment bank in August 2012 announced that it is exploring strategic alternatives including selling itself and raising money from outside investors.

Financial Analysis

Gleacher's sales declined 3% in 2011 vs. 2010 while the firm marked its second consecutive year of unprofitability as losses widened. Indeed underperforming Gleacher has been unprofitable in seven of the past 10 years.

Strategy

The firm put itself up for sale in 2012 despite a reorganization launched in mid-2011 designed to save the business by focusing on its fixed-income operations. Under CEO Tom Hughes the firm has tried to turn itself around by closing unprofitable units (including its equities business) slashing its workforce and overhauling management. It is looking to capitalize on opportunities in the mortgage-backed securities and credit markets while realigning the investment banking practice to enhance its position as a leading advisor and to deliver the capital-raising capabilities of its fixed income business to corporate clients. Gleacher is also looking to build out its mortgage origination platform following the acquisition of ClearPoint Funding in early 2011. Gleacher is looking to key industries such as real estate financial services aerospace and defense technology media and telecom and manufacturing.

The company exited its underperforming equities division in 2011 and realigned its investment banking division. The strategic shift underscores the firm's commitment to its core fixed income operations.

Mergers and Acquisitions

Gleacher & Co. launched a residential mortgage banking business in 2011 after it acquired ClearPoint Funding a residential mortgage lender based in Massachusetts. The deal extended Gleacher's mortgage platform and diversified its business.

Ownership

Private equity firm MatlinPatterson is Gleacher & Co's. largest shareholder with about 28% of its shares. Chairman Eric Gleacher owns about 11% of the firm.

Company Background

The firm was founded by its chairman and long-time Wall Street deal maker Eric Gleacher. National Westminster Bank bought Gleacher in 1995 for $135 million. Four years later Mr. Gleacher cut his ties with the British bank and took the firm private forming Gleacher Partners. In 2009 brokerage firm Broadpoint Securities acquired the firm and adopted the Gleacher name.

EXECUTIVES

Chairman, Eric J. Gleacher, age 71, $200,577 total compensation
CEO and Director, Thomas J. (Tom) Hughes, age 54
Managing Director Investment-Grade Fixed Income Trading, Robert B. Cox
COO, John Griff, age 56
Managing Director; Head Equity Capital Markets Origination, J. Scott Coburn
President DESCAP, Robert M. (Rob) Fine, $187,500 total compensation
Head Trading DESCAP, Robert Tirschwell
Managing Director Mergers and Acquisitions Advisory Services, David M. Reed Jr.
Chief Administrative Officer, Laurence Mascera
Managing Director and Head Investment Banking, Tim O'Connor
Managing Director and Co-Head Restructuring Advisory Group, Robert Kost
Secretary and General Counsel Broadpoint Gleacher Securities Group and Broadpoint Capital, Patricia A. Arciero-Craig, age 44, $250,000 total compensation
Managing Director Investment-Grade Fixed Income Sales, William F. (Bill) Parry
Managing Director; Head Capital Markets Origination, Keith (Lex) Malas
Executive Managing Director; Head Debt Capital Markets, Joseph Mannello
Vice Chairman Equity Capital Markets, Richard Prati
President Equity Capital Markets, Curt Snyder
CEO Equity Capital Markets, Robert (Bob) Meier
Head Trading Equity Capital Markets, Richard Brown
Acting CFO; Controller and COO Broadpoint Capital, Jeffrey H. Kugler, age 52
Principal Advisory Services, Sunny Cheung
VP Advisory Services, William Cooling
Managing Director; Head Real Estate, Steve Hentschel
Managing Director and Co-Head Restructuring and Recapitalization Advisory Group, Richard NeJame
VP, Matt Pennino
Managing Director and Head Sales Equity Capital Markets, Myles Lavelle
Head Research Equity Capital Markets, Mark Conley
Managing Director; Head High Yield Bank Loan and Convertible Institutional Sales, Gregory Sullivan
Managing Director; Co-Head Trading Debt Capital Markets, John Hale
Managing Director; Co-Head Trading Debt Capital Markets, Riaz Haidri
Managing Director; Co-Head Investment-Grade Fixed-Income Sales, Richard J. Crescenzo
Managing Director; Co-Head Investment-Grade Fixed-Income Sales, Douglas J. Scales
Managing Director; Head Investment-Grade Trading, Robert Gorham
Managing Director; Head Bank Loan Trading, Marc Berg
Managing Director Investment-Grade Fixed Income Desk Analyst, Douglas R. Colandrea
VP and Senior Research Analyst, Nam Sung Ji
Director, Bruce C. Rohde, age 63
Director, Marshall A. Cohen, age 76
Director, Henry S. Bienen, age 72
CEO and Director, Thomas J. (Tom) Hughes, age 54
Director, Mark R. Patterson, age 60
Director, Christopher R. Pechock, age 47
Director, Robert S. Yingling, age 50
Director, Robert A. Gerard, age 67
Auditors: PricewaterhouseCoopersLLP

LOCATIONS

HQ: Gleacher & Co, Inc. (DE)
1290 Avenue of the Americas, New York, NY 10104
Phone: 212 273-7100
Web: www.gleacher.com

PRODUCTS/OPERATIONS

2011 Sales

	$ mil.	% of total
Principal transactions	89	33
Commissions	71	26
Investment banking	33	12
Investment banking revenue from related party	-	-
Investment gains net	3	1
Interest income	66	24
Gains from acquisition	2	1
Total	**273**	**100**

COMPETITORS

Cowen Group
Jefferies Group
Ladenburg Thalmann
Oppenheimer Holdings
Robert W. Baird & Co.
Stifel Financial
Wedbush Securities
William Blair

HISTORICAL FINANCIALS

Company Type: Public

Income Statement FYE: December 31

	ASSETS ($ mil.)	NET INCOME ($ mil.)	INCOME AS % OF ASSETS	EMPLOYEES
12/11	3,303	(82)	—	453
12/10	1,657	(20)	—	368
12/09	1,216	54	4.5%	342
12/08	694	(17)	—	255
12/07	274	(19)	—	211
Annual Growth	86.3%	—	—	21.0%

2011 Year-End Financials

Debt ratio: 6.49%
Return on equity: (-31.69)%
Cash ($ mil.): 46
Current ratio: —
Long-term debt ($ mil.): 214
No. of shares (mil.): 120
Dividends
Yield: —
Payout: —
Market value ($ mil.): 203

	STOCK PRICE ($) FY Close	P/E High	P/E Low	PER SHARE ($) Earnings	Dividends	Book Value
12/11	1.68	—	—	(0.67)	0.00	2.14
12/10	2.37	—	—	(0.17)	0.00	2.65
12/09	4.46	16	3	0.53	0.00	2.65
12/08	2.97	—	—	(0.25)	0.00	1.23
12/07	1.18	—	—	(0.71)	0.00	1.42
Annual Growth	9.2%	—	—	—	—	10.8%

Global Partners LP

Global Partners (formerly Global Companies) imports petroleum products from global sources but its marketing is largely regional. The company wholesales heating oil residual fuel oil diesel oil kerosene and gasoline to commercial retail and wholesale customers in New England. A major player in the regional home heating oil market Global Partners operates storage facilities at 23 bulk terminals each with a storage capacity of more than 50000 barrels and with a collective storage capacity of 10.2 million barrels. It also owns and supplies a network of gasoline stations. Wholesale revenues accounts for the bulk of the company's sales.

Sales & Marketing

To secure an uninterrupted fuel supply Global Partners also maintains throughput or exchange agreements at more than 50 bulk terminals and inland storage facilities. In 2011 the company sold unbranded gasoline and diesel to more than 1110 wholesale distributors and home heating oil to 1015. It has a long term relationship with Exxon Mobil which accounted for 19% of sales that year. The company operates 540 outlets in New England New York New Jersey and Pennsylvania.

Financial Analysis

An improving economy reflected in robust refined petroleum product prices and increased demand for gasoline lifted Global Partners' revenues in 2010. However increased costs related to its terminal and gas station purchases and expansions cut into the company's net income.

In 2011 Global Partners almost doubled its revenues due to the expansion of its assets higher refined petroleum product prices and increased volume sales. However the same high product prices and expansion activities drove up operating expenses and trimmed the company's net income for the year.

Strategy

Global Partners is looking to expand both within and beyond the Northeast US. In this regard in 2012 Global Partners acquired Alliance Energy a gasoline distributor and gas stations/convenience store operator for $180 million. That year the company also signed a long-term lease agreement with Getty Realty Corp. to supply gasoline to and operate about 90 of Getty's gas station in Queens Manhattan and the Bronx as well as in Long Island and Westchester County.

In 2010 in order to expand its wholesale supply business the company acquired about 190 retail gas stations in three states in the Northeast from Exxon Mobil and some of its dealers for $202.3 million.

Pursuing a strategy of growing its storage capacity in 2010 Global Partners acquired three terminals in Newburgh New York from Warex Terminals for $47.5 million.

In addition in 2010 it completed an ethanol and rail expansion project that added 180000 barrels of ethanol storage at its Albany New York refined petroleum product terminal.

Ownership

The Slifka family controls about 21% of the company.

Company Background

Global Partners was founded in 1933 as a one-truck heating oil retailer by current CEO Eric Slifka's grandfather Abraham Slifka.

EXECUTIVES

VP Human Resources, Barbara E. Rosenbloom
Chairman Global GP LLC, Alfred A. Slifka, age 79
VP and CIO Global GP LLC, James R. (Jim) Shelton
SVP Light Oil Supply and Distribution, Mark Romaine
EVP Treasurer and Chief Accounting Officer, Charles A. (Chuck) Rudinsky, age 64, $273,000 total compensation
COO CFO and Director, Thomas J. (Tom) Hollister, age 57, $578,000 total compensation
VP Marine Transportation Fuels and Bunkering Manager, Dana Fraktman
Manager Premium Fuels Diesel Marine and BioFuels, Duane McLevedge
SVP Marketing, Joseph (Joe) DeStefano
VP Heavy Oil Marketing and Manager Industrial Fuels Marketing, Dennis Bowersox
SVP Heavy Oil Supply and Distribution, F. P. (Philip) Sears III
President CEO and Director, Eric Slifka, age 46, $800,000 total compensation
SVP Administration, Kathleen A. Schoeffler
Vice Chairman Global GP LLC, Richard Slifka, age 71
EVP General Counsel and Secretary, Edward J. Faneuil, age 59, $376,000 total compensation
Sales Unbranded Gasoline, Felecia LeBlanc
Marketing Operations Manager Home Heating Oil, Michael LaFrance
VP Municipal and Commercial Bids, Kevin Young
Marketing Coordinator Natural Gas and Electricity, Rana Foley
International Arbitrage Supply, Bela Nemeth
SVP Terminals and Operations, William G. Davidson
VP Credit, Robert J. Fraczkiewicz
VP Marketing, Ray Gincavage
VP Environmental Health and Safety Operations, Tom Keefe
Manager Wholesale Risk, Bill Braunig
VP Commercial Fuels, Miles Allen
Treasurer, Daphne H. Foster
Marketing Manager Home Heating Oil, Steve Schooley
Regional Marketing Manager Home Heating Oil, Judy Delaney
Regional Sales Manager Home Heating Oil, Margie Wong
Scheduling Supply, Bernie Kelly
Demurrage Supply, Gregory Rudoy
Ship Chartering Supply, Clay Sack
CIO, Kenneth J. Piddington
President Alliance Gasoline Division, Andrew Slifka
Director Global GP LLC, Kenneth I. Watchmaker, age 69
Director Global GP LLC, David K. McKown, age 74
COO CFO and Director, Thomas J. (Tom) Hollister, age 57
President CEO and Director, Eric Slifka, age 46
Vice Chairman Global GP LLC, Richard Slifka, age 71
Director Global GP LLC, Robert J. McCool, age 73
Auditors: Ernst&YoungLLP

LOCATIONS

HQ: Global Partners LP
800 South St. Ste. 200, Waltham MA 02154
Phone: 781-894-8800 **Fax:** 781-398-4160
Web: www.globalp.com

PRODUCTS/OPERATIONS

2011 Sales

	$ mil.	% of total
Wholesale	13,694	92
Commercial	1,082	8
Other	58	-
Total	**14,835**	**100**

Selected Products

Biofuels
Bunker oil
Diesel oil
Distillates
Gasoline
Home heating oil
Kerosene
Residual fuel oil

COMPETITORS

Bayside Fuel
Exxon Mobil
George Warren
Getty Petroleum Marketing
Gulf Oil
Highlands Fuel Delivery
Koch Industries Inc.
Sprague Resources
Tauber Oil
Warren Equities

HISTORICAL FINANCIALS

Company Type: Public

Income Statement FYE: December 31

	REVENUE ($ mil.)	NET INCOME ($ mil.)	NET PROFIT MARGIN	EMPLOYEES
12/11	14,835	19	0.1%	264
12/10	7,801	27	0.3%	286
12/09	5,818	34	0.6%	250
12/08	9,019	21	0.2%	220
12/07	6,757	47	0.7%	230
Annual Growth	21.7%	(19.9%)	—	3.5%

2011 Year-End Financials

Debt ratio: 42.48%
Return on equity: 6.14%
Cash ($ mil.): 48
Current ratio: 183.24
Long-term debt ($ mil.): 731
No. of shares (mil.): 21
Dividends
Yield: —
Payout: 229.89%
Market value ($ mil.): 472

	STOCK PRICE ($) FY Close	P/E High/Low		PER SHARE ($) Earnings	Dividends	Book Value
12/11	21.87	34	17	0.87	0.00	14.62
12/10	27.40	17	12	1.59	1.96	14.67
12/09	22.96	11	4	2.51	1.95	12.09
12/08	11.30	20	5	1.40	1.95	10.98
12/07	26.05	29	17	1.38	1.87	12.27
Annual Growth	(4.3%)	—	—	(10.9%)	—	4.5%

Goldman Sachs Group, Inc.

Goldman Sachs has traditionally possessed the Midas touch in the investment banking world. A global leader in mergers and acquisitions advice and securities underwriting Goldman offers a gamut of investment banking and asset management services to corporate and government clients worldwide as well as institutional and individual investors. It owns Goldman Sachs Execution & Clearing one of the largest market makers on the NYSE and a leading market maker for fixed income products currencies and commodities. Through affiliates GS Capital Partners GS Mezzanine Partners and others Goldman Sachs is also one of the largest private equity investors in the world.

HISTORY

German immigrant-cum-Philadelphia retailer Marcus Goldman moved to New York in 1869 and began buying customers' promissory notes from jewelers to resell to banks. Goldman's son-in-law came aboard in 1882 and the firm became Goldman Sachs & Co. in 1885.

Two years later Goldman Sachs began offering US-UK foreign exchange and currency services. To serve such clients as Sears Roebuck it expanded to Chicago and St. Louis. In 1896 it joined the NYSE.

While the firm increased its European contracts Goldman's son Henry made it a major source of financing for US industry. In 1906 it co-managed its first public offering United Cigar Manufacturers (later General Cigar). By 1920 it had underwritten IPOs for Sears B.F. Goodrich and Merck.

Sidney Weinberg made partner in 1927 and stayed until his death in 1969. In the 1930s Goldman Sachs entered securities dealing and sales. After WWII it became a leader in investment banking co-managing Ford's 1956 IPO. In the 1970s it pioneered buying blocks of stock for resale.

Under Weinberg's son John Goldman Sachs became a leader in mergers and acquisitions. The 1981 purchase of J. Aron gave the firm a significant commodities presence and helped it grow in South America.

Seeking capital after 1987's market crash Goldman Sachs raised more than $500 million from Sumitomo for a 12% nonvoting interest in the firm (since reduced to 3%). The Kamehameha Schools/Bishop Estate of Hawaii an educational trust also invested.

The 1994 bond crash and a decline in new debt issues led Goldman Sachs to cut staffing for the first time since the 1980s. But problems went deeper. Partners began leaving and taking their equity. Cost cuts a stronger bond market and the long bull market helped the firm rebound; firm members sought protection through limited liability partnership status. The firm also extended the period during which partners can cash out (slowing the cash drain) and limited the number of people entitled to a share of profits. Overseas growth in 1996 and 1997 focused on the UK and Asia.

After three decades of resistance the partners in 1998 voted to sell the public a minority stake in the firm but market volatility led to postponement. Goldman Sachs also suffered from involvement with Long-Term Capital Management ultimately contributing $300 million to its bailout.

In 1999 Jon Corzine then co-chairman and co-CEO announced that he would leave the group after seeing it through its IPO and Goldman Sachs finally went public that year in an offering valued at close to $4 billion. In 2000 Corzine was elected to a US Senate seat. The New Jersey Democrat spent more than $64 million on his campaign (a record) nearly $61 million of it from his own personal wealth (also a record). Corzine went on to win New Jersey's gubernatorial race in 2005.

In early 2004 Goldman president and COO John Thain left the firm to assume the helm of the New York Stock Exchange. Lloyd Blankfein was named his successor and became chairman and CEO in 2006 when his predecessor Henry "Hank" Paulson was named secretary of the US Treasury.

At the height of the economic crisis Goldman Sachs converted to a bank holding company. It formed subsidiary Goldman Sachs Bank USA (GS Bank USA) to manage bank loan trading mortgage originations and other activities. The Federal Reserve mandated the change for Goldman Sachs and fellow investment bank Morgan Stanley. The shift marked a monumental change on Wall Street as it put an end to the independent brokerage firm model that had been a mainstay in the US since reform measures were implemented during the Great Depression. Rivals Merrill Lynch Lehman Brothers and Bear Stearns had already merged with larger banks or filed for bankruptcy. The bank holding company structure brought increased regulation but allowed Goldman Sachs to acquire commercial banks –all in an effort to shore up the company's balance sheet.

In the days following the Federal Reserve announcement Warren Buffett's Berkshire Hathaway invested $5 billion in Goldman Sachs and acquired an option to assume $5 billion more of the company's common shares. Goldman Sachs made an additional $5 billion worth of stock available in a public offering. Additionally the US government stepped in with funding for Goldman Sachs in late 2008 when it announced an economic stimulus plan to buy some $250 billion worth of preferred shares of the nation's top banks; approximately $10 billion went to Goldman Sachs.

The capital infusions helped but didn't completely shield Goldman Sachs from the financial crisis the effects of which were felt worldwide. To cut costs the company trimmed some 10% of its workforce. It eventually returned to profitability in 2009 and paid back the money it received from the government but still drew ire from politicians over what have been perceived to be extravagant pay packages for its top employees. (The firm's extravagant year-end bonuses had become the stuff of legend.)

Goldman Sachs opened a new $1.8-billion headquarters building in New York City's lower Manhattan in 2009.

EXECUTIVES

Member Management Committee, Richard A. Friedman, age 54
EVP CFO and Head Operations Technology Finance and Services Division, David A. Viniar, age 56, $600,000 total compensation
EVP General Counsel and Co-Head Legal, Gregory K. Palm, age 63
EVP General Counsel and Co-Head Legal, Esta E. Stecher, age 54
Member Management Committee, Donald R. Mullen
Member Management Committee; Head Latin America, Kevin W. Kennedy, age 63
Chairman and CEO, Lloyd C. Blankfein, age 57, $600,000 total compensation
Vice Chairman; Co-Head Global Investment Banking Division, John S. Weinberg, age 54, $600,000 total compensation
Vice Chairman; Chairman Asia; Global Head Growth Markets Business, J. Michael (Mike) Evans, age 54, $837,365 total compensation
Member Management Committee Controller and Chief Accounting Officer, Sarah E. Smith
EVP and Global Head Compliance, Alan M. Cohen, age 61
Member Management Committee; Co-Head Investment Management Division, Edward C. Forst, age 51
Member Management Committee; Co-Head Investment Banking Division, David M. Solomon
Member Management Committee, Masanori Mochida
Vice Chairman; Co-CEO Goldman Sachs International, Michael S. Sherwood, age 46
Member Management Committee; Co-President Asia, David C. Ryan
EVP Chief of Staff and Secretary, John F. W. Rogers
President COO and Director, Gary D. Cohn, age 51, $600,000 total compensation
Member Management Committee; Co-Head Investment Management Division, Timothy J. O'Neill
Member Management Committee; Co-President Asia, Yusuf A. Alireza
EVP and Global Head Human Capital Management, Edith W. Cooper
Member Management Committee; Global Head Equities Sales and Securities Distribution Europe, Michael D. Daffey
Member Management Committee; Co-CEO Goldman Sachs International and Co-Chairman Investment Banking, Richard J. Gnoodde
Member Management Committee; Global Co-Head Securities Division, David B. Heller
Deputy General Counsel and International General Counsel, David J. Greenwald
Member Management Committee; Head Firmwide Business Selection and Conflicts Clearance Group, Gwen R. Libstag
Member Management Committee; Global Co-Head Securities Division, Harvey M. Schwartz
Global Head Equity Capital Markets, Matthew Westerman
Member Management Committee and Chief Administrative Officer, Jeffrey W. Schroeder
Member Management Committee; Co-Chairman Investment Banking, Gordon E. Dyal
Member Management Committee, Isabelle Ealet
Member Management Committee, Pablo J. Salame
Member Management Committee, Steven H. Strongin
Member Management Committee, Yoel Zaoui
Director, Lois D. Juliber, age 63
Director, William W. George, age 69
Director, John H. Bryan, age 75
Director, Stephen Friedman, age 74
Director, Claes Dahlback, age 64
Director, James A. Johnson, age 68
Director, Debora L. Spar, age 48
President COO and Director, Gary D. Cohn, age 51
Auditors: PricewaterhouseCoopersLLP

LOCATIONS

HQ: The Goldman Sachs Group Inc.
200 West St., New York NY 10282
Phone: 212-902-1000 **Fax:** 212-902-9316
Web: www.goldmansachs.com

PRODUCTS/OPERATIONS

2011 Sales

	$ mil.	% of total
Interest	13,174	36
Market making	9,287	25
Investment management	4,691	13
Investment banking	4,361	12
Commissions & fees	3,773	10
Other	1,507	4
Total	**36,793**	**100**

Selected Subsidiaries

Goldman Sachs & Co.
Goldman Sachs Bank USA
Goldman Sachs Credit Partners L.P. (Bermuda)
Goldman Sachs Financial Markets L.P.
Goldman Sachs International (UK)
Goldman Sachs Japan Co. Ltd.
Goldman Sachs Mortgage Company
GSTM LLC
  Goldman Sachs Execution & Clearing L.P.
J. Aron & Company

COMPETITORS

BMO Capital Markets
CIBC World Markets
Citigroup Global Markets
Credit Suisse (USA)
Deutsche Bank Securities (USA)
FMR
JPMorgan Chase
Lazard
Merrill Lynch
Morgan Stanley
Nomura Securities
RBC Capital Markets
UBS

HISTORICAL FINANCIALS

Company Type: Public

Income Statement FYE: December 31

	ASSETS ($ mil.)	NET INCOME ($ mil.)	INCOME AS % OF ASSETS	EMPLOYEES
12/11	923,225	4,442	0.5%	33,300
12/10	911,332	8,354	0.9%	35,700
12/09	848,942	13,385	1.6%	32,500
12/08*	1,112,225	(780)	—	0
11/08	884,547	2,322	0.3%	30,067
Annual Growth	1.1%	17.6%	—	2.6%

*Fiscal year change

2011 Year-End Financials

Debt ratio: 25.97%
Return on equity: 6.31%
Cash ($ mil.): 120,272
Current ratio: —
Long-term debt ($ mil.): 239,745
No. of shares (mil.): 485
Dividends
Yield: —
Payout: 31.04%
Market value ($ mil.): 43,901

	STOCK PRICE ($) FY Close	P/E High	P/E Low	PER SHARE ($) Earnings	Dividends	Book Value
12/11	90.43	37	19	4.51	0.00	144.97
12/10	168.16	13	9	13.18	1.40	152.42
12/09	168.84	8	2	22.13	1.52	137.28
12/08*	75.97	—	—	(2.15)	1.40	142.48
11/08	78.99	49	11	4.47	1.40	145.45
Annual Growth	3.4%	—	—	0.2%	—	(0.1%)

*Fiscal year change

Goodyear Tire & Rubber Co.

Folks at The Goodyear Tire & Rubber Company never worry about flat tires. The company leverages a global alliance with Sumitomo Rubber Industries designed to dominate the tire industry. (It trails Bridgestone and Michelin.) Goodyear sells mainly new tires under the Goodyear Dunlop Kelly Fulda Debica and Sava brand names. Through its alliance with Sumitomo Goodyear makes Dunlop tires for sale in North America and Western Europe. In Japan the tire makers own businesses that separately sell to OEMs and aftermarkets. Goodyear operates 50+ plants in more than 20 countries and about 1400 tire/auto repair centers. More than 60% of sales are made outside the US.

HISTORY

In 1898 Frank and Charles Seiberling founded a tire and rubber company in Akron Ohio and named it after Charles Goodyear (inventor of the vulcanization process 1839). The debut of the Quick Detachable tire and the Universal Rim (1903) made Goodyear the world's largest tire maker by 1916.

Goodyear began manufacturing in Canada in 1910 and over the next two decades it expanded into Argentina Australia and the Dutch East Indies. The company established its own rubber plantations in Sumatra (now part of Indonesia) in 1916.

Financial woes led to reorganization in 1921 and investment bankers forced the Seiberlings out. Succeeding caretaker management Paul Litchfield began three decades as CEO in 1926 a time in which Goodyear emerged to become the world's largest rubber company.

Goodyear blimps served as floating billboards nationwide by the 1930s. During that decade Goodyear opened company stores acquired tire maker Kelly-Springfield (1935) and began producing tires made from synthetic rubber (1937). After WWII Goodyear was an innovative leader in technologies such as polyester tire cord (1962) and the bias-belted tire (1967).

By 1980 Goodyear had introduced radial tire brands such as the all-weather Tiempo the Eagle and the Arriva as it led the US market.

Thwarting British financier Sir James Goldsmith's takeover attempt in 1986 CEO Robert Mercer raised $1.7 billion by selling the company's non-tire businesses (Motor Wheel Goodyear Aerospace) and by borrowing heavily.

Recession overcapacity and price-cutting in 1990 led to hard times for tire makers. After suffering through 1990 its first money-losing year since the Depression Goodyear lured Stanley Gault out of retirement. He ceased marketing tires exclusively through Goodyear's dealer network by selling tires through Wal-Mart Kmart and Sears. Gault also cut costs through layoffs plant closures and spending reductions and returned Goodyear to profitability in 1991.

The company increased its presence in the US retail market in 1995 when it began selling tires through 860 Penske Auto Centers and 300 Montgomery Ward auto centers. President Samir Gibara succeeded chairman Gault as CEO in 1996. That year Goodyear bought Poland's leading tire maker T C Debica and a 60% stake in South African tire maker Contred (acquiring the rest in 1998).

In 1997 Goodyear formed an alliance with Sumitomo Rubber Industries under which the companies agreed to make and market tires for one another in Asia and North America. The next year Goodyear sold its Celeron Oil subsidiary which operated the All American Pipeline and acquired the remaining 26% stake in tire distributor Brad Ragan (commercial and retail outlets in the US) for $20.7 million.

The company acquired Sumitomo Rubber Industries' North American and European Dunlop tire businesses in 1999. The acquisition returned Goodyear to its #1 position in the tire-making industry. However the company recorded drastically low profits that year because it had cut tire production and was unable to meet supplier demands.

To improve profitability Goodyear increased tire prices in 2000 and began consolidating its manufacturing operations. Goodyear also announced plans to combine its commercial tire service centers with those of Treadco through a joint venture named Wingfoot Commercial Tire Systems. Despite record sales in 2000 the company's profits hit some hard road prompting Goodyear to lay off 10% of its workforce and implement other cost-cutting efforts.

Early in 2001 the company announced that it would close its Mexican tire plant. The same year the company agreed to replace Firestone Wilderness AT tires with Goodyear tires for Ford owners as part of Ford's big Firestone tire recall.

Early in 2002 Goodyear announced that its recent job cuts and manufacturing consolidation resulted in an $85 million decrease in annual operating costs. Later in the year the tire maker became embroiled in an age discrimination lawsuit claiming unfair job evaluations for the company's older employees. Blaming a slow US economy Goodyear announced plans to cut 450 jobs at its Union City Tennessee manufacturing plant. The job cuts were just the beginning of what would be a series of operational adjustments made as part of a Capital Structure Improvement Plan formally launched in 2003.

Although Goodyear once owned about 10% of its Sumitomo Rubber Industries it sold more than 20 million shares of its Japanese counterpart stock back to the tire maker in 2003. Later in the year as the company was embroiled in a lengthy debate with the United Steelworkers union it was announced that the Huntsville Alabama tire manufacturing plant would be closed. Goodyear also announced that it would cut 500 non-union salaried employees in North America. Later that same year it was announced that Goodyear was chosen by Volvo to be the truck manufacturer's primary tire supplier in North America; Goodyear had a similar contract with Mack Trucks.

Qantas Airways announced in early 2004 that it chose Goodyear to provide tires for the Australia-based company's Jetstar Airways. Later in the year Goodyear acquired the shares of Slovenia-based Sava Tires it did not already own and the company's Goodyear Dunlop Tires Europe unit purchased the Sweden-based Dackia retail tire stores. The company announced more job cuts in the non-tire sector in 2004 affecting Goodyear's engineered products and chemical units.

In 2005 Goodyear sold its stake in Goodyear Sumatra Plantations (rubber plantations in Indonesia) to rival Bridgestone for $62 million. Later that year the company sold its Wingtack adhesive resin business to Sartomer Company Inc. (a subsidiary of France's TOTAL S.A.) for about $65 million. As 2005 wound to a close the company sold its farm tire business to Titan International for $100 million.

Goodyear called off plans to sell its Chemical Products division. Instead the company integrated its chemical operations with those of its North American Tire division to take greater advantage of operational synergies. The company did however move forward with plans to jettison its Engineered Products division. In 2005 Goodyear secured the services of J.P. Morgan Securities and Goldman Sachs to help it explore opportunities for the sale of Engineered Products. The company struck a deal for The Carlyle Group in 2007 to buy its Engineered Products division for about $1.5 billion.

EXECUTIVES

VP Business Development, David G. Campopiano, age 59

VP Corporate Communications, Edward W. (Ed) Markey

Chairman President and CEO, Richard J. (Rich) Kramer, age 48, $678,523 total compensation

VP and Controller, Richard J. (Rick) Noechel, age 43

President Latin America, Jaime C. Szulc, age 50

VP Government Relations, Isabel H. Jasinowski, age 63

SVP General Counsel and Secretary, David L. (Dave) Bialosky, age 54, $136,364 total compensation

EVP and CFO, Darren R. Wells, age 46, $450,000 total compensation

VP Finance North American Tire, Laura K. Thompson, age 47

VP Commercial Tire Systems North America, Joseph (Joe) Copeland, age 51

Director National Media Relations and Business Communications, Keith Price

SVP Human Resources, Joseph B. (Joe) Ruocco, age 53

VP Global Engineering and Manufacturing Technology, Robert A. (Bob) Novotny
VP Finance Global Procurement, John P. Cavanaugh, age 42
Chief Customer Officer Consumer Tires North American Tire, Jack Winterton
President North American Tire, Steve McCellan, age 46
President Eastern Europe Middle East and Africa, Michel Rzonzef, age 49
President Europe Middle East and Africa, Arthur de Bok, age 50, $500,000 total compensation
Assistant Secretary and Associate General Counsel, Bertram (Bert) Bell, age 61
Assistant Secretary and Associate General Counsel, Anthony E. (Tony) Miller, age 61
VP Global Product Development and Innovation Center Operations, Joe Zekoski, age 59
VP and General Manager Original Equipment Tires North American Tire, Johann Finkelmeier, age 57
VP Financial Planning and Analysis, Marc O. Voorhees, age 53
VP Investor Relations, Gregory A. (Greg) Fritz
SVP Global Operations, Gregory L. (Greg) Smith, age 48
VP Off-Highway North America, Pierre Jambon, age 52
Chief Marketing Officer North American Tire, R. Scott Rogers, age 42
VP and General Manager North American Holdings and Integration, Charles (Chuck) Mick, age 64
Plant Manager Topeka, Tim Davis
SVP Global Communications, Paul Fitzhenry, age 53
Director Corporate Compliance and Ethics, Pat Gorbach
VP and Chief Procurement Officer, Mark W. Purtilar, age 52
SVP and CTO, Jean-Claude Kihn, age 52
Senior Director External Science and Technology Programs, Surendra Chawla
General Director Innovation Center Luxembourg, Marc Junio
VP Supply Chain and Logistics, Kevin Olifiers
Director Finance Argentina, Greg Dooley
VP Internal Audit, Richard Pegher, age 59
Director Organizational Communications, Rob Whitehouse
VP Global Labor Relations, Jim Allen
VP and Treasurer, Scott Honnold, age 47
Director Communications Asia/Pacific Region, Ron D. Castro
Manager Brand and Product PR European Union and Eastern Europe Middle East and Africa, Jens Voelmicke
Manager Brand and Product PR Latin America, Eduardo Arguelles
Director, Rodney O'Neal, age 58
Director, W. Alan McCollough, age 62
Director, G. Craig Sullivan, age 72
Director, James A. (Jim) Firestone, age 57
Director, Peter S. Hellman, age 62
Director, Thomas H. (Tom) Weidemeyer, age 64
Director, Stephanie A. Streeter, age 54
Director, Shirley D. Peterson, age 70
Director, Werner Geissler, age 58
Director, Michael R. Wessel, age 52
Director, James C. (Jim) Boland, age 71
Auditors: PricewaterhouseCoopersLLP

LOCATIONS

HQ: The Goodyear Tire & Rubber Company
1144 E. Market St., Akron OH 44316-0001
Phone: 330-796-2121 **Fax:** 330-796-2222
Web: www.goodyear.com

2011 Sales

	$ mil.	% of total
US	8,397	37
Germany	2,962	13
Other countries	11,408	50
Total	**22,767**	**100**

PRODUCTS/OPERATIONS

2011 Sales

	$ mil.	% of total
North American Tire	9,859	43
Europe Middle East & Africa Tire	8,040	35
Latin American Tire	2,472	11
Asia/Pacific Tire	2,396	11
Total	**22,767**	**100**

Selected Products

Automotive repair services
Chemical products
Natural rubber
Tires
- Automotive
- Aviation
- Buses
- Construction
- Farm
- Mining
- Motorcycles
- Trucks

Tread rubber
Wholesale tires

Selected Subsidiaries

Celeron Corporation
Dapper Tire Co. Inc.
Dunlop Grund und Service Verwaltungs GmbH (Germany)
Dunlop Tyres Limited (UK)
Goodyear Canada Inc.
Goodyear Dalian Tire Company Ltd. (China)
Goodyear de Chile S.A.I.C.
Goodyear de Colombia S.A.
Goodyear do Brasil Productos de Borracha Ltda (Brazil)
Goodyear Dunlop Tires Austria GmbH
Goodyear Dunlop Tires Belgium N.V.
Goodyear Dunlop Tires Czech s.r.o.
Goodyear Dunlop Tires Danmark A/S
Goodyear Dunlop Tires Espana S.A. (Spain)
Goodyear Dunlop Tires Finland OY
Goodyear Dunlop Tires Hellas S.A.I.C. (Greece)
Goodyear Dunlop Tires Hungary Ltd.
Goodyear Dunlop Tires Ireland Ltd
Goodyear Dunlop Tires Italia SpA (Italy)
Goodyear Dunlop Tires Polska Sp z.o.o. (Poland)
Goodyear Dunlop Tires Portugal Unipessoal Lda
Goodyear Dunlop Tires Slovakia s.r.o.
Goodyear Dunlop Tires Suisse S.A. (Switzerland)
The Kelly-Springfield Tyre Company Ltd (UK)
Wingfoot Corporation

COMPETITORS

Bridgestone
Continental AG
Cooper Tire & Rubber
Hankook Tire
Kumho Tire
Marangoni
Michelin
Midas
Pep Boys
Pirelli
Sime Darby
Titan International
Toyo Tire & Rubber
Yokohama Rubber
Zeon

HISTORICAL FINANCIALS

Company Type: Public

Income Statement

FYE: December 31

	REVENUE ($ mil.)	NET INCOME ($ mil.)	NET PROFIT MARGIN	EMPLOYEES
12/11	22,767	343	1.5%	73,000
12/10	18,832	(216)	—	72,000
12/09	16,301	(375)	—	69,000
12/08	19,488	(77)	—	74,700
12/07	19,644	602	3.1%	72,000
Annual Growth	3.8%	(13.1%)	—	0.3%

2011 Year-End Financials

Debt ratio: 29.50%
Return on equity: 45.79%
Cash ($ mil.): 2,772
Current ratio: 165.49
Long-term debt ($ mil.): 4,789
No. of shares (mil.): 244
Dividends
Yield: —
Payout: —
Market value ($ mil.): 3,465

	STOCK PRICE ($) FY Close	P/E High	P/E Low	PER SHARE ($) Earnings	Dividends	Book Value
12/11	14.17	14	7	1.26	0.00	3.06
12/10	11.85	—	—	(0.89)	0.00	2.65
12/09	14.10	—	—	(1.55)	0.00	3.04
12/08	5.97	—	—	(0.32)	0.00	4.24
12/07	28.22	12	8	2.65	0.00	11.87
Annual Growth	(15.8%)	—	—	(17.0%)	—	(28.7%)

Google Inc

If you don't know what the term Google means there's a leading Internet search engine you can use to find out. Taking its name from "googol" – the mathematical term for the value represented by a one followed by 100 zeros –Google offers targeted search results from billions of Web pages. Results are based on a proprietary algorithm; its technology for ranking Web pages is called PageRank. The firm generates revenue through ad sales. Advertisers deliver relevant ads targeted to search queries or Web content. The Google Network is a network of third-party customers that use Google's ad programs to deliver relevant ads to their own sites. Founders Sergey Brin and Larry Page each have nearly 30% voting control.

HISTORY

Google is the product of two computer science grad students Sergey Brin and Larry Page who met in 1995 at Stanford University where they studied methods of searching and organizing large datasets. They discovered a formula to rank the order of random search results by relevancy and in 1997 they adopted the name Google to their findings.

In 1998 the two presented their discovery at the World Wide Web Conference and by 1999 they had raised almost $30 million in funding from private investors venture capital firms and Stanford University. Later that year the Google site was launched.

Brin and Page hired tech industry veteran Eric Schmidt (former CTO at Sun Microsystems and former CEO of Novell) in 2001 as Google's CEO. Brin previously the company's chairman adopted the role of president of technology and Page previously CEO of Google became president of product. Also in 2001 Google launched AdWords its search-based advertising service. The following year the company launched another advertising service the context-based AdSense.

In 2004 the company entered the social networking sphere with the launch of its Orkut product which allows users (by invitation only) to search and connect with one another through online networks of friends. Later that year the once highly secretive company went public in one of the most anticipated IPOs ever raising $1.6 billion.

In 2005 it invested $1 billion for a 5% stake in AOL. As part of a five-year search partnership with AOL it gained ad distribution throughout the content portal's network of sites. In 2006 Google made the most expensive purchase in its history with the $1.65 billion acquisition of online video-sharing site YouTube which it bought in order to complement its online video offering (Google Video). Also that year Google entered China. The company further broadened distribution options for advertisers with the 2006 purchase of dMarc Broadcasting (audio ads) for $102 million.

Also in 2006 the company made high-profile agreements with News Corp. and Viacom's MTV Networks. News Corp. selected Google as the $900 million high bidder for providing search on Myspace and other Fox properties in a multiyear search agreement and in the Viacom deal Google distributed MTV video (shows such as Laguna Beach and Sponge Bob Square Pants) to a variety of sites. (News Corp. sold Myspace in 2011.) Another acquisition included the 2007 purchase of email security company Postini for $625 million in cash a deal that furthered Google's push into business software. Google acquired digital ad firm DoubleClick for a whopping $3.2 billion in 2008.

In 2009 Google pulled out of its investment in AOL selling its 5% stake back to Time Warner for more than $280 million. (The deal helped set the stage for Time Warner's spinoff of AOL later that year.) The next year Google and AOL agreed to extend their partnership through 2015; as part of the deal Google provides mobile and video search services for AOL

Google responded to tougher economic times by cutting costs in 2008 and 2009 when it laid off 100 recruiters and closed down or halted development on a number of projects. These include a service for saving Web pages a catalog search product a virtual-world service and a failed program that sold print advertising for newspapers. It also exited the business of brokering radio ads. Later in 2009 it cut 200 more jobs the biggest round of layoffs not associated with a merger in the company's history.

In 2010 Google branched out from its online services and into the growing market for mobile computing to mixed results when it unveiled its own smart phone called Nexus One (manufactured by partner HTC). Google had high hopes for the phone which it designed to compete with Apple's iPhone Research in Motion's BlackBerry and Palm's Pre. The Nexus One operated on the Android operating system an open source mobile computing system Google acquired in 2005. However the phone's sales were sluggish primarily because Google sold it through the Web. Despite the lack of interest from general consumers the Nexus One was popular with Android developers. Google announced a new version of its Android phone called Nexus S. Not making the same mistake twice it made the phone available at Best Buy in the US and Carphone Warehouse in the UK.

In 2010 Google reversed its strategy of cutting costs by ramping up its acquisition activity. That year the company completed nearly 50 acquisitions for a total of more than $1.8 billion. Its biggest deal that year was the purchase of mobile advertising network AdMob for $681 million. AdMob enables Google to sell mobile advertising on the iPhone and other mobile platforms.

Other major purchases in 2010 included the $123 million buy of On2 Technologies a maker of maker of video compression technology; Slide a social networking widget maker worth $179 million; and Widevine Technologies an anti-piracy software firm it paid some $158 million for in order to boost its online video services. Also that year Google attempted to acquire Groupon an online provider of coupons for local goods and services in a deal that would have been its biggest purchase to date at more than $5 billion. Groupon however turned down the offer.

In 2011 Page re-entered the CEO role and Schmidt was appointed executive chairman. Google completed its biggest acquisition to date in 2012 when it bought phone hardware maker Motorola Mobility Holdings for $12.5 billion.

EXECUTIVES

Executive Chairman, Eric E. Schmidt, age 56, $1 total compensation
SVP Corporate Development and Chief Legal Officer, David C. Drummond, age 48, $450,000 total compensation
VP Access Services, Milo S. Medin, age 49
CEO and Director, Larry E. Page, age 39, $1 total compensation
Co-founder and Director, Sergey Brin, age 38, $1 total compensation
VP New Business Development; General Manager Google.org, Megan J. Smith
VP Engineering, Max R. Levchin, age 37
SVP and CFO, Patrick Pichette, age 49, $450,000 total compensation
SVP and Chief Business Officer, Nikesh Arora, age 44, $450,000 total compensation
VP Search Product and User Experience, Udi Manber
Head GEO and Local, Marissa Mayer
SVP Knowledge, R. Alan Eustace, age 55, $450,000 total compensation
SVP; CEO Google.org, Shona L. Brown, age 46, $250,000 total compensation
SVP Local and Commerce, Jeffrey T. (Jeff) Huber, age 44
SVP YouTube and Video, Salar Kamangar
SVP Ads, Susan Wojcicki
Manager Global Communications and Public Affairs, Lily Lin
VP People Operations, Laszlo Bock
SVP Mobile, Andy Rubin
VP eCommerce, Stephanie Tilenius, age 44
Product Management Director, Mike Huang
SVP, Vic Gundotra
President Operations Japan and Asia Pacific, Daniel Alegre
CIO, Ben Fried
SVP Chrome, Sundar Pichai
President Americas Region, Margaret H. (Margo) Georgiadis
Head India Operations, Rajan Anandan
VP Content, Robert Kyncl
Country Director Canada, Chris O'Neill
VP Mobile Ads, Omar Hamoui
Global Head Content, Dean Gilbert
Engineering Director, Libor Michalek
Product Manager, Scott Eblen
Managing Director Media and Platform Sales Japan and Asia Pacific, Shailesh Rao
Head Marketing Middle East and North Africa, Wael Ghonim, age 31
Director Consumer Marketing, Bernardo Hernandez
Director Google Display Network, Dan Taylor
Product Manager, Paul Joyce
VP Payments, Osama Bedier
Director, Paul S. Otellini, age 61
Director, John L. Hennessy, age 59
Director, L. John Doerr, age 60
Director, Ann Mather, age 52
CEO and Director, Larry E. Page, age 39
Co-founder and Director, Sergey Brin, age 38
Director, Diane B. Greene, age 57
Director, Shirley M. Tilghman, age 65
Director, K. Ram Shriram, age 55
Auditors: Ernst&YoungLLP

LOCATIONS

HQ: Google Inc.
1600 Amphitheatre Pkwy., Mountain View CA 94043
Phone: 650-253-0000 **Fax:** 650-253-0001
Web: www.google.com/intl/en/about/index.html

2011 Sales

	$ mil.	% of total
US	17,560	46
UK	4,057	11
Other countries	16,288	43
Total	**37,905**	**100**

PRODUCTS/OPERATIONS

2011 Sales

	$ mil.	% of total
Advertising		
Google sites	26,145	69
Google networks	10,386	27
Licensing & other	1,374	4
Total	**37,905**	**100**

Selected Operations and Products

Advertising programs
- AdSense (network ad program for online publishers)
- AdWords (text-based ad placement for advertisers)
- DoubleClick (digital marketing technology and services)

Internet search and content
- Google Alerts (news and search e-mail alerts)
- Google Earth (3-D satellite imagery)
- Google Image Search
- Google Labs (online services research and development)
- Google Local (localized search)
- Google Mobile (wireless device content)
- Google News
- Google Play Store (marketplace for digital content)
- Google Video
- Google Web Search
- YouTube

Tools and applications
- Android (mobile operating system)
- Blogger (blogging tools)
- Gmail (Web-based e-mail)
- Google Analytics (Web traffic measurement)
- Google Chrome (Web browser)
- Google Desktop Search
- Google Language Tools (translation tools)
- Google Talk (instant messaging)
- Google Toolbar (browser plug-in application)
- Nexus S (smart phone)
- Picasa (digital photo organization and sharing)

COMPETITORS

24/7 Real Media
AOL
Apple Inc.
Ask.com
Baidu
Blucora
CityGrid Media
craigslist
Daum Communications
MSN
Myspace
NetEase
Responsys
Shopping.com
Shopzilla
SINA
Sohu.com
Twitter

Facebook
LiveJournal
LookSmart
ValueClick
Vertro
Yahoo!

HISTORICAL FINANCIALS

Company Type: Public

Income Statement FYE: December 31

	REVENUE ($ mil.)	NET INCOME ($ mil.)	NET PROFIT MARGIN	EMPLOYEES
12/11	37,905	9,737	25.7%	32,467
12/10	29,321	8,505	29.0%	24,400
12/09	23,650	6,520	27.6%	19,835
12/08	21,795	4,226	19.4%	20,222
12/07	16,593	4,203	25.3%	16,805
Annual Growth	22.9%	23.4%	—	17.9%

2011 Year-End Financials

Debt ratio: 5.79%
Return on equity: 16.75%
Cash ($ mil.): 9,983
Current ratio: 591.92
Long-term debt ($ mil.): 2,986
No. of shares (mil.): 324
Dividends
Yield: —
Payout: —
Market value ($ mil.): 209,850

	STOCK PRICE ($) FY Close	P/E High/Low		PER SHARE ($) Earnings	Dividends	Book Value
12/11	645.90	21	16	29.76	0.00	178.97
12/10	593.97	23	16	26.31	0.00	143.92
12/09	619.98	30	14	20.41	0.00	113.30
12/08	307.65	51	19	13.31	0.00	89.61
12/07	691.48	55	32	13.29	0.00	72.51
Annual Growth	(1.7%)	—	—	22.3%	—	25.3%

Grainger (W.W.) Inc.

LOCATIONS

HQ: Grainger (W.W.) Inc.
100 Grainger Parkway, Lake Forest, IL 60045-5201
Phone: 847 535-1000 **Fax:** 847 535-0878
Web: www.grainger.com

HISTORICAL FINANCIALS

Company Type:

Income Statement FYE: December 31

	REVENUE ($ mil.)	NET INCOME ($ mil.)	NET PROFIT MARGIN	EMPLOYEES
12/11	8,078	658	8.2%	21,400
12/10	7,182	510	7.1%	18,500
12/09	6,221	430	6.9%	18,000
12/08	6,850	475	6.9%	18,334
12/07	6,418	420	6.5%	18,036
Annual Growth	5.9%	11.9%	—	4.4%

2011 Year-End Financials

Debt ratio: 10.95%
Return on equity: 25.05%
Cash ($ mil.): 335
Current ratio: 194.17
Long-term debt ($ mil.): 175
No. of shares (mil.): 69
Dividends
Yield: —
Payout: 27.78%
Market value ($ mil.): 13,096

	STOCK PRICE ($) FY Close	P/E High/Low		PER SHARE ($) Earnings	Dividends	Book Value
12/11	187.19	21	14	9.07	0.00	37.57
12/10	138.11	20	14	6.93	2.08	31.79
12/09	96.83	18	11	5.62	1.78	29.94
12/08	78.84	15	10	6.04	1.55	27.20
12/07	87.52	19	14	4.94	1.34	26.40
Annual Growth	20.9%	—	—	16.4%	—	9.2%

Graphic Packaging Holding Co

Ever toted a 12-pack home? If so you can appreciate Graphic Packaging Holding Company's (GPHC) work. Operating subsidiary Graphic Packaging International (GPII) is a leading maker of laminated coated and printed packaging such as beverage carriers cereal boxes microwavable food packaging and detergent cartons. Its two business segments include flexible packaging and paperboard packaging the latter of which generates most of GPII's sales. The company also produces strength promotional and barrier packaging. Customers include Kraft Foods Anheuser-Busch Molson Coors Brewing General Mills SABMiller and various Coca-Cola and Pepsi bottlers.

GPHC was formed after the businesses of Graphic Packaging Corporation (GPC) and Altivity Packaging were merged in 2008 with GPHC emerging as the publicly-traded parent company. With this transaction the company which had been averaging about $2.5 billion in revenues suddenly saw that number increase to more than $4 billion in 2008; sales numbers have remained somewhat flat ever since. Not so for GPHC's net income which switched from an almost $100 million net income loss in 2008 to a net income gain of more than $56 million in 2009; it dropped again in 2010 to about $11 million. While 2009 was impacted by the company's merger with Altivity Graphic Packaging blames its net income loss primarily on a $138 million alternative fuel tax credit it received in 2009 causing subsequent high input costs in 2010.

What generates these sales is the company's production of paper wares from its more than 55 mills and paperboard converting and flexible packaging plants in North America and Europe. Different products require different grades of paperboard including coated unbleached kraft (CUK) coated-recycled board (CRB) and uncoated-recycled board (URB) –these come from third-party suppliers. Graphic Packaging uses as much as 80% of its coated board output in its carton converting operations. In addition to paper products the company also makes heat transfer and lithographic labels as well as manufactures and installs company-designed packaging machines.

The above-mentioned merger with Altivity super sized Graphic Packaging. As one of the top producers of coated-recycled boxboard in North America Altivity pushed Graphic Packaging's capacity to more than 80 manufacturing and converting facilities. The merger diversified Graphic Packaging's product lines as well through Altivity's folding carton converting operations and ink manufacturing labeling and flexible packaging facilities.

Intent on competing as the lowest cost producer in its industry the company has aggressively moved to streamline manufacturing operations. Graphic Packaging closed several of Altivity paperboard packaging facilities in 2010. The shrink follows Graphic Packaging's closure in 2009 of one of its own paperboard packaging facilities and a multi-wall bag plant along with a 10% headcount reduction. Regulator-approval in acquiring Altivity also required Graphic Packaging to divest two coated-recycled paperboard mills.

Other belt-tightening programs were implemented due to the global economic crisis during which time Graphic Packaging made a concerted effort to do more with less; it chose to exit businesses deemed peripheral to its packaging activities. In 2009 the company sold certain assets and liabilities of its Handschy inks coatings and varnishes business to Sun Chemical for an undisclosed amount. Graphic Packaging is also moving to lower cost regions by entering into joint ventures with companies in China a region of potential growth especially in the multi-pack beverage packaging market.

As a new period of recovery arrived the company geared up again in 2011 and purchased the assets and business of California-based Sierra Pacific Packaging a manufacturer of packaging for consumer goods such as beverage carriers and corrugated boxes for approximately $53.5 million. The acquisition opens up the West Coast market to Graphic Packaging.

The company took its current form in 2003 when privately held Riverwood Holding owner of paperboard maker Riverwood International bought rival Graphic Packaging International Corporation. Parent company Riverwood Holding changed its name to Graphic Packaging Corporation and combined its operating units to form subsidiary Graphic Packaging International Inc. When the company merged with Altivity Packaging in 2008 it again changed its name to Graphic Packaging Holding Company. As a result former shareholders of Graphic Packaging own around 60% of the merged company including an 18% stake held by the family of board member Jeffrey Coors who also serves as trustee of several Adolph Coors trusts which hold about a 15% stake. Buyout firm TPG Capital by virtue of its former majority stake in Altivity controls 38% of Graphic Packaging.

EXECUTIVES

SVP and CFO, Daniel J. (Dan) Blount, age 56, $470,000 total compensation
President CEO and Director, David W. Scheible, age 55, $880,000 total compensation
Chairman, John R. Miller, age 74
SVP General Counsel and Secretary, Stephen A. Hellrung, age 64, $389,000 total compensation
SVP Beverage Packaging Division, Michael R. Schmal, age 58, $400,000 total compensation
SVP Consumer Packaging Division, Michael P. Doss, age 45, $440,000 total compensation
SVP Human Resources, Cynthia A. Baerman, age 49
VP Business Development, John C. Best, age 52
SVP Flexible Group, Kristopher L. Dover, age 47
VP and Chief Accounting Officer, Deborah R. Frank, age 51
VP Graphic Business Systems, Philip H. Geminder II, age 55
SVP Mills Division, Alan R. Nichols, age 49
SVP Supply Chain, Joseph P. Yost, age 44
VP and CIO, Joseph (Joe) Pekala
Director, Robert W. Tieken, age 72

Director, Kevin R. Burns, age 48
Director, Jeffrey H. Coors, age 67
Director, Harold R. Logan Jr., age 68
Director, George V. Bayly, age 69
Director, David A. Perdue Jr., age 61
President CEO and Director, David W. Scheible, age 55
Director, Kevin J. Conway, age 53
Director, G. Andrea Botta, age 58
Director, Lynn A. Wentworth, age 53
Director, Michael G. MacDougall, age 41
Director, Jeffrey Liaw, age 35
Auditors: Ernst&YoungLLP

LOCATIONS

HQ: Graphic Packaging Holding Co
814 Livingston Court, Marietta, GA 30067
Phone: 770 644-3000
Web: www.graphicpkg.com

2010 Sales

	$ mil.	% of total
US/Canada	3,860	91
Europe	168	4
Asia/Pacific	134	3
Central & South America	77	2
Adjustments	(145.6)	-
Total	**4,095**	**100**

PRODUCTS/OPERATIONS

2010 Sales

	$ mil.	% of total
Paperboard packaging	3,419	84
Flexible packaging (multi-wall & specialty)	675	16
Total	**4,095**	**100**

Selected Products & Services

Beverage machinery
Contract packaging
Laminations & coatings
  Aqueous release coatings
  Decorative metalized laminations
  Extrusion and adhesive laminations
  Extrusion coatings
  Specialty coatings
Packaging
  Bags
  Barrier
  Beverage
  Consumer packaging
    Candy & confections
    Cereal & dry food
    Facial tissue
    Gift boxes
    Health & beauty care
    Pet foods
    Refrigerated & frozen foods
Paperboard
  Containerboard
  PaceSetter brand coated recycled paperboard
  SUS brand coated unbleached kraft paperboard
  Uncoated recycled paperboard

COMPETITORS

Amcor
Atlas Container
Barry-Wehmiller
Bemis
Caraustar
Cascades Inc.
Exopack
Hood Packaging
International Paper
Klabin
MeadWestvaco
Mid-America Packaging
Mondi
Packaging Corp. of America
PaperWorks Industries
Rock-Tenn
Sonoco Products
Southern Container corp
Temple-Inland
The Newark Group

HISTORICAL FINANCIALS

Company Type: Public

Income Statement — FYE: December 31

	REVENUE ($ mil.)	NET INCOME ($ mil.)	NET PROFIT MARGIN	EMPLOYEES
12/11	4,206	276	6.6%	12,300
12/10	4,095	10	0.3%	12,400
12/09	4,095	56	1.4%	13,100
12/08	4,079	(99)	—	14,400
12/07	2,421	(74)	—	7,400
Annual Growth	14.8%	—	—	13.5%

2011 Year-End Financials

Debt ratio: 50.88%
Return on equity: 23.71%
Cash ($ mil.): 271
Current ratio: 203.58
Long-term debt ($ mil.): 2,335
No. of shares (mil.): 389
Dividends
Yield: —
Payout: —
Market value ($ mil.): 1,659

	STOCK PRICE ($) FY Close	P/E High/Low	PER SHARE ($) Earnings	Dividends	Book Value
12/11	4.26	8 4	0.73	0.00	3.00
12/10	3.89	134 97	0.03	0.00	2.17
12/09	3.47	23 4	0.16	0.00	2.12
12/08	1.14	— —	(0.32)	0.00	1.53
12/07	3.69	— —	(0.37)	0.00	0.72
Annual Growth	3.7%	— —	—	—	42.9%

Graybar Electric Co., Inc.

There's no gray area when it comes to Graybar Electric: it's one of the largest distributors of electrical products in the US. The employee-owned company distributes more than 1 million electrical communications and data networking products through a network of around 240 distribution facilities. Its diversified lineup includes a myriad of wire cable and lighting products from thousands of manufacturers and suppliers. It also offers supply chain management and logistics services. Affiliate Graybar Financial Services provides equipment leasing and financing. Graybar Electric sells to construction contractors industrial plants power utilities and telecommunications providers primarily in the US.

Uncertain economic conditions weighed on Graybar Electric in 2009 with sales down 25% from the prior year and net income cut in half. The company is especially affected by conditions in the commercial industrial and residential construction industries. Changes in commodity prices particularly for copper and steel are another factor in Graybar's results; such commodities are subject to volatile pricing fluctuations.

As the economy improved throughout 2010 Graybar's results improved. Overall sales were up 5% though fourth quarter sales were up 15% compared to the same period in 2009 as new construction began to pick up. Net income for 2010 rose 13% on higher sales but remained well below 2008 levels.

Among the company's strengths is a diverse and large customer base with more than 130000 clients. Graybar gets nearly half of its sales from electrical contractors. The company has expanded its sales presence to support its government business which continues to see strong growth.

HISTORY

After serving as a telegrapher during the Civil War Enos Barton borrowed $400 from his widowed mother in 1869 and started an electrical equipment shop in Cleveland with George Shawk. Later that year Elisha Gray a professor of physics at Oberlin College who had several inventions (including a printing telegraph) to his credit bought Shawk's interest in the shop and the firm of Gray & Barton moved to Chicago where a third partner joined.

The company incorporated as the Western Electric Manufacturing Co. in 1872 with two-thirds of the company's stock held by two Western Union executives. As the telegraph industry took off the enterprise grew rapidly providing equipment to towns and railroads in the western US.

Gray and his company missed receiving credit for inventing the telephone in 1875 when Gray's patent application for a "harmonic telegraph" reached the US Patent Office a few hours after Alexander Graham Bell's application for his telephone. However the telephone and the invention of the light bulb in 1879 opened new doors for Western Electric. The company began to grow into a major corporation selling and distributing a variety of electrical equipment including batteries telegraph keys and fire-alarm boxes. By 1900 the firm was the world's #1 maker of telephone equipment.

Western Electric formed a new distribution business in 1926 Graybar Electric Co. (from "Gray" and "Barton") the world's largest electrical supply merchandiser. In 1929 employees bought the company from Western Electric for $3 million in cash and $6 million in preferred stock. During the 1930s it marketed a line of appliances and sewing machines under the Graybar name.

In 1941 the company bought the outstanding shares of stock from Western Electric for $1 million. Graybar Electric was a vital link between manufacturers and US defense needs during WWII. Its men and equipment wired the Panama Canal with telephone cable; it also helped the US military during the Korean conflict and the Vietnam War.

By 1980 Graybar Electric reached nearly $1.5 billion in sales. Business was hurt when construction slowed in the late 1980s and the early 1990s and the company reorganized in 1991 closing regional offices and cutting jobs. Rebounding in 1992 as the US economy improved Graybar acquired New Jersey-based Square Electric Co.

In 1994 the company acquired a minority interest in R.E.D. Electronics a Canadian data communications and computer networking company and realigned its operations into two business segments: electrical products and communications and data products.

In 1995 Graybar Electric formed the Solutions Providers Alliance with wholesale distributors Kaman Industrial Technologies VWR Scientific Products and Vallen Corporation. In 1996 AT&T's Global Procurement Group named the company as one of only three suppliers for its electrical products. The next year Graybar Electric upped its stake in one of its Canadian operations Harris & Roome Supply Limited.

Graybar Electric in 1998 opened a subsidiary in Chile and formed a joint venture Graybar Financial Services with Newcourt Financial (formerly AT&T Capital). The next year Graybar Electric bought the Connecticut-based electrical wholesaler Frank A. Blesso Inc. and it expanded its distribution partnership with wire and cable manufacturer Belden Electronics in 2000.

In 2001 Graybar opened a new distribution location in northeastern Pennsylvania. The following year Graybar increased its presence in the telecommunications industry when it inked a deal to distribute products made by Copper Mountain Networks a US-based broadband equipment manufacturer.

The company received a five-year contract in 2003 from Los Angeles County to provide electrical supplies to local and state governments school districts and other tax-funded agencies participating in US Communities a government buying cooperative established in 1999.

During 2004 Graybar won several contracts from the Defense Logistics Agency worth a total of $195 million over two years. Also that year the company completed a multi-year project to implement an enterprise resource planning (ERP) system that linked its entire network of warehouses and distribution facilities.

Graybar signed a three-year supply contract in 2005 with Premier Purchasing Partners a group purchasing organization for the health care industry. In 2006 Graybar opened locations in Kent Washington and Wallingford Connecticut.

EXECUTIVES

Chairman, Robert A. Reynolds Jr., age 63, $658,548 total compensation
SVP Operations and Director, Lawrence R. (Larry) Giglio, age 57, $268,053 total compensation
District VP Richmond and Director, Thomas S. Gurganous, age 62
VP Sales Electric Utility, Peter R. Elkas
SVP North American Business and Director, Robert C. Lyons, age 55
District VP Chicago and Director, Richard A. Cole, age 62
District VP Dallas and Director, Randall R. Harwood, age 55
VP Corporate Accounts, John C. Mansfield
SVP CFO and Director, D. Beatty D'Alessandro, age 51, $264,256 total compensation
President and CEO, Kathleen M. Mazzarella, age 52
SVP Secretary General Counsel and Director, Matthew W. Geekie, age 50
SVP Human Resources and Director, Beverly L. Propst, age 42
VP and CIO, Scott Clifford
EVP and General Manager Graybar Canada, Peter Horncastle
District VP Boston, Todd McDonough
VP Sales Broadband Utility, Tom Moore
SVP Operations and Director, Lawrence R. (Larry) Giglio, age 57
District VP Richmond and Director, Thomas S. Gurganous, age 62
SVP North American Business and Director, Robert C. Lyons, age 55
District VP Chicago and Director, Richard A. Cole, age 62
District VP Dallas and Director, Randall R. Harwood, age 55
SVP CFO and Director, D. Beatty D'Alessandro, age 51
EVP Sales and Marketing COO and Director, Kathleen M. Mazzarella, age 52
SVP Secretary General Counsel and Director, Matthew W. Geekie, age 50
SVP Human Resources and Director, Beverly L. Propst, age 42
Auditors: Ernst&YoungLLP

LOCATIONS

HQ: Graybar Electric Company Inc.
34 N. Meramec Ave., St. Louis MO 63105
Phone: 314-573-9200 **Fax:** 713-746-5611
Web: www.grocerssupply.com

2010 Sales

	$ mil.	% of total
		% of total
US		94
Other		6
Total		**100**

PRODUCTS/OPERATIONS

2010 Sales

	% of total
Electrical	45
Data & voice	21
Commercial &	19
Other	15
Total	**100**

Selected Products

Ballasts
Batteries
Cable
Conduit
Connectors
Emergency lighting
Enclosures
Fiber-optic cable
Fittings
Fluorescent lighting
Fuses
Hand tools
Hangers/fasteners
Heating and ventilating equipment
Industrial fans
Lighting
Lubricants
Paints
Patch cords
Smoke detectors
Testing and measuring instruments
Timers
Transfer switches
Transformers
Utility products
Wire

Selected Subsidiaries

Commonwealth Controls Corporation
Distribution Associates Inc.
Graybar Business Services Inc.
Graybar Canada Limited
Graybar Commerce Corporation
Graybar Electric Canada Limited
Graybar Financial Services Inc.
Graybar International Inc.
Graybar Services Inc.

COMPETITORS

Anixter International
Border States Electric
Communications Supply
Consolidated Electrical
Gexpro
HD Supply
HWC
Premier Farnell
Rexel Canada
Rexel Inc.
Richardson Electronics
Sonepar USA
SUMMIT Electric Supply
United Electric Supply
W.W. Grainger
WESCO International

HISTORICAL FINANCIALS

Company Type: Private

Income Statement

FYE: December 31

	REVENUE ($ mil.)	NET INCOME ($ mil.)	NET PROFIT MARGIN	EMPLOYEES
12/11	5,374	81	1.5%	7,400
12/10	4,616	42	0.9%	7,000
12/09	4,377	37	0.9%	6,900
12/08	5,400	87	1.6%	8,100
12/07	5,258	83	1.6%	8,600
Annual Growth	0.5%	(0.6%)	—	(3.7%)

2011 Year-End Financials

Debt ratio: 5.54%
Return on equity: 14.40%
Cash ($ mil.): 71
Current ratio: 143.96
Long-term debt ($ mil.): 10
No. of shares (mil.): 12
Dividends
Yield: —
Payout: 28.77%
Market value ($ mil.): —

Great Southern Bancorp, Inc.

Despite its name Great Southern Bancorp is firmly entrenched in the heartland. It is the holding company for Great Southern Bank which operates more than 75 branches in Missouri plus more than two dozen locations in Iowa Kansas Nebraska and Arkansas. Founded in 1923 the bank offers checking and savings accounts CDs IRAs and credit cards. The firm's Great Southern Travel division is one of the largest travel agencies in Missouri. It serves both leisure and corporate travelers through about a dozen offices. Among other units Great Southern Insurance offers property/casualty and life insurance while Great Southern Financial provides investment products and services through an agreement with Ameriprise.

The company in late 2012 agreed to sell its Great Southern Travel division to Adelman Travel.

Great Southern's lending activities primarily consist of originating and buying real estate loans: Commercial real estate mortgages and construction and land development loans account for around half of its loan portfolio while single-family residential mortgages make up another 15%. The bank also writes consumer (including home equity) construction and business loans.

The bank expanded into new markets in 2009 nearly doubling its branch network with the FDIC-assisted transactions of the failed TeamBank and deposits of Vantus Bank. It made a similar deal in 2011 when it acquired assets and deposits of the troubled Sun Security Bank. That transaction added another 27 banking locations in Missouri. In a smaller FDIC-assisted deal Great Southern acquired the deposits and loans of Inter Savings Bank in 2012 adding four branches in the Minneapolis/St. Paul market.

The company has also grown by opening new branches. In 2010 it opened three locations including its first in northwest Arkansas and it opened two new branches in 2011. Great Southern strategy for growth includes plans to continue opening two or three new branches per year which will help diversify the bank's loan portfolio beyond its core market of Springfield. Great Southern

Travel has also made acquisitions in the bank's expanded market areas.

Despite the tough economic environment in the Midwest Great Southern's revenues and income saw growth in 2011. Adding loans through the FDIC-related acquisitions as well as by operating in new markets such as St. Louis has helped bring up the company's interest income. The company's portfolio of nonperforming loans and foreclosed assets –much of which were acquired in the FDIC purchases –dropped by about 2% each in 2011 (to $27.5 million and $46.9 million respectively) and are performing better than the company had originally expected. Potential problem loans have also decreased for Great Southern.

The bank introduced a smartphone banking application in early 2012. The addition of mobile banking services allows it to better compete with larger technologically advanced banks.

The Turner family including CEO Joseph Turner controls about a quarter of Great Southern Bancorp.

EXECUTIVES

Director Human Resources Great Southern Bank, Matt Snyder
Secretary; VP Operations and Secretary Great Southern Bank, Douglas W. (Doug) Marrs, age 54, $110,251 total compensation
SVP and Chief Lending Officer Great Southern Bank, Steven G. Mitchem, age 60, $195,215 total compensation
President CEO and Director Great Southern Bancorp and Great Southern Bank, Joseph W. (Joe) Turner, age 47, $258,869 total compensation
Treasurer; SVP and CFO Great Southern Bank, Rex A. Copeland, age 47, $186,640 total compensation
Chairman Great Southern Bancorp and Great Southern Bank, William V. Turner, age 79, $237,269 total compensation
VP Information Systems, Linton J. (Lin) Thomason, age 55
Director Marketing Great Southern Bank, Teresa Chasteen-Calhoun
Director Retail Banking Great Southern Bank, Barby Pohl
Director Corporate Communications Great Southern Bank, Kelly Polonus
Controller Great Southern Bank, Tammy Baurichter
Director Retail Services, Kris Conley
Director Credit Risk Management Great Southern Bank, Debbie Flowers
Insurance Agency Manager Great Southern Insurance, Byron Robison
Compliance Officer Great Southern Bank, Shannon Thomason
Director Risk Management Great Southern Bank, Bryan Tiede
President CEO and Director Great Southern Bancorp and Great Southern Bank, Joseph W. (Joe) Turner, age 47
Director, William E. Barclay, age 82
Director, Larry D. Frazier, age 74
Director, Thomas J. Carlson, age 59
Director, Julie Turner Brown, age 50
Director, Earl A. Steinert Jr., age 75
Director, Grant Q. Haden
Auditors: BKDLLP

LOCATIONS

HQ: Great Southern Bancorp Inc.
1451 E. Battlefield, Springfield MO 65804
Phone: 417-887-4400 **Fax:** 858-550-7506
Web: www.ligand.com

PRODUCTS/OPERATIONS

2011 Sales

	$ mil.	% of total
Interest		
Loans	171	69
Securities & other	27	11
Noninterest		
Service charges & ATM fees	18	7
Gain recognized on business acquisitions	16	7
Commissions	8	4
Net gains on loan sales	3	1
Other	3	1
Adjustments	(38.4)	-
Total	**210**	**100**

COMPETITORS

BancorpSouth
Bank of America
Commerce Bancshares
First Bancshares (MO)
Guaranty Federal
Hawthorn Bancshares
NASB Financial
U.S. Bancorp
UMB Financial
Wells Fargo

HISTORICAL FINANCIALS

Company Type: Public

Income Statement FYE: December 31

	ASSETS ($ mil.)	NET INCOME ($ mil.)	INCOME AS % OF ASSETS	EMPLOYEES
12/11	3,790	30	0.8%	1,256
12/10	3,411	23	0.7%	1,086
12/09	3,641	65	1.8%	1,047
12/08	2,659	(4)	—	741
12/07	2,431	29	1.2%	775
Annual Growth	11.7%	0.8%	—	12.8%

2011 Year-End Financials

Debt ratio: 5.68%
Return on equity: 9.33%
Cash ($ mil.): 336
Current ratio: —
Long-term debt ($ mil.): 215
No. of shares (mil.): 13
Dividends
Yield: —
Payout: 37.31%
Market value ($ mil.): 318

	STOCK PRICE ($) FY Close	P/E High/Low		PER SHARE ($) Earnings	Dividends	Book Value
12/11	23.59	12	8	1.93	0.00	24.08
12/10	23.59	17	13	1.46	0.72	22.60
12/09	21.36	5	2	4.44	0.72	22.30
12/08	11.44	—	—	(0.35)	0.72	17.49
12/07	21.96	14	10	2.15	0.68	14.17
Annual Growth	1.8%	—	—	(2.7%)	—	14.2%

Great-West Life & Annuity Insurance Co.

Great-West Life & Annuity Insurance is the southern arm of a northern parent. The company a subsidiary of Canada's Great-West Lifeco and a member of the Power Financial family represents the Great-West group's primary US operations. It offers life insurance and annuities to individuals and employer groups. Under the Great-West Retirement Services brand it administers employer-sponsored retirement products including defined-benefit pension and 401(k) plans. Additional Great-West services include investment consulting and fund management. Great-West Life & Annuity markets products through its sales representatives and regional offices as well as independent brokers.

Great-West Life & Annuity also distributes its individual life insurance and annuity products through partnerships with banking institutions and financial advisors including Bank of America Citigroup and Charles Schwab. Outside of its own retirement products which are marketed to corporate not-for-profit health care educational and government organizations the Great-West Retirement Services unit provides business services including record-keeping for plans offered by other financial institutions.

In 2008 the company sold its Great-West Healthcare division to CIGNA for $1.5 billion; the segment offered group life and medical insurance products to US businesses with an emphasis on self-funded programs for small and midsized employers. The divestiture of its health care unit was part of Great-West's strategy of focusing its efforts in the financial services arena.

In 2009 Mitchell Graye moved into the chief executive office when then-CEO Raymond McFeetors was named chairman of the board at Great-West Lifeco; Graye had previously been CFO of Great West Life & Annuity. One of the company's stated goals is to improve its financial services business and Graye came up through the investment banking side of the company.

EXECUTIVES

Chairman, Raymond L. McFeetors, age 67, $225,844 total compensation
VP Taxation, D. Robert Meyer Jr., age 55
EVP Individual Markets, Robert Shaw, age 56, $412,500 total compensation
Vice Chairman Power Corporation, Michel Plessis-Belair, age 70, $22,430 total compensation
President and CEO, Mitchell T. G. Graye, age 56, $900,000 total compensation
President Retirement Services, Charles P. Nelson, age 51, $611,250 total compensation
SVP Government Markets Retirement Services, Gregory E. Seller, age 57
SVP and Chief Marketing Officer, Joe Greene
VP Investments, Brian J. Schwartz
VP Investments, Eve A. Hampton
SVP and Corporate Controller, James H. Van Harmelen
Director Corporate Affairs, Lisa Gigax
EVP and Chief Investment Officer, S. Mark Corbett, age 52, $475,000 total compensation
SVP and Controller, Glen R. Derback, age 59
SVP Corporate Resources, Graham R. McDonald, age 65
Chief Compliance Officer and Chief Legal Counsel Financial Services, Beverly A. Byrne
SVP FASCore Operations Retirement Services, Miles R. Edwards, age 52
SVP and CIO, Scot A. Miller, age 53
SVP General Counse and Secretary, Richard G. Schultz, age 51
SVP Marketing Healthcare and National Accounts Retirement Servicesa, Christopher H. Cumming
SVP Executive Benefits Markets, Ron J. Laeyendecker, age 47
Sales Southern New Jersey, Marc Abruzzese
Sales Illinois, Jerry Ahler
Sales Iowa and Minnesota, Dan Armstrong
Sales Hawaii and Los Angeles, Michael Barry
Sales Arizona and New Mexico, Patty Bell
Sales Georgia and South Carolina, Jason Bouldin
Sales Southern Florida, Natasha Branzanti

Sales Okalahoma and Arkansas, Jonah Caldwell
Sales Northern New Jersey, Laura Catalano-Grassi
Sales San Francisco Bay Area and Sacremento, Keith Cattaneo
Sales San Francisco Bay Area, Octavio Cheung
Sales Michigan (Except Detroit), Mike Demler
Sales Southern Alabma and Northwest Florida, Ryan Derbes
Sales Northern New Jersey, Joe Carew
VP Financial Institutions Markets, Christopher R. Bergeon
VP Individual Markets Operations, Susan Gile
VP Group Special Accounts, James F. Biesterfelt
VP Financial Services Markets, Sara A. Richman
Regional VP 401K Retirement Services, Scott A. Barnett
VP Client Relations Retirement Services, Stephanie A. Bendrick
VP P/NP National Accounts Retirement Services, Perry Christie
VP 401K Business Development, Thomas Connolly
VP FASCore Administration Retirement Services, John P. Fellin
Regional VP 401K Retirement Services, Gary W. Gould
VP 401K Sales Retirement Services, William S. Harmon
VP Information Systems Retirement Services, David T. Jonasson
VP Bank Services Group Retirement Services, Joseph P. Kerrigan
VP National P/NP Client Relations Retirement Services, J. Chris Luttges
VP Adivsed Assets Group Retirement Services, David G. McLeod
Regional VP 401K Retirement Services, Brian P. Morris
VP P/NP Client Relations Retirement Services, Kent A. Morris
Regional VP 401K Retirement Services, Kenneth J. Munro
VP P/NP Client Relations Retirement Services, Theresa M. Myers
VP P/NP Client Relations Retirement Services, Brent Neese
Regional VP 401K Retirement Services, Joseph M. Smolen
VP FASCore Operations and Financial Control Retirement Services, Darlene Soderquist
SVP Investments, Ernie Friesen
SVP Investments, Catherine S. Tocher
Chief Risk Officer Chief Legal Counsel Litigation, David C. Aspinwall
VP Investments, Judith Gibbs
VP and Actuary, Kenneth T. Ledwos
VP Investment Operations, Mary C. Maiers
VP Internal Audit, Debra Muhlhauser
VP Finance and Accounting, Robert L. Onstad
VP Finance and Accounting, Dawn S. Smith
VP Reporting and Finance, Rebecca M. Southall
VP Actuarial Executive, Peter D. Tilley
Director, Andre R. Desmarais, age 55
Director, Raymond Royer, age 73
Director, Michel Plessis-Belair, age 70
Director, Paul Desmarais Jr., age 58
Director, Henri-Paul Rousseau, age 63
Director, James Balog, age 83
Director, Jerry E. A. Nickerson, age 75
Director, Brian E. Walsh, age 58
Director, Robert Jeffrey Orr, age 52
Director, Alain Louvel, age 66
Director, John L. Bernbach, age 68
Director, Philip K. Ryan, age 55
Director, T. Timothy Ryan Jr., age 66
Auditors: Deloitte&ToucheLLP

LOCATIONS

HQ: Great-West Life & Annuity Insurance Company
8515 E. Orchard Rd., Greenwood Village CO 80111
Phone: 303-737-3000 **Fax:** 303-737-4861
Web: www.greatwest.com

PRODUCTS/OPERATIONS

Selected Products and Services

Annuities
Life insurance
Retirement services
- Retirement plans for government corporate and not-for-profit employers
- Communication and education services
- Enrollment services
- Investment options
- Third-party administrative and record-keeping services (FASCore)

COMPETITORS

Allstate
AXA Financial
Industrial Alliance Insurance and Financial Servic
John Hancock Financial Services
Liberty Mutual
Lincoln Financial Group
Manulife Financial
MetLife
Mutual of Omaha
Nationwide Financial
Pacific Mutual
Prudential
State Farm
Sun Life
The Hartford
Western National

HISTORICAL FINANCIALS

Company Type: Subsidiary

Income Statement FYE: December 31

	ASSETS ($ mil.)	NET INCOME ($ mil.)	INCOME AS % OF ASSETS	EMPLOYEES
12/11	48,336	214	0.4%	3,200
12/10	47,627	202	0.4%	3,100
12/09	41,798	122	0.3%	3,100
12/08	36,175	1,098	3.0%	3,000
12/07	40,290	418	1.0%	6,600
Annual Growth	4.7%	(15.4%)	—	(16.6%)

2011 Year-End Financials

Debt ratio: 1.11%
Return on equity: 10.73%
Cash ($ mil.): 7
Current ratio: —
Long-term debt ($ mil.): 538
No. of shares (mil.): 7
Dividends
Yield: —
Payout: 96.38%
Market value ($ mil.): —

Greif Inc

Unlike a box of chocolates with Greif (rhymes with "life") you know what you're going to get. The company produces rigid industrial packaging products including steel plastic and fibre drums and related closure systems. Greif also makes flexible intermediate bulk containers (based on polypropylene woven fabric) and multiwall bags used to ship an array of bulk industrial and consumer goods. It sells corrugated products and containerboard as well for packaging home appliances and small machinery and grocery and building products. Greif caters to a diverse group of industries from chemical to food and beverage petroleum agricultural and pharmaceutical. It traces its history back to 1877.

Greif operates through four business segments: Rigid Industrial Packaging and Services; Paper Packaging; Flexible Products and Services; and Land Management. (This last segment is responsible for harvesting the company's timber properties in the southeastern US and in Canada.)

The company's operations span the Americas Europe the Middle East Africa and the Asia/Pacific region. Although North America remains the sole market for its multiwall bag and corrugated products (accounting for about 45% of total sales) Greif has evolved into a global player in distributing its packaging and container products. Europe the Middle East and Africa accounted for about 40% of 2011 sales; the Asia/Pacific around 15%.

After its net sales slumped during the recession Greif's revenues have steadily risen. In 2011 revenues increased by 22% to $4.3 billion its best total in at least 10 years. The company attributes the revenue milestone to higher sales volumes propelled by an 11% increase from acquisitions. Its Flexible Products and Services segment experienced the most growth (6%) accounting for 13% of total sales for 2011 (compared to 7% for 2010). Greif's profits were down however dipping 16% from $210 million in 2010 to $176 million in 2011 due to higher impairment and restructuring charges and a rise in operating costs.

Greif has managed to brighten its balance sheet through an aggressive acquisition strategy and by establishing joint ventures. It has gained global ground by taking over or partnering with strategically positioned businesses in North America South America Europe and Asia. Such acquisitions are intended to capitalize on a host of opportunities that increase manufacturing efficiencies as well as broaden Greif's customer base.

Greif made eight acquisitions in 2011 all within its flagship Rigid Industrial Packaging and Services segment. Throughout the year it obtained several European companies and entered two joint ventures residing in North America and the Asia/Pacific. The company in 2010 acquired a dozen industrial packaging companies: seven of which were in Rigid Industrial Packaging and Services and five businesses made flexible intermediate bulk containers. Through those five acquisitions Greif established a joint venture: Storsack one of the world's largest producers of such flexible containers. The venture partners with Dabbagh Group a Saudi Arabian company and National Scientific a Dabbagh subsidiary.

Judith Hook represented on the company's board of directors owns 23% of Greif's shares.

HISTORY

Charles Greif co-founded Vanderwyst and Greif a Cleveland-based maker of casks kegs and barrels in 1877. The next year his brothers William Louis and Thomas joined the company which was renamed Greif Bros. to reflect the sibling involvement. The thriving company bought timberland as a source for raw materials and in 1926 went public as Greif Bros. Cooperage. In 1946 Jack Dempsey became chairman (his wife and mother-in-law owned minority stakes) and acquired a controlling interest. Dempsey moved Greif beyond barrels and kegs into fiber containers and steel drums. The company relocated to Delaware Ohio in 1951.

Greif entered the multiwall bag and corrugated packaging businesses in the 1960s and cut "Cooperage" from its name in 1969. In the early 1970s it began making plastic containers. Greif teamed with Robert Macauley to form Virginia Fibre in 1974 and bought the supplier outright in 1992. In 1994 after 48 years at the helm Dempsey was succeeded by COO Michael Gasser.

Greif bought three corrugated container firms and a pair of steel drum makers during 1997. Low paper prices and excess capacity dropped containerboard prices to a 19-year low in 1997. Dempsey died that year. In 1998 Greif bought the industrial container business of Sonoco Products for $225 million in a deal that gave Greif control of two-thirds of the US fiber drum market. The company then announced a restructuring plan that would close plants and lay off workers. Greif joined with RDJ Holdings in a corrugated sheet joint venture CorrChoice. In 1999 Greif bought Sonoco's intermediate bulk containers business and box maker Great Lakes Corrugated.

Late in 2000 Greif agreed to buy Finland-based Huhtamaki's industrial packaging operations. The deal worth about $555 million closed in 2001.

In 2003 the company changed its name to Greif Inc. The company felt that Greif Bros. was a regional-sounding name unworthy of a global industrial giant.

In 2006 Greif expanded further when it acquired Delta Petroleum Company which blended and packaged lubricants and other chemical mixtures. Later that year Greif spent $270 million to buy the European and Asian steel drum manufacturing business of Blagden Packaging Group.

In 2008 subsidiary Delta Companies sealed a contract with Cognis Corp. to provide on-site chemical packaging services. Not only profitable the contract builds Greif's position as a fulfillment service provider. Earlier in the year Greif acquired a steel drum maker in Vietnam Petro-Summit Mechanical (subsidiary of Asian Steel Co. Singapore). In addition four acquisitions were completed –two in North America one in South America one in the Middle East.

However in order to cut down on costs the company closed 19 facilities in its industrial packaging segment in 2009 and in 2008 six and four in its paper and packaging. All told its workforce during 2008 through 2009 was slashed 20%. During 2010 seven plants in its rigid industrial packaging business two plants in its paper packaging and one plant in its flexible products were shuttered. (In 2010 headcount increased roughly 50% due a spree of business acquisitions.)

In 2011 David Fischer became the company's newest president and CEO.

EXECUTIVES

VP and Treasurer, John K. Dieker, age 48
Executive Chairman, Michael J. Gasser, age 61, $917,358 total compensation
Assistant Secretary, Sharon R. Maxwell, age 62
VP and Division President Paper Packaging & Services, Peter G. Watson, age 53
EVP General Counsel and Secretary; President Soterra LLC, Gary R. Martz, age 54, $428,103 total compensation
VP Communications, Debra (Deb) Strohmaier
CEO and President, David B. Fischer, age 49, $545,012 total compensation
VP and Controller, Kenneth B. (Ken) Andre III, age 46
SVP and Divisional President Industrial Packaging and Services Europe Middle East and Africa, Ivan Signorelli, age 59
SVP and CFO, Robert M. (Rob) McNutt, age 52
SVP People Services and Talent Development, Karen P. Lane, age 63
VP Global Sourcing and Supply Chain; VP Greif Business System (GBS) Worldwide, Brian Janki, age 39
VP and Division President Rigid Industrial Packaging and Services - North America, Addison Kilibarda, age 48
CIO, Douglas W. Lingrel
VP and Division President Flexible Products and Services, Michael S. Mapes
CSO, Scott Griffin
Product Manager, Rick Volker
Vice President Soterra LLC, Matt Bonham
Vice President; Treasurer, Nadeem Ali
Director, Vicki L. Avril, age 57
Director, Bruce A. Edwards, age 57
Director, Mark A. Emkes, age 59
Director, Patrick J. Norton, age 61
Director, Daniel J. Gunsett, age 63
Director, Judith D. Hook, age 58
Director, John F. Finn, age 61
Director, John W. McNamara
Auditors: Ernst&YoungLLP

LOCATIONS

HQ: Greif Inc
425 Winter Road, Delaware, OH 43015
Phone: 740 549-6000
Web: www.greif.com

2011 Sales

	$ mil.	% of total
North America	1,932	45
Asia Pacific & Latin America	669	16

PRODUCTS/OPERATIONS

2011 Sales

	$ mil.	% of total
Rigid Industrial Packaging & Services	3,014	71
Flexible Products & Services	538	13
Total	**4,248**	**100**

Selected Products

Rigid Industrial Packaging
- Closure systems for industrial packaging products
- Fibre drums
- Plastic drums
- Reconditioned containers
- Rigid intermediate bulk containers
- Steel containers
- Transit protection products
- Water bottles

Paper Packaging
- Containerboard
- Corrugated sheets and other corrugated products

Flexible Products
- Flexible intermediate bulk containers
- Multiwall bag products (for industrial and consumer products)

Land Management
- Harvesting of timber operations

COMPETITORS

Cascades SA
Georgia-Pacific
International Paper
Longview Fibre
Pactiv
RockTenn CP
Sonoco Products
Tegrant
Temple-Inland
TriMas
Weyerhaeuser

HISTORICAL FINANCIALS

Company Type: Public

Income Statement FYE: October 31

	REVENUE ($ mil.)	NET INCOME ($ mil.)	NET PROFIT MARGIN	EMPLOYEES
10/11	4,247	176	4.1%	15,660
10/10	3,461	209	6.1%	12,250
10/09	2,792	132	4.7%	8,200
10/08	3,776	234	6.2%	9,600
10/07	3,322	156	4.7%	10,300
Annual Growth	6.3%	3.0%	—	11.0%

2011 Year-End Financials

Debt ratio: 35.53%
Return on equity: 14.25%
Cash ($ mil.): 127
Current ratio: 140.39
Long-term debt ($ mil.): 1,345
No. of shares (mil.): 47
Dividends
Yield: 3.75%
Payout: 55.81%
Market value ($ mil.): 2,109

	STOCK PRICE ($) FY Close	P/E High/Low		PER SHARE ($) Earnings	Dividends	Book Value
10/11	44.78	22	14	3.01	1.68	26.23
10/10	58.74	17	13	3.58	0.00	27.11
10/09	53.52	25	11	2.28	0.00	23.28
10/08	40.58	18	8	3.99	1.32	22.64
10/07	63.60	46	19	2.65	0.92	21.41
Annual Growth	(8.4%)	—	—	3.2%	16.2%	5.2%

Group 1 Automotive, Inc.

Group 1 Automotive is only one in a group of firms (AutoNation and Penske Automotive Group are the largest) striving to consolidate US auto sales. The company owns and operates about 130 franchises at more than 100 dealerships as well as about 25 collision service centers in about 15 US states. More than half of Group 1's dealerships are located in Texas Oklahoma and California. Group 1 Automotive also has about five dealerships and several collision centers in the UK. The company's dealerships offer new (about 55% of sales) and used cars and light trucks under some 30 different brands. It also offers financing provides maintenance and repair services and sells replacement parts.

Operations

Group 1 Automotive's operations include four core business segments: New Vehicles (more than 50% of sales); Used Vehicles (28%); Parts & Service (13%); and Finance & Insurance. In the UK the auto dealer operates through its subsidiary Group 1 Automotive UK Ltd.

Geographic Reach

The auto dealer rings up 95% of its sales in the US; the remainder comes from the UK. In Britain it has locations in Brighton Farnborough Hailsham Hindhead and Worthington.

Financial Analysis

While Group 1's 2011 sales increased more than 10% vs. 2010 to top $6 billion they have not quite returned to prerecession levels (more than $6.2 billion in 2007). Still the company had a strong year with net income up nearly 64% vs.

2010 and cash flow from operations rose sharply (after taking a dive in 2010). Since 2008 the company and its rivals have suffered from declining consumer confidence high unemployment and tight credit availability which conspired to drive down demand for new and used vehicles. However the sales and profit picture brightened beginning in late 2010 and 2011 was a strong year for both new and used vehicle sales. Sales of new and used automobiles rose 4.6% and nearly 7% respectively.

Strategy

Like its rival AutoNation Group 1 Automotive is focusing on acquiring import and luxury brand dealerships. Most recently in May 2012 it acquired a Honda franchise and a Volkswagen franchise in Panama City Florida expanding its presence in Florida Panhandle. In 2011 it completed 14 franchise acquisitions including a Volkswagen dealership in Irving Texas adding to its four existing dealerships in the Dallas metropolitan area. Further adding to its Texas holdings in June it purchased a pair of dealerships (Ford and GM) in El Paso. In 2012 the company's strategy includes growing its higher margin parts and services business growing its share of the new and used vehicle market taking advantage of its size to boost efficiency and continuing to make strategic acquisitions. In recent years Group 1 has seen import and luxury brands account for an increased share of its business. Indeed in 2011 they accounted for about 80% of its sales mix with domestic brands contributing 19%. That's quite a switch from 2005 when domestic brands totaled about 36% of sales.

EXECUTIVES

Chairman, John L. Adams, age 67
VP Corporate Development, Mark J. Iuppenlatz, age 53
VP Human Resources, J. Brooks O'Hara, age 56, $240,890 total compensation
President CEO and Director, Earl J. Hesterberg, age 58, $908,333 total compensation
VP Financial Services and Manufacturer Relations, Peter C. DeLongchamps
Regional VP West Region, Frank Grese Jr.
SVP and CFO, John C. Rickel, age 50, $408,750 total compensation
VP Fixed Operations, Wade D. Hubbard
VP Marketing and Fixed Operations, David W. Hult
VP Western Region, Martin E. Collins
VP and General Counsel, Darryl M. Burman, age 53, $324,729 total compensation
VP and Corporate Controller, Lance A. Parker
VP Information Systems, James R. Druzbik
VP Purchasing, Gigi L. Myung
Manager Investor Relations, Kim Paper Canning
VP and Treasurer, Michael D. Welch, age 37
Corporate Secretary, Beth Sibley
Director Market, Chris Hayden, age 51
Regional VP East Region, Daryl Kenningham, age 48
VP Taxes, Ronald W. Barnhill
Director, Max P. Watson Jr., age 66
Director, Beryl B. Raff, age 61
President CEO and Director, Earl J. Hesterberg, age 58
Director, Louis E. Lataif, age 73
Director, Stephen D. Quinn, age 57
Director, J. Terry Strange, age 67
Auditors: Ernst&YoungLLP

LOCATIONS

HQ: Group 1 Automotive Inc.
800 Gessner Ste. 500, Houston TX 77024
Phone: 713-647-5700 **Fax:** 713-647-5858
Web: www.group1auto.com

2011 Dealerships

	No.
US	
Western	62
Eastern	42
International	
UK	5
Total	**109**

2011 Sales

	% of total
US	
Western	59
Eastern	36
International	
UK	5
Total	**100**

PRODUCTS/OPERATIONS

2011 Sales

	$ mil.	% of total
New vehicle	3,402	56
Used vehicle	1,416	24
Used vehicle wholesale	251	4
Parts & service	813	13
Finance insurance & other	195	3
Total	**6,079**	**100**

2011 New Vehicle Sales

	$ mil.	% of total
Import	1,422	42
Luxury	1,327	39
Domestic	652	19
Total	**3,402**	**100**

2011 New Vehicle Unit Sales

	% of total
Import	53
Luxury	28
Domestic	19
Total	**100**

Selected Brands

Domestic
- Ford
- Chevrolet
- Dodge
- Jeep
- GMC
- Chrysler
- Buick

Import
- Toyota
- Nissan
- Honda
- Volkswagen
- Hyundai
- Mazda
- Subaru
- Scion
- Kia
- Fiat
- Mitsubishi

Luxury
- BMW
- Acura
- MINI
- Audi
- Infiniti
- Volvo
- Cadillac
- Lincoln
- Porsche
- Maybach
- Sprinter
- smart

COMPETITORS

Ancira
Asbury Automotive
AutoNation
CarMax
David McDavid Auto Group
Herb Chambers
Lithia Motors
Penske Automotive Group
Phil Long Dealerships
Sonic Automotive

HISTORICAL FINANCIALS

Company Type: Public

Income Statement FYE: December 31

	REVENUE ($ mil.)	NET INCOME ($ mil.)	NET PROFIT MARGIN	EMPLOYEES
12/11	6,079	82	1.4%	8,267
12/10	5,509	50	0.9%	7,454
12/09	4,525	34	0.8%	6,990
12/08	5,654	(31)	—	7,687
12/07	6,393	67	1.1%	8,932
Annual Growth	(1.2%)	4.9%	—	(1.9%)

2011 Year-End Financials

Debt ratio: 51.00%
Return on equity: 10.21%
Cash ($ mil.): 14
Current ratio: 112.50
Long-term debt ($ mil.): 482
No. of shares (mil.): 22
Dividends
Yield: —
Payout: 13.83%
Market value ($ mil.): 1,176

	STOCK PRICE ($) FY Close	P/E High/Low		PER SHARE ($) Earnings	Dividends	Book Value
12/11	51.80	15	10	3.47	0.00	35.54
12/10	41.76	19	10	2.16	0.10	32.97
12/09	28.35	23	5	1.49	0.33	29.42
12/08	10.77	—	—	(1.39)	0.47	25.95
12/07	23.75	19	8	2.90	0.56	29.62
Annual Growth	21.5%	—	—	4.6%	—	4.7%

Halliburton Company

One of the largest oilfield services companies in the world Halliburton serves the upstream oil and gas industry in 80 countries with a complete range of services from the location of hydrocarbons to the production of oil and gas. It operates in two segments: Drilling and Evaluation and Completion and Production. Services include providing production optimization drilling evaluation fluid services and oilfield drilling software and consulting. It combines tried-and-true well drilling and optimization techniques with high-tech analysis and modeling software and services. Halliburton works in established oilfields from the North Sea to the Middle East as well as in newer sites in Southeast Asia and Africa.

HISTORY

Erle Halliburton began his oil career in 1916 at Perkins Oil Well Cementing. He moved to oil boomtown Burkburnett Texas to start his Better Method Oil Well Cementing Company in 1919. Halliburton used cement to hold a steel pipe in a well which kept oil out of the water table strengthened well walls and reduced the risk of explosions. Though the contribution would later be praised his technique was considered useless at the time.

In 1920 Halliburton moved to Oklahoma. Incorporating Halliburton Oil Well Cementing Company in 1924 he patented its products and services forcing oil companies to employ his firm if they wanted to cement wells.

Erle died in 1957 and his company grew through acquisitions between the 1950s and the 1970s. In 1962 it bought Houston construction giant Brown & Root an expert in offshore platforms. After the 1973 Arab oil embargo Halliburton benefited from the surge in global oil exploration and later as drilling costs surged it became a leader in well stimulation.

When the oil industry slumped in 1982 the firm halved its workforce. Three years later a suffering Brown & Root coughed up $750 million to settle charges of mismanagement at the South Texas Nuclear Project.

In the 1990s Halliburton expanded abroad entering Russia in 1991 and China in 1993. The next year Brown & Root was named contractor for a pipeline stretching from Qatar to Pakistan. Halliburton drilled the world's deepest horizontal well (18860 ft.) in Germany in 1995.

That year Dick Cheney a former US defense secretary became CEO. Brown & Root began providing engineering and logistics services to US Army peacekeeping troops in the Balkans in 1995 and won a major contract to develop an offshore Canadian oil field the next year.

In 1997 Halliburton completed a major reorganization started in 1993 uniting 10 businesses under the Halliburton Energy Services umbrella. The company nearly doubled in size in 1998 with its $7.7 billion acquisition of oil field equipment manufacturer Dresser Industries. The purchase coupled with falling oil prices in 1998 and 1999 prompted Halliburton to ax more than 9000 workers. (Even after oil prices rebounded in 2000 Halliburton had to wait for the effects of the upturn to reach the oil field services sector.)

Brown & Root Energy Services won a contract to provide logistics support for the US Army in Albania in 1999. Halliburton also invested in oil field emergency-response firm Boots & Coots and took a stake in Japanese engineering firm Chiyoda.

The company began to sell off portions of its Dresser acquisition in 1999. Partner Ingersoll-Rand bought Halliburton's stake in Ingersoll-Dresser Pump for $515 million and bought its stake in Dresser-Rand (industrial compressors) for $579 million in 2000. Cheney resigned as chairman and CEO that year after he was chosen as George W. Bush's vice presidential running mate. President and COO David Lesar was named to succeed him.

A group consisting of investment firms First Reserve and Odyssey Investment Partners and Dresser managers paid $1.55 billion in 2001 for Dresser Equipment Group. That year a number of multimillion-dollar verdicts against Halliburton in asbestos cases sparked rumors that the company was going to file for bankruptcy (flatly denied by Halliburton) and caused the firm's stock price to tumble.

In 2002 in part to protect the company's assets from the unresolved asbestos claims issue Lesar announced plans to restructure Halliburton into two independent subsidiaries separating the Energy Services Group from Halliburton's KBR engineering and construction operations. Halliburton took a $483 million (pretax) charge against earnings in the second quarter of 2002 to cover its estimated asbestos liability.

Halliburton settled more than 300000 asbestos-related lawsuits by paying about $4 billion in cash and in stock. As a result Halliburton placed its subsidiaries Dresser Industries and Kellogg Brown & Root under Chapter 11 bankruptcy protection. Later that year in an effort to boost its newly formed Energy Services unit Halliburton purchased Pruett Industries a fiber optic sensor technology company.

In 2003 Halliburton announced plans to divest its noncore assets in an effort to return its focus to its main operating divisions. The company began its disposal of assets with the sale of its mono pumping businesses to National-Oilwell. The company sold its Wellstream business to European buyout firm Candover Partners for $136 million. It also completed the sale of its interests in European Marine Contractors Bredero-Shaw and its Subsea operations. The company's Halliburton Measurement Systems subsidiary was sold to NuFlo Technologies.

In 2004 the company's KBR subsidiary was awarded nearly $1.4 billion worth of contracts to aid in the repair and restoration of Iraq's oil fields during the US-led invasion of Iraq. The US Army Corps of Engineers later withdrew the contracts after allegations that they were awarded to the subsidiary due to Halliburton's relationship to Cheney. KBR also came under fire when the Pentagon claimed the company overcharged US taxpayers $61 million to supply fuel to Iraq. After an investigation by the US Army Corp of Engineers Halliburton was cleared of any wrongdoing. The investigation was picked up by the Pentagon's criminal investigative unit and the US State Department. Following an internal audit Halliburton repaid $6 million after discovering an overcharge from one of its subcontractor companies.

Later that year Halliburton enhanced its Fluids division by acquiring ITS Drilling Services' SUPAVAC unit. It also restructured its Engineering and Construction group into two divisions: Energy and Chemicals and Government and Infrastructure. In anticipation of selling off its KBR unit the company reorganized its management team promoting KBR CEO Andrew Lane to COO for Halliburton and placing him in charge of all Halliburton subsidiaries.

The company agreed to pay more than $4 billion in cash and stock to settle more than 300000 asbestos and silica-related personal injury lawsuits filed against its DII Industries and KBR subsidiaries. Halliburton reorganized its DII and KBR subsidiaries and finalized its asbestos settlements. DII and KBR emerged from Chapter 11 bankruptcy protection in January 2005. The company also completed the sale of its 50% stake in Subsea 7 to joint venture partner Siem Offshore for $200 million.

In 2006 Halliburton was awarded a multimillion-dollar contract by Saudi Aramco as part of the Khurais oilfield development project the largest in the region since the 1950s. The same year it spun off KBR to the public.

EXECUTIVES

Chairman President and CEO, David J. (Dave) Lesar, age 58, $1,328,708 total compensation
EVP and CFO, Mark A. McCollum, age 53, $577,500 total compensation
SVP Tax, Joseph F. (Joe) Andolino
President Strategy and Corporate Development, Timothy J. (Tim) Probert, age 60, $433,125 total compensation
EVP and General Counsel, Albert O. (Bert) Cornelison Jr., age 62
EVP Administration and Chief Human Resources Officer, Lawrence J. Pope, age 43, $310,000 total compensation
SVP and Chief Accounting Officer, Evelyn M. Angelle, age 45
SVP Investor Relations, Christian A. Garcia
SVP and Chief Ethics and Compliance Officer, Sherry D. Williams
VP and Secretary, Christina Ibrahim
President Eastern Hemisphere, Joseph (Joe) Rainey, age 55
President Western Hemisphere, Jim Brown
EVP and COO, Jeff Miller
Director, James R. Boyd, age 65
Director, J. Landis (Lanny) Martin, age 66
Director, Abdallah S. Jum'ah, age 71
Director, Debra L. (Debbie) Reed, age 56
Director, Milton Carroll, age 62
Director, Alan M. Bennett, age 62
Director, Nance K. Dicciani, age 64
Director, Robert A. (Bob) Malone, age 60
Director, S. Malcolm Gillis, age 71
Auditors: KPMGLLP

LOCATIONS

HQ: Halliburton Company
3000 N. Sam Houston Pkwy. East, Houston TX 77032
Phone: 281-871-2699 **Fax:** 214-522-9254
Web: www.hallwood.com

2011 Sales

	$ mil.	% of total
North America	14,413	58
Middle East/Asia	3,478	14
Latin America	2,982	12
Total	24,829	100

PRODUCTS/OPERATIONS

2011 Sales

	$ mil.	% of total
Completion & production	15,143	61

COMPETITORS

Baker Hughes
Cudd Energy Services
GE Oil
RPC
Saipem
Schlumberger
Superior Energy
Technip
Transocean
Weatherford International
Wild Well Control

HISTORICAL FINANCIALS

Company Type: Public

Income Statement FYE: December 31

	REVENUE ($ mil.)	NET INCOME ($ mil.)	NET PROFIT MARGIN	EMPLOYEES
12/11	24,829	2,839	11.4%	68,000
12/10	17,973	1,835	10.2%	58,000
12/09	14,675	1,145	7.8%	51,000
12/08	18,279	1,538	8.4%	57,000
12/07	15,264	3,499	22.9%	51,000
Annual Growth	12.9%	(5.1%)	—	7.5%

2011 Year-End Financials

Debt ratio: 20.36%
Return on equity: 21.51%
Cash ($ mil.): 2,698
Current ratio: 280.93
Long-term debt ($ mil.): 4,820
No. of shares (mil.): 921
Dividends
Yield: —
Payout: 11.69%
Market value ($ mil.): 31,784

	STOCK PRICE ($) FY Close	P/E High/Low		PER SHARE ($) Earnings	Dividends	Book Value
12/11	34.51	19	9	3.08	0.00	14.33
12/10	40.83	20	10	2.01	0.36	11.40
12/09	30.09	25	12	1.27	0.36	9.68
12/08	18.18	31	8	1.70	0.36	8.63
12/07	37.91	11	7	3.68	0.35	7.80
Annual Growth	(2.3%)	—	—	(4.4%)	—	16.4%

Hancock Holding Co.

Hancock Holding holds its own as a Gulf Coast financial force. It is the holding company of Mississippi-based Hancock Bank and Louisiana-based Whitney Bank. Together the banks have about 300 branches throughout the Gulf South from Florida to Texas. The community-oriented banks offer traditional products and services such as deposit accounts trust services and consumer and business lending. Hancock Holding also has subsidiaries or business units that offer insurance discount brokerage services mutual funds and consumer financing. In 2011 the company acquired regional rival Whitney Holding for some $1.5 billion.

The combination of Hancock and Whitney brought together two of the largest (and oldest) financial companies in the Gulf region. Following the merger bank branches in Louisiana and Texas operate under the Whitney Bank name while branches in Mississippi Alabama and Florida have the Hancock Bank brand. Hancock Holding was required to divest nearly 10 locations acquired in the deal in Louisiana and Mississippi to satisfy antitrust concerns.

Hancock Holding reported net income of $76.8 million on revenues of nearly $800 million. The Whitney acquisition boosted both of those numbers. The company also benefitted from fewer provisions for loan losses and charged-off loans.

The company's market area has faced plenty of challenges in recent years. Devastating hurricanes the recession and a major oil spill have plagued Gulf Coast communities. However Hancock Holding has continued to grow across its market and enter new ones.

It is looking to increase its international profile. The company which operates in major Gulf of Mexico port cities sees opportunity to be more involved in trade work as the Panama Canal is expanded. The canal expansion (expected to be completed in 2014) will increase trade between Central and South America and North America.

EXECUTIVES

President CEO and Director; President and CEO Hancock Bank, Carl J. Chaney, age 50, $425,769 total compensation
SVP and Chief Credit Officer, Sam B. Kendricks, age 52
Chairman, James B. Estabrook Jr., age 67
CEO COO and Director; COO Hancock Bank, John M. Hairston, age 48, $425,769 total compensation
EVP and Chief Retail Banking Officer, Richard T. Hill, $249,231 total compensation
EVP and Chief Wealth Management Officer, Clifton J. Saik, $277,269 total compensation
VP Investor Relations, Paul D. Guichet
SVP and Internal Auditor, Alfreda A. Horne
EVP and General Counsel, Joy Lambert Phillips
Director; Chairman Hancock Bank of Louisiana, John H. Pace, age 81
EVP and Chief Commercial Banking Officer, Edward G. Francis
EVP and Chief Risk and Administrative Officer, D. Shane Loper
VP and Manager Corporate Communications, R. Paul Maxwell
SVP and Treasurer, Gerry Dugal
EVP and CFO, Michael M. Achary, $249,231 total compensation
SVP and Director Marketing, Robert A. Seals
SVP and Director Compliance, Sandra A. Wilbourn
President CEO and Director; President and CEO Hancock Bank, Carl J. Chaney, age 50
Director, Robert W. Roseberry, age 61
Director, Frank E. Bertucci, age 55
Director, James H. Horne, age 59
CEO COO and Director; COO Hancock Bank, John M. Hairston, age 48
Director, Anthony J. Topazi, age 62
Director, Alton G. Bankston, age 70
Director, Don P. Descant, age 63
Director; Chairman Hancock Bank of Louisiana, John H. Pace, age 81
Director, Christine L. Pickering, age 51
Director, Randy W. Hanna, age 53
Director, Jerry L. Levens, age 55
Director, Thomas H. Olinde, age 56
Auditors: PricewaterhouseCoopersLLP

LOCATIONS

HQ: Hancock Holding Co.
One Hancock Plaza, P.O. Box 4019, Gulfport, MS 39502
Phone: 228 868-4000
Web: www.hancockbank.com

2011 Sales

	$ mil.	% of total
Whitney	476	60
Hancock	272	34
Other	50	6
Total	**798**	**100**

PRODUCTS/OPERATIONS

2011 Sales

	$ mil.	% of total
Interest		
Loans including fees	499	63
Securities	90	11
Other	2	-
Noninterest		
Service charges on deposit accounts	55	7
Bank card fees	28	4
Trust fees	23	3
Accretion of indemnification asset	16	2
Insurance commissions and fees	16	2
Investment & annuity fees	15	2
ATM fees	14	2
Other	36	4
Total	**798**	**100**

Subsidiaries
Berwick LLC
Community First Inc.
Dudley Ventures Hancock Fund LLC
Gulf South Technology Center LLC
The Gulfport Building Inc.
Hancock Bank
Hancock Bank of Alabama
Hancock Bank Securities Corporation II
Hancock Community Investment Corporatio
Hancock Enterprise Investment Fund LLC
Hancock Insurance Agency
Hancock Insurance Agency of Alabama
Hancock Insurance Agency of Florida
Hancock Investment Services of Alabama Inc.
Hancock Investment Services of Florida Inc.
Hancock Investment Services of Louisiana Inc.
Hancock Investment Services of Mississippi Inc.
Hancock Investment Services Inc.
Harrison Finance Company
Harrison Loan Company
HBSC LLC
HMC LLC
Invest-Sure Inc.
J Everett Eaves Inc.
Lighthouse Services Corporatio
Peoples First Transportation Inc.
Town Properties Inc.
Whitney Bank

COMPETITORS

BancorpSouth
Capital One
First Horizon
IBERIABANK
MidSouth Bancorp
Regions Financial
Renasant
Trustmark

HISTORICAL FINANCIALS

Company Type: Public

Income Statement FYE: December 31

	ASSETS ($ mil.)	NET INCOME ($ mil.)	INCOME AS % OF ASSETS	EMPLOYEES
12/11	19,774	76	0.4%	4,745
12/10	8,138	52	0.6%	2,271
12/09	8,697	74	0.9%	5,837
12/08	7,167	65	0.9%	1,952
12/07	6,055	73	1.2%	1,888
Annual Growth	34.4%	1.0%	—	25.9%

2011 Year-End Financials

Debt ratio: 1.79%
Return on equity: 3.24%
Cash ($ mil.): 1,622
Current ratio: —
Long-term debt ($ mil.): 353
No. of shares (mil.): 84
Dividends
Yield: —
Payout: 83.48%
Market value ($ mil.): 2,708

	STOCK PRICE ($) FY Close	P/E High/Low		PER SHARE ($) Earnings	Dividends	Book Value
12/11	31.97	31	22	1.15	0.00	27.95
12/10	34.86	32	19	1.40	0.96	23.22
12/09	43.81	20	10	2.26	0.96	22.74
12/08	45.46	28	17	2.05	0.96	19.18
12/07	38.20	23	14	2.27	0.96	17.71
Annual Growth	(4.4%)	—	—	(15.6%)	—	12.1%

Hanesbrands Inc

Hanesbrands can't wait until it gets its Hanes on you. The company makes bras hosiery men's boxers socks and other intimate apparel under brand names including Bali Champion barely there Just My Size Hanes L'eggs Playtex and Wonderbra. Its bras are tops in the US; its underwear legwear and activewear units are market leaders as well. Hanesbrands also makes basic outerwear such as T-shirts and licensed logo apparel for collegiate bookstores legwear for Donna Karan and underwear for Polo Ralph Lauren. The lineup is sold to wholesalers major retail chains such as Wal-Mart Target and Kohl's and through Hanesbrands' value outlets and Internet site. The US generates more than 85% of sales.

Despite the uncertain and volatile economy that has impacted consumer purchases Hanesbrands posted more than a 25% uptick in earnings on a 7% increase in sales in 2011 over the prior year. Marking a second consecutive year of growth the improvement was driven by higher prices coupled with favorable currency exchange rates and incremental sales from Gear for Sports a licensed logo apparel maker for college bookstores and other outlets (acquired in late 2010).

Results are parsed into five operating segments: Innerwear Outerwear Hosiery Direct to Consumer and International. In general each segment is organized by product category geography and distribution channel. During 2011 sales of innerwear comprising women's bras and panties and men's and kids' underwear and socks rose modestly fueling 44% of total revenues. Outerwear and International business segments (generating 31% and 13% of sales respectively) jumped by double digits year-over-year. Hosiery and Direct to Consumer sales however slumped slightly hurt by the trend toward casual dress as well as the company's lower investment in Internet selling and marketing activities.

Mass merchandise customers are particularly vital to the company's performance. It holds contracts with Wal-Mart and Target as well as discount retailer Family Dollar. Hanesbrands also allies with mid-tier stores including J. C. Penney Macy's and Kohl's which are adding its lower-priced labels. In 2011 Wal-Mart represented 25% of the company's sales while Target helped to bring in 16% and Kohl's another 6%.

Going forward Hanesbrands is focusing on reducing production costs. It counts on improving operating efficiencies primarily by using a low-cost global supply chain based upon a combination of owned contracted and sourced manufacturing. It has successfully started and increased production at a textile plant in China its first company-owned facility in Asia. Hanesbrands meanwhile shuttered about 10 manufacturing plants and three distribution centers. The closings include the company's last large knit-fabric textile plant in the US.

Handesbrands' long-term vision targets the difficult task of generating more cash to reduce debt which stands at $1.8 billion as of the end of 2011. Former parent Sara Lee spun off the apparel maker in late 2006. During the years since the spinoff Hanesbrands has struggled to improve its capital structure by shuttering plants and eliminating up to 5300 jobs or some 10% of its workforce.

EXECUTIVES

Chief Human Resources Officer, Kevin W. Oliver, age 54, $375,000 total compensation
Co-COO, William J. Nictakis, age 51, $600,000 total compensation
Chief Legal Officer General Counsel and Secretary, Joia M. Johnson, age 51
Chairman and CEO, Richard A. (Rich) Noll, age 54, $800,000 total compensation
CFO, Richard D. Moss, age 54
Co-COO, Gerald W. Evans Jr., age 52, $600,000 total compensation
EVP; General Manager Outerwear Strategic, Kevin D. Hall, age 53
EVP and Chief Customer Officer, Joan P. McReynolds, age 61
Media Relations, Matthew (Matt) Hall
EVP; President Innerwear/Hosiery, W. Howard Upchurch Jr., age 47
Media Relations, Bernadette Wallace
Operating CFO, Dale W. Boyles
Chief Supply Chain Officer, Michael E. Faircloth, age 46
SVP; President Outerware, John T. Marsh, age 46
Director, James C. Johnson, age 59
Director, Lee A. Chaden, age 70
Director, Ann E. Ziegler, age 54
Director, Ronald L. (Ron) Nelson, age 60
Director, Andrew J. (Andy) Schindler, age 68
Director, J. Patrick (Pat) Mulcahy, age 67
Director, Bobby J. Griffin, age 63
Director, Jessica T. Mathews, age 65
Auditors: PricewaterhouseCoopersLLP

LOCATIONS

HQ: Hanesbrands Inc.
1000 E. Hanes Mill Rd., Winston-Salem NC 27105
Phone: 336-519-8080 **Fax:** 212-664-4085
Web: tv.msnbc.com

2011 Sales

	$ mil.	% of total
US	4,057	87
Canada	139	3
Japan	118	3
Mexico	79	2
Europe	72	2
Brazil	67	1
China	19	—
Central America & the Caribbean Basin	4	—
Other	77	2
Total	**4,637**	**100**

PRODUCTS/OPERATIONS

2011 Sales

	$ mil.	% of total
Innerwear	2,058	44
Outerwear	1,459	31
International	580	13
Direct to consumer	375	8
Hosiery	163	4
Total	**4,637**	**100**

Selected Brands

Bali
barely there
Champion
Duofold
Gear for Sports
Just My Size
Hanes
L' eggs
Outer Banks
Playtex
Rinbros
Sol y Oro
Stedman
Wonderbra
Zorba

COMPETITORS

Calvin Klein
Frederick' s of Hollywood Group
Fruit of the Loom
Gerber Childrenswear
Gildan Activewear
J. Crew
Jockey International
Limited Brands
Maidenform
PremiumWear
Redcats USA
Russell Brands
The Gap
Tommy Hilfiger
Top Form
Triumph Apparel
Under Armour
Wacoal
Warnaco Group
Warnaco Swimwear

HISTORICAL FINANCIALS

Company Type: Public

Income Statement FYE: December 31

	REVENUE ($ mil.)	NET INCOME ($ mil.)	NET PROFIT MARGIN	EMPLOYEES
12/11*	4,637	266	5.8%	53,300
01/11	4,326	211	4.9%	55,500
01/10	3,891	51	1.3%	47,400
01/09	4,248	127	3.0%	45,200
12/07	4,474	126	2.8%	47,600
Annual Growth	0.9%	20.6%	—	2.9%

*Fiscal year change

2011 Year-End Financials

Debt ratio: 50.51%
Return on equity: 39.16%
Cash ($ mil.): 35
Current ratio: 249.62
Long-term debt ($ mil.): 1,807
No. of shares (mil.): 97
Dividends
Yield: —
Payout: —
Market value ($ mil.): 2,132

	STOCK PRICE ($) FY Close	P/E High	P/E Low	PER SHARE ($) Earnings	Dividends	Book Value
12/11*	21.86	12	8	2.69	0.00	6.98
01/11	25.40	14	10	2.16	0.00	5.85
01/10	24.11	48	11	0.54	0.00	3.51
01/09	13.18	28	7	1.34	0.00	1.98
12/07	27.84	25	18	1.30	0.00	3.03
Annual Growth	(5.9%)	—	—	19.9%	—	23.2%

*Fiscal year change

Hanmi Financial Corp.

No hand-me-down operation Hanmi Financial is headquartered in a penthouse suite along Los Angeles' Wilshire Boulevard. The company owns Hanmi Bank which serves California's Korean-American community and others in the multi-ethnic Los Angeles San Diego San Francisco Bay and Silicon Valley areas. Hanmi Bank offers retail and small business banking with an emphasis on the latter from more than 25 California branches and loan offices throughout the US. Commercial and industrial loans including SBA and international trade finance loans account for about 60% of its loan portfolio; real estate loans make up most of the rest. Hanmi and Korean bank Woori Finance called off plans to merge in mid-2011.

Operations

In addition to its banking services Hanmi subsidiaries offer life and property/casualty insurance products through Chun-Ha Insurance Services and All World Insurance Services.

Financial Analysis

Hanmi's revenue fell 10% in 2011 vs. 2010 the fourth consecutive year of decline. Indeed since 2007 the bank's revenue has fallen more than 50%. The financial and housing crises particularly acute in California hurt Hanmi's customers many of whom operate small businesses and consequently the bank's finances. Decreased loan volume lower yields on investment securities and a shift to lower-cost products by it customers all contributed to the decline in interest income in 2011. Non-interest income fell on decreasing service charges on deposit accounts.

On the plus side Hanmi returned to profitability in 2011 posting net income of about $28 million. It was the bank's first profitable year since 2006.

Strategy

While its merger with Woori was called off in mid-2011 Hanmi and Woori Finance launched a business alliance later in the year. The pair teamed together to offer VIP customer services such as investment consulting and safe deposit boxes. Woori Bank also agreed to train Hanmi Bank personnel. Another aspect of the alliance will be conducting benchmark studies about private banking enterprise risk management and other topics.

EXECUTIVES

EVP and CFO, Brian E. Cho, age 52, $270,000 total compensation
SVP and Deputy Chief Credit Officer, Haekyong (Jane) Kim
Chairman, Joseph K. Rho, age 71
President CEO and Director, Jay S. Yoo, age 65, $172,404 total compensation
Investor Relations, Stephanie Yoon
Chief Administrative Officer, Greg Kim
Branch Manager Olympic Kingsley, Ho I. Min
Branch Manager Downtown Los Angeles, Judy Lee
Branch Manager Garden Grove Brookhurst, Ine Ja Kim
Branch Manager Rowland Heights, Sook R. Park
Branch Manager Koreatown Plaza, Elaine Chung
Branch Manager Olympic, Helen H. Kim
Branch Manager San Diego, Young H. Oh
Branch Manager Silicon Valley, Philip Whang
Branch Manager Western, Sun Y. Park
Branch Manager Wilshire Hobart, Suk Jin Yoon
Chief Credit Officer Hamni Bank, Jung Hak Son
SVP and Chief Lending Officer, Hassan Bouayad
Manager SBA Loan Center, James Kim
Manager Consumer Loan Center, Janette K. Mah
Branch Manager Garden Grove Magnolia, Michelle Kwon
Branch Manager Irvine, MeeHye J. Lee
SVP and Manager Consumer Loan Center, Jennifer Nam
Manager Insurance Department, James Yang
LPO Manager Northwest Region, Seong Tae (Steven) Yang
Branch Manager Fullerton, Hye J. Shin
Branch Manager Beverly Hills, Jin-Young (Lisa) Kim
Branch Manager Gardena, Sung H. Shin
Branch Manager Diamond Bar, Sharon J. Im
Branch Manager Cerritos Artesia, Mu J. Kim
Branch Manager Cerritos South, Hye R. Kim
Branch Manager Fashion District, Sharon Kim
Branch Manager Koreatown Galleria, Jennifer S. Cho
Branch Manager Northridge, Sang U. Hong
Branch Manager Rancho Cucamonga, Eunice Lee
Branch Manager San Francisco, Been Lee
Branch Manager Torrance Crenshaw, In K. An
Branch Manager Torrance Del Amo Mall, Jae H. Lee
Branch Manager Van Nuys, Lydia Kim
Branch Manager Vermont Branch, Woo Y. Chung
Manager Commercial Loan Department, Min S. Park
Manager Commercial Loan Department, Claire Yoon
Construction Manager Commercial Loan Department, George Badal
Chief Marketing Officer, Sang K. Lee
Chief Compliance and BSA Officer, Jean Lim
Manager International Department, Jin S. Lee
LPO Manager Virginia, Yong J. Park
Director, William J. Stolte, age 65
Director, I. Joon Ahn, age 72
Director, Joon H. Lee, age 68
Director, Paul S. H. Kim, age 67
President CEO and Director, Jay S. Yoo, age 65
Director, John A. (Jack) Hall, age 62
Auditors: KPMGLLP

LOCATIONS

HQ: Hanmi Financial Corporation
3660 Wilshire Blvd. Penthouse Ste. A, Los Angeles CA 90010
Phone: 213-382-2200 **Fax:** 213-384-0990
Web: www.hanmi.com

PRODUCTS/OPERATIONS

2011 Sales

	$ mil.	% of total
Interest		
Loans including fees	117	78
Investment securities	9	6
Other	1	1
Noninterest		
Service charges on deposit accounts	12	8
Insurance commissions	4	3
Other	6	4
Total	**152**	**100**

COMPETITORS

Bank of America
BBCN
Cathay General Bancorp
East West Bancorp
Far East National Bank
JPMorgan Chase
Saehan Bancorp
Wilshire Bancorp
Woori

HISTORICAL FINANCIALS

Company Type: Public

Income Statement FYE: December 31

	ASSETS ($ mil.)	NET INCOME ($ mil.)	INCOME AS % OF ASSETS	EMPLOYEES
12/11	2,744	28	1.0%	483
12/10	2,907	(88)	—	459
12/09	3,162	(122)	—	509
12/08	3,875	(102)	—	563
12/07	3,983	(60)	—	627
Annual Growth	(8.9%)	—	—	(6.3%)

2011 Year-End Financials

Debt ratio: 3.12%
Return on equity: 9.86%
Cash ($ mil.): 181
Current ratio: —
Long-term debt ($ mil.): 85
No. of shares (mil.): 31
Dividends
Yield: —
Payout: —
Market value ($ mil.): 233

	STOCK PRICE ($) FY Close	P/E High	P/E Low	PER SHARE ($) Earnings	Dividends	Book Value
12/11	7.40	6	1	1.38	0.00	9.07
12/10	1.15	—	—	(7.44)	0.00	9.17
12/09	1.20	—	—	(20.56)	0.00	23.41
12/08	2.06	—	—	(17.84)	0.00	45.99
12/07	8.62	—	—	(10.16)	0.00	64.81
Annual Growth	(3.7%)	—	—	—	—	(38.8%)

Hanover Insurance Group Inc

The Hanover Insurance Group is an all-around property/casualty insurance holding company. Through its Hanover Insurance Company it provides personal and commercial automobile homeowners workers' compensation and commercial multiple-peril insurance and professional liability coverage. The group sells its products through a network of 2000 independent agents throughout the US but Michigan Massachusetts and New York account for more than 40% of its business. In Michigan it operates as Citizens Insurance Company. Hanover's Opus Investment Management subsidiary provides institutional investment management services and it operates internationally through its UK subsidiary Chaucer Holdings.

Geographic Reach Michigan is Hanover's largest market accounting for nearly a quarter of all commercial and personal lines. Massachusetts and New York account for 10% and 9% respectively while California and New Jersey contribute an additional 6% each. About a quarter of international operations are concentrated in the UK with the Asia-Pacific and Americas regions accounting for about 9% each.

Financial Analysis Hanover saw revenue jump nearly 25% in 2011 to $3.9 billion as net premiums earned grew by more than $750 million. The majority of that growth is attributable to the mid-year acquisition of UK insurance firm Chaucer which added international operations to Hanover's business. Expenses related to the Chaucer purchase as well as an increase in catastrophe losses and non-catastrophe weather-related activity pushed net income down to $37 million a decline of 76% from the prior year. Strategy Hanover's written premiums are split more or less evenly between its personal and commercial products but competition is fierce in personal insurance so the company has placed more emphasis on expanding its commercial offerings. Wriggling into a niche is one method of expanding and Hanover has moved into several areas of specialty insurance in recent years. It created Hanover Architects & Engineers Advantage product line out of its 2010 acquisition of Benchmark Professional Insurance Services (insurance for the design industry including architects and engineers). Another 2010 acquisition –Campania Group –brought in liability coverage for the health care industry. In 2011 the company went international when it acquired UK-based Chaucer Holdings for $510 million. Chaucer operates two Lloyd's of London syndicates which manage and underwrite global property/casualty policies. The purchase also put Hanover into the reinsurance business and added specialty coverage in areas such as marine aviation and nuclear energy. Hanover has also expanded its less specialized commercial offerings. It secured the rights to a block of small and middle-market non-specialty commercial business worth $400 million from OneBeacon in 2009 which helped it build up its business in that area just as it was also expanding geographically with new offices opening in the western US. To support its growth in the area Hanover created a Pacific Region territory in 2012 with branch offices in Washington Oregon and California.

HISTORY

In 1842 a group of Worcester Massachusetts businessmen tried to form a mutual life insurance company. After a failed first attempt they succeeded with the help of lobbyist Benjamin Balch. In 1844 the State Mutual Life Assurance Co. of Worcester set up business in the back room of secretary Clarendon Harris' bookstore. The first president was John Davis a US senator. The company issued its first policy in 1845.

In the early years State Mutual reduced risk by issuing policies only for residents of such "civilized" areas as New England New Jersey New York Pennsylvania and Ohio. It also restricted movement requiring policyholders to get permission for travel outside those areas. By the 1850s the company had begun issuing policies in the Midwest (with a 25% premium surcharge) the South (for 30% extra) and California (for a pricey extra $25 per $1000) with a maximum coverage of $5000.

The Civil War was a problem for many insurers who had to decide what to do about Southern policyholders and payment on war-related claims. State Mutual chose to pay out its Northern policyholders' benefits despite the extra cost. In 1896 the firm began offering installment pay-out plans for policyholders concerned that their beneficiaries would fritter away the whole payment.

The first 30 years of the 20th century were for the company a time of growth that was stopped short by the Depression. But despite a great increase in the number of policy loans and surrenders for cash value State Mutual's financial footing remained solid.

After WWII the company entered group insurance and began offering individual sickness and accident coverage. In 1957 it was renamed State Mutual Life Assurance Co. of America. The firm added property/casualty insurance in the late 1950s through alliances with such firms as Worcester Mutual Fire Insurance. During the 1960s State Mutual continued to develop property/casualty buying interests in Hanover Insurance and Citizens Corp.

The firm followed the industrywide shift into financial services in the 1970s adding mutual funds a real estate investment trust and an investment management firm. This trend accelerated in the 1980s and State Mutual began offering financial planning services as well as administrative and other services for the insurance and mutual fund industries (the mutual fund administration operations were sold in 1995). Managing this growth was another story: Its acquisitions left it bloated and disorganized. Technical systems were in disarray by the early 1990s and the agency force had grown to more than 1400. In response the company began a five-year effort to upgrade systems cut fat and reduce sales positions.

In view of its shifting focus State Mutual became Allmerica Financial in 1992. Three years later it demutualized. In 1997 it bought the 40% of Allmerica Property & Casualty it didn't already own. The next year heavy spring storms hammered Allmerica's bottom line and the company incurred $15 million in catastrophe losses. Also in 1998 it bought the portion of Citizens it didn't previously own.

In 1999 Allmerica announced plans to sell its group life and health insurance operations to concentrate on its core businesses; Great-West Assurance bought them the next year. Its purchase that year of Advantage Insurance Network a group of affiliated life insurance agencies grew its distribution channels. In 2000 the firm reduced its workforce by 5% (some 6000 employees) in an efficiency move. In 2001 Allmerica sold its 401(k) business to Minnesota Life.

Raising some much-needed capital the company sold a large chunk of its life insurance and annuities operations in 2002 which led to an improved bottom line the following year.

Deep in the red the company in 2003 sold its fixed universal life insurance operations to John Hancock. The declining stock market forced the company to stop selling new variable annuities and life insurance products. The company rebounded somewhat thanks in part to the discontinuation of unprofitable lines of business.

The company changed its name from Allmerica Financial Corporation to The Hanover Insurance Group in late 2005.

To better focus on its property/casualty lines in 2008 the company sold its last remaining life insurance business to Goldman Sachs and its commercial-property finance company Amgro to Premium Financing Specialists.

EXECUTIVES

EVP CIO and COO, Gregory D. Tranter, age 55, $389,423 total compensation
President CEO and Director, Frederick H. (Fred) Eppinger, age 53, $934,615 total compensation
EVP General Counsel and Assistant Secretary, J. Kendall Huber, age 57, $430,385 total compensation
EVP Corporate Development; President Specialty Insurance, Andrew S. Robinson, age 46
Chairman, Michael P. Angelini, age 69
EVP; President Property and Casualty Companies, Marita Zuraitis, age 51, $571,154 total compensation
President and CEO Chaucer, Robert A. (Bob) Stuchbery, age 55
VP and Secretary, Charles F. Cronin
SVP and Chief Human Resources Officer, Bryan D. Allen, age 44
Investor Relations, Robert P. Myron, age 44
EVP CFO and Principal Accounting Officer, David B. Greenfield, age 49
Media Relations, Michael F. Buckley
SVP; President Business Insurance, John C. (Jack) Roche, age 48
Manager Media Relations, Amy L. Banek
VP Corporate Finance and Treasurer, John (JR) Reilly
Regional President West, John Casper
Head of Corporate Product and Underwriting Functions, Tony de Padua
CFO Property and Casualty, Ellen M. Rizzo
President Specialty Lines and Chief Underwriting Officer Commercial Lines, Antonio Z. dePadua, age 59
SVP; President Personal Lines, Mark R. Desrochers, age 43
Assistant VP, Oksana Lukasheva
President. Professional Liability, Gerald T. Merritt
Assistant Regional VP Wisconsin, John Vose
President Northeast Region, Kelly J. Stacy
SVP and Chief Marketing and Distribution Officer, Richard (Dick) Lavey
Director, Joseph R. Ramrath, age 55
Director, Robert J. Murray, age 70
Director, Neal F. Finnegan, age 74
Director, John J. (Jack) Brennan, age 57
President CEO and Director, Frederick H. (Fred) Eppinger, age 53
Director, Wendell J. Knox, age 64
Director, P. Kevin Condron, age 66
Director, David J. Gallitano, age 64
Director, Harriett (Tee) Taggart, age 64
Auditors: PricewaterhouseCoopersLLP

LOCATIONS

HQ: The Hanover Insurance Group Inc.
440 Lincoln St., Worcester MA 01653-0002
Phone: 508-855-1000 **Fax:** 508-853-6332
Web: www.hanover.com

PRODUCTS/OPERATIONS

2011 Net Premiums Written

	% of total
Commercial	
Multiple	18
Auto	8
Worker's	6
Other	22
Personal	
Auto	29
Homeowners	16
Other	1
Total	**100**

COMPETITORS

Allstate
American Automobile Association (AAA)
American Financial Group
Auto-Owners Insurance
GEICO
Liberty Mutual
Markel Insurance
Nationwide
Progressive Corporation
State Farm
Travelers Companies
USAA

HISTORICAL FINANCIALS

Company Type: Public

Income Statement FYE: December 31

	ASSETS ($ mil.)	NET INCOME ($ mil.)	INCOME AS % OF ASSETS	EMPLOYEES
12/11	12,624	37	0.3%	5,100
12/10	8,569	154	1.8%	4,400
12/09	8,042	197	2.5%	4,100
12/08	9,230	20	0.2%	4,000
12/07	9,815	253	2.6%	3,900
Annual Growth	6.5%	(38.1%)	—	6.9%

2011 Year-End Financials

Debt ratio: 7.22%
Return on equity: 1.48%
Cash ($ mil.): 820
Current ratio: —
Long-term debt ($ mil.): 911
No. of shares (mil.): 44
Dividends
Yield: —
Payout: 138.89%
Market value ($ mil.): 1,559

	STOCK PRICE ($) FY Close	P/E High/Low		PER SHARE ($) Earnings	Dividends	Book Value
12/11	34.95	60	38	0.81	0.00	56.27
12/10	46.72	14	12	3.34	1.00	54.80
12/09	44.43	12	7	3.86	0.75	49.65
12/08	42.97	128	80	0.40	0.45	37.08
12/07	45.80	10	8	4.83	0.40	44.38
Annual Growth	(6.5%)	—	—	(36.0%)	—	6.1%

Harbinger Group Inc

Harbinger Group (formerly Zapata Corporation) zapped its former image as an oil and gas company and is on the lookout for new acquisitions. The holding company has some $400 million to make investments across a diverse array of industries.

Former US President George H. W. Bush co-founded the company as Zapata in 1953. It sold its energy businesses in the 1990s and became a producer of marine protein through its holdings in Omega Protein. Omega's facilities suffered major hurricane damage in 2005 and Zapata sold Omega the next year. Hedge fund Harbinger Capital Partners bought a controlling stake in Harbinger Group in 2009.

In early 2011 Harbinger Group acquired a majority of consumer goods firm Spectrum Brands. Shortly afterwards it acquired Old Mutual U.S. Life Holdings from Old Mutual for $350 million. The life insurance units were rebranded as Fidelity & Guaranty Life Insurance Company and Fidelity & Guaranty Life Insurance Company of New York. Harbinger Group then acquired a minority stake in North American Energy Partners which primarily provides construction and pipeline services to the Canadian oil sands market. The deals are part of Harbinger's strategy is to acquire operating businesses across a range of industries such as consumer products insurance and financial products telecommunications agriculture power generation and water and natural resources.

Harbinger Group also owns almost all of Zap.Com Corporation; however it is a public shell company with no business operations. Zap.Com is seeking investments or it may develop a new business so that it can become an operating company.

HISTORY

Named for the movie "Viva Zapata!" Zapata was formed by the 1953 merger of the young George H. W. Bush's Bush-Overby oil company and another oil firm run by Hugh and Bill Liedtke. After going public in 1955 Bush and the Liedtkes split the company in 1959 with Bush taking over Zapata Off-Shore. He sold his stake in Zapata in 1966 after being elected to Congress. In 1973 the company bought fish processor Haynie Products. Zapata struggled through the oil slump of the 1980s sold assets and converted debt to stock to avoid bankruptcy.

Investor Malcolm Glazer took control of the company in 1993. He became CEO and chairman the following year and shifted the company's focus away from energy. In 1995 Zapata sold the natural gas compression business and acquired Glazer's 31% share of money-losing food packaging manufacturer Envirodyne (increased to 40% in 1996 and renamed Viskase Companies in 1998). In 1997 it sold its Bolivian operations the last of the energy holdings to Tesoro.

The company expanded its fishing business by purchasing two competitors in 1997 but it didn't hold them for long. The next year it spun off its fishing businesses to the public as Omega Protein retaining a majority stake.

Excited by the Internet's possibilities Zapata in 1998 resuscitated two e-zines that had been spiked by Icon CMT and it formed Zap.com to hold those and other Web sites that it planned to buy. Despite having few significant assets and no revenues in 1999 the company spun off Zap.com to its shareholders; Zapata retained nearly 98%. Also that year the company moved its headquarters from Houston to Rochester New York.

Zapata recorded big losses in 1999 mostly due to sluggish sales at Omega Protein which suffered from a glut in the protein meal and edible oil markets. In addition Viskase which has been struggling and selling operations for a few years sold its shrink film business in 2000 to help retire debt. Also that year Viskase announced that it was selling its plastics business. Zapata announced in 2000 that it would begin a new focus for "Charged" including expansion into wireless animation and creative multimedia. In 2001 however the company shut down both Zap.com and its Charged Productions operations. In September 2001 Zapata sold its interest in Viskase.

In 2003 Zapata rejected an unsolicited $108 million cash take-over bid from merger and acquisition group Hollingsworth Rothwell & Roxford. Later that year Zapata bought additional shares of Safety Components International bringing its ownership of the company to about 80%; however it sold its shares in Safety Components in 2005.

In late 2006 it began selling its holdings in Omega Protein. Omega bought back 36% of Zapata's shares for $47.5 million in November of that year. Zapata announced the sale of the last of its Omega holdings to a group of private investors for about $29 million in December 2006.

In 2009 the company changed its name to Harbinger Group.

EXECUTIVES

EVP and CFO, Thomas A. (Tom) Williams, age 52
Chairman and CEO, Philip Falcone
EVP Investments Managing Director and Director, David M. Maura
President and Director, Omar M. Asali
VP Investments, Phil Gass
VP Investments, Tyler S. Kolarik
VP and Corporate Controller, R. Grant Edwards
VP Counsel and Corporate Secretary, Ehsan Zargar
VP Investor Relations, Tara Glenn
Director, Robert V. Leffler Jr., age 66
Director, Thomas J. Hudgins, age 72
Director, Keith M. Hladek, age 37
EVP Investments Managing Director and Director, David M. Maura
Director, Robin Roger
President and Director, Omar M. Asali
Director, Lap Wai Chan
Auditors: Deloitte&ToucheLLP

LOCATIONS

HQ: Harbinger Group Inc
450 Park Avenue, 27th Floor, New York, NY 10022
Phone: 212 906-8555
Web: www.harbingergroupinc.com

PRODUCTS/OPERATIONS

COMPETITORS

Apollo Global Management
Berkshire Hathaway
Blackstone Group
Brookfield Asset Management
Hellman & Friedman
KKR
Lightyear Capital LLC
Onex
TPG

HISTORICAL FINANCIALS

Company Type: Public

Income Statement FYE: September 30

	REVENUE ($ mil.)	NET INCOME ($ mil.)	NET PROFIT MARGIN	EMPLOYEES
09/12	4,480	89	2.0%	6,000
09/11*	3,477	34	1.0%	6,000
12/10	0	(22)	—	8
12/09	0	(13)	—	8
12/08	0	(0)	—	7
Annual Growth	—	—	—	441.1%

*Fiscal year change

2012 Year-End Financials

Debt ratio: 8.60%
Return on equity: 5.98%
Cash ($ mil.): 1,470
Current ratio: 411.83
Long-term debt ($ mil.): 2,150
No. of shares (mil.): 140
Dividends
Yield: —
Payout: —
Market value ($ mil.): 1,182

	STOCK PRICE ($) FY Close	P/E High	P/E Low	PER SHARE ($) Earnings	Dividends	Book Value
09/12	8.43	69	27	0.15	0.00	10.68
09/11*	5.07	92	57	0.04	0.00	8.47
12/10	6.19	—	—	(1.16)	0.00	6.44
12/09	7.02	—	—	(0.69)	0.00	7.56
12/08	6.03	—	—	(0.00)	0.00	8.24
Annual Growth	8.7%	—	—	—	—	6.7%

*Fiscal year change

Harley-Davidson Inc

Put your a** on some class reads one (not necessarily official) Harley-Davidson T-shirt. Harley-Davidson is a major US maker of motorcycles and the nation's #1 seller of heavyweight cruisers. The company offers touring and custom Harleys through a worldwide network of more than 1300 dealers. The company manufactures and markets five families of motorcycles: Touring Dyna Softail Sportster and V-Rod. It also makes three-wheeled motorcycles. Harley-Davidson sells attitude with its brand-name products which include a line of clothing and accessories (MotorClothes). Harley-Davidson Financial Services (HDFS) offers financing to dealers and consumers in the US and Canada.

HISTORY

In 1903 William Harley and the Davidson brothers (Walter William and Arthur) of Milwaukee sold their first Harley-Davidson motorcycle which essentially was motor-assisted bicycle that required pedaling uphill. Demand was high and most sold before leaving the factory. Six years later the company debuted its trademark two-cylinder V-twin engine. By 1913 it had 150 competitors.

WWI created a demand for US motorcycles overseas that made foreign sales important. During the 1920s Harley-Davidson was a leader in innovative engineering introducing models with a front brake and the "teardrop" gas tank that became part of the Harley look.

The Depression took a heavy toll on the motorcycle industry. As one of only two remaining companies Harley-Davidson survived through exports and sales to the police and military. To improve sales the company added styling features such as art deco decals and three-tone paint. The 1936 EL model with its "knucklehead" engine (named for the shape of its valve covers) was a forerunner of today's models.

During WWII Harley-Davidson prospered from military orders. It introduced new models after the war to cater to a growing recreational market of consumers with money to spend: the K-model (1952) Sportster "superbike" (1957) and Duo-Glide (1958). Ever since competitor Indian Motorcycle Company gave up the ghost in the 1950s Harley-Davidson has been the US's only major motorcycle manufacturer. (Indian Motorcycle was revived in 1998 however.)

The company began making golf carts (since discontinued) in the early 1960s. It went public in 1965 and American Machine and Foundry (AMF) bought the company in 1969. But by the late 1970s sales and quality were slipping. Certain that Harley-Davidson would lose to Japanese bikes flooding the market AMF put the company up for sale. There was no buyer until 1981 when Vaughn Beals and other AMF executives purchased it. Minutes away from bankruptcy in 1985 then-CFO Richard Teerlink convinced lenders to accept a restructuring plan.

Facing falling demand and increasing imports Harley-Davidson made one of the greatest comebacks in US automotive history (helped in part by a punitive tariff targeting Japanese imports). Using Japanese management principles it updated manufacturing methods improved quality and expanded the model line. Harley-Davidson again went public in 1986 and by the next year it had control of 25% of the US heavyweight-motorcycle market up from 16% in 1985.

In 1993 the company acquired a 49% stake in Eagle Credit (financing insurance and credit cards for dealers and customers; it bought the rest in 1995) and a 49% share of Wisconsin-based Buell Motorcycle gaining a niche in the performance-motorcycle market. (Harley-Davidson bought most of Buell's remaining stock in 1998.) The recreational vehicle business Holiday Rambler was sold to Monaco RV in 1996.

Jeffrey Bleustein who had headed Harley-Davidson's manufacturing unit was named the company's chairman president and CEO in 1997. Two years later the company began production at its new assembly plant in Brazil with an eye on increasing sales in Latin America. Harley-Davidson bested Honda in the US in 1999 for the first time in 30 years.

In 2000 Harley-Davidson's production increased by more than 15% over 1999 reaching a little more than 200000 bikes. Despite the slowing economy in 2001 demand for Hogs continued to grow. To meet demand Harley-Davidson again increased production by about 15% –making more than 240000 bikes in 2001. Also in 2001 Harley introduced the V-Rod which drew design inspiration from Harley's legendary drag racing heritage.

Harley-Davidson marked its 100th year in operation in 2002. To celebrate all 2003 model Harleys were designated 100th anniversary models. Harley-Davidson introduced two new lines of Buell motorcycles in 2003 the Firebolt and the Lightning.

Jeffrey Bleustein retired as president and CEO in 2005; he remained chairman. VP/CFO James Ziemer was promoted to president and CEO to succeed him.

Harley had been tracking the maturation of its markets not only in North America but also in its bread-and-butter markets including certain Europe countries and Japan. Those three markets appeared unlikely to generate the sales volume necessary to take the company to the next level. The company however countered with a major step in 2006; it opened its first Chinese Harley dealership in Beijing. The move looked to protect the Harley brand in China against counterfeiting as well as snag a toehold in the developing country.

In 2006 Harley also acquired its Australian supplier of wheels and hubs Castalloy. Later that year Harley entered into a partnership with Lehman Trikes USA (a subsidiary of Lehman Trikes Inc. of Canada) to make Harley-branded trikes –or three-wheeled cycles that would be distributed through its regular dealer network.

Harley steadily grew sales and profits every year since 1995 –that is until fiscal 2007 when the company reported a 1% decrease in sales and more than a 10% drop in net income. Adding to its woes in the first quarter of 2007 the company lost about a month's worth of production to a strike at its York Pennsylvania assembly plant.

In early 2008 the company acquired MV Agusta Group an Italy-based motorcycle manufacturer for $109 million. Established in 1945 MV Agusta markets its sport bikes in Europe and North America. It manufactured the high performance MV Agusta brand and lightweight sport Cagiva motorcycle. The acquisition remained confusing to onlookers but Harley-Davidson explained that the company would complement Buell. The story of the two companies ended with the divestiture of MV Agusta in mid-2010 and the dissolution of the Buell line in 2009.

The Harley-Davidson Museum in Wisconsin opened in 2008. Moreover in an industry first the company designed the Skyline helmet expressly for women who happen to represent 12% of Harley buyers.

After much deliberation the company decided in late 2009 to keep its York Pennsylvania manufacturing plant open rather than moving operations to a "cheaper plant" but it signed a labor agreement involving job cuts to a tune of almost 50%. In the two years prior the company had lowered its headcount by approximately 1100 a 12% reduction in force.

James Ziemer was CEO and president at the start of the economic downturn. He confronted the recession from three directions by advocating tight control of costs reaching for new sources of financing to support sales and continuing on-going development of the Harley-Davidson brand. After 40 years of service Ziemer retired in 2009 and Keith Wandell took the handlebars. Wandell a veteran of Johnson Controls is the first CEO hired from outside of the company.

Harley-Davidson has aimed to revive North American Hog purchases by calling upon the federal government for help. The 2009 federal TALF program (Term Asset-Backed Securities Loan Facility) has helped to opened up consumer credit through asset-backed loans to Harley Davidson Financial Services and similar businesses. A second program the Temporary Liquidity Guarantee Program (TLGP) has also been courted. Under this alternative the Financial Services segment receives federal funds if the new motorcycle owner fails to make his loan payment.

Harley-Davidson ceased production of its Buell line in 2009. Soft sales were what spurred the company to jump across the Atlantic in the first place to pick up Italy-based Buell Motorcycle Company a manufacturer of four motorcycle families (Sportbike Street Adventure and Blast). Buell was acquired in 2003 to expand the company's line beyond cruisers; however the models never received adequate investment and were not readily accepted by the company's dealer network. Because Buell was integrated into the company's books it was dissolved rather than sold.

In 2010 it sold MV Agusta to Claudio Castiglioni and his holding company MV Agusta Motor Holding. Harley-Davidson had only acquired MV Agusta a year earlier from Claudio Castiglioni but the company decided to return to its core business of making cruisers.

The sale of non-core businesses as well as an increase in interest received was also credited with boosting the company's operating cash flow almost 50% in 2010. It also had something to do with Harley-Davidson raising capital for its Financial Services business in 2009 when legendary investor Warren Buffett bought a portion of the iconic company's unsecured debt. In 2009 Berkshire Hathaway paid $300 million to acquire debt issued by Harley-Davidson. Davis Selected Advisers (which owns about 11% of Harley-Davidson's shares) also bought $300 million worth of debt. Berkshire's investors and Warren Buffett as well as Davis scored attractive terms on the senior unsecured notes paying interest of 15%.

The company launched nine new models for 2010 including the Ultra Limited Fat Boy Lo Iron 883 Street Glide and XR1200XTM. Its new Forty Eight –named after 1948 the first year the company debuted the "peanut" gas tank –incorporated back-to-basics retro styling. A front phat tire makes the Forty Eight look like the post WWII Bob Job that started the cruiser craze.

EXECUTIVES

VP Government Affairs Harley-Davidson Motor Company, Timothy K. Hoelter

SVP and Chief Styling Officer Harley-Davidson Motor Company, William G. Davidson

VP Communications, Joanne M. Bischmann, age 50

President and COO Harley-Davidson Financial Services, Lawrence G. Hund, age 55

Chairman, Barry K. Allen, age 63

SVP Manufacturing Harley-Davidson Motor Company, Karl M. Eberle, age 64

President CEO and Director, Keith E. Wandell, age 62, $650,025 total compensation

VP; Chief Compliance Officer General Counsel and Secretary, Paul J. Jones, age 41

VP Harley-Davidson Museum and Factory Tours, Bill Davidson

VP and Managing Director Asia/Pacific Harley-Davidson Motor Company, Rodney J. Copes, age 45

President and COO Harley-Davidson Motor Company, Matthew S. (Matt) Levatich, age 47

SVP and CFO, John A. Olin, age 51, $297,223 total compensation

VP and CIO Harley-Davidson Motor Company, James E. Haney

VP Customer Service and Sales Operations Harley-Davidson Motor Company, Jeffrey A. Merten

SVP and Chief Marketing Officer Harley-Davidson Motor Company, Mark Hans Richer, age 45

Managing Director Australia and New Zealand, Peter Nochar

SVP Product Development Harley-Davidson Motor Company, Michelle Kumbier

Director Investor Relations, Amy S. Giuffre

Director Corporate Communications, Bob Klein

VP and Controller, Perry A. Glassgow

VP and General Manager General Merchandise Harley-Davidson Motor Company, Patrick Smith

VP and Managing Director Latin America, Mark Van Genderen

Chief Accounting Officer, Mark Kornetzke

VP and Treasurer, J. Darrell Thomas

General Manager Corporate Strategy Business Development and Sustainability, John P. Baker, age 44

VP Human Resources, Tonit M. Calaway, age 44

Director, James A. (Jim) Norling, age 70

Director, R. John Anderson, age 61

Director, George H. Conrades, age 73

Director, Jochen Zeitz, age 49

Director, N. Thomas (Tom) Linebarger, age 49

President CEO and Director, Keith E. Wandell, age 62

Director, Richard I. (Dick) Beattie, age 73

Director, Sara L. Levinson, age 61

Director, Donald A. (Don) James, age 68
Director, George L. Miles Jr., age 70
Director, Martha F. Brooks, age 52
Auditors: Ernst&YoungLLP

LOCATIONS

HQ: Harley-Davidson Inc
3700 West Juneau Avenue, Milwaukee, WI 53208
Phone: 414 342-4680 **Fax:** 414 343-4621
Web: www.harley-davidson.com

PRODUCTS/OPERATIONS

2011 Sales

	$ mil.	% of total
Motorcycle & related parts	4,662	88
Financial services	649	12
Total	**5,311**	**100**

2011 Unit Shipments

Number of units		
Harley-Davidson		
Touring	92,002	
Custom	91,459	
Sportster	49,656	
Buell	274	
Total	**0**	**233,391**

Selected Motorcycles

Harley-Davidson
- CVO (custom vehicle operations)
  - Road Gllide Ultra
  - Softail Convertible
  - Street Glide
  - Ultra Classic Electroglide
- Dyna
  - Fat BOB
  - Street BOB
  - Super Glide Custom
  - Wide Glide
- Softail
  - Black Line
  - Cross Bones
  - Fat Boy
  - Heritage Softail Classic
  - Night Train
  - Rocker C
  - Softail Deluxe
- Sportster
  - 883 (Low and Custom)
  - 1200 (Custom and Low)
  - Forty Eight
  - Iron 883
  - Nightster
  - SuperLow
  - XR1200X
- Touring
  - Electra Glide (Standard Classic and Ultra Classic)
  - Road Glide Ultra
  - Road King (and Classic)
  - Street Glide
  - Tri Glide Ultra Classic
- Trike
  - Street Glide Trike
  - Tri Glide Ultra Classic
- VRSC
  - Night Rod Special
  - V-Rod (and V-Rod Muscle)

Selected Operations

Motorcycles
- Harley-Davidson Motor Company

Financial services
- Harley-Davidson Financial Services Inc.
  - Harley-Davidson Credit
  - Harley-Davidson Insurance

COMPETITORS

BMW
Ducati
Honda
Indian Motorcycle
Polaris Industries
Triumph Motorcycles
Ultra Motorcycle
Viper Motorcycle

HISTORICAL FINANCIALS

Company Type: Public

Income Statement

FYE: December 31

	REVENUE ($ mil.)	NET INCOME ($ mil.)	NET PROFIT MARGIN	EMPLOYEES
12/11	5,311	599	11.3%	6,600
12/10	4,859	146	3.0%	6,900
12/09	4,781	(55)	—	7,900
12/08	5,971	654	11.0%	10,100
12/07	6,143	933	15.2%	9,000
Annual Growth	(3.6%)	(10.5%)	—	(7.5%)

2011 Year-End Financials

Debt ratio: 59.15%
Return on equity: 24.75%
Cash ($ mil.): 1,526
Current ratio: 168.32
Long-term debt ($ mil.): 3,843
No. of shares (mil.): 230
Dividends
Yield: —
Payout: 18.63%
Market value ($ mil.): 8,961

	STOCK PRICE ($) FY Close	P/E High/Low		PER SHARE ($) Earnings	Dividends	Book Value
12/11	38.87	18	12	2.55	0.00	10.50
12/10	34.67	56	34	0.62	0.40	9.37
12/09	25.20	—	—	(0.24)	0.40	9.00
12/08	16.97	17	4	2.79	1.29	9.09
12/07	46.71	20	12	3.74	1.06	9.96
Annual Growth	(4.5%)	—	—	(9.1%)	—	1.3%

Harman International Industries, Inc.

Harman International Industries is loud and clear. It makes high-end stereo and audio equipment for consumer and professional markets. The company makes loudspeakers CD and DVD players CD recorders and amplifiers under such brands as Mark Levinson JBL Harman/Kardon Revel AKG Infinity Logic 7 and others. Harman's auto unit sells branded audio systems through several carmakers including Toyota Lexus and BMW. Its professional unit makes audio equipment such as monitors amplifiers microphones and mixing consoles for recording studios cinemas touring performers and others. Harman also offers computer software and development tools to the automotive energy medical and telecom industries.

HISTORY

tiSidney Harman and his partner Bernard Kardon left their engineering jobs at a public address system company to found Harman/Kardon in 1953. The two marketed their home audio components to the general public instead of to the traditional audio buff. Their novel concept was to package amplifiers and a tuner in a single unit (called a receiver) that appealed to average consumers. Kardon cashed out in a 1956 IPO that left Harman with about 33% of the firm. Harman/Kardon acquired the respected JBL speaker business in 1969.

Harman was also interested in internal growth. He introduced new management techniques emphasizing workers' quality of life allowing employees to redesign their jobs and leave work after meeting production quotas. His projects which had varying degrees of success attracted the attention of President Carter's administration which brought Harman on board as undersecretary of commerce in 1977. Harman sold the company to Beatrice Foods that year to avoid a conflict of interest. The company did poorly under the conglomerate and Harman bought much of it back in 1980 taking it private. He then changed the name to Harman International Industries.

Through acquisitions he quickly expanded the business into the auto OEM market acquiring Essex Loudspeaker from United Technologies (1981) then moving into the professional audio equipment market with his purchase of Infinity (1983). In the mid-1980s Harman signed exclusive deals to supply JBL speakers to Ford (ended in 1995) and Chrysler (now DaimlerChrysler) and in 1985 it bought back the Harman/Kardon trade name (Beatrice Foods had sold it to Japanese company Shin Shirasuna). The company went public again the next year.

In 1991 Harman went into a tailspin (losing $20 million laying off 500) caused by a worldwide recession poor auto sales and four soured acquisitions. Harman who had been living in Washington DC with his politician wife Jane moved back to California site of the company's largest plant. President Donald Esters quit in 1992 and Harman set about reorganizing the firm.

The company bought AKG a leading Austrian microphone maker in 1993. Signaling its interest in the new digital age Harman created a new business unit Harman Interactive the following year to focus on PC and home theater systems.

It acquired Becker supplier of audio systems to Mercedes and high-end equipment manufacturer Madrigal Audio Laboratories in 1995. Harman expanded its customer base by selling to home electronics superstores and specialty stores for audiophiles.

A year later the company began supplying speakers for a Compaq line of computers. In 1997 it boosted its car audio business with new agreements to supply audio systems to certain models of BMW Toyota Hyundai and Peugeot and it purchased two car loudspeaker makers (Oxford International and Audio Electronic Systems).

In the 1990s Harman trimmed its consumer product lines from 2000 to 200. With its sales to Asia down and European sales ailing as well it closed plants and laid off workers in 1998. That year president Bernard Girod succeeded Harman as CEO. Also in 1998 the company created a remote control with Microsoft and divested several of its international distribution companies to focus on manufacturing and marketing. Harman sold its Orban broadcasting-products business in 1999 and replaced it with Crown International (maker of high-powered amplifiers) in 2000. (Crown has since ceased operations.)

In 2001 Harman sold its Allen & Heath subsidiary a maker of mixing consoles to a group consisting of some of the company's top management. In 2003 Harman acquired Wavemakers a Canadian developer of processors and software algorithms.

Longtime CEO Bernard Girod who took the reins from Sidney Harman in 1998 retired in 2006. Earlier that year Douglas Pertz took over as CEO but resigned from the company mid-year after a short stint. In 2007 Dinesh C. Paliwal joined the company as president CEO and vice chairman. He was tapped to take over the position of chairman in late 2008 succeeding the retiring Sidney Harman.

Turbulent financial markets wreaked havoc in 2007 when KKR & Co. and Goldman Sachs abandoned an $8 billion leveraged buyout of Harman. Under the reneged-upon agreement Harman stockholders would have received either $120 in cash for each Harman share they owned or they could have exchanged some or all of their stock for shares in the new entity. But amid a tightening credit market KKR and Goldman Sachs said unacceptable financial conditions at the stereo maker triggered a material adverse change that allows them to walk away from the deal. (Harman disagrees that a material adverse change had occurred or that it has breached the merger agreement.) As a peace offering of sorts KKR and Goldman agreed to invest $400 million in the audio product maker's debt.

In 2008 the company added to its premium loudspeaker lineup by partnering with B & W Group which owns the Bowers & Wilkins name. The agreement allows Harman to use Bowers & Wilkins technologies in its automotive unit. UK-based B & W which outfitted London's Abbey Road Studios makes and markets products under the Bowers & Wilkins Classe and Rotel names for home theater hi-fi and multimedia.

Also in 2008 the company partnered with Wipro Technologies (of Wipro Limited) to open an engineering center in India.

In 2010 Harman expanded to Brazil with the purchase of Eletronica Selenium there. The firm makes and sells professional loudspeakers primarily in Latin America. It bought Aha Mobile a provider of on-demand mobile and location-based Internet content services that year as well.

Sidney Harman 92 died in 2011.

EXECUTIVES

EVP and Chief Human Resources Officer, John Stacey, age 47
Chairman President and CEO, Dinesh C. Paliwal, age 54, $1,125,000 total compensation
EVP Corporate Development, David J. Slump, age 44, $380,000 total compensation
EVP and President - Professional Division, Blake Augsburger, age 49, $425,000 total compensation
EVP and Co-President Lifestyle and Infotainment, Sachin Lawande, age 45, $365,000 total compensation
EVP and CFO, Herbert K. Parker, age 54, $500,000 total compensation
EVP General Counsel and Secretary, Todd A. Suko, age 45
Director Corporate Communications, Darrin Shewchuk
VP Corporate Affairs, Jean Lepine
EVP and Co-President - Infotainment and Lifestyle Divisions, Michael Mauser, age 49
EVP and CTO, I. P. Park
Director Corporate Affairs and Communications Europe, Nicole Mehr
Director, Edward H. (Ed) Meyer, age 85
Director, Hellene S. Runtagh, age 64
Director, Ann McLaughlin Korologos, age 70
Director, Brian F. Carroll, age 41
Director, Harald Einsmann, age 78
Director, Kenneth M. (Ken) Reiss, age 69
Director, Gary G. Steel, age 60
Director, Jiren Liu, age 57
Auditors: KPMGLLP

LOCATIONS

HQ: Harman International Industries Incorporated
400 Atlantic St. Ste. 1500, Stamford CT 06901
Phone: 203-328-3500 **Fax:** 414-319-8520
Web: www.joyglobal.com

2011 Sales

	$ mil.	% of total
Europe		
Germany	1,662	38
Other countries	916	21
US	967	22
Other regions	817	19
Total	**4,364**	**100**

PRODUCTS/OPERATIONS

2011 Sales

	$ mil.	% of total
Infotainment	2,401	55
Lifestyle	1,330	30
Professional	630	15
Other	1	—
Total	**4,364**	**100**

Selected Products

Automotive
- Audio systems
- Information and entertainment systems

Professional
- Audio amplifiers
- Audio headphones
- Broadcasting studio equipment
- Cinema audio systems
- Digital audio workstations
- Equalizers
- Loudspeakers
- Microphones
- Mixing consoles
- Signal processing systems
- Sound reinforcement systems
- Special effects units
- Surround sound systems

Consumer
- Audio amplifiers
- Audio and video receivers
- CD players
- Digital signal processors
- DVD players
- Home theater systems
- Loudspeakers
- PC audio systems

Selected Brands

AKG
BSS
Crown
dbx
DigiTech
Harman/Kardon
Infinity
JBL
JBL Professional
Lexicon
Mark Levinson
Martin Professional
Revel
Selenium
Soundcraft
Studer

COMPETITORS

Aisin Seiki
Altec Lansing
ASK
Audio Research
Avid Technology
Bang & Olufsen
Bosch Communications Systems
Bose
Boston Acoustics
BSH Bosch und Siemens Hausgerate
Continental Automotive Group
Creative Technology
D&M
Delphi Automotive
JVC KENWOOD
Klipsch
Krell
Logitech
LOUD Technologies
Macintosh Retail Group
Marshall Amplification
Meyer Sound
Mitsubishi Electric & Electronics
Onkyo
Panasonic Corporation of North America
Peavey Electronics
Pioneer Corporation
Polk Audio
QSC Audio
Systems
Denon Electronics
DENSO
Fender Musical Instruments
Foster Electric (U.S.A.)
Harris Corp.
Sennheiser
Shure
Sony
TASCAM
TomTom
Visteon
Yamaha

HISTORICAL FINANCIALS

Company Type: Public

Income Statement FYE: June 30

	REVENUE ($ mil.)	NET INCOME ($ mil.)	NET PROFIT MARGIN	EMPLOYEES
06/12	4,364	329	7.6%	11,366
06/11	3,772	135	3.6%	10,103
06/10	3,364	158	4.7%	9,816
06/09	2,891	(422)	—	9,482
06/08	4,112	107	2.6%	11,694
Annual Growth	1.5%	32.2%	—	(0.7%)

2012 Year-End Financials

Debt ratio: 12.48%
Return on equity: 21.54%
Cash ($ mil.): 617
Current ratio: 153.14
Long-term debt ($ mil.): —
No. of shares (mil.): 67
Dividends
Yield: —
Payout: 6.57%
Market value ($ mil.): 2,665

	STOCK PRICE ($) FY Close	P/E High/Low		PER SHARE ($) Earnings	Dividends	Book Value
06/12	39.60	11	6	4.57	0.00	22.73
06/11	45.57	27	15	1.90	0.05	20.36
06/10	29.89	23	8	2.25	0.00	16.32
06/09	18.80	—	—	(7.19)	0.04	14.05
06/08	41.39	67	21	1.73	0.05	22.90
Annual Growth	(1.1%)	—	—	27.5%	—	(0.2%)

Harris Corp.

Harris has ways to make its customers communicate. The company which develops communications products for government and commercial customers in more than 125 countries makes radio-frequency (RF) and satellite communications and other wireless network transmission equipment; air traffic control systems; and digital network broadcasting and management systems. Harris also offers specialized IT services. Its primary customers are US government agencies including prime contractors and supported foreign militaries accounting for about 70% of sales. Harris' commercial clients come from the construction energy health care maritime oil transportation and utilities industries.

HISTORY

Harris was founded in Niles Ohio in 1895 by brothers Alfred and Charles Harris both jewelers and inventors. Among their inventions was a printing press that became Harris Automatic Press Company's flagship product.

Harris remained a small family-run company until 1944 when engineer George Dively was hired as general manager. Under Dively the company began manufacturing bindery typesetting and paper converting equipment while remaining a leading supplier of printing presses. In 1957 Harris merged with typesetter maker Intertype and became known as Harris-Intertype Corporation.

During the 1960s and 1970s Harris-Intertype grew through acquisitions. In 1967 it bought electronics and data processing equipment maker Radiation a company heavily dependent on government contracts and relocated to Radiation's headquarters in Melbourne Florida. The company also bought RF Communications (two-way radios 1969) General Electric's broadcast equipment line (1972) and UCC-Communications Systems (data processing equipment 1972).

The company changed its name to Harris Corporation in 1974. In 1980 Harris bought Farinon a manufacturer of microwave radio systems and Lanier Business Products the leading maker of dictating equipment. In 1983 it sold its printing equipment business.

Harris formed a joint venture with 3M called Harris/3M Document Products in 1986 to market copiers and fax machines and in 1989 it acquired the entire operation which became Lanier Worldwide. Other 1980s acquisitions included Scientific Calculations a CAD software developer (1986) and GE's Solid State semiconductor group (1988).

Harris won a contract with the FAA in 1992 to modernize voice communications between airports and airplanes. Later that year Harris acquired Westronic a supplier of automated control systems for electric utilities. In 1994 Harris began installing the world's largest private digital telephone network along Russia's gas pipeline and it spun off its computer products division as Harris Computer Systems.

In 1996 Harris became the first company to demonstrate a digital TV transmitter. That year it acquired NovAtel a maker of cellular and wireless local-loop systems for rural areas and it bought a stake in the Chile-based phone company Compa?ia de Telefonos. In 1997 it purchased digital broadcasting specialist Innovation Telecommunications Image and Sound.

The company in 1998 purchased German chemical manufacturer Bayer's Agfa-Gevaert photocopier business which doubled Lanier's share of the European office equipment market. Hurt by a tough semiconductor market that year Harris laid off about 8% of its workforce.

Shifting toward a strictly communications-related operation in 1999 Harris sold its semiconductor operations (which now does business as Intersil) in a deal valued at about $600 million and spun off Lanier to shareholders. It also sold its photomask manufacturing unit to Align-Rite.

In 2000 Harris expanded its broadcasting and wireless transmission product lines with the acquisitions of Louth Automation and Wavtrace. That year the company began outsourcing the assembly of its commercial printed circuit boards and folded its telephone switching and alarm management product lines.

The company broadened its communications product portfolio in 2001 with the acquisitions of Exigent a provider of satellite tracking and control software and Hirschmann a maker of digital broadcasting radio transmitters and cable systems. That year Harris sold its minority stakes in two industrial electronics joint ventures to majority owner GE.

The company also sold its telecom testing product lines which accounted for about $30 million in revenue to Danaher Corporation in 2004. Later that year the company bought Encoda a developer of software and services to customers in the broadcast media industry for $340 million.

The company invested in broadcast communications with the acquisition of broadcast video systems maker Leitch Technology in 2006. The buy gave Harris a stake in the transition to high-definition digital TV services. The company also purchased broadcast management software maker Optimal Solutions and the digital video business of Aastra Technologies that year. Harris acquired Multimax –a provider of government IT and communication services –for $400 million in 2007.

In 2007 Harris merged its Microwave Communication Division with its Stratex Networks subsidiary to form Harris Stratex Networks. It initially held a 56% stake in the combined company but in 2009 Harris spun off its shares of Harris Stratex to its shareholders. Harris Stratex later changed its name to Aviat Networks.

Harris acquired the wireless systems business of Tyco Electronics (now TE Connectivity) for $675 million in 2009. The business which makes wireless communications systems for law enforcement and other public service organizations became part of its RF Communications unit. Harris also bought the air traffic control business of SolaCom Technologies in 2009. The deal included voice and data communications equipment for air traffic control facilities along with radio systems for communication between air traffic control and in-flight airplanes.

In addition Harris acquired privately held Crucial Security which provides IT engineering applications and services aimed at identifying and monitoring security threats in 2009. The company also expanded its IT service lineup for the government health care market that year when it bought Patriot Technologies. Patriot provided IT imaging and software services for the US Department of Veterans Affairs.

EXECUTIVES

VP Investor Relations, Pamela (Pam) Padgett
SVP Human Resources Chief Human Resources and Administrative Officer, Jeffrey S. (Jeff) Shuman, age 57, $364,327 total compensation
President Healthcare Solutions, James A. (Jim) Traficant
EVP and COO, Daniel R. (Dan) Pearson, age 60, $415,000 total compensation
SVP and CFO, Gary L. McArthur, age 52, $500,000 total compensation
VP Corporate Development, Ricardo A. (Rick) Navarro, age 61
VP Government Relations, Peter Challan, age 65
President CapRock Communications, Peter Shaper
VP Corporate Communications, Jim Burke
VP EBO and CTO Broadcast Communications Division, Brian Cabeceiras
VP Sales and Services Asia-Pacific Broadcast Communications, Stephen Wong
VP Associate General Counsel and Secretary, Scott T. Mikuen, age 50
President and CEO, William M. (Bill) Brown, age 49
VP Engineering and CTO, R. Kent Buchanan, age 61
VP Information Services and CIO, Paul T. (Ted) Hengst
VP and Principal Accounting Officer, Lewis A. Schwartz, age 49
President RF Communications, Dana A. Mehnert, age 50, $400,000 total compensation
President Public Safety and Professional Communications, Stephen Marschilok, age 53
VP Tax and Treasurer, Charles J. (Chuck) Greene, age 57
Group President Government Communications Systems, Sheldon J. Fox, age 53
VP and General Manager Cyber Integrated Solutions, Maj. Gen. Dale W. Meyerrose
VP Sales Broadcast Communications, Dave Dougall
VP Sales Worldwide Broadcast Communications, Richard Scott
VP Financial Services and Assistant Treasurer, John L. Draheim, age 57
VP Internal Audit and Compliance, Terry L. Feiser, age 56
VP Human Resources Broadcast Communications, David Cunningham
VP Human Resources Government Communications Systems Division, Andrea R. Bortner, age 50
President Broadcast Communications, P. Harris Morris Jr.
VP Strategy and Chief Growth Officer, Wesley B. (Wes) Covell
Director Product Management Broadcast Communications Division, Joseph I. (Joe) Lampert
President Maritime Communication Services Government Communications Systems Division, Richard P. (Rick) Simonian
VP Environmental-Energy Solutions Business Government Communications Systems Division, Carl D'Alessandro
VP Harris Mission Critical Networks, John O'Sullivan
VP Advanced Information Solutions Government Communications Systems Division, Richard L. (Rich) White
VP Operations Government Communications Systems Division, William J. (Bill) Heiselman
VP Broadcast Technology Architect Broadcast Communications Division, Jay C. Adrick
VP Transmission Systems Broadcast Communications Division, Philip (Phil) Argyris
Senior Counsel Broadcast Communications, Laurie McCall
President International Tactical Radio Communications, Andy Start
VP Strategy and Marketing Broadcast Communications, Brad Turner
Corporate VP and CIO, Ted Hengst, age 57
President Information Technology Services Business, John Heller, age 50
VP and Deputy General Counsel, Anthony Deglomine, age 52
President DoD Tactical Radio Communications, Brendan O'Connell
VP Supply Chain Management and Operations, Janice M. Lindsay
President Integrated Network Solutions Business, James D. (Jim) Morris, age 47
VP North American Sales Public Safety and Professional Communications, Walt Paskowski
VP Air Force Programs Information Technology Services, Alex Heidt
VP; General Manager Department of Defense Programs, Mike Deloney
VP Commercial Market Development Commercial Managed Services, Bret Kinsella
VP Intel Programs IT Services, Sherry Covell
Managing Director Caribbean and Latin America RF Communications, Julio Villafane
Director Indirect Channels Public Safety and Professional Communications, Geno Viviano
VP Advanced Concepts, Wyatt Starnes
Director, Thomas A. (Tom) Dattilo, age 61
Director, Stephen P. (Steve) Kaufman, age 70
Director, David B. (Dave) Rickard, age 65
Director, Karen L. Katen, age 63
Director, Gregory T. (Greg) Swienton, age 62
Director, Terry D. Growcock, age 65
Director, Lewis (Lew) Hay III, age 56
Director, Hansel E. Tookes II, age 64

Director, Leslie F. Kenne, age 64
Auditors: Ernst&YoungLLP

LOCATIONS

HQ: Harris Corporation
1025 W. NASA Blvd., Melbourne FL 32919-0001
Phone: 321-727-9100 **Fax:** 321-674-4740
Web: www.harris.com

2012 Sales

	$ mil.	% of total
US	5,077	93
Other countries	374	7
Total	**5,451**	**100**

PRODUCTS/OPERATIONS

2012 Sales

	$ mil.	% of total
RF communicat		
Tactical	1,570	29
Public safety and professional	573	10
Government communications systems	1,833	33
Integrated network solutions	1,571	28
Adjustments	(97.8)	
Total	**5,451**	**100**

Selected Product Groups

Government Communications Systems
- Civil programs
  - Aviation
  - Weather
- IT services
- Mission command-and-control
- National intelligence programs

Radio-frequency (RF) Communications
- Antennas and accessories
- Information assurance
- Internet protocol voice and data networks
- Public safety
- Tactical radio communications

COMPETITORS

Advisory Board
Aetna
Alcatel-Lucent
Amper
Avid Technology
BAE Systems Inc.
Boeing
CACI International
Ceragon Networks
Chyron
Cisco Systems
Computer Sciences Corp.
Dell
EADS
Ericsson
Exelis
General Dynamics
Globecomm
GTSI
Harmonic
Hewlett-Packard
IBM
L-3 Communications
Lockheed Martin
ManTech
Motorola Solutions
NCI
NEC
Nokia Siemens Networks
Nortel Networks
Northrop Grumman
Orion HealthCorp
Pilat Media
Raytheon
RigNet
Rockwell Collins
Rohde & Schwarz
SAIC
SELEX SI
Sony
SRA International
Technicolor
Tektronix
Telos
Thales
Vizrt
WideOrbit

HISTORICAL FINANCIALS

Company Type: Public

Income Statement

FYE: June 29

	REVENUE ($ mil.)	NET INCOME ($ mil.)	NET PROFIT MARGIN	EMPLOYEES
06/12*	5,451	30	0.6%	15,200
07/11	5,924	588	9.9%	16,900
07/10	5,206	561	10.8%	15,800
07/09	5,005	37	0.8%	15,400
06/08	5,311	444	8.4%	16,500
Annual Growth	0.7%	(48.8%)	—	(2.0%)

*Fiscal year change

2012 Year-End Financials

Debt ratio: 36.60%
Return on equity: 1.58%
Cash ($ mil.): 356
Current ratio: 183.85
Long-term debt ($ mil.): 1,883
No. of shares (mil.): 112
Dividends
Yield: 2.92%
Payout: 469.23%
Market value ($ mil.): 4,693

	STOCK PRICE ($) FY Close	P/E High/Low		PER SHARE ($) Earnings	Dividends	Book Value
06/12*	41.85	176	128	0.26	1.22	17.29
07/11	45.55	11	9	4.60	1.00	20.32
07/10	41.18	13	6	4.28	0.88	17.18
07/09	28.59	186	96	0.28	0.00	14.23
06/08	51.18	20	14	3.26	0.60	17.02
Annual Growth	(4.9%)	—	—	(46.9%)	19.4%	0.4%

*Fiscal year change

Harris Teeter Supermarkets, Inc.

Harris Teeter Supermarkets has groceries to health and beauty items in the bag. Through operating subsidiary Harris Teeter Harris Teeter Supermarkets (formerly Ruddick Corporation) operates a regional chain of around 205 supermarkets in nine states primarily in the southeastern and mid-Atlantic US as well as Washington DC. The majority of the grocery stores house pharmacies and feature niceties such as sushi bars gourmet delis and cafes. Subsidiary American & Efird (A&E) which makes industrial and consumer sewing thread for the apparel automotive medical and footwear industries worldwide was sold to KPS Capital Partners for $180 million in cash in November 2011.

A&E's industrial thread business had been wavering since 2008 and accounted for only about 7% of the company's total sales in 2010. Even though A&E's business grew substantially in China and India Harris Teeter Supermarkets no longer felt it fit within the company's strategic goal as a US grocer. With the sale of A&E Harris Teeter Supermarkets plans to use the proceeds to open new stores and pay down some of its $296 million in debt. To follow along these strategy plans the company acquired 10 stores from Lowes Foods Stores in the central Carolinas region for $26.5 million.

The regional grocery chain's expansion is focused on the competitive Washington DC market and nearby suburbs in northern Virginia southern Maryland and coastal Delaware. About a dozen new stores were opened during fiscal 2010 and in fiscal 2011 Harris Teeter plans to open another seven new stores. Harris Teeter Supermarkets' core supermarket operation which includes its own dairy processing plant has grown with Harris Teeter adding about 15 new supermarkets in fiscal 2009.

EXECUTIVES

President American & Efird, Fred A. Jackson, age 62, $285,000 total compensation
Chairman and CEO, Thomas W. Dickson, age 57, $555,000 total compensation
EVP and CFO, John B. Woodlief, age 62, $397,500 total compensation
President and COO, Frederick J. (Fred) Morganthall II, age 60, $390,000 total compensation
Secretary, Douglas J. Yacenda
EVP, Rodney C. (Rod) Antolock
VP and Treasurer, Ronald H. Volger
Assistant Secretary and Assistant Treasurer, Jesse B. Libensperger
Director, William C. Warden Jr., age 59
Director, Robert H. (Rob) Spilman Jr., age 55
Director, John P. D. Cato, age 61
Director, John R. (Johnny) Belk, age 53
Director, Harold C. Stowe, age 65
Director, Isaiah Tidwell, age 67
Director, Anna Spangler Nelson, age 50
Director, James E. S. Hynes, age 71
Director, Bailey W. Patrick, age 50
Auditors: KPMGLLP

LOCATIONS

HQ: Harris Teeter Supermarkets Inc.
701 Crestdale Rd., Matthews NC 28105
Phone: 704-372-5404 **Fax:** 704-372-6409
Web: harristeetersupermarkets.com

2011 Harris Teeter Stores

	No.
North	136
Virginia	36
South	13
Maryland	6
Tennessee	5
Delaware	3
Distict of	3
Florida	1
Georgia	1
Total	**204**

PRODUCTS/OPERATIONS

COMPETITORS

CVS Caremark
Food Lion
Ingles Markets
Kroger
Publix
Rite Aid
Target Corporation
Wal-Mart
Walgreen
Winn-Dixie

HISTORICAL FINANCIALS

Company Type: Public

Income Statement FYE: October 2

	REVENUE ($ mil.)	NET INCOME ($ mil.)	NET PROFIT MARGIN	EMPLOYEES
10/12	4,535	82	1.8%	25,300
10/11	4,285	91	2.1%	24,500
10/10*	4,400	112	2.5%	25,200
09/09	4,077	85	2.1%	24,800
09/08	3,992	96	2.4%	25,500
Annual Growth	3.2%	(3.9%)	—	(0.2%)

*Fiscal year change

2012 Year-End Financials

Debt ratio: 10.88%
Return on equity: 7.95%
Cash ($ mil.): 212
Current ratio: 140.46
Long-term debt ($ mil.): 208
No. of shares (mil.): 49
Dividends
Yield: 1.45%
Payout: 32.74%
Market value ($ mil.): 1,867

	STOCK PRICE ($) FY Close	P/E High/Low		PER SHARE ($) Earnings	Dividends	Book Value
10/12	37.88	27	22	1.68	0.55	21.05
10/11	38.99	24	18	1.87	0.00	19.72
10/10*	34.88	16	11	2.31	0.00	18.25
09/09	26.62	18	11	1.78	0.00	16.73
09/08	33.65	20	15	2.00	0.00	17.06
Annual Growth	3.0%	—	—	(4.3%)	—	5.4%

*Fiscal year change

Hartford Financial Services Group Inc.

Despite its name at its heart The Hartford Financial Services Group is an insurer with a range of commercial and personal property/casualty and life insurance products. Its commercial property/casualty operations include auto liability workers' compensation policies as well as group benefits and specialty commercial coverage for large companies. The Hartford also offers consumer homeowners and auto coverage. Through its wealth management division the company offers individual life insurance policies and the financial services mentioned in its name (retirement plans and mutual funds). The Hartford in business since 1810 sells its products through a network of independent agents and brokerages.

HISTORY

In 1810 a group of Hartford Connecticut businessmen led by Walter Mitchell and Henry Terry founded the Hartford Fire Insurance Co. Frequent fires in America's wooden cities and executive ignorance of risk assessment and premium-setting often left the firm on the edge of insolvency. (In 1835 stockholders staged a coup and threw management out.) Still each urban conflagration –including the Great Chicago Fire of 1871 –gave The Hartford an opportunity to seek out and pay all its policyholders thus teaching the company to underwrite under fire as it were and to use such disasters to refine its rates.

The company's stag logo was initially a little deer as shown on a policy sold to Abraham Lincoln in 1861. A few years later however Hartford began using the majestic creature (from a Landseer painting) now familiar to customers. By the 1880s Hartford operated nationwide as well as in Canada and Hawaii.

The company survived both world wars and the Depression but emerged in the 1950s in need of organization. It set up new regional offices and added life insurance buying Columbian National Life (founded 1902) which became Hartford Life Insurance Co.

In 1969 Hartford was bought by ITT (formerly International Telephone and Telegraph) whose CEO Harold Geneen was an avid conglomerateur. Consumer advocate Ralph Nader strongly opposed the acquisition –he fought the merger in court for years and felt vindicated when ITT spun off Hartford in 1995. Others opposed it too because ITT had engineered the merger based on an IRS ruling (later revoked) that Hartford stockholders wouldn't have to pay capital gains taxes on the purchase price of their stock.

Insurance operations consolidated under the Hartford Life Insurance banner in 1978. Through the 1980s Hartford Life remained one of ITT's strongest operations. A conservative investment policy kept Hartford safe from the junk bond and real estate manias of the 1980s.

Hartford reorganized its property/casualty operations along three lines in 1986 and in 1992 it organized its reinsurance business into one unit. The company faced some liability in relation to Dow Corning's breast-implant litigation but underwriting standards after 1985 reduced long-term risk. In 1994 the company began selling insurance products to AARP members under an exclusive agreement. In 1996 the company finished its spin-off from ITT which was acquired by Starwood Hotels & Resorts two years later.

To grow its reinsurance operation Hartford acquired the reinsurance business of Orion Capital (now Royal & SunAlliance USA) in 1996. It posted a loss of $99 million due in large part to asbestos and pollution liabilities. Late that year the firm changed its name to The Hartford Financial Services Group.

To shore up reserves and fund growth in 1997 the company spun off 19% of Hartford Life. The Hartford expanded into nonstandard auto insurance in 1998 by buying Omni Insurance Group (since sold in 2006). The company also sold its London & Edinburgh Insurance Group in 1998 to Norwich Union (now part of Aviva formerly CGNU). In 1999 The Hartford acquired the reinsurance business of Vesta Fire Insurance a subsidiary of Vesta Insurance Group.

In 2000 Hartford bought back the part of Hartford Life it had spun off. The Hartford also bought the financial products and excess and surplus specialty insurance lines of Reliance Group Holdings. Assurances Generales de France bought the company's Dutch subsidiary Zwolsche Algemeene. In 2001 the company bought Fortis Financial a US subsidiary of Belgian insurer Fortis and sold Hartford Seguros its Spanish subsidiary to Liberty Mutual.

Before the financial crisis hit Hartford Life invested in its data management with the acquisition of a defined contribution recordkeeping business (Princeton Retirement Group 2007) and a web-based technology company (TopNoggin 2008). Following the same strategy The Hartford acquired Sun Life's US 401K plan administration business.

Like so many others in the insurance and financial services industry The Hartford had its share of losses during the 2008 financial crisis due to its investment holdings in Fannie Mae Freddie Mac and Lehman Brothers. In mid-2009 the US Treasury stepped in and offered The Hartford and other major life insurers access to its Troubled Asset Relief Program (TARP). The Hartford borrowed $3.4 billion to shore up its capital reserves. As the company and the economy stabilized the loan was repaid by early 2010 including an additional $21.7 million dividend payment.

Prior to the creation of TARP funds the Treasury first made money available to banks through its Capital Purchase Program (CPP). To make itself more eligible The Hartford worked quickly to transform itself into a bank –at least on paper. In 2009 The Hartford acquired Federal Trust Corporation a regional bank holding company for $10 million. However shortly thereafter TARP funds became available and The Hartford readily accepted them and the strings attached. Two years later the company recognized that banking was not among its core competencies or passions and made arrangements to sell Federal Trust Corporation to CenterState Banks.

Chairman and CEO Ramani Ayer had planned on retiring at the end of 2008 but agreed to stay at the helm through 2009. His final year was marked by efforts to stem the company's losses stemming from the global economic and financial crisis that began in 2008. Former head of consumer banking at Bank of America Liam McGee was appointed as the company's new CEO in late 2009.

EXECUTIVES

EVP; President Commercial Markets, Douglas G. Elliot, age 52
Chairman President and CEO, Liam E. McGee, age 57, $275,000 total compensation
EVP Human Resources, Eileen G. Whelley, age 58
EVP; President Wealth Management, David N. Levenson, age 45
EVP Marketing and Communications, Karen C. Tripp, age 56
EVP and General Counsel, Alan J. Kreczko, age 60, $500,000 total compensation
EVP and CFO, Christopher J. Swift, age 51
Chief Investment Officer, Brion Johnson
EVP Digital Commerce and Customer Analytics, Jonathan R. Bennett, age 48
SVP and Controller, Beth A. Bombara, age 44
EVP; President Consumer Markets, Andre (Andy) Napoli, age 47
EVP Human Resources, Martha (Marty) Gervasi
EVP and Chief Risk Officer, Robert R. Rupp, age 59
VP Annuity Product and Marketing Global Annuity, Steve Kluever
VP Retirement Plans Mid-Market, Denise Diana
VP Diversity and Inclusion, Grace Figueredo, age 54
VP Medical Practices Workers Compensation; Director Clinical Practices Group Benefits, Robert E. Bonner
EVP Strategic Initiatives and Enterprise Technology, James Eckerle, age 52
SVP and Secretary, David C. Robinson
Director, Thomas A. Renyi, age 66
Director, Michael G. (Mike) Morris, age 65
Director, Charles B. Strauss, age 69
Director, Trevor Fetter, age 52
Director, H. Patrick Swygert, age 69
Director, Paul G. Kirk Jr., age 74
Director, Kathryn A. Mikells, age 47
Director, Robert B. Allardice III, age 65
Auditors: Deloitte&ToucheLLP

LOCATIONS

HQ: The Hartford Financial Services Group Inc.
One Hartford Plaza, Hartford CT 06155
Phone: 860-547-5000 **Fax:** 860-547-2680
Web: www.thehartford.com

PRODUCTS/OPERATIONS

2011 Revenue

	$ mil.	% of total
Earned premiums fees & other		
Commercial markets		
Commercial property/casualty	6,127	28
Group benefits	4,147	19
Consumer markets	3,747	17
Wealth management		
Individual annuity	1,660	7
Individual life	899	4
Mutual funds	649	3
Retirement plans	380	2
Runoff operations (international annuity & life other life)	1,020	5
Corporate	209	1
Investment income	2,913	13
Net realized capital gains (losses)	(145)	-
Other revenues	253	1
Total	**21,859**	**100**

COMPETITORS

AEGON USA
AIG
Allstate
Berkshire Hathaway
Chubb Corp
CNA Financial
ING
Liberty Mutual
MetLife
Nationwide
New York Life
Northwestern Mutual
Prudential
State Farm
TIAA-CREF
Travelers Companies
Zurich Financial Services

HISTORICAL FINANCIALS

Company Type: Public

Income Statement FYE: December 31

	ASSETS ($ mil.)	NET INCOME ($ mil.)	INCOME AS % OF ASSETS	EMPLOYEES
12/11	304,064	662	0.2%	24,400
12/10	318,346	1,680	0.5%	26,800
12/09	307,717	(887)	—	28,000
12/08	287,583	(2,749)	—	31,000
12/07	360,361	2,949	0.8%	31,000
Annual Growth	(4.2%)	(31.2%)	—	(5.8%)

2011 Year-End Financials

Debt ratio: 2.15%
Return on equity: 2.89%
Cash ($ mil.): 2,581
Current ratio: —
Long-term debt ($ mil.): 6,530
No. of shares (mil.): 442
Dividends
Yield: —
Payout: 30.77%
Market value ($ mil.): 7,191

	STOCK PRICE ($) FY Close	P/E High	P/E Low	PER SHARE ($) Earnings	Dividends	Book Value
12/11	16.25	22	11	1.30	0.00	51.77
12/10	26.49	11	7	2.49	0.20	45.69
12/09	23.26	—	—	(2.93)	0.20	46.64
12/08	16.42	—	—	(8.99)	1.91	30.83
12/07	87.19	11	9	9.24	2.03	61.19
Annual Growth	(34.3%)	—	—	(38.8%)	—	(4.1%)

Hartford Life Insurance Co

LOCATIONS

HQ: Hartford Life Insurance Co
200 Hopmeadow Street, Simsbury, CT 06089
Phone: 860 547-5000
Web: www.thehartford.com

HISTORICAL FINANCIALS

Company Type:

Income Statement FYE: December 31

	ASSETS ($ mil.)	NET INCOME ($ mil.)	INCOME AS % OF ASSETS	EMPLOYEES
12/11	222,537	244	0.1%	0
12/10	231,752	744	0.3%	0
12/09	221,320	(2,157)	—	0
12/08	204,380	(3,525)	—	4,300
12/07	266,212	740	0.3%	4,000
Annual Growth	(4.4%)	(24.2%)	—	—

2011 Year-End Financials

Debt ratio: 0.14%
Return on equity: 2.53%
Cash ($ mil.): 1,183
Current ratio: —
Long-term debt ($ mil.): 314
No. of shares (mil.): 0
Dividends
Yield: —
Payout: 0.41%
Market value ($ mil.): —

Hasbro, Inc.

It's all fun and games at Hasbro the #2 toy maker in the US (after Mattel) and the producer of such childhood favorites as G.I. Joe Play-Doh Tonka toys Mr. Potato Head Nerf balls and My Little Pony. Besides toys Hasbro makes board games under its Milton Bradley ("Scrabble Candy Land") Cranium and Parker Brothers ("Monopoly Trivial Pursuit") brands as well as trading cards such as "Magic: The Gathering" (through its Wizards of the Coast unit) and Dungeons & Dragons. Hasbro also makes "Star Wars" action figures; the company's the licensee of action figures and games for the prequels. Besides Disney and Disney's Marvel Entertainment Hasbro licenses popular names and characters for toys and games.

HISTORY

Henry and Helal Hassenfeld formed Hassenfeld Brothers in Pawtucket Rhode Island in 1923 to distribute fabric remnants. By 1926 the company was manufacturing fabric-covered pencil boxes and shortly thereafter pencils.

Hassenfeld Brothers branched into the toy industry during the 1940s by introducing toy nurse and doctor kits. The company's toy division was the first to use TV to promote a toy product (Mr. Potato Head in 1952).

Expansion continued in the mid-1960s with the introduction of the G.I. Joe doll which quickly became its primary toy line. Hassenfeld Brothers went public in 1968 and changed its name to Hasbro Industries. It bought Romper Room (TV productions) the next year.

In the 1970s the toy and pencil divisions led by different family members disagreed over the company's finances future direction and leadership. The dispute caused the company to split in 1980. The toy division continued to operate under the Hasbro name; the pencil division (Empire Pencil Corporation in Shelbyville Tennessee led by Harold Hassenfeld) became a separate corporation.

Hasbro expanded rapidly in the 1980s under new CEO Stephen Hassenfeld. He reduced the number of products by one-third to concentrate on developing a line of toys aimed at specific markets. During that decade the firm released a number of successful toys including a smaller version of G.I. Joe (1982) and Transformers (small vehicles that transform into robots 1984). Hasbro acquired Milton Bradley a major producer of board games ("Chutes and Ladders Candy Land") puzzles and preschool toys (Playskool) in 1984.

The company acquired Cabbage Patch Kids "Scrabble Parcheesi" and other product lines in 1989. Stephen died that year. His brother Alan who had spearheaded Hasbro's international sales growth in the late 1980s became CEO.

Hasbro bought Tonka (including the Kenner and Parker Brothers brands) in 1991 and established operations in Greece Mexico and Hungary. Hasbro blocked a $5.2 billion hostile takeover attempt by Mattel in 1996 and in 1997 it beat them to an exclusive four-year deal to produce nearly all NFL-related toys and games. It also bought OddzOn Products (sports toys Koosh balls) and began cutting about 2500 jobs (20% of Hasbro's employees) that year.

Expanding in the high-tech toys niche in 1998 Hasbro made several acquisitions including Tiger Electronics (Giga Pets) the rights to some 75 Atari home console game titles ("Missile Command" "Centipede") MicroProse (3-D video games for PCs) and Galoob Toys a fellow "Star Wars" prequel licensee and maker of Micro Machines and Pound Puppies. Tiger Electronics had the hit of the 1998 holiday season: a chattering interactive doll called Furby.

In 1999 Hasbro bought game maker and retailer Wizards of the Coast (maker of "Pokemon" trading cards). In late 1999 the company purged another 19% of its workforce (about 2200 jobs) and launched Games.com with Go2Net (now Blucora) to feature online versions of its games.

Another 750 job cuts followed in late 2000. The company sold its Hasbro Interactive and Games.com units in early 2001 to Infogrames Entertainment SA.

The company's Trivial Pursuit 20th Anniversary Edition was one of the top-selling games in 2002. In November of that year Hasbro was fined $7.7 million in the UK for allegedly forcing distributors to fix toy and game prices; however due to the company's full cooperation during the investigation the fine was waived in February 2003.

In 2004 Hasbro shuttered its manufacturing plant in Valencia Spain and shifted operations to China and Ireland affecting about 500 employees. The company retained a sales and marketing team in Valencia. In December 2004 Hasbro laid off about 125 employees across several departments. Tapping into the company's research and development capabilities Hasbro launched a Tooth Tunes toothbrush that includes a song stored in a microchip which began selling for $10 apiece at CVS stores in late 2005. Music transmits through the brusher's jawbone to the ear when brushing.

Hasbro has tapped into cross-marketing for movies and other forms of media paying at least

$600 million for the right to make most of the toys for the Star Wars prequels (not to mention giving producer George Lucas warrants to buy about 10% of the company). The investment has paid off; sales of Star Wars products contributed nearly 20% of Hasbro's revenues in 2005.

With its sale of Hasbro Interactive and Games.com in 2001 to Infogrames Entertainment Hasbro gave the firm digital gaming rights. In June 2005 Hasbro reacquired some of those rights for some $65 million.

Launched in CVS stores in 2006 were Hasbro's new Playskool line of 50 baby care items including Playskool brand diapers baby wipes sippy cups and more.

In 2007 Hasbro bought rights to another nine franchises from Infogrames for some $20 million. To secure its foothold in games-making the company acquired popular game maker Cranium in 2008 for more than $75 million. It continued its shopping in 2008 when it picked up the intellectual property rights to the Trivial Pursuit brand for $80 million from Horn Abbot Ltd. and Horn Abbot International Ltd.

EXECUTIVES

SVP and Treasurer, Martin R. Trueb, age 59
President and CEO The Hub, Margaret A. Loesch, age 64
Chairman, Alfred J. (Al) Verrecchia, age 69, $1,200,000 total compensation
COO, David D. R. Hargreaves, age 59, $700,000 total compensation
President CEO and Director, Brian Goldner, age 49
Global Chief Development Officer, Duncan J. Billing, age 53, $412,501 total compensation
SVP and CIO, Denise Clark
President Hasbro Studios, Stephen J. Davis, age 49
Global Chief Marketing Officer, Johnathan A. (John) Frascotti, age 51, $425,000 total compensation
SVP Corporate Communications, Wayne S. Charness
SVP and CFO, Deborah M. (Deb) Thomas, age 48, $423,077 total compensation
VP Development Hasbro Studios, Michael J. Vogel
SVP Current Programming Hasbro Studios, Linda Steiner
VP Production Hasbro Studios, Kathy Page
VP Investor Relations, Debbie Hancock
SVP Chief Legal Officer and Secretary, Barbara Finigan, age 50
Director, Basil L. Anderson, age 66
Director, Jack M. Greenberg, age 69
Director, Alan G. Hassenfeld, age 63
Director, Michael W.O. Garrett, age 69
Director, Lisa Gersh, age 53
President CEO and Director, Brian Goldner, age 49
Director, Alan R. Batkin, age 67
Director, Tracy A. Leinbach, age 52
Director, Kenneth A. Bronfin, age 52
Director, Frank J. Biondi Jr.
Director, Edward M. (Ted) Philip, age 46
Director, John M. (Jack) Connors Jr., age 69
Auditors: KPMGLLP

LOCATIONS

HQ: Hasbro Inc.
1027 Newport Ave., Pawtucket RI 02862
Phone: 401-431-8697 **Fax:** 401-431-8535
Web: www.hasbro.com

PRODUCTS/OPERATIONS

Selected Brands and Products

Electronics
- Tiger Electronics
  - Furby
  - FurReal Friends
  - Giga Pets
  - Hitclips (micro music systems)
  - Luv Cubs
  - Thintronix (ultra-thin speakerphone FM radio)
  - VideoNow (personal video player)

Games and Puzzles
- Avalon Hill
  - Acquire
  - Axis & Allies
  - Battle Cry
  - Cosmic Encounter
  - Diplomacy
  - History of the World
  - Risk 2210 A.D.
  - Stratego Legends
- Jigsaw Puzzles
  - Big Ben
  - Croxley
  - Guild
- Milton Bradley
  - Battleship
  - Candy Land
  - Chutes and Ladders
  - Connect Four
  - The Game of Life
  - Hungry Hungry Hippos
  - Jenga
  - Mousetrap
  - Operation
  - PERFALOCK
  - Scattergories
  - Scrabble
- Tiger Games
  - Trouble
  - Twister
  - Yahtzee
- Parker Brothers
  - Boggle
  - Clue
  - Monopoly
  - Ouija
  - Risk
  - Sorry!
  - Trivial Pursuit
- Wizards of the Coast
  - Dungeons and Dragons
  - Harry Potter trading cards
  - Magic: The Gathering
  - Magic: The Gathering Online
  - NeoPets
  - Pokemon
  - Major League Baseball Showdown
- Wrebbit
  - PERFALOCK
  - PUZZ-3D

Boys' Toys
- BeyBlade spinning tops
- BTR (Built To Rule action building sets)
- Engine Gear spinning tops
- G.I. Joe action figures
- Hard Metal System spinning tops
- Micro Machines
- NakNak (stacking battle figures)
- Star Wars action figures
- Tonka (toy trucks)
- Transformers (small vehicles that transform into robots)

Preschool Toys
- 2-in-1 Tummy Time Gym
- Bob the Builder toys
- Busy Ball Popper
- Cool Crew
- First Starts (role-playing products)
- Gloworm
- Go-Bots
- Kick Start Gym
- Major Powers (action figure)
- Mr. Potato Head
- Playskool
- Sesame Street
- Silly Sports (action games)
- Sit ' N Spin
- Speedstars (race cars and track sets)
- Step Start Walk n' Ride
- Weebles

Creative Play
- Easy-Bake Oven
- Lite-Brite
- Lite-Brite Cube
- Play-Doh
- Spirograph
- Tinkertoys

Girls' Toys
- e-kera (handheld karaoke system)
- Makeup Mindy (dolls)
- My Little Pony
- Raggedy Ann and Raggedy Andy dolls
- Secret Central (dolls)
- TwinkleTwirls Dance Studio

Other
- The Incredibles toys
- Nerf (soft play toys)
- Power Air Surfer Sky Wolf (remote control airplane)
- Rave Master (games action figures and accessories)
- Shrek 2 (boys girls creative play plush board games and puzzles categories)
- Super Soaker water products
- Wheels on the Bus

COMPETITORS

Build-A-Bear
Cartoon Network
Enesco
Graco Children' s Products
JAKKS Pacific
LeapFrog
LEGO
Marvel Entertainment
Mattel
MGA Entertainment
Nakajima USA
Namco Bandai
Nickelodeon
Ohio Art
Playmates Toys
Playmobil
Poof-Slinky
Radio Flyer
RC2 Corporation
Sanrio
Simba Dickie Group
Smoby
Spin Master
TakaraTomy
Toy Quest
Ty
VTech Holdings
WHAM-O

HISTORICAL FINANCIALS

Company Type: Public

Income Statement

FYE: December 25

	REVENUE ($ mil.)	NET INCOME ($ mil.)	NET PROFIT MARGIN	EMPLOYEES
12/11	4,285	385	9.0%	5,900
12/10	4,002	397	9.9%	5,800
12/09	4,067	374	9.2%	5,800
12/08	4,021	306	7.6%	5,900
12/07	3,837	333	8.7%	5,900
Annual Growth	2.8%	3.7%	—	0.0%

2011 Year-End Financials

Debt ratio: 38.28%
Return on equity: 27.19%
Cash ($ mil.): 641
Current ratio: 239.16
Long-term debt ($ mil.): 1,400
No. of shares (mil.): 128
Dividends
Yield: —
Payout: 40.78%
Market value ($ mil.): 4,172

	STOCK PRICE ($) FY Close	P/E High	P/E Low	PER SHARE ($) Earnings	Dividends	Book Value
12/11	32.43	17	11	2.82	0.00	11.02
12/10	48.52	17	11	2.74	0.00	11.76
12/09	32.17	12	8	2.48	0.00	11.63
12/08	29.04	19	10	2.00	0.00	9.99
12/07	25.91	16	12	1.97	0.00	9.54
Annual Growth	5.8%	—	—	9.4%	—	3.7%

HCA Holdings Inc

HCA dispenses TLC for a profit. HCA Holdings through HCA Inc. (Hospital Corporation of America) operates more than 160 acute care psychiatric and rehabilitation hospitals in the US and UK. It also runs more than 100 ambulatory surgery centers as well as cancer treatment and outpatient rehab centers that form health care networks in many of the communities it serves. In total its hospitals are home to more than 40500 beds. HCA's facilities are located in 20 states; roughly half of its hospitals are in Florida and Texas. HCA International operates hospitals and clinics in the UK. In 2011 HCA Holdings went public through a $3.8 billion IPO. In 2011 HCA Holdings went public through a $3.8 billion IPO.

HISTORY

In 1987 Dallas lawyer Rick Scott and Fort Worth Texas financier Richard Rainwater founded Columbia Hospital Corp. to buy two hospitals in El Paso Texas. The partners eventually sold 40% of the hospitals to local doctors hoping that ownership would motivate physicians to increase productivity and efficiency.

The company entered the Miami market the next year and by 1990 had four hospitals. After merging with Smith Laboratories that year Columbia went public and then acquired Sutter Laboratories (orthopedic products). By the end of 1990 it had 11 hospitals.

Columbia moved into Florida in 1992 with the purchase of several hospitals and facilities. The next year it acquired Galen Health Care which operated 73 hospitals and had been spun off from health plan operator Humana earlier in the year. The merger thrust the hospital chain into about 15 new markets.

Columbia bought Hospital Corporation of America (HCA) in 1994. Thomas Frist his son Thomas Frist Jr. and Jack Massey (former owner of Kentucky Fried Chicken now part of TRICON) founded HCA in Nashville Tennessee in 1968. By 1973 the company had grown to 50 hospitals.

Meanwhile the medical industry was changing — insurers Medicare and Medicaid began scrutinizing payment procedures while the growth of HMOs (which aimed to restrict hospital admissions) cut hospital occupancy rates. HCA began paring operations in the late 1980s selling more than 100 hospitals. In 1989 the younger Frist led a $5.1 billion leveraged buyout of the company. He sold more assets and in 1992 took HCA public again but losses and a tumbling stock price made it a takeover target.

Later in 1994 the newly christened Columbia/HCA acquired the US's largest operator of outpatient surgery centers Dallas-based Medical Care America. A year later it bought 117-hospital HealthTrust a 1987 offshoot of HCA. Columbia/HCA was unstoppable in 1996 with some 150 acquisitions.

In 1997 the government began investigating the company's business practices. After executive indictments the company fired Scott and several other top officers. Frist Jr. became chairman and CEO pledging to shrink the company and tone down its aggressive approach. Columbia/HCA sold its home care business more than 100 of its less-desirable hospitals and almost all the operations of Value Health a pharmacy benefits and behavioral health care management firm it had recently bought.

The trimming continued in 1998: The company sold nearly three dozen outpatient surgery centers and more than a dozen hospitals. That year Columbia/HCA sued former financial executive Samuel Greco and several vendors accusing them of defrauding the company of several million dollars. In 1999 it spun off regional operators LifePoint Hospitals (23 facilities) and Triad Hospitals (34) to trim its holdings. The next year it sold some 120 medical buildings to MedCap Properties a joint venture formed with First Union Capital Partners.

During 2000 the company bought out partner Sun Life and Provincial Holdings' (now AXA UK) interest in several London hospitals and bought three hospitals there from St. Martins Healthcare. It also renamed itself HCA - The Healthcare Company. While continuing a strategy of consolidating and streamlining operations (and resolving remaining legal matters) in 2001 the company streamlined its name even further to simply HCA Inc.

By 2002 HCA began shaking off its shaky past. Profits stabilized allowing it to reinvest millions into modernizing facilities and equipment at its hospitals and surgery centers. It entered the Kansas City market in 2003 by acquiring a local hospital chain.

The company finally closed the books during 2003 on the numerous government investigations launched in 1997 into its business practices. In the five years leading up to 2003 HCA paid out some $2 billion in settlements for Medicare fraud and other claims. These settlements took their toll on the firm's bottom line.

To expand its outpatient services HCA beginning in 2004 began purchasing imaging centers. In early 2005 the firm acquired Tampa Florida's Total I Imaging and its five centers that offer diagnostic services. In 2005 HCA's iMage1 Network part of HCA's outpatient services group bought more than a handful of imaging centers located in the Tampa Florida area from Ultra Open MRI Corp.

The devastating hurricane season of 2005 hit HCA's operations hard as they are concentrated in the southern US. When Hurricane Katrina hit HCA evacuated its Tulane University Hospital and Clinic (it reopened in early 2006). Hurricane Rita spurred HCA to evacuate three Houston-area hospitals (Mainland Medical Center in Texas City East Houston Regional Medical Center in Houston and Clear Lake Regional Medical Center in Webster) and partially evacuate two others.

In 2006 a group of investors — including Thomas Frist Jr. as well as Bain Capital Kohlberg Kravis Roberts and the private equity arm of Merrill Lynch –took HCA private in a $30 billion leveraged buyout. In 2009 Richard Bracken became CEO of the company.

The hospital operator maintained its private status for several years until it once again went public in 2011 as a way to pay off some debt.

EXECUTIVES

President CFO and Director, R. Milton Johnson, age 54, $849,984 total compensation
SVP General Counsel and Chief Labor Relations Officer, Robert A. (Bob) Waterman, age 58, $569,988 total compensation
Chairman and CEO, Richard M. Bracken, age 59, $1,324,975 total compensation
SVP and Chief Ethics and Compliance Officer, Alan R. Yuspeh, age 62
SVP and CIO; President HCA Information Technology & Services Inc., Noel B. Williams, age 57
SVP Finance and Treasurer, David G. Anderson, age 65
SVP, Victor L. Campbell, age 65
President Operations, Samuel N. (Sam) Hazen, age 52, $788,672 total compensation
President Service Line and Operations Integration, A. Bruce Moore Jr., age 52
CFO Outpatient Service Group, William B. (Bill) Rutherford, age 48
SVP Internal Audit Services, Joseph N. (Joe) Steakley, age 58
President Business Services Subsidiary, Beverly B. Wallace, age 61, $700,000 total compensation
CFO Western Group, Richard J. (Rick) Shallcross, age 54
President Southwest Group, Jon M. Foster, age 50
President Capital Division, Margaret G. Lewis, age 58
SVP Human Resources, John M. Steele, age 57
President Central Group, W. Paul Rutledge, age 57, $675,000 total compensation
VP Investor Relations, Mark Kimbrough
CFO Central Group, Russell K. (Russ) Harms
SVP and Controller, Donald W. (Don) Stinnett, age 56
Chief Medical Officer; President HCA Clinical and Physician Services Group, Jonathan B. (Jon) Perlin, age 51
President National Group, Charles J. (Chuck) Hall, age 59
Director, Jay O. Light, age 70
SVP and Chief Development Officer, Joseph A. (Joe) Sowell III, age 56
Government Relations and Investor Relations, Greta J. Presley
SVP Communications, Jana J. Davis, age 53
President and CEO Parallon Business Solutions, Michael O?Boyle, age 55
SVP Strategic Pricing and Analytics, Juan Vallarino, age 51
SVP and CIO, Marty Paslick
President CFO and Director, R. Milton Johnson, age 54
Director, Geoffrey G. (Geoff) Meyers, age 67
Director, Michael W. (Mike) Michelson, age 61
Director, Kenneth W. (Ken) Freeman, age 62
Director, Stephen G. (Steve) Pagliuca, age 57
Director, John P. (JC) Connaughton, age 46
Director, Nathan C. (Nate) Thorne, age 58
Director, James C. (Jim) Momtazee, age 40
Director, Christopher R. (Chris) Gordon, age 39
Director, Jay O. Light, age 70
Director, William R. Frist, age 42
Director, James D. Forbes, age 52
Auditors: Ernst&YoungLLP

LOCATIONS

HQ: HCA Holdings Inc.
1 Park Plaza, Nashville TN 37203
Phone: 615-344-9551 **Fax:** 615-344-2266
Web: www.hcahealthcare.com

2010 Locations

US		
Texas	36	
Virginia	10	
Colorado	7	
Missouri	6	
California	5	
Nevada	3	
Idaho	2	
New Hampshire	2	
Alaska	1	
Mississippi	1	
Total	**0**	**163**

Selected US Facilities

Alaska
- Alaska Regional Hospital (Anchorage)

California
- Good Samaritan Hospital (San Jose)
- Los Robles Medical Center (Thousand Oaks)
- Regional Medical Center of San Jose
- Riverside Community Hospital
- West Hills Hospital & Medical Center

Colorado
- Centrum Surgical Center (Greenwood Village)
- Medical Center of Aurora
- North Suburban Medical Center (Thornton)
- Presbyterian/St. Luke' s Medical Center (Denver)
- Rose Medical Center (Denver)
- Sky Ridge Medical Center (Lone Tree)
- Spalding Rehabilitation Hospital (Aurora)
- Swedish Medical Center (Englewood)

Florida
- Aventura Hospital and Medical Center
- Blake Medical Center (Bradenton)
- Brandon Regional Hospital
- Capital Regional Medical Center (Tallahassee)
- Central Florida Regional Hospital (Sanford)
- Columbia Hospital (West Palm Beach)
- Doctors Hospital of Sarasota
- Edward White Hospital (St. Petersburg)
- Fawcett Memorial Hospital (Port Charlotte)
- Gulf Coast Medical Center (Panama City)
- JFK Medical Center (Atlantis)
- Kendall Regional Medical Center (Miami)
- Lake City Medical Center
- Largo Medical Center
- Memorial Hospital Jacksonville
- North Florida Regional Medical Center (Gainesville)
- Northwest Medical Center (Margate)
- Ocala Regional Medical Center
- Osceola Regional Medical Center (Kissimmee)
- Palms West Hospital (Loxahatchee)
- South Bay Hospital (Sun City Center)
- St. Lucie Medical Center (Port St. Lucie)
- Twin Cities Hospital (Niceville)
- University Hospital and Medical Center (Tamarac)
- West Florida Hospital (Pensacola)
- Westside Regional Medical Center (Plantation)

Georgia
- Atlanta Outpatient Surgery Center (Atlanta)
- Cartersville Medical Center
- Coliseum Medical Centers (Macon)
- Doctors Hospital (Augusta)
- Eastside Medical Center (Snellville)
- Fairview Park Hospital (Dublin)
- Northlake Surgical Center (Tucker)
- Polk Medical Center (Cedartown)
- Redmond Regional Medical Center (Rome)

Idaho
- Eastern Idaho Regional Medical Center (Idaho Falls)
- West Valley Medical Center (Caldwell)

Indiana
- Terre Haute Regional Hospital

Kansas
- Allen County Hospital (Iola)
- Menorah Medical Center (Overland Park)
- Overland Park Regional Medical Center
- Wesley Medical Center (Wichita)

Kentucky
- Frankfort Regional Medical Center
- Greenview Regional Hospital (Bowling Green)

Louisiana
- Dauterive Hospital (New Iberia)
- Lafeyette Surgicare
- Lakeview Regional Medical Center (Covington)
- Rapides Regional Medical Center (Alexandria)
- Regional Medical Center of Acadiana (Lafayette)
- Tulane Medical Center (Metarie)
- Tulane University Hospital & Clinic (New Orleans)
- Women' s & Children' s Hospital (Lafayette)

Mississippi
- Garden Park Medical Center (Gulfport)

Missouri
- Centerpoint Medical Center (Independence)
- Lafayette Regional Health Center (Lexington)
- Lee' s Summit Hospital
- Research Medical Center (Kansas City)
- Research Psychiatric Center (Kansas City)

Nevada
- Flamingo Surgery Center (Las Vegas)
- MountainView Hospital (Las Vegas)
- Southern Hills Hospital and Medical Center (Las Vegas)
- Sunrise Hospital and Medical Center (Las Vegas)

New Hampshire
- Parkland Medical Center (Derry)
- Portsmouth Regional Hospital
- Salem Surgery Center

Oklahoma
- Edmond Medical Center
- Oklahoma Surgicare (Oklahoma City)
- Oklahoma University Medical Center (Oklahoma City)

South Carolina
- Colleton Medical Cemter (Walterboro)
- Grand Dunes Surgery Center (Myrtle Beach)
- Grand Strand Regional Medical Center (Myrtle Beach)
- Summerville Medical Center
- Trident Regional Medical Center (Charleston)

Tennessee
- Centennial Medical Center (Nashville)
- Hendersonville Medical Center
- Horizon Medical Center (Dickson)
- Parkridge East Hospital (Chattanooga)
- Parkridge Valley Hospital (Chattanooga)
- Skyline Medical Center (Nashville)
- StoneCrest Medical Center (Smyrna)
- Summit Medical Center (Hermitage)

Texas
- Bailey Square Surgery Center (Austin)
- Bayshore Medical Center (Pasadena)
- Clear Lake Regional Medical Center (Webster)
- Conroe Regional Medical Center
- Corpus Christi Medical Center
- Del Sol Medical Center (El Paso)
- Denton Regional Medical Center
- Green Oaks Hospital (Dallas)
- Kingwood Medical Center
- Las Colinas Medical Center (Irving)
- Mainland Medical Center (Texas City)
- Medical Center of Arlington
- Medical Center of Lewisville
- Medical Center of McKinney
- Medical Center of Plano
- Medical City Dallas Hospital
- Methodist Hospital (San Antonio)
- Metropolitan Methodist Hospital (San Antonio)
- North Austin Medical Center
- North Hills Hospital (North Richland Hills)
- Plaza Medical Center of Fort Worth
- Rio Grande Regional Hospital (McAllen)
- Round Rock Medical Center
- South Austin Hospital
- St. David' s Medical Center (Austin)
- Valley Regional Medical Center (Brownsville)
- West Houston Medical Center
- Woman' s Hospital of Texas (Houston)

Utah
- Brigham City Community Hospital
- Lakeview Hospital (Bountiful)
- Ogden Regional Medical Center
- St. Mark' s Hospital (Salt Lake City)
- Timpanogos Regional Hospital (Orem)

Virginia
- CJW Medical Center (Richmond)
- Dominion Hospital (Falls Church)
- Henrico Doctors' Hospital (Richmond)
- John Randolph Medical Center
- LewisGale Medical Center (Salem)
- Pulaski Community Hospital
- Reston Hospital Center
- Spotsylvania Regional Medical Center (Fredricksburg)

Selected International Facilities

UK
- Harley Street Clinic (London)
- Lister Hospital (London)
- London Bridge Hospital (London)
- The Portland Hospital for Women and Children (London)
- Princess Grace Hospital (London)
- The Wellington Hospital (London)

PRODUCTS/OPERATIONS

2011 Revenue Sources

	% of total	
Managed care & other insurers	53	
Managed Medicaid	4	
Total	**0**	**100**

2011 Revenues

	$ mil.	% of total
National Group	12,224	41
Central Group	6,982	24
Total	**29,682**	**100**

COMPETITORS

Adventist Health
Adventist Health System Sunbelt Healthcare
AmSurg
Ascension Health
Banner Health
Baptist Hospital
Baylor Health
Catholic Health Initiatives
Children' s Medical Center of Dallas
CHRISTUS Health
Community Health Systems
Dignity Health
Health Management Associates
HealthSouth
Kaiser Permanente
LifePoint Hospitals
MedCath
SSM Health Care
Sutter Health
Tenet Healthcare
Texas Health Resources
Trinity Health (Novi)
United Surgical Partners
Universal Health Services
University Health Services
WellStar Health System

HISTORICAL FINANCIALS

Company Type: Public

Income Statement

FYE: December 31

	REVENUE ($ mil.)	NET INCOME ($ mil.)	NET PROFIT MARGIN	EMPLOYEES
12/11	29,682	2,465	8.3%	199,000
12/10	30,683	1,207	3.9%	194,000
12/09	30,052	1,054	3.5%	0
12/08	28,374	673	2.4%	0
Annual Growth	1.5%	54.1%	—	—

2011 Year-End Financials

Debt ratio: 100.57%
Return on equity: 987650001000000.00%
Cash ($ mil.): 373
Current ratio: 130.23
Long-term debt ($ mil.): 25,645
No. of shares (mil.): 437
Dividends
Yield: —
Payout: —
Market value ($ mil.): 9,638

	STOCK PRICE ($) FY Close	P/E High/Low		PER SHARE ($) Earnings	Dividends	Book Value
12/11	22.03	7	3	4.97	0.00	(18.88)
Annual Growth	—	—	—	—	—	—

HCC Insurance Holdings, Inc.

From corporate office to offshore rig HCC Insurance Holdings sells specialized property/casualty insurance for commercial and individual customers. Through Houston Casualty Corporation and other subsidiaries the company provides insurance and reinsurance coverage in specialty markets such as directors' and officers' liability errors and omissions and surety and credit policies. It also provides medical stop-loss coverage and policies for aviation marine and energy industries. HCC's underwriting agency division provides brokerage services for affiliated and unaffiliated insurance firms. The company operates in the US Ireland Spain and the UK and does business in some 180 countries.

While most of its business is garden-variety specialty insurance HCC has set up shop in some narrow niches such as insuring vintage military aircraft kidnap and ransom product recalls and professional athletes. The company's strategy includes buying attractive specialty insurers and building up its underwriting business. It prefers to sell products that have a short to medium life span —any claims that might be filed come in within months and years rather than over decades.

International property treaty business is the company's fastest growing area of business. However like all property/casualty insurers HCC experienced international catastrophe losses in 2010 and 2011 from extreme weather events earthquakes and the tsunami in Japan. The company's largest business segment Accident & Health specializes in medical stop-loss policies and accounts for 30% of all premiums.

HCC Insurance has been steadily acquiring smaller companies and either folding them into its existing operations or re-shaping them into fresh subsidiaries. The company also regularly examines the profitability of its business segments and sometimes exits less profitable areas of operation.

EXECUTIVES

CEO and Director, John N. Molbeck Jr., age 65, $1,743,548 total compensation
EVP and Chief Accounting Officer, Pamela J. Penny, age 57
VP Human Resources, Susan L. Howie, age 58
Chairman, Robert A. (Bob) Rosholt, age 62
EVP and Chief Underwriting Officer; CEO Houston Casualty Company, Michael J. Schell, age 61, $612,000 total compensation
VP Administration, Deborah L. Riffe
EVP International Operations; CEO HCC Insurance Holdings (International) Limited, Barry J. Cook, age 51, $804,170 total compensation
EVP Life Accident and Health Operations; President and CEO HCC Life Insurance Company, Craig J. Kelbel, age 58, $612,000 total compensation
President Aviation, Michael J. Donovan
VP Financial Reporting and Budgeting, Mark A. Buechler
EVP US Property and Casualty Operations, Cory L. Moulton, age 43, $441,667 total compensation
VP and COO Aviation Division US Specialty Insurance, Anthony R. Bacewicz
Chairman HCC Specialty Underwriters, William F. (Bill) Hubbard
COO HCC Insurance Holdings (International) Limited, Nicholas I. Hutton-Penman
Chief Underwriting Officer HCC International Insurance, Michael L. Onslow
General Manager HCC Europe, Michel A. Pascual
President HCC Global Financial Products, Andrew G. Stone
SVP General Counsel and Secretary, Randy D. Rinicella, age 54
President Avemco Insurance, James A. (Jim) Lauerman
President Professional Indemnity Agency, Robert M. (Rob) Fishman, age 62
VP and Tax Director, Sharon L. Brock
VP Enterprise Risk Management, Jackie S. Kellems
VP Litigation, Christy M. Schweikhardt
President and CEO HCC Indemnity Guaranty, Laurence Donnelly
President and CEO Perico Life Insurance, Jeff E. Petty Jr.
President and Director, Christopher J. B. Williams, age 56
CEO HCC Surety, Adam S. Pessin
VP and CIO, William W. (Bill) Lukefahr
EVP HCC Life Insurance, Daniel A. Strusz
CEO HCC Specialty Underwriters, Matthew C. Overlan
President and Chief Underwriting Officer HCC Specialty Underwriters, Marc D. Idelson
Chairman HCC Surety, Richard E. Klein
VP Regulatory Compliance, Joycelyn M. Ray
SVP and Chief Underwriting Officer HCC Life Insurance, Larry J. Stewart
EVP and CFO HCC Life Insurance, Mark R. Sanderford
VP Corporate Claims, Stefano S. Minale
VP and Treasurer, Frank H. Ahlborn
EVP and CFO, Brad T. Irick, age 45
Joint CEO HCC Global International Operations, Philippe Vezio
VP and Treasurer, Jonathan Lee
EVP and Chief Actuary, Mark W. Callahan
VP Internal Audit, Nancy R. Berndt
VP and Controller, Brenda K. Bull
VP Finance Processes Systems and Services, Nikki M. Davis
CEO HCC Global Financial Products, R. Matthew Fairfield
EVP and COO, William N. Burke
CEO and Director, John N. Molbeck Jr., age 65
Director, Thomas M. (Tom) Hamilton, age 68
Director, James C. Flagg, age 60
Director, James E. Oesterreicher, age 70
Director, Deborah H. Midanek, age 57
Director, Frank J. Bramanti, age 55
Director, Leslie Stone Heisz, age 51
Director, Walter M. Duer, age 65
President and Director, Christopher J. B. Williams, age 56
Director, Scott W. Wise, age 62
Director, Judy C. Bozeman, age 69
Auditors: PricewaterhouseCoopersLLP

LOCATIONS

HQ: HCC Insurance Holdings, Inc.
13403 Northwest Freeway, Houston, TX 77040-6094
Phone: 713 690-7300
Web: www.hcc.com

2011 Revenues

Domestic	1,779	75
Total	**2,374**	**100**

PRODUCTS/OPERATIONS

2011 Revenues

	$ mil.	% of total
Accident & health	808	34
Professional liability	411	17
International	374	16
US Property & casualty	357	15
US Surety & credit	211	9
Investing	211	9
Corporate & other	(0.3)	-
Total	**2,374**	**100**

Selected Subsidiaries

Insurance
American Contractors Indemnity Company
Avemco Insurance Company
HCC Europe
HCC International Insurance Company
HCC Life Insurance Company
HCC Reinsurance Company Limited
HCC Specialty Insurance Company
Houston Casualty Company
Houston Casualty Company-London
Lloyd' s of London Syndicate 4141
Perico Life Insurance Company
United States Surety Company
U.S. Specialty Insurance Company

Underwriting
HCC Specialty
HCC Global Financial Products
HCC Indemnity Guaranty Agency
HCC Underwriting Agency
HCC Medical Insurance Services

COMPETITORS

ACE Limited
AIG
Chubb Corp
HM Insurance Group
Lloyd' s
Markel
Symetra
Travelers Companies
UnitedHealth Group
W. R. Berkley
XL Group plc

HISTORICAL FINANCIALS

Company Type: Public

Income Statement

FYE: December 31

	ASSETS ($ mil.)	NET INCOME ($ mil.)	INCOME AS % OF ASSETS	EMPLOYEES
12/11	9,625	255	2.7%	1,874
12/10	9,064	345	3.8%	1,883
12/09	8,834	353	4.0%	1,864
12/08	8,332	304	3.7%	1,864
12/07	8,074	395	4.9%	1,682
Annual Growth	4.5%	(10.4%)	—	2.7%

2011 Year-End Financials

Debt ratio: 4.97%
Return on equity: 7.75%
Cash ($ mil.): 334
Current ratio: —
Long-term debt ($ mil.): 478
No. of shares (mil.): 104
Dividends
Yield: —
Payout: 26.09%
Market value ($ mil.): 2,863

	STOCK PRICE ($) FY Close	P/E High/Low		PER SHARE ($) Earnings	Dividends	Book Value
12/11	27.50	14	11	2.30	0.00	31.62
12/10	28.94	10	8	2.99	0.56	28.67
12/09	27.97	9	6	3.11	0.52	26.58
12/08	26.75	11	6	2.64	0.47	23.27
12/07	28.68	10	8	3.38	0.42	21.21
Annual Growth	(1.0%)	—	—	(9.2%)	—	10.5%

Health Management Associates, Inc.

William Schoen chairman of Health Management Associates (HMA) once described his company as the "Wal-Mart of the hospital business" because like Sam Walton's empire HMA thrives in small-town America. The company operates a network of some 70 hospitals and more than 460 clinics in 15 states mainly in the South (although it also has facilities in Washington and Pennsylvania). Combined the facilities have about 10500 licensed beds. HMA's hospitals provide general medical and surgical care along with outpatient and emergency room services and specialty care in such areas as cancer care and obstetrics. The organization also operates an increasing number of outpatient surgery centers.

Geographic Reach

HMA's network of hospitals and clinics operates in Alabama Arkansas Florida Georgia Kentucky Mississippi Missouri North Carolina Oklahoma Pennsylvania South Carolina Tennessee Texas Washington and West Virginia.

Operations

Because it serves smaller markets HMA's facilities aren't large research hospitals that offer such procedures as organ transplants and other highly specialized services. HMA operates on a decentralized model with local CEOs CFOs and Chief Nursing Officers overseeing the daily operations of each hospital. The company maintains central control of finances purchasing and other systems which gives it advantages of scale and the buying power that comes with operating dozens of facilities.

Sales & Marketing

In 2011 about half of HMA's revenues were generated through patient care reimbursements from commercial insurance firms. Self-pay admissions accounted for 10% and Medicare and Medicaid together contributed 40%. Like other hospital operators some of HMA's revenues are offset by caring for patients who cannot pay their bills.

Financial Analysis

In 2011 HMA continued a five-year trend of increased revenues achieving growth of more than 13% over 2010 to a record $5.8 billion. The company's net income hit a three-year high with a 19% jump over 2010 to $178.7 million. HMA closed out the year with $6 billion in assets. The company's strong balance sheet and capital position allow it to continue to invest in various acquisitions.

Strategy

Over the years HMA has built its portfolio through numerous acquisitions of hospitals that serve as the primary source of health care in their regions (basically ensuring a loyal patient base). It typically acquires underperforming hospitals in attractive non-urban markets and then upgrades the facilities and equipment thereby increasing patient volume and efficiency. The health system also enters into joint ventures with physicians allowing doctors to own a minority stake in the hospitals in which they practice.

HMA also upgrades existing hospitals and broadens its service offerings in order to prevent local populations from having to travel to urban medical centers for treatment. Other strategic initiatives include recruiting qualified primary care doctors specialists and administrators; investing in strategic partnerships; and working to effectively control its costs. From time to time HMA also divests operations that no longer fit into its plans.

Some of the company's quality and efficiency programs aim to prepare for upcoming changes to the way hospitals are reimbursed by the federal government. HMA's initiatives include a medication error prevention program using a handheld scanner; hardware and software upgrades of its emergency rooms' clinical systems; and improvements to the system's quality management systems including data collection and benchmark measurement processes.

Mergers & Acquisitions

In 2012 HMA the company established a joint venture with INTEGRIS Health involving five hospitals in Oklahoma. HMA took on an 80% controlling interest in the hospitals and oversees the day-to-day operations.

HISTORY

From its founding in 1977 by Joseph Greene until 1985 Health Management Associates (HMA) owned only a handful of hospitals mostly in urban areas. In 1983 CEO Greene brought aboard William Schoen an ex-Marine who ran a beer company in New York before founding a bank in Florida. Schoen became president and COO that year took a co-CEO position in 1985 and assumed full leadership in 1986 when Greene retired.

Schoen sold the urban hospitals and refocused on small-town hospitals in underserved mainly southern communities with growing populations. To finance acquisitions and hospital overhauls HMA went public in 1986. Two years later Schoen took it private but it went public again in 1991. In the early 1990s it had a growth spurt adding 10 hospitals.

HMA continued buying adding two facilities in 1996 another two in 1997 and five in 1998 (three in Mississippi and two in Florida). The acquisitions continued in 1999 as Medicare cutbacks and costly Y2K computer fixes forced many small hospitals to seek buyers; the company bought facilities in Florida Mississippi (two) and Pennsylvania. In 2000 HMA continued to be acquisitive buying three medical centers (in Florida North Carolina and Pennsylvania) although it shut down its treatment center for at-risk youth in Kansas due to security concerns. In 2001 HMA bought some hospitals from the financially troubled Clarent Hospital.

Also in 2001 William Schoen resigned as CEO and was replaced by Joseph Vumbacco. Schoen remained as chairman.

In 2003 HMA acquired five hospitals from Tenet and expanded into the US Northwest by purchasing two hospitals in Washington. The next year the company bought Chester County Hospital in South Carolina. In 2005 HMA acquired five hospitals in Florida Mississippi and Virginia.

HMA's 2006 acquisitions included Gulf Coast Medical Center in Mississippi (which it later closed) from Tenet Healthcare; Cleveland Clinic - Naples Hospital in Florida; and Barrow Community Hospital in Georgia. The same year it sold off two psychiatric hospitals in Florida to Psychiatric Solutions.

It spent the next couple of years expanding in its key markets in the south through acquisitions and joint ventures. In 2007 it paid $32 million to acquire the remaining interests in two Dallas facilities it didn't already own (the Dallas Regional Medical Center and the Woman's Center at Dallas Regional Medical Center). That same year it opened the Physicians Regional Medical Center in Florida its first psychiatric hospital.

HMA continued to grow by purchasing the Sparks Health System in Fort Smith Arkansas in 2009. The nearly $140 million buy included a 500-bed hospital and other health care related operations. It then purchased the 300-bed Wuesthoff Medical Center and 115-bed Wuesthoff Medical Center in Florida from Wuesthoff Health System for about $152 million in 2010. Then in 2011 the company made a bold move for growth in the Southeast by acquiring the seven-hospital Mercy Health Partners Tennessee system from Catholic Health Partners for some $525 million; HMA renamed the system as Tennova Healthcare following the transaction. That purchase added some 1300 beds to the HMA network.

EXECUTIVES

SVP Finance, Robert E. Farnham, age 56, $400,000 total compensation
Chairman, William J. Schoen, age 76, $300,000 total compensation
President CEO and Director, Gary D. Newsome, age 54, $900,000 total compensation
EVP Development, Peter M. Lawson, age 50
SVP Support Services, Johnny A. Owenby
SVP and Chief Marketing Officer, Eric Waller
SVP Clinical Affairs, Lisa Gore
Group President South and West, Joe D. Pinion
SVP Management Information Systems, James L. (Jim) Jordan
Western Division President, Ann M. Barnhart
EVP and CFO, Kelly E. Curry, age 57, $675,000 total compensation
VP and Treasurer, Joseph C. Meek, $231,750 total compensation
South Florida Division President, Kathy A. Burke
Group President Florida, Alan Levine
Acting General Counsel, Linda A. Epstein
Chief Medical Officer, Ronald N. Riner
Tennessee Division President, Michael W. (Mike) Garfield
CIO, Ken Chatfield
SVP Administration, Gary J. Link
SVP Human Resources, Patrick E. Lombardo
North Florida Division President, Mike Fencel
Southern Division President, Robert L. Hammond Jr.
EVP Operations Finance, Kerrin E. (Kerry) Gillespie
Director, Donald E. Kiernan, age 71
Director, William C. Steere Jr., age 75
Director, Vicki A. O'Meara, age 54
President CEO and Director, Gary D. Newsome, age 54
Director, Randolph W. Westerfield, age 70
Director, Kent P. Dauten, age 56
Director, Robert A. Knox, age 60
Director, Pascal J. Goldschmidt, age 58
Auditors: Ernst&YoungLLP

LOCATIONS

HQ: Health Management Associates Inc.
5811 Pelican Bay Blvd. Ste. 500, Naples FL 34108-2710
Phone: 239-598-3131 **Fax:** 239-598-2705
Web: www.hma-corp.com

Selected States of Operation

Alabama
Arkansas
Florida
Georgia
Kentucky
Mississippi
Missouri
North Carolina
Oklahoma
Pennsylvania
South Carolina
Tennessee
Texas
Washington
West Virginia

PRODUCTS/OPERATIONS

2011 Revenue by Source

Commercial insurance & other	50	
Self-pay	10	
Medicaid	9	
Total	**0**	**100**

Selected Hospitals

Barrow Regional Medical Center (Winder GA)
Bartow Regional Medical Center (Bartow FL)
Biloxi Regional Medical Center (Biloxi MS)
Brooksville Regional Hospital (physician joint venture; Brooksville FL
Carlisle Regional Medical Center (physician joint venture; Carlisle PA)
Carolina Pines Regional Medical Center (physician joint venture; Hartsville SC)
Central Mississippi Medical Center (Jackson MS)
Charlotte Regional Medical Center (Punta Gorda FL)
Chester Regional Medical Center (physician joint venture; Chester SC)
Crossgates River Oaks Hospital (Brandon MS)
Dallas Regional Medical Center (Mesquite TX)
Davis Regional Medical Center (Statesville NC)
East Georgia Regional Medical Center (physician joint venture; Statesboro GA)
Fishermen' s Hospital (Marathon)
Gilmore Memorial Regional Medical Center (Amory MS)
Heart of Florida Regional Medical Center (physician joint venture; Haines City FL)
Heart of Lancaster Regional Medical Center (physician joint venture; Lititz PA)
Highlands Regional Medical Center (Sebring FL)
Jamestown Regional Medical Center (Jamestown TN)
Lake Norman Regional Medical Center (physician joint venture; Mooresville NC)
Lancaster Regional Medical Center (physician joint venture; Lancaster PA)
Lehigh Regional Medical Center (Lehigh Acres FL)
Lower Keys Medical Center (Key West FL)
Madison Regional Medical Center (Canton MS)
Medical Center of Southeastern Oklahoma (physician joint venture; Durant OK)
Midwest Regional Medical Center (physician joint venture; MidwestOK)
Natchez Community Hospital (physician joint venture; Natchez MS)
Northwest Mississippi Regional Medical Center (Clarksdale MS)
Pasco Regional Medical Center (physician joint venture; Dade City FL)
Paul B. Hall Regional Medical Center (physician joint ventur; Paintsville KY)
Peace River Regional Medical Center (Port Charlotte FL)
Physicians Regional Medical Center-Collier Boulevard (Naples FL)
Physicians Regional Medical Center-Pine Ridge (Naples FL)
Poplar Bluff Regional Medical Center (physician joint venture; Poplar Bluff MO)
River Oaks Hospital (Flowood MS)
Riverview Regional Medical Center (Gadsden AL)
Sandhills Regional Medical Center (Hamlet NC)
Santa Rosa Medical Center (Milton FL)
Sebastian River Medical Center (Sebastian FL)
Seven Rivers Regional Medical Center (Crystal River FL)
Sparks Medical Center (physician joint venture; Van Buren AR)
Spring Hill Regional Hospital (physician joint venture; Spring Hill FL)
St. Cloud Regional Medical Center (physician joint venture; St. Cloud FL)
Stringfellow Memorial Hospital (Anniston AL)
Summit Medical Center (Van Buren AR)
Tennova Healthcare (formerly Mercy Health Partners Tennessee; Knoxville TN)
Toppenish Community Hospital (physician joint venture; Toppenish WA)
Twin Rivers Regional Medical Center (Kennett MO)
University Medical Center (physician joint venture; Lebanon TN)
Venice Regional Medical Center (Venice FL)
Walton Regional Medical Center (Monroe GA)
Williamson Memorial Hospital (physician joint venture; Williamson WV)
Woman' s Hospital at River Oaks (Flowood MS)
Wuesthoff Medical Center-Melbourne (Melbourne FL)
Wuesthoff Medical Center-Rockledge (Rockledge FL)
Yakima Regional Medical & Cardiac Center (physician joint venture; Yakima WA)

COMPETITORS

Ascension Health
Baptist Health Care
Baptist Memorial Health Care
Baylor Health
Catholic Health East
Catholic Health Initiatives
Catholic Health Partners
CHRISTUS Health
Community Health Corporation
Community Health Systems
FirstHealth of the Carolinas
Greenville Hospital System
HCA
Lee Memorial
LifePoint Hospitals
Methodist Healthcare
SSM Health Care
SunLink Health Systems
Tenet Healthcare
Texas Health Resources
Universal Health Services
University Health Services
WellStar Health System

HISTORICAL FINANCIALS

Company Type: Public

Income Statement FYE: December 31

	REVENUE ($ mil.)	NET INCOME ($ mil.)	NET PROFIT MARGIN	EMPLOYEES
12/11	5,804	178	3.1%	40,600
12/10	5,115	150	2.9%	43,100
12/09	4,617	138	3.0%	33,700
12/08	4,451	167	3.8%	32,700
12/07	4,392	119	2.7%	34,900
Annual Growth	7.2%	10.5%	—	3.9%

2011 Year-End Financials

Debt ratio: 59.54%
Return on equity: 18.43%
Cash ($ mil.): 64
Current ratio: 175.43
Long-term debt ($ mil.): 3,489
No. of shares (mil.): 254
Dividends
Yield: —
Payout: —
Market value ($ mil.): 1,873

	STOCK PRICE ($) FY Close	P/E High/Low		PER SHARE ($) Earnings	Dividends	Book Value
12/11	7.37	16	9	0.70	0.00	3.82
12/10	9.54	16	10	0.60	0.00	2.88
12/09	7.27	15	3	0.56	0.00	2.16
12/08	1.79	12	1	0.68	0.00	0.63
12/07	5.98	43	12	0.49	10.12	0.33
Annual Growth	5.4%	—	—	9.3%	—	84.5%

Health Net, Inc.

Health Net has woven together a web of health plan services. The company provides managed health care medical coverage to about 6 million members. The company's health plan services unit offers HMO PPO Medicare and Medicaid plans as well as vision dental care and pharmacy benefit programs to customers in Arizona California Oregon and Washington. Its Managed Health Network subsidiary provides behavioral health and employee assistance to employers and traditional health plan customers. Health Net's products are marketed to commercial clients through its sales force and external brokers; individual plans are sold mostly through independent agents.

Operations

Health Net's core health plan business is firmly focused on the western US with California comprising its largest health plan market. HN California Health Net's California HMO is part of the Children's Health Insurance Program (known as Healthy Families) and insures some 136000 children. Other key states include Arizona and Oregon.

In addition the company's Health Net Federal Services subsidiary holds a contract with the government's TRICARE program through which the company provides health benefits to some 3 million military members in the northern US. TRICARE serves employees within the US Department of Defense the US State Department and the US Department of Veterans' Affairs.

Financial Analysis

In recent years Health Net's earnings have softened due in part to inking a smaller TRICARE contract and losses in its non-core markets. Health Net's income was beginning to recover from recession-linked investment losses in 2008 and 2009 when it was pinched again in 2011 by a court ruling that cost it $181 million. That ruling came from litigation tied to a business it no longer owned but held liability for. During 2011 Health Net's revenues dropped by 13% to some $11.9 billion and its net income decreased 65% to about $72 million.

Strategy

In recent years Health Net has reshaped its operations to focus on the western US by steadily divested its non-western operations. It has made plans to sell its remaining Medicare Part D prescription drug plan business in Connecticut and New Jersey to an affiliate of CVS Caremark.

The company is also increasingly focused on creating tailored products targeting specific groups of people. Like traditional HMO capitated networks (in which a provider is given a set fee per patient regardless of service performed) these new products are intended to lower costs while still offering comprehensive benefits and a broad provider network with low copays. For example its HMO Silver Network is one such product and is a network of doctors specialists and hospitals in ten counties in California. Another tailored network product Salud Con Health Net has plans targeted at the Latino community in Southern California. More than 45% of Health Net's capitated members in California are enrolled in tailored products.

HISTORY

Foundation Health started as the not-for-profit Foundation Community Health Plan in the 1960s. In 1984 it was bought by AmeriCare Health which had HMOs in six states. The acquisition was a coup: Foundation Health soon accounted for the bulk of AmeriCare's sales.

AmeriCare went public in 1985. The next year it lost to another firm the rights to that name. Redubbed Foundation Health the company expanded into new states and unrelated businesses: commercial real estate silk flowers and furniture.

In late 1986 senior management led a $140 million LBO that left Foundation Health hobbled with debt when the industry started to slide. A 1988 Department of Defense (DOD) CHAMPUS contract brightened prospects but the five-year $3 billion contract to provide health care to 860000 military retirees and dependents in California and Hawaii provided little short-term relief against the effects of high debt and rapid growth: The company lost money again.

The CEO slot had been vacant a year when Dan Crowley a trained accountant with a good turnaround record came aboard in 1989. He cut staff slashed budgets sold unrelated and nonperforming units and kicked off a huge sales effort. To satisfy bankers and the DOD which was threatening to rescind its contract Crowley refinanced Foundation's debt. In a little over a year Foundation Health recorded its best results ever. In 1990 the company went public.

Back on solid ground the company expanded its services and markets buying such firms as Western Universal Life Insurance (renamed Foundation Health Benefit Life Insurance 1991) Occupational Health Services (employee assistance and substance abuse programs 1992) and California Compensation Insurance (workers' compensation insurance 1993).

Foundation Health lost the DOD Hawaii/California contract (almost half its revenues) in 1993 but managed to cope until it regained the business – by then worth $2.5 billion –two years later. Also that year Foundation Health won DOD's five-year $1.8 billion managed-care contract for Oklahoma and parts of Arkansas Louisiana and Texas.

Meanwhile the company had formed Integrated Pharmaceutical Services and bought CareFlorida Health Systems Intergroup Healthcare and Thomas-Davis Medical Centers in 1994.

In 1995 the company dropped an offer to buy Health Systems International. The next year it added behavioral health and employee assistance programs with the purchase of Managed Health Network.

Renewed discussions with Health Systems International resulted in the companies merging to become Foundation Health Systems in 1997. Crowley –whose aggressive style garnered profits but was denounced as brutal by some critics –resigned after the merger.

In 1998 the company pushed into the Northeast buying Connecticut-based HMO Physicians Health Services. It then sold its workers' compensation insurance operations. Chairman Malik Hasan (founder of Health Systems' nucleus QualMed) resigned that year partly because president Jay Gellert planned to focus on Arizona and California health plans CHAMPUS and behavioral health and pharmacy benefit management.

The financial aftershocks of the companies' merger continued and FHS pruned its operations in 1999 and 2000 exiting such states as Colorado New Mexico and Texas; trimming its Medicare operations; and selling certain non-core administrative business lines. In 2000 the California Medical Association sued the company under RICO statutes claiming it coerced doctors and interfered in doctor-patient relationships. Later that year the company changed its name to Health Net in its effort to build a national brand name.

In 2002 the company continued to divest certain noncore businesses by selling its EOS Claims Services subsidiary.

In an effort to further expand its business in the Golden State the company acquired the health plan assets of Universal Care in 2006 adding another 20000 Medi-Cal and Healthy Families members to its ranks (as well as some 5000 Medicare Advantage and 75000 commercial members). Simultaneously in 2006 the company exited its health plan operations in the Pennsylvania market (while continuing to offer TRICARE services in the state) in an effort to divest noncore businesses.

To focus on its core Western markets Health Net sold its Northeast subsidiaries (offering HMO commercial and Medicaid plans in Connecticut New Jersey and New York) to national provider UnitedHealth in 2009 in a deal worth close to $600 million. It retained its stand-alone Medicare Part D business in Connecticut and New Jersey but later made arrangements to sell that business as well.

EXECUTIVES

SVP Organization Effectiveness, Karin D. Mayhew, age 61, $429,159 total compensation
President CEO and Director, Jay M. Gellert, age 58, $1,200,000 total compensation
Chairman, Roger F. Greaves, age 74
SVP Chief Regulatory and External Relations Officer and Chief Compliance Officer, Patricia T. (Pat) Clarey, age 58
Health Care Services Officer; President Health Net Pharmaceutical Services, John P. Sivori, age 48
EVP and CFO, Joseph C. Capezza, age 57, $550,000 total compensation
EVP and COO, James E. (Jim) Woys, age 53, $700,000 total compensation
President Government Programs, Steven D. (Steve) Tough, age 61, $494,711 total compensation
President Health Net Federal Services LLC, Thomas F. (Tom) Carrato
President Health Net of Arizona, Bret A. Morris
President Western Region Health Plan and Health Net of California, Steven J. (Steve) Sell, age 45
President Health Net Health Plan of Oregon, Chris Ellertson, age 43
VP and Treasurer, Jonathan Rollins, age 48
Manager Public Relations Health Net of Arizona, Lori Rieger
SVP General Counsel and Secretary, Angelee F. Bouchard, age 44, $257,095 total compensation
Director, Vicki B. Escarra, age 57
Director, Theodore F. (Ted) Craver Jr., age 60
Director, Bruce G. Willison, age 63
President CEO and Director, Jay M. Gellert, age 58
Director, Gale S. Fitzgerald, age 61
Director, Patrick Foley, age 80
Director, Fredrick C. (Rick) Yeager, age 70
Director, Mary Anne Citrino, age 53
Auditors: Deloitte&ToucheLLP

LOCATIONS

HQ: Health Net Inc.
21650 Oxnard St., Woodland Hills CA 91367
Phone: 818-676-6000 **Fax:** 818-676-8591
Web: www.healthnet.com

PRODUCTS/OPERATIONS

2011 Sales

	$ mil.	% of total
Health plan services	10,364	87
Net investment income	74	1
Total	**11,901**	**100**

Selected Subsidiaries

FH Surgery Centers Inc.
FH Surgery Limited Inc.
Foundation Health Facilities Inc.
Health Net Federal Services Inc.
Health Net of Arizona Inc
Health Net of California Inc.
Health Net One Payment Services Inc.
Health Net Pharmaceutical Services
Health Net Services Inc.
Managed Health Network Inc.
National Pharmacy Services Inc.
QualMed Inc.
- Health Net Health Plan of Oregon Inc.
- QualMed Plans for Health of Colorado Inc.

COMPETITORS

Aetna
Anthem Blue Cross
Blue Cross
Blue Cross Blue Shield of Arizona
Blue Shield Of California
CIGNA
Humana
Kaiser Permanente
LifeWise Health Plan of Oregon
Magellan Health
Oregon Dental
PacificSource
Providence Health & Services
Regence BlueCross BlueShield of Oregon
UnitedHealth Group
WellPoint

HISTORICAL FINANCIALS

Company Type: Public

Income Statement

FYE: December 31

	REVENUE ($ mil.)	NET INCOME ($ mil.)	NET PROFIT MARGIN	EMPLOYEES
12/11	11,901	72	0.6%	7,471
12/10	13,619	204	1.5%	8,169
12/09	15,713	(49)	—	8,922
12/08	15,366	95	0.6%	9,646
12/07	14,108	193	1.4%	10,228
Annual Growth	(4.2%)	(21.9%)	—	(7.6%)

2011 Year-End Financials

Debt ratio: 14.18%
Return on equity: 5.00%
Cash ($ mil.): 230
Current ratio: 187.96
Long-term debt ($ mil.): 511
No. of shares (mil.): 81
Dividends
Yield: —
Payout: —
Market value ($ mil.): 2,493

	STOCK PRICE ($) FY Close	P/E High/Low	PER SHARE ($) Earnings	Dividends	Book Value
12/11	30.42	42 26	0.80	0.00	17.61
12/10	27.29	14 11	2.06	0.00	17.90
12/09	23.29	— —	(0.47)	0.00	16.44
12/08	10.89	59 9	0.88	0.00	16.89
12/07	48.30	34 27	1.70	0.00	17.00
Annual Growth	(10.9%)	— —	(17.2%)	—	0.9%

Heartland Financial USA, Inc. (Dubuque, IA)

Heartland Financial USA's heart is in the right place. The multibank holding company owns flagship subsidiary Dubuque Bank & Trust and nine other banks that together operate more than 60 branches in 40-plus communities in the Midwest and Southwest. In addition to standard deposit loan and mortgage services the banks also offer retirement wealth management trust insurance and investment services including socially responsible investing. Heartland Financial USA also owns consumer lender Citizens Finance which has about a dozen offices in Illinois Iowa and Wisconsin.

One of Heartland Financial's strategic goals is to expand its presence in the West so that region is home to half of its total assets balancing growth in those markets with the stability of the Midwest. Consistent with this strategy Heartland Financial has agreed to acquire Heritage Bank N.A. a Phoenix-based commercial bank in an all-cash deal valued at about $16 million. Previously Heartland Financial expanded its residential lending capabilities in Arizona with the 2010 acquisition of the profitable mortgage banking operations of the failed thrift First Arizona Savings. Operating as National Residential Mortgage the acquired business offers home loans through Arizona Bank & Trust.

Closer to home the company agreed to buy Wisconsin-based First Shares which owns First National Bank of Platteville in an $11 million deal. Upon closure of the deal the three-branch First National Bank of Platteville will become part of Heartland's Wisconsin Bank & Trust subsidiary.

Heartland Financial also pursues a strategy of opening de novo banks with local investors. Its Summit Bank & Trust and Minnesota Bank & Trust were established in this manner; local investor groups hold minority stakes in the banks. The company also considers purchases of other banks' branches and FDIC assisted acquisitions of failed financial institutions both in and outside its existing markets.

Heartland Financial USA's structure emphasizes local brands leadership and decision-making while centralizing common back-office operations such as account and loan processing investment management and collections. The company feels that its commitment to building relationships in the communities it operates coupled with a broad service menu helps it complete with national megabanks.

However like some other multibank holding companies Heartland Financial has announced plans to simplify by reducing the numbers of bank charters it owns. In 2011 it combined the charter of subsidiary First Community Bank with that of Dubuque Bank and Trust in an effort to save operating costs and regulatory fees.

Approximately 70% of Heartland Financial's loan portfolio comes from commercial loans and mortgages but in keeping with the bank's Midwestern identity it also makes agricultural residential mortgage and consumer loans; each are around 10% of its loan book.

Although revenues were flat in 2011 the company reported an 18% increase in net income (to $28 million). Its results were boosted by fewer provisions for loan losses loan sales and gains on securities.

EXECUTIVES

Chairman Arizona Bank & Trust, Paul F. Muscenti
SVP and Chief Risk Officer, David D. Keim, age 64
President and CEO Minnesota Bank & Trust, Catherine T. (Kate) Kelly
Chairman President and CEO; Vice Chairman Dubuque Bank and Trust Wisconsin Community Bank New Mexico Bank & Trust Arizona Bank & Trust Rocky Mountain Bank and Summit Bank & Trust; Chairman Citizens Finance, Lynn B. Fuller, age 62, $330,000 total compensation
EVP CFO COO Treasurer and Director; Vice Chairman Dubuque Bank & Trust Galena State Bank & Trust First Community Bank and Riverside Community Bank; Treasurer Citizens Finance, John K. Schmidt, age 52, $244,500 total compensation
EVP and Chief Credit Officer; EVP Lending Dubuque Bank & Trust; Vice Chairman Citizens Finance, Kenneth J. Erickson, age 59, $220,000 total compensation
SVP Lending; President and CEO Dubuque Bank & Trust, Douglas J. Horstmann, age 58, $195,000 total compensation
President New Mexico Bank & Trust, R. Greg Leyendecker
Vice Chairman; Chairman Dubuque Bank & Trust, Mark C. Falb, age 64
Vice Chairman Heartland and Dubuque Bank and Trust; Director Citizens Finance, Thomas L. Flynn, age 56
President Heartland Business Bank, Kevin Tenpas
VP Corporate Secretary and Transfer Agent, Lois K. Pearce
President and CEO Galena State Bank & Trust, Andrew E. (Drew) Townsend
President First Community Bank, James (Jim) Hankes
President Riverside Community Bank, Willard C. (Bill) Brenner
Chairman and President Wisconsin Community Bank, Thomas J. (Tom) Wilkinson
President and CEO Arizona Bank & Trust, William F. (Bill) Frank
SVP Human Resources Heartland Financial and Dubuque Bank & Trust, Nancy Wilson
President and CEO Rocky Mountain Bank, Danny T. Skarda
SVP Chief Accounting Officer, Janet M. Quick
VP General Counsel and Assistant Corporate Secretary, David J. (Dave) Kapler
SVP Finance, Jacquie M. Manternach
Chairman First Community Bank, John H. Smith
Chairman Galena State Bank & Trust, Jerry L. Murdock
Chairman Riverside Community Bank, Dan G. Loescher
Chairman Rocky Mountain Bank, Don E. Fraley
SVP and Cashier Arizona Bank & Trust, Richard Nyborg
Branch President Plains Branch Rocky Mountain Bank, Jim Jacobs
Operations Officer Stevensville Branch Rocky Mountain Bank, Linda Kamrath
Branch President Plentywood Branch Rocky Mountain Bank, Bill McCoy
Operations Officer Plentywood Branch Rocky Mountain Bank, Joni Brensdal
Operations Officer Whitehall Branch Rocky Mountain Bank, Pam Smith
Branch President Kalispell Branch Rocky Mountain Bank, Tom Lund
Branch President Bozeman Branch Rocky Mountain Bank, Jim Powell
President Summit Bank & Trust, John P. Carmichael
Chairman New Mexico Bank & Trust, Nadyne C. Bicknell
Chairman Summit Bank & Trust, James R. Hill
EVP and CIO of Heartland; SVP of Dubuque Bank and Trust Company, Melvin E. Miller, age 69
Executive Vice President Wealth Management, Bruce J. Rehmke
SVP Information Services, Marti A. Vandemore
Chairman Minnesota Bank & Trust, Steven M. Thul
President Citizens Finance Co., Al H. Green
EVP Commercial Sales, Frank Walter
Senior Vice President Senior General Counsel, Michael Coyle
EVP Marketing and Sales of Heartland, John J. Berg, age 60
EVP Operations, Brian J. Fox
Senior Vice President Treasury Management, Stephanie Ihbe
EVP CFO COO Treasurer and Director; Vice Chairman Dubuque Bank & Trust Galena State Bank & Trust First Community Bank and Riverside Community Bank; Treasurer Citizens Finance, John K. Schmidt, age 52
Vice Chairman; Chairman Dubuque Bank & Trust, Mark C. Falb, age 64
Director, John W. Cox Jr., age 64
Director, James F. Conlan, age 48
Vice Chairman Heartland and Dubuque Bank and Trust; Director Citizens Finance, Thomas L. Flynn, age 56
Director, James R. Hill, age 60
Auditors: KPMGLLP

LOCATIONS

HQ: Heartland Financial USA Inc.
1398 Central Ave., Dubuque IA 52001
Phone: 563-589-2100 **Fax:** 563-589-2011
Web: www.htlf.com

PRODUCTS/OPERATIONS

2011 Sales

	$ mil.	% of total
Interest		
Loans & leases including fees	149	60
Securities & other	42	17
Noninterest		
Service charges & fees	14	6
Gain on trading account securities	13	5
Gains on sales of loans	11	5
Trust fees	9	4
Loan servicing	5	2
Brokerage & insurance commissions	3	1
Other	1	-
Total	**251**	**100**

Selected Subsidiaries

Arizona Bank & Trust
Citizens Finance Co. (consumer lending)
Dubuque Bank and Trust (IA)
  DB&T Insurance Inc.
  DB&T Community Development Corp.
First Community Bank (IA)
Galena State Bank & Trust Co. (IL)
New Mexico Bank & Trust
Minnesota Bank & Trust (80%)
Riverside Community Bank (IL)
Rocky Mountain Bank (MT)
Summit Bank & Trust (87% CO)
Wisconsin Community Bank

COMPETITORS

Associated Banc-Corp
Bank of America
Bank of the West
Compass Bancshares
First Banks
U.S. Bancorp
Wells Fargo
Zions Bancorporation

HISTORICAL FINANCIALS

Company Type: Public

Income Statement

FYE: December 31

	ASSETS ($ mil.)	NET INCOME ($ mil.)	INCOME AS % OF ASSETS	EMPLOYEES
12/11	4,305	28	0.7%	1,195
12/10	3,999	23	0.6%	1,066
12/09	4,012	6	0.2%	1,001
12/08	3,630	11	0.3%	1,028
12/07	3,264	25	0.8%	982
Annual Growth	7.2%	2.3%	—	5.0%

2011 Year-End Financials

Debt ratio: 8.79%
Return on equity: 8.01%
Cash ($ mil.): 130
Current ratio: —
Long-term debt ($ mil.): 378
No. of shares (mil.): 16
Dividends
  Yield: —
  Payout: 32.52%
Market value ($ mil.): 253

	STOCK PRICE ($) FY Close	P/E High/Low		PER SHARE ($) Earnings	Dividends	Book Value
12/11	15.34	15	10	1.23	0.00	21.24
12/10	17.46	18	12	1.13	0.40	20.04
12/09	14.35	297	122	0.07	0.40	19.10
12/08	20.59	37	25	0.68	0.40	18.78
12/07	18.57	18	11	1.54	0.37	14.04
Annual Growth	(4.7%)	—	—	(5.5%)	—	10.9%

Heinz (H.J.) Co.

Forget those original 57 varieties. H. J. Heinz now has thousands of products. One of the world's largest food companies Heinz produces ketchup and other condiments soups sauces frozen foods beans pasta meals infant food and other processed food products. Its flagship product is ketchup of course and the company dominates the US ketchup market. Heinz's customers include food retailers the foodservice industry and the US military. Its leading brands include its namesake ketchup Lea & Perrins Worcestershire sauce Classico pasta sauces Ore-Ida frozen potatoes and its Boston Market T.G.I. Friday's and Weight Watchers frozen foods.

HISTORY

In 1852 8-year-old Henry J. Heinz started selling produce from the family garden to neighbors in Sharpsburg Pennsylvania. The young entrepreneur formed a partnership with his friend L. C. Noble in 1869 bottling horseradish sauce in clear glass but the business went bankrupt in 1875. The following year with the help of his brother John and his cousin Frederick Heinz created F. & J. Heinz; the enterprise developed ketchup (1876) and sweet pickles (1880). He gained financial control of the firm in 1888 and changed the name to the H. J. Heinz Company.

Heinz developed a reputation as an advertising and marketing genius. He introduced pickle pins a popular promotion at the 1893 Chicago World's Fair; coined the catchy "57 Varieties" slogan in 1897 (despite already having 60 products); and in 1900 raised New York City's first large electric advertising sign (a 40-foot pickle). By 1905 Heinz was manufacturing food products in the UK.

After Heinz's death in 1919 the business under the direction of his son and later his grandson continued to rely on its traditional product lines for the next four decades although some new ones were introduced such as baby food in 1931. The company went public in 1946.

Heinz changed its strategy in 1958 when it made its first acquisition a Dutch food processor. Major purchases that followed included StarKist (tuna and pet food 1963) and Ore-Ida (potatoes 1965). In 1966 Burt Gookin became CEO the first nonfamily-member to hold that position.

The company bought Weight Watchers in 1978. The next year former rugby star Anthony O'Reilly became the company's fifth CEO. He intensified the focus on international expansion and presided over a string of acquisitions throughout the 1980s. O'Reilly became chairman in 1987.

Acquisitions in the 1990s included Wattie's Limited (New Zealand 1992); Borden's foodservice business (1994); and pet food divisions from Quaker Oats (1995). However faced with weak sales growth in its stable markets in 1997 Heinz began shedding domestic units as it made global acquisitions. It sold its Ore-Ida foodservice operations (to McCain Foods 1997) and its bakery products division (Pillsbury 1998) but purchased John West Foods (UK tuna 1997) and Sonnen Basserman (Germany convenience meals 1998).

William Johnson who had turned around stagnant brands such as 9-Lives succeeded O'Reilly as CEO in 1998. In 1999 Heinz announced a restructuring intended to eliminate jobs and close or sell about 20 factories over several years. Heinz sold the diet business of Weight Watchers and seeking greater access to the US natural foods market purchased nearly 20% of The Hain Celestial Group.

In 2000 Heinz acquired International DiverseFoods (foodservice condiments) and Alden Merrell (frozen desserts). Also that year O'Reilly retired and Johnson was named chairman.

Heinz continued with global acquisitions during 2001 while at the same time being picky with its food back home. It sold its Budget Gourmet frozen entree business to rival Luigino's and then lapped up pasta sauce and soup businesses from Borden Foods. Overseas Heinz acquired CSM's food products division making it the #2 food maker in the Benelux countries and expanded into Central America by purchasing Productos Columbia and Distribuidora Banquete (makers of the Banquete brand of ketchup sauces and condiments). The company also purchased US-based Delimex Holdings (frozen Mexican foods) as well as the Poppers and T.G.I. Friday's lines of frozen appetizers from Anchor Food Products.

In an effort to focus on its core food products (sauces ketchup frozen foods) Heinz spun off a number of its North American businesses to Del Monte Foods in 2002. The all-stock transaction included the company's pet food (Kibbles 'n Bits) and snacks tuna (StarKist) private-label soup and infant feeding (Nature's Goodness) businesses. The divestitures totaled 20% of Heinz's revenues but the company gained a 75% stake in Del Monte.

Furthering expansion in China Heinz purchased Meiweiyuan Food Corp. (flavoring) along with Meiweiyuan Food Factory and Fanyu Jinmai Food Factory (food processing) in 2002. Keeping up with the health-food-Joneses it introduced Heinz organic ketchup that year.

In 2003 the company announced the restructuring of its North American operations into two units: Away from Home (restaurant and on-the-go eating businesses) and Consumer Products (ketchup condiments sauces and frozen meals and snacks). Also in 2003 the company's foodservice division acquired Truesoups a premium frozen soup maker.

The next year the company bought Canadian foodservice sauce and salad-dressing maker Unifine Richardson and sold its frozen-food brands Ethnic Gourmet and Rosetto to Hain. It also sold its Northern Europe bakery business that year. The next year Heinz's foodservice division bought frozen hors d'oeuvres company Appetizers And Inc. and Nancy's Specialty Foods.

Heinz also acquired a majority stake in Russian condiment and margarine maker Petrosoyuz and the HP Foods Group from Groupe Danone in 2005. The HP group (for which Heinz paid $820 million in cash) included Lea & Perrins HP and Amoy Asian sauces. In addition the company opened a new product-development and technical-assistance center consolidating all of its R&D in one place.

Heinz said that in order to focus on its core business (ketchup and sauces meals and snacks and infant nutrition) in 2006 it sold its 16% interest in Hain Celestial and its New Zealand poultry operations Tegel Foods to Pacific Equity Partners for $165 million.

In a continuing effort to concentrate on its core business that year Heinz also sold the ethnic foods sector of Lea & Perrins maker HP Foods (which it acquired the year before and which supplies products to the Chinese Indian and Thai restaurant sectors under the brand names Cathay Dynasty Green Dragon Lotus and Rajah) to Associated British Foods for an undisclosed sum. Later in 2006 Heinz sold its European seafood business to Lehman Brothers Merchant Banking for $506 million. The brands involved in the seafood sale include the canned-tuna brands Mareblu (in Italy) John West (the UK Ireland and the Netherlands) and Petit Navire (France). Continuing to shed noncore operations Heinz sold its UK chilled prepared foods business (including the Linda McCartney brand of frozen vegetarian entrees) to Hain Celestial.

Heinz announced changes in 2006 to its corporate governance policy as a result of its proxy battle with dissident shareholders led by Peltz's Trian Fund. The changes which Heinz disclosed after discussions with CalPERS and other large Heinz shareholders included adding two independent board members and the adoption of a majority voting process with regard to the election of directors.

After many Heinz and Trian press-release statements back and forth and much press surrounding the bitter struggle between Peltz and Heinz leadership it was announced that Heinz's board elected to add two of Trian's five nominees to its board: Peltz and Michael Weinstein. Heinz quietly announced the results as being a chance to increase shareholder value; Trian touted the results as a "big victory for Heinz shareholders."

Despite wrangling in the boardroom Heinz continued acquisitions with the $68 million purchase in 2007 of Canadian maker of dressings and sauces Renee's Gourmet Foods.

During 2008 it acquired the license to the Cottee's and Rose's branded jams jellies and toppings business in Australia and New Zealand for about $58 million. It also bought the remaining interest in its Shanghai LongFong Foods operation for approximately $18 million in cash and $15 million of deferred consideration. The company added the Wyko sauce business in the Netherlands in 2008 as well paying approximately $66 million for it. Later that year it purchased Benedicta a French manufacturer of tabletop sauces mayonnaises and salad dressings. It also acquired Golden Circle Australian maker of canned foods juices and baby food for some $196 million that year.

Also in 2008 the company sold its noncore private-label frozen dessert operations in the UK to Polestar Foods. The sale included the Heinz Ross American Dream and Devonshire brands and a co-packing agreement to produce Weight Watchers desserts in the UK. It also sold off frozen hors d'oeuvres unit Appetizers And which had been part of the company's US foodservice operations.

EXECUTIVES

Chairman President and CEO, William R. (Bill) Johnson, age 63, $1,245,211 total compensation

EVP Rest of World Global Enterprise Risk Management and Global Infant and Nutrition, Michael D. (Mike) Milone, age 55, $582,759 total compensation

EVP and General Counsel, Theodore N. (Ted) Bobby, age 61

SVP Corporate Audit, Diane B. Owen, age 56

SVP Business Development, Mitchell A. (Mitch) Ring, age 60

EVP and CFO, Arthur B. (Art) Winkleblack, age 55, $622,605 total compensation

SVP Finance, Edward J. (Ed) McMenamin, age 56

President US Foodservice, Brendan Foley

Corporate Secretary, Rene Biedzinski

Area Director Latin America and Caribbean, Fernando Pocaterra

SVP Corporate & Government Affairs, Michael Mullen, age 43

EVP President and CEO Heinz North America, C. Scott O'Hara, age 51, $618,621 total compensation

Director of UK Corporate and Government Affairs UK and Ireland, Nigel Dickie
Chief Supply Chain Officer, Robert P. (Bob) Ostryniec, age 51
EVP; President and CEO Heinz Europe, David C. (Dave) Moran, age 54, $648,506 total compensation
President and CEO Heinz Canada, Peter Luik
EVP Heinz Asia Pacific, Christopher (Chris) Warmoth, age 53
EVP Heinz North America, David Woodward, age 47
VP and Chief People Officer, Stephen S. (Steve) Clark, age 44
President Eastern Europe, Daniel G. (Dan) Milich
SVP Investor Relations and Global Program Management Officer, Margaret R. (Meg) Nollen, age 49
Manager Communications and Corporate Affairs Canada, Joan Patterson
President Heinz Continental Europe, Roel van Neerbos
VP European Technical Services and Chief Quality Officer, Andy Keatings
Regional CEO New Zealand Japan Korea and Papua New Guinea, Nigel Comer
President Global Infant and Nutrition, Stefano Clini
Group Leader Public Relations and Communications, Jessica Jackson
Manager Public Relations, Tracey Parsons
Director Communications Italy, Antonio Cartolari
Director Corporate Communications and KCS Category Director Netherlands, Peter Boterman
External Affairs Manager Netherlands, Hein Kroft
Manager Corporate Affairs Wattie's/Australia, Jessica Ramsden
Director Corporate Affairs China, Alice Wang
Senior Manager Public Relations Japan, Akemi Tahara
Chairman and Managing Director Heinz India, Nellaiappan Thiruambalam
Regional CEO Heinz ASEAN, Nilesh Patel
Chief Supply Chain Officer Europe Africa and Middle East, Christophe Muller
Managing Director Heinz Russia, Vadim Fomichev
Manager Shareholder Relations, Amy Beck
Public Relations Manager Poland, Katarzyna Gospodarek
VP Corporate Governance Compliance and Ethics, John Kraus
CIO, Isobel Thomson
VP Global Ketchup Health and Wellness and Marketing Development, Mike Pretty
President Global Wal-Mart Business, Wayne Callahan
Public Relations Mexico and Venezuela, Maria Gimenez
Director Investor Relations and Market Analysis, Mary Ann Bell
VP Strategic Partnerships and Chief Strategy Officer, Kristen Clark
Director, Dean R. O'Hare, age 70
Director, Charles E. (Chuck) Bunch, age 63
Director, John G. (Jack) Drosdick, age 69
Director, Nelson Peltz, age 70
Director, Thomas J. Usher, age 69
Director, Candace Kendle, age 65
Director, Dennis H. Reilley, age 59
Director, Michael F. (Mike) Weinstein, age 63
Director, Edith E. (Ede) Holiday, age 60
Director, Leonard S. Coleman Jr., age 63
Director, Lynn C. Swann, age 60
Auditors: PricewaterhouseCoopersLLP

LOCATIONS

HQ: H. J. Heinz Company
1 PPG Place Ste. 3100, Pittsburgh PA 15222-5448
Phone: 412-456-5700 **Fax:** 412-456-6128
Web: www.heinz.com

2011 Sales

	$ mil.	% of total
US	3,991	37
UK	1,506	14
Other	5,208	49
Total	**10,706**	**100**

PRODUCTS/OPERATIONS

2011 Sales

	$ mil.	% of total
Ketchups & sauces	4,608	43
Meals & snacks	4,282	40
Infant/nutrition	1,175	11
Other	640	6
Total	**10,706**	**100**

Selected Brands

Asia/Pacific
- ABC
- Bruno
- Chef
- Classico
- Complan
- Cottee' s (licensed)
- Craig' s
- Farley' s
- Glucon D
- Golden Circle
- Gourmet
- Greenseas
- Hamper
- Heinz
- Hellaby
- HP
- La Bonne Cuisine
- Lea & Perrins
- LongFong
- Master Weijixian
- Nurture
- Nycil
- Ore-Ida
- Rose' s (licensed)
- SinSin
- Tom Piper
- Wattie' s
- Weight Watchers (licensed)
- Winna

Europe
- Amoy (licensed)
- Aproten
- Aunt Bessie (licensed)
- Benedicta
- Bi-Aglut
- Brinta
- Daddies
- De Ruijter
- Derevenskoye
- Dieterba
- Farex
- Farley' s
- Heinz
- Honig
- HP
- Karvan Cevitam
- Lea & Perrins
- Mechta Hoziajki
- Moya Semya
- Mum' s Own
- Nipiol
- Orlando
- Picador
- Plasmon
- Pudliszki
- Roosvicee
- Ross
- Sonnen Bassermann
- Squeezme!
- Venz
- Weight Watchers (licensed)
- Wyko

North America
- Alden Merrell
- Arthur' s Fresh
- Bagel Bites
- Bella Rossa
- Boston Market (licensed)
- Bravo
- Catelli (licensed)
- Chef Francisco
- Classico
- Delimex
- Diana
- Dianne' s
- Escalon
- Heinz Bell ' Orto
- Heinz
- HP
- Jack Daniel' s (licensed)
- Lea & Perrins
- Nancy' s
- Ore-Ida
- Poppers
- PPI
- Quality Chef Foods
- Renee' s Gourmet
- Tater Tots
- T.G.I. Friday' s (licensed)
- Todd' s
- Truesoups
- Weight Watchers (licensed)
- Wyler' s

Rest of the world
- Banquete
- Classico
- Complan
- Farley' s
- Heinz
- HP
- Lea & Perrins
- Mama' s
- Today
- Wattie' s
- Wellington' s

COMPETITORS

Associated British Foods
B&G Foods
Barilla
Beech-Nut
Bellisio Foods
Campbell Soup
COFCO
ConAgra
Del Monte Foods
Frito-Lay
Gerber Products
Hain Celestial
Indofood
J & J Snack Foods
Jenny Craig
John Sanfilippo & Son
La Doria
McIlhenny
Mondelez International
Nestle
New Dragon
Nutrisystem
Otis Spunkmeyer
Pepperidge Farm
PepsiCo
Ralcorp
Sara Lee North American Retail
Slim-Fast
Smucker
Snyder' s-Lance
Uni-President
URC

HISTORICAL FINANCIALS

Company Type: Public

Income Statement FYE: April 29

	REVENUE ($ mil.)	NET INCOME ($ mil.)	NET PROFIT MARGIN	EMPLOYEES
04/12	11,649	923	7.9%	32,200
04/11	10,706	989	9.2%	34,800
04/10	10,494	864	8.2%	29,600
04/09	10,148	923	9.1%	32,400
04/08	10,070	844	8.4%	32,500
Annual Growth	3.7%	2.2%	—	(0.2%)

2012 Year-End Financials

Debt ratio: 41.95%
Return on equity: 33.46%
Cash ($ mil.): 1,330
Current ratio: 146.61
Long-term debt ($ mil.): 4,779

No. of shares (mil.): 320
Dividends
Yield: —
Payout: 67.37%
Market value ($ mil.): 17,023

	STOCK PRICE ($) FY Close	P/E High/Low		PER SHARE ($) Earnings	Dividends	Book Value
04/12	53.16	19	17	2.85	0.00	8.62
04/11	51.23	17	14	3.06	1.80	9.68
04/10	45.76	17	12	2.71	1.68	5.95
04/09	33.99	18	10	2.90	1.66	3.88
04/08	47.03	18	16	2.63	1.52	6.06
Annual Growth	3.1%	—	—	2.0%	—	9.2%

Hershey Company (The)

The Hershey Company works to bring you Almond Joy and lots of Kisses. The company makes such well-known chocolate and candy brands as Hershey's Kisses Reese's peanut butter cups Twizzlers licorice and under license Mounds candy bar York peppermint pattie and Kit Kat wafer bar. Hershey also makes grocery goods including baking chocolate chocolate syrup cocoa mix cookies snack nuts breath mints and bubble gum. Products from the chocolate king are sold to wholesale distributors and retailers of all kind throughout North America and exported overseas. The Hershey Trust –which benefits the Milton Hershey School for disadvantaged children –controls approximately 80% of Hershey's voting power.

HISTORY

The Hershey Company is the legacy of Milton Hershey of Pennsylvania Dutch origin. Apprenticed in 1872 at age 15 to a candy maker Hershey started Lancaster Caramel Company at age 30. In 1893 at the Chicago Exposition he saw a new chocolate-making machine and in 1900 he sold the caramel operations for $1 million to start a chocolate factory.

The factory was completed in 1905 in Derry Church Pennsylvania and renamed Hershey Foods the next year. Chocolate Kisses individually hand-wrapped in silver foil were introduced in 1907. Two years later the candy man founded the Milton Hershey School an orphanage; the company was donated to a trust in 1918 and for years existed solely to fund the school. Although Hershey went public in 1927 the school still controls the majority of shareholder votes.

The candy company pioneered mass-production techniques for chocolates and developed much of the machinery for making and packaging its own products. At one time Hershey supplied its own sugar cane from Cuba and enlarged the world's almond supply six fold through nut farm ownership. The Hershey bar became so universally familiar that it was used overseas during WWII as currency. Milton refused to advertise believing that quality would speak for itself. Even after his death in 1945 the company continued his policy. Then in 1970 facing a sluggish candy market and a diet-conscious public the company lost share to Mars and management relented.

During the 1960s and 1970s Hershey diversified in order to stabilize the effects of changing commodity prices. The company got into the pasta business with its 1966 purchase of San Giorgio Macaroni and it bought the Friendly Ice Cream chain in 1979 (sold 1988). The company expanded candy operations by bringing out large-sized bars (1980) and buying Cadbury's US candy business (Peter Paul Cadbury Caramello; 1988).

In 1990 Hershey formed a joint venture with Fujiya to distribute Hershey products in Japan and bought Ronzoni's pasta cheese and sauce operations. Kenneth Wolfe was named chairman and CEO in 1994.

Hershey boosted its presence in the non-chocolate candy market with acquisitions of Henry Heide (1995) and the North American operations of Leaf (Good & Plenty Jolly Rancher) from Finnish candy maker Huhtamaki Oyj (1996). In return it sold Huhtamaki Oyj its struggling European confectionery interests.

In 1999 the company sold its pasta business to New World Pasta for $450 million and a 6% interest in that company. Also that year the Hershey Trust wanting to diversify its holdings sold $100 million of its stock to Hershey. Business melted during the fall of 1999 when a new company-wide computer system delayed orders during the critical Halloween season. The glitches cost the company more than $100 million in lost sales.

Hershey bought Nabisco Holdings' breath freshener mints and gum businesses (including the Breath Savers Care*Free and Fruit Stripe brands) for about $135 million in 2000.

In 2001 Nabisco veteran Rick Lenny replaced Wolfe as CEO. Hershey established a manufacturing presence in South America that year by acquiring the chocolate and confectionery business of Brazilian company Visagis. It also cut about 400 salaried positions and closing three plants and a distribution facility.

In 2002 Wolfe retired as chairman and Lenny was selected to replace him. Also that year Hershey settled a bitter six-week factory-worker strike the longest in company history. It subsequently sold its non-chocolate Heide brands (Heide Jujyfruits Wunderbeans Amazin' Fruit) to Farley's & Sathers Candy Company.

Also in 2002 the Hershey Trust said that to diversify its holdings it wanted to sell its 77% interest in Hershey. However the sale was temporarily blocked while the state of Pennsylvania reviewed the impact it would have on the community. Despite the injunction against the sale the trust continued to look for a buyer and was considering a $12.5 billion offer from chewing gum giant Wm. Wrigley Jr. and a $10.5 billion joint offer from Nestle and Cadbury Schweppes.

Amid the community outcry and legal wrangling the sale was finally called off later in 2002 after 10 of the trust's 17 members changed their minds. Due to the uproar surrounding the proposed sale the trust board promised to restructure itself. Among the outgoing board members was William Lepley president and chief executive of the Milton Hershey School.

Due to sharply rising cocoa prices in 2003 Hershey implemented an approximate 3% price increase across its entire domestic product line. It also sold some of its gum brands (Fruit Stripe Rain-Blo and Super Bubble) to Farley & Sathers that year.

The company began marketing sugar-free chocolates (sweetened with lactitol) in its Hershey and Reese's lines in 2003. The company also introduced the first permanent addition to its Kisses brand in 10 years –a dark chocolate version of the familiar treat named Rich Dark Chocolates and wrapped in purple foil. Later that year it introduced a line of sugar-free chocolates; and (the unsuccessful and now discontinued) Swoops chocolate "potato chips" shaped like Pringles and packaged in a canister reminiscent of the Pringles can.

In order to expand its sales in the Hispanic market in 2004 Hershey announced a new line of Latin-inspired candies including those with chili-based flavors and dulce de leche fillings. The company also signed an endorsement deal with Latin singer Thalia. And in 2004 Hershey's Mexican subsidiary bought one of Mexico's top confectionery companies Grupo Lorena. Also that year it acquired Mauna Loa Macadamia Nut Corporation from The Shansby Group for approximately $112 million in cash and $18 million in assumed debt.

The company changed its name to The Hershey Company in 2005 dropping the "Foods" from its name in order to reflect the company's move away from coffee pasta and restaurant businesses and its concentration on confectionery. In addition Hershey acquired Scharffen Berger Chocolate Maker in 2005 a maker of premium dark chocolates. The deal marked Hershey's first foray into the premium chocolate market. Later that year it acquired its second high-end chocolate company Joseph Schmidt Confections. Both companies are located in California.

With continuuing increases in raw materials in 2006 the company began to reduce the total number of its products by up to 25% eliminating limited-edition and seasonal items and streamlining underperforming brands. It put its efforts toward expansion in its high-growth categories such as organic chocolate dark chocolate cookies and nuts; in addition it purchased organic chocolate confectioner Dagoba that year.

President and CEO Richard Lenny left the company in 2007 having been at Hershey's helm since 2001. It is generally thought that Lenny's resignation was due to disagreements between him and the trust regarding the company's business strategies. CFO David J. West was named as Lenny's successor as president and CEO. Wolfe (a former Hershey CEO) was tapped as chairman.

The company formed a joint venture with South Korean confectioner Lotte in 2007 to manufacture and sell Hershey's products in China. Continuing to expand its geographical reach that year Hershey acquired a 51% interest in the food and beverage operations of the Indian conglomerate Godrej Industries for $54 million. The purchase was made for the purpose of distributing Hershey's products in India (one of Asia's fastest growing markets). It did not hurt that Godrej owns Nutrine India's most popular confectionery brand.

In another 2007 move Hershey and Barry Callebaut formed an R&D and supply partnership. Under the terms of the agreement the companies combined their research and development activities in the areas of new products premium chocolate health and wellness and ingredients. In addition Barry Callebaut supplies Hershey's Mexican production plant chocolate –at least 88000 tons per year.

In 2011 David West stepped down as CEO replaced by John P. Bilbrey who joined Hershey in 2003.

EXECUTIVES

SVP and CIO, George F. Davis, age 63

President CEO and Director, John P. (J.P.) Bilbrey, age 56, $550,000 total compensation
SVP and Chief Growth Officer, Michele G. Buck, age 50, $430,000 total compensation
SVP General Counsel and Secretary, Burton H. (Burt) Snyder, age 64, $485,000 total compensation
VP and Chief Accounting Officer, David W. Tacka, age 58
SVP and Chief Commercial Officer, D. Michael Wege, age 49
SVP and Chief Human Resources Officer, Kevin R. Walling, age 46
Chairman, James E. Nevels, age 60
EVP CFO and Chief Administrative Officer, Humberto P. (Bert) Alfonso, $500,000 total compensation
VP Investor Relations, Mark K. Pogharian
SVP Global Operations, Terence L. O'Day, age 62, $450,000 total compensation
VP Public Affairs, Andy McCormick
Director, David L. Shedlarz, age 63
President CEO and Director, John P. (J.P.) Bilbrey, age 56
Director, Robert F. Cavanaugh, age 53
Director, Thomas J. (Tom) Ridge, age 66
Director, Anthony J. (Tony) Palmer, age 52
Director, Charles A. Davis, age 63
Director, James M. Mead, age 66
Director, Pamela M. Arway, age 58
Auditors: KPMGLLP

LOCATIONS

HQ: The Hershey Company
100 Crystal A Dr., Hershey PA 17033
Phone: 717-534-4200 **Fax:** 650-857-5518
Web: www.hp.com

2012 Sales

	% of total
US	84
Other	16
Total	**100**

PRODUCTS/OPERATIONS

Selected Mergers and Acquisitions

FY2012
- Brookside Foods ($172.9 million Canadian chocolate and fruit maker)

FY2009
- Van Houten Singapore

Selected Brands

Confectionery
- Hershey' s
  - Air Delight
  - Bliss
  - Cookies N' Creme
  - Drops
  - Extra dark
  - Hugs
  - Milk chocolate
  - Miniatures
  - Nuggets
  - Pot of Gold
  - Sugar free
- Kisses
  - Air Delight
  - Milk chocolates
  - Special Dark
- Reese' s
  - Big Cup
  - Fast Break
  - Nutrageous
  - Peanut butter cups
  - Pieces
  - Reesesticks
  - Sugar free
  - Wafer bars
  - Whipps
- Other
  - 5th Avenue
  - Almond Joy (worldwide license from Cadbury)
  - Cadbury (USA license from Cadbury)
  - Caramello (USA license from Cadbury)
  - Chipits (Canada)
  - Eat More (Canada)
  - Glosette (Canada)
  - Godrej (India)
  - Good & Plenty (worldwide license from Huhtamaki)
  - Heath (worldwide license from Huhtamaki)
  - IO-IO (Brazil)
  - Jolly Rancher (worldwide license from Huhtamaki)
  - Kit Kat (US license from Nestle)
  - Milk Duds (worldwide license from Huhtamaki)
  - Mounds (worldwide license from Cadbury)
  - Mr. Goodbar
  - Nutrine (India)
  - Oh Henry! (Canada)
  - Payday (worldwide license from Huhtamaki)
  - Pelon Pelo Rico (Mexico)
  - Pot Of Gold
  - Rolo (US license from Nestle)
  - Scharffen Berger
  - Skor
  - Special Dark
  - Symphony
  - Take5
  - Thingamajig
  - Twizzlers
  - Van Houten (under license in Asia and the Middle East)
  - Whatchamacallit
  - Whoppers (worldwide license from Huhtamaki)
  - York (worldwide license from Cadbury)
  - Zagnut
  - Zero

Food and beverage enhancers
- Bake Shoppe
- Goodnight Hugs
- Goodnight Kisses
- Granola Bars
- Toppings

Pantry items
- Heath
- Hershey' s
- Hershey' s Bliss
- Reese' s
- Scharffen Berger

Premium products
- Dagoba natural and organic chocolate
- Scharffen Berger high-cacao dark chocolate

Refreshment products
- Breath Savers
- Bubble Yum
- Ice Breakers

Snack products
- Hershey' s 100 calorie bars
- Mauna Loa macadamia snack nuts

COMPETITORS

Annabelle Candy
Anthony-Thomas Candy
Asher' s Chocolates
Betsy Ann Candies
Chase General
Chocolates a la Carte
Chupa Chups
Endangered Species Chocolate
Enstrom
Farley' s & Sathers
Fazer Konfektyr
Ferrero
Flowers Foods
Ghirardelli Chocolate
Godiva Chocolatier
Goetze' s Candy
Guittard
Harry London Candies
Hostess Brands
Jelly Belly Candy
Kellogg
Laura Secord
Lindt & Sprungli
Mars Incorporated
Mondelez International
Nestle
Otis Spunkmeyer
Perfetti Van Melle
Purdy' s Chocolates
Rocky Mountain Chocolate
Russell Stover
See' s Candies
Smucker
Spangler Candy
Sweet Shop USA
Tootsie Roll
Warrell Corporation
World' s Finest Chocolate
Wrigley
Zachary Confections

HISTORICAL FINANCIALS

Company Type: Public

Income Statement FYE: December 31

	REVENUE ($ mil.)	NET INCOME ($ mil.)	NET PROFIT MARGIN	EMPLOYEES
12/11	6,080	628	10.3%	13,800
12/10	5,671	509	9.0%	13,500
12/09	5,298	435	8.2%	13,700
12/08	5,132	311	6.1%	14,400
12/07	4,946	214	4.3%	12,800
Annual Growth	5.3%	30.9%	—	1.9%

2011 Year-End Financials

Debt ratio: 42.79%
Return on equity: 74.08%
Cash ($ mil.): 693
Current ratio: 174.36
Long-term debt ($ mil.): 1,748
No. of shares (mil.): 225
Dividends
Yield: —
Payout: 50.36%
Market value ($ mil.): 13,913

	STOCK PRICE ($) FY Close	P/E High/Low		PER SHARE ($) Earnings	Dividends	Book Value
12/11	61.78	22	16	2.74	0.00	3.77
12/10	47.15	23	16	2.21	1.28	3.97
12/09	35.79	21	16	1.90	1.19	3.16
12/08	34.74	30	23	1.36	1.19	1.40
12/07	39.40	59	40	0.93	1.14	2.61
Annual Growth	11.9%	—	—	31.0%	—	9.6%

Hertz Global Holdings Inc

If you've ever said "Don't worry about it it's just a rental" guess who hurts: Hertz a world leader in car rental. On its own and through agents and licensees Hertz operates some 8800 rental locations in about 150 countries worldwide. The US is home to about 2360 of Hertz's staffed rental sites of which about 70% are at airports. Its fleet includes approximately 444000 cars from Ford General Motors Toyota and other manufacturers. Car rental accounts for about 85% of its sales. Hertz also rents a variety of heavy equipment through about 315 locations in North America Europe and China. Not to be left at the curb Hertz is investing in electric and hybrid vehicles as well as car sharing.

HISTORY

In 1918 22-year-old John Jacobs opened a Chicago car rental business with 12 Model T Fords that he had repaired. By 1923 when Yellow Cab entrepreneur John Hertz bought Jacobs' business it had revenues of about $1 million. Jacobs continued as top executive of the company renamed Hertz Drive-Ur-Self System. Three years later General Motors acquired the company when it bought Yellow Truck from John Hertz. Hertz introduced the first car rental charge card in 1926 opened its first airport location at Chicago's Midway Airport in 1932 and initiated the first one-way (rent-it-here/leave-it-there) plan in 1933. The company expanded into Canada in 1938 and Europe in 1950.

Omnibus bought Hertz from GM in 1953 sold its bus interests and focused on vehicle leasing and renting. The next year Omnibus changed its name to The Hertz Corporation and was listed on the NYSE. Also in 1954 the company purchased Metropolitan Distributors a New York-based truck leasing firm. In 1961 Hertz began operations in South America.

The company formed its Hertz Equipment Rental subsidiary in 1965. RCA bought Hertz two years later but allowed the company to maintain its board of directors and management. In 1972 it introduced the first frequent traveler's club the #1 Club which allowed the rental location to prepare a rental agreement before the customer arrived at the counter. Three years later Hertz began defining the company's image through TV commercials featuring former football star O. J. Simpson running through airports. (Hertz canceled Simpson's contract in 1994 after his arrest on murder charges –the TV ads had stopped in 1992.) Frank Olson became CEO in 1977 after serving in the same position at United Airlines.

United Airlines bought Hertz from RCA in 1985 then sold it in 1987 for $1.3 billion to Park Ridge which had been formed by Hertz management and Ford Motor specifically for the purchase. (Hertz was Ford's largest customer.) In 1988 Ford which held 80% of Park Ridge sold 20% to Volvo North America for $100 million. (Ford later reduced its stake to 49% when it sold shares to Volvo.) Also that year Hertz sold its stock in the Hertz Penske truck leasing joint venture for $85.5 million and issued Penske a license to use its name.

Ford bought all the shares of Hertz it didn't already own in 1994. The next year it formed a unit to provide replacement cars for insurance companies. Taking advantage of heightened investor interest in rental car companies (stemming in part from the purchases of some competitors) Ford sold 17% of Hertz to the public in 1997.

Hertz acquired several equipment rental companies in 1998 including the Boireau Group (France) and Matthews Equipment (Canada). In 1999 the company's European acquisitions included French car rental franchise SST and German van rental company Yellow Truck. Also in 1999 Hertz created a referral network with Toyota Japan's #1 car dealer.

Olson retired as CEO in 1999 and president Craig Koch was named his successor. The next year Hertz continued its acquisitive trend by purchasing Seattle-based equipment leasing company AA Rentals.

Lackluster performance of Hertz stock in 2001 prompted Ford to pay about $735 million to buy back shares held by the public –once again making the car rental company a wholly owned Ford subsidiary. Also that year Hertz opened about 200 new suburban rental locations. In April 2001 Hertz eliminated commissions for negotiated corporate and government accounts in the US and Canada.

The decline in air travel that followed the terrorist attacks of September 11 2001 hampered Hertz's business during 2001 and 2002. As part of an effort to strengthen its balance sheet and focus on its core automotive manufacturing operations Ford sold Hertz to a group of investment firms –Clayton Dubilier & Rice The Carlyle Group and Merrill Lynch Global Private Equity –in December 2005 for $5.6 billion and nearly $10 billion in assumed debt.

Ford had filed for an IPO of the car rental company in June 2005 but that offering was withdrawn in favor of a new proposed IPO in July 2006. Proceeds of the offering which was completed in November 2006 were to be used to reduce debt –including a $1 billion loan taken out by the company in June 2006 –and to pay an additional dividend to the investment firms.

Koch stepped down as CEO in 2006 after having announced plans in 2005 to do so because of a family medical issue. He was named chairman and Tenneco's Mark Frissora was hired to be CEO of Hertz. Frissora became chairman upon Koch's retirement in January 2007. In July 2007 Hertz acquired Autotravel a UK-based car-rental business for an undisclosed sum. (Autotravel had operated a successful Hertz car and van rental franchise in the North West of England for nearly 30 years.)

Hertz acquired Advantage Rent A Car out of bankruptcy for nearly $33 million in early 2009. Advantage added about 45 rental locations in the US and Europe and more than a dozen affiliates in Latin America and the Caribbean to Hertz's rental network and bolstered its position in the leisure travel market.

In October 2012 HERC acquired Oklahoma-based Pioneer Equipment Rental & Sales with 10 branches in the state and North Texas. In November Hertz completed its hard-won acquisition of Dollar Thrifty Automotive Group which became a wholly-owned subsidiary of the company.

EXECUTIVES

Chairman and CEO; Chairman and CEO Hertz, Mark P. Frissora, age 56, $975,769 total compensation
VP and Treasurer; VP and Treasurer Hertz, R. Scott Massengill, age 49
EVP; President Hertz Equipment Rental Corporation, Lois I. Boyd, age 58
SVP and CIO; SVP and CIO Hertz, Joseph F. (Joe) Eckroth Jr., age 53
EVP; President International, Michel Taride, age 55, $443,367 total compensation
SVP and Chief Marketing Officer; SVP and Chief Marketing Officer Hertz, Michael P. (Mike) Senackerib, age 46
EVP Supply Chain Management; EVP Supply Chain Management Hertz, John A. Thomas, age 47
EVP and CFO; EVP and CFO Hertz, Elyse Douglas, age 55, $474,692 total compensation
SVP and Chief Human Resources Officer; SVP and Chief Human Resources Officer Hertz, LeighAnne G. Baker, age 53
VP Investor Relations, Leslie Hunziker
SVP Global Sales; SVP Global Sales and Marketing Hertz, Robert J. Stuart, age 50
SVP General Counsel and Secretary; SVP General Counsel and Secretary Hertz, J. Jeffrey Zimmerman, age 52, $372,308 total compensation
SVP Finance and Corporate Controller; SVP Finance and Corporate Controller Hertz, Jatindar S. Kapur, age 53
SVP Corporate Affairs and Communications; SVP Corporate Affairs and Communications Hertz, Richard D. Broome, age 53
Acting General Manager Advantage Rent-a-Car, Gary Fulena
EVP; President Car Rental and Leasing The Americas, Scott P. Sider, age 51
President Off-Airport Operations, Kenneth Seavey
VP; General Manager China, Edward Hu
VP Global Procurement; VP Global Procurement Hertz, Todd Poste, age 49
Director, Barry H. Beracha, age 70
Director, Linda F. Levinson, age 71
Director, Nathan K. Sleeper, age 38
Director, George W. Tamke, age 64
Director, David H. Wasserman, age 45
Director, Robert F. End, age 56
Director, Michael J. (Mike) Durham, age 61
Director, Gregory S. Ledford, age 54
Director, Michael F. (Mike) Koehler, age 59
Director, Carl T. Berquist, age 61
Director, Brian A. Bernasek, age 39
Director, Angel L. Morales, age 38
Director, Henry C. Wolf, age 69
Auditors: PricewaterhouseCoopersLLP

LOCATIONS

HQ: Hertz Global Holdings Inc.
225 Brae Blvd., Park Ridge NJ 07656-0713
Phone: 201-307-2000 **Fax:** 201-307-2644
Web: www.hertz.com

2011 Sales by Point of Rental

	% of total
US	
Airport	70
Off-airport	30
Total	100
International	
Airport	56
Off-airport	44
Total	100

2011 Sales

	$ mil.	% of total
US	5,413	65
Other countries	2,885	35
Total	8,298	100

PRODUCTS/OPERATIONS

2011 Sales

	$ mil.	% of total
Car rental	6,929	84
Equipment rental	1,208	14
Other	160	2
Total	8,298	100

2011 Type of Car Rental

	% of total
US	
Leisure	57
Business	43
Total	100
International	
Business	54
Leisure	46
Total	100

Selected Subsidiaries

Dollar Thrifty Automotive Group Inc.
Eileo Inc.
Hertz Equipment Rental Corp.
Hertz Entertainment Services Corp.
Hertz Equipment Rental International
Simply Wheelz LLC (dba Advantage Rent A Car)
The Hertz Corp. (dba Hertz Car Sales Hertz Rent-A-Car)

COMPETITORS

Avis Budget
Caterpillar
Dollar Thrifty Automotive
Enterprise Rent-A-Car
HD Supply
Neff Rental
NES Rentals
RSC Equipment Rental
Sixt
Sunbelt Rentals
United Rentals
Zipcar

HISTORICAL FINANCIALS

Company Type: Public

Income Statement FYE: December 31

	REVENUE ($ mil.)	NET INCOME ($ mil.)	NET PROFIT MARGIN	EMPLOYEES
12/11	8,298	176	2.1%	23,900
12/10	7,562	(48)	—	22,900
12/09	7,101	(126)	—	23,050
12/08	8,525	(1,206)	—	24,900
12/07	8,685	264	3.0%	29,350
Annual Growth	(1.1%)	(9.7%)	—	(5.0%)

2011 Year-End Financials

Debt ratio: 64.03%
Return on equity: 7.88%
Cash ($ mil.): 931
Current ratio: 136.64
Long-term debt ($ mil.): 11,317
No. of shares (mil.): 417
Dividends
Yield: —
Payout: —
Market value ($ mil.): 4,888

	STOCK PRICE ($) FY Close	P/E High/Low		PER SHARE ($) Earnings	Dividends	Book Value
12/11	11.72	41	19	0.40	0.00	5.36
12/10	14.49	—	—	(0.12)	0.00	5.12
12/09	11.92	—	—	(0.34)	0.00	5.07
12/08	5.07	—	—	(3.74)	0.00	4.55
12/07	15.89	33	18	0.81	0.00	9.05
Annual Growth	(7.3%)	—	—	(16.2%)	—	(12.3%)

Hess Corp

Integrated oil and gas company Hess Corporation has corporate exploration and production operations in Algeria Australia Azerbaijan Brazil China Denmark Egypt Equatorial Guinea France Gabon Ghana Indonesia Kurdistan Libya Malaysia Norway Peru Russia Thailand the UK and the US. In 2011 Hess reported proved reserves totaling more than 2.4 billion barrels of oil equivalent. It markets gasoline through more than 1360 HESS gas stations in 16 US states and operates a 50%-owned oil storage terminal (HOVENSA) in the US Virgin Islands and a refinery in New Jersey. It also provides power to Northeast and Mid-Atlantic customers.

Financial Analysis

Robust oil prices and higher refined petroleum product prices lifted Hess' revenue in 2011 despite a decline in crude oil and petroleum product sales volume. However net income was also down due to higher expenses primarily related to the higher prices of purchased refined petroleum products. The company's 2011 financial performance was also trimmed by operational issues (and related fiscal losses) at its HOVENSA refinery which led to that refinery being shut down and Hess taking $525 million in impairment-related charges.

Following a difficult 2009 when the global recession hammered commodity prices and weakened revenues and income an expanding economy (with its higher oil and gas prices and increased industrial demand) helped the company post higher revenues and income in 2010.

Geographic Reach

Hess' refinery in the US Virgin Islands was operated as a joint venture with Venezuela's state oil company Petroleos de Venezuela S.A (PDVSA). However the loss-making refinery was shut down in 2012 and converted to an oil storage terminal.

Hess' European properties account for more than 30% of its total proved oil and gas reserves. In 2009 it boosted its European assets further swapping some noncore properties with Royal Dutch Shell in return for major stakes in two Norwegian offshore fields. The company plans to exploit attractive properties in Algeria Australia Azerbaijan and Latin America as well as Asia (particularly in Malaysia and Thailand) to boost its reserves.

Strategy

The company is also looking to grow its position in the lucrative Bakken oil shale play in North Dakota. In 2010 the company acquired American Oil and Gas in a $450 million stock deal that added 85000 net acres to Hess' holdings. It also bought 167000 acres in the Bakken play from TRZ Energy LLC for $1 billion.

The Utica Shale in Ohio is another growth area. In 2011 Hess agreed to pay up to $593 million for joint exploration and development rights to CONSOL Energy's nearly 200000 Utica Shale acres in Ohio. It subsequently acquired acquired Marquette Exploration LLC and other Utica Shale leases for $750 million boosting its acreage position by 85000 net acres. (To help pay for this it sold noncore UK North Sea assets that year to generate $359 million in cash.)

Hess also seeks opportunities on the marketing side of the business. In late 2008 Hess expanded its electricity marketing business in its core US retail market acquiring power assets in the northeastern US from RRI Energy (now GenOn Energy. In 2011 the company was marketing a total of more than 4370 MW a day.

HISTORY

In 1919 British oil entrepreneur Lord Cowdray formed Amerada Corporation to explore for oil in North America. Cowdray soon hired geophysicist Everette DeGolyer a pioneer in oil geology research. DeGolyer's systematic methods helped Amerada not only find oil deposits faster but also pick up fields missed by competitors. DeGolyer became president of Amerada in 1929 but left in 1932 to work independently.

After WWII Amerada began exploring overseas and during the 1950s entered pipelining and refining. It continued its overseas exploration through Oasis a consortium formed in 1964 with Marathon Shell and Continental to explore in Libya.

Leon Hess began to buy stock in Amerada in 1966. The son of immigrants he had entered the oil business during the Depression selling "resid" – thick refining leftovers that refineries discarded – from a 1929 Dodge truck in New Jersey. He bought the resid cheap and sold it as heating fuel to hotels. Hess also speculated buying oil at low prices in the summer and selling it for a profit in the winter. He later bought more trucks a transportation network refineries and gas stations and went into oil exploration. Expansion pushed up debt so in 1962 Leon's company went public as Hess Oil and Chemical after merging with Cletrac Corporation.

Hess acquired Amerada in 1969 after an ownership battle with Phillips Petroleum. During the Arab oil embargo of the 1970s Amerada Hess began drilling on Alaska's North Slope. Oilman T. Boone Pickens bought up a chunk of Amerada Hess stock during the 1980s spurring takeover rumors. They proved premature.

Amerada Hess completed a pipeline in 1993 to carry natural gas from the North Sea to the UK. In 1995 Leon Hess stepped down as CEO (he died in 1999) and his son John took the position. Amerada Hess sold its 81% interest in the Northstar oil field in Alaska to BP and the next year Petro-Canada bought the company's Canadian operations. In 1996 the company acquired a 25% stake (sold in 2002) in UK-based Premier Oil.

The company teamed with Dixons Stores Group in 1997 to market gas in the UK. It also purchased 66 Pick Wick convenience store/service stations.

In 1998 Amerada Hess signed production-sharing contracts with a Malaysian oil firm as part of its strategy to move into Southeast Asia and began to sell natural gas to retail customers in the UK.

To offset losses brought on by depressed oil prices Amerada Hess sold assets worth more than $300 million in 1999 including its southeastern pipeline network gas stations in Georgia and South Carolina and Gulf Coast terminals. It also moved into Latin America acquiring stakes in fields in offshore Brazil.

In 2000 Amerada Hess acquired Statoil Energy Services which markets natural gas and electricity to industrial and commercial customers in the northeastern US. It also announced its intention to buy LASMO a UK-based exploration and production company before Italy's Eni topped the Amerada Hess offer.

Undeterred in 2001 the company bought Dallas-based exploration and production company Triton Energy for $2.7 billion in cash and $500 million in assumed debt. Amerada Hess also acquired the Gulf of Mexico assets of LLOG Exploration Company for $750 million. That year however stiff competition prompted Amerada Hess to put its UK gas and electricity supply business on the auction block. The unit was sold to TXU (now Energy Future Holdings) in 2002.

In 2003 Amerada Hess sold 26 oil and gas fields in the Gulf of Mexico to Anadarko Petroleum. Amerada Hess was granted permission by the Equatorial Guinea government in 2004 to develop 29 new wells in that country. That year Amerada Hess acquired a 65% stake in Trabant Holdings International a Russia-based production and exploration company.

The company re-entered its former oil and gas production operations in the Waha concessions in Libya in 2006. Also that year it changed its name to Hess Corporation.

EXECUTIVES

EVP and Director; President Refining and Marketing, F. Borden Walker, age 58, $900,000 total compensation
SVP Marketing and Refining Supply and Financial Controls, Lawrence H. Ornstein, age 60
SVP Energy Marketing, John A. Gartman, age 64
Chairman and CEO, John B. Hess, age 58, $1,500,000 total compensation
VP and Controller, Kevin B. Wilcox
VP Secretary and Deputy General Counsel, George C. Barry
VP Global Business Improvement, Harold I. Small
VP Sales and Retail Marketing, Richard J. Lawlor
SVP and CFO, John P. Rielly, age 49, $700,000 total compensation
Assistant Controller, Kevin G. Daley
VP and CIO, Jeff L. Steinhorn
SVP Global New Business Development, Howard Paver, age 61
VP Environment Health and Safety, Gerald I. Bresnick
VP Supply and Trading, David K. Kirshner

VP Investor Relations, Jay R. Wilson
SVP Finance and Corporate Development, John J. Scelfo, age 54
SVP Global Production and Technology, Scott M. Heck, age 54
VP and Chief Risk Officer, Jonathan C. Stein
Assistant Treasurer, Erin K. Macher
SVP Global Exploration and New Ventures, William (Bill) Drennen III, age 61
VP Corporate Communications, Jon L. Pepper
VP Corporate Tax, C. Martin Dunagin
Assistant Treasurer, Eric Fishman
SVP Terminals and Refining, Darius Sweet
SVP and General Counsel, Timothy B. Goodell, age 54, $650,000 total compensation
EVP and Director; President Worldwide Exploration and Production, Gregory P. Hill, age 51, $850,000 total compensation
SVP; CEO Hess LNG, R. Gordon Shearer, age 57
SVP Global Production, John V. Simon, age 58
SVP Global Production, Michael R. Turner, age 52
SVP Global Developments, Gary Boubel, age 57
SVP Human Resources, Mykel J. Ziolo, age 59
Assistant Secretary, Randy J. Pharr
Assistant Secretary, John Y. Christopher
Deputy General Counsel Environmental and Assistant Secretary, Christopher S. Colman
Deputy General Counsel and Assistant Secretary, Nicholas P. Brountas
Assistant Corporate Secretary, Jackie Asafu-Adjaye
VP Corporate Projects and Assistant Corporate Secretary, Terry B. Garcia
SVP Retail and Energy Marketing, Christopher Baldwin
VP and Treasurer, Robert M. Biglin, age 47
Director Corporate Communications, William D. (Will) Rea
VP Government Affairs & Public Policy, Drew Maloney
Chief Financial Officer; Senior Vice President; Treasurer, Alison Engel
Lead Independent Director, John Puerner
Chairman of the Board; President; Chief Executive Officer, Robert Decherd
VP Controller, Michael N. Lavey
Senior Vice President; Secretary, Daniel Blizzard
EVP and Director; President Refining and Marketing, F. Borden Walker, age 58
Director, Craig G. Matthews, age 68
Director, Robert N. Wilson, age 71
Director, Frank A. Olson, age 79
Director, Thomas H. (Tom) Kean, age 76
Director, Nicholas F. Brady, age 81
Director, Edith E. (Ede) Holiday, age 60
Director, Risa J. Lavizzo-Mourey, age 57
Director, John H. Mullin III, age 70
Director, Ernst H. Von Metzsch, age 72
EVP and Director; President Worldwide Exploration and Production, Gregory P. Hill, age 51
Director, Samuel W. Bodman, age 73
Independent Director, Louis Caldera
Independent Director, John Beckert
Independent Director, Ronald Mccray
Independent Director, Tyree Miller
Independent Director, Ernst Metzsch
Independent Director, Samuel Nunn
Auditors: Ernst&YoungLLP

LOCATIONS

HQ: Hess Corporation
1185 Avenue of the Americas, New York NY 10036
Phone: 212-997-8500 **Fax:** 212-536-8593
Web: www.hess.com

2011 Sales

	$ mil.	% of total
US	31,813	83
Europe	3,137	8
Africa	1,782	5
Asia & other regions	1,734	4
Adjustments	(595)	-
Total	**37,871**	**100**

PRODUCTS/OPERATIONS

2011 Sales

	$ mil.	% of total
Marketing & refining	27,935	73
Exploration & production	10,530	27
Adjustments	(594)	-
Total	**37,871**	**100**

COMPETITORS

Abraxas Petroleum
BP
Bucking Horse
CAMAC International
Chevron
CMA CGM
ConocoPhillips
Constellation Energy Group
Continental Energy
Derek Oil & Gas Corporation
Desire Petroleum
Devon Energy
Dominion Resources
Double Eagle Petroleum
Encana Oil & Gas (USA) Inc.
Eni
ERHC
Exxon Mobil
Gastar Exploration
Getty Petroleum Marketing
Gulf Oil
Koch Industries Inc.
Marathon Oil
Marathon Petroleum
Norsk Hydro ASA
Occidental Petroleum
PEMEX
Petrobank Energy and Resources
PETROBRAS
Petroleos de Venezuela
Pioneer Oil and Gas
Royal Dutch Shell
Serica Energy
Sinclair Oil
Sunoco
TOTAL
United Refining

HISTORICAL FINANCIALS

Company Type: Public

Income Statement FYE: December 31

	REVENUE ($ mil.)	NET INCOME ($ mil.)	NET PROFIT MARGIN	EMPLOYEES
12/11	37,871	1,703	4.5%	14,350
12/10	34,613	2,125	6.1%	13,800
12/09	29,569	740	2.5%	13,300
12/08	41,094	2,360	5.7%	13,500
12/07	31,924	1,832	5.7%	13,300
Annual Growth	4.4%	(1.8%)	—	1.9%

2011 Year-End Financials

Debt ratio: 15.48%
Return on equity: 9.20%
Cash ($ mil.): 351
Current ratio: 102.95
Long-term debt ($ mil.): 6,005
No. of shares (mil.): 339
Dividends
Yield: —
Payout: 7.98%
Market value ($ mil.): 19,311

	STOCK PRICE ($) FY Close	P/E High	P/E Low	PER SHARE ($) Earnings	Dividends	Book Value
12/11	56.80	17	10	5.01	0.00	54.46
12/10	76.54	12	8	6.47	0.40	49.42
12/09	60.50	30	21	2.27	0.40	40.90
12/08	53.64	18	5	7.24	0.40	37.74
12/07	100.86	18	8	5.74	0.40	30.49
Annual Growth	(13.4%)	—	—	(3.3%)	—	15.6%

Hewlett-Packard Co

Hewlett-Packard is slimming down to flex its muscle in big data cloud computing and security. HP provides one of the tech world's most comprehensive portfolios of hardware software and services. Products include PCs servers storage devices printers and networking equipment. Its services unit offers IT and business process outsourcing application development consulting systems integration and other technology services. HP generates software sales through enterprise IT management data management business intelligence and carrier communications applications. The 75-year-old company which serves customers worldwide is undergoing a major restructuring as part of its turnaround strategy.

HISTORY

Encouraged by Stanford professor Frederick Terman (considered the founder of Silicon Valley) in 1938 engineers Bill Hewlett and David Packard started Hewlett-Packard (HP) in a garage in Palo Alto California with $538. Hewlett was the idea man while Packard served as manager; the two were so low-key that the company's first official meeting ended with no decision on exactly what to manufacture. Finding good people took priority over finding something to sell. The first product ended up being an audio oscillator. Walt Disney Studios one of HP's first customers bought eight to use in the making of "Fantasia".

Demand for HP's electronic testing equipment during WWII spurred sales growth from $34000 in 1940 to nearly $1 million just three years later. HP went public in 1957. The company expanded beyond the US during 1959 establishing a marketing organization in Switzerland and a manufacturing plant in West Germany. HP entered the medical field in 1961 by acquiring Sanborn and the analytical instrumentation business in 1965 with the purchase of F&M Scientific. In 1969 Packard left the company to serve as deputy defense secretary under President Nixon for two years.

The company pioneered personal computing with the world's first handheld scientific calculator in 1972. Under the leadership of John Young the founders' chosen successor (named CEO in 1978) HP introduced its first PCs the first desktop mainframe and the LaserJet printer. Its initial PCs were known for their rugged build tailored for factory operations. They were also more expensive than rival versions and consequently didn't enjoy strong sales.

By 1986 a five-year $250 million R&D project — the company's largest at the time —produced a family of HP computers based on the reduced instruction set computing (RISC) architecture. Hewlett retired in 1987 (he died in 2001); sons of both Hewlett and Packard were named that year to the company's board of directors. HP became a leader in workstations with the 1989 purchase of market pioneer Apollo Computer despite technology delays with the merger that resulted in the loss of nearly $750 million in new business.

HP acquired Texas Instruments' line of UNIX-based computers in 1992 and committed to product cost-cutting. Lewis Platt an EVP since 1987 was named president and CEO that year. Packard retired in 1993 (he died in 1996). HP combined its varied computer operations in 1995. Continuing expansion through acquisition HP bought electronic commerce firm VeriFone in 1997.

Two years later HP formed Agilent Technologies for its test and measurement and other non-computer operations and spun off 15% of the company to the public. (HP distributed to its shareholders its remaining 85% in 2000). Also in 1999 Platt retired and HP became one of the first major US corporations to be headed by a woman when it appointed Lucent executive Carly Fiorina president and CEO. She was named chairman the following year.

The company acquired application server specialist Bluestone Software in 2001; the acquisition helped form HP's Netaction operations. Later that year the company sold its VeriFone division to high-tech acquisition specialist Gores Technology Group (now Gores Group). Soon after HP agreed to pay $400 million to Pitney Bowes to settle a 1995 patent infringement case related to printer technology.

After an unsuccessful bid for the IT services unit of equipment leasing company Comdisco HP acquired StorageApps for $350 million in stock. HP said in 2002 that it was cutting about 6000 jobs. Soon after it acquired network performance software maker Trinagy.

Next came the announcement of a blockbuster deal: HP agreed to buy rival Compaq Computer in a stock transaction initially valued at about $25 billion. The highly contentious deal eventually met with shareholder approval in 2002 after months of heated volleys between merger advocates and dissenters. At the time of closing the deal was valued at approximately $19 billion. Integration efforts included a workforce reduction of roughly 10% as the company eliminated redundant product groups.

Fiorina soon had to address the clash of disparate corporate cultures and subsequent morale problems without Michael Capellas; the former Compaq CEO who initially served as president under Fiorina and helped champion the deal left HP in 2002 to become CEO of troubled telecom giant WorldCom (later renamed MCI and acquired by Verizon).

While managing the challenge of merging operations and maintaining customer focus HP continued to make acquisitions. It bought Consera Software and Novadigm in 2004 and shortly after it purchased TruLogica.

Fiorina's differences with HP's board over strategic direction finally came to a head in 2005 and she stepped down as chairman and CEO. HP's CFO Robert Wayman was named interim CEO and director Patricia Dunn took over as nonexecutive chairman. Mark Hurd the former CEO of NCR was named to lead HP that year. (Hurd resigned in August 2010 and was replaced by former SAP CEO Leo Apotheker).

HP's leadership experienced another shakeup the following year this time prompted by negative attention related to tactics used in an investigation of boardroom leaks. The company's board came under fire after it was revealed that third-party investigators employed by HP impersonated board members and journalists to obtain their phone records (a practice known as "pretexting"). Dunn was asked to resign from the board in 2006 and Hurd replaced her as chairman. HP settled a related dispute with the California attorney general later that year agreeing to pay $14.5 million. ($13.5 million of the settlement was earmarked to create a Privacy and Piracy Fund to assist state prosecutors).

In 2007 HP announced a different business model for its camera business opting to outsource the design licensing and distribution of HP-branded devices to an OEM. HP gave its Business Technology Optimization (BTO) software portfolio a boost when it purchased Opsware a developer of data center automation software for approximately $1.6 billion in 2007.

In 2010 HP made an acquisition to complement its PC group buying smartphone maker and PDA pioneer Palm for about $1.2 billion. Palm the creator of the iconic Palm Pilot PDA had struggled to keep up with other vendors (most notably Apple HTC and Research In Motion) in the burgeoning smartphone market. HP made the purchase in an attempt to carve a niche for itself in the wireless market building a line of smartphones around Palm's nascent webOS mobile software platform. In addition the company threw its hat into the tablet computing ring with a tablet PC (TouchPad) also featuring webOS that targeted Apple's iPad and devices from other manufacturers. HP killed the short-lived phone and tablet lines the next year.

HP's software purchases in 2010 included Fortify Software a specialist in applications for analyzing source code to detect potential security risks. It also paid $1.5 billion that year for security software maker ArcSight a developer of applications used to track and monitor data flow throughout an organization in order to prevent network hacking theft and internal fraud. The fact that its products are used to guard networks and data centers made ArcSight an attractive target for HP as it expands its reach past the desktop PC.

EXECUTIVES

EVP and General Manager Enterprise Group, David A. (Dave) Donatelli, age 46
SVP and General Manager Palm Global Business Unit, Jonathan J. (Jon) Rubinstein, age 55
President CEO and Director, Margaret C. (Meg) Whitman, age 55
EVP HP Software, George Kadifa, age 52
VP Experience Marketing Personal Systems Group, Carlos O. Montalvo, age 55
EVP and COO, Bill Veghte
EVP and Chief Marketing Officer, Martin (Marty) Homlish
Chairman, Raymond J. (Ray) Lane, age 65
EVP Imaging and Printing Group, Vyomesh (VJ) Joshi, age 58, $743,125 total compensation
Media Relations Contact Workstations Personal Systems Group, Jim Christensen
EVP Printing and Personal Systems Group, R. Todd Bradley, age 53, $743,125 total compensation
EVP; President and CEO HP Financial Services, Irv Rothman
EVP Emerging Markets, Francesco Serafini
SVP and CIO, Craig Flower
SVP and General Manager Infrastructure Technology Outsourcing HP Enterprise Services, Pete Karolczak
SVP and General Manager HP StorageWorks; President and CEO 3PAR, David C. Scott, age 50
SVP Global Information Technology, Linda M. Dillman, age 55
General Manager China, Ruey-Bin Kao
EVP and CFO, Catherine A. (Cathie) Lesjak, age 52, $589,063 total compensation
SVP and General Manager HP Enterprise Services, Thomas J. (Tom) Iannotti, age 55
SVP Growth Markets Organization, Brian Humphries
EVP and Chief Communications Officer, Henry Gomez
VP Technology Support Enterprise Americas, Paul Tsaparis
SVP and Global CIO, Ramon F. Baez
SVP Enterprise Business; Managing Director for HP Europe the Middle East and Africa, Yves de Talhouet
SVP and Treasurer, John McMullen, age 53
EVP Technology and Business Processes, John Hinshaw, age 42
SVP Controller and Principal Accounting Officer, James T. (Jim) Murrin, age 51
EVP General Counsel and Secretary, Michael J. (Mike) Holston, age 49
SVP Research; Director HP Laboratories, Prith Banerjee, age 51
EVP Human Resources, Tracy Keogh, age 50
VP Worldwide Developer Relations Palm Global Business Unit, Richard Kerris
SVP Global Information Technology, Ahmed Mahmoud
VP Global Government Affairs and Deputy General Counsel, Gregg R. Melinson
Enterprise Sales Lead HP Networking Group Asia Pacific and Japan excluding China, Jeff Healey
VP Global Government Affairs, Larry Irving, age 57
Interim Chief Communications Officer, Lynn Anderson
VP; Managing Director Russia, Aleksandr Mikoyan
Director New Business Initiatives; Chief MagClouder MagCloud, Andrew Bolwell
VP Investor Relations, James (Jim) Burns
SVP Operations Personal Systems Group, Anthony (Tony) Prophet
Manager Worldwide Solution Virtualization, Robert (Bob) Meyer
President and CEO Canada, Peter Galanis, age 45
EVP Global Sales and Enterprise Marketing, Jan Zadak
Director Emerging Technologies ProCurve Networking; Director Advanced Technology Solutions HP Networking, Lin Nease
VP IT Infrastructure, Ken Gray
VP HP IT Operations Control, James Cook
CIO Software Division, Saum Mathur
VP HP Product Development and Engineering IT, Michael Wolfe
VP Global Telecommunications Architecture & Engineering, Tony Bolton
Senior Director IT End User Services, Terry Criscione
Director Data Center Transformation, Grant Folsom
Director Operations Automation, Mahesh Shah
Director Asset Change and Configuration Management, Tim Benson
Manager Global Portfolio Management Office, Hiram Davis
Senior Portfolio Analyst, Rosalynn Tuggle
Worldwide Marketing Lead ? Application Transformation, Paul Evans
Director and Global Manager Data Center Transformation Technology Services, Ewald Comhaire
Director Investor Relations, Beth Howe
Director Investor Relations, Catriona Fallon
VP Investor Relations, Steve Fieler
Director Investor Relations, Amar Maletira
Director Investor Relations, Charly Kevers
VP Corporate Communications, Connie Guglielmo
Director Corporate/Innovation and International PR, Christina Schneider
Director General/Breaking News, Mylene Mangalindan
Strategic Advisor MagCloud, Udi Chatow
Chief Technologist MagCloud, Andy Fitzhugh
Chief of Awesome MagCloud, Derek Powazek
Chief Designologist MagCloud, James Goode
Media Relations Contact Cross-PSG Inquiries Personal Systems Group, Marlene Somsak

Media Relations Contact General/Breaking News, Michael Thacker
VP Global Telecommunications Delivery and Service Management, David E. Flanagin
EVP and General Manager of Enterprise Services, John Visentin
Worldwide Applications Development Leader, Srinivas (Srini) Koushik
CEO Autonomy Corporation PLC, Mike Lynch
EVP Enterprise Services, Mike Nefkens
VP Media relations and Executive Communications, Howard Clabo
EVP and General Counsel, John F Schultz
SVP Sales Operations, Dave Ornelas
Sales IT Director, Vicki Vandemberg
VP Sales Operations & Capabilities, Kevin Leighton
Director, Gary M. Reiner, age 57
Director, Marc L. Andreessen, age 40
Director, John H. Hammergren, age 53
Director, Rajiv L. (Raj) Gupta, age 66
Director, Ralph V. Whitworth, age 56
Director, Sari M. Baldauf, age 56
Director, Lawrence T. (Larry) Babbio Jr., age 67
President CEO and Director, Margaret C. (Meg) Whitman, age 55
Director, Patricia F. (Pat) Russo, age 59
Director, G. Kennedy (Ken) Thompson, age 61
Director, Ann M. Livermore, age 53
Director, Shumeet Banerji, age 52
Director, Dominique Senequier, age 58
Auditors: Ernst&YoungLLP

LOCATIONS

HQ: Hewlett-Packard Co
3000 Hanover Street, Palo Alto, CA 94304
Phone: 650 857-1501
Web: www.hp.com

2011 Sales

	$ mil.	% of total
US	44,111	35
Other countries	83,134	65
Total	127,245	100

PRODUCTS/OPERATIONS

2011 Sales

	$ mil.	% of total
Products	84,757	67
Services	42,039	33
Financing income	449	-
Total	127,245	100

2011 Sales

	$ mil.	% of total
PSG	39,574	31
Services	35,594	27
IPG	25,783	20
ESSN	22,241	17
HPFS	3,596	3
HP Software	3,217	2
Adjustments	(2760)	-
Total	127,245	100

Selected Products and Services

Enterprise Systems
- Business technology optimization software
- Networking equipment
- Servers (Linux Unix Windows)
  - Blade
  - Carrier-grade
  - Rack-optimized
  - Server appliances
  - Super-scalable
  - Tower
- Services
  - Consulting
  - Design and installation
  - Education
  - Financing
  - Outsourcing
  - Printing
  - Support and maintenance
  - Web hosting
- Storage
  - Disks and disk arrays
  - Network-attached storage (NAS) devices
  - Optical disk drives
  - Storage area network (SAN) systems
  - Tape drives and libraries

Personal Systems
- Calculators
- Desktop PCs
- Digital entertainment centers
- DVD writers
- Handheld computers
- Notebook computers
- Televisions (LCD plasma)
- Workstations

Imaging and Printing
- Commercial printing
  - Digital presses
  - Printers
- Digital imaging
  - Projectors
  - Scanners
- Personal printing
  - All-in-ones (copier fax printer scanner)
  - Ink jet printers
  - Laser printers
- Shared printing
  - Networked inkjet laser and multifunction printers
  - Office all-in-ones
  - Services
- Supplies

Selected Acquisitions

Printelligent (2011 managed print services)
Vertica Systems (2011 database management software)
ArcSight (2010 security software)
3PAR (2010 storage software and hardware)
Fortify Software (2010 data security software)
Stratavia (2010 database and application automation software)
Palm (2010 wireless communications devices)
3Com (2010 networking hardware and software)
IBRIX (2009 data storage software)
LeftHand Networks (2008 data storage software and hardware)
Colubris Networks (2008 wireless networking equipment)
Electronic Data Systems (2008 IT and business consulting)
Tower Software (2008 document management software)
Exstream Software (2008 document management software)
NUR Macroprinters (2008 inkjet printers)
Bristol Technology (2007 application development software)
MacDermid ColorSpan (2007 wide-format inkjet printers)
Neoware (2007 thin-client computers)
Opsware (2007 data-center automation software)
SPI Dynamics (2007 Web-application security software and services)
Polyserve (2007 data storage software)
Tabblo (2007 Web content management software)
Bitfone (2007 mobile-device management software)

COMPETITORS

Accenture
Acer
ADP
Affiliated Computer Services
Apple Inc.
ASUSTeK
BMC Software
Brother Industries
CA Inc.
CACI International
Canon
Capgemini
CGI Group
Cisco Systems
Heidelberger Druckmaschinen
Hitachi
IBM
Infosys
Konica Minolta
Lenovo
Lexmark
Microsoft
NCR
NEC
NetApp
Oce
Oki Electric
Oracle
Computer Sciences Corp.
Convergys
Dell
Eastman Kodak
EMC
Epson
First Data
Fiserv
Fuji Xerox
Fujitsu
Fujitsu Technology Solutions
Panasonic Corp
Ricoh Company
Samsung Electronics
SAP
Sharp Corp.
Sony
Symantec
Tata Consultancy
Teradata
Toshiba
Unisys
Wipro Technologies
Xerox

HISTORICAL FINANCIALS

Company Type: Public

Income Statement

FYE: October 31

	REVENUE ($ mil.)	NET INCOME ($ mil.)	NET PROFIT MARGIN	EMPLOYEES
10/12	120,357	(12,650)	—	331,800
10/11	127,245	7,074	5.6%	349,600
10/10	126,033	8,761	7.0%	324,600
10/09	114,552	7,660	6.7%	304,000
10/08	118,364	8,329	7.0%	321,000
Annual Growth	0.4%	—	—	0.8%

2012 Year-End Financials

Debt ratio: 26.14%
Return on equity: (-56.38)%
Cash ($ mil.): 11,301
Current ratio: 108.51
Long-term debt ($ mil.): 21,789
No. of shares (mil.): 1,962
Dividends
Yield: 3.64%
Payout: -
Market value ($ mil.): 27,185

	STOCK PRICE ($) FY Close	P/E High	P/E Low	PER SHARE ($) Earnings	Dividends	Book Value
10/12	13.85	—	—	(6.41)	0.50	11.43
10/11	26.61	14	7	3.32	0.40	19.40
10/10	42.04	14	10	3.69	0.00	18.35
10/09	47.46	15	8	3.14	0.00	17.13
10/08	38.28	16	9	3.25	0.32	16.13
Annual Growth	(22.4%)	—	—	—	11.8%	(8.3%)

Hillshire Brands Co

What does Sara Lee like? Click meat beverage and select bakery products. These interests have been or soon will be transformed as the iconic maker and marketer of brand name foods sets a new course. Sara Lee International oversees coffee (Douwe Egberts and Senseo) tea and some bakery sales in Europe Australia Asia and Brazil. A North American Retail arm sells packaged meat (Ball Park Jimmy Dean) and frozen baked items including its namesake cheesecake. Its North American Foodservice supplies meat and baked goods to foodservice operators. To spur earnings growth in 2012 Sara Lee sold the coffee and tea business of its North American Foodservice unit to The J. M. Smucker Company for about $400 million.

HISTORY

Businessman Nathan Cummings bought the C. D. Kenny Co. a Baltimore coffee tea and sugar wholesaler in 1939. Cummings soon purchased several grocery firms and later changed the company's name to Consolidated Grocers (1945). The operation went public in 1946 and was renamed Consolidated Foods Corp. (CFC) in 1954.

Two years later CFC bought the Kitchens of Sara Lee a Chicago bakery founded by Charles Lubin in 1951. Introduced in 1949 and named after Lubin's daughter Sara Lee cheesecake had become the bakery's most popular product.

In 1968 CFC sold its Eagle Complex which included Piggly Wiggly Midwest supermarkets and Eagle Food Centers and it bought Bryan Foods. The firm continued to buy and sell businesses in the US including beverage appliance and chemical companies. Some major US purchases were Hanes Corp. (1979) Jimmy Dean Meat Co. (1984) Coach Leatherware International (1985) and Champion Products (athletic knitwear 1989). Cummings served as president until 1970.

CFC began building its international markets with its first European acquisition in 1962. Following that purchase it expanded its global presence with the purchases of Douwe Egberts (coffee tea and tobacco; the Netherlands; 1978) Nicholas Kiwi (shoe care and pharmaceuticals Australia 1984) and Dim (hosiery and underwear France 1989).

Using one of its most respected brand names to enhance the public's awareness of the company CFC changed its name to Sara Lee in 1985. It continued making acquisitions in the 1990s including Playtex Apparel.

In 1997 Sara Lee began a restructuring that included selling noncore businesses and increasing its use of outsourcing closed more than 90 manufacturing and distribution facilities and laid off 9400 employees (about 7% of its workforce). It also closed its Mark Cross leather goods business.

Sara Lee sold its loose tobacco business (Amphora Drum Van Nelle) in 1998 to the UK's Imperial Tobacco for $1.1 billion; bought undergarments maker Strouse Adler; and purchased Quaker Oats' coffee marketer Continental Coffee Products. Also that year Sara Lee recalled hot dogs and packaged meats produced by its Bil Mar Foods unit after the items were linked to nearly two dozen fatal food-poisoning cases. (The company settled class-action suits over the incident in 2000.)

While closing more than 100 facilities during 1999 Sara Lee continued acquiring including coffee company Chock Full o'Nuts and the Hills Bros. MJB and Chase & Sanborn coffee operations from Nestle. It also bought Royal Ahold's Dutch meat processing units Meester and Nistria; J.E. Morgan Knitting Mills (maker of Duofold thermal underwear); and the UK's leading intimate apparel and underwear producer Courtaulds Textiles. (It sold Courtaulds International Fabrics unit in April 2001 to Spanish fabric maker Dogi.)

During 2000 Sara Lee spun off its Coach (leather goods) business and sold off its foodservice operation PYA/Monarch to a Royal Ahold subsidiary as the first move to refocus on its core brands. In 2000 president Steven McMillan added the CEO title to his duties; he was named chairman that October.

In 2001 Sara Lee continued to dispose of noncore operations. However in that August it acquired The Earthgrains Company the second-largest fresh-bread company in the US; the combined bakery operations of the companies were renamed the Sara Lee Bakery Group.

The Sara Lee Bakery Group was slapped with a $5.25 million fine in 2003 when the EPA determined that ozone-depleting chemicals were leaking from refrigeration systems in many of its plants. The company agreed to pay the fine and spend an additional $5 million on repairs. Due to falling sales caused by more casual dressing habits the company that year also sold off its Italian hosiery business which had sold its products in France Italy and Spain.

In 2005 McMillan retired and handed over the titles of president CEO and chairman to Brenda Barnes who instituted a total reorganization of the company. Sara Lee is still in the process of this reorganization.

In 2006 Sara Lee sold off its European packaged meats business. Turning to its apparel operations the company sold its $1.2 billion European apparel business to Florida's Sun Capital Partners. The 2006 deal included the Dim Playtex Wonderbra Abanderado Nur Die and Unno brands. (Sara Lee had already sold its 23% stake in Delta Galil Industries an Israeli clothing manufacturer to GMM Capital for more than $27 million in 2005.)

In 2009 Sara Lee sold its commercial coffee operation Superior Coffee to Farmer Bros. for $45 million. In addition to Superior other coffee brands included in the sale were Cain's Ireland Justin Lloyd McGarvey Metropolitan Prebica Suntipt (in the US only) Wechsler Cafe Royal and Royal Kona. Sara Lee kept its Douwe Egberts and Java Coast brands which are sold through large wholesalers and food suppliers rather than a distributor network.

In mid-2010 Sara Lee sold its European airfreshener business including Ambi Pur to Procter & Gamble for E320 million ($470 million). Sara Lee said it would use the proceeds to invest in its core food businesses and buy back stock. Abandoning a decision to retain its International Household and Body Care business Sara Lee sold its global personal care and European laundry brands to Unilever for E1.2 billion (equal to $1.5 billion) in cash in late 2010. The deal included the Sanex Duschdas Radox and Switzal brands. Additionally in 2010 the company completed the sale of its 51% stake in the Godrej joint venture in India to its partner there for E185 million ($230 million).

Brenda Barnes stepped down as chairman and CEO of the company in August for medical reasons.

EXECUTIVES

CEO, Marcel H. M. Smits, age 50, $511,815 total compensation
EVP Human Resources, Stephen J. Cerrone, age 48, $495,600 total compensation
Chairman, Jan Bennink, age 55
CFO North America, Maria Henry, age 44
EVP and CFO, Mark A. Garvey, age 47, $335,800 total compensation
EVP; CEO International Household and Body Care, Vincent H. A. M. Janssen, age 58, $563,877 total compensation
SVP Global Communications, Jon Harris
Director International Communications Sara Lee International, Joost den Haan
Interim Corporate Controller, John P. Zyck
SVP Strategic Planning and Corporate Development, B. Thomas Hansson, age 51
Director Corporate Communications, Mike Cummins
Director Media Development/Communications Sara Lee Brands and Foodservice, Sara Matheu
CEO North American Retail and Foodservice, Sean Connolly, age 46
Senior Manager Corporate Communications, Alissa Bolton
Manager Media Development Sara Lee Brands and Foodservice, Ashley LaCroix
VP Investor Relations, Robin Jansen
Senior Manager International Communications Sara Lee International Beverage and Bakery; Interim Senior Manager International Communications Sara Lee Household & Body Care, Ernesto Duran
CIO, Anne Teague, age 52
EVP and CFO International Beverage and CoffeeCo, Michel M. G. Cup
Brand General Manager Ball Park, Aaron Alt
EVP; CEO International Beverage and CoffeeCo, Michiel Herkemij
Chief Marketing Officer International Beverage and CoffeeCo, Ingrid Baron
General Counsel and Corporate Secretary, Paulette Dodson
General Counsel and Corporate Secretary, Kent B. Magill
CFO, Maria Henry
CEO, Sean Connolly
President Retail, Andy Callahan
Chief Supply Chain Officer, Tom Hayes
SVP Research and Development, Jeff George
Chief Innovation Officer, Sally Grimes
Director, Christopher B. (Chris) Begley, age 59
Director, Laurette T. Koellner, age 57
Director, Norman R. Sorensen, age 66
Director, James S. Crown, age 57
Director, John D. G. McAdam, age 64
Director, Cornelis J. A. (Cees) van Lede, age 69
Director, Sir Ian M. G. Prosser, age 68
Director, Jonathan P. (Jon) Ward, age 57
Director, Virgis W. Colbert, age 72
Director, Jeffrey W. Ubben, age 49
Director, Crandall C. Bowles, age 64
Auditors: PricewaterhouseCoopersLLP

LOCATIONS

HQ: Sara Lee Corporation
3500 Lacey Rd., Downers Grove IL 60515-5424
Phone: 630-598-8100 **Fax:** 630-598-8482
Web: www.saralee.com

2010 Sales

	$ mil.	% of total
US	6,769	63
Netherlands	1,001	9
Spain	607	5
France	509	5
Other	1,907	18
Total	**10,793**	**100**

PRODUCTS/OPERATIONS

2011 Sales

	$ mil.	% of total
International beverage	3,548	41
North American retail	2,868	33
North American foodservice	1,566	18
International bakery	726	8
Adjustments (27) —		
Total	**8,681**	**100**

Selected Products and Brands

Bakery
- Bistro Collection
- Bon Gateaux
- Bony
- Chef Pierre
- CroustiPate
- Madame Brioche Martinez
- Rudy' s Farmo
- Sara Lee - desserts
- Sunbeam

Beverages
- Bravo
- Butter-Nut Cappuccino
- Caboclo
- Cafe Continental
- Cafe do Ponto

Cafe Pil?o
Cafitesse
Chat Noir
Douwe Egberts
Harris
Hornimans
Jacqmotte
Java Coast
Kanis & Gunnink
Kayo
Laurentis
Maison du Cafe
Marcilla
Maryland Club
Merrild
Moccona
Natreen
Natrena
Paradise
Piazza d' Oro
Pickwick
Prima
Seleto
Senseo
Soley
Steamers
Van Nelle

Meats
Ball Park
Bryan
Deli d' Italia
Deli Perfect
Galileo
Gallo Salame
Hillshire Farm
Jimmy Dean
Kahn' s
Mr. Turkey
R.B. Rice
Sara Lee - deli
State Fair

Selected Subsidiaries

United States
Aidell' s Sausage Company Inc.
Bryan Foods Inc.
Earthgrains Baking Companies Inc.
Egbert LLC
Flavor Corp.
Southern Family Foods L.L.C.

Foreign
Bimbo S.A. (Spain)
Coffenco International GmbH (Germany)
Douwe Egberts Coffee Systems NV (Belgium)
Kaffehuset Friele A/S (Norway)
Maison du Cafe Coffee Systems France SNC
Merrild Kaffee A/S (Denmark)
Merrild Kaffee Systems Sverige AB (Sweden)

COMPETITORS

Adam Matthews
Alderfer/Leidy' s
Atlantic Premium Brands
Awrey Bakeries
Bar-S Foods
Bimbo Bakeries
Boar' s Head
Bob Evans
Bridgford Foods
Cargill Meat Solutions
Carl Buddig
Clougherty Packing
ConAgra
ConAgra
Cranswick
Crider
Dawn Food Products
F. B. Purnell Sausage
Farmland Foods
Farmland Foods
Flowers Foods
Gaspar' s Sausage
Hormel
Karl Ehmer
Karl Ehmer
King' s Hawaiian
Kraft Foods
Kraft Foods Group Inc.
Land O' Frost
Maple Leaf Foods
Millstone
Moksel
Mondelez International
Nestle
Oberto Sausage Company
Pepperidge Farm
Plumrose USA
Procter & Gamble
Quality Sausage
Roger Wood Foods
Rubschlager Baking
Smithfield Foods Ltd.
Smucker
Specialty Foods Group Income Fund
Starbucks
Stroehmann Bakeries
Hormel
Hostess Brands
J & B Sausage
JBS USA
Johnsonville Sausage
Johnsonville Sausage
Jones Dairy Farm
Jones Dairy Farm
L.C.
Sysco
Tyson Foods
Tyson Foods
Usinger' s
Vienna Beef
Williams Sausage

HISTORICAL FINANCIALS

Company Type: Public

Income Statement FYE: June 30

	REVENUE ($ mil.)	NET INCOME ($ mil.)	NET PROFIT MARGIN	EMPLOYEES
06/12*	4,094	845	20.6%	9,500
07/11	8,681	1,287	14.8%	21,000
07/10	10,793	506	4.7%	33,000
06/09	12,881	364	2.8%	41,000
06/08	13,212	(79)	—	44,000
Annual Growth	(25.4%)	—	—	(31.8%)

*Fiscal year change

2012 Year-End Financials

Debt ratio: 38.53%
Return on equity: 359.57%
Cash ($ mil.): 235
Current ratio: 120.29
Long-term debt ($ mil.): 939
No. of shares (mil.): 120
Dividends
Yield: —
Payout: 16.13%
Market value ($ mil.): 3,497

	STOCK PRICE ($) FY Close	P/E High/Low		PER SHARE ($) Earnings	Dividends	Book Value
06/12*	28.99	4	2	7.13	0.00	1.95
07/11	19.32	2	1	10.30	0.00	16.56
07/10	13.99	4	2	3.65	0.00	11.23
06/09	9.58	6	3	2.60	0.00	14.63
06/08	12.18	—	—	(0.55)	0.00	19.90
Annual Growth	24.2%	—	—	—	—	(44.1%)

*Fiscal year change

HollyFrontier Corp.

HollyFrontier refines crude oil to produce gasoline diesel and jet fuel and sells it in erstwhile American frontier territories: the Southwest northern Mexico Kansas and the Rockies. Its major assets are a 52000 barrels-per-day refinery in Wyoming; the El Dorado Kansas refinery 135000 barrels; a Utah refinery 31000 barrels; a Tulsa refinery 125000 barrels and subsidiary Navajo Refining (New Mexico) which has a capacity of 100000 barrels a day. The company has a minority stake in Holly Energy Partners which operates crude oil and petroleum product pipelines. To expand market share in 2011 the company acquired regional rival Frontier Oil and Holly changed its corporate name to HollyFrontier.

The all-stock deal created an enterprise valued at $7 billion and added Frontier's Kansas and Wyoming refineries to the company's portfolio. The acquisition which boosted HollyFrontier's refining capacity to 443000 barrels a day is expected to create cost savings of at least $30 million per year.

Strategy

The purchase was part of a multi-year strategy of expanding refinery capacity through selective acquisitions of complementary assets. In 2009 the company bought Sunoco's 85000-barrels-per-day Tulsa refinery. Building the largest refinery complex in the Midcontinent in 2009 the company also acquired Sinclair Oil's 75000-barrels-per-day Tulsa refinery for $128.5 million.

Operations

HollyFrontier also owns and operates NK Asphalt Partners which manufactures and markets asphalt products from various terminals in Arizona and New Mexico.

Financial Analysis

The expanded capacity brought about by the Frontier purchase coupled with significantly higher refinery gross margins lifted HollyFrontier 2011 revenues by 85% and net income by more than 880%. The 2009 refinery purchases and high oil prices pushed up the company's revenue by 72% in 2010 and dramatically lifted its operating and net income.

HISTORY

HollyFrontier was founded in 1947 as General Appliance Corp. to process other companies' crude oil; the current name was adopted in 1952. As Holly the company grew with the number of gas-guzzling cars in the 1950s and 1960s and in the 1970s it developed its Navajo refinery in New Mexico. In 1981 Holly began producing higher-grade gasoline and started an asphalt company at Navajo.

In 1984 Holly became a partner in Montana Refining and later bought the entire business. It upgraded the Navajo refinery in the early 1990s to meet the demand for unleaded gasoline. In 1995 Amoco Mapco and Holly formed a joint venture the 265-mile Rio Grande Pipeline (completed in 1997) to transport natural gas liquids to Mexico.

Also in 1997 FINA and Holly allied to expand and use Holly's pipelines in the southwestern US. A proposed merger with another southwestern refiner Giant Industries died in 1998 because of federal antitrust concerns and a billion-dollar lawsuit filed against Holly by Longhorn Partners Pipeline. Court papers revealed in 2000 that Holly had paid $4 million to fight Longhorn's request for a permit to transport gasoline in its Houston-to-El Paso pipeline. The permit if approved would compete with Holly's own interests in western Texas.

Later in 2000 Holly cut its workforce by about 10% mostly at Navajo Refining. The next year Navajo Refining secured a $122 million contract to provide JP-8 jet fuel to the Defense Department.

In a move to expand its production capacity in 2003 Holly acquired ConocoPhillips' Woods Cross refinery and related assets for $25 million. Holly agreed to be acquired by Frontier Oil for about $450 million that year but the companies terminated the agreement and litigation between the parties resulted.

In 2004 the company spun off its Navajo refinery-related refined petroleum pipeline and other distribution assets as Holly Energy Partners L.P.; it retains a 45% interest in the company.

In 2005 the Delaware Chancery Court ruled that Frontier Oil had not proved that Holly had repudiated the merger agreement and awarded Frontier Oil only $1 in damages. Also that year Holly acquired the remaining 51% of NK Asphalt Producers that it did not already own. The company sold its intermediate feedstock pipelines connecting two refining facilities in Lovington and Artesia New Mexico to Holly Energy Partners for $81.5 million.

To free up cash in 2008 it sold 136 miles of crude oil trunk lines and some tankage assets to Holly Energy Partners for $180 million.

EXECUTIVES

VP Marketing and Product Supply Holly Refining & Marketing, Gregory A. White
VP Special Projects Holly Corporation and Holly Refining & Marketing, James G. Townsend, age 57
President CEO and Director, Michael C. (Mike) Jennings, age 47
VP and Project Manager Holly Refining & Marketing Company, Randall R. Howes
President Holly Energy Partners and Holly Logistic Services, David G. Blair, age 53
Chairman, Matthew P. (Matt) Clifton, age 60, $922,500 total compensation
VP and Controller, Scott C. Surplus
SVP Strategy and Corporate Development, Bruce R. Shaw, age 44, $325,000 total compensation
VP Navajo Refinery Holly Refining & Marketing, James E. (Jim) Resinger
SVP Refining Operations, James M. (Jim) Stump
EVP and COO, David L. Lamp, age 54, $553,500 total compensation
EVP and CFO, Douglas S. (Doug) Aron, age 38
VP Investor Relations Holly Corporation and Holly Logistic Services, M. Neale Hickerson, age 59
VP Asphalt Operations Holly Refining & Marketing, Mark A. Plake, age 49
VP and Treasurer Holly Corporation Holly Logistic Services and Holly Refining & Marketing, Stephen D. Wise
VP Merchant Crude Oil Holly Refining & Marketing, R. Scott Louderback
VP Woods Cross Refinery Holly Refining & Marketing, Lynn P. Keddington
SVP Supply and Marketing, George J. Damiris, age 52, $300,000 total compensation
VP Human Resources Holly Corporation Holly Refining & Marketing and Holly Logistic Services, Nancy F. Hartmann
VP Crude Supply Holly Corporation and Holly Refining & Marketing, Thomas G. Creery
VP and General Counsel, Denise C. McWatters, age 52, $250,000 total compensation
VP Information Technology, Nellson D. Burns
VP Operations Holly Logistic Services, Mark T. Cunningham
VP Corporate Environmental Health and Safety, David Jelmini
President CEO and Director, Michael C. (Mike) Jennings, age 47
Director, Leldon E. (Lel) Echols, age 56
Director, Paul T. Stoffel, age 78
Director, Robert G. McKenzie, age 74
Director, Jack P. Reid, age 75
Director, Buford P. Berry, age 76
Director, Tommy A. Valenta
Auditors: Ernst&YoungLLP

LOCATIONS

HQ: HollyFrontier Corporation
2828 N. Harwood Ste. 1300, Dallas TX 75201-1507
Phone: 214-871-3555 **Fax:** 214-871-3560
Web: hollyfrontier.com

PRODUCTS/OPERATIONS

2011 Sales

	$ mil.	% of total
Refining	15,392	99
HEP	213	1
Corporate & other	1	-
Adjustments	(167.7)	-
Total	**15,439**	**100**

COMPETITORS

BP
Crown Central
Exxon Mobil
George Warren
Marathon Petroleum
Sunoco
Tesoro
Valero Energy
Western Refining Inc.
Williams Companies

HISTORICAL FINANCIALS

Company Type: Public

Income Statement FYE: December 31

	REVENUE ($ mil.)	NET INCOME ($ mil.)	NET PROFIT MARGIN	EMPLOYEES
12/11	15,439	1,023	6.6%	2,382
12/10	8,322	103	1.2%	1,661
12/09	4,834	19	0.4%	1,632
12/08	5,867	120	2.1%	978
12/07	4,791	334	7.0%	909
Annual Growth	34.0%	32.3%	—	27.2%

2011 Year-End Financials

Debt ratio: 11.78%
Return on equity: 19.67%
Cash ($ mil.): 1,578
Current ratio: 177.22
Long-term debt ($ mil.): 1,214
No. of shares (mil.): 209
Dividends
Yield: —
Payout: 20.83%
Market value ($ mil.): 4,898

	STOCK PRICE ($) FY Close	P/E High	P/E Low	PER SHARE ($) Earnings	Dividends	Book Value
12/11	23.40	12	3	6.42	0.00	24.86
12/10	40.77	42	24	0.97	0.30	6.55
12/09	25.63	169	88	0.20	0.30	5.83
12/08	18.23	47	9	1.19	0.30	5.42
12/07	50.89	26	15	2.99	0.23	5.64
Annual Growth	(17.7%)	—	—	21.1%	—	44.9%

Home BancShares, Inc.

At this Home you don't have to stash your cash under the mattress. Home BancShares is the holding company for Centennial Bank which operates more than 100 branches in Arkansas Alabama and Florida. The bank offers traditional services such as checking savings and money market accounts; IRAs; and CDs. It focuses on commercial real estate lending including construction land development and agricultural loans which make up more than 60% of its lending portfolio. The bank also writes residential mortgage business and consumer loans. Nonbank subsidiaries offer trust and insurance services. Investments are available to customers through an agreement with third-party provider LPL Financial.

In 2010 Home BancShares capitalized on the mortgage crisis in Florida and expanded in the Orlando area by acquiring the seven branches and most of the assets and deposits of the failed Old Southern Bank in an FDIC-assisted transaction. Also in FDIC-assisted deals Home BancShares later acquired the operations of Wakulla Bank Coastal Community Bank Bayside Savings Bank and Gulf State Community Bank adding more than 25 more branches in Florida's panhandle a new market for the company.

Home BancShares entered another new market with the 2012 acquisition of Vision Bank from Park National. The deal included 17 branches along the Florida panhandle and Gulf Coast and gave Home BancShares its first locations in Alabama. Also in 2012 it bought Florida-based Premier Bank from Premier Bank Holding Company and Heritage Bank of Florida with offices in Tampa Lutz and Wesley Chapel. The company continues to look for additional acquisitions including other institutions seized by regulators in and contiguous to its geographical markets.

While the loans acquired through the FDIC are covered under loss-sharing agreements with the regulator Home Bancshares doesn't have that luxury with its own portfolio. Its loan charge-offs ballooned in 2010 creating a drag on the company's bottom line.

Home BancShares consolidated its banking subsidiaries including Bank of Mountain View Community Bank First State Bank Marine Bank and Twin City Bank into Centennial Bank in order to unify and strengthen its brand. The move which also reduced costs helped to goose earnings in 2009.

Chairman John Allison and his family own around 10% of Home BancShares; including his stake executives and directors together own nearly a quarter of the company. Allison and company vice chairman Robert "Bunny" Adcock formed Home BancShares in 1998.

EXECUTIVES

Chairman, John W. Allison, age 65, $31,731 total compensation
CFO Treasurer and Director, Randy E. Mayor, age 47, $196,266 total compensation
CEO and Director, C. Randall (Randy) Sims, age 57, $206,000 total compensation
Regional President Centennial Bank, Robert F. Birch Jr., age 62, $190,000 total compensation
Regional President Centennial Bank, Tracy M. French, age 50, $206,000 total compensation
CEO and Director Bank of Mountain View, Michael L. (Mickey) Waddington, age 69
Chief Accounting Officer and Investor Relations Officer, Brian S. Davis, age 46
Vice Chairman, Robert H. Adcock Jr., age 63
President CEO and Director Centennial Bank, Chris S. Roberts, age 43
Market President. Keys, Teresa Condas
Regional President Centennial Bank, Robert H. Padgett, age 53
Director, Alex R. Lieblong, age 61
CFO Treasurer and Director, Randy E. Mayor, age 47
CEO and Director, C. Randall (Randy) Sims, age 57
Director, Richard H. Ashley, age 56
Director, Dale A. Bruns, age 69
Director; Chairman Marine Bank, Richard A. Buckheim, age 68
Director, Jack E. Engelkes, age 62
Director; Chairman Bank of Mountain View, James G. Hinkle, age 63
Director, William G. Thompson, age 64
Vice Chairman, Robert H. Adcock Jr., age 63
Auditors: BKDLLP

LOCATIONS

HQ: Home BancShares Inc.
719 Harkrider Ste. 100, Conway AR 72032
Phone: 501-328-4797 **Fax:** 501-328-4679
Web: www.homebancshares.com

PRODUCTS/OPERATIONS

2010 Sales

	$ mil.	% of total
Interest		
Loans	137	64

Investment securities	12	6
Other	0	-
Noninterest		
Gain on acquisitions	34	16
Service charges on deposit accounts	13	6
Other service charges & fees	7	3
FDIC indemnification accretion	4	2
Mortgage lending	3	2
Other	2	1
Total	**216**	**100**

COMPETITORS

Arvest Bank
Bank of America
Bank of the Ozarks
BB&T
BBX Capital
First Federal Bancshares of Arkansas
Regions Financial
Simmons First
TIB Financial
Woodforest Financial

HISTORICAL FINANCIALS

Company Type: Public

Income Statement

FYE: December 31

	ASSETS ($ mil.)	NET INCOME ($ mil.)	INCOME AS % OF ASSETS	EMPLOYEES
12/11	3,604	54	1.5%	774
12/10	3,762	17	0.5%	698
12/09	2,684	26	1.0%	605
12/08	2,580	10	0.4%	594
12/07	2,291	20	0.9%	595
Annual Growth	12.0%	27.9%	—	6.8%

2011 Year-End Financials

Debt ratio: 5.19%
Return on equity: 11.55%
Cash ($ mil.): 184
Current ratio: —
Long-term debt ($ mil.): 187

No. of shares (mil.): 28
Dividends
Yield: —
Payout: 14.49%
Market value ($ mil.): 733

	STOCK PRICE ($) FY Close	P/E High/Low		PER SHARE ($) Earnings	Dividends	Book Value
12/11	25.91	14	11	1.85	0.00	16.77
12/10	22.03	56	38	0.52	0.22	16.76
12/09	24.07	26	14	1.02	0.22	16.45
12/08	26.95	67	41	0.45	0.20	12.96
12/07	20.97	25	19	0.84	0.12	12.35
Annual Growth	5.4%	—	—	21.8%	—	7.9%

Home Depot Inc

When embarking on household projects many start their journey at The Home Depot. As the world's largest home improvement chain and fourth-largest US retailer the company operates about 2250 stores in the US Canada Mexico and China as well as an online business. It targets the do-it-yourself (DIY) and professional markets with its selection of some 40000 items including lumber flooring plumbing supplies garden products tools paint and appliances. Home Depot also offers installation services for carpeting cabinetry and other products. Stung by the deep recession and housing crisis in the US the firm is beginning to regain its footing by focusing on its core Home Depot stores and exiting China.

HISTORY

Bernard Marcus and Arthur Blank founded The Home Depot in 1978 after they were fired (under disputed circumstances) from Handy Dan Home Improvement Centers. They joined Handy Dan coworker Ronald Brill to launch a "new and improved" home center for the do-it-yourselfer (DIY). In 1979 they opened three stores in the fast-growing Atlanta area and expanded to four stores in 1980.

Home Depot went public opened four stores in South Florida and posted sales of $50 million in 1981. The chain entered Louisiana and Arizona next. By 1983 sales were more than $250 million.

In 1984 Home Depot's stock was listed on the NYSE and the company acquired nine Bowater Home Centers in the South. Through subsequent stock and debenture offerings Home Depot continued to grow entering California (Handy Dan's home turf) with six new stores in 1985.

Back on track in 1986 sales exceeded $1 billion in the firm's 60 stores. Home Depot began the current policy of "low day-in day-out pricing" the following year achieving Marcus' dream of eliminating sales events. The company entered the competitive northeastern market with stores in Long Island New York in 1988 and opened its first EXPO Design Center in San Diego.

Home Depot's sales continued to rise during the 1990-92 recession and the retailer kept opening stores. It entered Canada in 1994 when it acquired a 75% interest in Aikenhead's a DIY chain that it converted to the Home Depot name (it bought the remaining 25% in 1998).

A series of gender-bias lawsuits plagued the company in 1994 as female workers claimed they were not treated on an equal basis with male employees. Home Depot reached a $65 million out-of-court settlement in 1997 but not before the company was ordered to pay another female employee $1.7 million in a case in California.

Troubles aside Home Depot roared past the 500-store mark in 1997. That year Blank succeeded Marcus as the company's CEO; Marcus remained chairman. Home Depot bought National Blind & Wallpaper Factory (a mail-order firm) and Maintenance Warehouse (a direct-mail marketer) that year.

The company introduced its 40000-sq.-ft. Villager's Hardware stores designed to compete with smaller hardware shops in 1999 in New Jersey. It also bought Georgia Lighting an Atlanta lighting designer distributor and retailer. Home Depot later began adding large appliances to some stores following competitor Lowe's (most stores had them by 2000).

In 2000 Home Depot bought Apex Supply (a 20-plus-location plumbing distributor in Georgia South Carolina and Tennessee) and opened a flooring-only test store in Texas. Later that year the company named General Electric executive Robert Nardelli as its president and CEO. Marcus and Blank were named co-chairmen.

The company opened 200 new stores in 2001 and bought Total HOME a home improvement chain with four stores in Mexico. Additionally Marcus was named chairman after Blank stepped down. Later in the year Marcus retired and Nardelli became chairman. Also that year the company said it was scrapping its Villager's Hardware experiment to test a small-store concept in urban areas.

In 2002 Home Depot opened its first small store a 61000-sq.-ft. outlet in New York City. Further increasing its presence in Mexico the company acquired the four-store Del Norte chain in Ciudad Juarez that year.

Also in 2002 Home Depot created a new subsidiary HD Builder Solutions through the acquisition of Floors Inc. Arvada Hardwood Floor Company and FloorWorks Inc. The next year the company acquired roofing installer IPUSA and replacement windows and siding installer RMA Home Services.

Home Depot expanded its business in the homebuilder market in January 2004 by purchasing Creative Touch Interiors a floor and counter installer in California and Nevada. Additionally early that year Home Depot opened its largest store ever –205000 sq. ft. –in wealthy Anaheim Hills California. It also announced in February 2004 that it had partnered with AARP to hire people older than 50.

In addition that month Home Depot became the exclusive retailer of Maytag's SkyBox a home beverage dispenser. It acquired Home Mart a 20-unit Mexican chain in that June giving it a total of more than 40 stores in Mexico. Also in 2004 the company acquired White Cap Construction Supply; agreed to settle discrimination claims of some Colorado employees for $5.5 million; opened two trend-setting urban-oriented stores in Manhattan; and bought 18 stores from Kmart.

In mid-2005 Home Depot acquired National Waterworks Holdings (now National Waterworks Inc.) and Williams Bros. Lumber of Georgia and folded them both into its The Home Depot Supply business (called HD Supply until it was sold). In September Home Depot Direct launched 10 Crescent Lane a high-end home decorating catalog and Web site offering furniture lighting and decorative accessories housewares and more. While some Home Depot locations in Louisiana and Texas were temporarily shut down by hurricanes Katrina and Rita its stores (and those of rival Lowe's and other building suppliers) are among the first places people visited in the wake of the disaster. In the immediate aftermath of the storms Home Depot stocked nontraditional items such as food and diapers in affected areas. Also in 2005 the company shuttered 15 EXPO Design Center stores which cater to affluent homeowners and converted five others to The Home Depot format. In all in 2005 Home Depot spent about $2.5 billion to acquire 21 companies.

The company's direct-to-consumer division launched a pair of high-end catalogs in 2005: 10 Crescent Lane and Paces Trading Company. However the catalogs which featured home furnishings and lighting products were discontinued in 2006 and selected products were folded back into the main Home Depot store catalog and website.

In January 2006 Home Depot acquired carpet and upholstery cleaning franchisor Chem-Dry and folded it into its At-Home Services division. (Chem-Dry has some 4000 franchises worldwide including 2500 in the US). In March the company completed its largest acquisition to date: the construction repair and maintenance products distributor Hughes Supply Inc. for $3.2 billion. That purchase was followed in May by the acquisition of Cox Lumber Co. a Tampa-based provider of trusses doors and lumber-related products. Also Home Depot acquired Home Decorators Collection a company specializing in catalog and online sales of home decor merchandise in 2006. Lured by the growth potential of the vast Chinese market the retailer purchased a majority stake in Taiwan-based HomeWay for about $100 million in late 2006. HomeWay operates DIY warehouse stores in northern China.

Joining the trend of big-box retailers adding gasoline and convenience store services to fuel sales Home Depot opened its first Home Depot Fuel locations in Tennessee and Georgia in 2006.

In early 2007 Nardelli left the company and vice chairman and EVP Frank Blake took the top spot. Home Depot decided to close its handful of flooring-only stores that year. The apparent nail in Nardelli's coffin was his autocratic management style and hefty compensation package (strategically based on options rather than shareholder returns and estimated at $245 million over five years). Nardelli left Home Depot with a $210 million severance package.

The company sold its HD Supply business in 2007 to Bain Capital Carlyle Group and Clayton Dubilier & Rice. The retailer used the proceeds to help it make a $10 billion stock repurchase of more than 15% of its market capitalization.

The Home Depot closed two stores in China in fiscal 2011.

EXECUTIVES

SVP Merchandising Decor, Gordon M. Erickson
EVP Corporate Services and CFO, Carol B. Tome, age 55, $910,000 total compensation
VP Corporate Communications and External Affairs, Brad Shaw
SVP and Chief Marketing Officer, Trish Mueller
President Mexico, Ricardo E. Saldivar, age 59
Chairman and CEO, Francis S. (Frank) Blake, age 62, $1,025,000 total compensation
President Canada, William (Bill) Lennie
EVP Merchandising, Craig A. Menear, age 54, $675,000 total compensation
SVP Supply Chain, Mark Holifield
SVP IT Store Field and Corporate Support, Cara D. Kinzey, age 45
EVP US Stores, Marvin R. Ellison, age 47, $625,000 total compensation
EVP and CIO, Matthew A. (Matt) Carey, age 47
SVP Merchandising Hardlines, Bill Boltz
EVP Human Resources, Timothy M. (Tim) Crow, age 56
President Western Division, Joseph (Joe) McFarland III, age 43
SVP Merchandising Building Materials, Giles Bowman
SVP Retail Finance, Edward P. (Ted) Decker
SVP Operations, Marc D. Powers
President Southern Division, Ann-Marie Campbell
President Online, Hal Lawton
SVP Merchandising Services, Kevin Scott
Senior Director Corporate Communications, Ron DeFeo
Director Enterprise Data Warehouse, Cynthia Czabal
EVP General Counsel and Corporate Secretary, Teresa W. Roseborough
SVP Brand and Product Development, John Deaton
President Northern Division, Aaron Flowe
Director, Albert P. (Al) Carey, age 60
Director, F. Duane Ackerman, age 69
Director, Karen L. Katen, age 63
Director, Ari Bousbib, age 50
Director, Ronald L. (Ron) Sargent, age 56
Director, Gregory D. (Greg) Brenneman, age 50
Director, J. Frank Brown, age 53
Director, Armando M. Codina, age 65
Director, Bonnie G. Hill, age 70
Auditors: KPMGLLP

LOCATIONS

HQ: Home Depot Inc
2455 Paces Ferry Road, N.W., Atlanta, GA 30339
Phone: 770 433-8211 **Fax:** 770 431-2707
Web: www.homedepot.com

2012 Locations

	No.
US	1,974
Canada	180
Mexico	91
China	7
Total	**2,252**

PRODUCTS/OPERATIONS

2012 Sales

	% of total
Plumbing electrical &	31
Hardware &	29
Building materials lumber &	21
Paint &	19
Total	**100**

Selected Private Labels and Proprietary Brands

Behr Premium Plus (paint)
Glacier Bay (fixtures)
Hampton Bay (lighting)
Husky (hand tools)
Mill' s Pride (cabinets)
Vigoro (lawn care products)

COMPETITORS

84 Lumber
Abbey Carpet
Ace Hardware
Amazon.com
B&Q
Best Buy
BMC
CCA Global
Costco Wholesale
Do it Best
F.W. Webb
Guardian Building Products Distribution
Improvement Direct
Kelly-Moore
Lowe' s
Menard
Northern Tool
Pacific Coast Building Products
RONA
Sears Holdings
Sherwin-Williams
Stock Building Supply
Sutherland Lumber
Target Corporation
Tractor Supply
True Value
W.E. Aubuchon
Wal-Mart
WinWholesale
Wolseley

HISTORICAL FINANCIALS

Company Type: Public

Income Statement FYE: January 29

	REVENUE ($ mil.)	NET INCOME ($ mil.)	NET PROFIT MARGIN	EMPLOYEES
01/12	70,395	3,883	5.5%	331,000
01/11	67,997	3,338	4.9%	321,000
01/10*	66,176	2,661	4.0%	317,000
02/09	71,288	2,260	3.2%	322,000
02/08	77,349	4,395	5.7%	331,000
Annual Growth	(2.3%)	(3.0%)	—	0.0%

*Fiscal year change

2012 Year-End Financials

Debt ratio: 26.63%
Return on equity: 21.70%
Cash ($ mil.): 1,987
Current ratio: 154.86
Long-term debt ($ mil.): 10,758
No. of shares (mil.): 1,537
Dividends
Yield: —
Payout: 42.11%
Market value ($ mil.): 68,965

	STOCK PRICE ($) FY Close	P/E High/Low		PER SHARE ($) Earnings	Dividends	Book Value
01/12	44.87	18	11	2.47	0.00	11.64
01/11	36.70	19	13	2.01	0.00	11.64
01/10*	28.01	19	11	1.57	0.00	11.42
02/09	21.53	23	14	1.34	0.00	10.48
02/08	30.45	18	10	2.37	0.00	10.48
Annual Growth	10.2%	—	—	1.0%	—	2.7%

*Fiscal year change

Honeywell International, Inc.

Thermostats and jet engines seem worlds apart but they're the wind beneath Honeywell International's wings. More than a century old the company is a diverse industrial conglomerate with four segments; the largest are Automation and Control Solutions (ACS –making HVAC and manufacturing process products) and Aerospace (turbo engines and flight safety and landing systems). Additional segments include Performance Materials and Technologies (PMT formerly Honeywell Specialty Materials thermal switches fibers and chemicals) and Transportation Systems (engine boosting systems and brake materials). The US government accounts for about 12% of revenue (primarily Aerospace). The US represents about 60% of sales.

HISTORY

During WWI Germany controlled much of the world's chemical industry causing dye and drug shortages. In response "Washington Post" publisher Eugene Meyer and scientist William Nichols organized the Allied Chemical & Dye Corporation in 1920.

Allied opened a synthetic ammonia plant in 1928 near Hopewell Virginia and became the world's leading producer of ammonia. After WWII Allied began making nylon refrigerants and other products. The company became Allied Chemical Corporation in 1958.

Seeking a supplier of raw materials for its chemical products Allied bought Union Texas Natural Gas in 1962. In the early 1970s CEO John Connor sold many of the firm's unprofitable businesses and invested in oil and gas exploration. By 1979 when Edward Hennessy became CEO Union Texas produced 80% of Allied's income.

Hennessy led the company into the electronics and technical markets. Under a new name Allied Corporation (1981) it bought the Bendix Corporation an aerospace and automotive company in 1983. In 1985 Allied merged with Signal Companies (founded by Sam Mosher in 1922) to form AlliedSignal. The company spun off more than 40 unprofitable chemical and engineering businesses over the next two years.

Larry Bossidy hired from General Electric in 1991 as the new CEO began to cut waste and buy growth businesses. In 1998 alone the company made 13 acquisitions. Late in 1999 the company acquired Honeywell (which dated back to 1906) in a deal valued at $15 billion and changed its name to Honeywell International. Honeywell after trying to make a go of it in the computer and telecommunications industries had refocused on its core products lines –thermostats security systems and other automation equipment. The chairman and CEO of the original Honeywell Michael Bonsignore took the same titles in the combined company.

In 2000 Honeywell picked up building security and fire systems company Pittway for $2 billion. The same year Honeywell sold its fluid connectors business to Eaton. Then amid lower-than-expected earnings the company announced plans to cut an additional 6000 jobs on top of the 11000 cuts already planned. It also announced plans to sell its Bendix (brake pads) and chlor-alkali chemical manufacturing businesses taking a $300 million to $350 million charge in the process. Around the same time school bus and truck manufacturers began recalling vehicles made with a Honeywell (Bendix) air-braking system that could fail due to a design flaw.

Late in 2000 Honeywell was reportedly close to inking a deal to be acquired by United Technologies but the talks ended when industrial behemoth GE made a better offer. Honeywell then agreed to be acquired by GE in a stock deal worth about $45 billion. After the deal was inked Honeywell shelved its plans to sell its friction materials automotive consumer products security monitoring and fine chemicals operations.

In 2001 Honeywell's shareholders approved the deal with GE; the US Justice Department also approved the deal if Honeywell sold its helicopter engine business and authorized other companies to perform maintenance and repair services on some of its aircraft engines. European Union regulators saw things differently and the deal apparently collapsed in June when GE –which had offered to sell assets that generated about $2.2 billion a year – balked at demands that it sell virtually all of Honeywell's avionics operations. Honeywell then offered itself at a reduced price but GE declined. The EU formally rejected the acquisition in July and Honeywell ousted CEO Bonsignore replacing him with Bossidy –not only the former head of AlliedSignal but a former GE executive and close friend of Jack Welch.

In September the company said that it would take cost-cutting measures with charges of almost $1 billion; it increased the total of previously announced layoffs cutting about 16000 jobs (approximately 13% of its workforce) by year's end. In December Honeywell agreed to pay Northrop Grumman $440 million to settle an antitrust and patent infringement lawsuit filed against it by Litton (now a part of Northrop Grumman) in 1990.

In 2002 David Cote (like Bossidy a former GE executive) the former chairman president and CEO of TRW was named president and CEO of Honeywell replacing Bossidy (Cote also replaced Bossidy as chairman in 2002). The same year the ACS division acquired Ultrak's closed-circuit television business. Honeywell also bought Invensys Sensor Systems which made vehicle appliance and aerospace sensors and controls from Invensys for $415 million. The company sold its Advanced Circuits operations to TTM Technologies for about $2 million in an effort to focus on its core businesses at the close of the year.

Honeywell sold its Engineering Plastics business to BASF in 2003 in exchange for BASF's nylon fiber business –which became part of Honeywell's Specialty Materials unit –and $90 million. Early in 2005 Honeywell acquired UK-based Novar plc for about $1.7 billion. Novar's operations included aluminum products building control and security systems and checkbook printing.

Late in 2005 Honeywell sold its US nylon fibers business to Shaw Industries and its Clarke American Checks (check printing) business to M&F Worldwide for $800 million. It also bought Dow Chemical's 50% stake in UOP their energy refining joint venture for $825 million.

Honeywell sold Novar's Indalex Aluminum Solutions operations to Sun Capital Partners for $425 million early in 2006. Not long after Honeywell completed the acquisition of First Technology PLC a maker of gas sensing automotive and safety equipment for $718 million.

While First Technology's gas sensing operations were integrated into Honeywell's ACS division Honeywell sold First Technology's crash test dummies business to HgCapital a European private equity company for about $94 million. Honeywell later agreed to sell First Technology Automotive – a maker of automotive sensor valves crash switch devices and electromechanical control devices –to Sensata Technologies for $90 million. The deal was completed late in 2006.

Honeywell acquired the Burtek Systems/Security Systems Division business of Richardson Electronics for $80 million in cash in 2007. Honeywell combined the business with its ADI security distribution business. Burtek/SSD was a distributor of low-voltage products for commercial and residential audio burglar and fire alarm CCTV access control sound and data/network communications. Its sales in fiscal 2006 exceeded $108 million.

In mid-2007 Honeywell acquired Dimensions International a provider of logistics support to the US military and other defense agencies. The deal was valued at about $230 million. Dimensions was integrated into the Honeywell Technology Solutions subsidiary.

The company completed the purchase of the Netherlands-based Enraf Holding B.V. for about $260 million later in 2007. Enraf a maker of measurement and controls solutions used in the exploration production and transportation of energy products became part of Honeywell's process solutions division. Also that same year Honeywell bought Hand Held Products Inc. a maker of automatic identification and data collection (AIDC) equipment. The company's products were used for on-site mobile transaction processing in the health care logistics retail and transportation industries. Honeywell paid $390 million for Hand Held which had 2006 sales of about $285 million. Hand Held became part of Honeywell's ACS division.

Just weeks after the Hand Held announcement Honeywell bought Maxon Corp. for about $185 million. Maxon a maker of industrial burners and combustion equipment became part of the Environmental and Combustion Controls business within ACS.

For a purchase price of approximately $715 million the company acquired Metrologic Instruments in mid-2008. The acquisition brought data capture and collection hardware and software for inclusion in the ACS products portfolio. In May of that year it picked up Norcross Safety Products (now called Honeywell Safety Products) for more than $1 billion. The acquisition expanded the division's life safety segment.

The company sold its Consumable Solutions segment to BE Aerospace for $1.15 billion in cash and stock in 2008. Consumable Solutions which distributed aerospace fasteners and hardware around the world to airlines distributors flight service centers OEMs and repair shops was considered a non-strategic business.

In a larger investment Honeywell purchased Germany-based RMG Group and subsidiaries in 2009 for $416 million. A maker of regulating and safety systems metering and shutoff and installation services for natural gas businesses RMG Group firmed up Honeywell's position in transporting storing and distributing natural gas.

Bolstering its ACS segment the company purchased Matrikon in mid-2010 for approximately $139 million (C$144 million). The company enhanced Honeywell's industrial lineup for monitoring and improving the performance and safety of oil and gas wells and mining equipment.

In the fall of 2010 the company purchased protective gear maker Sperian Protection. The $1.4 billion (E1 billion) all-cash offer outdid (by 63%) a previous bid made by European buyout firm Cinven.

EXECUTIVES

SVP and CFO, David J. (Dave) Anderson, age 62, $900,000 total compensation
Chairman and CEO, David M. (Dave) Cote, age 59, $1,800,000 total compensation
VP Strategy and Business Development, Rhonda G. Germany
VP Secretary and Deputy Corporate Counsel, Thomas F. Larkins
President and CEO Automation and Control Solutions, Roger Fradin, age 58, $1,050,000 total compensation
President and CEO Performance Materials and Technologies, Andreas Kramvis, age 59, $550,000 total compensation
President and CEO Aerospace, Timothy O. (Tim) Mahoney, age 55
SVP Human Resources and Communications, Mark R. James, age 50
Media Contact Corporate Public Affairs, Robert C. (Rob) Ferris
Media Contact Corporate Public Affairs, Victoria Streitfeld
President and CEO Global High Growth Regions, Shane Tedjarati
VP and CIO, Mike Lang, age 48
President and CEO Transportation Business, Alexandre (Alex) Ismail, age 47
SVP and General Counsel, Katherine L. (Kate) Adams, age 47
VP and Controller, Kathleen A. Winters, age 44
VP Investor Relations, Elena Doom
SVP Engineering and Operations; President HON Technology Solutions, Krishna Mikkilineni
President Honeywell China, Stephen Shang
Director, George Paz, age 56
Director, Gordon M. Bethune, age 70
Director, Lord Clive R. Hollick, age 67
Director, Jaime Chico Pardo, age 62
Director, Kevin Burke, age 62
Director, D. Scott Davis, age 60
Director, Bradley T. Sheares, age 55
Director, Linnet F. Deily, age 67
Director, Judd Gregg, age 65
Independent Director, Jaime Pardo
Auditors: PricewaterhouseCoopersLLP

LOCATIONS

HQ: Honeywell International Inc.
101 Columbia Rd., Morristown NJ 07962-1219
Phone: 973-455-2000 **Fax:** 973-455-4807
Web: www.honeywell.com

2011 Sales

	$ mil.	% of total
US	21,005	58
Europe	9,604	26
Rest of world	5,920	16
Total	**36,529**	**100**

PRODUCTS/OPERATIONS

2011 Sales

	$ mil.	% of total
Automation & control solutions	15,536	43
Aerospace	11,475	31
Performance materials & technologies	5,659	15
Transportation systems	3,859	11
Total	**36,529**	**100**

2011 Sales

	$ mil.	% of total
Product sales	28,745	79
Service sales	7,784	21
Total	**36,529**	**100**

Selected Products

Aerospace
- Aircraft engines (turbine propulsion)
- Aircraft information systems
- Aircraft landing systems
- Aircraft and airport lighting
- Auxiliary power units
- Avionics systems
- Control products
  - Guidance
  - Radar
  - Pressure
  - Thermal
- Electric power systems
- Environmental control systems
- Inertial sensors
- Space products and subsystems

Automation and Control Solutions
- Building Solutions and Services
  - Building information services
  - Energy management
  - Enterprise building integration
  - HVAC and building control
  - Security and asset management
- Environmental combustion controls and sensing controls
  - Heating and air-conditioning controls
  - Humidifiers and thermostats
  - Indoor air quality products
- Process Automation Products
  - Analytical instrumentation
  - Control software and industrial automation systems
  - Industrial control equipment and systems
  - Production management software
- Security and Life Safety Products
  - Access controls and closed-circuit TV
  - Emergency lighting
  - Fire products and systems
  - Gas-detection products
  - Home health monitoring and nurse call systems

Specialty Materials
- Absorbents
- Advanced fibers and composites
- Catalysts
- Electronic chemicals
- Fluorine products
- Fluorocarbons
- Hydrofluoric acid
- Imaging chemicals
- Nuclear services
- Performance chemicals
- Renewable fuels and chemicals
- Research and fine chemicals
- Resins and chemicals
- Semiconductor materials and services
- Specialty additives and films

Transportation Systems
- Aluminum radiators
- Anti-lock brakes
- Brake components and materials
  - Hydraulic components
  - Pads
  - Fluid
- Charge-air systems
- Friction materials
- Thermal systems
- Turbochargers

Selected Services

Aerospace
- Ground support
- Repair and overhaul
- Spare parts
- Training

Automation and Control Solutions
- Building information and energy management
- HVAC maintenance and repair

COMPETITORS

3M
ABB AG
Air Products
Akebono Brake
Arkema
Asahi Glass
Astronautics
BAE Systems Inc.
BASF SE
Bechtel
Boeing
BorgWarner
Clariant
Computer Sciences Corp.
Daikin
DSM
DuPont
DynCorp International
Eastman Chemical
Eaton
Emerson Electric
Endress + Hauser
Exxon Mobil
Federal-Mogul
Garmin
GE
Goodrich Corp.
Halma
Hella
Ingersoll-Rand
Intermec
Invensys
ITT Corp.
Jeppesen Sanderson
Johnson Controls
KVH Industries
Kyocera
L-3 Communications
Lockheed Martin
Lonza
LSI Industries
Merck KGaA
Mexichem
Mine Safety Appliances
Modine Manufacturing
Motorola Solutions
NGK SPARK PLUG
Northrop Grumman
Old World Industries
Parker-Hannifin
Pelco
Raytheon
Riken Corporation
Robert Bosch
Rockwell Automation
Rolls-Royce
SAFRAN
SAIC
Sauer-Danfoss
Schneider Electric
Shinko Electric
Siemens AG
Sigma-Aldrich
Solvay
Teijin
Thales
Thermo Fisher Scientific
Trimble Navigation
Tyco
United Technologies
Unitika
Universal Avionics
Valeo
Yokogawa Electric

HISTORICAL FINANCIALS

Company Type: Public

Income Statement — FYE: December 31

	REVENUE ($ mil.)	NET INCOME ($ mil.)	NET PROFIT MARGIN	EMPLOYEES
12/11	36,529	2,067	5.7%	132,000
12/10	33,370	2,022	6.1%	130,000
12/09	30,908	2,153	7.0%	122,000
12/08	36,556	2,792	7.6%	128,000
12/07	34,589	2,444	7.1%	122,000
Annual Growth	1.4%	(4.1%)	—	2.0%

2011 Year-End Financials

Debt ratio: 18.98%
Return on equity: 19.13%
Cash ($ mil.): 3,698
Current ratio: 131.44
Long-term debt ($ mil.): 6,881
No. of shares (mil.): 774
Dividends
Yield: —
Payout: 52.49%
Market value ($ mil.): 42,105

	STOCK PRICE ($) FY Close	P/E High/Low		PER SHARE ($) Earnings	Dividends	Book Value
12/11	54.35	23	16	2.61	0.00	13.95
12/10	53.16	21	14	2.59	1.21	13.62
12/09	39.20	14	8	2.85	1.21	11.57
12/08	32.83	16	6	3.76	1.10	9.78
12/07	61.57	19	14	3.16	1.00	12.35
Annual Growth	(3.1%)	—	—	(4.7%)	—	3.1%

Horace Mann Educators Corp.

Naming itself in honor of Horace Mann considered the father of public education Horace Mann Educators is an insurance holding company that targets K-12 school teachers and other public school employees throughout the US. Through its operating subsidiaries the company offers homeowners auto and individual and group life insurance as well as retirement annuities. Horace Mann employs some 750 agents many of whom are former teachers themselves. Writing business in 48 states and Washington DC the company derives about a third of its direct premiums and contract deposits from five states - California North Carolina Texas Minnesota and Illinois.

The company's strategy and business purpose is to serve educators and their families by providing tailored insurance and financial products personalized service and advice to support their long-term financial well-being through its dedicated sales force.

Horace Mann maintains a long-standing relationship with the country's biggest education association the National Education Association which has more than 3 million members. It has also established a number of advertising and sponsorship agreements with a host of smaller educator groups as a way to drum up new business leads.

In recent years the company has begun to move away from single-person agency operations to an agency business model (ABM) with multiple sales agents licensed product specialists and other support personnel based together in outside offices. The company saw enough success with the ABM model that it began migrating agents over to an exclusive agent agreement through which the agents become independent contractors that only sell Horace Mann products. By the end of 2011 more than 85% of its agency force was using the ABM and almost 75% were exclusive agents. The company plans to convert all of its agents to the exclusive agency model eventually.

To manage future risk in 2010 the company quit renewing and writing new homeowners policies in Florida. While this deflated the numbers of policies in force it helped the company reduce the cost of its reinsurance. Like other personal property/casualty insurers during the economic recession Horace Mann saw a drop in its new business generated as fewer people bought new cars or new homes.

In 2011 Horace Mann's revenue grew by 2% over 2010 but its net income of $70.5 million dropped from its 2010 level by 13%. This was mainly due to increased property and casualty catastrophe losses.

EXECUTIVES

Chief Compliance Officer Secretary and General Counsel, Ann M. Caparros, age 59, $190,800 total compensation
EVP and CFO, Dwayne D. Hallman, age 49, $246,132 total compensation
Chairman, Joseph J. (Joe) Melone, age 80
President CEO and Director, Peter H. (Pete) Heckman, age 66, $436,000 total compensation
SVP Human Resources and Administrative Operations, Paul D. Andrews, age 55, $228,000 total compensation
SVP and Controller, Bret A. Conklin, age 48
SVP Marketing, Robert B. Joyner, age 68, $190,425 total compensation
Chairman, Gabriel L. Shaheen, age 58
VP Field Sales Management, Richard R. Schulenburg, age 58
EVP Property and Casualty, Thomas C. Wilkinson, age 54, $300,000 total compensation
EVP and Chief Marketing Officer, Stephen P. Cardinal, age 43
SVP Annuity and Life, Brent H. Hamann, age 51
Investor Relations Administrator, Karen Ruffatto
EVP Annuity and Life, Matthew P. Sharpe
Director, Charles R. Wright, age 70
Director, Stephen J. Hasenmiller, age 62
President CEO and Director, Peter H. (Pete) Heckman, age 66
Director, Mary Hatwood Futrell, age 72
Director, Charles A. Parker, age 77
Director, Roger J. Steinbecker, age 69
Chairman, Gabriel L. Shaheen, age 58
Director, Ronald J. Helow, age 68
Director, Robert Stricker, age 64
Auditors: KPMGLLP

LOCATIONS

HQ: Horace Mann Educators Corp.
1 Horace Mann Plaza, Springfield, IL 62715-0001
Phone: 217 789-2500
Web: www.horacemann.com

PRODUCTS/OPERATIONS

2011 Revenues

	$ mil.	% of total
Insurance premiums & contract charges earned	667	67
Net investment income	288	29
Net realized investment gains	37	4
Other income	5	-
Total	**998**	**100**

2011 Insurance Premiums & Contract Charges Earned

	% of total
Property &	82
Life	15
Annuity	3
Total	**100**

Selected Subsidiaries

Insurance Subsidiaries
- Educators Life Insurance Company of America (Illinois)
- Horace Mann Insurance Company (Illinois)
- Horace Mann Life Insurance Company (Illinois)
- Horace Mann Lloyds (Texas)
- Horace Mann Property & Casualty Insurance Company (Illinois)
- Teachers Insurance Company (Illinois)

Other Subsidiaries:
- ABM Service Corporation (Delaware)
- Horace Mann General Agency Inc. (Texas)
- Horace Mann Investors Inc. (Maryland)
- Horace Mann Lloyds Management Corporation (Texas)
- Horace Mann MGA and Brokerage of Florida Inc.
- Horace Mann Service Corporation (Illinois)

COMPETITORS

AIG
Allstate
Farmers Group
GEICO
ING Americas
Liberty Mutual Agency
LSW
MetLife
Nationwide
Progressive Corporation
Security Benefit Group
State Farm
TIAA-CREF
USAA
VALIC

HISTORICAL FINANCIALS

Company Type: Public

Income Statement

FYE: December 31

	ASSETS ($ mil.)	NET INCOME ($ mil.)	INCOME AS % OF ASSETS	EMPLOYEES
12/11	7,483	70	0.9%	1,596
12/10	7,005	80	1.2%	1,684
12/09	6,343	73	1.2%	1,866
12/08	5,507	10	0.2%	2,200
12/07	6,259	82	1.3%	2,300
Annual Growth	4.6%	(3.9%)	—	(8.7%)

2011 Year-End Financials

Debt ratio: 2.67%
Return on equity: 6.48%
Cash ($ mil.): 7
Current ratio: —
Long-term debt ($ mil.): 199
No. of shares (mil.): 39
Dividends
Yield: —
Payout: 27.06%
Market value ($ mil.): 545

	STOCK PRICE ($) FY Close	P/E High	P/E Low	PER SHARE ($) Earnings	Dividends	Book Value
12/11	13.71	10	6	1.70	0.00	27.33
12/10	18.04	9	6	1.97	0.35	22.19
12/09	12.50	8	3	1.81	0.24	18.36
12/08	9.19	70	19	0.27	0.37	11.49
12/07	18.94	12	9	1.86	0.42	16.41
Annual Growth	(7.8%)	—	—	(2.2%)	—	13.6%

Hormel Foods Corp.

The maker of such thrifty pantry staples as Spam (spiced pork and ham) lunch meat and Dinty Moore stew has turned sophisticated. In addition to canned meats Hormel Foods produces a slew of refrigerated processed meats and deli items ethnic entrees and frozen foods sold under the Hormel brand as well as Don Miguel and MegaMex Mexican Country Crock (side dishes) and Lloyd's barbeque. Foodservice offerings include Hormel Natural Choice meats Cafe H ethnic Austin Blues barbeque and Bread Ready pre-sliced meats. Hormel is also a major US turkey and pork processor churning out Jennie-O turkey Cure 81 hams and Always Tender pork. Thirty-four Hormel brands are ranked #1 or #2 in their respective markets.

HISTORY

George Hormel opened his Austin Minnesota slaughterhouse in an abandoned creamery in 1891. By 1900 Hormel had modernized his facilities to compete with larger meat processors. In 1903 the enterprise introduced its first brand name (Dairy Brand) and a year later began opening distribution centers nationwide. The scandal that ensued after the discovery in 1921 that an assistant controller had embezzled over $1 million almost broke the company causing Hormel to initiate tighter controls. By 1924 it was processing more than a million hogs annually. Hormel introduced canned ham two years later.

Jay Hormel George's son became president in 1929; under his guidance Hormel introduced Dinty Moore beef stew (1936) and SPAM (1937). A Hormel executive won a contest and $100 by submitting the name a contraction of "spiced ham." During WWII the US government bought over half of Hormel's output; it supplied SPAM to GIs and Allied forces.

In 1959 Hormel introduced its Little Sizzlers pork sausage and sold its billionth can of SPAM. New products rolled out in the 1960s included Hormel's Cure 81 ham (1963). By the mid-1970s the firm had more than 750 products.

The company survived a violent nationally publicized strike triggered by a pay cut in 1985. In the end only 500 of the original 1500 strikers returned to accept lower pay scales.

Sensing the consumer shift toward poultry Hormel purchased Jennie-O Foods in 1986. Later acquisitions included the House of Tsang and Oriental Deli (1992) Dubuque (processed pork 1993) and Herb-Ox (bouillon and dry soup mix 1993). After more than a century as Geo. A. Hormel & Co. the company began calling itself Hormel Foods in 1993 to reflect its expansion into non-pork foods. Former General Foods executive Joel Johnson was named president and CEO that year (and chairman two years later).

Hormel proved it could take a joke with the 1994 debut of its tongue-in-cheek SPAM catalog featuring dozens of SPAM-related products. But when a 1996 Muppets movie featured a porcine character named Spa'am Hormel sued Jim Henson Productions; a federal court gave Spa'am the go-ahead.

Also in 1996 Hormel teamed up with Mexican food processor Grupo Herdez to sell Herdez sauces and other Mexican food products in the US. It then formed a joint venture with Indian food producer Patak Spices (UK) to market its products in the US. Late that year Hormel paid $64 million for a 21% interest in Spanish food maker Campofrio Alimentacion.

Earnings fell in 1996 due in part to soaring hog prices. The company was hit hard again in 1998 when production contracts with hog growers meant it wound up paying premium rates despite a market glut. In 1998 the Smithsonian Institution accepted two cans of SPAM (one from 1937 the other an updated 1997 version) for its History of Technology collection.

SPAM sales soared in 1999 as nervous consumers stockpiled provisions for the millennium. To build its growing HealthLabs division Hormel acquired Cliffdale Farms (2000) and Diamond Crystal Brands nutritional products (a division of Imperial Sugar) in 2001 –boosting its share of the market for easy-to-swallow foods sold to hospitals and nursing homes.

In early 2001 Hormel acquired family-owned The Turkey Store for approximately $334 million and folded it into its Jennie-O division.

Hormel produced its 6 billionth can of SPAM in 2002 and traded $115 million in stock to acquire the rest of Imperial Sugar's Diamond Crystal Brands unit which packages single-serve packets of sugar sweeteners seasonings and plastic cutlery for the foodservice industry.

To further diversify in 2003 Hormel acquired food manufacturer Century Foods International (whey-based protein powders beverages and nutrition bars) and added it to its burgeoning specialty foods group. In 2004 Hormel sold off its stake in Campofrio to Smithfield Foods.

Its last act of business in 2004 was to purchase Southern California's Clougherty Packing for about $186 million. The pork processor's facilities help extend Hormel's capacity for further-processed foods in the southwestern US.

In 2005 the company purchased Mexican food manufacturer Arriba Foods for $47 million in cash. Later that year it bought Lloyd's Barbecue Company from General Mills.

Responding to the growing trend of the US population to dine out Hormel expanded its foodservice segment (which it refers to as its specialty foods business) with the 2005 purchase of foodservice food manufacturer and distributor Mark-Lynn Foods. Mark-Lynn's products include salt and pepper packets ketchup mustard sauces and salad dressings creamers and sugar packets as well as jellies desserts and drink mixes.

Adding to its grocery product offerings in 2006 the company acquired canned ready-to-eat chicken producer Valley Fresh Foods for $78 million. It also bought pepperoni and pasta maker Provena Foods and sausage and sliced meat maker Saag's Products. It added another to its list of countries in which it has joint ventures in 2006 when it formed a JV with San Miguel to raise and market hogs and animal feed in Vietnam. The JV is 49%-owned by Hormel.

Johnson retired in 2006; company veteran Jeffrey Ettinger was tapped to be the new chairman and CEO.

Hormel acquired Burke Corporation a maker of pizza toppings and other fully cooked meat items in 2007 for $115 million in cash. The acquisition allowed Hormel to extend its pizza-topping operations into the foodservice sector. The following year it acquired Boca Grande Foods for $23.5 in cash. Boca Grande makes Poco Pac branded jams jellies and pancake syrup portion-control products for foodservice operators.

EXECUTIVES

Director Manufacturing and Technical Services International, Michael S. Forbes
EVP Corporate Strategy Planning and Development, Ronald W. Fielding, age 58, $333,170 total compensation
Group VP; President Hormel Foods International, Richard A. Bross, age 60, $269,860 total compensation
EVP and President Hormel Business Units, Steven G. Binder, age 54, $318,530 total compensation
VP; SVP Business Planning Consumer Products Sales, Kurt F. Mueller, age 55
VP; SVP Consumer Products Sales, Douglas R. Reetz, age 57
SVP Supply Chain, William F. Snyder, age 54
VP Legislative Affairs, Joe C. Swedberg, age 56
Group VP and President Consumer Products Sales, Larry L. Vorpahl, age 48
Chairman President and CEO, Jeffrey M. Ettinger, age 53, $956,040 total compensation
VP and Controller, James N. Sheehan, age 56
Group VP Foodservice, Thomas R. Day, age 53
VP Foodservice Marketing, Dennis B. Goettsch, age 58
EVP CFO and Director, Jody H. Feragen, age 55, $380,920 total compensation
VP; SVP Consumer Products Sales, Daniel A. Hartzog, age 60
VP Finance and Treasurer, Roland G. Gentzler, age 57
Director Investor Relations, Kevin C. Jones
Director Mergers Acquisitions and Strategy, Fred D. Halvin
Group VP Specialty Foods, Michael D. (Mike) Tolbert, age 55
Group VP Grocery Products, James M. Splinter, age 49
VP Corporate Communications, Julie H. Craven, age 56
VP Research and Development, Phillip L. (Phil) Minerich, age 58
VP Human Resources, David P. Juhlke, age 52
VP Quality Management, Bryan D. Farnsworth, age 54
VP Refrigerated Foods Operations, Bruce R. Schweitzer, age 60
VP Corporate Innovation and New Product Development, D. Scott Aakre, age 47
Group VP and President Jennie-O Turkey Store, Robert A. Tegt, age 60
Group Product Manager Associated Brands, Swen Neufeldt
Director Innovation, Dan Hernandez
VP Deli Development Consumer Products Sales Division, Mike Farrand
VP Asia-Pacific, David L. Longacre
President Diamond Crystal Brands, Karl A. Kaiser
Manager Regional Sales Southeast, David F. Weber
President Clougherty Packing, Greg N. Longstreet
VP Sales, Deanna T. Brady, age 46
VP Operations Grocery Products, Michael L. Devine, age 57
Manager Western Region Foodservice, James N. (Jim) Maurice
Group VP Specialty Foods Group, Donald H. (Don) Kremin, age 51
VP and Corporate Secretary, Brian D. Johnson, age 51
VP; SVP Hormel Foods International, James P. Snee, age 44
Director Purchasing, Melanie A. Faust
Director Industrial Engineering and Six Sigma, Scott R. Christensen
VP Engineering, James Schroeder, age 54
Director Engineering, James E. Mino
Assistant Controller, James T. (Jim) Anderson
VP of External Affairs General Counsel, Lori J. Marco, age 44
VP Meat Products Marketing, Steven J. Venenga, age 39
VP Marketing Grocery Products, Whitney Velasco-Aznar, age 42
VP Sales and Marketing Farmer John, Robert Samples
Group VP and President Jennie-O-Turkey Store, Glenn R. Leitch, age 51
VP Affiliated Business Units Refrigerated Foods, Mark A. Coffey, age 49
VP; SVP Sales Consumer Product Sales Wal-Mart, Patrick J. Connor, age 42
VP Operations Refrigerated Foods Division, Jeffrey A. Nuytten
VP Marketing, Jeffrey R. Baker
Director, Ronald D. (Ron) Pearson, age 71
Director, Terrell K. (Terry) Crews, age 57
EVP CFO and Director, Jody H. Feragen, age 55
Director, Robert C. (Bob) Nakasone, age 64
Director, John G. Turner, age 72
Director, Dakota A. Pippins, age 63
Director, John L. (Jack) Morrison, age 66
Director, Susan I. Marvin, age 56
Director, Hugh C. Smith, age 72
Director, Susan K. Nestegard, age 51
Director, Elsa A. Murano, age 52
Auditors: Ernst&YoungLLP

LOCATIONS

HQ: Hormel Foods Corporation
1 Hormel Place, Austin MN 55912-3680
Phone: 507-437-5611 **Fax:** 507-437-5129
Web: www.hormelfoods.com

2010 Sales

	$ mil.	% of total
US	6,874	95
Other	346	5
Total	**7,220**	**100**

PRODUCTS/OPERATIONS

2010 Sales

	$ mil.	% of total
Refrigerated foods	3,818	53
Jennie-O Turkey Store	1,310	18
Grocery products	1,040	14
Specialty foods	783	11
Other	268	4
Total	**7,220**	**100**

Selected Products and Brands

Refrigerated
- Country Crock Side Dishes
- Hormel
  - Hormel Always Tender flavored pork and beef products
  - Hormel Black Label and Microwave Ready bacon
  - Hormel Cure 81 ham
  - Hormel Fresh Pantry meats
  - Hormel Little Sizzlers pork sausage
  - Hormel Natural Choice meats
  - Hormel pepperoni minis and stix
  - Hormel refrigerated entrees
  - Hormel Wranglers franks
  - Hormel Snac Cups
- Lloyd' s Barbeque products
- Saag' s sausages

Jennie-O Turkey Store
- Bratwursts and breakfast/dinner sausages
- Breast meat products
- Deli
  - Di Lusso deli meats
  - Farmer John deli meats
  - Hormel 100 percent natural deli meats
  - Hormel Deli beef dry sausage ham and turkey
  - Hormel party trays
- Ground turkey
- Marinated turkey tenderloins
- So-Easy Entrees
- Turkey burger patties and franks
- Whole turkeys

Grocery products
- Dinty Moore stew Hearty Meals varieties microwave-ready products
- Herb-Ox bouillon
- Herdez Salsa
- Hormel
  - Hormel bacon toppings
  - Hormel Chili Master
  - Hormel chunk meats
  - Hormel Compleats microwave meals
  - Hormel corned beef and roast beef with gravy
  - Hormel dried beef
  - Hormel Kid's Kitchen microwave cups
  - Hormel Mary Kitchen hash
  - Hormel microwave cups
- Not-So-Sloppy-Joe sloppy joe sauce
- Skippy peanut butter
- SPAM products (classic hickory smoke flavored hot and spicy lite low-sodium spread singles and oven-roasted turkey)
- Stagg chili
- Valley Fresh chunk meats and broths

Specialty Foods
- Century Foods International (dairy and vegetable proteins nutraceuticals)
- Diamond Crystal Brands (salts sugar substitutes)
- Hormel Foods Ingredients (sauces powders broths oils Omega-3 additives)
- Private Label products (canned meats prepared foods and desserts bouillon sweeteners salts seasonings)

Other
- MegaMex Mexican brands

Bufalo hot sauces
CHI-CHI'S Mexican hot sauces taco tubs dips seasoning mixes and tortillas
Do?a Maria Authentic Mexican products
Don Miguel burritos appetizers empanadas taquitos tacos flautas chimichangas enchiladas
El Torito sauces dressings and corn cakes
Embasa Mexican peppers salsas
Herdez imported salsas
La Victoria Mexican salsas taco sauces enchilada sauces green chile peppers
Wholly Guacamole
World Food ethnic brands
House of Tsang entrees sauces and oils
Marrakesh Express Mediterranean products (couscous risotto)
Peloponnese Greek foods olives

Selected Foodservice Brands

Always Tender Pork
Austin Blues barbeque meats
Authentic Barbeque
Bread Ready pre-sliced meats
Cafe H ethnic meats
Cure 81 Ham
Dry Sausage
Fast ' N Easy Fully Cooked Meats
Hormel Chili
Masterpieces Toppings
Natural Choice meats
Old Smokehouse bacon
Old Tyme breakfast sausage
Old Tyme ham
Special Recipe Sausage
Stagg Chili

COMPETITORS

B&G Foods
Boar' s Head
Bob Evans
Bridgford Foods
Bush Brothers
Butterball
Campbell Soup
Cargill
ConAgra
Cooper Farms
Eberly Poultry
Foster Farms
General Mills
Gusto Packing
H. J. Heinz Limited
JBS USA
Mondelez International
Perdue Incorporated
Pilgrim' s Pride
Pinnacle Foods
Plainville Farms
Sanderson Farms
Sara Lee
Seaboard
Smithfield Foods
The Dial Corporation
Tyson Foods

HISTORICAL FINANCIALS

Company Type: Public

Income Statement FYE: October 28

	REVENUE ($ mil.)	NET INCOME ($ mil.)	NET PROFIT MARGIN	EMPLOYEES
10/12	8,230	500	6.1%	19,700
10/11	7,895	474	6.0%	19,500
10/10	7,220	395	5.5%	19,300
10/09	6,533	342	5.2%	18,600
10/08	6,754	285	4.2%	19,100
Annual Growth	5.1%	15.0%	—	0.8%

2012 Year-End Financials

Debt ratio: 5.48%
Return on equity: 17.74%
Cash ($ mil.): 682
Current ratio: 295.14
Long-term debt ($ mil.): 250
No. of shares (mil.): 263
Dividends
Yield: —
Payout: 32.26%
Market value ($ mil.): 7,718

	STOCK PRICE ($) FY Close	P/E High/Low		PER SHARE ($) Earnings	Dividends	Book Value
10/12	29.34	16	14	1.86	0.00	10.72
10/11	29.95	29	15	1.74	0.00	10.06
10/10	45.92	31	25	1.46	0.00	9.03
10/09	36.31	30	20	1.27	0.00	7.95
10/08	28.48	40	27	1.04	0.00	7.46
Annual Growth	0.7%	—	—	15.6%	—	9.5%

Horton (D.R.) Inc.

When this Horton heard a Who it built the little guy a house. D.R. Horton builds single-family homes for the entry-level and move-up markets. Homes range from 1000 sq. ft. to 4000 sq. ft. and sell for an average of about $212000; luxury homes cost up to $700000. One of the top US homebuilders D.R. Horton is active in about 75 markets in 25 states. The company also provides mortgage title and closing services. Like its peers D.R. Horton saw its sales plummet as a result of the housing market crash the subprime mortgage crisis the global credit crunch and years of industrywide overbuilding. As a sign of the recovering economy though orders for the company's homes have begun to rebound.

In fiscal 2010 the company sold some 20875 homes up from 16700 homes the previous year. A federal tax credit for first-time homebuyers the company's target market also led to a temporary boost in home orders that year. Conversely demand for new homes declined after the tax credit expired that year. In fiscal 2011 even as home sales prices inched up 3% from the previous year's average of $206100 the number of homes the company sold slipped back down to approximately 16700. Sales declined across all geographic regions with the exception of the south-central region (Louisiana Texas Oklahoma and New Mexico). As a result revenues from home sales the bulk of the company's earnings fell 18% to $3.5 billion and overall revenues fell 17% to $3.6 billion. Profits fell even further slipping 71% to $71.8 million that year.

D.R. Horton has been readying itself for financial recovery by strategically buying land at distressed prices seeking promising new markets to enter and renegotiating purchasing contracts. As one of the largest homebuilders the company has been able to survive the worst housing market in 25 years unlike many smaller builders with limited resources that have gone out of business or been acquired in recent years.

In addition to single-family detached homes which account for some 90% of sales D.R. Horton builds duplexes townhomes and condominiums. The company operates through some 30 divisions which are somewhat autonomously led by presidents familiar with their geographic markets. The divisions report to one of four regional offices.

Founder and chairman Donald Horton owns 9% of D.R. Horton.

HISTORY

Donald R. Horton was selling homes in Fort Worth Texas when he hit upon a strategy for increasing sales –add options to a basic floor plan. In 1978 he borrowed $33000 to build his first home added a bay window for an additional charge and sold the home for $44000. Donald soon added floor plans and options that appealed to regional preferences.

The depressed Texas market drove the company to expand beyond the Dallas/Fort Worth area in 1987 when it entered the then-hot Phoenix market. It continued to expand into the Southeast Mid-Atlantic Midwest and West in the late 1980s and early 1990s. By 1991 Horton and his family owned more than 25 companies that were combined as D.R. Horton which went public in 1992.

D.R. Horton acquired six geographically diverse construction firms in 1994 and 1995. In 1996 the company started a mortgage services joint venture expanded its title operations and added three more firms.

In 1998 the company bought four builders including Scottsdale Arizona-based Continental Homes. Continental had been expanding beyond its Arizona and Southern California base and had entered the lucrative retirement community market. After the Continental purchase Donald Horton stepped down as president remaining chairman. Richard Beckwitt took over as president and Donald Tomnitz became CEO. In 1999 the company acquired Century Title and Midwest builder Cambridge Properties.

D.R. Horton sold its St. Louis assets to McBride & Son Enterprises in 2000 after spending five years trying to break into the St. Louis homebuilding market. Tomnitz also took over the duties of president in 2000 when Beckwitt retired.

D.R. Horton gained homebuilding operations in Houston and Phoenix when it bought Emerald Builders in 2001. In February 2002 the company acquired Schuler Homes for $1.2 billion including debt.

Sales continued to climb in fiscal 2003 and 2004. D.R. Horton experienced its 27th consecutive year of earnings and revenue growth in 2004 and broke records by being the first residential homebuilder to sell more than 45000 homes in the US in a fiscal year; in fiscal 2005 the company closed 51172 homes. By 2007 however it was evident that the heady days were over with a rise in cancellations and a larger value of backlog orders.

CEO Donald Tomnitz summed up the housing market crash when he said "I don't want to be too sophisticated here but '07 is going to suck all 12 months of the calendar year." Indeed the company suffered a loss that year and the next when sales orders declined and cancellation rates rose due to tightened mortgage markets and severe liquidity shortages. Adding to homebuilders' difficulties an influx of foreclosed homes on the market brought down the demand for new homes.

D.R. Horton responded to the downturn in 2008 by reducing land and housing inventory controlling construction and inventory costs and using its cash to reduce debt. Despite drops in many markets D.R. Horton saw improvements in its eastern market where home affordability and employment led to a higher demand for new homes.

EXECUTIVES

Vice Chairman President and CEO, Donald J. (Don) Tomnitz, age 64, $900,000 total compensation
Chairman, Donald R. Horton, age 62, $1,000,000 total compensation
EVP Investor Relations and Treasurer, Stacey H. Dwyer, age 46, $250,000 total compensation
President North Region, George W. Seagraves, $175,000 total compensation
President West Region, Chris Chambers

EVP and CFO, William W. (Bill) Wheat, age 46, $250,000 total compensation
President Financial Services, Randall C. (Randy) Present
Director Information Technology, Rick Rawlings
Chief Legal Officer, Ted I. Harbour
President South Region, Rick Horton
President East Region, David Auld
Director Investor Relations, Jessica Hansen
VP and Assistant Secretary, Thomas Montano
VP and Director National Accounts, Brad Conlon
Vice Chairman President and CEO, Donald J. (Don) Tomnitz, age 64
Director, Bob G. Scott, age 74
Director, Bradley S. Anderson, age 51
Director, Michael R. (Mike) Buchanan, age 65
Director, Michael W. (Mike) Hewatt, age 63
Auditors: PricewaterhouseCoopersLLP

LOCATIONS

HQ: Horton (D.R.) Inc.
301 Commerce Street, Suite 500, Fort Worth, TX 76102
Phone: 817 390-8200
Web: www.drhorton.com

2011 Homebuilding Sales by Region

	% of total
South	30
West	24
Southeast	20
East	12
Midwest	7
Southwest	7
Total	**100**

PRODUCTS/OPERATIONS

2011 Sales

	$ mil.	% of total
Homebuilding		
Home sales	3542.3	98
Land & lot sales	7	.
Financial services	87	2
Total	**3,636**	**100**

COMPETITORS

Beazer Homes
David Weekley Homes
Gehan Homes
Hovnanian Enterprises
KB Home
Lennar
M.D.C.
Meritage Homes
NVR
PulteGroup
Ryan Building
Standard Pacific
The Ryland Group
Toll Brothers
Weyerhaeuser Real Estate

HISTORICAL FINANCIALS

Company Type: Public

Income Statement

FYE: September 30

	REVENUE ($ mil.)	NET INCOME ($ mil.)	NET PROFIT MARGIN	EMPLOYEES
09/12	4,354	956	22.0%	3,477
09/11	3,636	71	2.0%	3,010
09/10	4,400	245	5.6%	3,214
09/09	3,657	(545)	—	2,926
09/08	6,646	(2,633)	—	3,800
Annual Growth	(10.0%)	—	—	(2.2%)

2012 Year-End Financials

Debt ratio: 34.40%
Return on equity: 26.62%
Cash ($ mil.): 1,047
Current ratio: 1541.71
Long-term debt ($ mil.): 2,493
No. of shares (mil.): 320
Dividends
Yield: —
Payout: 5.42%
Market value ($ mil.): 6,620

	STOCK PRICE ($) FY Close	P/E High	P/E Low	PER SHARE ($) Earnings	Dividends	Book Value
09/12	20.63	7	3	2.77	0.00	11.19
09/11	9.04	59	39	0.23	0.15	8.29
09/10	11.12	19	13	0.77	0.15	8.20
09/09	11.41	—	—	(1.72)	0.15	7.12
09/08	13.02	—	—	(8.34)	0.45	8.95
Annual Growth	12.2%	—	—	—	—	5.7%

Hospira Inc

Hospira helps hospitals heal the hurting. The company makes specialty injectable pharmaceuticals (primarily generics) including cardiovascular anesthesia oncology and anti-infective therapies as well as the related drug delivery systems such as prefilled syringes. The firm's more complicated medication delivery systems include electronic drug pumps infusion therapy devices and related medication management software. In addition Hospira makes some IV nutritional solutions and provides contract manufacturing services. Key customers include hospitals alternate site facilities (such as nursing and outpatient surgical care facilities) wholesalers and other drug manufacturers.

Many of the firm's hospital customers are members of the major US group purchasing organizations (GPOs) and integrated delivery networks (IDNs) that Hospira has pricing arrangements with. Major GPO customers include Amerinet HealthTrust MedAssets Novation and Premier. About 80% of Hospira's sales take place in the Americas. More than 60% of total annual revenues come from sales of injectable pharmaceuticals.

The company operates marketing and distribution centers across the US and uses third party distributors in other countries. It also runs about a dozen manufacturing facilities globally with its North Carolina Texas Kansas Costa Rica India and Australia (Victoria) locations account for the majority of output. The firm also outsources some production to third-party suppliers. Hospira performs its product development efforts at a handful of research facilities in the US as well as in Australia Italy and India overseas.

Hospira works to grow its product offerings and keep its development pipeline flowing through a number of growth strategies including acquisitions licensing deals and partnered and independent R&D efforts. Hospira's internal research programs are largely focused on the areas of generic specialty injectable pharmaceuticals. The company introduces a number of new generic injectables each year with about a dozen launches in 2011 (including cancer drugs docetaxel and topotecan) and it is working to move existing products into new countries. Hospira also regularly develops new drug delivery systems for its injectables such as emergency needleless syringe systems and medication mixing systems.

In addition Hospira is looking to develop new generic biotech injectable drugs (biosimilars) and non-generic specialty injectables. It launched Nivestim a biosimilar of Novartis' Filgrastim for low white blood cell counts in chemotherapy patients in 2010. To boost its proprietary (non-generic) R&D efforts in 2010 the company formed a licensing agreement with DURECT to develop and market DURECT's Posidur a long-acting version of the anesthetic bupivacaine in clinical trials. Hospira added another proprietary candidate in 2010 through the purchase of drug developer Javelin Pharmaceuticals for some $145 million. The acquisition gave Hospira access Javelin's new pain medication Dyloject which has been submitted to the FDA for approval. If approved Dyloject will be marketed to anesthesiologists alongside Hospira's sedation drug Precedex.

Also in 2010 Hospira boosted its commercial offerings through the purchase of the generic injectable business of India-based Orchid Chemicals for $400 million adding a number of antibiotics and other injectable drugs to its product line. The purchase boosted Hospira's manufacturing and research operations by adding facilities in India. It also added a long-term exclusive agreement with Orchid to supply Hospira with APIs.

However the Orchid supply arrangement was altered in 2012 when Hospira agreed to acquire one of Orchid's API manufacturing plants for another $200 million. The plant covers beta-lactam antibiotic (penicillin and penem) APIs; Orchid will continue to supply cephalosporin APIs to the company. Hospira hopes to reduce costs and ensure supply continuity by increasing its direct manufacturing operations; the purchase also adds R&D facilities that will help the company increase future API development efforts.

The plant acquisition is part of a broader manufacturing reorganization being undertaken by Hospira following several years of regulatory troubles. After having to shut down some of its production lines at its two North Carolina plants during 2010 and 2011 to fix quality issues cited in a letter from the FDA Hospira had a bit of trouble meeting demand for some of its injectable drugs. The situation has caused some supply shortages and the company has taken a further hit in sales as clinicians who would normally order Hospira products are forced to prescribe drugs from other companies. Hospira has been shifting its manufacturing resources to meet customer demands; it is also expanding its capacity at its facility in India.

While Hospira has grown its revenues through increased product sales over the years including a 4% increase to a little more than $4 billion in 2011 net income has dropped in both 2010 and 2011 largely due to the company's injectable manufacturing and regulatory troubles (and the resulting expenses from remediation efforts at its plants). In addition to the North Carolina plant troubles and injectable shortages the company's medication management systems segment took a hit from a recall and voluntary sales freeze of its Symbiq drug pump due to alarm malfunctions in 2011; the freeze was lifted when the FDA approved the upgraded Symbiq system in 2012.

The company had already launched a number of corporate streamlining measures in 2009; the restructuring program which was completed in 2011 included a 10% workforce reduction a product optimization plan and a review of its noncore operations. As part of that plan Hospira sold its critical care product line to ICU Medical for $35 million. Hospira also sold its brain function monitoring business to SEDLine a private research firm backed by Masimo Corporation in early 2010.

Hospira was formed through the spinoff of drug manufacturer Abbott Laboratories' hospital supplies business in 2004.

EXECUTIVES

CEO and Director, F. Michael (Mike) Ball, age 56

SVP Finance and CFO, Thomas E. Werner, age 55, $445,000 total compensation
SVP Operations, John B. Elliot
Chairman, John C. (Jack) Staley, age 70
SVP Organizational Transformation and People Development, Kenneth F. (Ken) Meyers, age 50
SVP Devices, Neil Ryding
SVP Operations, James H. (Jim) Hardy Jr., age 52
SVP Research and Development Medical and Regulatory Affairs and Chief Scientific Officer, Sumant Ramachandra, age 43, $475,000 total compensation
SVP and CIO, Daphne E. Jones, age 55
SVP General Counsel and Secretary, Brian J. Smith, age 60
Corporate VP Global Marketing and Corporate Development, Anil G. D'Souza
SVP and Chief Commercial Officer, Richard Davies
CEO and Director, F. Michael (Mike) Ball, age 56
Director, Irving W. Bailey II, age 70
Director, Roger W. Hale, age 68
Director, Heino von Prondzynski, age 62
Director, Barbara L. Bowles, age 64
Director, Connie R. Curran, age 64
Director, Mark F. Wheeler, age 62
Director, Jacque J. Sokolov, age 57
Auditors: Deloitte&ToucheLLP

LOCATIONS

HQ: Hospira Inc.
275 N. Field Dr., Lake Forest IL 60045
Phone: 224-212-2000 **Fax:** 224-212-3350
Web: www.hospira.com

2011 Sales

	$ mil.	% of total
Americas	3,206	79
Asia Pacific (APAC)	333	8

PRODUCTS/OPERATIONS

2011 Sales

	$ mil.	% of total
Specialty injectables	2,562	63
Other pharma	507	13
Total	**4,057**	**100**

Selected Products

Specialty injectables and related drug delivery systems
- ADD-Vantage system (for mixing from powders and concentrates)
- Ansyr system (prefilled needleless emergency syringe system)
- Carpuject syringe system (drug delivery system)
- FirstChoice (ready to use premixes)
- Generic injectables
- iSecure syringes (drug delivery system)
- Nivestim (biosimilar filgrastim specialty injectable for low white blood cells in chemotherapy patients)
- Precedex (dexmedetomidine HCI specialty injectable for intensive care sedation licensed from Orion Corporation)
- Retacrit (biosimilar erythropoietin specialty injectable for kidney failure-related anemia)

Medication management
- GemStar (ambulatory infusion pump)
- LifeCare PCA (analgesia device)
- LifeShield CLAVE and MicroCLAVE (valves to connect syringes to IV lines)
- MedNet (drug library safety software)
- Plum XLD (infusion pump)
- Symbiq (infusion pump)
- TheraDoc (monitors safety and provides clinical decision support)

COMPETITORS

Actavis
Akorn
APP Pharmaceuticals
Fresenius
Mylan Pharmaceuticals
Patheon
B. Braun Medical
Baxter International
Becton Dickinson
Boehringer Ingelheim Pharmaceuticals
Cardinal Health
CareFusion
Edwards Lifesciences
Pfizer
Sandoz International GmbH
Sanofi
Sun Pharmaceutical
Terumo
Teva

HISTORICAL FINANCIALS

Company Type: Public

Income Statement FYE: December 31

	REVENUE ($ mil.)	NET INCOME ($ mil.)	NET PROFIT MARGIN	EMPLOYEES
12/11	4,057	(9)	—	15,000
12/10	3,917	357	9.1%	14,000
12/09	3,879	403	10.4%	13,500
12/08	3,629	320	8.8%	14,500
12/07	3,436	136	4.0%	14,000
Annual Growth	4.2%	—	—	1.7%

2011 Year-End Financials

Debt ratio: 30.14%
Return on equity: (-0.32)%
Cash ($ mil.): 597
Current ratio: 303.22
Long-term debt ($ mil.): 1,711
No. of shares (mil.): 164
Dividends
Yield: —
Payout: —
Market value ($ mil.): 5,002

	STOCK PRICE ($) FY Close	P/E High/Low		PER SHARE ($) Earnings	Dividends	Book Value
12/11	30.37	—	—	(0.06)	0.00	17.84
12/10	55.69	28	23	2.11	0.00	19.10
12/09	51.00	20	9	2.47	0.00	16.05
12/08	26.82	22	13	1.99	0.00	11.13
12/07	42.64	51	39	0.85	0.00	11.00
Annual Growth	(8.1%)	—	—	—	—	12.8%

Host Hotels & Resorts Inc

Host Hotels & Resorts will leave the chandelier on for you. One of the largest hospitality real estate investment trusts in the US Host Hotels owns about 120 luxury and upscale hotels with some 65000 rooms in North America South America and Europe. Its properties are managed by third parties; most operate under the Marriott brand and are managed by sister firm Marriott International. Other primary brands include Hyatt Ritz-Carlton Sheraton and Westin. To maintain its status as a real estate investment trust (REIT) which carries tax advantages Host operates through majority-owned Host Hotels & Resorts LP.

Host's strategy is to acquire hotels in central business districts of major cities resorts and convention centers while reducing its exposure to non-core suburban airport assets. The company also considers the acquisition of midscale properties to compliment its traditional focus on upscale and luxury hotels.

After acquiring four upscale hotels around the globe in 2010 Host continued its spree in 2011. The company bought the New York Helmsley Hotel from Helmsley Enterprises and announced plans to renovate the 775-room property and re-open it under the Westin brand. In a separate deal Host acquired the Manchester Grand Hyatt San Diego's largest hotel for $570 million.

While Host emphasizes US acquisitions it still looks to diversity its holdings at home and abroad sometimes through joint ventures. In 2012 it entered into a joint venture with an affiliate of Hyatt Hotels Corp. to develop sell and operate a 131-unit vacation ownership project adjacent to the company's Hyatt Regency Maui Resort & Spa. The Maui project is expected to open in late 2014. Host owns approximately a third of a joint venture with Dutch pension fund Stichting Pensioenfonds that owns more than a dozen hotels in six European countries. The REIT also holds a quarter of a joint venture with Singapore's GIC Real Estate that acquired a minority interest in another joint venture that is developing seven hotel properties in India. It is also looking at opportunities in Australia China Japan and Vietnam. Acting alone Host bought seven hotels in New Zealand in 2011.

The global recession severely impacted the hospitality industry and Host was no exception. Lodging demand fell in 2008 and 2009 and revenues followed. But Host's capital and asset management skills helped it weather the downturn. While still below historical levels demand increased in 2010 and 2011 as the economy exhibited signs of improvement. The company expects the trend to continue. Though the company remained in the red it cut its losses in 2011.

Formerly known as Host Marriott Host Hotels & Resorts split from Marriott International in 1993. The company adopted its current name in 2006 after it diversified its portfolio beyond the Marriott brand. The Marriott family has mostly sold its interest in Host.

HISTORY

That's right –The Four Seasons started as a root beer stand.

Newlyweds John and Alice Marriott left Marriott Utah (founded by John's grandparents) in 1927 and opened a root beer stand in Washington DC. As a way to attract customers during the winter they began selling tamales and tacos –recipes came from a cook at the Mexican Embassy. Dubbed the Hot Shoppe the Marriotts built the business into a regional chain.

In 1937 the Marriotts began providing boxed lunches for airlines. Hot Shoppes entered the hospital food service business in 1955 and two years later opened its first hotel in Arlington Virginia. John and Alice's son Bill became president in 1964. The company which operated four hotels 45 Hot Shoppes and the airline catering business became Marriott-Hot Shoppes.

In the 1960s the company acquired Bob's Big Boy restaurant chain (sold 1987) started Roy Rogers fast-food restaurants (sold 1990) and changed its name to Marriott Corp. Later Marriott bought an Athenian cruise line (Oceanic; sold 1987). Bill became CEO in 1972.

Marriott diversified its hotel operations in the 1980s moving into limited-service middle-priced hotels with the launch of Courtyard by Marriott in 1983. To accelerate growth the company began building hotels for sale retaining their control through management contracts. In 1987 it acquired Residence Inn Co. which targeted extended-stay travelers. The company also expanded its airline catering business and moved into retirement facilities. To fund the expansion Marriott formed limited partnerships and issued corporate bonds; when the late 1980s recession hit the company was deeply in debt.

In 1993 Marriott Corp. divided into Marriott International (hotel management services) and Host Marriott (real estate and food service) leaving Host Marriott with most of the corporation's debt. Host Marriott began focusing on full-service hotels. It raised money to buy more hotels (many of which belonged to its old limited partnerships) by taking loans from Marriott International and selling assets (including 14 retirement properties and 30 Fairfield Inns). In late 1995 the company further refined its focus by spinning off its food service and concessions business as Host Marriott Services (later acquired by Italy-based restaurant operator Autogrill).

Host Marriott acquired three Ritz-Carlton hotels in 1995 through Marriott International which owns the Ritz-Carlton name and in 1997 acquired the Forum Group owner of 29 retirement communities. The next year it spun off Crestline Capital (now Barcelo Crestline Corp.) to own its retirement properties and to lease its hotels.

In 1999 the company expanded its hotel brands adding controlling stakes in 13 luxury Ritz-Carlton Four Seasons Swissotel and Hyatt properties bought from the Blackstone Group investment firm in exchange for a stake in Host Marriott. It also restructured as a real estate investment trust or REIT.

Host Marriott and Marriott International were slapped with an investor fraud lawsuit in 2000 relating to its capital-raising efforts in the late 1980s; they reached a tentative settlement under which they would buy back the partnerships. The bulk of the settlements were awarded to about 2000 investors in two of the six limited partnerships in question. That year Marriott matriarch Alice died.

Host Marriott's New York Marriott World Trade Center hotel located at Three World Trade Center was completely devastated on September 11 2001. Two blocks south the New York Marriott Financial Center hotel sustained heavy damage.

Even before September 11 brought the hotel industry to a screeching halt the company had curtailed the buying binge that saw it add more than 100 hotels to its portfolio since 1994. It decided to sell less posh noncore hotels and focus on renovating remaining holdings. Crashing per-room revenue had the company waiting for the slow return of the health of the industry and when it had the company began a cautious acquisition spree.

After a tourism industry downturn made worse by the September 11 2001 terrorist attacks the company made a key acquisition in 2006: It purchased a portfolio of 25 domestic and 3 international hotels from Starwood Hotels & Resorts for more than $4 billion and changed its name to Host Hotels & Resorts in conjunction with that buy. The package expanded the company's reach into Europe South America and the South Pacific.

In 2009 Host sold its leasehold interest in CBM Joint Venture Partnership which owned 115 Courtyard by Marriott hotels. The deal earned Host about $13 million.

In late 2011 the company sold its 95% interest in the Toronto Airport Marriott Hotel for CAD$30.6 million ($30.7 million).

EXECUTIVES

President CEO and Director, W. Edward (Ed) Walter, age 56, $704,589 total compensation
Chairman, Richard E. Marriott, age 73, $289,452 total compensation
EVP and CFO, Larry K. Harvey, age 47, $350,000 total compensation
EVP and Managing Director Europe, James F. Risoleo, age 56, $500,000 total compensation
EVP Corporate Strategy and Fund Management, Gregory J. (Greg) Larson, age 47, $350,000 total compensation
EVP General Counsel and Secretary, Elizabeth A. Abdoo, age 53, $387,500 total compensation
EVP Asset Management, Minaz B. Abji, age 58, $430,000 total compensation
SVP and Corporate Controller, Brian G. Macnamara, age 52
SVP Acquisitions, Timothy (Tim) Marvin
EVP Human Resources, Joanne G. Hamilton, age 54
President CEO and Director, W. Edward (Ed) Walter, age 56
Director, Terence C. Golden, age 67
Director, John B. (Jay) Morse Jr., age 65
Director, Willard W. (Woody) Brittain Jr., age 64
Director, Ann McLaughlin Korologos, age 70
Director, Robert M. Baylis, age 73
Director, Gordon H. Smith, age 60
Auditors: KPMGLLP

LOCATIONS

HQ: Host Hotels & Resorts Inc.
6903 Rockledge Dr. Ste. 1500, Bethesda MD 20817
Phone: 240-744-1000 **Fax:** 240-744-5125
Web: www.hosthotels.com

2011 Sales

	$ mil.	% of total
US	4,722	95
Canada	115	2
Other	161	3
Total	**4,998**	**100**

PRODUCTS/OPERATIONS

2011 Sales

	$ mil.	% of total
Rooms	3,022	60
Food & beverage	1,427	29
Other	549	11
Total	**4,998**	**100**

2011 Brands

	No. of hotels	% of revenue
Marriott	66	54
Westin	13	10
Hyatt	7	9
Ritz-Carlton	8	8
Sheraton	7	8
W	3	3
Fairmont	1	2
Novotel	4	1
Hilton/Embassy Suites	3	1
Four Seasons	2	1
Delta	1	1
Swissotel	1	1
Other	5	1
Total	**121**	**100**

COMPETITORS

Ashford Hospitality Trust
Carlson Companies
FelCor
Hospitality Properties Trust
InterContinental Hotels
LaSalle Hotel Properties
Lodgian
Strategic Hotels
Sunstone Hotel Investors

HISTORICAL FINANCIALS

Company Type: Public

Income Statement

FYE: December 31

	REVENUE ($ mil.)	NET INCOME ($ mil.)	NET PROFIT MARGIN	EMPLOYEES
12/11	4,998	(15)	—	219
12/10	4,437	(130)	—	203
12/09	4,158	(252)	—	186
12/08	5,288	427	8.1%	215
12/07	5,426	727	13.4%	243
Annual Growth	(2.0%)	—	—	(2.6%)

2011 Year-End Financials

Debt ratio: 44.02%
Return on equity: (-0.22)%
Cash ($ mil.): 826
Current ratio: 492.57
Long-term debt ($ mil.): 5,753
No. of shares (mil.): 705
Dividends
Yield: —
Payout: —
Market value ($ mil.): 10,414

	STOCK PRICE ($) FY Close	P/E High/Low		PER SHARE ($) Earnings	Dividends	Book Value
12/11	14.77	—	—	(0.02)	0.00	9.47
12/10	17.87	—	—	(0.21)	0.04	9.33
12/09	11.67	—	—	(0.45)	0.30	9.58
12/08	7.57	23	6	0.76	0.65	10.50
12/07	17.04	21	12	1.33	1.00	10.41
Annual Growth	(3.5%)	—	—	—	—	(2.3%)

HSBC Finance Corp

LOCATIONS

HQ: HSBC Finance Corp
26525 North Riverwoods Boulevard, Suite 100, Mettawa, IL 60045
Phone: 224 880-7000
Web: www.us.hsbc.com

HISTORICAL FINANCIALS

Company Type:

Income Statement

FYE: December 31

	ASSETS ($ mil.)	NET INCOME ($ mil.)	INCOME AS % OF ASSETS	EMPLOYEES
12/11	63,469	(1,408)	—	5,350
12/10	76,532	(1,916)	—	6,650
12/09	94,553	(7,450)	—	11,900
12/08	130,785	(2,783)	—	19,020
12/07	165,504	(4,906)	—	27,980
Annual Growth	(21.3%)	—	—	(33.9%)

2011 Year-End Financials

Debt ratio: 75.71%
Return on equity: (-20.33)%
Cash ($ mil.): 1,365
Current ratio: —
Long-term debt ($ mil.): 48,052
No. of shares (mil.): 0
Dividends
Yield: —
Payout: —
Market value ($ mil.): 0

	STOCK PRICE ($) FY Close	P/E High/Low	PER SHARE ($) Earnings	Dividends	Book Value
12/11	21.25	— —	(0.00)	0.00	101,852,941
12/10	22.84	— —	(0.00)	1.59	16,969,696
12/09	20.64	— —	(0.00)	1.59	28,907,692
12/08	17.50	— —	(0.00)	1.59	223,950,000
12/07	20.25	— —	(0.00)	1.59	248,403,508
Annual Growth	1.2%	— —	—	—	(20.0%)

HSBC USA, Inc.

HSBC USA a subsidiary of British banking behemoth HSBC Holdings operates HSBC Bank USA one of the biggest foreign-owned banks in the country by assets. With about 175 offices (including 115 in New York City) the bank has one of the largest branch networks in New York State plus more than 100 additional locations in about a dozen other states and Washington DC; California New Jersey and Florida are its next largest markets. The bank offers personal commercial and mortgage banking services. Its personal financial services segment provides mutual funds investments and insurance. HSBC Bank USA also offers investment banking private banking brokerage and trust services.

In addition to its domestic branch network HSBC USA operates foreign branches and representative offices in the Caribbean Canada Latin America Europe and Asia.

Residential mortgages commercial loans and credit card loans make up most of the bank's lending activity. With so much of its loan portfolio secured by residential mortgages and consumer loans amid elevated unemployment rates and an increase in delinquent accounts the company upped its provisions for expected loan losses in 2008 and 2009 and sold several billions of dollars worth of loans into the secondary market. After posting two consecutive years of losses the HSBC USA returned to profitability as the economy improved even though the company's revenues were down. In 2011 restructuring charges and ongoing losses impacted the company's revenues which fell some 35% to $5.7 billion (down from $8.7 billion in 2010).

HSBC and HSBC USA announced plans to restructure their operations in 2011 which includes divesting operations and cutting staff. As part of the restructuring HSBC sold 195 retail branches in New York and Connecticut to First Niagara for $1 billion. Through HSBC USA and its HSBC Finance affiliate HSBC also sold its card and retail services business to Capital One Financial. In 2010 HSBC USA exited its noncore wholesale banknotes business. The company also closed and consolidated about a dozen branches in Connecticut and New Jersey. The moves are part of the company's strategy to focus more on commercial and corporate banking in New York and other key urban markets itself part of HSBC's restructuring to create a leaner group.

In 2011 HSBC USA was given a cease-and-desist order by the Office of the Comptroller of the Currency (OCC) when it was found to have deficiencies in its foreclosure practices. HSBC USA is working with the OCC to meet the regulators' requirements including reviewing foreclosures from 2009 and 2010 which is expected to bring servicing and remediation costs up.

EXECUTIVES

EVP and Secretary, Patrick D. Schwartz, age 54
SEVP Head of Retail Banking and Wealth Management, Kevin R. Martin, age 51
EVP and CFO, John T. McGinnis, age 45
SEVP Human Resources, Jon N. Couture, age 46
EVP and Head of Private Banking, Marlon Young, age 56, $389,423 total compensation
SEVP and Chief Auditor, Mark Martinelli, age 52
SEVP and Chief Risk Officer, Mark C. Gunton, age 55
President CEO and Director, Irene M. Dorner, age 57
SEVP and General Counsel, Stuart Alderoty, age 53
SEVP and Chief Compliance Officer, Eric Larson
SEVP and COO, Eli Sinyak
Director, William R. P. (Bill) Dalton, age 68
Director, Anthea Disney, age 67
Director, Louis Hernandez Jr., age 45
Director, Salvatore H. (Sal) Alfiero, age 74
Director, Richard A. (Dick) Jalkut, age 68
Auditors: KPMGLLP

LOCATIONS

HQ: HSBC USA Inc.
452 5th Ave., New York NY 10018
Phone: 212-525-5000 **Fax:** 212-818-8543
Web: www.itochu.com

2011 Branches

	No.
New	371
California	38
Florida	18
New	9
Virginia	6
Washington	4
Washington	4
Connecticut	3
Maryland	3
Pennsylvania	2
Delaware	1
Illinois	1
Oregon	1
Total	**461**

PRODUCTS/OPERATIONS

2011 Sa

	$ mil.	% of total
Interest		
Loans	1,812	32
Securities	1,242	22
Other	374	7
Noninterest		
Credit card fees	129	2
Other fees & commissions	777	14
Gain on instruments designated at fair value & related derivatives	471	8
Trading revenue	349	6
Other	541	9
Total	**5,695**	**100**

COMPETITORS

Astoria Financial
Bank of America
Capital One
Citibank
JPMorgan Chase
KeyCorp
M&T Bank
New York Community Bancorp
PNC Financial
RBS Citizens Financial Group
TD Bank USA
Wells Fargo

HISTORICAL FINANCIALS

Company Type: Subsidiary

Income Statement FYE: December 31

	ASSETS ($ mil.)	NET INCOME ($ mil.)	INCOME AS % OF ASSETS	EMPLOYEES
12/11	210,280	1,018	0.5%	9,000
12/10	183,813	1,564	0.9%	12,000
12/09	171,079	(142)	—	12,000
12/08	185,569	(1,689)	—	11,731
12/07	188,373	138	0.1%	12,000
Annual Growth	2.8%	64.8%	—	(6.9%)

2011 Year-End Financials

Debt ratio: 7.95%	No. of shares (mil.): 0
Return on equity: 5.50%	Dividends
Cash ($ mil.): 65,870	Yield: —
Current ratio: —	Payout: —
Long-term debt ($ mil.): 16,709	Market value ($ mil.): 0

	STOCK PRICE ($) FY Close	P/E High/Low	PER SHARE ($) Earnings	Dividends	Book Value
12/11	16.43	— —	(0.00)	0.00	25,985,955
12/10	23.67	— —	(0.00)	0.88	23,501,404
12/09	21.80	— —	(0.00)	0.89	21,316,011
12/08	14.50	— —	(0.00)	1.09	17,936,530
12/07	20.06	— —	(0.00)	1.54	15,916,430
Annual Growth	(4.9%)	— —	—	—	13.0%

Hudson City Bancorp, Inc.

Hudson City Bancorp is the holding company for Hudson City Savings Bank one of the largest thrifts in the US. Founded in 1868 the bank has more than 130 branches in the New York City metropolitan area including northern New Jersey; Long Island; and Fairfield County Connecticut; as well as central New Jersey and that state's Philadelphia suburbs. Serving middle- to high-income consumers it issues and purchases high-quality first residential mortgages which account for about 99% of its loan portfolio. It originates loans at its branches through mortgage bankers and brokers and (to a lesser extent) on a wholesale basis nationwide. Acquisitive M&T Bank is buying Hudson City Bancorp for some $3.7 billion.

Hudson City Savings gathers funds for its lending and investment activities by offering checking and savings accounts CDs and IRAs. It also collects deposits from customers nationwide through its online banking service. The bank offers consumer loans second mortgages and home equity lines of credit. It does not offer investment services. Subsidiary HC Value Broker Services sells insurance products to bank customers.

Hudson City Savings requires a minimum down payment of 20% of a loan's value on all mortgages (though the average down payment hovers closer to 40%). The thrift does not originate subprime mortgages option adjustable rate mortgage loans or business loans. Its conservative lending and investment policies helped the company post record earnings each year for more than a decade.

However Hudson City Bancorp has not been unscathed by the recessionary economy. Although it serves affluent clients that are less susceptible to swings in the financial climate the company has seen an increase in nonperforming loans. And much like other banks Hudson City has also been stung by low interest rates. Meanwhile the company has seen yields on its investments in mortgage-backed securities decrease as the Federal Reserve ramped up its securities acquisition activity to provide liquidity in the marketplace. The company's sales slipped slightly in 2010 then fell 23% to $2.3 billion in 2011. That year the company ended up losing $736 billion its first net loss in many years. The results were primarily attributed to balance sheet restructuring activities in which the company reported a $1.9 billion loss on extinguishment of high-cost debt.

By strengthening its balance sheet Hudson City Bancorp believes it has positioned itself for growth when the mortgage market picks back up. Furthermore its banking operations have been performing in line with expectations.

The thrift's nationwide wholesale loan purchasing activities declined significantly in 2010 and 2011 as a result of fewer buying opportunities so most of its recently acquired loans have been based in its local market areas. (Sellers have increasingly either held on to their loans rather than selling or they are selling to government-sponsored entities as part of the government's involvement in providing liquidity to the financial sector.) Loan originations have also declined as a result of lower demand in the soft market. Combined with the sale of low-yielding assets as part of its restructuring Hudson City Bancorp's assets decreased by about a quarter in 2011.

EXECUTIVES

SVP Hudson City Bancorp and Hudson City Savings Bank, Michael B. Lee, age 62
EVP and Chief Lending Officer Hudson City Bancorp and Hudson City Savings Bank, Thomas E. Laird, age 59, $389,423 total compensation
EVP and CFO Hudson City Bancorp and Hudson City Savings Bank, James C. Kranz, age 63, $443,623 total compensation
SVP; SVP Mortgage Servicing Hudson City Savings Bank, V. Barry Corridon, age 63
Chairman and CEO Hudson City Bancorp and Hudson City Savings Bank, Ronald E. Hermance Jr., age 64, $1,526,923 total compensation
President COO and Director Husdon City Bancorp and Hudson City Savings Bank, Denis J. Salamone, age 59, $924,327 total compensation
SVP Secretary and Treasurer Hudson City Bancorp and Hudson City Savings Bank, Veronica A. Olszewski, age 52
SVP Hudson City Bancorp and Hudson City Savings, Ronald J. Butkovich, age 62, $341,771 total compensation
SVP Hudson City Bancorp and Hudson City Savings, James A. Klarer, age 59
EVP Hudson City Savings and Hudson City Bancorp, Anthony J. Fabiano, age 51
SVP Hudson City Bancorp and Hudson City Savings Bank, Christopher L. Mahler, age 51
SVP Hudson City Bancorp and Hudson City Savings Bank, Michael D. McCambridge, age 49
SVP Information Services Hudson City Bancorp and Hudson City Savings Bank, Steven M. Schlesinger, age 56
Director, Scott A. Belair, age 64
Director, Donald O. Quest, age 72
Director, Victoria H. Bruni, age 70
President COO and Director Husdon City Bancorp and Hudson City Savings Bank, Denis J. Salamone, age 59
Director, Cornelius E. (Neal) Golding, age 64
Director, Michael W. Azzara, age 65
Director, Joseph G. Sponholz, age 68
Director, William G. Bardel, age 72
Auditors: KPMGLLP

LOCATIONS

HQ: Hudson City Bancorp Inc.
W. 80 Century Rd., Paramus NJ 07652
Phone: 201-967-1900 **Fax:** 201-967-0332
Web: www.hcsbonline.com

2011 Locations

	No.
New	97
New	29
Connecticut	9
Total	**135**

PRODUCTS/OPERATIONS

2011 Sales

	$ mil.	% of total
Interest & dividends		
First mortgage loans	1,493	65
Mortgage-backed securities available for sale	301	13
Mortgage-backed securities held to maturity	213	9
Investment securities held to maturity	100	4
Other	59	3
Noninterest		
Gains on securities transactions	102	5
Service charges & other	11	1
Total	**2,281**	**100**

Selected Subsidiaries

Hudson City Savings Bank
HC Value Broker Services (life insurance brokerage)
HudCiti Service Corporation
Hudson City Preferred Funding Corp. (real estate investment trust)
Sound REIT Inc.

COMPETITORS

Astoria Financial
Bank of America
Capital One
Citigroup
JPMorgan Chase
New York Community Bancorp
PNC Financial
TD Bank USA
Valley National Bancorp

HISTORICAL FINANCIALS

Company Type: Public

Income Statement FYE: December 31

	ASSETS ($ mil.)	NET INCOME ($ mil.)	INCOME AS % OF ASSETS	EMPLOYEES
12/11	45,355	(735)	—	1,645
12/10	61,166	537	0.9%	1,626
12/09	60,267	527	0.9%	1,552
12/08	54,145	445	0.8%	1,496
12/07	44,423	295	0.7%	1,362
Annual Growth	0.5%	—	—	4.8%

2011 Year-End Financials

Debt ratio: 17.91%
Return on equity: (-16.14)%
Cash ($ mil.): 194
Current ratio: —
Long-term debt ($ mil.): 8,125
No. of shares (mil.): 527
Dividends
Yield: —
Payout: —
Market value ($ mil.): 3,297

	STOCK PRICE ($) FY Close	P/E High/Low		PER SHARE ($) Earnings	Dividends	Book Value
12/11	6.25	—	—	(1.49)	0.00	8.64
12/10	12.74	14	10	1.09	0.60	10.46
12/09	13.73	15	8	1.07	0.59	10.14
12/08	15.96	22	15	0.90	0.45	9.43
12/07	15.02	27	20	0.58	0.33	8.89
Annual Growth	(19.7%)	—	—	—	—	(0.7%)

Hudson Valley Holding Corp.

Hudson Valley Holding is the parent company of Hudson Valley Bank which serves individuals businesses municipalities and not-for-profit organizations from more than 35 locations throughout metropolitan New York and lower Connecticut. The bank focuses on real estate lending which accounts for more than 80% of the company's loan portfolio. Other products include savings checking and money market accounts commercial and industrial loans consumer loans credit cards CDs and IRAs. Bank subsidiary A.R. Schmeidler & Co. offers investment management services.

Due to its exposure to commercial and residential real estate Hudson Valley Holding has felt the impact of the economic downturn as levels of problem loans remained elevated in 2010 and 2011. Increased provisions for loan losses contributed to an overall loss for the company in 2011 after it reported profits the previous two years. Hudson Valley Holding also implemented a plan to sell some $475 million worth of commercial real estate loans to reduce its exposure to the sector. But while demand for most types of loans continued to be muted the company increased its multifamily real estate lending in 2011.

Hudson Valley Holding is upgrading its technology systems in order to improve efficiencies. It also plans to expand within its existing market by acquiring smaller banks and opening branches. In 2006 the company acquired Bronx-based New York National Bank which operated as a standalone subsidiary until 2010 when it became a division of Hudson Valley Bank. The merger was made in order to reduce costs enhance efficiency and unify the company's brand.

Board member Gregory Holcombe and his wife Marie own about 20% of Hudson Valley Holding which was founded in 1982. Hudson Valley Bank was established in 1972.

EXECUTIVES

SVP and Relationship Officer Hudson Valley Bank, John P. Bartolotta
Chairman, William E. Griffin, age 79
President CEO and Director, James J. Landy, age 57, $379,913 total compensation
SEVP CFO Treasurer and Director, Stephen R. Brown, age 56, $361,684 total compensation
Director; EVP and Chief Banking Officer Hudson Valley Bank, Michael P. Maloney, age 50, $275,173 total compensation
EVP and Special Assistant to President, Mary B. Minieri, age 53

EVP and Chief Lending Officer Hudson Valley Bank, Vincent T. Palaia, age 65, $265,075 total compensation
EVP COO and Marketing Director Hudson Valley Bank, Frank J. Skuthan, age 59, $254,234 total compensation
Secretary, James M. Coogan, age 69
Vice Chairman, John A. Pratt Jr., age 81
First VP Shareholder Relations, Wendy Croker
First SVP and Controller, Andrew J. Reinhart
EVP Branch Banking Hudson Valley Bank, Michael J. Gilfeather, age 54
VP Investment Management and Trust Hudson Valley Bank, Mary Ann E. Alonso
President and CEO A. R. Schmeidler & Co., Arnold R. Schmeidler
CFO A. R. Schmeidler & Co., Peter G. Kandel
First SVP Hudson Valley Bank, Michael P. King
First VP Marketing Hudson Valley Bank, Joan T. Dupay
Director, Adam W. Ifshin, age 46
President CEO and Director, James J. Landy, age 57
SEVP CFO Treasurer and Director, Stephen R. Brown, age 56
Director; EVP and Chief Banking Officer Hudson Valley Bank, Michael P. Maloney, age 50
Director, Gregory F. Holcombe, age 50
Director, Angelo R. Martinelli, age 84
Vice Chairman, John A. Pratt Jr., age 81
Director, Cecile D. Singer, age 82
Director, Craig S. Thompson, age 58
Director, Mary-Jane Foster, age 61
Director, John P. Cahill, age 53
Auditors: CroweHorwathLLP

LOCATIONS

HQ: Hudson Valley Holding Corp.
21 Scarsdale Rd., Yonkers NY 10707
Phone: 914-961-6100 **Fax:** 914-961-7378
Web: www.hudsonvalleybank.com

PRODUCTS/OPERATIONS

2011 Sales

	$ mil.	% of total
Interest		
Loans including fees	111	76
Securities	16	11
Other	0	-
Noninterest		
Investment advisory fees	10	7
Service charges	7	5
Other	1	1
Total	**147**	**100**

COMPETITORS

Apple Bank for Savings
Astoria Financial
Citibank
Flushing Financial
HSBC USA
JPMorgan Chase
New York Community Bancorp
RBS Citizens Financial Group
Sterling Bancorp

HISTORICAL FINANCIALS

Company Type: Public

Income Statement FYE: December 31

	ASSETS ($ mil.)	NET INCOME ($ mil.)	INCOME AS % OF ASSETS	EMPLOYEES
12/11	2,797	(2)	—	489
12/10	2,669	5	0.2%	478
12/09	2,665	19	0.7%	498
12/08	2,540	30	1.2%	533
12/07	2,330	34	1.5%	471
Annual Growth	4.7%	—	—	0.9%

2011 Year-End Financials

Debt ratio: 0.59%
Return on equity: (-0.77)%
Cash ($ mil.): 78
Current ratio: —
Long-term debt ($ mil.): 16
No. of shares (mil.): 19
Dividends
Yield: —
Payout: —
Market value ($ mil.): 414

	STOCK PRICE ($) FY Close	P/E High/Low		PER SHARE ($) Earnings	Dividends	Book Value
12/11	21.22	—	—	(0.11)	0.00	14.22
12/10	24.76	104	61	0.26	0.59	14.92
12/09	24.66	40	19	1.24	1.05	15.15
12/08	49.95	32	23	2.06	0.00	14.34
12/07	58.00	26	21	2.32	1.24	14.14
Annual Growth	(22.2%)	—	—	—	—	0.1%

Humana Inc.

Medicare has made Humana a big-time player in the health insurance game. One of the country's largest Medicare providers and a top health insurer Humana provides Medicare Advantage plans and prescription drug coverage to more than 4.5 million members throughout the US. It also administers managed care plans for other government programs including Medicaid plans in Florida and Puerto Rico and TRICARE (a program for military personnel) in 10 southern states. Additionally Humana offers commercial health plans and specialty (life dental and vision) coverage; it also provides health management services and operates outpatient care clinics. All told it covers more than 11 million health plan members in the US.

HISTORY

In 1961 Louisville Kentucky lawyers David Jones and Wendell Cherry bought a nursing home as a real estate investment. Within six years their company Extendicare was the largest nursing home chain in the US (with only eight homes).

Faced with a glutted nursing home market the partners noticed that hospitals received more money per patient per day than nursing homes so they took their company public in 1968 to finance hospital purchases (one per month from 1968 to 1971). The company then sold its 40 nursing homes. Sales rose 13 times over in the next five years and in 1973 the firm changed its name to Humana.

By 1975 Humana had built 27 hospitals in the South and Southwest. It targeted young privately insured patients and kept its charity caseload and bad-debt expenses low. Three years later #3 for-profit hospital operator Humana moved up a notch when it bought #2 American Medicorp.

In 1983 the government began reimbursing Medicare payments based on fixed rates. Counting on its high hospital occupancy in 1984 the company launched Humana Health Care Plans rewarding doctors and patients who used Humana hospitals. However hospital occupancy dropped and the company closed several clinics. When its net income fell 75% in 1986 the firm responded by lowering premiums to attract employers.

In 1991 co-founder Cherry died. With hospital profits down in 1993 Jones spun off Humana's 76 hospitals as Galen Healthcare which formed the nucleus of what is now HCA - The Healthcare Company. Humana used the cash to expand its HMO membership buying Group Health Association (an HMO serving metropolitan Washington DC) and CareNetwork (a Milwaukee HMO). The next year Humana added 1.3 million members when it bought EMPHESYS and the company's income which had stagnated since the salad days of the late 1980s and early 1990s seemed headed in the right direction.

In the mid-1990s cutthroat premiums failed to cover rising health care costs as members' hospital use soared out of control particularly in the company's new Washington DC market. Profits dropped 94% and Humana's already tense relationship with doctors and members worsened. President and COO Wayne Smith and CFO Roger Drury resigned as part of a management shake-up and newly appointed president Gregory Wolf offered to drop the company's gag clause after the Florida Physicians Association threatened to sue.

A reorganized Humana rebounded in 1997. The company pulled out of 13 unprofitable markets including Alabama (though it did not drop TRICARE its military health coverage program in that state) and Washington DC. Refocusing on core markets in the Midwest and Southeast Humana bought Physician Corp. of America (PCA) and ChoiceCare a Cincinnati HMO. Wolf replaced Jones as CEO in 1997.

To cut costs Humana agreed in 1998 to be bought by United HealthCare (now UnitedHealth Group). The deal was abandoned however when United HealthCare took a $900 million charge in advance of the purchase. Humana found savings by pruning its Medicare HMO business.

Humana did everything "but" party in 1999. The company faced RICO charges for allegedly overcharging members for co-insurance; it agreed to repay $15 million in Medicare overpayments to the government; and it became the first health insurance firm to be slapped with a class-action suit over its physician incentives and other coverage policies.

Humana sold PCA in 2000 saying that it had paid too much for the company; subsidiary PCA Property & Casualty was also sold marking the company's exit from the workers' compensation business. That year Humana also sold its underperforming Florida Medicaid HMO to Well Care HMO and agreed to pay more than $14 million to the government for submitting false Medicare payment information.

In 2001 Humana bought a unit of Anthem (now WellPoint) that provides health benefits to the military. Expanding its holdings in the southeast Humana acquired Louisiana's Ochsner Health Plan in 2004.

It further grew its product line with the 2007 acquisition of Atlanta-based CompBenefits a provider of dental and vision benefits to nearly 5 million members. The acquisition gave Humana a full-service vision offering and expanded its dental benefits operations. Later that year the company bought KMG America a life and health insurer and third-party administrator for more than 1 million members. Humana combined CompBenefits KMG America and its previous dental benefits operations into a new unit in 2008 called Humana Specialty Benefits.

In 2008 Humana acquired about 25000 Medicare Advantage members in Nevada from UnitedHealth which was divesting the operations as part of its merger deal with Sierra Health Services for $225 million. And later that year it acquired smaller Florida-based Medicare Advantage provider Metcare Health Plans from Metropolitan Health Networks.

Additional acquisitions include the 2008 acquisition of OSF HealthPlans an Illinois-based managed care company belonging to OSF Healthcare. The deal worth about $90 million gave Humana another 60000 commercial members as well as some new Medicare customers in Illinois. The company had already wrapped up its acquisition of Tennessee-based PHP Companies (which does business as Cariten Healthcare) from Covenant Health. Humana spent $250 million in late 2008 to gain Cariten's managed care operations in East Tennessee adding 70000 commercial customers and 45000 Medicare members.

One of Humana's competitive TRICARE contracts was awarded to another party in 2009; however after Humana objected and bids were re-evaluated the decision was reversed in 2011 (with no negative impact on the company's operations).

In 2010 Humana moved into an all new specialty business area with its acquisition of Concentra a provider of occupational medicine urgent care and wellness programs from Welsh Carson Anderson & Stowe for some $790 million. Humana made the purchase to bolster its consumer-focused initiatives and provide a platform for future service-offering expansion efforts.

To widen its cost-control services and advance its IT offerings Humana partnered with software firm Anvita Health in 2010. The analytics firm provided analytics capabilities to identify at-risk members and also served other insurers benefit managers health care professionals and electronic health record providers. (Humana wound up acquiring Anvita in late 2011.)

Early in 2012 Humana purchased MD Care a Medicare Advantage provider serving some 15000 members in four Southern California counties. It also acquired Arcadian Management Services a Medicare Advantage HMO with some 64000 members in 15 states including California. To complete its acquisition of Arcadian Humana was required to sell select Medicare Advantage plans serving some 12000 former Arcadian members to CIGNA (in Texas and Arkansas) and WellCare Health Plans (in Arizona).

EXECUTIVES

COO, James E. (Jim) Murray, age 58, $670,000 total compensation
SVP and Chief Human Resources Officer, Bonita C. (Bonnie) Hathcock, age 63
SVP Strategy Initiatives, Bruce J. Goodman, age 70, $489,385 total compensation
Chairman and CEO, Michael B. (Mike) McCallister, age 59, $1,025,000 total compensation
SVP and General Counsel, Christopher M. (Chris) Todoroff, age 49
President, Bruce D. Broussard, age 49
SVP CFO and Treasurer, James H. (Jim) Bloem, age 61, $545,000 total compensation
SVP Senior Products, Thomas J. (Tom) Liston, age 50
CEO Commercial Operations Midwest, Larry D. Savage
SVP Public Relations, Heidi S. Margulis, age 58
SVP Chief Strategy Officer and Corporate Development Officer, Paul B. Kusserow, age 50, $406,397 total compensation
VP Investor Relations, Regina C. Nethery
VP Controller and Principal Accounting Officer, Steven E. McCulley, age 50
President Commercial Market Operations Illinois, Dave Reynolds
President Commercial Market Operations Nevada Arizona and Utah, Curt Howell
Market President Specialty Products Northern California, Stephen Macias
President Commercial Market Operations Louisiana, Rhonda Bagby
CEO Commercial Market Operations Southeast, Craig Drablos
SVP and Chief Service and Information Officer, Brian P. LeClaire, age 51
SVP and Chief Innovation and Marketing Officer, V. Rajamannar Madabhushi, age 50
Director, James J. (Jim) O'Brien Jr., age 57
Director, W. Roy Dunbar, age 51
Director, William J. (Bill) McDonald, age 56
Director, Kurt J. Hilzinger, age 51
Director, David A. Jones Jr., age 54
Director, William E. (Bill) Mitchell, age 68
Director, Frank A. D'Amelio, age 54
Director, Marissa T. Peterson, age 50
Director, David B. Nash, age 56
Auditors: PricewaterhouseCoopersLLP

LOCATIONS

HQ: Humana Inc.
500 W. Main St., Louisville KY 40202
Phone: 502-580-1000 **Fax:** 502-580-3677
Web: www.humana.com

PRODUCTS/OPERATIONS

2012 Sales

	$ mil.	% of total
Premiums		
Medicare Advantage	24,852	64
Fully insured commercial	6,000	15
Medicare stand-alone PDP	2,861	7
Specialty commercial	1,241	3
Military	1,017	3
Medicaid & other premiums	1,038	3
Services	1,726	4
Investment income	391	1
Total	**39,126**	**100**

2012 Sales

	$ mil.	% of total
Health plans		
Retail	24,655	48
Employer group	10,553	21
Health and well-being services	12,988	26
Other businesses	2,687	5
Adjustments	(11757)	-
Total	**39,126**	**100**

Selected Acquisitions

2012
- Certify Data Systems Inc. (undisclosed price; San Jose California; provider of health information exchange technology)
- Arcadian Management (undisclosed price; Oakland California; Medicare Advantage plans)
- Harris Rothenberg International Inc. (HRI) (undisclosed price; New York City; work/life services and employee assistance programs)
- MD Care (undisclosed price; California; Medicare Advantage plans)
- Metropolitan Health Networks ($850 million care coordination services for Medicare/Medicaid in Florida)
- SeniorBridge (undisclosed price; New York City; chronic care management)

2011
- Anvita Health ($177 million; San Diego California; health care analytics)

2010
- Concentra Inc. ($805 million; Addison Texas; urgent care center operator)

Selected Products and Services

Government
- Medicaid managed care plans
- Medicare Advantage plans
- Medicare prescription drug plans
- TRICARE (military personnel)

Commercial
- Administrative services only (ASO)
- Health care spending accounts (HSAs)
- HMO plans
- Humana Classic (traditional indemnity plan)
- HumanaOne (individual insurance)
- POS (point-of-service) plans
- PPO plans
- Specialty products
  - Dental insurance
  - Life insurance
  - Short-term disability insurance
  - Vision insurance

COMPETITORS

Aetna
AMERIGROUP
Assurant
Blue Cross and Blue Shield of Florida
Blue Cross and Blue Shield of Texas
Caremark Pharmacy Services
Centene
CIGNA
Coventry Health Care
Express Scripts
First Health Group
HCSC
Health Net
HealthSpring
Highmark
Kaiser Foundation Health Plan
Molina Healthcare
UnitedHealth Group
Universal American
WellCare Health Plans
WellPoint

HISTORICAL FINANCIALS

Company Type: Public

Income Statement

FYE: December 31

	ASSETS ($ mil.)	NET INCOME ($ mil.)	INCOME AS % OF ASSETS	EMPLOYEES
12/11	17,708	1,419	8.0%	40,000
12/10	16,103	1,099	6.8%	35,200
12/09	14,153	1,039	7.3%	28,100
12/08	13,041	647	5.0%	28,900
12/07	12,879	833	6.5%	25,000
Annual Growth	8.3%	14.2%	—	12.5%

2011 Year-End Financials

Debt ratio: 9.37%
Return on equity: 17.60%
Cash ($ mil.): 1,377
Current ratio: —
Long-term debt ($ mil.): 1,659
No. of shares (mil.): 164
Dividends
Yield: —
Payout: 8.87%
Market value ($ mil.): 14,368

	STOCK PRICE ($) FY Close	P/E High	P/E Low	PER SHARE ($) Earnings	Dividends	Book Value
12/11	87.61	10	6	8.46	0.00	49.16
12/10	54.74	9	7	6.47	0.00	41.10
12/09	43.89	7	3	6.15	0.00	33.94
12/08	37.28	22	6	3.83	0.00	26.40
12/07	75.31	16	10	4.91	0.00	23.70
Annual Growth	3.9%	—	—	14.6%	—	20.0%

Hunt (J.B.) Transport Services, Inc.

When it comes to hauling freight J.B. Hunt Transport Services knows how to deliver. Its intermodal unit the company's largest maintains about 2900 tractors and 54000 pieces of trailing equipment and moves customers' cargo by combinations of truck and train. J.B. Hunt's dedicated contract services unit supplies customers with drivers and equipment; it operates about 4500 company-owned trucks. The company's truckload transportation unit provides dry freight transportation with a fleet of about 1600 tractors. A fourth business segment integrated capacity solutions (ICS) manages freight transportation via third-party carriers as well as J.B. Hunt equipment.

Freight transported by J.B. Hunt includes automotive parts building materials chemicals food and beverages forest and paper products and general merchandise. Traditionally one of the company's top customers has been its Arkansas neighbor Wal-Mart.

The company divides its operations across four segments. JBI offers intermodal freight services to customers in Canada Mexico and the US; it generated almost 60% of J.B. Hunt's total sales in 2011. Dedicated contract services (DCS) provides supply chain services supplementing a variety of different types of transportation and accounted for almost 25% of total sales. Other segments include JBT (trucking) and ICS (integrated capacity solutions). The latter segment often arranges specialty trucking services such as transporting freight that requires the use of flatbed or refrigerated trailers.

The company has enjoyed sizable growth in the wake of the recession. From 2010 to 2011 its revenues increased almost 30% from $3.8 billion to a record-high $4.5 billion. Profits also surged by nearly 30% from around $200 million to historic levels of $257 million. J.B. Hunt attributes the growth to increases in demand across all its segments especially from its JBI and DCS segments (these segments combined represented about 88% of its overall growth in operating income). Higher load counts and a focus on cost reduction initiatives also proved beneficial to the trucking company.

J.B. Hunt hopes to continue its pathway to growth by concentrating on its operating segments as separate but overlapping businesses and by selling more value-added services to its customers. It has continued to expand its intermodal unit which has agreements with major North American railroads including Burlington Northern Santa Fe and Norfolk Southern railways. The arrangement also allows J.B. Hunt to cut down on costs.

HISTORY

Johnnie Bryan (J.B.) Hunt's life was a classic tale of rolling from rags to riches —with a little help from a Rockefeller.

Hunt grew up in a family of sharecroppers during the Depression and he left school at age 12 to work for his uncle's Arkansas sawmill. In the late 1950s after driving trucks for more than nine years Hunt noticed that the rice mills along his eastern Arkansas route were burning rice hulls. Believing the hulls could be used as poultry litter Hunt got a contract to haul away the hulls and began selling them to chicken farmers.

In 1961 he began the J.B. Hunt Company with help from future Arkansas governor Winthrop Rockefeller who owned Winrock grass company where Hunt bought sod for one of his side businesses. Hunt developed a machine to compress the rice hulls which made their transportation profitable and within a few years the company was the world's largest producer of rice hulls for poultry litter.

Still looking for new opportunities Hunt bought some used trucks and refrigerated trailers in 1969 though the company continued to focus on its original business. In the 1970s it found that the ground rice hulls made a good base for livestock vitamins and medications. Buyers of the ground hulls included Pfizer and Eli Lilly. J.B. Hunt with Pfizer's backing soon began selling a vitamin premix to feed companies.

In the 1980s J.B. Hunt's trucking division grew dramatically and became lucrative as the trucking industry was being deregulated. In 1981-82 the Hunt trucking business had higher margins than most trucking firms. In 1983 when J.B. Hunt Transport Services went public Hunt sold the rice hull business to concentrate on trucking.

By 1986 J.B. Hunt was the US's third-largest irregular-route trucking company. The time was ripe to expand and it began trucking in Canada (1988) and Mexico (1989). It also formed an alliance in 1989 with Santa Fe Pacific Railroad (now Burlington Northern Santa Fe) to provide intermodal services between the West Coast and the Midwest.

The company began adding computers to its trucks in 1992 to improve data exchange and communication on the road. J.B. Hunt also formed a joint venture with Latin America's largest transportation company Transportacion Maritima Mexicana. Founder Hunt retired in 1995 and became senior chairman.

J.B. Hunt tried hauling automobiles in 1996 but abandoned the idea when it found that cars were easily dented on intermodal trailers. More in line with the trucking company's long-term goals was an effort to stabilize its roster of drivers. It raised wages by one-third in 1997 to counteract driver shortages and high turnover. That year J.B. Hunt sold its underperforming flatbed-trucking unit (renamed Charger Inc.).

In 1998 the company reaped the benefits of greater profits from its efforts to retain drivers. The next year it began testing a satellite system from ORBCOMM Global to track empty trailers.

The company combined its J.B. Logistics (JBL) unit with the logistics businesses of five other truckers in 2000 to form Transplace.com (later known as Transplace). Also that year J.B. Hunt inked a $100 million deal with Wal-Mart to increase its full-truckload services to the retailer by 50%. In 2002 J.B. Hunt bought a 10% stake in Transplace from Werner Enterprises increasing its stake in the logistics company to 37%.

Founder Hunt stepped down from the company's board in 2004. He died in 2006.

J.B. Hunt was also engaged in transportation management through its 37% stake in Transplace a company formed from the logistics units of several truckload carriers. However an investment firm acquired all the shares of Transplace in late 2009.

EXECUTIVES

EVP and COO, Craig Harper, age 54, $353,077 total compensation
President CEO and Director, John N. Roberts III, age 48
Chairman, Kirk Thompson, age 58, $695,000 total compensation
EVP and CIO, Kay Johnson Palmer, age 48
VP Treasurer and Assistant Secretary, David N. Chelette, age 48
President Intermodal, Terrence D. (Terry) Matthews, age 53
EVP Finance and Administration CFO and Corporate Secretary, David G. Mee, age 51, $248,515 total compensation
Chief Marketing Officer; President Integrated Capacity Solutions, Shelley Simpson, age 40
EVP; President Dedicated Contract Services, Nick Hobbs, age 49
EVP Maintenance Properties and Equipment, Gary Anderson, age 45
VP and Controller, John Kuhlow, age 41
Director, Coleman H. (Cole) Peterson, age 63
President CEO and Director, John N. Roberts III, age 48
Director, Wayne Garrison, age 59
Director, Douglas G. Duncan, age 61
Director, John A. White, age 72
Director, J. Bryan Hunt Jr., age 53
Director, James L. (Jim) Robo, age 49
Director, Sharilyn S. Gasaway, age 43
Director, William J. Shea Jr., age 57
Director, Gary C. George, age 61
Director, Francesca Maher Edwardson, age 54
Auditors: Ernst&YoungLLP

LOCATIONS

HQ: J.B. Hunt Transport Services Inc.
615 J.B. Hunt Corporate Dr., Lowell AR 72745-0130
Phone: 479-820-0000 **Fax:** 479-820-3418
Web: www.jbhunt.com

PRODUCTS/OPERATIONS

2011 Sales

Intermodal (JBI)	2,673	58
Trucking (JBT)	504	11
Adjustments	(37)	-

COMPETITORS

APL Logistics
Canadian National Railway
Con-way Inc.
CSX
Hub Group
Kansas City Southern
Landstar System
Pacer International
Ryder System
Schneider National
Swift Transportation
U.S. Xpress
Union Pacific
Werner Enterprises
YRC Worldwide

HISTORICAL FINANCIALS

Company Type: Public

Income Statement FYE: December 31

	REVENUE ($ mil.)	NET INCOME ($ mil.)	NET PROFIT MARGIN	EMPLOYEES
12/11	4,526	257	5.7%	15,631
12/10	3,793	199	5.3%	16,233
12/09	3,203	136	4.3%	14,171
12/08	3,731	200	5.4%	14,667
12/07	3,489	213	6.1%	15,795
Annual Growth	6.7%	4.8%	—	(0.3%)

2011 Year-End Financials

Debt ratio: 33.04%
Return on equity: 45.28%
Cash ($ mil.): 5
Current ratio: 117.11
Long-term debt ($ mil.): 699
No. of shares (mil.): 116
Dividends
Yield: —
Payout: 24.64%
Market value ($ mil.): 5,270

	STOCK PRICE ($) FY Close	P/E High/Low		PER SHARE ($) Earnings	Dividends	Book Value
12/11	45.07	23	16	2.11	0.00	4.85
12/10	40.81	26	19	1.56	0.48	4.72
12/09	32.27	32	17	1.05	0.44	5.06
12/08	26.27	25	14	1.56	0.40	4.20
12/07	27.55	20	14	1.55	0.36	2.76
Annual Growth	13.1%	—	—	8.0%	—	15.1%

Huntington Bancshares, Inc

Huntington Bancshares is the holding company for The Huntington National Bank which operates about 650 branches in Indiana Kentucky Michigan Ohio Pennsylvania and West Virginia. The bank offers retail and commercial banking mortgage banking credit cards equipment leasing brokerage services wealth and investment management trust and estate services and personal and business insurance. The company's automobile finance business provides car loans to consumers and real estate and inventory finance to car dealerships throughout the Midwest and Northeast.

With the economy in the Midwest wracked by the recession Huntington posted losses in 2008 and 2009 –more than $3 billion in the latter year alone –mainly attributable to credit losses due to nonperforming assets and the write down of goodwill related to past acquisitions. It returned to profitability in 2010 thanks in part to higher interest margins as a result of the company's focus on lower-cost customer checking accounts.

The company continued its momentum into 2011 when its earnings grew again; it reported growth in its brokerage and trust segments in addition to fewer changed-off loans and provisions for credit losses. The bank's commercial and industrial loan volume began to pick up in 2010 while residential mortgage and home equity loans increased during 2011.

Meanwhile Huntington's automobile loan portfolio more than doubled in 2010 and the company extended the business into eastern Pennsylvania and most of New England during the year. The company has said it will continue to pursue expansion beyond its traditional Midwest base.

To prepare for further growth Huntington is getting back to basics. Its retail strategy is centered around simple financial products customer service and convenience. The bank offers extended hours at many locations and has an agreement with Giant Eagle to install up to 100 new branches inside the grocer's stores in Ohio. The company is also courting large corporate clients and looking to grow its fee-based activities such as treasury management foreign exchange and capital markets services. The company's equipment finance business expanded into business aviation rail and lender/lessor financing.

After acquiring two banks in FDIC-assisted transactions in 2009 the company bought the assets of failed Fidelity Bank of Dearborn Michigan in 2012. The latest deal added some 15 branches to Huntington's banking network.

HISTORY

Pelatiah Webster (P. W.) Huntington descendant of both a Revolutionary War leader and a Declaration of Independence signer went to work at sea in 1850 at age 14. He returned to go into banking and in 1866 founded what would become Huntington National Bank of Columbus. As the business grew he conscripted four of his five sons. The bank took a national charter in 1905 and became The Huntington National Bank of Columbus. It survived the hard times of 1907 and 1912 through the Huntington philosophy of sitting on piles of cash.

P. W. died in 1918 and his son Francis became president. Francis expanded the company into trust services. Unlike many bankers in the 1920s he refused to make speculative loans based on the stock market. Francis died in 1928 and was succeeded by brother Theodore. By 1930 Huntington's trust assets accounted for more than half of the total. The family's conservative philosophy helped the bank sail through the 1933 bank holiday although when it reopened the amount of cash it could pay out was restricted to 10% of deposits.

P. W.'s son Gwynne chaired the bank during its post-WWII expansion. His death in 1958 ended the Huntington family reign. The bank began opening branches and adding new services such as mortgage and consumer loans. In 1966 in order to expand statewide the bank formed a holding company Huntington Bancshares. In the 1960s and 1970s the corporation added new operations including mortgage and leasing companies and an international division to help clients with foreign exchange.

In 1979 the company consolidated its 15 affiliates into The Huntington National Bank. Three years later the company bit off more than it could chew with the acquisitions of Reeves Banking and Trust Company of Dover and Union Commerce Corporation of Cleveland. The latter purchase loaded the company with debt. Nevertheless it continued to expand particularly after 1985 when banking regulations allowed interstate branch banking and it soon had operations in Florida Indiana Kentucky Michigan and West Virginia.

Huntington Bancshares was largely insulated from the real estate problems of the late 1980s and early 1990s thanks to its continuing conservative lending policies. But the company was at risk from the nationwide consolidation of the banking industry which made it a potential takeover target. It increased its service offerings and bolstered its place in the market through acquisitions. In 1996 Huntington Bancshares bought life insurance agency Tice & Associates and began cross-selling bank and insurance products. Important banking acquisitions in 1997 included First Michigan Bank and several Florida companies.

Also in 1997 the company took advantage of deregulation to consolidate its interstate operations (except for The Huntington State Bank) into a single operating company. In 1998 Huntington Bancshares continued to build its Huntington insurance services unit with the acquisition of Pollock & Pollock. In 1999 the bank launched a mortgage program aimed at wealthy clients and sold its credit card receivables portfolio to Chase Manhattan (now JPMorgan Chase & Co.). In 2000 the company bought Michigan's Empire Banc Corporation.

Former BANK ONE executive Thomas Hoaglin was named president and CEO in 2001. Later that year he became chairman when Frank Wobst retired after leading the company for 20 years.

In 2002 the company consolidated some branches in the Midwest to cut costs and exited the retail banking market in Florida selling some 140 retail branches there to SunTrust. After the mid-2007 acquisition of Sky Financial Sky's CEO Marty Adams became president and COO of Huntington Bancshares. He retired at the end of 2007 and Hoaglin resumed the president's role until his own retirement in 2009; Stephen Steinour then took the helm.

EXECUTIVES

President Northwest Ohio, Sharon S. Speyer
General Counsel and Secretary; EVP General Counsel Secretary and Cashier The Huntington National Bank, Richard A. Cheap, age 60, $279,833 total compensation
SEVP and Senior Trust Officer, Daniel B. (Dan) Benhase, age 52, $330,000 total compensation
President Mahoning Valley Region, Frank Hierro
EVP and Chief Customer and Marketing Officer, David B. Clifton, age 62
SEVP and Chief Risk Officer, Kevin M. Blakely, age 60
SVP and Director Investor Relations, Jay S. Gould
Chairman President and CEO, Stephen D. (Steve) Steinour, age 53, $965,909 total compensation
SEVP and Head Auto Finance and Dealer Services, Nicholas G. (Nick) Stanutz, age 57, $338,333 total compensation
SEVP Retail and Business Banking Director, Mary W. Navarro, age 56
SEVP Corporate Risk Managing Director, Helga Houston, age 51
SEVP and Director Commercial Banking; Regional President West Michigan, James S. (Jim) Dunlap, age 59
President Central Ohio/Columbus Region, James E. Kunk
SEVP, Mark E. Thompson, age 53, $315,340 total compensation
EVP and Director Payments and Channels, Mark W. Sheehan
SEVP and CFO, Donald R. Kimble, age 52, $467,042 total compensation
EVP and Chief Auditor, Eric N. Sutphin
SVP and Director Community Development, Reza Aghamirzadeh
CFO Huntington Insurance, Dennis Raab
SVP Relationship Management Unified Fund Services, Jeff Young
EVP and CIO, Zahid Afzal, age 49
EVP and Director Human Resources, Keith D. Sanders, age 52
SEVP and Director Commercial Real Estate, Randy G. Stickler
President Central Indiana Region, Michael W. (Mike) Newbold
President Southern Ohio/Northern Kentucky Region, Mark Reitzes
President West Virginia Region, Clayton Rice
President Pittsburgh Region, David Hammer
SVP and Director Corporate Real Estate and Facilities, Norman P. Bertke
Director Technology Shared Services, Steve George
President Greater Akron/Canton Region, William C. Shivers
SVP and Director Commercial and Corporate Banking Operations, John Largent
SVP and Director Treasury Management, Douglas G. Hartsema
President Unified Fund Services, Brian Blomquist
Assistant Director Investor Relations, Todd Beekman
President Greater Cleveland Region, Daniel P. Walsh

President Southeast Michigan, Mike Fezzey
SEVP and Chief Credit Officer, Daniel J. Neumeyer, age 52
EVP and Director Corporate Public Relations and Communications Huntington National Bank, Elizabeth Heller Allen, age 58
Manager Corporate Communications, Maureen Brown
Senior Communications Specialist Corporate Communications, Brent Wilder
Director Business Segment Communications, LuJean Smith
Communications Manager Business Segment Communications, Cynthia Kincaid
Communications Manager Business Segment Communications, Matt Samson
Chief Technology and Operations Officer, Paul G. Heller
President Huntington Investment Company, Belinda Sherman
Director Huntington Wealth Advisors, Steven Short
Director, William J. Lhota, age 72
Director, Steven G. (Steve) Elliott, age 65
Director, Richard W. (Rick) Neu, age 56
Director, John B. (Jay) Gerlach Jr., age 57
Director, Michael J. Endres, age 64
Director, Gerard P. Mastroianni, age 56
Director, D. James Hilliker, age 64
Director, Jonathan A. Levy, age 51
Director, William R. (Bill) Robertson, age 70
Director, David P. Lauer, age 69
Director, Don M. Casto III, age 67
Director, Kathleen H. Ransier, age 64
Director, David L. Porteous, age 59
Director, Ann B. (Tanny) Crane, age 55
Auditors: Deloitte&ToucheLLP

LOCATIONS

HQ: Huntington Bancshares Incorporated
Huntington Center 41 S. High St., Columbus OH 43287
Phone: 614-480-8300 **Fax:** 614-480-5284
Web: www.huntington.com

2011 Bank Branches

	No.
Ohio	376
Michigan	123
Pennsylvania	58
Indiana	51
West	31
Kentucky	13
Total	**652**

PRODUCTS/OPERATIONS

2011 Sales

	$ mil.	% of total
Interest		
Loans & leases	1,727	58
Securities	217	8
Other	24	1
Noninterest		
Service charges on deposit accounts	243	8
Trust services	119	4
Electronic banking	111	4
Mortgage banking	83	3
Brokerage	80	3
Insurance	69	2
Bank-owned life insurance	62	2
Capital markets	36	1
Gain on sales of loans	31	1
Automobile operating lease income	26	1
Other	115	4
Total	**2,950**	**100**

COMPETITORS

Comerica
Fifth Third
FirstMerit
JPMorgan Chase
KeyCorp
Park National
PNC Financial
RBS Citizens Financial Group
Regions Financial
TFS Financial
U.S. Bancorp
Wells Fargo

HISTORICAL FINANCIALS

Company Type: Public

Income Statement FYE: December 31

	ASSETS ($ mil.)	NET INCOME ($ mil.)	INCOME AS % OF ASSETS	EMPLOYEES
12/11	54,450	542	1.0%	11,245
12/10	53,819	312	0.6%	11,341
12/09	51,554	(3,094)	—	10,272
12/08	54,352	(113)	—	10,951
12/07	54,697	75	0.1%	11,925
Annual Growth	(0.1%)	63.9%	—	(1.5%)

2011 Year-End Financials

Debt ratio: 5.69%
Return on equity: 10.01%
Cash ($ mil.): 1,206
Current ratio: —
Long-term debt ($ mil.): 3,097
No. of shares (mil.): 864
Dividends
Yield: —
Payout: 16.95%
Market value ($ mil.): 4,746

	STOCK PRICE ($) FY Close	P/E High/Low	PER SHARE ($) Earnings	Dividends	Book Value
12/11	5.49	13 8	0.59	0.00	6.27
12/10	6.87	38 19	0.19	0.04	5.77
12/09	3.65	— —	(6.14)	0.04	7.46
12/08	7.66	— —	(0.44)	0.66	19.74
12/07	14.76	96 54	0.25	1.06	16.24
Annual Growth	(21.9%)	— —	23.9%	—	(21.2%)

Huntington Ingalls Industries, Inc.

LOCATIONS

HQ: Huntington Ingalls Industries, Inc.
4101 Washington Avenue, Newport News, VA 23607
Phone: 757 380-2000
Web: www.huntingtoningalls.com

HISTORICAL FINANCIALS

Company Type:

Income Statement FYE: December 31

	REVENUE ($ mil.)	NET INCOME ($ mil.)	NET PROFIT MARGIN	EMPLOYEES
12/11	6,575	(94)	—	38,000
12/10	0	0	—	39,000
Annual Growth	—	—	—	(2.6%)

2011 Year-End Financials

Debt ratio: 30.98%
Return on equity: (-10.78)%
Cash ($ mil.): 915
Current ratio: 165.31
Long-term debt ($ mil.): 1,830
No. of shares (mil.): 48
Dividends
Yield: —
Payout: —
Market value ($ mil.): 1,527

	STOCK PRICE ($) FY Close	P/E High/Low	PER SHARE ($) Earnings	Dividends	Book Value
12/11	31.28	— —	(1.93)	0.00	17.86
Annual Growth	—	— —	—	—	—

Huntsman Corp

Huntsman Corporation has a long track record of successfully stalking profits in the world's chemical marketplace. The global chemical manufacturer operates its businesses through subsidiary Huntsman International. Its broad range of products include MDI (methylene diphenyl diisocyanate) amines surfactants epoxy-based polymers and polyurethanes. Huntsman's chemicals are sold worldwide to a variety of customers in the adhesives construction products electronics medical and packaging industries. Huntsman operates more than 75 manufacturing and R&D facilities in 30 countries worldwide and does more than a third of its business in the US.

Operations

The company operates through five business segments after spinning off its North American base chemicals and polymers (also called olefins and polyolefins) businesses.

The largest segment is the Polyurethanes unit which makes MDI propylene oxide and propylene glycol for automotive interiors footwear and furniture cushioning. It is one of the largest producers of MDI which is used in producing rigid and other types of polyurethanes and has boasted a growth rate of 7% annually since 1992. Other segments are Advanced Materials (epoxy acrylic and polyurethane-based polymers) Textile Effects (epoxy resins and adhesives) Performance Products (mostly ethylene-based chemicals used in detergents paints and fuel additives) and Pigments (the whitening agent titanium dioxide).

Financial Analysis

Revenues jumped 21% in 2011 to more than $11.2 billion as demand and selling prices increased for many of its products over the previous year. Despite the effects of raw material inflation and currency differences on its fixed costs that year the company's net income reached $247 million.

Growth in the company's Polyurethanes and Advanced Materials segments in 2011 was driven by increased demand as substitution of those businesses' products continued that year in a broad range of industries. In Polyurethanes that growth (23%) was driven largely by Asia's demand for MDI and other key products. Its growth in its Performance Products segment for 2011 (24%) compared to 2010 was due to higher average selling prices and higher sales volumes as the company responded to higher raw material costs and increased demand. The segment also benefited that year from the consolidation of the company's Sasol-Huntsman joint venture and its acquisition of Laffans Petrochemicals.

In 2011 sales dipped in its Textile Effects segment because of restructuring and plant closing costs lower sales volumes and currency differences. However the company's Pigments segment increased in revenues that year because of higher average selling prices in all regions again driven by higher raw material costs and increased demand.

Strategy

Huntsman's strategy is to increase sales to its current customers while seeking growth in emerging international markets such as India and China. Huntsman has relocated the headquarters of some of its divisions overseas to be closer to critical markets putting its Polyurethanes operation in Hong Kong and its Textile Effects unit in Singapore. Huntsman has also expanded its manufacturing capabilities overseas by expanding its current operations and acquiring other companies. The company believes that by integrating its different product operations in large facilities close to its customers it can cut transportation costs and exposure to cyclical prices.

Mergers & Acquisitions

In a move to expand its Asian operations Huntsman acquired Indian chemical producer Laffans Petrochemicals in 2011 in a deal valued at $50 million. The company also took ownership of Laffans' ethylene oxide derivatives facility in Gujarat. The plant produces specialty intermediates for use in agrochemicals household and personal care products oil and gas applications and automotive lubricants and brake fluids.

In 2011 the company invested $40 million to build a new magnesium sulfate fertilizer production operation at its titanium dioxide plant in Calais France. The new fertilizer plant will use spent acid from the Calais pigment operations and will enable closure of part of the Calais effluent treatment plant which will lower energy consumption and reduce carbon dioxide emissions. The operation will also result in lower costs.

As part of its global strategy to expand in key growth markets in late 2011 Huntsman acquired Turkish polyurethanes manufacturer EMA Kimya Sistemleri Sanayi ve Ticaret. EMA has the capacity to produce polyester polyols and blend MDI polyurethane systems used primarily in autos adhesives and coatings elastomers furniture and insulation.

In 2012 the company acquired full ownership of its Russian joint venture Huntsman NMG (HNMG) for an undisclosed amount. HNMG supplies polyurethane systems to the adhesives coatings and footwear markets in Russia Belarus and Ukraine.

Ownership

The founding Huntsman family controls about 19% of the company.

EXECUTIVES

Vice Chairman, Nolan D. Archibald, age 68
EVP and CFO, J. Kimo Esplin, age 49, $489,500 total compensation
Chairman, Jon M. Huntsman, age 74, $1,008,333 total compensation
President CEO and Director, Peter R. Huntsman, age 49, $1,464,500 total compensation
VP Corporate Development, Sean Douglas, age 47
VP and Controller, L. Russell Healy, age 56
SVP Purchasing, Brian V. Ridd, age 54
VP Tax, Kevin C. Hardman, age 48
CEO Asia Pacific; President Polyurethanes, Anthony P (Tony) Hankins, age 54, $521,900 total compensation
VP Treasury and Planning, John R. Heskett, age 43
President Advanced Materials, James H. Huntsman, age 37
EVP General Counsel and Secretary, James R. Moore, age 67
SVP Global Human Resources, R. Wade Rogers, age 46
President and CEO Huntsman Financial Corporation (HFC), H. E. (Bud) Scruggs, age 54
Division President Textile Effects, Paul G. Hulme, age 55, $508,531 total compensation
VP and CIO, Maria Csiba-Womersly, age 54
SVP and Deputy General Counsel, Russ R. Stolle, age 49
VP Accounting Shared Services and Internal Controls, Steven C. Jorgensen, age 43
Division President Pigments, Simon Turner, age 48
Division President Advanced Materials, Andre Genton, age 52
VP Investor Relations, Kurt D. Ogden, age 43
Senior Corporate Counsel Mergers and Acquisitions, Troy M. Keller
SVP Environmental Health and Safety and Manufacturing Excellence, Ronald W. (Ron) Gerrard, age 52
Media Contact, Gary Chapman
President Performance Products, Stewart A. (Stu) Monteith
VP Internal Audit, Pierre Poukens
VP and Controller, Randy Wright
Vice Chairman, Nolan D. Archibald, age 68
Director, M. Anthony Burns, age 69
Director, Sir Robert J. (Rob) Margetts, age 65
Director, Marsha J. (Marty) Evans, age 64
President CEO and Director, Peter R. Huntsman, age 49
Director, Alvin V. Shoemaker, age 73
Director, Wayne A. Reaud, age 64
Director, Patrick T. Harker, age 53
Director, Mary C. Beckerle, age 57
Auditors: Deloitte&ToucheLLP

LOCATIONS

HQ: Huntsman Corp
500 Huntsman Way, Salt Lake City, UT 84108
Phone: 801 584-5700
Web: www.huntsman.com

2011 Sales

	$ mil.	% of total
US	3,470	32
China	944	8
Germany	723	6
Mexico	638	6
Italy	558	5
Other	4,888	43
Total	**11,221**	**100**

PRODUCTS/OPERATIONS

2011 Sales

	$ mil.	% of total
Polyurethanes	3,605	39
Advanced Materials	1,244	12
Textile Effects	787	8
Total	**9,250**	**100**

Segments & Selected Products
Polyurethanes
Aniline
MDI (methylene diphenyl diisocyana
MTBE (methyl tertiary-butyl ether)
PG (propylene glycol)
PO (propylene oxide)
Polyols
TPU (thermoplastic polyuretha
Performance Products
Ethylene glycol
Ethylene oxide
Ethanolamines
Ethyleneamines
Maleic anhydride
Polyetheramines
Surfactants
Materials & Effects
Adhesives
Acrylic
Polyurethane-based
Epoxy
Epoxy resin compounds
Pigments
Titanium dioxide

COMPETITORS

Akzo Nobel
BASF SE
Bayer AG
Dow Chemical
DuPont
Eastman Chemical
Evonik Degussa
Kronos Worldwide
LyondellBasell
Momentive
National Titanium Dioxide Company
Tronox

HISTORICAL FINANCIALS

Company Type: Public

Income Statement FYE: December 31

	REVENUE ($ mil.)	NET INCOME ($ mil.)	NET PROFIT MARGIN	EMPLOYEES
12/11	11,221	247	2.2%	12,000
12/10	9,250	27	0.3%	12,000
12/09	7,763	114	1.5%	11,000
12/08	10,215	609	6.0%	12,600
12/07	9,650	(172)	—	12,900
Annual Growth	3.8%	—	—	(1.8%)

2011 Year-End Financials

Debt ratio: 45.58%
Return on equity: 14.86%
Cash ($ mil.): 554
Current ratio: 216.10
Long-term debt ($ mil.): 3,734
No. of shares (mil.): 235
Dividends
Yield: —
Payout: 39.22%
Market value ($ mil.): 2,357

	STOCK PRICE ($) FY Close	P/E High	P/E Low	PER SHARE ($) Earnings	Dividends	Book Value
12/11	10.00	20	8	1.02	0.00	7.05
12/10	15.61	151	75	0.11	0.40	7.56
12/09	11.29	23	4	0.48	0.40	7.88
12/08	3.44	10	1	2.60	0.40	6.89
12/07	25.70	—	—	(0.74)	0.40	8.26
Annual Growth	(21.0%)	—	—	—	—	(3.9%)

HY-VEE INC.

EXECUTIVES

Chairman Emeritus, Ronald D. (Ron) Pearson, age 71
President Perishable Distributors of Iowa, Andy McCann
EVP and Chief Administrative Officer, Ronald P. (Ron) Taylor
Chairman President and CEO, Richard N. (Ric) Jurgens
SVP Marketing, Jon S. Wendel, age 48
Assistant VP Pharmacy and Drug Town Operations, Gary A. Goodhall
Assistant VP Information Technology, Cevin R. Anderson

Assistant VP Media Relations, Ruth Comer
VP Management Information Systems, Eric Smith
Assistant Director Communications, Chris Friesleben
VP Western Region, Paula K. Correy, age 45
VP Eastern Region, Thomas E. (Tom) Watson
Assistant VP Food Service, Gregory L. (Greg) Frampton
Director Benefit Plan, Kristine Garms
VP Distribution, Tod B. Hockenson
Store Manager Madison Wisconsin, Rob Budd
Chairman President and CEO, Randall B. (Randy) Edeker, age 49
SVP and Secretary, Stephen P. Meyer
Assistant Secretary, Michael P. Jurgens
Controller, Kevin A. Reeve
VP Human Resources, Sheila Laing
CFO and Treasurer, Mike Skokan
Auditors: McGladreyLLP

LOCATIONS

HQ: Hy-Vee Inc.
5820 Westown Pkwy., West Des Moines IA 50266-8223
Phone: 515-267-2800 **Fax:** 515-267-2817
Web: www.hy-vee.com

PRODUCTS/OPERATIONS

2012 Stores

	No.
Supermarkets	212
Drugstores	23
Total	**235**

Selected Subsidiaries

D & D Foods Inc. (salads dips and meats)
Florist Distributing Inc. (flowers plants and florist supplies)
Hy-Vee Pharmacy Solutions (specialty pharmacy services)
Hy-Vee Weitz Construction L.C. (construction)
Lomar Distributing Inc. (specialty foods)
Midwest Heritage Bank FSB (banking)
Perishable Distributors of Iowa Ltd. (meat fish seafood and ice cream)

COMPETITORS

ALDI
Associated Wholesale Grocers
Ball' s Food
Casey' s General Stores
CVS Caremark
Dahl' s Foods
Fareway Stores
Kmart
Kroger
Nash-Finch
Niemann Foods
Rite Aid
Roundy' s
Save-A-Lot Food Stores
SUPERVALU
Target Corporation
Wal-Mart
Walgreen

HISTORICAL FINANCIALS

Company Type: Private

Income Statement FYE: September 30

	REVENUE ($ mil.)	NET INCOME ($ mil.)	NET PROFIT MARGIN	EMPLOYEES
09/12*	7,682	0	—	58,000
10/11	0	0	—	0
10/10	0	0	—	0
09/09	0	0	—	0
Annual Growth	—	—	—	—

*Fiscal year change

2012 Year-End Financials

Debt ratio: —
Return on equity: —
Cash ($ mil.): 7
Current ratio: 0.20
Long-term debt ($ mil.): —
Dividends
Yield: —
Payout: —
Market value ($ mil.): —

IBERIABANK Corp

IBERIABANK Corp. serves up financial services with a Cajun flare. Through its flagship bank subsidiary also called IBERIABANK the holding company operates some 185 branches in Louisiana and five other southern states. It also has about 20 title insurance offices in Louisiana and Arkansas in addition to some 60 mortgage loan offices in a dozen states. Offering deposit products such as checking and savings accounts CDs and IRAs the bank uses funds gathered mainly to make loans. Commercial real estate and business loans make up nearly three-quarters of the company's loan portfolio which also includes consumer loans and residential mortgages. Founded in 1887 IBERIABANK Corp. has $12.5 billion in assets.

Geographic Reach

Beyond Louisiana IBERIABANK has branches in Alabama Arkansas Florida Tennessee and Texas.

Operations

IBERIABANK has eight wholly-owned nonbank subsidiaries including brokerage unit Iberia Financial Services IBERIABANK Insurance Services Acadiana Holdings IBERIABANK Mortgage Company Little Rock Arkansas-based Lenders Title Company and several investment funds.

Financial Analysis

IBERIABANK's 2011 revenue increased 4% vs. 2010 while profits climbed 10% over the same period. The revenue gain was attributed to an increase in both interest and dividend income. The bank's 2011 results were driven by both organic growth and acquisitions.

Strategy

Acquisitions have been a big part of IBERIABANK's growth strategy since 2003. Most recently in 2012 IBERIABANK struck an agreement to buy Florida Gulf Bank. In 2011 the bank completed three acquisitions: OMNI Bank with 14 offices in New Orleans and Baton Rouge Louisiana; Cameron State Bank with 22 offices in Lake Charles Louisiana; and the assets of Florida Trust Company a subsidiary of the failed Bank of Florida Corporation. (Between 2003 and 2010 the bank completed 13 acquisitions with combined total assets of more than $6 billion.) All of the acquisition activity has expanded the company's assets and branch network helped it enter new markets such as Florida and Texas and strengthen its presence in existing ones.

EXECUTIVES

President CEO and Director; President and CEO IBERIABANK, Daryl G. Byrd, age 57, $467,010 total compensation
SEVP and Director Financial Strategy and Mortgage, John R. Davis, age 51, $287,308 total compensation
EVP Corporate Secretary and Director Corporate Operations, George J. Becker III, age 71, $177,308 total compensation
Market President New Iberia and Community Markets, Taylor F. Barras
Chairman, William H. Fenstermaker, age 63
Vice Chairman, E. Stewart Shea III, age 60
Vice Chairman and Managing Director Brokerage Trust and Wealth Management, Jefferson G. (Jeff) Parker, age 59
EVP and Director Communications, Beth Ardoin
EVP and Internal Audit Manager, Lewis P. Rogers, age 59
SEVP and CFO, Anthony J. Restel, age 42, $199,231 total compensation
Market President New Orleans, Karl E. Hoefer
SEVP Florida Markets, Michael A. Naquin, age 51, $241,154 total compensation
Market President Baton Rouge, J. Keith Short
Market President Shreveport, Mark D. Evans
Market President Lafayette, Pete M. Yuan
EVP and Director Enterprise Risk Management, Elise Latimer
Market President Northeast Louisiana, Paul E. Hutcheson Jr.
EVP and President Mobile Alabama, Lawrence G. (Russ) Ford Jr.
Vice Chairman and COO, Michael J. (Mike) Brown, age 55
EVP and Chief Risk Officer, James B. Gburek
President and CEO IBERIABANK Mortgage, Chuck M. Quick Jr.
President Mortgage Market Alabama and Georgia IBERIABANK, Barry Carroll
EVP; President Birmingham Alabama IBERIABANK, Gregory A. King
EVP and Chief Credit Officer, H. Gregg Strader, age 54
Executive Vice President and Director - Retail and Small Business, Robert Kottler
Senior Vice President; Chief Accounting Officer; Controller, Michael Price
Executive Vice President and Executive Credit Officer, Spurgeon Mackie
Executive Vice President; Director - Organizational Development, Barry Berthelot
Chief Risk Officer, Randolph Bryan
President CEO and Director; President and CEO IBERIABANK, Daryl G. Byrd, age 57
Director, John N. Casbon, age 63
Director, Elaine D. Abell, age 69
Director, Harry V. Barton Jr., age 57
Vice Chairman, E. Stewart Shea III, age 60
Director, Ernest P. Breaux Jr., age 67
Director, O. Miles Pollard Jr., age 74
Director, David H. Welch, age 63
Independent Director, John Koerner
Auditors: Ernst&YoungLLP

LOCATIONS

HQ: IBERIABANK Corp
200 West Congress Street, Lafayette, LA 70501
Phone: 337 521-4003
Web: www.iberiabank.com

PRODUCTS/OPERATIONS

2011 Sales

	$ mil.	% of total
Interest		
Loans including fees	436	79
Securities	50	9
Other	3	1
Adjustments (70.1) (13)		
Noninterest		
Gain on sale of loans net	44	8
Service charges on deposit accounts	25	5
Title revenue	18	3
ATM/debit card fees	11	2
Broker commissions	10	2
Net gain on sale of investments	3	1

Income from bank owned life insurance	3	-
Gain on sale of assets	0	-
Other	15	3
Adjustments	(1.7)	-
Total	**552**	**100**

Selected Mergers and Acquisitions

2012

Florida Gulf Bancorp Inc. (Fort Myers Florida; commercial banking)

2011

OMNI BANCSHARES Inc. (Metairie Louisiana; commercial banking)

Cameron Bancshares Inc. (Lake Charles Louisiana; commercial banking)

Florida Trust Company (Naples Florida; commercial banking)

Selected Subsidiaries

IB Aircraft Holdings LLC
IBERIA Asset Management Inc.
IBERIA Capital Partners LLC
IBERIABANK
- Acadiana Holdings LLC
- CB Florida RRE Holdings LLC
- Finesco LLC
- Iberia Financial Services LLC
- IBERIABANK Insurance Services LLC
- Jefferson Insurance Corporation

Lenders Title Company
- American Abstract and Title Company Inc.
- Asset Exchange Inc.
- United Title & Abstract LLC
- United Title of Louisiana Inc.

COMPETITORS

Bank of America
Bank of the Ozarks
Capital One
Hancock Holding
Home Bank
JPMorgan Chase
Louisiana Bancorp
MidSouth Bancorp
Regions Financial
Teche Holding

HISTORICAL FINANCIALS

Company Type: Public

Income Statement

FYE: December 31

	ASSETS ($ mil.)	NET INCOME ($ mil.)	INCOME AS % OF ASSETS	EMPLOYEES
12/11	11,757	53	0.5%	2,645
12/10	10,026	48	0.5%	2,193
12/09	9,700	151	1.6%	1,685
12/08	5,583	39	0.7%	1,356
12/07	4,916	41	0.8%	1,386
Annual Growth	24.4%	6.7%	—	17.5%

2011 Year-End Financials

Debt ratio: 3.85%
Return on equity: 3.61%
Cash ($ mil.): 573
Current ratio: —
Long-term debt ($ mil.): 452
No. of shares (mil.): 29
Dividends
Yield: —
Payout: 72.73%
Market value ($ mil.): 1,448

	STOCK PRICE ($) FY Close	P/E High/Low		PER SHARE ($) Earnings	Dividends	Book Value
12/11	49.30	32	23	1.87	0.00	50.48
12/10	59.13	33	26	1.88	1.36	48.50
12/09	53.81	7	5	8.03	1.36	45.99
12/08	48.00	20	13	3.04	1.36	46.17
12/07	46.75	17	12	3.27	1.34	38.99
Annual Growth	1.3%	—	—	(13.0%)	—	6.7%

Icahn Enterprises L P

Icahn Enterprises has a can-do attitude when it comes to making money. The holding company has stakes in firms in a variety of industries including manufacturing real estate gaming and household goods. Holdings include car parts maker Federal-Mogul; PSC Metals one of the largest scrap yard operators in the US; residential developer Bayswater which is active in Florida and Massachusetts; and WestPoint International a maker of bed bath and other home products. In 2010 Icahn Enterprised acquired control of American Railcar Industries Viskase and Tropicana Entertainment. Billionaire corporate raider Carl Icahn and his affiliates own around 93% of his namesake firm.

Icahn Enterprises' typical strategy is to acquire undervalued assets (including firms in bankruptcy) improve their operations and enhance their value for possible sale. It usually purchases substantial stakes in companies with an eye twoard gaining control of them oftern by waging proxy battles for seats on their boards of directors. In 2012 the company upped its stake in CVR Energy from some 15% to nearly 70%. CVR's board of directors had urged shareholders to reject the offer.

Icahn Enterprises made an unsolicited bid to take Clorox private in a deal worth more than $10 billion. (It first bought its stake in the cleaning products maker earlier in 2011 and is its largest shareholder.) The company encouraged Clorox to entertain other bids from competitors but said he would buy the company if other bids were too low. Clorox rejected the offer and is adopting a poison pill measure in efforts to keep Icahn Enterprises from taking over the company.

The company was also rebuffed in 2010 when it attempted to gain control of Dynegy of which it already owned some 15% for around $665 million. Dynegy had originally agreed to be acquired by The Blackstone Group for approximately $4.7 billion including the assumption of more than $4 billion in debt. But the energy company's shareholders rejected that offer as well as Icahn's.

In 2010 Icahn Enterprises bought the unfinished Fontainebleau property in Las Vegas for some $150 million; Icahn has said he will let the latter property remain dormant until the economy picks up.

Icahn Enterprises' holdings took a hit at the beginning of the recession and the company reported more than $3 billion in losses for 2008. It rebounded to post profits the next three years as the performance of its investment funds improved. Revenues were up some 30% in 2011 and the company's net income more than tripled.

EXECUTIVES

Chairman, Carl C. Icahn, age 76, $400,000 total compensation
President, Daniel A. (Dan) Ninivaggi, age 48
President and CEO WestPoint International Inc., John A. Piazza
CFO, Sung Hwan Cho
Chief Accounting Officer, Peter Reck
Director of Icahn Enterprises GP, Keith Cozza
Director, Jack G. Wasserman, age 75
Director, William A. Leidesdorf, age 66
Director, James L. Nelson, age 62
Director, Vincent J. Intrieri, age 55
Auditors: GrantThorntonLLP

LOCATIONS

HQ: Icahn Enterprises L.P.
767 5th Ave. Ste. 4700, New York NY 10153
Phone: 212-702-4300 **Fax:** 469-522-4299
Web: www.amrealtytrust.com

PRODUCTS/OPERATIONS

2011 Sales

	$ mil.	% of total
Automotive	6,937	59
Investment	1,909	16
Metals	1,096	9
Gaming	624	5
Railcar	514	4
Food packaging	338	3
Home fashion	325	3
Real estate	90	1
Holding company	36	-
Eliminations	(14)	-
Total	**11,855**	**100**

Selected Subsidiaries

American Casino & Entertainment LLC
American Railcar Industries Inc.
AREP Oil & Gas Holdings LLC
AREP Real Estate Holdings LLC
AREP Sands Holdings LLC
Atlantic Coast Entertainment Holdings Inc.
Bayswater Development LLC
The Bayswater Group LLC
Federal-Mogul Corporation
Icahn Capital LP
Icahn Capital Management LP
Icahn Offshore LP
Icahn Onshore LP
National Energy Group Inc.
New Seabury Properties L.L.C.
PSC Metals Inc.
Tropicana Entertainment Inc.
Viskase Companies Inc.
WestPoint International Inc.

COMPETITORS

Apollo Global Management
Berkshire Hathaway
Blackstone Group
Clark Enterprises
Colony Capital
D. E. Shaw
KKR
MSD Capital
Soros Fund Management
The Trump Organization
Vulcan
Wesco Financial

HISTORICAL FINANCIALS

Company Type: Public

Income Statement

FYE: December 31

	REVENUE ($ mil.)	NET INCOME ($ mil.)	NET PROFIT MARGIN	EMPLOYEES
12/11	11,855	750	6.3%	59,559
12/10	9,119	199	2.2%	56,647
12/09	7,865	234	3.0%	42,339
12/08	5,027	(43)	—	42,339
12/07	2,487	308	12.4%	6,013
Annual Growth	47.8%	24.9%	—	77.4%

2011 Year-End Financials

Debt ratio: 25.75%
Return on equity: 19.97%
Cash ($ mil.): 7,257
Current ratio: 200.14
Long-term debt ($ mil.): 6,473
No. of shares (mil.): 86
Dividends
Yield: —
Payout: 11.40%
Market value ($ mil.): 3,099

	STOCK PRICE ($) FY Close	P/E High/Low		PER SHARE ($) Earnings	Dividends	Book Value
12/11	35.80	6	4	8.23	0.00	43.38
12/10	35.26	22	13	2.31	0.99	37.13
12/09	39.95	15	7	2.94	0.99	35.00
12/08	26.45	—	—	(0.79)	0.99	31.70
12/07	129.72	86	54	1.56	0.55	32.44
Annual Growth	(27.5%)	—	—	51.6%	—	7.5%

Illinois Tool Works, Inc.

Illinois Tool Works (ITW) hammers out more than just tools and it operates well beyond the Land of Lincoln. With operations in about 60 countries ITW manufactures and services equipment for the automotive construction electronics food/beverage packaging power system decorative surfaces and medical (adhesives) industries. The largest of its eight segments is Transportation which provides metal and plastic fasteners fluids and body repair putties as well as truck remanufacturing. Second in sales Power Systems & Electronics churns out arc welding equipment and airport ground support equipment. ITW gets about half of its sales from North America.

HISTORY

In the early years of the 20th century Byron Smith founder of Chicago's Northern Trust Company recognized that rapid industrialization was outgrowing the capacity of small shops to supply machine tools. Smith encouraged two of his four sons to launch Illinois Tool Works (ITW) in 1912. Harold C. Smith became president of ITW in 1915 and expanded its product line into automotive parts.

ITW developed the Shakeproof fastener the first twisted-tooth lock washer in 1923. When Harold C. died in 1936 the torch passed to his son Harold B. who decentralized the company and exhorted salesmen to learn customers' businesses so they could develop solutions even before the customers recognized the problems. Smith plowed profits back into research as WWII spurred demand.

In the 1950s the company began exploring plastics and combination metal and plastic fasteners as well as electrical controls and instruments to become a leader in miniaturization. Its major breakthrough came in the early 1960s with the development of flexible plastic collars to hold six-packs of beverage cans. This item under a new division called Hi-Cone was ITW's most-profitable offering.

Silas Cathcart became CEO in 1970. Smith's son another Harold B. was president and COO until 1981 (he remained on the board of directors and served as chairman of the board's executive committee). By the early 1980s ITW had become bureaucratic and susceptible to foreign competition. It was forced to lower prices to hold on to customers. Wary after the 1982 recession ITW hired John Nichols as CEO.

Nichols broadened the company's product line introduced more-effective production methods and doubled ITW's size by buying 27 companies the largest being Signode Industries bought for $524 million (1986). Nichols broke Signode into smaller units to speed development of 20 new products.

ITW purchased Ransburg Corporation (electrostatic finishing systems 1989) and the DeVilbiss division of Eagle Industries (1990) and merged the two to form its Finishing Systems and Products division. In 1992 the company introduced the Ring Leader Recycling Program to recycle its plastic six-pack rings.

Through a stock swap ITW acquired ownership of the Miller Group (arc welding equipment and related systems) in 1993. An 11% increase in car building in Europe in 1994 caused revenues of the company's engineered-components segment to grow dramatically; that year 76% of ITW's international sales came from European operations.

In 1995 ITW named president James Farrell as CEO. He replaced Nichols as chairman in 1996. ITW acquired Hobart Brothers (welding products) and Medalists Industries (industrial fasteners) in 1996 and made 28 acquisitions and joint ventures in 1997. It entered the domestic spray-painting equipment business in 1998 by acquiring Binks Sames (now Sames Corporation) for $106 million.

ITW gained the technology to make bar-code printers in 1999 when it acquired industrial ink-jet maker Trident International in a $107 million deal. Other purchases that year included a polyester film-processing plant from South Korea's SKC Duo-Fast (pneumatic nailing and stapling tools) and for $3.5 billion Premark International (consumer products which it began selling off in 2002). ITW sold its Irathane Systems urethane linings and moldings division to Industrial Rubber Products.

The company added to its ink-jet operations in 2000 with the acquisition of Imaging Technologies LLC. Through its Hobart subsidiary ITW also acquired Trilectron Industries (ground support equipment) from HEICO in a deal worth about $57 million. Early in 2001 the company added to its welding operations by buying four welding component businesses from Dover Corporation. Later in the year it acquired hot stamp foil company Foilmark. In early 2002 the company's board of directors gave its stamp of approval for the divestiture of ITW's consumer products segment. That decision led to the sale of its Precor fitness equipment business to Finland's Amer Sports in October for about $180 million.

Farrell retired as CEO in 2005 though he remained chairman; he was replaced by president David Speer. Farrell retired as chairman in 2006 and was succeeded by Speer in that post. EVP Thomas Hansen was elevated to vice chairman as well.

ITW purchased the Wynn Oil segment of industrial products maker Parker Hannifin in early 2005. Wynn Oil manufactures chemical car care products and maintenance technology for the auto industry. It also bought Rippey Corporation a maker of polyvinyl alcohol (PVA) cleaning products for the semiconductor industry that year. ITW continued its streak of diverse acquisitions later in 2005 with the purchase of instrumentation maker Instron from investment group Kirtland Capital Partners. Instron's products include instruments software and services designed to test materials and structures. And the company rolled on into 2006 with more acquisitions with the purchase of Alpine Engineered Products a maker of connectors design software and related machinery from Stonebridge Partners which had just acquired the company in the middle of 2005. Alpine fit in well with other ITW companies like Truswal and Pryda.

Also in 2006 ITW acquired CFC International (multilayer coatings for a variety of markets including furniture) for about $90 million in cash. In mid-2006 ITW bought BagCo (plastic recloseable packaging) and Kester (solder and related materials). The company then acquired Click Commerce a developer of supply chain management software for about $292 million in cash. ITW saw the software company with its 1500 customers having strengths in industries served by ITW. In late 2006 ITW purchased Speedline Technologies a manufacturer of printed circuit board assembly and semiconductor packaging equipment.

In 2007 the acquisitive company accumulated another 52 firms following a record set in 2006 that picked up more than 50 companies at a cumulative investment of around $1.7 billion. Also that same year ITW acquired the assets of Avery Berkel a venerable manufacturer of retail scales and other food processing equipment from Avery Weigh-Tronix. The company bought the rest of Avery Weigh-Tronix in 2008.

Trymer was among the 50 businesses acquired worldwide in 2008; the maker of rigid foam products expanded ITW's mechanical insulation offerings in its industrial packaging segment as well as sports a plant in La Porte Texas. Trymer's product applications run from mechanical and panel insulation to floral arrangements and crafts. Its lines like many of ITW's products are sold under their original owner's name.

In late 2009 ITW acquired the assets of South Carolina-based Hartness International a manufacturer of conveyor systems and line automation for the beverage and food industries. The acquisition complements ITW's packaging business in a lower cost geography. Nineteen other acquisitions were made in 2009 including a savvy negotiation for Ride Rite an inflatable paper dunnage (packing) bag manufacturer from recession hit KapStone Paper and Packaging.

ITW also divested a number of companies that didn't pan out for growth. In mid-2009 it jettisoned its Click Commerce a business with a buffet of industrial software applications to private equity Marlin Equity Partners. Marlin bought three software divisions from Requisite Technology (formerly Click Commerce) and raked away Service Network Solutions Research and Healthcare Solutions and Contract Service and Management operations as well as the Click Commerce nameplate.

The company pushed to unload an automotive components business on the sale rack since 2007. Instead the business was reclassified as discontinued along with an automotive machinery business and two consumer packaging businesses. Its consumer products holdings (appliances and cookware exercise equipment and ceramic tile acquired with Premark International) were also curbed. In a surprise move ITW's decorative surfaces segment which could not find a buyer was revived in 2009 as a continuing business.

In 2010 ITW acquired Accessories Marketing (dba Slime) a maker of tire care products and accessories from private equity Friend Skoler & Co. Slime brings a flagship brand green Slime tire sealants and a lineup of tire gauges tire repair kits portable air compressors and self-healing tire tubes sold in more than 60000 retail stores worldwide.

To build on its automotive aftermarket business in 2011 the company purchased Shell's SOPUS Products unit a car care product distributor for Pennzoil-Quaker State brands such as Rain-X (window rain repellent) Black Magic (liquid wax) and Gumout (fuel system cleaner). SOPUS (an acronym for Shell Oil Products US) made about $300 million in annual sales.

Also in 2011 Minnesota-based Despatch Industries joined ITW. The acquisition expanded ITW's presence in thermal processing equipment for the solar carbon fiber and other thermal technology sectors —a high-growth market.

EXECUTIVES

SVP Taxes and Investments, Allan C. (Al) Sutherland, age 48
Chairman and CEO, David B. Speer, age 60, $1,100,000 total compensation
SVP Human Resources, Sharon M. Brady, age 61
EVP, Jane L. Warner, age 65
EVP, Steven L. (Steve) Martindale, age 56
VP Investor Relations, John L. Brooklier
Acting Chairman, Robert S. Morrison, age 69
EVP, Craig A. Hindman, age 57
President Acting CEO and COO, E. Scott Santi, age 50, $399,135 total compensation
SVP and CFO, Ronald D. (Ron) Kropp, age 46, $350,000 total compensation
Vice Chairman, David C. Parry, age 58
EVP, Roland M. Martel, age 57
VP Intellectual Property, Mark W. Croll
EVP, Juan Valls, age 50
EVP, Timothy J. Gardner, age 57
EVP Global Welding, Sundaram (Naga) Nagarajan, age 49
EVP Global Food Equipment, Christopher (Chris) O'Herlihy, age 49
EVP Global Construction Products, John Hartnett, age 52
Director, Kevin M. Warren, age 49
Director, William F. (Bill) Aldinger III, age 64
Director, James A. (Jim) Skinner, age 67
Director, Don H. Davis Jr., age 72
Director, Pamela B. (Pam) Strobel, age 59
Director, Marvin D. Brailsford, age 74
Director, Susan M. Crown, age 53
Director, Robert C. (Bob) McCormack, age 72
Director, Robert S. Morrison, age 69
Director, Anre D. Williams, age 47
Vice Chairman, E. Scott Santi, age 50
Vice Chairman, David C. Parry, age 58
Director, David B. Smith Jr., age 46
Auditors: Deloitte&ToucheLLP

LOCATIONS

HQ: Illinois Tool Works Inc.
3600 W. Lake Ave., Glenview IL 60026-1215
Phone: 847-724-7500 **Fax:** 847-657-4261
Web: www.itw.com

2011 Sales

	$ mil.	% of total
North America		
US	7,379	41
Other North America	1,161	7
Europe	5,491	31
Asia	1,931	11
Australia/New Zealand	884	5
Other	938	5
Total	**17,786**	**100**

PRODUCTS/OPERATIONS

2011 Sales

	$ mil.	% of total
Transportation	3,108	18
Power Systems & Electronics	2,872	16
Industrial Packaging	2,612	15
Food Equipment	1,982	11
Construction Products	1,958	11
Polymers & Fluids	1,364	7
Decorative Surfaces	1,083	6
Other	2,889	16
Adjustments	(83.4)	-
Total	**17,786**	**100**

Selected Products

Construction products
- Anchors for concrete applications
- Anchors for retail
- Fasteners concrete applications
- Fasteners for retail
- Fasteners for wood and metal applications
- Metal plate truss components
- Packaged hardware for retail

Decorative surfaces
- Decorative high-pressure laminate for furniture office and retail space and countertops
- High-pressure laminate worktops

Food equipment
- Cooking equipment
  - Ovens
  - Ranges
  - Broilers
- Food processing equipment
  - Slicers
  - Mixers
  - Scales
- Kitchen exhaust systems
- Pollution-control systems
- Refrigeration equipment
  - Refrigerators
  - Freezers
  - Prep tables
- Ventilation Systems
- Warewashing equipment

Industrial packaging
- Metal jacketing
- Paper products that protect goods in transit
- Plastic products that protect goods in transit
- Plastic strapping
- Plastic stretch film
- Steel strapping

Polymers and fluids
- Adhesives
  - Industrial
  - Construction
  - Consumer
- Chemical fluids that clean or add lubrication to machines
- Epoxy and resin-based coating products for industrial applications
- Hand wipes and cleaners for industrial applications
- Pressure-sensitive adhesives and components
  - Telecommunications
  - Electronics
  - Medical
  - Transportation
- Resin-based coating products for industrial applications

Power systems and electronics
- Airport ground support equipment
- Arc welding equipment
- Component packaging
- Electronic components
- Equipment for microelectronics assembly
- Metal arc welding consumables
- Metal solder materials for PC board fabrication

Transportation
- Fillers for auto body repair
- Fluids for auto aftermarket maintenance and appearance
- Metal components for automobiles and light trucks
- Patch products for the marine industry
- Plastic components for automobiles and light trucks
- Polyester coatings for the marine industry
- Polymers for auto aftermarket maintenance and appearance
- Putties for auto body repair

Other
- Equipment and related software for testing and measuring of materials and structures
- Film used to decorate consumer products
- Foil used to decorate consumer products
- Plastic reclosable packaging for consumer food storage
- Plastic consumables that multi-pack cans and bottles and related equipment
- Plastic for appliances and industrial applications
- Metal fasteners for appliances and industrial applications

COMPETITORS

3M
BASF SE
Cooper Industries
DuPont
Emerson Electric
ESAB
Federal Screw Works
GE
Graco
IBIDEN
Koch Enterprises
Lincoln Electric
Manitowoc
Marmon Group
NCH
Nordson
Park-Ohio Holdings
PennEngineering
Snap-on
Stanley Black and Decker
Textron
TriMas
TRW Automotive
Victor Technologies
W. R. Grace

HISTORICAL FINANCIALS

Company Type: Public

Income Statement

FYE: December 31

	REVENUE ($ mil.)	NET INCOME ($ mil.)	NET PROFIT MARGIN	EMPLOYEES
12/11	17,786	2,071	11.6%	65,000
12/10	15,870	1,527	9.6%	61,000
12/09	13,877	947	6.8%	59,000
12/08	15,869	1,519	9.6%	65,000
12/07	16,170	1,869	11.6%	60,000
Annual Growth	2.4%	2.6%	—	2.0%

2011 Year-End Financials

Debt ratio: 21.98%
Return on equity: 20.68%
Cash ($ mil.): 1,177
Current ratio: 230.10
Long-term debt ($ mil.): 3,488
No. of shares (mil.): 483
Dividends
Yield: —
Payout: 33.41%
Market value ($ mil.): 22,589

	STOCK PRICE ($) FY Close	P/E High	P/E Low	PER SHARE ($) Earnings	Dividends	Book Value
12/11	46.71	14	10	4.19	0.00	20.71
12/10	53.40	18	13	3.03	1.30	18.83
12/09	47.99	27	14	1.89	1.24	17.53
12/08	35.05	19	10	2.91	1.18	15.35
12/07	53.54	18	14	3.36	0.98	17.64
Annual Growth	(3.4%)	—	—	5.7%	—	4.1%

Impac Mortgage Holdings, Inc.

Did you feel the impact of the mortgage bust? Impac Mortgage Holdings did. The company was formerly a real estate investment trust that invested in primarily Alt-A (one step above subprime on the creditworthiness scale) residential mortgages second mortgages and mortgage-backed securities. As the credit markets fell and loan defaults rose Impac switched gears and began offering fee-based real estate and asset management services to lenders borrowers servicers and investors. Its Integrated Real Estate Services subsidiary offers mortgage lending portfolio monitoring and title and escrow services. Through Exel Mortgage the company once again began funding conforming residential mortgages in 2010.

Although the company is cautiously entering the mortgage lending pool again the market is still volatile due to high unemployment rates continued foreclosures and regulatory changes. Impac's largest revenue source remains its investment portfolio which comprises more than $6 billion of collateralized mortgage obligations and other securities.

Impac's troubles stemmed from major disruption in the mortgage industry which hampered its ability to sell or securitize mortgages. In 2007 the company discontinued the mortgage and retail operations of subsidiary Impac Funding Corporation. It also pulled the plug on the commercial operations conducted by its Impac Commercial Capital Corporation and its warehouse lending operations. In an effort to remain viable the company rolled out its line of services including asset management escrow services and financial consulting for banks and regulatory bodies. Impac dropped its REIT status in early 2009.

EXECUTIVES

President and Director, William S. Ashmore, age 62, $575,000 total compensation
Chairman and CEO, Joseph R. Tomkinson, age 64, $600,000 total compensation
EVP General Counsel and Secretary, Ronald M. (Ron) Morrison, age 61, $385,000 total compensation
EVP and CFO, Todd R. Taylor, age 47, $277,875 total compensation
Investor Relations, Justin Moisio
VP Human Resources, Sheralee Urbano
President Impac Commercial Capital, William Endresen, age 57, $261,442 total compensation
VP Servicing Analytics & REO, Jim Hutnyk
VP Servicing Master Servicing, Marc Burridge
EVP Secondary Marketing, Nancy Pollard
SVP Operations Real Estate Document Solutions, Kathy Murray
VP Operations Escrow, Linda Sepulveda
SVP National Sales, Steve Curry
SVP and Director National Sales & Marketing, Gregory P. Davis
SVP Asset Management, Jim Malloy
SVP Asset Management, John Woodruff
Director, Leigh J. Abrams, age 69
Director, Frank P. Filipps, age 65
President and Director, William S. Ashmore, age 62
Director, Stephan R. Peers, age 59
Director, James Walsh, age 62
Auditors: SquarMilnerPetersonMiranda&WilliamsonLLP

LOCATIONS

HQ: Impac Mortgage Holdings Inc.
19500 Jamboree Rd., Irvine CA 92612-2401
Phone: 949-475-3600 **Fax:** 269-961-2871

PRODUCTS/OPERATIONS

COMPETITORS

Annaly Capital Management
Aurora Loan Services
Bank of America
Credit Suisse (USA)
GMAC Mortgage
JPMorgan Chase
Nationstar Mortgage
NovaStar Financial
Rancon
Residential Capital

HISTORICAL FINANCIALS

Company Type: Public

Income Statement FYE: December 31

	ASSETS ($ mil.)	NET INCOME ($ mil.)	INCOME AS % OF ASSETS	EMPLOYEES
12/11	5,612	3	0.1%	394
12/10	6,153	10	0.2%	376
12/09	5,872	10	0.2%	299
12/08	6,715	(44)	—	127
12/07	17,391	(2,047)	—	137
Annual Growth	(24.6%)	—	—	30.2%

2011 Year-End Financials

Debt ratio: 97.50%
Return on equity: 10.76%
Cash ($ mil.): 7
Current ratio: —
Long-term debt ($ mil.): 5,471
No. of shares (mil.): 7
Dividends
Yield: —
Payout: —
Market value ($ mil.): 16

	STOCK PRICE ($) FY Close	P/E High	P/E Low	PER SHARE ($) Earnings	Dividends	Book Value
12/11	2.01	10	4	0.39	0.00	3.84
12/10	2.79	4	2	1.24	0.00	3.39
12/09	3.29	10	0	0.44	0.00	2.01
12/08	0.06	—	—	(7.34)	0.00	1.21
12/07	0.56	—	—	(271.00)	0.00	(141.63)
Annual Growth	37.6%	—	—	—	—	—

Independent Bank Corp. (MA)

Independent Bank wants to rock your financial world. Its banking subsidiary Rockland Trust operates some 80 retail branches as well as commercial lending centers investment management offices and mortgage banking centers in suburban Boston southeastern Massachusetts and Cape Cod. Serving area individuals and small to midsized businesses the bank offers such standard services such as checking and savings accounts CDs and credit cards in addition to financial planning and trust services. Commercial and industrial loans including mortgages construction loans and business loans account for some two-thirds of Rockland Trust's portfolio. The bank also writes consumer loans and mortgages.

Through an agreement with LPL Investment Holdings Rockland Trust offers investment products such as securities and insurance. The company has been expanding its fee-based revenue business especially in its investment management segment. In 2010 Independent Bank launched institutional asset manager Bright Rock Capital Management and introduced its first two proprietary mutual funds.

The moves have helped the company to post relatively strong returns even in the economic downturn. While many other banks retrenched during this time Rockland Trust has taken advantage of industry turmoil and grown its commercial loan portfolio as well. Despite a minor bump in 2011 (revenues slipped 0.5% to $248.5 million) overall earnings have been up for the company since the economic crisis hit and profits for the year rose 13% to $45.4 million. Noninterest income including service charges interchange and ATM fees and wealth management fees increased that year by about 12%. Assets under administration grew 5% to $1.7 billion that year thanks largely to strong sales and general market appreciation.

In addition to branching into other financial services areas Independent Bank has expanded via acquisitions. In 2012 the company agreed to buy Central Bancorp parent of Central Bank. That deal will add nine branches in Maryland's Middlesex County.

EXECUTIVES

EVP and Director Retail Banking and Corporate Marketing Rockland Trust, Jane L. Lundquist, age 58, $218,269 total compensation
SVP and Director Human Resources Rockland Trust, Raymond G. Fuerschbach, age 61, $154,229 total compensation
General Counsel Independent Bank Corp. and Rockland Trust, Edward H. Seksay, age 54, $228,770 total compensation
CFO and Treasurer; CFO Rockland Trust, Denis K. Sheahan, age 46, $262,231 total compensation
Chairman, Thomas J. Teuten, age 71
Chief Technology and Operations Officer Rockland Trust, Edward F. Jankowksi, age 61
President CEO and Director Independent Bank Corp. and Rockland Trust, Christopher (Chris) Oddleifson, age 53, $502,462 total compensation
SVP and Treasurer Rockland Trust, Robert D. Cozzone
VP Public Relations Rockland Trust, Joan Reid
SVP and Chief Investment Officer Rockland Trust, David Smith
SVP Branch Administration Rockland Trust, William E. Matteson
EVP Commercial Lending Division Rockland Trust, Gerard F. Nadeau, age 54, $238,947 total compensation
SVP Marketing Strategy and Communications Rockland Trust, Ralph Valente
Director, Richard S. Anderson, age 69
Director, Kevin J. Jones, age 60
Director, Richard H. Sgarzi, age 69
Director, Benjamin A. Gilmore II, age 64
Director, John H. Spurr Jr., age 65
Director, Robert D. Sullivan, age 69
Director, Brian S. Tedeschi, age 61
Director, Eileen C. Miskell, age 54
President CEO and Director Independent Bank Corp. and Rockland Trust, Christopher (Chris) Oddleifson, age 53
Director, Thomas R. Venables, age 56
Director, William P. (Bill) Bissonnette, age 66
Director, Donna A. Lopolito, age 53
Director, Carl Ribeiro, age 65
Director, Daniel F. O'Brien, age 56
Auditors: Ernst&YoungLLP

LOCATIONS

HQ: Independent Bank Corp.
288 Union St., Rockland MA 02370
Phone: 781-878-6100 **Fax:** 781-982-6130
Web: www.rocklandtrust.com

PRODUCTS/OPERATIONS

2011 Sales

	$ mil.	% of total
Interest		
Loans	174	70
Taxable securities including dividends	20	8
Other	1	-
Noninterest		

Service charges on deposit accounts	16	7
Wealth management	13	6
Interchange & ATM fees	7	3
Other	15	6
Adjustments	(0.2)	-
Total	**248**	**100**

COMPETITORS

Bank of America	Mayflower Bancorp
Chicopee	RBS Citizens Financial Group
Eastern Bank	Sovereign Bank
Hingham Institution for Savings	TD Bank USA

HISTORICAL FINANCIALS

Company Type: Public

Income Statement FYE: December 31

	ASSETS ($ mil.)	NET INCOME ($ mil.)	INCOME AS % OF ASSETS	EMPLOYEES
12/11	4,970	45	0.9%	909
12/10	4,695	40	0.9%	919
12/09	4,482	22	0.5%	907
12/08	3,628	23	0.7%	827
12/07	2,768	28	1.0%	742
Annual Growth	15.8%	12.5%	—	5.2%

2011 Year-End Financials

Debt ratio: 6.47%
Return on equity: 9.69%
Cash ($ mil.): 237
Current ratio: —
Long-term debt ($ mil.): 321
No. of shares (mil.): 21
Dividends
Yield: —
Payout: 35.85%
Market value ($ mil.): 587

	STOCK PRICE ($) FY Close	P/E High/Low		PER SHARE ($) Earnings	Dividends	Book Value
12/11	27.29	14	10	2.12	0.00	21.82
12/10	27.05	15	11	1.90	0.72	20.78
12/09	20.86	30	12	0.88	0.72	19.71
12/08	26.16	22	13	1.52	0.72	18.75
12/07	27.22	18	13	2.00	0.68	16.04
Annual Growth	0.1%	—	—	1.5%	—	8.0%

Ingram Micro Inc.

There's nothing micro about Ingram. The world's largest wholesale distributor of information technology products Ingram Micro provides thousands of products —desktop and notebook PCs servers storage devices monitors printers and software —to about 190000 resellers in some 145 countries worldwide. Its sells products from more than 1300 suppliers including many of the world's top manufacturers; Hewlett-Packard is the company's largest supplier. Ingram Micro also offers a wide range of services to its resellers and suppliers including supply chain management business intelligence financing logistics and network support services. The company rings up nearly 60% of sales outside North America.

Ingram Micro is on the upward path after a rough stretch during the global financial crisis that dampened demand for IT products and services as businesses worldwide cut back on investments in technology. As a result the company's sales declined two years in a row and it lost money in 2008. If not for Ingram Micro's geographic diversification its financial performance might have been worse as the firm was able to take advantage of markets in Asia and Latin America while North America and Europe struggled.

Now with the economy improving in some markets (particularly North America) and businesses reinvesting in technology the IT distributor's sales have grown 23% from $29.5 billion in 2009 to about $36.3 billion in 2011. In 2011 the firm posted a 5% sales jump vs. 2010. However net income fell by 23% in 2011 vs. the prior year due in part to potential liability for certain commercial taxes in Brazil. In 2011 demand for IT products was stronger in North America and Latin America but soft in Europe and the Asia-Pacific region.

Challenges facing the business going forward include raising its razor-thin margins in a cutthroat pricing environment and more vendors selling directly to end users reducing the need from Ingram's services. More than just a reseller of IT peripherals systems software and networking products Ingram offers its vendors and customers a variety of services including supply chain management and technical support and training which help distinguish it from its rivals and provide higher profit margins. Its Ingram Micro Services division provides managed services such as network security application hosting and remote monitoring under the Seismic brand along with professional services such as consulting staffing and warranty contract management.

In 2012 Ingram Micro is accelerating its mobile strategy to capture this fast-growing high-margin product segment comprising handsets smartphones accessories tablets laptops activation services and fully integrated mobile solutions. To that end Ingram Micro acquired Brightpoint Inc. in late 2012. Brightpoint caters to the wireless industry by providing a long list of device lifecycle services and systems. The deal valued at about $640 million is expected to strengthen Ingram Micro's geographic presence and customer base in the mobility market as well as drive $55 million in annual cost efficiencies and other synergies.

In 2010 the company introduced the online Cloud Marketplace for channel partners looking to take advantage of the booming cloud computing market. The website offers detailed information on cloud-based products and services available from Ingram Micro as well as technical information and collaboration tools. Its new Advanced Technology and Advanced Computing divisions were also formed that year to give channel partners access to more specialized and higher-end product lines including virtualization data center infrastructure and data storage products.

The company is also expanding its geographic presence primarily by making small regional acquisitions. Over the past decade the firm has completed 20 such acquisitions including Asiasoft Hong Kong which distributes business software from companies such as Adobe Systems and Symantec in order to expand sales in Asia. To grow in Europe it acquired Barcelona-based Arete Sistemas a value-added distribution company and Belgium-based interAct.

Closer to home in late 2012 it agreed to buy Promark Technology a Maryland-based value-added distributor of storage data management electronic document imaging and other technology products to customers including the US government.

Artisan Partners Holdings owns about 10% of the company's shares.

HISTORY

Micro D was founded in Fountain Valley California in 1979 by husband-and-wife entrepreneurs Geza Csige and Lorraine Mecca. As the company grew Mecca sought to merge the computer distributor with a partner that could take over daily operations. She relinquished control of Micro D to Linwood "Chip" Lacy in 1986 and sold her 51% share of the company to minority shareholder Ingram Distribution Group.

Sales bottomed out for Micro D that year. Lacy tightened Micro D's belt and took huge charges for outdated inventory it sold at a discount and overdue payments from customers that had gone bankrupt.

At the same time Ingram Industries was busy merging recently acquired Ingram Software Distribution Services of Buffalo New York with Compton California-based Softeam. The merger made the company one of the nation's largest wholesale distributors of computer software. Lacy saw Ingram's purchase of Micro D shares as a conflict of interest but he was too busy returning Micro D to profitability —centralizing its marketing and distribution functions cutting costs and expanding its market to include more small retailers which provided higher margins. Micro D went from the fourth-largest distributor of microcomputer products to #1 in just one year.

The surging PC market in the late 1980s fueled Micro D's growth. By 1988 the firm had expanded outside the US for the first time acquiring Canadian company Frantek Computer Products.

Ingram Industries offered to acquire the 41% of outstanding Micro D stock it did not own in 1988 but Lacy resisted preferring to let Ingram wait. Though Ingram owned a majority of Micro D stock it only controlled three of seven seats on the board. Ingram was forced to play Lacy's game and finally acquired the company at a higher cost in 1989. The new company which controlled 20% of the computer distribution market was called Ingram Micro D. The merger was anything but smooth and several Micro D executives jumped ship.

As the PC took hold in the US in the 1990s Ingram Micro D became the dominant industry player but relations between Lacy and the Ingram family never improved. The company shortened its name to Ingram Micro in 1991 and two years later as it was hitting stride Lacy announced plans to leave. To keep him Ingram Industries CEO Bronson Ingram (much to his distaste) promised to let Lacy take the company public.

Bronson Ingram died in 1995 and the next year his widow Martha forced Lacy's resignation. Lacy was replaced by Jerre Stead formerly CEO of software maker LEGENT (bought by CA) who devised a compensation package for himself consisting solely of stock options (no salary) and listed "Head Coach" on his business card. Ingram went public a few months after Stead took over.

In 1998 Ingram Micro forged a distribution alliance with Japanese computer giant SOFTBANK and bought a majority stake in German computer products distributor Macrotron. It also expanded into build-to-order PC manufacturing. Amid softer PC sales industrywide Ingram Micro in 1999 terminated nearly 600 employees as part of a worldwide realignment and signed a deal (worth an estimated $10 billion) with CompUSA to be its primary PC manufacturer and distributor.

Later in 1999 Stead –with Ingram Micro's sales slipping and its stock slumping —made plans to step down as CEO. The search for his replacement ended in 2000 when the company named GTE veteran Kent Foster to the post.

Ingram Micro expanded its portfolio of services for enterprises and began offering more extensive network and product support services. The company outsourced certain IT infrastructure operations along with the related personnel to Affiliated Computer Services (ACS) in 2002. Ingram Micro continued to expand international operations that year acquiring the 49% of a Singapore exporter it did not previously own and purchasing operations in Belgium and the Netherlands. In a move to expand its presence in the Asia/Pacific region Ingram acquired Australian distributor Tech Pacific in 2004.

Company president Greg Spierkel replaced Foster as CEO in 2005. Ingram Micro also acquired certain assets of consumer electronics distributor AVAD. The following year it expanded its reach in Northern Europe when it purchased the assets of SymTech Nordic. It also formed a North American services division focused on professional IT services warranty contract management and managed services. Ingram purchased consumer electronics distributor DBL Distributing for $96 million in 2007.

In 2009 Ingram Micro bought certain assets of Computacenter Distribution (CCD) a distributor of server storage and networking equipment in the UK that was previously a division of Computacenter.

EXECUTIVES

Chairman, Dale R. Laurance, age 66
SVP Communications and Brand Management, Ria Marie Carlson, age 50
VP Information Solutions and e-Commerce EMEA, Ken Jordan
VP and General Manager Ingram Micro V7 Global, Rainer Kozlik
VP Legal and Mergers and Acquisitions EMEA; Managing Director Ingram Micro Coordination Center Belgium, Karel Everaet
EVP Human Resources, Lynn Jolliffe, age 59
VP and General Manager Advanced Computing, Scott Zahl
VP Human Resources North America, Robyn Tingley
EVP General Counsel and Secretary, Larry C. Boyd, age 59
SEVP; President Europe Middle East and Africa, Alain Maquet, age 60, $530,561 total compensation
VP France and Nordics, Christian Bittebierre
Regional VP UK Belgium and Netherlands, Johan Vandenbussche
SEVP; President North America, Keith W. F. Bradley, age 48, $510,000 total compensation
Senior EVP and CFO, William D. Humes, age 47, $500,000 total compensation
VP and General Manager Ingram Micro Logistics North America, Bill Sanders
VP and CFO Latin America, David Schoenberger
EVP and CIO, Mario F. Leone, age 56
SEVP; President Asia/Pacific, Shailendra Gupta, age 49, $530,561 total compensation
President CEO and Director, Alain Monie, age 61
President Ingram Micro North America, Paul Bay, age 42
SVP Specialty Solutions Division North America, Brian Wiser
EVP Global Logistics, Robert K. Gifford, age 54
Executive Vice President; President; Latin America, John Soumbasakis
Specialist Corporate Communications, Nicole Trombly
Senior Director Investor Relations, Kay Leyba
VP and Treasurer, Erik Smolders
Managing Director Sweden, Derrick Wood
Executive Director and General Manager AVAD, James Annes
Executive Director and General Manager Data Capture and Point-of-Sale Division, Justin Scopaz
VP and General Manager Commercial Markets Division, Kirk Robinson
SVP and CFO Ingram Micro North America, Lisa Locklear
Senior Director Channel Programs, John Fago
VP Organizational Development, Gwen Whitfield
VP Vendor Management U.S., Kevin Prewett
Managing Director UK, Matthew Sanderson
EVP; President Latin America, Eduardo Araujo, age 55
SVP and CFO EMEA, Paul Lilley
VP Managed Services and Cloud Computing North America, Renee Bergeron
SVP Corporate Strategy, G. Sam Kamel
Senior Director Strategic Program Management and Governance Global Information Systems, Robert W. (Bob) White
VP and General Manager Direct and Consumer Markets Division, Tim Ament
VP Human Resources and Communications EMEA, Sven Joos
VP Business Operations Strategy EMEA, Erich Bernscherer
Senior Director Data Capture (DC) / Point-of-Sale (POS) EMEA, Ernesto Schmutter
Executive Director Logistics EMEA, Herbert Hufsky
SVP Vendor Management and Business Development EMEA, Vincenzo Baggio
SVP Central and Eastern European Region, Gerhard Schulz
VP Product Management Central and Eastern Europe and Pan European Business Unit, Robert Beck
Managing Director Netherlands, Eric Segers
Managing Director Belgium and Luxembourg, Steve Meynen
Managing Director Austria, Florian Wallner
Managing Director Hungary, Ferenc Lazar
Managing Director Switzerland, Joe T. Feierabend
VP Southern Europe and Managing Director Spain, Dominique Meyer
Worldwide Media Relations, Clifford Crisanti
President; Chief Executive Officer; Director, Alain Monie
Director, Michael T. (Mike) Smith, age 68
Director, Orrin H. Ingram II, age 51
Director, Howard I. Atkins, age 61
Director, Gerhard Schulmeyer, age 73
Director, Gregory M. E. (Greg) Spierkel, age 55
Director, Linda F. Levinson, age 71
Director, John R. Ingram, age 51
Director, Joe B. Wyatt, age 76
Director, Scott A. McGregor, age 55
Director, Linda Fayne Levinson, age 69
Director, Leslie Stone Heisz, age 51
President CEO and Director, Alain Monie, age 61
Independent Director, Paul Read, age 47
Auditors: PricewaterhouseCoopersLLP

LOCATIONS

HQ: Ingram Micro Inc.
1600 E. St. Andrew Place, Santa Ana CA 92705-4926
Phone: 714-566-1000 **Fax:** 714-566-7900
Web: www.ingrammicro.com

2011 Sales

	$ mil.	% of total
North America	15,250	42
Europe Middle East & Africa	11,371	31
Asia/Pacific	7,920	22
Latin America	1,786	5
Total	**36,328**	**100**

PRODUCTS/OPERATIONS

Selected Products

IT Peripheral/CE/AIDC/POS/Mobility and Others
- Barcode/card printers
- Cell phones
- Components
- Digital cameras
- Digital signage products
- Digital video disc players
- Game consoles
- Mass storage
- Printers
- Projectors
- Scanners
- Supplies and accessories
- Televisions

Networking
- Network interface cards
- Storage
- Switches hubs and routers
- Wireless local area networks

Software
- Business application software
- Developer software tools
- Entertainment software
- Middleware
- Operating system software
- Security software
- Storage software

Systems
- Desktops
- Personal digital assistants
- Portable personal computers
- Rack tower and blade servers

COMPETITORS

Agilysys
Arrow Electronics
ASI Computer Technologies
Avnet
Black Box
Computacenter
D & H Distributing
DHL
Digiland
Digital China
Dimension Data
GTSI
Intcomex
Menlo Worldwide
New Age Electronics
Redington Group
ScanSource
Schindler Holding
SED International
SHI International
Softmart
Supercom
SYNNEX
Tech Data
United Stationers
UPS Supply Chain Solutions
Westcon

HISTORICAL FINANCIALS

Company Type: Public

Income Statement

FYE: December 31

	REVENUE ($ mil.)	NET INCOME ($ mil.)	NET PROFIT MARGIN	EMPLOYEES
12/11*	36,328	244	0.7%	15,500
01/11	34,588	318	0.9%	15,650
01/10	29,515	202	0.7%	13,750
01/09	34,362	(394)	—	14,500
12/07	35,047	275	0.8%	15,000
Annual Growth	0.9%	(3.0%)	—	0.8%

*Fiscal year change

2011 Year-End Financials

Debt ratio: 4.29%
Return on equity: 7.46%
Cash ($ mil.): 891
Current ratio: 156.42
Long-term debt ($ mil.): 300
No. of shares (mil.): 149
Dividends
Yield: —
Payout: —
Market value ($ mil.): 2,719

	STOCK PRICE ($) FY Close	P/E High/Low		PER SHARE ($) Earnings	Dividends	Book Value
12/11*	18.19	14	10	1.53	0.00	21.89
01/11	19.09	10	8	1.94	0.00	20.42
01/10	17.45	15	8	1.22	0.00	18.32
01/09	13.98	—	—	(2.37)	0.00	16.46
12/07	18.36	14	11	1.56	0.00	19.82
Annual Growth	(0.2%)	—	—	(0.5%)	—	2.5%

*Fiscal year change

Ingredion Inc

Sweet sodas and diet desserts alike get their taste from Ingredion's ingredients. The company (formerly Corn Products International) makes food ingredients and industrial products from corn and other starch-based raw materials. Its customers include food beverage brewing and pharmceutical companies. More than 40% of sales come from sweeteners including high-fructose corn syrup which is used by just about every beverage maker and a good many food companies to sweeten their products. Ingredion also produces corn starch (a thickener for processed foods) corn oil and corn gluten (for animal feed). Ingredion operates manufacturing plants throughout Africa Asia Europe and North and South America.

Geographic Reach

North America (Canada Mexico and the US) is Ingredion's largest market accounting for more than half of the firm's $6.2 billion in 2011 sales. South America contributes about 25% of sales followed by the Asia-Pacific Region (12%) and Europe the Middle East and Africa (9%).

Financial Analysis

Ingredion's sales increased by more than 42% in 2011 vs. 2010 while net income grew by 146% over the same period. The double-digit sales gain was driven by a 22% increase in volume sales attributed to the acquisition of National Starch (in 2010). The company's starch products business has increased from about 20% of sales a decade ago to 36% in 2011. Sweetener products still contribute more than 40% of Ingredion's total sales. Ingredion's 2011 sales also got a boost from higher prices for its other products. The robust growth in 2011 followed a sales increase of about 19% and jump in net income of more than 300% in 2010 vs. the year earlier period. The $1.3 billion acquisition of New Jersey-based National Starch extended the company's global reach and product portfolio.

Strategy

Beyond acquisitions Ingredion is also growing organically. Outside of North America the company's second-largest market is South America. To support its growth there the company is investing up to $100 million to expand its operations in Brazil - its biggest market in the region. Ingredion currently operates about a half a dozen manufacturing plants and two ingredient development facilities there.

The purchase of National Starch reduced Ingredion's reliance on sweetener products (from 56% of sales in 2009 to 43% in 2011.) Besides being a key ingredient in processed foods starches have a wide range of industrial uses. Ingredion's sweeteners are used as sugar substitutes in everything from soft drinks and beer to confections and canned foods. Taking advantage of a recent development in artificial-sweeteners as well as customer demand for lower-calorie products Ingredion jumped on the stevia bandwagon. It gained the global marketing and distribution rights to a stevia-based sweetener developed by Japanese company Morita Kagaku Kogyo in 2008. Products made from the stevia plant have been found to be 400 times sweeter than cane sugar. Nutritional supplements containing stevia have a GRAS (generally regarded as safe) status with the USDA and may be used and sold in the US. The Ingredion/Morita sweetener is called Enliten.

The name change from Corn Products International to Ingredion in June 2012 followed the company's purchase of National Starch and is meant to showcase its role as a global ingredients supplier.

Mergers and Acquisitions

The purchase of National Starch from the Netherland's Akzo Nobel in the fourth quarter of 2010 extended the company's reach into Asia – giving it access to Chinese food businesses –and added higher-margin processed items and provided a platform for growth in Europe. The addition of National Starch gave Ingredion more than 35 manufacturing sites in 15 countries.

EXECUTIVES

SVP Corporate Strategy and Global Business Development, John F. Saucier, age 58, $400,000 total compensation
SVP General Counsel Corporate Secretary and Chief Compliance Officer, Mary Ann Hynes, age 64
EVP and President North America, Jack C. Fortnum, age 55, $460,000 total compensation
EVP and CFO, Cheryl K. Beebe, age 56, $475,000 total compensation
VP and Controller, Robin A. Kornmeyer, age 63
EVP; President Global Ingredient Solutions, James P. Zallie, age 50
SVP Human Resources, Diane J. Frisch, age 57
Corporate Treasurer, Kimberly A. (Kim) Hunter, age 50
VP Investor Relations and Corporate Communications, Aaron H. Hoffman
Chairman President and CEO, Ilene S. Gordon, age 58, $563,942 total compensation
Director Corporate Communications, Mark Lindley
SVP; President South America Ingredient Solutions, Julio dos Reis, age 56
CIO, Ronald E. (Ron) Lejcar
SVP General Counsel and Corporate Secretary, Christine M. Castellano
Director, Paul T. Hanrahan, age 54
Director, Karen L. Hendricks, age 63
Director, Gregory B. Kenny, age 59
Director, Richard J. Almeida, age 69
Director, James M. (Jim) Ringler, age 66
Director, Barbara A. (Barb) Klein, age 57
Director, Wayne M. Hewett, age 47
Director, Luis Aranguren-Trellez, age 50
Director, Dwayne A. Wilson, age 53
Auditors: KPMGLLP

LOCATIONS

HQ: Ingredion Incorporated
5 Westbrook Corporate Center, Westchester IL 60154
Phone: 708-551-2600 **Fax:** 708-551-2700
Web: www.ingredion.com

2011 Sales

	$ mil.	% of total
North America	3,356	54
South America	1,569	25
Asia Pacific	764	12
Europe the Middle East & Africa	530	9
Total	**6,219**	**100**

PRODUCTS/OPERATIONS

2011 Sales

	% of total
Sweetener	43
Starch	36
Co-products &	21
Total	**100**

Selected Products

Sweetener products
- Dextrose
- Glucose corn syrups
- High fructose corn syrup
- High maltose corn syrup
- Maltodextrins
- Polyols
- Stevia-derived sweetener (Enliten)

Starch products
- Corn starch (consumer and industrial)

Co-products and others
- Corn gluten feed
- Corn gluten meal
- Refined corn oil
- Steepwater

Selected Subsidiaries

Canada Starch Company Inc.
Colombia Millers Ltd.
CP Ingredients Limited (UK)
Derivados del Maiz S.A. (95% Peru)
Feed Products Limited
Globe Ingredients Nigeria Limited
GTC Oats Inc.

COMPETITORS

ACH Food Companies
ADM
Ajinomoto
Cargill
Casco
Cumberland Packing
DSM
Faultless Starch
Global Bio-chem
Grain Processing Corporation
Henkel
Imperial Sugar
Malt Products Corporation
Merisant
Nordzucker
NutraSweet
PureCircle
Roquette Freres
Sudzucker
Sweet Green Fields
Tate & Lyle Ingredients
Yamazaki Baking

HISTORICAL FINANCIALS

Company Type: Public

Income Statement

FYE: December 31

	REVENUE ($ mil.)	NET INCOME ($ mil.)	NET PROFIT MARGIN	EMPLOYEES
12/11	6,219	416	6.7%	11,100
12/10	4,367	169	3.9%	10,700
12/09	3,672	41	1.1%	8,100
12/08	3,944	267	6.8%	7,800
12/07	3,391	198	5.8%	7,100
Annual Growth	16.4%	20.4%	—	11.8%

2011 Year-End Financials

Debt ratio: 36.66%
Return on equity: 19.77%
Cash ($ mil.): 401
Current ratio: 227.00
Long-term debt ($ mil.): 1,801
No. of shares (mil.): 75
Dividends
Yield: —
Payout: 12.41%
Market value ($ mil.): 3,991

STOCK PRICE ($) FY Close		P/E High/Low		PER SHARE ($) Earnings	Dividends	Book Value
12/11	52.59	11	7	5.32	0.00	27.73
12/10	46.00	21	12	2.20	0.56	25.99
12/09	29.23	59	33	0.54	0.56	22.79
12/08	28.85	14	5	3.52	0.51	18.88
12/07	36.75	19	12	2.59	0.38	22.17
Annual Growth	9.4%	—	—	19.7%	—	5.8%

Insight Enterprises Inc.

With Insight Enterprises around the end of your technology woes could be in sight. The company distributes computer hardware and software and provides IT services for businesses schools and government agencies and departments. Insight offers thousands of products from major manufacturers (including Hewlett-Packard IBM and Cisco) and it provides networking and communications services through subsidiaries Insight Networking in the US and UK-based MINX. The company uses direct telesales field sales agents and an e-commerce site to reach its clients in North America and about 190 other countries across Europe the Middle East Africa and the Asia/Pacific region.

Geographic Reach

Insight Enterprises rings up 70% of its sales in North America. Second in importance is Europe the Middle East and Africa which contributes about 25%. The Asia-Pacific region accounts for the rest.

Financial Analysis

Insight has had its share of up's and down's in recent years largely due to the global economic downturn and sputtering recovery. Still the company looks to be on track for growth as it evolves into a complete IT solutions provider. In 2011 the company logged sales of $5.3 billion about a 10% increase from the previous year. The company also managed net earnings of $100 million in 2011 compared to $75 million in 2010. The company's sales improved as IT spending increased in the first half of 2011 while the second half of 2011 large customers reduced IT spending.

Strategy

Insight is growing at home and abroad by expanding its product line entering new markets and making acquisitions. The company gained ground and started selling hardware in the Netherlands and Germany which expanded its product footprint. In the US the company bought out Tempe-based Ensynch a professional services consulting firm whose client list includes Microsoft. Ensynch's revenues in 2010 were reported at around $16 million. Net sales increased 10% in North America 7% in Europe the Middle East and Africa and 36% in Asia/Pacific in 2011 compared to 2010.

As part of its strategy to further expand its hardware sales in Europe the company acquired Inmac a business-to-business hardware reseller based in Frankfurt Germany and the Netherlands which sells to customers primarily in Western Europe. The acquisition closed in early 2012.

Ownership

Financial services conglomerate FMR is the company's largest shareholder. It owns about a 15% stake.

HISTORY

Eric Crown worked for a small computer retail chain in the mid-1980s before leaving to market PCs. In 1986 he and his brother Tim pooled $2000 from credit cards and $1300 in savings and anticipating a drop in hard drive prices placed an ad for low-cost hard drives in a computer magazine. The ad pulled in $20000 worth of sales and since costs did indeed drop the profit was enough to start a new company Hard Drives International. In 1988 they changed the name to Insight Enterprises; by 1991 the Crowns also sold Insight-branded PCs software and peripherals (discontinued in 1995). The company passed the $100 million revenue mark in 1992.

Insight shifted its marketing focus to catalogs in 1993 and had a circulation of more than 7 million by 1995. The company went public that year and entered an alliance with Computer City (acquired by CompUSA in 1998) to handle its mail-order fulfillment. It also launched its website. The next year subsidiary Insight Direct began to offer on-site service warranties and in 1997 retailing subsidiary Direct Alliance was chosen to provide product fulfillment for Internet software firm Geo Publishing. That year the company began sponsoring the Copper Bowl a college football game played in Arizona which was renamed the Insight.com Bowl (and later the Insight Bowl).

Looking beyond the US in 1998 Insight established operations in Canada and acquired direct marketers Choice Peripherals (UK) and Computerprofis Computersysteme (Germany). At home it added direct marketer Treasure Chest Computers. Sales passed the billion-dollar mark that year.

The company formed an alliance with Daisytek International in 1999 that expanded its product line by more than 10000. Soon thereafter Insight walked away from a merger with UK-based computer wholesaler Action Computer Supplies when Action's profits slumped.

Insight withdrew its planned IPO and spinoff of Direct Alliance in 2001 due to poor market conditions. Also that month Eric became chairman and Tim became CEO (they had previously shared the title of co-CEO). Insight ended up buying Action Computer Supplies in 2001. It also shut down its German operations and acquired computer direct marketers in both the UK and Canada in late 2001.

In April 2002 Insight acquired Comark a leading private reseller of computers peripherals and computer supplies in the US and began integrating its operations into Insight North America's existing operational structure.

Tim stepped down as president and CEO and became chairman in late 2004 while Eric assumed the title of chairman emeritus. The company appointed IBM veteran Richard Fennessy to the position of president and CEO. That year Insight spun off its UK-based Internet service provider PlusNet.

In 2006 Insight Enterprises bought software and mobile solutions firm Software Spectrum.

To fund its expansion into the services sector Insight Enterprises has been offloading other units. Insight Enterprises in 2006 also sold its business process outsourcing (BPO) division Direct Alliance to TeleTech Holdings for $46 million. The company sold the PC Wholesale division (acquired in 2002) of its subsidiary Insight Direct USA to Synnex Corp. in 2007 for about $10 million plus approximately $20 million for net assets acquired.

In early 2008 Insight Enterprises purchased Calence a leading Cisco provider in the US for $125 million to extend its reach into the services sector once again. Complementing the deal across the Atlantic Insight acquired MINX a Cisco-accredited network integrator in the UK for $1 million and the assumption of nearly $4 million in debt. Following the purchases the company realigned its US sales organization and in late 2008 laid off some 240 employees.

In early 2009 Insight combined the management of its North American businesses with its corporate headquarters and relocated its headquarters to another facility in Tempe Arizona.

EXECUTIVES

Chairman, Timothy A. (Tim) Crown, age 48, $695,000 total compensation
President CEO and Director, Kenneth T. (Ken) Lamneck, age 57
CIO, Michael Guggemos
Chief Administrative Officer General Counsel and Secretary, Steven R. (Steve) Andrews, age 59
President Insight EMEA and APAC, Stuart A. Fenton, age 43, $417,318 total compensation
CFO, Glynis A. Bryan, age 53, $400,000 total compensation
SVP Corporate Controller and Principal Accounting Officer, David C. Olsen, age 50
SVP Investor Relations and Treasurer, Helen K. Johnson, age 43
SVP Operations, Stephen A. Speidel, age 47
Senior Manager Marketing Communications, Shana Diana
Investor Relations, Rosalind Berkley
Senior Manager Internal Communications, Amy Kweder
SVP Product Marketing, Brian Davis
Director Marketing, Gina Morkel
President Insight U.S., Steve Dodenhoff
Director, Robertson C. Jones, age 67
President CEO and Director, Kenneth T. (Ken) Lamneck, age 57
Director, Anthony A. (Tony) Ibarguen
Director, Michael M. Fisher, age 66
Director, Larry A. Gunning, age 68
Director, Kathleen S. Pushor, age 54
Director, Bennett Dorrance, age 66
Auditors: KPMGLLP

LOCATIONS

HQ: Insight Enterprises Inc.
6820 S. Harl Ave., Tempe AZ 85283
Phone: 480-902-1001 **Fax:** 410-625-0355
Web: www.carrolltonbank.com

2011 Sales

	$ mil.	% of total
North America	3,701	70
Europe Middle East & Africa	1,374	26
Asia/Pacific	211	4
Total	**5,287**	**100**

PRODUCTS/OPERATIONS

2011 Sales

	$ mil.	% of total
Hardware	2,802	53
Software	2,220	42
IT services	264	5
Total	**5,287**	**100**

Selected Products

Computer memory and processors
Desktop computers
Monitors
Networking equipment
Notebook computers
Printers and printing consumables
Servers
Software

Storage devices

Selected Services

Business optimization software
  Business productivity
  Core infrastructure
  Software asset management
Collaboration
  Call/contact center
  Unified communications/messaging
  Video collaboration/conferencing
Cloud services
  Collaboration
  Infrastructure
  Messaging
  Security
Data center
  Infrastructure solutions
  Server solutions
  Storage solutions
Infrastructure and security
  Network infrastructure
  Security infrastructure
Managed services
  Business process outsourcing
  Connected real estate and sports
  Financing and leasing
  IT asset disposal
  Maintenance
  Product provisioning
  Remote network operations
  Telecom expense management
  Warehouse/integration

COMPETITORS

Amazon.com
Best Buy
Buy.com
CDW
CompuCom
Convergys
Dell
Digital River
Dixons Retail
Fry' s Electronics
Gateway Inc.
Hewlett-Packard
HP Enterprise Services
IBM
Lenovo
Micro Electronics
Microsoft
ModusLink
Office Depot
OfficeMax
PC Connection
PC Mall
PFSweb
RadioShack
SHI International
Softchoice
Staples
Symantec
Systemax
Zones

HISTORICAL FINANCIALS

Company Type: Public

Income Statement FYE: December 31

	REVENUE ($ mil.)	NET INCOME ($ mil.)	NET PROFIT MARGIN	EMPLOYEES
12/11	5,287	100	1.9%	0
12/10	4,809	75	1.6%	5,115
12/09	4,136	33	0.8%	4,898
12/08	4,825	(239)	—	4,581
12/07	4,800	77	1.6%	4,763
Annual Growth	2.4%	6.5%	—	—

2011 Year-End Financials

Debt ratio: 6.28%
Return on equity: 16.79%
Cash ($ mil.): 128
Current ratio: 138.45
Long-term debt ($ mil.): 115
No. of shares (mil.): 43
Dividends
  Yield: —
  Payout: —
Market value ($ mil.): 672

	STOCK PRICE ($) FY Close	P/E High/Low		PER SHARE ($) Earnings	Dividends	Book Value
12/11	15.29	9	6	2.18	0.00	13.59
12/10	13.16	10	7	1.61	0.00	11.76
12/09	11.42	19	3	0.73	0.00	10.17
12/08	6.90	—	—	(5.15)	0.00	9.26
12/07	18.24	17	11	1.56	0.00	16.00
Annual Growth	(4.3%)	—	—	8.7%	—	(4.0%)

Integrys Energy Group Inc

Integrys Energy integrates energy activities in the Windy City and surrounding geographies. The energy holding company owns six regulated utilities: Michigan Gas Utilities Corporation (165000 gas customers) Minnesota Energy Resources Corporation (212000 gas customers) North Shore Gas Company (158000 customers in the northern suburbs of Chicago) Peoples Gas Light and Coke Company (819000 natural gas customers in Chicago) Wisconsin Public Service (439000 electric customers and 318000 natural gas customers in Wisconsin and Michigan) and Upper Peninsula Power (52000 electricity customers). The company's nonregulated subsidiary Integrys Energy Services provides retail energy supply and services.

In addition to its electric and gas utilties Integrys Energy also holds a 34% stake in American Transmission Company (an electric transmission firm which operates in Illinois Michigan Minnesota and Wisconsin).

Financial Analysis

The company reported a 9.5% decline in revenues led by a $423 million (23%) drop in sales caused by weaker natural gas commodity prices. By contrast Integrys Energy's utility business revenues dropped by only 2%. Regulated electric revenues were down by 0.37% due to lower sales volumes while regulated gas revenues were down by 3.4% due to the decrease in the average per-unit cost of natural gas sold and the negative impact of higher regulatory refunds.

The company's net income for 2011 grew by 3% thanks primarily to a $31.8 million after-tax decrease in impairment losses recorded on generation plants and losses on dispositions at Integrys Energy Services and $20.3 million after-tax net decrease in operating expenses across all segments driven by a decrease in employee benefit costs and lower depreciation and amortization expense.

Strategy

In 2011 Integrys Energy moved into the compressed natural gas fueling business through the acquisition of Pinnacle CNG Systems and Trillium USA for an undisclosed price. The company is anticipating a growth of this market as more companies and government agencies expand their natural gas vehicle fleets. In 2012 Trillium USA announced a joint venture with AMP Americas called AMP Trillium to build CNG stations along the I-65 and I-75 trucking corridors and major routes in Texas.

Growing its energy capacity in 2012 Wisconsin Public Service agreed to buy Fox Energy (with a 593 MW power plant) for $440 million.

In order to reduce its debt and refocus on lower-risk regulated operations the company has steadily sold its non-regulated segment (formerly the largest contributor to total revenues). In 2009 the company sold Integrys Energy Services' non-retail energy services operations to U.S. Energy Services (based in Minneapolis). In 2009 and 2010 it also sold that unit's wholesale natural gas and electric marketing and Canadian energy marketing businesses. Integrys Energy Services has narrowed its focus to retail accounts and renewable energy investments.

Company Background

Integrys Energy took its current name after the 2007 acquisition of Peoples Energy for $1.5 billion.

EXECUTIVES

VP Gas Engineering Integrys Business Support, William E. Morrow, age 55
President The Peoples Gas Light and Coke and North Shore Gas, Willard S. (Will) Evans Jr.
EVP Business Performance and Shared Services; President Integrys Business Support, Phillip M. (Phil) Mikulsky, age 63, $395,200 total compensation
President and COO Utilities, Lawrence T. (Larry) Borgard, age 50, $426,231 total compensation
EVP and Chief Strategy Officer, Mark A. Radtke, age 50, $378,000 total compensation
President Integrys Energy Services, Daniel J. (Dan) Verbanac, age 48
VP Information Technology and Project Services and Chief Security Officer Integrys Energy Group and Integrys Business Support, David W. (Dave) Harpole, age 57
SVP and CFO, Joseph P. (Joe) O'Leary, age 57, $486,000 total compensation
Chairman President and CEO, Charles A. (Charlie) Schrock, age 58, $806,519 total compensation
VP Energy Supply Operations Wisconsin Public Service, Terry P. Jensky, age 56
President Wisconsin Public Service Corporation and Upper Peninsula Power Company, Charles A. (Chuck) Cloninger, age 53
Assistant VP Energy Supply Operations Wisconsin Public Service, Howard R. Giesler
SVP Integrys Energy Services, Richard J. Bissing, age 50
VP External Affairs, James F. (Jim) Schott, age 54
VP and Corporate Controller, Linda M. Kallas, age 52
Assistant Treasurer, Janet K. McKee, age 56
VP Operations The Peoples Gas Light and Coke and North Shore Gas, Edward A. Doerk
Assistant Secretary Integrys Energy Group The Peoples Gas Light and Coke Wisconsin Public Service Minnesota Energy Resources Michigan Gas Utilities North Shore Gas Upper Peninsula Power and Integrys Energy Services; Assistant Secretary and Senior Counsel, Dane E. Allen
VP General Counsel and Assistant Secretary, Jodi J. Caro, age 46
Manager Investor Relations, Donna M. Sheedy
VP Integrys Energy Services, Ronnie E. Cardwell, age 42
VP and Treasurer, William J. (Bill) Guc, age 43
VP and Corporate Controller, Diane L. Ford, age 58
VP Chief Legal Officer and Secretary, Barth J. Wolf, age 54
VP Human Resources, William Laakso, age 49
VP Investor Relations, Steven P. Eschbach
Assistant Treasurer, David K. Waltz
President Minnesota Energy Resources and Michigan Gas Utilities, Barbara A. (Barb) Nick
Manager IT Planning Integrys Business Support, Michael J. (Mike) O'Connell

Assistant VP Corporate Communications, Kathryn A. (Kathy) Hartman
Assistant VP Government Relations, Patrick J. Shillinger
Assistant VP Tax Strategy and Services, John R. Wilde
VP Integrys Energy Services, Leonardo G. Caro
Controller Integrys Energy Services, Craig A. Vanderwerff
VP Customer Relations Integrys Business Support, Mary J. Boettcher
VP Gas Supply Integrys Business Support, Thomas E. Zack
Assistant VP Client and Workforce Relations Integrys Business Support, Gary D. De Wolfe
Assistant VP Total Compensation Integrys Business Support, James C. Hoover
Assistant VP Total Compensation Integrys Business Support, Noreen E. Cleary
Assistant Controller Integrys Business Support, Michael A. Small
VP and General Manager Upper Peninsula Power, Keith E. Moyle
VP Michigan Gas Utilities, Charles F. Hauska
VP Energy Supply and Control Wisconsin Public Service, Paul J. Spicer
Assistant VP Energy Supply Operations Wisconsin Public Service, Bruce E. Bruzina
VP Integrys Customer Relations, Larry Szumski
Director Government Relations, Christopher LaRowe
Director, Keith E. Bailey, age 70
Director, Kathryn M. Hasselblad-Pascale, age 64
Director, James L. (Jim) Kemerling, age 72
Director, Pastora S. J. Cafferty, age 71
Director, Michelle L. Collins, age 51
Director, William J. Brodsky, age 68
Director, Albert J. (Al) Budney Jr., age 64
Director, William F. (Bill) Protz Jr., age 67
Director, Michael E. Lavin, age 66
Director, John W. (Jack) Higgins, age 65
Director, Ellen Carnahan, age 56
Auditors: Deloitte&ToucheLLP

LOCATIONS

HQ: Integrys Energy Group Inc.
130 E. Randolph St., Chicago IL 60601
Phone: 312-228-5400 **Fax:** 616-866-0257
Web: www.wolverineworldwide.com

PRODUCTS/OPERATIONS

2011 Sales

	$ mil.	% of total
Utility		
Gas	1,987	42
Electric	1,307	28
Nonutility		
Integrys Energy Services	1,394	30
Other	19	-
Total	**4,708**	**100**

Selected Subsidiaries

Integrys Energy Services Inc. (energy supply & service)
Michigan Gas Utilities Corporation (gas utility)
Minnesota Energy Resources Corporation (gas utility)
North Shore Gas Company (gas utility)
The Peoples Gas Light and Coke Company (gas utility)
Upper Peninsula Power Company (electric utility)
Wisconsin Public Service Corporation (electric and gas utility)

COMPETITORS

AEP
AES
ALLETE
Alliant Energy
CMS Energy
Dairyland Power
DPL
DTE
Exelon
FirstEnergy
Maine & Maritimes
MGE Energy
Nicor Gas
SEMCO ENERGY
Southern Union
Wisconsin Energy
Xcel Energy

HISTORICAL FINANCIALS

Company Type: Public

Income Statement

FYE: December 31

	REVENUE ($ mil.)	NET INCOME ($ mil.)	NET PROFIT MARGIN	EMPLOYEES
12/11	4,708	230	4.9%	4,619
12/10	5,203	223	4.3%	4,612
12/09	7,499	(68)	—	5,025
12/08	14,047	129	0.9%	5,191
12/07	10,292	254	2.5%	5,231
Annual Growth	(17.8%)	(2.4%)	—	(3.1%)

2011 Year-End Financials

Debt ratio: 24.29%
Return on equity: 7.65%
Cash ($ mil.): 28
Current ratio: 109.51
Long-term debt ($ mil.): 1,872
No. of shares (mil.): 78
Dividends
Yield: —
Payout: 94.77%
Market value ($ mil.): 4,242

	STOCK PRICE ($) FY Close	P/E High/Low		PER SHARE ($) Earnings	Dividends	Book Value
12/11	54.18	19	15	2.87	0.00	38.48
12/10	48.51	19	14	2.83	2.72	38.23
12/09	41.99	—	—	(0.92)	2.72	38.30
12/08	42.98	32	25	1.64	2.68	41.46
12/07	51.69	17	14	3.50	2.56	43.06
Annual Growth	1.2%	—	—	(4.8%)	—	(2.8%)

Intel Corp

The intelligence inside your computer could very well be Intel. The company —which holds about 80% of the market share for microprocessors that go into desktop and notebook computers and also into computer servers –is still #1 in semiconductors. Archrival AMD ate into Intel's market share for a time but the big guy fought back with faster processors and advanced manufacturing technology. Intel also makes embedded semiconductors for the industrial medical and in-vehicle infotainment markets. While most computer makers use Intel processors PC giants Dell and Hewlett-Packard are the company's largest customers. The Asia/Pacific region generates two-thirds of Intel's revenues.

HISTORY

In 1968 three engineers from Fairchild Semiconductor created Intel in Mountain View California to develop technology for silicon-based chips. ("Intel" is a contraction of "integrated electronics.") The trio consisted of Robert Noyce (who co-invented the integrated circuit or IC in 1958) Gordon Moore and Andy Grove.

Intel initially provided computer memory chips such as DRAMs (1970) and EPROMs (1971). These successes funded the microprocessor designs that revolutionized the electronics industry. In 1971 Intel introduced the 4004 microprocessor promoted as "a micro-programmable computer on a chip."

In 1979 Moore became Intel's chairman and Grove its president. (Grove became CEO in 1987.) When Intel's 8088 chip was chosen for IBM's PC in 1981 Intel secured its place as the microcomputer standard-setter.

Cutthroat pricing by Japanese competitors forced Intel out of the DRAM market in 1985; in a breathtaking strategy shift that became the subject of countless business school case studies the company refocused on microprocessors. It licensed its 286 chip technology to Advanced Micro Devices (AMD) and others in an effort to create an industry standard. Reacting to AMD's escalating market share (which stood at more than half by 1990) Intel fiercely protected the technology of its 386 (1985) and 486 (1989) chips; AMD sued for breach of contract.

Intel and AMD settled several microcode suits in 1995: AMD got the code license and Intel won $58 million in damages. Rather than fight an accusation from Digital Equipment (later acquired by Compaq) that Intel stole its technology to develop the Pentium processor Intel bought Digital Equipment's semiconductor operations.

Grove handed the CEO reins to president Craig Barrett in 1998; Grove replaced Moore as chairman while Moore became chairman emeritus. (Thanks to a mandatory retirement age he helped set Moore retired from Intel's board in 2001.)

Also in 1998 Intel unveiled its low-end Celeron chip. After a wrenching delay Intel unveiled a chipset to support Rambus' RDRAM memory architecture in 1999. The delay contributed to a big loss of chipset market share allowing VIA Technologies to pull even with Intel. Late in 1999 the company began shipping prototypes of its Itanium 64-bit processor; Itanium's general release was delayed repeatedly ultimately into mid-2001.

A string of other problems beset Intel in 2000. The company recalled hundreds of thousands of its motherboards that were distributed with a defective chip and later cancelled development of a low-cost microprocessor for budget PCs. Also in 2000 Intel began debuting its line of consumer Web appliances and interactive toys. The company later released the long-awaited Pentium 4 processor.

After announcing plans in mid-2001 for a major deal with Compaq (under which Compaq would use the Itanium architecture in all of its high-end servers by 2004) Intel gained a license to Compaq's Alpha chip technology. (Intel later absorbed some Compaq chip design teams as well as Itanium-related engineering groups from Hewlett-Packard even before those two companies announced their gigantic merger.)

In a move widely seen as an indication of the company's succession plan for top management early in 2002 Intel promoted EVP Paul Otellini to president and COO. The company's board formalized the succession plan late in 2004.

While the fastest Pentium 4 clocked at more than 3 gigahertz Intel changed its marketing tune after years of emphasizing the top speed of its processors; it instead stressed speed along with other performance factors such as energy efficiency. One of its first ventures along these lines was a major marketing campaign in support of the Centrino product family for notebook computers. The Centrino bundle combined a wireless radio device with a chipset and Pentium microprocessor optimized to run at low power. In part this shift in emphasis reflected the reality that computer buyers —especially corporate IT managers —valued economy more and raw speed less than they previously had. It also related to a larger issue born from Intel's great technological success over the years: Intel shrunk the size and boosted the speed of transistors so consistently for so long that in some cases its chips were running into fundamental barriers imposed by physics. At some point for example circuits are so tiny and packed so closely together that the chip they sit on cannot adequately dissipate the heat they generate. Intel responded by changing its product roadmap to emphasize dual-core microprocessors and other designs that circumvented these problems. (It also scrapped plans to introduce the first processor to pass the 4 gigahertz speed mark.)

Intel spent billions developing the powerful 64-bit Itanium microprocessor with Hewlett-Packard. After being beset by problems stemming from the complexity of its all-new architecture Itanium debuted (years behind schedule) in mid-2001. Though sales of the initial generation of Itanium chips were far from impressive prompting some industry wags to dub it the "Itanic" processor cheaper and more powerful subsequent versions helped the chip gain some market acceptance. (HP dropped out of the development partnership late in 2004.)

Intel conceded one point to AMD that it had earlier contested: there was room in the market between standard 32-bit chips (such as Pentium) and high-horsepower 64-bit chips (such as Itanium). AMD stole a march on Intel by debuting Opteron models built as 32-bit chips but with software extensions that allowed them to run 64-bit programs as well. After it brought Itanium to market Intel insisted that it would not follow suit (despite many rumors to the contrary). In mid-2004 though Intel finally introduced 64-bit-compatible models in its Pentium Xeon server processor line.

Expanding the holistic approach it took with Centrino development in 2005 Intel reorganized its entire structure around five platform-based business units: Mobility Digital Enterprise Digital Home Digital Health and Channel Products (later called Channel Platforms). The company scored a coup in mid-2005 when it reached an agreement with Apple Computer (now just Apple) that resulted in that company transitioning from IBM's PowerPC architecture to Intel chips for its Macintosh computers. It acquired XML (Extensible Markup Language) technology developer Sarvega. The company also purchased part of Zarlink Semiconductor's radio-frequency chip operations for roughly $70 million.

In 2005 Grove retired from the board Barrett retired as CEO and succeeded Grove as chairman and Otellini succeeded Barrett as CEO.

In late 2005 Intel joined with Micron Technology to form a new company devoted to NAND flash memory. Each contributed roughly $1.3 billion to create IM Flash Technologies which manufactures memory exclusively for Micron and Intel. The two companies quickly lined up a customer; Apple agreed to prepay $250 million to each company.

IM Flash Technologies was established in early 2006 and started with two wafer fabrication plants (or fabs) in Idaho and Virginia. The joint venture brought a third fab in Utah online in early 2007. The JV partners announced plans to build a fourth fab in Singapore but poor business conditions later led the JV to postpone construction.

Intel opened 2006 with the debut of a new brand identity. In addition to redesigning its well-known logo the company replaced its famous "Intel Inside" tagline with "Intel. Leap Ahead." That same year the company unveiled its vPro technology for desktop PCs. vPro represented a comprehensive technology suite for business desktop PCs similar to the sweep of the Centrino suite for mobile computing.

vPro was the third brand in Intel's platform strategy with its predecessors being Centrino and Viiv. Viiv (rhymes with five) was Intel's technology for digital entertainment providing home PC users with new ways to work with digital photos games movies music and video.

Responding to reports of lost market share and other problems Otellini promised financial analysts in 2006 that the company would conduct a comprehensive look at its entire business over three months leading to a broad restructuring of the company. He said it represented the biggest changes at the company in two decades. Otellini also vowed to cut $1 billion from Intel's spending budget in 2006 and to trim $300 million from the company's capital expenditures budget which was expected to be nearly $7 billion in 2006. (The company later lowered the 2006 capex budget to less than $6 billion.)

In mid-2006 Intel cut 1000 management jobs to trim costs in the face of stiff competition and lower demand for PCs. It also announced a shakeup of senior management that summer. The company also said it would reduce its headcount by 10500 jobs by mid-2007 through attrition and workforce reductions particularly in management marketing and IT functions. The job cutbacks represented a 10% drop in employment.

Intel fired a competitive volley in the summer of 2006 with the rollout of its Core 2 Duo microprocessors and deep cuts in price tags for older processor models. The Core 2 Duo line initially launching with 10 different models offered higher performance while consuming less electrical power. Targeted at gaming applications the Core 2 Extreme was designed into high-end PCs from Alienware Dell and Gateway among others.

Intel's support of the WiMAX wireless networking technology paid off in 2006 when Sprint Nextel set plans to spend up to $3 billion over two years building a WiMAX-based network infrastructure. Intel and Samsung Electronics were among the suppliers for the ambitious project. Sprint Nextel's embrace of WiMAX was a blow to QUALCOMM which was promoting an alternative technology orthogonal frequency-division multiplexing or OFDM. Sprint PCS and Verizon Wireless were using QUALCOMM's EV-DO technology for Internet access with mobile devices. (Two years later Intel Capital invested $1 billion in a company merging Sprint's wireless broadband business with Clearwire. Intel Capital had previously invested $620 million in Clearwire.)

In 2006 Intel sold its communications and application processor line to Marvell Technology for $600 million in cash. The same year the chip maker sold its media and signaling business to Eicon Networks for $75 million in cash. The business included all of the products from Intel's 1999 acquisition of Dialogic plus Host Media Processing software and HMP-enabled blade computers. Eicon Networks later changed its name to Dialogic Corporation. Later that year Intel sold its optical-networking components business to Cortina Systems for around $115 million in cash and stock.

The European Commission brought formal anticompetitive charges against Intel on behalf of AMD in 2007. It filed a second "statement of objections" against Intel alleging that Intel paid hidden rebates to PC manufacturers to use only Intel's microprocessors in their computers and that the chip maker paid retailer MediaMarkt to stock only computers with Intel processors. (The commission smacked Intel with a $1.45 billion fine in 2009.)

The company's long-running battle with AMD heated up when that company's successful Athlon processor took market share away from Intel's Pentium models. AMD pulled off its coup through timely introductions of high-performance chips during a period in the early 21st century when Intel experienced uncharacteristic component shortages and manufacturing glitches. Intel struck back with rounds of price cuts and an unusually aggressive schedule for introducing faster Pentium models. After AMD brought out its faster quad-core Opteron processors for desktop PCs and servers Intel responded in 2008 with the Core i7 which it claimed to be the fastest desktop processor in the world.

In 2008 Intel combined its flash memory business with the flash memory lines of R&D partner STMicroelectronics into a new stand-alone company named Numonyx based in Switzerland. Intel sold its NOR flash memory assets to Numonyx.

AMD's antitrust suit against Intel alleging that its rival used improper subsidies and coercion to secure sales was settled in 2009 in AMD's favor. Intel agreed to pay $1.25 billion in damages and to implement new business sales practices. New York Attorney General Andrew Cuomo filed an additional antitrust lawsuit against Intel that year. This suit again centered on Intel's questionable payments to PC makers to use Intel products. The FTC also filed a formal investigation in 2009 issuing subpoenas to AMD Intel and other companies. (The Korea Fair Trade Commission had previously cited and fined Intel for allegedly violating antitrust laws in South Korea.)

In 2009 the company acquired Wind River Systems a supplier of software for embedded electronics for about $884 million in cash. Wind River –with its portfolio of operating systems middleware and software development tools –became a wholly owned subsidiary.

In 2010 the Numonyx JV was sold to Micron Technology for about $1.2 billion. Late that year Intel acquired CognoVision a Toronto-based digital signage company that used camera sensors and computers in its signs to detect faces and track people moving through a store in order to make real-time changes to advertising.

In early 2011 Intel completed two significant acquisitions. In January the company bought the Wireless Solutions Business of Infineon for $1.4 billion in cash. Intel's interest in the unit stemmed from the company's lack of a widely accepted chip for the booming smartphone market. The second acquisition was that of security software maker McAfee at a cost of about $7.7 billion. Marking Intel's most significant foray into the world of software the purchase was part of an initiative to provide a package of software hardware and services for the multitude of devices connected to the Web.

In much smaller deals Intel also acquired Fulcrum Microsystems (Ethernet switch silicon for data centers cloud platforms and converged networks) and Israel-based location and navigation company Telmap in 2011.

EXECUTIVES

SVP and Director Human Resources, Patricia Murray

VP Intel Architecture Group; Chief Architect Hybrid Parallel Computing, David R. Ditzel, age 55

EVP; Chairman Intel China, Sean M. Maloney, age 55, $500,000 total compensation

Vice Chairman, Andy D. Bryant, age 61, $500,000 total compensation

President CEO and Director, Paul S. Otellini, age 61, $1,000,000 total compensation

VP Intel Architecture Group; Director Strategy Planning and Operations Visual Computing Group, W. Eric Mentzer, age 52
VP Intel Labs; Director Microprocessor and Programming Research, Joseph D. Schutz
VP Finance and Director Global Tax and Trade, Ronald D. Dickel
EVP; President Intel Capital, Arvind Sodhani, age 58, $225,000 total compensation
VP; Director Netbook and Tablet Development and Enabling, Stephen L. Smith
VP and Director Finance, Leslie S. Culbertson
VP Sales and Marketing Group; General Manager Intel World Ahead Program, John E. Davies
SVP; General Manager Technology and Manufacturing Group, William M. (Bill) Holt, age 59
EVP and Chief Product Officer; General Manager Intel Architecture Group, David (Dadi) Perlmutter, age 58, $453,900 total compensation
VP Intel Architecture Group; General Manager System-on-Chip Enabling Group, Gadi Singer
VP, William A. Swope
Chairman, Jane E. Shaw, age 73
VP and Chief Marketing Officer, Deborah S. Conrad, age 50
VP Intel Architecture Group; Director Low Power Components Ultra Mobility Group, Gil G. Frostig
VP Intel Architecture Group; General Manager Visual Computing Group, James A. (Jim) Johnson
VP Technology and Manufacturing Group; General Manager Customer Fulfillment Planning and Logistics, Franklin B. Jones
SVP; General Manager Sales and Marketing Group, Thomas M. (Tom) Kilroy, age 54
VP; General Manager Europe Middle East Africa (EMEA), Christian Morales
VP Human Resources; Director Compensation and Benefits, Ogden M. Reid, age 44
VP and Director Human Resources, Richard G. A. Taylor
VP Intel Architecture Group; Director Microprocessor Architecture and Performance, Daniel J. Casaletto
VP Technology and Manufacturing Group; Director Corporate Quality Network, Nasser Bozorg-Grayeli, age 62
VP and Treasurer, Ravi Jacob, age 59
SVP and COO, Brian M. Krzanich, age 51
VP Sales and Marketing Group; Director Consumer Channels Group, Jeffrey P. (Jeff) McCrea, age 46
VP; General Manager Business Management Group, Stuart C. Pann, age 52
VP; General Manager Worldwide Sales and Operations Group, Gregory R. Pearson, age 51
SVP and CFO, Stacy J. Smith, age 49, $425,000 total compensation
VP; General Manager Netbook and Tablet Group (NTG), Douglas L. (Doug) Davis, age 50
VP Sales and Marketing Group; General Manager Worldwide Reseller Channel Organization, Steven J. (Steve) Dallman
VP Intel Architecture Group; Director Strategic Planning Platform Architecture and Software Ultra Mobility Group, Shane D. Wall, age 47
Director Communication Infrastructure and Architecture, Matthew J. Adiletta
Senior Fellow Technology and Manufacturing Group; Director Process Architecture and Integration, Mark T. Bohr, age 59
Senior Fellow Technology and Manufacturing Group; Director Advanced Lithography, Yan A. Borodovsky, age 65
Senior Fellow Technology and Manufacturing Group; Director Transistor Research and Nanotechnology, Robert S. Chau, age 52
Computer Architect, John H. Crawford
Director Microarchitecture Research, Joel S. Emer
Director IA-32 Microarchitecture Development, Glenn J. Hinton, age 55
Director Reliability Methods, Neal R. Mielke
Director Microprocessor Product Development, David B. Papworth
Senior Fellow; CTO Architecture Group; General Manager Cross-IAG Architecture and Pathfinding, Stephen S. Pawlowski, age 50
Director Operational Decision Support Technology, Devadas D. (Dev) Pillai
VP and CTO; Director Intel Labs; Senior Fellow, Justin R. Rattner, age 62
Director Circuit Technology, Clair Webb
Senior Fellow Technology and Manufacturing Group; Director Advanced Circuits and Technology Integration, Ian A. Young, age 58
Director Lithography, Swaminathan (Sam) Sivakumar, age 46
VP Software and Services Group General Manager Visual and Parallel Computing Group, Jonathan (Jon) Khazam, age 50
VP and Director Logic Technology Development, Sohail U. Ahmed
VP; General Manager Atom and System-on-a-Chip (SOC) Development Group, Robert B. Crooke
VP; General Manager PC Client Group, Shmuel (Mooly) Eden
VP Legal and Corporate Affairs Director Corporate Legal and Secretary, Cary I. Klafter
VP Technology and Manufacturing Group; General Manager Worldwide Material, Jacklyn A. Sturm, age 55
VP Intel Architecture Group; General Manager Platform Components Group, Thomas R. (Tom) Macdonald, age 49
VP Intel Architecture Group; General Manager Ultra Mobility Group, Michael Bell
VP Information Technology; General Manager IT Global Operations and Services, Kimberly S. (Kim) Stevenson
VP Sales and Marketing Group; General Manager Global Communications Group, Paul Bergevin
Director I/O Research, Randy Mooney, age 50
VP Technology and Manufacturing Group; General Manager Technology Manufacturing Engineering, Robert E. Bruck, age 55
VP Sales and Marketing Group; General Manager Services, Lee Fang (Sophia) Chew, age 51
VP Technology and Manufacturing Group; Director Fab materials, Timothy G. Hendry, age 51
SVP; General Manager Software and Services Group, Renee J. James, age 47
VP; Director Assembly Test and Technology Development, Babak Sabi, age 53
Director Memory Technology Development, Albert Fazio, age 51
VP and General Manager Datacenter and Connected Systems Group, Diane M. Bryant, age 51
VP Finance and Corporate Controller, James G. Campbell, age 57
VP Sales and Marketing Group; Director Global Accounts Hewlett Packard, Laura G. Crone, age 51
VP Technology and Manufacturing Group; General Manager Intel Israel; Plant Manager Fab 28, Maxine Fassberg, age 58
VP; General Manager Microprocessor and Chipset Development, Ron Friedman, age 56
VP Technology and Manufacturing Group; Director Components Research, Michael C. Mayberry, age 55
VP Legal and Corporate Affairs and Deputy General Counsel, Suzan A. Miller, age 48
VP Technology and Manufacturing Group; General Manager NAND Solutions Group, Thomas A. (Tom) Rampone, age 49
VP Sales and Marketing Group; Director Global Accounts Dell, Arthur W. Roehm, age 53
VP Intel Architecture Group; Director WiMAX Program Office, Rama K. Shukla, age 59
VP Technology and Manufacturing Group; General Manager Fab/Sort Manufacturing, Joshua M. Walden, age 50
VP Sales and Marketing Group; President Intel K.K. (Japan), Kazumasa Yoshida, age 54
VP Sales and Marketing Group; President Intel China, Ian (Ian) Yang
VP Finance and Director Investor Relations, R. Kevin Sellers
VP Intel Capital; Managing Director Manufacturing Sector and Taiwan Korea and Latin American Regions, Keith R. Larson, age 54
VP Technology and Manufacturing Group; Director Chandler Assembly Technology Development, Mostafa Aghazadeh
VP Technology and Manufacturing Group; Co-Executive Officer IM Flash Technologies, David A. (Dave) Baglee
VP Technology and Manufacturing Group; Director Derivative Logic Technology Development, Peng Bai
VP; General Manager Digital Home Group, Erik Huggers
VP Legal and Corporate Affairs; Director Global Public Policy, Peter M. Cleveland
VP Intel Architecture Group; General Manager Platform Validation Engineering, John D. Barton
VP Sales and Marketing Group; Director Marketing Strategy and Campaigns, Nancy Bhagat
VP; General Manager Microprocessor Development Group, Rani N. Borkar
VP Technology and Manufacturing Group; Director Yield Technology, Melton C. Bost
VP Sales and Marketing Group; President Intel Americas, Christopher J. (C. J.) Bruno
VP Sales and Marketing Group; Director Global Accounts Lenovo, Gregory M. Bryant
VP Technology and Manufacturing Group; Director PTD Patterning and Manufacturing, Peter Charvat
VP Digital Home Group; Director Software Engineering, Alan Crouch
VP Sales and Marketing Group; Director Global Operations and Productivity, Tammy L. Cyphert
VP Digital Home Group; Director System-on-Chip Engineering, Bradley D. Daniels
VP Sales and Marketing Group; General Manager Worldwide Embedded Sales Group, Richard P. Dwyer
VP Intel Architecture Group; General Manager Business Client Platform Division, Ricardo J. (Rick) Echevarria
VP Legal and Corporate Affaris; Director Corporate Affairs Group; President Intel Foundation, Shelly M. Esque
VP; General Manager Systems Software Division, Douglas W. (Doug) Fisher
VP Software and Solutions Group; General Manager Visual Computing Software Division, Elliot D. Garbus
VP Sales and Marketing Group; General Manager Enterprise Solution Sales, Gordon G. Graylish
VP Technology and Manufacturing Group; Plant Manager D1DR Fab, Gulsher S. Grewal
VP Software and Services Group; Director Strategic Business Development, Kostas A. Katsohirakis
VP Technology and Manufacturing Group; Director Product Health Enhancement Organization, Patricia A. McDonald
VP Intel Architecture Group; Director Microprocessor and Graphics Group, Rory M. McInerney

VP Technology and Manufacturing Group; General Manager Assembly Test and Manufacturing, Steven C. Megli
VP Finance and Controller Technology and Manufacturing Group, Christina S. Min
VP Technology and Manufacturing Group; Director Logic Technology Integration, Kaizad R. Mistry
VP Intel Architecture Group; Director Intel Architecture Strategic Platform Planning and Cross Platform Technology (CPT) Teams, Alexander D. (Alex) Peleg
VP Technology and Manufacturing Group; Plant Manager Fab 32/22, John R. Pemberton
VP Finance and Controller Intel Architecture Group, Corine Perez
VP Technology and Manufacturing Group; General Manager Custom Intel Architecture Foundry, Sunit Rikhi
VP Intel Capital; Director Mergers and Acquisitions, Raheel A. Shah
VP Sales and Marketing Group; General Manager Asia/Pacific Region, Navin Shenoy
VP Information Technology; General Manager Platform Engineering Capability, Kumud M. Srinivasan
VP Intel Architecture Group; General Manager Embedded and Communications Group, Ton H. Steenman
VP Intel Architecture Group; General Manager LAN Access Division, Thomas H. (Tom) Swinford
VP Sales and Marketing Group; General Manager Service Provider Group, Robert P. (Robby) Swinnen
VP Technology and Manufacturing Group; Director Thin Films and Chemical Mechanical Polish Technology, Chi-Hwa Tsang
VP Technology and Manufacturing Group; Director Corporate Services, Neil R. Tunmore
VP Intel Architecture Group; General Manager Incubation and Innovation Group, Sriram Viswanathan
VP Intel Labs; Director Circuits and System Research, Wen-Hann Wang
VP Technology and Manufacturing Group; Director Intel Mask Operation, Chiang Yuan Yang
VP Technology Manufacturing Group; General Manager Design and Technology Solutions, Siva K. Yerramilli
VP Intel Architecture Group; Director Atom and System-on-Chip Development Group, Elenora Yoeli
Senior Fellow Software and Services Group; Director Systems Software, Bryant E. Bigbee
Senior Fellow Technology and Manufacturing Group; Director I/O Architecture, Richard L. Coulson, age 56
Chief Client Platform Architect Architecture Group, Ajay V. Bhatt
Director Microprocessor Technology Lab, Shekhar Y. Borkar
Larrabee Chief Architect, Douglas M. Carmean
Director Circuit Technology Research, Vivek K. De
Director Microarchitecture Development, Tryggve Fossum
Director Technology Strategy, Paolo A. Gargini
Director Transistor Technology and Integration, Tahir Ghani
Director Storage Architecture, Knut S. Grimsrud
Director Tera-Scale Computing Research, James P. Held
Director Decision Engineering, Karl G. Kempf
Director Parallel and Distributed Solutions Division, David J. Kuck
Director Advanced Device Technology, Kelin J. Kuhn
Director Circuit and Low Power Technologies, Rajesh Kumar
Director Compiler and Architecture Advanced Development, P. Geoffrey Lowney
Director Logic Technology, Jose A. Maiz
Director Photonics Technology Lab, Mario J. Paniccia
Director Analytical and Microsystems Technologies, Valluri Rao
Director Chemical Mechanical Polish Technology, Joseph M. (Joe) Steigerwald
CTO Digital Home Group, Brendan Traw
Chief Virtualization Architect, Richard A. Uhlig
Director System-on-Chip Architecture, Raj Yavatkar
Director Advanced Design, Kevin X. Zhang
SVP and General Counsel, A. Douglas (Doug) Melamed, age 66
VP Technology and Manufacturing Group; Director Product Quality and Reliability, Mohsen Alavi
VP Intel Architecture Group; General Manager Data Center Group Marketing, Boyd A. Davis
VP Intel Architecture Group; General Manager Enterprise Platforms and Services Division, Lisa H. Graff
VP Intel Labs; Director Integrated Platform Research Lab, Vida Ilderem
VP Sales and Marketing Group Director Creative Services and Digital Marketing, Johan Jerv?e
VP Intel Capital; Managing Director Software and Services Sector, Lisa M. Lambert
VP Technology and Manufacturing Group; General Manager Assembly Test Manufacturing, Robin A. Martin
VP Information Technology; General Manager Customer Capability, Patricia N. Perry
VP Software and Services Group; General Manager Developer Products Division, William A. (Bill) Savage
VP Technology and Manufacturing Group; Director Manufacturing and Operations, Ralph A. Schweinfurth
VP Intel Architecture Group; Director PC Client Program Office, Isic Silas
VP Technology and Manufacturing Group; Plant Manager Fab 24 and Fab 10; General Manager Intel Ireland, Eamonn Sinnott
VP Human Resources; Director Human Resources Enterprise Services, Ardine Williams
VP Technology and Manufacturing Group; Director Portland Technology Development Patterning, Niraj Anand
VP Intel Architecture Group; General Manager Mobile Wireless Group, Aicha S. Evans
VP Software and Services Group; General Manager Developer Relations Division, Christos Georgiopoulos
VP Sales and Marketing Group; Director Microprocessor Marketing and Business Planning, Jason L. Grebe
Chief Information Security Officer; General Manager Information Risk and Security; VP Information Technology Group, Malcolm Harkins
VP Finance; Controller Sales and Marketing Group, Brice A. Hill
VP Intel Architecture Group; Director Strategic Planning and Business Development Microprocessor and Chipset Development Group, Yoav Hochberg
VP Technology and Manufacturing Group; Site Manager Fab 11X, Ann B. Kelleher
VP Technology and Manufacturing Group; Director Process Technology Integration, Sanjay Natarajan
VP Intel Architecture Group; General Manager Workstations and Many Integrated Core computing, Anthony Neal-Graves
VP Intel Architecture Group; General Manager Ultra Mobility Group, David P. Whalen
Director, David S. (Dave) Pottruck, age 63
Vice Chairman, Andy D. Bryant, age 61
President CEO and Director, Paul S. Otellini, age 61
VP Finance and Director Global Tax and Trade, Ronald D. Dickel
Director, Susan L. Decker, age 49
Director, Frank D. Yeary, age 48
Director, Reed E. Hundt, age 64
Director, Prof David B. Yoffie, age 56
Director, John J. Donahoe, age 51
Director, Charlene Barshefsky, age 61
Director, James D. Plummer, age 67
Auditors: Ernst&YoungLLP

LOCATIONS

HQ: Intel Corporation
2200 Mission College Blvd., Santa Clara CA 95054-1549
Phone: 408-765-8080 **Fax:** 760-744-9589
Web: www.nai-online.com

2011 Sales

	$ mil.	% of total
Asia/Pacific		
Taiwan	17,076	32
China	8,114	15
Japan	5,024	9
Other countries	5,532	10
Americas		
US	8,411	16
Other countries	2,887	5
Europe	6,955	13
Total	**53,999**	**100**

PRODUCTS/OPERATIONS

2011 Sales

	$ mil.	% of total
PC Client Group	35,406	66
Data Center Group	10,129	19
Other architecture	5,005	9
Software & services	1,870	3
Other	1,589	3
Total	**53,999**	**100**

Selected Products

Chipsets (communications consumer electronics desktop embedded handheld netbook notebook server storage workstation)
Communication infrastructure components
- Network processors
- Networked storage products

Device software optimization products (embedded handheld)
Digital home (chips for cable modems digital TVs high-definition media players set-top boxes and home network integration)
Microprocessors (communications consumer electronics desktop embedded handheld network netbook notebook server storage workstation)
- Atom
- Celeron
- Centrino
- Core i3 i5 i7
- Core Duo
- Core Quad
- Itanium
- Pentium
- Xeon

Motherboards (desktop server workstation)
NAND flash memory (all-in-one desktop digital camera memory card portable memory storage device solid-state drive tablet computer)
Software products (software development tools middleware operating systems software tools)
Ultra-Mobility (chips for high-end smartphones handheld devices)
Wired and wireless connectivity components (embedded wireless cards network adapters)

COMPETITORS

AMD
ARM Holdings
Atmel
Broadcom
Cisco Systems
Conexant Systems
Freescale Semiconductor
Fujitsu Semiconductor
IBM
LSI Corp.
Maxim Integrated Products
MediaTek
Microchip Technology
Micron Technology
NVIDIA
Oracle
QUALCOMM
Samsung Electronics
SanDisk
Silicon Integrated Systems
SK Hynix
Sony
ST-Ericsson
STMicroelectronics
Texas Instruments
Toshiba Semiconductor & Storage Products
VIA Technologies

HISTORICAL FINANCIALS

Company Type: Public

Income Statement FYE: December 31

	REVENUE ($ mil.)	NET INCOME ($ mil.)	NET PROFIT MARGIN	EMPLOYEES
12/11	53,999	12,942	24.0%	100,100
12/10	43,623	11,464	26.3%	82,500
12/09	35,127	4,369	12.4%	79,800
12/08	37,586	5,292	14.1%	83,900
12/07	38,334	6,976	18.2%	86,300
Annual Growth	8.9%	16.7%	—	3.8%

2011 Year-End Financials

Debt ratio: 10.31%—
Return on equity: 28.19%
Cash ($ mil.): 5,065
Current ratio: 215.10
Long-term debt ($ mil.): 7,084
Dividends
Yield: —
Payout: 32.74%
Market value ($ mil.): —

	STOCK PRICE ($) FY Close	P/E High	P/E Low	PER SHARE ($) Earnings	Dividends	Book Value
12/11	24.25	10	8	2.39	0.00	9.18
12/10	20.84	12	9	2.01	0.00	8.97
12/09	20.33	26	15	0.77	0.00	7.55
12/08	14.18	29	13	0.92	0.00	7.03
12/07	26.76	23	16	1.18	0.00	7.35
Annual Growth	(2.4%)	—	—	19.3%	—	5.7%

INTERMOUNTAIN HEALTH CARE INC

LOCATIONS

HQ: INTERMOUNTAIN HEALTH CARE INC
36 S STATE ST STE 2300, SALT LAKE CITY, UT
841111471
Phone: 8014422000

HISTORICAL FINANCIALS

Company Type:

Income Statement FYE: December 31

	REVENUE ($ mil.)	NET INCOME ($ mil.)	NET PROFIT MARGIN	EMPLOYEES
12/11	4,049	6	0.2%	23,000
12/10	4,381	716	16.3%	0
12/09	3,568	1,032	28.9%	0
12/07	3,048	298	9.8%	0
Annual Growth	9.9%	(72.4%)	—	—

2011 Year-End Financials

Debt ratio: —
Return on equity: 0.20%
Cash ($ mil.): 175
Current ratio: 0.60
Long-term debt ($ mil.): —
Dividends
Yield: —
Payout: —
Market value ($ mil.): —

International Bancshares Corp.

International Bancshares is leading post-NAFTA banking in South Texas. The institution's International Bank of Commerce (IBC) and Commerce Bank serve residents and businesses of Texas Oklahoma and northern Mexico through some 220 locations. The company facilitates trade between the US and Mexico and serves Texas' growing Hispanic population; about 30% of its deposits come from south of the border. In addition to commercial and international banking services International Bancshares provides retail deposit services insurance and investment products and mortgages and consumer loans. The bulk of the company's portfolio is made up of business and construction loans.

IBC maintains a decentralized structure in which local advisory boards made up of members of the communities in the bank is located direct operations of its branches including recruiting prospective clients and developing products and services to meet local customers' needs However IBC announced in 2011 that it would close some 55 bank branches inside grocery stores in response to recent regulations that put a cap on how much banks can charge stores for debit card transactions. The company intends for the cost savings from the closures to offset the expected decline in fee revenues.

International Bancshares has not had a problem making money however as it has benefitted from the Texas economy which remained relatively stable during the recession in comparison to other parts of the country. The company's provisions for loan losses decreased in 2010 but net income was down slightly as well in part due to a tax hit related to a 2004 acquisition.

With a large number of Hispanic shareholders International Bancshares is one of the largest minority-owned banks in the nation. Founder and board member Tony Sanchez who lost the 2002 race for Texas governor and his family own around 15% of International Bancshares.

EXECUTIVES

VP and Director; President and CEO International Bank of Commerce McAllen, R. David Guerra, age 59, $260,928 total compensation
Chairman and President; President and CEO International Bank of Commerce Laredo, Dennis E. Nixon, age 69, $533,504 total compensation
Treasurer and Director; SEVP CFO and COO International Bank of Commerce Laredo, Imelda Navarro, age 54, $200,807 total compensation
VP; EVP International Bank of Commerce Laredo, Edward J. Farias
EVP and Director of International Business Development International Bank of Commerce Laredo, Guillermo R. Garcia
EVP Operations International Bank of Commerce Laredo, Dalia F. Martinez
EVP International Department International Bank of Commerce Laredo, Gerald Schwebel
EVP and Director Sales and Marketing International Bank of Commerce Laredo, J. Jorge Verduzco
President and CEO International Bank of Commerce Brownsville Texas, Fred W. Rusteberg
President and CEO Commerce Bank Laredo Texas, Ignacio Urrabazo Jr.
President and CEO International Bank of Commerce Eagle Pass Texas, Hector J. Cerna
Chairman and CEO International Bank of Commerce Houston Texas, Jay Rogers
President and CEO International Bank of Commerce Port Lavaca and Bay City Texas, Richard A. Bothe
President and CEO International Bank of Commerce Oklahoma, Thomas L. (Tom) Travis
President and CEO International Bank of Commerce Zapata Texas, Renato Ramirez
President and CEO International Bank of Commerce San Antonio Texas, Steve E. Edlund
Secretary, Marisa V. Santos
President and CEO International Bank of Commerce Austin Texas, Robert B. (Bob) Barnes
President IBC Service Center International Bank of Commerce San Antonio Texas, Pat Stewart
SVP, Eliza Gonzalez
President and CEO International Bank of Commerce Corpus Christi Texas, Harold Shockley
President International Bank of Commerce Houston Texas, Jeff Samples
Assistant Secretary, Hilda V. Torres
First VP, Judy Wawroski
Vice President; Director; President of International Bank of Commerce McAllen and Texas Branch, David Guerra
VP and Director; President and CEO International Bank of Commerce McAllen, R. David Guerra, age 59
Director, Leonardo Salinas, age 78
Treasurer and Director; SEVP CFO and COO International Bank of Commerce Laredo, Imelda Navarro, age 54
Director, Antonio R. (Tony) Sanchez Jr., age 69
Director, Irving Greenblum, age 82
Director, Daniel B. Hastings Jr., age 64

Director, Sioma Neiman, age 84
Director, Peggy J. Newman, age 80
Director, Guillermo F. Trevino
Director, Douglas B. Howland, age 61
Director, Larry A. Norton, age 59
Auditors: McGladreyLLP

LOCATIONS

HQ: International Bancshares Corporation
1200 San Bernardo Ave., Laredo TX 78042-1359
Phone: 956-722-7611 Fax: 956-726-6637
Web: www.iboc.com

PRODUCTS/OPERATIONS

2011 Sales

	$ mil.	% of total
Interest		
Loans including fees	292	47
Taxable investment securities	113	18
Other	11	2
Noninterest		
Service charges on deposit accounts	98	16
Other service charges commissions & fees	58	9
Net investment securities transactions	17	3
Other investments net	16	3
Other	12	2
Total	619	100

COMPETITORS

BancFirst
Bank of America
Broadway Bancshares
Citigroup
Cullen/Frost Bankers
Falcon Bancshares
First Victoria National Bank
JPMorgan Chase
Lone Star National Bancshares
Midland Financial
Wells Fargo

HISTORICAL FINANCIALS

Company Type: Public

Income Statement FYE: December 31

	ASSETS ($ mil.)	NET INCOME ($ mil.)	INCOME AS % OF ASSETS	EMPLOYEES
12/11	11,739	127	1.1%	3,388
12/10	11,943	130	1.1%	3,747
12/09	11,762	142	1.2%	3,662
12/08	12,439	132	1.1%	3,832
12/07	11,167	121	1.1%	3,740
Annual Growth	1.3%	1.2%	—	(2.4%)

2011 Year-End Financials

Debt ratio: 5.83%
Return on equity: 7.95%
Cash ($ mil.): 261
Current ratio: —
Long-term debt ($ mil.): 684
No. of shares (mil.): 67
Dividends
Yield: —
Payout: 22.49%
Market value ($ mil.): 1,234

	STOCK PRICE ($) FY Close	P/E High/Low		PER SHARE ($) Earnings	Dividends	Book Value
12/11	18.34	12	7	1.69	0.00	23.78
12/10	20.03	14	9	1.72	0.36	21.56
12/09	18.91	11	4	1.90	0.34	20.67
12/08	21.83	17	10	1.92	0.66	18.33
12/07	20.94	18	11	1.75	0.65	13.64
Annual Growth	(3.3%)	—	—	(0.9%)	—	14.9%

International Business Machines Corp.

Big Blue? Try Huge Blue. International Business Machines (IBM) is the world's top provider of computer products and services. Among the leaders in almost every market in which it competes the company focuses primarily on its growing services business which accounts for more than half of sales. While IBM made its name in computer hardware the company's information technology business services and software units are now among the largest in the world. The company is also one of the largest providers of semiconductors and its computing hardware legacy lives on in the form of its industry-leading enterprise server and data storage products lines. IBM serves customers globally across most industries.

HISTORY

In 1914 National Cash Register's star salesman Thomas Watson left to rescue the flagging Computing-Tabulating-Recording (C-T-R) Company the pioneer in US punch card processing that had been incorporated in 1911. Watson aggressively marketed C-T-R's tabulators supplying them to the US government during WWI and tripling company revenues to almost $15 million by 1920. The company became International Business Machines (IBM) in 1924 and soon dominated the global market for tabulators time clocks and electric typewriters. It was the US's largest office machine maker by 1940.

IBM perfected electromechanical calculation (the Harvard Mark I 1944) but initially dismissed the potential of computers. When Remington Rand's UNIVAC computer (1951) began replacing IBM machines IBM quickly responded.

The company unveiled its first computer in 1952. With its superior research and development and marketing IBM built a market share near 80% in the 1960s and 1970s. Its innovations included the STRETCH systems which eliminated vacuum tubes (1960) and the first compatible family of computers the System/360 (1964). IBM also developed floppy disks (1971) and the first laser printer for computers (1975). The introduction of the IBM PC in 1981 ignited the personal computer industry sparking a barrage of PC clones. Through it all IBM was the subject of a 12-year government antitrust investigation that ended in 1982.

The shift to smaller open systems along with greater competition in all of IBM's segments caused wrenching change. Instead of responding to the market need for cheap PCs and practical business applications IBM stubbornly stuck with mainframes and rivals began capitalizing on Big Blue's technology. After posting profits of $6.6 billion in 1984 the company began a slow slide. It sold many noncomputer businesses including its copier division to Kodak in 1988 and its Lexmark typewriter business in 1991. Closing the book on its heritage IBM shuttered the last of its punch card plants that year.

In 1993 CEO John Akers was replaced by Louis Gerstner the first outsider to run IBM. He began to turn the ailing antiquated company around by slashing costs and nonstrategic divisions cutting the workforce shaking up entrenched management and pushing services. His $1 billion R&D budget cut caused an exodus of IBM scientists and created an operation geared more toward quick turnaround than lengthy research (however the company still leads the business world in patents each year). In 1994 Big Blue reported its first profit in four years. It also began making computer chips that year.

A pioneer in server operating system software IBM made an early move into messaging and network management software with its acquisitions of spreadsheet pioneer Lotus Development in 1995 and network management specialist Tivoli the next year. Expanding its Web focus to include small businesses IBM in 1999 bought Internet communications server maker Sequent. That year IBM exited the networking hardware market selling related intellectual property to Cisco Systems.

Hoping to turn around its ailing PC business IBM in 1999 axed manufacturing staff and halted sales of its PCs through US retailers. The following year the head of its server business Samuel Palmisano was named president and COO; the change fueled speculation that IBM's emperor had found his heir.

In a move intended to bolster its data management division IBM in 2001 purchased the database software unit of Informix for $1 billion. It also bought longtime partner CrossWorlds Software a maker of application integration products the next year.

Streamlining efforts in 2002 included increased outsourcing of manufacturing and refurbishing activities to Sanmina-SCI and Solectron (acquired by Flextronics in 2007); each had acquired manufacturing facilities from IBM. Also that year the company formed a joint venture with Hitachi to combine the companies' disk drive operations. After an initial investment of about $2 billion from Hitachi combined with further payments to IBM over the next three years Hitachi eventually took on full ownership of the business. Additionally IBM combined its Technology (microchips) and Systems (servers storage) groups.

Looking to extend its lead in technology and business services IBM also acquired PricewaterhouseCoopers' consulting and IT services unit PwC Consulting for an estimated $3.5 billion in 2002. While presenting IBM with a significant integration challenge the transaction served the dual purpose of augmenting IBM's standard array of outsourcing maintenance and integration services while moving the company into high-end management consulting. Palmisano succeeded Gerstner as CEO that year.

In 2003 IBM acquired development tool maker Rational Software for $2.1 billion and it acquired supply chain software developer Trigo Technologies early in 2004. Also that year the company purchased Daksh eServices one of India's largest call center businesses and the Business Continuity Services unit of Schlumberger.

The company in 2005 sold its PC business —a segment that had begun to yield little profit for the company —to Chinese manufacturing partner Lenovo. IBM received a minority ownership stake in the expanded Lenovo as part of the deal but it subsequently sold its shares.

Also in 2005 it expanded the presence of its service arm in the health care market when it acquired Healthlink as well as software partner Candle. In 2005 it acquired Ascential Software for about $1.1 billion. The next year the company bought FileNet a maker of content management software for $1.6 billion.

In 2007 IBM spent about $1 billion on 12 acquisitions; half of those were software companies that included Vallent Corporation Softek Storage

Solutions Watchfire and DataMirror (for which it paid $161 million).

Continuing the trend of divesting its hardware operations IBM in 2007 sold its digital business-printer operations –through a 49% stake in a new printing joint venture known as InfoPrint Solutions (between itself and Japan-based printing and imaging giant Ricoh) –for about $725 million. Ricoh acquired the remaining 49% of the venture in 2010.

Among the 15 purchases made by the company in 2008 (up from 12 the previous year) was software developer Cognos. IBM paid about $5 billion for Cognos in a bid to increase its portfolio of so-called business process optimization applications. The deal helped the company gain ground against enterprise software industry leaders Oracle and SAP specifically in the areas of business intelligence and performance management.

Another notable acquisition that year was the $885 million purchase of business process optimization and embedded systems software specialist Telelogic. The deal complemented the embedded systems capabilities of IBM's Rational Software as IBM worked to meet demand for such technology in sectors that included auto manufacturing. The company's key purchase for 2009 was of analytics provider SPSS for about $1.2 billion in cash. IBM integrated the SPSS software into its Business Analytics and Optimization consulting organization.

Its 2010 purchase of Unica for about $480 million added more tools for managing targeted marketing and advertising efforts. Meanwhile the company sold its declining product lifecycle management software business to Dassault Systemes in 2010 for $600 million in order to focus on core products.

IBM acquired the Sterling Commerce subsidiary of AT&T in 2010 for about $1.4 billion in cash and integrated the business with its software development operations. Sterling Commerce made software that helped businesses create and integrate networks of customers partners and suppliers. The Sterling Commerce deal complemented IBM's portfolio of applications that enable customers to automate and manage business processes across functions such as marketing selling ordering and fulfillment. It also provided IBM with a more complete platform for business process automation by adding to its selection of middleware the code that connects disparate software components and applications.

The company named its first female CEO in 2012 naming SVP and group executive of sales marketing and strategy Virginia "Ginni" Rometty as president and CEO. Former CEO Samuel Palmisano stayed on as chairman.

EXECUTIVES

Chairman, Samuel J. (Sam) Palmisano, age 60, $1,800,000 total compensation
SVP Human Resources, J. Randall (Randy) MacDonald, age 63
SVP and CFO Finance and Enterprise Transformation, Mark Loughridge, age 58, $720,000 total compensation
SVP Marketing and Communications, Jon C. Iwata, age 49
SVP and Director IBM Research, John E. Kelly III, age 58
SVP Global Technology Services, Michael E. (Mike) Daniels, age 58, $665,000 total compensation
Chairman President and CEO, Virginia M. (Ginni) Rometty, age 55, $630,000 total compensation
SVP Systems and Technology, Rodney C. (Rod) Adkins, age 54
SVP Enterprise Transformation and Information Technology, Linda S. Sanford, age 59
SVP; Group Executive Software and Systems, Steven A. (Steve) Mills, age 60, $695,000 total compensation
VP Open Source and Linux Middleware Software Group, Jeff S. Smith
Managing Director State of Georgia Account Global Sales and Distribution, Curtis H. Tearte
SVP Application Management Services, Colleen F. Arnold, age 55
SVP Middleware Software, Robert J. LeBlanc, age 53
General Manager Information Management Software, Arvind Krishna
General Manager Global Media and Entertainment Industry, Steven L. (Steve) Canepa
General Manager Business Analytics and Process Optimization Software, Ambuj Goyal
SVP Global Technology Services, Erich Clementi
VP Security Counsel and Chief Privacy Officer, Harriet P. Pearson
General Manager Global Markets Systems and Technology Group, James (Jim) Stallings
VP and Treasurer, Martin J. Schroeter
Manager Media Relations Italy, Alessandro Ferrari
General Manager Power Systems Systems and Technology Group, Ross A. Mauri
SVP Software Solutions Group, Michael D. (Mike) Rhodin, age 51
SVP Legal and Regulatory Affairs and General Counsel, Robert C. (Bob) Weber, age 61
SVP GTS Services Delivery, Timothy S. Shaughnessy, age 54
VP and CIO, Jeanette Horan
VP Open Systems Development Systems and Technology Group, Daniel D. Frye
Director Media Relations Global Business Services, John Buscemi
VP Worldwide Marketing and Strategy Power Systems Platform, Scott Handy
General Manager Global Business Partners, Rich Hume
VP Assistant General Counsel and Secretary, Andrew Bonzani
General Manager Power and z Systems, Tom Rosamilia
SVP Sales and Distribution, Bruno Di Leo
Manager Media Relations Canada, Carrie Bendzsa
VP and Controller, James J. Kavanaugh
VP Corporate Citizenship and Corporate Affairs; President IBM International Foundation, Stanley S. Litow
Manager External Communications UK, Ken Saunders
Director Media Relations Research and Development, Jenny Galitz McTighe
Director Media Relations Technology and Intellectual Property, Steve Malkiewicz
Manager Media Relations Asia Pacific, Harriet Ip
Director Media Relations Europe, Joe Hanley
Manager Media Relations France, Constance Bordes
Manager Media Relations India, Prashanth Balarama
Manager Media Relations Japan, Motoyuki Suzuki
Manager Media Relations Spain, Alfonso Gonzalez Herrero
VP Cloud Services, Ric Telford
Global and Americas Leader IBM Strategy and Change Consulting Group Global Business Services, Saul J. Berman
VP Technology, Nicholas S. (Nick) Bowen
VP Marketing and Sales Enablement Systems Software Systems and Technology Group, Inna Kuznetsova
Managing Partner Global Business Services North America, Marc B. Lautenbach
General Manager Global General Business, Steven C. Solazzo
General Manager System Storage and Networking Systems and Technology Group, Brian J. Truskowski
Program Manager WW Open Source Strategy and Business Development, Gerd Weishaar
Manager Media Relations Australia and New Zealand, Pip Arthur
Manager Media Relations Brazil, Fabiana Dos Santos Galetol
Manager Media Relations Central and Eastern Europe, Svetlana Stavreva
Manager Media Relations China, Teller Tang
Manager Media Relations Latin America, Carola Schaub
Manager Media Relations Middle East and Africa, Arlene Wainstein
Director External Communications North America, Clint Roswell
Director Media Relations Global Technology Services, Michael Moeller
Director Media Relations Software Group, Lori Bosio
VP and Treasurer, Robert DelBene
Manager Media Relations IBM Global Financing, John Simonds
Manager Media Relations Germany, Marie-Ann Maushart
VP External Relations Systems and Technology Group, Jeff Cross
SVP Global Business Services, Bridget A van Kralingen
SVP Growth Markets Unit, James (Jim) Bramante
Director, James W. (Jim) Owens, age 66
Director, David N. Farr, age 57
Director, Alain J. P. Belda, age 68
Director, Kenneth I. (Ken) Chenault, age 61
Director, Sidney Taurel, age 62
Director, William R. Brody, age 68
Director, Michael L. (Mike) Eskew, age 62
Director, Lorenzo H. Zambrano, age 69
President CEO and Director, Virginia M. (Ginni) Rometty, age 54
Director, Andrew N. Liveris, age 57
Director, W. James (Jim) McNerney Jr., age 62
Director, Shirley Ann Jackson, age 64
Director, Joan E. Spero, age 66
Auditors: PricewaterhouseCoopersLLP

LOCATIONS

HQ: International Business Machines Corporation
1 New Orchard Rd., Armonk NY 10504-1722
Phone: 914-499-1900 **Fax:** 800-314-1092
Web: www.ibm.com

2011 Sales

	$ mil.	% of total
Americas	44,944	42
Europe Middle East & Africa	33,952	32
Asia Pacific	25,273	24
Total	**106,916**	**100**

PRODUCTS/OPERATIONS

2011 Sales

	$ mil.	% of total
Global technology services	40,879	38
Software	24,944	23
Global business services	19,284	18
Systems & technology	18,895	18
Global financing	2,102	2
Other	722	1
Total	**106,916**	**100**

Selected Services

Business services
- Application management
- E-business
- Strategic consulting
- Systems integration

Financing

Technology services
- Business process outsourcing
- Infrastructure
- Maintenance
- Outsourcing
- Software integration
- Systems management
- Web hosting

Training

Selected Products

Microelectronics
- Application-specific integrated circuits (ASICs)
- Foundry services
- Memory chips
- Microprocessors and embedded processors
- Packaging and interconnect products and services

Printing systems

Servers

Software
- Application development
- Database and data management
- E-commerce
- Graphics and multimedia
- Groupware
- Networking and communication
- Operating systems
- Product life cycle management
- Security
- Speech recognition
- System management
- Transaction system
- Web application servers

Storage
- Hard drive systems
- Optical libraries
- Storage networking
- Tape drives systems and libraries

Selected Acquisitions

TRIRIGA (2011 real estate management software)
Netezza (2010 data storage and analysis devices)
BLADE Network Technologies (2010; network servers switches and software)
OpenPages (2010 financial risk and compliance management software)
Clarity Systems (2010 financial data management software)
PSS Systems (2010 legal software)
Unica (2010 enterprise marketing software)
Storwize (2010 data compression software)
Sterling Commerce (2010 business integration software)
Datacap (2010 document digitization and data management software)
Coremetrics (2010 Web analytics software)
BigFix (2010 corporate security software)
Lombardi (2010 business process management software)
SPSS (2009 enterprise data analysis software)
ILOG (2008 enterprise resource management software)
Telelogic (2008 embedded systems software)
Cognos (2008 business intelligence software)
Softek Storage Solutions (2007 storage management software)
NovusCG (2007 enterprise resource planning software)
DataMirror (2007 data integration software)
WebDialogs (2007 Web conferencing services)
Princeton Softech (2007 data management software)
Watchfire (2007 website management software)
Vallent (2007 network management software)
Consul Risk Management (2007 risk management software)

COMPETITORS

Accenture
Alcatel-Lucent
BMC Software
CA Inc.
Capgemini
Cisco Systems
Cognizant Tech Solutions
Computer Sciences Corp.
Dell
Deloitte Consulting
Deloitte Global Services
EMC
Epson
Ericsson
Fujitsu
GE
HCL Technologies
Hewlett-Packard
Hitachi
HP Enterprise Services
Infosys
Intel
Lexmark
Microsoft
Motorola Solutions
NEC
Novell
NTT DATA
Oracle
Panasonic Corp
Ricoh Company
SAP
Sony
Tata Consultancy
Texas Instruments
Toshiba
TSMC
Unisys
Wipro Technologies

HISTORICAL FINANCIALS

Company Type: Public

Income Statement

FYE: December 31

	REVENUE ($ mil.)	NET INCOME ($ mil.)	NET PROFIT MARGIN	EMPLOYEES
12/11	106,916	15,855	14.8%	433,362
12/10	99,870	14,833	14.9%	426,751
12/09	95,758	13,425	14.0%	437,776
12/08	103,630	12,334	11.9%	438,080
12/07	98,786	10,418	10.5%	426,969
Annual Growth	2.0%	11.1%	—	0.4%

2011 Year-End Financials

Debt ratio: 26.90%
Return on equity: 78.73%
Cash ($ mil.): 11,922
Current ratio: 120.90
Long-term debt ($ mil.): 22,857
No. of shares (mil.): 1,163
Dividends
Yield: —
Payout: 22.21%
Market value ($ mil.): 213,886

	STOCK PRICE ($) FY Close	P/E High/Low		PER SHARE ($) Earnings	Dividends	Book Value
12/11	183.88	15	11	13.06	0.00	17.31
12/10	146.76	13	10	11.52	2.50	18.77
12/09	130.90	13	8	10.01	2.15	17.34
12/08	84.16	14	8	8.93	1.90	10.06
12/07	108.10	16	12	7.18	1.50	20.55
Annual Growth	14.2%	—	—	16.1%	—	(4.2%)

International Lease Finance Corp.

John Travolta bought his own Boeing; if your company's cash flow is more limited International Lease Finance Corporation (ILFC) will lease you one. The company which leases the entire range of Boeing and Airbus commercial aircraft is the world's second-largest lessor of new aircraft and widebody carriers. It boasts of owning the world's most valuable fleet of leasable aircraft –about 930 planes. ILFC's airplane-parts management business maintains the aging aircraft in its fleet. Commercial airlines outside the US generate more than 95% of revenue; ILFC counts most of the world's airlines as customers. Parent AIG (American International Group) spun off ILFC's holding company ILFC Holdings as an IPO in 2011.

AIG formed ILFC Holdings in August 2011 and registered with the SEC less than two weeks later planning to raise $100 million in its initial public offering. AIG the insurance firm bailed out by the US government in 2009 had been selling off subsidiaries not related to its insurance business. AIG first tried to offload ILFC to raise much-needed funds in 2009 and failing that initiated an auction for the company.

An investor consortium backing ILFC founder and then-CEO Steven Udvar-Hazy emerged as the favored bidder for ILFC's aircraft portfolio. However wanting to avoid the burden of "undesirable assets" the federal government AIG's controlling stakeholder nixed parceling the fleet. Udvar-Hazy resigned as CEO in early 2010 to found another aircraft lessor Air Lease.

Australian investment bank Macquarie Group managed to do what Udvar-Hazy could not –it purchased 53 aircraft for $2 billion from ILFS in spring 2010. Throughout the year ILFC renegotiated some of its debt and managed to raise $14 billion in financing initiatives and aircraft sales along with $2.5 billion in revolving credit. ILFC also repaid a large loan to the Federal Reserve Bank of New York which it received through AIG's bailout. Nonetheless the company suffered a loss of more than $383 million in 2010 driven by unfavorable market conditions. Four of ILFC's lessees filed for bankruptcy protection or ceased operations in 2010.

Going forward ILFC is using its newly raised liquidity to expand its business. The company derives revenues from remarketing commercial jet aircraft (which is less costly for customers) and providing fleet management services. In mid-2011 it bought Miami-based AeroTurbine from The Netherlands-based AerCap Holdings for about $228 million. AeroTurbine leases and trades aircraft engines and buys and resells used airplane parts to commercial airlines and the aftermarket. By handling ILFC's older planes the acquisition allows ILFC to either maintain its fleet or sell its engines and other parts as spares. Meanwhile ILFC has signaled its plans to buy 115 new aircraft from Airbus and Boeing for approximately $13.5 billion with delivery through 2019.

ILFC's move comes as leadership steadies. Following Udvar-Hazy's retirement in early 2010 former president and long-time colleague of Udvar-Hazy John Plueger was tapped. He resigned as CEO the following month after Udvar-Hazy's bid for ILFC failed. AIG chose aviation banker and former Airbus CEO Henri Courpron to head the company. Courpron succeeds interim CEO Alan Lund (former ILFC CFO) who continued as president but then retired in spring 2011. Lund was replaced by CFO Fred Cromer who serves as both president and CFO.

Udvar-Hazy founded ILFC in 1973 with Air New Zealand as its first operating lease. AIG purchased the company in 1990.

EXECUTIVES

Chairman, Douglas M. (Doug) Steenland, age 60
SVP and Head of ILFC Asia Pacific, David Nixon
Vice Chairman, Alan H. Lund, $820,000 total compensation
CEO and Director, Henri Courpron, age 50
VP and CIO, Andrew Oh
SVP Treasurer and Assistant Secretary, Pamela S. Hendry
CFO, Elias Habayeb, age 40
Chief Investment Officer, Heinrich H. Loechteken, age 50
President, Fred S. Cromer
VP Contract Administration, Cathy Reid

SVP Chief Accounting Officer and Controller, Kurt H. Schwarz
VP Insurance and Risk Management, Patricia K. Cleary
VP Legal and Deputy General Counsel, Margaret L. Epstein
SVP Material Management and Aircraft Specifications, Terry S. Eastley
SVP Marketing, Joseph H. Hermosillo
VP Marketing and Special Operations, David Kingsley
SVP and Head of Aircraft Acquisitions and Sales, Martin T. Olson
SVP Technical Services, Richard G. Poutier
Chief Marketing Officer, Philip G. Scruggs, age 47
VP Marketing Head of Americas, Sean Sullivan
SVP Corporate Planning, Craig Segor
SVP and Head of ILFC Europe Middle East and Africa, Colin Bole
SVP Human Resources Communications and Employee Services, Maggie Williams
VP Flight Operations, Philippe J. Renault
VP Corporate Planning, Sergey Kulyagin
Director, William N. (Bill) Dooley, age 59
Director, Robert H. (Bob) Benmosche, age 67
Director, David L. Herzog, age 52
Vice Chairman, Alan H. Lund
CEO and Director, Henri Courpron, age 50
Director, Leslie L. Gonda
Auditors: PricewaterhouseCoopersLLP

LOCATIONS

HQ: International Lease Finance Corporation
10250 Constellation Blvd. Ste. 3400, Los Angeles CA 90067
Phone: 310-788-1999 **Fax:** 310-788-1990
Web: www.ilfc.com

2010 Sales

	$ mil.	% of total
Europe	2,103	45
Asia/Pacific	1,455	31
Central/South America & Mexico	585	12
Middle East & Africa	375	8
US & Canada	206	4
Total	**4,726**	**100**

PRODUCTS/OPERATIONS

Selected Plane Models

Airbus
- A300
- A320
- A330
- A340
- A350

Boeing
- 737
- 747
- 757
- 777

COMPETITORS

AAR Corp.
AerCap
AeroCentury
Air Lease Corp
Air Transport Services Group
Aircastle
ATEL Capital
Aviation Capital Group
Boeing Capital
Fly Leasing
GE Capital Aviation Services
ICON Capital
Jetscape
Willis Lease

HISTORICAL FINANCIALS

Company Type: Subsidiary

Income Statement FYE: December 31

	REVENUE ($ mil.)	NET INCOME ($ mil.)	NET PROFIT MARGIN	EMPLOYEES
12/11	4,526	(723)	—	497
12/10	4,798	(383)	—	194
12/09	5,321	895	16.8%	180
12/08	5,088	703	13.8%	180
12/07	4,729	604	12.8%	171
Annual Growth	(1.1%)	—	—	30.6%

2011 Year-End Financials

Debt ratio: 62.27%
Return on equity: (-9.61)%
Cash ($ mil.): 2,389
Current ratio: 79.43
Long-term debt ($ mil.): 24,384
No. of shares (mil.): 45
Dividends
Yield: —
Payout: —
Market value ($ mil.): —

	STOCK PRICE ($) FY Close	P/E High/Low		PER SHARE ($) Earnings	Dividends	Book Value
12/11	0.00	—	—	(0.00)	0.00	166.38
Annual Growth	—	—	—	—	—	—

International Paper Co.

For International Paper (IP) business is a global paper chase. It is one of the world's largest manufacturers of printing papers. Products include uncoated paper used in printers market pulp for making towels and tissues and coated paper and uncoated bristols (heavyweight art paper). In the US IP is #1 in containerboard production 70% of which is used in industrial corrugated boxes. A consumer packaging arm makes board to box cosmetics and food. IP's distribution unit xpedx sells products and supply chain services to multiple markets in North America. IP owns recycling plants mainly in the US and a pulp and paper business in Russia via a 50/50 venture with Ilim Holding.

HISTORY

In 1898 18 northeastern pulp and paper firms consolidated to lower costs. The resulting International Paper had 20 mills in Maine Massachusetts New Hampshire New York and Vermont. The mills relied on forests in New England and Canada for wood pulp. When Canada enacted legislation to stop the export of pulpwood in 1919 International Paper formed Canadian International Paper.

In the 1920s International Paper built a hydroelectric plant on the Hudson River. Between 1928 and 1941 the company called itself International Paper & Power. It entered the market for kraft paper (paper sacks) in 1925 with the purchase of Bastrop Pulp & Paper (Louisiana).

During the 1940s and 1950s the company bought Agar Manufacturing (shipping containers 1940) Single Service Containers (Pure-Pak milk containers 1946) and Lord Baltimore Press (folding cartons 1958). It diversified in the 1960s and 1970s buying Davol (hospital products 1968; sold to C. R. Bard 1980) American Central (land development 1968; sold to developers 1974) and General Crude Oil (gas and oil 1975; sold to Mobil Oil 1979).

In the 1980s International Paper modernized its plants to focus on less-cyclical products. After selling Canadian International Paper in 1981 the company bought Hammermill Paper (office paper 1986) Arvey (paper manufacturing and distribution 1987) and Masonite (composite wood products 1988). International Paper entered the European paper market in 1989 by buying Aussedat Rey (France) Ilford Group (UK) and Zanders (West Germany). In 1990 it bought Dixon Paper (distributor of paper and graphic arts supplies) Nevamar (laminates) and the UK's Cookson Group (printing plates).

International Paper expanded in the early 1990s with acquisitions such as Scaldia Papier (the Netherlands 1991) and Western Paper (1992) and through investments in Carter Holt Harvey (New Zealand) and Scitex (Israel) a leading maker of electronic prepress systems. In 1994 International Paper formed a Chinese packaging joint venture and bought two Mexican paper-distributing companies. The next year it bought Seaman-Patrick Paper and Carpenter Paper (paper distribution) Micarta (high-pressure laminates) and DSM (inks and adhesives resins). In 1996 it bought Federal Paper Board a forest- and paper-products firm.

After recording a loss in 1997 International Paper began downsizing: It sold $1 billion in marginal assets and cut its workforce by 10%. Branching its US box-making operations into the South and Midwest International Paper bought Weston Paper & Manufacturing in 1998; it also bought Mead's distribution business. Then the company announced that it would close 25 plants in the combined enterprise. It also sold xpedx's grocery-supply business to Bunzl in 1998.

To preserve competition in 1999 federal regulators axed International Paper's deal to sell its laminate business to Formica. However the company did sell Formica its Fountainhead solid-surfacing business. International Paper paid $7.9 billion in 1999 for rival Union Camp.

International Paper acquired Shorewood Packaging for $850 million in 2000. That year it made an unsolicited $6.2 billion bid for Champion International –which had previously agreed to be acquired by UPM-Kymmene –igniting a bidding war. UPM withdrew its offer however and International Paper acquired Champion for about $9.6 billion. Also in 2000 the company sold its 68% stake in Bush Boake Allen for about $640 million.

In 2001 International Paper sold its Masonite operations to Premdor for $500 million. The company also began cutting 10% (3000 jobs) of its US workforce as part of a restructuring program.

International Paper sold its orient strand board facilities to Nexfor in 2002 and also sold its decorative products division to an affiliate of Kohlberg & Company later that year. The company had planned to sell its Industrial Paper and Arizona Chemical businesses but failed to receive acceptable offers. International Paper closed its mill in Natchez Mississippi and exited the Chemical Cellulose pulp business in 2003. (The Natchez plant is the world's second-largest producer of acetate pulps.) Layoffs affected about 600 workers or 6% of International Paper's workforce.

The company experienced relatively stagnant growth in 2003 due to poor market conditions in the US where demand for paper and packaging products was down and average prices were weak.

In 2004 the company purchased Northbrook Illinois-based corrugated box maker Box USA Holdings Inc. for an undisclosed amount. Hurricane Ivan forced International Paper to close its

Pensacola Florida and southern Alabama operations.

At the close of 2004 International Paper sold more than 1 million acres of its Maine and New Hampshire forestlands to private forest investment management company GMO Renewable Resources LLC for roughly $250 million. It also completed the sale of its Weldwood of Canada Ltd. subsidiary to West Fraser Timber Co. Ltd. of Vancouver Canada for about $950 million (C$1.26 billion).

In 2005 International Paper sold its industrial papers business (lightweight packaging and pressure sensitive papers) to Kohlberg & Company for about $180 million and completed the sale of its fine papers business including its writing text and covers papers and artist papers segments to Mohawk Paper Mills Inc. for $60 million. The company also sold its 50.5% stake in Carter Holt Harvey for $1.14 billion in a deal that raised about $350 million in after-tax cash.

In 2006 International Paper began a campaign to divest its noncore assets. on the forestry front it sold 218000 acres of forest to The Nature Conservancy and the Conservation Fund for about $300 million. Soon thereafter it sold 4.2 million acres of forestland to an investor group led by Resource Management Service and another 900000 acres of forestland to an investor group led by TimberStar. Together the two deals brought International Paper more than $6 billion. In a separate deal International Paper sold 275000 acres of forestland in the Adirondacks to Lyme Timber Company for nearly $140 million.

It also divested several operational assets including its coated and supercalendared papers unit to Verso Paper an affiliate of investment firm Apollo Management for about $1.4 billion. It later sold its coated papers business in Brazil to Stora Enso for $420 million a deal including 50000 hectares (around 124000 acres) of forestland in Brazil's Parana state.

Near the end of 2006 International Paper announced three more big divestitures all of which were completed by April 2007. In the first deal the company sold its beverage packaging operations to Carter Holt Harvey for approximately $500 million. In the second deal the paper giant sold its Arizona Chemical subsidiary to Rhone Capital for about $485 million. Lastly IP sold five wood products plants to rival Georgia-Pacific for $237 million. The last deal involving mills in four states substantially closed out the company's wood products business.

In mid-2006 International Paper moved its headquarters to Memphis. Shortly thereafter the company announced a $3 billion stock buyback plan; $1.4 billion shares were purchased in the offer resulting in an 8% reduction in the number of the company's outstanding shares.

International Paper continued to massage its product offerings during 2007; It sold its kraft papers (strong papers used in bags and wrapping) business to Stone Arcade Acquisition for about $155 million in cash plus up to another $60 million that may be paid five years after the transaction closes. The deal included a kraft paper mill in North Carolina and a bag plant in Arkansas. IP also shed some $11 billion worth of its specialty (chemical) business.

The company followed with a joint-venture deal with Ilim Pulp through Ilim Holding. The company bought 50% of Ilim Holding for about $650 million. The JV Ilim Group will operate pulp and paper mills in the European and Siberian regions of Russia. The JV agreement calls for the partnering companies to invest around $1.5 billion over five years in Ilim Group's four mills.

In Brazil in 2007 IP exchanged an in-progress pulp mill project and certain forestland operations for Votorantim Celulose e Papel's (VCP) Luiz Antonio uncoated paper and pulp mill plus forestlands in the state of S?o Paulo.

The company was faced with hard choices after making a transformational albeit ill-timed decision that propelled the company to the top spot in the North American containerboard industry. On the cusp of the recession in 2008 it purchased the containerboard packaging and recycling business of rival Weyerhaeuser for $6 billion. The transaction was structured as an asset purchase with IP anticipating a tax benefit of about $1.4 billion on the deal. Despite the favorable tax implications the company financed almost half of the purchase by taking on additional debt something IP would have preferred to avoid. The new operations included 10 specialty packaging plants and four kraft bag and sack locations as well as 19 recycling facilities.

IP made one of its most significant acquisitions to date in 2012 when it acquired Temple-Inland one of North America's top producers of corrugated packaging in a transaction valued at $4.5 billion. IP first attempted a takeover of Temple-Inland in 2011 but was rebuffed.

EXECUTIVES

Chairman and CEO, John V. Faraci, age 62, $1,261,400 total compensation
SVP Corporate Development, C. Cato Ealy, age 55
SVP and CIO, John N. Balboni, age 63
SVP Container The Americas, William P. (Bill) Hoel
SVP; President IP Europe Middle East Africa and Russia, Maximo Pacheco, age 59
SVP and CFO, Carol L. Roberts, age 52, $541,700 total compensation
SVP Consumer Packaging and IP Asia, Thomas G. (Tom) Kadien, age 56
VP Environment Health Safety and Sustainability, David (Dave) Kiser
SVP; President xpedx, Mary A. Laschinger, age 51
Senior Communications Manager, Amy J. Sawyer
SVP Printing and Communications Papers the Americas, Timothy S. (Tim) Nicholls, age 51, $545,000 total compensation
VP and General Manager Containerboard and Recycling, Thomas A. Cleves, age 50
VP and Controller Finance, Terri L. Herrington, age 56
SVP Industrial Packaging, Mark S. Sutton, age 50
SVP Manufacturing Technology EHS&S and Global Sourcing, Tommy S. Joseph, age 52
SVP Human Resources and Communications, Paul J. Karre, age 59
Manager Investor Relations, Emily Nix
VP Commercial Printing, Teri Shanahan
SVP General Counsel and Corporate Secretary, Sharon R. Ryan, age 53
VP Investor Relations, Glenn Landau, age 43
Director, Stacey J. Mobley, age 67
Director, William G. (Bill) Walter, age 66
Director, David J. Bronczek, age 58
Director, Alberto Weisser, age 56
Director, J. Steven Whisler, age 57
Director, John F. Turner, age 70
Director, John L. Townsend III, age 56
Director, Joan E. Spero, age 66
Director, Ahmet C. Dorduncu
Auditors: Deloitte&ToucheLLP

LOCATIONS

HQ: International Paper Company
6400 Poplar Ave., Memphis TN 38197
Phone: 901-419-9000 **Fax:** 901-214-9682
Web: www.ipaper.com

2011 Sales

	$ mil.	% of total
Americas		
Other countries	1,610	6
Pacific Rim & Asia	1,807	7

PRODUCTS/OPERATIONS

2011 Sales

	$ mil.	% of total
Industrial packaging	10,376	40
Printing papers	5,510	21

Selected Operations and Products

Consumer Packaging
- Cold cups and lids
- Consumer-ready packaging (Shorewood Packaging folding carton set-up box)
- Folding carton board
- Food buckets and lids
- Hot cups and lids
- Milk container and lids
- Starcote tobacco board

Distribution North America (xpedx)
- Building services and away-from-home markets with facility supplies
- Commercial printers with printing papers and graphic pre-press printing presses post press equipment
- Manufacturers with packaging supplies and equipment
- Warehousing and delivery services

Industrial Packaging
- Automotive packaging
- Corrugated pallet
- Die-cut package
- Flapless
- Kraft linerboard
- Laminated bulk bin
- Liquid bulk
- Litho lamination
- Medium paper
- Retail displays
- Saturating kraft
- Slotted container
- White top liner

Papers
- HP (Hewlett-Packard) home and commercial papers
- Office papers

Pulp
- Fluff pulp
- Paper and tissue pulp

Recycling products
- Old corrugated containers and kraft corrugated cuttings
- Old newspaper

COMPETITORS

Alcoa
Amcor
Cascades Inc.
Domtar
ENCE
Environmental Mill & Supply
Georgia-Pacific
Louisiana-Pacific
M-real
MeadWestvaco
Mondi
Nippon Paper
Packaging Corp. of America
RockTenn CP
Smurfit Kappa
Stora Enso
UPM-Kymmene

HISTORICAL FINANCIALS

Company Type: Public

Income Statement FYE: December 31

	REVENUE ($ mil.)	NET INCOME ($ mil.)	NET PROFIT MARGIN	EMPLOYEES
12/11	26,034	1,341	5.2%	61,500
12/10	25,179	644	2.6%	59,500
12/09	23,366	663	2.8%	56,100
12/08	24,829	(1,282)	—	61,700
12/07	21,890	1,168	5.3%	51,500
Annual Growth	4.4%	3.5%	—	4.5%

2011 Year-End Financials

Debt ratio: 36.71%
Return on equity: 20.26%
Cash ($ mil.): 3,994
Current ratio: 220.68
Long-term debt ($ mil.): 9,189

No. of shares (mil.): 436
Dividends
Yield: —
Payout: 31.76%
Market value ($ mil.): 12,934

	STOCK PRICE ($) FY Close	P/E High/Low		PER SHARE ($) Earnings	Dividends	Book Value
12/11	29.60	11	7	3.07	0.00	15.15
12/10	27.24	19	13	1.48	0.40	15.62
12/09	26.78	18	3	1.55	0.33	13.90
12/08	11.80	—	—	(3.05)	1.00	9.75
12/07	32.38	15	12	2.70	1.00	20.40
Annual Growth	(2.2%)	—	—	3.3%	—	(7.2%)

Interpublic Group of Companies Inc.

Subsidiaries of this company come between brands and the general public. The Interpublic Group of Companies is one of the world's largest advertising and marketing services conglomerates operating through offices in more than 100 countries. Its flagship creative agencies include McCann Worldgroup DraftFCB and Lowe & Partners while such firms as Campbell-Ewald Deutsch and Hill Holliday are leaders in the US advertising business. Interpublic also offers direct marketing media services and public relations through such agencies as Initiative and Weber Shandwick. Its largest clients include General Motors Johnson & Johnson Microsoft and Unilever.

HISTORY

Standard Oil advertising executive Harrison McCann opened the H. K. McCann Company in 1911 and signed Standard Oil of New Jersey (later Exxon) as his first client. McCann's ad business boomed as the automobile became an integral part of American life. His firm merged with Alfred Erickson's agency (created 1902) in 1930 forming the McCann-Erickson Company. At the end of the decade the firm hired Marion Harper a top Yale graduate as a mailroom clerk. Harper became president in 1948.

Harper began acquiring other ad agencies and by 1961 controlled more than 20 companies. That year he unveiled a plan to create a holding company that would let the ad firms operate separately allowing them to work on accounts for competing products but giving them the parent firm's financial and information resources. He named the company Interpublic Inc. after a German research company owned by the former H. K. McCann Co. The conglomerate continued expanding and was renamed The Interpublic Group of Companies in 1964. Harper's management capabilities weren't up to the task however and the company soon faced bankruptcy. In 1967 the board replaced him with Robert Healy who saved Interpublic and returned it to profitability. The company went public in 1971.

The 1970s were fruitful years for Interpublic; its ad teams created memorable campaigns for Coke ("It's the Real Thing" and "Have a Coke and a Smile") and Miller Beer ("Miller Time" and Miller Lite ads). After Philip Geier became chairman in 1980 the company gained a stake in Lowe Howard-Spink (1983; it later became The Lowe Group) and bought Lintas International (1987). Interpublic bought the rest of The Lowe Group in 1990.

Interpublic bought Western International Media (now known as Initiative) and Ammirati & Puris (which was merged with Lintas to form Ammirati Puris Lintas) in 1994. As industry consolidation picked up in 1996 Interpublic kept pace with acquisitions of PR company Weber Group and Draft-Worldwide. Interpublic bought a majority stake in artist management and film production company Addis-Wechsler & Associates (now Industry Entertainment) in 1997 and later formed sports marketing and management group Octagon.

Interpublic acquired US agencies Carmichael Lynch and Hill Holliday Connors Cosmopulos in 1998. It also boosted its PR presence with its purchase of International Public Relations (UK) the parent company of public relations networks Shandwick and Golin/Harris. Interpublic strengthened its position in the online world in 1999 when it bought 20% of Stockholm-based Internet services company Icon Medialab International. That year the company merged agencies Ammirati and Lowe & Partners Worldwide to form Lowe Lintas & Partners Worldwide (in 2002 they changed the name to just Lowe & Partners Worldwide).

Interpublic bought market research firm NFO Worldwide for $580 million in 2000 and merged Weber Public Relations with Shandwick International to form Weber Shandwick Worldwide one of the world's largest PR firms. Later that year the company bought ad agency Deutsch for about $250 million. John Dooner took the position of chairman and CEO at the end of the year after Geier resigned. His first move proved a big one: Interpublic acquired True North Communications for $2.1 billion in stock in 2001.

The honeymoon was short lived; facing a recession the mounting debt from its buying spree and with the revelation of accounting discrepancies at McCann-Erickson WorldGroup (renamed McCann Worldgroup in 2004) Dooner stepped aside as chairman and CEO in 2003. Interpublic chose vice chairman David Bell (former CEO of True North) as Dooner's replacement. After almost two years of work to improve Interpublic's balance sheet Bell was replaced by former MONY Group chief Michael Roth.

In 2005 Roth was tasked with straightening out Interpublic's financial controls and improving its balance sheet. Later that year the company revealed extensive bookkeeping problems primarily in its overseas operations leading to a financial restatement going back to 2000.

In order to simplify its operating structure in 2006 Interpublic integrated direct marketer Draft Inc. with advertising agency Foote Cone & Belding (forming DraftFCB). A year later it restructured its vast network of media brands to report under a single management structure (Mediabrands).

Looking to India in mid-2007 Interpublic bought all the shares of FCB Ulka a top-five ad agency in the country that operated from six offices. Interpublic integrated the Indian agency with its DraftFCB operations. At the same time it acquired the remaining 51% stake it didn't hold in Lintas India Private Limited at a cost of $50 million in cash and integrated it into its Lowe Worldwide network.

In 2010 Interpublic acquired Brazilian creative advertising strategy firm CUBOCC and London-based marketing agency Delaney Lund Knox Warren & Partners (DLKW). During 2011 the company acquired several marketing agencies. In early 2012 Interpublic obtained German consumer lifestyle agency Nicole Weber Communications (NWC) and UK-based digital and interactive agency FUSE.

EXECUTIVES

CEO ICC Lowe, Steve Viviano
CEO McCann Healthcare Worldwide, John Cahill
SVP and Managing Director, Terry D. Peigh
CEO Weber Shandwick, Harris Diamond, age 59
EVP Emeritus, Barry R. Linsky, $380,000 total compensation
SVP General Counsel and Secretary, Nicholas J. (Nick) Camera, age 65, $361,250 total compensation
Chairman and CEO, Michael I. Roth, age 66, $1,400,000 total compensation
EVP and CFO, Frank Mergenthaler, age 51, $900,000 total compensation
President and CEO Octagon, Rick Dudley, age 63
Chairman and CEO ID Media, Lynn Fantom
CEO and Area Director McCann Worldgroup Greater China, T.H. Peng
Chairman Deutsch, Donny J. Deutsch, age 54
CEO Deutsch North America, Linda Sawyer, age 51
CEO Deutsch NY, Val DiFebo, age 50
SVP Investor Relations, Jerome J. (Jerry) Leshne
CEO Deutsch LA, Mike Sheldon, age 53
Executive Chairman DraftFCB, Howard Draft, age 59
Chairman and CEO Jack Morton Worldwide, Josh McCall
Chairman and CEO McCann Worldgroup, Nick Brien
Co-Chairman and Co-CEO PMK-BNC, Michael Nyman
EVP Chief Strategy and Talent Officer, Philippe Krakowsky, age 49, $670,000 total compensation
President and CEO Translation, Steve Stoute
SVP and CIO, Joseph W. (Joe) Farrelly, age 67
President and CEO Casanova Pendrill, Ingrid Otero-Smart, age 53
Executive Chairman and CEO Cassidy & Associates, Gerald S. J. Cassidy
President and CEO DraftFCB, Laurence J. Boschetto
Chairman and CEO Momentum Worldwide, Chris Weil
Chairman and CEO Campbell-Ewald, William J. (Bill) Ludwig
Chairman and CEO The Martin Agency, John B. Adams Jr.
Chairman and CEO IW Group, Bill Imada
Global CEO Universal McCann (UM), Jacki Kelley, age 46
Chairman and CEO Avrett Free Ginsberg, Frank Ginsberg
President and CEO Hacker Group, Spyro Kourtis
SVP Business Development, David I. Weiss
President Weber Shandwick Worldwide, Andy Polansky
CEO Campbell Mithun, Steve Wehrenberg
CEO DeVries Public Relations, Jim Allman
President Dailey & Associates Advertising, Tom Lehr
SVP and Treasurer, Ellen T. Johnson
CEO Lowe & Partners Worldwide, Michael Wall
SVP Leadership and Organizational Development, Frank Guglielmo
CEO FutureBrand, Patrick Smith
SVP Controller and Chief Accounting Officer, Christopher F. Carroll, age 45
CEO MRM Worldwide & Worldgroup EXP, Marc Landsberg

President DeVries Public Relations, Stephanie Smirnov
Managing Partner IPG Media Lab, Brian Monahan
President and CEO Tierney Communications, Mary Stengel Austen
President and CEO GolinHarris, Fred Cook
SVP and Global Director Talent, Beverly Popielarz
President and CEO Fitzgerald+CO, Dave Fitzgerald
President and CEO DraftFCB Healthcare, Dana Maiman
President MAGNAGLOBAL, Elizabeth Herbst-Brady
SVP Corporate Services, Richard J. Haray
Worldwide CEO Initiative, Richard Beaven
SVP and Managing Director, Peter Leinroth
Co-Chairman and Co-CEO PMK-BNC, Cindi Berger
President TM Advertising, Becca Weigman
SVP and Chief Diversity and Inclusion Officer, Heide Gardner
President McCann Worldgroup Europe, Gustavo Martinez
SVP Global Taxation, Anthony G. (Tony) Alexandrou
President The Axis Agency, Armando Azarloza
President Carmichael Lynch Spong, Doug Spong
President Current Lifestyle Marketing, Virginia Devlin, age 44
President and CEO ORION Trading, Brian T. McMahon
Chairman CEO and Global Creative Officer R/GA, Bob Greenberg
Managing Partner Regan Campbell Ward, Maureen C. (Mo) Regan
President Cassidy & Associates, Barry Rhoads
Chairman and CEO SIBONEYUSA, Jose M. Cubas
Executive Chairman and CEO McCann Worldgroup India, Prasoon Joshi
Co-CEO PMK-BNC, Chris Robichaud
SVP Audit and Chief Risk Officer, Julie M. Connors, age 40
VP Corporate Communications, Tom Cunningham
Managing Director ipm, Chris Marjoram
President and Managing Partner Accentmarketing, Lisette Hoyo
EVP Creative Director and Managing Partner Accentmarketing, Diana Ocasio-Fant
SVP and Account Group Director Accentmarketing, Alice Rivera
Director Media Services, Claudia A. Varela
SVP Account Group Director ? Promotions and Public Relations Accentmarketing, Vickie Gaston
CEO Ansible, Angela Steele
CEO Hill Holliday, Mike Sheehan
President Jay Advertising, Gregory W. Smith
CEO KRC Research, Bradley Honan
President KRC Research, Jennifer Sosin
President and CEO MacLaren McCann, Doug Turney
Chairman and CEO Marketel, Jacques Duval
President The Martin Agency, Mike Hughes
SVP and Managing Director Media Partnership Corp., Matt Thornbrough
SVP and Managing Director MedRageous, Hudson Plumb
Chairman and CFO NAS Recruitment Communications, Jim Miller
Managing Director NeOn, Matt Lane
President Reprise Media U.S., John Anagnost
President and COO Wahlstrom, Chris Hiland
SVP and Global Director Talent, Marge Hoey
Director, Richard A. Goldstein, age 70
Director, William T. (Bill) Kerr, age 70
Director, David M. Thomas, age 63
Director, H. John Greeniaus, age 67
Director, Jill M. Considine, age 67
Director, Reginald K. Brack, age 74
Director, Jocelyn E. Carter-Miller, age 54
Director, Mary J. Steele Steele Guilfoile, age 57
Auditors: PricewaterhouseCoopersLLP

LOCATIONS

HQ: The Interpublic Group of Companies Inc.
1114 Avenue of the Americas, New York NY 10036
Phone: 212-704-1200 **Fax:** 212-704-1201
Web: www.interpublic.com

2012 Sales

	% of total
US	55
Europe	
UK	8
Other	12
Asia	12
Latin	6
Other	7
Total	**100**

PRODUCTS/OPERATIONS

Selected Mergers and Acquisitions

FY2012
Nicole Weber Communications (undisclosed price; Hamburg Germany; consumer lifestyle agency)
FUSE (undisclosed price; London UK; digital and interactive agency)

Selected Operations

Advertising and marketing services
- Advertising agencies
  - Austin-Kelly
  - Avrett Free Ginsberg
  - Campbell-Ewald
  - Campbell Mithun
  - Carmichael Lynch
  - Dailey & Associates
  - Deutsch
  - Gotham
  - Hill Holiday
  - Jay Advertising
  - Lowe & Partners (UK)
  - The Martin Agency
  - McCann Erickson Worldwide
  - Mullen
  - Tierney Communications
  - TM Advertising
- Marketing agencies
  - DraftFCB
  - The Hacker Group
  - MRM Partners
  - Momentum
  - Rivet
  - Translation Consulting + Brand Imaging
- Media services
  - Initiative Media
  - MAGNA Global
  - Universal McCann

Public relations and corporate communications
- DeVries Public Relations
- MWW Group
- Weber Shandwick

COMPETITORS

Aegis Group
Dentsu
Hakuhodo
Havas
Omnicom
Publicis Groupe
WPP

HISTORICAL FINANCIALS

Company Type: Public

Income Statement FYE: December 31

	REVENUE ($ mil.)	NET INCOME ($ mil.)	NET PROFIT MARGIN	EMPLOYEES
12/11	7,014	532	7.6%	42,000
12/10	6,531	261	4.0%	41,000
12/09	6,027	121	2.0%	40,000
12/08	6,962	295	4.2%	45,000
12/07	6,554	167	2.6%	43,000
Annual Growth	1.7%	33.5%	—	(0.6%)

2011 Year-End Financials

Debt ratio: 13.74%
Return on equity: 21.62%
Cash ($ mil.): 2,302
Current ratio: 103.16
Long-term debt ($ mil.): 1,210
No. of shares (mil.): 449
Dividends
Yield: —
Payout: 24.24%
Market value ($ mil.): 4,374

	STOCK PRICE ($) FY Close	P/E High	P/E Low	PER SHARE ($) Earnings	Dividends	Book Value
12/11	9.73	12	6	0.99	0.00	5.48
12/10	10.62	19	11	0.47	0.00	5.17
12/09	7.38	38	16	0.19	0.00	5.14
12/08	3.96	18	5	0.52	0.00	5.19
12/07	8.11	48	28	0.26	0.00	4.95
Annual Growth	4.7%	—	—	39.7%	—	2.6%

INTL FCStone Inc.

Going global is the name of the game for securities broker INTL FCStone and its subsidiaries. The company specializes in niche international markets offering commodity risk management consulting and international securities. It offers clearing and execution services of listed futures and options on futures. Its INTL Trading subsidiary is a wholesale market-maker for some 800 foreign securities. The company also offers asset management and commodity financing and facilitation. INTL FCStone serves financial institutions corporations charitable organizations and other institutional investors in the US and abroad.

INTL FCStone serves more than 20000 customers in about 100 countries around the world. The company operates through a network of 30 offices in the US Canada Paraguay Uruguay Argentina Brazil UK Ireland China Singapore Arab Emirates and Australia.

INTL FCStone reported a 57% increase in operating revenue in 2011 (the financial gauge measures income from the company's everday business operations). That increase was attributed to a spike in operating revenues in the company's consulting and risk management segment which benefited from increase in trade volumes higher global demand and an expanded customer base.

INTL FCStone is focused on broadening its customer base in new markets by offering more services. The company is zeroing in on midsized commercial entities as many are relatively underserved and seeking risk management in the wake of the worldwide financial crisis. Key growth areas for INTL FCStone include Latin America Canada Asia Europe and Australia.

Acquisitions play a big part in INTL FCStone's growth strategy. In the past several years the company has bought other firms that have helped broaden its geographic reach and service capabilities. In 2011 INTL FCStone acquired Ambrian Commodities Limited a London metals exchange from Ambrian Capital. Ambrian Commodities joined INTL FCStone's subsidiary INTL Global Currencies. The deal helped the firm build its capabilities in Europe. Also that year INTL FCStone agreed to acquire the metals division of bankrupt MF Global. The division has staff in Hong Kong London New York and Sydney. In 2012 the company bought UK brokerage and clearing firm TRX Futures which targets coffee and cocoa customers as well as the energy and financial industries.

INTL FCStone which traces its roots to 1924 was created after the 2009 merger of FCStone Group and International Assets Holding.

EXECUTIVES

CEO and Director, Sean M. O'Connor, age 49, $175,000 total compensation
COO and Director, Scott J. Branch, age 49, $175,000 total compensation
President and Director, Paul G. (Pete) Anderson, age 59
Secretary and Corporate Counsel, David A. Bolte
VP and Global Head Compliance, Nancey M. McMurtry, age 64, $125,000 total compensation
Chief Legal and Governance Officer, Brian T. Sephton, age 54, $135,000 total compensation
Chairman, Jack Friedman, age 55
CFO, William J. (Bill) Dunaway, age 41
Manager Information Technology, Jorge Hierro
Group Controller, James W. Tivy, age 44, $120,000 total compensation
President FCStone, Pete Nessler
Head Brazilian Operations, Fabio Solferini
VP and Risk Management Consultant FCStone Canada ULC, Frank Kelton
VP and Head Food Service, Robert (Rob) Chesler
Managing Director Global Soft Commodities, Oscar Schaps
Director, Diego J. Veitia, age 68
Director, Robert A. Miller, age 69
CEO and Director, Sean M. O'Connor, age 49
COO and Director, Scott J. Branch, age 49
Director, John Radziwill, age 64
President and Director, Paul G. (Pete) Anderson, age 59
Director, Brent Bunte, age 55
Director, Justin R. Wheeler, age 40
Director, John M. Fowler, age 62
Director, Bruce Kriebiel, age 59
Director, Eric Parthemore, age 63
Director, Daryl K. Henze, age 68
Auditors: KPMGLLP

LOCATIONS

HQ: INTL FCStone Inc.
708 3rd Ave. Ste. 1500, New York NY 10017
Phone: 212-485-3500 **Fax:** 212-485-3505
Web: www.intlfcstone.com

PRODUCTS/OPERATIONS

2011 Sales

	$ mil.	% of total
Sale of physical commodities	75,123	100
Trading gains	205	-
Commission and clearing fees	134	-
Other	34	-
Total	**75,497**	**100**

2011 Sales

	$ mil.	% of total
Commodity and risk management services	75,274	100
Foreign Exchange	59	-
Securities	30	-
Clearing and execution services	66	-
Other	67	-
Total	**75,497**	**100**

Selected Subsidiaries

Blackthorn Mult-Advisor Fund LP
FCC Futures Inc.
FCC Investments Inc.
FCStone Advisory Inc.
FCStone Asia Pte. Ltd.
FCStone Australia Pty Ltd.
FCStone Canada ULC
FCStone Carbon LLC
FCStone Commodities Services (Europe) Ltd.
FCStone do Brazil Ltda.
FCStone Financial Inc.
FCStone Forex LLC
FCStone Group
FCStone Information LLC
FCStone International LLC
FCStone Investments Inc.
FCStone Merchant Services LLC
FCStone Paraguary S.R.L.
FCStone LLC
Gainvest Asset Management Ltd.
Gainvest S.A. Sociedad Gerente de Fondos Comunes de Inversion
Gainvest Uruguay Asset Management S.A.
Gletir S.A.
Hanley Alternative Trade Group LLC
HGC Advisory Services LLC
HGC Asset Management LLC
HGC Office Services LLC
HGC Trading LLC
IAHC Bermuda Ltd
INTL Asia Pte. Ltd
INTL Capital and Treasury Global Services Ltd. (Nigeria)
INTL Capital Limited (Dubai UAE)
INTL Capital S.A. (Argentina)
INTL CIBSA Sociedad de Bolsa S.A.
INTL Colombia Ltda.
INTL Commodities DMCC
INTL Commodities Inc.
INTL Commodities Mexico S de RL de CV
INTL FCStone Commodities Inc.
INTL FCStone (Europe) Ltd.
INTL FCStone (Netherlands) B.V.
INTL FCStone SA
INTL Gainvest Capital Assessoria Financeira Ltda. (formerly Gainvest do Brasil Ltda.).
INTL Global Currencies Ltd.
INTL Hanley LLC
INTL Hencorp Futures LLC
INTL Holding (U.K.) Limited
INTL Netherlands B.V.
INTL Participacoes Ltda.
INTL Provident Inc.
INTL Sieramet LLC
INTL Trading Inc.
INTL Universal Commercial (Shanghai) Co. Ltd.
Risk Management Incorporated
RMI Consulting Inc.
Westown Commodities LLC

Selected Mergers & Acquisitions

2012
TRX Futures Limited (London UK; brokerage and clearing)
2011
Coffee Network (online news and analysis portal)
Ambrian Commodities Limited (London UK; London Metals Exchange brokerage)
2010
Hencorp Becstone Futures (Miami Florida; (commodity risk management)
Provident Group (New York; investment bank)
Hanley Group Capital (Chicago; risk management)
Risk Management Incorporated/ RMI Consulting Inc. (Chicago; price-risk and credit-risk management)
2009
FCStone group ($130 million Kansas City: execution and advisory services)

COMPETITORS

CAPIS
Citigroup Global Markets
Credit Suisse (USA)
Goldman Sachs
ICAP
Interactive Brokers
J.P. Morgan Clearing
MF Global
Morgan Stanley
Newedge
Rosenthal Collins
Susquehanna International Group LLP

HISTORICAL FINANCIALS

Company Type: Public

Income Statement FYE: September 30

	REVENUE ($ mil.)	NET INCOME ($ mil.)	NET PROFIT MARGIN	EMPLOYEES
09/12	69,249	15	0.0%	1,074
09/11	75,486	37	0.0%	904
09/10	46,930	5	0.0%	729
09/09	43,596	27	0.1%	625
09/08	18,347	27	0.2%	195
Annual Growth	39.4%	(14.3%)	—	53.2%

2012 Year-End Financials

Debt ratio: 7.37%
Return on equity: 4.70%
Cash ($ mil.): 236
Current ratio: 96.51
Long-term debt ($ mil.): —
No. of shares (mil.): 18
Dividends
Yield: —
Payout: —
Market value ($ mil.): 362

	STOCK PRICE ($) FY Close	P/E High	P/E Low	PER SHARE ($) Earnings	Dividends	Book Value
09/12	19.06	35	23	0.75	0.00	16.81
09/11	20.76	13	9	1.96	0.00	15.89
09/10	18.10	64	46	0.30	0.00	13.71
09/09	16.51	8	2	2.80	0.00	13.76
09/08	24.11	11	6	2.95	0.00	8.38
Annual Growth	(5.7%)	—	—	(29.0%)	—	19.0%

Intuit Inc

Intuit knows that good accounting takes more than a pocket calculator. The company is a leading developer of software used to manage personal finances (Quicken) small business accounting (QuickBooks) and consumer tax preparation (TurboTax). Customers include consumers accountants and small businesses; Intuit claims more than 50 million users for its products and services. Other software offerings include industry-specific accounting and management applications for construction health care and retail organizations. Intuit also provides payroll services financial supplies and software for professional tax preparation as well as products and services geared for financial institutions.

ersIntuit believes the ease of use of its products give it a competitive edge over rivals especially for its consumer-oriented offerings such as TurboTax and QuickBooks which account for the majority of sales. The ubiquity of its products in prominent retail locations also gives the company an edge in the consumer space that competitors such as H&R Block Sage and Microsoft struggle to match.

Most of the company's sales are made in the US but it has key international offices and facilities in Canada the United Kingdom and India. Its presence in the Asia Pacific region comprises offices in Hong Kong Singapore Sydney and Tokyo.

Intuit's sales and net income continued their upward march in 2012 with total revenue reaching $4.1 billion (representing a 10% increase over the previous year) and profits rising to $792 million; the company's profit margin was 19% for the year. The company attributed growth largely to its small business division although its other product segments including financial management employee management and payment solutions also reported sales growth. Operating costs were higher for the year in part due to expenses associate with staffing and compensation.

The company's strategy is focused on ensuring that Intuit products and services are all accessible online and can be accessed via desktops laptops and mobile devices as well as through social communities such as online forums and social media sites.

Acquisitions in recent years have supported this effort including the 2011 purchase of the mobile Web banking technology assets of Mobile Money Ventures (MMV). MMV's technology was used by about 400000 consumers to access banking services from mobile devices.

The company has also used acquisitions to expand further beyond the consumer finance and accounting markets adding products for small and midsized businesses and industry-specific accounting and health care applications among others. In 2010 Intuit purchased Medfusion for $91 million in cash. Medfusion provides software tools and services that improve communication between patients and health care providers including applications for patients to schedule appointments access patient information online and to settle and track health care expenses. Shortly after buying Medfusion the company formed a new division Intuit Health that combined Medfusion and Quicken Health Group.

In 2012 the company paid $423.5 million in cash to buy San Francisco-based Demandforce a provider of hosted software used to automate marketing and customer communications. The acquisition furthered Intuit's expansion into software-as-a-service (SaaS) products for small and midsized businesses to address demand among many companies for cloud-based software delivery. Demandforce's e-mail mobile and social tools are used in such industries as automotive and health care.

HISTORY

After earning his MBA from Harvard founder Scott Cook spent three years in marketing at Procter & Gamble and four years with consultancy Bain & Company before establishing Intuit in 1983. Research showed that consumers wanted an easy-to-use personal finance software package. Quicken was introduced in 1984.

Intuit was near collapse in 1986 when it received its first big order from software retailer Egghead.com. Intuit released QuickBooks in 1992 and went public in 1993. The next year it acquired a number of firms including tax preparation software developer ChipSoft which brought TurboTax onboard.

In 1995 Microsoft's $2 billion bid to buy Intuit was halted by a Justice Department antitrust lawsuit. Also that year Intuit launched an online banking service and forged its first ties with the Web by bundling a browser and free Internet access with Quicken. It sold its online banking and bill presentation business to CheckFree in 1997. In 1998 the company bought Lacerte Software a provider of software and services to tax professionals.

In 1999 Intuit bought Computing Resources which had been providing the company's online payroll services for about $200 million. The company also purchased Rock Financial an online consumer mortgage company for about $370 million and renamed it Quicken Loans.

Stephen Bennett a former GE Financial Services executive became CEO in 2000. Later that year Intuit sold its QuickenInsurance business to InsWeb an online insurance service. Intuit also bought small business services provider EmployeeMatters for $39 million in stock from FrontLine Capital Group.

Moving to boost its small business offerings in 2001 the company expanded its QuickBooks software to include industry-specific versions designed for retailers and accountants and it acquired OMware a provider of business management software for the construction industry.

In 2002 it completed a string of acquisitions purchasing American Fundware (public-sector accounting software) Management Reports (property management software) Eclipse (business management software) CBS Payroll (outsourced payroll services) and Blue Ocean Software (information technology asset management software).

In 2002 the company sold its Quicken Loans mortgage operation followed by the sale of its wholly owned Japanese subsidiary Intuit KK in 2003. Intuit continued to pare down its product line over the next few years in order to focus on its core products selling its Intuit Public Sector Solutions and Intuit Information Technology Solutions businesses in 2005 its Master Builder operations in 2006 and its Distribution Management Solutions business in 2008.

Deals in 2007-2008 included the acquisitions of online banking software provider Digital Insight for about $1.35 billion and e-commerce and website software maker Homestead Technologies for about $170 million.

Acquisitions to further a push into the health care industry included the 2009 purchase of PayCycle (online payroll services) for $170 million as well as the 2008 purchase of Electronic Clearing House (ECHO) a provider of transaction processing services for about $131 million. Also in 2009 Intuit acquired Mint.com for about $170 million; the deal boosted Intuit's Web-based personal finance offerings and added a well-known consumer brand to its product catalog.

In 2010 the company sold Intuit Real Estate Solutions (IRES) (formerly called Management Reports International) to Vista Equity Partners for about $128 million in cash. Although the business had more than 1700 customers Intuit stated that it was no longer a strategic long-term fit for the company as part of the Connected Services strategy. IRES was renamed MRI Software LLC.

EXECUTIVES

SVP Sales, Caroline F. Donahue, age 49
VP Learning and Development, Brooks Fisher
SVP Payment Initiatives, Eric C.W. Dunn, age 54
Chairman, William V. (Bill) Campbell, age 71
VP Human Resources, Jennifer Jones Hall, age 48
VP Corporate Affairs, Bernard F. (Bernie) McKay
VP Consumer Advocacy, Robert (Bob) Meighan
SVP and General Manager Accounting Professionals Division, Jill A. Ward, age 52
Founder Chairman Executive Committee and Director, Scott D. Cook, age 59, $499,039 total compensation
SVP and Chief Human Resources Officer, Sherry Whiteley
SVP and Chief Innovation Officer, Per-Kristian (Kris) Halvorsen, age 60
EVP and General Manager Small Business Group, Kiran M. Patel, age 64, $700,000 total compensation
SVP Big Data Social Design and Marketing, Nora M. Denzel, age 49
VP Human Resources, Jim Grenier
SVP General Manager Employee Management Solutions, Ginny T. Lee
VP Innovation, Roy Rosin
Senior Manager Product Communications Accountant Products, Rich Walker
VP Shared Development and Services Technology Group, Miles Lewitt
VP Procurement, Scott Beth
VP and General Manager Global Tax, Rick W. Jensen, age 53
VP Quickbase, Allison Mnookin
VP Marketing QuickBooks Group, Ken Wach
President CEO and Director, Brad D. Smith, age 48, $800,000 total compensation
SVP General Counsel and Corporate Secretary, Laura A. Fennell, age 51
SVP and CIO, Sasan K. Goodarzi, age 44
Chief Communications Officer and Marketing Leader, Harry Pforzheimer
VP; General Manager Intuit Financial Services, CeCe Morken, age 53
SVP and CFO, R. Neil Williams, age 58, $600,000 total compensation
Senior Manager Corporate Public Relations, Diane Carlini
President Global Business Division, Alexander M. (Alex) Lintner, age 50, $585,000 total compensation
Manager Corporate Public Relations, Holly Perez
VP Marketing Small Business, Rob Lips
VP Finance Global, David Merenbach
VP and Corporate Controller, Jeffrey P. (Jeff) Hank, age 52
SVP and CTO, Tayloe Stansbury
SVP and General Manager Consumer Group, Daniel R. (Dan) Maurer, age 56
Managing Director India, Umang Bedi
VP New Market Development Global, Lindsey Argalas
VP Corporate Public Relations, Rob Lanesey
Group Product Manager Quicken, Jim Del Favero
Senior Manager Product Communications Intuit Canada, Cheryll Watson
VP and General Manager Consumer, Todd Stanley
Director Marketing Intuit Payroll, Cameron Schmidt
Senior Marketing Manager Product Communications Intuit Real Estate Solutions, Therese Susalla
Director Product Communications, Chris Repetto
Director Product Communications, Julie Miller
Director Product Communications, Heather McLellan
Manager Industry Analyst Relations, Allyson Casey
President and General Manager Intuit Health Group, Steve Malik
Manager Industry Analyst Relations Financial Institutions, Tobin Lee
Director, Diane B. Greene, age 57
Founder Chairman Executive Committee and Director, Scott D. Cook, age 59
Director, Christopher W. (Chris) Brody, age 67
Director, Dennis D. Powell, age 63
Director, Edward A. (Ed) Kangas, age 68
President CEO and Director, Brad D. Smith, age 48
Director, David H. Batchelder, age 62
Director, Suzanne Nora Johnson, age 54
Auditors: Ernst&YoungLLP

LOCATIONS

HQ: Intuit Inc.
2700 Coast Ave., Mountain View CA 94043
Phone: 650-944-6000 **Fax:** 401-884-4773
Web: www.amtrol.com

PRODUCTS/OPERATIONS

2012 Sales

	$ mil.	% of total
Consumer tax	1,441	35

Financial management	691	17
Employee management	512	12
Accounting professionals	423	10
Payment	417	10
Financial services	362	9
Other	305	7
Total	**4,151**	**100**

COMPETITORS

ADP
Bank of America
CA Inc.
CCH Incorporated
Deluxe Corporation
Elavon
Fidelity National Information Services
First Data
Fiserv
Global Payments
H&R Block
Jack Henry
Jackson Hewitt
JPMorgan Chase
Microsoft Dynamics
MYOB
NetSuite
Online Resources
Paychex
Sage Group
SAP
Sybase
Thomson Reuters
Universal Tax
Wells Fargo

HISTORICAL FINANCIALS

Company Type: Public

Income Statement FYE: July 31

	REVENUE ($ mil.)	NET INCOME ($ mil.)	NET PROFIT MARGIN	EMPLOYEES
07/12	4,151	792	19.1%	8,500
07/11	3,851	634	16.5%	8,000
07/10	3,455	574	16.6%	7,700
07/09	3,182	447	14.0%	7,800
07/08	3,070	476	15.5%	8,200
Annual Growth	7.8%	13.5%	—	0.9%

2012 Year-End Financials

Debt ratio: 10.65%
Return on equity: 28.86%
Cash ($ mil.): 393
Current ratio: 120.40
Long-term debt ($ mil.): 499
No. of shares (mil.): 295
Dividends
Yield: 1.03%
Payout: 23.08%
Market value ($ mil.): 17,133

	STOCK PRICE ($) FY Close	P/E High	P/E Low	PER SHARE ($) Earnings	Dividends	Book Value
07/12	58.02	23	15	2.60	0.60	9.29
07/11	46.70	27	19	2.00	0.00	8.70
07/10	39.75	22	15	1.77	0.00	8.99
07/09	29.70	23	15	1.35	0.00	7.92
07/08	27.33	23	18	1.41	0.00	6.43
Annual Growth	20.7%	—	—	16.5%	—	9.6%

Investors Bancorp Inc

Investors Bancorp is the holding company for Investors Savings Bank which serves New Jersey and New York from more than 85 branch offices. Founded in 1926 the bank offers such standard deposit products as savings and checking accounts CDs money market accounts and IRAs. Over the past few years Investors Savings Bank has increasingly focused on commercial lending; its residential mortgages have gone from more than 90% to around 60% of the bank's total loan portfolio. Other offerings include commercial mortgages multifamily loans and construction loans.

Investors Bancorp has been growing through acquisitions and by opening new branches. In 2012 it announced plans to acquire Marathon Banking Corporation (a subsidiary of Greece-based Piraeus Bank) for $135 million. The deal will add 13 branches in the New York metro area –more than doubling its branches in New York. The deal also will mark Investors Bancorp's entry into Manhattan and Staten Island.

In 2011 Investors acquired Brooklyn Federal Bancorp a deal that added five branches in Brooklyn and Long Island New York. The company has focused on expanding its geographic footprint since it entered New York in 2010 through its purchase of Millennium Bank which had 17 branches in New Jersey New York and Massachusetts. (It sold the four Massachusetts locations to Rhode Island-based Domestic Bank after the deal closed.)

The company's growth has helped it improve income and grow deposits. Sales grew by 10% in 2011 pushing that figure to half a billion. Net income also improved that year by more than 27%. Investors Bancorp's level of nonperforming loans has remained low as it sticks to conservative lending standards. The company's funding costs also have been low thanks to favorable interest rates.

Mutual holding company Investors Bancorp MHC owns a majority of Investors Bancorp's stock.

EXECUTIVES

Chairman, Robert M. Cashill, age 69, $960,000 total compensation
SEVP COO and Director, Domenick A. Cama, age 56, $437,500 total compensation
President CEO and Director, Kevin Cummings, age 57, $703,766 total compensation
SVP; Director Corporate Services, Diane C. Kraemer, age 53
SVP Accounting Special Project, Susan B. Olson, age 58
SVP; Manager Lending Administration, Debra A. Richardson, age 55
EVP and Chief Lending Officer, Richard S. Spengler, age 50, $245,004 total compensation
SVP and CFO, Thomas F. Splaine Jr., age 47, $191,002 total compensation
SVP; Summit Market Manager, William V. Cosgrove
Chief Accounting Officer, Kelly Pecoraro, age 43
Director, James H. Ward III, age 62
SEVP COO and Director, Domenick A. Cama, age 56
Director, Brian D. Dittenhafer, age 70
Director, Vincent D. Manahan III, age 74
Director, Stephen J. Szabatin, age 75
President CEO and Director, Kevin Cummings, age 57
Director, Richard Petroski, age 73
Auditors: KPMGLLP

LOCATIONS

HQ: Investors Bancorp Inc.
101 JFK Pkwy., Short Hills NJ 07078-2716
Phone: 973-924-5100 **Fax:** 973-924-5192
Web: www.isbnj.com

PRODUCTS/OPERATIONS

2011 Sales

	$ mil.	% of total
Interest		
Loans receivable and held-for-sale	434	87
Mortgage-backed securities	29	6
Municipal bonds & other debt	5	1
Other	4	1
Noninterest		
Fees & service charges	12	2
Gain on sales of mortgage loans	9	2
Income on bank owned life insurance	3	1
Other	1	-
Total	**500**	**100**

COMPETITORS

Bank of America
Bank of New York Mellon
Center Bancorp
Citigroup
Fulton Financial
M&T Bank
New York Community Bancorp
OceanFirst Financial
PNC Financial
Susquehanna Bancshares

HISTORICAL FINANCIALS

Company Type: Public

Income Statement FYE: December 31

	ASSETS ($ mil.)	NET INCOME ($ mil.)	INCOME AS % OF ASSETS	EMPLOYEES
12/11	10,701	78	0.7%	982
12/10	9,602	62	0.6%	892
12/09*	8,357	22	0.3%	731
06/09	8,136	(64)	—	705
06/08	6,419	16	0.2%	571
Annual Growth	13.6%	48.9%	—	14.5%

*Fiscal year change

2011 Year-End Financials

Debt ratio: 21.08%
Return on equity: 8.15%
Cash ($ mil.): 90
Current ratio: —
Long-term debt ($ mil.): 2,255
No. of shares (mil.): 110
Dividends
Yield: —
Payout: —
Market value ($ mil.): 1,495

	STOCK PRICE ($) FY Close	P/E High	P/E Low	PER SHARE ($) Earnings	Dividends	Book Value
12/11	13.48	21	17	0.73	0.00	8.72
12/10	13.12	25	19	0.56	0.00	7.99
12/09*	10.94	64	33	0.21	0.00	7.43
06/09	9.20	—	—	(0.62)	0.00	7.14
06/08	13.06	105	77	0.15	0.00	7.60
Annual Growth	0.8%	—	—	48.5%	—	3.5%

*Fiscal year change

iStar Financial Inc

iStar Financial is a real estate investment trust (REIT) that acts as a private banker for owners of high-end commercial real estate in the US and abroad. Its financing activities include first mortgages senior and mezzanine real estate debt and corporate capital net lease financing and equity investments. The REIT's loans typically range in size from $20 million to $150 million and are mainly secured by apartments or other residential properties office complexes land hotels or industrial retail entertainment or mixed-use properties. Founded in 1993 iStar has made more than $35 billion worth of commercial real estate investments. Its current portfolio weighs in at some $7.5 billion.

The company also owns a portfolio of real estate held for investment and properties acquired through foreclosures which it typically redevelops for sale. It has expertise in multifamily condominium and master-planned communities.

The economic crisis that began in 2008 impacted iStar in two critical ways. The tightening credit markets made it more difficult for the company to secure both debt and equity financing for its commercial real estate lending and investment activities. And the deterioration of the real estate markets caused the firm's nonperforming loans to balloon. iStar has limited new investments while focusing on resolving non-performing loans and improving credit quality. The company also shifted its focus to new investments sourced from its existing portfolio. iStar believes that these carry less risk since the company already has working relationships with the clients.

After losing nearly $1 billion in 2008 and 2009 combined iStar returned to profitability in 2010; however its results were inflated by the sale of more than 30 corporate tenant lease properties for more than $1 billion. Though the company reported losses of more than $22 million in 2011 there were some silver linings: Non-performing loans fell by nearly half (from $1.35 billion in 2010 to some $771 million) and provisions for expected loan losses dwindled from more $330 million to around $46 million.

EXECUTIVES

Chairman and CEO, Jay Sugarman, age 50, $1,000,000 total compensation
EVP and President iStar Asset Services, Barbara (Barb) Rubin, $250,000 total compensation
EVP Chief Legal Officer Chief Investment Officer and General Counsel, Nina B. Matis, age 61, $350,000 total compensation
EVP Investments, R. Michael Dorsch III, $250,000 total compensation
EVP Investments, Barclay G. Jones III, age 51
EVP Investments, Steven R. (Steve) Blomquist
EVP Investments, Michelle M. Mackay
EVP Credit, Chase S. Curtis Jr.
President AutoStar, Vernon B. Schwartz, age 57
SVP Investor Relations and Marketing, Andrew G. Backman
CFO, David DiStaso
Chief Accounting Officer, Collin Cochrane, age 35
Director, Robert W. Holman Jr., age 68
Director, Prof John G. (Jack) McDonald, age 74
Director, Robin Josephs, age 52
Director, George R. Puskar, age 68
Director, Jeffrey A. Weber, age 47
Director, Glenn R. August, age 50
Director, Dale A. Reiss, age 64
Auditors: PricewaterhouseCoopersLLP

LOCATIONS

HQ: iStar Financial Inc.
1114 Avenue of the Americas 39th Fl., New York NY 10036
Phone: 212-930-9400 **Fax:** 212-930-9494
Web: www.istarfinancial.com

PRODUCTS/OPERATIONS

2011 Sales

	$ mil.	% of total
Interest	226	52
Operating lease income	165	38
Other	40	10
Total	**432**	**100**

COMPETITORS

Annaly Capital Management
Capital Trust
Capstead Mortgage
CIFC
Dynex Capital
MFA Financial
NovaStar Financial
Redwood Trust

HISTORICAL FINANCIALS

Company Type: Public

Income Statement FYE: December 31

	ASSETS ($ mil.)	NET INCOME ($ mil.)	INCOME AS % OF ASSETS	EMPLOYEES
12/11	7,517	(22)	—	184
12/10	9,174	79	0.9%	200
12/09	12,810	(768)	—	247
12/08	15,296	(196)	—	270
12/07	15,848	238	1.5%	326
Annual Growth	(17.0%)	—	—	(13.3%)

2011 Year-End Financials

Debt ratio: 77.65%
Return on equity: (-1.44)%
Cash ($ mil.): 356
Current ratio: —
Long-term debt ($ mil.): 5,837
No. of shares (mil.): 81
Dividends
Yield: —
Payout: —
Market value ($ mil.): 433

	STOCK PRICE ($) FY Close	P/E High/Low	PER SHARE ($) Earnings	Dividends	Book Value
12/11	5.29	— —	(0.70)	0.00	18.66
12/10	7.82	20 6	0.39	0.00	17.85
12/09	2.56	— —	(7.88)	0.00	17.04
12/08	2.23	— —	(1.78)	2.86	22.66
12/07	26.05	35 17	1.51	3.60	21.65
Annual Growth	(32.9%)	— —	—	—	(3.6%)

Jabil Circuit, Inc.

Jabil Circuit is one of the leading providers of electronics manufacturing services (EMS) in the world. Its largest segment diversified manufacturing services includes higher-complexity specialized services products as well as healthcare and CleanTech (energy water and materials) offerings. Parts made by Jabil on a contract basis are also used in computing and telecommunications products as well as consumer products such as set-top boxes and printers. The company's services range from product design and component procurement to product testing order fulfillment and supply chain management. It serves customers worldwide and gets most of its sales from international operations.

Geographic Reach The company operates in nearly 30 countries. Mexico and China are Jabil's largest markets each accounting for about 20% of sales. The US comes in at about 15% and the company's fastest-growing market Malaysia accounts for more than 10%. Malaysian sales grew more than 115% year-over-year Sales and Marketing Jabil generates nearly half its sales from five customers. Its top customers include Apple (13% of sales) Cisco Systems (10%) and Research in Motion (10%).

Financial Analysis The company's sales rose by 4% to $17.2 billion in fiscal 2012 (ended August 31) as strong growth in its diversified manufacturing services (DMS) segments offset declines in the rest of the business. DMS sales rose nearly 25% as the company was able to secure additional business from existing clients. Net income was also up 4% to $395 million.

Strategy To compete in a rapidly consolidating industry Jabil provides production on a global scale and operates through semi-autonomous business units that are dedicated to individual customers. The company continues to add services and to expand globally through acquisitions including deals to acquire manufacturing operations from customers looking to reduce costs through outsourcing. Jabil has acquired or established manufacturing facilities in regions with lower operating costs including Brazil China Hungary India Malaysia Mexico Poland Russia Turkey Ukraine and Vietnam. In other regions the company has rid itself of operations particularly in Europe where production costs are higher. Jabil sold its French and Italian operations in 2010; however months later in 2011 Jabil bought back those operations to appease impacted customers. Mergers and Acquisitions Back on domestic soil Jabil acquired Texas-based Telmar Network Technology in late 2011 to bolster its aftermarket services. With nearly $150 million in sales in 2010 Telmar's communications and network products and services was to be integrated with Jabil's DMS segment.

HISTORY

Jabil Circuit was named for founders James Golden and Bill Morean. The duo who originally ran an excavation business started Jabil in suburban Detroit in 1966 to provide assembly and reworking services to electronics manufacturers. Jabil incorporated in 1969 and began making printed circuit boards for Control Data Corporation (later renamed Control Data Systems) that year.

William D. Morean the founder's son who had worked summers at Jabil while in high school joined the company in 1977. The next year the younger Morean took over Jabil's day-to-day operations. The company had entered the automotive electronics business in 1976 through a $12 million contract with General Motors.

During the 1980s Jabil began building computer components adding such customers as Dell NEC Sun Microsystems and Toshiba. Jabil moved its headquarters to St. Petersburg Florida in 1983. William Morean became Jabil's chairman and CEO in 1988.

Production design accounted for most of Jabil's sales for the first time in 1992. The next year the company went public and also opened a factory in Scotland. A major laptop computer manufacturing contract from Epson soured when in 1995 cracks appeared in the casings of the laptops and Epson balked at paying its tab.

Disk drive maker Quantum then Jabil's biggest client canceled production orders worth about $60 million in 1996. Jabil quickly filled production gaps by shifting its focus to the booming communications market. By 1997 it had successfully diversified beyond low-margin PC manufacturing becoming one of the top US circuit board manufacturers while adding higher-margin products such as networking hardware.

In 1999 the company expanded into China when it acquired electronics manufacturing services provider GET Manufacturing. The next year William Morean stepped down as CEO (he remained chairman); he was succeeded by president Timothy Main.

The company made plans in 2001 to buy five component factories from UK-based electronics distributor Marconi. Later that year Jabil announced it would cut about 3000 jobs or about 10% of its staff. Also in 2001 it signed an agreement with chip titan Intel under which Jabil would acquire an Intel plant in Malaysia and supply Intel with parts for three years.

In 2002 Jabil acquired most of the assets of Lucent Technologies of Shanghai a joint venture among Lucent (now Alcatel-Lucent) and three Chinese partners for $75 million; the deal included an agreement to supply Lucent with optical switching and other communications components for three years. Also that year the company acquired certain Mexican operations of Seagate Technology for about $26 million and bought Philips Contract Manufacturing Services an arm of the Dutch electronics giant for around $210 million. Philips signed a four-year product supply agreement with Jabil valued at E4 billion.

In late 2004 Jabil began expanding its manufacturing capacity in Asia by breaking ground on plants in India and China. The facilities represented the company's second plant in India and its fourth in China.

In early 2005 the company paid about $195 million to acquire the contract manufacturing business of Varian Inc. the instrument vendor. Later that year the Jabil Singapore plant was certified under the AS 9100 standard becoming the company's fifth facility to qualify for the certification.

Together with Carl Zeiss Jabil created a joint venture in early 2006 to manufacture optical modules for computer displays and other applications. Jabil took the majority interest in the JV.

In 2006 Jabil exercised an option to acquire Celetronix International an India-based electronics manufacturer. Jabil obtained the option when it loaned Celetronix $25 million in fiscal 2005. The company paid about $150 million in cash for Celetronix which had operations in India the UK and the US.

In 2007 Jabil sold Celetronix International's switching power supply business to Red Rocket Inc.

Also that year the company acquired Taiwan Green Point Enterprises a contract manufacturer with plants in China Malaysia and Taiwan. Jabil made a tender offer of NT$109 a share in cash for all shares of Green Point valuing the deal at nearly $900 million. Green Point specialized in plastic parts for cell phones and other portable electronics products. Jabil planned to operate Green Point as an autonomous subsidiary hiring about 30000 employees and keeping the company's management in place.

Further expanding into Asian markets Jabil opened a facility in Vietnam in mid-2007.

EXECUTIVES

President CEO and Director, Timothy L. Main, age 55, $1,000,000 total compensation
Chairman, William D. Morean, age 57
EVP Strategic Planning and Development, Joseph A. (Joe) McGee, age 50
Vice Chairman, Thomas A. Sansone, age 63
COO, Mark T. Mondello, age 48, $700,000 total compensation
General Counsel and Corporate Secretary, Robert L. Paver, age 56
EVP; CEO Materials Technology Group, John P. Lovato, age 52, $500,000 total compensation
EVP; CEO Manufacturing Services, William D. (Bill) Muir Jr., age 44, $500,000 total compensation
CFO, Forbes I. J. Alexander, age 52, $520,000 total compensation
EVP and CEO Aftermarket Services, Hartmut Liebel
SVP and Controller, Meheryar (Mike) Dastoor, age 47
SVP Corporate Development, Donald J. Myers
VP Global Business Unit Manufacturing Services, Carey A. Paulus
Treasurer, Sergio A. Cadavid, age 56
EVP and CEO Materials Technology Services, Hai Hwai (HH) Chiang
CIO, David D. Couch
VP Financial Planning, Daryn G. Smith
VP Financial Reporting, Timothy W. Traud
VP Finance Global Business Center, Steven A. Hodge
VP Global Business Units Manufacturing Services, David T. Wahl
VP Tax, Thomas R. Blythe
Senior Legal Counsel and Assistant Corporate Secretary, Susan Pritchard Allan
VP Operations Asia Manufacturing Services, Vait Leong Tan
VP Global Business Unit Manufacturing Services, Paul (Andrew) Williams
VP and Global Supply Chain Officer Aftermarket Services, Scott H. Sickels
VP Information Technology Service Operations, Linda L. Beaman
VP Global Legal Affairs, Samantha A. Brem
VP Information Technology Business Systems, Robert F. Hawthorne
VP Human Development, Audrey J. McGuckin
VP Risk and Assurance, Lawrence A. Stock
Director, Steven A. (Steve) Raymund, age 57
President CEO and Director, Timothy L. Main, age 55
Director, Frank A. Newman, age 64
Vice Chairman, Thomas A. Sansone, age 63
Director, David M. Stout, age 57
Director, Mel S. Lavitt, age 75
Director, Lawrence J. Murphy, age 70
Director, Kathleen A. (Kathy) Walters, age 61
Director, Martha F. Brooks, age 52
Auditors: KPMGLLP

LOCATIONS

HQ: Jabil Circuit Inc.
10560 Dr. Martin Luther King Jr. St. North, St. Petersburg FL 33716
Phone: 727-577-9749 **Fax:** 727-579-8529
Web: www.jabil.com

2012 Sales

	$ mil.	% of total
$ mil % of total		
Mexico	3,658	21
China	3,425	20
US	2,466	14
Singapore	2,030	12
Hungary	1,430	8
Malaysia	1,148	7
Brazil	661	4
Other	2,330	14
Total	**17,151**	**100**

PRODUCTS/OPERATIONS

2012 Sales

	$ mil.	% of total
Diversified Manufacturing Services	7,476	44
Enterprise & Infrastructure	5,080	29
High Velocity Systems	4,594	27
Total	**17,151**	**100**

Services
Component selection sourcing and procuremen
Design and prototypin
Engineering
Order fulfillmen
Printed circuit board and backplane assembly
Product testing
Repair and warranty
Systems assembly
Test developmen
Tooling design (molds and dies)

COMPETITORS

ASUSTeK
Benchmark Electronics
BenQ
Celestica
Compal Electronics
Flextronics
Hon Hai
Inventec
Key Tronic
Plexus
Sanmina
SMTC Corp.
Sparton
Venture Corp.
Wistron

HISTORICAL FINANCIALS

Company Type: Public

Income Statement FYE: August 31

	REVENUE ($ mil.)	NET INCOME ($ mil.)	NET PROFIT MARGIN	EMPLOYEES
08/12	17,151	394	2.3%	141,000
08/11	16,518	381	2.3%	121,000
08/10	13,409	168	1.3%	69,000
08/09	11,684	(1,165)	—	61,000
08/08	12,779	133	1.0%	61,000
Annual Growth	7.6%	31.0%	—	23.3%

2012 Year-End Financials

Debt ratio: 21.48%
Return on equity: 18.75%
Cash ($ mil.): 1,217
Current ratio: 146.13
Long-term debt ($ mil.): 1,658
No. of shares (mil.): 206
Dividends
Yield: 1.41%
Payout: 17.11%
Market value ($ mil.): 4,693

	STOCK PRICE ($) FY Close	P/E High/Low		PER SHARE ($) Earnings	Dividends	Book Value
08/12	22.78	14	8	1.87	0.32	10.22
08/11	16.85	13	6	1.73	0.28	9.18
08/10	10.25	23	13	0.78	0.28	7.50
08/09	10.95	—	—	(5.63)	0.28	6.90
08/08	16.86	39	14	0.65	0.00	13.16
Annual Growth	7.8%	—	—	30.2%	—	(6.1%)

Jacobs Engineering Group, Inc.

Jacobs Engineering fuels its rise up the ladder with oil gas and chemicals. The group provides technical professional and construction services for industrial government and commercial clients primarily in the US the UK and Canada. Jacobs handles project design and engineering construction operations maintenance and scientific consultation. Typical projects include oil refineries manufacturing plants and roads and highways. The company's largest single customer is the US government (about 25% of revenues) for which it chiefly performs aerospace and defense work. Jacobs Engineering has more than 160 offices around the world.

HISTORY

Joseph Jacobs graduated from the Polytechnic Institute of Brooklyn in 1942 with a doctorate in engineering. He went to work for Merck designing processes for pharmaceutical production. Later he moved to Chemurgic Corp. near San Francisco where he worked until 1947 when he founded Jacobs Engineering as a consulting firm. Jacobs also sold industrial equipment avoiding any apparent conflict of interest by simply telling his consulting clients.

When equipment sales outstripped consulting work by 1954 Jacobs hired four salesmen and engineer Stan Krugman who became his right-hand man. Two years later the company got its first big chemical design job for Kaiser Aluminum. Jacobs incorporated his sole proprietorship in 1957.

In 1960 the firm won its first construction contract to design and build a potash flotation plant and Jacobs Engineering became an integrated design and construction firm. In 1967 it opened its first regional office but kept management decentralized to replicate the small size and hard-hitting qualities of its home office. Three years later Jacobs Engineering went public.

The firm merged with Houston-based Pace Companies which specialized in petrochemical engineering design in 1974. Also that year the firm became Jacobs Engineering Group and began building its first major overseas chemical plant in Ireland.

By 1977 sales had reached $250 million. A decade of lobbying paid off that year when the firm won a contract for the Arab Potash complex in Jordan. Jacobs began to withdraw from his firm's operations in the early 1980s but the 1982-83 recession and poor management decisions pounded earnings. Jacobs returned from retirement in 1985 fired 14 VPs cut staff in half and pushed the firm to pursue smaller process-plant jobs and specialty construction.

After abandoning a 1986 attempt to take the company private Jacobs began making acquisitions to improve the firm's construction expertise. In 1992 he relinquished his role as CEO to president Noel Watson. The next year the company expanded its international holdings by acquiring the UK's H&G Process Contracting and H&G Contractors.

The firm's $38 million purchase of CRS Sirrine Engineers and CRSS Constructors in 1994 was the company's largest buy at that point and added new markets in the paper and semiconductor industries. By 1995 Jacobs Engineering was working on a record backlog.

Continuing its acquisition drive the company bought a 49% interest in European engineering specialist Serete Group in 1996; it bought the rest the next year. Also in 1997 it gained control of Indian engineering affiliate Humphreys & Glasgow (now Jacobs H&G) increasing its 40% stake to 70% and bought CPR Engineering a pulp and paper processing specialist. It also formed a joint venture with Krupp UHDE to provide design engineering and construction management services in Mexico.

In 1999 the company paid $198 million for St. Louis construction and design firm Sverdrup which had completed projects in some 65 countries. The next year Jacobs Engineering purchased half of Dutch firm Stork Engineering's business (it acquired the rest in 2001). But the company's bid to buy the assets of bankrupt power plant construction company Stone & Webster in 2000 was topped by Shaw Group.

After being accused of overcharging the US government Jacobs Engineering settled a whistleblower lawsuit (for $35 million) in 2000 while continuing to deny the allegations. However the next year Jacobs continued to receive federal contracts including contracts for boosting security at the US Capitol complex and providing logistics to the US Special Operations Command. Jacobs completed its acquisition of the UK-based GIBB unit of engineering consulting firm LawGibb Group in 2001 as well as the purchase of McDermott Engineers and Constructors (Canada).

After acquiring airport consulting firm Leigh Fisher Associates in 2003 Jacobs announced that it planned a larger acquisition. Jacobs then went on a shopping spree acquiring a controlling stake in Finland's largest engineering firm Neste Engineering and picking up Glasgow-based engineering firm Babtie Group.

In 2004 Jacobs acquired Scottish engineering firm Babtie Group (now Jacobs U.K.) an international firm that helped the group grow its UK presence. Also in 2004 the group's founder and chairman died at the age of 88. He was succeeded as chairman by Watson who retained the CEO post until 2005. Former president Craig Martin was named CEO the following year.

The company expanded its Middle East operations in 2008 by acquiring a 60% interest in the Saudi Arabia-based Zamel & Turbag Consulting Engineers. It also bought a 30% stake in AWE Management Limited which allowed it to partner with Lockheed Martin and Serco to manage the Atomic Weapons Establishment for the UK government.

In 2010 Jacobs bought Jordan Jones and Goulding broadening its aviation and transportation business as well as the government services operations of TechTeam Global boosting its federal strategic consulting capabilities. The previous year it bought Florida-based government contractor TYBRIN Corporation. Other similar deals included the acquisitions of Carter & Burgess and transportation specialist Edwards and Kelcey. Both deals added to the group's infrastructure business.

EXECUTIVES

EVP Operations, Gregory J. Landry, age 64, $632,692 total compensation
SVP and Controller, Nazim G. Thawerbhoy, age 65
President CEO and Director, Craig L. Martin, age 63, $1,165,385 total compensation
EVP Global Sales, George A. Kunberger Jr., age 60, $646,154 total compensation
EVP Operations, Thomas R. (Tom) Hammond, age 61, $694,615 total compensation
EVP Finance and Administration and Treasurer, John W. Prosser Jr., age 67, $612,308 total compensation
Chairman, Noel G. Watson, age 76, $850,000 total compensation
SVP and General Counsel, William C. Markley III, age 67
SVP Information Technology, Cora L. Carmody, age 55
SVP Global Human Resources, Patricia H. Summers, age 55
VP Global Communications Technology, Bradley P. (Brad) Wright
VP Marketing and Corporate Communications, Michelle Jones
EVP Operations, Joseph G. Mandel
President CEO and Director, Craig L. Martin, age 63
Director, Peter J. Robertson, age 65
Director, Benjamin F. Montoya, age 77
Director, Joseph R. (Joe) Bronson, age 64
Director, Edward V. Fritzky, age 62
Director, Robert C. (Bob) Davidson Jr., age 67
Director, Linda F. Levinson, age 71
Director, Linda Fayne Levinson, age 69
Director, Gen. John P. Jumper, age 66
Director, Thomas M. T. Niles, age 72
Director, John F. Coyne, age 62
Independent Director, Christopher Thompson
Independent Director, Ralph Eberhart
Auditors: Ernst&YoungLLP

LOCATIONS

HQ: Jacobs Engineering Group Inc.
1111 S. Arroyo Pkwy., Pasadena CA 91105
Phone: 626-578-3500 **Fax:** 626-568-7144
Web: www.jacobs.com

2011 Sales

	$ mil.	% of total
US	6,435	62
Canada	1,656	16
Europe	1,649	16
Australia	194	2
Middle East & Africa	130	1
South America & Mexico	109	1
India	103	1
Asia	102	1
Total	**10,381**	**100**

PRODUCTS/OPERATIONS

2011 Sales by Industry

	$ mil.	% of total
National government programs	2,313	22
Downstream refining	2,256	22
Chemicals & polymers	1,461	14
Infrastructure	1,219	12
Buildings	893	9
Upstream oil & gas	753	7
Mining & minerals	449	4
Pharmaceuticals & biotechnology	404	4
Industrial & other	630	6
Total	**10,381**	**100**

2011 Sales by Service

	$ mil.	% of total
Project services	5,070	49
Construction	3,060	29
Operations & maintenance	1,434	14
Process scientific and systems consulting	815	8
Total	**10,381**	**100**

COMPETITORS

AECOM
Aker Solutions
AMEC
Babcock & Wilcox
Bechtel
CH2M HILL
Computer Sciences Corp.
Day & Zimmermann
Fluor
Foster Wheeler
HDR
HNTB Companies
HOK
Honeywell International
KBR
KBR Building Group
Lockheed Martin
Louis Berger
Parsons Brinckerhoff
Parsons Corporation
Peter Kiewit Sons'
Raytheon
SAIC
Shaw Group
Technip
Tetra Tech
Turner Construction
URS
Weston Solutions

HISTORICAL FINANCIALS

Company Type: Public

Income Statement

FYE: September 28

	REVENUE ($ mil.)	NET INCOME ($ mil.)	NET PROFIT MARGIN	EMPLOYEES
09/12	10,893	378	3.5%	63,400
09/11*	10,381	331	3.2%	62,000
10/10	9,915	245	2.5%	52,200
10/09	11,467	399	3.5%	53,200
09/08	11,252	420	3.7%	57,100
Annual Growth	(0.8%)	(2.6%)	—	2.7%

*Fiscal year change

2012 Year-End Financials

Debt ratio: 7.72%
Return on equity: 10.18%
Cash ($ mil.): 1,032
Current ratio: 206.75
Long-term debt ($ mil.): 528
No. of shares (mil.): 129
Dividends
Yield: —
Payout: —
Market value ($ mil.): 5,253

	STOCK PRICE ($) FY Close	P/E High/Low		PER SHARE ($) Earnings	Dividends	Book Value
09/12	40.43	16	11	2.94	0.00	28.65
09/11*	32.29	20	12	2.60	0.00	25.93
10/10	39.01	25	17	1.96	0.00	22.71
10/09	43.51	17	8	3.21	0.00	21.14
09/08	54.31	29	14	3.38	0.00	18.30
Annual Growth	(7.1%)	—	—	(3.4%)	—	11.9%

*Fiscal year change

Jarden Corp.

More than 100 brands of consumer products for inside and outside the home make Jarden beam. It makes a variety of branded consumer products including Sunbeam and Oster appliances Coleman outdoor gear and First Alert home safety products. It also makes Ball canning jars Diamond matches and plastic cutlery Loew-Cornell art supplies K2 snowboards and Bee and Bicycle brand playing cards. Jarden sells its products primarily to retailers such as Wal-Mart Dick's Sporting Goods and Target. It also supplies copper-plated zinc penny blanks to the US Mint and the Royal Canadian Mint. To further diversify its products portfolio Jarden acquired the Mapa Spontex baby care and home care businesses from TOTAL.

Operations

Jarden operates its business through three segments: Outdoor Solutions Consumer Solutions and Branded Consumables. Outdoor Solutions focuses on making and marketing active lifestyle and outdoor-related products such as air beds camping stoves tents inflatable boats team sports equipment and all-terrain vehicle gear among other items. Its Consumer Solutions segment is responsible for manufacturing and distributing household products for making coffee purifying the air and slow-cooking meals. Branded Consumables concentrates on the basics such as brooms brushes kitchen matches arts and crafts paint brushes home canning jars and smoke and carbon monoxide alarms.

Strategy

Pumping out new products is what keeps Jarden's bottom line healthy. As part of its strategy the outdoor products maker expanded its line of Instant tents which can be set up in up to 60 seconds to include the largest shelters. Its Consumer Solutions segment is extending its reach of its core products to cater to trendy niche markets in consumer health pet products at-home food preparation and single-serve coffee. As a result it expanded its Keurig single-serve coffee offering and introduced a new FoodSaver model for hunters and fishermen. Across its Branded Consumables business Jarden focused on aerl-brand air filters and purifiers and Sunbeam pet electronics used to train pets.

Mergers and Acquisitions

Jarden has maintained a steady pace of acquiring companies with noteworthy names to add value to its stable of brands. The $415 million deal for Paris-based Mapa Spontex completed in 2010 is no different. The French manufacturer's baby care products (such as baby bottles and nipples) carry the NUK Tigex and Lillo brands its household cleaning items (sponges rubber gloves) bear the Mapa and Spontex names and its health care segment makes condoms under the Billy Boy name. The purchase has exposed Jarden to new product segments and helped to boost revenue from foreign markets extending the firm's presence beyond North America to include Europe and Latin America (Brazil and Argentina). Jarden also completed two smaller purchases in 2010 with a combined value of about $270 million: Aero Products International a maker of air-filled mattresses and Quickie Manufacturing Corp. a supplier and distributor of cleaning tools and supplies. Previously Jarden focused on accumulating outdoor and recreational brands. Jarden paid about $1.2 billion for outdoor products maker K2 which is known for its global reach with such brand names as Rawlings Penn Shakespeare Volkl and Worth. Jarden bought K2 back in 2007 to extend its reach nationally and internationally. The acquisition was also the largest of about 20 it had completed during the prior decade such as its purchase of Pure Fishing a family-found firm for more than $300 million.

Financial Analysis

The Mapa Spontex purchase helped boost sales in the company's branded consumables segment by a robust 70% while Jarden's overall sales increased by almost 17% to more than $6 billion in 2010 vs. 2009. Sales in the company's other two business segments: outdoor solutions and consumer solutions increased by about 9% and 2% respectively. The strong sales growth overall in 2010 vs. the year earlier period marked a turnaround for the consumer products company which saw its combined US and international sales decline by about 4% in 2009 vs. 2008 due to the downturn in the global economy and stalled sales of consumer products. Still net income and cash flow both declined in 2010 vs. 2009. The decrease in net income was primarily due to charges related to Jarden's operations in Venezuela. (In early 2010 the Venezuelan government devalued its currency relative to the US dollar.)

Ownership

Teachers Insurance and Annuity Association - College Retirement Equities Fund owns more than 12% of Jarden. FMR LLC holds another 10% stake in the company.

EXECUTIVES

Vice Chairman and CFO, Ian G. H. Ashken, age 51, $911,856 total compensation
Chairman, Martin E. Franklin, age 47, $1,975,688 total compensation
SVP Human Resources and Corporate Risk, J. David Tolbert, age 51, $290,000 total compensation
CEO, James E. Lillie, age 50, $643,366 total compensation
Executive Vice President FinanceRichard, Richard T. Sansone, age 45, $373,846 total compensation
Executive Vice President General Counsel, John E. Capps, age 47, $358,750 total compensation
SVP Business Operations and Supply Chain, Patricia J. Gaglione, $273,635 total compensation
SVP and Chief Transition Officer, Patricia A. Mount
Vice President; Principal Accounting Officer, James Cunningham
Director, Richard J. (Dick) Heckmann, age 68
Vice Chairman and CFO, Ian G. H. Ashken, age 51
Director, William P. Lauder, age 52
Director, Irwin D. Simon, age 54
Director, Michael S. Gross, age 50
Director, Robert L. Wood, age 57
Director, Rene-Pierre Azria, age 55
Director, William J. Grant, age 66
Auditors: PricewaterhouseCoopersLLP

LOCATIONS

HQ: Jarden Corporation
555 Theodore Fremd Ave. Ste. B-302, Rye NY 10580
Phone: 914-967-9400 **Fax:** 914-967-9405
Web: www.jarden.com

2011 Sales

	$ mil.	% of total
Domestic	4,082	61
International	2,597	39
Total	**6,679**	**100**

PRODUCTS/OPERATIONS

2011 Sales

	$ mil.	% of total
Outdoor solutions	2,772	41
Consumer solutions	1,880	28
Branded consumables	1,734	26
Process solutions	351	5
Adjustments (58.1) —		
Total	**6,679**	**100**

Selected Products

Branded consumables
- Baby bottles soothers and nipples
- Canning jars
- Clothespins
- Condoms (Billy B)
- Cord and twine
- Food preparation kits
- Fire safety equipment (First Alert)
- Home appliances (Mr. Coffee Oster Sunbeam)
- Infant accessories
- Kitchen matches
- Outdoor gear (Coleman Aero)
- Plastic cutlery
- Rope
- Rubber gloves
- Sponges
- Toothpicks

Consumer solutions
- Panini grills
- Vacuum packaging systems
- Waffle makers

Plastic consumables
- Closures
- Contact lens packaging
- Plastic cutlery
- Refrigerator door liners
- Shotgun shell casings
- Surgical devices
- Syringes

Other
- Zinc strip and fabricated products

Selected Brands

Aviator
Ball
Bee
Bernardin
Bicycle
Campingaz
Coleman
Crawford
Diamond
First Alert
FoodSaver
Forster
Health o meter
Hoyle
Java Log
K2
Kerr
Lehigh
Leslie-Locke

Loew-Cornell
Mr. Coffee
Oster
Sunbeam
Ugly Stick
Villawear
XTools

COMPETITORS

Academy Sports
adidas
Amazon.com
Amer Sports
Andis
AZZ
Bass Pro Shops
Bauer Hockey
Bed Bath & Beyond
Burton
BWAY
Cabela' s
CalCedar
Canadian Tire
Carrefour
Church & Dwight
Conair Consumer Products
Costco Wholesale
Crayola
Daiwa
De' Longhi
Deswell
Dick' s Sporting Goods
Easton-Bell Sports
EBSCO
Elmer' s Products
Energizer Holdings
Evenflo
Female Health
Gaming Partners International
Gerber Products
Habasit America
Hamilton Beach
Hanesbrands
Head N.V.
Hillerich & Bradsby
Home Depot
HoMedics
Honeywell ACS
Igloo Products
Intex DIY
Invensys
Johnson & Johnson
Johnson Outdoors
Kaz
Kellwood
Lasko Products
Lifetime Brands
Lowe' s
Mattel
Mayborn Group
MEGA Brands
Mizuno
NACCO Industries
New Balance
Newell Rubbermaid
NIKE
Owens-Illinois
Patch Products
Philips Avent
Procter & Gamble
Quiksilver
REI
Richco
Rollerblade
Rossignol
Russell Hobbs
Sealy
SEB
Simmons
Spectrum Brands
Suncast
Target Corporation
Tecnica
Tegrant
Universal Security Instruments
UTC Climate Controls & Security
VF Corporation
W.C. Bradley Co.
Wahl Clipper
West Pharmaceutical Services
Whirlpool
Worthington Industries

HISTORICAL FINANCIALS

Company Type: Public

Income Statement FYE: December 31

	REVENUE ($ mil.)	NET INCOME ($ mil.)	NET PROFIT MARGIN	EMPLOYEES
12/11	6,679	204	3.1%	23,000
12/10	6,022	106	1.8%	24,000
12/09	5,152	128	2.5%	20,000
12/08	5,383	(58)	—	20,000
12/07	4,660	28	0.6%	25,000
Annual Growth	9.4%	64.3%	—	(2.1%)

2011 Year-End Financials

Debt ratio: 44.39%
Return on equity: 10.71%
Cash ($ mil.): 808
Current ratio: 238.68
Long-term debt ($ mil.): 2,890
No. of shares (mil.): 90
Dividends
Yield: —
Payout: 14.94%
Market value ($ mil.): 2,716

	STOCK PRICE ($) FY Close	P/E High/Low		PER SHARE ($) Earnings	Dividends	Book Value
12/11	29.88	16	11	2.31	0.00	21.03
12/10	30.87	29	22	1.19	0.33	19.83
12/09	30.91	21	6	1.52	0.15	19.59
12/08	11.50	—	—	(0.78)	0.00	18.31
12/07	23.61	115	59	0.38	0.00	20.03
Annual Growth	6.1%	—	—	57.0%	—	1.2%

Jefferies Group, Inc.

Because smaller companies need hostile-takeover advice too. Jefferies Group (along with its main subsidiary Jefferies & Company) raises capital performs securities trading and research and provides advisory services for small and midsized companies in the US. Serving about 2500 institutional clients worldwide the company also trades derivatives and commodities and makes markets for some 5000 US and international equities. Jefferies Group also oversees more than $3 billion on behalf of investors private clients and national and local governments. The company operates in 30 cities in North America Europe the Middle East and Asia. In a friendly deal Jefferies has agreed to be acquired by Leucadia.

Investing conglomerate Leucadia National Corp. (LNC) will acquire Jefferies Group for nearly $4 billion. (It already owns about 29% of its shares.) The deal will place Jefferies CEO Rich Handler in the top job at LNC after its chairman and CEO Ian Cumming retires at the end of 2012. Jefferies Group will become a portfolio of LNC when the deal is done.

Despite a few troubles during the economic downturn which caused Jefferies Group to cut costs by closing some offices and reducing staff the company has been able to quickly regain momentum. In recent years it has enhanced its capabilities grown its staff and diversified its business..

After financial markets regained momentum Jefferies rebounded and operating results have grown steadily since 2009. Strong investment banking revenues and success in its trading business helped Jefferies' post a 26% increase in overall sales in 2011. That year profits also grew by more than 27%. But it wasn't exactly smooth sailing for Jefferies Group in 2011. The company struggled to deal with its exposure to European soverign debt.

The company also has restarted expanding its team once again in Asia Latin America and other emerging markets. Jefferies also launched a European government bond sales and trading platform in London. In 2012 Jefferies reopened an office in Dubai.

Jefferies is focusing on diversifying its business lines and growing its futures and swaps businesses. To that end the company acquired Prudential Bache's global commodities business from Prudential Financial for $430 million in 2011. It was the largest acquisition yet for Jefferies. The deal helped Jefferies grow in futures and commodities.Now Jefferies Bache Limited operates in the US and UK.

In 2012 Jefferies bought UK-based company Hoare Govett which provides corporate broking research and trading services from RBS. The deal expands the capabilities and reach of Jefferies' European investment banking and equities business.

In addition to serving government clients Jefferies has a long tradition of serving markets such as aerospace and defense consumer energy financial services gaming and leisure health care industrial maritime media and technology.

HISTORY

Former cowboy and stock exchange clerk Boyd Jefferies founded Jefferies & Company in 1962. The firm referred customers to brokers in exchange for cuts of their commissions. In 1969 mutual fund giant Investors Diversified Services (IDS) acquired the upstart. Because IDS was not a broker Jefferies was kicked off the NYSE and increased its off-exchange activities.

Boyd Jefferies bought back his company in 1973 and took it public in 1983. Because the SEC had less control over off-exchange trades Jefferies was a popular stop for greenmailers amassing stock for hostile takeovers. By 1986 the firm was in Japan Switzerland and the UK.

After 1987's "Black Monday" stock crash it was revealed that Jefferies had illegally "parked" stocks for Ivan Boesky. Boyd Jefferies pleaded guilty to SEC rules violations resigned and sold his interest in the company. New CEO Frank Baxter launched subsidiary Investment Technology Group (ITG). When Michael Milken's Drexel Burnham Lambert failed in 1990 Baxter hired scores of former Drexelites.

During the 1990s ITG grew along with demand for off-exchange trading. In 1999 Jefferies merged ITG into a separate company spinning off its other operations as the new Jefferies Group. Jefferies formed an alliance with Credit Lyonnais' US brokerage subsidiary and bought a stake in online bond trading system LIMITrader.com which had mostly ceased operations by 2001.

At the end of 2000 Baxter retired as CEO but stayed on as chairman until 2002. He was succeeded in both capacities by Jefferies Group veteran Richard Handler. Also in 2000 Jefferies bought The Europe Company to boost its international operations.

The company's Helfant Group subsidiary (which was renamed Jefferies Execution Services in 2004) was created from the 2002 merger of Lawrence Helfant and W&D Securities.

Jefferies Group enhanced its capital-raising capabilities by acquiring Helix Associates a UK-based private equity fund placement firm in 2005. Jefferies & Company was fined $5.5 million by the NASD and $4.2 million by the SEC in 2006 for giving nearly $2 million worth of improper gifts to equity traders at Fidelity.

Jefferies Group acquired the financial services investment banking business of Putnam Lovell from National Bank of Canada in 2007. Two years later it acquired First Albany Securities which specializes in municipal capital markets from DEPFA.

Jefferies Group was impacted by the uncertainty in the global markets in 2008 and struggled with declining revenue. It had been focused on expanding into Latin America and the Middle East but put the brakes on some of its expansion plans. The company also cut more than 10% of its workforce and closed offices in Dubai Singapore and Tokyo.

In 2010 Jefferies sold its noncore clearing and custody business to BNY Mellon subsidiary Pershing.

EXECUTIVES

Co-Head Investment Banking, Alec L. Ellison, age 48
SVP Investment Banking Technology Jefferies & Company, Omer Soykan
Chairman and CEO; President and CEO Jefferies & Company, Richard B. Handler, age 50, $1,000,000 total compensation
EVP and Co-Head of Investment Banking, Chris M. Kanoff, age 53
Head Mergers and Acquisitions Jefferies & Company, John E. Huwiler, age 45
Managing Director and Head Marketing Jefferies & Company Inc., Thomas E. (Tom) Tarrant
Co-Head of Restructuring Practice (Europe), Richard Nevins, age 65
Chairman Executive Committee and Director; President Jefferies Capital Partners, Brian P. Friedman, age 56, $500,000 total compensation
Vice Chairman and Co-Head of Investment Banking Jefferies & Company, Andrew R. Whittaker, age 48
Head U.S. Government Agency Jefferies & Company, Michael S. Effron
Vice Chairman Jefferies & Company, Roy L. Furman
Managing Director Senior Equity Research Analyst, Howard A. Rubel
Global Head Equity Research Jefferies & Company, Steven R. Black
Managing Director Senior Equity Research Analyst, Katherine Egbert
Director Convertible Research, Derrick Wenger
Global Head Equity Capital Markets Jefferies & Company Inc., Mark E. Connelly
Co-President Jefferies Financial Products, Adam De Chiara
Managing Director Equity Research, Susan F. Gilbertson
Managing Director Head of General Industrial Group, Ted Cook
Managing Director Co-Head Private Placement Group Jefferies & Company, Andrew Woolford
EVP General Counsel and Secretary, Michael J. (Mike) Sharp, age 56
SVP and Global Head of Compliance, Robert J. (Bob) Albano
Director Mortgage-backed Securities Bonds Direct Division, James Perillo
Managing Director Fixed Income Division Jefferies & Company, Thomas M. Thees
Director Jefferies International, Paul Edwards
Co-Director High Yield Research Jefferies & Company, Brett M. Levy
Co-Director High Yield Research Jefferies & Company, Robert J. Welch, age 48
Managing Director Communications Software and Enhanced Services, Robert Jackman
Managing Director Jefferies Broadview Technology Investment Banking Group, Philip (Phil) Berkowitz
Managing Director and Senior Equity Research Analyst Jefferies & Company, Eun K. Yang
Managing Director and Senior Research Analyst Bonds Direct Division Jefferies & Company, Edwin P. Dean
Managing Director and Global Head of Commodity Derivatives Jefferies Financial Products, Mazin Mirza
Managing Director Bonds Direct Division Jefferies & Company, F. Erich Bauer-Rowe
Managing Director Bonds Direct Division Jefferies & Company, Charles B. Cortellesi
Managing Director Bonds Direct Division Jefferies & Company, Miguel A. Santiago
Head Quantitative Strategies Jefferies & Company, Vlad Portnoy
Co-Head Equity Products Jefferies & Company, Jason Griffith
Chairman Randall & Dewey, Ralph Eads III
Managing Director Restructuring Group, Steven R. Strom
Managing Director and Senior Equity Research Analyst, William H. (Bill) Choi
Head of Structured Products Equities Department, Mark O'Donnell
Managing Director Jefferies & Company, Charles J. (Chuck) Hendrickson, age 61, $250,000 total compensation
SVP Private Client Services Department Jefferies & Company, Michael W. Hyde
Senior Equity Research Analyst Jefferies International, Milan Radia
Managing Director Equity Capital Markets Group Jefferies & Company, Matthew L. (Matt) Sperling
Head of Boston Equities, Brian T. Devlin
Senior Equity Research Analyst Jefferies & Company, Douglas J. (Doug) Mavrinac
Head Wealth Management Group Jefferies Group, A. Markman (Mark) Peters, age 53
Managing Director and Senior Equity Research Analyst, Subash Chandra
President International and Co-Head Investment Banking, David Weaver
Head of Equities Technology Trading Jefferies & Company, Thomas E. Labenz
SVP Prime Brokerage Services Jefferies & Company, Jeffrey M. McCarthy
SVP Prime Brokerage Services Jefferies & Company, Robin H. Fink
Managing Director Private Client Services Jefferies & Company, Wesley Caywood
Managing Director Private Client Services Jefferies & Company, Jin K. Park
Managing Director and Head Maritime Shipping Investment Banking Group Jefferies & Company, Hamish Norton
EVP and CFO, Peregrine C. de M. (Peg) Broadbent, age 48, $1,000,000 total compensation
Head Derivatives Strategy Group, Pat Neal
Managing Director Private Client Services Jefferies & Company, Jack Carvalho
Managing Director Private Client Services Jefferies & Company, S. Whit Yates
Head International Equity Capital Markets Jefferies International, Rupert Mitchell
Head U.S. Equity Capital Markets, Timothy E. Monfort
Managing Director Retail and Apparel Jefferies & Company, Steven J. Tricarico
Head Industrials Investment Banking Practice, Ian Williams
Head Healthcare Investment Banking, Ian Crosbie
Managing Director Jefferies Asset Management LLC, James P. (Jim) Crimmins
Managing Director Aerospace and Defense Jefferies Quarterdeck Jefferies & Company, David P. Baxt
Managing Director and Co-Head Jefferies Randall & Dewey, Stephen M. (Steve) Straty, age 56
Managing Director and Head of Whole Loan Trading and Sales Jefferies & Company, Thomas Dolan
Managing Director and Head of European Asset-Backed and Mortgage-Backed Securities Trading Jefferies & Company, Chander Gupta
Lead MBS and ABS Sales Chicago, Marc DeFife
SVP MBS and ABS Sales Chicago, Elizabeth Harper
Co-Head MBS and ABS Banking and Origination, Andrew Peisch
Managing Director and Head Par Loan Trading, Anthony LoGrippo
SVP Par Loan Trading, John Gally
Global Head Investment Banking and Capital Markets Jefferies & Company Inc., Benjamin D. (Ben) Lorello
Managing Director and Senior High-Yield Trader, Robert Leone
SVP and Chief Strategist Emerging Markets Sales and Trading Jefferies & Company, Eric Ollom, age 50
Managing Director and U.S. Head Real Estate Investment Banking Jefferies & Company, John P. Ockerbloom
Managing Director and European Head Fund Placement Group, Magnus Christensson
US Head Equity-Linked Origination Jefferies & Company Inc., Craig McCracken
Head International Communications Jefferies International Limited, Desiree Maghoo
Managing Director; Global Head Technology Mergers and Acquisitions and U.S. Head Mergers & Acquisitions Investment Banking Division, Michael Tedesco
Head of European Insurance Services Rates Group, Dirk Schlochtermeyer
Co-Head Fixed Income, Johan Eveland
Co-Head Fixed Income, William Jennings
Managing Director and European Head Lodging and Gaming Investment Banking, Steffen Doyle
Equity Strategist Japan, Naomi Fink
Head Securities Finance Trading Asia, Sean Huang
Global Treasurer, John F. Stacconi, age 49
Director, Joseph S. Steinberg, age 68
Director, W. Patrick Campbell, age 66
Director, Richard G. Dooley, age 82
Chairman Executive Committee and Director; President Jefferies Capital Partners, Brian P. Friedman, age 56
Director, Robert E. Joyal, age 67
Director, Michael T. O'Kane, age 66
Auditors: Deloitte&ToucheLLP

LOCATIONS

HQ: Jefferies Group Inc.
520 Madison Ave. 10th Fl., New York NY 10022
Phone: 212-284-2300 **Fax:** 212-284-2111
Web: www.jefco.com

US Offices
Atlanta
Boston
Chicago
Dallas
Foster City CA
Houston
Jersey City NJ
Los Angeles
Nashville TN
New Orleans
New York
San Francisco
Short Hills NJ
Stamford CT
Washington DC

International Offices
Calgary
Dubai
London
Paris
Shanghai
Zurich

PRODUCTS/OPERATIONS

2011 Sales

	$ mil.	% of total
Interest	1,248	35
Investment banking	1,122	32
Commissions	534	15
Principal transactions	428	12
Other	196	6
Total	**3,529**	**100**

Selected Subsidiaries

Jefferies & Company Inc.
Jefferies Asset Management LLC
Jefferies Bache Limited
Jefferies Bache LLC
Jefferies Bache (Hong Kong) Limited
Jefferies Execution Services Inc.
Jefferies Finance LLC
Jefferies Financial Products LLC
Jefferies High Yield Holdings LLC
Jefferies High Yield Trading LLC
Jefferies Hong Kong Limited
Jefferies India Private Ltd.
Jefferies International Limited (UK)
Jefferies International (Holdings) Limited (UK)
Jefferies Investment Management Limited (UK)
Jefferies Japan Ltd.
Jefferies Switzerland Ltd.

COMPETITORS

Arlington Asset Investment
Collins Stewart (US)
Cowen Group
Deutsche Banc Alex. Brown
Evercore Partners
Goldman Sachs
Houlihan Lokey
JPMorgan Chase
KBW
Lazard
Lehman Brothers
Lincoln International
Merrill Lynch
N M Rothschild & Sons
Piper Jaffray
RBC Wealth Management
Robert W. Baird & Co.
Thomas Weisel Partners
UBS Financial Services
Wedbush Securities
WR Hambrecht

HISTORICAL FINANCIALS

Company Type: Public

Income Statement FYE: November 30

	ASSETS ($ mil.)	NET INCOME ($ mil.)	INCOME AS % OF ASSETS	EMPLOYEES
11/11	34,971	284	0.8%	3,898
11/10*	36,726	223	0.6%	3,084
12/09	28,189	280	1.0%	2,628
12/08	19,978	(536)	—	2,270
12/07	29,793	144	0.5%	2,568
Annual Growth	4.1%	18.4%	—	11.0%

*Fiscal year change

2011 Year-End Financials

Debt ratio: 13.18%
Return on equity: 8.83%
Cash ($ mil.): 2,393
Current ratio: —
Long-term debt ($ mil.): 4,608
No. of shares (mil.): 197
Dividends
Yield: 2.62%
Payout: 23.44%
Market value ($ mil.): 2,256

	STOCK PRICE ($) FY Close	P/E High	P/E Low	PER SHARE ($) Earnings	Dividends	Book Value
11/11	11.44	21	8	1.28	0.30	16.35
11/10*	24.15	26	19	1.09	0.30	14.43
12/09	23.73	22	6	1.38	0.00	13.94
12/08	14.06	—	—	(3.23)	0.25	13.00
12/07	23.05	32	22	0.97	0.50	14.15
Annual Growth	(16.1%)	—	—	7.2%	(12.0%)	3.7%

*Fiscal year change

JetBlue Airways Corp

JetBlue Airways is counting on more than low fares to make its ledgers jet-black. The carrier offers one-class service —with leather seats satellite TV from DIRECTV satellite radio from XM and movies —to about 70 cities in more than 20 US states Puerto Rico Mexico and about a dozen countries in the Caribbean and Latin America. Most of its flights arrive or depart from Boston Los Angeles New York Orlando and Fort Lauderdale Florida and San Juan Puerto Rico. JetBlue's fleet of about 170 aircraft consists mainly of Airbus A320s but also includes Embraer 190s. It owns one subsidiary in-flight entertainment system developer LiveTV.

In many ways JetBlue has taken a lesson from —and set its sights on —Southwest Airlines the guru of the low-fare airline world. Like Southwest JetBlue works to keep costs down eliminating amenities such as airport lounges and full meal service. It also relies on electronic ticketing and a non-unionized staff. JetBlue departs from the Southwest model however by assigning seats and by operating more than one type of aircraft. (JetBlue believes it can serve smaller markets more efficiently with the Embraer 190s which have about 100 seats versus 150 for the A320s.) The company also prefers to expand its operations organically — through its operations rather than through acquisitions.

JetBlue's year-over-year 2011 operating revenues rose 19% thanks to an increase in passenger revenue as a result of more capacity and yield. Revenue from the company's Even More Space seats also contributed to the uptick. Higher fuel prices and maintenance for an aging fleet caused operating expenses to climb 21% however. The contribution of fuel costs to operating expenses rose from 32% in 2010 to 40% in 2011. Among the measures JetBlue is implementing for greater fuel efficiency are winglets (vertical extensions of wingtips) on its Airbus craft and a new A320 engine that improves fuel use by 16%.

Also to keep its bottom line soaring against the weight of rising fuel costs JetBlue has been launching a number of initiatives to improve the customer experience. In 2011 JetBlue rebranded its Even More Legroom option as Even More Space which offers early boarding and first access to overhead storage in addition to more legroom. Also in 2011 JetBlue introduced another branded customer service Even More Speed which allows faster security processing. In late 2012 JetBlue will begin providing in-flight Ka broadband connectivity through ViaSat.

From the beginning JetBlue was quicker than Southwest to enter major metropolitan markets. The New York-based carrier is the largest domestic airline at New York's JFK International Airport —the US's biggest travel market. JetBlue's strategy has been to identify routes with high average fares and beat the competition on price as well as to distinguish itself with service offerings such as TV and radio programming.

Traditionally focused on the leisure traveler JetBlue has been developing more service for the business customer to offset the seasonal limitations of the vacation market. Also to develop more business beyond vacation travelers JetBlue has been growing its operations in Latin America and the Caribbean (LACA) which has a strong presence of visiting-friends-and-relatives (VFR) travelers in addition to vacationers. LACA now accounts for more than 25% of JetBlue's revenue.

In 2011 JetBlue began offering service to seven new locations including Anchorage Alaska Martha's Vineyard Mass. Turks & Caicos the Dominican Republic Costa Rica and the US Virgin Islands. It additionally added eight slots each at La Guardia Airport in New York and Ronald Reagan National Airport in Washington DC. Also in 2011 JetBlue became the top carrier in San Juan and the Dominican Republic.

HISTORY

JetBlue took to the skies in 2000 as the third airline start-up for founder and CEO David Neeleman. The first airline Neeleman helped create Morris Air was formed in 1984. Named after his business partner June Morris the discount airline was operating 22 planes out of Salt Lake City by 1993. While with Morris Air Neeleman pioneered ticketless travel which a decade later would become an industry standard.

Impressed with Morris Air's efficient and strategic network its e-ticket system and Neeleman Southwest Airlines acquired its smaller rival in 1993. Neeleman left Southwest after just six months but not without signing a non-compete clause that prevented him from attempting to repeat his Morris Air success in the US for five years.

Not willing to sit still for long (a characteristic he attributes to attention deficit disorder) Neeleman partnered with David Evans to create Open Skies an integrated e-ticket Internet booking and sales management tool that they began to market to smaller airlines.

Meanwhile Neeleman had skirted the terms of his non-compete agreement to help the founders of Canadian low-fare carrier WestJet get their project off of the ground serving as a consultant and a board member.

In 1999 a year after his non-compete agreement expired Neeleman sold Open Skies to Hewlett-Packard and set to work creating a new airline. In a matter of weeks he had managed to gather $130 million the most ever raised for a start-up airline from investors that included Chase Capital and financier George Soros. Neeleman immediately began acquiring new Airbus A320 jets and fitting them with satellite TV.

JetBlue's first flight was from New York to Fort Lauderdale in 2000. During the year the airline added nine more destinations in California Florida New York Utah and Vermont. By 2001 the airline was operating 20 new A320s with an ambitious 131 on order.

On September 11 of that year terrorists commandeered four passenger aircrafts and turned them into instruments of destruction killing some 3000 people. The events shocked the world and crippled the airline industry. Despite the climate however JetBlue continued to expand its network and it went public in 2002.

The industry star took some heat in 2003 for violating its own privacy policy when it gave the personal information of 1.1 million customers to the Department of Defense as part of anti-terrorism project.

JetBlue added nine new destinations in 2004 including Boston —a major market not dominated by a single carrier and lacking what the company deemed to be sufficient low-fare domestic service.

Consecutive losses in the fourth quarter of 2005 and the first quarter of 2006 —caused in part by rising fuel costs—led the carrier to raise fares on some routes redouble its efforts to keep expenses down and slow some of its expansion plans.

As part of the effort to improve the company's operations JetBlue's board in May 2007 asked David Neeleman to step down as CEO in favor of former president Dave Barger. Neeleman remained with the company as nonexecutive chairman until May 2008.

To grow JetBlue increased capacity at its base at New York's JFK airport with the opening of a new terminal in October 2008. The 630000 sq. ft.

Terminal 5 has 26 gates solely used by JetBlue and can accommodate 250 daily departures. The $875 million renovation took three years; it has the largest single security checkpoint in the US and an adjacent 1500-space parking lot.

JetBlue expanded service in 2009 to Bogota Colombia and the Caribbean islands of St. Maarten and Jamaica.

In 2010 JetBlue ink a limited partnership with AMR Corp.'s legacy airline American; the two are sharing activities in New York and Boston including customer "interline" service one-stop booking and check-in and bag transfers for connecting flights. The partnership gives the younger low-cost carrier eight pairs of the Texas-based carrier's take-off and landing slots at Ronald Reagan Washington National Airport and swells American Airlines' New York market with 12 pairs of JetBlue's slots at John F. Kennedy International Airport.

In early 2011 the airline signed an interline agreement with Virgin Atlantic that allows passengers to make connecting flights on transatlantic routes using a single itinerary and baggage check.

EXECUTIVES

President CEO and Director, David (Dave) Barger, age 54, $591,667 total compensation
EVP and CIO, Joseph (Joe) Eng
Vice Chairman, Frank V. Sica, age 61
Chairman, Joel C. Peterson, age 64
SVP Corporate Finance Treasurer and Interim CFO, Mark D. Powers, age 58
VP Security, Ken Maxwell
EVP Corporate Affairs General Counsel and Secretary, James G. (Jim) Hnat, age 41, $350,000 total compensation
VP Safety, Steve Predmore
VP In-Flight Experience, Vicky Stennes
EVP and COO, Robert (Rob) Maruster, age 40, $327,917 total compensation
EVP and Chief Commercial Officer, Robin Hayes, age 45, $400,000 total compensation
SVP Marketing and Commercial Strategy, Martin (Marty) St. George
VP Airports, Alex Battaglia
VP Corporate Compliance and Audit, Glenn Cusano
VP Supply Chain and Fuel, Glenn Hipp
VP Controller and Chief Accounting Officer, Donald (Don) Daniels, age 44
VP Technology Services, Terry Dinterman
VP Network Planning, Scott Laurence
VP Sales and Revenue Management, Dennis Corrigan
VP IT Business Solution Delivery, Richard Zeni
VP Associate General Counsel and Assistant Secretary, Brandon Nelson
VP Flight Operations, Andres (Sandy) Sandoval
VP System Operations Planning and Control, Marc Gross
SVP Government Affairs and Associate General Counsel, Robert Land
Director Concession Management, Mitch Nadler
EVP People, Joanna Geraghty
VP Crew and Values Relations, Michael Elliott
VP JetBlue University, Warren Christie
VP Government Affairs, Jeffrey (Jeff) Goodell
VP Corporate Communications, Jenny Dervin
VP Benefits and Compensation, Harry L. Spencer
VP Corporate Real Estate, Richard (Rich) Smyth
EVP and CIO, Eash Sundaram
Director, David W. (Dave) Checketts, age 56
President CEO and Director, David (Dave) Barger, age 54
Director, Peter Boneparth, age 52
Vice Chairman, Frank V. Sica, age 61
Director, M. Ann Rhoades, age 67
Director, Virginia Gambale, age 52
Director, Stephan Gemkow, age 52
Director, Gen. Stanley A. McChrystal, age 57
Auditors: Ernst&YoungLLP

LOCATIONS

HQ: JetBlue Airways Corporation
118-29 Queens Blvd., Forest Hills NY 11375
Phone: 718-286-7900 **Fax:** 718-709-3621
Web: www.jetblue.com

2011 Sales

	$ mil.	% of total
Domestic	3,351	74
Caribbean & Puerto Rico	1,153	26
Total	**4,504**	**100**

PRODUCTS/OPERATIONS

2011 Sales

	$ mil.	% of total
Passenger	4,080	91
Other	424	9
Total	**4,504**	**100**

COMPETITORS

AirTran Airways
Alaska Air
AMR Corp.
Delta Air Lines
Frontier Airlines
Southwest Airlines
United Continental
US Airways
Virgin America
WestJet

HISTORICAL FINANCIALS

Company Type: Public

Income Statement FYE: December 31

	REVENUE ($ mil.)	NET INCOME ($ mil.)	NET PROFIT MARGIN	EMPLOYEES
12/11	4,504	86	1.9%	14,022
12/10	3,779	97	2.6%	12,948
12/09	3,286	58	1.8%	12,532
12/08	3,388	(76)	—	11,852
12/07	2,842	18	0.6%	11,632
Annual Growth	12.2%	47.8%	—	4.8%

2011 Year-End Financials

Debt ratio: 44.35%
Return on equity: 4.90%
Cash ($ mil.): 673
Current ratio: 115.30
Long-term debt ($ mil.): 2,850
No. of shares (mil.): 281
Dividends
Yield: —
Payout: —
Market value ($ mil.): 1,465

	STOCK PRICE ($) FY Close	P/E High	P/E Low	PER SHARE ($) Earnings	Dividends	Book Value
12/11	5.20	23	11	0.28	0.00	6.24
12/10	6.61	21	13	0.31	0.00	5.61
12/09	5.45	35	13	0.20	0.00	5.28
12/08	7.10	—	—	(0.34)	0.00	4.64
12/07	5.90	166	60	0.10	0.00	5.71
Annual Growth	(3.1%)	—	—	29.4%	—	2.2%

Johnson & Johnson

Is it possible to get well without Johnson & Johnson (J&J)? The diversified health care giant operates in three segments through more than 250 operating companies located in some 60 countries. Its Medical Devices and Diagnostics division offers surgical equipment monitoring devices orthopedic products and contact lenses among other things. J&J's Pharmaceuticals division makes drugs for an array of ailments such as neurological conditions blood disorders autoimmune diseases and pain. Top sellers are psoriasis drug Remicade and anemia medication Procrit. Its Consumer business makes over-the-counter drugs and products for baby skin and oral care as well as first aid and women's health.

HISTORY

Brothers James and Edward Mead Johnson founded their medical products company in 1885 in New Brunswick New Jersey. In 1886 Robert joined his brothers to make the antiseptic surgical dressings he developed. The company bought gauze maker Chicopee Manufacturing in 1916. In 1921 it introduced two of its classic products the Band-Aid and Johnson's Baby Cream.

Robert Jr. became chairman in 1932 and served until 1963. A WWII Army general he believed in decentralization; managers were given substantial freedom a principle still used today. Product lines in the 1940s included Ortho (birth control products) and Ethicon (sutures). In 1959 Johnson & Johnson bought McNeil Labs which launched Tylenol (acetaminophen) as an OTC drug the next year. Foreign acquisitions included Switzerland's Cilag-Chemie (1959) and Belgium's Janssen (1961). The company focused on consumer products in the 1970s gaining half the feminine protection market and making Tylenol the top-selling painkiller.

J&J bought Iolab a developer of intraocular lenses used in cataract surgery in 1980. Trouble struck in 1982 when someone laced Tylenol capsules with cyanide killing eight people. The company's response is now a damage-control classic: It immediately recalled 31 million bottles and totally redesigned its packaging to prevent future tampering. The move cost $240 million but saved the Tylenol brand. The next year prescription painkiller Zomax was linked to five deaths and was pulled.

New products in the 1980s included ACUVUE disposable contact lenses and Retin-A. The company bought LifeScan (blood-monitoring products for diabetics) in 1986. In 1989 it began a joint venture with Merck to sell Mylanta and other drugs bought from ICI Americas.

The firm continued its acquisition and diversification strategy in the 1990s. After introducing the first daily-wear disposable contact lenses in 1993 it bought skin-care product maker Neutrogena (1994) to enhance its consumer lines. To diversify its medical products and better compete for hospital business it bought Mitek Surgical Products (1995) and heart disease product maker Cordis (1996). The FDA cleared J&J's Renova wrinkle and fade cream in 1996. The company also began selling at-home HIV test Confide but pulled it the next year after low sales and other problems.

In 1997 J&J bought the OTC rights to Motrin from Pharmacia (now Pfizer). In 1998 the FDA approved artificial sweetener sucralose and its Indigo LaserOptic system to treat prostate enlargement. That year it bought DePuy and launched Benecol a margarine said to cut "bad" cholesterol by up to 15%.

In response to numerous negative events in 1998 —several drugs in late development fell through rights to an anemia drug were lost and the company's share of the coronary stent market fell

—the firm cut jobs and consolidated plants worldwide to control inventory and improve service.

In 1999 it purchased S.C. Johnson & Son's skin care business including the Aveeno line. That year the Ethicon Endo-Surgery unit settled three patent-infringement suits with Tyco International's U.S. Surgical. J&J also pulled its Hismanal antihistamine and bought biotechnology firm Centocor.

The firm bought sports medicine device maker Innovasive Devices in 2000. After more than 80 deaths were linked to its use J&J pulled heartburn drug Propulsid from the US market. That year the company started a health care services information-technology joint venture with Merrill Lynch and began selling Definity 2 trifocals as its first venture into eyeglass lenses.

In 2001 J&J bought minimally invasive heart-surgery equipment maker Heartport. Other buys included BabyCenter an online parenting resource; drug and drug-delivery system maker ALZA; and the diabetes-care businesses of Inverness Medical Technology (renamed Alere) which it merged with its LifeScan division.

The company made headlines in 2002 with its INDEPENDENCE iBOT a robotic wheelchair capable of climbing staircases and traversing rough terrain made by subsidiary Independence Technology. That year J&J acquired OraPharma a maker of oral antibiotics and other periodontal therapies.

In 2006 J&J aggressively pushed to add cardiac defibrillator maker Guidant to its medical device portfolio but was thwarted at every turn by counterbids from niche rival Boston Scientific. Boston Scientific emerged victorious from that battle paying some $27 billion for Guidant.

That year the company paid $16.6 billion to make the major coup of acquiring Pfizer's consumer products business which added about 40 brands to J&J's offerings. In order to clear some FTC hurdles J&J sold US marketing rights for Pfizer's Zantac to Boehringer Ingelheim Pharmaceuticals for a little more than $500 million. J&J also sold five brands (Act mouthwash Unisom sleep aid Cortizone anti-itch treatment Kaopectate anti-diarrhea medication and Balmex for diaper rash) to Chattem.

In 2007 J&J acquired drug-coated stent maker Conor Medsystems but it had to halt US development of Conor's Costar stent (and pull the product from international shelves) after it failed in a pivotal clinical trial. Also that year the company launched a new schizophrenia medication called Invega as well as antibacterial Doribax and antiretroviral Prezista.

J&J announced a major restructuring aimed at trimming costs in some areas and reinvesting in others in 2007. The restructuring included job cuts amounting to about 4% of J&J's global workforce with the bulk coming out of Cordis and various operating subsidiaries in its Pharmaceuticals segment.

To offset losses from certain products' shrinking markets J&J in 2008 consolidated Ortho Biotech (the marketer of troubled anemia drug Procrit) into Centocor (the successful maker of Remicade) which was then renamed Centocor Ortho Biotech. It also combined administrative functions of its Janssen (neurology) and Ortho-McNeil (birth control including the controversial Ortho Evra patch) divisions into holding company Ortho-McNeil-Janssen Pharmaceuticals.

In late 2008 the company expanded through the acquisition of biosurgical products maker Omrix Biopharmaceuticals for $438 million. Also that year J&J's consumer unit launched an OTC version of Zyrtec a former Pfizer allergy prescription that had gone off-patent. In addition the company won FDA approval for HIV drug Intelence that year.

Global blockbusters Risperdal (schizophrenia) and Topamax (epilepsy) lost patent protection in 2008 and 2009 respectively and began facing competition from cheaper generics. The company still had market exclusivity for Risperdal Consta a long-acting injectable version of Risperdal that received approval for the expanded application of bipolar disorder treatment in 2009.

In 2009 the company launched new products including Stelara for psoriasis Simponi for rheumatoid arthritis and Nucynta for pain. In addition J&J paid about $1.1 billion for Mentor Corporation (renamed Mentor Worldwide) a maker of devices for aesthetic procedures and some $1 billion for Cougar Biotechnology an oncology research and development firm with a promising prostate cancer candidate.

Also in 2009 the company paid $885 million for an 18% stake in Irish drug maker Elan. As a result J&J gained control of Elan's portion of an Alzheimer's disease treatment partnership with Pfizer which it incorporated into a new company Janssen Alzheimer Immunotherapy. (Elan retained a 50% equity stake in that entity.) Later that year J&J broke into the growing flu vaccine development market by making a similar investment in Dutch biotech firm Crucell buying an 18% stake for $443 million. (It acquired the rest of Crucell in 2011.)

To expand in the medical equipment industry in early 2010 Ethicon acquired ear nose and throat (ENT) device maker Acclarent for $785 million.

Invega Sustenna a long-acting injectable version of schizophrenia medication Invega was launched in 2010. Also that year DePuy launched its new Delta XTEND shoulder replacement system.

As part of its restructuring efforts J&J combined the Janssen mental health division (maker of Concerta and Risperdal) Ortho-McNeil (contraceptives) Ortho-McNeil Neurologics (Topamax) and a number of other units into the Janssen Pharmaceuticals unit. It formed an umbrella organization known as the Janssen Pharmaceutical Companies and rebranded some divisions under the Janssen name to unify the identities of the various pharmaceutical entities.

EXECUTIVES

Chairman, William C. (Bill) Weldon, age 63, $1,802,500 total compensation
VP Finance and CFO, Dominic J. Caruso, age 54, $723,739 total compensation
VP Corporate Affairs, Brian D. Perkins, age 58
Treasurer, John A. Papa
CEO, Alex Gorsky, age 52
Corporate Controller, Stephen J. Cosgrove
Director Investor Relations, Lesley Fishman
VP Corporate Communication, Jeffrey J. (Jeff) Leebaw
Worldwide Chairman Medical Devices & Diagnostics, Michael F. (Mike) Mahoney, age 47
VP Investor Relations, Louise Mehrotra
Senior Director Investor Relations, Stanley (Stan) Panasewicz
VP Public Affairs and Corporate Communications, Raymond C. Jordan
Worldwide Chairman Pharmaceuticals, Paul Stoffels
Director Corporate Media Relations, Marc Monseau
Director Corporate Media Relations, Bill Price
Director Investor Relations, Tina Pinto
Director Corporate Media Relations, Carol Goodrich
Worldwide Chairman Consumer, Jesse Wu
Worldwide Chairman Pharmaceuticals, Joaquin Duato
Worldwide VP Human Resources, Peter M. Fasolo, age 49
Corporate Secretary and Assistant General Counsel, Douglas K. Chia
President McNeil Consumer Division, Denise Torres
VP and General Counsel, Michael H. Ullmann, age 53
Director, Leo F. Mullin, age 69
Director, Anne M. Mulcahy, age 60
Director, Michael M. E. Johns, age 70
Director, Ronald A. (Ron) Williams, age 62
Director, William D. (Bill) Perez, age 64
Director, Charles O. (Chuck) Prince III, age 62
Director, James G. Cullen, age 69
Director, David Satcher, age 71
Director, Ian E. L. Davis, age 61
Director, Susan L. Lindquist, age 62
Auditors: PricewaterhouseCoopersLLP

LOCATIONS

HQ: Johnson & Johnson
One Johnson & Johnson Plaza, New Brunswick NJ 08933
Phone: 732-524-0400 **Fax:** 732-214-0332
Web: www.jnj.com

2011 Sales

	$ mil.	% of total
US	28,908	45
Europe	17,129	26
Asia/Pacific & Africa	12,575	19
Western Hemisphere excluding US	6,418	10
Total	**65,030**	**100**

PRODUCTS/OPERATIONS

2011 Sales

	$ mil.	% of total
Medical Devices & Diagnostic		
DePuy	5,809	9
Ethicon Endo-Surgery	5,080	8
Ethicon	4,870	8
Vision care (Vistakon)	2,916	4
Diabetes care (LifeScan)	2,652	4
Cardiovascular care (Cordis)	2,288	4
Ortho-Clinical Diagnostics	2,164	3
Pharmaceuticals		
Remicade	5,492	8
Procrit/Eprex	1,623	2
Risperdal Consta	1,583	2
Velcade	1,274	2
Concerta	1,268	2
Prezista	1,211	2
Aciphex/Pariet	975	2
Levaquin/Floxin	623	1
Other pharmaceuticals	10,319	16
Consumer		
OTC pharmaceuticals & nutritionals	4,402	7
Skin care	3,715	6
Baby care	2,340	4
Women's health	1,792	3
Oral care	1,624	2
Wound care & other	1,010	1
Total	**65,030**	**100**

Selected Products

Medical devices and diagnostics
- AcuVue contact lenses (Vistakon)
- Advanced sterilization products
- Animas insulin pump (LifeScan)
- Cordis diagnostic catheters
- Cypher (drug-coated stent Cordis)
- DePuy Mitek sports medicine products
- DePuy Orthopaedics hip and knee replacement products
- DePuy Spine repair products
- Electrophysiology products (Biosense Webster)
- Ethicon women' s health and urology

Harmonic scalpel (plastic surgery)
OneTouch blood glucose monitor (LifeScan)
Vitros diagnostic instrumentation systems (Ortho-Clinical)

Pharmaceuticals
Aciphex/Pariet (acid reflux)
Concerta (ADHD)
Duragesic/Fentanyl transdermal (pain management Durogesic outside the US)
Edurant (HIV)
Intelence (HIV)
Invega (schizophrenia)
Invega Sustenna (injectable Invega)
Levaquin/Floxin (anti-infective)
Nucynta (pain)
Ortho Evra (patch contraceptive)
Ortho Tri-cyclen (oral contraceptive)
Prezista (HIV)
Procrit/Eprex (anemia Eprex outside the US)
Remicade (rheumatoid arthritis psoriasis and Crohn' s disease)
Risperdal (schizophrenia and bipolar)
Risperdal Consta (injectable Risperdal)
Simponi (rheumatoid arthritis)
Stelara (psoriasis)
Topamax (epilepsy and migraines)
Velcade (multiple myeloma)
Xarelto (blood clots)
Zytiga (prostate cancer)

Consumer
Aveeno skin care products
Band-Aid bandages
Benecol food products
Carefree feminine hygiene products
Clean & Clear skin care products
Imodium A-D antidiarrheal
Johnson' s adult skin care products
Johnson' s baby care products
Lactaid nutritional products
Listerine mouthwash
Motrin IB analgesic
Mylanta gastrointestinal aid
Neutrogena skin and hair care products
Pepcid AC gastrointestinal aid (marketed with Merck)
Reach toothbrushes
Rembrandt toothpaste
RoC skin care products
Splenda non-caloric sugar substitute
Stayfree feminine hygiene products
Sudafed cold flu and allergy medications
Tylenol acetaminophen pain medicines
Viactiv calcium supplements
Zyrtec allergy products

Selected Subsidiaries and Divisions

ALZA Corporation
Biosense Webster Inc.
Conor Medsystems LLC
Cordis Corporation
Crucell N.V.
DePuy Inc.
Codman & Shurtleff Inc.
DePuy Mitek Inc.
DePuy Spine Inc.
Ethicon Endo-Surgery Inc.
Ethicon Inc.
Acclarent Inc.
Mentor Worldwide
Omrix Biopharmaceuticals Inc.
Johnson & Johnson Health Care Systems Inc.
Johnson & Johnson Medical Ltd. (UK)
Johnson & Johnson Pharmaceutical Research & Development L.L.C.
Johnson & Johnson Vision Care Inc.
Vistakon
LifeScan Inc.
Animas Corporation
McNeil Consumer Healthcare
McNeil Consumer Pharmaceuticals Co. (formerly Johnson & Johnson - Merck Consumer Pharmaceuticals Co.)
McNeil Nutritionals LLC
Neutrogena Corporation
Noramco Inc.
Ortho-Clinical Diagnostics Inc.
Janssen Pharmaceutical Companies
Janssen Biotech Inc. (formerly Centocor Ortho Biotech Services LLC)
Cougar Biotechnology Inc.
Janssen Pharmaceuticals Inc.
Janssen Therapeutics
Scios Inc.
Therakos Inc.

COMPETITORS

3M Health Care
Abbott Labs
Alcon
Allergan
Amgen
ArthroCare
AstraZeneca
B. Braun Melsungen
Bard
Bausch & Lomb
Baxter International
Bayer AG
Beckman Coulter
Becton Dickinson
Biogen Idec
Boehringer Ingelheim
Boston Scientific
Bristol-Myers Squibb
Chattem
Colgate-Palmolive
Cook Incorporated
Covidien
Dr. Reddy' s
Edwards Lifesciences
Elan
Eli Lilly
Forest Labs
Genzyme
GlaxoSmithKline
Kimberly-Clark Health
L' Oreal USA
Medtronic
Mentholatum Company
Merck
Mylan
Novartis
NutraSweet
Perrigo
Pfizer
Procter & Gamble
Roche Holding
Sanofi
Shire
Smith & Nephew
St. Jude Medical
Stryker
Terumo
Teva
The Dial Corporation
UCB
Unilever
Watson Pharmaceuticals
Zimmer Holdings

HISTORICAL FINANCIALS

Company Type: Public

Income Statement FYE: January 1

	REVENUE ($ mil.)	NET INCOME ($ mil.)	NET PROFIT MARGIN	EMPLOYEES
01/12	65,030	9,672	14.9%	117,900
01/11	61,587	13,334	21.7%	114,000
01/10*	61,897	12,266	19.8%	115,500
12/08	63,747	12,949	20.3%	118,700
12/07	61,095	10,576	17.3%	119,200
Annual Growth	1.6%	(2.2%)	—	(0.3%)

*Fiscal year change

2012 Year-End Financials

Debt ratio: 17.27%—
Return on equity: 16.94%
Cash ($ mil.): 24,542
Current ratio: 238.11
Long-term debt ($ mil.): 12,969
Dividends
Yield: —
Payout: 64.47%
Market value ($ mil.): —

	STOCK PRICE ($) FY Close	P/E High	P/E Low	PER SHARE ($) Earnings	Dividends	Book Value
01/12	65.58	19	16	3.49	0.00	20.95
01/11	61.85	14	12	4.78	0.00	20.66
01/10*	64.41	15	10	4.40	0.00	18.37
12/08	58.56	16	12	4.57	0.00	15.35
12/07	67.38	19	16	3.63	0.00	15.25
Annual Growth	(0.7%)	—	—	(1.0%)	—	8.3%

*Fiscal year change

Johnson Controls Inc

Johnson Controls (JCI) wants to put you in the driver's seat –an environmentally conscious one. The company makes car batteries and interior parts for combustion engine and hybrid electric vehicles as well as energy-efficient HVAC systems for commercial buildings. Products include seating instrument panels and a slew of electronics. OEM customers include GM Daimler and Ford. The battery unit supplies car batteries for retailers such as Advance Auto Parts AutoZone Pep Boys and Wal-Mart. The building efficiency unit makes installs and services mechanical equipment that controls HVAC lighting security and fire systems in commercial buildings. The unit also offers on-site facility management.

HISTORY

Professor Warren Johnson developed the electric telethermoscope in 1880 so that janitors at Whitewater Wisconsin's State Normal School could regulate room temperatures without disturbing classrooms. His device the thermostat used mercury to move a heat element that opened and shut a circuit. Milwaukee hotelier William Plankinton believed in the invention and invested $150000 to start production.

The two men formed Johnson Electric Service Company in 1885. They sold the marketing installation and service rights to concentrate on manufacturing. Johnson also invented other devices such as tower clocks and he experimented with the telegraph before becoming intrigued with the automobile and beginning production of steam-powered cars. He won the US Postal Service's first automotive contract but never gained support within his own company. Johnson continued to look elsewhere for financing until his death in 1911.

The renamed Johnson Services regained full rights to its thermostats in 1912 and sold its other businesses. During the Depression it produced economy systems that regulated building temperatures. Johnson Services became a public company in 1940. During WWII it aided the war effort building weather-data gatherers and radar test sets.

In the 1960s Johnson Services began developing centralized control systems for temperature fire alarm lighting and security regulation. The company was renamed Johnson Controls in 1974; it acquired automotive battery maker Globe-Union in 1978.

Johnson Controls bought auto seat makers Hoover Universal and Ferro Manufacturing in 1985. It expanded its controls business through the purchases of ITT's European controls group (1982) and Pan Am World Services (1989).

The company sold its car-door components business in 1990 and bought battery maker Varta's Canadian plant. The next year Johnson Controls purchased several car-seat component makers in Europe and in 1992 it bought a Welsh plastics manufacturer and a Czech seat-cover producer.

The battery unit faced a major setback in 1994 when Sears dropped the company as its battery maker. Two years later however the battery business was recharged by an exclusive supply contract with Target stores.

In 1996 Johnson Controls bought most of Roth Freres (auto components) and Prince Automotive (interior systems) becoming a major interior-systems integrator. The company sold its plastic-container operations to the Schmalbach-Lubeca unit of Germany's VIAG in 1997 and regained its Sears business with a three-year deal to make DieHard batteries.

The company bought Becker Group (automotive interior parts) Creative Control Designs (HVAC and lighting-control systems) and Italy-based Commerfin SpA (door systems) in 1998. To slim down after its buying binge Johnson Controls sold its plastics-machinery division to Cincinnati Milacron (now Milacron) and its industrial batteries unit to C&D Technologies.

The company announced in 1999 that it would develop integrated electronics for car interiors through a "keiretsu"-like partnership with Gentex Corporation (mirrors) Jabil Circuit (semiconductors and transistors) and Microchip Technology (microcontrollers). The next year Johnson Controls agreed to buy Nissan's 38% stake in seat maker Ikeda Bussan for about $100 million as well as Sweden's Gylling Optima Batteries for about $62 million. Late in 2000 the company bought a 15% stake in Donnelly Corporation (automotive components).

In 2001 Johnson Controls paid $435 million in cash for the automotive electronics business of France's Sagem (now SAFRAN). It then picked up German automotive-battery maker Hoppecke Automotive GmbH & Co. and finished out the year with the acquisition of SCIENTECH Security Services a design-build security-system integration services business specializing in US government projects. It added the automotive battery operations of Varta AG (Germany) in 2002 and Borg Instruments (automotive electronics) in 2003.

Johnson Controls in 2004 acquired complete control of the Mexican battery-making operations run as a joint venture with Grupo IMSA (now Ternium Mexico); Johnson Control was the joint venture's primary customer.

Early the following year Johnson Controls sold its engine electronics division (engine management systems and components) to France's Valeo for about $437 million. The company also sold its Johnson Controls World Services subsidiary to IAP Worldwide Services for about $260 million.

The company's controls division was complemented by Johnson Controls' late 2005 acquisition of York International the US's third-largest supplier of heating ventilation air-conditioning and refrigeration equipment. The deal was valued at $3.2 billion. The controls division also benefited from Johnson Controls' 2005 purchase of corporate real estate services firm United Systems Integrators Corporation (USI) for $80 million. The move allowed Johnson Controls to offer customers a single source for facilities management and real estate services.

Also in 2005 the company increased its presence in Asia particularly in China by purchasing Delphi's global auto battery operations. The deal was valued in excess of $200 million and was tied to a long-term global contract to supply GM with batteries.

Prompted by the acquisition of York Johnson Controls renamed its business units. Automotive experience handled the company's automotive interior and seating business; Building efficiency covered building systems controls and HVAC; and power solutions encompassed Johnson Controls' battery businesses.

In 2006 Johnson Controls bought Environmental Technologies Inc. a supplier of HVAC equipment. Terms of the purchase were undisclosed.

Also that year Johnson Controls announced it would take an estimated after-tax charge of between $130 million and $140 million in the third quarter for restructuring. The revamping was aimed at reducing costs at its automotive interiors and facilities management businesses. The plan included the cutting of 5000 jobs and the closure of 16 plants over one year. Specifically the moves were aimed at increasing efficiencies and profitability at its US interiors business and its European seating operations. The facilities management business in Europe also launched a systems redesign.

The following year Johnson Controls sold its European diagnostics division to SPX Corporation for nearly $44 million.

The building efficiency division also grew in 2007 with the acquisition of Skymark International a provider of indoor packaged HVAC equipment. Skymark's self-contained HVAC units were used in both new construction and retrofit markets.

As increasing numbers of consumers seek out fuel-efficient low-emission vehicles Johnson Controls is broadening its expertise in green energy through both acquisitions and collaborations. In 2008 the company acquired PWI Energy an independent provider of energy and greenhouse-gas-management services. It also bought financially strapped Plastech Engineered Products' automotive interiors operations.

Expanding its core building efficiency services JCI linked up with German-based Concentrix Solar (a subsidiary of Soitec Group) in 2010 to develop solar photovoltaic systems for North America.

Also in 2010 JCI expanded its lighting services to retail commercial and industrial markets by taking over National Energy Services (NES). Additionally that year JCI purchased Michel Thierry a France-based automotive fabrics and lamination supplier. Along with its customer base in the Czech Republic France and Spain Michel Thierry strengthened Johnson Controls' direction of the automobile seat manufacturing process.

Additionally in 2010 the power solutions segment acquired the remaining shares of its Korean Power Solutions as well as 90% of its joint venture with Delkor Corporation an automotive battery manufacturer in South Korea.

EXECUTIVES

VP Secretary and General Counsel, Jerome D. Okarma, age 60
EVP Human Resources, Susan F. Davis, age 59
Chairman President and CEO, Stephen A. Roell, age 62, $1,365,000 total compensation
VP; President Building Efficiency, C. David (Dave) Myers, age 49, $835,000 total compensation
VP and Treasurer, Frank A. Voltolina, age 52
VP; President Automotive Experience, Beda-Helmut Bolzenius, age 56, $779,000 total compensation
EVP and CFO, R. Bruce McDonald, age 52, $776,000 total compensation
VP Finance Power Solutions, Susan M. Kreh, age 50
VP Corporate Communication, Jacqueline F. Strayer, age 58
Group VP and General Manager Auto Experience Asia, Jeffrey S. Edwards, age 50
VP; President Power Solutions, Alex A. Molinaroli, age 53, $713,000 total compensation
VP Finance Building Efficiency, Jeffrey G. Augustin, age 50
VP Diversity and Public Affairs, Charles A. Harvey, age 60
VP and Corporate Controller, Brian J. Stief, age 56
EVP Operations and Innovation, William C. (Bill) Jackson, age 51
VP Information Technology and CIO, Colin Boyd, age 53
VP Government Affairs, Mark Wagner
Manager Brand and Corporate Communication, Anna Timms
Program Manager Public Relations Building Efficiency, Angela S. Adams
Manager Marketing Communications Building Efficiency Latin America, Cuky Pouparina
Communications Manager Building Efficiency Asia, Kay Cheung
Public Relations Manager Building Efficiency Europe and Africa, Nanda Aerts
Communications Manager Building Efficiency EMEA Global WorkPlace Solutions, Charlotte Ling
Regional Manager Communications Building Efficiency Middle East, Farhan Qureshy
Global Public Relations Manager Automotive Experience, Debra L. Lacey
Public Relations Manager Automotive Experience Europe, Astrid Schafmeister
External Communication Manager Automotive Experience Asia, Phyllis Gao
Global Communications Director Power Solutions, Rebecca K. Fitzgerald
External Communications Manager EMEA Power Solutions, Ina Longwitz
Manager Public Relations Building Efficiency, Kari B. Pfisterer
Director, Robert L. Barnett, age 72
Director, Jeffrey A. (Jeff) Joerres, age 53
Director, Robert A. Cornog, age 72
Director, William H. Lacy, age 67
Director, Dennis W. Archer, age 70
Director, Natalie A. Black, age 62
Director, David P. Abney, age 57
Director, Eugenio Clariond Reyes-Retana, age 69
Director, Richard A. Goodman, age 64
Auditors: PricewaterhouseCoopersLLP

LOCATIONS

HQ: Johnson Controls Inc.
5757 N. Green Bay Ave., Milwaukee WI 53209
Phone: 414-524-1200 **Fax:** 414-524-2077
Web: www.johnsoncontrols.com

2011 Sales

	$ mil.	% of total
US	14,367	35
Europe		
Germany	4,590	11
Other European countries	10,212	25
Mexico	1,869	5
Rest of the world	9,795	24
Total	**40,833**	**100**

PRODUCTS/OPERATIONS

2011 Sales

	$ mil.	% of total
Automotive experience	20,065	49
Building efficiency	14,893	37
Power solutions	5,875	14
Total	**40,833**	**100**

Selected Mergers & Acquisitions

FY2011
KEIPER ($450 million; Germany; metal seat structures and mechanisms supplier)
C. Rob. Hammerstein (Germany; metal seat structures parts and mechanisms supplier)
EnergyConnect (California; smart grid response services and technologies provider)

Selected Products

Automotive experience
Electronics
Body electronics
Driver information

- HomeLink (wireless car-to-home connectivity)
- Infotainment and connectivity

Interiors
- Cockpits and instrument panels
- Door panels
- Floor consoles
- Overhead products

Seating
- Climate seat systems
- Foam
- Metal structures and mechanisms
- Seat safety
- Trim

Building efficiency
- Building management systems
- Fire safety products
- HVAC systems
- Refrigeration
- Security products
- Snowmaking equipment
- York equipment

Power solutions
- Absorbent glass mat technology
- Lead-acid batteries
- Lithium-ion batteries

COMPETITORS

A123 Systems
Addison
Building Technologies
Comfort Systems USA
Delphi Automotive Systems
DENSO
Eagle-Picher
East Penn Manufacturing
Eaton
Exide
Faurecia
General Motors
Goodman Global
GS Yuasa
Honeywell International
Invensys
Lear Corp
Lennox
Magna International
Paloma Group
Rieter Automotive North America
Robert Bosch
SPX
Trane Inc.
Valeo
Visteon
Yazaki North America

HISTORICAL FINANCIALS

Company Type: Public

Income Statement FYE: September 30

	REVENUE ($ mil.)	NET INCOME ($ mil.)	NET PROFIT MARGIN	EMPLOYEES
09/12	41,955	1,226	2.9%	170,000
09/11	40,833	1,624	4.0%	162,000
09/10	34,305	1,491	4.3%	137,000
09/09	28,497	(338)	—	130,000
09/08	38,062	979	2.6%	140,000
Annual Growth	2.5%	5.8%	—	5.0%

2012 Year-End Financials

Debt ratio: 19.65%
Return on equity: 10.61%
Cash ($ mil.): 265
Current ratio: 116.75
Long-term debt ($ mil.): 5,321
No. of shares (mil.): 682
Dividends
Yield: —
Payout: 40.45%
Market value ($ mil.): 18,695

	STOCK PRICE ($) FY Close	P/E High/Low		PER SHARE ($) Earnings	Dividends	Book Value
09/12	27.40	20	13	1.78	0.00	16.94
09/11	26.37	18	11	2.36	0.64	16.23
09/10	30.50	16	11	2.19	0.52	14.95
09/09	25.56	—	—	(0.57)	0.52	13.67
09/08	30.33	73	17	1.63	0.52	15.95
Annual Growth	(2.5%)	—	—	2.2%	—	1.5%

Joy Global Inc

Joy Global is pretty happy for a company that builds equipment destined to spend the majority of its life down in a hole. The company makes heavy equipment for the mining industry through two subsidiaries. Its Joy Mining Machinery subsidiary makes underground coal-mining equipment that includes armored face conveyors roof supports longwall shearers and shuttle cars. Subsidiary P&H Mining Equipment makes electric mining shovels rotary blasthole drills and other equipment used in surface open-pit mining; it also provides parts and service through its P&H MinePro Services network. Joy Global operates manufacturing and service facilities worldwide; about half of its sales are made outside of the US.

In the aftermath of Caterpillar's 2010 acquisition of Joy Global's chief rival Bucyrus International the company has been in deal-making mode. In mid-2011 Joy Global acquired mining equipment manufacturer LeTourneau Technologies from Rowan Cos. (RDC) for about $1.1 billion. The deal gives Joy Global access to large electric-drive wheel loaders used in mining. LeTourneau's mining equipment business segment will be integrated with Joy's P&H mining business. However Joy said it will sell the drilling products business of LeTourneau to Cameron International for $375 million in order to use the cash for its acquisition of Chinese mining equipment maker International Mining Machinery Holdings Ltd. (IMM). Joy Global outlined a plan for acquiring 41% of IMM's share from private equity firm The Jordan Company and obtained the share through a tender offer to investors in late 2011. The deal valued at $584 million gave the company a 69% controlling stake in IMM and expanded its presence in the Chinese coal mining equipment market.

Although it is one of the largest producers of underground mining equipment Joy Global confronts a highly cyclical marketplace driven by commodity pricing and industry consolidation. In addition more than two-thirds of Joy Global's revenues come from coal mining customers exposing it to public outcry over climate change and other risks.

Although Joy Global experienced cancellations and deferred new orders throughout most of 2009 its backlog recovered and grew by almost 40% in 2010. About two-thirds of the increase was driven by demand for new equipment and the remainder for aftermarket parts and service. Net sales declined slightly due to flagging shipments of original underground equipment. Nevertheless earnings increased buoyed by higher interest income coupled with lower interest expense and income taxes. Cash generated from operations reached a new high.

Joy Global benefits from focusing on aftermarket sales and service (about 60% of sales). This capability extends the life of its installed base of (expensive) machinery through spare parts and repair services as well as supports long-term customer relationships and a steady revenue stream. Its surface mining equipment business also offers aftermarket services for equipment made by other OEMs.

To optimizing aftermarket sales and services the company has built service centers in key mining regions –Canada Chile Australia and South Africa – and plans to open new centers in Russia and India. The latter initiatives are anticipated to help offset some of the decline experienced in more mature domestic markets. Concurrently it has managed to shift an increasing portion of its aftermarket revenue from one-time transactions to extended maintenance and repair contracts or machine exchange programs. The company has also introduced remote equipment monitoring systems allowing maintenance personnel to check machines for reliability and safety fleet status productivity and other performance related issues using wireless technology.

HISTORY

In the mid-1880s German immigrant Henry Harnischfeger and partner Alonzo Pawling started Pawling and Harnischfeger (P&H) a small machine and pattern shop in Milwaukee. The company shipped its first overhead electric crane in 1888. After a fire destroyed its main shop in 1903 P&H built a new plant in West Milwaukee the following year that became the world's leading manufacturer of overhead cranes. The company became Harnischfeger Corporation after Pawling died in 1914. In remembrance of Pawling Harnischfeger kept its P&H trademark.

The highly cyclical heavy-equipment industry encountered a big upswing with WWI. After the war Harnischfeger began selling excavating and mining equipment to help weather downturns in the industry. Harnischfeger died in 1930 and his son Walter became president. The Depression was hard for the company as it lost money every year from 1931 to 1939. Harnischfeger diversified into welding equipment diesel engines and prefabricated houses during the 1930s and 1940s.

WWII and the postwar period boosted the company and Harnischfeger was listed on the AMEX in 1956. Walter became chairman in 1959 and his son Henry became president. Harnischfeger streamlined operations in the 1960s keeping its construction and mining division and its industrial and electrical division.

Harnischfeger was listed on the NYSE in 1971. After the 1973 oil embargo its machinery sales increased with the opening of coal reserves and the construction of oil pipelines and mass transit systems. By the end of the 1970s however recession and high interest rates took their toll on the company.

On the verge of bankruptcy in the early 1980s Harnischfeger revived itself by trimming down diversifying and making key acquisitions. It formed Harnischfeger Engineering in 1984 (sold in the early 1990s) and in 1986 the company bought Beloit (papermaking equipment) and formed Harnischfeger Industries as a holding company.

Harnischfeger began moving away from systems handling in the early 1990s. It bought underground mining equipment maker Joy Technologies (now Joy Mining Machinery) in 1994 and Longwall International (through the acquisition of Dobson Park Industries) in 1995. The next year Harnischfeger bought Ingersoll-Rand's pulp machinery division. In 1997 the company's $631 million bid for Giddings & Lewis (machine tools) was thwarted when Giddings & Lewis agreed to be acquired by Thyssen (now ThyssenKrupp AG).

After the Asian economic crisis and other factors weakened demand for its papermaking and mining equipment Harnischfeger announced in 1998 it would be laying off about 20% of its workforce –about 3100 jobs. Harnischfeger also sold an 80% stake in P&H Material Handling to Chartwell Investments for $340 million that year.

In 1999 Harnischfeger rearranged the terms of $500 million in loans and obtained an additional $250 million term loan. CEO Jeffery Grade also chairman since 1993 stepped down. Grade spearheaded the company's aggressive growth strategy which was stymied by slips in demand for the company's machinery due to weak prices for metal and paper. President John Hanson succeeded Grade as CEO. Unable to keep up with its debt the company filed for Chapter 11 bankruptcy protection.

Creditors accepted a $160 million offer from Metso Corporation in 2000 to buy Beloit's assets including its roll cover division paper machine aftermarket assets and related paper machine technology. Harnischfeger emerged from bankruptcy and changed its name to Joy Global Inc. in 2001.

Orders for new equipment were soft in 2002 although limited sales were offset by paced revenue growth through the company's operations in China. In 2003 Joy Global completed the purchase of the remaining 25% interest in P&H-Australia (surface mining equipment) that it didn't already own.

P&H sold its subsidiary The Horsburgh & Scott Co. a manufacturer of industrial gears and mechanical gear drives in November 2005. The following year Joy Global purchased the Stamler business of Oldenburg Group Inc. for $118 million. Stamler's products used in underground and surface coal mining included feeder breakers battery haulers and continuous haulage systems.

EVP Michael Sutherlin succeeded John Hanson as president and CEO in 2006. Hanson remained chairman. Sutherlin previously served as president and COO of Joy Mining Machinery for three years.

Joy Global acquired Continental Global Group which was renamed Continental Crushing & Conveying in 2008; the company makes conveyor systems and material-handling machinery used in mining and other industrial applications. Also that year the company purchased Wuxi Shengda a China-based firm that makes longwall shearing machines giving it a foothold in the domestic equipment manufacturing sector of the country. An armored face conveyor factory and a shovel transmission factory followed enabling low-cost performance and local delivery.

EXECUTIVES

Chairman, John N. (Nils) Hanson, age 70, $315,600 total compensation
President CEO and Director, Michael W. Sutherlin, age 66, $828,333 total compensation
EVP Administration, Dennis R. Winkleman, age 61, $312,500 total compensation
EVP CFO and Treasurer, Michael S. (Mike) Olsen, age 61, $364,741 total compensation
EVP; President and COO Joy Mining Machinery, Edward L. (Ted) Doheny II, age 50, $469,021 total compensation
VP Controller and Chief Accounting Officer, Ricky T. Dillon, age 42
EVP General Counsel and Secretary, Sean D. Major, age 47, $347,833 total compensation
VP Investor Relations and Corporate Communications, Sara Leuchter Wilkins, age 57
EVP; President and COO P&H Mining Equipment, Randal W. (Randy) Baker, age 48
Executive Assistant, Sandra L. McKenzie
EVP Business Development, Eric A. Nielsen, age 52
President and COO Continental Crushing & Conveying and EVP Joy Global Inc., Terry Nicola
Director, Ken C. Johnsen, age 53
President CEO and Director, Michael W. Sutherlin, age 66
Director, Gale E. Klappa, age 61
Director, Steven L. Gerard, age 66
Director, Richard B. (Dick) Loynd, age 84
Director, P. Eric Siegert, age 46
Auditors: Ernst&YoungLLP

LOCATIONS

HQ: Joy Global Inc
100 East Wisconsin Avenue, Suite 2780, Milwaukee, WI 53202
Phone: 414 319-8500
Web: www.joyglobal.com

2010 Sales

	$ mil.	% of total
US	2,135	50
Australia	527	12
Europe	315	8
Other regions	1,290	30
Adjustments	(744.4)	-
Total	**3,524**	**100**

PRODUCTS/OPERATIONS

2010 Sales

	$ mil.	% of total
Undergroung mining machinery	2,126	58
Surface mining equipment	1,518	42
Adjustments	(121.1)	-
Total	**3,524**	**100**

2010 Sales

	$ mil.	% of total
Aftermarket	2,097	60
Original equipment	1,426	40
Total	**3,524**	**100**

Selected Products

Surface mining equipment (P&H Mining Equipment)
- Electric mining shovels
- Rotary blasthole drills
- Walking draglines

Underground mining machinery (Joy Mining Machinery)
- Armored face conveyors
- Battery haulers
- Complete longwall mining systems
- Continuous haulage systems
- Continuous miners
- Conveyor systems
- Crushing equipment
- Feeder breakers
- Flexible conveyor trains
- High angle conveyors
- Longwall shearers
- Roof bolters
- Roof supports
- Shuttle cars

COMPETITORS

Caterpillar
Hitachi
Howle Holdings
Ingersoll-Rand
Jervis B. Webb
Komatsu
Marmon Group
Metso
Multi-Shifter
Rowan Companies
Sandvik
Sime Darby

HISTORICAL FINANCIALS

Company Type: Public

Income Statement FYE: October 26

	REVENUE ($ mil.)	NET INCOME ($ mil.)	NET PROFIT MARGIN	EMPLOYEES
10/12	5,660	762	13.5%	18,019
10/11	4,403	609	13.8%	14,500
10/10	3,524	461	13.1%	11,900
10/09	3,598	454	12.6%	11,300
10/08	3,418	374	10.9%	11,800
Annual Growth	13.4%	19.5%	—	11.2%

2012 Year-End Financials

Debt ratio: 22.34%
Return on equity: 29.57%
Cash ($ mil.): 263
Current ratio: 177.23
Long-term debt ($ mil.): 1,306
No. of shares (mil.): 105
Dividends
Yield: 1.14%
Payout: 9.82%
Market value ($ mil.): 6,520

	STOCK PRICE ($) FY Close	P/E High/Low		PER SHARE ($) Earnings	Dividends	Book Value
10/12	61.55	13	7	7.13	0.70	24.33
10/11	91.19	18	10	5.72	0.70	18.57
10/10	70.95	16	10	4.40	0.70	13.09
10/09	50.41	13	3	4.41	0.70	7.90
10/08	28.98	25	6	3.45	0.63	5.18
Annual Growth	20.7%	—	—	19.9%	2.7%	47.2%

JPMorgan Chase & Co.

JPMorgan Chase was born with a silver spoon in its mouth but that hasn't stopped it from wanting more. With more than $2 trillion in assets the largest bank holding company in the US has more than 5500 branches in a couple dozen states (and counting) and is among the nation's top mortgage lenders and credit card issuers (it holds some $132 billion in credit card loans). Active in some 60 countries it also boasts formidable investment banking and asset management operations. The firm's subsidiaries include the prestigious JPMorgan Private Bank and institutional investment manager JPMorgan Asset Management (with some $1.9 trillion under supervision). It also owns private equity firm One Equity Partners.

HISTORY

JPMorgan Chase & Co.'s roots are in The Manhattan Company created in 1799 to bring water to New York City. A provision buried in its incorporation documents let the company provide banking services; investor and future US Vice President Aaron Burr brought the company (eventually the Bank of Manhattan) into competition with The Bank of New York founded by Burr's political rival Alexander Hamilton. JPMorgan Chase still owns the pistols from the notorious 1804 duel in which Burr mortally wounded Hamilton.

In 1877 John Thompson formed Chase National naming it for Salmon Chase Abraham Lincoln's secretary of the treasury and the architect of the national bank system. Chase National merged with John D. Rockefeller's Equitable Trust in 1930 becoming the world's largest bank and beginning a long relationship with the Rockefellers. Chase National continued growing after WWII and in 1955 it merged with the Bank of Manhattan. Christened Chase Manhattan the bank remained the US's largest into the 1960s.

When soaring 1970s oil prices made energy loans attractive Chase invested in Penn Square an obscure oil-patch bank in Oklahoma and the first notable bank failure of the 1980s. (The legal aftereffects of Penn Square's 1982 failure dragged on until 1993.) Losses following the 1987 foreign loan crisis hit Chase hard as did the real estate crash. In 1995 the bank went looking for a partner. After talks with Bank of America it settled on Chemical Bank.

Chemical Bank opened in 1824 and was one of the US's largest banks by 1900. As with Chase Chemical Bank began as an unrelated business (New York Chemical Manufacturing) in 1823 largely in order to open a bank (it dropped its chemical operations in 1844). Chemical would merge with Manufacturers Hanover in 1991.

After its 1996 merger with Chase Chemical Bank was the surviving entity but assumed Chase's more prestigious name. Initial cost savings from the merger were substantial as jobs and branch offices were eliminated. In 1997 Chase acquired the credit business of The Bank of New York and the corporate trustee business of Mellon Financial but underwent another round of belt-tightening the next year when it took a $320 million charge and cut 4500 jobs. The bank also suffered losses related to its involvement with the ill-starred Long-Term Capital Management hedge fund.

In 1999 Chase focused on lending buying two mortgage originators and forming a marketing alliance with subprime auto lender AmeriCredit (now General Motors Financial Company). Chase also bought Mellon Financial's residential mortgage unit and Huntington Bancshares' credit card portfolio. It bought UK investment bank Robert Fleming Holdings in 2000.

In 2001 it closed its $30 billion buy of J.P. Morgan and renamed itself JPMorgan Chase & Co. The new firm eliminated some 10% of its combined workforce as a result of the merger. Chairman Sandy Warner (who ran J.P. Morgan) retired at year-end and was replaced by former Chase Manhattan leader CEO William Harrison.

JPMorgan Chase had more than $1 billion in exposure to Enron but in 2003 recovered some $600 million after a court battle with the failed energy trader's insurers which claimed the losses stemmed from loans by JPMorgan Chase disguised as oil and gas transactions. Nonetheless JPMorgan Chase ended up paying some $135 million to settle actions relating to the questionable loans.

In 2004 JPMorgan Chase joined forces with venerable investment bank Cazenove; the joint venture called JPMorgan Cazenove handles corporate finance and capital markets activities in the UK.

The next year JPMorgan Chase and its investment banking arm J.P. Morgan Securities avoided a trial by paying some $2 billion to settle claims from investors who lost money on bonds that the firm underwrote in 2000 and 2001 for scandal-ridden WorldCom which eventually declared bankruptcy (WorldCom became MCI and later was acquired by Verizon Communications).

On the heels of the its massive BANK ONE buy in 2004 JPMorgan Chase made several smaller purchases including global trade management and logistics software maker Vastera (renamed JPMorgan Chase Vastera) trading technology firm Neovest and the credit card business of Sears Canada. JPMorgan Chase also sold online brokerage subsidiary J.P. Morgan Invest and its BrownCo unit to E*TRADE. The following year the company acquired student lender Collegiate Funding Services which JPMorgan Chase combined with its existing Chase Education Finance division. The company also got the go-ahead from the FTC and bought Kohl's $1.6 billion credit card portfolio.

Enron continued to haunt the company: in 2005 it forked over $2.2 billion to settle part of an investor class-action suit over fraud charges related to the Enron debacle and paid another $350 million to the infamous energy trading firm which asserted that JPMorgan Chase and about 10 other banks aided and abetted the company's collapse. However the next year the company got some good news regarding its alleged involvement with the collapse of Enron when the class action suit against it was dismissed.

Also in 2006 the company cut ties with private equity investment arm J.P. Morgan Partners which divided into two companies CCMP Capital and Panorama Capital. JPMorgan Chase retained the former private equity operations of BANK ONE One Equity Partners.

In keeping with the lesson learned regarding its $2 billion fine to settle claims in the WorldCom debacle in 2006 the bank was quick to settle its part of another class-action lawsuit this time brought by investors claiming they were cheated in the dot-com IPO boom. JPMorgan Chase paid $425 million to settle that case. It paid a much smaller settlement of $3.8 million for its part in the demise of the ill-fated telecom Global Crossing.

All was not lawsuits and settlements in 2006 however: that year it swapped its corporate trust business for Bank of New York's nearly 340-branch network in the New York metropolitan area. Both units were valued at about $2 billion with JPMorgan Chase paying Bank of New York around $150 million more to make up the difference.

William Harrison retired as chairman at the end of 2006; he was succeeded by president and CEO (and the CEO of BANK ONE when it was acquired) Jamie Dimon.

As one of the largest mortgage and home equity providers in the country JPMorgan Chase was hurt by the subprime mortgage crisis and subsequent fall in home values in 2007. About a third of its loans were home equity loans and it had to write off more than $500 million in home equity loans that year.

In 2008 the bank assumed full ownership of payments processor Chase Paymentech Solutions which had been a joint venture with First Data. First Data assumed 49% of Chase Paymentech's assets and clients in the deal.

Also that year as part of a plan to stimulate the economy the US government invested in JPMorgan Chase and other banks. The bank got $25 billion of the $700 billion taxpayer-funded bailout package that was approved in late 2008 with the stipulation that the banks use the money and not hoard it. The investment came with restrictions on executive pay and other rules and JPMorgan returned the money the following year saying it was doing just fine without it.

Led by CEO Jamie Dimon JPMorgan Chase closed a couple of very high profile deals as the economic crisis claimed numerous victims. It acquired Bear Stearns one of Wall Street's top investment banks and the operations of Washington Mutual (WaMu) the largest bank to fail in US history. Both deals closed in 2008.

Initially JPMorgan Chase made a bargain-basement offer of $270 million (around $2 a share) for the struggling Bear Stearns which was drowning in subprime mortgage investment debt. It ultimately raised its offer to around $10 a share or some $1.2 billion. The deal came after the Fed extended a $30 billion lifeline to Bear Stearns to keep the firm afloat; JPMorgan Chase was one of the lenders.

The company also stepped in to buy WaMu when that bank failed and was seized by regulators. It paid $1.9 billion for the bank's operations and assumed some $31 billion in losses. JPMorgan began integrating WaMu's branches with its own retail network phasing out the WaMu brand and closing about 10% of the combined branches (especially in markets where there was overlap). Shortly after the acquisition JPMorgan cut 9200 WaMu jobs –about 20% of its workforce.

In 2009 JPMorgan Chase sold specialist firm Bear Wagner acquired in the Bear Stearns deal to Barclays Capital.

JPMorgan Chase agreed to pay more than $153 million to the Securities and Exchange Commission in order to settle a claim that it misled investors during the 2007 housing market crash. The company was among others that were investigated for improper sales practices.

EXECUTIVES

President International, Heidi G. Miller, age 57
Executive Committee Member Europe Middle East and Africa, Walter A. Gubert
Executive Committee Member; Chairman Midwest Business, Glenn F. Tilton, age 64
Executive Committee Member Pacific Northwest, Phyllis J. Campbell, age 60
Head of Corporate and Regulatory Affairs, Barry L. Zubrow, age 58
Executive Committee Member Asset Management, Michael O'Brien
Executive Committee Member Retail Financial Services, Michael J. Cleary, age 53
Executive Committee Member Audit, Martha J. Gallo
Executive Committee Member Investment Bank, Carlos M. Hernandez, age 50
Chairman and CEO, James (Jamie) Dimon, age 56, $1,000,000 total compensation
Executive Committee Member Consumer Practices, Stephanie B. Mudick, age 54
CEO Retail Financial Services, Charles W. (Charlie) Scharf, age 46, $500,000 total compensation
Executive Committee Member JPMorgan Chase International, Jacob A. Frenkel, age 69
Executive Committee Member Investment Bank, James B. (Jimmy) Lee Jr.
Executive Committee Member One Equity Partners, Richard M. (Dick) Cashin Jr., age 58
Consumer and Community Banking Co-CEO, James E. (Jes) Staley, age 55, $500,000 total compensation
General Counsel, Stephen M. (Steve) Cutler, age 50
Consumer and Community Banking Co-CEO, Gordon A. Smith, age 53, $500,000 total compensation
Head Strategy and Business Development, Jay Mandelbaum, age 49
Co-COO and CEO Mortgage Banking, Frank J. Bisignano, age 52, $500,000 total compensation
Head of Human Resources, John L. Donnelly, age 55
Executive Committee Member Asset Management, Paul T. Bateman
Executive Committee Member Asset Management, Catherine M. Keating, age 50
Executive Committee Member Treasury and Securities Services, Donald H. (Don) McCree III, age 44
Executive Committee Member Chief Investment Office, Achilles O. Macris
Chief Investment Officer, Ina R. Drew, age 55
EVP and Head Corporate Services and Finance, Peter J. (Pete) Bocian, age 56
Executive Committee Member Florida Mexico Central America and Caribbean, Mel R. Martinez, age 65
Corporate and Investment Bank Co-CEO, Michael J. (Mike) Cavanagh, age 45, $500,000 total compensation
Executive Committee Member Banking and Consumer Lending Operations, Scott E. Powell
CEO Consumer & Business Banking, Samuel Todd (Todd) Maclin, age 55

Executive Committee Member Home Lending, David B. (Dave) Lowman, age 53
Executive Committee Member Investment Bank, Kevin D. Willsey
CFO, Douglas L. (Doug) Braunstein, age 50
Executive Committee Member Chief Investment Office, Richard Sabo
Head North America Healthcare Coverage Group, Jeff Stute
Vice Chairman Investment Banking, Robbie Huffines
Executive Committee Member Asia Pacific, Gaby A. Abdelnour
Executive Committee Member Corporate Banking, Philip F. Bleser
Executive Committee Member Investment Bank, Klaus Diederichs
Executive Committee Member Auto and Education Finance, Marc Sheinbaum
Executive Committee Member Retail Financial Services, Kevin P. Watters
Executive Committee Member Controller, Louis Rauchenberger
Executive Committee Member Investment Management, Clive S. Brown
Executive Committee Member Philanthropy, Kimberly B. Davis
Executive Committee Member Corporate Communications, Joseph M. Evangelisti
Executive Committee Member Investment Bank, Blythe S. Masters
Executive Committee Member Card Services, William S. Wallace
Global Head Marketing and Communications Investment Bank, Kristin Lemkau
Executive Committee Member Strategy and Marketing, Jack M. Stephenson
CIO, Guy Chiarello
Corporate and Investment Bank Co-CEO, Daniel E. Pinto
Global Head Equity Derivatives and Regional Head Equities Europe Middle East and Africa, Tim Throsby
Managing Director Investment Banking India, Sidharth Punshi
Executive Committee Member Global Government Relations and Public Policy, Peter L. Scher
Chief Risk Officer, John J. Hogan
Executive Committee Member Worldwide Securities Services, Conrad J. Kozak
Executive Committee Member Card Services, Eileen M. Serra
Co-COO, Matthew E. Zames
Corporate Media Relations, Jennifer R. Zuccarelli
Media Contact Retail Financial Services and the US Region, Tom Kelly
Media Contact Credit Card Services, Paul Hartwick
Head Media Relations Americas, Brian J. Marchiony
Media Contact Americas, Tasha Pelio
Media Contact Americas, Justin G. Perras
Media Contact Asia/Pacific, Ray B. Bashford
Executive Committee Member Investment Bank, Emilio Saracho
Executive Committee Member Asset Management, Phil Di Iorio
Executive Committee Member California, Peter Barker
Media Contact Europe Middle East and Africa, Axel Luedeke
Executive Committee Member Retail Financial Services, Barry Sommers
Executive Committee Member Investment Bank, Jeffrey J. (Jeff) Urwin
Chief Investment Officer North America, Irene Tse
Global Chairman Mergers and Acquistions, Jimmy Elliott
Co-Head Mergers and Acquistions North America, Jim Woolery
Co-Head Investment Banking North America, Chris Ventresca
Executive Committee Member Investment Bank, Nicolas Aguzin
Executive Committee Member Chief Investment Office, Althea L. Duersten
Executive Committee Member Commercial Banking, Scott Geller
Executive Committee Member International, Gregory L. Guyett
Executive Committee Member Commercial Bank, Robert C. Holmes
Executive Committee Member Retail Financial Services, Ryan McInerney
Chief Executive Officer Commercial Banking and Executive Committee Member, Douglas B. (Doug) Petno
Head of Retail Claims Collections Fraud and Fulfillment, John Samenuk
CFO Consumer Banking, David Owen
CEO Asset Management, Mary Callahan Erdoes
Director, Stephen B. (Steve) Burke, age 53
Director, Lee R. Raymond, age 73
Director, William C. (Bill) Weldon, age 63
Director, David M. (Dave) Cote, age 59
Director, James S. Crown, age 58
Director, Ellen V. Futter, age 62
Director, David C. Novak, age 59
Director, William H. (Bill) Gray III, age 70
Director, Laban P. (Labe) Jackson Jr., age 69
Director, James A. Bell, age 63
Director, Timothy P. Flynn, age 61
Director, Crandall C. Bowles, age 65
Auditors: PricewaterhouseCoopersLLP

LOCATIONS

HQ: JPMorgan Chase & Co.
270 Park Ave., New York NY 10017-2070
Phone: 212-270-6000 **Fax:** 212-270-1648
Web: www.jpmorganchase.com

PRODUCTS/OPERATIONS

2011 Sales

	$ mil.	% of total
Interest		
Loans	37,098	34
Trading assets	11,142	10
Securities	9,215	8
Federal funds sold & securities purchased under resale agreements	2,523	
2		
Other	1,315	1
Noninterest		
Asset management administration & commissions	14,094	13
Principal transactions	10,005	9
Lending & deposit-related fees	6,458	6
Credit card income	6,158	6
Investment banking fees	5,911	5
Mortgage fees & related income	2,721	2
Other	4,198	4
Total	**110,838**	**100**

2011 Assets

	$ mil.	% of total
Cash & equivalents	380,195	17
Securities borrowed	142,462	6
Trading assets	443,963	20
Securities	364,793	16
Net loans	696,111	31
Other	238,268	10
Total	**2,265,792**	**100**

COMPETITORS

American Express
Bank of America
Barclays
Credit Suisse (USA)
Deutsche Bank
Goldman Sachs
Capital One
CIBC
Citigroup
Citigroup Global Markets
HSBC
Morgan Stanley
RBC Financial Group
UBS
Wells Fargo

HISTORICAL FINANCIALS

Company Type: Public

Income Statement

FYE: December 31

	ASSETS ($ mil.)	NET INCOME ($ mil.)	INCOME AS % OF ASSETS	EMPLOYEES
12/11	2,265,792	18,976	0.8%	260,157
12/10	2,117,605	17,370	0.8%	222,316
12/09	2,031,989	11,728	0.6%	222,316
12/08	2,175,052	5,605	0.3%	224,961
12/07	1,562,147	15,365	1.0%	180,667
Annual Growth	9.7%	5.4%	—	9.5%

2011 Year-End Financials

Debt ratio: 11.33%—
Return on equity: 10.34%
Cash ($ mil.): 144,881
Current ratio: —
Long-term debt ($ mil.): 256,775
Dividends
Yield: —
Payout: 17.86%
Market value ($ mil.): —

	STOCK PRICE ($) FY Close	P/E High	P/E Low	PER SHARE ($) Earnings	Dividends	Book Value
12/11	33.25	11	6	4.48	0.00	48.66
12/10	42.42	12	9	3.98	0.20	45.04
12/09	41.67	21	7	2.26	0.53	41.95
12/08	31.53	35	16	1.37	1.52	44.71
12/07	43.65	12	9	4.38	1.44	36.59
Annual Growth	(6.6%)	—	—	0.6%	—	7.4%

Juniper Networks Inc

Juniper Networks has blossomed in a landscape dominated by Cisco. The company designs and sells network infrastructure equipment used to deploy and manage services and applications across Internet protocol (IP) networks. Its products include routers network traffic management software virtual private network and firewall devices data center and WAN acceleration tools and intrusion prevention systems. Juniper sells directly and through resellers to network service providers enterprises government agencies and schools. The company has resale agreements with Ericsson IBM and Nokia Siemens and it counts Ingram Micro and NEC among its distribution partners. More than half of its sales are made overseas.

Juniper has two primary product segments: infrastructure and service layer technologies (SLT). The infrastructure group which accounts for about three-quarters of the company's revenues encompasses Juniper's switching and routing equipment; sales of switches account for more than 60% of sales. The SLT segment includes data and network protection application performance and bandwidth optimization tools.

The company's revenue rose in 2011 due to strong global demand from both telecom network operators and enterprise customers primarily for its infrastructure products; meanwhile sales of its SLT products slipped. Juniper's income rose in 2011 as well despite higher operating costs particularly in the areas of research and development sales and marketing.

Juniper has historically relied on telecom network operators including AT&T and Verizon which both accounted for about 10% of sales in 2010 to make large equipment purchases. However no single customer accounted for more than 10% of sales in 2011.

Juniper uses acquisitions to supplement its internal product development efforts and enter new markets. In 2012 Juniper bought Web security software developer Mykonos for about $80 million in cash to expand its selection of network security products. The previous year the company bought assets related to network timing synchronization and monitoring systems designed by California-based Brilliant Telecommunications for $4.5 million. Juniper's interest in Brilliant's technology stemmed from its effort to improve the flexibility of core product lines as the complexity and intersections of wired and mobile networks increases.

Breaking a five year hiatus from acquisitions the company bought five companies in 2010 to add new products and technology to its portfolio. It bought Ankeena Networks a developer of new media infrastructure technology to help it address the fast-rising volume of video traffic on fixed and mobile networks. Juniper also bought Internet video storage and delivery systems specialist Blackwave that year to complement its Media Flow digital media delivery product family and it acquired SMobile Systems for about $70 million to add security technology for smart phones and tablets to its Junos Pulse product line.

The company additionally paid $152 million to buy Trapeze Networks from Belden to boost its enterprise business in acknowledgement that demand from telecommunications companies may be set to diminish. Finally it paid $95 million in cash to acquire Altor Networks a provider of network security systems for virtual (cloud-based) servers as demand for secure cloud computing services from businesses in many industries increases.

Juniper's technology opened a market long dominated by rival Cisco Systems and has helped it take a chunk out of the powerhouse's market share. Juniper is among a number of companies that have touted superior technology to differentiate their offerings but designs its equipment to be compatible with that of the ubiquitous Cisco platforms.

EXECUTIVES

EVP Software Solutions, Robert L. (Bob) Muglia, age 52
Vice Chairman and CTO, Pradeep S. Sindhu, age 59, $381,872 total compensation
Chairman, Scott G. Kriens, age 54, $675,000 total compensation
CEO and Director, Kevin R. Johnson, age 51, $740,000 total compensation
EVP Service Support and Operations, Michael J. (Mike) Rose, age 59, $481,250 total compensation
EVP Office of the CEO, Kim Perdikou, age 54, $357,938 total compensation
SVP Manufacturing Operations, Martin J. Garvin, age 59
EVP General Counsel and Secretary, Mitchell L. (Mitch) Gaynor, age 52
EVP and Chief Marketing Officer, Lauren P. Flaherty
EVP and General Manager Data Center Business Unit, R. K. Anand
EVP and General Manager Fabric and Switching Technologies Business Group, David W. Yen, age 60
Investor Relations, Kathleen Bela
EVP and Chief Sales Officer, Gerri Elliott
EVP and CFO, Robyn M. Denholm, age 48, $481,250 total compensation
EVP Strategy and Corporate Development, Luis Avila-Marco
Media Contact, Jessica Kersey
EVP Services Support and Operations, Mark Bauhaus, age 50, $352,750 total compensation
EVP Human Resources, Steven Rice
SVP and General Manager Emerging Technologies, Nawaf Bitar
VP Corporate Communications, David Shane
VP Worldwide Enterprise Marketing and Solutions, Brad Brooks
EVP Worldwide Sales and Services, John Morris, age 51, $481,250 total compensation
EVP and General Manager Junos Ready Software (JRS) Business Group, Manoj Leelanivas
SVP Europe Middle East and Africa, Sean Dolan
VP Finance and Corporate Controller, Gene Zamiska, age 50
EVP and General Manager Platform Systems Division, Stefan Dyckerhoff, age 39
SVP and CIO, Bask Iyer
Media Relations, Ellen Roeckl
SVP Worldwide Partners, Emilio Umeoka
VP Global Partner Marketing, Luanne Tierney
Media Relations, Stefani Carver
Director, David L. (Dave) Schlotterbeck, age 64
Director, Mercedes Johnson, age 58
Vice Chairman and CTO, Pradeep S. Sindhu, age 59
CEO and Director, Kevin R. Johnson, age 51
Director, Mary B. Cranston, age 64
Director, Robert M. (Bob) Calderoni, age 52
Director, William R. (Bill) Stensrud, age 61
Director, Stratton D. Sclavos, age 51
Director, J. Michael Lawrie, age 58
Director, William F. (Bill) Meehan Jr., age 59
Director, J. Michael (Mike) Lawrie
Auditors: Ernst&YoungLLP

LOCATIONS

HQ: Juniper Networks Inc.
1194 N. Mathilda Ave., Sunnyvale CA 94089-1206
Phone: 408-745-2000 **Fax:** 408-745-2100
Web: www.juniper.net

2011 Sales

	$ mil.	% of total
Americas		
US	2,015	45
Other countries	222	5
Europe Middle East & Africa	1,339	30
Asia Pacific	870	20
Total	**4,448**	**100**

PRODUCTS/OPERATIONS

2011 Sales

	$ mil.	% of total
Infrastructure		
Routers	2,894	64
Switches	528	13
Service layer technology	1,026	23
Total	**4,487**	**100**

2011 Sales by Market

	$ mil.	% of total
Service providers	2,833	64
Enterprises	1,615	36
Total	**4,448**	**100**

COMPETITORS

ADTRAN
Alcatel-Lucent
Brocade Communications
Check Point Software
Cisco Systems
Citrix Systems
Enterasys
Ericsson
Extreme Networks
F5 Networks
Fortinet
Hewlett-Packard
Huawei Technologies
IBM Internet Security Systems
MRV Communications
Nokia Siemens Networks
Riverbed Technology
SonicWALL
Sycamore Networks

HISTORICAL FINANCIALS

Company Type: Public

Income Statement FYE: December 31

	REVENUE ($ mil.)	NET INCOME ($ mil.)	NET PROFIT MARGIN	EMPLOYEES
12/11	4,448	425	9.6%	9,129
12/10	4,093	618	15.1%	8,772
12/09	3,315	117	3.5%	7,231
12/08	3,572	511	14.3%	7,014
12/07	2,836	360	12.7%	5,879
Annual Growth	11.9%	4.2%	—	11.6%

2011 Year-End Financials

Debt ratio: 10.01%
Return on equity: 6.00%
Cash ($ mil.): 2,910
Current ratio: 302.70
Long-term debt ($ mil.): 999
No. of shares (mil.): 526
Dividends
Yield: —
Payout: —
Market value ($ mil.): 10,744

	STOCK PRICE ($) FY Close	P/E High/Low	PER SHARE ($) Earnings	Dividends	Book Value
12/11	20.41	56 21	0.79	0.00	13.47
12/10	36.92	32 19	1.15	0.00	12.58
12/09	26.67	128 58	0.22	0.00	11.21
12/08	17.51	35 14	0.93	0.00	11.20
12/07	33.20	56 26	0.62	0.00	10.24
Annual Growth	(11.5%)	— —	6.2%	—	7.1%

Kansas City Life Insurance Co. (Kansas City, MO)

They're not just standing on the corner of 12th Street and Vine! Kansas City Life Insurance and subsidiary Sunset Life provide insurance products throughout the US to individuals (life and disability coverage and annuities) and to groups (life dental vision and disability insurance). Subsidiary Old American Insurance focuses on burial and related insurance. The insurance companies sell through more than 1400 independent agents brokers and third-party marketers. Kansas City Life Insurance also operates its own insurance and investment brokerage network through its Sunset Financial Services unit. Chairman and CEO R. Philip Bixby and his family control the company.

Kansas City Life offers both universal and variable life policies throughout the US. Some of its largest state markets include Missouri Texas Kansas California and Colorado. The company is focused on expanding its individual life insurance operations by widening its distribution network and enhancing its marketing efforts. For instance it has marketing agreements with health plan provider American Republic Insurance and property/casualty firm GuideOne Insurance which distribute the life policies of Kansas City Life to their respective members and policyholders.

Founded in 1895 the company built up its operations through a number of historical acquisitions including GuideOne Life (2003) Old American (1991) and Sunset Life (1974). The company exited its banking operations (Generations Bank) in 2007.

Kansas City Life Insurance recorded a 3% drop in revenues to $419 million in 2011 compared to 2010. Its net income however showed positive growth at $26 million with a 15% increase over 2010. Increased investment revenues and lower policyholder benefits were the main factors contributing to its improved results. The company's assets and life insurance in force were $4 billion and $29 billion respectively.

The Bixby family owns about 60% of the company through trusts and investment partnerships.

EXECUTIVES

SVP and Actuary Kansas City Life; VP and Actuary Sunset Life, Mark A. Milton, age 53, $287,520 total compensation
SVP Operations, Charles R. Duffy Jr., age 64, $288,360 total compensation
Chairman President and CEO; Chairman and President Sunset Life, R. Philip Bixby, age 58, $688,740 total compensation
Vice Chairman; President Old American Insurance, Walter E. (Web) Bixby, age 53
SVP Finance CFO and Director, Tracy W. Knapp, age 49, $284,100 total compensation
SVP Sales and Marketing Kansas City Life; VP Sales and Marketing Sunset Life, Donald E. Krebs, age 54, $267,600 total compensation
VP Underwriting and New Business, Robert J. Milroy
VP Computer Information Services, J. Todd Salash
VP and Auditor, Dan L. Schick
VP Taxes, John L. Nogalski
VP Customer Services and Claims, Richard D. Ropp
VP Securities, Philip A. Williams
VP Controller and Chief Accounting Officer, David A. Laird, age 51
VP Group, Jeffrey M. Seeman, age 54
Director, Kevin G. Barth, age 51
Director, Richard L. Finn, age 70
Vice Chairman; President Old American Insurance, Walter E. (Web) Bixby, age 53
Director, William R. (Bill) Blessing, age 56
Director, Bradford T. (Brad) Nordholm, age 56
Director, Nancy Bixby Hudson, age 59
Director, Michael Braude, age 76
SVP Finance CFO and Director, Tracy W. Knapp, age 49
Director, William A. (Bill) Schalekamp, age 67
Director, Cecil R. Miller, age 78
Director, John C. Cozad, age 67
Auditors: KPMGLLP

LOCATIONS

HQ: Kansas City Life Insurance Company
3520 Broadway, Kansas City MO 64111-2565
Phone: 816-753-7000 **Fax:** 816-753-0138
Web: www.kclife.com

PRODUCTS/OPERATIONS

2011 Sales

	$ mil.	% of total
Individual insurance	303	70
Old American	77	18
Group insurance	50	12
Adjustments	(0.5)	
Total	**419**	**100**

2011 Revenues

	$ mil.	% of total
Insurance	288	55
Investment	180	43
Other	10	2
Total	**419**	**100**

Selected Subsidiaries

Old American Insurance Company
Sunset Financial Services
Sunset Life Insurance Company of America

COMPETITORS

Advance Insurance of Kansas
AEGON USA
American Equity Life
American Heritage Life Insurance
American National Insurance
Americo
Citizens Inc.
Delphi Financial Group
Homesteaders Life
MassMutual
MetLife
National Western
Nationwide
New York Life
Northwestern Mutual
Phoenix Companies
Prudential
Security Benefit Group
The Hartford
Torchmark
Universal American

HISTORICAL FINANCIALS

Company Type: Public

Income Statement FYE: December 31

	ASSETS ($ mil.)	NET INCOME ($ mil.)	INCOME AS % OF ASSETS	EMPLOYEES
12/11	4,398	26	0.6%	444
12/10	4,333	22	0.5%	446
12/09	4,176	10	0.3%	447
12/08	3,967	(17)	—	512
12/07	4,352	35	0.8%	527
Annual Growth	0.3%	(7.5%)	—	(4.2%)

2011 Year-End Financials

Debt ratio: —
Return on equity: 3.68%
Cash ($ mil.): 10
Current ratio: —
Long-term debt ($ mil.): —
No. of shares (mil.): 11
Dividends
Yield: —
Payout: 47.16%
Market value ($ mil.): 371

	STOCK PRICE ($) FY Close	P/E High/Low	PER SHARE ($) Earnings	Dividends	Book Value
12/11	32.82	16 12	2.29	0.00	62.84
12/10	33.03	18 13	1.95	1.08	59.25
12/09	29.75	48 17	0.93	1.08	54.33
12/08	43.35	— —	(1.47)	1.08	46.11
12/07	43.59	17 13	3.01	3.08	58.17
Annual Growth	(6.8%)	— —	(6.6%)	—	1.9%

KBR Inc

KBR builds big projects for the US government. But the engineering and construction services company also lends its capabilities to the hydrocarbon energy minerals civil infrastructure and power and industrial markets. The company is widely known for its service to the government and infrastructure sector (the US government accounts for about 25% of revenue) however that figure is slowly declining as the military pulls its presence in the Middle East. KBR is increasingly focused on projects in the oil and gas industry. It has designed many of world's liquefied natural gas production facilities and develops new technologies such as coal gasification.

KBR has operations in the US Australia Africa the UK Asia and the Middle East. The company's diverse customer base includes international oil and gas companies such as Chevron and Exxon petrochemical producers fertilizer producers and domestic and foreign governments.

The Infrastructure Government and Power (IGP) segment has traditionally been a major revenue maker for KBR. However in 2011 the hydrocarbons segment became the company's biggest money maker contributing more than 45% of revenue.

The growing hyrdocarbons market has improved considerably since the global economic downturn. Energy demand is helping contribute to long-term growth for projects in the offshore oil and gas production liquified natural gas biofuels motor fuels chemicals and fertilizer markets. Geographically KBR is focused on the Middle East Brazil North Sea and Africa. Shale gas supplies in North America also represent opportunites for KBR to grow at home. In 2012 KBR formed a new entity to perform engineering work in Saudi Arabia.

As focus shifts to the hydrocarbon segment KBR continues to support the US government's activities in Afghanistan and other Middle Eastern countries. KBR was the sole government contractor serving the US military in Iraq. However the company no longer enjoys that enviable position. After 2011 KBR must bid alongside competitors for those jobs. In 2011 KBR demobilized its units in Iraq in conjunction with the US withdrawal from that country. As a result the company's revenues in those areas have decreased and will likely continue to decrease over the next several years.

Lagging sales in KBR's Infrastructure Government and Power segment along with its services arm contributed to an 8% drop in overall revenues in 2011. But the company isn't standing still. It is trying to shift its business focus and invest in new areas such as the global minerals. KBR plans to grow in the mining minerals and materials handling markets. It has potential to support mining work around the globe by building roads camps water and power infrastructure and port and marine infrastructure.

Former parent Halliburton spun off about 20% of KBR through an IPO in 2006 and divested the rest in 2007. KBR's link to Halliburton brought the company trouble in 2009. KBR pleaded guilty to foreign bribery charges for its participation in a decade-long scheme to bribe Nigerian officials in exchange for government contracts. The company was ordered to pay a $402 million fine. Additionally the company (along with Halliburton) was fined $177 million for violating SEC anti-bribery rules. Halliburton agreed to pay most of the fines leaving KBR paying about $20 million to the Department of Justice. In 2012 a former KBR chief executive was sentenced to 30 months in prison for his role in the bribe scheme.

EXECUTIVES

EVP and CFO, Susan K. (Sue) Carter, age 53, $83,521 total compensation
SVP and Chief Accounting Officer, Dennis S. Baldwin, age 51
Chairman President and CEO, William P. (Bill) Utt, age 55, $928,932 total compensation
President Downstream, John Quinn
Director Investor Relations, Rob Kukla Jr.
EVP Operations, John L. Rose, age 66, $448,083 total compensation
EVP and General Counsel, Andrew D. Farley, age 48, $430,316 total compensation
EVP Administration, Klaudia J. Brace, age 55
Group President Government & Defense Infrastructure & Minerals and Power & Industrial, Mark S. Williams, age 54
President Oil & Gas, Dennis Calton
President Services, David Zimmerman, age 58, $416,158 total compensation
President Power and Industrial, James T. (Jim) Stewart, age 64
President International Government Defence and Support Services, Andrew Pringle
President Middle East, Khaled Abu-Nasrah
President Gas Monetization, Mitch Dauzat
Group President Hydrocarbons, Roy Oelking
President Infrastructure, Colin Elliott
SVP; Chairman and CEO Building Group, Luther Cochrane
VP Canada Operations, Brian Cole
Manager Media Relations, Gabriela Segura
SVP Commercial, Thomas R. Hewitt
SVP Corporate Development; General Manager KBR Ventures, Mark P. Barry
SVP Industrial Services, Darrell Hargrave
SVP U.S. Construction, Danny Hicks
President Technology, John Derbyshire
President Minerals, Mark Read
SVP Human Resources, Clare Kinahan
President - Downstream Business Unit, David Zelinski
Executive Vice President - Operations, Farhan Mujib
Group President - Services, Ivor Harrington
President - North American Government & Logistics, Richard Ambrose
Director, Loren K. Carroll, age 68
Director, Jeffrey E. Curtiss, age 63
Director, W. Frank Blount, age 73
Director, Richard J. Slater, age 65
Director, Gen. Lester L. Lyles, age 65
Independent Director, Jack Moore
Independent Director, Linda Cook
Auditors: KPMGLLP

LOCATIONS

HQ: KBR Inc.
601 Jefferson St. Ste. 3400, Houston TX 77002
Phone: 713-753-3011 **Fax:** 713-753-5353
Web: www.kbr.com

2011 Sales

	$ mil.	% of total
Africa	2,113	23
US	1,994	22
Iraq	1,969	21
Asia/Pacific	1,439	16
Other Middle East	707	8
Europe	587	6
Other countries	452	4
Total	**9,261**	**100**

PRODUCTS/OPERATIONS

2011 Sales

	$ mil.	% of total
$ in mil. % of total		
Services	9,103	98
Equity in earnings of unconsolidated affiliates net	158	2
Total	**9,261**	**100**

2011 Sales by Segment

$ in mil. % of total		
Hydrocarbons	4,258	46
Infrastructure government and power	3,328	36
Services	1,590	17
Other	85	1
Total	**9,261**	**100**

COMPETITORS

Aker Solutions
AMEC
American Bridge Company
ARB
Bechtel
Bechtel National
Bovis Lend Lease
CH2M HILL
Chicago Bridge & Iron
Chiyoda Corp.
DynCorp International
Fluor
Foster Wheeler
Grunley Construction
Hyundai Heavy Industries
Jacobs Engineering
JGC
John Wood Group
Kiewit Offshore
McDermott
Parsons Corporation
Performance Contractors
Peter Kiewit Sons'
Petrofac
Saipem
Shaw Group
Technip
Tutor Perini
URS
Yates Companies

HISTORICAL FINANCIALS

Company Type: Public

Income Statement FYE: December 31

	REVENUE ($ mil.)	NET INCOME ($ mil.)	NET PROFIT MARGIN	EMPLOYEES
12/11	9,261	480	5.2%	27,000
12/10	10,099	327	3.2%	35,000
12/09	12,105	290	2.4%	51,000
12/08	11,581	319	2.8%	57,000
12/07	8,745	302	3.5%	52,000
Annual Growth	1.4%	12.3%	—	(15.1%)

2011 Year-End Financials

Debt ratio: 1.73%
Return on equity: 19.24%
Cash ($ mil.): 966
Current ratio: 150.70
Long-term debt ($ mil.): 88
No. of shares (mil.): 148
Dividends
Yield: —
Payout: 6.33%
Market value ($ mil.): 4,129

	STOCK PRICE ($) FY Close	P/E High/Low		PER SHARE ($) Earnings	Dividends	Book Value
12/11	27.87	12	7	3.16	0.00	16.84
12/10	30.47	15	8	2.07	0.20	14.86
12/09	19.00	14	7	1.79	0.20	14.27
12/08	15.20	21	5	1.91	0.20	12.69
12/07	38.80	24	11	1.79	0.00	13.36
Annual Growth	(7.9%)	—	—	15.3%	—	6.0%

Kearny Financial Corp

Kearny Financial is the holding company for Kearny Federal Savings Bank which has some 40 branches in northern New Jersey. Kearny Federal Savings Bank offers such standard services as checking and savings accounts CDs ATM and debit cards IRAs and loans. Residential mortgages make up about two-thirds of its loan portfolio; multifamily and commercial mortgages and home equity loans round out most of the rest. Kearny also invests in mortgage-backed securities government and municipal bonds and other securities. In 2010 the company acquired Central Jersey Bancorp for approximately $72 million adding 13 branches to its network.

In 2011 CEO John Hopkins resigned after more than 35 years with the company including nearly a decade as chief executive. He was replaced by Craig Montanaro who previously was president and COO.

Mutual holding company Kearny MHC owns some 70% of Kearny Financial.

EXECUTIVES

SVP and Branch Administrator Kearny Federal Savings Bank, Erika S. Parisi, age 47, $238,149 total compensation
SVP Chief Investment Officer and Treasurer Kearny Financial and Kearny Federal Savings Bank, Albert E. Gossweiler, age 64, $238,149 total compensation
President CEO and Director Kearny Financial; President and CEO Kearny Federal Savings Bank, Craig L. Montanaro, age 46
Chairman, John J. Mazur Jr., age 58
EVP and COO Kearny Financial; EVP and COO Kearny Federal Savings Bank, William C. (Bill) Ledgerwood, age 58, $238,149 total compensation
SVP and Corporate Secretary Kearny Financial and Kearny Federal Savings Bank, Sharon Jones, age 58, $147,500 total compensation
SVP and Chief Lending Officer Kearny Federal Savings Bank, Patrick M. Joyce, age 47, $238,149 total compensation
VP and Chief Accounting Officer, Eric B. Heyer, age 49
President CEO and Director Kearny Financial; President and CEO Kearny Federal Savings Bank, Craig L. Montanaro, age 46
Director, Leopold W. Montanaro, age 72
Director, John N. Hopkins, age 65
Director, Theodore J. Aanensen, age 67
Director, Joseph P. Mazza, age 68
Director, John F. Regan, age 67

LOCATIONS

HQ: Kearny Financial Corp.
120 Passaic Ave., Fairfield NJ 07004
Phone: 973-244-4500 **Fax:** 914-848-4777
Web: www.pernod-ricard-usa.com

PRODUCTS/OPERATIONS

2008 Sales

	$ mil.	% of total
Interest income		
Loans	55	55
Mortgage-backed securities	34	35
Other securities	2	2
Other interest-earning assets	5	5
Noninterest income	2	3
Total	**100**	**100**

COMPETITORS

Bank of America
Capital One
Hudson City Bancorp
PNC Financial
Sovereign Bank
TD Bank USA
Valley National Bancorp

HISTORICAL FINANCIALS

Company Type: Public

Income Statement

FYE: June 30

	ASSETS ($ mil.)	NET INCOME ($ mil.)	INCOME AS % OF ASSETS	EMPLOYEES
06/12	2,937	5	0.2%	459
06/11	2,904	7	0.3%	436
06/10	2,339	6	0.3%	285
06/09	2,124	6	0.3%	284
06/08	2,083	5	0.3%	286
Annual Growth	9.0%	(3.7%)	—	12.6%

2012 Year-End Financials

Debt ratio: 8.50%
Return on equity: 1.03%
Cash ($ mil.): 155
Current ratio: —
Long-term debt ($ mil.): 249
No. of shares (mil.): 66
Dividends
Yield: —
Payout: 187.50%
Market value ($ mil.): 649

	STOCK PRICE ($) FY Close	P/E High/Low	PER SHARE ($) Earnings	Dividends	Book Value
06/12	9.69	127100	0.08	0.00	7.35
06/11	9.11	86 69	0.12	0.20	7.19
06/10	9.16	117 84	0.10	0.20	7.11
06/09	11.44	155 87	0.09	0.20	6.89
06/08	11.00	154111	0.09	0.20	6.69
Annual Growth	(3.1%)	— —	(2.9%)	—	2.4%

Kellogg Co

Location as irony –Battle Creek Michigan-based Kellogg Company is in a constant battle for the #1 spot in the US cereal market with its main rival General Mills. (General Mills' fiscal 2011 sales totaled about $16.6 billion compared to Kellogg's $13.2 billion.) But Kellogg founded in 1906 boasts many a familiar brand name including Kellogg's Corn Flakes Frosted Flakes Corn Pops and Rice Krispies. While the company works to fill cereal bowls globally it puffs up its bottom line with snacks and cookies (Keebler Cheez-It and Famous Amos) along with convenience foods such as Eggo waffles and Nutri-Grain and Bear Naked cereal bars. Its products are sold in more than 180 countries worldwide.

HISTORY

Will Keith (W. K.) Kellogg first made wheat flakes in 1894 while working for his brother Dr. John Kellogg at Battle Creek Michigan's famed homeopathic sanitarium. While doing an experiment with grains (for patients' diets) the two men were interrupted; by the time they returned to the dough it had absorbed water. They rolled it anyway toasted the result and accidentally created the first flaked cereal. John sold the flakes via mail order (1899) in a partnership that W. K. managed. In 1906 W. K. started his own firm to produce corn flakes.

As head of the Battle Creek Toasted Corn Flake Company W. K. competed against 42 cereal companies in Battle Creek (one run by former patient C. W. Post) and roared to the head of the pack with his innovative marketing ideas. A 1906 Ladies' Home Journal ad helped increase demand from 33 cases a day earlier that year to 2900 a day by year-end. W. K. soon introduced Bran Flakes (1915) All-Bran (1916) and Rice Krispies (1928). International expansion began in Canada (1914) and followed in Australia (1924) and England (1938).

Diversifying a little the company introduced the Pop-Tart in 1964 and acquired Eggo waffles in the 1970s. By the early 1980s Kellogg's US market share dipped due to strong competition from General Mills and other rivals. The company pitched new cereals to adults and aggressively pursued the fast-growing European market.

Kellogg spent the mid-1990s reengineering itself creating the USA Convenience Foods Division and selling such noncore assets as its carton container and Argentine snack-food makers (1993). It teamed with ConAgra in 1994 to create a cereal line sold under the latter's popular Healthy Choice label.

In 1997-98 the company expanded operations in Australia the UK Asia and Latin America and it slashed about 25% of its salaried North American workforce and hiked prices on about two-thirds of its cereals. Several top officers left in 1998-99 and Cuban-born president and COO Carlos Gutierrez became CEO.

The company sold the disappointing Lender's division (frozen bagels) to Aurora Foods in 1999 for just $275 million. (Aurora later merged with Pinnacle Foods to become Pinnacle Foods Group —now Pinnacle Foods Finance and owned by Blackstone.) Kellogg took another crack at non-breakfast foods when it bought Worthington Foods (Morningstar Farms meat alternatives Harvest Burgers) for $307 million.

By the beginning of 2000 cereal competitor General Mills had closed the gap with Kellogg in US market share (in 2001 it passed Kellogg as the #1 cereal maker). In 2000 Kellogg added Kasha Company (natural cereals) to its pantry. Later that year Kellogg reorganized its operations into two divisions (USA and International) to reduce costs.

In 2001 Kellogg bulked up its snacks portfolio by acquiring Keebler's Foods for $4.5 billion (in cash and assumed debt). In the aftermath of the acquisition the company trimmed jobs at Keebler's and its own headquarters.

To boost enthusiasm among kids for breakfast in 2002 Kellogg launched new cereals featuring Disney characters Buzz Lightyear Mickey Mouse and Winnie the Pooh –the first such alliance for The Walt Disney Company. That move combined with better marketing and General Mills being distracted by its purchase of Pillsbury helped Kellogg grab back the top spot in the US.

As part of Kellogg's digestion of Keebler's it consolidated some manufacturing operations and reconfigured parts of Keebler's distribution system in 2002. To better focus on its branded products the company sold off Keebler's private-label Bake-Line division to Atlantic Baking Group for $65 million in cash.

In 2004 Kellogg sold the Athens Re-packaging business of Keebler's to Total Logistics. Later that year Kellogg reached an agreement with then New York Attorney General Eliot Spitzer to stop using promotional toys identified as a possible environmental risk in its cereal products. In addition the company agreed to phase out the sale or distribution of promotional products containing mercury by the end of 2004 recycle mercury batteries returned by consumers and educate consumers as to the need to dispose of mercury properly.

Continuing its integration of Keebler's in 2004 the company did some geographic juggling: The US snack division was relocated from Elmhurst Illinois to Kellogg's main headquarters in Battle Creek Michigan. The Food Away From Home (FAFH) business unit and the Information Technology Center remained in Elmhurst.

In 2005 Gutierrez resigned from Kellogg to become secretary of the Department of Commerce in the George W. Bush administration. He was succeeded at the cereal behemoth by advertising executive and Kellogg board member James Jenness. In 2006 David Mackay was appointed Kellogg's CEO replacing Jenness who remained as chairman.

The company began using oils derived from genetically modified soybeans in some of its products in 2006 in order to lower their fat content –a real toss-up move considering consumer concern about obesity and heart disease and the fear of scientists altering genes. It added to its meatless menu with its 2007 acquisition of Wholesome & Hearty Foods the maker of Gardenburger. It also acquired Bear Naked a small seller of natural granola in 2007.

Kellogg acquired Chinese cookie and cracker manufacturer Zhenghang Food Company (dba Navigable Foods) in 2008. Also that year Kellogg acquired The United Bakers Group a top cracker biscuit and breakfast cereal manufacturer in Russia as well as Specialty Cereals an Australian cereal manufacturer. The company wrapped up 2008 in a sweet fashion a little closer to home with the purchase of the recipes and trademarks from the bankrupt (but traditionally popular in the western US) Mother's Cake & Cookie Co. Kellogg added the brands which include Chips Deluxe Fudge Shoppe and Sandies to its snacks business unit and hopes to expand their distribution.

President and CEO David Mackay retired at the end of 2010 and was succeeded by the company's COO John Bryant in January 2011.

EXECUTIVES

SVP Corporate Development General Counsel and Secretary, Gary H. Pilnick, age 48
Chairman, James M. (Jim) Jenness, age 66, $928,846 total compensation
President CEO and Director, John A. Bryant, age 47, $830,763 total compensation
SVP Global Public Policy and External Relations and Chief Sustainability Officer, Celeste A. Clark, age 58
SVP and Global Chief Marketing Officer, Mark R. Baynes, age 51
VP Investor Relations, Kathryn C. Koessel, age 49
SVP; President Kellogg International, Paul T. Norman, age 48, $623,079 total compensation
SVP; President Kellogg North America, Bradford J. (Brad) Davidson, age 51, $675,000 total compensation
Associate Director Corporate Communications Kellogg Canada, Lores Tome
Director Corporate Affairs and Communications Kellogg Europe, Paul Fitzsimmons
Senior Manager Corporate Communications and Regulatory Affairs Kellogg Australia/New Zealand, Rebecca Boustead
SVP Global Human Resources, Dennis W. Shuler, age 57
SVP Research Quality and Technology, Margaret R. Bath, age 48
SVP and CFO, Ronald L. (Ron) Dissinger, age 54
SVP and CIO, Brian S. Rice, age 49

Director Marketing and Innovation Kellogg Asia, Kalyan Bandyopadhyay
Director Marketing Kellogg India Pakistan Sri Lanka Nepal Maldives and Bangladesh, Vikram Bahl
Manager Corporate Affairs Kellogg Latin America, Jose F. Rios
President Kellogg Canada Inc., Carol Stewart
SVP Global Supply Chain, Steven (Steve) Sterling
VP Global Communications and Philanthropy, Kris Charles
VP Government Relations, Brigitte Schmidt Gwyn
Senior Director Diversity and Inclusion, Mark King
VP; President Kellogg Latin America, Carols E. Mejia
VP and Treasurer, Joel A. Vander Kooi
Vice President; Corporate Controller, Maribeth Dangel
Director, Rogelio M. Rebolledo, age 67
Director, Donald R. (Don) Knauss, age 61
Director, John T. Dillon, age 73
Director, Gordon Gund, age 72
Director, John L. Zabriskie, age 72
Director, Benjamin S. Carson Sr., age 60
Director, Dorothy A. Johnson, age 71
Director, Ann McLaughlin Korologos, age 70
President CEO and Director, John A. Bryant, age 47
Director, Robert A. (Rob) Steele, age 57
Director, Sterling K. Speirn, age 64
Auditors: PricewaterhouseCoopersLLP

LOCATIONS

HQ: Kellogg Co
One Kellogg Square, P.O. Box 3599, Battle Creek, MI 49016-3599
Phone: 269 961-2000 **Fax:** 616 961-2871
Web: www.kelloggcompany.com

2011 Sales

	$ mil.	% of total
North America	8,873	67
Europe	2,334	18
Latin America	1,049	8
Asia/Pacific	942	7
Total	**13,198**	**100**

PRODUCTS/OPERATIONS

2011 Sales

	$ mil.	% of total
Retail channel cereal	6,725	51
Retail channel snacks	4,940	37
Frozen & specialty channels	1,533	12
Total	**13,198**	**100**

Selected Cereal Brands

Asia and Australia
- BeBig
- Cerola
- Chex
- Frosties
- Goldies
- Kellogg' s Iron Man Food
- Nutri-Grain
- Rice Bubbles
- Sultana Bran

Canada
- Vector
- Vive

Europe
- Choco Pops
- Chocos
- Country Store
- Frosties
- Fruit n' Fibre
- Honey Loops
- Kellogg' s Crunchy Nut Corn Flakes
- Kellogg' s Crunchy Nut Red Corn Flakes
- Kellogg' s Extra
- Muslix
- Optima
- Pops
- Ricicles
- Smacks
- Start
- Sustain

Latin America
- Choco Krispis
- Choco Zucaritas
- Crusli Sucrilhos
- Musli
- NutriDia
- Sucrilhos Chocolate
- Vector
- Zucaritas

US
- All-Bran
- Apple Jacks
- Bran Buds
- Cinnamon Crunch
- Cocoa Krispies
- Complete Bran Flakes
- Complete Wheat Flakes
- Corn Pops
- Cracklin' Oat Bran
- Crispix
- Crunch
- Cruncheroos
- Froot Loops
- Frosted Krispies
- Frosted Mini-Wheats
- Just Right
- Kellogg' s Corn Flakes
- Kellogg' s Frosted Flakes
- Kellogg' s Low-Fat Granola
- Kellogg' s Raisin Bran
- Mueslix
- Pops
- Product 19
- Raisin Bran
- Rice Krispies
- Smacks/Honey Smacks
- Smart Start
- Special K
- Special K Red Berries

Selected Other Brands

Cereal Bars and Granola
- All-Bran
- Bear Naked
- Choco Krispies
- Froot Loops
- GoLean
- Kashi

Convenience Foods
- Austin
- Cheez-It
- Chips Deluxe
- Club
- Croutettes Croutons
- E. L. Fudge
- Famous Amos
- Fudge Shoppe
- Hi-Ho
- Keebler
- Kellogg' s Corn Flake Crumbs
- Krispy Munch' Ems
- Murray
- Pop-Tarts
- Pop-Tarts Pastry Swirls
- Pop-Tarts Snak-Stix
- Pringles
- Ready Crust
- Rice Krispies Squares
- Rice Krispies Treats
- Right Bites
- Sandies
- Soft Batch
- Stretch Island
- Sunshine
- Toasteds
- Town House

Frozen Waffles and Pancakes
- Eggo
- Froot Loops
- Nutri-Grain
- Special K

Water and Water Mixes
- Special K
- Special K2O

Meat and Egg Alternatives
- Gardenburger
- Loma Linda
- Morningstar Farms
- Natural Touch
- Worthington

COMPETITORS

Amy' s Kitchen
Barbara' s Bakery
Bob' s Red Mill Natural Foods
Boca Foods
Campbell Soup
ConAgra
Frito-Lay
General Mills
Gilster-Mary Lee
Goodman Fielder
granoVita
Hain Celestial
Hostess Brands
J & J Snack Foods
Jordans & Ryvita
McKee Foods
MOM Brands
Mondelez International
Nestle
Patty King
PepsiCo
Pinnacle Foods
PowerBar
Ralcorp
Ralston Food
Schulze and Burch
Snyder' s-Lance
Weetabix
Wellness Foods
Wessanen

HISTORICAL FINANCIALS

Company Type: Public

Income Statement FYE: December 31

	REVENUE ($ mil.)	NET INCOME ($ mil.)	NET PROFIT MARGIN	EMPLOYEES
12/11*	13,198	1,231	9.3%	30,700
01/11	12,397	1,247	10.1%	30,645
01/10	12,575	1,212	9.6%	30,949
01/09	12,822	1,148	9.0%	32,400
12/07	11,776	1,103	9.4%	26,500
Annual Growth	2.9%	2.8%	—	3.7%

*Fiscal year change

2011 Year-End Financials

Debt ratio: 50.68%
Return on equity: 69.94%
Cash ($ mil.): 460
Current ratio: 91.37
Long-term debt ($ mil.): 5,037
No. of shares (mil.): 357
Dividends
Yield: —
Payout: 49.41%
Market value ($ mil.): 18,069

	STOCK PRICE ($) FY Close	P/E High	P/E Low	PER SHARE ($) Earnings	Dividends	Book Value
12/11*	50.57	17	14	3.38	0.00	4.93
01/11	51.08	17	14	3.30	0.00	5.90
01/10	53.20	17	11	3.16	0.00	5.96
01/09	45.05	19	14	2.99	0.00	3.79
12/07	52.92	20	18	2.76	0.00	6.48
Annual Growth	(1.1%)	—	—	5.2%	—	(6.6%)

*Fiscal year change

Kelly Services, Inc.

These days a lot of "Kelly Girls" are men. Once a business that supplied only female clerical help Kelly Services has expanded to include male and female temporary employees in light industrial technical and professional sectors including information technology specialists engineers and accountants. It also places lawyers (Kelly Law Registry) scientists (Kelly Scientific Resources) substitute teachers (Kelly Educational Staffing) nurses and other medical staff (Kelly Healthcare Resources) and teleservices personnel (KellyConnect). Kelly Services assigns some 550000 temporary employees around the world each year. Chairman Terence Adderley owns a controlling stake in the company.

Operations

The company provides additional personnel in areas such as electronics (Kelly Electronic Assembly Services) merchandising (Kelly Marketing Services) and catering (Kelly Catering and Hospitality). It also offers career transition outplacement and human resources consulting services through its Ayers Group division.

Financial Analysis

Like most companies involved in the employment industry the recession has had a punishing grip on Kelly's ability to remain profitable. As the economy turned the corner the company recognized $26 million in profit for 2010 and $63.7 million in profit for 2011. It suffered a net loss of $105 million in 2009 and $82 million in 2008.

Sales & Marketing

Although Kelly is not totally dependent on any one customer it is somewhat dependent on its larger customers. No single customer of Kelly accounted for more than 4% of total revenue in 2011 but roughly 50% of revenue came from 100 large customers.

Mergers & Acquisitions

In 2011 Kelly improved its position in the Brazilian market through the acquisition of Tradicao Tecnologia e Servicos a temporary staffing firm owning 12 branch locations throughout the country.

Geographic Reach

Kelly has its eye fixed on the emerging markets of Brazil Russia India and China.

HISTORY

William Russell Kelly a college dropout and former car salesman went to Detroit after WWII to seek his fortune. An owner of modern business equipment he set up Russell Kelly Office Service in 1946 to provide copying typing and inventory services for other businesses; first-year sales from 12 customers totaled $848.

Although companies began to acquire their own machines Kelly knew that they still needed people to work at their offices. He reincorporated his rapidly expanding business as Personnel Service in 1952 and opened the company's first branch office in Louisville Kentucky in 1955; by the end of that year he had 35 offices throughout the US. In 1957 the company was renamed Kelly Girl Service to reflect its all-female workforce.

In the 1960s Kelly ventured beyond office services and began placing convention hostesses blue-collar workers data processors door-to-door marketers and drafters among others. Kelly Girl went public in 1962 boasting 148 branches at the time. In 1966 the company adopted the name Kelly Services. It opened its first non-US office in Toronto in 1968 and one in Paris followed in 1972.

A tough US economy in the 1970s saw a surge in corporate interest in temporary employees. Employers saw the benefits of hiring "Kelly Girls" to meet seasonal needs and special projects. In 1976 Kelly Services acquired a modest health care services company and used it to form Kelly Home Care. In the 1980s this division abandoned the Medicaid and Medicare markets and shifted to private-sector care. Renamed Kelly Assisted Living Services in 1984 (and later known as Kelly Home Care Services) the unit offered aides to perform household duties and nurses to conduct home visits for the elderly and disabled. Also in the 1980s Kelly Services began hiring retired people as part of its ENCORE Program.

In 1988 Kelly began a program of international expansion that would see the company add operations in the Asia/Pacific region and in Europe.

The company developed specialty services in the US in the 1990s. It acquired ComTrain (testing and training software products) and Your Staff (an employee-leasing firm providing companies with entire human resources departments including benefits and payroll services) in 1994. The following year it bought the Wallace Law Registry (renamed Kelly Law Registry) a provider of lawyers paralegals and clerks. Kelly also established Kelly Scientific Resources to place science professionals. In 1996 that subsidiary acquired Oak Ridge Research Institute which provided scientists to the defense and energy industries.

William Kelly died at the age of 92 in 1998 and the company named president and CEO Terence Adderley his adopted son to replace him as chairman. (Adderley relinquished the title of president in late 2001.) The next year the company made four additions to its staffing services: Kelly Healthcare Resources Kelly Financial Resources Kelly Educational Staffing (substitute teachers) and KellyConnect (teleservices).

In 2000 the company made three acquisitions: Extra ETT in Spain (automotive staffing) ProStaff Group in the US (general staffing) and Business Trends Group in Singapore (general staffing). Kelly Services continued with its acquisition strategy the following year purchasing the engineering services business of Compuware among others. In 2002 the company opened new offices in the US Europe and Canada. In 2003 Kelly Services launched Kelly FedSecure which provides professionals with security clearances to companies and government contractors.

Citing medical reasons Adderley stepped down as chairman and CEO in 2006. President and COO Carl Camden took over as CEO but by May 2006 Adderley had recovered and was named chairman again.

In order to augment its portfolio of career transition services and business effectiveness consulting Kelly Services bought New York-based The Ayers Group. It also expanded its reach to the Czech Republic and Poland with the buyout of executive search firm Talents Technology in 2007. Also that year its presence in Japan grew when it acquired all the shares of former joint venture Tempstaff Kelly. Looking to China Hong Kong and Singapore Kelly Services acquired executive search and HR outsourcing services firm P-Serv.

At the same time the company shed some non-core operations. Kelly Services sold its Home Care Services unit to Res-Care in 2007 and sold its staff leasing operations to Oasis Outsourcing Holdings the year before. Kelly Services also closed 22 underperforming branches in the UK.

EXECUTIVES

EVP and General Manager Americas, Michael S. (Mike) Webster, age 56, $450,000 total compensation
SVP and Chief Innovation Officer, Rolf E. Kleiner, age 57, $343,750 total compensation
SVP Outsourcing and Consulting Group Global Administration, James H. Bradley
President CEO and Director, Carl T. Camden, age 57, $930,000 total compensation
Chairman, Terence E. (Terry) Adderley, age 78, $929,167 total compensation
EVP and COO, George S. Corona, age 53, $550,000 total compensation
SVP Global Marketing, Michael S. Morrow
Senior Director Investor and Public Relations, James M. (Jim) Polehna
SVP Outsourcing and Consulting Group Europe Middle East and Africa, Bernard Tommasini
SVP General Counsel and Corporate Secretary, Daniel T. Lis, age 65, $323,333 total compensation
SVP; General Manager KellyConnect, Jonathan D. Means
SVP Controller and Chief Accounting Officer, Michael E. Debs, age 54, $263,333 total compensation
SVP and Chief Human Resources Officer, Antonina M. (Nina) Ramsey, age 57
SVP; General Manager Asia Pacific, Dhiren Shantilal
SVP; General Manager U.S. Operations, Steve S. Armstrong
SVP Global Solutions and Services, Pamela M. Berklich
SVP and General Manager U.S. Commercial, W. Edward Meisenheimer
SVP and General Manager Europe Middle East and Africa, Leif Agneus
SVP Global CWO Practice Leader Outsourcing and Consulting Group, Teresa S. Carroll
SVP Global Client Relationships, Peter W. Quigley
EVP and CFO, Patricia Little, age 52, $500,000 total compensation
SVP and CIO, Joseph (Joe) Drouin
Manager Kelly Scientific Resources, Niall Clerkin
VP Kelly Healthcare, Connie Gray
VP and Managing Director Canadian Operations, Karin French
VP and Division Manager Kelly Government Solutions, James Hoen
Manager Public Relations, Jane Stehney
SVP Global Service, Debra Thorpe
Director, Donald R. Parfet, age 59
President CEO and Director, Carl T. Camden, age 57
Director, B. Joseph White, age 64
Director, Maureen A. Fay, age 77
Director, Leslie A. Murphy, age 60
Director, Conrad L. Mallett Jr., age 58
Director, Jane E. Dutton, age 59
Director, Terrence B. (Terry) Larkin, age 57
Director, Carol M. Adderley, age 52
Director, Toshio Saburi
Auditors: PricewaterhouseCoopersLLP

LOCATIONS

HQ: Kelly Services Inc.
999 W. Big Beaver Rd., Troy MI 48084-4782
Phone: 248-362-4444 **Fax:** 704-873-1275
Web: www.kewaunee.com

2011 Sales

	$ mil.	% of total
US	3,445	62
Total	**5,551**	**100**

PRODUCTS/OPERATIONS

2011 Sales

	$ mil.	% of total
Americas		
Professional & Technical	982	18
Commercial	1,387	24
Other	317	6
Total	**5,551**	**100**

Selected Services

CGR/seven (creative services staffing)

Kelly Catering and Hospitality (chefs porters)
Kelly Educational Staffing (substitute teachers)
Kelly Electronic Assembly Services
Kelly Engineering Resources (engineers)
Kelly Financial Resources (accounting analysts)
Kelly Government Solutions (US federal government staffing)
Kelly Healthcare Resources (nurses medical technicians)
Kelly Information Technology Resources
Kelly Law Registry
Kelly Light Industrial
Kelly Marketing Services
Kelly Office Services (clerical staffing)
Kelly Scientific Resources (science staffing)
KellyConnect (call center staffing)
KellyDirect (permanent placement service)
KellySelect (temporary-to-hire service)

COMPETITORS

Adecco
Allegis Group
ATC Healthcare
Insperity
ManpowerGroup
On Assignment
Randstad Holding
Robert Half
Technical Aid Corporation
TrueBlue
Volt Information

HISTORICAL FINANCIALS

Company Type: Public

Income Statement FYE: January 1

	REVENUE ($ mil.)	NET INCOME ($ mil.)	NET PROFIT MARGIN	EMPLOYEES
01/12	5,551	63	1.1%	558,200
01/11	4,950	26	0.5%	538,000
01/10*	4,314	(104)	—	487,900
12/08	5,517	(82)	—	660,100
12/07	5,667	61	1.1%	760,000
Annual Growth	(0.5%)	1.1%	—	(7.4%)

*Fiscal year change

2012 Year-End Financials

Debt ratio: 6.25%
Return on equity: 9.43%
Cash ($ mil.): 81
Current ratio: 159.77
Long-term debt ($ mil.): —
No. of shares (mil.): 36
Dividends
Yield: —
Payout: 5.92%
Market value ($ mil.): 505

	STOCK PRICE ($) FY Close	P/E High/Low		PER SHARE ($) Earnings	Dividends	Book Value
01/12	13.68	13	6	1.69	0.00	18.31
01/11	18.80	28	15	0.71	0.00	17.00
01/10*	11.93	—	—	(3.00)	0.00	16.18
12/08	12.55	—	—	(2.37)	0.00	18.78
12/07	19.29	20	11	1.67	0.00	22.48
Annual Growth	(8.2%)	—	—	0.3%	—	(5.0%)

*Fiscal year change

Kemper Corp. (DE)

Kemper (formerly Unitrin) is among the largest property and casualty insurance groups in the nation. Its Kemper Preferred and Kemper Specialty businesses offer automobile homeowners and fire coverage through independent agents and brokers. Its Kemper Direct business sells standard and non-standard auto coverage directly to consumers online and through employer-sponsored voluntary benefit programs. The company's Kemper Home Service Companies primarily sell life insurance the old-fashioned way –through home visits to individual customers. The company operates in the southern Midwestern and western parts of the US. The company changed its name from Unitrin Inc. to Kemper Corp. in 2011.

Operations

Following its name change in August 2011 the company rebranded its business units by renaming its largest property and casualty business unit (36% of sales) as "Kemper Preferred" and its largest life and health insurance business unit (34% of sales) as "Kemper Home Service Companies."

The name change followed a downsizing where the company shed or shuttered several operations. Its Fireside Bank subsidiary which purchased (subprime) loan contracts from used automobile dealers halted all lending back in 2009. Its remaining business was then wound down gradually in the process known as "run-off" whereby existing loans are serviced but no new business is conducted. After all of its remaining active and inactive auto loans were sold off Fireside (and thus Kemper) ceased all banking operations in mid-2012.

Financial Analysis

Kemper's revenue fell 9% in 2011 vs. 2010 while net income dropped by nearly 55%. (Indeed revenue has declined in three of the past four annual comparisons.) The company blamed the decline in 2011 on a decrease in earned premiums in the Direct Specialty and Preferred segments as a result of lower sales. Higher premium rates partially offset the decline in sales. Net income declined on lower net investment income.

Strategy

Kemper is also preparing to shed its Reserve National subsidiary which sells individual accident and health insurance and Medicare supplement policies. The sale will mark the company's exit from the sale of certain specialty lines such as scheduled benefit hospitalization and surgical plans home health care and first-occurrence cancer and heart-attack policies. An earlier deal to sell the unit to life insurer Physicians Mutual fell apart in 2010.

Kemper's disposal-heavy strategy followed a period of expansion in its traditional consumer insurance options. The company enriched its Unitrin Direct business segment through acquisitions of smaller companies.

Ownership

Singleton Group LLC owns about 18% of Kemper's shares.

EXECUTIVES

SVP Secretary and General Counsel, Scott Renwick, age 60, $530,000 total compensation
Chairman President CEO, Donald G. (Don) Southwell, age 60, $925,000 total compensation
Chairman Emeritus, Richard C. Vie, age 74
VP and Chief Accounting Officer, Richard Roeske, age 51, $320,000 total compensation
EVP Life and Health Group; President Kemper Home Service Companies, Edward J. Konar, age 55, $214,250 total compensation
VP and Chief Investment Officer, John M. Boschelli, age 43, $223,750 total compensation
SVP and CFO, Dennis R. Vigneau, age 45
Corporate Actuary, Ronald E. Greco
CIO, Shawn R. Crawford
President Reserve National Insurance, Orin L. Crossley
VP Planning and Analysis, Frank J. Sodaro, age 43
VP and Treasurer, Christopher L. Moses, age 40
VP Human Resources, Lisa M. King, age 52
VP Tax, Dennis J. Sandelski, age 51
President Kemper Specialty, Timothy D. Burns
Director Internal Audit, Joseph A. Dutcher
VP Investor Relations & Corporate Identity, Diana Hickert-Hill
Chief Risk Officer, Shekar Jannah
Director, David P. Storch, age 59
Chairman President CEO, Donald G. (Don) Southwell, age 60
Chairman Emeritus, Richard C. Vie, age 74
Director, Julie M. Howard, age 49
Director, Fayez S. Sarofim, age 83
Director, James E. Annable, age 68
Director, Douglas G. (Doug) Geoga, age 56
Director, Reuben L. Hedlund, age 75
Director, Wayne Kauth, age 78
Auditors: Deloitte&ToucheLLP

LOCATIONS

HQ: Kemper Corporation
1 E. Wacker Dr., Chicago IL 60601-1802
Phone: 312-661-4600 **Fax:** 312-494-6995
Web: www.kempercorporation.com

PRODUCTS/OPERATIONS

2011 Revenues

Preferred	909	36
Specialty	466	19
Other	29	1

Selected Subsidiaries

United Insurance Company of America
The Reliable Life Insurance Company
Union National Life Insurance Company
Mutual Savings Life Insurance Company
United Casualty Insurance Company of America
Union National Fire Insurance Company
Mutual Savings Fire Insurance Company
Reserve National Insurance Company

COMPETITORS

Allstate
Citizens Financial
Citizens Inc.
GEICO
Liberty Mutual Agency
Nationwide
Penn-America
Security National Financial
State Farm
USAA

HISTORICAL FINANCIALS

Company Type: Public

Income Statement FYE: December 31

	ASSETS ($ mil.)	NET INCOME ($ mil.)	INCOME AS % OF ASSETS	EMPLOYEES
12/11	8,085	83	1.0%	0
12/10	8,358	184	2.2%	0
12/09	8,573	164	1.9%	7,230
12/08	8,818	(29)	—	7,700
12/07	9,405	217	2.3%	7,400
Annual Growth	(3.7%)	(21.3%)	—	—

2011 Year-End Financials

Debt ratio: 7.55%
Return on equity: 3.78%
Cash ($ mil.): 251
Current ratio: —
Long-term debt ($ mil.): 610
No. of shares (mil.): 60
Dividends
Yield: —
Payout: 69.57%
Market value ($ mil.): 1,760

	STOCK PRICE ($)	P/E		PER SHARE ($)		
	FY Close	High/Low		Earnings	Dividends	Book Value
12/11	29.21	23	16	1.38	0.00	36.78
12/10	24.54	10	7	2.98	0.88	34.61
12/09	22.05	9	3	2.64	1.07	30.75
12/08	15.94	—	—	(0.47)	1.88	26.46
12/07	47.99	16	12	3.30	1.82	35.76
Annual Growth	(11.7%)	—	—	(19.6%)	—	0.7%

KeyCorp

Financial services giant KeyCorp unlocks its customers' monetary potential. With a focus on retail operations flagship subsidiary KeyBank operates about 1000 branches in more than a dozen states scattered throughout the Northeast the Midwest the Rocky Mountains and the Pacific Northwest including Alaska. Its operations are divided into two groups: Community banking offers traditional services such as deposits loans and financial planning; while national banking provides real estate capital equipment financing and capital markets services to large corporate clients nationwide.

Like many of its peers KeyCorp was hit by the economic downturn resulting in lower revenues and billions of dollars in losses. In response the company more than doubled its allowance for loan losses from 2008 to 2009 and curbed risky lending. KeyCorp also wound down noncore businesses such as hedge fund manager Austin Capital Management to focus on consumer and corporate banking.

So far the changes have served the company well as its loan charge-offs have declined. Net income has dramatically increased and was up by more than 66% in 2011. The company returned to profitability in 2010 and remained profitable the following year. The improvements were due to lower credit costs and increased noninterest expense. Poor market conditions due to the slowly recovering economy created a lag in revenues in 2011.

KeyCorp's main goals are to grow profitability by increasing revenues and controlling costs. Much of the company's growth comes from attracting and retaining new customers. Those new customers often come by expanding the company's geographic footprint and improving products.

The company's community banking group continues to grow despite the economic turmoil. In 2012 KeyCorp acquired nearly 40 branches in the Buffalo and Rochester New York areas from First Niagara which is divesting the branches in order to satisfy antitrust concerns related to its acquisition of nearly 200 branches in upstate New York from HSBC USA. KeyCorp has also been opening about 40 new branches a year and plans to continue to do so.

HISTORY

KeyCorp predecessor Commercial Bank of Albany was chartered in 1825. In 1865 it joined the new national banking system and became National Commercial Bank of Albany. After WWI National Commercial consolidated with Union National Bank & Trust as National Commercial Bank and Trust which then merged with First Trust and Deposit in 1971.

In 1973 Victor Riley became president and CEO. Under Riley National Commercial grew during the 1970s and 1980s through acquisitions. Riley sought to make the company a regional powerhouse but was thwarted when several New England states passed legislation barring New York banks from buying banks in the region.

As a result the company renamed Key Bank in 1979 turned west targeting small towns with less competition. Thus situated it prospered despite entering Alaska just in time for the 1986 oil price collapse. Its folksy image and small-town success earned it a reputation as the "Wal-Mart of banking."

Meanwhile in Cleveland Society for Savings followed a different path. Founded as a mutual savings bank in 1849 the institution succeeded from the start. It survived the Civil War and postwar economic turmoil and built Cleveland's first skyscraper in 1890. It continued to grow even during the Depression and became the largest savings bank outside the Northeast in 1949.

In 1955 the bank formed a holding company Society National. Society grew through the acquisitions of smaller banks in Ohio until 1979 when Ohio allowed branch banking in contiguous counties. Thereafter Society National opened branches as well. In the mid-1980s and the early 1990s the renamed Society Corporation began consolidating its operations and continued growing.

A 1994 merger of National Commercial with Society more than doubled assets for the surviving KeyCorp; compatibility of the two companies' systems and software simplified consolidation. KeyCorp sold its mortgage-servicing unit to NationsBank (now Bank of America) in 1995 and over the next year bought investment management finance and investment banking firms.

In 1997 KeyCorp began trimming its branch network divesting 200 offices including its 28-branch KeyBank Wyoming subsidiary. It expanded its consumer lending business that year by buying Champion Mortgage. In cooperation with USF&G (now part of The St. Paul Travelers Companies) and three HMOs KeyCorp began offering health insurance to the underserved small-business market.

In 1998 the company bought Leasetec which leases computer storage systems globally through its StorageTek subsidiary; it also bought McDonald & Company Investments (now McDonald Investments; sold in 2007) with an eye toward reaching its goal of earning half of its revenues from fees. Also in 1998 KeyCorp began offering business lines of credit to customers of Costco Wholesale the nation's largest wholesale club.

As part of a restructuring effort KeyCorp sold 28 Long Island New York branches to Dime Bancorp in 1999. The next year the company sold its credit card portfolio to Associates First Capital (now part of Citigroup) and bought National Realty Funding a securitizer of commercial mortgages. In 2001 it acquired Denver-based investment bank The Wallach Company.

The company expanded further in the Denver area with its 2002 purchase of Union Bankshares. Two years later KeyCorp bought Seattle-area bank EverTrust Financial Group.

In 2007 the company bought Tuition Management Systems which provides outsourced tuition billing accounting and counseling services for schools and colleges; the unit was later merged into its Key Education Resources operations. Also that year KeyCorp sold investment bank and brokerage McDonald Investments to UBS Financial Services.

The company bought New York-based U.S.B. Holding Co. and its Union State Bank subsidiary for some $550 million in early 2008. The deal added more than 30 branches nearly doubling KeyCorp's presence in the Hudson River Valley region.

EXECUTIVES

CFO Key National Bank, Patricia J. Jamieson, age 53
EVP and Chief Human Resources Officer, Thomas E. (Tom) Helfrich, age 59
Vice Chairman and Chief Administrative Officer, Thomas C. (Tom) Stevens, age 62, $798,077 total compensation
SEVP and CFO, Jeffrey B. Weeden, age 55, $725,000 total compensation
Chief Marketing and Communications Officer, Karen R. Haefling
EVP and Director Corporate Diversity and Philanthropy, Margot J. Copeland
EVP KeyBank; President Community Development Banking, Bruce D. Murphy
President Key Corporate Bank, Christopher M. (Chris) Gorman, age 51
EVP General Counsel and Secretary, Paul N. Harris, age 53
SEVP and Chief Risk Officer, Charles S. (Chuck) Hyle, age 60, $300,000 total compensation
CEO Victory Capital Management, Robert (Bob) Wagner
EVP Key Enterprise Operations KeyBank, Michael P. (Mike) Barnum
EVP and Treasurer, Joseph M. Vayda
Head National Business Banking Segment, Maria C. Coyne
EVP; Group Head Real Estate and Corporate Banking Services Key National Banking, E.J. Burke
Regional President Northwest KeyBank, Wes Lawrence
Chief Accounting Officer, Robert L. Morris, age 59
President Key Community Bank and President KeyBank NA, William R. (Bill) Koehler, age 47
EVP and Segment Head Commercial Bank Key Community Banking, Cindy P. Crotty
EVP and Segment Head Consumer Bank Key Community Banking, Robert A. DeAngelis
EVP Chief Risk Review Officer and General Auditor, Kevin T. Ryan
COO KeyBanc Capital Markets; Co-Lead KeyBank National Association, Douglas W. Preiser
EVP Key National Bank Servicing and Support Group, Marty L. O'Connor
Media Contact, William C. (Bill) Murschel
Co-CEO Victory Capital Management, David C. Brown
President Northeast Region KeyBank, Hugh Donlon
EVP and and Chief Credit Officer, William L. (Bill) Hartmann
President Greater Cleveland District, Lisa Oliver
Co-Lead KeyBank National Association, Andrew Paine
Chairman President and CEO, Beth E. Mooney, age 56, $849,231 total compensation
Director Strategy, Mark J. R. Williams
SVP and Head Public Sector Group, Amer Ahmad
EVP and Chief Human Resources Officer, Johnni Beckel
CIO and Head Key Enterprise Technology, Amy G. Brady
Director, Alexander M. (Sandy) Cutler, age 60
Vice Chairman and Chief Administrative Officer, Thomas C. (Tom) Stevens, age 62
Director, Edward P. (Ed) Campbell, age 62
Director, Barbara R. Snyder, age 56

Director, Edward W. (Ed) Stack, age 57
Director, Ruth Ann M. Gillis, age 58
Director, William R. (Bill) Sanford, age 67
Director, Carol A. Cartwright, age 70
Director, H. James Dallas, age 53
Director, Kristen L. Manos, age 52
Director, Joseph A. Carrabba, age 59
Director, Elizabeth R. Gile, age 56
Auditors: Ernst&YoungLLP

LOCATIONS

HQ: KeyCorp
127 Public Sq., Cleveland OH 44114-1306
Phone: 216-689-3000 **Fax:** 972-448-1408
Web: www.keystoneconsolidated.com

PRODUCTS/OPERATIONS

2011 Sales

	$ mil.	% of total
Interest		
Loans	2,206	47
Securities	595	13
Other	88	2
Noninterest		
Trust & investment services	434	9
Service charges on deposits	281	6
Letter of credit & loan fees	213	4
Investment banking and capital markets income	134	3
Operating lease income	122	3
Other	624	13
Total	**4,697**	**100**

COMPETITORS

Bank of America
Citigroup
Comerica
Fifth Third
Flagstar Bancorp
HSBC USA
Huntington Bancshares
JPMorgan Chase
M&T Bank
Northern Trust
PNC Financial
RBS Citizens Financial Group
Sovereign Bank
U.S. Bancorp
Wells Fargo

HISTORICAL FINANCIALS

Company Type: Public

Income Statement FYE: December 31

	ASSETS ($ mil.)	NET INCOME ($ mil.)	INCOME AS % OF ASSETS	EMPLOYEES
12/11	88,785	920	1.0%	15,381
12/10	91,843	554	0.6%	15,610
12/09	93,287	(1,335)	—	16,698
12/08	104,531	(1,468)	—	18,095
12/07	99,983	919	0.9%	18,934
Annual Growth	(2.9%)	0.0%	—	(5.1%)

2011 Year-End Financials

Debt ratio: 10.72%
Return on equity: 9.29%
Cash ($ mil.): 1,317
Current ratio: —
Long-term debt ($ mil.): 9,520
No. of shares (mil.): 953
Dividends
Yield: —
Payout: 11.49%
Market value ($ mil.): 7,329

	STOCK PRICE ($) FY Close	P/E High/Low		PER SHARE ($) Earnings	Dividends	Book Value
12/11	7.69	11	7	0.87	0.00	10.39
12/10	8.85	20	12	0.44	0.04	12.62
12/09	5.55	—	—	(2.34)	0.09	12.14
12/08	8.52	—	—	(3.36)	1.00	21.17
12/07	23.45	17	9	2.32	1.46	19.92
Annual Growth	(24.3%)	—	—	(21.7%)	—	(15.0%)

Kimberly-Clark Corp.

Nobody knows noses and bottoms better than Kimberly-Clark. One of the world's largest makers of personal paper products the company operates through four business segments: personal care consumer tissue K-C Professional and health care. Kimberly-Clark's largest unit personal care makes products such as diapers (Huggies Pull-Ups) feminine care items (Kotex) and incontinence care products (Poise Depend). Through its consumer tissue segment the manufacturer offers facial and bathroom tissues paper towels and other household items under the names Cottonelle Kleenex Viva and Scott (including the Scott Naturals line). Kimberly-Clark's professional unit makes WypAll commercial wipes among other items.

Operations

Amid a troubled global economy that has put pressure on cash-strapped consumers and inflated the cost of fuel pulp and paper Kimberly-Clark manages to hold on to the #1 or #2 position in 80-plus countries. Its largest customer uber worldwide retailer Wal-Mart represented about 12% of sales in 2011 and 13% in both 2010 and 2009.

Financial Analysis

The company posted a modest increase in year-over-year sales in 2011. Results reflect sluggish sales in its largest market North American personal care products coupled with lower selling prices and a tepid product mix. Volumes were flat despite product innovations to mainstay lines –baby wipes adult incontinence and feminine care. Its top line was buoyed by demand in Europe and in South Korea China and Latin America as well as favorable currency exchange rates. Consumer tissue lines (which generate nearly a third of Kimberly-Clark's sales) across all geographic markets remained strong as did higher sales volumes and sales prices for health care products such as exam gloves and medical devices. Earnings however declined for a second consecutive year driven mainly by $415 million in pretax charges for restructuring its consumer tissues operations and exiting its ailing pulp manufacturing business. Kimberly-Clark's plan which aims to bolster profitability has focused on streamlining or closing half a dozen manufacturing facilities and axing production of mainly non-branded offerings. Most of the restructuring charges are associated with the consumer tissue and K-C Professional businesses in North America followed by Australia. Although net sales are likely to fall in 2012 operating profit is projected to increase over the next two years thanks to the resulting savings.

Geographic Reach

Kimberly-Clark is maintaining a broad global presence as part of its growth strategy. It boasts manufacturing facilities in more than 35 countries and products that reach about 175 countries. Developing regions Asia Latin America and others now generate more than a third of the company's revenue due to expansion efforts such as building a $40 million plant in Singapore and acquisitions such as the remaining 31% of its Bogota Colombia-based subsidiary Colombiana Kimberly Colpapel (CKC). The deal secured the company's foothold in the developing markets of Bolivia Colombia Ecuador Peru and Venezuela. Kimberly-Clark also holds Kimberly-Clark Kenko Industria e Comercio Ltda based in Brazil.

Strategy

Kimberly-Clark's strategy includes building upon its well-branded position in the personal care and consumer tissue space. It typically invests more than $300 million a year in research and development of new and/or improved products. Notable introductions are Huggies Little Movers Slip-On Diapers Poise Hourglass Shape Pads and Kleenex Cool Touch Facial Tissue among several others. The company has simultaneously moved into making higher-margin disposable medical products. It produces sterilization wrap face masks surgical drapes and gowns and closed-suction respiratory products. Its health care unit which accounted for 8% of 2011 sales has logged increasingly higher year-over-year sales volumes helped by acquisitions. Among them Kimberly-Clark took over Baylis Medical's pain management business which focuses on chronic spinal pain and I-Flow a developer and marketer of drug-delivery systems for post-surgical pain relief and surgical site care.

Mergers & Acquisitions

Kimberly-Clark's Professional business representing about 16% of 2011 sales has also benefited from the acquisition of Jackson Products a maker of welding and work-zone protective gear. The company known as Jackson Safety paved the way for Kimberly-Clark to sell safety products in the US and Europe. To boost its revenue further the professional unit inked a deal in 2012 to acquire Slovenia-based safety products company Balder. Specializing in eye and face protection Balder complements Kimberly-Clark's Jackson Products welding purchase with its own electro-optic device production and research and development activities.

Sales & Marketing

To gain recognition for its brands the company averages about $650 million in advertising expenses each year. In fiscal 2011 Kimberly-Clark logged $686 million in ad spending. As business and economic conditions change the consumer paper company will spend more aggressively on adverting and promoting its products.

HISTORY

John Kimberly Charles Clark Havilah Babcock and Frank Shattuck founded Kimberly Clark & Company in Neenah Wisconsin in 1872 to manufacture newsprint from rags. The company incorporated as Kimberly & Clark Company in 1880 and built a pulp and paper plant on the Fox River in 1889.

In 1914 the company developed cellu-cotton a cotton substitute used by the US Army as surgical cotton during WWI. Army nurses used cellu-cotton pads as disposable sanitary napkins and six years later the company introduced Kotex the first disposable feminine hygiene product. Kleenex the first throwaway handkerchief followed in 1924. Kimberly & Clark joined with The New York Times Company in 1926 to build a newsprint mill (Spruce Falls Power and Paper) in Ontario Canada. Two years later the company went public as Kimberly-Clark.

The firm expanded internationally during the 1950s opening plants in Mexico Germany and the UK. It began operations in 17 more foreign locations in the 1960s.

CEO Guy Minard who retired in 1971 sold the four mills that handled Kimberly-Clark's unprofitable coated-paper business and entered the paper towel and disposable diaper markets. Minard's successor Darwin Smith introduced Kimbies diapers in 1968 but they leaked and were withdrawn from the market. An improved version came out in 1976 followed by Huggies a premium-priced diaper with elastic leg bands two years later.

The company formed Midwest Express Airlines from its corporate flight department in 1984 (a business it exited in 1996). Smith moved Kimberly-Clark's headquarters from Neenah to Irving Texas the following year.

In 1991 Kimberly-Clark and The New York Times Company sold Spruce Falls Power and Paper. Smith retired as chairman in 1992 and was succeeded by Wayne Sanders who was largely responsible for designing Huggies Pull-Ups (introduced in 1989). Kimberly-Clark entered a joint venture to make personal care products in Argentina in 1994 and also bought the feminine hygiene units of VP-Schickedanz (Germany) and Handan Comfort and Beauty Group (China).

Kimberly-Clark bought Scott Paper in 1995 for $9.4 billion. The move boosted its market share in bathroom tissue from 5% to 31% and its share in paper towels from 6% to 18% but led to some headaches as the company absorbed Scott's operations.

In 1997 Kimberly-Clark sold its 50% stake in Canada's Scott Paper to forest products company Kruger and bought diaper operations in Spain and Portugal and disposable surgical face masks maker Tecnol Medical Products. A tissue price war in Europe bruised the company's bottom line that year and the company began massive job cuts. (By the end of 1999 nearly 4000 jobs mostly in the tissue-based businesses had been axed.)

In part to focus on its health care business which it entered in 1997 the company in 1999 sold some of its timber interests and its timber fleet to Cooper/T. Smith Corp. Augmenting its presence in Germany Switzerland and Austria in 1999 the company paid $365 million for the tissue business of Swiss-based Attisholz Holding. Adding to its lineup of medical products the company bought Ballard Medical Products in 1999 for $744 million and examination glove maker Safeskin in 2000 for about $800 million.

Also in 2000 the company bought virtually all of Taiwan's S-K Corporation; the move made Kimberly-Clark one of the largest manufacturers of consumer packaged goods in Taiwan and set the stage for expanded distribution in the Asia/Pacific region. The company later purchased Taiwan Scott Paper Corporation for about $40 million and merged the two companies forming Kimberly-Clark Taiwan. In 2001 Kimberly-Clark bought Italian diaper maker Linostar and announced it was closing four Latin American manufacturing plants.

In 2002 Kimberly-Clark purchased paper-packaging rival Amcor's stake in their Kimberly-Clark Australia joint venture. Adding to its global consumer tissue business in 2003 Kimberly-Clark acquired the Polish tissue-maker Klucze.

In early 2004 Chairman and CEO Thomas Falk began rolling out the global business plan the company had detailed in July 2003. The firm combined its North American and European groups for personal care and consumer tissue under North Atlantic groups and was working to ensure that Asian Latin American and Eastern European markets were covered specifically in the areas of value-tiered diapers light-end incontinence and health care products.

Kimberly-Clark combined its North Atlantic Personal Care and Family Care businesses in 2005 to form a North Atlantic Consumer Products unit which serves North America and Europe.

Its 2005 $16 million acquisition of Microcuff extended Kimberly-Clark's reach into medical devices and catheter technology. Adding to its medical business Kimberly-Clark in late 2009 acquired Baylis Medical to boost its high-margin medical device business.

EXECUTIVES

Chairman and CEO, Thomas J. (Tom) Falk, age 54, $1,224,996 total compensation
Group President North Atlantic Consumer Products, Robert E. Abernathy, age 57, $625,000 total compensation
Group President Kimberly-Clark International, Robert W. (Bob) Black, age 52, $560,000 total compensation
SVP and Chief Human Resources Officer, Lizanne C. (Liz) Gottung, age 55
SVP and CFO, Mark A. Buthman, age 52, $660,000 total compensation
VP Investor Relations, Paul J. Alexander
Senior Marketing Officer, Clive Sirkin
President Health Care, Joanne B. Bauer, age 57
CIO, Ramon F. Baez
SVP Continuous Improvement Sourcing and Sustainability, Jan B. Spencer, age 56
Chief Strategy Officer and Treasurer, Nancy S. Loewe, age 45
President Global Brands and Innovation, Anthony J. (Tony) Palmer, age 52, $500,000 total compensation
SVP Law and Government Affairs and Chief Compliance Officer, Thomas J. (Tom) Mielke, age 54
President North America Consumer Products, Michael Hsu, age 48
President Kimberly-Clark Professional, Christian A. (Chris) Brickman, age 47
General Manager Corporate Services Australia New Zealand and Southern Asia Pacific, Ross Hearne
Press Contact Argentina Chile Uruguay and Paraguay, Fernando Hofmann
Press Contact Brazil, Marco A. Iszlaji
VP Global Sustainability, Suhas Apte
VP and Controller, Michael T. Azbell, age 48
SVP and Chief Strategy Officer, Elane B. Stock, age 48
VP and Global Diversity Officer, Sue Dodsworth
VP and Secretary, John W. Wesley
Manager External Communications, Joanna McCarthy
Press Contact China, Jessica Cai
Press Contact Central America and Caribbean, Anabell Iglesias
Press Contact Colombia Peru Ecuador Bolivia and Venezuela, Juan Steverlynck
Director Shopper Marketing, Richard Moulton
Director Enterprise Integrated Marketing Planning, Deborah Hannah
Director, Abelardo E. (Al) Bru, age 63
Director, Robert W. Decherd, age 61
Director, G. Craig Sullivan, age 72
Director, John R. Alm, age 66
Director, Linda Johnson Rice, age 54
Director, James M. (Jim) Jenness, age 66
Director, Marc J. Shapiro, age 64
Director, John F. Bergstrom, age 65
Director, Nancy J. Karch, age 64
Director, Mae C. Jemison, age 55
Director, Fabian T. Garcia, age 52
Director, Ian C. Read, age 59
Auditors: Deloitte&ToucheLLP

LOCATIONS

HQ: Kimberly-Clark Corporation
351 Phelps Dr., Irving TX 75038
Phone: 972-281-1200 **Fax:** 972-281-1490
Web: www.kimberly-clark.com

2011 Sales

	$ mil.	% of total
North America		
US	10,463	48
Canada	726	3
Asia Latin America & other	7,467	34
Europe	3,401	15
Intergeographic sales	(1211)	-
Total	**20,846**	**100**

PRODUCTS/OPERATIONS

2011 Sales

	$ mil.	% of total
Personal care products	9,128	44
Consumer tissue	6,770	32
K-C Professional & other	3,294	16
Health care	1,606	8
Corporate & other	48	—
Total	**20,846**	**100**

2011 Sales

	$ bil.	% of total
Consumer tissue products	6	32
Diapers	4	24
Away-from-hom professional products	3	16
All other	5	28
Total	**20**	**100**

Selected Products and Brands

Medical
- Closed-suction respiratory products
- Examination gloves
  - Safeskin
- Face masks
- Infection-control products
- Scrub suits and apparel
- Sterile wrap
  - Kimguard
- Surgical drapes and gowns

Personal Care
- Baby wipes
  - Huggies
- Disposable diapers
  - GoodNites
  - Huggies
  - Pull-Ups
- Feminine hygiene products
  - Kotex
  - Lightdays
  - New Freedom
- Incontinence products
  - Depend
  - Poise
- Swimpants
  - Little Swimmers

Tissue-Based
- Bathroom tissue
  - Cottonelle
  - Scott
- Commercial wipes
  - Kimwipes
  - WypAll
- Facial tissue
  - Kleenex
- Paper napkins
  - Scott
- Paper towels
  - Kleenex
  - Scott
  - Viva

COMPETITORS

3M
Ansell
Becton Dickinson
Bristol-Myers Squibb
Cardinal Health Medical
CCA Industries
DSG International Ltd
Energizer Holdings
Georgia-Pacific
Johnson & Johnson
Medline Industries
Nice-Pak Products
Potlatch
Procter & Gamble
SSI Surgical Services
Suominen

HISTORICAL FINANCIALS

Company Type: Public

Income Statement FYE: December 31

	REVENUE ($ mil.)	NET INCOME ($ mil.)	NET PROFIT MARGIN	EMPLOYEES
12/11	20,846	1,591	7.6%	57,000
12/10	19,746	1,843	9.3%	57,000
12/09	19,115	1,884	9.9%	56,000
12/08	19,415	1,690	8.7%	53,000
12/07	18,266	1,822	10.0%	53,000
Annual Growth	3.4%	(3.3%)	—	1.8%

2011 Year-End Financials

Debt ratio: 31.65%
Return on equity: 27.45%
Cash ($ mil.): 764
Current ratio: 116.42
Long-term debt ($ mil.): 5,426
No. of shares (mil.): 395
Dividends
Yield: —
Payout: 70.18%
Market value ($ mil.): 29,108

	STOCK PRICE ($) FY Close	P/E High/Low		PER SHARE ($) Earnings	Dividends	Book Value
12/11	73.56	18	16	3.99	0.00	14.65
12/10	63.04	15	13	4.45	2.64	15.87
12/09	63.71	15	10	4.52	2.40	15.49
12/08	52.74	17	13	4.04	2.32	11.82
12/07	69.34	17	16	4.09	2.12	14.80
Annual Growth	1.5%	—	—	(0.6%)	—	(0.3%)

Kinder Morgan Energy Partners, L.P.

Kinder Morgan Energy Partners (KMP) keeps energy on the move throughout the North America. The company holds stakes in more than 37000 miles of natural gas and petroleum product pipelines and owns 180 bulk terminals and rail transloading facilities with 200 millions barrels of storage capacity that handle 100 million tons of coal petroleum coke and bulk products annually. KMP transports refined petroleum products (gasoline diesel and jet fuel) through 8400 miles of pipelines and stores the products in 60 terminals in the US. Through its CO2 subsidiary KMP transports carbon dioxide. Kinder Morgan owns about 13% of KMP and through its Kinder Morgan Management unit acts as general partner.

KMP operates five business segments: Natural Gas Pipelines Products Pipelines CO2 Terminals and Kinder Morgan Canada. Its business strategy includes acquiring and integrating additional businesses expanding existing assets and constructing new facilities for midstream energy holdings. These assets provide earnings well in excess of KMP's capital costs which in turn is distributed to limited partners and its general partner.

Expanding its ethanol business in 2010 the company formed an ethanol terminal joint venture with U.S. Development Group LLC. The deal includes the purchase of three terminals for $195 million and the creation of and a US-wide ethanol distribution network. It also acquired four liquids and liquid bulk terminals from Slay Industries for $98 million giving it a foothold in the St. Louis market.

That year the company also acquired a 50% stake in Petrohawk Energy's Haynesville Shale gathering and treating business for $921 million. The purchase gives KMP an entry into one of the largest onshore gas fields the US. It also teamed up with Copano Energy to form the Eagle Ford Gathering LLC joint venture to provide gathering transportation and processing services to natural gas production companies in South Texas.

In 2010 reported an overall jump in revenues and income thanks largely to increased capacity and product volumes as the result of acquisitions and expansions and higher commodity prices. The products pipeline segment was the only unit to report a dip in earnings largely due to increased operating costs (mainly rate case liability related).

Growing its coke operations in 2011 the company acquired a new petroleum coke terminal from TGS Development Group for $74 million.

In a major move to become North America's largest natural gas pipeline and midstream company (with about 80000 miles of pipeline) in 2012 parent Kinder Morgan acquired El Paso Corp. for about $38 billion.

In 2012 KMP agreed to buy 50% stake in a KKR natural gas midstream joint venture operating in the Uinta Basin and the Eagle Ford shale for $300 million.

EXECUTIVES

VP; President Products Pipelines, Thomas A. Bannigan, age 58
VP General Counsel and Secretary, Joseph Listengart, age 44, $257,692 total compensation
VP Human Resources and Administration, James E. Street, age 56
Chairman and CEO, Richard D. (Rich) Kinder, age 67, $1 total compensation
President and Director, C. Park Shaper, age 44, $257,692 total compensation
VP; President CO2, Richard T. (Tim) Bradley, age 56
VP Corporate Development Treasurer and Investor Relations, David D. Kinder, age 38, $200,000 total compensation
EVP and COO, Steven J. (Steve) Kean, age 51, $257,692 total compensation
VP and Chief Tax Officer, Jordan H. Mintz
VP and CFO, Kimberly A. (Kim) Dang, age 42, $257,692 total compensation
VP; President Terminals, Jeffrey R. Armstrong, age 43, $200,000 total compensation
President Kinder Morgan Canada, Ian D. Anderson, age 54
Media Relations, Joe Hollier
VP Corporate Communications, Larry S. Pierce
Investor Relations, Mindy Mills Thornock
VP; President Natural Gas Pipelines, Thomas A. (Tom) Martin, age 50
VP and CIO, Henry W. (Hank) Neumann Jr.
VP and Controller, Debra M. Witges
VP Internal Audit, W. Garner Dotson
President Texas Intrastate Natural Gas Pipelines, Duane Kokinda
VP Internal Audit, Patrick Bourgoyne
Director, C. Berdon Lawrence, age 69
President and Director, C. Park Shaper, age 44
Director, Gary L. Hultquist, age 68
Director, Perry M. Waughtal, age 76
Director, Ted A. Gardner, age 54
Auditors: PricewaterhouseCoopersLLP

LOCATIONS

HQ: Kinder Morgan Energy Partners L.P.
500 Dallas St. Ste. 1000, Houston TX 77002
Phone: 713-369-9000 **Fax:** 713-369-9410
Web: www.kindermorgan.com

2010 Sales

	$ mil.	% of total
US	7,701	96
Canada	356	4
Mexico & other countries	19	-
Total	**8,077**	**100**

PRODUCTS/OPERATIONS

2010 Sales

	$ mil.	% of total
Natural gas pipelines	3,614	45
Services	3,024	37
Product sales & other	1,438	18
Total	**8,077**	**100**

COMPETITORS

Buckeye Partners
Crosstex Energy
Enterprise Products
K-Sea Transportation
Koch Industries Inc.
Plains All American Pipeline
Sunoco Logistics
TransMontaigne
Williams Companies

HISTORICAL FINANCIALS

Company Type: Public

Income Statement FYE: December 31

	REVENUE ($ mil.)	NET INCOME ($ mil.)	NET PROFIT MARGIN	EMPLOYEES
12/11	8,211	1,257	15.3%	8,120
12/10	8,077	1,316	16.3%	0
12/09	7,003	1,267	18.1%	0
12/08	11,740	1,304	11.1%	0
12/07	9,217	590	6.4%	0
Annual Growth	(2.8%)	20.8%	—	—

2011 Year-End Financials

Debt ratio: 57.57%
Return on equity: 16.75%
Cash ($ mil.): 409
Current ratio: 50.51
Long-term debt ($ mil.): 12,238
No. of shares (mil.): 336
Dividends
Yield: —
Payout: 1832.00%
Market value ($ mil.): 28,586

	STOCK PRICE ($) FY Close	P/E High/Low		PER SHARE ($) Earnings	Dividends	Book Value
12/11	84.95	340258		0.25	0.00	22.31
12/10	70.26	51	43	1.40	4.32	22.81
12/09	60.98	52	35	1.18	4.20	22.38
12/08	45.75	31	22	1.94	3.89	22.70
12/07	53.99	—	—	(0.09)	3.39	17.89
Annual Growth	12.0%	—	—	—	—	5.7%

Kinder Morgan Inc.

Kinder Morgan Inc. (KMI formerly Kinder Morgan Holdco) is the top layer of a large oil and gas cake. It owns Kinder Morgan Management which manages the general partner of Kinder Morgan Energy Partners (KMP). KMP operates pipeline that transport natural gas crude oil gasoline and other products along with terminals used to store chemicals and petroleum products. It produces carbon dioxide (CO2) which is used in oil field production. In a major move to become the largest natural gas pipeline and midstream enterprise in North America (with about 75000 miles of natural gas pipeline and 180 terminals) in 2012 KMI acquired El Paso Corp. (which had 44000 miles of natural gas pipeline) for about $38 billion.

Apart from greatly expanding the company's size and scope the deal is expected to save KMI more than $400 million of cost savings per year through the integration of the two organizations and the elimination of redundancies. KMI also owns 51% of El Paso Pipeline Partners and about 20% of natural gas pipeline NGPL PipeCo.

Operations

The company is a leader in petroleum product transportation terminal operations and coke and CO2 transportation; it serves more than 1.1 million customers in the US and Canada.

Financial Analysis

In 2011 KMI reported a 1% increase in revenues thanks largely to higher prices for its CO2 and petroleum products compensating for weakness in natural gas prices. However those same lower natural gas prices resulted in lower gas expenses helping to substantially lift the company's net income for the year.

Strategy

KMI's strategy is focused on building and maintaining energy transportation and storage assets which are central components to a growing natural gas and petroleum products infrastructure across North America.

Ownership

Following its $2.9 billion IPO the company is 30% controlled by chairman and CEO Richard Kinder. Other investors include several board members and other management as well as four investment funds.

Company Background

Kinder led a group of investors in taking KMI private in 2007. It then adopted the Knight name. To take advantage of its better-known brand it reverted to the Kinder Morgan name in 2009. Kinder Morgan went public in 2011 and changed its name to Kinder Morgan Inc. IPO proceeds went to the aforementioned selling shareholders.

EXECUTIVES

VP General Counsel and Secretary, Joseph Listengart, age 44
VP Human Resources and Administration, James E. Street, age 56
Chairman and CEO, Richard D. (Rich) Kinder, age 67
President and Director, C. Park Shaper, age 44
VP Corporate Development and Treasurer, David D. Kinder, age 38
COO and Director, Steven J. (Steve) Kean, age 51
VP and CFO, Kimberly A. (Kim) Dang, age 42
VP and CIO, Henry W. (Hank) Neumann Jr.
VP IT Infrastructure, Paul Davis
Director, Michael C. (Mike) Morgan, age 44
President and Director, C. Park Shaper, age 44
Director, Glenn A. Youngkin, age 45
Director, Fayez S. Sarofim, age 83
Director, Kenneth A. Pontarelli
COO and Director, Steven J. (Steve) Kean, age 51
Director, Henry Cornell, age 56
Director, John Stokes, age 61
Director, Michael Miller, age 54
Director, R. Baran Tekkora, age 39
Auditors: PricewaterhouseCoopersLLP

LOCATIONS

HQ: Kinder Morgan Inc.
500 Dallas St. Suite 1000, Houston TX 77002
Phone: 713-369-9000 **Fax:** -14799
Web: www.isoftstone.com

2011 Sales

	$ mil.	% of total
US	7,834	95
Canada	411	5
Mexico & other countries	18	-
Total	**8,264**	**100**

PRODUCTS/OPERATIONS

2011 Sales

	$ mil.	% of total
Pipelines	5,179	63
CO2	1,433	17
Terminals	1,313	16
Kinder Morgan Canada	302	4
NGPL PipeCo	35	-
Other	1	-
Total	**8,264**	**100**

COMPETITORS

AltaGas
BC Hydro
Buckeye Partners
Canadian Utilities
Colorado Interstate Gas
Crosstex Energy
Enterprise Products
K-Sea Transportation
Koch Industries Inc.
Plains All American Pipeline
Royal Vopak
Spectra Energy
Sunoco Logistics
TransMontaigne
Williams Companies

HISTORICAL FINANCIALS

Company Type: Public

Income Statement FYE: December 31

	REVENUE ($ mil.)	NET INCOME ($ mil.)	NET PROFIT MARGIN	EMPLOYEES
12/11	8,264	594	7.2%	8,120
12/10	8,190	(41)		8,142
12/09	7,185	495	6.9%	7,900
12/08	12,094	(3,599)	—	0
Annual Growth	(11.9%)	—	—	—

2011 Year-End Financials

Debt ratio: 56.17%
Return on equity: 17.90%
Cash ($ mil.): 411
Current ratio: 36.73
Long-term debt ($ mil.): 14,356
No. of shares (mil.): 803
Dividends
Yield: —
Payout: 100.00%
Market value ($ mil.): 25,844

	STOCK PRICE ($) FY Close	P/E High/Low	PER SHARE ($) Earnings	Dividends	Book Value
12/11	32.17	43 32	0.74	0.00	4.13
Annual Growth	—	— —	—	—	—

Kindred Healthcare Inc

Families unable to provide 24-hour care to their kin can at least turn to Kindred Healthcare. As a leading provider of long-term health care Kindred operates about 225 nursing and rehabilitation centers and some 120 long-term acute care hospitals in 26 states. Its facilities have a combined capacity of more than 36000 beds. In addition Kindred's RehabCare business provides contract rehabilitation therapy services at thousands of facilities. The firm also runs sub-acute and inpatient rehabilitation centers as well as home health and hospice agencies. The company owns many of its facilities but leases many more facilities from Ventas and other third parties.

Kindred is composed of four divisions including hospital nursing center rehabilitation services and home health and hospice. The hospital division operates its long-term acute care and inpatient rehabilitation hospitals while its nursing center division operates the nursing and (outpatient) rehabilitation centers and a handful of assisted living facilities. The company seriously bulked up its rehabilitation services unit when it acquired RehabCare in 2011. Kindred has grown its home care and hospice business in recent years but that remains the company's smallest division.

The hospital division includes both free-standing long term acute care hospitals and "hospitals-within-hospitals" which are co-located with short-term acute care facilities and sometimes receive patients as they are discharged from the host facility. All of Kindred's hospitals care for patients with complex medical conditions: those who are recovering from major surgery are experiencing multiple organ failure or have brain or spinal cord injuries for instance. The hospital division brings in 45% of Kindred's yearly income. Medicare and Medicaid reimbursements make up more than half of Kindred's revenue.

Kindred Healthcare operates its hospitals and nursing care facilities in over half of the US but it has the largest numbers of licensed beds in California Florida Indiana Massachusetts North Carolina Texas and Wisconsin.

After several static years Kindred Healthcare's revenues jumped nearly 26% in 2011 to $5.5 billion as a result of the RehabCare acquisition. However that same splashy acquisition also affected the company's net income which fell from 2010's nearly $57 million down to some $54 million in 2011.

Kindred's strategy involves dominating the post-acute care sector and it has diversified accordingly. It has clustered its services in certain markets where it can provide rehabilitation services across several possible sites: hospital inpatient center outpatient center or private homes. In those geographic areas no matter where a patient needs to receive rehabilitation (or where Medicare is willing to pay for it) Kindred will have a means of providing that care.

To that end the company paid $1.3 billion in 2011 to acquire post-acute care services provider RehabCare. The purchase added about 35 rehabilitation hospitals as well as contracts to manage post-acute therapy for another 1250 facilities.

Kindred's home care and hospice business operates under the PeopleFirst banner. In recent years this part of its business has grown steadily through acquisitions of smaller regional operations. It continued this strategy in 2012 with its acquisition of IntegraCare Holdings. The $71 million price (with up to $4 million more based on earnings) added 47 locations in Texas.

Acquisitions of existing facilities have been Kindred's primary means of growth though it occasionally opens a new facility. It also regularly sheds underperforming assets.

HISTORY

After a stint as Kentucky's commerce secretary in the 1980s Bruce Lunsford was approached by respiratory therapist Michael Barr with the idea of establishing long-term hospitals for ventilator-dependent patients. Barr said these hospitals would be cheaper to run than full-service facilities which require additional equipment. Lunsford (who became chairman president and CEO) and Barr (who was COO) founded Vencare in 1983 with backing from Gene Smith (a wealthy political associate of Lunsford). They bought a money-losing 62-bed Indiana hospital and soon turned the operation around.

Vencare expanded into Florida and Texas and by the end of the 1980s operated more than 420 beds in seven facilities. Revenues jumped from less than $1 million in 1985 to $54 million by 1989 the year it changed its name to Vencor.

During the early 1990s Vencor added facilities in Arizona California Colorado Georgia and Missouri. Vencor ran 29 facilities by the end of 1993 the same year it launched its Vencare respiratory care program.

Vencor acquisitions in 1995 included hospital respiratory and cardiopulmonary departments in seven states. Later that year it bought the much-larger Hillhaven the US's #2 nursing home operator at that time. (In 1990 Hillhaven had been spun off from what is now Tenet Healthcare.) When Vencor bought it Hillhaven owned 310 nursing homes 60 pharmacies and 23 retirement communities. The buy furthered Lunsford's vision of creating a network of long-term-care facilities and services. Vencor also debuted VenTouch an electronic-pad-based record-keeping system for its facilities in 1995.

In 1996 Vencor spun off its assisted and independent living properties as Atria Communities; as part of the Hillhaven assimilation it also consolidated its MediSave pharmacy unit into its hospital operations and sold 34 nursing homes to Lennox Healthcare.

Vencor's 1997 buys included TheraTx (216 rehabilitation centers 28 nursing centers 16 occupational health clinics) and Transitional Hospitals (long-term acute care hospitals). That year Vencor formed an alliance with insurer CNA to develop an insurance product for long-term care.

In 1998 the company split into Ventas (real estate) and Vencor (operations). It also sold most of its remaining interest in an assisted living company (now called Atria Senior Quarters) it had spun off in 1996. To attract wealthier residents it also launched a program in 1998 to turn away –and turn out –Medicaid patients. Vencor soon abandoned the plan amid heated attacks from advocacy groups. (Welcoming back the evictees didn't stop Florida regulators from fining Vencor.) Several other states and the federal government also began probing Vencor's practices; in 1999 the affair prompted Congressional action designed to protect Medicaid patients. Lunsford and Barr were ousted in the turmoil. The government also demanded that Vencor return $90 million in overpayments over 60 months ($2 million a month) or risk losing Medicare payments.

The company filed for Chapter 11 bankruptcy later in 1999. Despite bankruptcy protection the Justice Department in 2000 filed claims for more than $1 billion from Vencor for Medicare fraud since 1992. Vencor settled the majority of these claims the next year. The company emerged from bankruptcy in April 2001 and changed its name to Kindred Healthcare. In 2003 the company sold all of its Texas and Florida nursing center operations. Kindred Healthcare began operating its contract rehabilitation business as a separate division in 2004.

In 2006 the company bought the long-term care operations of Commonwealth Communities Holdings gaining six long-term acute care hospitals and 11 nursing homes in Massachusetts. The company entered lease agreements for eight nursing homes in San Francisco in 2007.

In 2007 Kindred spun off its Kindred Pharmacy Services unit which distributed drugs to long-term care facilities. The unit was combined with the institutional pharmacy unit of AmerisourceBergen to form a new entity named PharMerica. Kindred Pharmacy Services contributed more than 40 institutional pharmacies in 26 states to the combined company.

To keep its portfolio robust Kindred has engaged in some construction of new facilities. It completed construction of a 60-bed hospital in Florida in 2009 and it opened a new long-term care hospital to replace an aging facility in Houston in 2010; the older Houston facility was converted into a rehabilitation facility.

EXECUTIVES

CEO and Director, Paul J. Diaz, age 50, $1,040,839 total compensation
EVP and CFO, Richard A. (Rich) Lechleiter, age 53, $451,462 total compensation
EVP and Chief Administrative and Information Officer, Richard E. Chapman, age 63, $369,893 total compensation
Chairman, Edward L. (Eddie) Kuntz, age 67, $898,408 total compensation
Chief Diversity Officer and General Counsel, M. Suzanne Riedman, age 60
EVP Strategy Policy and Integrated Care, William M. Altman, age 52
EVP; President Nursing Center Division, Lane M. Bowen, age 61, $442,411 total compensation
SVP Operational Reimbursement Health Services Division, Dennis J. Hansen
EVP Central Region Hospital Division, Steven L. (Steve) Monaghan
SVP Clinical and Residential Services Health Services Division, Barbara L. Baylis
Co-General Counsel and Corporate Secretary, Joseph L. Landenwich, age 47
VP Communications, Susan E. Moss
President and COO, Benjamin A. Breier, age 41, $415,390 total compensation
Chief Development Officer, Gregory C. (Greg) Miller, age 42
SVP Finance and Corporate Controller, John J. Lucchese
VP Managed Care, Kathleen M. (Kathy) Wiljanen
VP Rehabilitation Services Rehabilitation Division, Vonda Black
SVP and Chief Compliance Officer, Kim Martin
President Peoplefirst Rehabilitation Division, Christopher M. (Chris) Bird, age 47
EVP; President Hospital Division, Jeffrey P. (Jeff) Winter
VP Information Systems, Kathy J. Markham
Director, Isaac Kaufman, age 65
CEO and Director, Paul J. Diaz, age 50
Director, Frederick J. (Fred) Kleisner, age 67
Director, Jonathan D. Blum, age 54
Director, Joel Ackerman, age 47
Director, Thomas P. Cooper, age 68
Director, Ann C. Berzin, age 59
Director, Phyllis R. Yale, age 54
Director, Eddy J. Rogers Jr., age 71
Auditors: PricewaterhouseCoopersLLP

LOCATIONS

HQ: Kindred Healthcare Inc.
680 S. 4th St., Louisville KY 40202-2412
Phone: 502-596-7300 **Fax:** 502-596-4170
Web: www.kindredhealthcare.com

PRODUCTS/OPERATIONS

2011 Revenues

	$ mil.	% of total
Hospital division	2,550	44
Nursing center division	2,254	39
Rehabilitation division		
Skilled nursing rehabilitation services	775	13
Hospital rehabilitation services	200	3
Home health & hospice division	60	1
Adjustments	(319.0)	-
Total	**5,521**	**100**

2011 Sales by Payer

Medicare	41	
Medicare Advantage	18	
Total	**0**	**100**

Selected Acquisitions

2012
IntegraCare Holdings Inc. (up to $75 million; home health hospice and community services; Texas)
2011
RehabCare Group Inc. ($1.3 billion rehabilitation hospitals long term acute care hospitals rehabilitation therapy services)
Professional HealthCare (home health and hospice operations)
2010
Vista (California hospitals)

COMPETITORS

Ascension Health
Catholic Health Partners
Covenant Care
Emeritus Corporation
Ensign Group
Extendicare
Five Star Quality Care
Genesis HealthCare
Golden Horizons
HCA
HCR ManorCare
HealthSouth
Life Care Centers
NHC
Omnicare
Paradigm Management Services
Physiotherapy Associates
SavaSeniorCare
Select Medical
Skilled Healthcare Group
Sun Healthcare
Sunrise Senior Living
Tenet Healthcare
U.S. Physical Therapy

HISTORICAL FINANCIALS

Company Type: Public

Income Statement

FYE: December 31

	REVENUE ($ mil.)	NET INCOME ($ mil.)	NET PROFIT MARGIN	EMPLOYEES
12/11	5,521	(53)	—	77,800
12/10	4,359	56	1.3%	56,800
12/09	4,270	40	0.9%	54,100
12/08	4,151	36	0.9%	53,700
12/07	4,220	(46)	—	52,500
Annual Growth	7.0%	—	—	10.3%

2011 Year-End Financials

Debt ratio: 37.27%
Return on equity: (-4.15)%
Cash ($ mil.): 41
Current ratio: 145.28
Long-term debt ($ mil.): 1,531
No. of shares (mil.): 52
Dividends
Yield: —
Payout: —
Market value ($ mil.): 613

	STOCK PRICE ($) FY Close	P/E High/Low		PER SHARE ($) Earnings	Dividends	Book Value
12/11	11.77	—	—	(1.16)	0.00	24.73
12/10	18.37	14	8	1.43	0.00	26.12
12/09	18.46	19	11	1.02	0.00	24.72
12/08	13.02	34	9	0.93	0.00	23.52
12/07	24.98	—	—	(1.17)	0.00	22.90
Annual Growth	(17.1%)	—	—	—	—	1.9%

KKR Financial Holdings LLC

KKR Financial Holdings is a specialty finance company that invests in a variety of financial products primarily below-investment-grade corporate debt as well as public and private equity. Its portfolio which weighs in at more than $8 billion includes syndicated bank loans mezzanine loans high-yield corporate bonds asset-backed securities commercial real estate and debt and equity securities. KKR Financial Holdings is externally managed by KKR Financial Advisors; both firms are affiliates of private equity and leveraged buyout giant KKR & Co.

KKR Financial Holdings was formerly a real estate investment trust (REIT) with significant investments in residential mortgages and related securities. During the mortgage meltdown that began in 2007 the company restructured dropped its REIT status and stopped investing in residential mortgages. After reporting more than $1 billion in losses in 2008 (mainly due to losses from investments and impaired securities) the company tweaked its investment focus to include mezzanine financing natural resources commercial real estate and distressed situations as other investors shied away from these activities in the wake of the credit crisis. The strategy paid off as KKR Financial cut its losses significantly in 2009 and returned to profitability in 2010.

William Sonneborn formerly president of The TCW Group was named CEO of KKR Financial in 2008. He succeeded Saturnino Fanlo who resigned. Sonneborn was also tapped to head KKR's newly created asset management division (which includes KKR Financial).

EXECUTIVES

Chairman, Paul M. Hazen, age 70
President CEO and Director, William C. (Bill) Sonneborn, age 42
EVP and Director Tax, Jeffrey B. Van Horn, age 51
COO and CFO, Michael R. (Mike) McFerran, age 40
General Counsel, Nicole J. Macarchuk
Director, Deborah H. McAneny, age 53
Director, Willy R. Strothotte, age 67
President CEO and Director, William C. (Bill) Sonneborn, age 42
Director, Scott C. Nuttall, age 39
Director, Ross J. Kari, age 53
Director, R. Glenn Hubbard, age 53
Director, Ely L. Licht, age 64
Director, Scott A. Ryles, age 53
Director, Tracy L. Collins, age 48
Director, Vincent P. Finigan, age 65
Auditors: Deloitte&ToucheLLP

LOCATIONS

HQ: KKR Financial Holdings LLC
555 California St. 50th Fl., San Francisco CA 94104
Phone: 415-315-3620 **Fax:** 415-391-3077
Web: ir.kkr.com/kfn_ir/kfn_overview.cfm

PRODUCTS/OPERATIONS

2010 Sales

	$ mil.	% of total
Interest		
Loans	397	60
Securities	104	16
Other	3	-
Noninterest		
Net gains on investments	109	16
Net gain on restructuring & extinguishment of debt	40	6
Other	10	2
Adjustments	(16.8)	-
Total	**648**	**100**

COMPETITORS

Arlington Asset Investment
Capital Trust
iStar Financial Inc
Opus Investment Management
Prospect Capital
Resource America

HISTORICAL FINANCIALS

Company Type: Public

Income Statement FYE: December 31

	ASSETS ($ mil.)	NET INCOME ($ mil.)	INCOME AS % OF ASSETS	EMPLOYEES
12/11	8,647	318	3.7%	0
12/10	8,418	371	4.4%	0
12/09	10,300	76	0.7%	0
12/08	12,515	(1,075)	—	0
12/07	19,046	(100)	—	67
Annual Growth	(17.9%)	—	—	—

2011 Year-End Financials

Debt ratio: 78.39%
Return on equity: 18.98%
Cash ($ mil.): 392
Current ratio: —
Long-term debt ($ mil.): 6,778
No. of shares (mil.): 178
Dividends
Yield: —
Payout: 38.29%
Market value ($ mil.): 1,555

	STOCK PRICE ($) FY Close	P/E High	P/E Low	PER SHARE ($) Earnings	Dividends	Book Value
12/11	8.73	6	4	1.75	0.00	9.41
12/10	9.30	4	2	2.33	0.43	9.24
12/09	5.80	12	1	0.50	0.05	7.37
12/08	1.58	—	—	(7.68)	1.30	4.40
12/07	14.05	—	—	(1.11)	1.62	14.27
Annual Growth	(11.2%)	—	—	—	—	(9.9%)

Kohl's Corp.

Kohl's wants to be easy on shoppers and tough on competition. It operates more than 1100 discount department stores in 49 states. Nearly half of its stores are in the Midwest and West where Kohl's continues to grow while rapidly expanding into other markets. Moderately priced name-brand and private-label apparel shoes accessories and housewares are sold through centrally located cash registers designed to speed checkout and keep staff costs down. Kohl's competes with discount and mid-level department stores. Merchandising relationships allow Kohl's to carry top brands (NIKE Levi's OshKosh B'Gosh) not typically available to discounters; it sells them cheaper than department stores by controlling costs.

HISTORY

Max Kohl (father of Sen. Herbert Kohl of Wisconsin) opened his first grocery store in Milwaukee in the late 1920s. Over the years he and his three sons developed it into a chain and in 1938 Kohl's incorporated.

Kohl opened a department store (half apparel half hard goods) in 1962 next door to a Kohl's grocery. In the mid-1960s he hired William Kellogg a twentysomething buyer in the basement discount department at Milwaukee's Boston Store for his expertise in budget retailing. Kellogg came from a retailing family (his father was VP of merchandising at Boston Store; the younger Kellogg had joined that firm out of high school). Kohl and Kellogg began developing the pattern for the store carving out a niche between upscale department stores and discounters (offering department store quality at discount store prices).

The Kohl family entered real estate development in 1970 building the largest shopping center in the Milwaukee area. By 1972 the family's 65 food stores and five department stores were generating about $90 million in yearly sales. That year the Kohls sold 80% of the two operations to British American Tobacco's Brown & Williamson Industries division (later called BATUS) the first in a string of department store acquisitions that would eventually include Marshall Field's and Saks Fifth Avenue.

BATUS bought the rest of Kohl's in 1978. Herb and Allen Kohl left the business to concentrate on real estate and politics and Kellogg was named president and CEO. The next year BATUS separated the food and department store operations and eventually sold the food store chain to A&P in 1983.

Kohl's discount image did not fit in with BATUS's other retail operations so it decided to sell the department store chain. In 1986 Kellogg and two other executives with the backing of mall developers Herbert and Melvin Simon led an LBO to acquire the chain's 40 stores and a distribution center; annual sales were about $288 million.

Two years later Kohl's acquired 26 Main Street department stores from Federated Department Stores (now Macy's) moving the company into new cities such as Chicago and Detroit. When Kohl's went public in 1992 it had 81 stores in six states and sales topped $1 billion.

In 1996 Kohl's began its mid-Atlantic expansion by opening stores in North Carolina. Sales topped $2 billion in fiscal 1997 and same-store sales were up more than 11%. Early in 1997 the firm acquired a former Bradlees store to enter New Jersey and opened stores in Washington DC; Philadelphia; New York; and Delaware.

Kohl's continued its expansion in 1998 entering Tennessee and building its mid-Atlantic presence. In early 1999 Kohl's named Larry Montgomery as CEO. The company also bought 30 stores from bankrupt Caldor (mostly in the New York City area) and reopened them as Kohl's in 2000. In 2001 Kohl's opened a total of 62 new stores. The following year it opened 75 new outlets including 12 in Houston a new market for Kohl's. In December 2002 Kohl's opened a distribution center in San Bernardino California to support its planned expansion into Southern California and the Southwest.

Montgomery was named chairman of Kohl's in February 2003 succeeding Kellogg who retired after 34 years with the company. Kohl's which had become one of the fastest-growing and most successful US department store chains in the last decade hit some serious bumps in 2003 including excess inventory (built up based on previous years of strong sales). Its same-store sales for the fiscal year decreased 1.6%. The company's one-floor stores (averaging about 85000 sq. ft.) have fewer areas with a more limited selection than full-line department stores.

In 2004 Kohl's launched a new private label Apt. 9 which was designed to compete with the likes of Banana Republic Liz Claiborne and Perry Ellis.

It entered the Florida market in 2005. In 2006 Kohl's sold its private-label credit card business to JPMorgan Chase for about $1.6 billion. (Kohl's continues to handle all customer and marketing services for JPMorgan Chase as they relate to credit card customers.) The retailer opened 65 stores (including its first in the Pacific Northwest) that year. It introduced a more appealing modern store format in the fall of 2006 designed to broaden its appeal beyond its current customer base.

In 2007 the company expanded its online shopping offerings to include some items not generally available in its stores including furniture and electronics.

In late 2007 Kohl's partnered with Fila in a multiyear licensing agreement to be Fila's exclusive US retailer of the FILA SPORT collection. Having debuted in fall 2008 the collection consists of apparel footwear and accessories for women men and children. As part of the deal Fila heads the footwear manufacturing while Kohl's heads the manufacturing production distribution sales and marketing of the FILA SPORT apparel and accessories.

In late 2009 Larry Montgomery retired as chairman after 21 years with the company. Montgomery stepped down as CEO in 2008 and was succeeded by Kevin Mansell.

EXECUTIVES

Chairman President and CEO, Kevin B. Mansell, age 59, $1,212,500 total compensation
SEVP and CFO, Wesley S. (Wes) McDonald, age 50, $751,700 total compensation
SEVP General Counsel and Secretary, Richard D. (Rick) Schepp, age 51
SVP Corporate Governance, Brian F. Miller
Chief Merchandising Officer, Donald A. (Don) Brennan, age 52, $837,031 total compensation
SEVP Product Development, Peggy Eskenasi, age 57, $595,833 total compensation
SEVP Logistics, Kenneth (Ken) Bonning, age 54
SVP Public Relations, Vicki Shamion
Chief Administrative Officer, John M. Worthington, age 48, $830,903 total compensation
Director, Steven A. (Steve) Burd, age 62
Director, R. Lawrence (Larry) Montgomery, age 63
Director, William S. (Bill) Kellogg, age 68
Director, Peter Boneparth, age 52
Director, Stephanie A. Streeter, age 54
Director, Stephen E. (Steve) Watson, age 67
Director, John F. Herma, age 64
Director, Peter M. Sommerhauser, age 69
Director, Frank V. Sica, age 61
Director, Dale E. Jones, age 52
Director, Nina G. Vaca, age 40
Auditors: Ernst&YoungLLP

LOCATIONS

HQ: Kohl' s Corp.
N56 W17000 Ridgewood Drive, Menomonee Falls, WI 53051
Phone: 262 703-7000 **Fax:** 262 703-6373
Web: www.kohls.com

2012 Stores

	No.
California	128
Texas	84
Illinois	64
Ohio	59
Florida	52
New	50
Michigan	45
Pennsylvania	47
Wisconsin	40
Indiana	38
New	38
Georgia	33
North	29
Virginia	29
Arizona	26
Minnesota	26
Colorado	24
Missouri	24
Massachusetts	23
Maryland	22
Tennessee	20
Connecticut	18
Washington	17
Kentucky	16
Iowa	15
South	14
Alabama	13
Utah	12
Nevada	12
Kansas	11
Oklahoma	10
Oregon	10
New	9
Arkansas	8
Nebraska	7
West	7
Louisiana	6
Delaware	5
Idaho	5
Maine	5
Mississippi	5
New	5
North	3
Rhode	3
South	3
Montana	2
Wyoming	2
Alaska	1
Vermont	1
Total	**1,127**

PRODUCTS/OPERATIONS

2012 Sales

	% of total
Women's	31
Men's	19
Home	19
Children's	13
Accessories	10
Footwear	8
Total	**100**

2012 Stores

	No.
Prototype	987
Small	135
Urban	5
Total	**1,127**

Selected National Brands

adidas
apt. 9
Arrow
Calphalon
Candies
Carter' s
Chaps
Columbia
Cuisinart
Daisy Fuentes
Dickies
Dockers
everGirl
George Foreman
Gloria Vanderbilt Home
Gold Toe
Haggar
Hanes
Healthtex
Henckels
HoMedics
Jockey
Jumping Beans
KitchenAid
Krups
Laura Ashley Lifestyles
Lee
l.e.i.
Levi' s
Mudd
NIKE
Nine & Company
Oneida
OshKosh B' Gosh
Pfaltzgraff
Pyrex
Reebok
Skechers
Speedo
Unionbay
Urban Pipeline
Villager

Selected Private-label Brands

Apt. 9
Bobby Flay
ELLE
Jennifer Lopez
Jumping Beans
Marc Anthony

COMPETITORS

Bed Bath & Beyond
Belk
BJ' s Wholesale Club
Dillard' s
J. C. Penney
Kmart
Macy' s
Men' s Wearhouse
Old Navy
Ross Stores
Saks
Sears
Shopko Stores
Target Corporation
TJX Companies
Wal-Mart

HISTORICAL FINANCIALS

Company Type: Public

Income Statement

FYE: January 28

	REVENUE ($ mil.)	NET INCOME ($ mil.)	NET PROFIT MARGIN	EMPLOYEES
01/12	18,804	1,167	6.2%	142,000
01/11	18,391	1,114	6.1%	136,000
01/10	17,178	991	5.8%	133,000
01/09*	16,389	885	5.4%	126,000
02/08	16,473	1,083	6.6%	125,000
Annual Growth	3.4%	1.9%	—	3.2%

*Fiscal year change

2012 Year-End Financials

Debt ratio: 15.86%
Return on equity: 17.93%
Cash ($ mil.): 1,205
Current ratio: 184.36
Long-term debt ($ mil.): 2,141
No. of shares (mil.): 247
Dividends
Yield: —
Payout: 23.26%
Market value ($ mil.): 11,532

	STOCK PRICE ($) FY Close	P/E High	P/E Low	PER SHARE ($) Earnings	Dividends	Book Value
01/12	46.69	13	10	4.30	0.00	26.35
01/11	51.20	16	12	3.65	0.00	27.84
01/10	50.37	19	10	3.23	0.00	25.58
01/09*	36.71	19	9	2.89	0.00	22.10
02/08	45.93	23	11	3.39	0.00	19.65
Annual Growth	0.4%	—	—	6.1%	—	7.6%

*Fiscal year change

Kraft Foods Group Inc

LOCATIONS

HQ: Kraft Foods Group Inc
Three Lakes Drive, Northfield, IL 60093-2753
Phone: 847 646-2000
Web: www.kraftfoodsgroup.com

HISTORICAL FINANCIALS

Company Type:

Income Statement FYE: December 31

	REVENUE ($ mil.)	NET INCOME ($ mil.)	NET PROFIT MARGIN	EMPLOYEES
12/11	18,655	1,839	9.9%	23,500
12/10	17,797	3,531	19.8%	0
12/09	17,278	2,170	12.6%	0
Annual Growth	3.9%	(7.9%)	—	—

Kroger Co.

Kroger may be the nation's largest traditional grocer but it still must watch out for falling prices; Wal-Mart long ago overtook Kroger as the largest seller of groceries in the US. While Kroger has diversified through acquisitions adding jewelry and general merchandise to its mix supermarkets still account for more than 90% of sales. The company operates about 3575 stores including some 2435 supermarkets and multidepartment stores under two dozen banners in about 30 states. It also runs 790 convenience stores under names such as Quik Stop and Kwik Shop. Kroger's Fred Meyer Stores subsidiary operates about 130 supercenters which offer groceries general merchandise and jewelry in the western US.

HISTORY

Bernard Kroger was 22 when he started the Great Western Tea Company in 1883 in Cincinnati. Kroger lowered prices by cutting out middlemen sometimes by making products such as bread. Growing to 40 stores in Cincinnati and northern Kentucky the company became Kroger Grocery and Baking Company in 1902. It expanded into St. Louis in 1912 and grew rapidly during the 1910s and 1920s by purchasing smaller cash-strapped companies. Kroger sold his holdings in the company for $28 million in 1928 the year before the stock market crash and retired.

The company acquired Piggly Wiggly stores in the late 1920s and bought most of Piggly Wiggly's corporate stock which it held until the early 1940s. The chain reached its largest number of stores –a whopping 5575 –in 1929. (The Depression later trimmed that total.) A year later Kroger manager Michael Cullen suggested opening self-service low-price supermarkets but company executives demurred. Cullen left Kroger and began King Kullen the first supermarket. If he was ahead of his time at Kroger it wasn't by much; within five years the company had 50 supermarkets.

During the 1950s Kroger acquired companies with stores in Texas Georgia and Washington DC. It added New Jersey-based Sav-on drugstores in 1960 and it opened its first SupeRx drugstore in 1961. The company began opening larger supermarkets in 1971; between 1970 and 1980 Kroger's store count grew just 5% but its selling space nearly doubled.

In 1983 the grocer bought Kansas-based Dillons Food Stores (supermarkets and convenience stores) and Kwik Shop convenience stores. Kroger sold most of its interests in the Hook and SupeRx drug chains (which became Hook-SupeRx) in 1987 and focused on its food-and-drugstores. (It sold its remaining stake to Revco in 1994.) The next year it faced two separate takeover bids from the Herbert Haft family and from Kohlberg Kravis Roberts. The company warded off the raiders by borrowing $4.1 billion to pay a special dividend to shareholders and to buy shares for an employee stock plan.

To reduce debt Kroger sold most of its equity in Price Saver Membership Wholesale Clubs and its Fry's California stores. In 1990 the company made its first big acquisition since the 1988 restructuring by buying 29 Great Scott! supermarkets. Joseph Pichler became CEO that year.

Kroger sold its Time Saver Stores unit in 1995. In 1999 Kroger acquired Fred Meyer operator of about 800 stores mainly in the West in a $13 billion deal. Late in 1999 it announced it was buying nearly 75 stores (mostly in Texas) from Winn-Dixie Stores; the deal was called off in 2000 shortly after the FTC withheld its approval. But the company kept buying –acquisitions included 20 former Hannaford stores in Virginia in 2000 as well as 16 Nebraska food stores bought from food distributor Fleming and seven New Mexico stores bought from Furrs Supermarkets in 2001. Also in 2001 it sold five Smith's stores to Fleming. In late 2001 Kroger said it would cut 1500 jobs. With mega-discounter Wal-Mart breathing down its neck (Wal-Mart Supercenters compete on roughly 55% of Kroger's turf) Kroger cut prices in December 2001.

Kroger acquired 17 supermarkets (16 in the Houston area) from Albertson's (now Albertsons LLC) and another seven stores from Winn-Dixie in the Dallas/Fort Worth area in 2002.

In April 2003 Kroger introduced Naturally Preferred its own brand of some 140 natural and organic items including baby food pastas cereal snacks milk and soy products. In June Pichler stepped down as CEO (but remained chairman) and was succeeded by David Dillon. Also in 2003 Kroger consolidated its leadership position in Colorado with the acquisition of four Cub Foods stores and a warehouse from SUPERVALU and combined operations in Michigan and Ohio reducing the number of retail divisions at Kroger to 17.

A four-and-a-half-month-long strike by grocery workers at Kroger's Ralphs chain in Southern California ended in March 2004. The dispute pitted workers' demands for continued generous health care benefits against management's call to control costs in the face of increasing non-union competition. The grocery chain spent about $120 million in 2004 to open about nine new stores and remodel others in Tennessee where Wal-Mart is introducing its smaller Neighborhood Market stores.

Pichler retired as chairman in June 2004 and was succeeded by Dillon. In November 2004 the company opened the largest store that operates under the Kroger banner boasting 105000 sq. ft. in the Cincinnati area. Also that month Kroger opened its newest store concept Kroger Marketplace in Columbus Ohio.

In August 2006 Kroger sold 11 Cala Foods and Bell Markets in the San Francisco Bay area to DeLano Retail Partners headed by Hartley DeLano the former president of the Cala chain for an undisclosed sum.

In July 2007 Kroger bought 20 Farmer Jack stores in the Detroit area from A&P. Also in 2007 the firm purchased 18 Scott's Food & Pharmacy stores in Indiana from rival SUPERVALU for an undisclosed amount. Kroger retained the Scott's banner and incorporated the business into its Indianapolis-based Central division.

In February 2010 Kroger made in-store walk-in medical chain The Little Clinic a wholly-owned subsidiary. (Kroger first acquired a majority stake in the chain in mid-2008.)

EXECUTIVES

SVP Human Resources, Kathleen S. (Katy) Barclay, age 56
President King Soopers, Russell J. (Russ) Dispense
Group VP; President Manufacturing, Calvin J. Kaufman, age 49
Group VP Corporate Affairs, Lynn Marmer, age 59
EVP Secretary and General Counsel, Paul W. Heldman, age 60, $697,638 total compensation
President COO and Director, W. Rodney McMullen, age 51, $875,062 total compensation
SVP Retail Operations, Geoffrey J. Covert, age 60
Chairman and CEO, David B. Dillon, age 61, $1,239,822 total compensation
SVP and CFO, J. Michael Schlotman, age 54, $556,280 total compensation
SVP and CIO, Christopher T. (Chris) Hjelm, age 50
President Columbus Division, Bruce A. Macaulay
SVP Merchandising, Michael J. (Mike) Donnelly, age 53
VP and Controller, M. Elizabeth Van Oflen, age 54
VP and Treasurer, Scott M. Henderson, age 56
SVP, R. Pete Williams, age 57
President Southwest Division, William H. (Bill) Breetz Jr.
President Quality Food Centers, Donna F. Giordano
President Cincinnati/Dayton, Sukanya R. Madlinger, age 49
President Food 4 Less, Bryan H. Kaltenbach, age 56
President Fry's Food and Drug Stores, Jon C. Flora
SVP, M. Marnette Perry, age 60
President Mid-South Division, John P. Hackett
President Atlanta Division, Bruce A. Lucia
President Central Division, Robert Moeder
President Turkey Hill Minit Markets, Darel Pfeiff
President Tom Thumb, Mark W. Salisbury
President Loaf 'N Jug, Arthur (Art) Stawski Sr.
President Convenience Stores and Supermarket Petroleum, Van Tarver
President Smith's Food and Drug Centers, Mark Tuffin
President Dillon Companies, Joseph A. (Joe) Grieshaber Jr., age 54
President Fred Meyer Stores, Michael L. (Mike) Ellis
Group VP Logistics, Kevin M. Dougherty, age 59
President Jay C, Paul L. Bowen
President Delta Division, D. Mark Prestidge
President Mid-Atlantic Division, Jay A. Cummins
Director and Assistant Treasurer, Carin Fike, age 43
President Fred Meyer Jewelers, Peter M. (Pete) Engel
President Quik Stop, Ron Stewart
President Fred Meyer Stores, Lynn Gust, age 59
President Michigan Division, Rick Going
President Kwik Shop, Jeffrey A. (Jeff) Parker
CEO The Little Clinic, Michael J. Stoll

Group VP Perishables Merchandising and Procurement, Jeffrey D. Burt, age 50
Director Investor Relations, Cindy Holmes, age 43
Director External Corporate Communications, Keith Dailey
Chief Diversity Officer, Reuben Shaffer, age 61
President Kroger Personal Finance, Gary Millerchip
Director, John T. LaMacchia, age 70
Director, Susan J. Kropf, age 64
Director, Bobby S. Shackouls, age 59
President COO and Director, W. Rodney McMullen, age 51
Director, Jorge P. Montoya, age 65
Director, Steven R. (Steve) Rogel, age 69
Director, Ronald L. (Ron) Sargent, age 56
Director, Robert D. Beyer, age 52
Director, David B. Lewis, age 68
Director, Reuben V. Anderson, age 69
Director, Clyde R. Moore, age 58
Director, James A. (Jim) Runde, age 65
Director, Susan M. Phillips, age 67
Auditors: PricewaterhouseCoopersLLP

LOCATIONS

HQ: The Kroger Co.
1014 Vine St., Cincinnati OH 45202-1100
Phone: 513-762-4000 **Fax:** 513-762-1160
Web: www.kroger.com

PRODUCTS/OPERATIONS

2012 Stores

	No.
Supermarkets & multidepartment	2,435
Convenience	791
Jewelry	348
Total	**3,574**

2012 Grocery Stores

	No.
Combo	2,094
Price-impact warehouse	145
Multidepartment	126
Marketplace	70
Total	**2,435**

2012 Sales

	$ mil.	% of total
Supermarket	71,109	79
Supermarket fuel sales	12,995	14
Other stores & manufacturing	6,270	7
Total	**90,374**	**100**

Selected Kroger Stores

Multidepartment stores
- Fred Meyer

Supermarkets
- Baker' s
- City Market Food & Pharmacy
- Dillon Food Stores
- Fry' s Food & Drug Stores
- Gerbes Supermarkets
- Jay C Food Stores
- King Soopers
- Kroger
- Kroger Fresh Fare
- Owen' s
- Pay Less Super Markets
- Quality Food Centers (QFC)
- Ralphs
- Scott' s Food & Pharmacy
- Smith' s Food & Drug Centers

Warehouse stores
- Food 4 Less
- FoodsCo

Convenience stores
- Kwik Shop
- Loaf ' N Jug
- Quik Stop Markets
- Tom Thumb Food Stores
- Turkey Hill Minit Markets

Jewelry stores
- Barclay Jewelers
- Fox' s Jewelers
- Fred Meyer Jewelers
- Littman Jewelers

Food Production
- Bread and other baked goods
- Cheese
- Coffee
- Crackers
- Cultured products (cottage cheese yogurt)
- Deli products
- Fruit juices and fruit drinks
- Ice cream
- Juice
- Meat
- Milk
- Nuts
- Oatmeal
- Peanut butter
- Snacks
- Soft drinks
- Spaghetti sauce
- Water

Selected Private-Label Brands
- Bath & Body Therapies (body and bath)
- Banner brands (Kroger Ralphs King Soopers)
- Everyday Living (kitchen gadgets)
- FMV (For Maximum Value)
- HD Design (upscale kitchen gadgets)
- Moto Tech (automotive)
- Naturally Preferred (premium quality natural and organic brand)
- Office Works (office and school supplies)
- Private Selection (premium quality brand)
- Splash Spa (body and bath)
- Splash Sport (body and bath)

COMPETITORS

7-Eleven
99 Cents Only
A&P
Ahold U.S.A.
Albertsons
Chevron
Costco Wholesale
CVS Caremark
Delhaize America
Dollar General
Exxon Mobil
Family Dollar Stores
Giant Eagle
H-E-B
Hy-Vee
IGA
Kmart
Marsh Supermarkets
Meijer
Publix
Raley' s
Randall' s
Rite Aid
Safeway
Save Mart
Stater Bros.
Sterling Jewelers
SUPERVALU
Target Corporation
Tesco
Valero Energy
Wal-Mart
Walgreen
Wegmans
Whole Foods
Winn-Dixie
Zale

HISTORICAL FINANCIALS

Company Type: Public

Income Statement FYE: January 28

	REVENUE ($ mil.)	NET INCOME ($ mil.)	NET PROFIT MARGIN	EMPLOYEES
01/12	90,374	602	0.7%	339,000
01/11	82,189	1,116	1.4%	338,000
01/10	76,733	70	0.1%	334,000
01/09*	76,000	1,249	1.6%	326,000
02/08	70,235	1,181	1.7%	323,000
Annual Growth	6.5%	(15.5%)	—	1.2%

*Fiscal year change

2012 Year-End Financials

Debt ratio: 34.78%
Return on equity: 15.12%
Cash ($ mil.): 188
Current ratio: 80.45
Long-term debt ($ mil.): 6,850
No. of shares (mil.): 561
Dividends
Yield: —
Payout: 42.57%
Market value ($ mil.): 13,632

	STOCK PRICE ($) FY Close	P/E High/Low		PER SHARE ($) Earnings	Dividends	Book Value
01/12	24.30	26	21	1.01	0.00	7.10
01/11	21.29	14	11	1.74	0.00	8.54
01/10	21.43	224	177	0.11	0.00	7.53
01/09*	22.50	16	12	1.90	0.00	7.98
02/08	25.98	18	15	1.69	0.00	7.41
Annual Growth	(1.7%)	—	—	(12.1%)	—	(1.1%)

*Fiscal year change

L-3 Communications Holdings, Inc.

L-3's good defense is its best commercial offense. L-3 Communications Holdings provides products and services to the government based on Command Control Communications Intelligence Surveillance and Reconnaissance (C3ISR) including systems for satellite avionics (aircraft electronics) security and marine communications. It also provides aircraft maintenance and modernization. The US government primarily the Department of Defense (DoD) accounts for 75% of its business but L-3 is expanding its commercial offerings. The company derives all of its income from operating subsidiary L-3 Communications Corporation (L-3).

HISTORY

In the early 1970s Frank Lanza caught defense giant Lockheed's eye by building Loral Corporation into an aerospace industry contender through acquisitions of smaller defense technology firms. Lockheed (now Lockheed Martin) eventually bought Loral in 1996 and made Lanza the head of defense electronics. Looking for more action Lanza formed L-3 Communications Holdings in 1997 by convincing Lockheed Martin's CEO to spin off a group of 10 communications technology units and put him at the helm. The operations were units from General Electric and Loral acquired by Lockheed Martin in 1993 and 1996 respectively.

In charge were two of the L's in the L-3 name: 20-year Loral executives Lanza (chairman and CEO by then old enough to retire) and Robert LaPenta (president and CFO). The third L stood for major backer Lehman Brothers. The company embarked on an acquisition binge (just as Loral had originally done) in 1997. L-3 targeted strapped independent companies and the potential noncore operations of large corporate mergers.

Much as he had at Loral Lanza remained a hands-off executive a surprising approach in a red tape-wrapped industry. As a result L-3's divisions developed an entrepreneurial freedom. In 1998 the year L-3 went public it purchased the Ocean Systems unit of AlliedSignal (now Honeywell International; sonar products) ILEX Systems (information technology and support for the US government) SPD Technologies (electronics and power products) and the satellite transmission systems unit of California Microwave. The next year L-3 bought Microdyne (telemetry receivers) and AYDIN (electronic products for military government and aerospace).

In 2000 L-3 sold its network security software division to Symantec. Its 10 acquisitions that year included Honeywell's Traffic Alert and Collision Avoidance System (TCAS) avionics safety technology 53% of wireless network infrastructure equipment maker LogiMetrics and Raytheon's training devices and services division.

The next year L-3 sued Raytheon for not disclosing material liabilities before the sale of the division. The company later dropped the lawsuit saying it intended to improve its relations with Raytheon to benefit the Defense Department following September 11. Also that same year L-3 added to its aircraft repair overhaul and technical services with the purchase of Spar Aerospace (absorbed into L-3 Communications MAS in 2008) and what are now L-3 Communications Integrated Systems L-3 Communications Vertex Aerospace and L-3 Communications Cincinnati Electronics.

L-3 made its largest acquisition to date in 2002 buying Raytheon's Aircraft Integration Systems unit for $1.13 billion in cash. Also that year the company bought the Detection Systems (X-ray screening) business of PerkinElmer and Westwood Corporation (shipboard power systems). Late in the year L-3 acquired some Northrop Grumman operations (electron devices and displays-navigation systems) as well as Wescam Inc. (image capture/transmission).

The company acquired Vertex Aerospace a company that provides technical services for government agencies for about $650 million in 2003 and renamed it L-3 Communications Vertex Aerospace. The company shelled out another $40 million for BEAMHIT a maker of laser-based firearms training systems in 2004. Later that year L-3 spent $36 million for Brashear (electro-optical systems) and agreed to acquire CMC Electronics Cincinnati from CMC Electronics for about $172 million (the deal closed in 2004). In mid-2004 DRS Technologies a maker of combat ship equipment rebuffed an unsolicited $42 a share bid from L-3.

L-3's acquisition of optical/homeland defense businesses continued late in 2004 with a $43 million deal for Raytheon's commercial infrared unit. L-3 finished up the year with the acquisition of BAI Aerosystems a maker of small reconnaissance UAVs.

The acquisition roll continued in 2005 as L-3 acquired the Marine Controls division (shipboard control systems) of CAE the Propulsion Systems business unit (transmissions engines suspensions and turret drives) of General Dynamics and most of Boeing's Electron Dynamic Devices business including the space and military traveling wave tubes traveling wave tube amplifiers passive microwave devices and electric propulsion operations. L-3 also acquired Mobile-Vision. a maker of video surveillance systems used in police cars.

L-3 completed its $150 million acquisition of SAM Electronics a German naval electronics company in 2006. Not long afterwards it added CyTerra Corp. (military and homeland security sensors) and SafeView Inc. (security systems). Later that year the company acquired Germany's Magnet-Motor GmbH a maker of high-tech electric and energy systems for propulsion of commercial and combat vehicles and marine vessels. The company was renamed L-3 Communications Magnet-Motor. Also in 2006 L-3 acquired radio and satellite communications systems maker TRL Electronics PLC of the UK for about $176 million.

L-3 kept the acquisitions spree going with an agreement to purchase Crestview Aerospace Corporation (airframe assemblies and military aircraft modifications) for $135 million. Crestview became part of L-3's Aircraft Modernization and Maintenance division when the transaction closed in late 2006. L-3 also bought SSG Precision Optronics a maker of optics telescopes and optical subsystems for government defense and commercial customers.

Lanza died suddenly in 2006. Shortly after his death L-3 completed its acquisition of Nautronix Defence Group a provider of mine warfare and anti-submarine systems. L-3 purchased Nautronix Defence Group from Nautronix Holdings PLC for $65 million in cash. Later that year L-3 purchased Nova Engineering a maker of communication systems for network-centric warfare and technology applications.

Speculation sparked immediately that Lanza's death might spur rivals such as BAE SYSTEMS to seek to acquire L-3 —either as a whole or in parts. Within days of Lanza's death L-3 CFO Michael Strianese was named interim CEO. Board member Robert Millard was named chairman. Overtures by potential suitors however never materialized.

L-3 created a division as an organization of its security-related businesses called The L-3 Homeland Security Group in 2006. The group included security and detection systems as well as L-3's SafeView (military and public safety security systems) and CyTerra (military sensors) subsidiaries.

The company acquired Global Communications Solutions renamed L-3 Global Communications Solutions (L-3 GCS) a maker of portable satellite communications equipment for $152 million in 2007. L-3 GCS became part of the company's Electronic Systems segment. The purchase was the largest of four acquisitions that year that also included MKI Systems Geneva Aerospace and APSS S.r.l.

L-3 picked up several companies in 2008. Important acquisitions included the purchase of night vision technology developer Electro-Optical Systems (renamed L-3 EOS) from Northrop Grumman for $178 million. L-3 purchased International Resources Group (IRG) for $58 million late in the year adding professional services for government policy and training support. IRG —which specializing in energy environment natural resources relief and reconstruction and economic development — expands L-3's service capabilities and provides access to new international and domestic markets. Smaller acquisitions included HSA Systems (nautical charts and custom software) and METI which L-3 increased its stake in and then sold the same year. L-3 also sold the Electronic Technologies Passive Microwave Devices product line in 2008.

As it bolstered its product lines through acquisitions in 2008 L-3 also realigned several businesses in the Electronic Systems (formerly Specialized Products) segment and formed a Marine and Power Systems Group. Gathered into the $1.2 billion group are the Power and Control Automation Navigation Undersea Warfare and Offshore businesses.

The company acquired Chesapeake Sciences Corp. (CSC) a manufacturer of anti-submarine warfare systems in 2009. Renamed L-3 CSC it became part of the Marine and Power Systems Group.

L-3 was awarded a five-year contract worth $152 million to provide IT and operational support to the US Air Force Central Command (USAFCENT) through its STRATIS division in spring 2010. The contract expands on its existing cybersecurity operational support for the US Central Command. L-3 will manage maintain and monitor network operations as well as provide support Web development project management and global command and control services. Earlier the company's WESCAM subsidiary won a contract worth $110 million to provide the US Air Force with electro-optic/infrared imaging turrets along with training courses and services.

Also in 2010 L-3 acquired Insight Technology Incorporated a maker of night vision goggles thermal imaging systems and laser aiming and illumination devices for about $611 million. Insight's products expanded and broadened L-3's existing electro-optical and infrared product lines; a new Warrior Systems Sector group was formed from the combination of products in order to target the homeland security and military markets. The company beefed up its secure satellite capabilities by acquiring 3Di Technologies (for about $60 million) a company that specialized in installing communications solutions in remote areas with a history of providing support for all branches of the US military. 3Di was rolled into L-3's Microwave Group. Both Insight and 3Di reside now in L-3's Electronic Systems segment.

For $34 million L-3 purchased Airborne Technologies (ATI) an aeronautical engineering firm that specialized in UAS manufacture and operations support. ATI joined the L-3 family with an existent DoD contract to produce an air-launched small expendable UAS. Another addition to the segment was the $50 million purchase of FUNA a Germany-based provider of control and safety systems for cruise ships ferries and mega yachts. That purchase served the company's commercial sector which makes up around 10% of overall sales. Products from this business included flight recorders (black boxes) display systems and aircraft modification and maintenance services.

EXECUTIVES

VP; President Microwave Group, John S. Mega

SVP; President Products Group, Charles J. Schafer, age 64, $380,000 total compensation

Chairman President and CEO, Michael T. Strianese, age 56, $1,284,231 total compensation

EVP Corporate Strategy and Development, Curtis Brunson, age 64, $562,846 total compensation

SVP; President Sensors and Simulation Group, James W. Dunn, age 68, $534,462 total compensation

SVP and CFO, Ralph G. D'Ambrosio, age 44, $560,423 total compensation

SVP; President Services, Steven (Steve) Kantor, age 67

SVP Corporate Secretary and General Counsel, Steven M. (Steve) Post, age 59

SVP; President Integrated Systems Group, John C. McNellis, age 59

SVP Washington Operations, Gen. Richard A. Cody, age 61

VP; President Communications Systems Group, Susan D. Opp

VP Controller and Principal Accounting Officer, Dan Azmon, age 48

EVP L-3 Services Group (LSG), Anthony (Tony) Smeraglinolo, age 59

VP; President Marine and Power Systems, Robert E. (Bob) Leskow

Director, Alan H. Washkowitz, age 71

Director, Robert B. Millard, age 61

Director, Arthur L. Simon, age 80

Director, Thomas A. (Tom) Corcoran, age 67

Director, Gen. Henry H. (Hugh) Shelton, age 70

Director, Claude R. Canizares, age 66

Director, John P. White, age 75

Director, Lewis Kramer, age 64

Auditors: PricewaterhouseCoopersLLP

LOCATIONS

HQ: L-3 Communications Holdings Inc.
600 3rd Ave., New York NY 10016
Phone: 212-697-1111 **Fax:** 212-805-5477
Web: www.l-3com.com

2011 Sales

US	13,064	86
UK	310	2
Australia	118	1
Italy	98	1
South Korea	93	1
Other countries	839	5

PRODUCTS/OPERATIONS

2011 Sales

Electronic systems	5,539	37
Command control & communications intelligence surveillance & reconnaissance (C3ISR)	3,568	23
Total	**15,169**	**100**

2011 Sales

Services	7,606	50
Total	**15,169**	**100**

2011 Sales by Customer

US Government		
Army	3,931	25
Air Force	3,864	25
Navy & Marines	2,358	15
Other US government	1,113	7
Commercial		
Domestic commercial	630	4

Selected Operations

Aircraft Modernization and Maintenance (AM&M)
- Aircraft engineering maintenance modification upgrades and logistics services
- Airborne traffic and collision avoidance systems
- Life cycle management services
- Ruggedization of displays computers and electronics
- Supply chain management
- Voice recorders flight data recorders and maritime hardened voyage recorders

Command Control and Communications and Intelligence Surveillance and Reconnaissance (C3ISR)
- Airborne space and surface data link terminals ground stations and transportable tactical SATCOM systems
- Communication systems for surface and undersea vessels and manned space flights
- Fleet management of special mission aircraft
- Ground-based satellite communications terminals and payloads
- Prime mission systems integration sensor development and operations and support
- Satellite command and control sustainment and support
- Satellite communication and tracking systems
- Secure communication terminals and equipment and secure network encryption products
- Shipboard communications

Electronic Systems
- Avionics and displays
- Electro-optic/infrared (EO/IR)
- Marine services
- Microwave
- Power and control systems
- Precision engagement
- Propulsion systems
- Security and detection
- Simulation and training
- Telemetry and advanced technology
- Undersea warfare
- Warrior systems

COMPETITORS

BAE SYSTEMS
CACI International
CAE Inc.
Cubic Corp.
DRS Technologies
DynCorp International
ITT Corp.
Lockheed Martin
Meggitt
Northrop Grumman
Orbital Sciences
Raytheon
FLYHT Aerospace Solutions
General Dynamics
Harris Corp.
Herley Industries
Honeywell International
Rockwell Collins
Sierra Nevada Corp
telent
Thales
Trimble Navigation
United Technologies

HISTORICAL FINANCIALS

Company Type: Public

Income Statement FYE: December 31

	REVENUE ($ mil.)	NET INCOME ($ mil.)	NET PROFIT MARGIN	EMPLOYEES
12/11	15,169	956	6.3%	61,000
12/10	15,680	955	6.1%	63,000
12/09	15,615	901	5.8%	67,000
12/08	14,901	949	6.4%	65,000
12/07	13,960	756	5.4%	64,600
Annual Growth	2.1%	6.0%	—	(1.4%)

2011 Year-End Financials

Debt ratio: 26.68%
Return on equity: 14.41%
Cash ($ mil.): 764
Current ratio: 194.94
Long-term debt ($ mil.): 4,135
No. of shares (mil.): 98
Dividends
Yield: —
Payout: 19.93%
Market value ($ mil.): 6,600

	STOCK PRICE ($) FY Close	P/E High/Low		PER SHARE ($) Earnings	Dividends	Book Value
12/11	66.68	10	6	9.03	0.00	67.03
12/10	70.49	12	8	8.25	1.60	62.27
12/09	86.95	12	8	7.61	1.40	56.93
12/08	73.78	15	8	7.72	1.20	49.15
12/07	105.94	19	13	5.98	1.00	48.23
Annual Growth	(10.9%)	—	—	10.9%	—	8.6%

Laboratory Corp. of America Holdings

This company pricks and prods for profit. Laboratory Corporation of America Holdings (LabCorp) is a top provider of clinical laboratory services performing tests on more than 450000 patient specimens each day on behalf of managed care organizations hospitals doctors government agencies drug companies and employers. Its services range from routine urinalyses HIV tests and Pap smears to specialty testing for diagnostic genetics disease monitoring forensics identity clinical drug trials and allergies. LabCorp operates about 1700 service sites across the US (and select overseas markets) that collect patient specimens and ship them to one of its 50 primary laboratories where tests are performed.

Most of the tests LabCorp performs each year are routine tests (including blood chemistry analyses blood cell counts and HIV tests) with the segment accounting for about 60% of annual revenues. The genomic and esoteric testing segment which includes LabCorp's Esoterix Monogram Biosciences and Integrated Genetics subsidiaries has grown to account for a larger percentage of sales (nearly 40%) in recent years.

Most of LabCorp's operations are conducted through its extensive network of facilities in the US. The company also has joint ventures in Canada where it provides diagnostic testing services in several provinces and it has also established a presence in Belgium China Japan Puerto Rico Singapore and the UK.

All of LabCorp's efforts towards expanding its offerings and geographic presence helped keep the company's finances healthy for several consecutive years with its revenue and cash flow growing pretty much in tandem annually between 2008 and 2010. In 2011 the company reported an 11% increase in sales to some $5.5 billion largely due to a 21% increase in the growing genomic and esoteric testing segment (routine testing operations also reported a 5% increase in revenues that year). However LabCorp's profits (net income) declined some 7% to $520 million that year largely due to increased expenses from restructuring efforts acquisitions legal settlements and other operational activities.

The company is focused on expanding its advanced testing capabilities especially in the areas of genetic and cancer testing. One particular area of focus for the company's product development efforts is the field of personalized medicine. It has introduced a number of "companion" diagnostic tests that determine whether a patient will react well or poorly to certain drugs. LabCorp is developing such tests internally as well as through partnerships with life science entities such as Duke University and Johns Hopkins University.

LabCorp has also expanded the genetic testing segment through acquisitions including the purchase of Orchid Cellmark for some $85 million in late 2011. The buy fortified the company's position in the DNA identity testing market in the US and marked its entry into the UK testing market. The UK expansion is part of LabCorp's overall goal of growing outside the US.

Back in the US in mid-2012 LabCorp paid some $241 million to acquire MEDTOX Scientific in order to secure its diagnostics products and services. MEDTOX provides forensic and toxicology testing and counts health care and criminal justice facilities among its largest customers.

As payments from managed care entities (HMOs and PPOs) make up about half of LabCorp's annual revenue gaining and maintaining contracts with these clients is a main thrust of the company's strategy and LabCorp strives to capitalize on its nationwide presence to strengthen managed care partnerships. For instance LabCorp has a multi-year contract with UnitedHealth that makes LabCorp the insurer's exclusive national laboratory services provider. Meanwhile LabCorp's specialty subsidiaries such as kidney stone analysis firm Litholink work to control costs for payers by focusing on providing patient-specific tools to manage chronic conditions.

In addition to maintaining its relationships with managed care companies LabCorp looks to keep its physician customers happy with education tools and integrated information management systems including eLabCorp a Web-based tool that allows doctors to access testing services online.

EXECUTIVES

Divisional Medical Director DIANON Systems, James B. Amberson
SVP and Chief Medical Officer, Mark E. Brecher, age 55
SVP Chief Legal Officer Secretary and Chief Compliance Officer, F. Samuel Eberts III, age 52, $311,643 total compensation
Chairman President and CEO, David P. (Dave) King, age 55, $810,000 total compensation

EVP CFO and Treasurer, William B. (Brad) Hayes, age 46, $419,333 total compensation
VP Specimen Quality, Michael Roberts
EVP Atlantic Region, Benjamin R. Miller, age 49
Director Hematopathology US LABS/DIANON and Medical Director US LABS, Ronald W. Thomason
EVP Esoteric Business, Andrew S Walton, age 45, $335,000 total compensation
SVP, Eric Lindblom
EVP and COO, James T. Boyle Jr., age 55
SVP and CIO, Lidia L. Fonseca, age 43
Manager Corporate Communications, Donna F. Schuetz
SVP Human Resources, Lisa Hoffman Starr
Director Investor Relations, Stephen Anderson
VP Clinical Development, Hawazin Faruki
VP and Director Department of Science and technology, James K. Fleming
VP; Global Head Esoterix Clinical Trials Services, David Johnston
SVP Research and Development/Science and Technology, Marcia Eisenberg
Medical Director Atlantic Division, Alicia Carter
Medical Director LabCorp/DIANON-Florida, Sean E. Farrier
Medical Director, Pamela D. Holder
Medical Director, Michael J. Mahoney
Medical Director, Richard C. Marsella
Medical Director North Central Division, Patricia Ann Miller-Canfield
Assistant Director and Medical Director, Antonius Sehonanda
VP and Laboratory Director Center for Esoteric Testing, Andre A. Valcour
Technical Director Genetics Principal, Geraldine McDowell
Associate VP Science and Technology US LABS, Horacio G. Vail
Director Laboratory Operations, W. Allen Taylor
Medical Director Coagulation and Co-director Special Coagulation Esoterix Coagulation, Dorothy M. Adcock
National Director Cytogenetics, Peter Pappenhausen
Director Cytogenetics and Discipline Director for FISH, James H. Tepperberg
Associate VP and National Director Microbiology Special Microbiology Esoteric Immunology/Serology Kidney Stone Analysis and Routine Virology, Barbara A. Body
Divisional Medical Director LabCorp Hematology, Betty M. Garvin Burns
VP and Director Cytology/Histology, Tiea L. Kesler
Chief Scientific Officer Oncology and Genetics LabCorp and Monogram Biosciences, Steven M. Anderson
Director Esoteric and Core Laboratories and Co-discipline Director Infectious Disease Immunology, Mary Ann Meiser
Discipline Director Medical Genetics, Kenneth Friedman
Strategic Director and National Director Mass Spectrometry, Russell P. Grant
Technical Director Infectious Diseases Center for Molecular Biology and Pathology, Joe Sebastian
Associate VP and Director Microbiology and Immunology, Melinda B. Nye
Discipline Director Medical Oncology, Li Cai
Associate VP and Technical Director DNA Identification Testing Division, Uwe Heine
Associate VP Laboratory Director and Technical Leader DNA Identification Testing Division, George C. Maha
Discipline Director, Frank Ryan
Technical Director Infectious Disease and Co-Discipline Director LabCorp, Howard D. Engler
Supervisor III and Laboratory Manager III, Rita Parke
Technical Director, James K. Farquhar
Associate VP and Executive Director Endocrinology, Donald W. Chandler
VP Operations Quality Assurance and Quality Control, Randolph M. Young
Director, Thomas P. Mac Mahon, age 65
Director, M. Keith Weikel, age 74
Director, Kerrii B. Anderson, age 55
Director, Jean-Luc Belingard, age 63
Director, Wendy E. Lane, age 60
Director, Robert E. Mittelstaedt Jr., age 68
Director, Arthur H. Rubenstein, age 74
Director, Robert Sanders (Sandy) Williams, age 63
Auditors: PricewaterhouseCoopersLLP

LOCATIONS

HQ: Laboratory Corporation of America Holdings
358 S. Main St., Burlington NC 27215
Phone: 336-229-1127 **Fax:** 336-436-1205
Web: www.labcorp.com

PRODUCTS/OPERATIONS

2011 Sales

Routine testing	3,143	57
Ontario Canada	309	5

2011 Sales by Payer

Managed care	49	
Medicare and Medicaid	18	
Total	**0**	**100**

Selected subsidiaries

DIANON Systems Inc. (pathology Connecticut)
Dynacare Laboratories Inc. (clinical labs; Tennessee Washington Wisconsin Canada)
Esoterix Inc. (esoteric testing Colorado)
Integrated Genetics (formerly Genzyme Genetics fertility testing labs across the US)
Integrated Oncology (formerly US Labs esoteric oncology tests US)
Litholink Corporation (kidney patient testing Illinois)
Monogram Biosciences Inc. (HIV resistance testing and personalized medicine California)
National Genetics Institute (NGI infection testing and blood screening California
Viro-Med Laboratories Inc. (molecular microbial testing Minnesota)

Selected Acquisitions

2012
MEDTOX Scientific Inc. ($241 million; St. Paul Minnesota; forensic and pathology testing)
2011
Orchid Cellmark ($85 million; Princeton New Jersey; DNA identity testing including paternity in US and UK)
2010
Genzyme Genetics ($925 million; Westborough Massachusetts; genetic reproductive blood disease and oncology testing plus drug trial services)
2009
Monogram Biosciences ($155 million; San Francisco California; personalized genetic tests for infectious disease and cancer)

Selected Services

General and specialty laboratory testing
Ambulatory monitoring services
Bone marrow/HLA services
Clinical trials services
Drug testing services
DNA identification services
Forensic indentity services
Health care provider services
Hospital services
Insurance/health plan services
Paternity testing
Patient services

COMPETITORS

Arup Laboratories
Bio-Reference Labs
Celera
CML HealthCare
Commonwealth Biotechnologies
CompuNet Clinical Laboratories
Covance
eScreen
IDENTIGENE
Kroll Background America
Laboratory Sciences of Arizona
MEDTOX Laboratories
Medtox Scientific
Mid America Clinical Laboratories
NeoGenomics
Oncolab
Orchid Cellmark
Pathology Associates Medical Laboratories
Pharmaceutical Product Development
Psychemedics
Quest Diagnostics
Solstas
Sonic Healthcare

HISTORICAL FINANCIALS

Company Type: Public

Income Statement

FYE: December 31

	REVENUE ($ mil.)	NET INCOME ($ mil.)	NET PROFIT MARGIN	EMPLOYEES
12/11	5,542	519	9.4%	31,000
12/10	5,003	558	11.2%	31,000
12/09	4,694	543	11.6%	28,000
12/08	4,505	464	10.3%	28,000
12/07	4,068	476	11.7%	26,000
Annual Growth	8.0%	2.2%	—	4.5%

2011 Year-End Financials

Debt ratio: 36.19%
Return on equity: 20.76%
Cash ($ mil.): 159
Current ratio: 136.04
Long-term debt ($ mil.): 2,085
No. of shares (mil.): 97
Dividends
Yield: —
Payout: —
Market value ($ mil.): 8,408

	STOCK PRICE ($) FY Close	P/E High/Low		PER SHARE ($) Earnings	Dividends	Book Value
12/11	85.97	19	15	5.11	0.00	25.60
12/10	87.92	16	13	5.29	0.00	24.08
12/09	74.84	15	11	4.98	0.00	20.00
12/08	64.41	19	13	4.16	0.00	15.60
12/07	75.53	20	16	3.93	0.00	15.54
Annual Growth	3.3%	—	—	6.8%	—	13.3%

Lakeland Bancorp, Inc.

Lakeland Bancorp is shoring up in the Garden State. It's the holding company for Lakeland Bank which serves northern New Jersey from about 50 branch offices. Targeting individuals and small to midsized businesses the bank offers standard retail products such as checking and savings accounts money market and NOW accounts and CDs. It also offers financial planning and advisory services for consumers. The bank's lending activities primarily consist of commercial loans and mortgages (more than half of the company's loan portfolio) and residential mortgages. Lakeland also offers commercial lease financing for office systems and heavy equipment.

The company has been minimizing its exposure to commercial leases though as its leasing portfolio contributed to Lakeland's first reported annual loss in 2009. The company cut its leasing portfolio by about half —a move made to de-emphasize that line of business. Instead Lakeland has focused on strengthening its mortgage and commercial loan portfolios. In fact commercial loans have recently been the area of greatest growth for the bank.

Lakeland has been working to shrink its portfolio of nonperforming loans and leases and in 2011 it lowered its provision of loan losses by 3% to $18.8. That year the company's overall revenues shrunk 6% to $135.6 million. However profits grew 3% to $19.9 million. Despite the troubles during the recession Lakeland has an ongoing strategy of focusing on organic growth and expanding its market presence by opening new branches. The company's deposits have grown as a result.

EXECUTIVES

Chairman Lakeland Bancorp and Lakeland Bank, John W. Fredericks, age 75
EVP CFO and Chief Accounting Officer, Joseph F. Hurley, age 61, $240,000 total compensation
President CEO and Director; President and CEO Lakeland Bank, Thomas J. Shara Jr., age 54, $292,308 total compensation
EVP and Chief Retail Officer, Ronald E. (Ron) Schwarz, age 55
SVP and Controller Lakeland Bank, Rita A. Myers
SEVP and COO, Robert A. Vandenbergh, age 60, $268,846 total compensation
EVP Government and Business Services, Jeffrey J. Buonforte, age 60, $205,075 total compensation
EVP and Chief Operations Officer, Louis E. Luddecke, age 65, $205,000 total compensation
Chairman Lakeland Bancorp and Lakeland Bank, Mary Ann Deacon, age 60
Secretary and Director, George H. Guptill Jr., age 73
EVP and Chief Credit Officer, James R. Noonan, age 60
SVP Southern Regional Administration Lakeland Bank, Karen Garrera
SVP Auditing Lakeland Bank, Joseph M. Gallo
SVP Bank Secrecy Act and Anti-Money Laundering Lakeland Bank, Rasiel Kleiner
SVP Loan Operations Lakeland Bank, Gail D. Martin
SVP Information Systems Lakeland Bank, Mary Kaye Nardone
SVP Computer Services Lakeland Bank, Elaine C. Petit
VP Government Banking Lakeland Bank, Robin Hulmes
SVP and Director Retail Sales, Ellen Lalwani
SVP Leasing Division, Robert Ingram
EVP and Chief Lending Officer Lakeland Bancorp and Lakeland Bank, David Yanagisawa
SVP Commercial Loans and Team Leader Oak Ridge, Bradley Bloss
SVP Commercial Loans and Team Leader Montville, Christopher M. Gorey
SVP Asset Based Lending, Thomas R. Keady
SVP Commercial Loans and Team Leader Newton, Mary T. Karakos
SVP General Counsel and Corporate Secretary, Timothy J. Matteson, age 42
SVP Commercial Loans and Team Leader Teaneck, Michael J. Vessa
SVP Commercial Loans and Team Leader Caldwell, Carl A. Monaco
Office Manager West Caldwell, Susan Scimone-Bellini
VP Enterprise Program Office, Thomas Askin
Assistant Treasurer and Consumer Loan Officer Lakeland Administration, Lisa Johnson
Assistant VP and Financial Consultant Lakeland Bank Teaneck Region, Margaret Laquidara
VP Business Development Lakeland Montville Lakeland Bank, Mark McCoy
Assistant Treasurer Lakeland Bank, Linda E. Redyke
Assistant VP and Manager Network Services Lakeland Bank, Stephen Loy
Chairman Lakeland Bancorp and Lakeland Bank, John W. Fredericks, age 75
Director, Roger Bosma, age 69
President CEO and Director; President and CEO Lakeland Bank, Thomas J. Shara Jr., age 54
Chairman Lakeland Bancorp and Lakeland Bank, Mary Ann Deacon, age 60
Director, Mark J. Fredericks, age 51
Director, Joseph P. O'Dowd, age 65
Director, Stephen R. Tilton Sr., age 66
Secretary and Director, George H. Guptill Jr., age 73
Director, Robert B. Nicholson III, age 47
Director, Brian M. Flynn, age 52
Director, Janeth C. Hendershot, age 57
Director, Robert E. McCracken, age 54
Director, Paul G. Viall Jr., age 65
Director, Bruce D. Bohuny, age 43
Auditors: GrantThorntonLLP

LOCATIONS

HQ: Lakeland Bancorp, Inc.
250 Oak Ridge Road, Oak Ridge, NJ 07438
Phone: 973 697-2000
Web: www.lakelandbank.com

PRODUCTS/OPERATIONS

2011 Sales

	$ mil.	% of total
Interest		
Loans & fees	104	77
Investment securities	12	9
Other	0	-
Noninterest		
Service charges on deposit accounts	10	8
Commissions & fees	3	3
Net gains ons sales and calls of securities	1	1
Other	2	2
Total	**135**	**100**

COMPETITORS

Bank of America
Bank of New York Mellon
Capital One
Clifton Savings
Hudson City Bancorp
Investors Bancorp
JPMorgan Chase
New York Community Bancorp
PNC Financial
Sovereign Bank
Sussex Bancorp
TD Bank USA
Valley National Bancorp
Wells Fargo

HISTORICAL FINANCIALS

Company Type: Public

Income Statement FYE: December 31

	ASSETS ($ mil.)	NET INCOME ($ mil.)	INCOME AS % OF ASSETS	EMPLOYEES
12/11	2,825	19	0.7%	527
12/10	2,792	19	0.7%	529
12/09	2,723	(5)	—	533
12/08	2,642	15	0.6%	521
12/07	2,513	17	0.7%	540
Annual Growth	3.0%	2.5%	—	(0.6%)

2011 Year-End Financials

Debt ratio: 8.22%
Return on equity: 7.64%
Cash ($ mil.): 72
Current ratio: —
Long-term debt ($ mil.): 232
No. of shares (mil.): 26
Dividends
Yield: —
Payout: 34.37%
Market value ($ mil.): 231

	STOCK PRICE ($) FY Close	P/E High	P/E Low	PER SHARE ($) Earnings	Dividends	Book Value
12/11	8.62	18	11	0.66	0.00	9.68
12/10	10.97	20	10	0.57	0.19	9.81
12/09	6.39	—	—	(0.33)	0.27	10.18
12/08	11.26	27	13	0.58	0.36	8.46
12/07	11.59	22	15	0.70	0.35	8.24
Annual Growth	(7.1%)	—	—	(1.5%)	—	4.1%

Lakeland Financial Corp.

American dollars are preferred over Polish zloty in this Warsaw bank. Lakeland Financial is the holding company for Lake City Bank which serves area business customers and individuals through more than 40 branches scattered across about a dozen northern Indiana counties. Founded in 1872 in Warsaw Indiana the bank offers such standard retail services as checking and savings accounts money market accounts and CDs. Commercial loans including agricultural loans and mortgages make up about 80% of the bank's loan portfolio. Lake City Bank also offers investment products and services such as corporate and personal trust brokerage employee benefit plans and estate planning.

EXECUTIVES

Chairman and CEO Lakeland Financial and Lake City Bank, Michael L. Kubacki, age 60, $453,841 total compensation
EVP Lakeland Financial and Lake City Bank, Charles D. Smith, age 67, $230,288 total compensation
EVP Retail Lakeland Financial and Lake City Bank, Kevin L. Deardorff, age 50, $189,077 total compensation
President CFO and Director; President and CFO Lake City Bank, David M. Findlay, age 50, $283,993 total compensation
SVP and Trust Officer Lakeland Financial; Head Wealth Advisory Group, James D. Westerfield, age 54, $144,984 total compensation
Corporate Secretary, Kristin Pruitt, age 40
SVP Wealth Advisory, Eric H. Ottinger, $168,247 total compensation
Director, Charles E. Niemier, age 56
Director, L. Craig Fulmer, age 70
Director, Steven D. Ross, age 57
Director, M. Scott Welch, age 51
Director, Richard L. Pletcher, age 70
President CFO and Director; President and CFO Lake City Bank, David M. Findlay, age 50
Director, Robert E. (Rob) Bartels Jr., age 47
Director, Emily E. Pichon, age 48
Director, Thomas A. Hiatt, age 64
Director, Ron Truex
Auditors: CroweHorwathLLP

LOCATIONS

HQ: Lakeland Financial Corporation
202 E. Center St., Warsaw IN 46581-1387
Phone: 574-267-6144 **Fax:** 574-267-6063
Web: www.lakecitybank.com

PRODUCTS/OPERATIONS

2008 Sales

	$ mil.	% of total
Interest		
Loans	99	72
Securities	18	13
Short-term investments	0	-
Noninteresst		
Service charges on deposit accounts	8	6
Merchant card fees	3	3
Wealth advisory fees	3	2
Loan insurance and service fees	2	2
Other	3	2
Total	**139**	**100**

COMPETITORS

1st Source Corporation
KeyCorp
Northeast Indiana Bancorp
PNC Financial

HISTORICAL FINANCIALS

Company Type: Public

Income Statement FYE: December 31

	ASSETS ($ mil.)	NET INCOME ($ mil.)	INCOME AS % OF ASSETS	EMPLOYEES
12/11	2,889	30	1.1%	482
12/10	2,681	24	0.9%	467
12/09	2,571	18	0.7%	461
12/08	2,377	19	0.8%	446
12/07	1,989	19	1.0%	447
Annual Growth	9.8%	12.4%	—	1.9%

2011 Year-End Financials

Debt ratio: 1.59%
Return on equity: 11.22%
Cash ($ mil.): 104
Current ratio: —
Long-term debt ($ mil.): 45
No. of shares (mil.): 16
Dividends
Yield: —
Payout: 32.98%
Market value ($ mil.): 418

	STOCK PRICE ($) FY Close	P/E High/Low		PER SHARE ($) Earnings	Dividends	Book Value
12/11	25.87	14	10	1.88	0.00	16.92
12/10	21.46	17	13	1.32	0.62	15.36
12/09	17.25	19	11	1.26	0.62	17.52
12/08	23.82	16	11	1.58	0.61	12.22
12/07	20.90	16	12	1.55	0.55	12.08
Annual Growth	5.5%	—	—	4.9%	—	8.8%

Las Vegas Sands Corp

Las Vegas Sands brings a touch of Venice to the US and China. Replete with gondoliers and a replica of the Rialto Bridge the company's Venetian Las Vegas Hotel Resort & Casino offers a 120000-sq.-ft. casino and a 4000-suite hotel as well as a shopping dining and entertainment complex. Through its majority-owned Sands China subsidiary the firm operates The Venetian Macau on the Cotai Strip (the Chinese equivalent of the Las Vegas Strip) as well as two other properties in Macao. Properties also include the Marina Bay Sands in Singapore and the partially-owned Sands Bethlehem in Bethlehem Pennsylvania. Billionaire casino mogul Sheldon Adelson and trusts for his family own about 55% of Las Vegas Sands.

Geographic Reach

The company's 70%-owned Sands China subsidiary consist of three casinos in Macao the only place in China where casinos are legal. These properties include the Sands Macau the Venetian Macau Resort Hotel Casino and the Four Seasons Macau. Elsewhere in Asia the company's Marina Bay Sands in Singapore opened in 2010 at a total cost of about $5.5 billion. In the US additional Las Vegas properties include The Palazzo Casino next door to the Venetian and the nearby Sands Expo Center trade show and convention center. Another US property is its Sands Casino Resort Bethlehem in Pennsylvania.

Financials

Las Vegas Sands in 2011 benefitted from a recovering Las Vegas market as well as an Asia-heavy portfolio. About 50% of the company's revenues come from Macao and another 30% is from Singapore. In 2011 Las Vegas Sands reported revenues of more than $9.4 billion up from about $6.8 billion the previous year and its profits increased to more than $1.5 billion compared to about $599 million in 2010.

Strategy

Las Vegas Sands is in the middle of a major growth initiative with several projects in various stages of development. The company's $4.1 billion expansion plan for its Macao operations includes a new resort complex Sands Cotai Central that will house hotels under brands such as Sheraton and St. Regis. Construction is being completed in phases with certain operations to be opening in 2012 and 2013. Driven by its success in Macao and Singapore in 2011 Las Vegas Sands completed a major expansion at its Sands Casino Resort Bethlehem. Included in the remodel was the addition of a hotel retail space and an entertainment center.

Despite these ambitious expansion plans abroad and at home in Pennsylvania the company remains cautious in Las Vegas. A challenging economic environment caused Las Vegas Sands in 2009 to halt construction of a high-rise residential condominium tower located next to The Venetian. The company has reported that construction will resume when conditions improve and demand for condos on the Strip increases.

EXECUTIVES

EVP and CFO, Kenneth J. (Ken) Kay, age 57, $916,667 total compensation
President COO Secretary and Director; Acting CEO Sands China, Michael A. (Mike) Leven, age 74, $1,561,539 total compensation
EVP Global Operations, Chris J. Cahill, age 58
Chairman CEO and Treasurer, Sheldon G. Adelson, age 78, $1,000,000 total compensation
President Global Gaming Operations, Robert G. (Rob) Goldstein, age 56, $1,203,692 total compensation
VP Sales The Venetian Resort and The Palazzo, Eric Bello
SVP; President and COO Venetian Casino Resort, John P. Caparella Jr., age 54
VP Compliance, Kim McCabe
Director Race and Sports Operations The Venetian Resort and The Palazzo, Mark Goldman
VP Casino Credit The Venetian Resort and The Palazzo, Guy Gethers
Director Surveillance The Venetian Resort and The Palazzo, Daniel Eitnier
VP and CTO, Steve Vollmer
SVP Operations The Venetian Resort and The Palazzo, Pete Boyd
VP Casino Marketing Administration The Venetian Resort and The Palazzo, Jeff Ross
EVP and Chief Casino Officer Sands China, David R. Sisk, age 50
SVP and General Counsel, Gayle M. Hyman
VP Public Relations, Ron Reese
President and COO Sands China, Edward M. (Ed) Tracy, age 59
EVP and Global General Counsel, Ira H. Raphaelson, age 58
CIO, Manjit Singh, age 42
VP Investor Relations, Daniel J. Briggs
VP Government Relations, Andrew Abboud
VP Hotel Operations The Venetian Resort and The Palazzo, Kirsten Dimond
Corporate Controller, Michael Quartieri, age 44, $261,227 total compensation
VP Procurement, Norbert Riezler
Managing Director Global Development; President and CEO Marina Bay Sands, George Tanasijevich, age 51
COO Marina Bay Sands, Benny Zin
President COO Secretary and Director; Acting CEO Sands China, Michael A. (Mike) Leven, age 74
Director, Charles D. Forman, age 65
Director, Irwin Chafetz, age 76
Director, Irwin A. Siegel, age 71
Director, George P. Koo, age 73
Director, Jason N. Ader, age 44
Director, Jeffrey H. Schwartz, age 52
Auditors: PricewaterhouseCoopersLLP

LOCATIONS

HQ: Las Vegas Sands Corp.
3355 Las Vegas Blvd. South, Las Vegas NV 89109
Phone: 702-414-1000 **Fax:** 702-414-4884
Web: www.lasvegassands.com

2011 Sales

	$ mil.	% of total
Asia		
Macao		
The Venetian Macau	2,827	30
Sands Macau	1,282	13
Four Seasons Macau	687	7
Singapore		
Marina Bay Sands	2,912	30
Other Asian locations	147	2
US		
Las Vegas Operating Properties	1,324	14
Sands Bethlehem	399	4
Adjustments	(170.5)	-
Total	**9,410**	**100**

PRODUCTS/OPERATIONS

2011 Sales

	$ mil.	% of total
Casino	7,437	76
Rooms	1,000	10
Food & beverage	598	6
Convention retail & other	826	8
Promotional allowances	(451.6)	-
Total	**9,410**	**100**

Selected Properties

Las Vegas
The Palazzo Resort Hotel Casino
The Sands Expo and Convention Center
The Venetian Resort Hotel Casino
China

The Sands Macau (70%)
The Venetian Macau (70%)
Singapore
The Marina Bay Sands

COMPETITORS

Boyd Gaming
Caesars Entertainment
Galaxy Entertainment
Genting Singapore
Melco Crown Entertainment
MGM Resorts
Penn National Gaming
Pinnacle Entertainment
Rio All-Suite Hotel & Casino
Tropicana Entertainment
Wynn Resorts

HISTORICAL FINANCIALS

Company Type: Public

Income Statement FYE: December 31

	REVENUE ($ mil.)	NET INCOME ($ mil.)	NET PROFIT MARGIN	EMPLOYEES
12/11	9,410	1,560	16.6%	40,000
12/10	6,853	599	8.7%	34,000
12/09	4,563	(354)	—	27,000
12/08	4,389	(163)	—	28,500
12/07	2,950	116	4.0%	28,000
Annual Growth	33.6%	91.2%	—	9.3%

2011 Year-End Financials

Debt ratio: 45.10%
Return on equity: 19.87%
Cash ($ mil.): 3,902
Current ratio: 216.00
Long-term debt ($ mil.): 9,577
No. of shares (mil.): 733
Dividends
Yield: —
Payout: 5.39%
Market value ($ mil.): 31,332

	STOCK PRICE ($) FY Close	P/E High/Low	PER SHARE ($) Earnings	Dividends	Book Value
12/11	42.73	29 21	1.56	0.00	10.71
12/10	45.95	87 24	0.51	0.00	10.13
12/09	14.94	— —	(0.82)	0.00	10.48
12/08	5.93	— —	(0.48)	0.00	7.39
12/07	103.05	438221	0.33	0.00	6.36
Annual Growth	(19.8%)	— —	47.5%	—	13.9%

Lauder (Estee) Cos., Inc. (The)

LOCATIONS

HQ: Lauder (Estee) Cos., Inc. (The)
767 Fifth Avenue, New York, NY 10153
Phone: 212 572-4200
Web: www.elcompanies.com

HISTORICAL FINANCIALS

Company Type:

Income Statement FYE: June 30

	REVENUE ($ mil.)	NET INCOME ($ mil.)	NET PROFIT MARGIN	EMPLOYEES
06/12	9,713	856	8.8%	38,500
06/11	8,810	700	8.0%	32,300
06/10	7,795	478	6.1%	31,200
06/09	7,323	218	3.0%	31,300
06/08	7,910	473	6.0%	32,000
Annual Growth	5.3%	16.0%	—	4.7%

2012 Year-End Financials

Debt ratio: 19.54%
Return on equity: 31.35%
Cash ($ mil.): 1,347
Current ratio: 181.35
Long-term debt ($ mil.): 1,069
No. of shares (mil.): 388
Dividends
Yield: —
Payout: 24.31%
Market value ($ mil.): 21,047

	STOCK PRICE ($) FY Close	P/E High/Low	PER SHARE ($) Earnings	Dividends	Book Value
06/12	54.12	54 24	2.16	0.00	7.03
06/11	105.19	59 31	1.74	0.38	6.66
06/10	55.73	58 25	1.19	0.28	4.93
06/09	32.67	97 36	0.55	0.28	4.17
06/08	46.45	40 31	1.20	0.28	4.24
Annual Growth	3.9%	— —	15.8%	—	13.5%

Lear Corp.

Lear doesn't take a back seat to anyone when it comes to manufacturing automotive seats. The company's Seating business by far its most lucrative segment is a leader in the global market for manufacturing car seat systems and their components. The company's Electrical Power Management Systems (EPMS) segment produces automotive electronics including the manufacture of wire harnesses junction boxes terminals and connectors and body control modules. It operates from some 200 facilities in 35 countries. Its largest customers include BMW Ford and General Motors Fiat and Volkswagen. Lear gets about 80% of its sales outside the US.

HISTORY

Lear dates back to 1917 when American Metal Products began supplying seats to Detroit's fledgling car industry. The seat maker incorporated in 1928 and grew during the 1950s and 1960s by buying other auto parts makers.

Siegler Heating an industrial conglomerate with interests in the aerospace auto parts and manufacturing industries was founded in 1950 as a maker of climate-control equipment. Entrepreneur John Brooks and a group of associates bought the company (renamed Siegler Corporation) in 1954 and led it through a series of acquisitions including that of aerospace firm Lear in 1962. The company then became Lear Siegler.

Lear Siegler acquired American Metal Products in 1966. Beset by project delays the company's aerospace unit sputtered in the 1970s but the seat business did well. By 1985 metal seat frames had become Lear Siegler's major auto parts revenue producer. Spurred by growing competition with Japanese carmakers the company built a plant near a General Motors factory in Michigan to allow for swift delivery of its car seats.

In 1986 Forstmann Little bought the financially troubled Lear Siegler and began selling off the parts. Two years later the investment firm offered Lear Seating to its management (including Ken Way who had been with the company since 1966). Way took the company private in a $500 million LBO with the help of Kidder Peabody and the company's name was changed to Lear Seating. Kidder sold its stake in Lear Seating to Lehman Brothers in 1991.

Lear Seating bought a slice of Ford's North American automotive and trim operation and manufacturing factory in Ciudad Juarez Mexico in 1993. As a result of the purchase the company entered into a long-term supply agreement with Ford.

In another strategic buy of a customer's seat business Lear Seating acquired Fiat's seat operations in 1994. This purchase encompassed Sepi Poland Sepi S.p.A. (Italy) and a 35% stake in a Turkish joint venture giving Lear Seating a presence in those countries. The purchase also made the company Europe's largest seat maker and gave it access to Fiat's 5% of the global automotive market. That year Lear Seating went public.

In 1995 Lear Seating bought Automotive Industries and inked a contract to provide seats for Brazil's top-selling car the Volkswagen Gol. To reflect the broader scope of its business the company dropped "Seating" from its name and became Lear Corporation in 1996. That year the company acquired Pennsylvania-based Masland for $475 million and formed a joint venture with China's Jiangling Motors to make seats and interior trim for Ford and Isuzu vehicles.

Lear bought German manufacturer Keiper Car Seating in 1997 and BTR's Dunlop Cox which made a patented seat-adjusting system. It also bought ITT Industries' main North American seat-making unit. In 1998 Lear purchased the automotive seating unit of GM's Delphi Automotive Systems subsidiary (now the independent Delphi) giving it a bigger chunk of GM's business as well as parts companies in the UK and Italy. To cut costs the company announced that it would shut down 18 plants and cut 2800 jobs in the US Europe and South America. Acquisitions continued however.

The company paid $2.3 billion for United Technologies' auto unit (but sold the electric motors unit to Johnson Electric Holdings for $310 million) to complete its instrument panel offerings in 1999. Lear also bought Hyundai Motor's seat business to boost Pacific Rim sales. The following year Lear sold its sealants and foam rubber business to GSC Industries' AcoustiSeal.

Early in 2002 Lear announced it would cut 6500 more jobs and close 21 manufacturing facilities. In light of the tightening automotive market Lear planned to shutter older plants and move work to more cost-efficient locations. In 2004 Lear acquired German automotive electronics maker Grote & Hartmann GmbH & Co. for $220 million.

In 2006 Lear sold $200 million in common stock to activist investor Carl Icahn whose funds already held 5% of the company. The sale gave Icahn a combined 16% stake in Lear. Early in 2007 Icahn offered to buy the entire company in a deal valued at $2.8 billion. Amid skepticism among shareholders Icahn raised his bid to $2.9 billion. However shareholders voted to reject the offer. Icahn then sold two-thirds of his Lear holdings in late 2008.

The company narrowed its product focus and sold its interior product lines (instrument panels door panels flooring acoustic systems and other interior products) in 2006. Before the year was out Lear struck a deal with Wilbur Ross whereby Lear contributed its North American interiors business and $25 million in cash to the International Automotive Components Group North America joint venture. The deal was completed in 2007. Lear got a 25% stake in the venture and warrants for an additional 7% equity interest.

In the midst of the Great Recession Lear filed for Chapter 11 bankruptcy emerging in late 2009. The company came out of bankruptcy with less than $1 billion in debt and $1.6 billion in cash. Lear received debtor-in-possession financing of about $500 million from secured lenders led by J.P. Morgan and Citigroup allowing it to continue its operations during reorganization.

EXECUTIVES

Chairman, Henry D. G. Wallace, age 66
EVP; President Seating, Raymond E. Scott, age 46, $635,152 total compensation
SVP Communications Human Resources and Investor Relations, Melvin L. (Mel) Stephens, age 56
VP and Treasurer, Shari L. Burgess, age 53
President CEO and Director, Matthew J. (Matt) Simoncini, age 51, $635,152 total compensation
VP Corporate Controller and Chief Accounting Officer, Wendy L. Foss, age 54
EVP Business Development General Counsel and Corporate Secretary, Terrence B. (Terry) Larkin, age 57, $594,432 total compensation
VP and Interim CFO, Jason M. Cardew
VP; Interim President Electrical Power Management Systems, Frank C. Orsini, age 39
Director, Thomas P. (Tom) Capo, age 61
Director, Gregory C. (Greg) Smith, age 60
Director, Donald L. Runkle, age 66
Director, Curtis J. Clawson, age 52
Director, Conrad L. Mallett Jr., age 58
President CEO and Director, Matthew J. (Matt) Simoncini, age 51
Director, Jonathan F. (Jon) Foster, age 51
Auditors: Ernst&YoungLLP

LOCATIONS

HQ: Lear Corporation
21557 Telegraph Rd., Southfield MI 48033
Phone: 248-447-1500 **Fax:** 248-447-1772
Web: www.lear.com

2011 Sales

	$ mil.	% of total
US	2,542	18
Mexico	1,659	12
Other countries	6,069	43

PRODUCTS/OPERATIONS

2011 Sales

Seating	10,943	77
Total	**14,156**	**100**

2011 Sales by Customer

General Motors		19
BMW		12
Total	**0**	**100**

Selected Mergers & Acquisitions

FY2012
Guilford Mills ($257 million; North Carolina; maker of fabrics used in water filtration and window covering markets)

Selected Products

Seating
- Adjusters
- Automotive seats
- Fabrics
- Head restraints
- Mechanisms
- Seat foam
- Structure systems
- Trim covers

Electrical power management
- Electrical distribution and power management systems
  - Fuse boxes
  - Junction boxes
  - Terminals and connectors
  - Wire harness assemblies
- High-power electrical systems
- Hybrid electrical systems
- Specialty electronics
  - Audio sound systems
  - In-vehicle television tuner module
  - LED electronics (interior/exterior)
  - Lighting control module
  - Media console
  - Radio amplifiers
- Wireless systems
  - Keyless entry systems
  - Passive entry systems
  - Tire pressure monitoring systems

COMPETITORS

Delphi Automotive Systems
DENSO
Faurecia
Johnson Controls
LEONI
Magna International
Methode Electronics
Mitsubishi Electric
Robert Bosch
Stoneridge
Toyota Boshoku
TRW Automotive
Valeo
Visteon
Yazaki

HISTORICAL FINANCIALS

Company Type: Public

Income Statement

FYE: December 31

	REVENUE ($ mil.)	NET INCOME ($ mil.)	NET PROFIT MARGIN	EMPLOYEES
12/11	14,156	540	3.8%	97,800
12/10	11,954	438	3.7%	86,800
12/09*	1,580	(3)	—	75,000
11/09	8,158	818	10.0%	0
12/08	13,570	(689)	—	80,000
Annual Growth	1.1%	—	—	5.2%

*Fiscal year change

2011 Year-End Financials

Debt ratio: 9.92%
Return on equity: 22.19%
Cash ($ mil.): 1,754
Current ratio: 155.43
Long-term debt ($ mil.): 695
No. of shares (mil.): 100
Dividends
Yield: —
Payout: 9.84%
Market value ($ mil.): 4,007

	STOCK PRICE ($) FY Close	P/E High/Low		PER SHARE ($) Earnings	Dividends	Book Value
12/11	39.80	21	7	5.08	0.00	24.20
12/10	98.71	23	15	4.06	0.00	23.39
12/09*	67.64	—	—	(0.06)	0.00	28.27
Annual Growth	(23.3%)	—	—	—	—	(7.5%)

*Fiscal year change

Level 3 Communications, Inc.

Level 3 Communications wants to help businesses get their network functions to the next level. The company operates one of the world's largest fiber-optic communications networks connecting customers in 45-plus countries. Services include broadband Internet access wholesale voice origination and termination enterprise voice content distribution broadband transport and colocation. Level 3's wholesale customers include ISPs telecom carriers cable-TV operators wireless providers and the US government. Level 3 markets directly to businesses state agencies and schools. Its content delivery unit targets video distributors Web portals online gaming and software companies and social networking sites.

HISTORY

Thoroughly modern Level 3 Communications was the brainchild of an Omaha Nebraska construction company that traces its roots to 1884 – the multinational Peter Kiewit Sons'. With cash to invest in the 1980s Kiewit acquired Metropolitan Fiber Systems which built fiber-optic networks for phone companies. In 1986 Kiewit executive James Crowe convinced CEO Walter Scott that Kiewit should build some phone circuits of its own and by 1987 Kiewit had created MFS Communications headed by Crowe to build networks in business districts. Kiewit slated $500 million for the project in 1989.

By 1995 MFS had gone public and was the biggest of the competitive local-exchange carriers (CLECs). That year Crowe and Scott heard Bill Gates speak on the power of the Internet to destroy traditional phone traffic. MFS launched "Project Silver" to decide how to respond. The answer: Buy UUNET. In 1996 MFS acquired the giant ISP and Internet backbone operator and in the process made itself an acquisition target. WorldCom bought MFS for $14 billion by year's end.

Within a month Crowe walked away from WorldCom (with several MFS execs in tow) to head Kiewit Diversified Group which had holdings in telecommunications technology and energy.

In 1998 Kiewit split into the Peter Kiewit Sons' construction group headed by Ken Stinson and a diversified company called Level 3 Communications headed by Crowe. Level 3 kept stakes in telecom companies RCN and C-TEC (now Commonwealth Telephone Enterprises). The Level 3 name came from the seven-layer Open Systems Interconnect (OSI) network model: The company saw its field of play in the bottom three levels –the physical plant data link and network layers.

Kiewit provided Crowe with a $2.5 billion grubstake; Level 3 went public and sold its oil interests and Michigan cable-TV operation. It retained its coal-mining and toll-road interests to help fund the buildout of a new fiber-optic network to be based on Internet protocol (IP) technology instead of the old circuit-switching system.

Level 3 secured rights-of-way from Burlington Northern and Union Pacific. The company found a new angel in Craig McCaw whose INTERNEXT agreed to plunge $700 million into the Level 3 network in return for capacity. By year's end the company had begun local networks in 25 US cities and had completed gateway sites in 17.

In 1999 Level 3 moved from Omaha to Broomfield Colorado deciding that it could grow faster in the Rockies. The company opened London and Frankfurt gateway sites after buying UK and German ISPs and it agreed to share construction costs on Western European routes with COLT . Level 3 hired Tyco International to develop an Atlantic undersea cable and agreed to participate in the building of the Japan-US Cable Network across the Pacific.

Fellow fiber baron Global Crossing agreed to buy a 50% interest in the transatlantic cable in 2000. By mid-year Level 3 had installed fiber across more than a third of its planned US intercity network. In early 2001 the company announced the completion of its network construction and said it would expand its European network to eight additional markets despite cutting about 6% of its workforce. Later that year Level 3 announced plans to buy McLeodUSA's wholesale dial-up Internet access assets for $55 million and in 2002 it completed the deal which enabled Level 3 to support dial-up Internet access in all 50 states.

For Level 3 as for many of its rivals demand for bandwidth capacity and services failed to reach expected levels and the company in 2001 scaled back its revenue estimates and cut almost 25% of its workforce. It also sold its Asian operations including its Tiger network and its capacity on a Japan-US submarine cable and backhaul network to Reach the wholesale carrier partnership of Telstra and PCCW.

However Level 3 received a shot in the arm in 2002 when an investment group that included Warren Buffett's Berkshire Hathaway invested $500 million in the company (it sold the stake in 2004). Level 3 acquired most of the assets of network services provider Genuity in a deal valued at $242 million. It later withdrew from Genuity's managed hosting business sending customers to CSC and sold the Midwest Fiber Optic Network a regional system acquired from Genuity to CenturyTel. The company had made an earlier unsuccessful bid to purchase Tulsa-based Williams Communications Group now WilTel Communications which later completed reorganization under bankruptcy protection.

Also in 2002 Level 3 acquired Massachusetts-based software distributor CorpSoft and Software Spectrum a business software distributor based in Texas. The companies were combined and Level 3 soon derived much of its revenues from software distribution which provided relief from the telecom sector's hard times. That year it sold its stake in Pennsylvania phone company Commonwealth Telephone Enterprises and its stake in RCN was written off following that company's bankruptcy.

In 2003 the company gained $46 million in cash and $139 million in reduced debt from its 65% interest in California Private Transportation Company following its sale of the SR-91 Toll Road to the Orange County (California) Transportation Authority. That year it teamed up with PanAmSat combining the two companies' network capabilities to form a hybrid fiber-optic and satellite delivery system for entertainment content and information to cable and TV broadcasters ISPs and others (PanAmSat was acquired in 2006 by Intelsat). In a separate deal Level 3 agreed to provide Internet access through its satellite platform to the 500000 Internet access customers of Hughes Electronics' DIRECTV unit.

The company acquired the managed modem business of ICG Communications in 2004.

Vyvx was acquired in 2005 when Level 3 bought WilTel Communications Group from Leucadia National. The company also sold its computer outsourcing services unit (i)Structure in 2005.

Level 3 made a number of acquisitions in 2006 including Progress Telecom TelCove metro transport services provider Looking Glass Networks and the rest of ICG Communications. It also sold its Software Spectrum subsidiary that year.

The company acquired Broadwing a provider of voice and data communications services for $254 million in early 2007. To diversify its services Level 3 also purchased SAVVIS's content delivery network services business for approximately $132 million and it bought online video management firm Servecast for $45 million.

Due to declining revenues from transport services for audio and video programming Level 3 sold the advertising portion of it Vyvx content distribution unit to DG FastChannel (now Digital Generation) for $129 million in 2008.

EXECUTIVES

EVP Chief Administrative Officer and Secretary, Thomas C. (Tom) Stortz, age 60
CEO and Director, James Q. (Jim) Crowe, age 62, $812,692 total compensation
Chairman, J. Walter (Walter) Scott Jr., age 80
CTO and President Global Network Services, John F. (Jack) Waters Jr., age 47
EVP and Vice Chairman, Charles C. (Buddy) Miller III, age 59, $502,692 total compensation
President and COO, Jeffrey K. (Jeff) Storey, age 52
EVP and CFO, Sunit S. Patel, age 50, $438,846 total compensation
SVP Strategic Asset Investment Group, Robin Grey
SVP and Controller, Eric J. Mortensen, age 53
President EMEA, James Heard, age 49
Regional President North America, Andrew Crouch, age 41
CIO, Mark Martinet
Chief Customer Experience Officer and Business Process Engineering Lead, Peter Neill
EVP Chief Legal Officer and Assistant Secretary, John M. Ryan, age 49
Regional President Latin America, Hector R. Alonso, age 54
Director, Arun N. Netravali, age 65
CEO and Director, James Q. (Jim) Crowe, age 62
Director, Michael B. Yanney, age 78
EVP and Vice Chairman, Charles C. (Buddy) Miller III, age 59
Director, Michael J. (Mike) Mahoney, age 62
Director, Richard R. Jaros, age 60
Director, Albert C. Yates, age 70
Director, R. Douglas Bradbury, age 61
Director, Robert E. Julian, age 72
Director, John T. Reed, age 68
Director, Douglas C. Eby, age 53
Director, Rahul N. Merchant, age 56
Director, Adm. James O. Ellis Jr., age 64
Auditors: KPMGLLP

LOCATIONS

HQ: Level 3 Communications Inc.
1025 Eldorado Blvd., Broomfield CO 80021-8869
Phone: 720-888-1000 **Fax:** 720-888-5085
Web: www.level3.com

2010 Sales

	$ mil.	% of total
North America	3,335	91
Europe		
UK	131	4
Germany	62	2
Other countries	123	3
Total	**3,651**	**100**

2011 Sales

	$ mil.	% of total
North America	3,669	85
Europe		
UK	267	6
Germany	72	2
Other Europe	163	4
Latin America		
Brazil	68	2
Argentina	23	-
Colombia	23	-
Other Latin America	44	1
Rest of world	4	
Total	**4,333**	**100**

PRODUCTS/OPERATIONS

2011 Sales

	$ mil.	% of total
Core network services		
Wholesale	1,433	33
Mid-market	640	15
Large enterprise & federal	605	14
European	324	7
Global Crossing invest & grow	590	14
Wholesale voice services	672	15
Other communications services	69	2
Total	**4,333**	**100**

2011 Sales

	$ mil.	% of total
Level 3	3,679	85
Global Crossing	654	15
Total	**4,333**	**100**

Selected Services

Communications services
- Transport and infrastructure
  - Colocation
  - Dark fiber (unconnected fiber)
  - Metropolitan and intercity wavelengths
  - Private line
  - Professional services
  - Transoceanic
- Voice
  - Enterprise
  - Wholesale voice origination and termination
  - Wholesale VoIP component services
- IP and data
  - ATM and frame relay
  - Content delivery network (CDN) services
  - Dedicated Internet access
  - High-speed Internet access
  - VPNs
- Managed IP (low-speed services primarily from Genuity acquisition)
- Managed modem (dial-up Internet access)
- Reciprocal compensation (interconnection agreements with carriers)
- Vyvx (audio and video program broadcasting)

SBC contract services

COMPETITORS

AboveNet
Akamai
AT&T
Belgacom
BT
Cable & Wireless Communications
CenturyLink
Cogent Communications
COLT Group
Deutsche Telekom
Equinix
France Telecom
Hewlett-Packard
IBM
Internap Network Services
Interoute
InterXion
KPN
Limelight
PAETEC
SAVVIS
TCS America
TeleCity
Telefonica
TeliaSonera
Telmex
tw telecom
Verizon Enterprise Solutions
XO Holdings

HISTORICAL FINANCIALS

Company Type: Public

Income Statement FYE: December 31

	REVENUE ($ mil.)	NET INCOME ($ mil.)	NET PROFIT MARGIN	EMPLOYEES
12/11	4,333	(756)	—	10,900
12/10	3,651	(622)	—	5,500
12/09	3,762	(618)	—	5,200
12/08	4,301	(290)	—	5,300
12/07	4,269	(1,114)	—	6,680
Annual Growth	0.4%	—	—	13.0%

2011 Year-End Financials

Debt ratio: 64.07%
Return on equity: (-63.37)%
Cash ($ mil.): 918
Current ratio: 102.96
Long-term debt ($ mil.): 8,385
No. of shares (mil.): 207
Dividends
Yield: —
Payout: —
Market value ($ mil.): 3,532

	STOCK PRICE ($) FY Close	P/E High/Low	PER SHARE ($) Earnings	Dividends	Book Value
12/11	16.99	— —	(5.51)	0.00	5.74
12/10	0.98	— —	(5.55)	0.00	(1.41)
12/09	1.53	— —	(5.70)	0.00	4.48
12/08	0.70	— —	(2.85)	0.00	8.12
12/07	3.04	— —	(10.95)	0.00	10.44
Annual Growth	53.8%	— —	—	—	(13.9%)

Levi Strauss & Co.

Yes Levi Strauss & Co. (LS&CO.) has jeans but it gets the casual workday wardrobe inside and out. A global manufacturer of brand-name clothing LS&CO. sells jeans and sportswear under the Levi's Dockers Signature by Levi Strauss and Denizen labels in more than 110 countries. It also markets men's and women's underwear and loungewear. Levi's Red Tag jeans department store staples and once the uniform of American youth have expanded outside their niche to markets beyond the US. LS&CO. has further transformed its products portfolio to include wrinkle-free and stain-resistant fabrics used in making some of its Levi's and Dockers slacks. The Haas family (descendants of founder Levi Strauss) controls LS&CO.

LS&CO.'s operations are divided among three geographic regions: the Americas Europe and the Asia/Pacific region. While Levi's is marketed as an authentically American brand approximately 50% of the company's net revenues come from outside the US.

Worldwide LS&CO.'s clothing is sold in about 55000 retail locations of which 2300 stores sell only the Levi's brand. Outside of the US its lineup is found in department and specialty stores and some 1800 franchised and other brand-dedicated outlets.

Like many other apparel makers which have traditionally relied on chain retailers and department stores to distribute their products in the US LS&CO. is developing its own retail network to increase the global availability and visibility of the Levi's brand. LS&CO. distributes Levi's and Dockers clothing through approximately 500 company-operated stores in 32 countries as well as sells apparel online. Company-operated stores have generated an increasing share of sales 18% 15% and 11% in 2011 2010 and 2009 respectively. LS&CO. added 62 company-operated stores and closed 34 during 2011.

In fiscal 2011 (ends November) LS&CO. hit a five-year low posting an 8% decline in earnings over the prior year. Sales climbed 6% over 2010 driven by the company's expanding retail network across all geographic regions. The top line was underpinned by the Levi's brand products which accounted for 83% of sales in 2011 while Dockers-branded products represented only 12% slipping from 21% in 2007. In addition although LS&CO. boasts a broad range of apparel its jeans and casual and dress pants account for more than 80% of all sales (2009 through 2011). Men's products generated more than 70% of sales during the same period.

Part of the struggle toward growth is attributable to higher costs as well as growing competitive pressures. LS&CO has lost market share to rival V.F. Corporation (maker of Lee and Wrangler brand jeans and apparel) and others over the past decade. It is further squeezed between makers of pricey premium denim (True Religion Diesel S.p.A.) and purveyors of trendy low-priced denim (Wal-Mart and J.C. Penney).

In addition to opening company-owned stores the jeans maker created the Signature by Levi Strauss and Denizen brands sold through the mass market. In 2011 the Denizen entered more than 1700 Target stores in the US. Abroad the brand has developed a following in China and India. Results to date however are modest. Demand for the company's value-priced brands has remained flat accounting for roughly 5% of sales.

LS&CO. simultaneously is aiming to take advantage of its category and brand strength. In its first-ever global product launch it introduced Levi's Curve ID jeans for women which is reportedly selling ahead of the brand's overall growth. It also developed the Water

HISTORY

Levi Strauss arrived in New York City from Bavaria in 1847. In 1853 he joined his brother-in-law David Stern in San Francisco selling dry goods to the gold rushers. Shortly after a prospector told Strauss of miners' problems in finding sturdy pants. Strauss made a pair out of canvas for the prospector; word of the rugged pants spread quickly.

Strauss continued his dry-goods business in the 1860s. During this time he switched the pants' fabric to a durable French cloth called serge de Nimes soon known as denim. He colored the fabric with indigo dye and adopted the idea from Nevada tailor Jacob Davis of reinforcing the pants with copper rivets. In 1873 Strauss and Davis produced their first pair of waist-high overalls (later known as jeans). The pants soon became "de rigueur" for lumberjacks cowboys railroad workers oil drillers and farmers.

Strauss continued to build his pants and wholesaling business until he died in 1902. Levi Strauss & Co. passed to four Stern nephews who carried on their uncle's jeans business while maintaining the company's philanthropic reputation.

After WWII Walter Haas and Peter Haas (a fourth-generation Strauss family member) assumed leadership of LS&CO. In 1948 they ended the company's wholesaling business to concentrate on Levi's clothing. In the 1950s Levi's jeans ceased to be merely functional garments for workers; they became the uniform of American youth. In the 1960s LS&CO. added women's attire and expanded overseas.

The company went public in 1971. That year it added a women's career line and bought Koret sportswear (sold in 1984). By the mid-1980s profits declined. Peace Corps-veteran-turned-McKinsey-consultant Robert Haas (Walter's son) grabbed the reins of LS&CO. in 1984 and took the company private the next year (he became chairman in 1989). He also instilled a touchy-feely corporate culture often at odds with the bottom line.

In 1986 LS&CO. introduced Dockers casual pants. The company's sales began rising in 1991 as consumers forsook the designer duds of the 1980s for more practical clothes. LS&CO. says seven out of every 10 American men own a pair of Dockers. However LS&CO. missed out on the birth of another trend: the split between the fashion sense of US adolescents and their Levi's-loving baby boomer parents.

In 1996 the company introduced Slates dress slacks. That year LS&CO. bought back nearly one-third of its stock from family and employees for $4.3 billion. Grappling with slipping sales and debt from the buyout in 1997 LS&CO. closed 11 of its 37 North American plants laying off 6400 workers and 1000 salaried employees; it granted generous severance packages even to those earning minimum wage.

In 1998 citing improved labor conditions in China LS&CO. announced it would step up its use of Chinese subcontractors. Further restructuring added a third of its European plants to the closures list that year. LS&CO.'s sales fell 13% in fiscal 1998. Also that year Haas handed his CEO title to Pepsi executive Philip Marineau; Haas remained chairman.

LS&CO. closed 11 of 22 remaining North American plants in 1999. It also unleashed several new jeans brands that eschewed the company's one-style-fits-all approach of old..

In April 2002 LS&CO. announced it would close six of its last eight US plants and cut 20% of its worldwide staff (3300 workers). In September 2003 it cut another 5% of its global staff (650 workers). That month the company opened its first girls-only store located in Paris. In December LS&CO. replaced CFO Bill Chiasson with an outside turnaround specialist.

Pinpointing 2006 as the best time to step down as the company's chief executive Philip Marineau retired at the end of 2006. John Anderson president of LS&CO.'s Asia/Pacific division and head of the firm's global supply chain unit replaced Marineau as president and CEO.

Levi Strauss chairman Robert Haas retired in 2008 after 18 years in that role. His successor was Dryer's ice cream executive T. Gary Rogers who became the first leader in the company's history who was not a descendant of the founder. In August 2008 CFO Hans Ploos van Amstel left the company the and was replaced by Heidi Manes its corporate controller and principal accounting officer.

Looking to gain a more active role in its store business LS&CO. in July 2009 bought the operating rights for more than 70 Levi's and Dockers Outlet locations from store operator Anchor Blue Retail Group which had filed for bankruptcy for $72 million. Anchor Blue said the US recession and drop in consumer spending especially among teens severely affected its financial performance. LS&CO. said the acquisition will enable it to better manage its brands' positioning.

Rogers retired in late 2009 and Richard Kauffman became chairman.

EXECUTIVES

Chairman Emeritus, Robert D. (Bob) Haas, age 69
Chairman, Stephen C. Neal, age 62
EVP and CFO, Blake J. Jorgensen, age 52
President CEO and Director, Charles V. (Chip) Bergh, age 55
Chief Strategy Officer and SVP Strategy and Business Development, Lawrence W. (Larry) Ruff, age 55
SVP and CIO, Tom Peck
SVP and Chief Supply Chain Officer, David Love, age 49
SVP Corporate Affairs and Chief Communications Officer, Jill Nash
SVP Global Human Resources, Cathleen L. Unruh, age 63
EVP; President Global Denizen; and President Commercial Operations Asia Pacific, Aaron B. K. Boey, age 51
Global Chief Marketing Officer, Rebecca (Becca) Van Dyck
SVP Women?s Merchandising and Design, Laurie Etheridge
EVP; President Commercial Operations Americas and Europe; President Dockers Brand, Anne Rohosy, age 53
Director, Vanessa J. Castagna, age 62
Director, Leon J. (Lee) Level, age 71
Director, Robert D. (Bob) Haas, age 69
Director, Patricia Salas Pineda, age 60
Director, Robert A. Eckert, age 57
Director, Peter E. Haas Jr., age 64
Director, Stephen C. Neal, age 62
Director, Fernando G. Aguirre, age 54
President CEO and Director, Charles V. (Chip) Bergh, age 55
Auditors: PricewaterhouseCoopersLLP

LOCATIONS

HQ: Levi Strauss & Co.
1155 Battery St., San Francisco CA 94111
Phone: 415-501-6000 **Fax:** 415-501-7112
Web: www.levistrauss.com

2011 Sales

	% of total
Americas	57
Europe	25
Asia/Pacific	18
Total	**100**

2011 Retail & Outlet Stores

	No.
Americas	211
Europe	178
Asia/Pacific	109
Total	**498**

PRODUCTS/OPERATIONS

2011 Sales

	% of total
Levi's	83
Dockers	12
Signature by Levi Strauss & Denizen	5
Total	**100**

Selected Brands

Denizen
Dockers
 Dockers Alpha Khaki
 Dockers for Men
 Dockers for Women
Levi' s
 Levi' s 501 Original
 Levi' s 505 Straight
 Levi' s 511 Skinny
 Levi' s 513 Slim
 Levi' s 514 Slim Straight
 Levi' s Curve ID
Signature by Levis Strauss & Co.

COMPETITORS

Abercrombie & Fitch
adidas
American Eagle Outfitters
Benetton
Calvin Klein
Diesel SpA
Fast Retailing
Fifth & Pacific
Fruit of the Loom
FUBU
Guess?
Haggar
Hugo Boss
Inditex
J. C. Penney
J. Crew
Jockey International
Joe' s Jeans
Jones Group
Kmart
Kohl' s
Lands' End
Macy' s
Nautica Apparel
NIKE
OshKosh B' Gosh
Oxford Industries
Perry Ellis International
PVH
Ralph Lauren
Sean John
Sears
Target Corporation
The Gap
True Religion Apparel
Under Armour
VF Corporation
Victoria' s Secret Stores
Wacoal
Wal-Mart
Warnaco Group

HISTORICAL FINANCIALS

Company Type: Private

Income Statement FYE: November 27

	REVENUE ($ mil.)	NET INCOME ($ mil.)	NET PROFIT MARGIN	EMPLOYEES
11/11	4,761	137	2.9%	17,000
11/10	4,410	156	3.5%	16,200
11/09	4,105	151	3.7%	11,800
11/08	4,400	229	5.2%	11,400
11/07	4,360	460	10.6%	11,550
Annual Growth	2.2%	(26.0%)	—	10.1%

2011 Year-End Financials

Debt ratio: 60.25%
Return on equity: 987650001000000.00%
Cash ($ mil.): 204
Current ratio: 199.85
Long-term debt ($ mil.): 1,819
No. of shares (mil.): 37
Dividends
 Yield: —
 Payout: 14.82%
Market value ($ mil.): —

Lexmark International, Inc.

Lexmark International attacks printing with a host of jets and lasers. A leading maker of printers and related supplies the company provides color monochrome and multifunction laser printers; color and multifunction ink jet printers; dot matrix printers; and ink cartridges. Lexmark markets to customers ranging from individual consumers to large organizations in the financial services government health care manufacturing and retail sectors. Its Perceptive Software subsidiary provides software and services used to manage documents workflows imaging and other content. The company sells products in more than 170 countries; it gets more than half of sales from outside the US.

In 2011 sales for Lexmark were flat falling by less than 1% compared to 2010. Sales of supplies –the company's largest and most profitable product line –were flat on a year-over-year basis. Hardware sales were down 7% while software and other sales increased 22% due to the inclusion of a full year of results for Perceptive Software. Lexmark's net earnings were down 6% compared to 2010 primarily due to lower operating income and higher income taxes. The company's sales have trended downwards since 2006 (though it benefited from a jump in 2010 sales when it bought Perceptive Software mid-year). Lexmark has maintained profitability by restructuring on a regular basis including headcount reductions and related project costs and lease terminations.

The company continues to expand its printer supplies business which makes up about 70% of sales by growing its base of installed hardware and software. Lexmark is shifting the focus of its Imaging Solutions segment to higher-end products designed for greater volume usage. It establishes relationships with large customers and channel partners including office retailers distributors and value-added resellers in order to expand printer sales. Another area the company is targeting for growth is managed print services with Lexmark taking over the maintenance and replenishment of a customer's printing and imaging equipment infrastructure. Customers for its managed print services include Anheuser-Busch Columbia Sportswear Cummins and the USDA.

Lexmark added to its managed print services offerings in 2012 with the purchase of Brainware a developer of intelligent data capture software. The $148 million acquisition added software used to select critical data from paper or electronic documents and validate it prior to sending it to a document or content management system. Brainware part of Perceptive Software was part of the larger purchase of Luxembourg-based BDGB from Vista Equity Partners. Lexmark also boosted its Perceptive subsidiary with the purchase of Australia-based ISYS Search Software (enterprise search software) and US-based Nolij (Web-based imaging document and workflow management software for the higher education market).

Lexmark acquired Perceptive Software in 2010. The purchase allowed the company to build on its existing document workflow products and managed print services. Perceptive which makes most of its sales in the US is a fast-growing software business that has experience in the health care higher education and government segments. Lexmark operates Perceptive as a stand-alone business retaining the Perceptive Software name. In a move to build the business in 2011 Lexmark acquired Palla Athena for an estimated $50.2 million. The Dutch developer of business process management (BPM) document object model and process mining software for government insurance and life science applications expanded Perceptive's reach to markets in Belgium the Caribbean Germany and the UK.

Under an agreement with Dell Lexmark manufactures printers that the PC maker sells under its own brand. Dell accounts for approximately 10% of Lexmark's revenues. The companies expanded their business relationship in 2009 extending the number of printer models involved and related aftermarket cartridges.

HISTORY

During the late 1980s as a horde of Davids took aim at Goliath IBM the computer giant began downsizing to become more competitive. IBM cut its workforce by 100000 between 1986 and 1992 and began to sell off its peripherals businesses. One of these was Lexmark ("Lex" as in "lexicon" and "mark" as in "marks on paper").

In 1991 IBM sold Lexmark to a group led by investment firm Clayton Dubilier & Rice for $1.5 billion. Martin Dubilier who helped found the firm in 1978 learned the leveraged buyout (LBO) ropes as a turnaround expert for Jerome Kohlberg founder of investment firm Kohlberg Kravis Roberts (now KKR) during the 1970s. Clayton Dubilier's LBO of Lexmark was financed primarily with bank loans leaving the new company over $1 billion in debt. Marvin Mann a 32-year IBM veteran was appointed Lexmark's chairman.

Mann took a cue from his former bosses and did some downsizing of his own at Lexmark cutting the number of employees from 5000 to 3000. Mann also put more of the responsibility for running the company in the hands of his line managers allowing them to come up with their own goals and business plans rather than take strategy from above.

Although many employees were given their walking papers Mann put up a "Help Wanted" sign in his sales department. As an IBM subsidiary Lexmark relied on Big Blue's general sales force and Mann now needed to create one from scratch. By the end of 1991 staff rose to 4000.

As another sign of Lexmark's break from IBM where it sometimes got lost in the shuffle Mann reorganized the company into four operating groups and made each group's financial information available to everyone in the company.

Lexmark began to flex its muscles as an independent in 1992 when it introduced the first products (IBM PC-compatible keyboards) bearing its own name rather than the IBM logo. That year Lexmark's first color printer debuted. Lexmark's operating profits doubled in 1992 its second year of operation. Using the additional cash flow the company reduced its debt ahead of schedule to about $750 million. In 1993 it made its first acquisition when it bought Australian printer maker Gestetner Lasers; the purchase increased Lexmark's presence in the Pacific Rim.

Lexmark began removing the IBM logo from its printers in 1994 and kicked off retail distribution of its own brand of ink jet printers and low-end laser printers. In 1995 the company went public and introduced its first color laser printer. In 1996 Lexmark doubled the number of its manufacturing facilities opening ink jet plants in the US Mexico and the UK to help keep up with rising demand and put its products closer to burgeoning markets.

In continuing efforts to swipe market share from Hewlett-Packard Lexmark in 1997 revamped its line of office and home printers. Clayton Dubilier & Rice sold its remaining 23% stake in Lexmark in 1998. COO Paul Curlander who developed IBM's first laser printer replaced Mann as CEO that year and as chairman the next.

Lexmark in 2000 opened an ink jet plant in the Philippines and a second such plant in Mexico. Later that year the company announced it would move some manufacturing operations to Mexico and China and cut about 900 jobs. In 2001 the company announced further jobs cuts —about 1600 –and the closure of one of its plants in Mexico.

Sales and profits peaked in 2004 and began a gradual decline in following years as Lexmark was pressured by a wide number of competitors around the world. Net cash from operating activities waxed and waned during the latter half of the decade until 2009 when the company threw off its smallest amount of cash from operations in five years due to the global recession.

Longtime CEO Paul Curlander retired late in 2010. He was replaced by Paul Rooke who has been with Lexmark since it was formed. Rooke also replaced Curlander as chairman the following year.

EXECUTIVES

Chairman and CEO, Paul A. Rooke, age 54, $572,192 total compensation
Director Investor Relations, John Morgan
EVP and CFO, John W. Gamble Jr., age 49, $496,904 total compensation
VP Human Resources, Jeri L. Isbell, age 54, $337,577 total compensation
VP Asia Pacific and Latin America, Ronaldo M. Foresti, age 59, $356,365 total compensation
VP; President and CEO Preceptive Software, Scott Coons
EVP; President Imaging Solutions and Services (ISS), Martin S. (Marty) Canning, age 49, $451,731 total compensation
VP General Counsel and Secretary, Robert J. (Bob) Patton, age 51
Director, Jean-Paul L. Montupet, age 64
Director, Kathi P. Seifert
Director, Sandra L. (Sandy) Helton, age 62
Director, J. Edward (Ed) Coleman, age 60
Director, Ralph E. Gomory, age 82
Director, Michael J. (Mike) Maples Sr., age 69
Director, William R. (Bill) Fields, age 62
Director, Robert Holland Jr., age 71
Director, Jared L. Cohon, age 64
Director, Stephen R. Hardis, age 76
Auditors: PricewaterhouseCoopersLLP

LOCATIONS

HQ: Lexmark International Inc.
740 W. New Circle Rd., Lexington KY 40550
Phone: 859-232-2000 **Fax:** 859-232-2403
Web: www.lexmark.com

2012 Sales

	$ mil.	% of total
US	1,695	45
Europe Middle East & Africa	1,320	35
Other regions	781	20
Total	**3,797**	**100**

PRODUCTS/OPERATIONS

2012 Sales

	$ mil.	% of total
Supplies	2,640	70
Printers	826	24
Software & other	331	6
Total	**3,797**	**100**

2012 Sales

	$ mil.	% of total
Imaging Solutions & Services	3,641	96
Perceptive Software	156	4
Total	**3,797**	**100**

Selected Products

Printers
- Dot matrix
- Ink jet
- Laser
- Multifunction
- Refurbished
- Wide-format

Software
- Drivers
- Network management

Supplies
- Labels
- Paper
- Print cartridges

COMPETITORS

Appian
Brother Industries
Canon
EMC
Epson
Hewlett-Packard
Hyland Software
IBM
Kofax plc
Konica Minolta
Kyocera Document Solutions
Oki Data
Open Text
Pegasystems
Ricoh Company
Samsung Electronics
Static Control Components
Xerox

HISTORICAL FINANCIALS

Company Type: Public

Income Statement FYE: December 31

	REVENUE ($ mil.)	NET INCOME ($ mil.)	NET PROFIT MARGIN	EMPLOYEES
12/11	4,173	320	7.7%	13,300
12/10	4,199	340	8.1%	13,200
12/09	3,879	145	3.8%	11,900
12/08	4,528	240	5.3%	14,000
12/07	4,973	300	6.0%	13,800
Annual Growth	(4.3%)	1.6%	—	(0.9%)

2011 Year-End Financials

Debt ratio: 17.85%
Return on equity: 23.06%
Cash ($ mil.): 356
Current ratio: 196.63
Long-term debt ($ mil.): 649
No. of shares (mil.): 71
Dividends
Yield: —
Payout: 6.07%
Market value ($ mil.): 2,361

	STOCK PRICE ($) FY Close	P/E High/Low		PER SHARE ($) Earnings	Dividends	Book Value
12/11	33.07	10	6	4.12	0.00	19.49
12/10	34.82	11	6	4.28	0.00	17.74
12/09	25.98	15	8	1.86	0.00	12.98
12/08	26.90	14	9	2.69	0.00	10.45
12/07	34.86	23	10	3.14	0.00	13.50
Annual Growth	(1.3%)	—	—	7.0%	—	9.6%

Liberty Global Inc

Liberty Global Inc. (LGI) may call the US home but Europe is its land of plenty. The holding company's subsidiaries provide cable-based TV phone and Internet access to about 20 million users both residential and commercial mostly in Europe. Its core market is Western Europe where it does business through UPC; in Germany through Unitymedia; in Switzerland through Cablecom and in Belgium through a controlling stake in Telenet. In the Ameicas LGI also serves Puerto Rico through Liberty Cablevision and Chile via an 80% stake in VTR Global Com SA. The company also offers satellite TV service. Its Chellomedia subsidiary which includes Chello Zone in the UK produces and distributes programming.

Operations The Chellomedia unit produces and distributes 45 channels (31 owned 14 joint ventures) including US favorites such as the Biography Channel the Food Network and the History Channel as well as Spain's popular cooking channel Canal Cocina owned by Canal Plus. Geographic

Reach Germany Switzerland and the Netherlands combine to represent 40% of LGI's sales. Altogether Liberty Global Inc. (LGI) operates in more than a dozen countries including Chile and Puerto Rico. With acquisitions in 2010 and 2011 LGI not only entered the German market but built it up to its largest revenue generator at 15% of sales. Switzerland and the Netherlands are nearly as significant for LGI with both only a couple of percentage points behind Germany. Belgium comes in at a fifth of sales with Chile nearly a tenth. LGI is the largest cable network operator in most of its markets; it is the second-largest in Germany the Netherlands and Romania. Financial Analysis LGI's revenue growth ended in 2010 when sales fell nearly 20% but the company bucked its historical trend by turning in a profit nearly $390 million. It got back to growth in 2011 with sales up 5% to $9.5 billion but fell back into the red with nearly $775 million in losses.

Mergers and Acquisitions LGI continues to make acquisitions and buy stakes in subsidiaries to position itself as the largest cable company outside the US. Its purchases in Germany are a striking example of this. LGI's entry into the German market came in 2010 when it bought Unitymedia for about E3.4 billion ($4.4 billion). Along with nearly 5 million subscribers LGI picked up Europe's largest cable infrastructure. The following year LGI paid $4.1 billion for Germany's third-largest cable services provider Kabel BW (KBW). Also that year LGI acquired Polish cable company Aster for about $785 million. In 2012 LGI found an opportunity to boost its market share in the Americas agreeing to buy San Juan Cable dba OneLink Communications for about $585 million. Once LGI combines it with existing operations it can add Puerto Rico to the list of countries in which LGI is the largest cable operator. To focus on its core market LGI exited Asia/Pacific by selling its stake in Jupiter Telecommunications Japan's top cable provider to Tokyo-based carrier KDDI for $4 billion in 2010. Two years later LGI sold AUSTAR its publicly traded satellite cable company in Australia to rival Foxtel for about A$ 1 billion ($1.1 billion). Ownership Chairman John Malone controls more than 35% of the company's voting power.

HISTORY

Liberty Global was formed through the 2005 merger of cable operators Liberty Media International (LMI) and UnitedGlobalCom (UGC) each of which was previously spun off from TV programming behemoth Liberty Media Corporation.

The company had a busy first fiscal year as it tweaked its holdings through divestitures and acquisitions. It unloaded its Norwegian and Belgian cable businesses (UPC Norge AS and UPC Belgium respectively) in 2005; the former was sold to a European private equity firm for about $540 million and the latter went to Belgian cable operator Telenet Group Holding for $245 million. LGI also sold its French cable subsidiary UPC France to Cinven in a 2006 deal valued at more than $1.5 billion.

The company's 2005 acquisitions included Swiss cable firm Cablecom ($2.2 billion) and Romanian telecommunications provider Astral Telecom. It also bought out Walt Disney's stake in IPS Multicanal which operated seven television channels in Spain and Portugal.

LGI expanded in Japan during 2008 when subsidiary J:COM acquired cable TV and Internet services provider Mediatti. The company was also active in Belgium where its Telenet subsidiary acquired cable TV assets from a handful of municipalities around the country.

EXECUTIVES

Chairman, John C. Malone, age 71
SVP Investor Relations and Corporate Communications, Frederick G. (Rick) Westerman III, age 46
President CEO and Director, Michael T. (Mike) Fries, age 49, $957,000 total compensation
EVP Co-CFO and Principal Accounting Officer, Bernard G. Dvorak, age 52, $507,000 total compensation
EVP Co-CFO and Principal Financial Officer, Charles H. R. (Charlie) Bracken, age 46, $595,643 total compensation
SVP and Chief Policy Officer, Manuel Kohnstamm
Corporate Communications, Bert Holtkamp
President Liberty Global Latin America and Liberty Cablevision of Puerto Rico; CEO VTR, Mauricio Ramos, age 44
SVP and Chief Strategy Officer; President Chellomedia, Shane O'Neill, age 51, $656,469 total compensation
EVP Secretary and General Counsel, Bryan H. Hall, age 49
SVP Global Human Resources, Amy M. Blair, age 46
EVP and CTO, Balan Nair, age 45
SVP Programming, Robert M. (Bob) Leighton, age 56
EVP European Broadband Operations, Diederik Karsten
Investor Relations, Christopher (Chris) Noyes
Director Corporate Communications, Hanne Wolf
Investor Relations, Molly Bruce
SVP and Chief Development Officer, Andrea Salvato
SVP and Chief Strategy Officer, James Ryan
Director, Miranda Curtis, age 56
President CEO and Director, Michael T. (Mike) Fries, age 49
Director, J. C. Sparkman, age 79
Director, John P. Cole Jr., age 82
Director, John W. Dick, age 74
Director, Paul A. Gould, age 66
Director, David E. Rapley, age 70
Director, Larry E. Romrell, age 72
Director, J. David Wargo, age 58
Director, Richard R. Green, age 74
Auditors: KPMGLLP

LOCATIONS

HQ: Liberty Global Inc.
12300 Liberty Blvd., Englewood CO 80112
Phone: 303-220-6600 **Fax:** 303-220-6601
Web: www.lgi.com

2011 Sales

	$ mil.	% of total
Europe		
UPC Broadband		
Germany	1,450	15
Switzerland	1,292	13
The Netherlands	1,273	13
Austria	453	5
Ireland	430	4
Poland	390	4
Hungary	270	3
The Czech Republic	251	3
Romania	143	2
Slovakia	65	1
Direct-to-home satellite	122	1
Telenet (Belgium)	1,918	20
Chellomedia		
Poland	118	1
The Netherlands	108	1
Spain	73	1
Hungary	66	1
Other	133	1
The Americas		
VTR (Chile)	889	9
Other Americas	144	2
Adjustments	(86.4)	-
Total	**9,510**	**100**

PRODUCTS/OPERATIONS

2011 Sales

	$ mil.	% of total
Subscription		
Video	4,405	46
Broadband Internet	2,203	23
Telephony	1,294	14
Other	1,607	17
Total	**9,510**	**100**

2011 Sales

	$ mil.	% of total
UPC Broadband	6,144	64
Telenet (Belgium)	1,918	20
VTR (Chile)	889	9
Chellomedia (programming)	500	5
Other	144	2
Adjustments	(86.4)	-
Total	**9,510**	**100**

Countries of Operation
Austria
Belgium
The Czech Republic
Chile
Germany
Hungary
Ireland
The Netherland
Poland
Puerto Rico
Romania
Slovakia
Switzerland

COMPETITORS

AAPT
Asia Satellite Telecommunications
BBC
BSkyB
BT
Cableuropa
CANAL+
Central European Media
Deutsche Telekom
DNA Ltd.
Elisa Corporation
Eutelsat
FOXTEL
France Telecom
ITV
Kabel Deutschland
KPN
M6
Net Servicos de Comunicac?o
NHK
Optus
PCCW Ltd.
PrimaCom
SES Group
Sky Network Television
Swisscom
Tele2
Telecom Corporation of New Zealand
Telecomunicaciones de Chile
Telefonica
Telekom Austria
Telenor
TeliaSonera
Telstra
TF1

HISTORICAL FINANCIALS

Company Type: Public

Income Statement FYE: December 31

	REVENUE ($ mil.)	NET INCOME ($ mil.)	NET PROFIT MARGIN	EMPLOYEES
12/11	9,510	(772)	—	22,000
12/10	9,016	388	4.3%	20,000
12/09	11,080	(412)	—	23,000
12/08	10,561	(788)	—	22,300
12/07	9,003	(422)	—	22,000
Annual Growth	1.4%	—	—	0.0%

2011 Year-End Financials

Debt ratio: 68.00%
Return on equity: (-27.54)%
Cash ($ mil.): 1,651
Current ratio: 90.53
Long-term debt ($ mil.): 24,573

No. of shares (mil.): 274
Dividends
Yield: —
Payout: —
Market value ($ mil.): 11,282

	STOCK PRICE ($)	P/E		PER SHARE ($)		
	FY Close	High/Low		Earnings	Dividends	Book Value
12/11	41.03	—	—	(2.93)	0.00	10.20
12/10	35.38	26	14	1.54	0.00	12.55
12/09	21.89	—	—	(1.53)	0.00	11.66
12/08	15.92	—	—	(2.50)	0.00	12.06
12/07	39.19	—	—	(1.11)	0.00	16.48
Annual Growth	1.2%	—	—	—	—	(11.3%)

Liberty Interactive Corp

Liberty Interactive Corp. (formerly Liberty Media Corp.) stands by your right to shop at home and online. The company is focused on video and e-commerce through its QVC home-shopping subsidiary and numerous online retail businesses. They include e-tailer Provide Commerce online costume and party supply provider Celebrate Interactive (dba Celebrate Express) Backcountry.com Bodybuilding.com the online invitation site Evite and Internet travel service Expedia among other activities. Liberty Interactive Corp. was formed in 2011 when its predecessor restructured by merging and splitting off its Liberty Capital and Liberty Starz businesses under a newly-formed holding company also called Liberty Media.

HISTORY

The man who would be king of cable programming got his start on the hardware end of the business. In 1970 John Malone became president of General Instrument's Jerrold Communications subsidiary which supplied equipment to the then-new cable TV industry. One of Jerrold's customers was Bob Magness a former Texas rancher who in the 1950s started the company that eventually became Denver-based cable operator Tele-Communications Inc. (TCI). In the early 1970s TCI struggled in need of leadership. In 1973 the 32-year-old Malone was named CEO of TCI.

Malone restructured TCI's debt in 1977 paving the way for expansion into bigger cable markets after deregulation in 1984. He also acquired programming buying stakes in Black Entertainment Television (33% 1979 sold to Viacom in 2001) the Discovery Channel (14% 1986) and American Movie Classics (50% 1986). In 1987 TCI helped save debt-plagued Turner Broadcasting and came away with 12% of Turner Broadcasting's stock.

Due in part to antitrust pressure from government regulators in 1991 TCI spun off much of its programming assets along with interests in 14 cable systems as Liberty Media. Malone became chairman and principal shareholder. In its first year the company launched Court TV in a joint venture and introduced film channel Encore. The next year it bought an interest in the Home Shopping Network (which became USA Networks in 1998 and later changed names to USA Interactive in 2002 InterActiveCorp in 2003 and finally IAC/InterActiveCorp in 2004).

In 1994 TCI reacquired Liberty Media; it issued a tracking stock the next year to reflect the value of Liberty's program assets. Also in 1995 Liberty Media and News Corp. joined forces to create FOX/Liberty Networks a national sports network designed to compete with Disney's ESPN.

Control of TCI's stake in Turner Broadcasting was passed to Liberty Media after Turner was acquired by Time Warner in 1996 giving Liberty Media a 9% holding in entertainment giant Time Warner. (AOL acquired Time Warner in 2001 to form AOL Time Warner but the company resumed the Time Warner name in 2003.) Magness died in 1996 and Malone became TCI's chairman. In 1998 Liberty Media and BET's former chairman Robert Johnson bought out BET in a $380 million deal.

AT&T bought TCI for $55 billion in 1999 to form AT&T Broadband. As part of the deal AT&T folded TCI Ventures into Liberty Media including stakes in Sprint PCS (now Sprint FON) United Video Satellite Group (now Gemstar-TV Guide) General Instrument (Motorola bought General Instrument in 2000) and TCI International and issued a new tracking stock for Liberty Media. The company later traded its interest in FOX/Liberty Networks (now called FOX Sports Net) for an 8% interest (later increased to 19%) in News Corp. and agreed to buy Associated Group and a stake in wireless communications company Teligent (the deal closed in early 2000). It called off a deal to acquire Ascent Entertainment Group provider of in-room entertainment services because Ascent could not sell its sports teams.

In 2000 Liberty Media invested about $400 million in Cendant (now Avis Budget Group) and about $200 million in media conglomerate PRIMEDIA and it bought about 20% of Canadian media group Corus Entertainment. It also finalized a deal to buy 60% of postproduction businesses Todd-AO (renaming it Liberty Livewire). Later that year it revived a dead deal and bought the majority of Ascent Media. Liberty Media promptly sold Ascent's sports teams to Wal-Mart heir Stan Kroenke. That year Liberty Media folded various Latin American broadband assets into UnitedGlobalCom in exchange for a 45% stake and merged Japan-based Jupiter Telecommunications (35%) with Microsoft's Titus Communications.

In 2001 AT&T spun off Liberty Media as part of a plan to restructure the phone giant into four separate companies. The firm came solely under Malone's control. In fall 2001 the company agreed to buy most of Germany's Deutsche Telekom's cable assets for $4.8 billion. (The deal fell through in early 2002 when German regulators nixed the purchase.) Shortly afterward Liberty Media agreed to buy the network assets of Germany's #3 cable operator TeleColumbus owned by Deutsche Bank. This deal also failed when it did not meet government conditions.

The company restructured its deal with European cable operator UnitedGlobalCom in late 2001 upping its proposed 45% stake to 72% and retaining its Latin American assets. Also that year Liberty Media contributed its ownership of Ascent Entertainment and 89% stake in Liberty Satellite in exchange for shares in Liberty Satellite & Technology Inc. In early 2003 the firm rebranded Liberty Livewire under the Ascent Media name. Later that year the company bought the remaining 10% stake in Ascent Media that it did not own.

Liberty Media completed its purchase of the remaining UnitedGlobalCom stake that it did not own in 2004. Later that year the company spun off all of its international assets (including UnitedGlobalCom) into a new firm called Liberty Media International. Liberty Media no longer owns any interest in the international business. And in 2005 the company spun off Ascent Media and its stake in Discovery Communications by placing those assets in a new public company (Discovery Holding) in which it no longer has any interest.

In August 2005 president and CEO Robert Bennett announced that he would retire but remain a board member in 2006. Former TCI head Malone took over the CEO position briefly until the company named former Oracle executive Gregory Maffei near the end of 2005. Maffei officially took over the role of president and CEO in March 2006. His spot at the top was secured through 2014 in late 2009.

Liberty Media bought Provide Commerce an e-tailer of flowers and perishable food items early in 2006. The purchase furthered its push into online and television shopping. In May the company changed its name to Liberty Media Corp. and reorganized to form two tracking stocks: Liberty Interactive Group and Liberty Capital Group. Also in May the company sold its 50% stake in Court TV to Time Warner for $735 million. In August Liberty Media purchased Buyseasons operator of the BuyCostumes.com website to add to Liberty Interactive's growing stable of non-store retail operations.

In May 2007 the firm acquired the Atlanta Braves baseball team from Time Warner. The complex deal involved Liberty Media giving up part of its stake in Time Warner in exchange for the baseball team a collection of craft magazines owned by Time Inc. and nearly $1 billion in cash. Also in 2007 Liberty Media sold its controlling interests in OpenTV and On Command. Its Liberty Genius an indirect wholly owned subsidiary of Liberty acquired FUN Technologies in December. FUN provides online and interactive sports games and sports information.

In March 2008 a third tracking stock was formed: Liberty Entertainment Group is traded on the NASDAQ stock exchange and holds a 48% stake in The DIRECTV Group among other Liberty Media subsidiaries and investments. In late August Liberty Media acquired Celebrate Express a direct marketer of party supplies and costumes for about $31 million.

The company announced its decision to spin off Liberty Entertainment in September 2008.

In March 2009 Liberty Media invested $530 million in SIRIUS MX Radio in the form of high-interest loans in exchange for a 40% equity stake in the troubled company and seats on its board of directors.

In September 2011 Liberty Media Corp. changed its name to Liberty Interactive Corp. following the split-off of its Liberty Capital and Liberty Starz tracking stocks.

EXECUTIVES

Chairman, John C. Malone, age 71, $2,600 total compensation
EVP and General Counsel, Charles Y. Tanabe, age 61, $875,500 total compensation
SVP and Treasurer, David J. A. Flowers, age 56, $650,000 total compensation
SVP and CFO, Christopher W. (Chris) Shean, age 47, $650,000 total compensation
President CEO and Director, Gregory B. (Greg) Maffei, age 50, $1,000,000 total compensation
President and CEO Starz LLC, Chris Albrecht
SVP, Albert E. Rosenthaler, age 52, $650,000 total compensation
SVP, Michael P. Zeisser, age 47
SVP, Mark D. Carleton, age 50

VP Deputy General Counsel and Secretary, Pamela L. Coe
Investor Relations, Courtnee Ulrich
Investor Relations, Reggie Salazar
Investor Relations, Heather Lipp
Media Relations, Amanda Cheslock
Director, Robert R. Bennett, age 54
President CEO and Director, Gregory B. (Greg) Maffei, age 50
Director, Donne F. Fisher, age 73
Director, Larry E. Romrell, age 72
Director, Andrea L. Wong, age 45
Director, David E. Rapley, age 70
Director, M. La Voy Robison, age 77
Director, Evan D. Malone, age 41
Director, M. Ian G. Gilchrist, age 62
Auditors: KPMGLLP

LOCATIONS

HQ: Liberty Interactive Corporation
12300 Liberty Blvd., Englewood CO 80112
Phone: 720-875-5300 **Fax:** 765-456-6905
Web: www.haynesintl.com

2011 Sales

	$ mil.	% of total
US	6,670	69
Japan	1,133	12
Germany	1,068	11
Other countries	745	8
Total	**9,616**	**100**

PRODUCTS/OPERATIONS

2011 Sales

	$ mil.	% of total
QVC	8,268	86
E-commerce	1,348	14
Total	**9,616**	**100**

Selected Subsidiaries and Investments

Backcountry.com Inc. (87% online backcountry gear)
Bodybuilding.com LLC (86% online bodybuilding products and equipment)
Celebrate Interactive Holdings LLC (100% online costume and party supply retail)
Evite Inc. (100% online party planning)
Expedia Inc. (25% online travel)
Gifts.com (100% online gifts)
HSN Inc. (36% online and TV shopping)
LMC Right Start (100% baby products)
LOCKERZ (38%)
Provide Commerce Inc. (100% e-commerce)
QVC (100% home shopping network)
TripAdvisor (57% online travel site)

COMPETITORS

1-800-FLOWERS
Access TV
Amazon.com
Bluestem Brands
FTD
Hallmark
Harry & David Holdings
IAC
KaBloom
Orbitz Worldwide
priceline.com
Teleflora
Travelocity
ValueVision Media
Viacom
Wal-Mart

HISTORICAL FINANCIALS

Company Type: Public

Income Statement

FYE: December 31

	REVENUE ($ mil.)	NET INCOME ($ mil.)	NET PROFIT MARGIN	EMPLOYEES
12/11	9,616	912	9.5%	22,077
12/10	10,982	1,892	17.2%	24,073
12/09	10,158	6,462	63.6%	23,073
12/08	10,084	3,479	34.5%	22,075
12/07	9,423	2,114	22.4%	19,070
Annual Growth	0.5%	(19.0%)	—	3.7%

2011 Year-End Financials

Debt ratio: 34.83%
Return on equity: 14.05%
Cash ($ mil.): 847
Current ratio: 87.44
Long-term debt ($ mil.): 4,850
No. of shares (mil.): 578
Dividends
Yield: —
Payout: —
Market value ($ mil.): 9,381

	STOCK PRICE ($) FY Close	P/E High/Low	PER SHARE ($) Earnings	Dividends	Book Value
12/11	16.22	— —	(0.00)	0.00	11.23
12/10	15.77	— —	(0.00)	0.00	15.41
12/09	10.84	— —	(0.00)	0.00	13.56
12/08	3.12	— —	(0.00)	0.00	16.24
12/07	19.08	— —	(0.00)	0.00	(0.00)
Annual Growth	(4.0%)	— —	—	—	—

Liberty Mutual Holding Co., Inc.

LOCATIONS

HQ: Liberty Mutual Holding Co., Inc.
175 Berkeley Street, Boston, MA 02116
Phone:
Web: www.libertymutualgroup.com

HISTORICAL FINANCIALS

Company Type:

Income Statement

FYE: December 31

	REVENUE ($ mil.)	NET INCOME ($ mil.)	NET PROFIT MARGIN	EMPLOYEES
12/11	34,671	365	1.1%	0
12/10	33,193	1,678	5.1%	0
12/09	31,035	1,023	3.3%	0
Annual Growth	5.7%	(40.3%)	—	—

2011 Year-End Financials

Debt ratio: 4.74%—
Return on equity: 2.06%
Cash ($ mil.): 5,972
Current ratio: 14538.05
Long-term debt ($ mil.): 5,341
Dividends
Yield: —
Payout: —
Market value ($ mil.): —

Lilly (Eli) & Co.

Healthwise Eli Lilly hopes everything will come up roses for you. Best known for its neuroscience products the company also makes endocinology (hormone-related) oncology (cancer-related) and cardiovascular medicines for a wide variety of ailments. Its top-selling drug is Zyprexa (schizophrenia and bipolar disorder) although patent rights for the drug expired in 2011. Other top-sellers include Cymbalta (depression anxiety disorder and other indications) Alimta (lung cancer) and Humalog insulin (diabetes). Lilly also makes erectile dysfunction medication Cialis and osteoporosis drug Evista; anti-infective agents; and animal health products. Lilly sells its products in some 130 countries.

HISTORY

Colonel Eli Lilly pharmacist and Union officer in the Civil War started Eli Lilly and Company in 1876 with $1300. His process of gelatin-coating pills led to sales of nearly $82000 in 1881. Later the company made gelatin capsules which it still sells. Lilly died in 1898 and his son and two grandsons ran the business until 1953.

Eli Lilly began extracting insulin from the pancreases of hogs and cattle in 1923; 6000 cattle glands or 24000 hog glands made one ounce of the substance. Other products created in the 1920s and 1930s included antiseptic Merthiolate sedative Seconal and treatments for pernicious anemia and heart disease. In 1947 the company began selling diethylstilbestrol (DES) a drug to prevent miscarriages. Eli Lilly researchers isolated the antibiotic erythromycin from a species of mold found in the Philippines in 1952. Lilly was also the major supplier of Salk polio vaccine.

The company enjoyed a 70% share of the DES market by 1971 when researchers noticed that a rare form of cervical cancer afflicted many of the daughters of women who had taken the drug. The FDA restricted the drug's use and Lilly found itself on the receiving (and frequently losing) end of a number of trailblazing product-liability suits that stretched into the 1990s.

The firm diversified in the 1970s buying Elizabeth Arden (cosmetics 1971; sold 1987) and IVAC (medical instruments 1977). It launched such products as analgesic Darvon and antibiotic Ceclor.

Lilly's 1982 launch of Humulin a synthetic insulin developed by Genentech made it the first company to market a genetically engineered product. In 1986 the company introduced Prozac; that year it also bought biotech firm Hybritech for $300 million (sold in 1995 for less than $10 million). In 1988 Lilly introduced anti-ulcerative Axid. It founded pesticides and herbicides maker DowElanco with Dow Chemical in 1989.

Trying to find a new product outlet the firm bought pharmacy benefit management company PCS Health Systems from what is now McKesson in 1994. But an FTC mandate to offer rival drugs and a lack of mail-order sales contributed to poor results which ultimately led Lilly to sell PCS to Rite Aid and exit this arena completely in 1998.

Eli Lilly in 1995 bought medical communications network developer Integrated Medical Systems. That year the firm and developer Centocor introduced ReoPro a blood-clot inhibitor used in angioplasties. The next year it launched antipsychotic Zyprexa Humalog and Gemzar and Prozac was approved to treat bulimia nervosa.

In 1997 the firm sold its DowElanco stake to Dow. In 1998 the Lilly Endowment passed the Ford Foundation as the US's largest charity largely due to Prozac (it has since been passed by the Bill & Melinda Gates Foundation). That year Lilly began trying to stop Chinese drugmakers from infringing on its patents for Prozac's active ingredient.

In 1999 a US federal judge found the firm illegally promoted osteoporosis drug Evista as a breast cancer preventative similar to AstraZeneca's Nolvadex. Lilly halted tests on its variation of heart drug Moxonidine after 53 patients died. Also that year Zyprexa was approved to treat bipolar disorder.

In 2000 the firm began marketing Prozac under the Sarafem name for severe premenstrual syndrome. A federal appeals court knocked more than two years off Prozac's patent reducing the expected 2003 expiration date to 2001 creating a negative impact on Lilly's annual sales (Prozac had accounted for 30% of revenues). Lilly suffered another blow when a potential successor to Prozac failed in clinical trials and became embroiled in legal maneuverings with generics maker Barr Pharmaceuticals.

While the firm fretted over Prozac and its patents it continued work to find its next blockbuster. In 2000 Lilly and partner ICOS announced favorable results from a study of erectile dysfunction treatment Cialis which was approved in Europe in 2002 and in the US in 2004. (Several years later Lilly acquired ICOS and with it full ownership of the Cialis franchise.)

In 2001 Lilly bought a minority stake in Isis Pharmaceuticals a developer of antisense drugs and licensed from it an antisense lung cancer drug. Also that year the firm launched Lilly BioVentures a venture fund aimed at private biotech startup companies. In 2002 the company settled with eight states in an infringement-of-privacy case involving the company's accidental disclosure of e-mail addresses for more than 600 Prozac patients.

In late 2004 the druggernaut was one of several pharmas hit by bad news about drug side effects. Lilly announced its attention-deficit disorder drug Strattera had been linked to rare liver problems. The company agreed to add warning labels about the potential side effects to the drug's packaging and advertisements. The company also began facing trouble over Zyprexa as consumer lawsuits claiming diabetes and high blood pressure began pouring in. The majority of suits were settled in 2005 and 2007 for some $1.2 billion.

Generalized anxiety disorder drug Cymbalta was approved by the FDA and released in 2006 and osteoporosis drug Evista was approved for an expanded indication as a breast cancer preventative for postmenopausal women in 2007.

Also in 2007 the company acquired and absorbed development partner ICOS for $2.1 billion; the deal gave Lilly full ownership of Viagra-competitor Cialis. Lilly dropped a joint-development effort with another partner Alkermes for an inhaled insulin device in 2008.

The company gradually reduced its workforce by more than 10% between 2003 and 2008 to fight off the effects of generic competition and other challenges. Other restructuring measures included an employee attrition plan announced in 2007 a management restructuring in 2008 and a manufacturing consolidation program launched in 2008.

After a lengthy lawsuit regarding its patents for its top seller Zyprexa a federal judge ruled in Lilly's favor in 2008 against generic manufacturers IVAX Dr. Reddy's Laboratories and Teva Pharmaceutical Industries. Federal courts ruled that the drug's patents would remain valid until October 2011.

To fuel growth in the biopharmaceuticals market the firm completed a $1 billion biotech research facility in Indianapolis in 2008. It further expanded through the 2008 acquisition of biotech firm ImClone for about $6.5 billion; ImClone began operating as a research subsidiary of Lilly following the transaction. ImClone already had one approved blockbuster therapy Erbitux for colorectal and head/neck cancers and was developing numerous other cancer therapy candidates. Lilly also expanded its biotech oncology program earlier that year by purchasing development partner SGX Pharmaceuticals for $64 million. SGX was absorbed into Lilly's research operations.

The company agreed in 2009 to pay $1.4 billion in government fines to settle allegations over its marketing tactics for Zyprexa.

EXECUTIVES

SVP Corporate Strategy and Business Development, Gino Santini, age 55
Chairman President and CEO, John C. Lechleiter, age 58, $1,483,333 total compensation
VP Six Sigma, Elizabeth H. Klimes
VP Global Public Policy Pricing Reimbursement and Access (PRA) and International Corporate Affairs, Newton F. Crenshaw
VP and General Counsel, Alecia A. DeCoudreaux, age 56
EVP Science and Technology; President Lilly Research Laboratories, Jan M. Lundberg, age 58
SVP and General Counsel, Robert A. Armitage, age 63, $811,167 total compensation
SVP Enterprise Risk Management and Chief Ethics and Compliance Officer, Anne Nobles, age 55
SVP Finance and Treasurer, Thomas W. Grein, age 60
VP Global Communications, Jeffrey A. (Jeff) Winton, age 54
SVP Information Technology and CIO, Michael C. (Mike) Heim, age 57
SVP Development Center of Excellence Lily Research Laboratories, Thomas Verhoeven
EVP Global Services and CFO, Derica W. Rice, age 47, $892,500 total compensation
VP Lilly Research Labs Operations and Lily Resarch Laboratories Europe, Andrew M. Dahlem
VP Portfolio Project Management Lily Research Laboratories, Johanna C. Egan
VP Human Resources - Global Compensation and Human Resources Services, Sharon L. Sullivan
SVP; President Emerging Markets, Jacques Tapiero, age 53
President Lilly USA, Alex M. Azar II, age 45
SVP Corporate Affairs and Communications, Barton R. (Bart) Peterson, age 53
VP Global External Research and Development Lilly Research Laboratories, Robert W. Armstrong
VP Corporate Strategic Planning, Peter J. Johnson
VP Global Diversity, Patricia A. Martin
SVP Global Quality, Fionnuala Walsh, age 52
VP and Chief Procurement Officer, James A. Ward
VP Neuroscience Cardiovascular Acute Care Urology Product Development Lilly Bio-Medicines, J. Anthony Ware
SVP; President Elanco Animal Health, Jeffrey N. (Jeff) Simmons, age 44
SVP; President Diabetes Business Unit, Enrique A. Conterno, age 45
SVP Global API Manufacturing, E. Paul Ahern
President European Operations, Karim Bitar
VP Biotechnology Discovery Research; President Applied Molecular Evolution Lily Research Laboratories, Thomas F. Bumol
President Manufacturing Operations, Maria Crowe, age 52
Chief Medical Officer; SVP Development Center of Excellence, Timothy J. (Tim) Garnett
SVP Product Research and Development Lily Research Laboratories, William F. Heath Jr.
VP Corporate Engineering and Continuous Improvement, W. Darin Moody
SVP and Controller, Elizabeth G. O'Farrell
VP MS&T Supply Chain Global Packaging, Andreas (Andrew) Witzel
President and General Manager Lilly Japan, Alfonso G. (Chito) Zulueta
SVP; President Lilly Oncology, Susan (Sue) Mahony, age 47
SVP and President Lilly Bio-Medicines, David Ricks, age 44
VP External Communications and Corporate Responsibility, Angela M. Sekston
Senior Director Lilly USA Bio-Medicines Diabetes and Oncology, Tarra Ryker
SVP Human Resources and Diversity, Steve Fry, age 46
SVP Marketing and Chief Marketing Officer, Robert B. Brown
Senior Director Global Corporate Communications, Ed Sagebiel
Director Diversity and Human Relations Communications, Janice Chavers
Manager Corporate Communications, Carole Copeland
Director Government Legislation and Access and Public Policy Issues, Greg Kueterman
Director Corporate Responsibility, David J. Marbaugh
Director Corporate Financial Performance and Parnerships and Alliances, Mark Taylor
Director Lilly USA Communications, J. Scott MacGregor
Associate Consultant Lilly USA Communications, Tammy Lieber
Director Lilly Bio-Medicines, Morry Smulevitz
Manager Lilly Bio-Medicines, Tamara Hull
Manager Lilly Bio-Medicines, Sonja Popp-Stahly
Manager Lilly Bio-Medicines, Stefanie Prodouz
Manager Lilly Bio-Medicines, Teresa Shewman
Director Lilly Diabetes, Kelley Murphy
Manager Lilly Diabetes, Carole Puls
Manager Lilly Diabetes, Kindra Strupp
Director Lilly Oncology, Carla Cox
Manager Lilly Oncology, Amy Sousa
Director Emerging Markets, Eunice Kim
Director Lilly Development Center of Excellence and Lilly Research, Christine Van Marter
Manager Lilly Development Center of Excellence and Lilly Research, Judy Kay Moore
Manager Global Communications Lilly Development Center of Excellence and Lilly Research, Colleen Parr Dekker
Vice President of China Research, Bei Zhang
SVP and Chief Ethics and Compliance Officer, Melissa Barnes
Director, R. David (Dave) Hoover, age 67
Director, Kathi P. Seifert
Director, Michael L. (Mike) Eskew, age 62
Director, Sir Winfried F. W. (Win) Bischoff, age 71
Director, Douglas R. (Doug) Oberhelman, age 59
Director, J. Erik Fyrwald, age 52
Director, Alfred G. Gilman, age 70
Director, Karen N. Horn, age 68
Director, Martin S. Feldstein, age 72
Director, Ellen R. Marram, age 65
Director, Franklyn G. Prendergast, age 67
Director, Raul Alvarez, age 56

Independent Director, Katherine Baicker
Auditors: Ernst&YoungLLP

LOCATIONS

HQ: Eli Lilly and Company
Lilly Corporate Center 893 S. Delaware St.,
Indianapolis IN 46285
Phone: 317-276-2000 **Fax:** 317-276-4878
Web: www.lilly.com

2011 Sales

	$ mil.	% of total
US	12,977	53
Europe	5,290	22
Japan	2,104	9
Other regions	3,914	16
Total	24,286	100

PRODUCTS/OPERATIONS

2011 Sales

	$ mil.	% of total
Neurosciences	9,723	41
Endocrinology	6,135	27
Oncology	3,744	16
Cardiovascular	2,171	9
Animal health	1,391	6
Other pharmaceuticals	214	1
Total	24,286	100

2011 Sales

	$ mil.	% of total
Zyprexa	4,622	19
Cymbalta	4,161	17
Alimta	2,461	10
Humalog	2,367	10
Cialis	1,875	8
Animal health products	1,678	7
Humulin	1,248	5
Evista	1,066	4
Forteo	949	4
Strattera	620	2
Gemzar	452	2
Other pharmaceuticals	2,100	9
Collaboration & other	681	3
Total	24,286	100

Selected Products and Indications

Neuroscience
- Cymbalta (duloxetine hydrocholoride; depression anxiety pain; also for managing fibromyalgia and chronic musculoskeletal pain in the US)
- Prozac (fluoxetine hydrochloride; depression panic disorder obsessive-compulsive disorder and bulimia nervosa)
- Strattera (atomoxetine hydrochloride ADHD)
- Symbyax (olanzapine and fluoxetine hydrochloride bipolar and treatment-resistant depression)
- Zyprexa (olanzapine schizophrenia and bipolar)
- Zyprexa Relprevv/Zypadhera in the EU (long-acting injectable Zyprexa)

Endocrinology (including diabetes)
- Actos (pioglitazone hydrochloride type 2 diabetes)
- Alimta (non-small cell lung cancer)
- Axiron (testosterone topical for testosterone deficiency)
- Erbitux (colorectal cancers head and neck cancers)
- Evista (raloxifene hydrochloride osteoporosis and breast cancer prevention in postmenopausal women)
- Forteo (osteoporosis)
- Gemzar (pancreatic cancer metastatic breast cancer non-small cell lung cancer; bladder cancer in the EU)
- Humalog (insulin lispro injection rDNA origin; diabetes)
- Humalog Mix 75/25 (75% Insulin lispro protamine suspension 25% insulin lispro injection rDNA origin; diabetes)
- Humalog Mix 50/50 (50% Insulin lispro protamine suspension 50% insulin lispro injection rDNA origin; diabetes)
- Humalog Pen (insulin lispro rDNA origin; diabetes)
- Humatrope (somatropin for injection rDNA origin; growth disorders)
- Humulin (human insulin rDNA origin; diabetes)
- Humulin Pen (human insulin rDNA origin; diabetes)
- Tradjenta (type 2 diabetes)

Oncology (cancer)
- Alimta (pemetrexed non-small cell lung cancer and malignant pleural mesothelioma)
- Erbitux (colorectal head and neck cancers; from ImClone)
- Gemzar (gemcitabine hydrochloride; pancreatic breast lung bladder and ovarian cancers)

Cardiovascular
- Adcirca (pulmonary arterial hypertension)
- Cialis (tadalafil erectile dysfunction; benign prostatic hyperplasia in US)
- Efient/Effient (atherothrombotic events)
- Livalo (statin high cholesterol)
- ReoPro (percutaneous coronary intervention)

Animal Health
- Apralan (antibiotic to control enteric infections in calves and swine)
- Coban Monteban and Maxiban (anticoccidal for poultry)
- Comfortis (flea infestation prevention tablets for dogs)
- Micotil Pulmotil and Pulmotil AC (antibiotics for respiratory disease in cattle swine and poultry respectively)
- Paylean Optaflexx (leanness and performance enhancers for swine and cattle respectively)
- Posilac (protein supplement for enhanced milk productivity in cows)
- Reconcile (separation anxiety for dogs)
- Rumensin (feed additive)
- Surmax/Maxus (performance enhancer for swine and poultry)
- Trifexis (chewable tablet for dogs to prevent flea infestations and heartworm disease and control intestinal parasite infections)
- Tylan (antibiotic)

Other pharmaceuticals
- Ceclor (bacterial infections)
- Vancocin (staphylococcal infections)

COMPETITORS

Abbott Labs	Merck KGaA
Amgen	Mylan
AstraZeneca	Myriad Genetics
Baxter International	Novartis
Bayer AG	Novo Nordisk
Boehringer Ingelheim	Pfizer
Bristol-Myers Squibb	Ranbaxy Laboratories
Dr. Reddy' s	Roche Holding
Elan	Sanofi
Forest Labs	Shire
GlaxoSmithKline	Takeda Pharmaceutical
Johnson & Johnson	Teva
Merck	

HISTORICAL FINANCIALS

Company Type: Public

Income Statement

FYE: December 31

	REVENUE ($ mil.)	NET INCOME ($ mil.)	NET PROFIT MARGIN	EMPLOYEES
12/11	24,286	4,347	17.9%	38,080
12/10	23,076	5,069	22.0%	38,350
12/09	21,836	4,328	19.8%	40,360
12/08	20,378	(2,071)	—	40,450
12/07	18,633	2,953	15.8%	40,600
Annual Growth	6.8%	10.2%	—	(1.6%)

2011 Year-End Financials

Debt ratio: 20.76%	No. of shares (mil.): 1,157
Return on equity: 32.11%	Dividends
Cash ($ mil.): 6,897	Yield: —
Current ratio: 159.54	Payout: 50.26%
Long-term debt ($ mil.): 5,464	Market value ($ mil.): 48,118

	STOCK PRICE ($) FY Close	P/E High/Low		PER SHARE ($) Earnings	Dividends	Book Value
12/11	41.56	11	9	3.90	0.00	11.70
12/10	35.04	8	7	4.58	1.96	10.78
12/09	35.71	10	7	3.94	1.96	8.29
12/08	40.27	—	—	(1.89)	1.88	5.93
12/07	53.39	22	18	2.71	1.70	12.05
Annual Growth	(6.1%)	—	—	9.5%	—	(0.7%)

Limited Brands Inc.

Limited Brands is as much of a shopping-mall mainstay as food courts and teenagers. The company operates about 2940 specialty stores throughout North America primarily under the Victoria's Secret Bath & Body Works (BBW) and La Senza (in Canada) banners as well as corresponding websites and catalogs. Originally focused on apparel Limited Brands sold its ailing Limited Stores and Express chains –leaving the company free to focus on two core businesses: Victoria's Secret and BBW. Limited Brands also owns apparel importer MAST Industries accessories boutique operator Henri Bendel apothecary C.O. Bigelow and The White Barn Candle Co. Limited Brands was founded in 1963 by its chairman Leslie Wexner.

HISTORY

After a disagreement with his father in 1963 over the operation of the family store (Leslie's) Leslie Wexner then 26 opened the first Limited store in Columbus Ohio with $5000 borrowed from his aunt. The company was named from Wexner's desire to do one product line well –moderately priced fashionable attire for teenagers and young women.

When The Limited went public in 1969 it had only five stores but the rapid development of large covered malls spurred growth to 100 stores by 1976. Two years later The Limited acquired MAST Industries an international apparel purchasing and importing company. The company opened Express in 1980 to serve the teen market.

The Limited grew with acquisitions including the 1982 purchases of Lane Bryant (large sizes) and Victoria's Secret (lingerie). That year it formed the Brylane fashion catalog division and acquired Roaman's a bricks-and-mortar and catalog merchandiser of plus sizes.

Wexner bought The Lerner Stores (budget women's apparel) and Henri Bendel (high fashion) in 1985 sportswear retailer Abercrombie & Fitch (A&F) in 1988 and London-based perfumer Penhaligon's in 1990 (sold in 1997). The Limited introduced several in-store shops including Cacique (French lingerie) in 1988 and Limited Too (girls' fashions) which were later expanded into stand-alone stores. It also launched Structure (men's sportswear) in 1989 and Bath & Body Works shops in 1990. All of these stores were in malls often strategically clustered together.

The company closed many The Limited and Lerner stores in 1993 and sold 60% of its Brylane catalog unit to Freeman Spogli (Brylane went public in 1997). It opened four Bath & Body Works stores in the UK (its first non-US stores) to compete with British rival The Body Shop.

In 1994 The Limited bought Galyan's Trading Company a chain of sporting goods superstores. The company began spinning off its businesses while keeping controlling stakes; it spun off Intimate Brands (Victoria's Secret Cacique and Bath & Body Works) in 1995 and A&F in 1996. (The Limited sold its remaining 84% in A&F in 1998.)

The Limited closed more than 100 of its women's apparel stores in 1997 and Intimate Brands shuttered the Cacique chain; the next year The Limited closed nearly 300 more stores companywide (excluding the Intimate Brands chains) and the majority of its Henri Bendel stores.

In 1998 The Limited launched White Barn Candle Co. (candle and home fragrance stores). The following year the company spun off Limited Too its most successful chain as Too Inc. and reduced its interest in Galyan's to 40%. (Galyan's management and buyout firm Freeman Spogli own 60% of the sporting goods chain.) The Limited (as well as Intimate Brands) declared a two-for-one stock split in 2000.

To boost profits in 2001 The Limited folded the Structure brand into the Express unit and spun off its Galyan's and Alliance Data Systems subsidiaries retaining 22% and 20% respectively. The Limited sold its Lane Bryant unit to Charming Shoppes for $335 million that year.

The Limited bought back the remaining shares of Intimate Brands it did not already own in March 2002 and over the course of the year phased it into a business segment. In May 2002 the company changed its name to Limited Brands from The Limited. Later that year Limited Brands sold off its remaining stake in Lerner New York and in late 2003 sold its Structure label (which it had rebranded as Express Men's) to Sears Roebuck and Co.

Limited Brands in 2004 sold 1.6 million shares of the plus-size United Retail Group Inc. after a decade of investment and it acquired New York-based Slatkin & Co. (a prestige home fragrance company distributing scented candles potpourris and room sprays under the names Slatkin & Co. Oscar Home Elton John C.Z. Guest and Kabbalah). Later that year Limited Brands laid off 25% of the headquarters workforce of its Express division –including managers and support personnel but not store employees or warehouse workers –in the face of slipping earnings.

Bath and Body Works launched an Internet store bathandbodyworks.com in 2005.

In January 2007 Limited Brands completed its acquisition of lingerie maker and retailer La Senza based in Montreal for about $600 million. La Senza is a specialty retailer offering lingerie and sleepwear for women age 18 to 35 as well as apparel for girls in the 7 to14 age group. Independently owned La Senza stores operate in 34 other countries. In July Limited Brands sold a 75% interest in its Express chain to affiliates of Golden Gate Capital for about $425 million. Limited Brands retained a 25% stake in the 625-store chain. In a similar transaction completed in August Limited Brands sold a 75% stake in its 251-store Limited Stores business to Sun Capital Partners taking a loss on the sale.

Former vice chairman and COO Len Schlesinger retired in September 2007 after eight years with the firm. Wexner and administrative executive Martyn Redgrave took over Schlesinger's responsibilities.

In 2008 BBW opened its first stores in Canada. In 2009 Limited Brands closed 53 La Senza Girl stores exiting that business. The company in mid-2010 sold off the remaining 25% stake it held in Limited Stores LLC which operates The Limited retail locations.

In fsical 2009 the company closed 53 la Senza Girl stores in Canada.

In November 2011 Limited Brands sold a 51% stake in its third-party apparel sourcing division Mast Global Fashions to the private equity firm Sycamore Partners.

EXECUTIVES

EVP and CFO, Stuart B. Burgdoerfer, age 49, $725,000 total compensation
President and Chief Marketing Officer Brand and Creative Services, Edward G. Razek
SVP Law Policy and Governance and Secretary, Samuel P. Fried
Chairman and CEO, Leslie H. Wexner, age 74, $1,924,000 total compensation
VP Treasury Mergers and Acquisitions, Timothy J. Faber, age 50
EVP and Chief Administrative Officer, Martyn R. Redgrave, age 59, $1,040,000 total compensation
CEO Bath & Body Works, Diane L. Neal, age 55, $927,000 total compensation
CEO Henri Bendel, Edward (Ed) Bucciarelli, age 52
President and CEO Victoria's Secret, Sharen J. Turney, age 55, $1,250,000 total compensation
VP External Communication, Tammy Roberts Myers
COO Victoria's Secret Stores, Peter Z. Horvath, age 54
President Brand Development Bath & Body Works, Camille McDonald
VP Investor Relations, Amie Preston
President and CEO Victoria's Secret PINK, Denise Landman
EVP Human Resources, Jane L. Ramsey, age 54
EVP Retail Real Estate, Jamie Bersani
SVP and General Merchandise Manager Fashion Henri Bendel, Scott Schramm
CEO Victoria's Secret Stores, Lori Greeley
SVP and General Counsel, Douglas L. Williams
VP Government Affairs, Ted Adams
President International, Martin Waters
Chief Administrative Officer Victoria's Secret Direct, Will Matt
VP Loss Prevention and Safety Services, John Talamo
VP Leadership Talent and Inclusion, Marvin Clayton
President La Senza and Limited Brands Canada, Joanne Nemeroff
President Victoria's Secret Beauty, Sashi Batra
President and CEO Mast Global, Charles C McGuigan
Director, William R. Loomis Jr., age 64
Director, Allan R. Tessler, age 75
Director, Raymond Zimmerman, age 79
Director, Donna A. James, age 54
Director, E. Gordon Gee, age 68
Director, David T. Kollat, age 73
Director, Jeffrey H. Miro, age 69
Director, Abigail S. Wexner, age 50
Director, Prof James L. (Jim) Heskett, age 79
Director, Dennis S. Hersch, age 65
Auditors: Ernst&YoungLLP

LOCATIONS

HQ: Limited Brands Inc.
3 Limited Pkwy., Columbus OH 43216
Phone: 614-415-7000 **Fax:** 614-415-7440
Web: www.limitedbrands.com

PRODUCTS/OPERATIONS

2012 Stores

	No.
Victoria's Secret	
Victoria's Secret Stores	1,017
La Senza	230
Victoria's Secret	19
Bath & Body Works	1,587
Bath & Body Works	69
Henri	19
Total	**2,941**

2012 Sales

	$ mil.	% of total
Victoria's Secret Stores	4,564	44
Victoria's Secret Direct	1,557	15
Bath & Body Works	2,674	26
Other (includes Henri Bendel La Senza Mast & BBW Canada)	1,569	15
Total	**10,364**	**100**

Selected Retail Brands

Bath & Body Works
C.O. Bigelow
Henri Bendel
La Senza
Pink
Victoria' s Secret

COMPETITORS

Abercrombie & Fitch
American Eagle Outfitters
Avon
Body Shop
CVS Caremark
Dillard' s
Estee Lauder
Frederick' s of Hollywood
Fruit of the Loom
Hanesbrands
J. C. Penney
Jockey International
Kiehl' s
Macy' s
Mary Kay
Natori
Nordstrom
Revlon
Saks
Sephora USA
Shiseido Americas
Target Corporation
The Gap
Ulta
VF Corporation
Wal-Mart
Warnaco Group

HISTORICAL FINANCIALS

Company Type: Public

Income Statement

FYE: January 28

	REVENUE ($ mil.)	NET INCOME ($ mil.)	NET PROFIT MARGIN	EMPLOYEES
01/12	10,364	850	8.2%	97,000
01/11	9,613	805	8.4%	96,500
01/10	8,632	448	5.2%	92,100
01/09*	9,043	220	2.4%	90,900
02/08	10,134	718	7.1%	175,600
Annual Growth	0.6%	4.3%	—	(13.8%)

*Fiscal year change

2012 Year-End Financials

Debt ratio: 57.92%
Return on equity: 620.44%
Cash ($ mil.): 935
Current ratio: 155.18
Long-term debt ($ mil.): 3,481
No. of shares (mil.): 295
Dividends
Yield: —
Payout: 140.74%
Market value ($ mil.): 12,231

	STOCK PRICE ($) FY Close	P/E High	P/E Low	PER SHARE ($) Earnings	Dividends	Book Value
01/12	41.46	16	10	2.70	0.00	0.46
01/11	28.92	14	8	2.42	0.00	4.60
01/10	19.02	15	5	1.37	0.00	6.76
01/09*	7.92	33	11	0.65	0.00	5.84
02/08	19.33	16	8	1.89	0.00	6.41
Annual Growth	21.0%	—	—	9.3%	—	(48.2%)

*Fiscal year change

Lincoln National Corp.

Who better to trust with your nest egg than the company that took its name from Honest Abe? Lincoln National which operates as Lincoln Financial Group provides retirement planning and life insurance to individuals and employers in the form of annuities 401k savings plans and a variety of life dental and disability insurance products. It does business through such subsidiaries as Lincoln National Life Insurance and Lincoln Life & Annuity Company of New York. The company is also active in the investment management business offering individual and institutional clients such financial services as pension plans trusts and mutual funds through its subsidiaries.

HISTORY

Wilbur Wynant a sort of Johnny Appleseed of shady fraternal benefits societies arrived in Fort Wayne Indiana in 1902. He persuaded several respected businessmen and professionals to help him found the Fraternal Assurance Society of America an assessable mutual organization in which surviving members contributed to the death benefits of deceased members. Wynant absconded within a couple of years and the local organizers restructured the society's remains as a stock company in 1905. To clean up the organization's reputation they obtained permission from Abraham Lincoln's son Robert to use his father's name and image.

In 1905 when the company wrote its first policy it had three agents including its leading executive Arthur Hall. By 1911 the company had 106 agents. Careful risk assessment was an early hallmark of the company and allowed it to accept business that other companies rejected based on more superficial analysis.

From a very early period the company grew through acquisitions. WWI increased claims but not as much as the global flu epidemic that followed the war. Organic growth continued in the 1920s.

Death and disability claims increased abnormally during the Depression and the company's underwriting became more stringent. Lincoln National used the financial turmoil of the period to buy other troubled insurers. Reinsurance became the firm's primary line until after WWII.

The company bought up other firms in the 1950s and 1960s and in 1968 it formed holding company Lincoln National. Soon it began diversifying buying Chicago Title and Trust (1969; sold 1985) as well as more life and reinsurance companies. Lincoln National also went into the health benefits business setting up its own HMO and investing in EMPHESYS (which it took public in 1994 divesting the remainder of its stock in 1995).

The collapse of the real estate market in many areas nicked results in the late 1980s and in 1990 the company accepted an infusion of cash from Dai-Ichi Mutual Life Insurance. Property/casualty results were hurt in the early 1990s by an unprecedented string of natural disasters.

With the growth of retirement savings from baby boomers hitting their 50s the company shifted gears into wealth management. In 1995 Lincoln National expanded its investment management capacities by purchasing Delaware Management Holdings and Laurentian Financial Group. The next year it bought the group tax-qualified annuity business of disability insurer UNUM (now UNUMProvident) and in 1997 bought Voyageur Fund Managers a tax-free-bond fund business. The company also took a 49% stake in a Mexican insurance company owned by Grupo Financiero Santander Serfin (sold in 2000). It sold its 83% interest in property/casualty firm American States Financial in 1996.

Lincoln National bought CIGNA's annuity and individual life insurance business and Aetna's US individual life insurance operations in 1998. It reorganized that year to help it absorb these businesses causing earnings to take a substantial hit.

In 1999 after nearly a century in the heartland Lincoln National moved its headquarters to Philadelphia. Other transformations included the sale of its individual disability income business in 1999. In 2001 it sold its reinsurance operations to Swiss Re to re-focus on wealth and asset accumulation products and services. The reshaping continued in 2002 when the company acquired employee benefits record-keeping firm The Administrative Management Group.

Lincoln National completed a merger/acquisition of Jefferson-Pilot in early 2006. The $7.5 billion deal combined the Lincoln Financial Group with the Jefferson Pilot Financial group (the operating brand for Jefferson-Pilot Corporation) and created a new company operating as Lincoln Financial Group. Led by management from both former organizations the new group expanded insurance and financial products offerings and national retail and wholesale distribution platforms.

The Jefferson-Pilot purchase came with several media businesses which Lincoln National promptly deemed to be noncore. In early 2008 the company sold off three television stations and a sports syndication business to Raycom Media for $548 million and it sold three radio stations to Greater Media for a total of $100 million.

When the economic waters turned murky and cold in 2008 Lincoln Financial sought relief under the US Treasury's TARP program. As the TARP was originally structured to assist banks Lincoln's earliest efforts were focused on making itself more eligible by acquiring regional banking company Newton Country Loan & Savings of Goodland Indiana. The Office of Thrift Supervision now technically recognizes the company as a savings and loan holding company. However while Lincoln Financial was still waiting for approval to participate in the Capital Purchase Programs as a bank in 2009 the feds instead decided to extend its funds to major life insurers including Lincoln Financial. The company received approval for up to $2.5 billion of TARP funds to shore up its capital but only issued some $2.1 billion in equity debt and preferred stock to the Treasury.

Having secured itself to a life raft Lincoln Financial chose to jettison several businesses in 2009 to lighten its load. To better focus on the US markets it sold its UK retirement products and financial services subsidiary Lincoln National (UK) to Canada-based Sun Life Financial for some $307 million. It then sold its asset management subsidiary Delaware Management Holdings to Australian financial services firm Macquarie Group for $405 million. Lincoln National divested the investment business to focus on its insurance and retirement operations. However it was an amicable divestiture and Delaware Management agreed to continue managing some of Lincoln National's insurance assets.

EXECUTIVES

President Defined Contribution, Charles C. (Chuck) Cornelio, age 52
President Retirement and Insurance Solutions, Mark E. Konen, age 52, $908,563 total compensation
President CEO and Director; President Lincoln National Life Insurance, Dennis R. Glass, age 62, $2,239,123 total compensation
President and Managing Director Lincoln National (UK), Michael Tallett-Williams, age 58
Chairman, William H. Cunningham, age 68
President and CEO Lincoln Financial Advisors, Robert W. (Bob) Dineen, age 62, $419,754 total compensation
VP; Head Finance and Strategy Defined Contribution, Duane L. Bernt
VP Digital Strategy and User Experience, Anand S. Rao
VP Head of Enterprise Litigation, Kelley A. Grady
President Lincoln National Investment Company Inc. and Delaware Management Holdings Inc, Patrick P. (Pat) Coyne, age 48, $2,501,110 total compensation
VP Profitability and Risk Management Individual Annuity Life Insurance and Group Protection Businesses, Jeff Coutts
Media Inquiries Life Insurance and Group Benefits, Heidi St. Jean
VP Corporate Development, Lisa Marie DeSimone
SVP and Chief Human Resources Officer, Lisa M. Buckingham, age 46
VP and Head of IRA Strategies Retirement Solutions, Tom McGirr
President and CEO Lincoln Financial Distributors, Wilford H. (Will) Fuller, age 41, $355,385 total compensation
VP Investor Relations, Jim Sjoreen
Media Inquiries Individual Annuities and Defined Contribution, Daniela Palmieri
Head Distribution MoneyGuard Reserve Lincoln Financial Distributors, Andrew Bucklee
Large Market Product Manager Defined Contribution Product, Ray Radikas
VP Brand Management, Charlie Armstrong
SVP and Head Defined Contribution Products, Eric Levy
Head Product Retirement Solutions, Robert (Rob) Grubka
VP Defined Contribution Strategy, Andrew J. (Drew) Powers
VP and Business Leader Large Market Defined Contribution, Sharon Scanlon
EVP and CFO, Randal J. Freitag, age 49
VP Small Market Business Leader Defined Contribution Products, Michael Conte
Chief Risk Officer, John Rhodes
Director, William J. Avery, age 71
President CEO and Director; President Lincoln National Life Insurance, Dennis R. Glass, age 62
Director, David A. Stonecipher, age 71
Director, Gary C. Kelly, age 56
Director, George W. Henderson III, age 63
Director, Patrick S. Pittard, age 66
Director, William P. Payne, age 64
Director, Eric G. Johnson, age 61
Director, Isaiah Tidwell, age 67
Director, M. Leanne Lachman, age 69
Director, William H. Cunningham, age 67
Director, Michael F. Mee, age 69
Auditors: Ernst&YoungLLP

LOCATIONS

HQ: Lincoln National Corporation
150 N. Radnor Chester Rd., Radnor PA 19807
Phone: 484-583-1400 **Fax:** 484-583-1421
Web: www.lfg.com

PRODUCTS/OPERATIONS

2011 Revenues		
Insurance		
Group protection	1,939	18
Annuities	2,865	26
Retirement plan services	1,017	9
Other operations	461	4
Total	**10,636**	**100**

2011 Revenues		
Net investment income	4,652	43
Insurance premiums	2,294	21
Amortization of deferred gain on business sold through reinsurance		75
1		
Other revenues & fees	477	4

Selected Subsidiaries

First Penn-Pacific Life Insurance Company
Hampshire Funding Inc.
Jefferson-Pilot Investments Inc.
Lincoln Financial Investment Services Corporation
Lincoln Financial Securities Corporation
Lincoln Insurance Services Limited
Lincoln Investment Management Company
The Lincoln National Life Insurance Company
Lincoln National Management Corporation
Lincoln National Reinsurance Company (Barbados) Limited
Lincoln Reinsurance Company of Bermuda Limited

COMPETITORS

AEGON
AIG
American Equity Investment Life Holding Company
AXA Financial
Guardian Life
ING
John Hancock Financial Services
MassMutual
MetLife
Nationwide Financial
New York Life
Northwestern Mutual
Pacific Mutual
Principal Financial
Prudential
The Hartford
TIAA-CREF
Torchmark
Unum Group

HISTORICAL FINANCIALS

Company Type: Public

Income Statement FYE: December 31

	ASSETS ($ mil.)	NET INCOME ($ mil.)	INCOME AS % OF ASSETS	EMPLOYEES
12/11	202,906	294	0.1%	8,564
12/10	193,824	980	0.5%	8,270
12/09	177,433	(485)	—	9,619
12/08	163,136	57	0.0%	9,696
12/07	191,435	1,215	0.6%	10,870
Annual Growth	1.5%	(29.9%)	—	(5.8%)

2011 Year-End Financials

Debt ratio: 2.81%
Return on equity: 2.08%
Cash ($ mil.): 4,510
Current ratio: —
Long-term debt ($ mil.): 5,691
No. of shares (mil.): 291
Dividends
Yield: —
Payout: 21.74%
Market value ($ mil.): 5,657

	STOCK PRICE ($) FY Close	P/E High/Low		PER SHARE ($) Earnings	Dividends	Book Value
12/11	19.42	34	15	0.92	0.00	48.62
12/10	27.81	13	8	2.54	0.04	40.56
12/09	24.88	—	—	(1.85)	0.24	38.71
12/08	18.84	265	23	0.22	1.66	31.18
12/07	58.22	17	12	4.43	1.58	44.35
Annual Growth	(24.0%)	—	—	(32.5%)	—	2.3%

Live Nation Entertainment, Inc.

Live Nation Entertainment holds center stage as the world's largest ticket seller and promoter of live entertainment. In 2010 the company significantly expanded its ticketing services with the purchase of Ticketmaster Entertainment. The deal worth some $889 million created a powerful live-music conglomerate. The firm also owns or operates more than 130 venues in North America and Europe. Annually about 50 million people attend some 20000 Live Nation events. Live Nation also owns House of Blues venues through HOB Entertainment and dozens of prestigious concert halls. In addition Live Nation owns a stake in about 250 artists' music including albums tours and merchandise.

Operations

The combination of Live Nation and Ticketmaster established a giant in the music industry that controls concert promotion ticketing services and artist management all under one roof. Live Nation promotes shows or tours for approximately 2000 artists globally.

Before the Ticketmaster acquisition Live Nation had sold many of its tickets through Ticketmaster; however Live Nation parted ways with the ticketing giant at the end of 2008 when it formed its own ticketing division. While Live Nation had mixed results with the division the company managed to secure a five-year deal which started in late 2009 to sell tickets for SMG Management one of the largest venue operators in the US.

Strategy

Live Nation has been investing its dance music promotion activities as of late. In 2012 the company acquired Hard Events a Los Angeles firm that puts on electronic dance music and festivals and concerts across North America. Also in 2012 Live Nation bought Cream Holdings a major British dance promoter. After that deal closed the company appointed Cream founder as president of Live Nation's electronic music division.

Live Nation has also been busy forming joint ventures to expand its operations. In 2011 it launched a joint venture with online discount giant Groupon. Through the partnership Groupon Live offers group discounts and special promotions to help sell tickets to concerts sporting events and other attractions. Also that year its business unit Front Line Management an artist managment company fomed a joint venture with Universal Music Group. The JV's goal is to provide artists and their brands a variety of sponsorships campaigns and extensions through ticketing and bundling opportunities.

Ownership

After the Ticketmaster acquisition closed in 2010 media conglomerate Liberty Media upped its stake in Live Nation to 18% and expressed a desire to eventually increase its share to about 35%.

HISTORY

Robert Sillerman began his career teaching advertisers how to reach young consumers. He started investing in radio and TV stations and founded SFX Broadcasting (named for a scrambling of his initials) in 1992. In early 1997 the firm entered the live entertainment field with the formation of SFX Concerts and the purchase of concert promoter Delsener/Slater.

When SFX Broadcasting agreed to be bought in 1997 by Capstar Broadcasting 87% controlled by investment firm Hicks Muse Tate & Furst (now HM Capital) SFX Entertainment was formed to house the live entertainment operations (it was spun off in 1998). In 1998 the company continued its rapid acquisition rate with the purchases of sports marketing and management team FAME New England concert promoter Don Law and national concert producer PACE Entertainment.

In 1999 the company bought concert promoter The Cellar Door Companies (which almost doubled SFX's size) sports marketing firm Integrated Sports International sporting event management company The Marquee Group sports talent agency Hendricks Management 50% of urban-music producer A.H. Enterprises and troubled theatrical producer Livent. SFX also made its first foray abroad through its purchase of Apollo Leisure a UK-based live entertainment firm. The company rolled all of its sports talent and marketing businesses into a new division SFX Sports Group that year.

In 2000 SFX jumped on the other side of the acquisition train when it was bought by radio station owner Clear Channel Communications for about $4 billion. Sillerman stepped down as chairman and CEO and was replaced by Clear Channel EVP Brian Becker. Later that year SFX acquired Philadelphia-based concert promoter and venue operator Electric Factory Concerts; Core Audience Entertainment Canada's second-largest concert promoter and events marketer; and the Cotter Group a North Carolina-based motorsports marketing agency.

In 2001 SFX acquired a majority interest in the International Hot Rod Association. It also bought professional golf talent agency Signature Sports Group. Later that year the company changed its name to Clear Channel Entertainment. It also continued expansion into Europe with the acquisition of Trident Agency and Milano Concerti music promotion businesses in Italy.

While operating as Clear Channel Entertainment Live Nation spent nearly $2 billion on acquisitions (Pace Entertainment Livent) almost singlehandedly consolidating the live entertainment industry.

Before being spun off in December 2005 the company changed its name to CCE Spinco then Live Nation. Also that year Randall Mays became chairman and Michael Rapino replaced Becker as CEO. As part of the Clear Channel spinoff the company relocated from Houston to headquarters in tony Beverly Hills. It trimmed the fat by shutting down operating divisions such as museum exhibitions and music publishing (and laying off about 400 employees in the process) in order to focus on its core businesses of live music concerts venue management and website brand development.

In 2006 the company acquired rival HOB Entertainment for $354 million. Live Nation used the acquisition to expand its presence in the midsized venue business and fill in geographic gaps in its existing amphitheater network. As part of the deal Live Nation gained high-profile House of Blues-branded music venues such as San Francisco's Fillmore Auditorium Jones Beach in New York and London's Apollo Theatre and Wembley Arena. The company subsequently began re-branding many of its midsize clubs "Fillmore" after the San Francisco venue.

The company had in 2005 formed Delirium Concert LP a joint venture with Cirque du Soleil. The Delirium tour began in 2006. The following year Live Nation signed a $120 million deal with pop icon Madonna. Through its North American Music segment in 2007 Live Nation promoted or produced some 10000 live music events including tours for Van Halen Dave Matthews Band and Kenny Chesney. International Music operations for the year included Cirque De Soleil's Delirium as well as UK's Reading Festival. Also in 2007 the company produced global tours for legends such as The Police The Rolling Stones Genesis and The Who and presented some 5000 theatrical performances such as the UK touring production of Chicago through its Global Theater operations.

In 2008 the company divested itself of its North American theatrical assets. Later that year the company signed pacts with U2 and Jay-Z. Michael Cohl chairman and Live Nation Artists chief who spearheaded the deals later resigned over conflicts with CEO Rapino. Also in 2008 the company sold its motor sports operations. In early 2010 the company acquired Ticketmaster Entertainment and Live Nation changed its name to Live Nation Entertainment.

EXECUTIVES

CEO House of Blues Entertainment Division, Ronald (Ron) Bension
EVP and General Counsel, Michael G. Rowles, age 46, $517,475 total compensation
President Talent Live Nation International Music, Shane Bourbonnais
President Arenas, Michael R. (Mike) Evans
President Onsite Products, Brian Yost
President North America Concerts Regions North, Mark Campana
President CEO and Director, Michael (Mike) Rapino, age 46, $1,501,140 total compensation
CEO Global Touring; Chairman Global Music, Arthur Fogel, age 58
Executive Chairman, Irving L. Azoff, age 64
Chairman International Concerts, Thomas O. Johansson, age 63
President Marketing Artist Marketing Products, Faisel Durrani, age 46
COO, Joe Berchtold
President TicketsNow.com and Ticketmaster, Eric Korman
President International and Emerging Markets, Alan Ridgeway, age 45, $579,165 total compensation
EVP and CFO, Kathy Willard, age 45, $533,330 total compensation
Chief Strategic Officer, Robert Peters
President North America Sponsorships, Russell Wallach
President Concert Tours Strategy, Rick Franks
President Music Sales North America, Maureen Ford
SVP Live Nation New York, Phil Ernst
President and Chief Creative Officer Merchandising; CEO and Creative Director TRUNK, Brad Beckerman
General Manager Recorded Music Division Live Nation Artists, Bill Hein
Director Booking Asia, Luke Hede
SVP Touring, Bruce Kapp
EVP Business Development and Strategy Ticketing, Greg Bettinelli
Chief Accounting Officer, Brian Capo, age 45
EVP and General Manager LiveNation.com, Noah T. Maffitt, age 40
CEO Ticketing, Nathan Hubbard, age 36
CIO Ticketing, Joe Manna
COO International, Paul Latham
President Touring Live Nation International Music, Phil Bowdery
EVP Mergers and Acquisitions and Strategic Finance, John Hopmans, age 53
Chief Marketing Officer Global, Seth Matlins
VP Engineering International Digital, Stephen Williams
VP, Jim McPartlin
President Live Nation Nashville, Brian O'Connell
President North America Concerts Regions South, Bob Roux
CEO Live Nation Europe Sponsorship and Concerts, Simon Lewis
Director, James S. (Jim) Kahan, age 64
Director, Randall T. Mays, age 46
Director, Jeffrey T. Hinson, age 57
Director, Robert (Ted) Enloe III, age 73
Director, Jonathan L. Dolgen, age 67
Director, Jonathan F. (Jon) Miller, age 55
President CEO and Director, Michael (Mike) Rapino, age 46
Director, Ariel Z. (Arie) Emanuel, age 51
Director, Mark D. Carleton, age 51
Director, Mark S. Shapiro, age 42
Auditors: Ernst&YoungLLP

LOCATIONS

HQ: Live Nation Entertainment Inc.
9348 Civic Center Dr., Beverly Hills CA 90210
Phone: 310-867-7000 **Fax:** 310-867-7001
Web: www.livenation.com

PRODUCTS/OPERATIONS

COMPETITORS

Brillstein
CAA
Dial Global
Dodger Properties
Feld Entertainment
IMG
International Creative Management
Jujamcyn Theaters
Madison Square Garden
Nederlander Producing Company
Octagon
On Stage Entertainment
Palace Sports & Entertainment
Ryman
Shubert Organization
SMG Management
TBA Global
United Talent
Universal Music Group
Warner Music
William Morris Endeavor Entertainment

HISTORICAL FINANCIALS

Company Type: Public

Income Statement FYE: December 31

	REVENUE ($ mil.)	NET INCOME ($ mil.)	NET PROFIT MARGIN	EMPLOYEES
12/11	5,384	(83)	—	6,600
12/10	5,063	(228)	—	6,500
12/09	4,181	(60)	—	4,300
12/08	4,166	(231)	—	4,700
12/07	4,184	(11)	—	4,700
Annual Growth	6.5%	—	—	8.9%

2011 Year-End Financials

Debt ratio: 33.72%
Return on equity: (-5.68)%
Cash ($ mil.): 844
Current ratio: 105.64
Long-term debt ($ mil.): 1,663
No. of shares (mil.): 188
Dividends
Yield: —
Payout: —
Market value ($ mil.): 1,570

	STOCK PRICE ($) FY Close	P/E High/Low	PER SHARE ($) Earnings	Dividends	Book Value
12/11	8.31	— —	(0.46)	0.00	7.73
12/10	11.42	— —	(1.39)	0.00	7.84
12/09	8.51	— —	(0.73)	0.00	8.20
12/08	5.74	— —	(3.04)	0.00	8.49
12/07	14.52	— —	(0.17)	0.00	12.11
Annual Growth	(13.0%)	— —	—	—	(10.6%)

Lockheed Martin Corp.

Lockheed Martin takes flight in times of crisis. A leading global military contractor the company serves the civil and commercial sectors but it is firmly on the defense/government side of the aerospace industry; sales to the US government accounts for about 82% of revenue with the US DoD accounting for about 61%. Electronic Systems is its largest segment providing such products as surface ship and submarine combat systems. Other segments include Aeronautics (combat aircraft and UAVs) Information Systems & Global Services (IS&GS; data protection and intelligence) and Space Systems (satellites and space travel). Lockheed Martin also provides engineering logistics and information services.

HISTORY

Brothers Allan and Malcolm Loughead (pronounced "Lockheed") started their first aviation venture the Alco Hydro-Aeroplane Company in 1912. Alco's first product the Model G floatplane didn't sell. In 1916 the brothers relocated from Santa Barbara to San Francisco and formed the Loughead Aircraft Manufacturing Company. That company's first product the F-1 seaplane made a successful debut in early 1918 but the end of WWI effectively ended the potential market for the F-1. Loughead Aircraft went bankrupt in 1921.

The Loughead brothers joined Fred Keeler in 1926 to form the Lockheed Aircraft Company in Southern California. John Northrop (who later founded Northrop Corporation) designed Lockheed's first airplane the Vega (flown by Amelia Earhart). The company was acquired in 1929 by Detroit Aircraft Corporation which went bankrupt in 1931 as the Great Depression devastated the airplane industry.

Robert Gross Carl Squier and Lloyd Stearman bought Lockheed in 1932. The company produced such aviation classics as the P-38 Lightning fighter the U-2 spy plane and the SR-71 Blackbird spy plane. It also produced submarine-launched ballistic missiles (Polaris 1958) military transports (C-5 Galaxy 1968) and the L-1011 TriStar airliner (1971).

Lockheed suffered from the cancellation of its Cheyenne attack helicopter the C-5A cost overrun scandal and financial problems with the L-1011. Government loans saved the firm from bankruptcy in 1971.

In the late 1970s Lockheed was at the center of a corporate bribery scandal that overturned governments in Japan and Italy and led to tougher US anti-bribery laws. During the 1970s and 1980s Lockheed developed the Hubble Space Telescope and the F-117A stealth fighter. Shrinking orders forced Lockheed to close its main aircraft plant in 1990. Lockheed merged with Martin Marietta in 1995 to form Lockheed Martin.

Glenn Martin started Martin Marietta in 1917. Martin Marietta made the first US-built bombers as well as military and commercial flying boats. During the 1950s Martin Marietta made missiles electronics and nuclear systems. In 1961 it merged with American-Marietta Company (construction materials and chemical products).

Strapped with debt after defeating a hostile takeover by Bendix in 1982 Martin Marietta sold many of its businesses. It bought General Electric's aerospace business (1992) and became part of Lockheed in 1995.

In 1996 Lockheed Martin sold its Defense Systems and Armament Systems units to General Dynamics and bought most of Loral Corporation (advanced electronics). In 1997 it spun off 10 non-core technology units as L-3 Communications Holdings. A prospective deal to buy Northrop Grumman for $11.6 billion ended in 1998 when the US government raised antitrust issues.

Using global satellite communications to build its non-defense business Lockheed Martin bought 30% of Asia Cellular Satellite in 1999 and invested in the Astrolink wireless broadband satellite system. It also acquired a 49% stake in COMSAT a satellite network company that is the centerpiece of Lockheed Martin's communications business.

A series of launch failures in 1999 destroyed about $4 billion in rockets and payloads and led to an inquiry that blamed poor management oversight and quality-control problems. Company profits —two-thirds lower than the prior year's — prompted it to restructure and sell many non-core operations.

In 2000 the Pentagon bailed out Lockheed Martin by agreeing to buy 24 C-130J transports. The company also won a $3.97 billion contract from the Pentagon to develop the Theater High-Altitude Area Defense (THAAD) anti-missile defense system. Lockheed sold some defense electronics units including its Sanders unit (aerial electronic warfare and countermeasure systems) to UK-based BAE SYSTEMS for around $1.7 billion; in a separate deal it also sold its Lockheed Martin Control Systems unit to BAE. That year Lockheed Martin purchased the 51% of COMSAT it didn't already own.

Lockheed Martin announced in 2001 that it would cut nearly $3 billion in costs. That year the US Department of Defense named Lockheed Martin as the lead contractor for the F-35 Lightning II program (previously known as the Joint Strike Fighter or J-35). The deal was expected to be worth more than $200 billion and the plane was to serve as the main fighter aircraft for the US and its allies for decades. Later in 2001 Lockheed Martin (along with TRW) was awarded a $2.7 billion contract for the US military's next-generation communications satellite system. In late 2001 Israel exercised an option to purchase an additional 52 F-16I fighter jets (potentially worth more than $1.3 billion) and Lockheed jettisoned its plans to exit its global telecommunications services business.

In 2002 Lockheed Martin sold COMSAT's Mobile Communications operations to Telenor for about $100 million. The company was then awarded a $12.7 billion US contract (spread out over 23 years) to provide support work for single-seat F-16s flown by 16 different countries. Late in the year Lockheed agreed to sell 48 F-16s to Poland for about $3.5 billion.

Lockheed Martin acquired the government technology services business of Affiliated Computer Services for about $650 million in 2003. That year the company announced a two-year initiative to create another unit Maritime Systems & Sensors. The move to consolidate its naval seafaring operations was designed to make for better customer efficiency but would also allow Lockheed Martin to reduce its workforce and save money.

In 2003 Lockheed agreed to buy Titan Corporation a US-based defense-oriented computer systems company in a half-cash half-stock deal worth about $2.4 billion ($1.8 billion plus assumed debt). In 2004 the deal's value was amended to $2.2 billion amid a federal probe into illegal overseas payments allegedly made by Titan. The deal was scuttled in mid-2004 as the allegations remained unresolved.

Lockheed acquired naval electronics maker Sippican in 2004. Sippican's businesses included electronic warfare countermeasures oceanographic and meteorological systems navigation and communications systems and autonomous underwater vehicles.

In 2005 the US Navy selected Lockheed (prime contractor) and AgustaWestland to build a new fleet of 23 Presidential Marine One helicopters in a deal worth about $6 billion. Lockheed Martin also completed its acquisition of STASYS Ltd. a UK-based network communications company. A wholly owned subsidiary the company was renamed Lockheed Martin STASYS Limited. Lockheed also acquired the SYTEX Group (now SYTEX Lockheed) a provider of IT services and technical support services to the US government for $462 million.

Lockheed Martin acquired ISX Corporation a privately held provider of military decision systems and other government IT systems in 2006. Also that year the company bought Pacific Architects and Engineers Incorporated (PAE) a provider of services that support military readiness peacekeeping missions and disaster relief. Lockheed Martin additionally acquired Savi Technology a supplier of radio-frequency identification products for cargo and freight. Savi became a subsidiary of Integrated Systems & Solutions.

A busy year 2006 brought a bonanza of business for Lockheed when NASA awarded the company with the coveted Orion manned lunar spaceship contract. It beat out competing bids by Northrop Grumman and Boeing. Orion was slated to be NASA's next generation of manned spacecraft and to eventually replace the space shuttle. Orion was anticipated to take astronauts to the moon and possibly to Mars. That same year Lockheed launched the inaugural flight of the F-35 Lightning II.

In 2007 Lockheed combined its Information Technology & Global Services and Integrated Systems and Solutions divisions into a single entity Information Systems & Global Services. Not long into 2008 the company landed a $345 million deal with the DoD to provide operation and maintenance of computing centers at four research sites.

The company teamed up with rivals Northrop Grumman and Alliant Techsystems in 2008 to develop multi-role weapons for Lockheed's F-22 Raptor and F-35 Lightning II. The partnership was forged to address a void the companies saw in the weapons market for the aircraft. The companies pooled their weapons technologies to stave off potential competitors.

Lockheed has faced program terminations when the DoD cut two significant Lockheed programs in 2009: the VH-71 Presidential Helicopter Replacement and the Transformational Communications Satellite (TSAT) and TSAT Mission Operations System contracts.

Lockheed put its Enterprise Integration Group (EIG) and its Pacific Architects and Engineers (PAE) businesses on the sale rack. It managed to sell off EIG to Veritas Capital in late 2010 for $815 million. EIG part of Lockheed's IS&GS division advises government agencies on weapons platforms. Lockheed sold PAE which specializes in mission readiness peacekeeping and disaster relief services to private equity Goldberg Lindsay (dba Lindsay Goldberg) in spring 2011. The deals follow the Pentagon's proposed rules that crack down on organizational conflicts of interest at its major contractors.

EXECUTIVES

Chairman and CEO, Robert J. (Bob) Stevens, age 60, $1,834,615 total compensation

President and COO, Christopher E. Kubasik, age 51, $1,007,115 total compensation

VP and Associate General Counsel, David A. Dedman

EVP Information Systems and Global Solutions, Linda R. Gooden, age 59, $591,154 total compensation

VP Ethics and Business Conduct, Leo S. Mackay Jr., age 51

SVP General Counsel and Corporate Secretary, Maryanne R. Lavan, age 53

CEO Lockheed Martin UK Holdings, Stephen R. Ball

EVP Aeronautics, Larry Lawson

EVP Space Systems Company, Joanne M. Maguire, age 57, $558,077 total compensation

EVP Electronic Systems, Marillyn A. Hewson, age 58

Director Strategic Development Information Systems and Global Solutions-Defense, Sam Guthrie

EVP and CFO, Bruce L. Tanner, age 52, $742,019 total compensation

President MS2, Dale P. Bennett

VP and Controller, Christopher J. (Chris) Gregoire, age 43

VP Worldwide Media Relations, Jennifer M. Whitlow, age 39

SVP and CTO, Ray O. Johnson

SVP Human Resources, John T. Lucas, age 52

VP and General Manager F-35, Orlando D. Carvalho, age 54

VP Communications Mission Systems and Sensors, Kimberly Ramalho, age 44

President Information Systems and Global Solutions-Defense, Gerard A. (Gerry) Fasano

VP C-130 Program, George Shultz

Media Contact, Keith Little

VP Communications Information Systems and Global Solutions, Nettie R. Johnson
VP and Deputy F-35 program, Lorraine Martin
VP Command Control Communications Computers and Intelligence and General Manager San Diego Mission Systems and Sensors (MS2), Michael (Mike) Feeley
SVP Operations and Program Management, Michael (Mike) Joyce
VP Energy Environment Safety and Health, David J. C. Constable
VP and Treasurer, Kenneth R. (Ken) Possenriede, age 51
VP and Associate General Counsel Enterprise Legal Activities, Alice M. Eldridge
President Global Training and Logistics, Denise A. Saiki
SVP Enterprise Business Services and CIO, Sondra L. Barbour
VP Leadership and Organizational Development, Marilyn Figlar
VP Investor Relations, Jerry F. Kircher III
Director Investor Relations, Shamala N. Littlefield
VP Corporate Internal Audit, Erich Sanchack, age 42
VP Corporate Internal Audit, Stephanie C. Hill, age 47
Director, Nolan D. Archibald, age 68
Director, Thomas J. (Tom) Falk, age 54
Director, Douglas H. McCorkindale, age 72
Director, Anne L. Stevens, age 63
Director, Gwendolyn S. King, age 71
Director, David B. (Dave) Burritt, age 56
Director, Joseph W. Ralston, age 68
Director, Adm. James O. Ellis Jr., age 64
Director, James M. Loy, age 69
Director, Rosalind G. Brewer, age 49
Auditors: Ernst&YoungLLP

LOCATIONS

HQ: Lockheed Martin Corporation
6801 Rockledge Dr., Bethesda MD 20817
Phone: 301-897-6000 **Fax:** 301-897-6704
Web: www.lockheedmartin.com

PRODUCTS/OPERATIONS

2011 Sales

	$ mil.	% of total
Products	36,925	79
Services	9,574	21
Total	**46,499**	**100**

2011 Sales by Segment

	$ mil.	% of total
Electronic Systems	14,622	31
Aeronautics	14,362	31
Information Systems & Global Solutions	9,381	20
Space Systems	8,134	18
Total	**46,499**	**100**

2011 Sales by Customer

	$ mil.	% of total
US Government	38,001	82
International	8,068	17
US Commercial & other	430	1
Total	**46,499**	**100**

Selected Products and Services

Electronic Systems
- Advanced aviation management
- Air and theater missile defense systems
- Anti-submarine and undersea warfare systems
- Avionics and ground combat vehicle integration
- Homeland security systems
- Missiles and fire control systems
- Platform integration systems
- Postal automation systems
- Radars
- Security and information technology solutions
- Simulation and training systems
- Surface ship and submarine combat systems
- Surveillance and reconnaissance systems

Aeronautics
- C-5 (strategic airlift aircraft)
- C-130J (tactical airlift aircraft)
- F-2 (Japanese combat aircraft)
- F-16 (multi-role fighter)
- F-22 (air-superiority fighter)
- F-35 Joint Strike Fighter (next-generation multi-role fighter)
- Special mission and reconnaissance aircraft (S-3 Viking U-2 P-3 Orion)
- T-50 (Korean advanced trainer)

Information Systems & Global Services
- Aircraft and engine maintenance and modification services
- Application development
- Command control and communication systems
- Computer system design and service
- Engineering science and information services for NASA
- Engineering science and technology services
- Enterprise solutions
- Government technology services
- Information technology integration and management
- Intelligence
- Launch mission and analysis services for military classified and commercial satellites
- Nuclear operations and materials management (Oak Ridge Tennessee and other locations)
- Operation maintenance training and logistics support for military homeland security and civilian systems
- Surveillance

Space Systems
- Airborne defense systems
- Defensive missiles
- Missile launch vehicles
- Satellites (for commercial and government use)
- Satellite launch services
- Strategic missiles

COMPETITORS

Alliant Techsystems
Arianespace
BAE SYSTEMS
Boeing
CACI International
Cubic Corp.
DynCorp International
EADS
Finmeccanica
General Dynamics
Goodrich Corp.
Herley Industries
Honeywell International
ITT Corp.
L-3 Communications
Northrop Grumman
Orbital Sciences
Raytheon
Saab AB
SAFRAN
SAIC
Textron
Thales
United Technologies
URS

HISTORICAL FINANCIALS

Company Type: Public

Income Statement

FYE: December 31

	REVENUE ($ mil.)	NET INCOME ($ mil.)	NET PROFIT MARGIN	EMPLOYEES
12/11	46,499	2,655	5.7%	123,000
12/10	45,803	2,926	6.4%	132,000
12/09	45,189	3,024	6.7%	140,000
12/08	42,731	3,217	7.5%	146,000
12/07	41,862	3,033	7.2%	140,000
Annual Growth	2.7%	(3.3%)	—	(3.2%)

2011 Year-End Financials

Debt ratio: 17.04%
Return on equity: 265.23%
Cash ($ mil.): 3,582
Current ratio: 116.19
Long-term debt ($ mil.): 6,460
No. of shares (mil.): 321
Dividends
Yield: —
Payout: 41.61%
Market value ($ mil.): 25,969

	STOCK PRICE ($) FY Close	P/E High	P/E Low	Earnings	Dividends	Book Value
12/11	80.90	10	8	7.81	0.00	3.12
12/10	69.91	11	8	7.94	2.64	10.72
12/09	75.35	11	7	7.78	2.34	11.07
12/08	84.08	15	8	7.86	1.83	7.29
12/07	105.26	15	13	7.10	1.47	23.97
Annual Growth	(6.4%)	—	—	2.4%	—	(39.9%)

Loews Corp.

When it comes to diversification Loews definitely has the low-down. The holding company's main interest is insurance through publicly traded subsidiary CNA Financial which offers commercial property/casualty coverage. Other wholly owned and partially owned holdings include hotels in the US and Canada through its Loews Hotels subsidiary. Its energy holdings include contract oil-drilling operator Diamond Offshore Drilling (which operates roughly 50 offshore oil rigs) interstate natural gas transmission pipeline systems operator Boardwalk Pipelines and HighMount Exploration & Production (also natural gas). Loews is controlled and run by the Tisch family including co-chairmen and cousins Andrew and Jonathan.

Geographic Reach

Through its subsidiaries diversified Loews has operations in Canada and beyond. Loews Hotels has two properties in Canada while Diamond Offshore has drilling rigs located off the coasts of about a dozen countries in addition to the US.

Operations

Loews' flagship unit CNA Financial is the company's cash cow accounting for nearly two-thirds of its annual revenue. Rig operator Diamond Offshore Drilling represents nearly a quarter of annual sales while pipeline systems operator Boardwalk Pipeline accounts for most of the rest. Hotels contribute just 2% of annual sales.

CNA's affiliates include The Continental Insurance Company and CNA Surety. While commercial insurance is generally stable stuff CNA has faced the same downturn other big insurers have seen over the past couple of years. With commercial lending still sluggish businesses have less to insure and fewer workers to cover.

Financial Analysis

Loews Corp's. 2011 revenue declined 3% vs. 2010 driven by declines at two of its largest businesses —CNA Financial and Diamond Offshore down nearly 3% and 1% respectively. (While CNA's premium revenue increased in 2011 vs. 2010 investment income declined and the insurer suffered investment losses.) Boardwalk Pipeline posted a modest gain in revenue in 2011 while Loews Hotels logged a 9% gain vs. the prior year.

Consolidated net income declined 17% in 2011 vs. the prior year on lower investment income from partnership results at CNA higher catastrophe losses and investment losses among other factors.

Strategy

With business growing at its hotels (sales are up 19% since 2009) the company has made a commitment to growing the Loews brand. Indeed Loews Hotels agreed to purchase the Renaissance Hollywood Hotel along the renowned Walk of

Fame and rename it the Loews Hollywood Hotel in 2012.

In keeping with the Loews strategy of acquiring what can be turned around letting go of what can't and the wisdom to know the difference the company spent $4 billion to acquire oil and gas exploration operator HighMount Exploration & Production and disposed of its tobacco interests and Bulova subsidiary in 2008.

Ownership

Members of the Tisch family including co-chairmen cousins Andrew and Jonathan Tisch CEO James Tisch and their mothers control more than 20% of the company. Investment firm Davis Selected Advisers owns about 10% of Loews' shares.

HISTORY

In 1946 Larry Tisch who earned a business degree from New York University at age 18 dropped out of Harvard Law to run his parents' New Jersey resort. Younger brother Bob joined him in creating a new entity Tisch Hotels. The company bought two Atlantic City hotels in 1952 quickly making them profitable. Later Tisch purchased such illustrious hotels as the Mark Hopkins The Drake the Belmont Plaza and the Regency.

Moving beyond hotels the brothers bought money-losing companies with poor management. Discarding the management along with underperforming divisions they tightened operational control and eliminated such frills as fancy offices company planes and even memos.

In 1960 Tisch Hotels gained control of MGM's ailing Loew's Theaters to take advantage of their desirable city locations. The company then began demolishing more than 50 stately movie palaces and selling the land to developers. In 1968 the company bought Lorillard the oldest US tobacco company; it shed Lorillard's unprofitable pet food and candy operations and reversed its slipping tobacco market share.

Taking the Loews name in 1971 the company bought CNA Financial in 1974. The Tisch method turned losses of more than $200 million to profits of more than $100 million the very next year. It bought Bulova Watch in 1979 and guided by Larry's son Andrew it gradually returned to profitability.

In the early 1980s Loews entered the energy business by investing in oil supertankers. The company sold its last movie theaters in 1985. Then in 1987 Loews helped CBS fend off a takeover attempt by Ted Turner and ended up with about 25% of the company. Larry became president of the broadcaster.

In 1989 Loews acquired Diamond M Offshore a Texas drilling company and with the acquisition of Odeco Drilling in 1992 the company amassed the world's largest fleet of offshore rigs. The next year Loews grouped its drilling interests as Diamond Offshore Drilling.

In 1994 CNA expanded its insurance empire buying The Continental Corp. The next year Loews sold its interest in CBS and the following year Diamond Offshore Drilling merged with Arethusa (Off-Shore) Limited.

As deft as the Tisch brothers had been in accumulating their riches Larry's bearish investment strategy (short-selling stocks) cost Loews in the late 1990s (more than $900 million alone during 1997's bull market). Larry and Bob retired as co-CEOs at the end of 1998; Larry's son James already president and COO became CEO.

That year Lorillard signed on to the 46-state tobacco lawsuit settlement; the first payment cost the company $325 million (payments continue until 2025). Facing a softened insurance market CNA sold unprofitable lines to focus on commercial insurance; in 1999 it transferred its auto and homeowners lines to Allstate (it continues writing and renewing these policies) and put its life and life reinsurance units up for sale in 2000. Also that year Lorillard was hit with $16 billion of a record-breaking $144 billion punitive damage award in a smokers' class-action suit in Florida. CNA Financial paid out over $450 million in 2001-02 for claims related to the attacks on the World Trade Center.

In 2004 the company continued to expand its natural resource offerings when its subsidiary Boardwalk Pipelines (formerly known as TGT Pipeline) acquired Gulf South Pipeline which operates natural gas pipeline and gathering systems in Texas Louisiana Mississippi Alabama and Florida including several major supply hubs. Loews had acquired gas pipeline operator Texas Gas Transmission in 2003. Texas Gas operates natural gas pipeline systems reaching from the Louisiana Gulf Coast and East Texas north through Louisiana Arkansas Mississippi Tennessee Kentucky Indiana and into Ohio and Illinois.

Tobacco had long been a staple in Loews' portfolio until the company kicked the habit. Prior to quitting the company kept its 62% ownership of Lorillard rolled up as Carolina Group and traded it as a tracking subsidiary. Lorillard which included the Kent Newport and True cigarette brands in the US accounted for more than 20% of Loews' revenues. However after a steady stream of tobacco-related litigation the company spun Lorillard off into an independent public company in 2008 eliminating the Carolina Group and exiting the industry. Additionally while accessories make the outfit in 2008 Loews slipped its Bulova subsidiary off of its wrist and handed it to competitor Citizen Watch for $250 million.

Larry Tisch died at the age of 80 in 2003. Chairman Bob Tisch died of cancer in late 2005. Tisch also was co-owner of the New York Giants of the National Football League.

EXECUTIVES

SVP and CFO, Peter W. Keegan, age 67, $990,000 total compensation
SVP, Herbert C. Hofmann, age 69
Co-Chairman Office of the President and Chairman Executive Committee, Andrew H. Tisch, age 62, $975,000 total compensation
Co-Chairman and Office of the President; Chairman and CEO Loews Hotels, Jonathan M. Tisch, age 58, $975,000 total compensation
President CEO and Director, James S. Tisch, age 59, $975,000 total compensation
SVP, David B. Edelson, age 52, $975,000 total compensation
VP Human Resources, Alan Momeyer
VP Tax, Susan Becker
SVP General Counsel and Secretary, Gary W. Garson, age 65
Treasurer, John J. Kenny
Public Affairs, Candace Leeds
Controller, Mark S. Schwartz, age 53
Investor Relations, Darren Daugherty
VP Internal Audit, Robert F. Crook
VP Corporate Development, Jonathan Nathanson
VP Risk Management, Audrey A. Rampinelli
SVP and Chief Investment Officer, Richard W. Scott, age 58
SVP, Kenneth I. Siegel, age 55
VP and CIO, Robert D. Fields
Co-Chairman and Office of the President; Chairman and CEO Loews Hotels, Jonathan M. Tisch, age 58
President CEO and Director, James S. Tisch, age 59
Director, Charles M. Diker, age 77
Director, Paul J. Fribourg, age 57
Director, Philip A. (Phil) Laskawy, age 71
Director, Jacob A. Frenkel, age 69
Director, Gloria R. Scott, age 73
Director, Joseph L. Bower, age 73
Director, Ken Miller, age 69
Director, Ann E. Berman, age 59
Director, Walter L. Harris, age 60
Auditors: Deloitte&ToucheLLP

LOCATIONS

HQ: Loews Corporation
667 Madison Ave., New York NY 10065-8087
Phone: 212-521-2000 **Fax:** 212-521-2525
Web: www.loews.com

PRODUCTS/OPERATIONS

2011 Revenues

Insurance premiums	6,603	47
Net investment income	2,063	14
Other	2,259	16
Total	**14,127**	**100**

2011 Revenues

	$ mil.	% of total
CNA Financial		
CNA Commercial	4,071	29
CNA Specialty	3,512	25
Life & group non-core	1,334	9
Other insurance	44	
Diamond Offshore	3,334	24
Boardwalk Pipeline	1,144	8
HighMount	390	3
Loews Hotels	337	2
Corporate & other	(39)	-
Total	**14,127**	**100**

Selected Subsidiaries

Boardwalk Pipeline Partners LP (61%)
CNA Financial Corporation (90%)
Diamond Offshore Drilling Inc. (50%)
HighMount Exploration & Production LLC (100%)
Loews Hotels Holding Corporation (100%)

COMPETITORS

ACE Limited
AIG
American Financial Group
Apache
Berkshire Hathaway
Chubb Corp
Cincinnati Financial
Four Seasons Hotels
Hilton Worldwide
Hyatt
Marriott
Noble
Pride International
Starwood Hotels & Resorts
Statoil
The Hartford
Transocean
Travelers Companies
Wyndham Worldwide

HISTORICAL FINANCIALS

Company Type: Public

Income Statement FYE: December 31

	ASSETS ($ mil.)	NET INCOME ($ mil.)	INCOME AS % OF ASSETS	EMPLOYEES
12/11	75,375	1,064	1.4%	18,250
12/10	76,277	1,288	1.7%	18,400
12/09	74,070	564	0.8%	18,500
12/08	69,857	4,530	6.5%	19,100
12/07	76,079	2,489	3.3%	21,700
Annual Growth	(0.2%)	(19.1%)	—	(4.2%)

2011 Year-End Financials

Debt ratio: 11.82%
Return on equity: 5.65%
Cash ($ mil.): 129
Current ratio: —
Long-term debt ($ mil.): 8,913
No. of shares (mil.): 396
Dividends
Yield: —
Payout: 9.51%
Market value ($ mil.): 14,917

	STOCK PRICE ($) FY Close	P/E High/Low		PER SHARE ($) Earnings	Dividends	Book Value
12/11	37.65	17	13	2.63	0.00	47.54
12/10	38.91	13	10	3.07	0.25	44.51
12/09	36.35	28	14	1.30	0.25	39.76
12/08	28.25	6	2	9.05	0.25	30.17
12/07	50.34	14	11	3.65	0.25	33.21
Annual Growth	(7.0%)	—	—	(7.9%)	—	9.4%

Lorillard, Inc.

Money smells of menthol at Lorillard the #3 cigarette maker in the US (behind Philip Morris USA and Reynolds American). Flagship brand Newport is its best-selling menthol cigarette and #2-top selling cigarette name in the US accounting for more than 85% of sales. Other brands include the premium and discount lines of Kent Old Gold True and Maverick as well as the blu e-cigarette. The company sells its lineup to wholesale distributors (who supply retail and chain stores and government agencies). Lorillard was known as the Carolina Group until 2008 when it split from former parent Loews. Founded in 1760 by French immigrant Pierre Lorillard it is the nation's oldest continuously operating tobacco business.

Despite the declining number of American smokers Lorillard is maintaining its financial momentum. Year-over-year net income has increased approximately 7% to 9% between 2009 and 2011. In 2011 sales rose 9% from the prior year driven by higher sales volume and higher pricing offset by an increase in sales incentives. Total wholesale unit volume inched up almost 7% throughout 2010. Volume shipments of the Newport brand of menthol cigarettes increased some 6%. Reflecting the sputtering economy shipments of Maverick the company's discount brand increased 16% compared to 2010.

The rise in wholesale shipments contrasts with the domestic cigarette industry's decline of more than 3%. Lorillard has strategically introduced a non-menthol version of its Newport brand (Newport Red). In addition it has strengthened its position in the discount cigarette segment with Maverick. Its five core brands include more than 40 different product offerings differentiated by price taste flavor length and packaging.

The tobacco company is also chasing after the fast-growing electronic cigarette market as more restaurants companies and municipalities cave to antismoking campaigns. In 2012 Lorillard acquired blu ecigs an electronic cigarette company based in Charlotte North Carolina for $135 million in cash in its effort to capture this niche of the market with a top brand. Without the tobacco smoke ash or smell of a real burning cigarette blu ecigs help smokers looking to kick the habit maintain the social aspects of lighting up. As part of the agreement blu ecigs will operate as a subsidiary of Lorillard which expects to give the blu ecigs brand a boost with its experience in regulatory issues and established infrastructure.

Lorillard supplies about 500 direct buy customers primarily wholesale distributors that service more than 400000 retail outlets chain stores and government agencies such as the US Armed Forces. McLane Company comprises more than a quarter of the company's sales. The cigarette maker purchases more than 70% of its tobacco from Alliance One International (formerly DIMON).

Lorillard and its rivals face an ever challenging regulatory environment following the passage of the Family Smoking and Tobacco Control Act by the US Congress in June 2009. The landmark legislation grants the US Food and Drug Administration (FDA) substantial power to regulate tobacco products including authority over marketing as well as candy flavorings (such as menthol) and nicotine in tobacco products.

Responding the cigarette maker along with Reynolds American and others filed suit against the FDA protesting its "unprecedented restriction" of First Amendment rights. In 2010 a court axed the law's ban on using color and graphics in certain tobacco products and on statements by tobacco makers about the regulation; a subsequent ruling in 2012 by a federal judge declared unconstitutional the FDA's requirement for stronger warnings and pictures on the top half of cigarette packages. An appeal by the Justice Department in the US Court of Appeals for the District of Columbia was heard in April 2012 with a decision to be announced at a later date.

An equally significant legal challenge that Lorillard and other cigarette makers face is small scale civil litigation from individual plaintiffs seeking significant judgments. For example a Florida court in spring 2012 ordered Lorillard to pay a widow $25 million in punitive damages after she was awarded $16 million in compensatory damages. The company plans to appeal.

EXECUTIVES

Chairman President and CEO, Murray S. Kessler, age 53
SVP Legal and External Affairs Secretary and General Counsel, Ronald S. Milstein, age 55, $639,298 total compensation
EVP Marketing and Sales, Randy B. Spell, age 60, $663,837 total compensation
EVP Finance and Planning and CFO, David H. Taylor, age 56, $872,219 total compensation
VP Controller and Chief Accounting Officer, Anthony B. Petitt, age 41
Director Investor Relations, Robert W. (Bob) Bannon, age 47
EVP Production Operations, Charles E. Hennighausen, age 57, $631,277 total compensation
Director, Nigel Travis, age 62
Director, Andrew H. (Andy) Card Jr., age 64
Director, Virgis W. Colbert, age 73
Director, Dianne Neal Blixt, age 52
Director, Richard W. (Rich) Roedel, age 62
Director, David E. R. Dangoor, age 62
Director, Kit D. Dietz, age 55
Director, Robert C. (Bob) Almon, age 60
Auditors: Deloitte&ToucheLLP

LOCATIONS

HQ: Lorillard Inc.
714 Green Valley Rd., Greensboro NC 27408-7018
Phone: 336-335-7000 **Fax:** 336-335-7550
Web: www.lorillard.com

PRODUCTS/OPERATIONS

Selected Brands

Kent
Maverick
Newport
Old Gold
TRUE

COMPETITORS

British American Tobacco
Commonwealth Brands
JT International
Philip Morris USA
Reynolds American
Smokin Joes
Star Scientific
Swisher International
Vector Group

HISTORICAL FINANCIALS

Company Type: Public

Income Statement

FYE: December 31

	REVENUE ($ mil.)	NET INCOME ($ mil.)	NET PROFIT MARGIN	EMPLOYEES
12/11	6,466	1,116	17.3%	2,800
12/10	5,932	1,029	17.3%	2,700
12/09	5,233	948	18.1%	2,700
12/08	4,204	887	21.1%	2,800
12/07	3,969	898	22.6%	2,800
Annual Growth	13.0%	5.6%	—	0.0%

2011 Year-End Financials

Debt ratio: 86.27%
Return on equity: 987650001000000.00%
Cash ($ mil.): 1,634
Current ratio: 172.66
Long-term debt ($ mil.): 2,595
No. of shares (mil.): 396
Dividends
Yield: —
Payout: 195.25%
Market value ($ mil.): 45,144

	STOCK PRICE ($) FY Close	P/E High/Low		PER SHARE ($) Earnings	Dividends	Book Value
12/11	114.00	44	28	2.66	0.00	(3.82)
12/10	82.06	39	31	2.26	4.25	(0.51)
12/09	80.23	42	28	1.92	3.84	0.19
12/08	56.35	52	32	1.72	1.84	1.25
12/07	85.30	52	37	1.72	0.00	1.94
Annual Growth	7.5%	—	—	11.5%	—	—

Lowe's Companies Inc

No longer a low-profile company Lowe's Companies has evolved from a regional hardware store operator into a nationwide chain of home improvement superstores bent on international expansion. The #2 US home improvement chain (after The Home Depot) Lowe's has more than 1745 superstores in 50 states and more than 30 locations in Canada and Mexico as well as an e-commerce site. Its stores sell some 40000 products for do-it-yourselfers and professionals for home improvement and repair projects such as lumber paint plumbing and electrical supplies tools and gardening products as well as appliances lighting and furniture. Lowe's is the second-largest US home appliance retailer after Sears.

Geographic Reach

Since entering Canada in 2007 Lowe's has grown to number 31 stores there. Seeking to get bigger faster in Canada Lowe's in July 2012 bid C$1.8 billion (or roughly $1.8 billion) to acquire its

Canadian rival RONA. (Based in Quebec RONA operates about 800 hardware stores across Canada including about 40 in Quebec where Lowe's has no retail presence.) However RONA rejected the offer and Lowe's formally withdrew its bid in September.

Financial Analysis

Sales topped $50 billion in fiscal 2012 (ends January) up nearly 3% vs. the prior year. Sales at stores open longer than 13 months were flat however and net income however declined more than 8% over the same period. Still fiscal 2012 marked the second consecutive year of sales growth for Lowe's after two years of falling sales during the recession and housing crisis. Despite the sales reversal Lowe's has kept its expansion plans conservative opening only about 25 new outlets in fiscal 2011. Going forward the company revised its new store opening schedule to only 10 to 15 locations per year beginning in 2012 down from a previous target of 30.

Strategy

The slower pace of store openings reverses the trend at Lowe's which grew its store base by more than 50% since 2005. The company typically concentrates on small and midsized markets but it also targets large metropolitan areas (with populations of 500000 or more). Lowe's which entered Canada five years ago sees potential in the North American market for up to 2500 locations but the economic downturn slowed its progress on making that a reality. Indeed in October 2011 Lowe's announced plans to shutter 20 of its underperforming US locations and eliminate nearly 2000 jobs. Beyond North America Lowe's has set its sights on the land down under. Through a joint venture formed in 2009 with Australia's top retailer Woolworths Ltd. Lowe's owns a one-third share in seven DIY stores under the Master banner there. The partnership expects to open as many as 20 Masters stores in the coming year. To drive sales Lowe's is trying to differentiate itself from its rivals by forming strategic partnerships with select suppliers including GE (appliances) Stainmaster (carpets) and Pella (windows) to offer brand-name merchandise in its stores. It's also trying to attract more female customers who the company claims call the shots on about 80% of home improvement decisions. To make its big-box stores appealing the company makes effective use of lighting and signage and caters to women and baby boomers with an attractive store layout. The retailer has also increased the number of sales representatives working the floor on weekends its peak shopping period.

HISTORY

Lowe's Companies was founded in 1921 as Mr. L. S. Lowe's North Wilkesboro Hardware in North Wilkesboro North Carolina. A family operation by 1945 Mr. Lowe's store (which also sold groceries snuff and harnesses) was run by his son Jim and his son-in-law H. Carl Buchan. Buchan bought Lowe's share of the company in 1956 and incorporated as Lowe's North Wilkesboro Hardware; he wanted Lowe's as part of the company name because he liked the slogan "Lowe's Low Prices." The chain expanded from North Carolina into Tennessee Virginia and West Virginia. By 1960 Buchan had 15 stores and sales of $31 million — up $4 million from a decade before.

Buchan planned to create a profit-sharing plan for Lowe's employees but in 1960 he died of a heart attack at age 44. In 1961 Lowe's management and the executors of Buchan's estate established the Lowe's Employees Profit Sharing and Trust which bought Buchan's 89% of the company (later renamed Lowe's Companies). That year they financed the transaction through a public offering which diluted the employees' stock. Lowe's was listed on the NYSE in 1979.

Robert Strickland who had joined the company in 1957 became chairman in 1978. Revenues increased from $170 million in 1971 to more than $900 million with a net income of $25 million in 1979. Traditionally the majority of Lowe's business was in sales to professional homebuilders but in 1980 housing starts fell and company profits dropped. Concurrently The Home Depot introduced its low-price warehouse concept. Instead of building warehouse stores of its own Strickland changed the stores' layouts and by 1982 had redesigned half of the 229 stores to be more oriented toward do-it-yourself (DIY) consumers. The new designs featured softer lighting and displays of entire room layouts to appeal to women who made up over half of all DIY customers. In 1982 Lowe's made more than half of its sales to consumers for the first time in its history.

Although Lowe's had more than 300 stores by 1988 its outlets were only about 20000 sq. ft. (one-fifth the size of Home Depot's warehouse stores). By 1989 Lowe's which had continued to target contractors as well as DIYers was overtaken by Home Depot as the US's #1 home retail chain.

Since 1989 the company has focused on building larger stores taking a charge of $71 million in 1991 to phase out smaller stores and build warehouse outlets. In 1993 Lowe's opened 57 large stores (half were replacements for existing stores) almost doubling its total floor space.

The retailer opened 29 new stores in 1995. During 1996 Lowe's added a net of 37 stores and in 1997 it opened 42 stores in new markets. Also that year president and CEO Leonard Herring retired and was replaced by former COO Robert Tillman who also took the post of chairman when Strickland stepped down in 1998.

Also in 1998 the company entered a joint venture to sell an exclusive line of Kobalt-brand professional mechanics' tools produced by Snap-on and to better serve commercial customers began allowing them to special order items not stocked in stores. In addition Lowe's announced it would spend $1.5 billion over the next several years on a 100-store push into the western US. Lowe's westward expansion was fueled when it purchased Washington-based 38-store Eagle Hardware & Garden in 1999 in a stock swap deal worth $1.3 billion. The company gradually converted the Eagle stores into Lowe's.

In 2001 the company earmarked $2.4 billion of its $2.7 billion capital budget for store expansions and new distribution centers.

Robert Niblock was promoted from CFO to president in March 2003. Lowe's sold its some 30 outlets operating as The Contractor Yard to The Strober Organization in February 2004. In April 2004 the company opened its first predominantly urban-oriented store suited to the needs of city dwellers and building superintendents in Brooklyn.

Chairman and CEO Robert Tillman retired in January 2005. He was succeeded by president Robert Niblock.

Lowe's entered the Canadian market in 2007.

The home improvement chain expanded its distribution footprint in 2008 opening a regional distribution center in Pittston Pennsylvania and a flatbed distribution center in Purvis Mississippi.

During 2010 Lowe's opened its first location in Mexico (in Monterrey).

EXECUTIVES

EVP Human Resources, Maureen K. Ausura, age 56
Chairman and CEO, Robert A. Niblock, age 49, $1,100,000 total compensation
SVP Product Development; President Global Sourcing, Michael K. Menser, age 56
EVP Business Development, Gregory M. (Greg) Bridgeford, age 57, $590,000 total compensation
EVP Merchandising, Robert J. Gfeller Jr., age 50
Director, Richard W. (Rick) Dreiling, age 59
EVP and CIO, Michael K. (Mike) Brown, age 48
SVP and General Merchandising Manager Outdoor Living, Eric D. Sowder, age 55
EVP and CFO, Robert F. (Bob) Hull Jr., age 47, $660,000 total compensation
SVP and Chief Risk Officer, Marshall A. Croom, age 51
EVP Store Operations, Rick D. Damron, age 47
EVP Logistics and Distribution, Joseph M. (Mike) Mabry Jr., age 49
SVP International Operations and Customer Support Services, William D. (Doug) Robinson, age 50
SVP Store Operations South Central Division, William W. (Bill) Edwards, age 50
SVP and Chief Accounting Officer, Matthew V. Hollifield, age 45
SVP Corporate Affairs, N. Brian Peace, age 46
SVP Distribution, Stephen J. Szilagyi
SVP and General Merchandising Manager Home Decor, Patricia M. (Patti) Price
SVP and General Merchandising Manager Kitchen and Bath, Clinton T. (Clint) Davis
SVP Specialty Sales and Store Operations Support, Dennis R. Knowles
EVP General Counsel Secretary and Chief Compliance Officer, Gaither M. Keener Jr., age 62
SVP Operations North Central Division, Brent G. Kirby
SVP Marketing and Advertising, Thomas J. (Tom) Lamb
SVP Learning and Organizational Effectiveness, Cedric T. Coco
SVP Store Planning and Environment, Ronnie E. Damron
SVP Human Resources, Robert (Bob) Ihrie Jr.
SVP Financial Planning and Analysis, Kelly C. Ross
SVP IT Retail Solutions, Joyce L. Vonada
SVP Real Estate Engineering and Construction, Gary E. Wyatt
SVP Deputy General Counsel and Assistant Secretary, Janet M. Saura, age 47
VP Corporate Communications, Chris C. Ahearn
Media Contact, Julie V. Yenichek
SVP Strategy, Richard D. Maltsbarger
SVP and General Manager Merchandising Hardlines and Building Products, Troy J. Dally
SVP Logistics, William L. (Leroy) Allen
SVP Information Technology Business Management, Everett B. (Britt) Dayton
SVP Store Operations West Division, Kevin S. Measel
SVP IT Infrastructure and Operations, Paul D. Ramsay
SVP Deputy General Counsel and Assistant Secretary, M. Lee Reeves
Director, Stephen F. (Steve) Page, age 72
Director, Marshall O. Larsen, age 63
Director, Robert L. (Bob) Johnson, age 66
Director, Richard W. (Rick) Dreiling, age 59
Director, David W. Bernauer, age 68
Director, Richard K. Lochridge, age 68
Director, Peter C. Browning, age 70
Director, Leonard L. Berry, age 69
Director, Raul Alvarez, age 56
Director, Dawn E. Hudson, age 54
Auditors: Deloitte&ToucheLLP

LOCATIONS

HQ: Lowe' s Companies Inc.
1000 Lowe' s Blvd., Mooresville NC 28117
Phone: 704-758-1000 **Fax:** 704-758-4766
Web: www.lowes.com

2012 Stores

	No.
US	1,712
Canada	31
Mexico	2
Total	1,745

PRODUCTS/OPERATIONS

2012 Sales

	$ mil.	% of total
Appliances	5	11
Lawn & landscape products	4	10
Fashion electrical	4	8
Lumber	3	7
Building materials	3	6
Paint	3	6
Home fashions storage & cleaning	3	6
Rough plumbing	2	6
Flooring	2	6
Tools	2	6
Seasonal living	2	5
Millwork	2	5
Hardware	2	5
Fashion plumbing	2	5
Nursery	2	4
Cabinets & countertops	1	3
Other	0	1
Total	50	100

Selected Proprietary Brands

allen+roth
Aquasource
Garden Treasures
Harbor Breeze
Kobalt
Portfolio
Reliabilt
Top Choice
Utilitech

Selected Subsidiaries

Lowe' s Home Centers Inc.
Lowe' s HIW Inc.

COMPETITORS

84 Lumber
Abbey Carpet
Ace Hardware
Best Buy
CCA Global
Do it Best
HD Supply
Home Depot
McCoy Corp.
Menard
Northern Tool
Sears
Sherwin-Williams
Sutherland Lumber
True Value
Wal-Mart
Wolseley

HISTORICAL FINANCIALS

Company Type: Public

Income Statement

FYE: February 3

	REVENUE ($ mil.)	NET INCOME ($ mil.)	NET PROFIT MARGIN	EMPLOYEES
02/12*	50,208	1,839	3.7%	248,000
01/11	48,815	2,010	4.1%	234,000
01/10	47,220	1,783	3.8%	239,000
01/09	48,230	2,195	4.6%	229,000
02/08	48,283	2,809	5.8%	216,000
Annual Growth	1.0%	(10.0%)	—	3.5%

*Fiscal year change

2012 Year-End Financials

Debt ratio: 22.73%
Return on equity: 11.12%
Cash ($ mil.): 1,014
Current ratio: 127.64
Long-term debt ($ mil.): 7,035
No. of shares (mil.): 1,241
Dividends
Yield: 1.95%
Payout: 37.06%
Market value ($ mil.): 33,755

	STOCK PRICE ($) FY Close	P/E High	P/E Low	PER SHARE ($) Earnings	Dividends	Book Value
02/12*	27.20	19	13	1.43	0.53	13.32
01/11	25.25	20	14	1.42	0.42	13.38
01/10	21.65	20	11	1.21	0.36	13.07
01/09	18.27	18	11	1.49	0.34	12.28
02/08	25.55	18	11	1.86	0.29	11.04
Annual Growth	1.6%	—	—	(6.4%)	16.3%	4.8%

*Fiscal year change

M & T Bank Corp

M&T Bank Corporation is making a splash in the mid-Atlantic region. It is the holding company of M&T Bank which offers deposit loan trust investment brokerage and insurance services to more than two million individuals and small and midsized business customers. The bank has operates about 775 branches in New York Pennsylvania New Jersey Delaware Maryland Virginia West Virginia and Washington DC as well as major cities throughout the US. Its residential mortgage origination operations span more than a dozen states in the South and West. The company also manages a proprietary line of mutual funds the Wilmington Funds. M&T is buying Hudson City Bancorp for some $3.7 billion.

Acquisitions are nothing new for M&T. The company often buys smaller banks in order to expand its reach or solidify its presence in existing markets. It has averaged roughly one acquisition a year since 1990.

The Hudson City acquisition is the latest in a series of transformational deals for the company. It will bring in 135 branches in the New York City metropolitan area and will greatly expand M&T's presence in New Jersey.

The company bought Wilmington Trust Corporation in 2011 for some $350 million. The deal which added some 50 branches in Delaware plus two dozen more locations throughout the US not only grew M&T's banking operations but should strengthen its wealth management and corporate client businesses as well. The addition helped to boost M&T's 2011 results.

M&T purchased Provident Bankshares for approximately $400 million in stock in 2009. That deal added more than 130 branches mainly in Maryland and Virginia to M&T Bank's network. In 2009 and 2010 the company acquired two failed institutions that had been seized by regulators Bradford Bank and K Bank. The FDIC-assisted deals added about 15 bank branches in Maryland.

Allied Irish Banks (AIB) owned more than 20% of M&T but divested its interest in 2010 in order to raise capital. It assumed the stake when M&T bought troubled Maryland-based bank Allfirst Financial from AIB in 2003. Now insiders own more than 20% of M&T's stock.

EXECUTIVES

Vice Chairman M&T Bank Corporation and M&T Bank; Chairman and CEO Mid-Atlantic Region M&T Bank, Michael P. (Mike) Pinto, age 56, $571,154 total compensation
Chairman and CEO M&T Bank Corporation and M&T Bank, Robert G. (Bob) Wilmers, age 77, $675,000 total compensation
EVP M&T Bank Corporation and M&T Bank Wealth and Institutional Services Division, William J. (Bill) Farrell II, age 54
Vice Chairman, Jorge G. Pereira, age 78
EVP M&T Bank Corporation and M&T Bank; President and COO Mid-Atlantic Division, Atwood Collins III, age 65, $283,846 total compensation
President and Director M&T Bank Corporation and M&T Bank, Mark J. Czarnecki, age 56, $571,154 total compensation
EVP M&T Bank Corporation and M&T Bank, Brian E. Hickey, age 59, $299,231 total compensation
EVP M&T Bank Corporation and M&T Bank, Kevin J. Pearson, age 50, $379,039 total compensation
Administrative VP and Secretary, Marie King
EVP Human Resources M&T Bank Corporation and M&T Bank, Stephen J. Braunscheidel, age 55
EVP M&T Bank Banking Services Division, James J. Beardi, age 65
EVP and Chief Credit Officer M&T Bank Corporation and M&T Bank, Robert J. Bojdak, age 56
EVP and CIO M&T Bank Corporation and M&T Bank, Michele D. Trolli, age 50
SVP and Controller, Michael R. Spychala
Group VP, Clifford P. Johnson
Group VP, Ayan Das Gupta
Assistant Secretary, Deborah R. Pokerwinski
VP and Assistant Secretary, Randall A. Krolewicz
VP and Assistant Secretary, Donald J. MacLeod
Administrative VP, Darlene A. Spychala
Administrative VP and Assistant Secretary, Brian R. Yoshida
EVP and CFO M&T Bank Corporation and M&T Bank, Rene F. Jones, age 47, $311,538 total compensation
SVP and General Auditor, John L. D'Angelo
EVP M&T Bank Corporation and M&T Bank Residential Mortgage Consumer Lending and Business Banking Divisions, Richard S. Gold, age 51
EVP and Treasurer M&T Bank Corporation and M&T Bank, D. Scott N. Warman
SVP and General Counsel, Drew J. Pfirrman
SVP and Assistant Treasurer, Douglas A. Sheline
VP, Mark E. Wood
Assistant VP, Kathleen M. Dewyea
EVP M&T Bank Corporation and M&T Bank Retail Banking Division, Darren J. King
Director, Robert E. (Bob) Sadler Jr., age 66
Vice Chairman M&T Bank Corporation and M&T Bank; Chairman and CEO Mid-Atlantic Region M&T Bank, Michael P. (Mike) Pinto, age 56
Director, Brent D. Baird, age 72
Director, Robert T. (Bob) Brady, age 71
Director, T. Jefferson Cunningham III, age 69
Director, Donald E. Foley, age 60
Director, Michael D. Buckley, age 67
Vice Chairman, Jorge G. Pereira, age 78
Director, Robert J. (Bob) Bennett, age 70
Director, C. Angela Bontempo, age 71
Director, Richard G. King, age 67
Director, Herbert L. Washington, age 61
President and Director M&T Bank Corporation and M&T Bank, Mark J. Czarnecki, age 56
Director, Eugene J. Sheehy, age 57
Director, Melinda R. (Mindy) Rich, age 54

Director, Patrick W. E. Hodgson, age 70
Director, Gary N. Geisel, age 63
Auditors: PricewaterhouseCoopersLLP

LOCATIONS

HQ: M&T Bank Corporation
1 M&T Plaza, Buffalo NY 14203
Phone: 716-842-5445 **Fax:** 716-842-5839
Web: www.mandtbank.com

PRODUCTS/OPERATIONS

2011 Sales

	$ mil.	% of total
Interest		
Loans & leases including fees	2,522	58
Fully taxable investment securities	256	6
Other	13	-
Noninterest		
Service charges on deposit accounts	455	10
Trust income	332	8
Mortgage banking	166	4
Gain on bank investment securities	150	3
Brokerage services	56	1
Other	422	10
Total	**4,375**	**100**

COMPETITORS

Citigroup
First Niagara Financial
Fulton Financial
HSBC USA
JPMorgan Chase
KeyCorp
Northwest Bancshares
PNC Financial
RBS Citizens Financial Group
Sovereign Bank
SunTrust
Susquehanna Bancshares

HISTORICAL FINANCIALS

Company Type: Public

Income Statement FYE: December 31

	ASSETS ($ mil.)	NET INCOME ($ mil.)	INCOME AS % OF ASSETS	EMPLOYEES
12/11	77,924	859	1.1%	15,666
12/10	68,021	736	1.1%	13,365
12/09	68,880	379	0.6%	14,226
12/08	65,815	555	0.8%	13,620
12/07	64,875	654	1.0%	13,869
Annual Growth	4.7%	7.1%	—	3.1%

2011 Year-End Financials

Debt ratio: 8.58%
Return on equity: 9.27%
Cash ($ mil.): 2,166
Current ratio: —
Long-term debt ($ mil.): 6,686
No. of shares (mil.): 125
Dividends
Yield: —
Payout: 44.09%
Market value ($ mil.): 9,595

	STOCK PRICE ($) FY Close	P/E High	P/E Low	PER SHARE ($) Earnings	Dividends	Book Value
12/11	76.34	14	11	6.35	0.00	73.77
12/10	87.05	17	12	5.69	2.80	69.82
12/09	66.89	24	11	2.89	2.80	65.58
12/08	57.41	19	11	5.01	2.80	61.48
12/07	81.57	21	13	5.95	2.60	59.04
Annual Growth	(1.6%)	—	—	1.6%	—	5.7%

Macys Inc

LOCATIONS

HQ: Macys Inc
151 West 34th Street, New York, NY 10001
Phone: 212 494-1602 **Fax:** 212 494-1838
Web: www.macys.com

HISTORICAL FINANCIALS

Company Type:

Income Statement FYE: January 28

	REVENUE ($ mil.)	NET INCOME ($ mil.)	NET PROFIT MARGIN	EMPLOYEES
01/12	26,405	1,256	4.8%	171,000
01/11	25,003	847	3.4%	166,000
01/10	23,489	350	1.5%	161,000
01/09*	24,892	(4,803)	—	167,000
02/08	26,313	893	3.4%	182,000
Annual Growth	0.1%	8.9%	—	(1.5%)

*Fiscal year change

2012 Year-End Financials

Debt ratio: 35.11%
Return on equity: 21.17%
Cash ($ mil.): 2,827
Current ratio: 140.14
Long-term debt ($ mil.): 6,655
No. of shares (mil.): 414
Dividends
Yield: —
Payout: 11.99%
Market value ($ mil.): 14,008

	STOCK PRICE ($) FY Close	P/E High	P/E Low	PER SHARE ($) Earnings	Dividends	Book Value
01/12	33.82	12	7	2.92	0.00	14.32
01/11	22.99	13	8	1.98	0.00	13.06
01/10	15.93	25	8	0.83	0.00	11.17
01/09*	8.95	—	—	(11.40)	0.00	11.06
02/08	28.00	23	11	1.97	0.00	23.60
Annual Growth	4.8%	—	—	10.3%	—	(11.7%)

*Fiscal year change

MainSource Financial Group Inc

MainSource Financial wants to be the main source of financial services for residents and businesses in Indiana and beyond. It is the holding company of MainSource Bank which operates about 80 branches in the Hoosier State as well as neighboring portions of Ohio Illinois and Kentucky. The bank offers standard deposit and lending products in addition to trust and insurance services. Real estate loans account for some 85% of MainSource Financial's lending portfolio which also includes other commercial and consumer loans. Through MainSource Insurance the company provides annuities and credit life insurance.

The company has made several acquisitions over the years including National City Corporation's Madison Bank & Trust Union Community Bancorp Peoples Ohio Financial and 1st Independence Financial Group. MainSource has also opened new offices and acquired operating branches from other banks to boost its network and enter new markets. However the economic downturn brought a slowdown for the company which lost $64 million in 2009.

The decline was largely attributed to loan losses. MainSource sold some assets the following year which helped it return to profitability. In late 2010 the company sold its property/casualty and health insurance operations. The divestiture marked a turnaround for MainSource which had built up its insurance holdings. The company retained its annuities and credit life businesses which align more closely with its core banking operations.

Net income continued to improve in 2011 growing 60% to $23.8 million. Among the factors contributing to the gains were a decline in loan loss provision expenses higher earnings on trust and investment product fees increased interchange income and higher realized gains on securities. However overall revenues declined 5% to $166.9 million. Interest on loans which makes up the majority of the company's earnings have been declining as the bank's loan portfolio has shrunk. In 2011 the company ceased writing development and construction loans in the sluggish economy; MainSource also sells a portion of its residential real estate loans to the secondary market. The sale of the property/casualty business has also cut into MainSource's revenues.

EXECUTIVES

SVP and Chief Banking Officer, Daryl R. Tressler, $225,887 total compensation
Chairman, Robert E. Hoptry, age 73, $186,619 total compensation
SVP CFO and Secretary, James M. (Jamie) Anderson, age 38, $174,592 total compensation
Chairman President and CEO, Archie M. Brown Jr., age 51, $109,038 total compensation
President and CEO MainSource Insurance, Jerry J. Vollmer
VP Retail Services MainSource Bank of Ohio, Richard K. Bender
SVP Commercial Lending MainSource Bank - Illinois, William J. Krones
SVP Wealth Management MainSource Bank of Indiana, Daniel F. Anderson
President MainSource Title; SVP Retail Lending MainSource Bank of Indiana, Mark W. Dunevant
President and CEO MainSource Bank of Ohio, David J. Dippold
SVP and Chief Credit Officer, William J. (Bill) Goodwin
SVP and Senior Commercial Lending Officer MainSource Bank of Indiana, Keith A. Lindauer
SVP Branch Administration MainSource Bank of Indiana, Chris M. Harrison
Chairman President and CEO MainSource Bank of Illinois, W. Brent Hoptry
VP and Director Retail Services MainSource Bank of Illinois, Raul P. Flores
SVP Commercial Lending MainSource Bank of Ohio, Jesse E. Westmeyer Sr.
Director, Charles J. Thayer, age 68
Director, William G. Barron, age 62
Director, Philip A. Frantz, age 67
Director, Rick S. Hartman, age 56
President CEO and Director, Archie M. Brown Jr., age 51
Director, Brian J. Crall, age 52
Director, D. J. Hines, age 60
Director, Kathleen L. Bardwell, age 56
Director, Thomas M. O'Brien
Auditors: CroweHorwathLLP

LOCATIONS

HQ: MainSource Financial Group Inc.
2105 N. State Rd. 3 Bypass, Greensburg IN 47240
Phone: 812-663-6734 **Fax:** 651-686-9331
Web: www.pattersoncompanies.com

PRODUCTS/OPERATIONS

2011 Sales

	$ mil.	% of total
Interest		
Loans including fees	92	55
Investment securities	28	17
Other	0	-
Noninterest		
Service charges on deposit accounts	18	11
Net realized gains on securities	11	7
Interchange income	6	3
Mortgage banking	5	3
Other	6	4
Adjustments	(2.7)	
Total	**166**	**100**

COMPETITORS

1st Source Corporation
Bank of America
Fifth Third
First Merchants
German American Bancorp
KeyCorp
Old National Bancorp
U.S. Bancorp

HISTORICAL FINANCIALS

Company Type: Public

Income Statement FYE: December 31

	ASSETS ($ mil.)	NET INCOME ($ mil.)	INCOME AS % OF ASSETS	EMPLOYEES
12/11	2,754	23	0.9%	805
12/10	2,769	14	0.5%	926
12/09	2,906	(64)	—	934
12/08	2,899	19	0.7%	915
12/07	2,536	21	0.9%	805
Annual Growth	2.1%	2.2%	—	0.0%

2011 Year-End Financials

Debt ratio: 7.32%
Return on equity: 7.08%
Cash ($ mil.): 109
Current ratio: —
Long-term debt ($ mil.): 201
No. of shares (mil.): 20
Dividends
Yield: —
Payout: 3.88%
Market value ($ mil.): 178

	STOCK PRICE ($) FY Close	P/E High/Low		PER SHARE ($) Earnings	Dividends	Book Value
12/11	8.83	10	7	1.03	0.00	16.66
12/10	10.41	19	8	0.58	0.04	15.03
12/09	4.78	—	—	(3.33)	0.26	14.62
12/08	15.50	21	12	1.00	0.58	14.90
12/07	15.56	16	12	1.17	0.56	14.22
Annual Growth	(13.2%)	—	—	(3.1%)	—	4.0%

ManpowerGroup

Millions of men (and women) have helped power this firm to the upper echelon of the staffing industry. Doing business as ManpowerGroup the company is one of the world's largest providers of temporary employees placing about 3.5 million people in office industrial and professional positions every year. It offers services through different brands including ManpowerGroup Solutions Manpower Experis (accounting finance health and engineering positions) and Right Management which provides management consulting services focused on leadership development and assessment. ManpowerGroup has some 3800 owned or franchised offices in 80 countries and territories.

Strategy

Supplying temporary employees to businesses on an as-needed basis accounts for the bulk of the company's business with most of its sales coming from office and light-industrial placements. ManpowerGroup is focused on its professional staffing services (Experis) division however which has been its fastest-growing segment.

Geographic Reach

Operations outside the US including Manpower UK account for about 85% of Manpower's sales. During 2011 Manpower acquired Proservia SA a provider of information technology and systems engineering solutions in France. The company has also been expanding its Asia/Pacific presence where Manpower made acquisitions in China and India in 2012 as well.

Mergers & Acquisitions

In keeping with its strategic focus on professional staffing services ManpowerGroup acquired COMSYS IT Partners in 2010 for about $375 million. The Houston-based firm provided information technology staffing through more than 50 offices in the US Canada and the UK. ManpowerGroup integrated the staffing operations into its Experis unit.

HISTORY

Milwaukee lawyers Elmer Winter and Aaron Scheinfeld founded Manpower in 1948. It originally concentrated on supplying temporary help to industry during the first few years of the postwar boom. In the next few years the company expanded and in 1956 it began franchising. During the 1960s Manpower opened franchises in Europe Asia and South America. Unlike many of its competitors however it continued to emphasize blue-collar placements.

Manpower embarked on a series of acquisitions in the 1970s and began to shift its emphasis from industrial to clerical placements. It was Mitchell Fromstein Manpower's advertising account executive in the 1960s who orchestrated the company's growth into a powerhouse. Fromstein joined the board in 1971 and became president and CEO in 1976.

Mid-decade with Scheinfeld deceased and Winter eager to sell the Parker Pen Company came along. Parker Pen also based in Wisconsin was trying to re-energize its fading fortunes after the arrival of the disposable pen. Parker Pen bought Manpower in 1976 sold the pen business 10 years later and became Manpower Inc. Fromstein continued as president and CEO with a 20% interest in the company.

In the late 1970s Manpower entered the computer age instituting a computer training program for its temporary employees. The company grew as the character of employment in the US changed from career-long employment with one company to a series of shorter-term jobs with many employers. In addition to providing short-term workers Manpower began offering hiring and training services for permanent employees thus saving companies in-house recruitment and training costs.

Blue Arrow a temporary-employment agency based in the UK acquired the firm in 1987. The combined companies operated as Manpower and almost immediately tensions arose between Fromstein and his new boss Antony Berry who accused Fromstein of obstructing efforts to unite the two companies. Fromstein was fired in 1988.

Manpower's worldwide franchisees revolted against Berry and the UK began an investigation of how the acquisition of Manpower was financed —a $1.5 billion stock sale by UK bank NatWest (now Royal Bank of Scotland Group). Berry was ousted in 1989 and Fromstein regained control. A push by US interests changed the US composition of the company's ownership during that year from just 9% in January to over 60% by the end of the year. This gave Fromstein the support he needed to move Manpower back to Wisconsin in 1991.

Fromstein then worked to disentangle the two companies by selling off all Blue Arrow holdings not related to employment. During the mid-1990s the company opened hundreds of new offices in the US and abroad. It spent more than $15 million in 1995 to upgrade its computerized worker-to-job matching system. An alliance with HR services firm Drake Beam Morin the following year gave the company access to more than 200000 new clients.

Manpower began two pilot programs in 1997 – one to place inner-city welfare recipients in the workforce and one offering free technology-related training to company applicants via the Internet. In 1998 the company acquired Australia's Kirby Contract Labour which added 15 branches to the 55 already operating in Australia and New Zealand. The following year Fromstein retired after leading Manpower for 23 years. Jeffrey Joerres took over as CEO (and added chairman to his title in 2001).

Later in 1999 Manpower changed the name of its Manpower Technical division to Manpower Professional to better indicate the variety of disciplines it supported and compete in an increasingly tight market for professional workers. In 2001 the company bought financial services provider Jefferson Wells International. Manpower started a program to provide internships for high school students in 2002. In 2003 the company launched its Business Resource Center to offer online human resources information for small and midsized businesses. Manpower acquired Right Management in 2004.

Manpower was awarded a temporary staffing business license in China in 2007 making it the first global staffing company to be allowed to offer those services in that market. The company made several acquisitions the following year including Clarendon Parker Middle East a professional recruitment provider with operations in Bahrain Kuwait Qatar Saudi Arabia and the United Arab Emirates. Other acquisitions included Dutch professional recruitment provider Vitae and Los-Angeles based business process outsourcer CRI.

In 2010 Manpower acquired Houston-based COMSYS IT Partners for about $375 million. The following year it officially changed its business name to ManpowerGroup and launched its Experis unit.

EXECUTIVES

Chairman President and CEO, Jeffrey A. (Jeff) Joerres, age 53, $980,769 total compensation

EVP Global Strategy and Talent, Mara E. Swan, age 52

EVP and CFO, Michael J. (Mike) Van Handel, age 52, $539,423 total compensation

EVP; President Asia-Pacific and Middle East, Darryl E. Green, age 51, $425,000 total compensation

EVP; President Specialty Brands, Owen J. Sullivan, age 54, $420,000 total compensation

SVP Innovation and Workforce Solutions, Tammy Johns
President Corporate and Government Affairs, David Arkless
Director Communications US Canada and Puerto Rico, Juan Carlos Cruz
EVP; President The Americas, Jonas Prising, age 46, $384,615 total compensation
EVP; President Southern Europe, Francoise Gri, age 54, $524,880 total compensation
SVP Chief Legal Officer and Secretary, Kenneth C. (Ken) Hunt, age 62
Director Global Strategic Communications, Britt Zarling
SVP and Global Chief Information Officer, Denis Edwards
EVP; President Northern Europe, Hans Leentjes
Manager Communications ? Manpower France Immeuble Eureka, Christian Boghos
Director, John R. Walter, age 65
Director, Jack M. Greenberg, age 69
Director, Elizabeth P. (Libby) Sartain, age 57
Director, Terry A. Hueneke, age 69
Director, Edward J. Zore, age 67
Director, William A. (Bill) Downe, age 60
Director, Roberto G. Mendoza, age 66
Director, Ulice Payne Jr., age 56
Director, Patricia A. (Pat) Hemingway Hall, age 59
Director, Marc J. (M. J.) Bolland, age 52
Director, Gina R. Boswell, age 49
Director, Cari M. Dominguez, age 62
Auditors: Deloitte&ToucheLLP

LOCATIONS

HQ: Manpower Inc.
100 Manpower Place, Milwaukee WI 53212
Phone: 414-961-1000 **Fax:** 734-207-6500
Web: www.metaldyne.com

PRODUCTS/OPERATIONS

Selected Services

Staffing
Industrial trades
Manpower Professional
  Engineering
  Finance
  Information technology
  Telecommunications
Office and clerical

COMPETITORS

Adecco
Kelly Services
Korn/Ferry
Michael Page
Randstad Holding
Robert Half
TrueBlue
Volt Information

HISTORICAL FINANCIALS

Company Type: Public

Income Statement FYE: December 31

	REVENUE ($ mil.)	NET INCOME ($ mil.)	NET PROFIT MARGIN	EMPLOYEES
12/11	22,006	251	1.1%	31,000
12/10	18,866	(263)	—	30,000
12/09	16,038	(9)	—	28,000
12/08	21,552	218	1.0%	33,000
12/07	20,500	484	2.4%	33,000
Annual Growth	1.8%	(15.1%)	—	(1.6%)

2011 Year-End Financials

Debt ratio: 10.15%
Return on equity: 10.13%
Cash ($ mil.): 580
Current ratio: 132.65
Long-term debt ($ mil.): 266
No. of shares (mil.): 79
Dividends
  Yield: —
  Payout: 26.32%
Market value ($ mil.): 2,857

	STOCK PRICE ($) FY Close	P/E High/Low		PER SHARE ($) Earnings	Dividends	Book Value
12/11	35.75	23	11	3.04	0.00	31.08
12/10	62.76	—	—	(3.26)	0.74	29.32
12/09	54.58	—	—	(0.12)	0.74	32.28
12/08	33.99	25	8	2.75	0.74	31.86
12/07	56.90	16	10	5.73	0.69	33.42
Annual Growth	(11.0%)	—	—	(14.7%)	—	(1.8%)

Marathon Oil Corp.

In the long-running competition for profits in the oil and gas industry Marathon Oil is keeping up a steady pace. The company explores for and produces oil and gas primarily in Angola Canada Equatorial Guinea Iraq Libya Norway Poland the UK and the US. In 2011 it reported proved reserves of 1.8 billion barrels of oil equivalent including 623 million barrels of synthetic oil from oil sands. Seeking stronger financial returns in 2011 Marathon Oil (formerly a holding company with both upstream and downstream operations) spun off its downstream unit Marathon Petroleum (which had accounted for the bulk of its revenues) and became a pure-play exploration and production company.

Operations

Marathon Oil's Houston-based operations retained the exploration oil sands mining and natural gas businesses and the company name while the Findlay Ohio operations (Marathon Petroleum) kept the marketing refining pipeline and transportation functions.

Financial Analysis

The reconfigured exploration and production company saw its revenues and net income grow further in 2011 thanks to higher oil prices increased production and ramped up product sales. Revenue was up 25% and net income about 15%.

However while exploration and production and oil sands mining reported robust revenue growth in 2011 Marathon's natural gas products segment's revenue declined due to the closing of the company's LNG facility in Alaska to cut costs.

In 2010 a recovering global economy higher oil prices and stronger demand lifted Marathon Oil's overall revenues (especially in the refining and marketing and exploration and production segments) and net income.

Strategy

A key part of Marathon's strategy involves making large divestitures and acquisitions. It plans to make divestitures worth $1.5 billion to $3 billion over the period of 2011 to 2013 in an effort to position the company for profitable growth. Included in this plan is an agreement to divest its exploration and production assets in Alaska for $375 million.

In 2010 the company sold 20% of its 30% stake in its Angola-based oil and gas operations to CNOOC and Sinopec in order to raise about $1.3 billion.

On the acquisition side Marathon has so far in 2012 acquired or agreed to acquire about $1 billion worth of acreage in the South Texas Eagle Ford resource play where it has already made significant investments –namely $3.5 billion in assets already acquired from KKR and Hilcorp Energy in 2011. All told acquisitions at Eagle Ford are expected to add a number of drilling locations to Marathon's inventory and will boost its position to about 225000 net acres.

HISTORY

Marathon Oil was founded in 1887 in Lima Ohio as The Ohio Oil Company by 14 independent oil producers to compete with Standard Oil. Within two years Ohio Oil was the largest producer in the state. This success did not go unnoticed by Standard Oil which proceeded to buy Ohio Oil in 1889. In 1905 the company moved to Findlay Ohio where it remained until it relocated to Houston in 1990.

When the US Supreme Court broke up Standard Oil in 1911 Ohio Oil became independent once again and expanded its exploration activities to Kansas Louisiana Texas and Wyoming.

In a 1924 attempt to drill three wells west of the Pecos River in Texas Ohio Oil mistakenly drilled three dry holes to the east. The company was on the verge of abandoning the project until a geologist reported the error. Ohio Oil drilled in the right area and the wells flowed. That year the company bought Lincoln Oil Refining –its first venture outside crude oil production.

Ohio Oil continued its expansion into refining and marketing operations in 1927. Following WWII the company began international exploration. Through Conorada Petroleum (later Oasis) a partnership with Continental Oil (later Conoco and then ConocoPhillips) and Amerada Hess the company explored in Africa and South and Central America. Conorada's biggest overseas deal came in 1955 when it acquired concessions on more than 60 million acres in Libya.

In 1962 the company acquired Plymouth Oil and changed its name to Marathon Oil Company; it had been using the Marathon name in its marketing activities since the late 1930s. Marathon added a 200000-barrel-a-day refinery in Louisiana to its operations in 1976 when it acquired ECOL Ltd.

After a battle with Mobil U.S. Steel acquired Marathon in 1982 for $6.5 billion. U.S. Steel changed its name to USX in 1986 and acquired Texas Oil & Gas. That year the US government introduced economic sanctions against Libya putting Marathon's Libyan holdings in suspension.

USX consolidated Texas Oil and Marathon in 1990. After a protracted struggle with corporate raider Carl Icahn USX split Marathon and U.S. Steel into two separate stock classes in 1991. A third offering USX-Delhi Group (the pipeline operator division) followed the next year. (Koch Industries bought USX-Delhi in 1997.)

A consortium led by USX-Marathon signed an agreement with the Russian government in 1994 to develop oil and gas fields off Sakhalin Island (although USX-Marathon sold its stake in the project in 2000). In 1996 Marathon formed a venture ElectroGen International with East Coast utility DQE to develop power generation projects in the Asia/Pacific region.

In 1998 Marathon and Ashland merged their refining and retail operations creating Marathon Ashland Petroleum (MAP) with Marathon owning 62%. That year Marathon in a deal that boosted its reserves by 18% acquired Calgary-based Tarragon Oil and Gas.

As part of a restructuring drive in 1999 MAP sold its crude oil gathering business Scurlock Permian to Plains All American Pipeline. With oil prices rebounding Marathon ramped up its oil exploration in 2000 buying more deepwater leases in the Gulf of Mexico and acquiring an interest in an oil and gas play offshore the Republic of Congo.

The company bought Pennaco Energy a Colorado-based producer of coalbed methane gas for about $500 million in 2001 and it agreed to buy CMS Energy's Equatorial Guinea (West Africa) oil and gas assets in a $993 million deal that was completed in 2002. At the end of 2001 USX spun off U.S. Steel and changed the name of the remaining company to Marathon Oil Corporation. In 2002 Marathon acquired Globex Energy a privately held exploration and production company with assets in West Africa for $155 million.

In 2005 Ashland sold its 38% stake in Marathon Ashland to Marathon Oil for about $3.7 billion.

In addition to acquiring MAP Marathon Oil also obtained Ashland's maleic anhydride business a share of its Valvoline Instant Oil Change business in Michigan and Ohio and other assets.

In 2006 the company sold its oil and gas assets in the Khanty-Mansiysk autonomous region of western Siberia to LUKOIL for $787 million. That year Marathon Oil announced a plan to spend $3.2 billion to expand the crude oil refining capacity of its refinery in Garyville Louisiana.

As a way to expand its hydrocarbon asset base the company has been investing heavily in non-conventional exploration and production areas. In 2006 as part of a five-year $1.5 billion investment the company announced plans to drill as many as 225 new wells in western North Dakota in the Bakken Oil Formation (tight shale layers) over a five-year period. The following year Marathon Oil expanded into the Canadian oil sands market through the acquisition of Western Oil Sands for about $5.8 billion.

EXECUTIVES

VP Corporate Compliance and Ethics, Daniel J. Sullenbarger, age 56
EVP and CFO, Janet F. Clark, age 57, $650,000 total compensation
Chairman President and CEO, Clarence P. Cazalot Jr., age 61, $1,400,000 total compensation
VP Public Policy, Eileen M. Campbell, age 54
SVP Exploration, Annell R. Bay
VP and CIO, Thomas K. Sneed
VP Technology, Linda A. Capuano
EVP and COO, David E. (Dave) Roberts Jr., age 51, $775,000 total compensation
VP Finance and Accounting Controller and Treasurer, Michael K. Stewart, age 54
VP Tax, Stephen J. Landry
VP Investor Relations and Public Affairs, Howard J. Thill, age 53
VP Strategic Planning and Portfolio Management, Robert E. Estill
Media Relations Corporate/Upstream, Lee Warren
VP Health Environment Safety and Security, R. Douglas Rogers
VP General Counsel and Secretary, Sylvia J. Kerrigan, age 47
VP Human Resources, Robert L. Sovine
Chief Procurement Officer, Michael W. Tweedy
Manager Investor Relations, Chris C. Phillips
IT Manager Corporate Client Services, Myra Egbert
VP Business Development, Steven P. Guidry, age 53
Director, David A. Daberko, age 67
Director, William L. Davis III, age 68
Director, Michael E. J. Phelps, age 63
Director, Dennis H. Reilley, age 59
Director, Charles R. Lee, age 72
Director, Philip Lader, age 66
Director, Shirley Ann Jackson, age 64
Director, Seth E. Schofield, age 72
Director, Gregory H. (Greg) Boyce, age 57
Director, John W. Snow, age 72
Director, Pierre R. Brondeau, age 54
Auditors: PricewaterhouseCoopersLLP

LOCATIONS

HQ: Marathon Oil Corporation
5555 San Felipe Rd., Houston TX 77056-2723
Phone: 713-629-6600 **Fax:** 713-296-2952
Web: www.marathon.com

2011 Sales

	$ mil.	% of total
& of total		
US	47	
Norway	23	
Canada	11	
UK	10	
Libya	2	
Other	7	
Total	0	100

PRODUCTS/OPERATIONS

2011 Sales

	% of total
Exploration &	88
Oil sands	11
Natural gas	1
Total	100

COMPETITORS

BP
Chevron
ConocoPhillips
Exxon Mobil
Hess Corporation
Koch Industries Inc.
Occidental Petroleum
PEMEX
Petroleos de Venezuela
Royal Dutch Shell

HISTORICAL FINANCIALS

Company Type: Public

Income Statement FYE: December 31

	REVENUE ($ mil.)	NET INCOME ($ mil.)	NET PROFIT MARGIN	EMPLOYEES
12/11	15,282	2,946	19.3%	3,322
12/10	73,621	2,568	3.5%	29,677
12/09	54,139	1,463	2.7%	28,855
12/08	78,569	3,528	4.5%	30,360
12/07	65,207	3,956	6.1%	29,524
Annual Growth	(30.4%)	(7.1%)	—	(42.1%)

2011 Year-End Financials

Debt ratio: 15.35%
Return on equity: 17.18%
Cash ($ mil.): 493
Current ratio: 73.37
Long-term debt ($ mil.): 4,674
No. of shares (mil.): 704
Dividends
Yield: —
Payout: 19.37%
Market value ($ mil.): 20,606

	STOCK PRICE ($) FY Close	P/E High/Low		PER SHARE ($) Earnings	Dividends	Book Value
12/11	29.27	13	5	4.13	0.00	24.36
12/10	37.03	10	8	3.61	0.99	33.48
12/09	31.22	17	10	2.06	0.96	30.95
12/08	27.36	12	4	4.95	0.96	30.32
12/07	60.86	23	9	5.69	0.92	27.07
Annual Growth	(16.7%)	—	—	(7.7%)	—	(2.6%)

Marathon Petroleum Corp.

Marathon Petroleum has a long running commitment to fuel its customers. Spun off from Marathon Oil Corporation in 2011 the company operates six refineries with the capacity to process about 1.2 million barrels of crude oil a day. Marathon Petroleum sells refined products through a nationwide network of branded gas stations. It also holds stakes in pipelines and is one of the largest asphalt and light oil product terminal operators in the US. The company distributes petroleum products wholesale to private-brand marketers and to large commercial and industrial consumers as well as to the spot market.

Operations

Marathon Petroleum sells refined products at some 5000 Marathon-branded gas stations in 18 states and through retail subsidiary Speedway SuperAmerica's 1350 outlets. It also holds stakes in 8300 miles of pipeline and is one of the largest asphalt and light oil product terminal operators in the US (with 83 terminals in 2011).

Financial Analysis

With an improving economy in 2011 Marathon Oil spun off Marathon Petroleum to improve shareholder returns by having two publicly traded companies –an exploration and production entity and a refining and marketing company.

That year thanks to high oil prices and a strong demand for refined products Marathon Petroleum reported a rise in company's revenues of 26% and 384% jump in net income.

Strategy

Growing its retail network in 2012 Marathon Petroleum's Speedway America unit bought 88 gas stations in Indiana and Ohio from GasAmerica Services.

In March 2012 Marathon Petroleum formed a tax-exempt limited partnership MPLX to take over some of its midstream operations. MPLX has an indirect 51% stake in about 2800 miles of pipeline across nine states in the Midwest and Gulf Coast as well as a Mississippi River barge dock and tank farms. (Marathon Petroleum retains the other 49% stake.) MPLX filed a $365 million initial public offering in July 2012 and should the company successfully go public Marathon Petroleum intends for MPLX to be the primary growth vehicle for its midstream business by transferring even more assets to the tax-exempt entity.

To expand its refining capacity Marathon Petroleum invested $3.3 billion in a conventional refinery expansion at its Garyville Louisiana plant (completed in 2009) and is putting up $2.2 billion to upgrade its heavy oil processing unit in Detroit (expected to be completed in 2012). To free up cash and to help it meet expansion costs in 2010 sold its Minnesota downstream assets (including a refinery and more than 230 gas stations/convenience stores) to investment firms TPG Capital and ACON Investments for about $900 million. It also agreed to buy BP's 451000 barrels-of-oil-per-day refinery in Texas City for $2.5 billion.

EXECUTIVES

President, Gary R. Heminger, age 58
VP Human Resources and Administrative Services, Rodney P. Nichols

VP General Counsel and Secretary, J. Michael Wilder, age 59
EVP Corporate Planning and Investor and Government Relations, Garry L. Peiffer, age 60
VP Investor Relations and Government and Public Affairs, Pamela K. M. Beall
President Speedway, Anthony R. (Tony) Kenney, age 58
SVP Marketing, Thomas M. (Tom) Kelley
Manager Brand Marketing, Bill McCleave
Manager Real Estate, Paul Smith
Manager Asphalt Marketing, Gary Hewitt
SVP Supply Distribution and Planning, C. Michael Palmer
Manager Wholesale Marketing, David Heppner
Manager Environmental Safety and Security, Tim Haley
Manager Communications, Shane Pochard
Manager Environmental Safety and Security, Jeffrey Cleemput
SVP and CFO, Donald (Don) Templin
SVP Refining, Richard D. Bedell
SVP Transportation and Logistics, George P. Shaffner, age 53
VP and Controller, Michael G. Braddock, age 54
VP Environment Health and Security, John S. Swearingen
VP and CIO, Donald W. Wehrly
Auditors: PricewaterhouseCoopersLLP

LOCATIONS

HQ: Marathon Petroleum Corporation
539 S. Main St., Findlay OH 45840-3295
Phone: 419-422-2121 **Fax:** 419-425-7040
Web: www.marathonpetroleum.com

PRODUCTS/OPERATIONS

2011 Sales

	$ mil.	% of total
Refining & marketing	65,028	83
Speedway	13,490	17
Pipeline transportation	65	-
Total	**78,583**	**100**

COMPETITORS

BP
Chevron
CITGO
Exxon Mobil
Motiva Enterprises
Shell Oil Products
Sunoco
Valero Energy

HISTORICAL FINANCIALS

Company Type: Public

Income Statement FYE: December 31

	REVENUE ($ mil.)	NET INCOME ($ mil.)	NET PROFIT MARGIN	EMPLOYEES
12/11	78,759	2,389	3.0%	24,210
12/10	62,605	623	1.0%	25,803
12/09	45,639	449	1.0%	0
12/08	65,258	1,215	1.9%	0
Annual Growth	6.5%	25.3%	—	—

2011 Year-End Financials

Debt ratio: 12.85%
Return on equity: 25.13%
Cash ($ mil.): 3,079
Current ratio: 125.13
Long-term debt ($ mil.): 3,292
No. of shares (mil.): 357
Dividends
Yield: —
Payout: 6.75%
Market value ($ mil.): 11,885

	STOCK PRICE ($) FY Close	P/E High/Low		PER SHARE ($) Earnings	Dividends	Book Value
12/11	33.29	7	4	6.67	0.00	26.62
Annual Growth	—	—	—	—	—	—

Markel Corp (Holding Co)

Have you ever thought about who insures the manicurist or an antique motorcycle? Specialty insurer Markel Corporation takes on the risks other insurers won't touch from amusement parks to thoroughbred horses and summer camps. Coverage is also available for one-time events such as golf tournaments and auto races. Markel's commercial excess and surplus products include a wide range of liabilities (professional pollution) while its specialty admitted segment covers businesses ranging from martial arts schools to dude ranches. Markel International provides specialty insurance internationally from its base in the UK. The company distributes its products through independent agents and brokers.

While the company is a diverse financial holding company more than 75% of its revenues are generated through its specialty insurance (excess and surplus specialty admitted and international) products and service to niche markets. Excess insurance kicks in when a company's regular insurance fizzles out. For example a regular policy might pay up to $100000 on claims but the excess policy could then pay any amounts over $100000 and up to $1 million. Surplus insurance is coverage that no regular insurance company can offer and typically comes with a higher level of risk and higher-priced premiums.

The company has been working to grow its specialty admitted business segment which serves clients that engage in highly specialized activities requiring niche insurance coverage typically not offered by standard insurers. In 2010 Markel added workers' compensation to its roster of US specialty insurance offerings when it acquired Aspen Holdings which does business as FirstComp Insurance for some $135 million (plus stock option value). FirstComp now operates as a separate business unit.

In early 2012 Markel added another US specialty unit when it acquired Kennesaw Georgia-based Thompson Insurance Enterprises (THOMCO) for an undisclosed amount. The new business unit which operates independently under the specialty admitted division offers industry specific insurance programs for fields including medical transportation senior and childcare facility services and fitness center operations. Other underwriting entities in the specialty admitted segment include Markel Insurance and Markel American Insurance.

Higher premium volume (primarily in its excess and surplus segment) and improved results by its previously struggling international business have helped to increase Markel's underwriting profits. Rather than sit on its hands while its investment portfolio tanked during 2008 Markel chose to sell off portions of its investments and took substantial write-downs that year.

By 2010 the company's investment arm Markel Ventures had stabilized enough to resume investing in a slew of new non-insurance businesses. A buying spree ensued and by late 2011 its acquisitions included a food-processing equipment manufacturer; manufactured housing communities; a behavioral health management firm; a dredge systems maker; a medical and executive health program manager; a supplier of continuous baking systems; and a majority interest in WI Holdings known as Weldship and its Texas Trailer division. In 2012 Markel Ventures acquired a majority interest in privately held Havco WP LLC and Havco Wood Products a leading maker of laminated oak and composite wood flooring for truck trailers intermodal containers and truck bodies.

In fiscal 2011 Markel's underwriting results were impacted by higher losses related to the Japanese earthquake and tsunami tornadoes in the US floods in Thailand and other natural catastrophes that occurred at a higher-than-expected frequency during the year. The company continued to grow however by making strategic acquisitions in its insurance and non-insurance operations. Its revenues grew to $2.6 billion an increase of about 18% from 2010 while its net income dropped by almost 45% to $148 million.

Markel's strategy for growth is to leverage its expertise and specialized market knowledge of niche markets to differentiate its business from competitors. Financially the company's aim is to generate consistent underwriting and operating profits and produce superior returns on its investments to increase its value.

Cousins and co-vice chairmen Anthony Markel and Steven Markel own about 5% of the company.

HISTORY

In the 1920s Sam Markel formed a mutual insurance company for "jitneys" (passenger cars refurbished as public transportation buses). In 1930 he founded Markel Service to expand nationally. To keep up with industry growth the company revamped itself as a managing general agent and independent claims service organization in the late 1950s. In 1978 Markel began covering taverns restaurants and vacant buildings. It created excess and surplus lines underwriter Essex Insurance in 1980.

Markel went public in 1986. The next year it invested in Shand Morahan and Evanston Insurance (specialty coverage including architects engineers and lawyers professional liability; officers and directors insurance; errors and omissions; and medical malpractice). It bought summer camp insurer Rhulen Agency in 1989.

In the 1990s Markel began buying insurers with their own offbeat niches. In 1990 it bought the rest of Shand Morahan and Evanston Insurance. In 1995 it bought Lincoln Insurance (excess and surplus lines) from media giant Thomson (now Thomson Reuters). The next year the company bought Investors Insurance Holding (excess and surplus lines). Markel which already owned nearly 10% of Gryphon Holdings (commercial property/casualty) bought the rest in 1999.

Expanding internationally Markel bought Bermuda-based Terra Nova Holdings a reinsurer and a Lloyd's managing agency in 2000. The company experienced heavy losses in 2001 not only related to the events of September 11 but also to its slumping international business (the company took a $100 million charge).

Unlike standard insurers (whose rates are generally regulated) specialty insurers can charge the rates they consider reasonable. To that end after taking significant losses from the 2005 hurricane season (Katrina Rita Wilma) and additional hits from the 2008 season (Gustav Ike) the company decided to raise the rates on its catastrophe-exposed businesses.

Markel moved to expand its international specialty property/casualty operations in 2009 by acquiring Elliott Special Risks a Canadian general agent providing underwriting services for non-standard policies for $70 million. Elliot Special Risks was then housed within Markel International.

EXECUTIVES

Vice Chairman, Anthony F. (Tony) Markel, age 70, $600,000 total compensation
Vice Chairman, Steven A. Markel, age 63, $600,000 total compensation
Chairman and CEO, Alan I. Kirshner, age 76, $650,000 total compensation
President and Chief Investment Officer, Thomas S. Gayner, age 50, $525,000 total compensation
CIO, David Egbert
VP Investor Relations, Bruce A. Kay
Managing Director Marketing Markel American Insurance, Audrey Hanken
President and Co-COO, Richard R. Whitt III, age 48, $475,000 total compensation
President and Co-COO, F. Michael (Mike) Crowley, age 60, $493,846 total compensation
President Wholesale, John K. Latham, age 65
Chief Administrative Officer, Britton L. (Britt) Glisson, age 55
EVP and Chief Underwriting Officer, Gerard Albanese Jr., age 60, $400,000 total compensation
Secretary, D. Michael Jones
Director Marketing Market West, Chris Behymer
VP CFO and Treasurer, Anne G. Waleski, age 45
Chief Accounting Officer and Controller, Nora N. Crouch, age 52
Manager Marketing Markel Southeast, Glenn Harris
Director Marketing Markel Northeast, Daniel Confalone
Director Marketing Market Mid South, Wendy Houser
Director Marketing and Public Relations Markel International, Sean Martin
Vice Chairman, Anthony F. (Tony) Markel, age 70
Vice Chairman, Steven A. Markel, age 63
Director, Darrell D. Martin, age 63
Director, Stewart M. Kasen, age 72
Director, J. Alfred Broaddus Jr., age 73
Director, Douglas C. Eby, age 53
Director, Jay M. Weinberg, age 79
Director, Debora J. Wilson, age 54
Auditors: KPMGLLP

LOCATIONS

HQ: Markel Corporation
4521 Highwoods Pkwy., Glen Allen VA 23060-6148
Phone: 804-747-0136 **Fax:** 804-965-1600
Web: www.markelcorp.com

PRODUCTS/OPERATIONS

2011 Revenues

Earned premiums		
London insurance market	695	27
Net investment income	263	10
Other revenues	351	13

2011 Gross Premium Volume

	$ mil.	% of total
Excess & surplus lines	893	39
London insurance market	825	36
Specialty admitted	572	25
Total	**2,291**	**100**

Selected Acquisitions

2012
- Tromp Bakery Equipment B.V. (global supplier of baking equipment; Gorinchem The Netherlands)
- IDRECO GmbH (IDRECO; deep-digging electrical suction and cutter suction dredges; Heerenberg The Netherlands)
- Havco WP LLC (majority interest; laminated oak and composite wood flooring that is utilized in the assembly of truck trailers intermodal containers and truck bodies; Cape Girardeau Missouri)
- Thompson Insurance Enterprises LLC (THOMCO; Program Administrator underwriting multi-line industry-focused insurance programs; Kennesaw Georgia)

2011
- WI Holdings Inc. (dba Weldship; majority interest; manufactures leases and sells high-pressure tube trailers certified ISO containers and other gas and liquid containers; Bethlehem Pennsylvvania)
- Baking Technology Systems Inc. (renamed AMF/BAKETECH; supplier of ovens and other related equipment; Tucker Georgia)
- PartnerMD LLC (concierge medical and executive health programs; Richmond Virginia)
- Rohr Bagger GmbH (European and US operations; manufactures automated floating clamshell and bucket ladder dredge systems; Germany)
- Diamond Healthcare Corporation (manages behavioral health programs throughout the US; Richmond Virginia)

Selected Subsidiaries

Associated International Insurance Company
Essex Insurance Company
Mark IV Realty Corporation
Markel American Insurance Company
Markel Aspen Inc.
  FirstComp Insurance Company
Markel Capital Holdings Limited
  Markel Capital Limited
  Markel International Limited
    Markel International Insurance Company Limited
Markel Insurance Company
  Deerfield Insurance Company
Markel Properties LLC
Markel Ventures Inc.
  AMF Bakery Systems
  Ellicott Dredge Enterprises LLC
    Rohr International Dredge Holdings Inc.
MINT Canadian Specialty Underwriters Limited
Shand/Evanston Group Inc.
  Evanston Insurance Company

COMPETITORS

Assurant
Chubb Corp
CNA Financial
Fireman' s Fund Insurance
Great American Insurance Company
HCC Insurance
Liberty International Underwriters
Meadowbrook Insurance
Medical Liability Mutual Insurance
National Indemnity Company
Nationwide
Penn-America
Philadelphia Insurance Companies
ProSight Specialty Insurance Group
RLI
Travelers Companies
United States Liability Insurance Group
XL Group plc

HISTORICAL FINANCIALS

Company Type: Public

Income Statement

FYE: December 31

	ASSETS ($ mil.)	NET INCOME ($ mil.)	INCOME AS % OF ASSETS	EMPLOYEES
12/11	11,532	142	1.2%	5,400
12/10	10,825	266	2.5%	4,800
12/09	10,241	201	2.0%	2,800
12/08	9,477	(58)	—	2,000
12/07	10,134	405	4.0%	2,000
Annual Growth	3.3%	(23.1%)	—	28.2%

2011 Year-End Financials

Debt ratio: 11.22%	No. of shares (mil.): 9
Return on equity: 4.19%	Dividends
Cash ($ mil.): 775	Yield: —
Current ratio: —	Payout: —
Long-term debt ($ mil.): 1,293	Market value ($ mil.): 3,990

	STOCK PRICE ($) FY Close	P/E High/Low	PER SHARE ($) Earnings	Dividends	Book Value
12/11	414.67	29 24	14.60	0.00	352.10
12/10	378.13	14 12	27.27	0.00	326.36
12/09	340.00	18 10	20.52	0.00	282.55
12/08	299.00	— —	(5.95)	0.00	222.20
12/07	491.10	13 11	40.64	0.00	265.26
Annual Growth	(4.1%)	— —	(22.6%)	—	7.3%

Marriott International, Inc.

Marriott International signs in at the top of the lodging industry. The company is one of the world's leading hoteliers with some 3700 operated or franchised properties in more than 70 countries. Its hotels include such full-service brands as Renaissance Hotels and its flagship Marriott Hotels & Resorts as well as select-service and extended-stay brands Courtyard and Fairfield Inn. It also owns the Ritz-Carlton luxury chain and resort and manages about 45 golf courses. The firm spun off its time-share business Marriott Vacations Worldwide in 2011 and is selling its ExecuStay corporate housing business in 2012. The Marriott family including J. W. Marriott Jr. owns about 30% of Marriott International.

Strategy

Marriott's business model focuses on managing and franchising hotels rather than owning them. About 53% of its hotel rooms are operated by franchisees that pay the company fees and royalties as well as a percentage of their food and beverage revenue. The company operates 44% of its hotel rooms under management agreements. It has long-term management agreements with properties that are owned or leased by Host Hotels & Resorts a major customer that accounts for about 18% of Marriott's sales. While the bulk of its hotels are located in the US about 15% of its properties are international.

Marriott in 2012 announced that it is selling its ExecuStay corporate and temporary apartment housing business to Oakwood a provider of corporate housing and serviced apartments. It is making the deal to focus on its hotel business but will continue to maintain a relationship with Oakwood. Terms of the deal have ExecuStay customers continuing to earn Marriott Rewards guest loyalty program points for stays at ExecuStay.

The previous year Marriott added about 170 hotel properties to its portfolio. Also in 2011 it formed a joint venture with Spanish hotel group AC Hotels. The venture operates under a new co-brand called AC Hotels by Marriott that is pursuing growth in Europe and Latin America. As a result of the deal some 80 existing AC hotels in Spain Italy and Portugal were re-branded AC by Hotels Marriott which operate in the urban four-star hotel category.

Financials

Revenues increased by $626 million (5%) to $12317 million in 2011 from $11691 million in 2010 driven by a continuation of the rebound in the hospitality market that began in 2010. However Marriott's net income dropped in 2011 due to a one time impairment charge related to the spinoff of its time share business as well as higher income taxes.

The time-share business was a particularly weak spot for the company. While the subsidiary was a large revenue generator when the economy was booming the business lost its luster during the recession. Time share sales –which target vacationing consumers –continued to fall as hotel room sales recovered. As a result Marriott spun off the business (which accounted for about 10% of total sales) as a new publicly traded company at the end of 2011. It made the separation to allow both companies to tailor business strategies to their respective market segment.

Mergers & Acquisitions

On the hotel side of things in 2012 the company acquired the Gaylord brand and hotel management operations from Ryman Hospitality Properties (then called Gaylord Entertainment) for $210 million. The deal included four hotels (in Texas Tennessee Florida and Washington DC). Under the agreement Ryman will continue to own the hotels and Marriott will assume management of the properties through long-term contracts. Marriott made the deal to expand its group and meetings portfolio –the deal will roughly 2 million square feet of meeting and event space and approximately 7800 rooms to its holdings.

HISTORY

The company began in 1927 as a Washington DC root beer stand operated by John and Alice Marriott. Later they added hot food and named their business the Hot Shoppe. In 1929 the couple incorporated and began building a regional chain.

Hot Shoppes opened its first hotel the Twin Bridges Marriott Motor Hotel in Arlington Virginia in 1957. When the Marriotts' son Bill became president in 1964 (CEO in 1972 chairman in 1985) he focused on expanding the hotel business. The company changed its name to Marriott Corp. in 1967. With the rise in airline travel Marriott built several airport hotels during the 1970s. By 1977 sales had topped $1 billion.

Marriott became the #1 operator of airport food beverage and merchandise facilities in the US with its 1982 acquisition of Host International and it introduced moderately priced Courtyard hotels in 1983. Acquisitions in the 1980s included a time-share business foodservice companies and competitor Howard Johnson. (Marriott later sold the hotels but kept the restaurants and turnpike units.)

The company entered three new market segments in 1987: Marriott Suites (full-service suites) Residence Inn (moderately priced suites) and Fairfield Inn (economy hotels). It also began developing "life-care" communities which provide apartments meals and limited nursing care to the elderly in 1988.

Marriott split its operations into two companies in 1993: Host Marriott to own hotels and Marriott International primarily to manage them. However Marriott International still owned some of the properties and in 1995 it bought 49% of the Ritz-Carlton luxury hotel group.

In 1996 Marriott purchased the Forum Group (assisted living communities and health care services) and merged it into Marriott Senior Living Services.

Marriott introduced its Marriott Executive Residences in 1997. Also that year the firm expanded overseas operations with its purchase of the 150-unit Hong Kong-based Renaissance Hotel Group a deal that included branding rights to the Ramada chain.

In 1998 after the division of its lodging and food distribution services the new Marriott International then began trading as a separate company. That year Marriott also acquired the rest of Ritz-Carlton and established SpringHill Suites by Marriott.

Marriott entered the corporate housing business in 1999 through its acquisition of ExecuStay Corporation (renamed ExecuStay by Marriott) which provided fully furnished and accessorized apartments for stays of 30 days or more. The following year it joined Italy's Bulgari the world's #3 jeweler in a $140 million venture of luxury hotels sporting the Bulgari name.

Marriott refocused its operations on the lodging market in 2003 when it exited both the senior living and distribution services businesses. It sold Marriott Distribution Services (food and beverage distribution) to Services Group of America and sold Marriott Senior Living Services to Sunrise Assisted Living (the management business) and CNL Retirement Properties (nine communities). The following year Marriott sold the international branding rights to the Ramada and Days Inn chains to Cendant (now Avis Budget Group) for about $200 million.

In 2005 Marriott acquired about 30 properties from CTF Holdings (an affiliate of Hong Kong-based New World Development) for nearly $1.5 billion. It sold 14 properties immediately to Sunstone Hotel Investors and Walton Street Capital. The deal put an end to an ongoing legal battle between Marriott and CTF Holdings which had alleged that the hotelier had pocketed kickbacks and fees from outside vendors.

Marriott invested about $200 million in 2005 to upgrade its hotel beds with higher thread-count sheets and triple-sheeted tops and it renovated and upgraded many of its Courtyard and Residence Inn locations during 2006. A difficult 2009 called for the elimination of more than 1000 jobs. Also that year the company cut costs by modifying menus and restaurant hours adjusting room amenities and relaxing some brand standards.

In 2010 Marriott introduced two new hotel brands into the market: Edtion (a boutique luxury chain) and Autograph Collection (independent luxury properties that each have their own unique identity). The firm spun off its time-share business Marriott Vacations Worldwide in 2011.

EXECUTIVES

President Marriott Vacation Club International, Stephen P. (Steve) Weisz, age 61

President COO and Director, Arne M. Sorenson, age 53, $859,538 total compensation

President and Managing Director Marriott International Lodging, Edwin D. (Ed) Fuller, age 66

Chairman and CEO, J. W. (Bill) Marriott Jr., age 80, $1,182,692 total compensation

Group President The Americas and Global Lodging Services, Robert J. (Bob) McCarthy, age 58, $659,535 total compensation

EVP Finance and Global Treasurer, Carolyn B. Handlon

VP Canadian Operations, Scott Allison

President and Managing Director Asia Pacific, Simon F. Cooper, age 66

Vice Chairman, John W. Marriott III, age 50

Chief Development Officer Select Service and Extended Stay Brands, Joel M. Eisemann

President The Americas, David J. Grissen, age 55

SVP Investor Relations, Laura E. Paugh

EVP Finance Marriott Lodging, Kevin M. Kimball

SVP and Deputy General Counsel, Nancy C. Lee

EVP Development Planning and Feasibility, Scott E. Melby

EVP Lodging Development Select-Service and Extended-Stay Brands, Daryl A. Nickel

EVP Taxes, M. Lester Pulse Jr.

EVP Global Human Resources, David A. Rodriguez, age 53

EVP and General Counsel, Edward A. (Ed) Ryan, age 58

EVP and CFO, Carl T. Berquist, age 61, $576,896 total compensation

Chief Development Officer Asia Pacific, Paul T. Foskey

SVP and Associate General Counsel, Steven M. Goldman

President and Managing Director Europe, Amy C. McPherson, age 50

EVP Mergers Acquisitions and Business Development, Richard S. Hoffman

SVP North American Lodging Development, Norman K. (Norm) Jenkins

President and COO The Ritz-Carlton Hotel, Herve Humler

SVP Operations Planning and Support, Robin J. Uler

Director Edition, Tim Miller

EVP Global Communications and Public Affairs, Kathleen Matthews

SVP External Affairs and Global Diversity Officer, Jimmie Walton Paschall

VP Senior Counsel and Corporate Secretary, Bancroft S. Gordon

SVP Government Affairs, Deborah Marriott Harrison, age 55

EVP Global Development, Anthony G. (Tony) Capuano, age 46

Chief Development Officer Europe, Carlton Ervin

EVP Lodging Operations United Kingdom Ireland Middle East and Africa, Jurgen Giesbert

EVP Brand Management and Operations, Donald J. Semmler

SVP Global Sales, Stephanie Linnartz

SVP Lifestyle Brands and Renaissance Operations, Tina Edmundson

SVP Lodging Development Select Service and Extended Stay Brands East Region, Ray Bennett

General Manager Oceana Palms, Joseph (Joe) Smith

SVP Global Sales, David Townshend

VP Global Sales Europe, Neal Jones

General Manager Doral Golf Resort & Spa, Paige D. Koerbel

Director Marketing The Nashville Airport Marriott, Amanda Sensibaugh

Assistant General Manager Gaithersburg Marriott Washingtonian Center, Tom Gilliland

General Manager Gaithersburg Marriott Washingtonian Center, Michele Pajot
Chief Development Officer Caribbean and Latin America, Laurent de Kousemaeker
SVP Mixed Use Development, Tim Grisius
Chief Development Officer Middle East and Africa, Jean-Marc Grosfort
Regional Director Global Sales India and Subcontinent, Anant N. Joshi
Regional Director Global Sales Latin America Caribbean and Mexico, Aldo Ruiz
VP Global Sales Middle East and Africa, Vladimir Dabbah
Chief Development Officer North America Full-Service Hotels, Yoav Gery
VP Project Management, Gary Gosztonyi
VP Eastern Lodging Development, Robin Kennedy
VP Central Lodging Development, Paul Loehr
SVP Western Lodging Development, Chris Rose
VP Western Lodging Development, Alison Cumberland
VP Western Lodging Development, Julie Purnell
SVP Lodging Development Canada, Michael Beckley
VP Lodging Development Canada, Manlio Marescotti
SVP Central Lodging Development Atlanta Office, Tom Papelian
VP Lodging Development Eastern Europe and Russia, John Litzengerger
VP Lodging Development Germany Austria Switzerland, Markus Lehnert
VP Lodging Development United Kingdom and Ireland, Tim Walton
VP Lodging Development France, Xavier Grange
VP Lodging Development Middle East and Africa, Nawfal Bendefa
VP Lodging Development Middle East and Africa, Aboudi Asali
VP Lodging Development Middle East and Africa, Samir Baidas
SVP Lodging Development Select Service and Extended Stay Brands Central Region, Tom Onken
SVP Lodging Development Select Service and Extended Stay Brands West Region, Eric Jacobs
VP Lodging Development Latin America and Caribbean, Alejandro Acevedo
VP and Global Brand Manager Residence Inn, Katie Tyson
General Manager Oklahoma City Marriott, Tom Russell
VP Global Procurement, Stephane C. Masson
SVP Global Operations Services, John Adams
Global CIO, Bruce Hoffmeister
Global Officer Architecture and Construction, Ronald T. Harrison
General Manager Marriott's Harbour Point and Marriott's Sunset Pointe Hilton Head Island S.C., Mark Harney
VP Development, Paul Adan
Regional Director Sales and Marketing Selective Service, Christopher (Chris) O'Donnell
President and Managing Director; Middle East and Africa, Alex Kyriakidis
Director, Harry J. Pearce, age 69
Director, Debra L. Lee, age 57
Director, Steven S. (Steve) Reinemund, age 64
Director, Lawrence M. Small, age 69
Director, Lawrence W. (Larry) Kellner, age 53
President COO and Director, Arne M. Sorenson, age 53
Director, Mary K. Bush, age 63
Vice Chairman, John W. Marriott III, age 50
Director, George Mu?oz, age 61
Independent Director, George Munoz
Auditors: Ernst&YoungLLP

LOCATIONS

HQ: Marriott International, Inc.
10400 Fernwood Road, Bethesda, MD 20817
Phone: 301 380-3000
Web: www.marriott.com

2011 Locations

	No.
Americas	
US	3,122
Other	141
Europe	
UK &	61
Other	221
Asia	130
Middle East &	37
Australia	6
Total	**3,718**

PRODUCTS/OPERATIONS

2011 Sales

	$ mil.	% of total
Lodging		
North American full-service	5,450	44
North American limited-service	2,358	19
Luxury	1,673	13
Former timeshare business	1,438	12
International	1,278	10
Other	120	1
Total	**12,317**	**100**

Selected Operations and Brands

International lodging
- Courtyard by Marriott
- Fairfield Inn by Marriott
- JW Marriott Hotels & Resorts
- Marriott Executive Apartments
- Marriott Hotels & Resorts
- Ramada International
- Renaissance Hotels & Resorts
- Residence Inn by Marriott

Luxury hotels
- Bulgari Hotels & Resorts
- The Ritz-Carlton

North American full-service hotels
- JW Marriott Hotels & Resorts
- Marriott Conference Centers
- Marriott Hotels & Resorts
- Renaissance ClubSport
- Renaissance Hotels & Resorts

North American limited-service hotels
- Courtyard by Marriott
- Fairfield Inn by Marriott
- Marriott ExecuStay
- Residence Inn by Marriott
- SpringHill Suites by Marriott
- TownePlace Suites by Marriott

COMPETITORS

Accor
Best Western
Carlson Hotels
Choice Hotels
Club Med
Fairmont Raffles
Four Seasons Hotels
Hilton Worldwide
HVM
Hyatt
InterContinental Hotels
Loews Hotels
LXR Luxury Resorts
Starwood Hotels & Resorts

HISTORICAL FINANCIALS

Company Type: Public

Income Statement FYE: December 30

	REVENUE ($ mil.)	NET INCOME ($ mil.)	NET PROFIT MARGIN	EMPLOYEES
12/11	12,317	198	1.6%	120,000
12/10*	11,691	458	3.9%	129,000
01/10	10,908	(346)	—	137,000
01/09	12,879	362	2.8%	146,000
12/07	12,990	696	5.4%	151,000
Annual Growth	(1.3%)	(27.0%)	—	(5.6%)

*Fiscal year change

2011 Year-End Financials

Debt ratio: 36.73%
Return on equity: 987650001000000.00%
Cash ($ mil.): 102
Current ratio: 51.76
Long-term debt ($ mil.): 1,816
No. of shares (mil.): 333
Dividends
Yield: 1.33%
Payout: 70.45%
Market value ($ mil.): 9,714

	STOCK PRICE ($) FY Close	P/E High	P/E Low	PER SHARE ($) Earnings	Dividends	Book Value
12/11	29.17	75	47	0.55	0.39	(2.35)
12/10*	41.54	34	20	1.21	0.21	4.32
01/10	27.25	—	—	(0.97)	0.00	3.19
01/09	20.06	36	12	0.99	0.34	3.95
12/07	34.12	28	17	1.75	0.29	4.00
Annual Growth	(3.8%)	—	—	(25.1%)	7.7%	—

*Fiscal year change

Marsh & McLennan Companies Inc.

Marsh & McLennan Companies (MMC) is the ultimate insurance middleman. The company is one of the world's largest insurance brokers. Through core subsidiary Marsh the company provides a broad array of insurance-related brokerage consulting and risk management services to clients in 100 countries including large and small companies government entities and not-for-profit organizations. Its global reinsurance brokerage business is handled by subsidiary Guy Carpenter. MMC also owns Mercer which provides human resources and financial consulting services to customers in 40 nations worldwide and Oliver Wyman which provides management consulting services.

HISTORY

Marsh & McLennan Companies dates back to the Dan H. Bomar Company founded in 1871 after the Great Chicago Fire. In 1885 a plucky Harvard dropout named Henry Marsh joined the company then known as R.A. Waller and Company. When Robert Waller died in 1889 Marsh and fellow employee Herbert Ulmann bought a controlling stake and renamed the company Marsh Ulmann & Co. Marsh pioneered insurance brokering and in 1901 set up U.S. Steel's self-insurance program.

In 1904 different directors at Burlington Northern Railroad promised their account to Marsh Ulmann as well as Manley-McLennan of Duluth (railroad insurance) and D.W. Burrows (a small Chicago-based railroad insurance firm). Rather than fight over it the firms joined forces to form the world's largest insurance brokerage. When Burrows retired in 1906 the firm became Marsh & McLennan.

In the early 20th century Marsh won AT&T's business and McLennan landed the account of Armour Meat Packing.

In 1923 Marsh & McLennan became a closely held corporation. Marsh sold out to McLennan in 1935. The company weathered the Depression without major layoffs by cutting pay and branching into life insurance and employee-benefits consulting after passage of the Social Security Act (1935).

The firm grew through acquisitions in the 1950s went public in 1962 and in 1969 formed a holding company that became Marsh & McLennan Companies. In the 1970s it diversified buying Putnam Management (investment management). It set up subsidiary William M. Mercer's employee-benefits consulting business in 1975 and in 1980 it acquired a foothold in the UK with C.T. Bowring Reinsurance. In 1982 Marsh & McLennan formed Seabury & Smith to manage its insurance group programs.

As the insurance business slowed in the 1980s the financial and consulting fields grew. In 1992 the firm formed Mercer Consulting Group as an umbrella for its various consulting companies. With J.P. Morgan (now J.P. Morgan Chase & Co.) the company (through Marsh & McLennan Risk Capital) formed Mid Ocean Reinsurance and Underwriters Capital (Merrett) Ltd. in 1993 and the Trident Fund in 1994.

In 1995 Marsh & McLennan opened global brokering centers to centralize its insurance placement services to mid-market businesses. In 1997 it required that these accounts be handled at the centers rather than at its regional offices. Also that year the company expanded its insurance brokering and money management by buying Johnson & Higgins. In addition Marsh & McLennan formed Marsh & McLennan Securities a broker-dealer to broker insurance- and reinsurance-related securities.

In 1998 a group of Johnson & Higgins' retired directors filed suit over alleged manipulation of the partnership's rules which they charged prevented them from participating in the vote to join Marsh & McLennan. The same year the company bought Sedgwick Group a UK-based insurance services firm. In 2000 Marsh & McLennan launched MMC Enterprise Risk an enterprise risk management unit.

In 2001 revenue decreased in the Marsh & McLennan investment management segment as the level of assets under management declined along with the sagging equity market. The risk and insurance services segment saw some growth due to the impact of higher commercial insurance premium rates. In an attempt to strengthen its position the company sought to acquire British reinsurer Benfield Group but the offer was turned down.

With offices in the World Trade Center the company lost some 300 employees in the September 11 terrorist attacks. Following the attacks on the World Trade Center Marsh & McLennan launched a new subsidiary (AXIS Specialty) to deal with the capacity shortage in the insurance industry. The company saw its total revenue increase in 2003 partly thanks to insurance rate hikes and renewed risk awareness (in the aftermath of September 11 and various accounting scandals).

Two major Marsh & McLennan units came under legal fire in probes of the mutual fund and insurance brokerage industries respectively. In 2003 Putnam agreed to settle securities fraud charges with the SEC and reimburse investors; many of Putnam's top officers were replaced and its compliance procedures were restructured.

The following year Marsh found itself at the center of a price-fixing investigation that involved several insurance companies including AIG and ACE Limited. At least nine employees of Marsh and AIG pled guilty to criminal charges. Jeffery Greenberg the son of outspoken AIG chairman and CEO Maurice Greenberg who had served as Marsh & McLennan's chairman and CEO since 1999 resigned in 2004 as a result of the price-fixing allegations.

Strengthening its risk management operations Marsh & McLennan acquired risk consulting company Kroll for about $2 billion in 2004. (It later divested the unit in 2010.)

Michael Cherkasky was named as Greenberg's successor. Before entering the insurance industry Cherkasky had headed the investigations unit of the New York County district attorney's office. Cherkasky guided the company during Marsh's alleged bid-rigging investigation which ended with an $850 million settlement agreement in early 2005. Following the settlement the company slashed its dividend and cut jobs.

As part of an effort to relieve possible conflicts of interest following the investigation MMC divested its US-based wholesale insurance brokerage Crump Group in late 2005. It also sold its private equity subsidiary MMC Capital (now Stone Point Capital) to the unit's management team.

The company then sold its money management operation Putnam Investments to Power Financial Corporation subsidiary Great-West Lifeco for $3.9 billion in 2007. At the same time the company reorganized its management consultancy operations melding three firms Mercer Oliver Wyman Mercer Management Consulting and Mercer Delta Organizing under one new brand: Oliver Wyman.

Late in 2007 the company ousted CEO Michael Cherkasky. While Cherkasky had seen the company through rough times he was unable to lead a recovery of the company following the bid-rigging scandal. The company's board replaced him with insurance executive Brian Duperreault formerly of ACE Limited at the start of 2008.

Duperreault immediately launched a number of restructuring measures to cut costs and reduce risks within the MMC business including revamping the company's management structure and rearranging Marsh's operating divisions.

Duperreault started carving off underperforming portions of the Kroll business including the Kroll's Corporate Advisory and Restructuring division and the Kroll Government Services business in 2008 and 2009. Then in 2010 MMC sold the Kroll Laboratory Specialists division which conducted drugs-of-abuse testing to diagnostic firm Inverness for $110 million.

In 2009 the company settled a shareholder class-action lawsuit –which was related to the 2004 bid-rigging investigation –for some $425 million. It also completed purchase of NIA Group in 2009. The following year the Mercer unit agreed to a $500 million payment to settle litigation matters with an Alaska retirement fund.

As a result of its various struggles MMC reported a net income loss in 2008; however it returned to profitability in 2009.

EXECUTIVES

Chairman and CEO Mercer, M. Michele Burns, age 53, $850,000 total compensation
President CEO and Director, Brian Duperreault, age 65, $1,000,000 total compensation
President and CEO Mercer, Julio A. Portalatin, age 53
SVP Chief Innovation Officer and CIO, Benjamin F. Allen, age 47
Chairman, Rt. Hon. Lord Lang of Monkton, age 71
President and CEO Guy Carpenter; Chairman Marsh & McLennan Companies International, Alexander (Alex) Moczarski, age 56
Vice Chairman Office of the CEO, David A. Nadler, age 63
President and CEO Oliver Wyman Group, John P. Drzik, age 49, $600,000 total compensation
Group President and COO, Daniel S. (Dan) Glaser, age 51, $1,000,000 total compensation
EVP and General Counsel, Peter J. Beshar, age 50, $875,000 total compensation
SVP and Chief Risk and Compliance Officer, E. Scott Gilbert, age 56
Deputy General Counsel and Corporate Secretary, Luciana (Lucy) Fato, age 46
VP and Head Corporate Communications and Brand, Silvia Davi
SVP and Chief Human Resources and Communications Officer, Orlando D. Ashford, age 43
President and CEO Marsh, Peter Zaffino, age 45
SVP International and Client Development, David R. Frediani
VP and Director Government Relations, Erick Gustafson
National Brokerage Leader, Regina M. Spratt
Head of Business Development, Edward Lynch
Chief Diversity Officer, Kathryn Komsa
CFO, J. Michael Bischoff, age 64
Director, Marc D. Oken, age 65
Director, H. Edward (Ed) Hanway, age 60
Director, Leslie M. (Bud) Baker Jr., age 69
President CEO and Director, Brian Duperreault, age 65
Director, Steven A. (Steve) Mills, age 60
Director, Bruce P. Nolop, age 61
Director, Adele Simmons, age 70
Director, Oscar Fanjul, age 62
Director, Lloyd M. Yates, age 51
Director, Zachary W. Carter, age 62
Auditors: Deloitte&ToucheLLP

LOCATIONS

HQ: Marsh & McLennan Companies Inc.
1166 Avenue of the Americas, New York NY 10036-2774
Phone: 212-345-5000 **Fax:** 212-345-4808
Web: www.marshmac.com

2011 Sales

	$ mil.	% of total
US	5,131	44
UK	1,922	17
Continental Europe	1,906	17
Asia/Pacific	1,287	11
Other regions & countries	1,320	11
Adjustments	(40)	-
Total	**11,526**	**100**

PRODUCTS/OPERATIONS

2011 Sales

	$ mil.	% of total
Risk & insurance services		
Marsh	5,253	45
Guy Carpenter	1,048	9
Consulting		
Mercer	3,782	33
Oliver Wyman Group	1,483	13
Adjustments	(40)	-
Total	**11,526**	**100**

Selected Acquisitions

2012

Eidson Insurance (property/casualty and employee benefits Florida)

2011

Alexander Forbes (South Africa)
Prescott Pailet Benefits
RJF Agencies
Seitlin Insurance

2010

Bostonian Group
Haake Companies
HSBC Insurance Brokers (London)
Rutherford

COMPETITORS

Accenture
Affiliated Computer Services
Anthony Clark International Insurance Brokers
Aon
Bain & Company
BB&T
Bollinger Inc.
Booz Allen
Brown & Brown
Fortegra Financial
FTI Consulting
Gallagher
Hub International
ING
Jardine Lloyd
McKinsey & Company
National Financial Partners
THB Group
Towers Watson
USI
Wells Fargo Insurance Services
Willis Group Holdings

HISTORICAL FINANCIALS

Company Type: Public

Income Statement FYE: December 31

	REVENUE ($ mil.)	NET INCOME ($ mil.)	NET PROFIT MARGIN	EMPLOYEES
12/11	11,526	993	8.6%	52,400
12/10	10,550	855	8.1%	51,000
12/09	10,493	227	2.2%	52,000
12/08	11,587	(73)	—	54,400
12/07	11,350	2,475	21.8%	56,100
Annual Growth	0.4%	(20.4%)	—	(1.7%)

2011 Year-End Financials

Debt ratio: 18.95%
Return on equity: 16.88%
Cash ($ mil.): 2,113
Current ratio: 151.06
Long-term debt ($ mil.): 2,668
No. of shares (mil.): 539
Dividends
Yield: —
Payout: 48.04%
Market value ($ mil.): 17,049

	STOCK PRICE ($) FY Close	P/E High/Low	PER SHARE ($) Earnings	Dividends	Book Value
12/11	31.62	18 14	1.79	0.00	10.91
12/10	27.34	18 13	1.55	0.81	11.78
12/09	22.08	59 41	0.42	0.80	11.00
12/08	24.27	— —	(0.14)	0.80	11.13
12/07	26.47	7 5	4.53	0.76	15.03
Annual Growth	4.5%	— —	(20.7%)	—	(7.7%)

Masco Corp.

Masco's ideal customer is a home improvement junkie with a thing for cabinets –and a hand-washing fetish. The company is a leading manufacturer of a variety of home improvement and building products, with cabinet and plumbing products accounting for more than half of its sales. Cabinet brands include KraftMaid, Quality Cabinets, and Merillat in the US and The Moores Group and Tvilum-Scanbirk in Europe. Faucets and bath and shower accessories are sold under the Delta and Peerless brands in the US and as Hansgrohe in Europe. Masco also makes BEHR paints and stains, windows, doors, staple guns, locksets, and HVAC products. If you're more comfortable on the couch, Masco also provides installation services.

HISTORY

Masco founder Alex Manoogian moved to the US at age 19 in 1920. He wound up in Detroit, and with partners Harry Adjemian and Charles Saunders, he started Masco (the first letters of their last names plus "co" for "company") Screw Products Company eight days before the crash of 1929. Manoogian's partners left within the year. Largely reliant on Detroit's auto industry, Masco grew slowly during the Depression, making custom parts for Chrysler, Ford, and others. With sales of $200,000 by 1937, it went public on the Detroit Stock Exchange. During WWII Masco focused on defense, and in 1942 sales passed $1 million.

A new plant opened in 1948 in Dearborn, Michigan, as Masco resumed peacetime business, mainly in the auto industry.

In 1954 Masco began selling Manoogian's one-handle kitchen faucet (Delta). Sales of faucets passed $1 million by 1958, and Masco opened a new faucet factory in Indiana. Under Manoogian's son Richard –whose dinner was often delayed while his father used the stove to test the heat tolerance of new faucet parts –Masco Corporation (so renamed in 1961) diversified. From 1964 to 1980 it bought more than 50 companies, concentrating on tool and metal casting, energy exploration, and air compressors.

In 1984 the firm split. Masco Corporation pursued the course set by its successful faucet sales, expanding its interests in home improvement and furnishings. The industrial products business was spun off as Masco Industries, a separate public corporation (later Metaldyne) in which Masco maintained a sizable stake.

Masco Corporation became the #1 US furniture maker in the late 1980s by buying Lexington Furniture (1987) and Universal Furniture (1989), both of North Carolina. In 1990 Masco acquired KraftMaid cabinets.

Two years later the company sold its interests in Mechanical Technology, Payless Cashways, and Emco Limited of Canada (Masco bought back 40% of Emco in 1997). Masco reduced its stake in Metaldyne from 47% to 35% in 1993.

Masco sought to establish itself in Europe, and in 1994 it bought a German cabinetmaker and a UK producer of handheld showers. In 1996 founder Manoogian died, but the company flowed on. It added a UK cabinetmaker, a German shower manufacturer, and a German insulation firm. That year Masco sold its troubled furniture unit to a group of investors and executives (who renamed the unit LifeStyle Furnishings International) for about $1 billion and further reduced its stake in Metaldyne to less than 20% (and later sold it all).

Acquisitions in 1997 included cabinetmakers Texwood Industries of Texas and Liberty Hardware Manufacturing of Florida. The next year it bought Vasco (heating systems and equipment, Belgium) and Brugman (building and home-improvement products, the Netherlands). It sold its Thermador unit (ovens and ranges) to US joint venture Bosch-Siemens Hausgerate.

Masco made 13 acquisitions from 1999 through early 2000, including Heritage Bathrooms (bathroom equipment, UK), Faucet Queens (plumbing and hardware supply), GMU Group (kitchen cabinets, Spain), Avocet Hardware (locks and hardware, UK), BEHR Process (coatings), and Mill's Pride (cabinets). Boosting its services in 1999, it acquired The Cary Group, an installer of fiberglass insulation.

To increase its geographic reach, Masco bought Tvilum-Scanbirk (ready-to-assemble furniture, Denmark), Masterchem Industries (specialty paint products), and Glass Idromassaggio (bathroom equipment, Italy), in 2000. In late 2000 and early 2001 it acquired two US-based installation services companies, Davenport Insulation Group and BSI Holdings, respectively. Also in 2001 Masco acquired Milgard Manufacturing, a vinyl window and patio door maker.

During 2002 Masco acquired home improvement products and service companies that included Bristan Ltd. (kitchen and bath faucets and shower and bath accessories), Brasstech, Inc. (faucets, plumbing specialties, and bath accessories; California), Cambrian Windows Ltd. (vinyl window frames), Duraflex Ltd. (extruded vinyl frame components), Premier Manufacturing Ltd. (vinyl window and door frames), SCE Unlimited (siding, shutters, gutters; Illinois), IDI Group (fireplaces, garage doors, shower enclosures; Atlanta), Service Partners LLC (insulation and other building products, Virginia), several small installation and other service companies, and Diversified Cabinet Distributors (cabinets and countertops, Atlanta). Masco also increased its interest in Hansgrohe AG (kitchen and bath faucets, hand-held and fixed showerheads, luxury shower systems, and steam showers; Germany) to 64%. The company sold its StarMark Cabinetry business for about $15 million.

In 2003 Masco increased its ownership interest in Hansgrohe AG (kitchen and bath faucets, hand-held and fixed showerheads, luxury shower systems, and steam showers; Germany) to 64% from 27%. The company established Color Solutions Centers in more than 1,500 Home Depot stores throughout the US. Masco sold its Baldwin Hardware and Weiser Lock businesses (builders' hardware and locksets) to Black & Decker (now Stanley Black & Decker) and The Marvel Group, a provider specialty products such as office work stations and machine stands, to members of Marvel's management team (led by president John Dellamore) for $289 million in total. Acquisitions in 2003 included PowerShot Tool Company, Inc. (fastening products, New Jersey) and several small installation service companies for a combined $63 million.

The next year Masco sold its Jung Pumpen (pumps), The Alvic Group (kitchen cabinets), Alma Kuchen (kitchen cabinets), E. Missel (acoustic insulation), and SKS Group (shutters and ventilation systems) businesses for $199 million. Masco continued its business review in 2005, selling two operating companies that made and distributed cabinets, vanities, medicine cabinets, shower rods, and bath accessories.

After reorganizing its European business operations, Masco sold off several of its operating units, including Gebhardt Consolidated (HVAC), The Heating Group (radiators), and GMU Group (cabinets). The company also disposed of North American businesses that were not core to its long-term growth strategy, which included Computerized Security Systems (CSS) and Zenith Products (bathroom storage).

In 2008 the company merged its Mill's Price brand with KraftMaid to form the Masco Retail Cabinet Group. It also merged Merillat and Quality Cabinets to form Masco Builder Cabinet Group.

LOCATIONS

HQ: Masco Corp.
21001 Van Born Road, Taylor, MI 48180
Phone: 313 274-7400 **Fax:** 313 792-4177
Web: www.masco.com

HISTORICAL FINANCIALS

Company Type:

Income Statement FYE: December 31

	REVENUE ($ mil.)	NET INCOME ($ mil.)	NET PROFIT MARGIN	EMPLOYEES
12/11	7,467	(575)	—	31,000
12/10	7,592	(1,043)	—	32,500
12/09	7,792	(183)	—	35,400
12/08	9,600	(391)	—	39,000
12/07	11,770	386	3.3%	52,000
Annual Growth	(10.8%)	—	—	(12.1%)

2011 Year-End Financials

Debt ratio: 55.16%	No. of shares (mil.): 347
Return on equity: (-109.11)%	Dividends
Cash ($ mil.): 1,656	Yield: —
Current ratio: 145.11	Payout: —
Long-term debt ($ mil.): 3,222	Market value ($ mil.): 3,646

	STOCK PRICE ($) FY Close	P/E High/Low	PER SHARE ($) Earnings	Dividends	Book Value
12/11	10.48	— —	(1.66)	0.00	1.52
12/10	12.66	— —	(3.00)	0.30	3.97
12/09	13.81	— —	(0.53)	0.46	7.50
12/08	11.13	— —	(1.11)	0.93	8.10
12/07	21.61	32 20	1.03	0.91	11.21
Annual Growth	(16.5%)	— —	—	—	(39.3%)

MasterCard Inc

Surpassing Visa in market share —now that would be priceless. Serving approximately 22000 member financial institutions worldwide MasterCard is the #2 payment system in the US. The company does not issue credit or its namesake cards; rather it markets the MasterCard (credit debit and prepaid cards) and Maestro (debit and prepaid cards mainly in Europe) brands provides a transaction authorization network establishes guidelines for use and collects fees from members. The company provides its services in more than 210 countries and territories and its cards are accepted at more than 31 million locations around the planet. MasterCard also operates the Cirrus ATM network.

There are more than 1.6 billion MasterCard- and Maestro-branded cards in circulation worldwide and the company annually processes some 27 billion transactions worth some $3.2 trillion. Long considered more down-market than Visa MasterCard is working to lure more affluent users by offering such products as the World MasterCard which has no spending limit.

While not entirely recession-proof (revenues are directly tied to consumer business and government spending) MasterCard has proven resilient during the economic downturn as consumers increasingly migrate to electronic payments. Though the number of MasterCard-branded cards in circulation has declined along with the number of financial institutions that issue them the company's transaction volume not to mention the corresponding processing fees it collects from them has increased. This has brought the company's revenues and net income up for the past three years. With the US market virtually saturated MasterCard has been focusing its expansion efforts overseas. (Revenue generated in the US accounts for less than half of the company's sales and has been declining.) However a protracted recession in Europe could hurt the company if consumer spending there declines.

MasterCard offers computer chip-enabled cards in several markets including Europe Latin America and the Caribbean and the Asia/Pacific region. US consumers have been slower to adopt this technology but not for the company's lack of trying. One "smart" product however that's showing signs of success stateside is the company's MasterCard PayPass which allows customers to quickly tap or swipe their payment cards at specially equipped merchant terminals. In 2011 the company partnered with the New York City-area Metropolitan Transportation Authority to pilot a program allowing commuters to ride using tap-and-go payments. The program was successful if not in its overwhelming usage but as far as showcasing the company's ability to process the payments securely.

In keeping with its strategy of developing its online and mobile payments business in non-US markets MasterCard acquired British payment services provider DataCash Group in 2010. The $525 million deal expanded the company's e-commerce business and increased its ability to process payments online especially in Europe. The following year MasterCard bought the prepaid card business of Travelex for some $460 million. It will use the acquisition as a platform to expand its prepaid card operations around the world as its operations in that segment are already well-established at home. To gain traction in the burgeoning personalized shopping offers and rewards business MasterCard acquired Silicon Valley firm Truaxis in 2012.

MasterCard which in 2008 agreed to a $1.8 billion settlement with American Express over antitrust issues faces further ongoing litigation which could cost it billions. Some 5 million retailers have filed another antitrust suit against MasterCard Visa and about a dozen large banks claiming that the defendants have worked together to unfairly increase interchange fees. (MasterCard does not earn interchange fees itself.) The 2011 Durbin amendement cut the interchange fees on debit cards which has already cut into the banks' revenues. If interchange fees charged to merchants decreases the banks that issue the cards could ultimately pressure MasterCard and Visa to reduce their fees and assessments further cutting revenues.

HISTORY

A group of bankers formed The Interbank Card Association (ICA) in 1966 to establish authorization clearing and settlement procedures for bank credit card transactions. This was particularly important to banks left out of the rapidly growing BankAmericard (later Visa) network sponsored by Bank of America.

By 1969 ICA was issuing the Master Charge card throughout the US and had formed alliances in Europe and Japan. In the mid-1970s ICA modernized its system replacing telephone transaction authorization with a computerized magnetic strip system. ICA had members in Africa Australia and Europe by 1979. That year the organization changed its name (and the card's) to MasterCard.

In 1980 Russell Hogg became president when John Reynolds resigned after disagreeing with the board over company performance and direction. Hogg made major organizational changes and consolidated data processing in St. Louis. MasterCard began offering debit cards in 1980 and traveler's checks in 1981.

MasterCard issued the first credit cards in China in 1987. The next year it bought Cirrus then the world's largest ATM network. It also secured a pact with Belgium-based card company Eurocard (which later became Europay) to supervise MasterCard's European operations and help build the brand.

Hogg resigned in 1988 after disagreements with the board and was succeeded by Alex Hart. In 1991 the Maestro debit card was unveiled.

The 1990s were marked by trouble in Europe: The pact with Europay hadn't resulted in the boom MasterCard had hoped for customer service was below par and competition was keen. Alex Hart retired in 1994 and was succeeded by Eugene Lockhart who tackled the European woes. Lockhart considered ending the relationship but eventually worked things out with Europay. By the end of the decade Europay was locked in a vicious battle to undercut Visa's market share through lower fees.

MasterCard in 1995 invested in UK-based Mondex International maker of electronic set-value refillable smart cards. But US consumer resistance to cash cards and competition in the more advanced European market delayed growth in this area.

In October 1996 a group of merchants including Wal-Mart and Sears filed class-action lawsuits against both MasterCard and Visa challenging the "honor all cards" rule. Because usage fees are higher merchants balked at accepting consumers' MasterCard- or Visa-branded off-line or signature-based debit cards and claimed the card issuers violated antitrust laws by tying acceptance of debit to that of credit. In a dramatic twist minutes before the trial was set to begin in 2003 MasterCard announced a settlement (the card issuer was required to pay $125 million in 2003 and $100 million annually from 2004 through 2012).

Just months later armed with the lawsuit's settlement which also freed merchants to pick which credit and debit card services they use Wal-Mart (along with a handful of others) stopped accepting signature debit cards issued by MasterCard.

Lockhart resigned in 1997 and was succeeded by former head of overseas operations Robert Selander. Yet another management upheaval began in 1999 as the company moved to streamline its organizational structure and shift away from geographical divisions. It also said member banks could boost visibility by putting their logos on card fronts and moving MasterCard's logo to the back.

In 2002 MasterCard merged with Europay with which it already had close ties. As part of the transaction holding company MasterCard Incorporated was formed; MasterCard International become the company's main subsidiary and MasterCard Europe (formerly Europay) became its European subsidiary.

After some 40 years as a private entity MasterCard went public in 2006 in one of the largest IPOs of its time. Following the offering the approximately 1400 financial institutions that wholly owned MasterCard before the offering retained a stake of more than 40%. Two of the top three US banks (Citigroup and JPMorgan Chase) remained among MasterCard's largest shareholders.

Some of the proceeds from the company's IPO were used to fight antitrust lawsuits from such rivals as American Express and Discover as well as other payment processors. In 2008 the company agreed to a $1.8 billion settlement with American Express which had claimed that MasterCard and others tried to stop financial institutions from issuing its AmEx cards. Later that year MasterCard settled the Discover lawsuit agreeing to pay $862.5 million.

Also in 2008 MasterCard bought Ireland-based software provider Orbiscom. The acquired company's technology was used to create MasterCard inControl a platform for making secure Internet and telephone purchases.

MasterCard promoted president and COO Ajay Banga to CEO in 2010. He succeeded Robert Selander who stepped down after more than a dozen years at the helm.

EXECUTIVES

Chairman, Richard N. Haythornthwaite, age 55
CFO MasterCard Incorporated and MasterCard International Incorporated, Martina Hund-Mejean, age 51, $500,000 total compensation
Vice Chairman, Walter M. (Walt) Macnee, age 57
President CEO and Director, Ajaypal S. (Ajay) Banga, age 52, $269,744 total compensation
President Global Products and Solutions MasterCard Incorporated and MasterCard International, Gary J. Flood, age 53, $500,000 total compensation
Chief Franchise Integrity Officer General Counsel and Secretary MasterCard Incorporated and MasterCard International, Noah J. Hanft, age 59, $475,000 total compensation
President US Markets MasterCard Incorporated and MasterCard International, Christopher A. (Chris) McWilton, age 53, $550,000 total compensation
President International Markets MasterCard Incorporated and MasterCard Worldwide, Ann Cairns
President Access Prepaid Worldwide, Steve Grigg
Group Executive Global Prepaid Solutions, Ronald C. (Ron) Hynes
President MasterCard Technologies, Robert (Rob) Reeg, age 56
Chief Human Resources Officer MasterCard Incorporated and MasterCard International, Stephanie E. Voquer, age 60
Group Executive Research and Development Mastercard Labs, Garry Lyons
SVP Mobile Product Development, James Anderson
Group Executive MasterCard Integrated Processing Solutions, Cathy McCaul
Director, Marc R. Olivie, age 58
Director, Jackson P. Tai, age 61
Director, Edward S. Tian, age 48
Director, Nancy J. Karch, age 64
Vice Chairman, Walter M. (Walt) Macnee, age 57
President CEO and Director, Ajaypal S. (Ajay) Banga, age 52
Director, Steven J. Freiberg, age 55
Director, David R. (Dave) Carlucci, age 57
Director, Mark Schwartz, age 57
Director, Silvio Barzi, age 64
Director, Jose O. Reyes Lagunes, age 60
Director, Rima Qureshi, age 47
Auditors: PricewaterhouseCoopersLLP

LOCATIONS

HQ: MasterCard Incorporated
2000 Purchase St., Purchase NY 10577
Phone: 914-249-2000 **Fax:** 402-351-2775
Web: www.mutualofomaha.com

PRODUCTS/OPERATIONS

2011 Sales

	$ mil.	% of total
Domestic assessments	3,246	36
Transaction processing fees	2,595	29
Cross-border volume fees	2,094	24
Other	1,000	11
Adjustments	(2221)	-
Total	**6,714**	**100**

COMPETITORS

American Express
Discover
Fifth Third
First Data
JCB International
NYCE Payments Network
PULSE Network
Total System Services
Visa Inc
Visa International

HISTORICAL FINANCIALS

Company Type: Public

Income Statement FYE: December 31

	REVENUE ($ mil.)	NET INCOME ($ mil.)	NET PROFIT MARGIN	EMPLOYEES
12/11	6,714	1,906	28.4%	6,700
12/10	5,539	1,846	33.3%	5,600
12/09	5,098	1,462	28.7%	5,100
12/08	4,991	(253)	—	5,500
12/07	4,067	1,085	26.7%	5,000
Annual Growth	13.3%	15.1%	—	7.6%

2011 Year-End Financials

Debt ratio: —
Return on equity: 32.48%
Cash ($ mil.): 3,734
Current ratio: 183.57
Long-term debt ($ mil.): —
No. of shares (mil.): 126
Dividends
Yield: —
Payout: 4.04%
Market value ($ mil.): 47,297

	STOCK PRICE ($) FY Close	P/E High/Low		PER SHARE ($) Earnings	Dividends	Book Value
12/11	372.82	26	15	14.85	0.00	46.25
12/10	224.11	19	14	14.05	0.60	39.76
12/09	255.98	23	11	11.16	0.60	27.00
12/08	142.93	—	—	(1.95)	0.60	14.91
12/07	215.20	28	12	8.00	0.54	23.06
Annual Growth	14.7%	—	—	16.7%	—	19.0%

Mattel Inc

Barbie is the platinum blonde in power at Mattel the #1 toy maker in the world. Its products include Barbie and Polly Pocket dolls Fisher-Price toys Hot Wheels and Matchbox cars American Girl dolls and books and various Barney Ferrari and other licensed items. Mattel also sells action figures and toys based on Walt Disney and Warner Bros. movies. To satisfy techie kids Mattel has accessorized Barbie with interactive games software and a line of MP3 players. The company has even licensed the Barbie name for eyewear. It also sells games (UNO) and puzzles. Mattel is trying to reduce its reliance on its biggest customers –Wal-Mart Toys "R" Us and Target –through its own catalog and Internet sales.

HISTORY

A small California toy manufacturer began operating out of a converted garage in 1945 producing dollhouse furniture. Harold Matson and Elliot Handler named their new company Mattel using letters from their last and first names. Matson soon sold his share to Handler and his wife Ruth who incorporated the business in 1948.

The company's toy line had expanded by 1952 to include burp guns and musical toys and sales exceeded $5 million. Sponsorship of Walt Disney's "Mickey Mouse Club" (debuted 1955) a first in toy advertising was a shrewd marketing step for Mattel providing direct year-round access to millions of young potential customers.

In 1959 Mattel introduced the Barbie doll named after the Handlers' daughter Barbara and later introduced Ken named after their son. Barbie with her fashionable wardrobe and extensive line of accessories was an instant hit and eventually became the most successful brand-name toy ever sold.

Mattel went public in 1960 and within two years sales had jumped from $25 million to $75 million. It launched the popular Hot Wheels miniature cars line in 1968.

The Handlers were ousted from management in 1974 after an investigation by the SEC found irregularities in reports of the company's profits. The new management moved into non-toy businesses adding Western Publishing (Golden Books) and the Ringling Brothers-Barnum & Bailey Combined Shows circus in 1979.

By the 1980s Mattel was a high-volume business with heavy overhead expenses and high development costs. By 1984 in an effort to recapitalize the company had sold all its non-toy assets. Sales were more than $1 billion in 1987 but Mattel lost $93 million. Toying with bankruptcy newly appointed chairman John Amerman cut Mattel's manufacturing capacity by 40% and fired 22% of its corporate staff.

The early 1990s saw several acquisitions – Fisher-Price (toys for preschoolers) and Kransco (battery-powered ride-on vehicles). But Mattel backed down from a 1996 hostile bid for rival Hasbro when it realized the purchase would be too costly.

Amerman relinquished his roles as chairman and CEO in 1997 and was replaced by COO Jill Barad who had enlivened the Barbie brand. Also in 1997 the company bought #3 US toy maker Tyco Toys (Tickle Me Elmo and Matchbox cars). In 1998 Mattel bought mail-order firm Pleasant Company (now known as American Girl) maker of

American Girl-brand books dolls and clothing and the UK's Bluebird Toys.

Barad started restructuring Mattel in 1999 closing plants and laying off 3000 workers.

The company entered unfamiliar territory in 1999 paying $3.6 billion for leading educational software maker The Learning Company ("Carmen Sandiego Reader Rabbit") in a deal that would be Barad's downfall. The Learning Company unexpectedly lost money leading to the resignations of the unit's top brass. Additional losses followed and Barad left in 2000. Mattel soon put its software business (mostly consisting of The Learning Company) up for sale and it named Kraft Foods veteran Bob Eckert chairman and CEO.

Later in 2000 Mattel finally found a buyer for its beleaguered Learning Company software business –an affiliate of privately owned Gores Technology Group. Mattel also cut 350 jobs.

To take advantage of its well-known brand name subsidiary Fisher-Price announced in late 2000 that it would begin selling children's apparel online and through direct-mail catalogs. In 2001 Mattel signed several licensing deals including one for toys and games based on Barney TV's purple dinosaur.

Mattel and two former employees agreed in 2002 to pay $477000 in fines for making political donations in other people's names the third-largest fine imposed by the Federal Election Commission. Also that year the company closed its Kentucky manufacturing and distribution facilities and in early 2003 consolidated two of its manufacturing facilities in Mexico.

In February 2003 Mattel consolidated its US Girls and US Boys-Entertainment divisions into one segment called Mattel Brands and separated the Pleasant Company (now American Girl) from the US Girls division.

Mattel's Fisher-Price was sued by interactive learning bookmaker LeapFrog for patent violations concerning its talking book technology. The product in question was Fisher-Price's Power-Touch Learning System which was launched in August 2003. A federal court ruled in favor of Fisher-Price in 2006.

In early 2004 the Pleasant Company changed its name to American Girl to match the American Girl brand.

On Valentine's Day 2004 Mattel announced the breakup of Barbie and Ken who had been together for over 43 years. The couple according to the company decided to "spend some time apart" but will "always remain the best of friends."

The company also partnered with Scholastic Entertainment in 2005 to produce Read With Me DVD! and Ready for School educational learning systems. In late 2005 Mattel consolidated its flagship and Fisher-Price divisions under the direction of one executive in order to better streamline its operations. Only the company's American Girl brand has its own unit.

Looking to further its presence in the electronic toys business Mattel acquired Hong Kong-based Radica Games for $230 million in 2006. The products appeal to children older than Mattel's typical consumer as well as adults. Also that year Mattel selected Activision Blizzard in a multiyear deal to be the exclusive worldwide distributor for Barbie-branded video games.

In December 2008 the company agreed to pay $12 million to 39 states to settle an investigation over Chinese-made lead-tainted toys (shipped to the US in 2007) and to lower acceptable levels of lead in imported toys. In response to hard economic times Mattel in late 2008 cut 1000 jobs (less than 5% of its worldwide workforce) thus reducing its professional and management ranks by nearly 10%.

2009 marked Barbie's 50th birthday an event that Mattel marked with a yearlong celebration. After about a decade making Sesame Street-branded toys for Sesame Workshop Mattel saw its licensing business awarded to competitor Hasbro in December 2009.

In a stinging defeat for Mattel in April 2011 a federal jury sided with MGA Entertainment in the long-running legal battle over ownership of the billion-dollar Bratz doll franchise. (MGA and Mattel started their catfight a decade ago.) The jury rejected Mattel's copyright infringement claims. Instead it found that Mattel has stolen trade secrets from MGA and said it owed the company $88.5 million. The decision reversed a 2008 ruling in which a jury sided with Mattel.

EXECUTIVES

EVP and Chief Human Resources Officer, Alan Kaye, age 58
CFO, Kevin M. Farr, age 54, $725,000 total compensation
EVP; President American Girl, Ellen L. Brothers, age 56
SVP Asia Pacific Sourcing, Douglas E. Kerner, age 52
SVP and Corporate Controller, H. Scott Topham, age 51
EVP Chief Legal Officer and Secretary, Robert (Bob) Normile, age 52
Chairman, Robert A. Eckert, age 57, $1,250,000 total compensation
CEO and Director, Bryan G. Stockton, age 58, $750,000 total compensation
EVP Worldwide Operations, Thomas A. Debrowski, age 61, $710,000 total compensation
SVP and CIO, Paul Rasmusson
SVP Investor Relations, Dianne Douglas, age 55
SVP Product Integrity and Chief Regulatory Officer, Jim Walter
VP International PR and Brand Communications, Julia Jensen
SVP Strategic Iniatives, Jerry Bossick
EVP North America, Jean-Christophe Pean
Director US Logistics, Selwyn Moore
Director Corporate Communications, Jules Andres
SVP Inventor Relations Licensing and New Business Fisher-Price Brands, Stan Clutton
VP Entertainment, Rob Hudnut
EVP Mattel Brands El Segundo, Tim Kilpin, age 51
SVP Global Entertainment and Franchise Development, Doug Wadleigh
VP Corporate Affairs, Lisa Marie Bongiovanni
EVP Fisher-Price, David Allmark, age 48
VP PR and Brand Communications, Sara Rosales
Director Fisher-Price PR, Brenda Andolina
EVP International, Geoff Massingberd, age 54
SVP Marketing Barbie, Stephanie Cota
SVP Design Barbie Brand, Evelyn Viohl
SVP Tax, Clara Wong
Director Investor Relations, David Zbojniewicz
Director American Girl PR, Julie Parks
SVP and Treasurer, Mandana Sadigh, age 52
Director, Dean A. Scarborough, age 56
Director, Kathy Brittain White, age 62
Director, G. Craig Sullivan, age 72
Director, Ronald L. (Ron) Sargent, age 56
Director, Dominic Ng, age 53
Director, Michael J. (Mike) Dolan, age 65
Director, Vasant M. Prabhu, age 52
CEO and Director, Bryan G. Stockton, age 58
Director, Tully M. Friedman, age 70
Director, Andrea L. Rich, age 68
Director, Christopher A. Sinclair, age 61
Director, Frances D. Fergusson, age 67
Auditors: PricewaterhouseCoopersLLP

LOCATIONS

HQ: Mattel Inc.
333 Continental Blvd., El Segundo CA 90245-5012
Phone: 310-252-2000 **Fax:** 310-252-2179
Web: www.mattel.com

2011 Sales

	$ mil.	% of total
US	3,580	57
Europe	1,656	26
Latin America	991	16
Asia/Pacific	384	6
Other regions	228	4
Adjustments (575.1) (9)		
Total	**6,226**	**100**

PRODUCTS/OPERATIONS

2011 Sales

	$ mil.	% of total
Domestic		
Mattel Girls & Boys Brands US	1,776	28
Fisher-Price Brands US	1,293	21
American Girl Brands	510	8
International	3,260	52
Adjustments (575.1) (9)		
Total	**6,266**	**100**

Selected Brands

Boys
- Batman
- DC Universe
- Fireman Sam
- Hot Wheels
- Kung Fu Panda
- Magic 8 Ball
- Masters of the Universe
- Matchbox
- Mattel
- Max Steel
- Nickelodeon Rugrats
- Radica
- Scrabble (International)
- Speed Racer
- Tyco Radio Control
- Yu-Gi-Oh!

Girls
- American Girl
- Angelina Ballerina
- Barbie
- Bitty Baby
- Boom-O
- Cabbage Patch Kids
- Coconut
- Disney
- Diva Starz
- ello
- Fashion Avenue
- Flavas
- High School Musical
- Just Like You
- Little Mommy
- Polly Pocket!

Infant and preschool
- BabyGear
- Barney
- Blue' s Clues
- Bob the Builder
- Disney
- Dora the Explorer
- Fisher-Price
- Geo Trax
- Go-Diego-Go!
- Little People
- Matchbox Kids
- Mickey Mouse
- Pixter
- Power Wheels
- See ' n Say
- Thomas & Friends
- UNO

View-Master
Winnie the Pooh

COMPETITORS

Electronic Arts	Playmobil
Hasbro	Radio Flyer
JAKKS Pacific	Sanrio
LeapFrog	Simba Dickie Group
LEGO	Spin Master
Marvel Entertainment	TakaraTomy
MGA Entertainment	Toy Quest
Motorsports Authentics	Ty
Namco Bandai	VTech Holdings
Ohio Art	

HISTORICAL FINANCIALS

Company Type: Public

Income Statement FYE: December 31

	REVENUE ($ mil.)	NET INCOME ($ mil.)	NET PROFIT MARGIN	EMPLOYEES
12/11	6,266	768	12.3%	28,000
12/10	5,856	684	11.7%	31,000
12/09	5,430	528	9.7%	27,000
12/08	5,918	379	6.4%	29,000
12/07	5,970	599	10.1%	31,000
Annual Growth	1.2%	6.4%	—	(2.5%)

2011 Year-End Financials

Debt ratio: 27.47%
Return on equity: 29.44%
Cash ($ mil.): 1,369
Current ratio: 331.47
Long-term debt ($ mil.): 1,500
No. of shares (mil.): 337
Dividends
Yield: —
Payout: 42.20%
Market value ($ mil.): 9,355

	STOCK PRICE ($) FY Close	P/E High/Low		PER SHARE ($) Earnings	Dividends	Book Value
12/11	27.76	13	10	2.18	0.00	7.75
12/10	25.43	14	10	1.86	0.83	7.53
12/09	19.98	14	7	1.45	0.75	6.99
12/08	16.00	21	11	1.05	0.75	5.91
12/07	19.04	19	12	1.54	0.75	6.38
Annual Growth	9.9%	—	—	9.1%	—	5.0%

MB Financial Inc

The "MB" in MB Financial doesn't stand for "Midsized Businesses" though that's its target market. The holding company owns MB Financial Bank which has about 90 branches in the Chicago area and one in Philadelphia. Commercial-related credits including mortgages operating loans lease financing and construction loans make up nearly 75% of the bank's loan portfolio. In addition to serving small and middle-market businesses MB Financial provides retail banking and lending to consumers. The company also offers wealth management and trust services through its Cedar Hill Associates subsidiary and brokerage through Vision Investment Services. LaSalle Systems leases technology-related equipment to corporations.

Taking advantage of the dozens of bank failures in 2009 MB Financial acquired Heritage Community Bank InBank Corus Bank and Benchmark Bank in separate FDIC-assisted transactions. In 2010 it acquired failed Chicago-area institutions Broadway Bank and New Century Bank in similar deals. Gains on these acquisitions helped the company's revenues (and profits) grow in 2010. Although the company didn't have the benefit of gains on acquisitions in 2011 (and revenues fell 20% to $493.7 million) profits continued to climb that year growing 89% to $38.7 million largely due to a lowered provision for loan losses. Also that year the bank got millions of dollars of nonperforming loans off of its books via a sale to Colony Capital.

The company has said it will continue to acquire failed banks with FDIC assistance if the opportunity arises. It believes such transactions are more profitable because they usually include loss-share agreements with the regulator and often afford the acquirer more flexibility than traditional takeovers. Other strategies for growth include expanding its private banking and asset managements operations as well as its fee-based business services including treasury management and leasing.

EXECUTIVES

VP; EVP Administration and Director MB Financial Bank, Rosemarie Bouman, age 54, $233,615 total compensation
President CEO and Director; President MB Financial Bank, Mitchell S. Feiger, age 53, $629,000 total compensation
VP; President Lease Banking and Director MB Financial Bank, Burton J. Field, age 76, $419,905 total compensation
EVP and Director MB Bank; President MB Financial Commmunity Development and MB Charitable Foundation, Thomas P. (Tommy) FitzGibbon Jr., age 67, $216,300 total compensation
SVP MB Financial Bank, James Mann
VP and CFO; EVP CFO and Director MB Financial Bank, Jill E. York, age 48, $294,000 total compensation
Vice Chairman, James N. Hallene, age 51
Chairman, Thomas H. Harvey, age 51
EVP and Chief Retail Banking Officer and Director MB Financial Bank, Susan G. Peterson, age 62
EVP Operations and Technology and Director MB Financial Bank, Larry J. Kallembach, age 55
VP Commercial Real Estate MB Financial Bank, Rick J. Chang, age 40
EVP Wealth Management Commercial Services and Director MB Financial Bank, Brian Wildman, age 49
SVP and Head Personal Trust Administration MB Financial Bank, Sally Larson Sargent
Chief Credit Officer, Tom Watts
COO Commercial Banking, Tom Prothero, age 42
SVP Real Estate MB Financial Bank, Christina Frank
President Cedar Hill Associates, Alan Cole
EVP Credit Management MB Financial Bank, Mark A. Heckler
EVP Commercial Banking MB Financial Bank, Edward F. Milefchik
Director, Robert S. Engelman Jr., age 70
President CEO and Director; President MB Financial Bank, Mitchell S. Feiger, age 53
Director, David P. Bolger, age 55
Director, Karen J. May, age 54
Vice Chairman, James N. Hallene, age 51
Director, Patrick Henry, age 72
Director, Richard J. Holmstrom, age 54
Director, Charles J. Gries, age 66
Auditors: McGladreyLLP

LOCATIONS

HQ: MB Financial Inc.
800 W. Madison St., Chicago IL 60607
Phone: 888-422-6562 **Fax:** 337-364-1171
Web: www.iberiabank.com

PRODUCTS/OPERATIONS

2011 Sales

	$ mil.	% of total
Interest		
Loans	324	64
Investment securities	58	12
Other	1	-
Noninterest		
Deposit service fees	39	8
Lease financing net	26	5
Asset management & trust fees	17	3
Loan service fees	7	2
Card fees	7	1
Other	24	5
Adjustments	(13.6)	-
Total	**493**	**100**

Selected Subsidiaries

MB Financial Bank N.A.
- Ashland Management Agency Inc.
- Cedar Hill Associates LLC (80%)
- LaSalle Systems Leasing Inc.
  - LaSalle Business Solutions LLC
  - Melrose Equipment Company LLC
- MB Deferred Exchange Corporation
- MB Financial Center LLC
- MB Financial Center Land Owner LLC
- MB Financial Community Development Corporation
- Vision Investment Services Inc.
  - Vision Insurance Services Inc.

COMPETITORS

Bank of America	Northern Trust
Citigroup	PNC Financial
Fifth Third	PrivateBancorp
Harris	U.S. Bancorp
JPMorgan Chase	Wintrust Financial

HISTORICAL FINANCIALS

Company Type: Public

Income Statement FYE: December 31

	ASSETS ($ mil.)	NET INCOME ($ mil.)	INCOME AS % OF ASSETS	EMPLOYEES
12/11	9,833	38	0.4%	1,684
12/10	10,320	20	0.2%	1,703
12/09	10,865	(26)	—	1,638
12/08	8,819	16	0.2%	1,342
12/07	7,834	93	1.2%	1,282
Annual Growth	5.8%	(19.9%)	—	7.1%

2011 Year-End Financials

Debt ratio: 4.32%
Return on equity: 2.79%
Cash ($ mil.): 244
Current ratio: —
Long-term debt ($ mil.): 424
No. of shares (mil.): 54
Dividends
Yield: —
Payout: 7.69%
Market value ($ mil.): 935

	STOCK PRICE ($) FY Close	P/E High/Low		PER SHARE ($) Earnings	Dividends	Book Value
12/11	17.10	42	27	0.52	0.00	25.44
12/10	17.32	140	75	0.19	0.04	24.66
12/09	19.71	—	—	(0.91)	0.15	24.49
12/08	27.95	81	43	0.44	0.72	30.52
12/07	30.83	14	11	2.58	0.72	24.91
Annual Growth	(13.7%)	—	—	(33.0%)	—	0.5%

McDonald's Corp

Serving billions of hamburgers has put a shine on these arches. McDonald's is the world's #1 fast-food company by sales with more than 33500 restaurants serving burgers and fries in 119 countries. (There are more than 14000 Golden Arches locations in the US.) The popular chain is well-known for its Big Macs Quarter Pounders and Chicken McNuggets. Most of the outlets are free-standing units offering dine-in and drive-through service but McDonald's also has many eateries located in airports retail areas and other high-traffic locations. About 80% of the restaurants are run by franchisees or affiliates.

HISTORY

The first McDonald's opened in 1948 in San Bernardino California. In 1954 owners Dick and Mac McDonald signed a franchise agreement with 52-year-old Ray Kroc (a malt machine salesman) and a year later Kroc opened his first restaurant in Des Plaines Illinois. By 1957 Kroc was operating 14 McDonald's restaurants in Illinois Indiana and California. In 1961 Kroc bought out the McDonald brothers for $2.7 million.

In 1962 the now-ubiquitous Golden Arches appeared for the first time and the company sold its billionth burger. Ronald McDonald made his debut the following year and the company introduced its first new menu item –the Filet-O-Fish. Two years later McDonald's went public and ran its first TV ads. The company opened its first stores outside the US (in Canada) in 1967 and the next year it added the Big Mac to the menu and opened its 1000th restaurant.

During the 1970s McDonald's grew at the rate of about 500 restaurants per year and the first Ronald McDonald House (a temporary residence for families of hospitalized children) opened in 1974. The drive-through window appeared in 1975.

McDonald's introduced Chicken McNuggets in 1983. Kroc who had become senior chairman in the 1970s died the next year. Growing competition slowed the company's US sales growth to about 5% per year at the end of the 1980s. In response McDonald's added specially priced "value menu" items.

In 1990 the company made history and headlines when it opened the first McDonald's in Moscow. Two years later the Golden Arches expanded into China. The company stumbled with the pricey Arch Deluxe hamburger in 1996 and its Campaign 55 discount promotion the next year. However the giveaway of Teenie Beanie Babies in 1997 was its most successful promotion ever. McDonald's decentralized US operations that year to bring decision-making closer to local franchises. US division CEO Edward Rensi retired and was replaced by division chairman Jack Greenberg.

The next year Greenberg launched the Made For You food preparation system designed to reduce waste and produce a better tasting burger. He was named CEO later that year. McDonald's also made its first investment in another restaurant concept in 1998 when it bought a stake in Chipotle Mexican Grill a Denver-based chain of Mexican food restaurants. That same year saw the death of co-founder Dick McDonald who died at age 89.

During Greenberg's first year he slowed US expansion and stepped up international growth. In 1999 McDonald's added a third brand to its family when it acquired the Ohio-based Donatos Pizzeria chain. The company's biggest deal though came in 2000 when it purchased the Boston Market chain from struggling Boston Chicken for about $175 million.

Early in 2001 McDonald's unveiled its New Tastes Menu in which local markets could feature up to four regional or seasonal foods out of a 40-item national selection. The company continued its move toward diversification and international expansion purchasing a 33% stake in the UK limited-service sandwich chain Pret A Manger for $40 million. It also spun off its Japanese unit to the public retaining a 50% ownership stake.

But even with all its size and power McDonald's found out it was not immune to economic trouble and corporate blunders. The company suffered from ill-thought product changes less-than-successful marketing plans and the growing public preference for lighter fast-food options such as sub sandwiches and salads. Following three quarters of declining profits in 2001 McDonald's announced a major restructuring of its US operations. It cut about 700 corporate jobs hired five new managers and consolidated its service regions.

Business failed to improve however and in 2002 it laid off approximately 600 corporate employees and closed about 175 underperforming units. At the end of 2002 after the company posted its first quarterly loss in history vice chairman and president Jim Cantalupo a veteran of McDonald's international operation replaced Jack Greenberg as chairman and CEO.

McDonald's business began to improve during 2003 with the introduction of healthier menu fare. Late that year the company sold Donatos Pizza back to its founder Jim Grote and closed all Boston Market locations outside the US in order to focus more attention on its core chains. The company ended a joint venture with Seed Restaurant Group that would have led to the development of new Fazoli's locations. Japan however remained a particularly rough market: McDonald's Holdings (Japan) posted losses for both 2002 and 2003. It also gave up on efforts to establish the Pret A Manger sandwich shops in Japan.

Putting its advertising dollars to work McDonald's introduced a global branding campaign in 2003 to help change its image. Called "I'm Lovin' It" the campaign attempted to up the restaurant chain's hip factor and draw young customers. These efforts showed positive results: McDonald's posted steady sales increases through most of 2003 and into early 2004 and investors were encouraged by the progress.

Cantalupo died in 2004. Director Andrew McKenna was named chairman and president. Charlie Bell became CEO. Diagnosed with cancer and undergoing surgery a month later Bell curtailed his workload but returned to his job full-time later that month. He underwent a second surgery procedure later that year again cancer-related and eventually stepped down near the end of 2004 in order to devote all his time to fighting cancer. (Bell died early the next year.) Vice chairman Jim Skinner assumed the mantle of CEO becoming the company's third chief executive in seven months. Mike Roberts the CEO of McDonald's USA assumed the additional titles of president and COO.

In a David and Goliath scenario the Venezuelan government ordered all 80 of the country's McDonald's restaurants closed for three days in 2005 as punishment for not following the country's tax laws. McDonald's sold a 35% stake in Chipotle through an IPO in 2006 and disposed of its remaining holdings later that year. It sold Boston Market to private equity firm Sun Capital Partners for $250 million the following year and in 2008 McDonald's cashed out its stake in Pret A Manger as part of a $670 million buyout by private equity firm Bridgepoint Capital.

In 2011 McDonald's sold its 50% stake in Hardcastle Restaurants one of two joint ventures operating McDonald's restaurants in India and converted it to a franchisee operation.

EXECUTIVES

Vice Chairman and CEO, James A. (Jim) Skinner, age 67, $1,391,667 total compensation

Honorary Chairman, Fred L. Turner, age 79

Chairman, Andrew J. (Andy) McKenna Sr., age 82

EVP and Chief Human Resources Officer, Richard R. (Rich) Floersch, age 54

President and CEO, Donald (Don) Thompson, age 48

EVP General Counsel and Secretary, Gloria Santona, age 61

VP and Chief Creative Officer, Marlena Peleo-Lazar

Corporate VP Associate General Counsel and Assistant Secretary, Denise A. Horne

President McDonald's USA, Janice L. (Jan) Fields, age 56

President McDonald's Asia Pacific Middle East and Africa, Timothy J. (Tim) Fenton, age 54, $563,750 total compensation

EVP Worldwide Supply Chain Development and Franchising, Jose Armario, age 52

Global Chief Diversity Officer, Patricia (Pat) Harris, age 63

EVP and Chief Restaurant Officer, Jeffrey P. (Jeff) Stratton, age 56

US Division President West, Steven (Steve) Plotkin

US Division President East, Karen King

President McDonald's Europe, Douglas M. (Doug) Goare, age 59

SVP Shared Services and Chief Information Officer, Dave Weick

VP Corporate Media Relations, Walt Riker

Senior Director Corporate Media Relations, Lisa Howard

Administrative Coordinator Corporate Media Relations, Theresa Riley

EVP and CFO, Peter J (Pete) Bensen, age 49, $554,167 total compensation

SVP and President Northern Europe, Gillian McDonald

EVP and COO McDonald's USA, James (Jim) Johannesen, age 58

SVP; Division President Eastern Europe, Khamzat Khasbulatov

SVP; Division President Western Europe, Bane Knezevic

EVP and Division President Southern Europe, Jean-Pierre Petit

Chief Marketing Officer McDonald's USA, Neil Golden

Corporate SVP and Controller, Kevin M. Ozan, age 48

Director Nutrition McDonald's USA, Cynthia M. Goody

VP Communications McDonald's USA, William (Bill) Whitman Jr.

Managing Director McDonald's Australia, Catriona Noble

VP and General Manager Southern California Region, Steve Norby

SVP North America Supply Chain Management McDonald's USA, Dan Gorsky

Managing Director McDonald's Norway, Olli Kilpi

CEO McDonald's China, Kenneth Chan

Division President Greater Asia and Middle East, Peter Rodwell

US Division President Central, Michael (Mike) Andres

Senior Director Corporate Media Relations, Heidi Barker
Senior Manager Corporate Media Relations, Lisa McComb
Manager Corporate Media Relations, Becca Hary
Manager U.S. Communications, Ashlee Yingling
Director U.S. Communications, Danya Proud
Supervisor Corporate Media Relations, Lizzie Roscoe
EVP and Global Chief Brand Officer, Kevin Newell, age 54
SVP Corporate Relatiions, Bridget Coffing
SVP and President Pacific Africa Singapore Malaysia and Korea, David Murphy
VP IS Management McDonald?s USA, Frank Liberio
CTO, Frank Ellermeyer
Manager Sourcing, Mike Spera
Director, Susan E. Arnold, age 58
Director, Miles D. White, age 57
Vice Chairman and CEO, James A. (Jim) Skinner, age 67
Honorary Chairman, Fred L. Turner, age 79
Director, Cary D. McMillan, age 54
Director, Richard H. Lenny, age 60
Chairman, Andrew J. (Andy) McKenna Sr., age 82
Director, Jeanne P. Jackson, age 60
Director, Robert A. Eckert, age 57
Director, Walter E. Massey, age 74
Director, Enrique (Rick) Hernandez Jr., age 56
Director, Roger W. Stone, age 77
President COO and Director, Donald (Don) Thompson, age 48
Director, John W. Rogers Jr., age 53
Director, Sheila A. Penrose, age 66
Auditors: Ernst&YoungLLP

LOCATIONS

HQ: McDonald' s Corp
One McDonald' s Plaza, Oak Brook, IL 60523
Phone: 630 623-3000
Web: www.mcdonalds.com

2011 Sales

	$ mil.	% of total
Europe	10,886	40
Asia/Pacific Middle East & Africa	6,019	22
Total	27,006	100

2011 Locations

US	14,098	
Europe	7,156	
Total	0	33,510

PRODUCTS/OPERATIONS

2011 Sales

	$ mil.	% of total
Restaurants	18,293	68
Total	27,006	100

2011 Locations

Franchised	27,075	
Total	0	33,510

Selected Products

Big Mac
Chicken McNuggets
Happy Meal
Filet-O-Fish
Mac Snack Wrap
McCafe
McChicken
McDouble
McRib
Quarter Pounder

COMPETITORS

AFC Enterprises
Burger King
Chick-fil-A
Church' s Chicken
CKE Restaurants
Dairy Queen
Jack in the Box
Panda Restaurant Group
Quiznos
Sonic Corp.
Starbucks
Subway
Tim Hortons
Wendy' s
YUM!

HISTORICAL FINANCIALS

Company Type: Public

Income Statement FYE: December 31

	REVENUE ($ mil.)	NET INCOME ($ mil.)	NET PROFIT MARGIN	EMPLOYEES
12/11	27,006	5,503	20.4%	420,000
12/10	24,074	4,946	20.5%	400,000
12/09	22,744	4,551	20.0%	385,000
12/08	23,522	4,313	18.3%	400,000
12/07	22,786	2,395	10.5%	390,000
Annual Growth	4.3%	23.1%	—	1.9%

2011 Year-End Financials

Debt ratio: 37.89%
Return on equity: 38.24%
Cash ($ mil.): 2,335
Current ratio: 125.47
Long-term debt ($ mil.): 12,133
No. of shares (mil.): 1,021
Dividends
Yield: —
Payout: 48.01%
Market value ($ mil.): 102,477

	STOCK PRICE ($) FY Close	P/E High/Low		PER SHARE ($) Earnings	Dividends	Book Value
12/11	100.33	19	14	5.27	0.00	14.09
12/10	76.76	17	13	4.58	2.26	13.89
12/09	62.44	15	12	4.11	2.05	13.03
12/08	62.19	17	13	3.76	1.63	12.00
12/07	58.91	31	21	1.98	1.50	13.11
Annual Growth	14.2%	—	—	27.7%	—	1.8%

McGraw-Hill Cos., Inc. (The)

LOCATIONS

HQ: McGraw-Hill Cos., Inc. (The)
1221 Avenue Of The Americas, New York, NY 10020
Phone: 212 512-2000
Web: www.mcgraw-hill.com

HISTORICAL FINANCIALS

Company Type:

Income Statement FYE: December 31

	REVENUE ($ mil.)	NET INCOME ($ mil.)	NET PROFIT MARGIN	EMPLOYEES
12/11	6,246	911	14.6%	22,660
12/10	6,168	828	13.4%	21,000
12/09	5,951	730	12.3%	21,077
12/08	6,355	799	12.6%	21,649
12/07	6,772	1,013	15.0%	21,171
Annual Growth	(2.0%)	(2.6%)	—	1.7%

2011 Year-End Financials

Debt ratio: 18.64%
Return on equity: 60.41%
Cash ($ mil.): 944
Current ratio: 85.59
Long-term debt ($ mil.): 798
No. of shares (mil.): 276
Dividends
Yield: —
Payout: 33.33%
Market value ($ mil.): 12,412

	STOCK PRICE ($) FY Close	P/E High/Low		PER SHARE ($) Earnings	Dividends	Book Value
12/11	44.97	15	12	3.00	0.00	5.46
12/10	36.41	15	10	2.65	0.94	7.19
12/09	33.51	15	7	2.33	0.90	5.86
12/08	23.19	18	7	2.51	0.88	4.08
12/07	43.81	24	15	2.94	0.82	4.98
Annual Growth	0.7%	—	—	0.5%	—	2.3%

McKesson Corp.

McKesson moves medicine. As a top pharmaceuticals distributor in North America McKesson delivers prescription and generic drugs as well as health and beauty care products to more than 40000 retail and institutional pharmacies throughout the US. The company is also a major medical supplies wholesaler providing medical and surgical equipment to alternate health care sites such as doctors' offices surgery centers and long-term care facilities. In addition to distribution services McKesson offers software and technical services that help pharmacies health care providers and insurers manage supply chain clinical administrative and financial operations.

Operations

The McKesson Distribution Solutions division which brings in about 95% of the company's annual revenues primarily provides prescription and over-the-counter (OTC) pharmaceuticals to retailers and health care institutions in the US; it also is a wholesaler of drugs in Canada and owns about half of Nadro a Mexican pharma distributor. The distribution division also supplies medical equipment through its Medical-Surgical unit including first aid kits and workplace safety supplies distributed by subsidiary ZEE Medical. Major US pharmacy operators CVS Caremark Rite Aid and Wal-Mart are among the company's key clients each accounting for about 10% of accounts receivable.

McKesson Distribution Solutions also holds operations outside the traditional retail and institutional distribution realm. For instance its specialty pharmaceutical distribution unit coordinates the delivery of complex medicines directly to physicians including cancer drugs through subsidiary US Oncology (which also provides clinical management services). Additionally the company supplies automated pharmacy dispensing systems through its minority-owned Parata Systems as well as institutional medication preparation services through its SKY Packaging unit and plasma products delivery through the Plasma and BioLogics unit. Other Distribution Solutions services include consulting and inventory management services for pharmacies (such as EnterpriseRx data management software and the Health Mart franchise program) and for drugmakers (including discount and patient management programs).

The company's smaller Technology Solutions division provides IT-focused solutions primarily for non-pharmacy customers including hospitals doctors' offices and health insurance companies. Its McKesson Automation unit provides drug dispensing inventory management and claims processing systems for hospitals while its Health Solutions business offers claims processing and disease management programs for health providers insurers and employers; in addition the Provider Technologies unit provides revenue cycle management and electronic health record (EHR) software for doctors' offices and other care providers.

Geographic Reach

While the Distribution Solutions division is focused solely on the North American marketplace (primarily through the US distribution unit as well as the McKesson Canada business and its stake in Mexico's Nadro) the Technology Solutions businesses provide a more global scope. McKesson's IT-focused division provides services in countries including the UK the Netherlands France and Israel. Overall international operations account for about 10% of McKesson's annual revenues.

Financial Analysis

As one of the top wholesale drug distributors in North America McKesson has maintained healthy earnings and profit growth through the years. For instance in fiscal 2012 the company's revenues increased nearly 10% to some $123 billion and its net income grew by about 17% to $1.4 billion. McKesson attributes its success to organic and acquisitive growth measures that have helped it nurture all of its business segments. The firm has especially benefited from its acquisition of US Oncology (2010) as well as increases in generic drug distribution and high-margin technology services.

Strategy

Strategic acquisitions have long been important to the growth of the company's core distribution operations as the company regularly purchases small to midsized regional distributors and distribution support companies to extend its network. McKesson also widens its product offerings by forming new partnerships with suppliers.

McKesson is also focused on expanding its smaller but increasingly important Technology Solutions division. The firm is especially taking advantage of the fact that many health care providers and insurance firms are looking to prepare for the implementation of health reform measures as well as to qualify for federal incentive programs that encourage more efficient data systems and methods of care.

Mergers and Acquisitions

In October 2012 McKesson struck a $2.1 billion deal ($1.6 billion cash plus debt assumptions) to acquire PSS World Medical to expand its medical supply distribution business. The purchase will expand McKesson's US warehouse delivery and marketing organizations and strengthen its supply business in key areas including diagnostic tests and private-label products.

Earlier in 2012 McKesson expanded its Canadian pharmaceutical distribution and services business by acquiring the independent banner (Drug Trading Company) and franchise (Medicine Shoppe Canada) businesses of Katz Group Canada for C$920 million ($926 million).

To expand its Technology Solutions unit in 2011 the company paid about $90 million for Portico Systems a company that manages IT systems (including billing and claims) for payer and provider networks. In early 2012 the company acquired peerVue to add to its medical imaging workflow technology platform.

HISTORY

John McKesson opened a Manhattan drugstore in 1833 and Daniel Robbins joined him as a partner in 1840. McKesson-Robbins soon expanded into chemical and drug production and the enterprise grew steadily. In 1926 after differences arose between the McKesson and Robbins heirs the company was sold to Donald Coster.

Coster was actually convicted felon Philip Musica who purchased McKesson-Robbins with fraudulently obtained bank loans. For more than a decade his real identity remained secret from all but one blackmailer. By 1930 McKesson-Robbins had wholesale drug operations in 33 states. The company appeared to be growing but a treasurer discovered a Musica-orchestrated accounting scam and a cash shortfall of $3 million. Faced with exposure Musica killed himself in 1939; company bankruptcy followed. McKesson-Robbins emerged from bankruptcy in 1941.

In a hostile takeover in 1967 San Francisco-based Foremost Dairies bought McKesson-Robbins to form Foremost-McKesson. Over the next 20 years the company bought liquor chemical and software wholesalers as well as several bottled-water companies. It sold Foremost Dairies in 1983 to focus on distribution changed its name to McKesson the next year and continued to build its drug wholesaling business through acquisitions. By 1985 it was the US's largest distributor of drugs and medical equipment wine and liquor bottled water and car waxes and polishes.

In 1986 McKesson narrowed its focus to the health industry by selling its liquor and chemical distributors. It acquired Canadian drug distributor Medis by halves in 1990 and 1991 and a 23% stake in Mexican drug distributor Nadro in 1993.

McKesson sold PCS the US's #1 prescription claims processor (acquired in 1970) to Eli Lilly in 1994. In 1996 the firm bought bankrupt distributor FoxMeyer Drug and sold its stake in Armor All (auto and home cleaning products) to Clorox.

In 1997 the company purchased General Medical the US's largest distributor of medical surgical supplies for about $775 million. McKesson began to focus on health care selling its Millbrook Distribution Services unit (health and beauty products general merchandise and specialty foods).

Under new CEO Mark Pulido it agreed to buy drug wholesaler AmeriSource Health (now AmerisourceBergen) but withdrew the offer in 1998 facing FTC opposition. Instead McKesson moved into information systems paying $14 billion for health care information top dog HBO & Company and forming McKesson HBOC. HBO a highflyer in the high-growth health information systems segment balanced its rather dowdy drug and medical distribution operations.

But just months after the deal closed accounting inconsistencies at HBO prompted McKesson to restate fourth-quarter results for fiscal 1999 twice triggering shareholder lawsuits and a housecleaning of top brass. Five ex-HBO executives including McKesson HBOC chairman Charlie McCall (who was later indicted for securities fraud) were canned for using improper accounting methods. McKesson's veteran CEO Pulido and CFO Richard Hawkins were forced to resign for not seeing the problems coming.

The company changed its name to McKesson Corporation in 2001. The National Health Services Information Authority entered into an agreement with McKesson to develop a human resources and payroll system for use at the more than 600 NHS locations throughout the UK.

To catch then #1 pharmaceutical distributor Cardinal Health McKesson built up its core areas in 2003 and 2004 while trimming away some of the dead weight (Abaton.com Amysis Managed Care Systems and ProDental Corp.). The company bought PMO a specialty mail-order prescription business. It also acquired Canadian firm A.L.I. Technologies which provided systems for managing medical images.

In 2007 McKesson acquired Oncology Therapeutics Network a specialty pharmaceuticals distributor for $519 million. McKesson launched a new Plasma and BioLogics division in 2008 to deliver plasma and plasma-related products to hospital pharmacies and it expanded its regional drug distribution network through the purchase of Midwest pharmacy distributor McQueary Brothers for $190 million.

To trim noncore operations it also sold specialty pharmacy unit ivpcare to Walgreen in 2008. In addition in 2010 the Technology Solutions segment sold its MAP unit which provided telehealth services in the Asia/Pacific region for some $109 million.

The company made a large purchase in 2010 when it expanded its offering of cancer treatment drugs and entered the oncology practice management business through the acquisition of US Oncology for some $2.2 billion in a combination of cash and assumed debt. It then combined US Oncology with its existing specialty pharmaceutical distribution business; the combined organization is headquartered at US Oncology's facilities in Texas.

EXECUTIVES

VP and Treasurer, Nicholas A. Loiacono
Chairman President and CEO, John H. Hammergren, age 53, $1,580,000 total compensation
EVP Human Resources, Jorge L. Figueredo, age 51
President Provider Technologies, David A. (Dave) Souerwine
EVP and CFO, Jeffrey C. (Jeff) Campbell, age 52, $798,000 total compensation
Chairman President and CEO US Oncology, Bruce D. Broussard, age 49
EVP and Group President, Paul C. Julian, age 56, $986,000 total compensation
EVP Corporate Strategy and Business Development, Marc E. Owen, age 53, $630,000 total compensation
CFO Pharmacy Systems, Todd Baldanzi
VP and Controller, Nigel A. Rees
President and CEO McKesson Canada, Domenic Pilla
SVP Research and Development Pharmacy Systems, Rick Hronicek
EVP CTO and CIO, Randall N. (Randy) Spratt, age 61
President McKesson U.S. Pharmaceutical, Brian S. Tyler, age 45
EVP and Group President McKesson Technology Solutions, Patrick J. (Pat) Blake, age 48
President Health Solutions, Emad Rizk
EVP General Counsel and Chief Compliance Officer, Laureen E. Seeger, age 51, $615,000 total compensation
Public Relations Medical-Surgical, Jenny Graves
SVP Marketing and Supplier Management Medical-Surgical, Joan Eliasek
Director Marketing Communications U.S. Pharmaceutical Solutions, Catherine Brew
VP Public Relations and Executive Communications Provider Technologies, Leslie White
VP Investor Relations, Ana Schrank

Group President International Operations, Patrick Carter
President RelayHealth Connectivity Solutions, Jim Bodenbender
VP Pharmacy Operations Health Mart, Chuck Wilson
President Specialty Care Solutions, Mark Walchirk
VP Advanced Diagnostics Management Health Solutions, Matthew Zubiller
Secretary, Willie C. Bogan
President McKesson Medical-Surgical, Stanton McComb
VP Infrastructure and Data Management Pharmacy Systems, Brian Grobbel
VP Human Resources Pharmacy Systems, Dena Barcome-King
SVP Customer Operations Pharmacy Systems, Anan Khaldi
SVP High Volume Solutions/MailRx Pharmacy Systems, Michael Jordan
SVP Strategy Product Management and Marketing Pharmacy Systems, Brenton Burns
General Counsel Pharmacy Systems, Mike Missailidis
CFO Specialty Care Solutions, Jennifer Webster
Director Marketing Communications McKesson Specialty, Anna Buxbaum
Senior Director Marketing Pharmacy Systems and Automation, Andrea Serra
Assisant VP Marketing Communications Health Solutions - Products, Christine Scarlett
Manager Public Relations Health Solutions - Services, Jordan Gruener
Director Corporate Communications McKesson Canada, Daniele Dufour
Senior Manager Corporate Communications, Kris Fortner
SVP Pharmacy Optimization, Mark Eastham
President and Acting SVP Sales Pharmacy Systems, Nathan Mott
Director Investor Relations, Holly Weiss
SVP McKesson U.S. Pharmaceutical, Rex Catton
VP and Medical Director, David Nace
President McKesson Foundation, Carrie Varoquiers
Senior Director Corporate Marketing, Jane Paolucci
Executive Director Marketing Communications and Public Relations RelayHealth, Lynne Durham
Director, Marie L. Knowles, age 65
Director, Andy D. Bryant, age 61
Director, M. Christine Jacobs, age 61
Director, David M. Lawrence, age 71
Director, Edward A. (Ed) Mueller, age 65
Director, Wayne A. Budd, age 70
Director, Jane E. Shaw, age 73
Director, Alton F. Irby III, age 71
Auditors: Deloitte&ToucheLLP

LOCATIONS

HQ: McKesson Corporation
1 Post St., San Francisco CA 94104
Phone: 415-983-8300 **Fax:** 415-983-7160
Web: www.mckesson.com

2012 Sales

	$ mil.	% of total
US	112,230	91
Other countries	10,504	9
Total	**122,734**	**100**

PRODUCTS/OPERATIONS

2012 Sales

	$ mil.	% of total
Distribution Solutions		
US pharmaceutical distribution	105,976	86
Canada pharmaceutical distribution & services	10,303	8
Medical-surgical distribution & services	3,145	3
Technology Solutions		
Services	2,594	2
Software & software systems	596	1
Hardware	120	-
Total	**122,734**	**100**

Selected Operations and Services

Distribution Solutions (North America)
- McKesson Canada (drug distribution pharmacy and provider services)
- McKesson Medical-Surgical (includes ZEE Medical and Moore Medical supplies and equipment distribution)
- McKesson Patient Relationship Solutions (consumer adherence coaching outreach discount/trial programs)
- McKesson Pharmaceutical (drug health and beauty care products distribution)
  - Institutional pharmacy services (consulting inventory management cost control SKY Packaging)
  - Retail pharmacy services (Health Mart franchising consulting data and claims management cost control inventory management value brands redistribution repackaging refilling software)
- McKesson Pharmacy Systems (EnterpriseRx and PharmacyRx software financial operational and clinical solutions for retail and institutional pharmacies)
- McKesson Plasma and BioLogics (plasma-derivative products for hospitals)
- McKesson Specialty Health (solutions for specialty drug manufacturers and specialist care providers includes iKnowMed EHR)
  - The US Oncology Network (cancer drug distribution)
- Nadro S.A. de C.V. (49% drug distribution Mexico)
- Parata Systems LLC (39% automated pharmacy and supply management systems and services)

Technology Solutions (North America Europe Israel)
- McKesson Automation (hospital dispensing and inventory management InterQual claims payment)
- McKesson Health Solutions (disease and case management claims management)
- McKesson Provider Technologies (clinical automation and physician practice management hospital inventory management and dispensing electronic health records software enterprise imaging revenue cycle outsourcing)
- RelayHealth (connectivity vendor neutral health information exchange)

Selected Acquisitions

2012
- Drug Trading Company and Medicine Shoppe Canada (former units of Katz Group Canada $926 million Canadian distribution and pharmacy services)
- peerVue (undisclosed price medical imaging workflow technology)

2011
- Portico Systems ($90 million claims processing and efficiency services for payers/provider networks)

2010
- US Oncology ($2.2 billion oncology management and supply services)

Key Customers
CVS Caremark (16% of revenues 17% of accounts receivable)
Rite Aid (10% of revenues 9% of accounts receivable)
Wal-Mart (10% of accounts receivable)

COMPETITORS

Allscripts
AmerisourceBergen
Apothecary Products
athenahealth
BioScrip
Cardinal Health
Catamaran
Cerner
CuraScript
Emdeon
FFF Enterprises
Franz Haniel
GE Healthcare
Grifols
H. D. Smith Wholesale Drug
Henry Schein
Imperial Distributors
Kinray
Medline Industries
Omnicare
Owens & Minor
PharMerica
PSS World Medical
Quality King
Quality Systems
Siemens Healthcare
Surgical Express
The Harvard Drug Group

HISTORICAL FINANCIALS

Company Type: Public

Income Statement

FYE: March 31

	REVENUE ($ mil.)	NET INCOME ($ mil.)	NET PROFIT MARGIN	EMPLOYEES
03/12	122,734	1,403	1.1%	37,700
03/11	112,084	1,202	1.1%	36,400
03/10	108,702	1,263	1.2%	32,500
03/09	106,632	823	0.8%	32,500
03/08	101,703	990	1.0%	32,900
Annual Growth	4.8%	9.1%	—	3.5%

2012 Year-End Financials

Debt ratio: 12.03%
Return on equity: 20.54%
Cash ($ mil.): 3,149
Current ratio: 108.84
Long-term debt ($ mil.): 3,072
No. of shares (mil.): 235
Dividends
Yield: —
Payout: 14.31%
Market value ($ mil.): 20,626

	STOCK PRICE ($) FY Close	P/E High	P/E Low	PER SHARE ($) Earnings	Dividends	Book Value
03/12	87.77	16	12	5.59	0.00	29.07
03/11	79.05	17	12	4.57	0.72	28.65
03/10	65.72	14	7	4.62	0.48	27.79
03/09	35.04	20	10	2.95	0.48	22.85
03/08	52.37	20	15	3.32	0.24	22.10
Annual Growth	13.8%	—	—	13.9%	—	7.1%

MDU Resources Group Inc.

MDU Resources has branched out from its roots as a regional utility to cover a range of natural resources businesses. Utility subsidiaries Montana-Dakota Utilities Great Plains Natural Gas and Cascade Natural Gas deliver gas to more than 839000 customers and electricity to more than 124000 customers. MDU Resources' energy businesses include natural gas transmission gathering and storage; and oil and gas exploration and production (645.6 billion cu. ft. of natural gas in 2010). Its construction materials and contracting division (including Knife River) mines and sells concrete gravel and other materials. MDU Resources' MDU Construction Services unit builds power lines pipelines and telecom systems.

The company's strategy is to expand the customer base of its regulated utilities through organic growth and acquisitions while developing its non regulated businesses as separate revenue sources. At the same time it seeks to save costs by securing better integration of its diverse operations and by eliminating cost redundancies.

In 2009 as part of an emphasis on creating power from renewable sources MDU Resources teamed up with ITC Holdings to build the Green Power Express a 3000-mile grid project which would transport renewable energy from the Plains states to major urban markets. In 2010 MDU subsidiary Montana-Dakota Utilities began operating two new wind farm sites at Cedar Hills in southwest North Dakota and at Diamond Willow near Baker Montana. The operations are capable of generating a combined 50 MW of power.

That year the company reported a dip in revenues primarily due to the lingering effects of the recession on its construction businesses and warmer weather that cut demand from gas customers. However it also reported a jump in net income thanks to the absence of a major property write-down (which it had in 2009) and higher oil prices.

Expanding its natural gas assets to support its gas utility operations in 2010 the company acquired producing natural gas properties in the Green River Basin in southwest Wyoming for $106.4 million.

Further growing its oil and gas asset base in 2011 MDU Resources acquired 20000 additional leasehold acres in the Bakken shale play boosting its total holdings to 90000 acres.

EXECUTIVES

Chairman, Harry J. Pearce, age 69
President CEO and Director, Terry D. Hildestad, age 62, $625,000 total compensation
Assistant VP Accounting and Financial Reporting, Daniel B. (Dan) Moylan, age 47
EVP Bakken Development, William E. (Bill) Schneider, age 64, $422,000 total compensation
VP Administration, Cynthia J. Norland, age 57
General Counsel and Secretary, Paul K. Sandness, age 57
President and CEO WBI Holdings, Steven L. (Steve) Bietz, age 53
Assistant Treasurer Enterprise Risk Management, Ken Dolan
VP and CFO, Doran N. Schwartz, age 42
VP and Controller, Nicole A. Kivisto, age 38
VP Strategic Planning, John P. Stumpf, age 52
Director Investor Relations, Phyllis A. Rittenbach
CEO MDU Construction Services Group Inc.and Knife River Corporation, John G. Harp, age 59, $341,000 total compensation
VP Human Resources, Mark Del Vecchio, age 52
President and CEO Montana-Dakota Utilities Great Plains Natural Gas Cascade Natural Gas and Intermountain Gas, David L. Goodin, age 51
Director Communications and Public Affairs, Rick Matteson
VP Renewable Resources, Bill Connors, age 51
Treasurer and Assistant Secretary, Douglass A. Mahowald
Director Shared Technology Services, Peggy Monson
President and CEO Fidelity Exploration and Production, J. Kent Wells
Director, Patricia L. Moss, age 58
Director, Thomas C. (Tom) Knudson, age 66
Director, Thomas S. Everist, age 62
Director, Dennis W. Johnson, age 62
Director, Sister Thomas Welder, age 71
President CEO and Director, Terry D. Hildestad, age 62
Director, John K. Wilson, age 57
Director, Richard H. (Dick) Lewis, age 62
Director, Karen B. Fagg, age 58
Director, A. Bart Holaday, age 69
Auditors: Deloitte&ToucheLLP

LOCATIONS

HQ: MDU Resources Group Inc.
1200 W. Century Ave., Bismarck ND 58506-5650
Phone: 701-530-1000 **Fax:** 701-530-1698
Web: www.mdu.com

PRODUCTS/OPERATIONS

2010 Sales

	$ mil.	% of total
Energy operations		
Natural gas distribution	892	22
Construction services	789	19
Natural gas & oil production	434	11
Pipeline & energy services	329	8
Electric	211	5
Construction materials & contracting	1,445	35
Other	7	-
Adjustments	(200.7)	-
Total	**3,909**	**100**

?

COMPETITORS

Basin Electric Power
Bechtel
Black & Veatch
Black Hills
Exxon Mobil
Gas Natural
HeidelbergCement
Henkels & McCoy
Lehigh Hanson
NorthWestern
Otter Tail
Vulcan Materials

HISTORICAL FINANCIALS

Company Type: Public

Income Statement FYE: December 31

	REVENUE ($ mil.)	NET INCOME ($ mil.)	NET PROFIT MARGIN	EMPLOYEES
12/11	4,050	213	5.3%	8,021
12/10	3,909	240	6.2%	7,895
12/09	4,176	(123)	—	8,081
12/08	5,003	293	5.9%	10,074
12/07	4,247	432	10.2%	12,293
Annual Growth	(1.2%)	(16.2%)	—	(10.1%)

2011 Year-End Financials

Debt ratio: 21.73%
Return on equity: 7.68%
Cash ($ mil.): 162
Current ratio: 132.92
Long-term debt ($ mil.): 1,285
No. of shares (mil.): 188
Dividends
Yield: —
Payout: 58.48%
Market value ($ mil.): 4,052

	STOCK PRICE ($) FY Close	P/E High/Low		PER SHARE ($) Earnings	Dividends	Book Value
12/11	21.46	21	16	1.12	0.00	14.70
12/10	20.27	19	14	1.27	0.64	14.30
12/09	23.60	—	—	(0.67)	0.62	13.69
12/08	21.58	22	10	1.59	0.60	15.03
12/07	27.61	13	10	2.36	0.56	13.88
Annual Growth	(6.1%)	—	—	(17.0%)	—	1.4%

MeadWestvaco Corp.

MeadWestvaco (MWV) has got your products covered —literally. MWV's packaging business — folding cartons corrugated boxes and printed plastics —serves many of the world's major brands. MWV wraps up health care personal and beauty care food and tobacco as well as home and garden goods. MWV also packages pharmaceuticals and manufactures packaging equipment for dairy and beverage OEMs. It operates through four segments: Packaging Resources (its core segment generating about 40% of total sales) Consumer Solutions Specialty Chemicals and Community Development and Land Management. MWV owns 125 facilities spanning North America South America Europe and Asia.

Operations

In 2012 MWV spun off its former Consumer & Office Products business (12% of total sales in 2011) which makes and markets office and planning products and merged it with ACCO Brands a provider of office supplies and computer products. As part of the spinoff/merger transaction valued at around $433 million MWV gave ACCO ownership of the Mead Five Star At-A-Glance and Tilibra brands. The spinoff allows MWV to focus on the food beverage health care personal care tobacco and home and garden global packaging markets.

Financial Analysis

Despite its breadth of activities MWV has seen its revenues and profits consistently rise and fall over the years. After experiencing declines in 2010 the company saw its revenues increase by 6% for 2011 mostly due to a 5% revenue jump in the US region and growth in emerging markets such as China and Brazil. Growth from emerging markets accounted for more than 28% of total sales in 2011 an increase of 8% from the previous year.

MWV's profits skyrocketed by over 100% from roughly $110 million to nearly $250 million. The significant growth was attributed to the overall increase in total sales along with previous cost-cutting initiatives that included workforce reductions.

Strategy

In addition to spinning off its Consumer & Office Products segment MWV has been making divestments in order to sharpen its focus on its core activities. In early 2011 it shed its envelope products (part of its former Office Supplies segment) to Cenveo. MWV in 2010 sold its global media and entertainment packaging business (for DVDs music and video games) to Atlas Holdings for $68 million. MWV also exited its visual packaging brand Klearfold selling it to the North American affiliate of Hip Lik Packaging Products (Hong Kong).

Mergers and Acquisitions

MWV is looking to acquisitions to shore up its core segments. In 2012 it obtained AARDEX Group a maker of electronic medication event monitoring systems and technology designed to measure analyze and manage patient adherence in clinical drug trials. The deal widened MWV's portfolio in the pharmaceuticals sphere allowing it to provide other products to its customers besides packaging.

In late 2011 MWV snapped up Polytop Corporation a designer of closures serving the food home and garden and beauty and personal care packaging markets.

MWV in 2010 acquired Spray Plast an Italy-based manufacturer of all-plastic trigger sprayers used in household and industrial cleaning and other global markets. The $60 million deal added an ergonomic high-performing eco-friendly lineup to MWV's home and garden portfolio (part of its Consumer Solutions segment).

HISTORY

Late in August 2001 Mead agreed to merge with Westvaco to form MeadWestvaco. Together the two companies had combined annual sales of about $7 billion and a market capitalization of some $6 billion; their combined debt tallied to $4.4 billion. The combined company —50.2%-owned by former Mead shareholders —had an equally split board. Westvaco executives occupied the new CEO CFO and transition officer positions while the new corporate headquarters were Westvaco's Connecticut offices. The two companies merged as MeadWestvaco Corporation in January 2002.

To quickly expand its production capability in Europe MeadWestvaco also bought Kartoncraft Limited near Dublin Ireland a leading pharmaceutical packaging producer. In July 2002 the company reported that it had eliminated 2100 jobs of the 2500 it expected to cut by the end of the year. As part of its plan to divest 950000 nonstrategic acres the company sold 95500 acres of forest land in West Virginia for $50 million; the purchase was made through The Forestland Group LLC for Heartwood Forestland Fund IV Limited Partnership in December 2002.

In 2003 the company bought AMCAL a maker of stationery products including journals notepads decorative calendars and holiday cards.

Sticking with its consolidation and realignment strategy in mid-2004 MeadWestvaco eliminated some 600 jobs by closing both its Garland Texas and St. Joseph Missouri facilities. Also in 2004 MeadWestvaco acquired Brazilian-based Tilibra S.A. Produtos de Papelaria a maker of office products.

In 2005 MWV decided it would rather box than shuffle paper; it sold its Papers business –which made labels book/catalog/magazine papers and business forms –to Cerberus Capital Management. The decision marked a particularly strategic step toward global leadership in premium packaging. Papers accounted for a little less than 30% of MWV's sales prior to the deal but the segment had consistently struggled in the red. (Cerberus set up the divested business as an independent company NewPage Group Inc.) The deal included mills in Kentucky Maine Maryland Michigan and Ohio and about 900000 acres of forest land in Illinois Kentucky Michigan Missouri Ohio and Tennessee.

Striving to play a larger role in its customers' packaging process rather than just as a supplier the company established a packaging research facility in collaboration with North Carolina State University in Raleigh and moved its headquarters to Richmond Virginia in 2006. MWV realigned operations as well by launching into packaging made from materials other than paperboard. The company burned through $714 million to acquire Saint-Gobain Calmar (now MeadWestvaco Calmar) from Compagnie de Saint-Gobain. The French packager specializes in plastic dispensing and spraying systems for personal and healthcare products. MWV also snatched up Netherlands-based Keltec Dispensing Systems and California-based Hayes Products.

The company began to reinvent itself around 2008 –moving away from a paper mill oriented business to that of a global partner to major companies. It divested a number of its kraft paper and specialty paper mills as well as its packaging plant in Pennsylvania. MWV partnered with pharmaceutical-packaging company Bilcare to acquire pharmaceutical package-maker International Labs for an undisclosed amount. In late 2008 MWV also formed a joint venture with Wadco Packaging an Indian manufacturer of corrugated boxes. The venture of which MWV owns 51% churns out packaging to protect fresh produce in transit from field to market. At the same time MWV's Specialty Chemicals division grew by acquiring Eastman Chemical Company's pine chemical products. The chemicals are used in the production of paper as well as paints coatings and other building materials.

EXECUTIVES

SVP and CFO, E. Mark Rajkowski, age 53, $551,358 total compensation
SVP General Counsel and Secretary, Wendell L. Willkie II, age 60, $457,161 total compensation
Chairman and CEO, John A. Luke Jr., age 63, $1,007,105 total compensation
VP Corporate Affairs, Ned W. Massee, age 62
President, James A. Buzzard, age 57, $655,985 total compensation
SVP Healthcare and Innovation, Bruce V. Thomas, age 55
VP and Treasurer, Robert E. Birkenholz, age 51
SVP Human Resources and Communications MeadWestvaco Foundation, Linda V. Schreiner, age 52
SVP Technology, Mark T. Watkins, age 58, $443,796 total compensation
President Global Business Services, Mark V. Gulling, age 58
VP and Controller, John E. Banu, age 64
SVP Packaging, Mark S. Cross, age 55, $489,250 total compensation
SVP Packaging Resources Group, Robert A. (Bob) Feeser, age 50
President Consumer & Office Products Group, Neil A. McLachlan, age 55
Assistant Secretary and Associate General Counsel, John J. Carrara, age 56
President Tobacco, Kevin Clark, age 52
President Healthcare, T. D. Lithgow, age 58
VP Communications, Donna O. Cox, age 48
President Food Packaging, Diane Teer
President Rigesa, Robert K. (Bob) Beckler, age 50
VP Safety Health and Environment, Dirk Krouskop, age 54
SVP; President Community Development and Land Management, Kenneth T. Seeger, age 61
President Food Service, John K. Sanfacon
President Beverage and Consumer Electronics, Stephen R. Scherger, age 47
President Beauty & Personal Care and Home & Garden, Thomas Y. Jonas, age 42
President Global Innovation, Alejandro (Alex) Cede?o
President Primary Plastics Operations, John C. Taylor, age 49
President Specialty Chemicals Division, Edward A. Rose, age 50
VP and Chief Strategy Officer, Peter C. Durette, age 38
President PRG Systems, Charles E. Johnson Jr.
President Commercial Print, Joseph McNamara
Director Corporate Communications, Tucker McNeil
President Global Business Services, Jason Chapman
Director, Richard B. (Rick) Kelson, age 65
Director, Susan J. Kropf, age 64
Director, Timothy H. (Tim) Powers, age 63
Director, Michael E. Campbell, age 64
Director, James M. (Jim) Kilts Jr., age 64
Director, James G. Kaiser, age 69
Director, Douglas S. Luke, age 70
Director, Robert C. (Bob) McCormack, age 72
Director, Thomas W. Cole Jr., age 71
Director, Jane L. Warner, age 65
Director, Alan D. Wilson, age 54
Auditors: PricewaterhouseCoopersLLP

LOCATIONS

HQ: MeadWestvaco Corporation
501 S. 5th St., Richmond VA 23219-0501
Phone: 804-444-1000 **Fax:** -7263
Web: www.freightwatchgroup.com

2011 Sales

	$ mil.	% of total
US	3,972	66
Brazil	731	12
Total	**6,060**	**100**

PRODUCTS/OPERATIONS

Selected Mergers and Acquisitions

2012
- Ruby Macons Limited (undisclosed price; India; producer of corrugated packaging materials)
- AARDEX Group SA (undisclosed price; Switzerland; designer of electronic medication event monitoring systems and applications)

2011
- Polytop Corporation (undisclosed price; Rhode Island; manufacturer of dispensing closures)

2010
- Spray Plast SpA (undisclosed price; Italy; manufacturer of trigger sprayers)

COMPETITORS

3M
Alcoa
Amcor
Anglo American
Ball Corp.
Bemis
Boise Cascade
Cascades Inc.
Disc Graphics
Georgia-Pacific
Graphic Packaging Holding
Iggesund Paperboard
International Paper
Pratt Industries USA
RockTenn CP
Sonoco Products
Temple-Inland
UPM-Kymmene
Weyerhaeuser

HISTORICAL FINANCIALS

Company Type: Public

Income Statement FYE: December 31

	REVENUE ($ mil.)	NET INCOME ($ mil.)	NET PROFIT MARGIN	EMPLOYEES
12/11	6,060	246	4.1%	17,000
12/10	5,693	106	1.9%	17,500
12/09	6,049	225	3.7%	20,000
12/08	6,637	90	1.4%	22,000
12/07	6,906	285	4.1%	24,000
Annual Growth	(3.2%)	(3.6%)	—	(8.3%)

2011 Year-End Financials

Debt ratio: 24.34%
Return on equity: 7.73%
Cash ($ mil.): 656
Current ratio: 151.49
Long-term debt ($ mil.): 1,880
No. of shares (mil.): 170
Dividends
Yield: —
Payout: 70.42%
Market value ($ mil.): 5,118

	STOCK PRICE ($) FY Close	P/E High	P/E Low	PER SHARE ($) Earnings	Dividends	Book Value
12/11	29.95	24	16	1.42	0.00	18.62
12/10	26.16	48	34	0.62	0.94	19.52
12/09	28.63	22	6	1.30	0.92	19.89
12/08	11.19	60	18	0.52	0.92	17.37
12/07	31.30	23	18	1.56	0.92	21.33
Annual Growth	(1.1%)	—	—	(2.3%)	—	(3.3%)

Medtronic, Inc.

Sometimes the best medicine is a short sharp shock; that's why Medtronic's products reside in its customers' hearts and minds (among other places). A leading maker of implantable biomedical devices the company makes defibrillators and pacemakers that shock the heart to help it beat normally. Its Cardiac and Vascular group also produces catheters stents valves balloons and surgical ablation technologies used to treat vascular and heart disease. The company's Restorative Therapies Group makes nerve and brain stimulation devices defibrillators implantable drug delivery systems products used to manage diabetes and surgical devices for ear nose and throat (ENT) and spinal conditions.

Geographic Reach

Medtronic markets its products in more than 120 countries around the globe with more than half of revenues coming from the US market. The company operates almost 40 manufacturing plants mainly in the US and Europe.

Operations

Minnesota-based Medtronic got its start treating heart disease (it was a leader in the development of pacemakers in the 1950s) and a majority of its revenue still comes from sales of products used to treat heart or vascular conditions. However it has expanded its reach into the rest of the human body and the rest of the world.

Within the Cardiac and Vascular group reside its Cardiac Rhythm Disease Management (CRDM) and Medtronic CardioVascular units. CRDM is Medtronic's largest single unit accounting for more than 30% of sales. The unit makes pacemakers defibrillators heart monitors and other products used to keep the heart beating properly. The CardioVascular unit accounts for around 20% of the company's sales with a focus on minimally invasive technologies including drug-eluting stents (to prevent reclogging of arteries) heart valves and surgical ablation systems.

Under the Restorative Therapies Group is Medtronic's Spinal unit which accounts for around 20% of sales. Through its Medtronic Sofamar Danek business the unit manufactures spinal devices and implants as well as surgical instruments used in spine surgery; and bone grafting tissue used in spinal dental and oral surgical procedures.

The company's Neuromodulation division (also housed within the Restorative Therapies Group) makes electrical stimulation devices and drug delivery systems that help control conditions including chronic pain tremors and urinary incontinence. Additionally its Diabetes segment manufactures and sells supplies including glucose monitoring systems and insulin pumps. The firm's ENT offerings are housed in its smaller Surgical Technologies segment.

Sales and Marketing

Medtronic sells through direct representatives in the US while using a combination of independent distributors and direct marketing methods in overseas markets. Its products are marketed to customers including hospitals physicians wholesalers and group purchasing organizations.

Financial Analysis

In 2012 Medtronic achieved modest sales growth (2%) over 2011 achieving more than $16 billion in sales. Growth was mainly attributable to new products brought on line in the past three years (38% of sales) and 21% growth in emerging markets which contributed 10% of total sales. The company's net income of $3.6 billion represented a leap of almost 17% over 2011. These increases continued the company's trend of year-over-year improvements over the past five years.

Strategy

Strategically the company maintains a steady stream of new product introductions through a mixture of internal research and development and acquisitions to fuel its growth. (In fiscal 2011 alone Medtronic brought some 60 new products to market across all of its units.) While the company has grown steadily its growth has slowed somewhat as recession-worn patients have delayed non-emergency surgical procedures.

Medtronic is also focusing on expanding its international business which has increased over the past three years to account for 45% of company sales in fiscal 2012. Medtronic has an especially keen eye on the emerging markets of Brazil China India and Russia. It has laid plans to increase sales in those markets to eventually account for some 20% of company sales.

Medtronic sold its smallest segment Physio-Control to Bain Capital for some $487 million in 2012. The business provides professional emergency medical response solutions worldwide.

Mergers and Acquisitions

In 2012 Medtronic made progress towards its goal of growing in international markets when it agreed to acquire device manufacturer China Kanghui for some $816 million. The purchase will add direct distribution operations in the Chinese market as well as a product portfolio and R&D pipeline containing spinal trauma and joint reconstruction devices.

HISTORY

In 1949 electrical engineer Earl Bakken and brother-in-law Palmer Hermundslie founded Medtronic in Minneapolis as a medical equipment repair outfit. After branching into custom-made products Bakken made history in 1957 by crafting the world's first external battery-powered cardiac pacemaker. In 1960 Medtronic began making and selling the first implantable pacemakers; the company quickly claimed about 80% of the market.

In the late 1960s and early 1970s Medtronic acquired other medical devices companies. Calamity struck in 1976 when the firm had to recall more than 35000 Xytron pacemakers (some of which were already in patients) because body moisture was seeping into the battery chamber. Market share plunged to about 35%.

Medtronic recruited former Pillsbury COO Winston Wallin as chairman and CEO in 1985. The next year Medtronic released its Activitrax pacemaker which snagged about 20% of the market. Under Wallin (who retired in 1996) the firm opened facilities in Europe and Asia and resumed acquisitions adding companies in Italy the Netherlands and the US.

In the early 1990s Medtronic sought to expand its position in the vascular market. Its 1990 purchase of Bio-Medicus made the company the world's top maker of centrifugal blood pumps; it also entered the lucrative cardiac defibrillator market (1992) and increased other lines with the purchase of a maker of blood recycling devices and a company that produced disposable tubing and detection kits for breast and prostate cancer.

With an eye on the hot stent market Medtronic in 1996 acquired InStent and AneuRx makers of devices used to keep diseased arteries open. The company failed to become a leader in the market because its new units did not perform.

Using its expertise in implant devices the company developed (and in 1997 received FDA approval for) devices aimed at the growing tremor control and incontinence markets.

In the late 1990s Medtronic undertook a flurry of acquisitions both to solidify its leadership in the cardiovascular market and to broaden its operations. These purchases included external defibrillator maker Physio-Control International as well as a maker of power instruments for neurological bone and plastic surgery procedures in 1998. The next year Medtronic bought #1 spinal implant product maker Sofamor Danek to boost its neurosurgical business. The company took one more stab at the stent market buying market-leader Arterial Vascular Engineering. Its share of the market fell after it was acquired however so Medtronic closed five facilities. Later that year the company bought Xomed Surgical Products (renamed Medtronic Xomed) a maker of products for ear nose and throat specialists.

In 2000 the company announced a partnership with health care companies –including Johnson & Johnson and GE Medical Systems –to provide online product ordering. Medtronic also partnered with WebMD (now WebMD Health) to provide health care information on the Internet.

The following year the firm bought medical device makers MiniMed and Medical Research Group and combined them to form Medtronic MiniMed. In 2002 Medtronic bought VidaMed to grow its urology offerings. In 2005 the company voluntarily notified physicians that some of its defibrillators could experience a battery shorting mechanism; the action resulted in a number of individual and payor lawsuits. (A majority of the suits were settled for $123 million in 2008.)

In 2007 the company's CRDM division suspended sales of one of its defibrillator leads (the wires that connect the device to the heart) after determining that a flaw in the wire may have contributed to several deaths. The lead called Sprint Fidelis had been implanted in nearly 270000 patients. (Medtronic settled 8100 personal-injury cases that resulted from the product suspension – which the FDA had classified as a recall –for some $268 million in 2010.)

The company combined its Cardiac Surgery and Vascular business units into the new CardioVascular division in 2007. Medtronic also built up its spinal surgery business in 2007 with the acquisition of Kyphon a maker of orthopedic medical devices used to treat compression fractures of the spine. The following year Medtronic settled federal allegations that Kyphon had defrauded Medicare agreeing to pay a $75 million fine.

EXECUTIVES

EVP and Group President Cardiac and Vascular Group, Michael J. Coyle, age 49

SVP; President Surgical Technologies, Bob Blankemeyer, age 65

SVP; President Cardiac Rhythm Disease Management, James Patrick (Pat) Mackin, age 45, $506,354 total compensation

SVP; President Diabetes, Catherine M. (Katie) Szyman, age 45

SVP Quality and Operations, H. James Dallas, age 53, $520,000 total compensation

SVP and Chief Regulatory Officer, Susan Alpert, age 66

SVP Medicine and Technology, Stephen N. (Steve) Oesterle, age 61

Senior Manager Corporate Public Relations, Chuck Grothaus

EVP; Group President International, Jean-Luc Butel, age 55, $498,750 total compensation

SVP General Counsel and Corporate Secretary, D. Cameron Findlay, age 52

Manager Public Relations Spine and Biologics, Victor Rocha, age 48

SVP and CFO, Gary L. Ellis, age 55, $604,200 total compensation

Director Public Relations Neuromodulation, Cindy Resman
SVP Human Resources, Caroline Stockdale, age 48
Chairman and CEO, Omar S. Ishrak, age 56
SVP and Chief Scientific Clinical and Regulatory Officer, Richard E. (Rick) Kuntz, age 55
Director Investor Relations, Jeff Warren
President Physio-Control, Brian Webster
EVP AND President Restorative Therapies Group, Christopher J. (Chris) O'Connell, age 45, $478,820 total compensation
Senior Director Public Relations and Communications Spinal and Biologics, Marybeth Thorsgaard
VP New Therapies and Diagnostics Cardiac Rhythm Disease Management, Rebecca M. (Becky) Bergman, age 55
VP Public Relations Cardiac Rhythm Disease Management, Christopher Garland
Manager Public Relations Cardiac Rhythm Disease Management, Catherine Peloquin
Manager Corporate and Public Relations Foundation and Community Affairs, Rich Fischer
VP International Public Relations and Communications, Yvan Deurbroeck
Senior Global Communications Manager Physio-Control, Jennifer Roth
Director Public Relations CardioVascular, Joe McGrath
SVP and President United States, Michael C. (Mike) Genau, age 51
SVP; President Neuromodulation, Tom Tefft
VP Medical Affairs Coronary and Peripheral Vascular Business, Prof Martin Rothman
Senior Director Media Relations, Brian Henry
Program Director Public Relations Communications and Media Cardiac Rhythm Disease Management, Wendy Dougherty
Director Public Relations Diabetes, Amanda Sheldon
VP Cardiac and Vascular Sales Group, David Roberts
CIO, Michael Hedges
SVP Strategy and Business Development, Geoffrey S. (Geoff) Martha
SVP; President EMEA & Canada, Rob ten Hoedt
SVP and Group President Diabetes, Katie Szyman
Director, Richard H. Anderson, age 56
Director, Kendall J. (Ken) Powell, age 58
Director, James T. Lenehan, age 63
Director, Robert C. (Bob) Pozen, age 65
Director, Jack W. Schuler, age 71
Director, Jean-Pierre Rosso, age 72
Director, David L. (Dave) Calhoun, age 55
Director, Shirley Ann Jackson, age 64
Director, Victor J. Dzau, age 66
Director, Denise M. O'Leary, age 55
Auditors: PricewaterhouseCoopersLLP

LOCATIONS

HQ: Medtronic Inc.
710 Medtronic Pkwy., Minneapolis MN 55432-5604
Phone: 763-514-4000 **Fax:** 763-514-4879
Web: www.medtronic.com

2012 Sales

	$ mil.	% of total
US	8,828	54
Asia/Pacific	2,399	15
Total	**16,184**	**100**

Selected Manufacturing Locations

North America
- Canada
- Mexico
- US and Territories
  - Arizona
  - California
  - Colorado
  - Connecticut
  - Florida
  - Indiana
  - Massachusetts
  - Minnesota
  - New Jersey
  - Texas
  - Puerto Rico

Europe
- France
- Germany
- Ireland
- Italy
- The Netherlands
- Switzerland

Asia/Pacific
- Singapore

PRODUCTS/OPERATIONS

2012 Sales

	$ mil.	% of total
Cardiac & Vascular Group	8,482	52
Restorative Therapies Group	7,702	48
Total	**16,184**	**100**

2012 Sales

	$ mil.	% of total
Cardiac & Vascular Group		
Cardiac rhythm disease management	5,007	31
Cardiovascular	3,475	21
Restorative Therapies Group		
Spinal	3,267	20
Neuromodulation	1,700	11
Diabetes	1,481	9
Surgical technologies	1,254	8
Total	**16,184**	**100**

Selected Products

Cardiac and Vascular Group
- Cardiac Rhythm Disease Management
  - Cryoablation catheters
  - Implantable defibrillators
  - Monitoring devices
  - Pacemakers
  - Resynchronization therapy devices (CRT-Ds)
- CardioVascular
  - Cardiac surgery instruments and grafts
  - Coronary stents
  - Drug-eluting stents
  - Endovascular stent grafts
  - Heart stabilizers
  - Heart valves
  - Peripheral vascular stents
  - Surgical tissue ablation systems

Restorative Therapies Group
- Diabetes
  - Blood glucose meters
  - Glucose monitoring systems
  - Insulin pumps
  - Patient management software
- Neuromodulation
  - Deep brain stimulation systems
  - Implantable drug delivery systems
  - Implantable neurostimulation devices
  - Urology & gastroenterology devices
- Spinal
  - Bone graft materials
  - Cervical and thoracolumbar fixation systems
- Surgical Technologies
  - Ear nose throat surgical systems
  - Neurological surgical products
  - Surgical navigation products

Selected Acquisitions

2011
- Ardian ($1 billion; hypertension catheter system - CardioVascular)
- Jolife (LUCAS chest compression system - Cardiac Rhythm Disease Management; sold in 2012)
- PEAK Surgical (S113 million; PlasmaBlade surgical devices - Surgical Technologies)
- Salient Surgical Technologies ($497 million; AQUAMANTYS system - Surgical Technologies)

2010
- ATS Medical ($394 million; heart valves cryoablation devices - CardioVascular)
- Axon Surgical ($62 million; spinal neuromonitoring technology - Surgical Technologies)
- Invatec ($500 million including contingency payments; drug-eluting balloon devices - CardioVascular)
- Osteotech ($123 million; bone graft materials - Surgical Technologies)

2009
- Ablation Frontiers (ablation therapies - Cardiac Rhythm Disease Management)

2008
- CryoCath Technologies (cryotherapy products - Cardiac Rhythm Disease Management)
- Restore Medical (soft palate implant system - Surgical Technologies)

COMPETITORS

Abbott Labs
Alphatec Spine
American Medical Systems
ArthroCare
Biomet
Boston Scientific
Cardiac Science Corporation
Cook Incorporated
Covidien
DePuy Spine
DexCom
Edwards Lifesciences
Endologix
GE Healthcare
Globus Medical
Gyrus ACMI
Insulet Corporation
Integra LifeSciences
Johnson & Johnson
NuVasive
Orthofix
Philips Electronics
Philips Healthcare
Roche Holding
Siemens Healthcare
Sorin
St. Jude Medical
Stryker
Synthes
Terumo Medical Corporation
Urologix
W.L. Gore
Zimmer Holdings
ZOLL

HISTORICAL FINANCIALS

Company Type: Public

Income Statement

FYE: April 27

	REVENUE ($ mil.)	NET INCOME ($ mil.)	NET PROFIT MARGIN	EMPLOYEES
04/12	16,184	3,617	22.3%	44,944
04/11	15,933	3,096	19.4%	45,000
04/10	15,817	3,099	19.6%	43,000
04/09	14,599	2,169	14.9%	41,000
04/08	13,515	2,231	16.5%	40,000
Annual Growth	4.6%	12.8%	—	3.0%

2012 Year-End Financials

Debt ratio: 32.14%
Return on equity: 21.14%
Cash ($ mil.): 1,248
Current ratio: 162.46
Long-term debt ($ mil.): 7,359
No. of shares (mil.): 1,037
Dividends
Yield: 2.57%
Payout: 28.45%
Market value ($ mil.): 39,092

	STOCK PRICE ($) FY Close	P/E High	P/E Low	PER SHARE ($) Earnings	Dividends	Book Value
04/12	37.69	13	9	3.41	0.97	16.50
04/11	41.75	15	11	2.86	0.90	14.92
04/10	43.69	16	11	2.79	0.82	13.33
04/09	29.58	29	13	1.93	0.75	11.48
04/08	49.42	29	23	1.95	0.50	10.25
Annual Growth	(6.5%)	—	—	15.0%	18.0%	12.6%

Merck & Co., Inc

Merck makes medicines for a number of maladies from stuffy noses and asthma to hypertension and arthritis. The pharmaceutical giant's top prescription drugs include asthma medication Singulair diabetes drug Januvia anti-inflammatory Remicade cholesterol combatants Vytorin and Zetia and hypertension fighters Cozaar and Hyzaar. In addition Merck makes childhood and adult vaccines for such diseases as measles mumps hepatitis and shingles as well as veterinary pharmaceuticals through Merck Animal Health. The company's OTC drug and personal care offerings include Claritin allergy pills and Dr. Scholl's foot care products.

HISTORY

Merck traces its roots to the formation of Schering-Plough in 1851 and the founding of the original Merck entity in 1887. (The two companies merged in 2009.)

Schering-Plough dates back to 1851 when Berlin chemist Ernst Schering began to sell chemicals to apothecary shops. By 1880 Schering's business (which eventually became Bayer Schering Pharma) was exporting pharmaceuticals to the US where a subsidiary (the predecessor to Schering-Plough) was established in 1928.

At the outbreak of WWII the US government seized the US Schering subsidiary severing links with its German parent. The company went on to develop such new drugs as Chlor-Trimeton one of the first antihistamines and the cold medicine Coricidin. The US government sold Schering in 1952 to Merrill Lynch which took it public. Schering bought White Labs (which made Coppertone sunscreen) in 1957. In the 1960s the company introduced Garamycin (antibiotic 1964) Tinactin (antifungal 1965) and Afrin (decongestant 1967).

Schering's 1971 merger with Memphis-based Plough expanded the product line to include such cosmetics and consumer items as Coppertone and Di-Gel. Plough's founder Abe Plough had borrowed $125 from his father to found the company in 1908. Abe remained chairman at Schering-Plough until 1976. Schering-Plough introduced many products after the merger including Lotrimin AF (antifungal 1975) antibiotic Netromycin (1980) and Drixoral (a cold remedy made nonprescription in 1982).

The company was one of the first drug giants to make significant investments in biotechnology: It bought DNAX Research Institute of Palo Alto California in 1982. Acquisitions in the late 1970s and 1980s included Scholl (foot care 1979) Key Pharmaceuticals (cardiovascular drugs 1986) and Cooper Companies (eye care 1988).

In 1993 Schering-Plough began marketing its non-sedating antihistamine Claritin in the US. (Claritin became an OTC drug in 2002.) The next year it gained FDA approval to market the first colored disposable contact lenses only to sell its contact lens business later in the year. In 1996 Schering-Plough bought Canji to strengthen its gene therapy research program. It strengthened its veterinary medicine segment in 1997 when it bought Mallinckrodt's animal health operations.

The firm bought the marketing rights to Centocor's treatment for Crohn's disease in 1998. In 1999 the FDA approved the company's Temodar a chemotherapy treatment for brain tumors and it bought the US rights to Pfizer's Bain de Soleil sun care product line. In 2000 Schering-Plough formed its first collaboration with Merck. In 2002 the company paid a $500 million fine to the FDA over manufacturing concerns.

As Schering-Plough's revenues started to decline in 2003 the company brought in several executives from Pharmacia including CEO Fred Hassan (who retired following the 2009 merger with Plough) to help streamline its operations and expand its R&D programs and product offerings. The firm gave itself a major boost by acquiring Akzo Nobel's Organon unit in 2007 growing in the areas of women's health care neurology vaccines animal health (Intervet) and third-party biologics manufacturing (through Diosynth).

The original Merck was started in 1887 when German chemist Theodore Weicker came to the US to set up a branch of German firm E. Merck AG (which was founded in 1668 and later became Merck KGaA). George Merck (grandson of the German company's founder) came in 1889 and formed a partnership with Weicker and eventually bought out Weicker's shares. At first the firm imported and sold drugs and chemicals from Germany but in 1903 it began manufacturing its own products. During WWI Merck gave the US government the 80% of the US Merck unit's stock owned by the family in Germany (George kept his shares). After the war the stock was sold to the public.

The firm acquired Powers-Weightman-Rosengarten of Philadelphia (a producer of antimalarial quinine) in 1927. Merck opened its first research lab in 1933; Merck scientists there developed the first steroid cortisone in 1944. Five Merck scientists received Nobel Prizes in the 1940s and 1950s. In 1953 Merck bought drugmaker Sharp & Dohme of Philadelphia which brought with it a strong sales force.

The 1958 introduction of Diuril (antihypertensive) and several other drugs (including the first measles vaccine) in the early 1960s was followed by a dry spell. In the 1970s an accelerated R&D organization created new products including Clinoril (antiarthritic) Flexeril (muscle relaxant) and Timoptic (for glaucoma). Merck introduced 10 major new drugs in the 1980s including Mevacor (high cholesterol) and Vasotec (high blood pressure).

In 1990 the company bought the nonprescription drug segment of ICI Americas; products from the purchase were contributed to a Consumer Pharmaceuticals joint venture with Johnson & Johnson. Merck bought pharmacy benefits manager Medco Containment Services in 1993. New drug launches in 1995 and 1996 included Cozaar (for reducing hypertension) and Pepcid AC (antacid). Also in 1996 Merck expanded its pharmacy benefit management operations with the purchase of Systemed.

In 1997 Merck and Rhone-Poulenc (now part of Sanofi-Aventis) merged their animal health units to form Merial. Merck also sold its insecticide and fungicide business to Novartis that year. In 1998 DuPont bought out Merck's 50% stake in a drug-marketing joint venture formed by the two firms in 1991. In 1999 the FDA approved Merck's preservative-free hepatitis B vaccine Recombivax HB.

In 2001 Merck acquired biotech firm Rosetta Inpharmatics. The company spun off its highly successful Medco Health Solutions drug distribution subsidiary in 2003.

In 2004 Merck pulled its blockbuster pain medication Vioxx off the market after studies linked the drug to increased risks of strokes and heart attacks. (Merck settled thousands of class-action and personal-injury lawsuits related to Vioxx in 2007 for $4.85 billion.) The Vioxx safety scandal along with the pending loss of patent protection on some of its biggest sellers like Zocor (which began facing competition in 2006) sent the company into recovery mode. Merck announced restructuring plans to make the company's operations leaner and more cost-effective in 2005 under new CEO Richard (Dick) Clark a longtime Merck executive. Between 2005 and 2008 the company eliminated more than 10000 jobs and closed a handful of manufacturing plants.

From 2006 to 2009 Merck worked aggressively to expand its biotech operations through the acquisition of companies including GlycoFi (biologic drug molecules) Abmaxis (monoclonal antibodies) Sirna Therapeutics (RNA interference or RNAi) and NovaCardia (cardiology drugs) as well as the follow-on (generic) biologic assets of Insmed. New drug launches included HIV drug Isentress and diabetes therapy Janumet in 2007 and blockbuster HPV vaccine Gardasil the world's first anti-cancer vaccine which was approved by the FDA in 2006.

In 2008 Merck sold off the assets of its Rosetta Inpharmatics subsidiary to Covance (gene expression laboratory assets) and Microsoft (expression analysis software assets). It also sold another research lab to PPD and contracted out certain lab functions to the buyer. Merck launched a new product Emend for chemotherapy side-effects that year. New drug launches in 2009 included Saphris a treatment for schizophrenia and bipolar disorder and Simponi the next-generation version of top-selling drug Remicade.

Cholesterol drug Vytorin —a combination of Schering-Plough's Zetia and Merck's Zocor — began facing controversy in 2008 when study results were released questioning the drug's effectiveness compared to Merck's older medication Zocor. Controversy over Vytorin along with some other pipeline setbacks (including the FDA's rejection of a Merck/Schering-Plough combo asthma drug and Merck's Cordaptive cholesterol candidate) led both predecessors Merck and Schering-Plough to announce layoffs and restructuring measures in 2008. Each company reduced its workforce by around 10% that year with their respective US sales teams bearing the brunt of the cuts.

The companies' troubles with Vytorin came to a head in 2009 when they agreed to pay about $42 million to settle class-action lawsuits filed by consumers and health plans over Vytorin's efficacy. Later that year Merck and Schering-Plough decided to merge taking the logical step of marriage to strengthen their defenses against future troubles (especially in light of increasing competitive challenges in the market) as well as to create cost savings opportunities and expanded avenues for revenue growth.

The $41 billion transaction was conducted through a reverse-merger transaction in which the legacy Schering-Plough entity acquired the legacy Merck entity and took on the Merck name. Following the merger Merck began simplifying its global branding under the Merck and MSD names gradually phasing out the Schering-Plough moniker. The purchase expanded Merck's offerings in areas including inflammation allergy and cancer treatment as well as biotech drugs. The acquisition also greatly expanded Merck's operations in the animal health and consumer health arenas.

However to gain Schering-Plough's animal health unit Intervet (later renamed Merck Animal Health) Merck had to sell its stake in veterinary joint venture Merial to partner Sanofi-Aventis for about $4 billion later that year to avoid anti-trust issues. (Merck and Sanofi-Aventis later explored options to strike a fresh veterinary medicine joint venture by combining Merial with Intervet; however after a year of planning the two companies called off the deal in 2011 due to concerns over further anti-trust issues.)

The company experienced a sharp gain in profits that year (reporting net income of $12.9 billion) due to gains on the sale of the Merial stake and on recognized equity from assets previously owned jointly with Schering-Plough.

When the Merck/Schering-Plough merger closed the existing Merck CEO Dick Clark took the helm at the new Merck. Once the dust from the merger settled however Clark retired from the CEO post at the end of 2010 while remaining as chairman. President Kenneth Frazier stepped into the CEO role.

EXECUTIVES

Chairman President and CEO, Kenneth C. (Ken) Frazier, age 57, $1,044,688 total compensation

EVP; President Animal Health, Raul E. Kohan, age 59, $479,250 total compensation

SVP; President Global Supply Chain, Ian A.T. McInnes, age 58

EVP; President Consumer Care, Bridgette P. Heller, age 50

EVP Global Services and CIO, J. Chris Scalet, age 53

SVP Research and Development Schering-Plough K. K. (Japan), Peder K. Jensen, age 52

EVP; President Merck Research Laboratories, Peter S. Kim, age 53, $1,066,004 total compensation

EVP and Chief Medical Officer, Michael Rosenblatt, age 64

EVP and CFO, Peter N. Kellogg, age 56, $903,978 total compensation

VP and Controller, Steven H. (Steve) Koehler, age 60

SVP and Chief Communications Officer, Adele D. Ambrose, age 55

SVP Global Medical Affairs, Hans M. Vemer

Group VP EUCAN Region II (Austria Belgium Greece the Netherlands Portugal Switzerland Central and Eastern Europe the Middle East and Africa), Bruno Strigini

Group VP Global Project Management Schering-Plough Research Institute (SPRI), Gregory Joseph Szpunar, age 54

President Merck Vaccines, Julie Louise Gerberding, age 57

EVP and Chief Ethics and Compliance Officer, Richard S. Bowles III, age 60

SVP Primary Care Customer Group Global Pharmaceuticals, Ellen Geisel

VP Investor Relations, Alex Kelly

VP and General Manager UK and Ireland, Gordon Coutts

VP Alliance Management, Ratnakar Mitra

VP Global Communications Europe Canada Middle East Africa Japan Latin America and Far East Regions, Gail S. Thornton

VP and Head Global Pharmacovigilance, Jean-Louis Saillot

Group VP Finance Global Pharmaceuticals, Charles Schultes

VP and General Manager Schering-Plough Mexico, Armando Trujillo

VP Global Information Technology Global Supply Chain and Global Quality Operations, Christopher Kelly

VP Global Clinical Development Early Clinical Research and Experimental Medicine Schering-Plough Research Institute, James F. McLeod

Group VP Global Clinical Development Cardiovascular and Early Clinical Research and Experimental Medicine, Enrico Veltri

VP Finance Consumer Health Care, Anne Renahan, age 53

VP and General Manager Schering-Plough France, Gilles Picard

SVP External Manufacturing, Didier Colombeen

EVP; President Merck Manufacturing, Willie A. Deese, age 56

Group VP Research and Development Consumer Health Care, John O'Mullane

VP Commercial Operations Schering-Plough K.K., Tony Alvarez

VP and General Manager Schering Canada, Carlos G. Dourado

Group VP; President Latin America Region, Pierre Verstraete

VP Global Cholesterol Marketing, Raymond Russo

EVP; President Global Human Health, Adam H. Schechter, age 47

VP Global Internal Audits, John M. Carroll, age 51

SVP Finance and Global Controller, John Canan, age 55

General Manager Argentina, Eduardo Cortes

President Director P.T. Schering-Plough Indonesia, Thierry Powis

General Manager Schering-Plough Australia/New Zealand, Shaju Backer

EVP and General Counsel, Bruce N. Kuhlik, age 55, $706,234 total compensation

EVP The Merck Company Foundation, Ellen W. Lambert

VP Global Pharmacovigilance SPRI, Martin Huber Jr.

Deputy Chief Medical Officer SPRI Europe, Hans Rekers

EVP Human Resources, Miriam M. Graddick-Weir, age 57

VP Strategic Planning & Financial Forecasting, Lisa DeBeradine

VP Global Clinical Research SPRI, Thomas Haverty

VP Global Animal Health Regions, Hugo Wahnish

Chief Strategy Officer; SVP Emerging Markets R&D Merck Research Laboratories, Mervyn (Merv) Turner, age 65

Head Media Relations, David Caouette

Media Contact Financial Communications Manufacturing and Corporate Responsibility, Amy Rose

Media Contact Scientific Affairs R&D and Licensing and Partnerships, Ian McConnell

Media Contact Product Communications, Pamela Eisele

Media Contact Policy and Litigation, Ronald Rogers

VP Emerging Markets, Greg Guyer

Head Administration and Coordination GCTO, Hassan Ansari

VP Franchise Project Management Head, Sandra A. Morris

Discovery Technologies Head, Marvin Bayne

Marketing Director Oncology, Jane Brandman

VP Clinical Research Merck Research Laboratories, Robin Isaacs

VP Cardiovascular Disease Clinical Research Merck Research Laboratories, Yale Mitchel

SVP Biologics and Therapeutic Protein Operations Merck Manufacturing Division, John T. McCubbins

VP and General Manager USA Intervet/Schering-Plough Animal Health, Paul Casady

Senior Director Investor Relations, Joe Romanelli

VP Neuroscience Clinical Research, David Michelson

EVP; President Merck Animal Health, Richard R. DeLuca Jr., age 49

EVP and Chief Strategy Officer, Cuong V. Do, age 45

Director, Wendell P. Weeks, age 52

Director, Thomas H. (Tom) Glocer, age 52

Director, William B. (Bill) Harrison Jr., age 68

Director, Steven F. (Steve) Goldstone, age 66

Director, Thomas R. (Tom) Cech, age 64

Director, Harry R. Jacobson, age 64

Director, Carlos E. Represas, age 66

Director, Peter C. Wendell, age 61

Director, Patricia F. (Pat) Russo, age 59

Director, Rochelle B. (Shelly) Lazarus, age 64

Director, Anne M. Tatlock, age 72

Director, William N. Kelley, age 72

Director, Thomas E. (Tom) Shenk, age 65

Director, C. Robert (Bob) Kidder, age 67

Director, Craig B. Thompson, age 59

Director, Leslie A. Brun, age 59

Auditors: PricewaterhouseCoopersLLP

LOCATIONS

HQ: Merck & Co. Inc.
1 Merck Dr., Whitehouse Station NJ 08889-0100
Phone: 908-423-1000 **Fax:** 908-735-1253
Web: www.merck.com

2011 Sales

	$ mil.	% of total
US	20,495	43
Europe Middle East & Africa	13,782	29
Japan	4,835	10
Other regions	8,935	18
Total	**48,047**	**100**

PRODUCTS/OPERATIONS

2011 Sal

	$ mil.	% of total
Pharmaceuticals		
Respiratory & immunology		
Singulair	5,479	11
Remicade	2,667	6
Nasonex	1,286	3
Clarinex/Aerius	621	1
Other respiratory & immunology	1,152	2
Diabetes & obesity		
Januvia	3,324	7
Janumet	1,363	3
Infectious disease		
Isentress	1,359	3
PegIntron	657	2
Cancidas	640	1
Primaxin	515	1
Other infectious disease	1,464	3
Cardiovascular		
Zetia	2,428	5
Vytorin	1,882	4
Integrilin	230	1
Vaccines		
Gardasil	1,209	3
ProQuad/M-M-R II/Varivax	1,202	3
RotaTeq	651	1
Other vaccines	830	2
Diversified brands		
Cozaar/Hyzaar	1,663	3
Other diversified brands	1,912	4
Women's health & endocrine		
Fosamax	855	2
NuvaRing	623	1
Follistim AQ	530	1
Other women's health & endocrine	562	1
Oncology		
Temodar	935	2
Other oncology	613	1
Neurosciences & Ophthalmol		
Maxalt	639	1
Other Neurosciences & Opthalmology	477	1
Other pharmaceuticals	3,521	7
Other operating segments (including Animal Health & Consumer Care)	6,327	13
Corporate & other	431	1
Total	**48,047**	**100**

Selected Products

Pharmaceuticals
  Respiratory and Immunology
    Arcoxia (arthritis and pain)

- Asmanex (asthma)
- Clarinex/Aerius (allergies)
- Dulera (asthma)
- Nasonex (allergies)
- Proventil (asthma)
- Remicade (rheumatoid arthritis and Crohn's disease)
- Singulair (asthma and allergic rhinitis)
- Simponi (rheumatoid arthritis)

Diabetes and Obesity
- Janumet (diabetes)
- Januvia (diabetes)
- Juvisync (diabetes)

Infectious Disease
- Avelox (antibiotic with Bayer)
- Cancidas (antifungal)
- Crixivan/Stocrin (HIV)
- Invanz (antibacterial)
- Isentress (antifungal HIV)
- Noxafil (antifungal)
- PegIntron (hepatitis C)
- Primaxin (antibiotic)
- Rebetol (hepatitis C)
- Victrelis (hepatitis C)

Cardiovascular
- Brinavess (vernakalant atrial fibrillation)
- Integrilin (injectable for acute coronary syndrome)
- Vytorin (combination Zetia and Zocor cholesterol)
- Zetia/Ezetrol (cholesterol)

Vaccines
- Gardasil (cervical cancer caused by HPV virus)
- M-M-R II (measles mumps and rubella)
- Pneumovax (pneumococcal disease)
- ProQuad (measles mumps rubella varicella)
- RotaTeq (rotavirus gastroenteritis)
- Varivax (chicken pox)
- Zostavax (shingles)

Diversified Brands (non-patent protected products)
- Claritin Rx (allergies)
- Cozaar/Hyzaar (hypertension)
- Propecia (male pattern hair loss)
- Proscar (benign prostate enlargement)
- Remeron (antidepressant)
- Vasotec/Vaseretic (hypertension/heart failure)
- Zocor (elevated cholesterol)

Women' s Health & Endocrine
- Cerazette (contraceptive)
- Follistim/Puregon (fertility)
- Fosamax/Fosavance (osteoporosis)
- Implanon (contraceptive)
- NuvaRing (contraceptive)
- Zoely (contraceptive)

Oncology
- Emend (chemotherapy-induced nausea and vomiting)
- Intron A (melanoma)
- Sylatron (melanoma)
- Temodar/Temodal (brain tumors)

Neurosciences and Ophthalmology
- Cosopt/Trusopt (glaucoma)
- Maxalt (migraine)
- Saphris (schizophrenia bipolar)
- Zioptan/Saflutan (glaucoma)

Animal Health (Intervet)
- Aquaflor (antibiotic for farm-raised fish)
- Banamine (nonsteroid anti-inflammatory)
- Coccivac (poultry vaccine)
- Exspot/Scalibor (canine topical insecticide)
- M+PAC (swine pneumonia vaccine)
- Nuflor (antimicrobial)
- Otomax (canine otitis)
- Paracox (poultry vaccine)

Consumer Health Care
- Afrin (nasal decongestant)
- Claritin (allergy)
- Coppertone (sun care)
- Coricidin HBP (cold medicine)
- Dr. Scholl' s (foot care products)
- MiraLAX (constipation)
- Tinactin (antifungal)
- Zegerid OTC (heartburn)

COMPETITORS

Abbott Labs
Alcon
Allergan
Amgen
AstraZeneca
Heska
Johnson & Johnson
Meda Pharmaceuticals
Merck KGaA
Mylan
Bausch & Lomb
Baxter International
Bayer AG
Biogen Idec
Boehringer Ingelheim
Bristol-Myers Squibb
Chattem
Eli Lilly
Enanta
Forest Labs
Genzyme
Gilead Sciences
GlaxoSmithKline
Novartis
Perrigo
Pfizer
Roche Holding
Sandoz International GmbH
Sanofi
Shire
Teva
Virbac Corporation
Warner Chilcott
Watson Pharmaceuticals

HISTORICAL FINANCIALS

Company Type: Public

Income Statement FYE: December 31

	REVENUE ($ mil.)	NET INCOME ($ mil.)	NET PROFIT MARGIN	EMPLOYEES
12/11	48,047	6,272	13.1%	86,000
12/10	45,987	861	1.9%	94,000
12/09	27,428	12,901	47.0%	175,600
12/08	23,850	7,808	32.7%	55,200
12/07	24,197	3,275	13.5%	59,800
Annual Growth	18.7%	17.6%	—	9.5%

2011 Year-End Financials

Debt ratio: 16.66%—
Return on equity: 11.50%
Cash ($ mil.): 13,531
Current ratio: 204.25
Long-term debt ($ mil.): 15,525
Dividends
Yield: —
Payout: 77.23%
Market value ($ mil.): —

	STOCK PRICE ($) FY Close	P/E High/Low	PER SHARE ($) Earnings	Dividends	Book Value
12/11	37.70	19 15	2.02	0.00	17.93
12/10	36.04	147114	0.28	1.52	17.64
12/09	36.54	7 4	5.65	0.38	19.00
12/08	30.40	17 6	3.64	0.00	8.90
12/07	58.11	40 28	1.49	0.00	8.37
Annual Growth	(10.3%)	— —	7.9%	—	21.0%

Mercury General Corp.

Named after the Roman god of commerce and travel Mercury General hopes to combine the two. The company is the parent of a group of insurers including Mercury Casualty Company that write automobile insurance for all risk classifications in about a dozen states. Plain old private auto insurance accounts for more than 80% of premiums written. However Mercury General also sells commercial vehicle insurance and a bit of homeowners mechanical breakdown and fire insurance. The company sells its policies through more than 5500 independent agents mainly in California and Florida. Chairman George Joseph founded Mercury Casualty in 1961; he and his wife own just over 50% of the company.

While Mercury General has ventured from its California comfort zone California still accounts for more than 75% of its total premiums. The company operated solely in its home state until 1990; it now underwrites auto insurance in a dozen other states as well. These include Arizona Florida Georgia Illinois Michigan Nevada New Jersey New York Oklahoma Pennsylvania Texas and Virginia.

Mercury General paid $120 million to acquire AIS Management the US car insurance business of Aon Corporation. The 2009 deal gave Mercury General ownership of AIS' operating companies Auto Insurance Specialists and PoliSeek AIS Insurance Solutions. AIS was already Mercury General's largest independent broker and brought with it a significant chunk of California premiums.

Like most of its property/casualty brethren Mercury General saw its revenues drop during the credit crisis as its investment income turned mushy. However just as it was seeing its investments recover its net income was again sorely tested in 2010 when its reserves were heavily tapped by large homeowners claims in California (from catastrophic rainstorms) and Florida (from sinkholes). In response the company has decided to withdraw from the Florida homeowners market.

Mercury General's revenues in 2011 increased slightly over 2010 edging even closer to $2.8 billion. The company's net income however increased to $191 million representing an almost 26% increase from $152 million in 2010. The increase was due in part to improved investment gains. Premiums earned (more than 90% of total revenues) remained fairly flat although premiums written increased (except in California where there was a slight decrease) by about $20 million from 2010. More products and improvements in its products together with higher average premiums per policy have driven the company's growth outside of California.

Core to its strategy for growth is managing rates to achieve the right balance between attracting customers through lower rates and remaining competitve. The company places value in its agent relationships and underwriting processes to achieve favorable margins. To encourage policy growth and broaden its customer base Mercury General offers multi-policy discounts to those who bundle their home and car insurance together. It also employs marketing initiatives to build brand recognition and generate leads. Technology is another key aspect it uses to build the business. For example in 2011 the company enhanced its Mercury First internet agency portal with its point of sale (POS) system to make writing new business easier. Of the $18 million in capital expenditures that year most was spent on information technology.

EXECUTIVES

VP Corporate Affairs and Secretary, Judy A. Walters, age 65

VP and Chief Underwriting Officer, Kenneth G. Kitzmiller, age 65

SVP and Chief Claims Officer, Joanna Y. Moore, age 56, $275,714 total compensation

President CEO and Director, Gabriel Tirador, age 47, $750,000 total compensation

Chairman, George Joseph, age 90, $850,000 total compensation

Director; Executive Consultant, Michael D. Curtius, age 61

VP and CFO, Theodore R. Stalick, age 48, $488,250 total compensation

VP and Chief Investment Officer, Christopher Graves, age 46, $306,984 total compensation

VP and Chief Actuary, Charles Toney, age 50

SVP and Chief Information Officer, Allan Lubitz, age 53, $330,000 total compensation

SVP Customer Service, John Sutton, age 64

VP Southeast Region, Ronald Deep, age 56

VP and Chief Product Officer, Robert Houlihan, age 56, $281,167 total compensation

Director Human Resources, Clarisa Eng

State Director Marketing Northeast Region, Cynthia VanHoesen
Vice President - Marketing, Brandt N. Minnich
President CEO and Director, Gabriel Tirador, age 47
Director; Executive Consultant, Michael D. Curtius, age 61
Director, Donald P. Newell, age 74
Director, Donald R. Spuehler, age 77
Director, Nathan Bessin, age 86
Director, Bruce A. Bunner, age 78
Director, Richard E. Grayson, age 82
Director, Martha E. Marcon, age 63
Auditors: KPMGLLP

LOCATIONS

HQ: Mercury General Corporation
4484 Wilshire Blvd., Los Angeles CA 90010
Phone: 323-937-1060 **Fax:** 323-857-7116
Web: www.mercuryinsurance.com

PRODUCTS/OPERATIONS

Selected Products

Auto
- Commercial auto
- Mechanical breakdown (extended warranty coverage)
- Niche commercial
- Personal auto

Condo
- Contents coverage
- Guest medical protection and liability
- Personal liability protection
- Personal property

Homeowners
- Apartments
- Condominiums
- Single-family homes

Personal umbrella

Renter
- Liability protection
- Personal property

Selected Operating Brands and Divisions

AIS Management
American Mercury Insurance
American Mercury Lloyds Insurance
American Mercury MGA
Auto Insurance Specialists
California Automobile Insurance
California General Underwriters Insurance
Concord Insurance Services
Mercury Casualty
Mercury County Mutual Insurance
Mercury Group
Mercury Indemnity
Mercury Insurance
Mercury National Insurance
Mercury Select Management
PoliSeek AIS Insurance Solutions

COMPETITORS

21st Century Insurance
Allstate
Auto Club of Southern California
Covanta Holding
Farmers Group
GEICO
State Farm
USAA

HISTORICAL FINANCIALS

Company Type: Public

Income Statement FYE: December 31

	ASSETS ($ mil.)	NET INCOME ($ mil.)	INCOME AS % OF ASSETS	EMPLOYEES
12/11	4,070	191	4.7%	4,500
12/10	4,203	152	3.6%	4,800
12/09	4,232	403	9.5%	5,000
12/08	3,950	(242)	—	5,000
12/07	4,414	237	5.4%	5,200
Annual Growth	(2.0%)	(5.3%)	—	(3.6%)

2011 Year-End Financials

Debt ratio: 3.44%
Return on equity: 10.29%
Cash ($ mil.): 211
Current ratio: —
Long-term debt ($ mil.): 140
No. of shares (mil.): 54
Dividends
Yield: —
Payout: 69.05%
Market value ($ mil.): 2,503

	STOCK PRICE ($) FY Close	P/E High/Low		PER SHARE ($) Earnings	Dividends	Book Value
12/11	45.62	13	10	3.49	0.00	33.86
12/10	43.01	17	13	2.78	2.37	32.75
12/09	39.26	6	3	7.32	2.33	32.33
12/08	45.99	—	—	(4.42)	2.32	27.28
12/07	49.81	13	11	4.34	2.08	34.02
Annual Growth	(2.2%)	—	—	(5.3%)	—	(0.1%)

Meritor Inc

Whether it's building axles or drum brakes for big rigs or buses this company's products are meritorious. Meritor (formerly ArvinMeritor) makes axles brakes drivelines suspension systems undercarriages and aftermarket transmissions for commercial truck trailer off-highway construction military bus and specialty vehicle manufacturers. It also makes U-joints shafts clutches and ABS and stability control systems. The company divides its operations across three primary segments: Commercial Truck; Industrial; and Aftermarket & Trailer. Meritor operates around the globe through operations in roughly 20 countries including Canada China France India Mexico Sweden and South America.

HISTORY

Meritor's earliest progenitor was the Wisconsin Parts Company a small axle plant Willard Rockwell bought in 1919 to build a truck axle he had designed himself. In 1953 Rockwell merged Wisconsin Parts with Standard Steel and Spring and Timken-Detroit Axle to form Rockwell Spring and Axle Company. Timken-Detroit was a 1909 spinoff of the Timken Roller Bearing Axle Company whose buggy springs predated the invention of the automobile.

Rockwell Spring and Axle changed its name in 1958 to Rockwell-Standard Corp. In 1967 Rockwell-Standard took over North American Aviation. North American Aviation needed to improve its public image by burrowing into a reputable company after the Apollo space capsule it had built ignited during a ground test killing all three astronauts aboard. The new company called North American Rockwell was headed by Willard.

North American Rockwell made car and truck parts tools printing presses industrial sewing machines and electronic flight and navigation instruments. In 1973 North American Rockwell bought Willard Rockwell Jr.'s Rockwell Manufacturing and changed its name once again to Rockwell International (now Rockwell Automation).

Under Willard Jr.'s leadership Rockwell bought a number of high-risk businesses. During one period in the early 1970s the company was losing a million dollars a day. Willard Jr. retired in 1979 and Robert Anderson who had come to Rockwell in 1968 from Chrysler became chairman. Anderson moved the company away from the high-profile consumer market that Willard Jr. had been so keen on. He also required all company divisions to submit profit goals. Under Anderson's management Rockwell's debt fell dramatically.

In 1986 Rockwell brought out a new line of single-speed and two-speed drive axles for heavy vehicles and in 1989 it introduced a family of nine- and 13-speed on-highway transmissions. The next year the company's Meritor WABCO unit (a joint venture with American Standard Companies) began supplying antilock brakes for trailers and tractors.

In the 1990s Rockwell's automotive division began growing through acquisitions and overseas expansion. It bought Czech auto parts maker Skoda Miada Boleslav in 1993 and Dura Automotive Systems' window-regulator business in 1995. The next year the division entered into a joint venture with China's Xuzhou Construction Machinery Axle and Case Co. It also introduced the Engine Synchro Shift transmission system designed to shift gears easily.

Rockwell spun off Meritor Automotive in 1997 as an independent publicly traded company. The new company derived its name from the Latin word "meritum" meaning service worth and benefit. In 1999 Meritor bought UK-based LucasVarity's heavy vehicle braking system division; Volvo's heavy-duty truck axle unit; and Euclid Industries which made replacement parts for medium- and heavy-duty trucks. Meritor further enhanced its aftermarket offerings through an agreement with Pressure Systems International to market automatic tire-inflation systems. Meritor sold its auto seat adjusting system operations for $130 million that year.

Meritor's Suspension Systems joint venture with Mitsubishi Steel acquired Tempered Spring Co. a UK-based supplier of automotive suspension components. It also acquired Arvin Industries. Renamed ArvinMeritor the combined companies formed an automotive systems titan with $7.5 billion in sales.

In 2001 it sold certain electric seat motor assets of its light vehicle systems division to Johnson Electric Holdings for $11.7 million. In late 2002 it announced it would buy the remaining 51% of Zeuna Starker GmbH & Co. KG (a maker of exhaust and emissions components) that it didn't already own. The transaction was completed in early 2003. The next year the company announced plans to exit the aftermarket business to focus on the needs of its OEM customers. Meritor sold its coil coating operations as well as its off-highway brake parts business to Carlisle Companies for about $39 million.

Meritor also sold its light vehicle aftermarket Purolator filters business to Robert Bosch and MANN+HUMMEL in 2006. Soon afterward the company sold its North American light vehicle aftermarket exhaust business to IMCO (International Muffler Company) as well as its light vehicle aftermarket motion control business to AVM Industries LLC.

Chassis Systems was started in 2007. Meritor formed a joint venture with China's Chery Automobile and named it ArvinMeritor Chassis Systems Wuhu Co.; it produced chassis systems at first and then later produced shocks and struts. The venture was meant to expand the customer base in Asia as well as insulate the company from the steadily contracting North American market and the mature European market.

The company formed a joint venture in China to build sunroofs for Chinese-built Volkswagens and established two more joint ventures in France to provide AB Volvo with commercial vehicle drive axles.

In 2007 Meritor fully exited the automotive aftermarket in order to focus on meeting the needs of its OEM automotive and heavy-duty truck customer base. It sold its emissions technologies business to One Equity Partners an affiliate of JPMorgan Chase for about $310 million and its light vehicle aftermarket European exhaust division to Klarius Group of the UK. Meritor earmarked the proceeds of the divestitures to pay down debt and invest in the growth of its core business.

The company moved to exit the automotive business for light vehicles and focus on global commercial vehicle and industrial products for OEM and aftermarket customers. Late in 2008 it put the LVS division up for sale. Unable to attract a buyer in part due to the credit crisis Meritor called off the sale in early 2009 and instead began divesting LVS piece by piece. Throughout 2009 and 2010 it divested substantially all of its LVS and Chassis businesses to focus on its core businesses of Commercial Truck Industrial and Aftermarket & Trailer.

As part of a major wave in cost-cutting measures Meritor in 2009 laid off about 2800 employees worldwide more than 10% of its workforce. It shuttered a brake plant and a coil spring operation in Canada and closed its commercial truck machining and casting facility in Kentucky. Restructuring efforts also included salary reductions as well as the elimination of training programs and all non-priority discretionary spending. The restructuring moves provided about $195 million in cost savings for fiscal 2009.

After 11 years as ArvinMeritor the company changed its name back to Meritor Inc. in 2011.

EXECUTIVES

SVP and General Counsel, Vernon G. Baker II, age 59, $500,833 total compensation
SVP Communications, Linda (Lin) Cummins, age 65
Chairman President and CEO, Charles G. (Chip) McClure Jr., age 57, $1,151,917 total compensation
VP; President Industrial, Pedro Ferro, age 53
SVP and CFO, Jeffrey A. (Jay) Craig, age 53, $466,713 total compensation
VP and CIO, Deborah Henderson
Senior Director Corporate Communications and Media Relations, Krista Sohm
General Manager Worldwide Aftermarket Operations, Craig Cartmill, age 50
SVP Treasury and Corporate Development, Mary Lehmann, age 54, $340,567 total compensation
VP Purchasing, Art Waldowski
VP and Corporate Secretary, Barbara Novak
General Manager Aftermarket United States and Canada, Terry Livingston
VP Aftermarket Americas, Daniel R. (Dan) Hopgood, age 40
Controller, Kevin Nowlan, age 40
Assistant Treasurer, Carl Anderson
Senior Director Investor Relations, Brett Penzkofer
VP; President Aftermarket and Trailer, Joseph Mejaly
SVP Human Resources, Larry Ott
Director IS Business Solutions, Ryan Olivier
VP; President Commercial Truck, Timothy E. (Tim) Bowes
Director Europe and Asia/Pacific Communications, Malte Raddatz
Director Global Brand Management and Marketing Communications, Mike Pennington
VP; General Manager Worldwide Trailer Systems, Larry Burgin
VP Engineering, Joe Elbehairy
VP Quality, Steven Foster
VP Truck Europe, Alessandro Mortali
VP Truck, Joseph Plomin
VP Manufacturing and Supply Chain Management, Christopher Snodgrass
Director, David W. (Dave) Devonshire, age 65
Director, Rhonda L. Brooks, age 58
Director, Ivor J. (Ike) Evans, age 68
Director, William R. (Bill) Newlin, age 71
Chairman President and CEO, Charles G. (Chip) McClure Jr., age 57
Director, Steven G. (Steve) Rothmeier, age 64
Director, Victoria B. Jackson, age 55
Director, Joseph B. Anderson Jr., age 69
Director, James E. Marley, age 75
Auditors: Deloitte&ToucheLLP

LOCATIONS

HQ: Meritor Inc.
2135 W. Maple Rd., Troy MI 48084-7186
Phone: 248-435-1000 **Fax:** 248-435-1393
Web: www.meritor.com

2011 Sales

North America		
Mexico	597	13
Europe		
France	264	6
South America	746	16
Asia Pacific		
China	312	7
India	240	5
Total	**4,622**	**100**

PRODUCTS/OPERATIONS

2011 Sales

Commercial Truck	2,806	57
Industrial	1,113	22
Total	**4,622**	**100**

Selected Products

Aftermarket and Trailer
- Remanufactured parts
- Undercarriage and related products

Commercial and Industrial Vehicle Systems
- Axles
- Brakes
- Brake wheel-end components (hubs drums and rotors)
- Clutches
- Drivelines
- Exhaust products
- Ride control products
- Shock absorbers
- Suspension systems
- Trailer products (including axles and air suspension products)
- Universal joints

COMPETITORS

Accuride
American Axle & Manufacturing
ASC Inc.
AxleTech International
Haldex
Hayes Lemmerz
Magna International
MAN
Robert Bosch
Bendix Commercial Vehicle Systems
Benteler Group
Boler
BorgWarner
Brembo
Carlisle Brake & Friction
Carlisle Companies
Carraro
Daimler
Dana Holding
DURA Automotive
Eaton
Federal-Mogul
SAF-HOLLAND
SOGEFI
Superior Industries
Tenneco
Titan International
Topy
Tower International
TRW Automotive
Visteon
Voith
WABCO
Westinghouse Air Brake
Williams Controls
ZF Friedrichshafen

HISTORICAL FINANCIALS

Company Type: Public

Income Statement

FYE: September 30

	REVENUE ($ mil.)	NET INCOME ($ mil.)	NET PROFIT MARGIN	EMPLOYEES
09/12*	4,418	52	1.2%	9,300
10/11	4,622	63	1.4%	10,500
10/10	3,590	12	0.3%	14,051
09/09	4,108	(1,212)	—	13,200
09/08	7,167	(101)	—	19,800
Annual Growth	(11.4%)	—	—	(17.2%)

*Fiscal year change

2012 Year-End Financials

Debt ratio: 42.38%
Return on equity: 987650001000000.00%
Cash ($ mil.): 257
Current ratio: 126.26
Long-term debt ($ mil.): 1,042
No. of shares (mil.): 96
Dividends
Yield: —
Payout: —
Market value ($ mil.): 409

	STOCK PRICE ($) FY Close	P/E High	P/E Low	PER SHARE ($) Earnings	Dividends	Book Value
09/12*	4.24	19	7	0.54	0.00	(10.60)
10/11	7.06	34	10	0.65	0.00	(10.52)
10/10	15.69	120	52	0.14	0.00	(11.20)
09/09	7.82	—	—	(16.72)	0.30	(17.26)
09/08	13.04	—	—	(1.40)	0.40	6.26
Annual Growth	(24.5%)	—	—	—	—	—

*Fiscal year change

Merrill Lynch Life Insurance Co.

LOCATIONS

HQ: Merrill Lynch Life Insurance Co.
4333 Edgewood Road, N.E., Cedar Rapids, IA 52499-0001
Phone: 800 346-3677

HISTORICAL FINANCIALS

Company Type:

Income Statement FYE: December 31

	ASSETS ($ mil.)	NET INCOME ($ mil.)	INCOME AS % OF ASSETS	EMPLOYEES
12/11	10,516	18	0.2%	0
12/10	11,491	137	1.2%	0
12/09	11,612	(203)	—	0
12/08	11,113	(138)	—	0
12/07	14,709	110	0.8%	0
Annual Growth	(8.0%)	(35.9%)	—	—

2011 Year-End Financials

Debt ratio: —
Return on equity: 1.48%
Cash ($ mil.): 328
Current ratio: —
Long-term debt ($ mil.): —
No. of shares (mil.): 0
Dividends
Yield: —
Payout: —
Market value ($ mil.): —

MetLife Inc

While its name evolved from "metropolitan" MetLife's insurance policies are found in villages towns and huge cities around the world. Operating through its Metropolitan Life Insurance Company subsidiary MetLife is the largest life insurer in the US. Its Insurance Products segment includes all of its group and individual life insurance and non-medical health insurance products (dental disability illness). Its Retirement Products segment includes annuity products. MetLife's Auto & Home segment works through subsidiary Metropolitan Property and Casualty Insurance. Internationally MetLife is a big player in Japan and growing in over 50 other countries.

HISTORY

New York merchant Simeon Draper tried to form National Union Life and Limb Insurance to cover Union soldiers in the Civil War but investors were scared away by heavy casualties. After several reorganizations and name changes the enterprise emerged in 1868 as Metropolitan Life Insurance (MetLife) a stock company.

Sustained at first by business from mutual assistance societies for German immigrants MetLife went into industrial insurance with workers' burial policies. The firm was known for its aggressive sales methods. Agents combed working-class neighborhoods collecting small premiums. If a worker missed one payment the company could cancel the policy and keep all premiums paid a practice outlawed in 1900.

MetLife became a mutual company (owned by its policyholders) in 1915 and began offering group insurance two years later.

After a period of conservative management under the Eckers family from 1929 to 1963 MetLife began to change dropping industrial insurance in 1964. It started offering auto and homeowners insurance in 1974.

To diversify the company bought State Street Research & Management (1983) Century 21 Real Estate (1985 sold 1995) London-based Albany Life Assurance (1985) and Allstate's group life and health business (1988). In 1987 it took over the annuities segment of the failed Baldwin United Co. and expanded into Spain and Taiwan in 1988. During the early 1990s MetLife reemphasized insurance adding such new products as long-term-care insurance.

In 1993 MetLife was charged with improper sales practices in 13 states. Legal fees fines and refunds in these cases exceeded $100 million; bad publicity had a chilling effect on sales. MetLife in turn instituted new training and sales practices. (In 1998 it agreed to pay an additional $25 million civil penalty to settle the federal investigation.)

In 1996 MetLife bought New England Mutual Life Insurance expanding its customer base to include wealthier middle-class customers (it also sought to obliterate its 1995 loss by retroactively restating results on combined sales).

MetLife's problems continued with a suit over its sales of insurance to Americans in Europe and an investigation in Florida related to churning (agents inducing customers to buy more expensive policies).

In 1997 MetLife acquired Los Angeles-based Security First Group (annuity contracts for public employees). In 1998 it sold its UK insurance operations and its Canadian business then cut 10% (about 1900) of its administrative employees.

In 1999 MetLife followed the industry trend of buying and selling single product lines rather than whole companies. Also in 1999 the company agreed to pay $1.7 billion to settle policyholder lawsuits related to churning allegations.

MetLife saw numerous changes in 2000. Most notably it went public bought fellow insurer GenAmerica and purchased Grand Bank a one-office nationally chartered bank in New Jersey which was renamed MetLife Bank. Plans to use Grand Bank as a ticket into the financial services arena met with opposition from community and consumer groups concerned about how MetLife's ownership would comply with the Community Reinvestment Act. The Federal Reserve Board approved the acquisition in 2001.

To trim expenses MetLife cut employees and consolidated some offices and in 2001 it exited the large-market 401(k) business and sold asset manager Conning to Swiss Re.

Solidifying its position as a major group benefits provider MetLife bought John Hancock's group life insurance operations in 2003.

MetLife in 2005 exited the asset management business when it sold State Street Research to BlackRock. That same year it acquired The Travelers Insurance Company and The Travelers Life and Annuity Company from Citigroup in a cash and equity deal valued at $11.8 billion. The deal which included Citigroup's international insurance businesses made MetLife the largest individual life insurer in North America. In 2006 it changed the acquired business' name to MetLife Insurance Company of Connecticut and MetLife Life and Annuity Company of Connecticut and in 2007 it merged the latter into the former.

Until 2008 the company participated in reinsurance by holding 52% of Reinsurance Group of America. However MetLife sold off its shares that year to focus on its core activities. The same year the company purchased dental plan provider SafeGuard the reverse mortgage business of EverBank and the mortgage business of First Tennessee Bank.

While MetLife is primarily known as an insurance company over the years it amassed a solid real estate portfolio valued at more than $7 billion. However the company has sold off some of its largest properties including Chicago's Sears Tower (divested in 2004 the tower was renamed Willis Tower in 2009) and even its own landmark headquarters in New York (in 2005 for $1.5 billion). It also sold the Peter Cooper and Stuyvesant Town housing complexes that it helped build with government funding in 1947. Tishman Speyer Properties and BlackRock paid $5.4 billion for the property in late 2006; the sale boosted MetLife's 2006 net income to a record $6.29 billion. However the buyers didn't fare as well and in 2010 they handed the keys to the iconic complexes over to their lenders.

Like all of its life insurance brethren MetLife experienced some queasiness during the recession of 2008 and 2009. As its investments roller-coasted some of its ratings also bobbed up and down and losses from its investments contributed to the company's first net income loss of the decade. However the company's operations were never in serious trouble and it did not seek or receive any federal support. It even saw some of its business swell from increased mortgage refinancing and from an influx of nervous customers who switched from other insurers to MetLife and the firm made a swift return to profitability in 2010.

EXECUTIVES

Vice Chairman EMEA and Asia, William J. Toppeta, age 63, $630,000 total compensation
EVP and Interim CFO, Eric T. Steigerwalt
President Americas, William J. (Bill) Wheeler, age 50, $568,750 total compensation
EVP and Chief Human Resources Officer, Frans Hijkoop
Chairman President and CEO, Steven A. (Steve) Kandarian, age 60, $583,333 total compensation
EVP Office of the Chairman, Gwenn L. Carr, age 66
VP Public Relations, John Calagna
VP International Communications, Peter Stack
Chief Accounting Officer, Peter M. (Pete) Carlson, age 48
EVP and CFO, John C. R. Hele, age 53
SVP and Head of Finance European Regions, Conor Murphy
EVP Global Employee Benefits, Maria R. Morris, age 49
VP U.S. Business MetLife Mature Market Institute, Joe Madden
Assistant VP Corporate and Investments, Christopher (Chris) Breslin
President and CEO MetLife Foundation, Dennis White
Assistant VP Individual Business, Holly Sheffer Liapis
Director Institutional Business (Group Insurance/Employee Benefits), Karen Eldred
Director MetLife Auto & Home MetLife Bank MetLife Foundation and Information Technology, David Hammarstrom
Director International, Christina Tso
EVP Human Resources, Kathleen A. Henkel

EVP and Chief Investment Officer, Steven J. Goulart, age 53
President EMEA, Michel Khalaf
VP Vendor Sourcing and Corporate Services and Chief Procurement Officer, John M. Vazquez
VP Global Brand and Marketing Services, Richard Hong
EVP International Business, Eugene Marks
VP Product and Market Strategies Corporate Benefits Funding Group, Cynthia Mallett
VP Life Products Management, Graham Cox
EVP Employee Benefits Sales, Anthony Nugent
EVP and General Counsel, Nicholas D. Latrenta, age 60
VP and Director Warehouse Lending Home Loan Unit, Charlie Clark
VP Home Loan Unit, Paul Chmielinski
VP and Head of Investor Relations, John McCallion
VP Disability Product Management, Paul D. Taylor
VP MetLife Dental Products, David Guarrera
VP and Secretary, Christine M. DeBiase
SVP and Treasurer, Marlene Debel
EVP Global Brand Marketing and Communications, Beth M. Hirschhorn
EVP Global Technology and Operations, Martin (Marty) Lippert
Director, Alfred F. (Al) Kelly Jr., age 53
Director, Cheryl W. Grise, age 60
Director, Catherine R. (Cathy) Kinney, age 60
Director, James M. (Jim) Kilts Jr., age 64
Director, Hugh B. Price, age 70
Director, Kenton J. Sicchitano, age 67
Director, Sylvia Matthews Burwell, age 46
Director, Eduardo Castro-Wright, age 57
Director, David Satcher, age 71
Director, John M. Keane, age 69
Director, R. Glenn Hubbard, age 54
Director, Lulu C. Wang, age 67
Auditors: Deloitte&ToucheLLP

LOCATIONS

HQ: MetLife Inc.
200 Park Ave., New York NY 10166-0188
Phone: 212-578-2211 **Fax:** 212-578-3320
Web: www.metlife.com

PRODUCTS/OPERATIONS

2011 Revenues

	$ mil.	% of total
Insurance products	27,841	40
Retirement products	9,015	13
Corporate benefit funding	8,613	12
International		
Japan	8,822	12
Other international	10,538	15
Auto & Home	3,217	5
Corporate & other	2,216	3
Total	**70,262**	**100**

Selected Subsidiaries and Affiliates

American Life Insurance Co. (ALICO)
General American Life Insurance Company
Hyatt Legal Plans Inc. (prepaid legal plans)
MetLife Bank N.A. (consumer banking)
MetLife Insurance Company of Connecticut
MetLife Investors Group Inc. (distribution)
Metropolitan Property and Casualty Insurance Company
New England Life Insurance Company
Walnut Street Securities Inc. (mutual funds securities)

COMPETITORS

AEGON USA
Aetna
Aflac
AIG
Allianz
Allstate
MassMutual
Meiji Yasuda Life
Mutual of Omaha
Nationwide
New York Life
Nippon Life Insurance
American General
Aon
AXA
CIGNA
COUNTRY Financial
Genworth Financial
Guardian Life
ING
John Hancock Financial Services
Liberty Mutual
Lincoln Financial Group
Northwestern Mutual
Pacific Mutual
Principal Financial
Prudential
State Farm
The Hartford
TIAA-CREF
USAA
Zurich Financial Services

HISTORICAL FINANCIALS

Company Type: Public

Income Statement FYE: December 31

	ASSETS ($ mil.)	NET INCOME ($ mil.)	INCOME AS % OF ASSETS	EMPLOYEES
12/11	799,625	6,981	0.9%	67,000
12/10	730,906	2,790	0.4%	66,000
12/09	539,314	(2,246)	—	54,000
12/08	501,678	3,209	0.6%	57,000
12/07	558,562	4,317	0.8%	49,000
Annual Growth	9.4%	12.8%	—	8.1%

2011 Year-End Financials

Debt ratio: 3.94%
Return on equity: 11.65%
Cash ($ mil.): 10,461
Current ratio: —
Long-term debt ($ mil.): 31,531
No. of shares (mil.): 1,057
Dividends
Yield: —
Payout: 11.76%
Market value ($ mil.): 32,987

	STOCK PRICE ($) FY Close	P/E High	P/E Low	PER SHARE ($) Earnings	Dividends	Book Value
12/11	31.18	8	4	6.29	0.00	56.62
12/10	44.44	16	11	3.00	0.74	49.44
12/09	35.35	—	—	(2.89)	0.74	40.45
12/08	34.86	15	4	4.14	0.74	29.91
12/07	61.62	13	11	5.48	0.74	48.24
Annual Growth	(15.7%)	—	—	3.5%	—	4.1%

MetLife Insurance Company of Connecticut

LOCATIONS

HQ: MetLife Insurance Company of Connecticut
1300 Hall Boulevard, Bloomfield, CT 06002
Phone: 860 656-3000
Web: www.metlife.com

HISTORICAL FINANCIALS

Company Type:

Income Statement FYE: December 31

	ASSETS ($ mil.)	NET INCOME ($ mil.)	INCOME AS % OF ASSETS	EMPLOYEES
12/11	171,771	1,240	0.7%	0
12/10	154,885	757	0.5%	0
12/09	127,689	(446)	—	0
12/08	112,024	573	0.5%	0
12/07	128,582	695	0.5%	0
Annual Growth	7.5%	15.6%	—	—

2011 Year-End Financials

Debt ratio: 2.25%
Return on equity: 12.19%
Cash ($ mil.): 745
Current ratio: —
Long-term debt ($ mil.): 3,857
No. of shares (mil.): 34
Dividends
Yield: —
Payout: —
Market value ($ mil.): —

Metro Bancorp Inc PA

Metro Bancorp (formerly Pennsylvania Commerce Bancorp) is the holding company for Metro Bank (formerly Commerce Bank/Harrisburg) which has more than 30 branches in south-central Pennsylvania many of them with extended hours and open seven days a week. The bank provides standard services such as checking savings and money market accounts CDs IRAs and credit cards. Commercial loans including lines of credit and construction land development real estate and operating loans account for the majority of the bank's lending activities. It also originates consumer loans and residential mortgages.

2010 Metro Bancorp canceled plans to acquire Philadelphia-based Republic First Bancorp. The two banks terminated the agreement due to regulatory difficulties related to the transaction. The combined firm would have had about 45 branches stretching from Harrisburg to Philadelphia. The merger was announced in 2008 after Canadian bank Toronto-Dominion acquired Commerce Bancorp (now part of TD Bank) which had owned more than 10% of Pennsylvania Commerce Bancorp and shared branding. The company and the bank changed their names in 2009.

Metro Bancorp reported losses in 2009 and 2010 as the deterioration in general economic conditions led to an uptick in nonperforming loans and the company increased its provisions for expected losses. Undaunted by the losses or the demise of its attempted acquisition Metro Bancorp plans to grow by opening new branches in central Pennsylvania and the Philadelphia metropolitan area.

EXECUTIVES

Chairman President and CEO Metro Bancorp and Metro Bank, Gary L. Nalbandian, age 69, $397,600 total compensation
EVP and CFO Metro Bancorp and Metro Bank, Mark A. Zody, age 48, $205,500 total compensation
COO, Mark A. Ritter, age 52, $205,300 total compensation
Public Relations, Jason S. Kirsch
Investor Relations, Sherry Richart

SVP and Chief Credit Officer Metro Bancorp and Metro Bank, James R. Ridd, age 50, $167,300 total compensation
SVP Operations, Victoria G. (Vicki) Chieppa, age 62
Secretary, Peter J. Ressler
Director, Douglas S. Gelder, age 62
Director, Alan R. Hassman, age 72
Director, Howell C. Mette, age 84
Director, Michael A. Serluco, age 71
Director, Samir J. Srouji, age 75
Director, James R. Adair, age 64
Director, John J. Cardello, age 51

LOCATIONS

HQ: Metro Bancorp Inc.
3801 Paxton St., Harrisburg PA 17111
Phone: 717-412-6000 **Fax:** 717-412-6171
Web: www.mymetrobank.com

PRODUCTS/OPERATIONS

2010 Sales

	$ mil.	% of total
Interest		
Loans receivable including fees	74	59
Securities & other	22	18
Noninterest		
Service charges fees & other operating income	26	21
Other	2	2
Total	**126**	**100**

COMPETITORS

Bryn Mawr Bank Corp.
Codorus Valley Bancorp
Fulton Financial
M&T Bank
Pennsylvania State Employees Credit Union
PNC Financial
Sovereign Bank
Stonebridge Financial

HISTORICAL FINANCIALS

Company Type: Public

Income Statement FYE: December 31

	ASSETS ($ mil.)	NET INCOME ($ mil.)	INCOME AS % OF ASSETS	EMPLOYEES
12/11	2,421	0	0.0%	957
12/10	2,234	(4)	—	959
12/09	2,147	(1)	—	1,043
12/08	2,140	12	0.6%	1,077
12/07	1,979	7	0.4%	922
Annual Growth	5.2%	(54.9%)	—	0.9%

2011 Year-End Financials

Debt ratio: 2.03%
Return on equity: 0.13%
Cash ($ mil.): 47
Current ratio: —
Long-term debt ($ mil.): 49
No. of shares (mil.): 14
Dividends
Yield: —
Payout: —
Market value ($ mil.): 118

	STOCK PRICE ($) FY Close	P/E High/Low		PER SHARE ($) Earnings	Dividends	Book Value
12/11	8.38	645	398	0.02	0.00	15.58
12/10	11.01	—	—	(0.33)	0.00	14.94
12/09	12.57	—	—	(0.24)	0.00	14.87
12/08	26.66	16	11	1.97	0.00	17.76
12/07	27.85	29	23	1.07	0.00	17.79
Annual Growth	(25.9%)	—	—	(63.0%)	—	(3.3%)

MetroPCS Communications Inc

MetroPCS Communications has an urban outlook on communications. The regional wireless service provider offers use of its phone networks without requiring its customers to sign long-term contracts. Unlike other providers that charge by the minute MetroPCS offers monthly unlimited usage flat-rate plans for local and domestic long distance services to its approximately 9 million customers. It operates in about 20 states primarily in major metropolitan areas as Atlanta Dallas/Fort Worth Detroit Las Vegas Los Angeles Miami Sacramento and San Francisco. In 2012 Deutsche Telekom agreed to acquire MetroPCS via a reverse merger and combine it with T-Mobile USA.

MetroPCS will acquire T-Mobile while at the same time issuing 74% of its common stock to Deutsche Telekom. The combined entity which will retain the T-Mobile name will serve more than 42 million subscribers. The carriers have relatively complementary networks and MetroPCS has upgraded much of its network to LTE technology which is one of T-Mobile's strategic goals.

MetroPCS focuses largely on serving densely populated markets which creates efficiencies for the company in regard to network deployment and product distribution. To keep pace with market demand for higher bandwidth wireless connections as more consumers adopt Web-enabled smartphones MetroPCS began rolling out 4G wireless service in key parts of its national service area in 2010; network upgrades are ongoing. The company also fortified its presence in its home state of Texas that year with the purchase of the remaining 15% of Dallas-based Royal Street Communications that it did not already own.

MetroPCS's revenue rose again in 2011 about 19% over 2010 due to an increase in subscribers of 1.2 million (a jump of nearly 15%); it added more than 1 million customer in each of the previous two years as well. MetroPCS boosted its equipment sales by 10% in 2011. Profits were also up again for the year jumping 55%.

MetroPCS achieved strong fiscal performance in 2011 despite higher operating expenses in all areas of the business. In particular costs of service and equipment rose substantially due to investments in additional network infrastructure to support 4G upgrades and a growing customer base as well as upgrades to customer handsets.

MetroPCS plans to expand its subscriber base in part by simplifying its billing as consumers look increasingly to mobile accounts to replace their landline telephones. The company introduced service plans in 2010 that include all taxes and fees in the advertised flat rates. Also that year MetroPCS expanded its voice text and mobile Web services for new subscribers to include nationwide coverage. Looking ahead the company is betting that the availability of faster data connections for smartphone users will continue to drive new sales and subscriber plan upgrades.

HISTORY

CEO Roger Linquist and CTO Malcolm Lorang founded General Wireless in 1994 to bid on PCS licenses being auctioned by the US government. Linquist was formerly CEO of PacTel Personal Communications (later called AirTouch and now part of the Vodafone Group) and founded PageMart Wireless (now WebLink Wireless). In 1996 Japanese trading house Mitsui and audio-equipment maker Kenwood agreed to invest $10 million in General Wireless. The US electronics unit of Hyundai also made a substantial financial commitment and Lucent Technologies said it would provide $300 million in vendor financing to build the networks.

Also in 1996 the firm successfully bid $1 billion for 14 PCS licenses. But before the licenses were awarded the FCC held another auction where similar licenses sold for far less. General Wireless scrapped its IPO in 1997 because of poor market conditions. A year later it filed for Chapter 11 bankruptcy protection and sought to reduce the price of its licenses. In 1999 a federal bankruptcy court ruled that the licenses were worth only $166 million and that the company could reorganize and keep the licenses. The FCC launched an appeal but the bankruptcy court's decision was upheld by a Texas district court. The FCC then lobbied the US Congress to reclaim the licenses but the resulting bill was blocked.

After emerging from bankruptcy protection the firm changed its name to MetroPCS Communications. The legal wrangling continued into 2000 when the FCC appealed the decision to the 5th US Circuit Court of Appeals in New Orleans which ruled in favor of the company. The next year the Supreme Court denied a review of the case upholding the lower court's decision. MetroPCS then began rolling out operations in its major markets.

In 2007 the company went public and bought $1.4 billion in spectrum licenses covering regions such as Boston New York and Philadelphia during the federal government's auction.

Also in 2007 the company's more than $5 billion bid to acquire Leap Wireless was rejected. MetroPCS had hoped to significantly expand its service area in order to better compete with nationwide carriers like Sprint Nextel and AT&T Mobility through a merger with Leap.

In late 2008 the company entered into a national roaming agreement with Leap Wireless (which MetroPCS unsuccessfully tried to acquire in 2007) as well as agreeing to settle outstanding litigation between the two companies. The pact also included a spectrum exchange agreement that saw Leap acquiring from MetroPCS spectrum rights in San Diego Fresno Seattle and other Washington and Oregon markets and MetroPCS acquiring from Leap additional spectrum in Dallas/Fort Worth and other markets in Louisiana and Florida.

EXECUTIVES

VP and Regional General Manager, Michael C. Ward
SVP and CTO, Malcolm M. Lorang, age 78, $305,385 total compensation
Chairman and CEO, Roger D. Linquist, age 73, $804,192 total compensation
SVP Corporate Marketing, Phillip R. (Phil) Terry
EVP and CFO, J. Braxton Carter, age 53, $472,308 total compensation
EVP General Counsel and Secretary, Mark A. Stachiw, age 50, $380,962 total compensation
SVP Market Operations West, Herbert (Chip) Graves IV, age 56, $216,073 total compensation
VP Finance and Treasurer, Keith D. Terreri, age 47
SVP and CIO, John J. Olsen, age 55
SVP Chief Accounting Officer and Controller, Christine B. Kornegay, age 48
President and COO, Thomas C. Keys, age 53, $511,539 total compensation
VP and Regional General Manager, Tracy Lange
VP Network Operations, David Walker

SVP Corporate Operations, Douglas S. (Doug) Glen, age 54
SVP Engineering and Network Operations, Ed Chao
VP Human Resources, Dennis T. (Tom) Currier, age 43
VP Market Finance and Control, Charles Moore
VP Customer Operations, Greg Pressly
VP Revenue Assurance and Accounting, Terri Smith
VP Corporate Engineering, Ron Unger
VP and Regional General Manager, John Shelton
Director Investor Relations, Jim Mathias
Director, Richard A. (Dick) Anderson, age 53
Director, Arthur C. Patterson, age 68
Director, C. Kevin Landry, age 67
Director, James N. (Jim) Perry Jr., age 51
Director, John F. (Jack) Callahan Jr., age 54
Director, W. Michael Barnes, age 69
Auditors: Deloitte&ToucheLLP

LOCATIONS

HQ: MetroPCS Communications Inc.
2250 Lakeside Blvd., Richardson TX 75082
Phone: 214-570-5800 **Fax:** 214-570-5859
Web: www.metropcs.com

PRODUCTS/OPERATIONS

2011 Sales

	$ mil.	% of total
Service	4,428	91
Equipment	419	9
Total	**4,847**	**100**

COMPETITORS

AT&T Mobility
Boost Mobile
Cellco
Clearwire
Comcast Cable
Cox Communications
Cricket Communications
DISH Network
Leap Wireless
LightSquared
Sprint Nextel
T-Mobile USA
Time Warner Cable
TracFone
U.S. Cellular
Virgin Mobile
Vonage
XO Holdings

HISTORICAL FINANCIALS

Company Type: Public

Income Statement FYE: December 31

	REVENUE ($ mil.)	NET INCOME ($ mil.)	NET PROFIT MARGIN	EMPLOYEES
12/11	4,847	301	6.2%	3,700
12/10	4,069	193	4.8%	3,600
12/09	3,480	176	5.1%	3,600
12/08	2,751	149	5.4%	3,200
12/07	2,235	100	4.5%	2,498
Annual Growth	21.3%	31.6%	—	10.3%

2011 Year-End Financials

Debt ratio: 50.03%
Return on equity: 10.29%
Cash ($ mil.): 1,943
Current ratio: 335.93
Long-term debt ($ mil.): 4,711
No. of shares (mil.): 362
Dividends
Yield: —
Payout: —
Market value ($ mil.): 3,146

	STOCK PRICE ($) FY Close	P/E High	P/E Low	PER SHARE ($) Earnings	Dividends	Book Value
12/11	8.68	23	9	0.82	0.00	8.08
12/10	12.63	24	10	0.54	0.00	7.15
12/09	7.63	38	12	0.49	0.00	6.49
12/08	14.85	51	25	0.42	0.00	5.80
12/07	19.45	139	52	0.28	0.00	5.31
Annual Growth	(18.3%)	—	—	30.8%	—	11.1%

MFA Financial, Inc.

MFA Financial (formerly MFA Mortgage Investments) has three good buddies: Fannie Freddie and Ginnie. This self-advised mortgage real estate investment trust (REIT) was incorporated in 1997 to invest in mortgage-backed securities and mortgages such as those guaranteed by government-related entities Fannie Mae Freddie Mac and Ginnie Mae. The REIT's investment portfolio mainly consists of agency mortgage-backed securities AAA-rated mortgage-backed securities corporate and government bonds and cash. MFA Financial buys its securities and loans from the banks savings and loans investment banks and mortgage banking institutions that originate them. Its portfolio weighs in at approximately $8 billion.

The company's investments are typically secured by pools of adjustable-rate fixed-rate or hybrid mortgages on single-family residences. Although MFA Financial is in the thick of the mortgage industry it has largely avoided the fallout that has hampered or brought down other mortgage investment companies by focusing on the safest mortgage-backed securities.

Per company policy at least half of its portfolio consists of agency-backed securities or those rated highest by agencies like Fitch Moodys or Standard & Poors. At the end of 2010 these securities accounted for nearly three-quarters of MFA Financial's portfolio. However the company is been increasing its investments in non-agency securities beginning in 2009 taking advantage of bargains in the recessionary environment and diversifying its holdings. This has resulted in a decline in interest income but higher profits.

EXECUTIVES

EVP, Ronald A. Freydberg, age 51, $712,500 total compensation
President and Director, William S. Gorin, age 53, $737,500 total compensation
Chairman and CEO, Stewart Zimmerman, age 67, $900,000 total compensation
SVP Chief Accounting Officer and Treasurer, Teresa D. Covello, age 46, $250,000 total compensation
SVP General Counsel and Corporate Secretary, Timothy W. Korth II, age 46, $325,000 total compensation
EVP, Craig L. Knutson, age 52
SVP Accounting, Kathleen A. Hanrahan, age 46
CFO, Stephen D. Yarad
President and Director, William S. Gorin, age 53
Director, Stephen R. Blank, age 66
Director, Alan L. Gosule, age 71
Director, Michael L. Dahir, age 63
Director, George H. Krauss, age 70
Director, Robin Josephs, age 52
Director, Edison C. (Ted) Buchanan, age 57
Director, James A. Brodsky, age 66
Auditors: KPMGLLP

LOCATIONS

HQ: MFA Financial Inc.
350 Park Ave. 21st Fl., New York NY 10022
Phone: 212-207-6400 **Fax:** 212-207-6420
Web: www.mfa-reit.com

PRODUCTS/OPERATIONS

2010 Sales

	$ mil.	% of total
Agency mortgage-backed securities	250	52
Non-agency mortgage-backed securities	140	29
Net gain on linked transactions	53	11
Net gain on sale of mortgage-backed securities	33	7
Other	1	1
Net impairment losses	(12.3)	-
Loss on termination of repurchase agreements	(26.8)	-
Total	**4,412**	**100**

COMPETITORS

AG Mortgage Investment Trust
Annaly Capital Management
Anworth Mortgage Asset
Capstead Mortgage
CIFC
Cobalt Holdings
Impac Mortgage Holdings
iStar Financial Inc
JAVELIN Mortgage
Newcastle Investment
Redwood Trust
Webster Preferred Capital

HISTORICAL FINANCIALS

Company Type: Public

Income Statement FYE: December 31

	ASSETS ($ mil.)	NET INCOME ($ mil.)	INCOME AS % OF ASSETS	EMPLOYEES
12/11	11,750	316	2.7%	35
12/10	8,687	269	3.1%	29
12/09	9,627	268	2.8%	25
12/08	10,641	45	0.4%	22
12/07	8,605	30	0.4%	16
Annual Growth	8.1%	79.9%	—	21.6%

2011 Year-End Financials

Debt ratio: 7.45%
Return on equity: 12.67%
Cash ($ mil.): 394
Current ratio: —
Long-term debt ($ mil.): 875
No. of shares (mil.): 356
Dividends
Yield: —
Payout: 111.67%
Market value ($ mil.): 2,393

	STOCK PRICE ($) FY Close	P/E High	P/E Low	PER SHARE ($) Earnings	Dividends	Book Value
12/11	6.72	10	7	0.90	0.00	7.01
12/10	8.16	9	7	0.93	0.89	8.02
12/09	7.35	8	5	1.06	0.99	7.74
12/08	5.89	52	21	0.21	0.81	5.73
12/07	9.25	39	25	0.24	0.42	7.55
Annual Growth	(7.7%)	—	—	39.2%	—	(1.8%)

MGIC Investment Corp. (Milwaukee, WI)

Since a pinkie-promise isn't good enough for most lenders there's MGIC Investment's mortgage insurance to protect lenders from homebuyers who don't hold up their end of the bargain. MGIC Investment owns Mortgage Guaranty Insurance Corporation (MGIC) the largest provider of private mortgage insurance in the US. Such coverage allows otherwise-qualified buyers who aren't able to scrape up the standard 20% down payment to get mortgages. MGIC writes primary insurance on individual loans. The company's customers include banks mortgage brokers credit unions and other residential mortgage lenders.

MGIC Investment's businesses include a range of investment subsidiaries reinsurance subsidiaries and assurance corporations. The company also offers some online products: eMagic.com a web portal where mortgage providers can shop for a variety of loan origination tools and Myers Internet a web hosting provider and lead generator.

MGIC operates in the District of Columbia and in every state of the US as well as in Puerto Rico and Guam. Before the mortgage mess unfolded in the US MGIC had marked its entry into the global market by opening offices in Toronto and in Sydney Australia. In less than two years however MGIC closed its Canadian office stopped issuing new policies abroad and began searching for a buyer for its Australian operations in order to focus on its domestic operations.

Despite the diversity of its operations and the company's careful pruning MGIC Investment's capital reserves are still vulnerable and have dipped below some regional regulatory requirements. To operate in markets where it doesn't meet minimum capital requirements the company created MGIC Indemnity Corporation (MIC) in 2010 and gave it a tidy pile of capital reserves and nice fresh books with no murky liabilities. MGIC Investment expects to conduct more and more of its business through MIC as it moves forward.

As the entire private mortgage insurance industry nervously gauges its future government-sponsored enterprises Freddie Mac and Fannie Mae have taken over a huge share of the business during the past few years. To gain customers MGIC has lowered its rates based upon borrower's credit scores.

In 2011 MGIC Investment's revenues remained fairly flat at $1.5 billion dropping only a percentage point from 2010 revenues. For its fifth straight year the company operated with net losses due to conditions that continue to affect the private mortgage insurance industry as a whole –slowed activity in the housing market and in the creation of jobs decreased payrolled employment and dropped prices for homes. In 2011 its net loss was about $486 million compared to its net loss of about $364 million for 2010.

HISTORY

Milwaukee lawyer Max Karl founded MGIC in 1957 reinventing private mortgage guaranty insurance which had gone out of favor in the Depression. MGIC went public in 1961 suffered in the stagflated 1970s and entered the 1980s ready to expand. But poorly underwritten loans in such trouble spots as Texas and Oklahoma slammed MGIC.

Piano builder Baldwin United made a fruitless foray into financial services in 1982 paying too much for MGIC and going bankrupt in 1983. Northwestern Mutual bankrolled a management LBO in 1985. Surviving the weak real estate market of the 1980s MGIC went public again in 1991.

In 1995 MGIC debuted professional liability insurance products for lenders. Two years later it began selling homeowners extended warranties for appliances.

In the late 1990s changes in Fannie Mae and Freddie Mac mortgage insurance requirements hit MGIC hard. News reports that some insurers and lenders failed to inform homeowners when they could cancel their mortgage insurance also gave the industry a black eye.

In 1998 MGIC began insuring second mortgages and joined with Enhance Financial Services Group (now owned by Radian Group) to form C-BASS to buy and securitize nonperforming mortgages. Meanwhile MGIC was busy buffing up its in-house appraisal default and prepayment prediction tools and bundling them with a variety of mortgage origination services that it began offering over its eMAGIC website in 1999. In 2000 the decision by Illinois to allow insurance of 100% home loans meant that MGIC could begin to insure such loans nationwide.

With low interest rates high employment rates and some key legislative pushes to encourage home ownership lenders and homebuilders enjoyed a heyday from 2001 to late-2006. These were also good years for MGIC which wrote up a storm of mortgage insurance on all of those home purchases.

The subprime mortgage loan crisis that began in 2007 was brutal on MGIC and its competitors. MGIC responded by yanking hard on its own leash and tightening its underwriting standards to reduce its losses. The company stopped writing insurance on riskier loans and the blocks of pooled insurance sold on the secondary market curbed its coverage in states hardest hit by the resulting housing slump and raised its premium rates.

During its headier days MGIC had set up two joint ventures with Radian Group: debt collections firm Sherman Financial and Credit-Based Asset Servicing and Securitization LLC (C-BASS) which invested in riskier mortgage assets. Both ventures were among the first to feel pain from the collapse of the subprime mortgage market and credit freezes. To cut its losses MGIC sold its 25% interest in Sherman Financial Group to Sherman in 2008 for about $125 million in cash and an $85 million promissory note. Around that same C-BASS of which MGIC held less than a 50% interest ceased operations but only after costing MGIC roughly the value of its entire equity in the venture. (By late 2010 C-BASS filed for Chapter 11 bankruptcy protection.)

Faced with a pipeline full of pending claims investigations MGIC also turned to rescinding policies (known as rescissions) to help offset its losses. The company managed to shave $1 billion off its substantial 2009 losses by dropping policies with looming claims.

EXECUTIVES

VP and Managing Director Mortgage Guaranty Insurance, W. Thomas Hughes
SVP Regulatory Relations Assistant Secretary and Associate General Counsel MGIC Investment and Mortgage Guaranty Insurance, Joseph J. Ziino Jr.
SVP Chief Investment Officer and Treasurer MGIC Investment and Mortgage Guaranty Insurance, James A. Karpowicz, age 64
SVP Capital Markets Mortgage Guaranty Insurance, Steven T. Snodgrass
VP Claims Operations Mortgage Guaranty Insurance, Sandra K. Dunst
President and COO MGIC Investment and Mortgage Guaranty Insurance, Patrick Sinks, age 55, $524,423 total compensation
EVP General Counsel and Secretary MGIC Investment and Mortgage Guaranty Insurance, Jeffrey H. Lane, age 62, $415,385 total compensation
EVP Risk Management Mortgage Guaranty Insurance, Lawrence J. Pierzchalski, age 59, $449,654 total compensation
EVP and CFO MGIC Investment and Mortgage Guaranty Insurance, J. Michael Lauer, age 67, $460,039 total compensation
Chairman and CEO MGIC Investment and Mortgage Guaranty Insurance, Curt S. Culver, age 59, $898,269 total compensation
VP and Managing Director Mortgage Guaranty Insurance, James J. Hughes
VP Risk Management Mortgage Guaranty Insurance, Steven M. Thompson
VP and Managing Director Mortgage Guaranty Insurance, Stephen M. Dempsey
VP Sales Mortgage Guaranty Insurance, Malcolm T. Hurst
VP Sales Mortgage Guaranty Insurance, Eric L. Rice
VP National Accounts Mortgage Guaranty Insurance, Jerry L. Wormmeester
SVP Investor Relations Mortgage Guaranty Insurance, Michael J. (Mike) Zimmerman
SVP Field Operations Mortgage Guaranty Insurance, Cheryl L. Webb
VP Human Resources Mortgage Guaranty Insurance, Kurt J. Thomas
VP Marketing Mortgage Guaranty Insurance, Salvatore A. Miosi
VP and Assistant Treasurer Mortgage Guaranty Insurance, Lisa M. Pendergast
VP Controller and Chief Accounting Officer, Timothy J. Mattke, age 36
Corporate Relations Director, Katie Monfre
VP National Accounts Mortgage Guaranty Insurance, Mark J. Krauter
VP International Strategic Initiatives and Regulatory Affairs Mortgage Guaranty Insurance, Eric B. Klopfer
VP Financial Planning/Analysis Mortgage Guaranty Insurance, Jeffrey N. Nielsen
VP Internal Audit Mortgage Guaranty Insurance, Gary A. Antonovich
VP Analytic Services Mortgage Guaranty Insurance, Edward G. Durant
SVP Claims Mortgage Guaranty Insurance, Carla A. Gallas
VP Credit Policy Mortgage Guaranty Insurance, David A. Greco
VP Securities Law Counsel and Assistant Secretary Mortgage Guaranty Insurance, Ralph J. Gundrum
VP National Accounts Mortgage Guaranty Insurance, Steven F. Himebauch
VP and Managing Director Mortgage Guaranty Insurance, John S. Wiseman
VP Risk Management Mortgage Guaranty Insurance, Bernhard W. Verhoeven
VP Loss Mitigation Mortgage Guaranty Insurance, Kathleen E. Valenti
VP and Managing Director Mortgage Guaranty Insurance, Robin D. Mallory
VP Mortgage Banking Strategies Mortgage Guaranty Insurance, Mark E. Marple

VP Risk Management Mortgage Guaranty Insurance, John R. Schroeder
VP Assistant General Counsel Chief Compliance Officer and Assistant Secretary Mortgage Guaranty Insurance, Dan D. Stilwell
VP Regulatory Relations and Assistant Secretary Mortgage Guaranty Insurance, Heidi Heyrman
VP and Assistant Controller Mortgage Guaranty Insurance, Julie K. Sperber
SVP and CIO, Gregory Chi
Director, Kenneth M. (Kenny) Jastrow II, age 64
Director, Leslie M. (Les) Muma, age 67
Director, Michael E. Lehman, age 61
Director, Thomas M. Hagerty, age 49
Director, Daniel P. Kearney, age 72
Director, James A. Abbott, age 72
Director, William A. McIntosh, age 72
Director, David S. Engelman, age 74
Director, Donald T. (Don) Nicolaisen, age 67
Director, Bruce L. Koepfgen, age 59
Director, Mark Zandi
Auditors: PricewaterhouseCoopersLLP

LOCATIONS

HQ: MGIC Investment Corporation
MGIC Plaza 250 E. Kilbourn Ave., Milwaukee WI 53202
Phone: 800-558-9900 **Fax:** 888-601-4440
Web: www.mgic.com

PRODUCTS/OPERATIONS

2011 Sales

	$ mil.	% of total
Net premiums earned	1,123	75
Realized investment gains	142	10
Total	**1,504**	**100**

Selected Direct and Indirect Subsidiaries

eMagic.com LLC
MGIC Assurance Corporation
MGIC Australia Pty Limited
MGIC Credit Assurance Corporation
MGIC Indemnity Corporation
MGIC Insurance Services Corporation
MGIC Investor Services Corporation
MGIC Mortgage and Consumer Asset I LLC
MGIC Mortgage and Consumer Asset II LLC
MGIC Mortgage Reinsurance Corporation
MGIC Mortgage Services LLC
MGIC Reinsurance Corporation
MGIC Reinsurance Corporation of Vermont
MGIC Reinsurance Corporation of Wisconsin
MGIC Residential Reinsurance Corporation
MGICA Pty Limited
MIC Reinsurance Corporation
MIC Reinsurance Corporation of Wisconsin
Mortgage Guaranty Insurance Corporation

COMPETITORS

Allied Home Mortgage
Freddie Mac
Genworth Financial
Genworth Mortgage Insurance
GMAC Mortgage
PMI Group
Radian Group
Regions Mortgage
Republic Mortgage Insurance
United Guaranty
VBA
Wells Fargo Home Mortgage

HISTORICAL FINANCIALS

Company Type: Public

Income Statement FYE: December 31

	ASSETS ($ mil.)	NET INCOME ($ mil.)	INCOME AS % OF ASSETS	EMPLOYEES
12/11	7,216	(485)	—	920
12/10	9,333	(363)	—	1,010
12/09	9,404	(1,322)	—	1,020
12/08	9,182	(518)	—	1,160
12/07	7,716	(1,670)	—	1,250
Annual Growth	(1.7%)	—	—	(7.4%)

2011 Year-End Financials

Debt ratio: 11.92%
Return on equity: (-40.60)%
Cash ($ mil.): 995
Current ratio: —
Long-term debt ($ mil.): 859
No. of shares (mil.): 201
Dividends
Yield: —
Payout: —
Market value ($ mil.): 750

	STOCK PRICE ($) FY Close	P/E High/Low	PER SHARE ($) Earnings	Dividends	Book Value
12/11	3.73	— —	(2.42)	0.00	5.95
12/10	10.19	— —	(2.06)	0.00	8.33
12/09	5.78	— —	(10.65)	0.00	10.41
12/08	3.48	— —	(4.55)	0.08	18.93
12/07	22.43	— —	(20.54)	0.78	31.72
Annual Growth	(36.1%)	— —	—	—	(34.2%)

MGM Resorts International

It's not your imagination –MGM Resorts International (formerly MGM MIRAGE) is one of the world's largest gaming firms. The company's more than 15 partially or wholly owned properties include some of the biggest names on the Las Vegas Strip including MGM Grand The Mirage and the Monte Carlo as well as Luxor Bellagio and Mandalay Bay. MGM Resorts also owns or has a stake in other casinos in Nevada as well as in Michigan (MGM Grand Detroit) and Mississippi (Beau Rivage). Internationally it operates in China and Dubai. The company changed its name from MGM MIRAGE in 2010 to better reflect its family of hotel brands and its expanding global presence. Founder Kirk Kerkorian owns more than 20% of the firm.

HISTORY

Billionaire Kirk Kerkorian purchased a stake in famed movie studio Metro-Goldwyn-Mayer (MGM; formed 1924) for just over $80 million in 1970. Around the same time he began acquiring property in Las Vegas and started construction on the city's largest hotel.

Financial difficulties led Kerkorian to sell his new hotel as well as many of MGM's assets in the early 1970s. But he kept the MGM name and used it for MGM Grand hotels in Las Vegas and Reno Nevada. In 1986 Kerkorian sold MGM Grand Hotels to Bally but he retained the rights to the MGM Grand name and logo. That year Kerkorian founded MGM Grand Inc. and took the company public in 1987. He set about snapping up Las Vegas property in the late 1980s and early 1990s.

In 1993 Kerkorian and company unveiled Las Vegas' MGM Grand a $1.1 billion complex featuring a 33-acre theme park and at the time the largest casino on the planet (171500 sq. ft.). The project was a success ($742 million in revenues its first year) and spawned plans for expansion.

The 1990s proved a challenge for MGM Grand however as attendance figures at the theme park dropped off and the company struggled to maintain profitability. In 1996 MGM Grand began planning for an Atlantic City casino and signed on as developer and manager for gaming company Tsogo Sun which was opening casinos in South Africa. The following year through its joint venture with Primadonna Resorts it opened the 2035-room hotel and casino New York-New York. In 1998 MGM Grand narrowly won its bid to become one of three groups to build casinos in Detroit. (The MGM Grand Detroit opened the following year and pulled in $4.8 million in its first three days.)

In 1999 the company bought Primadonna Resorts which gave MGM Grand complete ownership of New York-New York and three casino properties in Primm Nevada. (It sold the Primm properties in 2007.) The company appointed co-CEOs John Redmond and Daniel Wade to their posts in late 1999. (Redmond and Wade moved to other positions in the company when Terrence Lanni became CEO in 2001.)

In a landmark deal MGM Grand bought rival Mirage Resorts for $6.4 billion (including $2 billion in debt) in 2000 and became one of the top gaming companies in the world. (Mirage Resorts' newer casinos had posted less-than-exciting financial results and the company had become an attractive acquisition target.)

The purchase of Mirage Resorts allowed MGM Grand to add a string of opulent casinos to its collection. Among the casinos the deal brought to the MGM Grand fold were Las Vegas strip properties Bellagio a luxurious European-style casino and The Mirage a tropical-themed casino. The Mirage Resorts acquisition also put Las Vegas' Treasure Island the Golden Nugget and Monte Carlo (50%-owned with Mandalay Resort Group) under the MGM Grand umbrella. Mirage Resorts' Beau Rivage in Biloxi Mississippi and the Golden Nugget in Laughlin Nevada also became MGM Grand properties.

Steven Wynn who had propelled Mirage Resorts from a single casino (the Golden Nugget) to its spot as one of the world's leading gaming companies opted not to join the merged firm. Later in 2000 MGM Grand changed its name to MGM MIRAGE. MGM MIRAGE laid off more than 6700 employees due to declining guest numbers in the wake of the September 11th terrorist attacks. In 2002 the company withdrew its $615 million bid for Chicago's Emerald Casino after the Illinois legislature passed a bill to increase gaming taxes by as much as 50%. Also that year the company ended its operations in South Africa where it managed four casinos.

In 2003 MGM MIRAGE closed its online casino citing an absence of sound regulatory policies regarding Internet gambling. The following year the company sold its Golden Nugget properties in Las Vegas and Laughlin to a private investment firm for $215 million. Also in 2004 MGM MIRAGE sold its MGM Grand Hotel and Casino in Darwin Australia.

The following year MGM MIRAGE purchased rival Mandalay Resort Group for about $7.9 billion briefly creating the world's largest gaming company. (It was surpassed later in 2005 when Harrah's bought Caesars.) In 2006 MGM Mirage and

Boyd Gaming debuted a $200 million expansion of its Borgata casino.

Kerkorian's Tracinda Corp. entered into talks with MGM Mirage in 2007 to purchase the Bellagio and CityCenter properties. However it later scrapped those plans reportedly in part because Tracinda disagreed with the valuation of a separate development deal between MGM MIRAGE and Kerzner International.

Also in 2007 the company opened MGM Grand Macau a hotel that operates through MGM Resorts' majority-owned MGM China. The following year Lana resigned as chairman and CEO. He was replaced by James Murren. In 2009 the company opened CityCenter an $8 billion-plus mixed-use development on the Las Vegas Strip a joint venture with Dubai World. In order to lighten its debt in 2009 it sold Treasure Island Hotel & Casino on the Las Vegas Strip to Ruffin Acquisition LLC for $775 million.

The following year MGM MIRAGE changed its name to MGM Resorts International to emphasize the brand's scope. In 2011 MGM China filed an IPO.

EXECUTIVES

COO, Corey I. Sanders, age 49
President and Chief Marketing Officer, William J. (Bill) Hornbuckle IV, age 54
Chairman and CEO, James J. (Jim) Murren, age 50, $2,038,462 total compensation
General Manager Gold Strike Casino Jean NV and Railroad Pass Henderson NV, Michael Shaunnessy, age 58
Chief Design and Construction Officer and Director, Robert H. Baldwin, age 61, $1,500,000 total compensation
President and COO Luxor and Excalibur Resorts, Renee West
EVP Special Counsel-Litigation and Chief Diversity Officer, Phyllis A. James, age 59
SVP Public Affairs, Alan Feldman, age 53
EVP CFO and Treasurer, Daniel J. D'Arrigo, age 43, $500,000 total compensation
EVP and Chief Accounting Officer, Robert C. Selwood, age 56, $439,286 total compensation
President MGM Resorts International Development, Kenneth (Ken) Rosevear
SVP Taxes, Shawn T. Sani, age 46
President and CEO Hospitality, Gamal Aziz, age 55
SVP Sales and Marketing MGM Resorts Hospitality; SVP Sales and Marketing MGM Grand, David Van Kalsbeek
President and COO ARIA Hotel and Casino, Bill McBeath
President and COO MGM Grand Las Vegas, Scott Sibella
President and COO Regional Operations, George P. Corchis Jr.
President and COO Bellagio, Randy Morton
President and COO New York-New York Hotel & Casino, Cynthia Kiser Murphy, age 54
EVP and Chief Administrative Officer, Aldo Manzini, age 48, $500,000 total compensation
VP Diversity and Community Affairs, Debra Nelson
President and COO Monte Carlo Resort & Casino, Anton Nikodemus
SVP and CFO ARIA Hotel and Casino, Jon Corchis
VP and CFO Bellagio, Mike Longi
VP and CFO Beau Rivage Resort, Jorge Perez
EVP Global Development MGM Resorts Hospitality, Michael Evans
EVP General Counsel and Secretary, John M. McManus, age 44
VP Strategic Sourcing, Mark Stolarczyk
Director Global Security MGM Resorts, Tom Lozich
President and COO The Mirage Resort, Felix Rappaport
President and COO Circus Circus Las Vegas, Don Thrasher
EVP Corporate Strategy and Special Counsel, William M. (Bill) Scott IV, age 51, $152,528 total compensation
SVP and Corporate Controller, Rick Arpin, age 39
General Manager Circus Circus Reno, Tony Mavrides
General Manager MGM Grand Detroit, Steve Zanella
SVP Capital Markets and Strategy, James A. Freeman, age 43
SVP Human Resources, Michelle DiTondo
VP Treasury, Pat Murphy
EVP Operations, Christopher Nordling, age 51
Director, Anthony L. Mandekic, age 71
Chief Design and Construction Officer and Director, Robert H. Baldwin, age 61
Director, Willie D. Davis, age 77
Director, Roland A. Hernandez, age 54
Director, Melvin B. Wolzinger, age 91
Director, Alexis M. Herman, age 64
Director, Daniel J. (Dan) Taylor, age 55
Director, Rose E. McKinney-James, age 60
Director, William A. (Bill) Bible, age 67
Director, Burton M. Cohen, age 88
Auditors: Deloitte&ToucheLLP

LOCATIONS

HQ: MGM Resorts International
3600 Las Vegas Blvd. South, Las Vegas NV 89109
Phone: 702-693-7120 **Fax:** 810-342-7090
Web: www.citizensonline.com

2011 Sales

	$ mil.	% of total
Wholly owned domestic resorts	5,892	75
MGM China	1,535	20
Corporate & other	421	5
Total	**7,849**	**100**

PRODUCTS/OPERATIONS

2011 Sales

	$ mil.	% of total
Casino	4,003	47
Non-casino		
Rooms	1,547	18
Food & beverage	1,425	17
Entertainment retail & other	1,556	18
Adjustments	(683.4)	
Total	**7,849**	**100**

Selected Properties

Nevada
Las Vegas
Bellagio
Circus Circus
CityCenter (50%)
Excalibur
Luxor
Mandalay Bay Resort & Casino
MGM Grand
The Mirage
Monte Carlo
New York-New York
Reno
Circus Circus Reno
Silver Legacy (50%; Reno NV)
Other
Railroad Pass (Henderson)
Gold Strike (Jean)
Other US
Beau Rivage (Biloxi MS)
Gold Strike (Tunica County MS)
MGM Grand Detroit
China
MGM Grand Macau (51%; Macau)

COMPETITORS

Boyd Gaming
Caesars Entertainment
Galaxy Entertainment
Las Vegas Sands
Pinnacle Entertainment
Rio All-Suite Hotel & Casino
Riviera Holdings
Sands China
SJM
Star City
Station Casinos
Stratosphere
Tropicana Entertainment
Trump Resorts
Wynn Resorts

HISTORICAL FINANCIALS

Company Type: Public

Income Statement FYE: December 31

	REVENUE ($ mil.)	NET INCOME ($ mil.)	NET PROFIT MARGIN	EMPLOYEES
12/11	7,849	3,114	39.7%	61,000
12/10	6,019	(1,437)	—	61,000
12/09	5,978	(1,291)	—	62,000
12/08	7,208	(855)	—	61,000
12/07	7,691	1,584	20.6%	67,400
Annual Growth	0.5%	18.4%	—	(2.5%)

2011 Year-End Financials

Debt ratio: 48.51%
Return on equity: 51.17%
Cash ($ mil.): 1,865
Current ratio: 161.21
Long-term debt ($ mil.): 13,470
No. of shares (mil.): 488
Dividends
Yield: —
Payout: —
Market value ($ mil.): 5,099

	STOCK PRICE ($) FY Close	P/E High	P/E Low	PER SHARE ($) Earnings	Dividends	Book Value
12/11	10.43	3	1	5.62	0.00	12.45
12/10	14.85	—	—	(3.19)	0.00	6.14
12/09	9.12	—	—	(3.41)	0.00	8.77
12/08	13.76	—	—	(3.06)	0.00	14.37
12/07	84.02	18	10	5.31	0.00	20.63
Annual Growth	(40.6%)	—	—	1.4%	—	(11.9%)

Micron Technology Inc.

Don't let Micron Technology's name mislead you: The circuits on its chips are well under one micron across but the company is one of the largest memory chip makers in the world. It makes DRAM (Dynamic Random Access Memory) NAND Flash and NOR Flash memory and other memory technologies. The company sells to customers in networking and storage consumer electronics and mobile telecommunications but the bulk of its sales are in the computer market. Intel and Hewlett-Packard are leading customers. Micron has manufacturing plants in Asia Europe and the US. About two-thirds of sales come from the Asia/Pacific region.

HISTORY

Micron Technology was founded in 1978 by twins Joe and Ward Parkinson and colleague Doug Pitman in the basement of a dentist's office. They started it as a semiconductor design firm but dreamed of manufacturing their own chips. In

1980 they persuaded several local businessmen including J. R. Simplot and Allen Noble to provide financial backing. They built their own production facility and in 1982 sold their first DRAM products.

Micron went public in 1984. The following year Japanese chip makers began dumping chips on the US market to capture market share causing huge losses for US DRAM makers. Micron filed an antidumping petition with the International Trade Commission and in 1986 the US and Japan agreed to a semiconductor trade pact to curb dumping.

By 1988 a shortage of memory chips had developed and Micron cashed in. The company began to diversify into SRAM (static random-access memory) chips and other add-in memory products for PCs. (The company wound down its SRAM product line in 2003 in the face of a dire industry slump.)

In the 1990s Micron expanded into PC manufacturing in part to soften the impact of the volatile cycles of the memory chip industry. It bought PC manufacturer ZEOS in 1995 merging it with two other Micron units to form Micron Electronics (later Interland and then Web.com prior to its 2007 acquisition by Website Pros) which it took public that year.

Also in 1995 Micron CEO and co-founder Joe Parkinson left the company after a clash with Simplot. Steve Appleton who had started as a production operator in 1983 became the new CEO. In early 1996 an internal power struggle triggered by longtime director Noble resulted in Appleton's ouster. But within a few days as several executives loyal to Appleton threatened to revolt Simplot wooed the CEO back. Noble resigned.

In 1998 Micron bought the memory chip business of Texas Instruments (TI) including plants in Texas Italy and Singapore. The complex deal made TI Micron's largest shareholder –it owned 15% of the company at the time –until TI sold off its remaining shares in Micron late in 2003.

In 1999 Micron sold its display division to flat-panel display maker PixTech; it received a 30% stake in PixTech (which folded in 2002). Later in 1999 Micron announced deals making it the primary supplier of memory chips for PC makers Compaq and Gateway. Also that year it acquired Rendition a designer of graphics chips as a part of its strategy to enter the logic chip business. The initial flagship project based on Rendition's technology was phased out in 2000 though Micron went ahead with development of other embedded chipsets –designed for use with AMD's Athlon microprocessor –using Rendition designs.

In 2001 the company acquired full ownership of Japan-based DRAM maker KMT Semiconductor when it bought out joint venture partner Kobe Steel for about $350 million. (KMT was subsequently renamed Micron Japan Ltd.)

Later in 2001 subsidiary Micron Electronics underwent a major overhaul when it sold its MicronPC business (now MPC Computers) to Gores Technology Group (now The Gores Group) and its SpecTek DRAM reselling business to parent Micron Technology. Micron Electronics then acquired Web hosting company Interland and took its name. The deal reduced Micron Technology's stake in the company from 61% to about 40% –a stake that Micron later gave to the not-for-profit Micron Technology Foundation. (Micron also gave up its two seats on Interland's board.)

Also that year the company acquired Photobit a small developer of CMOS image sensors an image-capturing chip that would become widely used in camera phones and digital still cameras among other uses. The acquisition launched Micron into a new semiconductor business line that would help the company withstand the volatile cycles of the memory chip business.

At the end of 2001 Micron struck a surprise deal with Toshiba to acquire the Japanese giant's Dominion Semiconductor unit in Virginia. (The deal was closed in 2002; Micron paid about $300 million in cash and stock for Dominion.)

In late 2001 and early 2002 Micron and rival Hynix Semiconductor engaged in round after round of negotiations about Micron's possible acquisition of some or all of Hynix's chip lines. In April 2002 the companies finally announced a complex provisional agreement for Micron to acquire Hynix's memory operations and invest in its other lines; a week later though Hynix's board of directors canceled the deal.

The company used a strong balance sheet to grow capacity during the steep industry swoon of the early 21st century but also stumbled a bit with slow product introductions. Micron surprised the industry in 2002 by announcing an agreement to buy the DRAM operations of Toshiba. The Toshiba purchase which cost Micron about $300 million in cash and stock saddled Micron with too much production capacity in the midst of an especially soft DRAM market. Micron rose on improved industry conditions after the chip industry slump ended in 2003 and returned to black ink by 2004.

In 2004 Intel made a $450 million investment in Micron giving the chip giant rights to a 5% ownership stake in the company.

In early 2006 Micron merged its mobile memory and systems memory business units into one memory products group responsible for NAND flash memory DRAM and specialty memory devices. The company also paid nearly $5 million to acquire a wafer fabrication facility in Nampa Idaho from ZiLOG. Micron planned to use the fab to make image sensor chips for camera phones digital still cameras and machine vision equipment among other applications.

In mid-2006 Micron acquired flash memory maker Lexar Media for about $850 million. The Lexar acquisition bolstered Micron's position in NAND flash memory the type of memory found in many MP3 players (such as the iPod nano and the iPod shuffle) digital still cameras and other portable electronics.

Also that year Photronics formed a joint venture with Micron Technology called MP Mask Technology Center. The memory chip manufacturer took ownership of slightly more than half of MP Mask. The JV would operate Micron's mask shop in Boise Idaho. The two companies built a facility called US NanoFab in Boise to conduct R&D on advanced technology in photomasks with Photronics contributing between $100 million and $150 million toward construction and equipping of the facility.

In late 2006 Micron bolstered its product portfolio in CMOS image sensors chips that are used in camera phones digital still cameras and other applications by acquiring the imaging sensor business of Avago Technologies. The company paid around $53 million and hired about 90 employees from Avago as part of the transaction.

Micron moved into the market for solid-state drives based on NAND flash memory with the rollout of its RealSSD product line in late 2007. The line was aimed at data storage applications in notebook computers enterprise computer servers and data networks. Its embedded USB drives can store from 1GB to 8GB while its 1.8-inch and 2.5-inch SSDs can hold from 8GB to 64GB. The introduction of RealSSD moved Micron into competition with manufacturers of hard-disk drives such as Hitachi Global Storage Seagate Technology and Western Digital. While HDDs were generally cheaper than SSDs the continually falling price of NAND flash made SSDs more price-competitive.

After months of speculation that the company would spin off its CMOS image sensor business Micron in 2008 launched a separate identity for the business as a division called Aptina Imaging. Image sensors were used in camera phones digital still cameras and high-definition video cameras among other applications. Micron was the leading supplier of CMOS image sensors in the world; the product line accounted for 11% of its sales (the rest was memory chips).

The volatile semiconductor market hit a cyclical downturn in 2008 and a global economic downturn followed in 2009 making the year particularly painful for chip makers. Responding to rapidly falling prices for DRAMs and NAND flash memory devices due to oversupply in the global market and declining customer demand Micron reduced its workforce by about 20% and phased out production of 200mm wafers at its Boise plant. The company also cut executive salaries by 20% and suspended its performance-based bonus plan for officers. Micron CEO Steve Appleton who is known to fly stunt jets for fun has steered Micron through the wild cycles of the memory chip market with an intense focus on cost control. Appleton took an additional 10% reduction in his base salary for 2009.

Furthering its non-memory ambitions in 2009 Micron entered the microdisplay market through its acquisition of Displaytech a designer of display panels and modules based on ferroelectric liquid crystal on silicon technology which is manufactured with a CMOS process on a single chip. The microdisplays marketed by Micron can be used in head-mounted display products or embedded in mobile phones to work as small projectors. The company has touted the integrated approach taken with the product which doesn't require any companion devices as digital micromirror devices do.

The company has also ventured into the solar market since photovoltaic production processes are similar to semiconductor production. In late 2009 Micron and Australia-based Origin Energy established a joint venture that develops and manufactures photovoltaic solar panels.

Also in 2009 Micron sold a 65% interest in its Aptina Imaging (imaging sensors) business to Riverwood Capital and TPG Capital for about $35 million; Micron retained a 35% equity stake in Aptina. The transaction allows Aptina and Micron to focus on their respective core businesses while retaining their ties in manufacturing marketing and product development. A portion of the buyers' 65% stake was in convertible preferred shares with a liquidation preference over common shares which resulted in Micron's ownership in Aptina's common stock to climb to 64% in 2011.

Longtime CEO Steve Appleton died unexpectedly in February 2012. He was replaced by president and COO Mark Durcan who was also named a director. Robert Switz a director since 2006 was named chairman. Sales VP Mark Adams was appointed president of the company.

EXECUTIVES

VP Corporate Development, Michael W. Sadler, age 54, $348,789 total compensation

VP Information Systems, James E. (Ed) Mahoney

Assistant Secretary, Jan R. Reimer

VP Backend Manufacturing; President Micron Italy Micron Japan and Micron Puerto Rico, Jay L. Hawkins, age 52, $263,631 total compensation

Chairman, Robert E. (Bob) Switz, age 65

CEO and Director, D. Mark Durcan, age 51, $462,231 total compensation

VP Investor Relations, Kipp A. Bedard, age 53
VP Legal Affairs General Counsel and Corporate Secretary, Roderic W. Lewis, age 57, $366,722 total compensation
VP Memory System Development, Dean A. Klein
VP Worldwide OEM Sales, Michael W. Bokan
VP Wireless Business Group, Mario Licciardello, age 70
VP Finance and CFO, Ronald C. (Ron) Foster, age 62, $375,923 total compensation
VP Worldwide Operations, Brian J. Shields, age 51
Treasurer, Philippe Morali, age 49
VP DRAM Solutions, Brian M. Shirley, age 43, $400,589 total compensation
VP DRAM Development, John F. Schreck
VP NAND Development, Frankie F. Roohparvar, age 48
Executive Director Micron Technology Foundation, Dee K. Mooney
Director Global Media Relations, Daniel Francisco
President, Mark W. Adams, age 48, $331,731 total compensation
VP Human Resources, Patrick T. (Pat) Otte, age 50
VP Process Development, Scott J. DeBoer
VP Worldwide Procurement and Chief Procurement Officer, Steven L (Steve) Thorsen Jr.
VP DRAM Marketing, Robert A. Feurle
Administrator Government Affairs, Jennafer R. Hopkins
Manager Idaho Government Affairs, Mike Reynoldson
Manager Utah Government Affairs, Stan Lockhart
Manager Virginia Government Affairs, Todd House
Investor Relations, Ivan Donaldson
VP Embedded Solutions, Glen W. Hawk, age 50
Media Relations Technology, Kirstin Bordner
Media Relations Corporate, Jill Thompson
Director, James W. (Jim) Bagley, age 73
Director, Mercedes Johnson, age 58
CEO and Director, D. Mark Durcan, age 51
Director, Robert L. (Bob) Bailey, age 55
Director, Lawrence N. (Larry) Mondry, age 52
Director, Teruaki Aoki, age 71
Auditors: PricewaterhouseCoopersLLP

LOCATIONS

HQ: Micron Technology Inc.
8000 S. Federal Way, Boise ID 83716-9632
Phone: 208-368-4000 **Fax:** 208-368-4435
Web: www.micron.com

2012 Sales

	$ mil.	% of total
Asia/Pacific		
China	2,936	36
Taiwan	1,022	12
Malaysia	546	7
Other countries	1,241	15
US	1,262	15
Europe	827	10
Other	400	5
Total	**8,234**	**100**

PRODUCTS/OPERATIONS

2012 Sales

	$ mil.	% of total
DRAM Solutions Group	2,691	33
NAND Solutions Group	2,853	35
Wireless Solutions Group	1,184	14
Embedded Solutions Group	1,054	13
Other	452	5
Total	**8,234**	**100**

2012 Sales

	$ mil.	% of total
DRAM	3,178	39
NAND Flash	3,627	44
NOR Flash	977	12
Other	452	5
Total	**8,234**	**100**

Semiconductor Products
Dynamic random-access memories (DRAMs)
Direct Rambus DRAMs (RDRAMs)
Synchronous DRAMs (SDRAMs)
Double data rate synchronous DRAMs (DDR SDRAMs)
Flash memory devices
Memory modules
Photomasks

COMPETITORS

Atmel
Cypress Semiconductor
Elpida Memory
Integrated Device Technology
Kingston Technology
Mosel Vitelic
Nanya
PNY Technologies
Quantum Corporation
Rambus
Samsung Electronics
SanDisk
Seagate Technology
Sharp Corp.
SK Hynix
SMART Modular Technologies
Spansion
Toshiba Semiconductor & Storage Products
Viking Modular Solutions
Western Digital

HISTORICAL FINANCIALS

Company Type: Public

Income Statement FYE: August 30

	REVENUE ($ mil.)	NET INCOME ($ mil.)	NET PROFIT MARGIN	EMPLOYEES
08/12*	8,234	(1,032)	—	27,400
09/11	8,788	167	1.9%	26,100
09/10	8,482	1,850	21.8%	25,900
09/09	4,803	(1,835)	—	18,200
08/08	5,841	(1,619)	—	22,800
Annual Growth	9.0%	—	—	4.7%

*Fiscal year change

2012 Year-End Financials

Debt ratio: 23.67%
Return on equity: (-13.40)%
Cash ($ mil.): 2,459
Current ratio: 256.71
Long-term debt ($ mil.): 3,038
No. of shares (mil.): 1,017
Dividends
Yield: —
Payout: —
Market value ($ mil.): 6,289

	STOCK PRICE ($) FY Close	P/E High/Low		PER SHARE ($) Earnings	Dividends	Book Value
08/12*	6.18	—	—	(1.04)	0.00	7.57
09/11	5.74	69	31	0.17	0.00	8.61
09/10	6.83	5	3	1.85	0.00	8.06
09/09	7.17	—	—	(2.29)	0.00	5.48
08/08	4.29	—	—	(2.10)	0.00	8.12
Annual Growth	9.6%	—	—	—	—	(1.7%)

*Fiscal year change

Microsoft Corporation

Microsoft's ambitions are anything but small. The world's #1 software company develops and sells a variety of products used by consumers and businesses. Its core products are the ubiquitous Windows PC operating system and the Office business productivity application suite that are sold in part through PC makers such as Acer Lenovo Dell Hewlett-Packard and Toshiba who pre-install the software on devices. Microsoft also sells directly online and through resellers. Other products include enterprise applications (Microsoft Dynamics) server and storage software video game consoles (Xbox) and digital music players (Zune). The company also makes mobile phone software (Windows Phone 7).

HISTORY

Bill Gates founded Microsoft (originally named Micro-soft) in 1975 after dropping out of Harvard at age 19 and teaming with high school friend Paul Allen to sell a version of the programming language BASIC. While Gates was at Harvard the pair wrote the language for Altair the first commercial microcomputer. The company was born in an Albuquerque New Mexico hotel room and grew by modifying BASIC for other computers.

Gates moved Microsoft to his native Seattle in 1979 and began developing software that let others write programs. The modern PC era dawned in 1980 when IBM chose Microsoft to write the operating system for its new machines. Although hesitant at first Gates bought QDOS short for "quick and dirty operating system" for $50000 from a Seattle programmer renaming it the Microsoft Disk Operating System (MS-DOS).

Allen fell ill with Hodgkin's disease and left Microsoft in 1983. In the mid-1980s Microsoft introduced Windows a graphics-based version of MS-DOS that borrowed from rival Apple's Macintosh system. The company went public in 1986 and Gates became the industry's first billionaire a year later. Microsoft introduced Windows NT in 1993 to compete with the UNIX operating system popular on mainframes and large networks.

The early 1990s brought monopoly charges from inside and outside the industry. In 1995 antitrust concerns scotched a $1.5 billion acquisition of personal finance software maker Intuit.

When the Internet began transforming business practices holdout Gates at last embraced the medium; the Microsoft Network (MSN) debuted in 1995. That year Microsoft licensed the Java Web programming language from Sun and introduced its Internet Explorer Web browser. It also launched Expedia an online travel site.

In 1997 Sun sued Microsoft for allegedly creating an incompatible version of Java; Microsoft countersued. (The ongoing court battle settled by Microsoft in 2001 for $20 million prevented the company from releasing new Java tools or accessing any of Sun's advances.) Microsoft also purchased WebTV Networks for $425 million.

The US Justice Department backed by 18 states filed antitrust charges in 1998 against the software giant claiming that it stifled Internet browser competition and limited consumer choice. Gates turned over the president's job to longtime Microsoft executive Steve Ballmer.

In 1999 Microsoft agreed to invest $5 billion for a minority stake in AT&T as part of that company's move to acquire cable operator MediaOne. In addition Microsoft bought Windows-based technical drawing software specialist Visio for $1.3 billion and sold a stake in Expedia to the public.

Gates named Ballmer CEO in 2000. Gates who had held the CEO spot since the company's founding remained chairman and added the title of chief software architect.

A federal judge's ruling later that year that Microsoft used its monopoly powers to violate antitrust laws left the prospect of two (smaller) Microsofts a decision the company aggressively appealed. (The initial ruling to split Microsoft into two companies was later struck down leading to a settlement between the company and the US Justice Department. Under the terms of the settlement Microsoft agreed to uniformly license its Windows operating systems cease to offer exclusive contracts with manufacturers and allow competing software to be included with its operating systems.)

In 2001 Microsoft completed the acquisition of longtime partner Great Plains Software a specialist in applications for midsized and small businesses in a $1.1 billion deal. A federal appeals court struck down the initial ruling to break up Microsoft leading to a tentative settlement (pending approval by the 18 US states involved in the trial) between the company and the US Justice Department. The settlement would leave Microsoft intact but impose restrictions on the company's licensing policies for its operating systems.

Netscape Communications filed suit in 2002 against Microsoft seeking unspecified damages and injunctions against the company's alleged antitrust actions. Later that year the company transferred its controlling stake in Expedia to InterActiveCorp (formerly USA Interactive) in exchange for stock. The company also acquired enterprise software provider Navision for about $1.5 billion.

Microsoft settled the suit with Netscape in 2003 agreeing to pay AOL $750 million as part of a larger settlement that includes AOL licensing Microsoft's Internet Explorer browser and its digital media technology.

In part due to increasing demands from shareholders to explore alternatives for its evergrowing cash hoard in 2003 the company declared its first-ever dividend for common stock. Microsoft also eliminated stock options instead moving to a system of distributing shares of its stock directly to employees.

In 2004 the company announced plans to spend up to $75 billion of its cash reserves over four years including boosting its dividend payments and repurchasing up to $30 billion of its own stock.

Microsoft announced late in 2005 a reorganization designed to streamline its decision making and speed up execution across its divisions. Its units include Microsoft Platform Products and Services (Windows Client Group Server and Tools Group MSN) Microsoft Business (Information Worker Group Microsoft Business Solutions) and Entertainment and Devices (Home and Entertainment Group Mobile and Embedded Devices Group).

In 2005 it acquired collaboration software maker Groove Networks (founded by Lotus Notes developer Ray Ozzie) anti-virus security provider Sybari Software email security developer FrontBridge Technologies and identity management software provider Alacris. Microsoft also bought file synchronization specialist FolderShare and media-streams.com a developer of VoIP technology.

Early in 2006 Microsoft acquired Apptimum a developer of software used to transfer data between computers and Onfolio an Internet content collection and organization technology provider. In 2007 the company acquired speech-recognition software developer Tellme Networks. Other smaller acquisitions included Caligari YaData Kidaro Komoku Farecast Powerset and Greenfield Online.

In an attempt to keep pace with Google and other competitors in a consolidating online advertising and search market the company acquired aQuantive for about $6 billion in 2007. Later in the year Microsoft reached an agreement to acquire a minority stake in social networking site Facebook for $240 million; the deal expanded the pre-existing advertising partnership between the two companies. In 2008 the company moved to beef up its enterprise search offerings by purchasing Fast Search & Transfer ASA (FAST) for about $1.2 billion; FAST specializes in Internet search technology and business intelligence applications for enterprises.

Microsoft put many of its legal woes from antitrust issues behind it from 2004 to 2008 reaching major settlement agreements with Netscape (paying the company about $750 million) Sun Microsystems ($1.6 billion in addition to royalty payments on certain technologies) Novell ($536 million to settle a suit tied to Novell's NetWare software) Gateway ($150 million) IBM ($775 million and extending $75 million in credit toward Microsoft software deployment) and RealNetworks ($761 million in cash and promotions).

In 2007-08 the company also partnered with mobile devices makers such as Hewlett-Packard and Motorola (which later became Motorola Mobility) to develop handheld computers and mobile phones that utilize Microsoft Windows Mobile and Windows Media software. As part of that push Microsoft acquired ScreenTonic a provider of mobile advertising products and services. It also purchased chat specialist Parlano and online mapping services provider Multimap as well as Danger (maker of the software for T-Mobile's Sidekick devices) in early 2008.

In 2008 Microsoft tried repeatedly to acquire Yahoo! but was ultimately rebuffed; the two companies would instead sign a deal in 2009 to combine their search operations. Yahoo!'s board of directors refused multiple offers from Microsoft (including proposals to buy certain parts of Yahoo!) insisting that the offers undervalued the company.

Microsoft's primary interest in acquiring Yahoo! was to bulk up its search offerings to better compete with search leader Google. Amid persisting rumors that Yahoo! still might give in and sell its search business to the company in 2009 Microsoft overhauled and rebranded its own search business as a new search engine called bing.com replacing its Live Search product. Shortly after the launch of bing.com Yahoo! and Microsoft finally came to terms on a 10-year agreement in which Microsoft took over the search engine responsibilities on Yahoo! with Yahoo! receiving 88% of all search-related advertising revenue for the first five years of the deal.

Microsoft introduced a new version of its PC operating system software Windows 7 in 2009. It followed the beleaguered Windows Vista which drew much fire from critics and reviewers due to compatibility issues among other problems following its release in 2007. Vista largely went on to surpass Microsoft's revenue target becoming the second most widely used OS in the world at one point.

In October 2012 Microsoft acquired mobile security provider Kansas-based PhoneFactor for an undisclosed sum. The purchase will help Microsoft bring effective and easy-to-use multifactor authentication to thier cloud services and on-premises applications.

EXECUTIVES

Corporate VP Finance and Administration and Chief Accounting Officer, Frank H. Brod
Chief Research and Strategy Officer, Craig J. Mundie, age 63, $377,707 total compensation
Corporate VP Microsoft Office Data and Business Intelligence, Derek J. Burney, age 49
President Interactive Entertainment Business, Don A. Mattrick, age 48
SVP Windows Development, Jon S. DeVaan, age 51
CEO and Director, Steven A. (Steve) Ballmer, age 56, $670,000 total compensation
Corporate VP Media and Entertainment Group, Blair Westlake
Corporate VP and CFO Windows and Windows Live, Tami Reller
Chairman, William H. (Bill) Gates III, age 57, $616,667 total compensation
Corporate VP Health Solutions Group, Peter M. Neupert, age 55
Corporate VP Microsoft Business Solutions Sales Marketing and Operations, Michael Park
Corporate VP Internal Audit, Melvin L. Flowers, age 59
Corporate VP and Chief Advisor to the COO; Chairman Emerging Markets, Orlando Ayala, age 56
Chief Marketing Officer Interactive Entertainment Business, Yusuf Mehdi
SVP Research, Richard F. (Rick) Rashid, age 60
President Windows and Windows Live Division, Steven J. Sinofsky, age 46
President Microsoft International, Jean-Philippe Courtois, age 53
Chief Technical Strategy Officer, Eric D. Rudder
SVP Developer Division, Sivaramakichenane (Soma) Somasegar
Corporate VP Strategic and Emerging Business Development, Dan'l Lewin
COO, B. Kevin Turner, age 47, $645,000 total compensation
SVP Strategy and Partnerships, Henry P. (Hank) Vigil, age 53
President Server and Tools Business, Satya Nadella, age 44
Corporate VP Corporate Communications, Frank X. Shaw
President Microsoft Business Solutions Division, Kirill Tatarinov
Chief People Officer, Lisa E. Brummel, age 52
President Microsoft Office Division, Kurt DelBene, age 52
SVP Windows Live, Chris Jones
Corporate VP Customer and Partner Advocacy, Richard (Rich) Kaplan
Corporate VP Worldwide Retail Sales and Marketing Group Entertainment and Devices Division, Mitchell L. (Mitch) Koch
SVP Business Platform Division, Ted Kummert
EVP Legal and Corporate Affairs and General Counsel, Bradford L. (Brad) Smith, age 53
Corporate VP Windows Test Sustaining Engineering Operations, Grant George
Corporate VP Deputy General Counsel Law and Corporate Affairs Department, Mary E. Snapp
Corporate VP Business and Marketing Group North America, Allison L. Watson
President, Andrew (Andy) Lees, age 47
Corporate VP Israel Research and Development, Moshe Lichtman
Corporate VP Microsoft Online, David Thompson
President Skype Division, Tony Bates
Corporate VP Worldwide Small and Midmarket Solutions and Partners Group, Vahe Torossian
Corporate VP Human Resources for Sales Marketing and Services Group Worldwide, Susan E. (Sue) Bevington
Corporate VP; Chairman and CEO Microsoft Greater China Region, Simon L. K. Leung
Corporate VP Startup Business Group, Amit Mital
Corporate VP and Deputy General Counsel Litigation Group, Tom Burt

SVP Windows Web Services, Antoine Leblond
Corporate VP Communications Sector, Austen Mulinder
Chief Marketing Officer and SVP Consumer Channels and Central Marketing Group, Chris Capossela
Corporate VP Consumer and Online, Darren R. Huston, age 46
Corporate VP Windows Phone Marketing, Achim Berg, age 46
Corporate VP Windows Live User Experience Group, Steve Liffick
Corporate VP, Ya-Qin Zhang, age 46
Corporate VP and Treasurer, George Zinn
Corporate VP US Enterprise and Partner Group, Ron Markezich
Corporate VP Directory Access and Information Protection, Lee R. Nackman
President Online Services Division, Qi Lu, age 50
President North America Sales and Marketing, Robert H. Youngjohns, age 60
Corporate VP; President and CEO Microsoft Japan, Yasuyuki Higuchi
Corporate VP Search Product Development, Harry Shum
Corporate VP and CFO Sales Marketing and Services Group, Alain Crozier
Corporate VP Global Marketing Interactive Entertainment Business, Michael Delman
Corporate VP Microsoft Research Connections, Tony Hey
Corporate VP Microsoft Services, Kathleen Hogan
Corporate VP Interactive Entertainment Business Hardware, Todd Holmdahl
Corporate VP Office Lync and Speech Group, Gurdeep Singh Pall
Corporate VP Interactive Entertainment Business, David Treadwell
Corporate VP TV and Service Business Interactive Entertainment Business, Tom Gibbons
Corporate VP US Small and Mid-market Solutions and Partners, Phil Sorgen
CFO, Peter S. Klein, age 50, $437,508 total compensation
Corporate VP and Director Windows Phone Program Management, Joe Belfiore
Corporate VP Microsoft Exchange, Rajesh Jha
Corporate VP Windows Experience, Julie Larson-Green
Corporate VP and CFO Online Services Division, Mindy Mount
Corporate VP Business Platform Marketing Group, Eduardo Rosini
Corporate VP Office Authoring Applications Microsoft Business Division, Jeanne Sheldon
Corporate VP Office Business Platform Microsoft Business Division, Jeff Teper
Corporate VP Trustworthy Computing Engineering Excellence and Environmental Sustainability, Scott Charney
Area VP Western Europe and VP Microsoft Corporate, Klaus Holse Andersen
Corporate VP and CIO, Tony Scott, age 60
Corporate VP Developer and Platform Evangelism Group, Walid Abu-Hadba
Corporate VP Original Equipment Manufacturer Division, Steve Guggenheimer
Corporate VP .NET Developer Platform, Scott Guthrie
Corporate VP Manufacturing Supply Chain Information and Services Interactive Entertainment Business, Brian Tobey
Corporate VP Microsoft Dynamics ERP Research and Development Microsoft Business Solutions, Hal Howard
Corporate VP and Deputy General Counsel Legal and Corporate Affairs, Nancy J. Anderson
Corporate VP Advertising and Online Business, Frank Holland
Corporate VP Bing Mobile, Erik Jorgensen
Corporate VP Server and Cloud Platform Marketing, Robert (Bob) Kelly
Corporate VP Core Search Program Management, Brian MacDonald
Corporate VP and Deputy General Counsel Global Corporate Affairs, Pamela S. Passman
Corporate VP Human Resources Talent and Organization Capability Group, Scott Pitasky
Corporate VP Server and Tools Marketing, Robert Wahbe
Corporate VP Worldwide Licensing and Pricing, Joe Matz
Corporate VP Windows Phone Division, Terry Myerson
Corporate VP Compensation Benefits and Human Resources Operations, J. Ritchie
Corporate VP Worldwide Partner Group, Jon Roskill
Corporate VP Advertiser and Publisher Solutions Group, Rik van der Kooi
Corporate VP Microsoft Game Studios, Phil Spencer
Corporate VP Retail Stores, David Porter
Corporate VP Xbox Live, Marc Whitten
Chief Creative Officer, Gayle Troberman
Chief Strategy Officer, David Webster
Corporate VP Management and Security Division, Brad Anderson
Corporate VP Technology Policy and Strategy and eXtreme Computing Group, Dan Reed
Corporate VP MSN, Ted Cahall
Corporate VP Strategy and Business and Marketing Operations Worldwide Sales Marketing and Services Group, Peter Cray
Corporate VP Advertising Platform Development, Don Gagne
Corporate VP Customer Service and Support, Barbara Gordon
Corporate VP and Deputy General Counsel, Horacio E. Gutierrez
Corporate VP Internet Explorer, Dean Hachamovitch
Corporate VP and CFO Microsoft Business Division, Amy Hood
Corporate VP Office Program Management, P.J. Hough
Corporate VP and Deputy General Counsel Litigation Group, David Howard
Corporate VP Specialized Devices and Accessories Group, Rusty Jeffress
Corporate VP Office Communications and Mobile Experiences Microsoft Business Division, William Kennedy
Corporate VP Microsoft Office Division Product Management Group, Kirk Koenigsbauer
Corporate VP Server and Cloud Division, Bill Laing
Corporate VP Office Product Management Group, Takeshi Numoto
Corporate VP Office Test, Tara Roth
Corporate VP Advertising and Commerce Platform, Rajat Taneja
Corporate VP Visual Studio, Jason Zander
General Manager Investor Relations, Bill Koefoed
Chairman India, Bhaskar Pramanik
Corporate VP Windows Planning Hardware and PC Ecosystem, Michael Angiulo
Corporate VP Business Platform Cloud Services, Tom Casey
Corporate VP Database Systems Group Microsoft SQL Server, Quentin Clark
Corporate VP Test and Systems Engineering Windows Live, Arthur de Haan
Corporate VP Ad Platform Online Services Division, David Ku
SVP Global Foundation Services, Dayne Sampson
Corporate VP and Director Development Windows Phone Engineering, Henry Sanders
Corporate VP Hardware Architecture Interactive Entertainment Business, Ilan Spillinger
General Manager and Chief Procurement Officer, Chris Drews
Director, Charles H. (Chuck) Noski, age 60
Director, Dina Dublon, age 59
Director, Raymond V. Gilmartin, age 69
CEO and Director, Steven A. (Steve) Ballmer, age 56
Director, Stephen J. (Steve) Luczo, age 55
Director, John W. Thompson, age 62
Director, David F. Marquardt, age 63
Director, Reed Hastings, age 51
Director, Helmut Panke, age 66
Director, Maria M. Klawe, age 60
Auditors: Deloitte&ToucheLLP

LOCATIONS

HQ: Microsoft Corporation
1 Microsoft Way, Redmond WA 98052-6399
Phone: 425-882-8080 **Fax:** 425-936-7329
Web: www.microsoft.com

2012 Sales

	$ mil.	% of total
US	38,846	53
Other countries	34,877	47
Total	**73,723**	**100**

PRODUCTS/OPERATIONS

2012 Sales

	$ mil.	% of total
Microsoft Business	23,963	32
Windows & Windows Live	18,818	26
Server & tools	18,696	25
Entertainment & services	9,585	13
Online services	2,934	4
Total	**73,723**	**100**

Selected Products

Consumer software services and devices
- Xbox (video game console)
- Zune (digital media player)

Desktop applications
- Access (relational database management)
- Excel (integrated spreadsheet)
- FrontPage (website publishing)
- MS Office (business productivity software suite)
- Outlook (messaging and collaboration)
- PowerPoint (presentation graphics)
- Project (project scheduling and resource allocation)
- Word (word processing)

Enterprise software
- BackOffice (server software suite)
- Content Management Server (content management)
- Exchange Server (messaging server)
- Proxy Server (Internet gateway)
- Site Server (website management)
- SQL Server (database and data analysis management)
- Systems Management Server (centralized management)
- Visio (visualization and diagramming suite)

Selected Acquisitions

2012
- PhoneFactor (multifactor authentication software)

2010
- Canesta (3-D image sensors)
- Sentillion (healthcare software)

2009
- BigPark (online game developer)
- 3DV Systems (digital 3-D cameras)

2008
- Greenfield Online (online consumer data collection)
- DATAllegro (data storage devices)
- Powerset (semantic search software)
- MobiComp (mobile software)
- Navic Networks (TV advertising software)
- Kidaro (desktop virtualization software)

Fast Search & Transfer (enterprise search software)
Danger (mobile software)
Farecast (online airfare pricing technology)
Komoku (security software)
Rapt (advertising management software)
YaData (advertising software)
Caligari (3-D modeling and animation software)
2007
Multimap (online mapping services)
Parlano (messaging software)
aQuantive (digital advertising software and services)
ScreenTonic (mobile advertising software)
devBiz Business Solutions (application development software)
Tellme Networks (voice recognition services)

COMPETITORS

Adobe Systems	Nintendo
Amazon.com	Nokia
Apple Inc.	Novell
CA Inc.	Opera Software
EMC	Oracle
Google	Red Hat
Hewlett-Packard	salesforce.com
IBM	SAP
Logitech	Sony
Mozilla	Yahoo!

HISTORICAL FINANCIALS

Company Type: Public

Income Statement FYE: June 30

	REVENUE ($ mil.)	NET INCOME ($ mil.)	NET PROFIT MARGIN	EMPLOYEES
06/12	73,723	16,978	23.0%	94,000
06/11	69,943	23,150	33.1%	90,000
06/10	62,484	18,760	30.0%	89,000
06/09	58,437	14,569	24.9%	93,000
06/08	60,420	17,681	29.3%	91,000
Annual Growth	5.1%	(1.0%)	—	0.8%

2012 Year-End Financials

Debt ratio: 9.85%—
Return on equity: 25.58%
Cash ($ mil.): 6,938
Current ratio: 260.29
Long-term debt ($ mil.): 10,713
Dividends
Yield: —
Payout: 38.00%
Market value ($ mil.): —

	STOCK PRICE ($) FY Close	P/E High	P/E Low	PER SHARE ($) Earnings	Dividends	Book Value
06/12	30.59	16	12	2.00	0.00	7.92
06/11	26.00	11	8	2.69	0.61	6.82
06/10	23.01	15	11	2.10	0.52	5.33
06/09	23.77	17	9	1.62	0.50	4.44
06/08	27.51	20	14	1.87	0.43	3.97
Annual Growth	2.7%	—	—	1.7%	—	18.8%

Mohawk Industries, Inc.

Mohawk Industries doesn't mind being trampled under foot. The company is the second-largest maker of commercial and residential carpets rugs and other floor coverings in the US (after Shaw Industries) and one of the largest carpet makers in the world. It produces a range of broadloom carpets and rugs under such names as Mohawk Aladdin Durkan Karastan Lees and Bigelow. Mohawk's Dal-Tile International division is one of the US's largest makers of ceramic tile and stone flooring. Unilin's laminate and wood flooring and other wood products round out Mohawk's operations. The company sells its wares to carpet retailers home centers mass merchandisers department stores and dealers.

Geographic Reach

Mohawk Industries generates around 80% of its revenues in North America. It has manufacturing facilities located in Georgia Oklahoma North Carolina Mexico and Belgium.

Operations

Once focused exclusively on carpets and rugs Mohawk has evolved adapting itself to changing customer tastes and spending habits. The company now offers popular alternatives to carpet such as hardwood laminate and ceramic tile. It has also reached outside of its premium-priced portfolio by rolling out a do-it-yourself flooring line that mimics the elegant look of materials like marble or limestone without the coldness chipping or costly installation of real stone. Its breadth of operations is matched by its depth; Mohawk maintains a strong distribution and wide customer base (in addition to residential customers it serves government healthcare and educational institutions as well as corporate retail and public venues) which creates strong brand recognition.

Financial Analysis

Mohawk faces many obstacles including the downturn in US home remodeling and new construction markets as well as weak commercial real estate demand at home and abroad. Revenue levels have declined over the last three years but in 2011 total sales reached 5.4 billion an increase of 6% compared to 2010. After suffering a $5-plus million net loss in 2009 the company posted $185 million and $174 million in net income for 2010 and 2011 respectively. The overall improvement was attributed to a higher sales volume of around $143 million coupled with favorable foreign exchange rates and lower operating expenses. Cash generated from operations enabled Mohawk to pay down debt and fuel working capital.

Strategy

The company is looking to grow through acquisitions and joint ventures. After buying an Australian distribution business to add to its Unilin segment in 2011 the company acquired a 34% stake in a joint venture with China-based Sanfi Ceramics in 2010. The joint venture manufactures and distributes ceramic tile in that country a region which industry insiders see as the largest ceramic tile market in the world with growth forecast at 10% annually. Mohawk has also undertaken a series of restructuring initiatives aimed to optimize its manufacturing footprint and reduce its overhead costs including its workforce.

Ownership

Chairman and CEO Jeffrey Lorberbaum holds almost a 16% stake in Mohawk directly and additional ownership through his interest in Aladdin Partners which owns more than 12%.

HISTORY

Mohawk Carpet was an ailing unit of Mohasco until 1988 when division president David Kolb led an LBO to separate Mohawk from its parent and became CEO of the new company. Mohawk traces its origins to the Shuttleworth family who founded the company in Amsterdam New York in 1878 setting up their business with 14 second-hand looms imported from England. The company was incorporated as Shuttleworth Brothers in 1902. It introduced the popular Karnak carpet design in 1908.

The firm acquired carpet maker McLeary Wallin and Crouse and began to consolidate the fragmented carpet industry in the Northeast. The company renamed itself Mohawk Carpet Mills and was the only maker of a complete line of domestic carpets under the Wilton Axminster Velvet and Chenille styles. Over the next three decades the company pioneered a number of carpet industry firsts: the first texture design (Shuttlepoint) the first sculptured weave (Raleigh) and the first knitted carpet (Woven Interlock).

Mohawk Carpet Mills like the rest of the industry moved into synthetics such as nylon and acrylics during the late 1940s and early 1950s. The company merged with Alexander Smith in 1956 to form Mohasco Industries the largest carpet maker in the world at the time.

By 1980 the company was facing a fiercely competitive market. Mohasco had failed to keep up with changing fashions and was no longer the leading carpet maker. Allied Fibers veteran David Kolb was brought in to turn Mohasco's unprofitable Mohawk division around. He moved the company's headquarters to the carpet-making center of the US Georgia. Kolb began modernizing equipment and refocused the company on its high-margin carpet products and emphasized direct sales to retailers.

Kolb took Mohawk public in 1992 and began acquiring other carpet makers including Horizon Industries (carpet mills 1992) American Rug Craftsmen (household rugs and mats 1993) and Fieldcrest Cannon's Karastan and Bigelow divisions (carpets and rugs 1993).

In 1994 Mohawk bought Aladdin Mills then the fourth-largest carpet maker in the US. Jeffrey Lorberbaum son of Aladdin founder Alan Lorberbaum became Mohawk's president and COO.

The company's spending spree continued acquiring Galaxy Carpet Mills in 1995. In 1996 Mohawk added capacity at all its plants: The acquisition of Fiber One boosted Mohawk's annual polypropylene extrusion capacity by 40 million pounds and in 1997 Mohawk added approximately 100 million pounds of annual polypropylene extrusion capacity by acquiring certain assets of Diamond Rug. In 1998 Mohawk purchased American Weavers and floorcoverings maker World Carpets.

In 1999 the company paid $232 million for Image Industries a unit of Maxim Group that makes residential polyester carpet from recycled plastic bottles and $98 million for commercial carpet supplier Durkan Patterned Carpets. Mohawk entered the market for hardwood floors by introducing a product line in 2000. Also that year the company purchased the Wovens Division of Crown Crafts (woven throws bedspreads and coverlets). Lorberbaum succeeded Kolb as CEO in 2001.

Early in 2002 Mohawk acquired ceramic tile maker Dal-Tile International for $1.5 billion. Dal-Tile added nearly $1 billion in sales (or nearly a quarter of Mohawk's total revenues) and gave the company an automatic stronghold in the hard flooring business. Mohawk followed that up by acquiring bankrupt Burlington Industries' carpet division Lees Carpet for about $350 million in 2003. In 2005 Mohawk acquired Unilin Holding NV a European manufacturer of laminate flooring. The purchase price for Unilin which has about $1 billion in annual sales was $2.6 billion. Unilin not only diversified the company as a total flooring business but widened Mohawk's presence in the US and European marketplace.

In 2007 Mohawk added the wood flooring assets of Columbia Forest Products for $147 million. The deal which included three plants in the US and one in Malaysia built upon an established relationship; Columbia manufactures the wood flooring that Mohawk distributes.

Throughout 2008 and 2009 Mohawk was profusely pinched by the painful effects of the recession as demand in the overall construction sector tanked. It posted a staggering net loss of $1.4 billion for 2008 but after significant restructuring initiatives it shrunk its losses down to $5.5 million in 2009.

EXECUTIVES

Chairman President and CEO, Jeffrey S. Lorberbaum, age 57, $990,000 total compensation
COO and Director, W. Christopher (Chris) Wellborn, age 57, $850,000 total compensation
President Dal-Tile, John C. Turner Jr., age 56
VP General Counsel and Assistant Secretary, James T. Lucke, age 51
President Mohawk Flooring Business, Brian M. Carson
VP Finance and CFO, Frank H. Boykin, age 56, $525,000 total compensation
Secretary, Barbara M. Goetz
President Unilin, Bernard P. Thiers, age 56, $729,866 total compensation
Corporate Controller and Chief Accounting Officer, James F. Brunk, age 46
Director, Joseph A. Onorato, age 63
Director, David L. Kolb, age 73
Director, John F. Fiedler, age 73
COO and Director, W. Christopher (Chris) Wellborn, age 57
Director, Phyllis O. Bonanno, age 69
Director, Bruce C. Bruckmann, age 58
Director, Frans G. De Cock, age 69
Auditors: KPMGLLP

LOCATIONS

HQ: Mohawk Industries Inc.
160 S. Industrial Blvd., Calhoun GA 30701
Phone: 706-629-7721 **Fax:** 706-624-3825
Web: www.mohawkind.com

2011 Sales

	$ mil.	% of total
North America	4,619	82
Total	5,642	100

PRODUCTS/OPERATIONS

2011 Sales

	$ mil.	% of total
Mohawk	2,927	51
Unilin	1,344	23
Total	5,642	100

Selected Operations

Mohawk
- Bath rugs
- Blankets
- Carpets
- Carpet pad
- Ceramic tile
- Decorative throws and pillows
- Doormats
- Hardwood flooring
- Laminate flooring
- Resilient flooring
- Rugs
- Woven and tufted rugs

Dal-Tile
- Ceramic tile
- Glazed floor tile
- Glazed wall tile
- Glazed and unglazed ceramic mosaic tile
- Porcelain tile
- Quarry tile
- Stone products

Unilin
- Hardwood flooring
- Insulation panels
- Laminate flooring
- Roofing systems

Selected Brand Names

Mohawk
- Aladdin
- Bigelow Commercial
- Durkan
- Horizon
- Karastan
- Lees
- Merit
- Mohawk
- Mohawk Home

Dal-Tile
- American Olean
- Dal-Tile

Unilin
- Century Flooring
- Columbia Flooring
- Mohawk
- Quick-Step
- Universal Flooring

COMPETITORS

Armstrong World Industries
Beaulieu of America
Couristan
Dixie Group
Formica
Guilford Mills
Hollander Home Fashions
Interface Inc.
Mannington Mills
Perstorp
Shaw Industries
Tarkett Inc.
Wilsonart International

HISTORICAL FINANCIALS

Company Type: Public

Income Statement FYE: December 31

	REVENUE ($ mil.)	NET INCOME ($ mil.)	NET PROFIT MARGIN	EMPLOYEES
12/11	5,642	173	3.1%	26,200
12/10	5,319	185	3.5%	26,900
12/09	5,344	(5)	—	27,400
12/08	6,826	(1,458)	—	31,200
12/07	7,586	706	9.3%	36,200
Annual Growth	(7.1%)	(29.6%)	—	(7.8%)

2011 Year-End Financials

Debt ratio: 25.56%
Return on equity: 5.09%
Cash ($ mil.): 311
Current ratio: 217.75
Long-term debt ($ mil.): 1,200
No. of shares (mil.): 68
Dividends
Yield: —
Payout: —
Market value ($ mil.): 4,117

	STOCK PRICE ($) FY Close	P/E High/Low		PER SHARE ($) Earnings	Dividends	Book Value
12/11	59.85	27	16	2.52	0.00	49.66
12/10	56.76	24	16	2.65	0.00	47.67
12/09	47.60	—	—	(0.08)	0.00	46.74
12/08	42.97	—	—	(21.32)	0.00	46.09
12/07	74.40	10	7	10.32	0.00	68.86
Annual Growth	(5.3%)	—	—	(29.7%)	—	(7.8%)

Molina Healthcare Inc

Navigating the murky waters of federal health care plans is no easy feat but Molina Healthcare's mission is to help Medicaid and Medicare members find their way to health care. Its Health Plan segment arranges for the delivery of health services to some 1.8 million people who receive their care through Medicaid Medicare and other government-funded programs in 9 states. Its Medicaid Solutions segment provides business process outsourcing solutions to Medicaid agencies in five states for their Medicaid Management Information Systems (MMIS) the tool used to support administration of state health care entitlement programs. The family of founder C. David Molina controls the company through holdings and trusts.

Operations

A third segment of the company referred to as the direct delivery line of business consists of about 20 primary care community clinics primarily in California and other western US states. Molina manages three county-owned primary care community clinics through a contract with Fairfax County Virginia.

Financial Analysis

As the company remains concerned over state deficits it is keeping a close eye on its operations and ways to improve performance. Despite a 15% increase in earned premium revenues and improvements in its health plans segment in 2011 Molina's net income was $20.8 million a decrease of 66% over 2010 which was attributed to a $65 million impairment charge related to the expiration of the company's contract with the state of Missouri in mid-2012. The Missouri health plan had contributed premium revenue of about $230 million or 5% of total premium revenue in 2011 and held about 5% of the health plans segment's total membership.

Strategy

Molina grows in its existing markets by broadening its service areas and adding physicians to those provider networks. Additionally it looks to add new members by increasing its brand awareness through marketing and advertising campaigns.

In addition Molina enters new markets through acquisitions targeting entry into large markets with competitive provider communities. Molina's growth strategy also consists of opening additional primary care clinics in existing and new territories. The addition of more clinics helps Molina diversify its operations by expanding its involvement in the direct delivery of primary care. About 20% of Molina's California health plan membership is being served by its primary care clinics there.

Molina is preparing to meet health care reform changes by growing the direct delivery component of its business and developing additional community care clinics for some of its health plans during 2011. Components of the health care reform bill call for increased health insurance coverage and changes to the way government health plans are reimbursed (which could include significant decreases). Molina expects the requirements to cause a shortage in health care services.

Mergers & Acquisitions

In 2010 the company entered a high-growth market with the acquisition of Abri Health Plan for about $15 million. Abri Health provides Medicaid managed care services in Wisconsin.

Also in 2010 Molina purchased the information management business that now operates as Molina Medicaid Solutions.

Company Background

Founded in 1980 Molina Healthcare is headed by founder C. David Molina's sons: Dr. J. Mario Molina who serves as chairman and CEO and John C. Molina who is a director and the company's CFO.

EXECUTIVES

Chief Accounting Officer, Joseph W. White, age 53
Chairman President and CEO, J. Mario Molina, age 53, $850,000 total compensation
CFO and Director, John C. Molina, age 47, $775,000 total compensation
President Utah, Paul Muench
President Florida, David Pollack
COO, Terry P. Bayer, age 61, $500,000 total compensation
President Molina Healthcare of Washington, Glen Bogner
Regional VP Molina Healthcare of Ohio and Molina Healthcare of Missouri, Kathie Mancini
President New Mexico, D. Lynn Allen
President Molina Healthcare of Ohio, Amy Schultz Clubbs
President California, Lisa Rubino
VP Investor Relations and Marketing, Juan J. Orellana
President Texas, Don Hairston
Chief Medical Officer Molina Healthcare of Washington, John Robinson
VP Consolidated Plan Solutions, Marianne Czapla
SVP General Counsel and Secretary, Jeff D. Barlow, age 49
President Molina Healthcare of Michigan, Craig Bass
CIO, Rick Hopfer
Associate VP IT, Nitin Gotmare
President Molina Medicaid Solutions, Norman Nichols
Director IT Operations, Sri Bharadwaj
CFO and Director, John C. Molina, age 47
Director, Ronna E. Romney, age 68
Director, Sally K. Richardson, age 79
Director, John P. Szabo Jr., age 47
Director, Steven J. Orlando, age 60
Auditors: Ernst&YoungLLP

LOCATIONS

HQ: Molina Healthcare Inc.
200 Oceangate Ste. 100, Long Beach CA 90802
Phone: 562-435-3666 **Fax:** 562-499-0790
Web: www.molinahealthcare.com

2011 Membership by Health Plan

Washington	355,000	21
California	355,000	21
Michigan	222,000	13
New Mexico	88,000	5
Utah	84,000	5
Wisconsin	42,000	2

2011 Membership by State for Medicare Advantage Plans

	No. of members	% of total
Utah	8,400	27
Michigan	8,200	26
California	6,900	22
Washington	5,000	16
New Mexico	800	3
Florida	800	3
Texas	700	2
Ohio	200	1
Total	**31,000**	**100**

2011 Membership by State for the Aged Blind or Disabled

	No. of members	% of total
Texas	63,700	33
Michigan	37,500	20
California	31,500	16
Ohio	29,100	15
Florida	10,400	5
Utah	8,500	4
New Mexico	5,600	3
Washington	4,800	3
Wisconsin	1,700	1
Total	**192,800**	**100**

PRODUCTS/OPERATIONS

2011 Revenues

Premiums	4,603	97
Services	160	3
Investments	5	-
Total	**4,769**	**100**

Selected Subsidiaries

American Family Care Inc.
Molina Center LLC
Molina Healthcare Data Center Inc.
Molina Healthcare of California
Molina Healthcare of California Partner Plan Inc.
Molina Healthcare of Florida Inc.
Molina Healthcare of Georgia Inc.
Molina Healthcare of Illinois Inc.
Molina Healthcare of Michigan Inc.
Molina Healthcare of New Mexico Inc.
  Molina Healthcare of New Mexico Medical Clinics Inc.
Molina Healthcare of Ohio Inc.
Molina Healthcare of Texas Inc.
  Molina Healthcare of Texas Insurance Company
Molina Healthcare of Utah Inc.
Molina Healthcare of Virginia Inc.
Molina Healthcare of Washington Inc.
Molina Healthcare of Wisconsin Inc.
Molina Information Systems LLC dba Molina Medicaid Solutions
Molina Pathways LLC

Selected Plans

Abria Health Plan
Molina Healthcare Plans by individual state subsidiaries
Molina Medicare Options (Medicare plan with prescription drug benefit)
Molina Medicare Options Plus (Medicare plan for dual-eligible individuals)

COMPETITORS

Aetna
AMERIGROUP
Blue Cross Blue Shield of Michigan
Blue Shield Of California
Cambia Health Solutions
Centene
CIGNA
CNSI
Community Health Group
Computer Sciences Corp.
Coventry Health Care
HCSC
Health Net
HealthPlus of Michigan
HP Enterprise Group
Humana
Kaiser Foundation Health Plan
L. A. Care Health Plan
Premera Blue Cross
Priority Health
Total Health Care
UnitedHealth Group
WellCare Health Plans
WellPoint

HISTORICAL FINANCIALS

Company Type: Public

Income Statement

FYE: December 31

	REVENUE ($ mil.)	NET INCOME ($ mil.)	NET PROFIT MARGIN	EMPLOYEES
12/11	4,769	20	0.4%	5,200
12/10	4,085	54	1.3%	4,200
12/09	3,669	30	0.8%	2,800
12/08	3,112	62	2.0%	2,500
12/07	2,492	58	2.3%	2,300
Annual Growth	17.6%	(22.7%)	—	22.6%

2011 Year-End Financials

Debt ratio: 13.20%	No. of shares (mil.): 45
Return on equity: 2.76%	Dividends
Cash ($ mil.): 493	Yield: —
Current ratio: 174.15	Payout: —
Long-term debt ($ mil.): 216	Market value ($ mil.): 1,023

	STOCK PRICE ($) FY Close	P/E High/Low		PER SHARE ($) Earnings	Dividends	Book Value
12/11	22.33	96	32	0.45	0.00	16.48
12/10	27.85	24	15	1.32	0.00	15.82
12/09	22.87	32	21	0.79	0.00	14.13
12/08	17.61	26	11	1.50	0.00	13.34
12/07	38.70	30	22	1.37	0.00	12.00
Annual Growth	(12.8%)	—	—	(24.3%)	—	8.3%

Momentive Specialty Chemicals Inc

Momentive Specialty Chemicals (formerly Hexion Specialty Chemicals) is the world's largest thermosetting resins (or thermosets) maker ahead of competitor Georgia-Pacific. Thermosets add a desired quality (heat resistance gloss adhesion etc.) to a number of different paints coatings and adhesives. They include an array of resins: phenolic epoxy polyester acrylic and urethane. The company also is a leading producer of adhesive and structural resins and coatings. It serves several markets including paints consumer products and automotive coatings. It was created after Hexion merged with Momentive Performance Materials in 2010. Both companies are owned by Momentive Performance Materials Holdings.

Operations

Under the terms of the merger Momentive Performance Materials and Momentive Specialty Chemicals became subsidiaries of the newly formed Momentive Performance Materials Holdings. The capital and legal structures of both companies remain separate entities under the holding company.

Momentive Specialty Chemicals has reorganized into two main operating divisions: Forest Products Resins and Epoxy Phenolic and Coating Resins. Its business segments produce a wide variety of products. The Epoxy Phenolic and Coating Resins segment is the largest accounting for nearly half of sales. It markets its products to the auto aerospace electronics and oil and gas industries. The epoxy resins are the fundamental components of many types of materials and are used in a number of products for their adhesion strength and durability properties –including protective coatings for the industrial flooring automotive coatings and industrial flooring industries. The unit also is one of the world's largest producers of versatic acids which are additives for finished coatings pharmaceuticals and personal care products.

Its next largest unit is the Forest Products Resins segment whose forest resins go into lumber plywood particle board and decorative laminates. It also has formaldehyde applications used in herbicides fungicides fabric softeners and oil and gas production.

Geographic Reach

In 2011 Momentive Specialty Chemicals operated 70 production sites around the world and served customers in about 100 countries.

Financial Analysis

Momentive Specialty Chemicals performed well in 2011 recording net sales of $5.2 billion a 13%

increase over the previous year's sales of $4.6 billion. The company attributed the hike to its ability to pass on the increases in its raw material costs to customers as well as a favorable currency translation due to the weaking US dollar. It also posted a net income in 2011 of $118 million although earnings were down from $214 the previous year associated with insurance recoveries from previous legal settlements.

Strategy

The company's strategy for growth includes developing and marketing new products expanding in higher growth regions shifting to high-margin specialty products and continuing to pursue key add-on acquisitions and joint ventures.

To raise cash in early 2011 Momentive sold its IAR business which produced naturally derived resins for a variety of applications to Japan's Harima Chemicals for about $120 million. The unit had been one of the company's Coating and Inks' segments.

That year Momentive also sold its North American composites and coating resins business to a subsidiary of Investindustrial a European investment group specializing in chemicals resins and intermediates. The business which has manufacturing locations in Illinois Texas Georgia and California had $230 million in sales in 2010.

Momentive formed a joint venture in 2011 with China-based UPC Technology Corporation a maker of specialty chemicals and materials to produce specialty phenolic resins. The venture plans to build its first manufacturing plant in Zhenjiang in Jiangsu Province which will produce specialty novolac and resole phenolic resins used in refractories friction and abrasives applications. The plant is slated for startup in 2012.

In 2012 the company's joint venture with China-based Shanxi Sanwei Group began production at a VeoVa-brand vinyl ester plant that supplies Momentive's monomer products for the coatings and adhesives industry. The monomer is used to provide a variety of qualities to water-based paints wood stains and coatings as well as to adhesives and powders used in construction.

That year the company also announced that it is building a new plant in Thailand to expand its production of acrylic-based resins used in coatings adhesives and building applications in the Southeast Asia region. The plant is part of the company's strategy for global growth.

EXECUTIVES

Vice Chairman, Marvin O. Schlanger, age 63
EVP CFO and Director, William H. (Bill) Carter, age 58, $604,492 total compensation
Chairman President and CEO, Craig O. Morrison, age 56, $810,048 total compensation
Director Investor Relations, John Kompa
EVP; President Coatings and Inks Division, Julia D. Harp, age 59, $281,785 total compensation
EVP; President Epoxy Phenolic and Coating Resins Division, Joseph P. (Jody) Bevilaqua, age 56, $462,885 total compensation
SVP Finance and Treasurer, George F. Knight, age 55
EVP Human Resources, Judith A. (Judy) Sonnett, age 55, $327,352 total compensation
VP Public Affairs, Peter F. (Pete) Loscocco
EVP Environmental Health and Safety, Richard L. Monty, age 64, $267,401 total compensation
EVP Procurement, Nathan E. Fisher, age 46
VP Business Processes and IT, Kevin W. McGuire, age 52
EVP and General Counsel, Mary Ann Jorgenson, age 70
EVP; President Forest Products Division, Dale N. Plante, age 54
EVP and Managing Director Asia, Joseph Chan, age 56
VP Ink and Adhesive Resins, Brad Crocker
Business Director Epoxy Resins and Intermediates, Harold Schweitzer
VP Performance Adhesives, David Hemm
VP and CIO, Dean Meyer
VP Corporate Strategy and Development, Michael Schuler
Vice Chairman, Marvin O. Schlanger, age 63
EVP CFO and Director, William H. (Bill) Carter, age 58
Director, Jan Secher, age 54
Director, Joshua J. (Josh) Harris, age 47
Director, Scott M. Kleinman, age 38
Director, Robert V. Seminara, age 40
Director, Jordan C. Zaken, age 37
Auditors: PricewaterhouseCoopersLLP

LOCATIONS

HQ: Momentive Specialty Chemicals Inc.
180 E. Broad St., Columbus OH 43215
Phone: 614-225-4000 **Fax:** 909-843-6350
Web: www.axmpharma.com

2011 Sales

	$ mil.	% of total
US	2,130	41
Netherlands	1,051	20
Germany	402	8
Canada	304	6
Other	1,320	25
Total	**5,207**	**100**

PRODUCTS/OPERATIONS

2011 Sales

	$ mil.	% of total
Epoxy Phenolic & Coating Resins	3,424	66
Total	**5,207**	**100**

COMPETITORS

Aditya Birla Chemicals
Akzo Nobel
Arizona Chemical
Arkema US
Ashland Inc.
BASF SE
Celanese
Cytec
DIC Corporation
Dow Chemical
Dynea
ExxonMobil Chemical
Georgia-Pacific
Huntsman International
Mitsui Chemicals
Nan Ya Plastics
Reichhold
SI Group
Thermoset Resins
Valspar
Wacker Chemie

HISTORICAL FINANCIALS

Company Type: Private

Income Statement FYE: December 31

	REVENUE ($ mil.)	NET INCOME ($ mil.)	NET PROFIT MARGIN	EMPLOYEES
12/11	5,207	118	2.3%	5,300
12/10	4,818	214	4.4%	6,000
12/09	4,030	92	2.3%	6,200
12/08	6,093	(1,190)	—	6,800
12/07	5,810	(65)	—	6,400
Annual Growth	(2.7%)	—	—	(4.6%)

2011 Year-End Financials

Debt ratio: 113.87%
Return on equity: 98765000100000000.00%
Cash ($ mil.): 431
Current ratio: 187.77
Long-term debt ($ mil.): 3,420
No. of shares (mil.): 82
Dividends
Yield: —
Payout: —
Market value ($ mil.): —

Mondelez International Inc

Mondelez International (formerly Kraft Foods Inc.) makes what it takes to survive a global snack attack. The company's pantry of billion-dollar brands includes: Cadbury and Milka chocolates; LU Nabisco and Oreo biscuits; Trident gum; Tang powdered beverages; and Jacobs coffees. Mondelez International comprises the global snacking and food brands of the former Kraft Foods following the spin-off of its North America grocery operations (now Kraft Foods Group). The two companies split in a tax-free spinoff in October 2012. Mondelez with about $36 billion in annual sales and operations in more than 80 countries is the larger of the two businesses.

HISTORY

The Kraft tale began in 1903 when James L. Kraft began delivering cheese to Chicago grocers. His four brothers joined in forming the J.L. Kraft & Bros. Company in 1909. By 1914 the company had opened a cheese factory and was selling cheese across the US. Kraft developed its first blended pasteurized cheese the following year.

Kraft went public in 1924; four years later it merged with Philadelphia cream-cheese maker Phoenix and also created Velveeta cheese spread. In 1930 Kraft was bought by National Dairy but its operations were kept separate. New and notable products included Miracle Whip salad dressing (1933) macaroni and cheese dinners (1937) and Parkay margarine (1940). In the decades that followed Kraft expanded into foreign markets.

National Dairy became Kraftco in 1969 and Kraft in 1976 hoping to benefit from its internationally known trademark. To diversify Kraft merged with Dart Industries in 1980; Dart's subsidiaries (including Duracell batteries) and Kraft kept separate operations. With non-food sales sagging Dart & Kraft split up in 1986. Kraft kept its original lines and added Duracell (sold 1988); the rest became Premark International. Tobacco giant Philip Morris Companies bought Kraft in 1988 for $12.9 billion. The next year Philip Morris joined Kraft with another unit General Foods.

General Foods began when Charles Post who marketed a wheat/bran health beverage established the Postum Cereal Co. in 1896; he expanded the firm with such cereals as Grape-Nuts and Post Toasties. The company went public in 1922. Postum bought the makers of Jell-O (1925) Baker's chocolate (1927) Log Cabin syrup (1927) and Maxwell House coffee (1928) and in 1929 it acquired control of General Foods (owned by frozen vegetable pioneer Clarence Birdseye) and changed its own name to General Foods.

Its later purchases included Perkins Products (Kool-Aid 1953) and Kohner Brothers (toys 1970). Most of its non-food lines proved unsuccessful and were sold throughout the years. General Foods bought Oscar Mayer the US's #1 hot dog maker in 1981. Philip Morris bought General Foods for $5.6 billion in 1985.

The 1989 combination of Kraft and General Foods (the units still ran independently) created the largest US food maker Kraft General Foods. In the 1990s Kraft General Foods lost market share in areas such as frozen vegetables and processed meat. It introduced "light" meat products and stopped making nearly 300 food items. In 1993 it bought RJR Nabisco's cold cereal business (Shredded Wheat) and sold its Breyers ice-cream business to Unilever.

To streamline management Philip Morris integrated Kraft and General Foods in 1995. Newly named Kraft Foods sold off lower-margin businesses including its bakery unit and its North American table spreads business. Kraft bought Del Monte's shelf-stable pudding business (1995) and Taco Bell's grocery line (1996). It also sold its Lender's bagels (1996) and Log Cabin (1997) lines.

Deciding to eat healthy in early 2000 Kraft bought Boca Burger (soy products) for about $100 million and Balance Bar (meal-replacement snack bars drink mixes and beverages) for $268 million.

In 2000 parent Philip Morris (which renamed itself the Altria Group in 2003) outbid Danone and Cadbury Schweppes (later Cadbury) and agreed to buy Nabisco Holdings. It completed the deal that December for $18.9 billion (including $4 billion in debt) and began integrating those operations into Kraft Foods and Kraft Foods International. Then Philip Morris created a holding company for the newly combined food operations under the Kraft Foods Inc. name in 2001. The original Kraft Foods was renamed Kraft Foods North America.

Kraft Foods International CEO Roger Deromedi was appointed co-CEO of the new holding company along with Betsy Holden. Kraft Foods Inc. was spun off by Altria in 2001 in what was the US's second-largest IPO ever at the time (behind AT&T Wireless now AT&T Mobility).

Kraft cut 7500 jobs in 2002 as a result of the integration of Nabisco operations paying out $373 million in cash for severance and related costs. That year Kraft was also part of a $9 million settlement of a federal lawsuit regarding the use of genetically modified corn in its taco shells.

A strategy to shed brands that do not fit with the rest of the company's portfolio led Kraft to sell Farley's and Sathers in 2002 to FS Partners which renamed the company Farley's & Sathers Candy Company. Later that year Kraft sold some of its candy brands (Now and Later Intense Fruit Chews and Mity Bite) to FS Partners.

In a move to combat the population's growing obesity problem Kraft said in 2003 that it intended to reduce the fat and sugar content and cut the portion sizes of its food products as well as cease marketing in schools.

Deromedi shared the CEO slot with co-CEO Betsy Holden until 2003 at which time Deromedi was named sole CEO. (Holden was demoted to a marketing slot in the company and eventually left Kraft in 2005.) During his tenure as CEO Deromide was dogged by Kraft's looming spinoff from Altria and struggled to improve company profits by selling off underperforming and non-core brands.

The company in 2004 formed an alliance with Dr. Arthur Agatston of low-carb South Beach Diet fame to use the South Beach Diet trademark on some of its products including cereal meal replacements cereal bars refrigerated sandwich wraps and frozen entrees and pizza.

As part of Deromedi's plan to refashion Kraft's product lineup in 2005 the company sold its Altoids breath mints LifeSavers and CremeSavers candies brands whose combined sales were at the time estimated to be about $660 million a year. Wm. Wrigley Jr. Company paid about $1.4 billion for the popular brands.

Despite his best efforts to improve the bottom line Deromedi was shown the door in 2006. He was replaced by Frito-Lay's CEO Irene Rosenfeld (a former top Kraft executive who was instrumental in the company's acquisition and integration of Nabisco). She returned to Kraft after being head of Pepsico's Frito-Lay from 2004 to 2006.

Kraft extricated itself from the haze of secondhand tobacco smoke when it was spun off from Altria in 2007. Having edged toward splitting from its former parent for years the separation relieved the food maker of many headaches. It freed Kraft from any tobacco-related liability that Altria may be found guilty of post-spinoff. It also eliminated a significant layer of management which made it easier for Kraft to improve its sluggish sales.

Focusing on sharpening its brand portfolio Kraft sold off its hot cereals business in 2007. The $200 million sale to B&G Foods included two old favorites Cream of Wheat and Cream of Rice. It also sold its Fruit2O and Veryfine juice brands and operations to Sunny Delight Beverages.

As part of its plan to offer new product categories Kraft entered the lucrative and popular premade salad market in 2007 with the introduction of South Beach Living brand chicken-salad kits.

Adding more on the expansion front Kraft bought the Spanish and Portuguese operations of United Biscuits that year; the deal returned to Kraft the rights to Nabisco trademarks such as Oreo Ritz and Chips Ahoy! in Europe the Middle East and Africa.

Kraft further expanded its foreign operations with its 2007 purchase of the cookie/biscuit business of Groupe Danone for some $7.6 billion. The purchase gave the company brands such as LU Petit Ecolier and Creme Roulee and made biscuits (cookies to us Yanks) the company's largest global business. It also added the Tiger and Prince brands to its Egyptian portfolio.

Billionaire Warren Buffett acquired a small percentage of Kraft in 2007 (less than 5% at the time) joining the also famously rich and famous-on-Wall Street corporate raiders Nelson Peltz (whose estimated Kraft holdings are 3%) and Carl Icahn (who owns about 3%) in ownership of the Velveeta vendor. Peltz and Ichan are typically activist investors making suggestions regarding company operations. Peltz has suggested that Kraft concentrate on its core brands as well as undertake divestitures to fund overseas expansion.

Kraft acquiesced to Peltz on one front agreeing with his investment operations collectively known as Trian Partners by adding two directors (selected by the company and supported by Trian) to its board in 2007. Kraft also signed a "standstill" agreement with Trian agreeing to support the board's full list of nominees at Kraft's next two annual meetings.

Late in 2007 Kraft announced the re-rebranding of its South Beach products from South Beach Diet to South Beach Living saying that it wanted to capture a more positive image for the products. That year the company also sold its Veryfine juice and Fruit2O water brands and operations to the Sunny Delight company.

Kraft's 2008 sale of its slow-growing Post (Shredded Wheat Raisin Bran Honeycomb Grape-Nuts Pebbles and others) to Ralcorp a maker of private-label cereals and other foods is part of Kraft's strategy to pare down its brand offerings and concentrate on high-yield products. Ralcorp paid some $1.6 billion in stock for the acquisition. Post is the #3 US cereal maker by sales after General Mills and Kellogg. Post brought in more than $1 billion for Kraft in both 2006 and 2007.

In February 2010 Kraft acquired Cadbury for about $19 billion of which 60% was cash and 40% was stock. A majority of Cadbury's shareholders (almost 72% according to Kraft) accepted the offer effectively making Cadbury part of Kraft.

In October 2012 Kraft Foods split into two companies: a global snacks business Mondelez International and Kraft Foods Group (formerly Kraft Foods North America).

EXECUTIVES

Chairman Project Management Office, Timothy R. (Tim) McLevish, age 56, $700,000 total compensation
SVP Health and Wellness and Sustainability, Lance Friedmann
EVP Research Development and Quality, Jean E. Spence, age 54
Chairman and CEO, Irene B. Rosenfeld, age 58, $1,470,000 total compensation
President Kraft Biscuits Europe, Georges Casala
EVP and Chief Category and Marketing Officer, Mary Beth West, age 49
President Eastern Europe Middle East and Africa Region, Maurizio Calenti, age 57
EVP Global Human Resources, Karen J. May, age 54
President Health and Wellness, Rhonda Jordan, age 54
VP Finance and Investor Relations, Christopher M. (Chris) Jakubik
SVP Global Research and Technology Strategy, Todd Abraham
President Latin America Region, Gustavo H. Abelenda, age 51
VP Global Media Resources, Donald J. (Don) Miceli
President Foodservice, Thomas H. (Tom) Sampson, age 53
President Commercial Operations European Union, Pascal Houssin, age 60
EVP Strategy, Sam B. Rovit, age 54
Director Corporate Affairs UK and Ireland, Jonathan Horrell
EVP; President Developing Markets, Sanjay Khosla, age 60, $720,000 total compensation
EVP and CFO, David A. (Dave) Brearton, age 51
VP Global Nutrition, Richard Black
Senior Manager Planters Brand, Heath Osburn
SVP Sales International Commercial, Franco Suardi
President Oscar Meyer, Nick Meriggioli
Director Integrated Marketing Snacks, Michael Brandstaedter
President Kraft Foods Europe, Jean-Paul Rigaudeau
SVP and Corporate Controller, Kim Harris Jones, age 52
Senior Director Kraft Kitchens, Janet Myers
President Kraft Canada, Dino Bianco, age 50
SVP Corporate Affairs, Perry Yeatman
Director Corporate Affairs Nordic, Annica Johansson
SVP Corporate Affairs Business Units Kraft North America, Nancy Daigler
Director Corporate Affairs EU, Laurie Guzzinati
Senior Director Corporate Affairs North America Sector Communications and Consumer Innovation and Marketing Services, Renee Zahery
Director Sustainability Strategy, Elisabeth Wenner
Associate Director Corporate Affairs Convenient Meals Sector, Sydney Lindner
Manager Corporate Affairs Austria, Nicole Stege
Senior Manager Corporate Affairs Health and Wellness, Valerie Moens
Manager Corporate Affairs Czech Republic and Slovakia, Jitka Hofmanova
Manager Corporate Affairs France, Pascal Tanchoux
Manager Corporate Affairs Greece, Evi Dimitrakaki
Manager Corporate Affairs Hungary, Judit Turza
Director Corporate Affairs Italy and Greece, Stefano Robba

Manager Corporate Affairs Baltics and Central Europe, Rasa Bagdoniene
Manager Corporate Affairs Poland, Malgosia Faras
Manager Corporate Affairs Iberia, Ricardo Hernandez
Managing Director Russia, Michael Boon
Manager Consumer Promotions, David Rizzo
Director Media Buying, Gary Gruneberg
Director Corporate Affairs European Union, Richard Johnson
Associate Director Corporate Affairs Canada, Lynn Galia
Director Corporate Affairs Germany Austria and Switzerland, Silke Troesch
Director Corporate Affairs Developing Markets, Lisa Gibbons
EVP; President Kraft North America, W. Anthony (Tony) Vernon, age 56
VP and Area Director Middle East and Africa, Patrick Satamian
President Grocery North America, Michael Osanloo, age 45
VP and Corporate Secretary, Carol J. Ward
Director Marketing Cheese and Dairy, Chitra Ebenezer
President Beverages, Robert (Bob) Levi
President Grocery, Michael Hsu
President Asia Pacific Region, Pradeep Pant
Senior Director Corporate External Communications, Michael Mitchell
Managing Director Romania, Lachlan Grave
VP Retail Northern California, John LeGuluche
President Central and Eastern Europe (CEE) and Chief Customer Officer, Trevor Bond, age 50
President Middle East and Africa, Lawrence MacDougall, age 55
President Strategy North Asia and Asia-Pacific, Amit Banati, age 43
Director Corporate Affairs Asia Pacific Region, Jin Montesano
General Manager Immediate Consumption Channel; President Confectionery, Jim Chambers
President Biscuits Division, Pascal Bourdin, age 50
President France, Jean-Philippe Pare, age 54
SVP and Controller, Pamela King
SVP Global Information Systems and CIO, Mark Dajani
EVP Supply Chain, Daniel Myers, age 57
EVP; President Europe, Timothy P. Cofer, age 43
EVP Legal Affairs and General Counsel, Gerard W. (Gerd) Pleuhs, age 55
Director, Lois D. Juliber, age 63
Director, Mackey J. McDonald, age 65
Director, John C. (Jack) Pope, age 63
Director, Fredric G. (Fred) Reynolds, age 61
Director, Jean-Francois M. L. van Boxmeer, age 50
Director, Richard A. Lerner
Director, Ajaypal S. (Ajay) Banga, age 52
Director, Myra M. Hart, age 71
Director, Mark D. Ketchum, age 62
Director, Peter B. Henry, age 42
Auditors: PricewaterhouseCoopersLLP

LOCATIONS

HQ: Mondelez International Inc.
3 Pkwy. N., Deerfield IL 60015
Phone: 847-943-4000 **Fax:** -6755
Web: www.madame-tussauds.co.uk

2012 Sales

	% of total
Developing	44
Europe	37
North	19
Total	**100**

PRODUCTS/OPERATIONS

2012 Sales

	% of total
Biscuits	30
Chocolate	27
Beverages	17
Gum &	16
Cheese &	10
Total	**100**

Selected Products and Brands

Biscuits
- Barni
- BelVita
- Chips Ahoy
- Club Social
- Oreo
- Tuc

Chocolate
- Cadbury
- Lacta
- Milka
- Toblerone

Gum & Candy
- Chicklets
- Halls
- Stride
- Trident

Other
- Philadelphia (cream cheese)

COMPETITORS

Amy' s Kitchen
Associated British Foods
Boar' s Head
Campbell Soup
Clif Bar
Coca-Cola
Community Coffee
ConAgra
Dairy Crest
Dairy Farmers of America
Danone
Dean Foods
Del Monte Foods
Dr Pepper Snapple Group
Eden Foods
Farmland Foods
Fehr Foods
Frito-Lay
Fromageries Bel
Galaxy Nutritional Foods
General Mills
Goya
Green Mountain Coffee
Hain Celestial
Heinz
Hershey
Hillshire Brands
Hormel
Hostess Brands
Jenny Craig
Johnsonville Sausage
Kellogg
Kellogg U.S. Snacks
Kerry Group
Lactalis
Land O' Lakes
Lindt & Sprungli
Manischewitz Company
Maple Leaf Foods
Mars Incorporated
Michael Foods
Mott' s
Mrs. Fields
Naked Juice
Nestle
Newman' s Own
Northern Foods
Nutrisystem
Odwalla
Old Orchard
Otis Spunkmeyer
Parmalat Canada
Pepperidge Farm
PepsiCo
PowerBar
Procter & Gamble
Ralcorp
Rich Products
Russell Hobbs
Saputo
Sara Lee North American Retail
Sargento
Schwan' s
Seneca Foods
Slim-Fast
smart balance
Smucker
Snapple
Snyder' s-Lance
Starbucks
Stonyfield Farm
Tofutti Brands
Tropicana
Tyson Foods
Unilever
Voortman Cookies
Weight Watchers International
Welch' s
WhiteWave

HISTORICAL FINANCIALS

Company Type: Public

Income Statement

FYE: December 31

	REVENUE ($ mil.)	NET INCOME ($ mil.)	NET PROFIT MARGIN	EMPLOYEES
12/11	54,365	3,527	6.5%	126,000
12/10	49,207	4,114	8.4%	127,000
12/09	40,386	3,021	7.5%	97,000
12/08	42,201	2,901	6.9%	98,000
12/07	37,241	2,590	7.0%	103,000
Annual Growth	9.9%	8.0%	—	5.2%

2011 Year-End Financials

Debt ratio: 28.70%
Return on equity: 10.02%
Cash ($ mil.): 1,974
Current ratio: 87.84
Long-term debt ($ mil.): 23,095
No. of shares (mil.): 1,767
Dividends
Yield: —
Payout: 58.29%
Market value ($ mil.): 66,049

	STOCK PRICE ($) FY Close	P/E High	P/E Low	PER SHARE ($) Earnings	Dividends	Book Value
12/11	37.36	19	15	1.99	0.00	19.92
12/10	31.51	14	11	2.39	1.16	20.50
12/09	27.18	15	10	2.03	1.16	17.51
12/08	26.85	18	13	1.92	1.12	15.11
12/07	32.63	22	18	1.62	1.04	17.80
Annual Growth	3.4%	—	—	5.3%	—	2.9%

Monsanto Co.

An ear of corn the size of a Trident missile? Not quite but Monsanto is all about bioengineered crops. The company helps farmers grow more crops like corn cotton oilseeds and vegetables by applying biotechnology and genomics to seeds and herbicides. It produces genetically altered seeds that tolerate Roundup (its flagship product and the world's #1 herbicide) and resist bugs. The company also produces Asgrow DEKALB Deltapine and Seminis seeds. During the past decade Monsanto re-made itself into a seed and biotech company as opposed to one focused on agrochemicals a transition that was sped up with the acquisition of Delta and Pine Land.

HISTORY

Realizing he had only a German source for saccharin and foreseeing growing US demand for the product in 1901 drug firm buyer John Queeny spent $5000 to found Monsanto Chemical Works (using his wife's maiden name) to make saccharin in St. Louis. Monsanto soon added caffeine vanillin antiseptic phenol and aspirin; it went public in 1927.

Queeny's son Edgar became president in 1928. He branched out into rubber additives and plastics through acquisitions. In 1943 Monsanto began making styrene monomer used to produce the US Army's first synthetic rubber tires.

Monsanto and American Viscose joined forces to form synthetic-fiber firm Chemstrand in 1949 (Monsanto bought it in 1961). Chemstrand also developed Acrilan fibers (1952) and the synthetic surface AstroTurf (first used commercially in Houston's Astrodome 1966). In 1954 Monsanto and Bayer formed a joint venture to develop urethane foams (sold to Bayer 1967). Monsanto debuted the herbicides Lasso (1969) and Roundup (1973) and stopped making saccharin in 1972.

Monsanto bought drugmaker G. D. Searle (founded 1868) in 1985 inheriting lawsuits relating to its Copper-7 contraceptive IUD. It also got the rights to artificial sweetener aspartame (NutraSweet). In 1993 Monsanto bought Chevron's Ortho lawn and garden business for $416 million. It launched its first biotech product (to increase milk yields) the next year.

Searle's Robert Shapiro became CEO in 1995 and set out to create genetically altered foods. That year Monsanto bought Merck's specialty chemicals unit Syntex (birth-control pills) and 50% of biotech firm Calgene (it bought the rest in 1997).

In 1996 Monsanto bought a stake in DEKALB Genetics (it bought the rest in 1998) and introduced a Roundup-tolerant soybean. It bought Holden's Foundation Seeds (corn seed) in 1997 and spun off chemicals unit Solutia. Purchases in 1998 included the seed business of Cargill and the wheat-breeding business of Unilever (UK). It also said it would buy #1 cottonseed producer Delta and Pine Land but that deal was delayed by regulators and dropped altogether in 1999.

After calling off a $35 million merger with drugmaker American Home Products in 1998 Monsanto laid off workers and sold Ortho to The Scotts Company (now Scotts Miracle-Gro).

In 1999 Monsanto launched Celebrex an arthritis drug that set new prescription records. Meanwhile concerns about genetically modified foods prompted bans in the UK and Brazil (and later in other countries). Negative public reaction led Monsanto to stop developing seeds with a terminator gene that rendered them sterile.

To pay for acquisitions Monsanto sold its pharmaceutical intermediates business to Great Lakes Chemical (now Chemtura) and its algins (derived from algae) food ingredients business to International Specialty Products. Late in 1999 activists stepped up protests over bioengineered crops and lawyers filed a class-action suit alleging inadequate testing and unfair price influence.

Monsanto merged with Pharmacia & Upjohn in 2000 and the new entity Pharmacia Corporation (with Monsanto now a wholly owned subsidiary) set about restructuring selling Monsanto's NutraSweet Equal and Canderel sweeteners (in part to a group led by Michael Dell) as well as its biogums (food texturing and processing) business. The "new" Monsanto is focused solely on using advanced technology to grow better crops –the pharmaceutical and other operations of the old Monsanto have been assumed by Pharmacia. Consumer apprehension over so-called "Frankenfoods" and the like prompted Pharmacia to spin off about 15% of Monsanto to the public in 2000; the company spun off the remainder as a dividend to shareholders in 2002.

After two disappointing years of results in December 2002 CEO Hendrik Verfaillie resigned and chairman Frank AtLee assumed the position. In late May 2003 COO Hugh Grant was named president and CEO with AtLee returning to chair the board of directors. Less than a month later Grant initiated a reorganization of Monsanto placing focus on growing the company's seed business and redefining its goals and strategies for public acceptance of biotechnology. The company elected Grant chairman at its annual meeting in October of that year with AtLee staying on the board as a director.

The company formed American Seeds Inc. in 2004 as a holding company that would acquire and build up regional seed businesses. First on its plate was Indiana seed company Channel Bio Corp. which Monsanto bought for $120 million. Channel has three main lines of seed –Crow's Hybrid Corn Company Midwest Genetics Seed Genetics Inc. and Wilson Seeds –and 2% of the US corn seed market. Monsanto already had 14% of that market. It added Nebraskan corn-seed producer NC Hybrids in 2005 at a price of $40 million.

In a more significant move Monsanto announced in the spring of 2005 that it had acquired fruit and vegetable seed maker Seminis for about $1.4 billion in cash and assumed debt. Seminis is among the world's largest fruit and vegetable seed producers with about 3500 varieties of seed sold in more than 150 countries. It continues as a wholly owned subsidiary of Monsanto with its own management remaining in place. The deal furthered the company's recent emphasis on growing its seeds business and changing its focus from agricultural chemicals.

Many analysts saw the move for Seminis as an indication Monsanto was trying to broaden its seed portfolio to give the company something to balance out its biotech business. Perhaps but Monsanto isn't content with the size of its GM seed business either. Later in 2005 the company purchased the cotton business of Emergent Genetics for $300 million. That business gives Monsanto a foothold in the cotton seed business similar to its existing corn and soybean product lines. Emergent ranked among the top three cotton seed companies with 12% of the market.

In 2010 Monsanto completed the purchase of the Chesterfield Village Research Center located in Chesterfield Missouri from Pfizer. In 2011 the company acquired Beeologics a start-up company engaged in the R&D of biological tools to provide targeted pest and disease control (with a focus on bee health).

EXECUTIVES

EVP and CTO, Robert T. (Robb) Fraley, age 59, $602,308 total compensation
Chairman and CEO, Hugh Grant, age 53, $1,409,179 total compensation
SVP Chief of Staff and Community Relations, Janet M. Holloway, age 58
EVP Human Resources, Steven C. Mizell, age 52
EVP Sustainability and Corporate Affairs, Gerald A. (Jerry) Steiner, age 52
President and Chief Commercial Officer, Brett D. Begemann, age 51, $542,077 total compensation
SVP Global Strategy, Kerry J. Preete, age 52
EVP Secretary and General Counsel, David F. (Dave) Snively, age 58, $481,846 total compensation
VP and Controller, Nicole M. Ringenberg, age 51
VP and Treasurer, Thomas D. (Tom) Hartley, age 53
President US Seeds and Traits, Michael Stern
VP Global Vegetable and Asia Commercial, Consuelo E. Madere, age 51
Lead Media, Kelli Powers
SVP and CFO, Pierre Courduroux, age 46
CIO, Shirley Cunningham
Lead Investor Relations, Bryan Hurley
Director Investor Relations, Manny Cruz
Director Investor Relations, Ruben Mella
Director, Robert J. (Bob) Stevens, age 60
Director, C. Steven (Steve) McMillan, age 66
Director, George H. Poste, age 67
Director, Gwendolyn S. King, age 71
Director, William U. (Bill) Parfet, age 65
Director, David L. Chicoine, age 64
Director, Arthur H. (Art) Harper, age 56
Director, Janice L. (Jan) Fields, age 56
Director, Laura K. Ipsen, age 47
Auditors: Deloitte&ToucheLLP

LOCATIONS

HQ: Monsanto Company
800 N. Lindbergh Blvd., St. Louis MO 63167
Phone: 314-694-1000 **Fax:** 314-694-8394
Web: www.monsanto.com

2012 Sales

	$ mil.	% of total
US	7,367	55
Brazil	1,588	12
Argentina	873	6
Mexico	385	3
Total	**13,504**	**100**

PRODUCTS/OPERATIONS

2012 Sales

	$ mil.	% of total
Seeds & genomics		
Soybean seed & traits	1,771	13
Cotton seed & traits	779	6
Agricultural productivity	3,715	28

Selected Brands

Crop protection
- Bullet
- Degree Brands
- Field Master
- Harness Brands
- INTRRO
- Landmaster II
- Lariat
- Maverick
- Micro-Tech
- PARRLAY
- Roundup PowerMAX
- Roundup WeatherMAX
- Roundup with CROPSHIELD Formulas
- RT 3

Industrial turf and ornamental
- AquaMaster
- Campaign
- Certainty Turf Herbicide
- Outrider
- QuikPRO
- Roundup Original MAX
- Roundup Pro
- Roundup ProConcentrate
- Roundup ProDry

Input traits
- Bollgard II
- Bollgard II Cotton with Roundup Ready Flex
- Roundup Ready Canola
- Roundup Ready Corn 2
- Roundup Ready Flex Cotton
- Roundup Ready Soybeans
- YieldGard Corn Borer
- YieldGard Plus
- YieldGard Plus with Roundup Ready Corn 2
- YieldGard Rootworm
- YieldGard Rootworm with Roundup Ready Corn 2
- YieldGard VT

Output traits
- Processor Preferred
- High Extractable Corn
- I-85 Program
- Vistive

Seed
- Asgrow
- DEKALB
- Interstate Seed
- Deltapine
- NC Hybrid

Selected Subsidiaries

Alellyx S.A.
American Seeds LLC
Asgrow Seed Company LLC
CanaVialis S.A. (Brazil)
Corn States LLC
Seminis Vegetable Seeds Inc.
WestBred LLC

COMPETITORS

ADM
BASF SE
Nippon Soda
Origin Agritech

Bayer CropScience
Dow AgroSciences
DuPont Agriculture
FMC
GROWMARK
NC Hybrids
Pfister Hybrid Corn
Pioneer Hi-Bred
Sakata Seed
Scotts Miracle-Gro
Syngenta
Syngenta Seeds

HISTORICAL FINANCIALS

Company Type: Public

Income Statement FYE: August 31

	REVENUE ($ mil.)	NET INCOME ($ mil.)	NET PROFIT MARGIN	EMPLOYEES
08/12	13,504	2,045	15.1%	26,000
08/11	11,822	1,607	13.6%	26,100
08/10	10,502	1,109	10.6%	27,600
08/09	11,724	2,109	18.0%	27,000
08/08	11,365	2,024	17.8%	26,400
Annual Growth	4.4%	0.3%	—	(0.4%)

2012 Year-End Financials

Debt ratio: 10.26%
Return on equity: 17.28%
Cash ($ mil.): 3,283
Current ratio: 228.81
Long-term debt ($ mil.): 2,038
No. of shares (mil.): 534
Dividends
Yield: 1.38%
Payout: 31.66%
Market value ($ mil.): 46,549

	STOCK PRICE ($) FY Close	P/E High	P/E Low	PER SHARE ($) Earnings	Dividends	Book Value
08/12	87.11	23	16	3.79	1.20	22.14
08/11	68.93	25	16	2.96	1.12	21.57
08/10	52.65	42	22	2.01	1.06	18.69
08/09	83.88	31	17	3.80	1.01	18.44
08/08	114.25	39	19	3.62	0.00	17.09
Annual Growth	(6.6%)	—	—	1.2%	—	6.7%

Morgan Stanley

One of the world's top investment banks Morgan Stanley serves up a smorgasbord of financial services. The company operates in three primary business segments: institutional securities (capital raising corporate lending financial advisory services for corporate and institutional investors); global wealth management group (brokerage and investment advisory services financial planning for individual investors and businesses); and asset management (services and products including alternative investments equity fixed income; merchant banking; investment activities). Morgan Stanley has more than 1300 office in more than 40 nations serving corporate institutional government and individual clients.

HISTORY

In 1934 the Glass-Steagall Act required the J. P. Morgan bank (now part of JPMorgan Chase & Co.) to sell its securities-related activities. The next year Henry Morgan Harold Stanley and others established Morgan Stanley as an investment bank. Capitalizing on old ties to major corporations the firm handled $1 billion in issues its first year. By 1941 when it joined the NYSE it had managed 25% of all bond issues underwritten since Glass-Steagall took effect.

In the 1950s Morgan Stanley was known for handling large issues alone. Clients included General Motors U.S. Steel General Electric and DuPont. The firm avoided the merger wave of the 1960s but in the early 1970s it formed Wall Street's first mergers and acquisitions (M&A) department. In 1974 Morgan Stanley handled its first hostile takeover International Nickel's (now Vale Inco) buy of ESB the world's #1 battery maker.

Morgan Stanley went public in 1986. It escaped the carnage of the 1987 crash but a lawsuit arising from investor dissatisfaction with its M&A and LBO activities during that period lasted well into the 1990s.

By 1994 it was talking to possible merger mates including Dean Witter and finally merged with Dean Witter Discover in 1997 creating Morgan Stanley Dean Witter & Co. The San Francisco brokerage founded by Dean Witter in 1924 had remained regional for 40 years serving wealthy customers. In 1977 the firm merged with Reynolds Securities another regional retail brokerage started by Richard Reynolds Jr. the son of the founder of Reynolds Metals (now part of Alcoa) and grandnephew of the founder of R.J. Reynolds Tobacco. The new company Dean Witter Reynolds became the #2 US brokerage after Merrill Lynch and one of the top 10 US underwriters.

Dean Witter needed capital in the early 1980s and sold itself to Sears which hoped to turn it into a financial Allstate. Sears put in a retail-oriented management team and tried to shoehorn Dean Witter into in-store brokerages. Sears' indifference to the investment side hobbled operations.

The Discover card introduced by Sears and Dean Witter in 1986 was a hit but by the late 1980s it was obvious Sears would never be a financial giant. The retailer spun off Allstate Insurance and the newly renamed Dean Witter Discover in 1993.

Amazingly all but six of Morgan Stanley's 3700 World Trade Center employees survived the September 11 2001 terrorist attack on the towers. Hoping to capitalize on deregulations and privatizations in Europe as well as the rise of the individual investor Morgan Stanley acquired UK-based private bank Quilter & Co. in 2001 (then later sold it to Citigroup in 2006). Also that year the firm dropped the public use of "Dean Witter" in 2001 for promotional purposes and then dropped it completely in 2002.

When regulatory scrutiny fell on the mutual fund industry Morgan Stanley was charged with failing to adequately disclose the incentives its brokers and managers received for selling certain funds. In 2003 the firm agreed to pay a $50 million fine and adopt a "plain English" approach to informing investors about its product fees and broker compensation.

In mid-2004 the firm agreed to pay $54 million to settle a sex discrimination lawsuit filed on behalf of more than 300 female employees who claimed they were denied promotions and salary raises.

Unhappy with the firm's performance eight former Morgan Stanley executives (dubbed the Group of Eight) publicly called for the ouster of chairman and CEO Philip Purcell in 2005; Purcell was replaced by John Mack. That same year a jury ordered Morgan Stanley to pay more than $1.5 billion to Ronald Perelman now the chairman of cosmetics giant Revlon. (Morgan Stanley in 2003 rejected an offer from Perelman to settle the dispute for $20 million.) Perelman contended that Morgan Stanley withheld knowledge of massive accounting fraud at appliance maker Sunbeam when he sold his camping gear firm Coleman to that company for some $1.5 billion in cash and stock in 1998; a Florida appeals court overturned the verdict in 2007.

In 2006 the firm agreed to pay a $15 million fine to settle charges that it was uncooperative and did not produce documents during investigations performed by the Securities and Exchange Commission (SEC). In addition the company settled charges (while not pleading guilty) that it falsely claimed to arbitration claimants and regulators that it lost e-mails on September 11 2001; it agreed to pay $12.5 million in 2007.

Morgan Stanley had been one of the largest credit card issuers through Discover Financial Services. However it spun those operations off in 2007. Discover was the last remnant of the company's merger with the venerable Dean Witter at the end of the previous century.

After the company wrote down more than $9 billion in mortgage-related investments in 2007 it was compelled to sell part of itself to an investment arm of the Chinese government China Investment Corp. for some $5 billion in order to raise capital. The equity units included in the deal could be converted to a nearly 10% stake in Morgan Stanley.

As its traditional investment banking business faced hard times Morgan Stanley increasingly focused on private equity investing. In 2008 the company's Infrastructure unit teamed up with Ontario Teachers' Pension Plan to acquire electrical services provider SAESA the Chilean subsidiary of Public Service Enterprise Group. In 2007 Morgan Stanley teamed up with Apax Partners Worldwide to buy insurance brokerage Hub International. The previous year Morgan Stanley acquired TransMontaigne a Denver-based oil and gas transportation company and Heidmar Group a Connecticut-based marine transportation and logistics firm (it later sold Heidmar's lightering business).

In order to shore up the big banks during the financial crisis the US government invested $250 billion in healthy banks to help them jumpstart their operations; Morgan Stanley received about $10 billion of that. The cash –part of the $700 billion taxpayer-fueled bailout in 2008 –came with several stipulations including restrictions on executive pay and the order to use the funds not hoard them. Deciding it didn't need the money that badly Morgan Stanley repaid the $10 billion in 2009. The company announced in late 2008 that it would cut its staff by 10% in an effort to reduce costs.

Also in 2008 the Federal Reserve mandated that Morgan Stanley and Goldman Sachs (the other remaining independent bulge-bracket US investment bank) convert to a bank holding company structure. The structure subjected them to tighter scrutiny but enabled them to acquire a commercial bank to shore up their balance sheets if need be. The move came after rivals Bear Stearns Merrill Lynch and Lehman Brothers were either acquired or went bankrupt.

In 2009 Morgan Stanley sold its remaining stake in investment analysis and market index firm MSCI to raise capital. The deal brought the company some $625 million.

Morgan Stanley also shook up its top leadership. John Mack stepped down as CEO in early 2010; he remained chairman but stepped down at the end of 2011. James Gorman the firm's co-president succeeded Mack at the helm of the company and as chairman. The change marked a significant shift for Morgan Stanley as it scaled back its operations in riskier proprietary trading.

EXECUTIVES

Head Americas Real Estate Investing and Global Real Estate Debt Investing, John R. Klopp, age 57

Chairman President and CEO, James P. Gorman, age 54, $734,247 total compensation
EVP and COO, James A. (Jim) Rosenthal, age 58
EVP; President of Morgan Stanley Smith Barney; President of Morgan Stanley Investment Management, Gregory J. (Greg) Fleming, age 49
EVP; Chairman and CEO Morgan Stanley International, Walid Chammah, age 58, $719,347 total compensation
Chief Administrative Officer Sales and Trading, Karen C. Jamesley
Head Products Morgan Stanley Smith Barney, Mark Connolly
Co-CEO Asia Pacific, Wei Sun Christianson
EVP; Co-President Institutional Securities, Paul J. Taubman, age 51
Global Head Fixed Income Sales and Trading, Kenneth M. (Ken) deRegt, age 56, $634,932 total compensation
Chairman and CEO MSRE Investing, Owen D. Thomas, age 49
EVP; Co-President Institutional Securities, Colm Kelleher, age 55, $628,476 total compensation
Managing Director and Senior Client Relationship Manager, Harold E. Ford Jr.
Global Head Operations, Stephen C. Daffron
EVP and CFO, Ruth Porat, age 55
EVP; President Morgan Stanley Smith Barney, Charles D. Johnston, age 58
Co-Head FIG Japan, Yoichiro Ito
Global Co-Head Financial Institutions Group, Jonathan Pruzan, age 43
Global Co-Head Financial Institutions Group, Eric Bischof, age 47
Chief Legal Officer, Francis P. (Frank) Barron, age 61
EVP and Chief Legal Officer, Eric F. Grossman, age 45
COO Investment Strategy Products Morgan Stanley Smith Barney, Colbert Narcisse
CEO Taiwan, Sean Chao, age 57
Head Morgan Stanley Investment Management International Sales, Paul Price
COO Distribution and Development Wealth Management U.S. Morgan Stanley Smith Barney, James J. Tracy
CEO Private Bank Morgan Stanley Smith Barney, Shelley Hanan
Media Relations, Sandra Hernandez
Head European Technology, Enrique Perez-Hernandez
Co-CEO Asia Pacific Region, William H. (Bill) Strong, age 59
Head Private Wealth Management US, Douglas J. Ketterer
Secretary, Martin M. Cohen
Head Interest Rates, Glenn Hadden
Head Investment Strategy and Solutions Morgan Stanley Smith Barney, Paul Hatch
Interim Chief Risk Officer; Head Market Risk Department, Keishi Hotsuki, age 49
Director, James W. (Jim) Owens, age 66
Director, Roy J. Bostock, age 71
Chairman President and CEO, James P. Gorman, age 54
Director, Erskine B. Bowles, age 66
Director, James H. (Jim) Hance Jr., age 67
Director, Laura D. Tyson, age 65
Director, Donald T. (Don) Nicolaisen, age 67
Director, C. Robert (Bob) Kidder, age 67
Director, Sir Howard J. Davies, age 61
Director, Ryosuke Tamakoshi, age 64
Director, O. Griffith (Griff) Sexton, age 68
Director, Hutham S. Olayan, age 58
Director, Masaaki (Masa) Tanaka, age 59
Auditors: Deloitte&ToucheLLP

LOCATIONS

HQ: Morgan Stanley
1585 Broadway, New York NY 10036
Phone: 212-761-4000 **Fax:** 516-338-7220
Web: www.nathansfamous.com

PRODUCTS/OPERATIONS

2011 Sales

	$ mil.	% of total
Principal transactio		
Trading	12,392	31
Investments	573	1
Asset management distribution & administration fees	8,502	22
Investment banking	4,991	13
Commissions & fees	5,379	14
Interest & other	7,473	19
Total	**39,310**	**100**

COMPETITORS

Brown Brothers Harriman
Charles Schwab
CIBC
Citigroup
Citigroup Global Markets
Deutsche Bank
FMR
Franklin Templeton
Goldman Sachs
JPMorgan Chase
Lehman Brothers
Marsh & McLennan
Merrill Lynch
MF Global
Nomura Securities
Oppenheimer Holdings
Raymond James Financial
State Street
T. Rowe Price
TD Bank
UBS
Wells Fargo Securities

HISTORICAL FINANCIALS

Company Type: Public

Income Statement FYE: December 31

	ASSETS ($ mil.)	NET INCOME ($ mil.)	INCOME AS % OF ASSETS	EMPLOYEES
12/11	749,898	4,110	0.5%	61,899
12/10	807,698	4,703	0.6%	62,542
12/09	771,462	1,346	0.2%	61,388
12/08*	676,764	(1,288)	—	0
11/08	658,812	1,707	0.3%	46,964
Annual Growth	3.3%	24.6%	—	7.1%

*Fiscal year change

2011 Year-End Financials

Debt ratio: 24.57%
Return on equity: 6.62%
Cash ($ mil.): 76,766
Current ratio: —
Long-term debt ($ mil.): 184,234
No. of shares (mil.): 1,926
Dividends
Yield: —
Payout: 16.26%
Market value ($ mil.): 29,155

	STOCK PRICE ($) FY Close	P/E High/Low		PER SHARE ($) Earnings	Dividends	Book Value
12/11	15.13	25	10	1.23	0.00	32.20
12/10	27.21	12	9	2.63	0.20	37.84
12/09	29.60	—	—	(0.77)	0.44	34.31
12/08*	16.04	—	—	(1.62)	1.08	45.37
11/08	14.75	36	6	1.45	0.00	48.52
Annual Growth	0.6%	—	—	(4.0%)	—	(9.7%)

*Fiscal year change

Mosaic Co (The)

LOCATIONS

HQ: Mosaic Co (The)
3033 Campus Drive, Suite E490, Plymouth, MN 55441
Phone: 800 918-8270 **Fax:** 763 577-2990
Web: www.mosaicco.com

HISTORICAL FINANCIALS

Company Type:

Income Statement FYE: May 31

	REVENUE ($ mil.)	NET INCOME ($ mil.)	NET PROFIT MARGIN	EMPLOYEES
05/12	11,107	1,930	17.4%	8,000
05/11	9,937	2,514	25.3%	7,700
05/10	6,759	827	12.2%	7,500
05/09	10,298	2,350	22.8%	7,500
05/08	9,812	2,082	21.2%	7,400
Annual Growth	3.1%	(1.9%)	—	2.0%

2012 Year-End Financials

Debt ratio: 6.31%
Return on equity: 16.11%
Cash ($ mil.): 3,811
Current ratio: 343.18
Long-term debt ($ mil.): 1,010
No. of shares (mil.): 425
Dividends
Yield: 0.58%
Payout: 6.22%
Market value ($ mil.): 20,286

	STOCK PRICE ($) FY Close	P/E High/Low		PER SHARE ($) Earnings	Dividends	Book Value
05/12	47.68	16	10	4.42	0.28	28.16
05/11	70.85	16	7	5.62	0.00	26.07
05/10	46.17	36	22	1.85	0.00	19.58
05/09	54.70	30	4	5.27	0.00	19.11
05/08	125.32	30	7	4.67	0.00	15.16
Annual Growth	(21.5%)	—	—	(1.4%)	—	16.7%

Motorola Solutions Inc.

Once a perennial favorite in the cell phone game Motorola Solutions (formerly Motorola) hung up that business as mobile phone users enjoyed a wider selection of phones offered by industry leaders such as Nokia and Samsung. The company focused instead on products for business and government clients including two-way radios mobile computers bar code scanners and wireless broadband products used in private voice and data networks and public safety communications systems. More than half of sales come from customers in the US. Motorola changed its name to Motorola Solutions when it spun off its handset and set-top box units as Motorola Mobility in 2011.

HISTORY

Paul Galvin started his first business as a popcorn vendor when he was 13. In 1928 at age 33 he founded Galvin Manufacturing in Chicago to make battery eliminators so early radios could run on household current instead of batteries. The following year Galvin began making car radio receivers and trying to develop a mobile radio for the police. In 1940 the company developed the first handheld two-way radio for the US Army.

In 1947 Galvin renamed the company Motorola after its car radios. In the late 1950s Motorola started making integrated circuits and microprocessors stepping outside its auto industry mainstay. When Galvin died in 1959 his son Robert became CEO. The company's purchase that year of a hospital communications systems maker led it to produce some of the first pagers.

Motorola began to change focus in the 1970s. The company invested in the data communications hardware market by acquiring Codex (1977) and Universal Data Systems (1978). In 1977 Motorola began developing its first cellular phone system. By 1985 sales of the company's cellular systems had taken off. In 1987 Motorola made its last car radio.

In 1990 Motorola organized the 66-satellite Iridium communication system (which went online in 1998). The company began developing the PowerPC chip with Apple and IBM in 1991. In 1996 China adopted Motorola's technology as its national paging standard.

The founder's grandson Christopher Galvin took over as CEO in 1997 on the heels of a major drop in profits –the result of increasing competition in the cellular phone market and a downturn in semiconductor sales. Chris who had sold police radios for the company as a university student began a full-scale restructuring that included the sale of noncore assets and the layoffs of 15000 employees.

The next year Motorola recorded a $2 billion restructuring charge that contributed to a loss for 1998. The last vestiges of the PowerPC alliance evaporated that year when Motorola and IBM announced plans to work separately on the technology.

In 1999 the company signed deals to develop Internet protocol-based products with Cisco (wireless networks) Sun Microsystems (wireless network servers and base stations) and Lucent Technologies (telephony and high-speed data over cable TV systems). Motorola also sold its DRAM gate array and smart card semiconductor operations (now called ON Semiconductor) to Texas Pacific Group.

In 2000 Motorola acquired General Instrument in a deal valued at $17 billion. That spring Iridium went out of business leaving Motorola to oversee the de-orbiting and destruction of its satellites. Also that year Motorola agreed to outsource about 15% of its manufacturing to Flextronics. As part of the $30 billion deal (the largest outsourcing contract to date) Motorola took a small stake in Flextronics.

Late in 2000 Iridium gained a reprieve from destruction when it was acquired for $25 million (it cost about $5 billion to build) by a consortium of private investors that signed the US Department of Defense as its first customer.

In early 2001 Motorola led by Chris Galvin cut more than 30000 jobs amid slow sales of semiconductors and mobile phones. Motorola also cut back on its manufacturing outsourcing and sold its stake in Flextronics back to that company; it also sold its North American IT operations.

Motorola bought RiverDelta Networks (cable network equipment) in an attempt to strengthen its broadband product line. It also formed a subsidiary Thoughtbeam to market new compound semiconductor-on-silicon technology (Thoughtbeam's operations were scaled back to research and development in early 2003).

EVP and former General Instrument CEO Ed Breen took over as president and COO in early 2002 replacing Robert Growney (Breen left Motorola later that year to become chairman and CEO of Tyco International). Motorola also bought optical networking equipment maker Synchronous.

Faced with continuing weak sales the company continued to make layoffs through 2002. That year the company formed a joint venture called StarCore with Infineon and Agere to develop DSP (digital signal processing) chips for communications systems wireless phones and consumer electronics. Motorola ceased production of pagers in 2002 to focus on the development of new wireless handsets but continued to license its pager technology to other manufacturers.

Motorola acquired the shares of network equipment manufacturer Next Level Communications that it did not already own in 2003. That year sales slipped slightly across all but two business segments: Commercial Government and Industrial Solutions and Integrated Electronic Systems which each increased sales and profits. After disagreeing with the board of directors about Motorola's future in late 2003 Chris Galvin retired as chairman and CEO and Ed Zander the former head of Sun Microsystems took over in 2004 becoming the first person from outside the Galvin family to lead the company.

The company in 2004 acquired embedded computing systems Force Computers from Solectron and passive optical networking equipment maker Quantum Bridge. Also in 2004 Motorola handed off its stake in StarCore when it spun off its semiconductor operations as Freescale Semiconductor a publicly traded company. The semiconductor business had accounted for about 17% of Motorola's sales in each of the fiscal years from 2001 through 2003.

Motorola's other restructuring efforts included selling some IT services units shifting some production to contractors and using extensive layoffs to reduce costs. The company also sold its automotive products unit which manufactured telematics products used for vehicle safety and navigation to German auto supplier Continental in a 2006 deal valued at about $1 billion.

In 2007 activist investor Carl Icahn bought up Motorola shares about 6% in total in a successful attempt to obtain seats on the company's board of directors. Icahn indicated his intent to decrease Motorola's debt and return cash to investors in an effort to counter weakened sales and profits. He also called for the replacement of CEO Ed Zander and for the breakup of the company into parts.

Aiming to boost its home video and network technology business Motorola paid $140 million for Terayon Communication Systems in 2007. Other 2007 video technology purchases included digital video technology company Tut Systems for approximately $39 million and Modulus Video a developer of video coding compression systems used in VoIP cable broadcast and satellite applications.

Early in 2008 Zander was replaced by COO and communications industry veteran Greg Brown; Zander stayed on as chairman. The change in leadership was precipitated by Motorola's inability despite early successes with the RAZR cell phone model to consistently gain ground in the handset space against global leader Nokia. Former AT&T CEO David Dorman was named chairman upon Zander's retirement in mid-2008 and Sanjay Jha joined Brown as co-CEO that same year.

Partly spurred by uneven performance from its core handset business Motorola has made a string of acquisitions in an effort to diversify and strengthen other product lines. It expanded its broadcast products division with the purchase of privately held TV-on-demand services provider Broadbus Technologies. It also purchased Netopia a maker of broadband routers and software based on DSL technology for $208 million. The company also bought Symbol Technologies a manufacturer of bar-code scanners and other devices for about $3.9 billion. The Symbol purchase formed the core of Motorola's enterprise wireless products business.

Motorola also acquired a mobile devices R&D facility (located in the "Danish Silicon Valley" at Aalborg Denmark) from BenQ Mobile UK-based mobile phone software and chip maker TTP Communications and wireless software developer Good Technology. Motorola later sold Good Technology to Visto in 2009 for $163 million.

In 2009 Motorola bought the iDEN (integrated digital enhanced network) business of RadioFrame Networks. The purchase expanded the company's selection of products based on the iDEN transmission standard which was developed by Motorola to enable radio transmission on frequencies outside of typical cellular spectrum.

In January 2011 Motorola changed its name to Motorola Solutions when it spun off its handset and home products business as Motorola Mobility. Motorola Mobility took ownership of the Motorola brand though Motorola Solutions continued to use the brand under license. At the same time Sanjay Jha resigned as co-CEO and a director of Motorola to become CEO of the Motorola Mobility business. Greg Brown continued as sole CEO and a director of Motorola Solutions.

EXECUTIVES

Chairman and CEO, Gregory Q. (Greg) Brown, age 51, $905,769 total compensation
Lead Director, David W. (Dave) Dorman, age 58
EVP Product and Business Operations, Eugene A. (Gene) Delaney, age 55, $569,500 total compensation
SVP and Chief Marketing Officer, Eduardo Conrado, age 45
SVP Public Affairs, Karen P. Tandy, age 58
SVP and CIO, Leslie M. Jones, age 65
EVP and CFO, Edward J. (Ed) Fitzpatrick, age 46, $398,647 total compensation
SVP Business Development and Ventures, Michael D. Annes, age 48
SVP Human Resources, Michele (Shelly) Aguilar Carlin, age 50
Corporate VP and Chief Accounting Officer, John K. Wozniak, age 40
SVP and General Manager Networks, Bruce Brda
Director Corporate Communications, Tama McWhinney
Corporate VP Strategy and Staff Operations, Kelly S. Mark, age 40
EVP Sales and Field Operations, Mark F. Moon, age 48
SVP General Counsel and Secretary, Lewis A. Steverson, age 48
VP Global Communications, Nicholas (Nick) Sweers
Corporate VP Law Corporate Securities and Transactions, Michelle Warner
VP Investor Relations, Shep Dunlap
Manager Media Center and PR Specialist, Katie Shaykin
Director Investor Relations, Jason J. Winkler
President Canada, George Krausz
Senior Vice President - Human Resources, Michele Carlin
Director, Kenneth C. (Ken) Dahlberg, age 67
Director, Judy C. Lewent, age 63
Director, Samuel C. (Sam) Scott III, age 68
Lead Director, David W. (Dave) Dorman, age 58
Director, John A. White, age 72
Director, Gen. Michael V. Hayden, age 66

Director, Vincent J. Intrieri, age 55
Director, William J. (Bill) Bratton, age 64
Independent Director, Bradley Singer
Auditors: KPMGLLP

LOCATIONS

HQ: Motorola Solutions Inc.
1303 E. Algonquin Rd., Schaumburg IL 60196
Phone: 847-576-5000 **Fax:** 952-979-1717
Web: www.premiumwear.com

2011 Sales

	$ mil.	% of total
US	4,399	54
UK	670	8
China	322	4
Israel	173	2
Japan	97	1
Other countries	2,542	31
Total	**8,203**	**100**

PRODUCTS/OPERATIONS

2011 Sales by Market

	$ mil.	% of total
Government	5,358	65
Enterprise	2,845	35
Total	**8,203**	**100**

2011 Sales

	$ mil.	% of total
Products	6,068	74
Services	2,135	26
Total	**8,203**	**100**

Selected Products and Services

Devices
- Bar code scanners
- Micro kiosks
- Mobile computers
- Mobile-to-mobile wireless modules
- Public safety LTE infrastructure devices and services (handheld USB modem vehicle modem)
- Radio-frequency identification products (RFID) and accessories
- Tablets
- Two-way radios and pagers
- Two-way radio accessories

Networks
- Mobile broadband (public safety LTE)
- Private broadband networks
- Wireless broadband networks
- Wireless local area networks (WLAN) and accessories

Services
- Enterprise
  - Enterprise video solutions
  - Integrated enterprise communications
  - Managed network infrastructure
  - Managed security and compliance
  - Supply chain visibility solutions
- Government and Public Safety
  - Advanced video security systems
  - Complex network design and integration
  - Interoperability and unified communications
  - Next-generation command and control
  - Public safety managed services

Software
- Application development framework
- Mobility software
- Network design software
- Public sector applications
- Support and help desk applications
- WLAN management and security software

Systems
- Dispatch systems
- Enterprise voice systems
- SCADA Systems (real-time facilities monitoring and control)

COMPETITORS

Cisco Systems
EADS
EF Johnson Technologies
Harris Corp.
Honeywell International
Intermec
JVC KENWOOD
Sepura

HISTORICAL FINANCIALS

Company Type: Public

Income Statement

FYE: December 31

	REVENUE ($ mil.)	NET INCOME ($ mil.)	NET PROFIT MARGIN	EMPLOYEES
12/11	8,203	1,158	14.1%	23,000
12/10	19,282	633	3.3%	51,000
12/09	22,044	(51)	—	53,000
12/08	30,146	(4,244)	—	64,000
12/07	36,622	(49)	—	66,000
Annual Growth	(31.2%)	—	—	(23.2%)

2011 Year-End Financials

Debt ratio: 11.02%
Return on equity: 22.21%
Cash ($ mil.): 1,881
Current ratio: 229.83
Long-term debt ($ mil.): 1,130
No. of shares (mil.): 318
Dividends
Yield: —
Payout: 12.90%
Market value ($ mil.): 14,757

	STOCK PRICE ($) FY Close	P/E High/Low	PER SHARE ($) Earnings	Dividends	Book Value
12/11	46.29	14 3	3.41	0.00	16.36
12/10	9.07	5 3	1.87	0.00	32.37
12/09	7.76	— —	(0.14)	0.00	29.59
12/08	4.43	— —	(13.09)	0.00	29.23
12/07	16.04	— —	(0.14)	0.00	47.78
Annual Growth	30.3%	— —	—	—	(23.5%)

MRC Global Inc

LOCATIONS

HQ: MRC Global Inc
2 Houston Center, 909 Fannin, Suite 3100, Houston, TX 77010
Phone: 877 294-7574
Web: www.mrcpvf.com

HISTORICAL FINANCIALS

Company Type:

Income Statement

FYE: December 31

	REVENUE ($ mil.)	NET INCOME ($ mil.)	NET PROFIT MARGIN	EMPLOYEES
12/11	4,832	28	0.6%	4,100
12/10	3,845	(51)	—	0
12/09	3,661	(339)	—	0
Annual Growth	14.9%	—	—	—

2011 Year-End Financials

Debt ratio: 47.30%
Return on equity: 4.02%
Cash ($ mil.): 46
Current ratio: 259.65
Long-term debt ($ mil.): 1,526
No. of shares (mil.): 84
Dividends
Yield: —
Payout: —
Market value ($ mil.): —

Murphy Oil Corp

Murphy's Law? Turn that oil into money. Murphy Oil explores for and produces oil and gas –primarily in the US but also in Canada Malaysia and the UK and has major refining and marketing assets. In 2011 the company produced 17100 barrels of oil per day and 47 million cubic feet of natural gas per day and about 13500 barrels of synthetic crude oil per day. The company sells refined products through more than 1000 Murphy Oil USA gas stations. Most of these US retail stations are located in the parking lots of Wal-Mart stores although the company also operates stand-alone Murphy Express stations. It markets petroleum products through distribution systems under the Murphy USA and SPUR brands in the US.

Operations

On the exploration and production side of the business the company has more than 12700 net acres of developed and undeveloped properties in 11 countries. Murphy Oil's 5% stake in Syncrude Canada helps diversify the company's oil holdings. Syncrude is the world's #1 producer of light sweet crude oil; the synthetic blend is refined into gasoline and various kinds of fuel as well as chemical feedstocks.

Geographic Reach

Murphy Oil has exploration and operations in Canada Malaysia Republic of the Congo the UK and the US. Murphy Oil USA operates more than 1100 stores in 23 states throughout the US. Murphy Oil's more than 400 UK gas stations operate primarily under the MURCO brand.

Financial Analysis

In 2011 the company reported a significant financial improvement as a recovering global economy increased demand resulting in higher commodity prices that lifted revenues. Murphy Oil's revenues improved by almost 38% that year. Refining and Marketing segment revenues jumped by 41% reflecting higher oil prices. The Exploration and Production segment's revenues increased by 18%.

Net income reported a more modest 9% growth in 2011 primarily due to a $368.6 million impairment charge to reduce the carrying value of the Azurite oil field offshore Republic of the Congo to fair value as well as higher dry hole costs lower crude oil sales volumes lower North American natural gas sales prices and higher extraction costs for oil and gas produced in 2011.

Strategy

As part of a strategic restructuring focused on exiting the refining business to raise cash to pay down debt and to invest in its other core activities in 2011 the company sold its Superior Wisconsin refinery to Calumet Specialty Products Partners for $434 million. It also sold its refinery in Meraux Louisiana to Valero Energy for $585 million. Some of Murphy Oil's cost-cutting measures have included exiting the sale of its exploration operations in Ecuador to a unit of Repsol YPF for about $85 million in 2009.

Boosting its exploration and production profile in 2011 the company acquired 156000 net acres of mineral rights in the northeastern British Columbia Montney area including Tupper and Tupper West and also acquired 146000 net acres of land in Southern Alberta that is prospective for light oil. That year it also signed a production sharing contract with Suriname's state oil company Staatsolie Maatschappij Suriname N.V. giving it

100% working interest and operatorship of Block 48 offshore Suriname.

To supplement its US petroleum products operations Murphy Oil has entered the renewable fuels business. It acquired an ethanol production facility in North Dakota in 2009 and also purchased an unfinished ethanol production facility in Texas in 2010 that was completed and began operations in 2011.

EXECUTIVES

VP and Controller, John W. Eckart, age 53, $285,417 total compensation
Chairman, William C. Nolan Jr., age 72
EVP and CFO, Kevin G. Fitzgerald, age 56, $483,708 total compensation
EVP Corporate Planning & Business Development, Bill H. Stobaugh, age 60, $425,000 total compensation
SVP and General Counsel, Walter K. Compton, age 49
President CEO and Director, David M. Wood, age 55, $1,150,000 total compensation
VP International Downstream; Managing Director Murco Petroleum, Charles A. Ganus, age 57
VP Refining Support Murphy Oil USA, Ernest C. Cagle
VP and Treasurer, Mindy K. West, age 42
VP Renewable Fuels Murphy Oil USA, Marn Cheng
Secretary Murphy Oil Company Ltd., Georg R. McKay
Community Relations, Katie Sandifer
President Murphy Oil Company Ltd., Michael McFadyen
Director Retail Information Technology, Charles Jarrett
EVP Exploration and Production; President Murphy Exploration & Production, Roger W. Jenkins, age 50, $541,667 total compensation
EVP World Wide Downstream Operations, Thomas (Tom) McKinlay, age 48
VP Administration, Kelli M. Hammock, age 40
VP Joint Ventures and Business Development Murphy Oil Company Ltd., Cal Buchanan
VP Finance Murphy Oil Company Ltd., Dennis Ward
VP Finance and Administration, Keith S. Caldwell
SVP U.S. Latin America West Africa Murphy Exploration & Production Company, Derek M. Stewart
VP Africa Europe and Latin America Murphy Exploration & Production, Harry J. Howard
VP Business Development and Planning Murphy Exploration & Production, Daniel R. Hanchera
VP Worldwide Exploration Murphy Exploration & Production, Sam Algar
SVP South East Asia Murphy Exploration & Production, Eugene T. Coleman
VP World Wide Refining Murphy Oil USA, Stephen F. Hunkus
Secretary Murco Petroleum, Patricia E. Haylock
Financial Director Murco Petroleum, Simon V. Rhodes
Supply Director Murco Petroleum, Bernard Pouille
Marketing Director Murco Petroleum, Jeremy Clarke
General Manager Information Systems, Ronald (Ron) McDaniel
Manager Network and Desktop Support Global IT Operations, Joe Pieratt
Manager Law and Corporate Secretary, John A. Moore
President; Chief Executive Officer; Director, Steven Cosse
Vice President - Corporate Planning & Development, Thomas Mireles
Director, R. Madison Murphy, age 54
Director, Claiborne P. Deming, age 57
Director, James Virgil (Jim) Kelley, age 62
Director, Frank W. Blue, age 70
Director, Neal E. Schmale, age 65
Director, David J. H. Smith, age 70
Director, Robert A. Hermes, age 72
Director, Caroline G. Theus, age 68
President CEO and Director, David M. Wood, age 55
Independent Director, Walentin Mirosh
Auditors: KPMGLLP

LOCATIONS

HQ: Murphy Oil Corporation
200 Peach St., El Dorado AR 71731-7000
Phone: 870-862-6411 **Fax:** 870-864-6373
Web: www.murphyoilcorp.com

2011 Sales

US	18,209	66
Malaysia	2,045	8
UK	107	-
Total	**23,345**	**100**

PRODUCTS/OPERATIONS

2011 Sales

Refining marketing & transportation	23,502	85
Adjustments	33	-

Selected Subsidiaries

Murphy Eastern Oil Company
Murphy Exploration & Production Company - International
Murphy Exploration & Production Company - USA
Murphy Oil Company Ltd.
Murphy Oil USA Inc.

COMPETITORS

7-Eleven
ADM
Apache
BP
Canadian Natural
Chevron
Encana
Exxon Mobil
Marathon Petroleum
Nexen
Noble Energy
Racetrac Petroleum
Repsol
Royal Dutch Shell
Suncor

HISTORICAL FINANCIALS

Company Type: Public

Income Statement

FYE: December 31

	REVENUE ($ mil.)	NET INCOME ($ mil.)	NET PROFIT MARGIN	EMPLOYEES
12/11	27,745	872	3.1%	8,610
12/10	23,345	798	3.4%	8,994
12/09	19,012	837	4.4%	8,369
12/08	27,512	1,739	6.3%	8,277
12/07	18,439	766	4.2%	7,539
Annual Growth	10.8%	3.3%	—	3.4%

2011 Year-End Financials

Debt ratio: 4.24%
Return on equity: 9.94%
Cash ($ mil.): 513
Current ratio: 122.04
Long-term debt ($ mil.): 249
No. of shares (mil.): 193
Dividends
Yield: —
Payout: 24.50%
Market value ($ mil.): 10,798

	STOCK PRICE ($) FY Close	P/E High/Low		PER SHARE ($) Earnings	Dividends	Book Value
12/11	55.74	17	9	4.49	0.00	45.31
12/10	74.55	18	12	4.13	1.05	42.52
12/09	54.20	15	9	4.35	1.00	38.44
12/08	44.35	11	4	9.06	0.88	32.92
12/07	84.84	21	11	4.01	0.68	26.70
Annual Growth	(10.0%)	—	—	2.9%	—	14.1%

Mutual of Omaha Insurance Co. (NE)

In the wild kingdom that is today's insurance industry Mutual of Omaha Insurance Company wants to distinguish itself from the pack. The company provides individual group and employee benefits products through a range of affiliated companies. It offers Medicare supplement disability illness and long-term care coverage as well as life insurance and annuities through its United of Omaha Life Insurance unit. Its Mutual of Omaha Investor Services offers brokerage services pension plans and mutual funds while the Mutual of Omaha Bank operates regionally. Mutual of Omaha is owned by its policyholders.

Operations

Taking advantage of changes in regulatory restrictions Mutual of Omaha has expanded into banking through acquisitions. Operating as Mutual of Omaha Bank it provides commercial and personal banking through nearly 50 locations in 10 states. Its key markets are rapidly growing cities where it already has high numbers of insurance customers. While banking only accounted for 10% of the company's operating results in 2011 it has been growing steadily and the bank intends to eventually offer Internet banking nationwide.

Sales & Marketing

Mutual of Omaha offers its products through its agency sales force and independent agents as well as via direct marketing.

Financial Analysis

Mutual of Omaha's revenues and income bounced back from the investment losses it (and most other insurers) incurred in 2008 and 2009. However weakness in its Medicare Supplement Plan N products prompted Moody's and Standard & Poor's to lower Mutual of Omaha's ratings a notch in 2011. In response the company halted sales of the product and re-jiggered its premiums to cover the problems. The company's revenues in 2011 ended up exceeding $5.9 billion representing an increase of more than 12% over 2010. Even though its net income in 2011 dropped by almost half from 2010 to $130 million mainly due to an increase of about 17% in benefit and expense costs Mutual of Omaha remains strong and positioned for future growth with total assets of more than $29 billion.

Strategy

To build up its Retirement Plans division in 2011 the company struck an alliance with Triad Advisors whereby regional advisors will help to distribute Mutual of Omaha's 401(k) plans. It is also cozying up to third-party administrators (TPAs) by making its retirement products easier to customize for clients.

Company Background

The company's sponsorship of the long-running "Mutual of Omaha's Wild Kingdom" introduced it to a generation of Americans. Recognizing that the connection remained strong the company has revived the television series which now runs on Discovery Communications' Animal Planet cable channel and YouTube.

HISTORY

Charter Mutual Benefit Health & Accident Association got its start in Omaha Nebraska in 1909. A year later half of its founders quit leaving a group headed by pharmaceuticals businessman H. S. Weller in charge. He tapped C. C. Criss as principal operating officer general manager and treasurer. Criss brought in his wife Mabel and brother Neil to help run the business.

Formed to offer accident and disability protection at a time when there were many fraudulent benefit societies Charter Mutual Benefit Health faced consumer resistance that slowed growth in its first 10 years. By 1920 it was licensed in only nine states. Experience helped it refine its products and improve its policies' comprehensibility. By 1924 the firm had more than doubled its penetration gaining licensing in 24 states.

The US was nearing the depths of the Depression when Weller died in 1932. Criss succeeded him as president. The stock crash had brought a steep decline in the value of the firm's asset base and premium income dropped (accompanied by an increase in claims). Even so Mutual Benefit Health expanded its agency force the scope of its benefits and its operations. It went into Canada in 1935 and began a campaign to obtain licensing throughout the US.

By 1939 the company was licensed in all 48 states. During WWII it wrote coverage for civilians killed or injured in acts of war in the US (including Hawaii) and Canada. With paranoia running high and consumer goods in short supply the insurance industry boomed during the war (and payouts on stateside act-of-war claims were low to nonexistent). Criss retired in 1949.

Gearing up its postwar sales efforts in 1950 the company changed its name to Mutual of Omaha and adopted its distinctive chieftain logo. During the 1950s it added specialty accident and group medical coverage. In 1963 it made an advertising coup when it launched "Mutual of Omaha's Wild Kingdom." Hosted by zoo director Marlin Perkins and later naturalist sidekick Jim Fowler the show was one of the most popular nature programs of all time. Later that decade the company added investment management to its services.

Changes in the health care industry during the 1990s led Mutual of Omaha to de-emphasize its traditional indemnity products in favor of building managed care alternatives. In 1993 it joined with Alegent Health System to form managed care company Preferred HealthAlliance. Mutual of Omaha also stopped writing new major medical coverage in such states as California Florida New Jersey and New York where state laws made providing health care onerous. This led the company to cut its workforce by about 10% in 1996.

In 1999 it bought out Alegent's interest in their joint venture and entered the credit card business (offering First USA Visa cards). The firm also lifted its $25000 limit for coverage of AIDS-related illnesses (its standard limit is $1 million); the company had been sued over the policy.

In the new millennium the company enhanced its products targeted towards seniors as well as introducing more flexible personal health care plans.

Focusing on its core individual and employer-based lines in 2003 the company sold the renewal rights to all of its Omaha Property and Casualty Co. (OPAC) policies to Fidelity National Financial. After all the actual operations had been transferred in 2005 the UK's Beazley Group bought up the OPAC operating license.

In 2006 the company sold its innowave water purification subsidiary to Waterlogic International. The next year Mutual of Omaha sold its employer-based group health business to Coventry Health Care in 2007. Then in 2010 the company sold its employer stop loss line of business to HM Life Insurance.

EXECUTIVES

EVP CFO and Treasurer, David A. (Dave) Diamond, age 56
SVP Information Services Applications, John A. Brown
EVP and Chief Investment Officer, Richard A. (Rick) Witt
Chairman and CEO Mutual of Omaha Insurance Company and United of Omaha Life Insurance Company, Daniel P. (Dan) Neary, age 60
EVP Individual Financial Services; President United World Life Insurance, Michael C. (Mike) Weekly
EVP Group Benefit Services, Daniel P. Martin
EVP Corporate Operations, Stacy A. Scholtz
President and CEO Omaha Financial Holdings, Jeffrey R. (Jeff) Schmid
EVP Customer Service, Madeline R. Rucker
SVP Business Information and Project Management, Michelle A. Lebens
SVP Group Insurance Products, T. Scott Ault
SVP Brand Management and Public Relations, John H. Hildenbiddle III
SVP State Government Relations, Galen F. Ullstrom
SVP Individual Producer Sales, John L. Haver
SVP Direct to Customer Marketing, Stephen J. Abels
EVP Information Services, James T. Blackledge
SVP Individual Underwriting, William L. (Bill) Vigliotte
SVP Corporate Strategy, Pat H. Shiverdecker
SVP and Corporate Chief Actuary, Paul Ochsner
SVP Enterprise Reporting and Analysis, Michael J. (Mike) Jareske
EVP and General Counsel, Richard C. (Rich) Anderl
SVP and Deputy General Counsel; General Counsel and Corporate Secretary Mutual of Omaha Bank, Michael E. (Mike) Huss
SVP Private Investment Sourcing and Trading, Curt R. Caldwell
SVP Mortgage and Real Estate Investment Management, B. Peter Newland III
SVP Securities Risk Management, Kent Knudsen
SVP Investment Portfolio Strategies and Management, Patrick M. (Pat) Miner
SVP Information Services Operations, Robert C. (Bob) Johnson
SVP and Medical Director, Tom A. Reeder
EVP and CFO Mutual of Omaha Bank, Marjorie J. (Margie) Heller
EVP and Chief Credit Officer Mutual of Omaha Bank, Dwayne Sieck
EVP Bank Operations and Services Mutual of Omaha Bank, M. Lynn Crane
SVP Corporate Tax, Kurt S. Christiansen
SVP Information Services Applications, Judith A. Henderson
SVP Corporate Accounting, Dee A. Henry
SVP Retirement Plans, Scott L. Herchenbach
SVP Information Services Applications, Michael A. (Mike) Lechtenberger
VP Enterprise Architecture and Security, George Royce
Director, W. Gary Gates, age 61
Director, Derek R. McClain, age 56
Director, James G. McFarlane, age 56
Director, Adm. Richard W. Mies, age 67
Director, Anthony J. Principi, age 68
Director, Paula R. Meyer, age 57
Director, Jeffrey M. Heller, age 72
Director, Robert L. (Bob) Clarke, age 69
Auditors: Deloitte&ToucheLLP

LOCATIONS

HQ: Mutual of Omaha Insurance Co. (NE)
Mutual Of Omaha Plaza, Omaha, NE 68175
Phone: 402 342-7600
Web: www.mutualofomaha.com

PRODUCTS/OPERATIONS

2011 Revenues

Health & accident	3,158	53
Net investment income	1,078	18
Other	89	1

Selected Products

Individual
- Annuities
- Critical illness insurance
- Disability insurance
- Investment products
- Life insurance
- Long-term care insurance
- Medicare supplement insurance
- Structured settlements

Group Benefits and Retirement Solutions
- Dental insurance
- Disability insurance
- Employee assistance program
- Group annuities
- Institutional investments
- Life insurance
- Retirement services
- Special risk insurance

Selected Subsidiaries and Affiliates

Companion Life Insurance Company (individual and group life insurance plans and annuities New York)
Continuum Worldwide Corporation (operational risk management services)
East Campus Realty LLC (oversees a mixed-use urban development property adjacent to company headquarters)
Mutual of Omaha Investor Services Inc. (mutual funds)
Omaha Financial Holdings (holding company for banking operation)
Omaha Insurance Company (health and accident coverage)
Retirement Marketing Solutions (national wholesaling organization specializing in retirement products)
United of Omaha Life Insurance Company (life insurance fixed annuities and other insurance and financial services)
United World Life Insurance Company (specialty life plans and health and accident coverage)

COMPETITORS

Aetna
Allstate
Assurant
CNO Financial
Guardian Life
John Hancock Financial Services
MassMutual
MetLife
National Life Insurance
New York Life
Northwestern Mutual
Physicians Mutual Insurance
Prudential
State Farm
Unum Group
USAA

HISTORICAL FINANCIALS

Company Type: Private - Mutual Company

Income Statement FYE: December 31

	ASSETS ($ mil.)	NET INCOME ($ mil.)	INCOME AS % OF ASSETS	EMPLOYEES
12/11	29,198	130	0.4%	0
12/10	26,906	247	0.9%	0
12/09	23,819	143	0.6%	0
12/08	21,245	47	0.2%	0
12/07	19,446	217	1.1%	0
Annual Growth	10.7%	(12.0%)	—	

2011 Year-End Financials

Debt ratio: 4.08%—
Return on equity: 2.84%
Cash ($ mil.): 233
Current ratio: —
Long-term debt ($ mil.): 1,191

Dividends
Yield: —
Payout: —
Market value ($ mil.): —

Mylan Inc

Mylan knows you probably don't know its name but hopes you'll appreciate the prices of its drugs. Through Mylan Pharmaceuticals and other subsidiaries the company is one of the top global manufacturer of prescription generic drugs. Mylan's medicine cabinet holds generic versions of antibiotics antidepressants anti-inflammatories and respiratory agents in a range of delivery forms. Its specialty division makes branded nebulized and injectable drugs. In addition to finished drugs Mylan Laboratories Limited is a major producer of active pharmaceutical ingredients for generic drugs. The company's customers in more than 150 countries include wholesalers distributors retailers and government agencies.

Operations

The company's generic drug operations account for about 90% of annual revenues. The remainder of sales comes from Mylan's specialty pharmaceutical division which is led by Mylan Specialty (formerly Dey Pharma) whose best-selling product is the EpiPen Auto-Injector used to treat severe allergic reactions. The division's name was changed from Dey Pharma to Mylan Specialty in early 2012 as part of an effort by Mylan to align its businesses under the Mylan brand.

Financial Analysis

As Mylan has expanded its operations and as generic drugs have grown in popularity so have the company's revenues grown over in recent years. Mylan reported a 12% increase in sales to some $6.1 billion in 2011. Profits also rose 55% to some $534 million that year.

Strategy

Mylan Laboratories has more than doubled its size over the last decade through a series of ambitious acquisitions that helped the company expand its geographic footprint and gave it the capacity to produce active pharmaceutical ingredients.

To build its presence in Japan and grow the generics business in that country Mylan formed a strategic long-term partnership with Pfizer in 2012 to develop manufacture and commercialize a portfolio of more than 350 generic drugs (and more than 125 additional products in development) in Japan. Mylan's focus will be on the development and manufacturing end and Pfizer will focus on sales and marketing; both companies will share costs.

Mylan also has a partnership with Indian biotech firm Biocon to expand into the growing field of generic biotech drugs. While biologic drugs are trickier to copy and finicky to produce they do promise splendid profits. The two companies co-develop and market biologic therapies in numerous countries.

In addition to acquisitions and partnerships a key piece of Mylan's strategy is to be the first to file with the FDA to manufacture generic versions of popular drugs as they become fair game. Being first in line gives a generics manufacturer a three-month window of exclusivity while its competitors have to wait before they can produce an equivalent product. To that end the company's research and development pipeline depends on a steady flow of Abbreviated New Drug Applications (ANDAs) being filed with the FDA.

HISTORY

Milan Puskar and a colleague founded Milan as a drug distributor in 1961 and shifted to vitamin manufacturing in 1965. It added generic penicillin in 1966 and tetracycline three years later. The next year Parke-Davis (now part of Pfizer) became the first major drug company to purchase Milan's products. Puskar left in 1972 after a management dispute and the company changed its name to Mylan. The company went public in 1973. Chairman Roy McKnight brought Puskar back as president in 1976 when the two bought control of Mylan. In 1984 the company launched its first proprietary drug. Mylan became the #1 independent drugmaker in the US in 1985 specializing in generics.

In 1988 Mylan formed research joint venture Somerset Pharmaceuticals with Circa Pharmaceuticals (later bought by Watson Pharmaceuticals). The venture helped produce the successful anti-Parkinson's disease drug Eldepryl. The firm absorbed dermatological products maker Dow Hickam Pharmaceuticals in 1991 and drug-delivery specialist Bertek in 1993.

Puskar became chairman and CEO after McKnight died in 1993. Mylan launched cimetidine a generic ulcer drug in 1994 and by the following year it held 39% of the market for all new cimetidine prescriptions. Mylan got FDA approval for Etodolac a generic version of arthritis drug Lodine in 1997. The next year it bought Penederm Inc. maker of topical antifungal treatment Mentax.

In 2000 Mylan paid $135 million to settle price-fixing and antitrust charges relating to popular antianxiety drugs lorazepam and chlorazepate (generic versions of Ativan and Tranxene). On a happier note that year the FDA approved the sale of Mylan's generic version of GlaxoSmithKline's Wellbutrin antidepressant. The following year the company's generic version of Merck's cholesterol drug Mevacor was approved by the FDA and in 2002 its version of Eli Lilly's Prozac won FDA approval.

The company's proposed acquisition of troubled King Pharmaceuticals rankled investor Carl Icahn a minority stakeholder in Mylan. In late November 2004 Icahn made a buyout offer of Mylan to end its bid to buy King. That bid became moot after asset manager Perry Corp. led by Richard Perry increased its stake in Mylan just enough to edge out Icahn as largest shareholder. However Icahn filed suit against the company and Perry Corp. making charges of hedging to allow Mylan to complete its acquisition of King. The scuffle between shareholders was for naught.

At the end of February 2005 Mylan and King terminated their deal and Perry announced plans to unload his entire near-10% stake in the company. Ichan dropped his lawsuit against Perry and then re-set his sights on a hostile buyout of Mylan. In retaliation the company bought back 25% of its stock and closed its Mylan Bertek division —the branded drug unit that would have benefited most from the King Pharmaceuticals acquisition. In the end Mylan incurred $22.9 million in expenses related to the fizzled plan during its 2005 fiscal year.

With an eye on global expansion Mylan first bought 20% of Matrix Laboratories in 2006. It then secured control of 51% of the company in 2007. With 10 manufacturing facilities Matrix was one of the largest companies in India and the world's largest supplier of the generic anti-retroviral pharmaceutical ingredients used to treat HIV/AIDS. Additionally by having its own API producer in-house Mylan sought to gain an edge over competitors who must obtain their ingredients from outside manufacturers. Over the following two years Mylan slowly increased its holdings to 97% of Matrix.

Committed to growth through big acquisitions Mylan spent nearly $7 billion in 2007 to acquire Generics (UK) Ltd. from Merck. Mylan won out in a bidding war that included rivals Actavis Group and Teva with the prize being a business almost twice Mylan's size. Following the acquisition the company changed its name from Mylan Laboratories to just plain Mylan. Akin to a frog swallowing a salmon Mylan spent the next two years digesting its catch.

Following the acquisitions both businesses were eventually rebranded with the Mylan name. However Mylan kept the Matrix name for its institutional antiretroviral franchise serving non-governmental organizations and other alliances.

Mylan paid private-equity firm RoundTable Healthcare Partners $550 million in cash in 2010 to acquire Bioniche Pharma Holdings. Adding Bioniche increased Mylan's presence in the North American injectables market. Following the acquisition Mylan combined Bioniche with its existing unit dose business UDL Laboratories to form Mylan Institutional serving customers including group purchasing organizations hospitals and long-term care facilities.

EXECUTIVES

SVP Chief Accounting Officer and Corporate Controller, Daniel C. Rizzo Jr., age 49, $350,025 total compensation
EVP and COO, Harry A. (Hal) Korman, age 54, $441,436 total compensation
SVP and Global Head Human Biologics, Patrick Vink
Executive Chairman, Robert J. Coury, age 51, $1,566,184 total compensation
EVP and CFO, John D. Sheehan, age 51
President, Rajiv Malik, age 51, $581,438 total compensation
Vice Chairman, Rodney L. (Rod) Piatt, age 59
CEO and Director, Heather Bresch, age 42, $633,173 total compensation
SVP and Chief Compliance Officer, Brian Roman
President Europe Middle East and Africa, Didier Barret, age 47, $514,808 total compensation
SVP and Treasurer, Brian Byala
VP Global Public Affairs, Michael Laffin
VP Investor Relations, Kris King
SVP and Global CIO, Greg Sheldon
EVP and Global General Counsel, Joe Haggerty

VP Communications, Nina Devlin
VP Government Relations, Lara Ramsburg
President North America and Mylan Pharmaceuticals, Anthony (Tony) Mauro, age 39
Director, Neil F. Dimick, age 62
Director, Clarence B. (C. B.) Todd, age 78
Director, Douglas J. Leech, age 57
Director, Wendy Cameron, age 52
Director, Randall L. (Pete) Vanderveen, age 61
Director, Mark W. Parrish, age 56
Director, Robert J. Cindrich, age 68
Vice Chairman, Rodney L. (Rod) Piatt, age 59
CEO and Director, Heather Bresch, age 42
Auditors: Deloitte&ToucheLLP

LOCATIONS

HQ: Mylan Inc.
1500 Corporate Dr., Canonsburg PA 15317
Phone: 724-514-1800 **Fax:** 724-514-1870
Web: www.mylan.com

PRODUCTS/OPERATIONS

2011 Sales

	$ mil.	% of total
Generic drugs	5,579	91
Total	**6,129**	**100**

2011 Sales by Therapeutic Category

	% of total
Central nervous	20
Cardiovascular	17
Anti-infective	16
Endocrine &	9
Gastrointestinal	8
Allergy	8
Respiratory	4
Other	18
Total	**100**

Selected Products

Albuterol (Proventil Ventolin)
Alprazolam (Xanax)
Azithromycin (Zithromax)
Bupropion Hydrochloride (Wellbutrin)
Cimetidine (Tagamet)
Clonidine Hydrochloride (Catapres)
Diazepam (Valium)
Diltiazem Hydrochloride (Cardizem)
Estradiol (Estrace)
Fentanyl (Duragesic)
Fluoxetine (Prozac)
Gabapentin (Neurontin)
Linsinopril (Prinivil Zestril)
Metformin hydrochloride (Glucophage)
Metoprolol Tartrate (Lopressor)
Naproxen (Naprosyn)
Nifedipine (Procardia)
Omeprazole (Prilosec)
Propanolol Hydrochloride (Inderal)
Risperidone (Risperdal)
Selegiline Hydrochloride (Eldepryl)
Sertraline Hydrochloride (Zoloft)
Tizanidine Hydrochloride (Zanaflex)
Warfarin Sodium (Coumadin)
Zidovudine (Retrovir)

COMPETITORS

Abbott Labs
Actavis
Bayer AG
Bristol-Myers Squibb
Daiichi Sankyo
Dr. Reddy' s
Eisai
Eli Lilly
GlaxoSmithKline
Hovione
Johnson & Johnson
Merck
Par Pharmaceutical Companies
Perrigo
Pfizer
Roche Holding
Roxane Laboratories
Sandoz International GmbH
Sun Pharmaceutical
Teva
Watson Pharmaceuticals
Wockhardt

HISTORICAL FINANCIALS

Company Type: Public

Income Statement FYE: December 31

	REVENUE ($ mil.)	NET INCOME ($ mil.)	NET PROFIT MARGIN	EMPLOYEES
12/11	6,129	536	8.8%	18,000
12/10	5,450	345	6.3%	16,000
12/09	5,092	232	4.6%	15,500
12/08	5,137	(181)	—	15,000
12/07	2,178	(1,138)	—	12,000
Annual Growth	29.5%	—	—	10.7%

2011 Year-End Financials

Debt ratio: 39.72%
Return on equity: 15.37%
Cash ($ mil.): 375
Current ratio: 139.24
Long-term debt ($ mil.): 4,479
No. of shares (mil.): 426
Dividends
Yield: —
Payout: —
Market value ($ mil.): 9,157

	STOCK PRICE ($) FY Close	P/E High/Low	PER SHARE ($) Earnings	Dividends	Book Value
12/11	21.46	20 13	1.22	0.00	8.18
12/10	21.13	34 24	0.68	0.00	8.26
12/09	18.43	61 32	0.30	0.00	10.22
12/08	9.89	— —	(1.05)	0.00	8.87
12/07	14.06	— —	(4.49)	0.18	11.18
Annual Growth	11.2%	— —	—	—	(7.5%)

Nash Finch Co

Nash-Finch knows what's in store for food retailers. One of the largest US wholesale grocery distributors the company supplies food and general merchandise to about 1700 retail grocery stores in some 36 states. It operates 14 distribution centers located in the Midwest the Great Lakes region and the Southeast. The company is also one of the leading suppliers to the US armed forces distributing goods to approximately 480 military commissaries and exchanges in both the US and abroad. In addition to its food distribution businesses Nash-Finch operates more than 50 of its own supermarkets under such banners as Avanza Econofoods Family Thrift Center and Sun Mart Foods.

Geographic Reach

Nash-Finch serves customers in 36 US states the District of Columbia Puerto Rico Cuba Europe the Azores and Egypt. The company's military business segment rings up about 17% of its sales overseas.

Operations

Nash-Finch operates three business segments which include military (49% of sales) food distribution (41% of sales) and retail (10% of sales). In 2011 the company's overall sales declined by around 4% compared to the previous year. The company's military segment is made up of seven distribution centers that distributes mainly to military commissaries and exchanges. The distribution centers are located near the largest concentration of military bases and close to Atlantic ports to distribute grocery products overseas. The company's 10 largest manufacturer customers accounted for some 43% of the military segment's sales in 2011.

Nash-Finch's food distribution segment sells and distributes an array of nationally branded and private label grocery and perishable food products from around 14 distribution centers. It distributes to about 1500 independent retailers primarily in the Midwest and Southeast.

Its retail segment operates some 46 company-owned stores located primarily in the Upper Midwest. The company's retail sales decreased by around 9% in 2011 compared to 2010. The reason was due in part to the sale and closing of seven retail stores and same-store sales were down by 2% in 2011. After launching a start-up retail grocery operation designed to appeal to Hispanic consumers –called AVANZA –in 2009 it sold four of the five markets in 2011.

Strategy

On the retail side of its business Nash-Finch has been actively adding to its supermarket holdings. It acquired the No Frills Supermarkets chain of 18 stores in Nebraska and Iowa in mid-2012. The deal builds on the company's purchase of Bag 'N Save which has 12 supermarkets in Omaha and York Nebraska earlier in the year. In late 2011 Nash Finch bought a Wally's Supermarket in Devils Lake North Dakota where Nash Finch was founded in 1885.

Ownership

Mutual fund company T. Rowe Price owns around 10% of Nash-Finch.

HISTORY

Vermont farmers Warren and Mary Nash operated a small country store in the mid-1800s. In 1884 their son Fred followed the homesteading rush to the Dakota Territory where the next year he opened a small confectionery and tobacco shop in railroad boomtown Devils Lake. His brothers Edgar and Willis soon joined him and by 1887 there was a Nash Brothers store in Devils Lake and another in Grand Forks.

Two years later North Dakota entered the Union and the Nash brothers bought an unclaimed boxcar of peaches and turned it into a quick profit. That year the company hired 14-year-old Harry Finch to sort lemons for $4 a week a job he took to support his ailing father. Also in 1889 Edgar moved to California where he established ties between the Nashes' wholesale business and California produce growers. He died in 1896; Finch became a manager that year.

Acquisitions expanded the company in the late 1890s and early 1900s. It partnered with local produce brokerage C. H. Robinson in 1905; Nash Brothers controlled it by 1913.

Over the next several decades Nash Brothers expanded its growing packaging and shipping operations forming companies in California and Texas. It started the Nash Coffee Company and fruit and vegetable packager Nash DeCamp in 1916. Three years later the company moved its headquarters to Minneapolis. Nash Brothers' 60-plus companies incorporated as Nash-Finch in 1921. When Fred died in 1926 Finch became president. During the 1930s the company introduced its own brand Our Family.

Nash-Finch returned to retailing in the 1950s with 17 supermarkets in Nebraska. Finch by then a partner retired in 1953 after 64 years with the company. During the 1960s the FTC limited C. H. Robinson's role with Nash-Finch and the grocer sold its remaining stake in the broker in 1976. The company reached $1 billion in sales in 1981 and was the US's 10th-largest grocery wholesaler by the mid-1980s.

It made acquisitions throughout the 1990s including a division of military distributor B. Green & Co. (Maryland 1992); Easter Enterprises a 16-store Iowa chain (1993); and 23 Food Folks stores (1994). In 1994 chairman Harold Finch grandson of Harry died in an auto accident. President Alfred Flaten became chairman and CEO and separated the wholesale and retail divisions.

The company sold two convenience store subsidiaries (Thomas & Howard and T&H Service Merchandisers) in 1995. In 1996 Nash-Finch bought Military Distributors of Virginia a distributor of groceries to military bases in the eastern US and Europe and grocery wholesalers T. J. Morris and Super Food Services.

A year later it bought most of the assets of Nebraska-based grocery distributor United-A.G. Cooperative. Former Pathmark executive Ron Marshall succeeded Flaten as CEO in 1998.

In ensuing years it replaced most of its management team consolidated distribution centers and sold produce and dairy subsidiaries to focus more on retailing. In 1999 Nash-Finch sold its Nash DeCamp produce unit to Agriholding sold Gillette Dairy and Nebraska Dairies to Royal Wessanen reduced its number of store banners and closed unprofitable warehouses and stores.

It purchased retailer Erickson's Diversified (18 stores in Minnesota and Wisconsin) and in 2000 bought Hinky Dinky Supermarkets (12 locations in Nebraska). In 2001 Nash-Finch announced that it would sell its North and South Carolina supermarkets as it continued focusing on the market in the Midwest. To that end it acquired U Save Foods (14 supermarkets in Nebraska Kansas and Colorado) in mid-2001; most of the stores were renamed Sun Mart.

In 2003 the company purchased five Sunshine Food stores in South Dakota and converted some of those to the Econofoods banner. It also started two specialty retail food operations: Buy?n?Save (aimed at low-income customers) and AVANZA (aimed at the Hispanic market). Nash-Finch closed about 20 underperforming retail food stores in 2004 including all of its Buy?n?Save locations and several AVANZA stores.

In the midst of an investigation into internal trading practices in 2006 Marshall stepped down as CEO. Alec Covington formerly North American chief for Dutch food distributor Koninklijke Wessanen was named as his replacement.

EXECUTIVES

Chairman, William R. Voss, age 58
SVP Human Resources, Michael W. Rotelle III, age 52
EVP CFO & Treasurer, Robert B. (Bob) Dimond, age 50, $382,906 total compensation
President and CEO, Alec C. Covington, age 55, $869,340 total compensation
EVP Supply Chain Management, Jeffrey E. (Jeff) Poore, age 53, $333,014 total compensation
SVP Center Store Services, Howard Befort
EVP and CIO, Calvin S. (Cal) Sihilling, age 62, $386,152 total compensation
SVP; President and COO MDV, Edward L. Brunot, age 48, $295,133 total compensation
EVP; President and COO Nash Finch Wholesale/Retail, Kevin Elliott, age 46
EVP General Counsel & Secretary, Kathleen M. (Kathy) Mahoney, age 57
EVP; President and COO Wholesale, Christopher A. Brown, age 49, $484,549 total compensation
VP Internal Audit, Blaine T. McGuire
Director, Douglas A. (Doug) Hacker, age 56
Director, Mickey P. Foret, age 66
President and CEO, Alec C. Covington, age 55
Director, Sam K. Duncan, age 60
Director, Christopher W. (Chris) Bodine, age 57
Director, Hawthorne L. (Peet) Proctor, age 65
Auditors: GrantThorntonLLP

LOCATIONS

HQ: Nash-Finch Company
7600 France Ave. South, Minneapolis MN 55440-0355
Phone: 952-832-0534 **Fax:** 952-844-1237
Web: www.nashfinch.com

PRODUCTS/OPERATIONS

2011 Sales

	$ mil.	% of total
Military	2,340	49
Food distribution	1,996	41
Retail	470	10
Total	**4,807**	**100**

2011 Retail Banners

	No.
Sun	20
Econofoods	13
Family Thrift	4
Family Fresh	2
Pick'n	2
AVANZA	1
Prairie	1
Savers	1
Wallys	1
Wholesale Food	1
Total	**46**

COMPETITORS

ALDI
Alex Lee
Associated Wholesale Grocers
C&S Wholesale
Coastal Pacific Food Distributors Inc.
Core-Mark
Costco Wholesale
Hy-Vee
JTM Provisions
Kroger
McLane
Piggly Wiggly Midwest
Purity Wholesale Grocers
Roundy' s
Shopko Stores
Spartan Stores
SUPERVALU
UniPro Foodservice
United Natural
Wal-Mart

HISTORICAL FINANCIALS

Company Type: Public

Income Statement FYE: December 31

	REVENUE ($ mil.)	NET INCOME ($ mil.)	NET PROFIT MARGIN	EMPLOYEES
12/11*	4,807	35	0.7%	6,342
01/11	4,991	50	1.0%	6,822
01/10	5,212	2	0.1%	7,563
01/09	4,703	36	0.8%	7,410
12/07	4,532	38	0.9%	7,475
Annual Growth	1.5%	(2.0%)	—	(4.0%)

*Fiscal year change

2011 Year-End Financials

Debt ratio: 27.70%
Return on equity: 8.85%
Cash ($ mil.): 0
Current ratio: 193.03
Long-term debt ($ mil.): 294
No. of shares (mil.): 12
Dividends
Yield: —
Payout: 26.28%
Market value ($ mil.): 357

	STOCK PRICE ($) FY Close	P/E High/Low	PER SHARE ($) Earnings	Dividends	Book Value
12/11*	29.28	15 9	2.74	0.00	33.20
01/11	42.51	11 8	3.86	0.00	31.14
01/10	37.09	219125	0.21	0.00	27.36
01/09	45.94	16 11	2.75	0.00	26.22
12/07	35.77	18 9	2.84	0.00	24.05
Annual Growth	(4.9%)	— —	(0.9%)	—	8.4%

*Fiscal year change

National Beef Packing Co. LLC/NB Finance Corp.

Beef it's what's for dinner thanks to National Beef Packing Co. (NBPC). One of the biggest US beef processor it produces name brand boxed case-ready portion-controlled and other fresh and frozen beef products for 900-plus domestic and export markets. The company offers Naturewell Natural Beef and NatureSource brand beef marketed as US-raised corn and pasture grass-fed Angus cattle free of antibiotics or added hormones. National Carriers a 700-unit refrigerated trucking subsidiary transports the meaty lineup within the US. Leucadia in 2011 acquired about a 79% stake in the beef processor (formerly 68% controlled by beef producers) and NBPC's parent U.S. Premium Beef which markets beef through NBPC.

The takeover by Leucadia reflects NBPC's frustrated attempt to raise additional capital. To this end National Beef Inc. (NBI) was created to enable NBPC to enter the stock market. NBI filed an IPO with the SEC in fall 2009 but postponed selling the shares due to a lack of public investors.

Meanwhile NBPC has grown through acquisition. In 2009 it acquired Prime Tanning Leathers. Renamed National Beef Leathers the company sells hides to tanners who use the tanned pieces to produce finished leather goods for the automotive luxury goods apparel and furniture industries.

NBPC also holds a majority interest in Kansas City Steak Company which sells beef and other products to foodservice operators and retailers. Kansas City Steak sells to consumers too through direct mail the Internet and the home-shopping cable television channel QVC.

Wal-Mart and SAM'S CLUB together have accounted for about 10% of NBPC's sales. Other NBPC customers include food retailers C&S Grocers and Topco; branded meat companies Oscar Mayer Sara Lee and ConAgra; and foodservice operators SYSCO and U.S. Foodservice. The beef processor does business with Beef Products Inc. too a customer that both purchases NBPC beef trimmings and sells processed lean beef to NBPC.

Eldon Roth founder and chairman of Beef Products Inc. owns a minority interest in NBPC (through NBPCo Holdings). Roth is the inventor of a process for producing 95% lean ground beef from fatty beef trimmings which otherwise have little value.

NBPC itself was the target of an acquisition in 2008 by rival Brazilian meat producer JBS. It was forced to drop its bid for NBPC after the US Department of Justice filed a suit to block the sale claiming that the acquisition would place more than 80% of the US's cattle slaughter capacity in the hands of three companies —JBS Tyson and Cargill. A similar suit was also filed by the Ranchers Cattlemen Action Legal Fund the United Stockgrowers of America (R-CALF) and the Organization for Competitive Markets (OCM).

EXECUTIVES

CEO and President, Timothy M. (Tim) Klein, age 55, $565,385 total compensation
EVP Sales and Marketing, Monte E. Lowe, age 54, $266,347 total compensation
VP Marketing, Keith Welty
Director Human Resources, Mike Eckman
Treasurer and Chief Accounting Officer, Jay D. Nielsen, age 57, $190,000 total compensation
EVP Business Planning and Analysis, David L. Grosenheider, age 55, $266,347 total compensation
COO, Terry L. Wilkerson, age 61, $275,000 total compensation
General Counsel and Secretary, Scott H. Smith, age 59
Chairman, Steven D. (Steve) Hunt, age 53
CFO, Simon P. McGee, age 45
EVP Beef Operations, Carey Hoskinson

LOCATIONS

HQ: National Beef Packing Company LLC
12200 N. Ambassador Dr. Ste. 500, Kansas City MO 64163
Phone: 816-713-8500 **Fax:** 816-713-8863
Web: www.nationalbeef.com

PRODUCTS/OPERATIONS

2009 Sales

	$ mil.	% of total
Core beef	5,494	96
Other	239	4
Adjustments (284.9) —		
Total	**5,449**	**100**

Selected Products and Brands

Black Canyon Angus Beef
Black Canyon Premium Reserve
Certified Angus Beef
Certified Angus Beef Prime
Certified Hereford Beef
Certified Premium Beef
Imperial Valley Premium Beef
Naturewell Natural Beef
NatureSource Natural Angus Beef
Vintage Natural Beef

COMPETITORS

Birchwood Meat & Provision
Brown Packing Company
Buckhead Beef
C.R. England
Cargill Meat Solutions
Central Refrigerated Service
Clougherty Packing
Covenant Transportation
Ellison Meat Company
Freedman Meats
Fremont Beef
Frozen Food Express
Greater Omaha Packing
Hormel
Indiana Packers
JBS USA
Jobbers Meat Packing
John Morrell
Nueske' s
Omaha Steaks
Pioneer Wholesale Meat
Plumrose USA
Sam Kane Beef Processors
Trim-Rite Food
Tyson Foods
Willis Shaw Express
Wolverine Packing

HISTORICAL FINANCIALS

Company Type: Subsidiary

Income Statement

FYE: August 27

	REVENUE ($ mil.)	NET INCOME ($ mil.)	NET PROFIT MARGIN	EMPLOYEES
08/11	6,849	258	3.8%	9,100
08/10	5,807	247	4.3%	9,100
08/09	5,449	142	2.6%	8,900
08/08	5,847	124	2.1%	0
08/07	5,578	20	0.4%	0
Annual Growth	5.3%	89.6%	—	—

2011 Year-End Financials

Debt ratio: 36.09%
Return on equity: 76.46%
Cash ($ mil.): 50
Current ratio: 169.88
Long-term debt ($ mil.): 321

No. of shares (mil.): 219
Dividends
Yield: —
Payout: —
Market value ($ mil.): —

National Oilwell Varco Inc

National Oilwell Varco is the tool man that provides goods and services to exploration and production companies operating in oil patches around the world. The company makes distributes and services oil and gas drilling equipment for land and offshore drilling rigs. Its mechanical components include drawworks mud pumps cranes jacking systems automated pipehandling tools top drives and traveling equipment. Other products include masts derricks substructures and cranes. National Oilwell Varco operates in more than 900 locations on six continents including a network of 270 distribution service centers to serve its oil and gas company customers.

Operations

Its Rig Technology segment (its largest segment) serves supplies drilling contractors oilfield service companies and oil and gas companies with major drilling equipment and spare parts. Its Petroleum Services & Supplies segment provides a range of products and services used to drill complete remediate oil and gas wells and service pipelines along with other oilfield tubular products. Both segments are dependent to a large degree on oil prices and the global demand for oil exploration. Finally its Distribution & Transmission segment provides maintenance repair and operating supplies (MRO) and spare parts to drill site and production locations across the globe.

Financial Analysis

The robust oil and gas market in 2011 spurred greater demand for National Oilwell Varco's products and services which coupled with acquisitions helped to lift the company's revenues and net income by about 20% for the fiscal year. Each of its business segments - Rig Technology Petroleum Services & Supplies and Distribution & Transmission - saw revenues increase 12% 35% and 21% respectively in 2011 over 2010.

Mergers and Acquisitions

Acquisitions continue to play a big part of National Oilwell Varco's strategy. In mid-2012 it agreed to acquire Robbins & Myers a provider of services and equipment to the upstream oil and gas industry in an all-cash transaction for $2.5 billion. Robbins & Myers' complementary products include downhole tools pumps and valves. This will be the company's second-largest acquisition since it bought Grant Prideco for about $7.2 billion in 2008. That year it also bought Canadian equipment distributor CE Franklin for about $240 million.

Earlier in 2012 National Oilwell Varco bought parts and supplies provider Wilson International from Schlumberger. Wilson has an extensive supply chain portfolio with which National Oilwell Varco expects to take advantage of new market opportunities. It also bought Denmark-based flexible pipe maker NKT Flexibles (a joint venture between NKT Holding and Subsea 7) for $670 million.

In total National Oilwell Varco bought 10 companies for more than $1 billion in 2011 and 12 companies for $556 million in 2010. Significant acquisitions include that of oilfield equipment maker and services provider Ameron in a $777 million deal a move that helped to expand National Oilwell Varco's Fiberglass & Composite Tubulars business.

Company Background

National Oilwell Varco took its current form when National Oilwell and Varco International merged in 2005.

EXECUTIVES

EVP and CFO, Clay C. Williams, age 49, $550,000 total compensation
SVP Sales and Marketing, Jerry N. Gauche
Chairman President and CEO, Merrill A. (Pete) Miller Jr., age 61, $823,077 total compensation
President Services, Haynes B. Smith III, $385,000 total compensation
Group President Rig Technology, Mark A. Reese, age 53, $490,000 total compensation
President Distribution Services, Robert Workman
VP CIO and Chief Administrative Officer, Howard E. Davis
SVP General Counsel and Secretary, Dwight W. Rettig, age 51, $450,000 total compensation
President Downhole and Pumping Solutions, Jeremy Thigpen
VP Corporate Controller and Chief Accounting Officer, Robert W. Blanchard, age 50, $300,000 total compensation
VP and CTO, Hege Kverneland
SVP Distribution Services, Santosh Mathilakath
Assistant CIO, Tony Duran
Senior Accountant International Tax, Jennifer Hetmaniak
VP, Raymond W. Chang
Director, Robert E. (Bob) Beauchamp, age 52
Director, Roger L. Jarvis, age 58
Director, Eric L. Mattson, age 60
Director, Ben A. Guill, age 61
Auditors: Ernst&YoungLLP

LOCATIONS

HQ: National Oilwell Varco Inc.
7909 Parkwood Circle Dr., Houston TX 77036-6565
Phone: 713-375-3700 **Fax:** 212-656-2126
Web: www.nyse.com

2011 Sales

	$ mil.	% of total
US	5,449	37
South Korea	2,257	15
Canada	913	6
Singapore	721	5
Norway	689	5
UK	465	4
Other countries	4,164	28
Total	**14,658**	**100**

PRODUCTS/OPERATIONS

2011 Sales

	$ mil.	% of total
Rig technology	7,788	51
Petroleum services & supplies	5,654	37
Distribution services	1,873	12
Adjustments	(657)	-
Total	**14,658**	**100**

Selected Products and Services

Automation systems
Computer control systems
Derricks
Drawworks
Drilling motors
Electrical power systems
Masts
Mud pumps
Specialized downhole tools (including fishing tools drilling jars shock tools)
Substructures
Supply chain management
Top drives
Well drilling and servicing (drill stem technology)

COMPETITORS

Aker Solutions
Baker Hughes
Bechtel
Cameron International
FMC Technologies
GE Oil
Halliburton
McDermott
Schlumberger
Weatherford International

HISTORICAL FINANCIALS

Company Type: Public

Income Statement FYE: December 31

	REVENUE ($ mil.)	NET INCOME ($ mil.)	NET PROFIT MARGIN	EMPLOYEES
12/11	14,658	1,994	13.6%	49,475
12/10	12,156	1,667	13.7%	41,027
12/09	12,712	1,469	11.6%	36,802
12/08	13,431	1,952	14.5%	40,205
12/07	9,789	1,337	13.7%	31,198
Annual Growth	10.6%	10.5%	—	12.2%

2011 Year-End Financials

Debt ratio: 2.00%
Return on equity: 11.32%
Cash ($ mil.): 3,535
Current ratio: 223.60
Long-term debt ($ mil.): 159
No. of shares (mil.): 423
Dividends
Yield: —
Payout: 9.57%
Market value ($ mil.): 28,821

	STOCK PRICE ($) FY Close	P/E High/Low		PER SHARE ($) Earnings	Dividends	Book Value
12/11	67.99	18	11	4.70	0.00	41.56
12/10	67.25	17	8	3.98	0.41	37.39
12/09	44.09	14	6	3.52	1.10	33.73
12/08	24.44	19	4	4.90	0.00	30.26
12/07	73.46	39	14	3.76	0.00	18.67
Annual Growth	(1.9%)	—	—	5.7%	—	22.1%

National Penn Bancshares Inc (Boyertown, Penn.)

LOCATIONS

HQ: National Penn Bancshares Inc (Boyertown, Penn.)
Philadelphia and Reading Avenues, Boyertown, PA 19512
Phone: 610 367-6001 **Fax:** 610 369-6349
Web: www.nationalpennbancshares.com

HISTORICAL FINANCIALS

Company Type:

Income Statement FYE: December 31

	ASSETS ($ mil.)	NET INCOME ($ mil.)	INCOME AS % OF ASSETS	EMPLOYEES
12/11	8,486	87	1.0%	1,791
12/10	8,844	21	0.2%	1,843
12/09	9,483	(348)	—	1,756
12/08	9,403	32	0.3%	1,941
12/07	5,824	65	1.1%	2,141
Annual Growth	9.9%	7.6%	—	(4.4%)

2011 Year-End Financials

Debt ratio: 8.97%
Return on equity: 7.42%
Cash ($ mil.): 451
Current ratio: —
Long-term debt ($ mil.): 761
No. of shares (mil.): 151
Dividends
Yield: —
Payout: 16.07%
Market value ($ mil.): 1,282

	STOCK PRICE ($) FY Close	P/E High/Low		PER SHARE ($) Earnings	Dividends	Book Value
12/11	8.44	16	11	0.56	0.00	7.77
12/10	8.03	85	56	0.10	0.04	8.32
12/09	5.79	—	—	(3.52)	0.28	8.51
12/08	14.51	46	27	0.42	0.68	14.62
12/07	15.14	16	11	1.31	0.66	11.49
Annual Growth	(13.6%)	—	—	(19.1%)	—	(9.3%)

National Western Life Insurance Co. (Austin, TX)

National Western Life Insurance sells life insurance and annuity products including individual universal whole and term plans. The company operates throughout the US except in New York and internationally in Central and South America the Caribbean Eastern Europe Asia and the Pacific Rim. Annuities sold by independent agents make up most of its US sales. Some two-thirds of its life insurance premiums come from outside the US where the company targets wealthy individuals. Investments mainly in fixed debt securities account for some 70% of revenues.

Operations The company has more than 60000 US life insurance policies and some 140000 annuity contracts representing $7 billion. Internationally it claims nearly 75000 life insurance policies. National Western also operates two nursing homes (in Nevada and Texas) which account for less than 5% of sales.

Financial Analysis National Western's revenue was flat in 2011 down less than 1% to $573 million. The company experienced growth in its life and annuity product segments but investment income (its largest revenue contributor) was hit by derivative losses. Net income fell in 2011 declining nearly 25% to $56 million because of increased amortization costs.

Ownership CEO Robert Moody a member of the powerful Moody family of Galveston Texas owns one-third of the company and effectively controls its board of directors.

EXECUTIVES

SVP and Secretary, James P. Payne, age 67
Chairman and CEO, Robert L. Moody Sr., age 76, $1,648,582 total compensation
SVP and Chief Investment Officer, Patricia L. Scheuer, age 60
SVP Mortgage Loan and Real Estate and Director, Charles D. Milos Jr., age 66, $249,130 total compensation
SVP and Chief Actuary, Paul D. Facey, age 60
President COO and Director, Ross R. Moody, age 49, $588,956 total compensation
SVP CFO and Treasurer, Brian M. Pribyl, age 53, $253,165 total compensation
SVP and CIO, Michael P. Hydanus, age 60
SVP and Chief Marketing Officer, S. Christopher Johnson, age 43, $150,200 total compensation
SVP International Marketing, Scott E Arendale, age 67, $158,878 total compensation
VP Controller and Assistant Treasurer, Thomas F. Kopetic, age 52
VP Domestic life Underwritng, John Ptaszynski
VP Marketing, Gary L. Fischer
VP and Associate Actuary, Mark. D. Gulas
VP Policy Benefits, Doris N. M. N. Kruse
VP Actuarial Services, Sean L. Mcintosh
VP Policyowner Services, Jo N. Morris
VP Human Resources, Linda G. Wishard
VP Marketing, Charles S. Blundo
VP Marketing, Paul T. Garofoli
VP Information Technology, Allison G. Hasselmeier Jr.
VP Valuation Actuary, Kitty S. Kennedy
VP International Life Underwriting, Carlos A. Martinez
VP Policyowner Services, Larry D. White
SVP Mortgage Loan and Real Estate and Director, Charles D. Milos Jr., age 66
President COO and Director, Ross R. Moody, age 49
Director, Frances A. Moody-Dahlberg, age 42
Director, Russell S. Moody, age 50
Director, E. Douglas McLeod, age 70
Director, Louis E. Pauls Jr., age 76
Director, E. J. (Jere) Pederson, age 64
Director, Stephen E. Glasgow, age 49
Auditors: KPMGLLP

LOCATIONS

HQ: National Western Life Insurance Company
850 E. Anderson Ln., Austin TX 78752-1602
Phone: 512-836-1010 **Fax:** 512-835-2729
Web: www.nationalwesternlife.com

PRODUCTS/OPERATIONS

2011 Revenues

	$ mil.	% of total
Investment income	391	68
Universal life & annuity contract revenues	132	23
Life & annuity premiums	18	3
Other income	25	5
Gains on investments	6	1
Total	**572**	**100**

COMPETITORS

Allstate
American Equity Life
American Fidelity Assurance Company
Aviva
BMI Financial Group
Citizens Inc.
FBL Financial
Lincoln Benefit Life
Lincoln Life
Old Mutual (US)
Pan-American Life
Presidential Life
Sammons Financial
Securian Financial

HISTORICAL FINANCIALS

Company Type: Public

Income Statement FYE: December 31

	ASSETS ($ mil.)	NET INCOME ($ mil.)	INCOME AS % OF ASSETS	EMPLOYEES
12/11	9,728	55	0.6%	278
12/10	8,773	72	0.8%	292
12/09	7,518	45	0.6%	294
12/08	6,786	33	0.5%	296
12/07	6,835	85	1.2%	290
Annual Growth	9.2%	(10.2%)	—	(1.1%)

2011 Year-End Financials

Debt ratio: —
Return on equity: 4.36%
Cash ($ mil.): 119
Current ratio: —
Long-term debt ($ mil.): —
No. of shares (mil.): 3
Dividends
Yield: —
Payout: 2.29%
Market value ($ mil.): 495

	STOCK PRICE ($) FY Close	P/E High/Low		PER SHARE ($) Earnings	Dividends	Book Value
12/11	136.16	11	8	15.73	0.00	351.27
12/10	166.72	9	6	20.61	0.36	335.83
12/09	173.62	15	5	12.87	0.36	307.24
12/08	169.17	29	12	9.48	0.36	271.99
12/07	207.37	11	8	23.95	0.36	279.29
Annual Growth	(10.0%)	—	—	(10.0%)	—	5.9%

Navigators Group, Inc. (The)

The Navigators Group writes specialty lines of insurance and reinsurance to clients whom it hopes are good navigators themselves. The company's various subsidiaries write marine liability and other lines of business primarily in the US and the UK. Its Navigators Insurance and Navigators Underwriting Agency (NUA) units specialize in ocean marine insurance including hull energy and cargo insurance as well as property insurance for inland marine and onshore energy concerns. Navigators Specialty primarily provides excess and surplus (high risk) lines. The firm's subsidiaries are also involved in professional liability especially directors and officers' coverage as well as general liability for contractors.

Geographic Reach

Outside its core markets of the US and the UK Navigators has operations in several European nations such as Belgium Denmark and Sweden mainly through NUA's activity on the European Lloyd's of London insurance exchange (via Lloyd's Syndicate 1221). The firm has also established offices in emerging markets such as Brazil and China.

Operations

Navigator's NUA unit serves as a Lloyd's of London underwriting agency which manages Lloyd's Syndicate 1221. The company primarily underwrites marine and related lines of business along with offshore energy professional liability insurance and construction coverages for onshore energy business at Lloyd's of London.

Navigators' global product lines are distributed through a network of retail and wholesale brokers. In addition to its specialty property/casualty insurance and reinsurance policies the company and its subsidiaries provide catastrophe risk management services.

Financial Analysis

The company's revenues decreased by 1% in 2011 due to drop in net investment income as a result of lower investment yields and shorter portfolio duration as well as lower net realized gains as a result of decrease in gains and increase in losses from fixed maturities.

By contrast Navigators' net income dropped by 63% in 2011 because of a decrease in operating earnings caused by unfavorable underwriting results related to a large loss activity from its energy business and significant current year loss stemming from its Professional Liability division. Another factor included a decrease in net investment income primarily due to lower investment yields and shorter portfolio duration and an increase in commission expenses.

Strategy

The company is focused on strengthening and controlling costs within its existing operations. At the same time Navigators is looking for opportunities to expand into new niche coverage areas and regions aiming for underserved commercial markets with high-value assets and low-frequency loss levels.

In 2012 its principal underwriting agency subsidiary Navigators Management Company has launched a new operating unit Navigators Specialty to focus exclusively on working with US clients.

In 2011 the company launched a new Global Life Sciences suite of products Navigators LS Elite a set of property & casualty products addressing the complex needs of the life sciences industry.

That year through subsidiary Navigators Insurance Company it entered into a deal with Tower Insurance Company of New York a subsidiary of Tower Group to sell the renewal rights for the middle market commercial package and commercial automobile business underwritten through its NAV PAC division.

In 2010 the group formed a new subsidiary Navigators Re to provide medical cost property treaty and agriculture exposures in the Americas.

EXECUTIVES

President CEO and Director; Chair Navigators Insurance and Navigators Management, Stanley A. (Stan) Galanski, age 53, $600,000 total compensation
Chairman, Terence N. Deeks, age 72, $325,000 total compensation
SVP and CFO, Francis W. (Frank) McDonnell, age 55, $177,083 total compensation
EVP Field Operations and Regional VP West Coast and Pacific Northwest Navigators Management, Noel Higgitt, $285,000 total compensation
SVP and Chief Administrative Officer, R. Scott Eisdorfer, age 48
EVP and COO Navigators Management, Michael L. Civisca, age 49, $296,667 total compensation
SVP Chief Compliance Officer General Counsel and Secretary, Bruce J. Byrnes, age 44
SVP Chief Underwriting Officer and Chief Risk Officer, H. Clay Bassett Jr., age 46
President and CEO Navigators Management, Christopher C. (Chris) Duca, age 46, $305,833 total compensation
SVP and Chief Actuarial Officer, Anthony G. Martella Jr., age 45
President Accident and Health Navigators Re, Joann DeBlasis
Active Underwriter Navigators Underwriting Agency, Richard P. Bardwell, age 54
President Navigators Technical Risk, Stephen R. Coward, age 58, $331,650 total compensation
President Professional Liability Navigators Management, Reina L. Gregorio
President Navigators Holdings (UK), Paul V. Hennessy, age 64
SVP Navigators Management, LoriAnn Lowery-Biggers, age 45
Regional VP Central Region Navigators Management, Henry A. Lopez
President Marine and Inland Marine Navigators Management, Edward J. Helfers Jr.
Media Contact, Taha Ebrahimi
Global Human Resources Officer, Denise Tinger Lowsley
President Global Management Liability Navigators Management, Scott H. Misson
President Excess Casualty Navigators Management, Jeff L. Saunders
SVP; Head Navigators Global Life Sciences, Lyn Rossano
President Primary Casualty Division Navigators Management, Mark J. Richards
President Inland Marine Division Navigators Management, Lisa M. Uzzo
Director, Robert V. (Bob) Mendelsohn, age 65
Director, W. Thomas Forrester, age 63
President CEO and Director; Chair Navigators Insurance and Navigators Management, Stanley A. (Stan) Galanski, age 53
Director, Marc M. Tract, age 52
Director, Marjorie D. Raines, age 65
Director, John F. (Jack) Kirby, age 65
Director, H. J. Mervyn Blakeney, age 74
Director, Janice C. Tomlinson, age 61
Auditors: KPMGLLP

LOCATIONS

HQ: The Navigators Group Inc.
6 International Dr., Rye Brook NY 10573
Phone: 914-934-8999 **Fax:** 650-583-3789
Web: www.poniard.com

PRODUCTS/OPERATIONS

Selected Subsidiaries

Millennium Underwriting Ltd. (UK)
Navigators A/S (Denmark)
Navigators Corporate Underwriters Ltd. (UK)
Navigators Holdings (UK) Ltd.
Navigators Insurance Company
Navigators Management Company Inc.

Navigators Management (UK) Limited
Navigators NV (Belgium)
Navigators Specialty Insurance Company
Navigators Underwriting Agency Ltd. (UK)
Navigators Underwriting Limited (UK)
NUAL AB (Sweden)

Selected Products and Services:

Commercial Surety
Standard Transactional
Non Standard Transactional
Account
Program
Energy and Engineering
Onshore Energy
Offshore Energy
Construction
Operational Engineering
Excess Casualty
Umbrella & Excess (Wholesale Brokerage)
Umbrella & Excess (Retail Agency)
Environmental Casualty
Contractors Pollution Liability
Site Pollution Legal Liability
NP3 sm General & Environmental Liability (Mfg. & Distributors)
NP4 sm General Environmental & Professional Liability (Env' l Consultants)
Environmental Excess
Inland Marine
Commercial Output Policy
Construction
Specialty
Transportation
Management Liability
Directors & Officers Liability
Employment Practices Liability
Fiduciary Liability
Crime Liability
Nonprofit D & O Liability
Marine
Bluewater Hull
Brownwater Hull
Cargo
Specie
Transportation
Marine & Energy Liability
War
Protection & Indemnity
Primary Casualty
General Liability
NAVIGATORS RE
Accident & Health
Agriculture
Latin American & Caribbean
Professional Liability Reinsurance
Property & Casualty
Life Sciences
Global Package Solutions
Commercial Auto
Professional Liability
Lawyers Professional Liability
Accountants Professional Liability
Miscellaneous Professional Liability
Insurance Agents & Brokers E&O
Technology Media & Cyber Liability
Design Professionals Liability
Real Estate Professionals E&O

COMPETITORS

AIG
Allianz
Amica Mutual
Arch Insurance Group
Aspen Insurance
AXA Corporate Solutions
Berkshire Hathaway
Chubb Corp
CNA Financial
Global Indemnity
ProSight Specialty Insurance Group
RLI
Safeco
Specialty Underwriters' Alliance
Travelers Companies
White Mountains Insurance Group
XL Group plc
Zurich American

HISTORICAL FINANCIALS

Company Type: Public

Income Statement FYE: December 31

	ASSETS ($ mil.)	NET INCOME ($ mil.)	INCOME AS % OF ASSETS	EMPLOYEES
12/11	3,670	25	0.7%	522
12/10	3,531	69	2.0%	494
12/09	3,453	63	1.8%	503
12/08	3,349	51	1.5%	445
12/07	3,143	95	3.0%	401
Annual Growth	3.9%	(28.1%)	—	6.8%

2011 Year-End Financials

Debt ratio: 3.11%
Return on equity: 3.19%
Cash ($ mil.): 127
Current ratio: —
Long-term debt ($ mil.): 114
No. of shares (mil.): 13
Dividends
Yield: —
Payout: —
Market value ($ mil.): 665

	STOCK PRICE ($) FY Close	P/E High	P/E Low	PER SHARE ($) Earnings	Dividends	Book Value
12/11	47.68	32	23	1.69	0.00	57.57
12/10	50.35	12	9	4.24	0.00	52.68
12/09	47.11	15	12	3.65	0.00	47.58
12/08	54.91	21	14	3.04	0.00	40.89
12/07	65.00	12	8	5.62	0.00	39.24
Annual Growth	(7.5%)	—	—	(25.9%)	—	10.1%

Navistar International Corp.

Navistar's gonna roll its truckin' convoy 'cross the USA and beyond. The company makes its products under brand names International (commercial trucks and military/defense vehicles) MaxxForce (diesel engines) IC (school and commercial buses) Workhorse (chassis for motor homes) and Navistar RV (recreational vehicles). It makes diesel engines for the pickup truck van and SUV markets. Navistar's parts group supplies engine parts and its financial sector offers sales and lease financing for dealers and customers. Navistar which operates production plants in Argentina Brazil Canada Mexico and the US derives most of its sales from North America. The US government accounts for 13% of its total sales.

HISTORY

Virginia-born inventor Cyrus McCormick perfected the reaper in 1831 and moved west to open a factory in Chicago in 1846. Before his death in 1884 McCormick had implemented such innovations as installment plans written guarantees and factory-trained repairmen. In 1902 with help from banker J. P. Morgan the company merged with Deering Harvester (agricultural machinery) and several smaller companies to form International Harvester (IH); it soon controlled 85% of US harvester production.

IH set up its first overseas plant in 1905 in Sweden. It entered the tractor industry in 1906 and in 1907 it began making the forerunner of the truck –the Auto Buggy. By 1910 IH was making 1300 trucks and 1400 tractors annually and had exceeded $100 million in sales.

Cyrus Jr. borrowed $5 million from John D. Rockefeller in 1913 and took control of IH. In 1924 IH introduced the Farmall the first all-purpose tractor. IH began making heavy trucks in 1928 and by 1937 it was the top US producer of medium and heavy trucks.

Overextended and underfinanced after WWII IH's market share declined. It produced more trucks than agricultural equipment for the first time in 1955. By 1958 Deere had taken over the lead in farm equipment. IH lost its medium-duty industry sales lead to Ford in the 1960s and its construction equipment business faltered as well.

A six-month strike by the UAW in 1980 coupled with a recession sent IH to the edge of bankruptcy. Over the next two years IH lost $2.3 billion. In 1982 the company sold its construction equipment unit and in 1985 it sold its agricultural equipment business and the International Harvester name. Employee numbers had dropped 85% by 1986 and plants decreased from 48 worldwide to six in North America.

The company was renamed Navistar International in 1986. It redesigned 85% of its truck line by 1987. In 1989 Navistar introduced a nine-speed heavy-truck transmission –its first all-new design in more than 25 years. In 1991 Navistar raised its stake in truck maker Dina Camiones (Mexico) to 17% and inked OEM deals for its engines with Perkins Group (UK) and its North American distributor Detroit Diesel.

A boom in demand for heavy trucks in 1992 and 1993 resulted in Navistar's retail deliveries rising nearly 33%. Navistar unveiled an engine for vans and trucks in 1994 that was the cleanest burning of its kind increasing the company's share of the diesel engine market. Company veteran John Horne became CEO in 1995.

Intense competition in the heavy-truck market caused sales to drop in 1996. In 1997 Navistar sold its Columbus Plastics subsidiary to RYMAC Mortgage retaining a 45% stake in the company renamed Core Materials. Navistar also launched its first new line of trucks since 1989.

In 1998 Navistar's earnings nearly doubled the result of a stable economy simplification of products and operations and railroad mergers that delayed shipments and forced many companies to switch to long-haul trucking. Navistar opened a plant in Mexico and began marketing trucks and truck parts in Brazil. In 1999 Navistar bought half of Maxion Motores Brazil's largest maker of diesel engines. The joint venture was renamed Maxion International Motores. Maxion provided diesel engines to Ford and GM factories in South America.

Navistar adopted International Truck and Engine Corporation as its operating name in 2000 and initiated plans to put its engine business under newly formed subsidiary International Engine Corporation. Anticipating a decline in demand Navistar announced plans to cut jobs including about 1850 jobs at its Springfield Ohio plant by 2003.

In 2001 Navistar and Ford announced the formation of a 50/50 joint venture to produce commercial trucks in Mexico. The venture named Blue Diamond Truck began operation in 2002. In late 2003 the company created an operating unit for the sole purpose of conducting business with the US military.

An agreement to supply the US Postal Service with 1700 medium-duty trucks was signed in early

2004. The following year through subsidiary International Truck and Engine Navistar bought Workhorse Custom Chassis for an undisclosed sum from Grand Vehicle Works Holdings Corporation a Carlyle Group company. Later that year the company entered into a joint venture with the India-based Mahindra & Mahindra Limited to build light-medium- and heavy-duty commercial vehicles.

The company was challenged to keep the delivery pace up in 2007 during a seven-week UAW strike against International Truck and Engine. During that year Navistar trimmed down its partnerships and joint ventures. It sold its stake in Siemens Diesel Systems Technology to its partner Siemens VDO Automotive (later VDO Automotive and now part of Continental AG).

In late 2007 Navistar signed a tentative agreement with General Motors to acquire GM's medium-duty truck business. The deal expired the following year due to what Navistar claimed was a major change in the industry. The agreement would have included the rights to manufacture GMC and Chevrolet brand trucks and to sell GMC and Chevy trucks and parts through GM dealers in Canada and the US.

Navistar launched the energy-efficient International ProStar and LoneStar long-haul trucks in 2007 to the US Canada and Mexico. It plans to expand modified versions throughout Latin America and other world markets. The company's MaxxForce engine built to current US emissions standards has been modified for use in Brazil and Mexico and ultimately for China India and Russia. Navistar continues to expand its global truck business into new markets like the Middle East and South Africa.

In 2008 Navistar partnered to manufacture public and commercial buses with Brazilian bus body maker San Marino Onibus e Implementos which sells internationally under the Neobus brand. The buses will be managed by Navistar's Global Bus Operations and initially target Latin American markets and ultimately the US and Canada.

In 2009 Navistar bought the recreational vehicle manufacturing assets of Monaco RV which had filed for Chapter 11 bankruptcy protection earlier in the year for about $47 million. The deal expanded its diesel and RV chassis business and provided Navistar with additional manufacturing facilities in the US.

The company's Navistar Defense subsidiary in 2009 secured more than $1.6 billion in contracts with the US armed forces for military vehicles used to protect troops from roadside bombs in Iraq. The company received orders for nearly 3000 MaxxPro MRAP (mine-resistant ambush-protected) vehicles more than any other supplier.

Navistar and Ford settled a long legal battle over an engine contract in 2009 essentially closing one chapter in their 30-year relationship. The companies ended their current diesel engine supply agreement earlier than planned with Ford paying an undisclosed amount to Navistar. (Ford generated more than 40% of the company's unit volume.) The companies continued to collaborate on the existing Blue Diamond Truck and Parts joint venture which offered medium-duty trucks as well as parts support for a variety of Ford products to dealers and customers. The companies continued their diesel engine supply relationship in South America. A reduction in Ford production schedules brought about 400 layoffs at the Indianapolis engine plant in 2008; with the contract issue settled Navistar closed its engine-casting operations in Indianapolis in mid-2009.

Navistar's purchase of Monaco RV (later renamed Navistar RV) in 2009 not only offered a twist to its portfolio offerings but it also made two plants available in Indiana in 2010 for Navistar to utilize for the development and construction of its all-electric delivery trucks in 2010 using part of a $39 million US Department of Energy grant it received when President Obama visited Navistar's manufacturing plant in 2009. That same year it launched the eStar medium-duty all-electric commercial vehicle.

Also in 2009 the company introduced the industry's first hybrid four-wheel-drive commercial truck an outcome to its partnerships with the EPA UPS and Eaton to develop a diesel "series" hydraulic urban delivery vehicle. The vehicle uses hydraulic pumps and hydraulic storage tanks to capture and store energy. Navistar is making school buses and midsize commercial vehicles with hybrid-electric powertrains as well.

In 2010 Navistar bought privately held Continental Mfg. one of the largest cement mixer manufacturers in North America. The purchase expanded the company's portfolio of purpose-built products with rear-discharge cement mixers for the construction industry and parts for all mixer models; the products will be sold and serviced in part through its International network of dealers.

EXECUTIVES

Chairman President and CEO, Daniel C. (Dan) Ustian, age 61, $1,180,000 total compensation
SVP Sales Operations North America, James L. Hebe, age 63
SVP; President and CEO Navistar Financial, David Johanneson
President Truck Group, Deepak T. (Dee) Kapur, age 58, $640,000 total compensation
President North American Truck Operations, John J. (Jack) Allen, $453,200 total compensation
President Parts Group, Phyllis E. Cochran, age 60
Media Inquiries General Business, Roy Wiley
SVP General Counsel and Chief Ethics Officer, Steven K. (Steve) Covey, age 61, $495,000 total compensation
SVP Human Resources and Administration, Gregory W. (Greg) Elliott, age 51
VP Investor Relations, Heather Kos, age 41
VP and Corporate Controller, John P. Waldron, age 48
VP and Treasurer, James M. (Jim) Moran, age 47
VP and General Manager Heavy Vehicle Center, Thomas Baughman
President Navistar Defense, Archie Massicotte
Group VP Product Development, Ramin Younessi
Corporate Secretary, Curt A. Kramer, age 44
Director Global Logistics, Ed Melching
Regional VP Navistar South Africa, Tim Quinlan
EVP and CFO, Andrew J. (A.J.) Cederoth, age 47, $321,534 total compensation
VP and General Manager Light Duty Vehicles and Joint Ventures; CEO Workhorse Custom Chassis, David Tarrant
Media Contact Engine, Pat McAuley
Media Contact Navistar Defense, Elissa Koc
Media Contact Truck, Steve Schrier
Vice President; Principal Accounting Officer; Controller, Richard C. Tarapchak, age 46
President - Truck and Engine, Troy Clarke
President - Global Truck And Engine, Eric Tech
Executive Chairman of the Board; Interim Chief Executive Officer, Lewis Campbell
Director, James H. (Jim) Keyes, age 71
Director, David D. Harrison, age 64
Director, Diane H. Gulyas, age 55
Director, Michael N. (Mike) Hammes, age 70
Director, John D. Correnti, age 64
Director, Steven J. (Steve) Klinger, age 52
Director, Eugenio Clariond, age 68
Director, Dennis D. Williams, age 58
Director, Gen. Stanley A. McChrystal, age 57
Independent Director, John Pope
Independent Director, Mark Rachesky
Independent Director, Vincent Intrieri
Auditors: KPMGLLP

LOCATIONS

HQ: Navistar International Corp.
2701 Navistar Drive, Lisle, IL 60532
Phone: 331 332-5000 **Fax:** 630 753-3982
Web: www.navistar.com

2011 Sales

US & Canada	10,674	76
Total	**13,958**	**100**

PRODUCTS/OPERATIONS

2011 Sales

Trucks	9,738	61
Parts	2,155	13
Financial services	291	2
Total	**13,958**	**100**

2011 Sales

Sales of manufactured products	13,758	99
Total	**13,958**	**100**

Selected Brands Products and Services

Engines
- MaxxForce
- MWM International

Services
- Navistar Electronics
- Navistar Financial
- Navistar Parts

Vehicles
- IC Bus
- International Trucks
- Mahindra Navistar
- Navistar Defense
- Navistar RV
- Workhorse

COMPETITORS

All American Group
BAE SYSTEMS
Blue Bird
Cummins
Daimler
Deere
Detroit Diesel
Eaton
Fiat
Force Protection
Ford Motor
Forest River
Freightliner Custom Chassis
General Dynamics
General Dynamics Land Systems
General Motors
Hino Motors
Isuzu
Leyland Trucks
Mercedes-Benz U.S. International
Mitsubishi Motors North America
Oshkosh Truck
PACCAR
Scania
Spartan Motors
Thor Industries
Tiffin Motorhomes
Toyota
UD Trucks
Volvo
Winnebago

HISTORICAL FINANCIALS

Company Type: Public

Income Statement FYE: October 31

	REVENUE ($ mil.)	NET INCOME ($ mil.)	NET PROFIT MARGIN	EMPLOYEES
10/12	12,948	(3,010)	—	16,900
10/11	13,958	1,723	12.3%	19,000
10/10	12,145	223	1.8%	15,800
10/09	11,569	320	2.8%	15,100
10/08	14,724	134	0.9%	15,900
Annual Growth	(3.2%)	—	—	1.5%

2012 Year-End Financials

Debt ratio: 52.42%
Return on equity: 987650001000000.00%
Cash ($ mil.): 1,553
Current ratio: 134.09
Long-term debt ($ mil.): 3,566
No. of shares (mil.): 79
Dividends
Yield: —
Payout: —
Market value ($ mil.): 1,485

	STOCK PRICE ($) FY Close	P/E High/Low		PER SHARE ($) Earnings	Dividends	Book Value
10/12	18.75	—	—	(43.56)	0.00	(41.73)
10/11	42.07	3	1	22.64	0.00	(0.31)
10/10	48.18	18	10	3.05	0.00	(13.55)
10/09	33.14	10	4	4.46	0.00	(25.46)
10/08	30.12	42	12	1.82	0.00	(18.96)
Annual Growth	(11.2%)	—	—	—	—	—

NBT Bancorp. Inc.

NBT Bancorp is the holding company for NBT Bank and its Pennstar Bank and Hampshire First Bank divisions which together operate about 140 branches mainly in suburban and rural areas of central and northern New York northeastern Pennsylvania western Massachusetts southern New Hampshire and northwestern Vermont. The banks offer services such as checking and savings accounts CDs and trust services. Its loan portfolio is dominated by business and commercial real estate loans. Its EPIC Advisors unit administers retirement plans while Mang Insurance Agency sells personal and commercial coverage. NBT Capital provides venture funding to growing area businesses. It's acquiring Alliance Financial.

Valued at $233 million NBT's purchase of Alliance strengthens its presence in central New York where the company operates nearly 100 branches.

NBT has expanded its market area through acquisitions. It purchased Hampshire First Bank in 2012 adding its first five branches in New Hampshire. The company entered Massachusetts through the 2011 purchase of four branches in Berkshire County that were divested by Berkshire Hills Bancorp to satisfy antitrust concerns regarding its takeover of Legacy Bancorp. It opened a fifth branch in the state in 2012.

In 2009 the bank entered northwest Vermont by establishing a branch in Burlington. It has since opened additional locations in that state as well and plans to continue to do so. NBT is eying growth in several other areas as well including upstate New York's Capital Region and northeastern Pennsylvania's Luzerne and Monroe counties.

NBT Bancorp remained profitable through the recession that began in 2008 even as real estate values fell and the number of non-performing loans in its portfolio grew. In response the company increased its loan collection efforts and focused on selling conforming real estate mortgages. It also stopped originating auto leases.

Although the company's revenues were down in 2011 its net income crept up from $57.4 million to $57.9 million. Its results were boosted by fewer loan losses and growth in its trust financial services and insurance businesses.

NBT Bancorp was founded in 1986. However NBT Bank traces its roots to 1856.

EXECUTIVES

SVP General Counsel and Secretary, F. Sheldon Prentice, age 61
President CEO and Director; President and CEO NBT Bank, Martin A. Dietrich, age 56, $495,000 total compensation
Chairman NBT Bancorp and NBT Bank, Daryl R. Forsythe, age 69, $495,000 total compensation
SEVP CFO and Secretary NBT Bancorp and NBT Bank, Michael J. Chewens, age 50, $345,000 total compensation
President Retail Banking NBT Bank; President and CEO Pennstar Bank, David E. Raven, age 49, $330,000 total compensation
EVP; President Commercial Banking NBT Bank and President Capital Region, Jeffrey M. Levy, age 50, $208,600 total compensation
President EPIC Advisors, Robert F. Judd
EVP EPIC Advisors, James M. Genthner
VP and Agricultural Lending Officer NBT Bank, Thomas Weingart
SVP and Chief Trust Officer NBT Bank, Timothy Handy
SVP and Regional Manager NBT Bank, Patricia Garrow
SVP and Regional Corporate Banking Manager NBT Bank, John Buffa
VP and Commercial Loan Officer Commercial Banking Division NBT Bank, Mary Ann Hallak-Serwatka
VP and Senior Financial Analyst Finance Division, William Whitaker Jr.
VP and Investment and Funding Systems Manager Treasury Services Department, Dewitt Yarnall
Corporate SVP and CIO, Joseph A. Stagliano
EVP and Director Human Resources, Catherine M. Scarlett
EVP Risk Management, Howard L. Atkinson
President CEO and Director; President and CEO NBT Bank, Martin A. Dietrich, age 56
Director, William C. Gumble, age 74
Director, William L. Owens, age 62
Director, John C. Mitchell, age 61
Director, Joseph G. Nasser, age 54
Director, Richard Chojnowski, age 69
Director, Joseph A. Santangelo, age 59
Director, Michael M. Murphy, age 50
Director, Patricia T. Civil, age 62
Director, Timothy E. (Tim) Delaney, age 49
Director, Robert A. Wadsworth, age 63
Director, James H. (Jim) Douglas
Auditors: KPMGLLP

LOCATIONS

HQ: NBT Bancorp Inc.
52 S. Broad St., Norwich NY 13815
Phone: 607-337-2265 **Fax:** 607-336-6545
Web: www.nbtbancorp.com

PRODUCTS/OPERATIONS

2011 Sales

	$ mil	% of total
Interest		
Loans & leases	204	63
Securities available for sale	31	10
Other	4	1
Noninterest		
Service charges on deposit accounts	21	7
Insurance & other financial services	20	6
ATM & debit card fees	11	4
Retirement plan administration fees	8	3
Trust	8	3
Other	8	3
Total	320	100

Selected Subsidiaries

Broad Street Property Associates Inc.
CNB Realty Trust
Colonial Finance Services Inc.
EPIC Advisors Inc.
FNB Financial Services Inc.
Hathaway Agency Inc.
LA Lease Inc.
Mang Insurance Agency LLC
NBT Bank National Association
NBT Capital Corp.
NBT Financial Services Inc.
NBT Holdings Inc.
NBT Services Inc.
Pennstar Bank Services Company
Pennstar Financial Services Inc.

COMPETITORS

Astoria Financial
Community Bank System
First Niagara Financial
HSBC USA
KeyCorp
M&T Bank
Sovereign Bank
TrustCo Bank Corp NY

HISTORICAL FINANCIALS

Company Type: Public

Income Statement FYE: December 31

	ASSETS ($ mil.)	NET INCOME ($ mil.)	INCOME AS % OF ASSETS	EMPLOYEES
12/11	5,598	57	1.0%	1,565
12/10	5,338	57	1.1%	1,499
12/09	5,464	52	1.0%	1,437
12/08	5,336	58	1.1%	1,411
12/07	5,201	50	1.0%	1,253
Annual Growth	1.9%	3.6%	—	5.7%

2011 Year-End Financials

Debt ratio: 7.96%
Return on equity: 10.76%
Cash ($ mil.): 129
Current ratio: —
Long-term debt ($ mil.): 445
No. of shares (mil.): 33
Dividends
Yield: —
Payout: 46.78%
Market value ($ mil.): 734

	STOCK PRICE ($) FY Close	P/E High/Low		PER SHARE ($) Earnings	Dividends	Book Value
12/11	22.13	14	10	1.71	0.00	16.23
12/10	24.15	16	12	1.66	0.80	15.46
12/09	20.37	18	10	1.53	0.80	14.69
12/08	27.96	19	10	1.80	0.80	13.24
12/07	22.82	17	11	1.51	0.79	12.29
Annual Growth	(0.8%)	—	—	3.2%	—	7.2%

NCR Corp.

Want to find NCR? Follow the money. Born during the waning days of the Wild West as National Cash Register NCR is a leading maker of ATMs. The company also makes point-of-sale (POS) terminals bar code scanners and related printer consumables. Other retail and financial systems offerings include check image processing systems and self-service kiosks for hospitality retail and travel applications. NCR's services segment provides maintenance and support as well as professional services such as systems integration and managed services. A direct sales force handles most of its sales. North America makes up about 40% of revenue and Europe about 25%.

HISTORY

John Patterson bought control of a Dayton Ohio cash register factory in 1882 and founded National Cash Register (NCR). Colonel Edward Deeds (who later became chairman) joined NCR in 1889 and hired inventor Charles Kettering in 1904 to develop an electric cash register. (The duo also developed an electric car ignition system and left NCR to start Dayton Engineering Laboratories Co. or Delco.)

By the 1920s NCR controlled 90% of the cash register market. That decade NCR introduced accounting machines which became almost as important to the company as cash registers. NCR's stock dropped from $154 to $6.87 in the crash of 1929 but by 1936 the company had fully recovered.

Responding to the commercialization of computers following WWII NCR bought computer developer Computer Research in 1952. During the 1960s the company introduced mainframe computers opened data processing centers established microelectronics research facilities and introduced disk-based computers. However NCR failed to automate its primary products –cash registers and accounting machines. In 1969 the company had record profits of $50 million; by 1971 they had plunged to $2 million.

William Anderson who became president in 1972 is credited with saving NCR. He slashed its Dayton workforce by 75% and focused the company on computing with an emphasis on retail scanners and ATMs.

In the early 1980s NCR moved from proprietary to UNIX operating systems and introduced networking equipment. In 1990 it began developing parallel processing technologies with database management specialist Teradata. That year the company won a contract to supply workstations to JCPenney stores.

Hoping to become one of the world's top PC makers in 1991 AT&T bought NCR in a $7.4 billion hostile takeover. AT&T also acquired Teradata and merged the two companies as Global Information Systems (GIS). Lars Nyberg a Swede who had led a divisional turnaround at electronics giant Philips took over GIS in 1995 and began a reorganization that would eventually cut 11000 jobs. When he joined GIS it was losing $2 million a day.

In 1996 AT&T spun off the company (renamed NCR); it suffered losses totaling nearly $4 billion during its years with AT&T. Nyberg jettisoned NCR's financially draining PC operations but beefed up the company's ATM and retail automation business by acquiring Compris Technologies (grocery automation and management products) and Dataworks (check processing software).

But losses prompted NCR to restructure in 1997 and the company slimmed down its 130-country network of independent operating units into a handful of global business units. The next year the company announced a partnership with Microsoft to further integrate NCR's Teradata systems with Microsoft's server technology making it easier for companies to create data warehouses. Also in 1998 NCR sold factories in Ireland and the US to contract manufacturer Solectron which agreed to produce NCR's hardware products for the next five years.

The following year with a narrowed focus on ATM banking retail and data warehousing systems the company acquired IBM's financial self-service operations and financial industry automation software company Gaspar.

In 2000 NCR bought Ceres Integrated Solutions a provider of customer relationship management software and it acquired information technology and outsourcing service provider 4Front Technologies for $250 million. In 2003 Nyberg handed the CEO reins to NCR president and former Teradata head Mark Hurd. Nyberg retained his chairmanship.

NCR acquired Kinetics a provider of self-service check-in systems for airlines and hotels in 2004; Kinetics' products also included systems for restaurant preordering and event ticketing.

In 2005 Hurd resigned to become CEO of Hewlett-Packard; NCR director Jim Ringler was appointed CEO on an interim basis and was named chairman. Soon after former Symbol Technologies CEO Bill Nuti was named the company's chief exec.

NCR agreed to acquire the ATM business of Tidel Technologies in 2005; the deal closed early the following year. It also acquired the assets of ID-Velocity a developer of RFID infrastructure and process management software in 2006.

The company purchased Touch Automation a developer of kiosks used to distribute DVDs in 2007. NCR also spun off its Teradata unit that year.

The company reorganized its operational structure in 2008 shifting from product-based business units to geographic divisions. The restructuring allowed NCR to reduce redundancies and process inefficiencies. Continuing to struggle with profitability in 2009 due to the global economic downturn the company cut about 10% of its workforce.

In 2009 NCR acquired TNR Holdings and DVD-Play both operators of DVD rental kiosks. TNR's kiosks operated under the Blockbuster Express brand an alliance which NCR began in 2008. NCR continued to deploy Blockbuster Express kiosks in venues such as supermarkets and convenience stores across the country.

NCR acquired Scotland-based mobile content provider Mobiqa in 2010 as part of its effort to build out its mobile software platform and expand its business in the UK. Mobiqa specialized in mobile boarding passes for airlines.

EXECUTIVES

EVP Industry Solutions Group and Global Operations, Peter A. Dorsman, age 56, $380,000 total compensation
Chairman President and CEO, William R. (Bill) Nuti, age 48, $1,000,000 total compensation
SVP CFO and Chief Accounting Officer, Robert P. (Bob) Fishman, age 48, $240,000 total compensation
SVP Human Resources, Andrea L. Ledford, age 46
SVP General Counsel and Corporate Secretary, Jennifer M. Daniels, age 48
EVP Corporate Development and CTO, John G. Bruno, age 47, $750,000 total compensation
EVP Global Sales Professional Services and Consumables, Peter A. Leav, age 41, $417,945 total compensation
VP and CIO IT Services Division, William T. (Bill) VanCuren
SVP Financial Services, Michael O'Laughlin
VP Channel Sales North America, Kathleen Curry
CEO NCR Partner North Country Business Products, Dean Crotty
Director, Edward P. (Pete) Boykin, age 73
Director, Gary J. Daichendt, age 60
Director, Richard L. (Rick) Clemmer, age 60
Chairman President and CEO, William R. (Bill) Nuti, age 48
Director, Quincy L. Allen, age 51
Auditors: PricewaterhouseCoopersLLP

LOCATIONS

HQ: NCR Corporation
3097 Satellite Blvd., Duluth GA 30096-5810
Phone: 937-445-5000 **Fax:** -1059760025
Web: www.sinopecgroup.com

2011 Sales

	$ mil.	% of total
North America	2,272	42
Europe	1,421	26
Brazil India China Middle East & Africa	849	16
South Asia Pacific	345	6
Japan & Korea	332	6
Caribbean & Latin America	224	4
Total	**5,443**	**100**

PRODUCTS/OPERATIONS

2011 Sales

	$ mil.	% of total
Product	2,744	50
Service	2,699	50
Total	**5,443**	**100**

2011 Sales

	$ mil.	% of total
Financial services	2,999	55
Retail solutions	1,755	32
Emerging industries	385	7
Entertainment	163	3
Hospitality & specialty retail	141	3
Total	**5,443**	**100**

Selected Acquisitions

Radiant Systems (2011 point-of-sale systems and services)
Mobiqa (2010 mobile content optimization)
Netkey (2009 kiosk and digital signage software)
NCI (2008 teller connectivity software)
Ambient Partners (2008 digital media merchandising)
Touch Automation (2007 digital media merchandising)

Selected Products and Services

Consumables
- Ink
- Paper
- Printer cartridges

Customer service
- Maintenance
- Professional and installation-related

Financial self-service
- Automated teller machines (ATMs)
- Support services

Payment and imaging
- Consulting outsourcing and support services
- Transactions processing systems

Retail store automation
- Consulting implementation and maintenance services
- Electronic shelf labels
- Point-of-sale workstations and scanners
- Software
- Web-enabled kiosks

COMPETITORS

ACI Worldwide
Acxiom
BancTec
Coinstar
Cummins-Allison
Datalogic Scanning
De La Rue
Dell
Diebold
Equinox Payments
Fidelity National
 Information Services
Fiserv
Fujitsu
Gilbarco
Hewlett-Packard
Honeywell
 International
IBM
Ingenico
MICROS Systems
Motorola Solutions
Netflix
Oki Electric
Optimal Group
Oracle
PAR Technology
Retalix
SANYO
SITA
Toshiba TEC
Triton Systems
Unisys
VeriFone
Wincor Nixdorf

HISTORICAL FINANCIALS

Company Type: Public

Income Statement FYE: December 31

	REVENUE ($ mil.)	NET INCOME ($ mil.)	NET PROFIT MARGIN	EMPLOYEES
12/11	5,443	53	1.0%	23,500
12/10	4,819	134	2.8%	21,000
12/09	4,612	(33)	—	21,500
12/08	5,315	228	4.3%	22,400
12/07	4,970	274	5.5%	23,200
Annual Growth	2.3%	(33.7%)	—	0.3%

2011 Year-End Financials

Debt ratio: 15.26%
Return on equity: 6.63%
Cash ($ mil.): 398
Current ratio: 160.70
Long-term debt ($ mil.): 852
No. of shares (mil.): 157
Dividends
 Yield: —
 Payout: —
Market value ($ mil.): 2,594

	STOCK PRICE ($) FY Close	P/E High	P/E Low	PER SHARE ($) Earnings	Dividends	Book Value
12/11	16.46	61	45	0.33	0.00	5.07
12/10	15.37	19	13	0.83	0.00	5.53
12/09	11.13	—	—	(0.21)	0.00	3.53
12/08	14.14	20	9	1.36	0.00	2.78
12/07	25.10	36	15	1.50	0.00	9.86
Annual Growth	(10.0%)	—	—	(31.5%)	—	(15.3%)

Netapp, Inc.

NetApp knows storage backwards and forwards. The company makes data storage systems used by businesses for archiving and backup. Its devices are used in network-attached storage (NAS) Fibre Channel and IP-based storage area network (SAN) settings. NetApp's OnCommand software product enables storage systems management while other applications focus on data loss (MetroCluster) and protection (SnapProtect). The company mainly sells to the energy financial services government health care and IT sectors through distributors including Arrow Electronics and Avnet ; direct sales account for less than one quarter of total revenue. Clients have included Deutsche Telekom and Boeing.

NetApp took an early lead in the NAS market but the rise in popularity of the relatively inexpensive devices attracted a host of competitors. Never content to cede market share for any storage offering industry leader EMC sells NAS products. Companies such as Sun Microsystems used acquisitions to crack the market and even former customer Dell now makes its own NAS devices. Dell is one of a number of companies that make Microsoft Windows-based NAS products.

However NetApp moved beyond the role of pure-play NAS vendor. Responding to customer demand it expanded the functionality of its storage filers to work within more complex SAN configurations. The company also provides data security appliances and controllers for storage virtualization. Its products are branded with yet another three letter designation FAS which stands for fibre-attached storage which denotes a storage system connecting to an IP network via a Fibre channel connection.

NetApp continues to add functionality to its product line to enter new markets and adapt to evolving technology. In 2011 the company bought Massachusetts-based Akorri Networks a developer of data center management software. The deal was intended to better position NetApp to offer products to the growing market for outsourced data management and give it a leg up in the areas of data capacity and network performance planning and management.

Also that year NetApp purchased the Engenio external storage systems business of LSI in an all-cash transaction valued at around $480 million. The company made the acquisition to address emerging segments of the storage market namely video (including video capture and video surveillance) and high-performance computing (used in genomics sequencing and other scientific research applications). It also benefited from the unit's established OEM business for server-attached and embedded storage products.

NetApp's sales rose 22% in fiscal 2012 due to healthy demand for its storage efficiency and data management products; the company also saw sales of hardware maintenance contracts rise. Profits however shrank for the year compared with 2011 due to lower margin products (E-Series) and the impact of discounting; reduced manufacturing costs offset those decreases to some degree. NetApp's revenue has grown steadily over the past decade as has its net income with the exception of 2009 when profits dipped.

HISTORY

David Hitz and James Lau (both EVPs) along with Michael Malcolm founded Network Appliance in 1992. The trio saw a market for file servers hardware that takes the storage duties out of high-performance UNIX-based computers and speeds data flow.

Donald Valentine of Sequoia Capital invested in Network Appliance in 1994 and was named chairman. He promptly brought on board as CEO Daniel Warmenhoven the top executive of telecommunications company Network Equipment Technologies. (It was the return of a favor –Warmenhoven had given Valentine a tip on investing in a late-1980s fledgling named Cisco Systems.) Warmenhoven ditched the company's network of resellers and built an in-house sales and marketing unit. Network Appliance went public in 1995.

The company in 1996 forged a deal with Microsoft to let Network Appliance's file servers support the software giant's Internet-based network file storage standard. The beefed-up sales emphasis helped the company turn its first profit in fiscal 1996. The next year it bought online caching software specialist IMC. Acquisition costs dropped earnings for fiscal 1997.

Network Appliance furthered its inroads into Europe the next year when it sold data storage and retrieval equipment to UK-based Internet service provider Demon Internet. In 1999 the company introduced servers that transmitted audio and video data streams.

Network Appliance acquired two software companies in 2000: Orca Systems (Windows NT and UNIX systems clustering) and WebManage Technologies (data management and distribution). Responding to a slumping economy the following year the company announced a restructuring plan that included job cuts.

In 2004 it acquired Spinnaker Networks for approximately $300 million in stock. The following year it acquired tape emulation software maker Alacritus for about $11 million in cash and network security appliance maker Decru for $272 million in cash and stock.

Network Appliance sold its NetCache content delivery business in 2006 to Blue Coat Systems. Later that year Network Appliance acquired data management software developer Topio for about $160 million in cash.

In 2008 Network Appliance officially changed its name to NetApp. Also that year the company acquired storage resource management specialist Onaro. The purchase gave NetApp software that enterprises use to optimize storage service levels.

Dan Warmenhoven who joined NetApp as its CEO in 1994 stepped aside in 2009 to become executive chairman in a planned management succession. Tom Georgens a NetApp executive since 2005 who became president and COO in 2008 was promoted to CEO while keeping the president's title.

EXECUTIVES

President CEO and Director, Thomas (Tom) Georgens, age 52, $754,038 total compensation
Vice Chairman, Thomas F. (Tom) Mendoza, age 60
Chairman, Daniel J. Warmenhoven, age 61, $591,923 total compensation
EVP, David Hitz, age 49, $322,500 total compensation
EVP, James K. Lau, age 53
SVP and Chief Scientist, Steve Kleiman
VP; General Manager NAS and V-Series Business Units, Brendon Howe
VP; General Manager Virtualization and Enterprise Applications Business Unit, Philip (Phil) Brotherton, age 51
SVP Operations, Mark J. Bluth
EVP Customer Advocacy, Ed Deenihan
EVP Field Operations, Robert E. (Rob) Salmon, age 51, $530,000 total compensation
EVP Product Operations, Manish Goel, age 47, $425,576 total compensation
EVP HR, Gwendolyn (Gwen) McDonald
SVP and Chief Technology Officer, John A. (Jay) Kidd
Chief Marketing Officer, Christine Heckart
SVP Business Operations, Tom Gerstenberger
SVP and CIO, Marina Levinson
VP Solutions and Alliances, Patrick Rogers
VP Global Partner Sales, Julie Parrish
SVP and Chief Strategy Officer, Jonathan Kissane, age 42
SVP and CTO, Brian Pawlowski
SVP; General Manager Technology Enablement and Solutions Organization, Rich Clifton
VP Strategy and Market Development, Bob Pearse
VP; General Manager SAN/iSAN Business Unit, Joel Reich
VP Americas Channel Sales, Todd Palmer

SVP; General Manager Europe Middle East and Africa, Andreas Konig
VP; General Manager Cloud Solutions and Core Product Software, Tim Russell
SVP; General Manager US Public Sector, Mark Weber
VP Advanced Technology Group, Scott Dawkins
VP; General Manager Asia Pacific, Simon Green
SVP Sales Americas, Eric Mann
VP Strategic Support, Clay Hendrix
VP Customer Advocacy, Dick Pocock
VP; General Manager Japan, Ty McConney
VP; General Manager Storage Management and Application Integration Business Unit, Krishnan Padmanabhan
Director Industry Standards; Chair SNIA IP Storage Forum, David Dale
VP Investor Relations, Tara Dhillon
General Manager Latin America and the Caribbean, Matt Gharegozlou
General Manager Canada, Jeff Goldstein
VP; General Manager Data Protection Group, Edward Sharp
SVP General Counsel and Secretary, Matthew K. Fawcett, age 44
Office of CTO, Val Bercovici
Manager Product Public Relations, Ryan Lowry
VP Global System Integrators, W. Thomas Stanley
VP; General Manager IBM Global Alliance, Richard J. Scurfield
Chief Strategy Officer, Vic Mahadevan
CFO and EVP Finance, Nicholas R. Noviello, age 42
President CEO and Director, Thomas (Tom) Georgens, age 52
Director, George T. Shaheen, age 68
Director, Richard P. (Rick) Wallace, age 52
Vice Chairman, Thomas F. (Tom) Mendoza, age 60
Director, Jeffry R. Allen, age 60
Director, Nicholas G. (Nick) Moore, age 69
Director, Robert T. Wall, age 67
Director, Alan L. Earhart, age 68
Director, T. Michael (Mike) Nevens, age 62
Director, Gerald D. (Jerry) Held, age 64
Auditors: Deloitte&ToucheLLP

LOCATIONS

HQ: NetApp Inc.
495 E. Java Dr., Sunnyvale CA 94089
Phone: 408-822-6000 **Fax:** 408-822-4501
Web: www.netapp.com

2012 Sales

	$ mil.	% of total
Americas	3,529	57
Europe Middle East & Africa	1,936	31
Asia Pacific	767	12
Total	**6,233**	**100**

PRODUCTS/OPERATIONS

2012 Sales

	$ mil.	% of total
Product	4,238	68
Software	810	13
Service	1,184	19
Total	**6,233**	**100**

COMPETITORS

Data Domain
Dell
Dot Hill
EMC
Hewlett-Packard
Hitachi Data Systems
IBM
Isilon Systems
LSI Corp.
Microsoft
Oracle
Quantum Corporation
XIO
Xyratex

HISTORICAL FINANCIALS

Company Type: Public

Income Statement

FYE: April 27

	REVENUE ($ mil.)	NET INCOME ($ mil.)	NET PROFIT MARGIN	EMPLOYEES
04/12	6,233	605	9.7%	12,149
04/11	5,122	673	13.1%	10,212
04/10	3,931	400	10.2%	8,333
04/09	3,406	86	2.5%	7,976
04/08	3,303	309	9.4%	7,645
Annual Growth	17.2%	18.2%	—	12.3%

2012 Year-End Financials

Debt ratio: 12.61%
Return on equity: 14.10%
Cash ($ mil.): 1,549
Current ratio: 193.95
Long-term debt ($ mil.): —
No. of shares (mil.): 364
Dividends
Yield: —
Payout: —
Market value ($ mil.): 14,230

	STOCK PRICE ($) FY Close	P/E High	P/E Low	PER SHARE ($) Earnings	Dividends	Book Value
04/12	39.03	33	20	1.58	0.00	11.78
04/11	52.11	32	17	1.71	0.00	10.11
04/10	34.67	31	14	1.13	0.00	7.29
04/09	18.63	105	40	0.26	0.00	5.00
04/08	23.44	44	22	0.86	0.00	4.98
Annual Growth	13.6%	—	—	16.4%	—	24.0%

New York Community Bancorp Inc.

It's big banking in the Big Apple and beyond. New York Community Bancorp is the holding company for one of the largest thrifts in the US New York Community Bank as well as New York Commercial Bank (also dba Atlantic Bank) and seven other banking divisions. In its home state New York Community Bank operates through Queens County Savings Bank Richmond County Savings Bank Roosevelt Savings Bank and Roslyn Savings Bank. It serves customers in New Jersey through its Garden State Community Bank division. New York Community Bank also does business asAmTrust Bank which operates in Arizona and Florida and Ohio Savings Bank. Altogether New York Community Bancorp has about 275 bank branches in five states.

Serving both consumers and business customers the banks provide standard services such as checking and savings accounts CDs IRAs credit cards mortgages and loans. They offer life and long-term care insurance through an agreement with third-party provider LPL Financial. New York Community Bancorp also owns investment advisory firm Peter B. Cannell & Co.

Multifamily mortgage loans (with an emphasis on rent-regulated apartment buildings) are the company's key assets making up approximately 70% of its loan book. New York Community Bancorp prefers rent-regulated properties because they tend to have lower-than-average tenant turnover and can often be expected to bring in steady income during economic downturns. The company also focuses on loans secured by commercial real estate in New York and New Jersey.

It originates one- to four-family residential mortgages and home equity loans through brokers in all 50 states but usually sells these loans to government-sponsored entities like Fannie Mae and Freddie Mac with servicing rights retained. After the economic downturn that began in 2007 New York Community Bancorp curtailed its business construction and real estate acquisition and development lending. Weakened demand for home loans cut into the company's mortgage banking fee income and contributed to a decline in earnings in 2011.

New York Community Bancorp has been growing through acquisitions; it has made about ten since 2000. It acquired the failed AmTrust Bank through an FDIC-assisted transaction in 2009. The deal which also brought in Ohio Savings added about 65 branches in new markets and marked the company's first foray beyond the New York metropolitan area. In 2010 New York Community Bancorp expanded its presence in Arizona by acquiring the six branches of the failed Desert Hills Bank also in an FDIC-assisted transaction. The acquired institution became part of AmTrust Bank. In 2012 New York Community Bank acquired some $2.3 billion in deposits mainly short-term CDs but also money market accounts from Aurora Bank.

New York Community Bancorp typically does not open new stand-alone branches but has been increasing its presence in its market areas by adding locations inside grocery stores and extending business hours.

EXECUTIVES

SEVP COO and Director; SEVP and COO New York Community Bank; SEVP New York Commercial Bank, Robert Wann, age 57, $700,000 total compensation
President CEO and Director New York Community Bankcorp New York Community Bank and New York Commercial Bank, Joseph R. Ficalora, age 65, $1,000,000 total compensation
SEVP and CFO New York Community Bancorp and New York Community Bank, Thomas R. (Tom) Cangemi, age 43, $560,000 total compensation
EVP Chief Corporate Governance Officer and Corporate Secretary, R. Patrick Quinn
Chairman, Dominick Ciampa, age 78
Director; President and CEO Atlantic Bank Division New York Commercial Bank, Spiros J. Voutsinas, age 78
EVP and Director Investor Relations and Corporate Communications, Ilene A. Angarola
SEVP and Chief Lending Officer New York Community Bancorp and New York Community Bank; SEVP New York Commercial Bank, James J. Carpenter, age 51, $500,000 total compensation
EVP and Chief Accounting Officer; EVP New York Community Bank and New York Commercial Bank, John J. Pinto, age 41, $330,000 total compensation
Director, James J. O'Donovan, age 69
SEVP COO and Director; SEVP and COO New York Community Bank; SEVP New York Commercial Bank, Robert Wann, age 57
President CEO and Director New York Community Bankcorp New York Community Bank and New York Commercial Bank, Joseph R. Ficalora, age 65
Director, John M. Tsimbinos, age 74
Director, Max L. Kupferberg, age 92
Director, Michael J. Levine, age 67
Director, Maureen E. Clancy, age 80

Director; President and CEO Atlantic Bank Division New York Commercial Bank, Spiros J. Voutsinas, age 78
Director, Robert S. Farrell, age 86
Director, William C. Frederick, age 84
Director, Guy V. Molinari, age 83
Director, Hanif W. (Wally) Dahya, age 56
Auditors: KPMGLLP

LOCATIONS

HQ: New York Community Bancorp Inc.
615 Merrick Ave., Westbury NY 11590
Phone: 516-683-4100 **Fax:** 410-740-2985
Web: www.martekbio.com

2011 Locations

	No.
New	157
New	51
Ohio	28
Florida	25
Arizona	14
Total	**275**

PRODUCTS/OPERATIONS

2011 Sales

	$ mil.	% of total
Interest		
Mortgage & other loans	1,638	78
Securities & money market investments	228	11
Noninterest		
Mortgage banking income	80	4
Fee income	44	2
Net gain on sales of securities	36	2
Bank-owned life insurance	28	1
Other	44	2
Total	**2,251**	**100**

COMPETITORS

Apple Bank for Savings
Astoria Financial
Bank of America
Citigroup
Emigrant Bank
Flushing Financial
HSBC USA
Investors Bancorp
JPMorgan Chase
Provident Financial Services
Ridgewood Savings Bank
Safra Bank
TD Bank USA
Valley National Bancorp
Wells Fargo

HISTORICAL FINANCIALS

Company Type: Public

Income Statement FYE: December 31

	ASSETS ($ mil.)	NET INCOME ($ mil.)	INCOME AS % OF ASSETS	EMPLOYEES
12/11	42,024	480	1.1%	3,348
12/10	41,190	541	1.3%	3,883
12/09	42,153	398	0.9%	3,970
12/08	32,466	77	0.2%	2,699
12/07	30,579	279	0.9%	2,834
Annual Growth	8.3%	14.5%	—	4.3%

2011 Year-End Financials

Debt ratio: 23.40%
Return on equity: 8.63%
Cash ($ mil.): 2,001
Current ratio: —
Long-term debt ($ mil.): 9,835
No. of shares (mil.): 437
Dividends
Yield: —
Payout: 91.74%
Market value ($ mil.): 5,410

	STOCK PRICE ($) FY Close	P/E High	P/E Low	PER SHARE ($) Earnings	Dividends	Book Value
12/11	12.37	17	10	1.09	0.00	12.73
12/10	18.85	16	12	1.24	1.00	12.69
12/09	14.51	13	7	1.13	1.00	12.39
12/08	11.96	90	48	0.23	1.00	12.23
12/07	17.58	22	18	0.90	1.00	12.92
Annual Growth	(8.4%)	—	—	4.9%	—	(0.4%)

Newell Rubbermaid, Inc.

Newell Rubbermaid wants to get its products into your drawers your kitchen cabinets and your workbench. The go-to company for men women and children makes housewares (Rubbermaid plastic products Calphalon cookware) hardware (Amerock cabinet hardware IRWIN and Lenox hand tools) home furnishings (Levolor blinds) juvenile products (Graco) hair products (Goody) and office items (DYMO Sanford Sharpie). Newell Rubbermaid sells its items to mass retailers (Target) and home and office supply stores (Staples). Past Gillette executive Michael Cowhig is chairman. Michael Polk took over as president and CEO in 2011 prior to the 2012 retirement of ex-Procter & Gamble executive and former CEO Mark Ketchum.

HISTORY

Businessmen in Ogdensburg New York advanced curtain rod maker W.F. Linton Co. $1000 to relocate from Rhode Island in the early 1900s. Local wholesaler Edgar Newell signed off on the loan; when the company went bankrupt in 1903 he was forced to take over. The company renamed Newell Manufacturing set up plants in Canada and Freeport Illinois to ease shipping costs and speed delivery.

Production expanded into towel racks ice picks and other items; Woolworth's decision to carry Newell's products turned the company into a national supplier. Edgar Newell died in 1920. The company made its first acquisition in 1938 buying window treatment specialist Drapery Hardware.

The Newell companies were consolidated in the mid-1960s into a single corporation. Daniel Ferguson was named president in 1965 and served alongside his CEO father Leonard one of Newell's original employees. During his tenure Daniel hitched the company's future to the growing dominance of large discount stores. Newell went from a $14 million family business to a global multiline conglomerate by acquiring products that it distributed to these big buyers. The company went public in 1972 and bought paint applicator maker EZ Paintr the next year. By 1978 sales reached $100 million.

Newell moved into housewares with the acquisitions of Mirro (cookware 1983) and the much larger Anchor Hocking (glassware 1987). It then bought office supply companies W.T. Rogers and Keene Manufacturing in 1991 and Sanford (writing instruments) in 1992. That year Daniel bowed out of active management.

The company began a global push with its purchase of Corning's European Consumer Products business (1994) and it kept busy at home by buying Insilco's Rolodex unit and Rubbermaid's office products business (both 1997). William Sovey succeeded Daniel as chairman in 1997 and John McDonough became CEO. Its 1998 acquisitions included Calphalon (upscale cookware) Panex (Brazil bakeware) and Rotring Group (Germany writing instruments).

Originally a balloon maker in the 1920s by the mid-1930s Ohio's Wooster Rubber had acquired the Rubbermaid product line of rubber housewares. It went public in 1955 and two years later changed its name to Rubbermaid. During the 1980s the company enjoyed a decade of phenomenal growth. However —despite product innovations —increased material costs a competitive retail climate and weak customer service began dulling Rubbermaid's luster. Profits plunged even as it reached record sales.

Newell's $6 billion purchase of Rubbermaid in 1999 sealed its biggest deal yet and resulted in a name change: Newell Rubbermaid. Also in 1999 Newell Rubbermaid bought the consumer products division of McKechnie (window furnishings and cabinet hardware) and three French firms: Ateliers 28 (drapery hardware) Reynolds (pens and pencils) and Ceanothe Holdings (picture frames). The company in 2000 bought Mersch (picture frames; France Germany) and Brio (picture frames France).

In late 2000 CEO McDonough resigned and Sovey replaced him. In 2001 Newell Rubbermaid acquired Gillette's stationery business including the Parker Paper Mate Liquid Paper and Waterman brands. The same month Joseph Galli succeeded Sovey as CEO; Sovey reassumed his position as chairman (and left in mid-2004).

In April 2002 Newell completed its acquisition of American Tool Companies (now IRWIN Industrial Tool Company North America) and announced the creation of two new operating divisions —North American hand tools and North American power tool accessories –to focus on its US and Canadian business segments. In June 2002 after multiple challenges from the FTC Newell Rubbermaid abandoned plans to sell its Anchor Hocking glass business to glassware maker Libbey Inc.

In January 2003 Newell Rubbermaid acquired American Saw & Manufacturing for $450 million in cash and in March the company sold its Cosmolab business to CSI East an affiliate of Cosmetic Specialties. The same year Newell Rubbermaid moved its corporate headquarters from Illinois to Alpharetta Georgia (relocated again in 2004 to Atlanta). In February 2004 the company sold Panex and the remainder of its European picture frames business. That April Newell sold its Anchor Hocking Glass Burnes Picture Frame and Mirro Cookware divisions to Global Home Products LLC. In July Newell Rubbermaid sold Little Tikes Commercial Play Systems a unit of Newell's Little Tikes division to PlayPower Inc. Newell retained the consumer portion of its Little Tikes division until November 2006 when it was sold to MGA Entertainment.

CEO Joseph Galli resigned in October 2005. A board member with three decades of experience at Procter & Gamble Mark Ketchum stepped in as interim CEO. He was made permanent in February 2006. Michael Cowhig with 38 years at Gillette became Newell Rubbermaid's chairman in 2010.

In a move that expanded the company's juvenile products business and positioned it to expand in Asia Newell Rubbermaid acquired Japan's Aprica Kassai a maker of strollers car seats and other children's gear in April 2008. Later in the year it closed on Aprica's operations in China. Also in 2008 the company purchased Illinois-based Technical Concepts Holdings LLC a provider of washroom hygiene products.

Mark Ketchum who retired in 2012 as chief executive was replaced by Mike Polk a former Unilever and Kraft Foods executive.

EXECUTIVES

President CEO and Director, Michael B. (Mike) Polk, age 51
President DYMO, Philip Damiano
President Technology GBU, David A. Klatt Jr., age 43
SVP and Chief Customer Officer, Paul G. Boitmann, age 51
President Rubbermaid Canada, Ric L. Kern Jr.
President Decor GBU, Kristine L. (Kristie) Juster
President Rubbermaid Consumer Products GBU, Jeffrey D. (Jeff) Hohler
Chairman, Michael T. Cowhig, age 65
CFO, Douglas L. (Doug) Martin, age 49
President Corporate Development, Hartley D. (Buddy) Blaha, age 47, $447,917 total compensation
President Everyday Writing GBU, Bill Mullenix
President Newell Rubbermaid International, J. Eduardo Senf, age 53
EVP Human Resources and Corporate Communications and Chief Human Resources Officer, James M. (Jim) Sweet, age 60
SVP and Chief Marketing Officer, Theodore W. (Ted) Woehrle, age 50
Group VP Finance Tools and Hardware, Ronald L. Hardnock, age 40
Corporate Director Packaging, David Hoffer
VP Investor Relations, Nancy O'Donnell
VP Global Licensing, Nathaniel S. (Nat) Milburn, age 39
President Rubbermaid Commercial Products, Neil Eibeler
President Baby & Parenting Essentials GBU, Doug McGraw
President Newell Professional Group, William A. (Bill) Burke III, age 51
VP Supply Chain Home and Family Group, Chris Van Dyke
SVP Program Management Office and CIO, Gordon C. Steele, age 61
President Beauty and Style GBU, A.J. Ross
EVP and CFO, Juan R. Figuereo, age 56, $35,666 total compensation
VP Corporate Controller and Chief Accounting Officer, John B. Ellis
VP Marketing Rubbermaid Consumer Global Business Unit, Steve Pawl
President Newell Consumer Group, G. Penny McIntyre, age 50, $515,625 total compensation
VP E-Business and Interactive Marketing, Bert DuMars
Senior Manager Investor Relations, Alisha Pennix
Manager Public Relations, Connie Bryant
Manager Public Relations Office Products Group, Susan Wassel
VP Corporate Communications, David Doolittle
SVP General Counsel and Secretary, John Stipancich, age 43
President Office Products North Americaand Markers Highlighters Art and Office Organization GBU, Ben Gadbois
VP Global Marketing Services Office Products, Krista DiBerardino
VP Corporate Philanthropy; President Newell Rubbermaid Foundation, Jackie Parker
VP Marketing Newell Rubbermaid Baby and Parenting Essentials Global Business Unit, Andrea Freeman
President Industrial Products and Services GBU, Rich Wuerthele
President Fine Writing GBU, Jean-Charles Hita
President Culinary Lifestyles GBU, Michael Halak
President Construction Tools & Accessories GBU, Ross Porter
President Hardware GBU, Tony Hair
Chief Design and Research & Development Officer, Charles Jones
Chief Supply Chain Officer, Meredith Stevens
Director, Raymond G. Viault, age 67
Director, Thomas E. Clarke, age 60
Director, Domenico De Sole, age 68
President CEO and Director, Michael B. (Mike) Polk, age 51
Director, Michael A. (Mike) Todman, age 55
Director, Elizabeth Cuthbert-Millett, age 55
Director, Cynthia A. Montgomery, age 59
Director, Scott S. Cowen, age 65
Director, Kevin Conroy, age 51
Director, Mark D. Ketchum, age 62
Director, Steven J. (Steve) Strobel, age 54
Independent Director, Domenico Sole
Auditors: Ernst&YoungLLP

LOCATIONS

HQ: Newell Rubbermaid Inc.
3 Glenlake Pkwy., Atlanta GA 30328
Phone: 770-418-7000 **Fax:** 661-255-3960
Web: valencia.com

2011 Sales

	$ mil.	% of total
US	3,915	67
Europe Middle East & Africa	815	15
Asia/Pacific	438	7
Canada	376	6
Latin America	318	5
Total	**5,864**	**100**

PRODUCTS/OPERATIONS

2011 Sales

	$ mil.	% of total
Home & family	2,390	41
Office products	1,778	30
Tools hardware & commercial products	1,695	29
Total	**5,864**	**100**

Selected Brands and Trade Names

Cleaning organization and decor
- Brute
- Kirsch
- Levolor
- Roughneck
- Rubbermaid
- TakeAlongs
- TC

Office products
- Accent
- Berol
- DYMO
- Eberhard Farber
- Expo
- Liquid Paper
- Paper Mate
- Parker
- rotring
- Sharpie
- Uni-Ball (under license)
- Vis-a-vis
- Waterman

Tools and hardware
- Amerock
- Bulldog
- Irwin
- Lenox
- Quick-Grip
- Marathon
- Shur-Line
- Strait-Line
- Unibit
- Vise-Grip

Home and family
- Ace
- Aprica
- Calphalon
- Calphalon One
- Cooking with Calphalon
- Goody
- Graco
- Katana
- Kitchen Essentials
- Solano
- Teutonia

COMPETITORS

ACCO Brands
Acme United
Alticor
Avery Dennison
Beam
BIC
Bridgestone
Coleman
Cooper Industries
Crayola
Decorator Industries
Dixon Ticonderoga
Faber-Castell
Home Products International
Katy Industries
Knape & Vogt
Lancaster Colony
Libbey
Lifetime Brands
Myers Industries
Owens-Illinois
Springs Global US
Sterilite
Tupperware Brands
Uniek
Wilton Brands
WKI Holding
ZAG Industries

HISTORICAL FINANCIALS

Company Type: Public

Income Statement

FYE: December 31

	REVENUE ($ mil.)	NET INCOME ($ mil.)	NET PROFIT MARGIN	EMPLOYEES
12/11	5,864	125	2.1%	19,900
12/10	5,759	292	5.1%	19,400
12/09	5,577	285	5.1%	19,500
12/08	6,470	(52)	—	20,400
12/07	6,407	467	7.3%	22,000
Annual Growth	(2.2%)	(28.0%)	—	(2.5%)

2011 Year-End Financials

Debt ratio: 35.33%
Return on equity: 6.77%
Cash ($ mil.): 170
Current ratio: 129.33
Long-term debt ($ mil.): 1,809
No. of shares (mil.): 288
Dividends
Yield: —
Payout: 69.05%
Market value ($ mil.): 4,656

	STOCK PRICE ($) FY Close	P/E High/Low		PER SHARE ($) Earnings	Dividends	Book Value
12/11	16.15	47	26	0.42	0.00	6.41
12/10	18.18	18	13	0.96	0.20	6.55
12/09	15.01	16	4	0.97	0.26	6.40
12/08	9.78	—	—	(0.19)	0.84	5.83
12/07	25.88	19	15	1.68	0.84	8.12
Annual Growth	(11.1%)	—	—	(29.3%)	—	(5.7%)

Newmont Mining Corp. (Holding Co.)

Newmont Mining goes for the gold. Once the clear #1 gold producing company in the world Newmont now ranks #2 behind Barrick. Newmont produces about 6 million ounces of gold annually and has proved and probable reserves of about 99 million ounces of gold and 10 million pounds of copper. It has significant assets in the US mining in Nevada since 1965. It also has assets in Australia Canada Ghana Indonesia Mexico Peru and New Zealand. Newmont mines copper mostly through its Batu Hijau project in Indonesia and Boddington project in Australia. The company produced about 350 million pounds of copper in 2011. Operations in North America and South America account for about half of Newmont's gold production.

Operations

The company's North American operations include mines in Nevada's Carlin Trend one of the largest gold-mining areas in North America. Newmont also holds stakes in gold mines in Mexico (44% in the La Herradura joint venture and related properties in the Sonora Desert) and in Indonesia (Batu Hijau a 32%-owned mine that produces both copper and gold). It also owns the Boddington project one of Australia's largest gold mining properties. Newmont placed its development of Hope Bay in Canada on hold in early 2012 to shift focus to other projects in its pipeline with better near-term potential.

The company entered a joint venture with Canada-based miner Stellar Pacific Ventures in 2011 to move into Mali in Western Africa and participate in the exploration of the Namarana gold property. The agreement allows Newmont to earn as much as a 51% stake in the project during its first phase and up to 85% during the second phase.

Newmont's operations in Ghana consist of one operating mine and a development project; it sees the country as the site of its next big operating district. The company's Akyem project could produce between 8 million to 9 million ounces of gold over time which along with the Subika expansion could boost annual production in Ghana to approximately 1 million ounces and make Africa Newmont's fastest growing region.

Financial Analysis

Although production dipped by 4% in 2011 a rise in the market prices of gold and copper pushed Newmont's revenues to $10.4 billion up 9% over the previous year. Net income however was down significantly falling from $2.3 billion in 2010 to $366 million in 2011 after a $1.6 billion write-down of the company's Hope Bay project in Canada and another charge related to its Fronteer acquisition. However in 2011 gold was selling for a net average price of $1562 an ounce (up 28% from 2010) and copper for $3.43 a pound (up 3% from the previous year) which helped offset the loss.

Strategy

Newmont's long-term strategy includes developing its assets to grow its annual attributable gold production to about 7 million ounces by 2017 an increase of 35% from its attributable gold production in 2011 of 5.2 million ounces.

The company moved to advance its project pipeline in 2011 by initiating construction at its Akyem project in Ghana Conga in Peru and the Tanami shaft in Australia. However Newmont halted construction on its Conga project in 2011 following several protests in the region. An independent review confirmed that Newmont's environmental impact assessment met Peruvian and international standards so Newmont will continue development of Conga based on the costs required to generate acceptable returns as well as support from the local community and government of Peru. Newmont estimated that potential delays on developing Conga and its other Peruvian projects could defer as much as 1 million ounces of gold production by 2017.

In addition to aggressively developing its projects the company pursues strategic acquisitions. In 2011 Newmont acquired Fronteer Gold a Canadian company with properties in the US Turkey and Peru for $2.3 billion. The deal significantly expands Newmont's holdings in Nevada.

HISTORY

Colonel William Boyce Thompson a flamboyant trader founded the Newmont Co. in 1916 to trade his various oil and mining stocks. The Newmont name was a combination of New York and Montana where Thompson grew up. The company was renamed Newmont Corporation in 1921 and Newmont Mining Corporation in 1925 when it went public. Thompson died five years later. During its first 10 years Newmont focused on investing and trading stocks in promising mineral properties including US copper and gold mines.

Newmont's gold mines bolstered the company throughout the Depression. During the 1940s its focus shifted to copper and Africa. It bought Idarado Mining in 1943 and Newmont Oil in 1944 (sold 1988). The company grew during the 1950s by acquiring stakes in North American companies involved in offshore oil drilling nickel mining and uranium oxide production. It also bought stakes in copper mines in South Africa and South America.

Newmont started producing gold from the Carlin Trend in Nevada in the mid-1960s. It bought a one-third stake in Foote Mineral (iron alloys and lithium) in 1967; by 1974 it controlled 83% of the company (sold 1987). In 1969 Newmont merged with Magma Copper one of the US's largest copper companies. A Newmont-led consortium bought Peabody Coal the US's largest coal producer from Kennecott Copper in 1977 (sold 1990).

After its 1980 discovery of one of the century's most important gold stakes Gold Quarry in the Carlin Trend Newmont spent a decade fending off takeover attempts. The company began selling off noncore operations to focus on gold. Magma Copper was spun off to stockholders in 1988.

A proposed merger with American Barrick Resources a major stockholder collapsed in 1991. Former Freeport-McMoRan VP Ronald Cambre became CEO in 1993 and that year the company began mining in Peru. A 1994 action by the French government one of Newmont's partners in Peru's Yanacocha Mine kicked off a protracted battle over the property's ownership. The claim was upheld in 1998 raising Newmont's stake to more than 50%. Reflecting its increasing interest in Indonesia in 1996 Newmont and Japan's Sumitomo formed a joint venture to exploit gold reserves on Sumbawa Island. In 1997 the company increased its gold reserves and territory by acquiring Santa Fe Pacific Gold for about $2.1 billion.

For years Newmont and Barrick Gold Corporation operated interlocked mining claims in Nevada's Carlin Trend which prevented optimal exploitation by either company. In 1999 both companies agreed to a mutually advantageous land swap in the region.

In 2000 an Indonesian court ordered the closure of the Minahasa mine over a local tax dispute; the company's joint venture agreed to pay a $500000 penalty to settle the matter. Newmont was fined $500000 after a mercury spill at its Yanacocha mine. That year Newmont settled the lingering ownership dispute over the Yanacocha.

Company president Wayne Murdy became CEO early in 2001 (he replaced Cambre as chairman in 2002). Newmont acquired Battle Mountain Gold in 2001 for nearly $600 million. Late that year Newmont moved to acquire Australia's top gold producer Normandy Mining (setting off a bidding war with AngloGold) as well as Canadian gold miner France-Nevada Mining Corp. AngloGold bowed out of the "battle for Normandy" in early 2002 but later completed a three-way deal in which it acquired Normandy and Franco-Nevada.

In 2003 Newmont reduced its stake in Kinross Gold from 14% to 5% and it considered selling off the Ghanaian interests it had gained in the Normandy merger. However in 2004 Newmont literally discovered a gold mine in Ghana –a major district with some 16 million equity ounces of gold.

Murdy retired in 2007; taking the helm was former CEO Richard O'Brien. In 2007 Newmont spun off its royalty assets acquired in 2002 as Franco-Nevada Corporation. Those assets then operated as Newmont Mining Corporation of Canada now a subsidiary of Newmont.

In 2008 Newmont bought Canadian gold producer Miramar Mining which controls the Hope Bay project for about $1.5 billion. It also acquired in 2009 a 33% stake in Boddington from AngloGold Ashanti for about $1 billion giving Newmont 100% of the Boddington project.

EXECUTIVES

SVP and Chief Sustainability Officer, David A. Baker
Chairman, Vincent A. Calarco, age 69
SVP Asia Pacific Operations, Jeffrey R. Huspeni, age 56
VP and Controller, David A. Ottewell
President ceo and Director, Richard T. O'Brien, age 57, $1,025,000 total compensation
SVP South American Operations, Carlos Santa Cruz, age 56
VP and Treasurer, Thomas P. Mahoney, age 56
EVP and CFO, Russell D. Ball, age 43, $544,667 total compensation
VP Internal Audit, John W. Kitlen
Director Investor Relations, Karli Anderson
EVP Discovery and Development, Guy Lansdown, age 51, $574,000 total compensation
EVP Strategic Development, Randy Engel, age 45, $486,917 total compensation
SVP General Counsel and Secretary, Stephen P. Gottesfeld, age 44
VP Planning and Tax, David V. Gutierrez, age 57
VP Indonesia Country Manager and Corporate Development, Blake M. Rhodes
SVP Business Opportunity Delivery, Ramzi R. Fawaz
VP Corporate Development, David R. Faley
EVP Sustainability and External Affairs, Brian A. Hill, age 52, $625,660 total compensation
EVP Human Resources and Communications, Bill MacGowan, age 54
Group Executive Communications, Omar Jabara
VP Investor Relations, John Seaberg
SVP North America Operations, Thomas R. Kerr, age 51
VP Health Safety and Security, Michael J. Byrne

VP Information Technology and CIO, Gerald Gluscic
VP Value Assurance, Tom McCulley
President Secretary, Jeffrey K. Reeser
Senior Vice President Exploration, Grigore Simon
VP Business Opportunity Creation, Cindy Williams
President Business Opportunity Development, Alan Fitzpatrick
VP Business Excellence, Todd White
VP Government Relations, Mary Beth Donnelly
SVP African Operations, David C. Schummer, age 40
Director Investor Relations, Monica Brisnehan
President; Chief Operating Officer, Gary J. Goldberg, age 53
Senior Vice President - South American Operations, Carlos Cruz
Regional Vice President Human Resources, Dave Kern
Chief Executive Officer; Director, Richard Brien
Vice President; Controller, Christopher Howson
Chief Executive Officer; Director, Richard OBrien
Director, Glen A. Barton, age 72
President ceo and Director, Richard T. O'Brien, age 57
Director, Simon R. Thompson, age 52
Director, Michael S. Hamson, age 71
Director, John B. Prescott, age 71
Director, Donald C. Roth, age 68
Director, Joseph A. Carrabba, age 59
Director, Noreen Doyle, age 62
Director, Veronica M. Hagen, age 66
Independent Director, Bruce Brook
Independent Director, Jane Nelson
Independent Director, Kofi Bucknor
Auditors: PricewaterhouseCoopersLLP

LOCATIONS

HQ: Newmont Mining Corporation
6363 S. Fiddler' s Green Cir. Ste. 800, Greenwood Village CO 80111
Phone: 303-863-7414 **Fax:** 303-837-5837
Web: www.newmont.com

2011 Sales

	$ mil.	% of total
Asia/Pacific	4,455	43
North America	3,031	29
South America	2,003	19
Africa	869	9
Total	**10,358**	**100**

PRODUCTS/OPERATIONS

2011 Sales

	$ mil.	% of total
Gold	9,096	88
Total	**10,358**	**100**

COMPETITORS

AngloGold Ashanti
Barrick Gold
Freeport-McMoRan
Gold Fields
Goldcorp
Harmony Gold
Inmet Mining
Kinross Gold
Newcrest Mining

HISTORICAL FINANCIALS

Company Type: Public

Income Statement FYE: December 31

	REVENUE ($ mil.)	NET INCOME ($ mil.)	NET PROFIT MARGIN	EMPLOYEES
12/11	10,358	366	3.5%	17,100
12/10	9,540	2,277	23.9%	15,500
12/09	7,705	1,297	16.8%	14,500
12/08	6,199	853	13.8%	15,450
12/07	5,526	(1,886)	—	15,000
Annual Growth	17.0%	—	—	3.3%

2011 Year-End Financials

Debt ratio: 15.70%
Return on equity: 2.84%
Cash ($ mil.): 1,760
Current ratio: 136.75
Long-term debt ($ mil.): 3,624
No. of shares (mil.): 494
Dividends
Yield: —
Payout: 136.99%
Market value ($ mil.): 29,689

	STOCK PRICE ($) FY Close	P/E High/Low	PER SHARE ($) Earnings	Dividends	Book Value
12/11	60.01	97 68	0.73	0.00	26.07
12/10	61.43	14 9	4.55	0.50	27.08
12/09	47.31	21 13	2.66	0.40	21.81
12/08	40.70	30 11	1.87	0.40	15.62
12/07	48.83	— —	(4.17)	0.40	16.66
Annual Growth	5.3%	— —	—	—	11.8%

News Corp

This News is heard seen and read all over the globe. The world's #2 media conglomerate (behind Walt Disney) News Corporation (or News Corp.) owns film TV and publishing businesses. It makes and distributes movies through Fox Filmed Entertainment while its FOX Broadcasting has more than 200 affiliate stations in the US. It also owns and operates about 25 TV stations as well as a portfolio of cable networks. Publishing assets include newspaper publishers Dow Jones (The Wall Street Journal) and News International (The Times The Sun) and book publisher HarperCollins. In addition News Corp. has stakes in British Sky Broadcasting (BSkyB) and Sky Deutschland. The company has announced plans to split in two.

HISTORY

In 1952 Rupert Murdoch inherited two Adelaide Australia newspapers from his father. After launching the "Australian" the country's first national daily in 1964 Murdoch moved into the UK market. He bought tabloid "News of the World" a London Sunday paper in 1968 and London's "Sun" the next year. In 1973 Murdoch hit the US buying the "San Antonio Express-News" and founding the "Star" tabloid. He followed this up in 1976 by buying the "New York Post." Murdoch formed News Corporation in Australia in 1979.

Moving upmarket in 1981 Murdoch bought the London "Times" and 40% of Collins Publishers a London book publisher. After buying the "Chicago Sun-Times" in 1983 (sold 1986) Murdoch bought 13 US travel hotel and aviation trade magazines from Ziff-Davis as well as film studio Twentieth Century Fox in 1985. In 1986 Murdoch bought six Metromedia stations and launched FOX Broadcasting the first new US TV network since 1948.

Print was not forgotten however and in the late 1980s News Corp. picked up US book publisher Harper & Row as well as Triangle Publications ("TV Guide" and other magazines). It also bought textbook publisher Scott Foresman and the rest of Collins Publishers. (Harper & Row was later merged with Collins to form HarperCollins.)

In 1996 Murdoch launched the FOX News Channel an all-news cable channel. The next year News Corp.'s FOX Kids joint venture bought Pat Robertson's International Family Entertainment.

In 1998 the company bought the Los Angeles Dodgers and stakes in the new Los Angeles-area Staples Center sports arena. (It sold its stake in the Staples Center in 2004.) Also that year News Corp. spun off part of Fox Entertainment in one of America's largest IPOs raising $2.7 billion.

That year News Corp. sold "TV Guide" to Tele-Communications Inc.'s United Video Satellite Group (now Gemstar-TV Guide International) for $800 million in cash and a 21% stake. The company also bought the 50% of FOX/Liberty Networks (now FOX Sports Net) it didn't own and transferred ownership to Fox Entertainment. The deal gave John Malone's Liberty Media holding company an 8% stake (later 19%) in News Corp.

In 1999 News Corp. purchased a 10% stake of wireless ISP OmniSky. The following year BSkyB acquired nearly 25% of Kirch PayTV the German pay-TV operation of KirchGruppe. Murdoch placed all of the company's satellite holdings into a new entity Sky Global Networks. (News Corp. folded Sky Global back into its operations in 2002 when it failed in its initial bid to buy DIRECTV.) Also that year News Corp. bought a stake in China's state-owned telecom operator Netcom.

In 2001 along with partner Haim Saban News Corp. sold the Fox Family Channel to Disney for about $5.2 billion. That year the FCC approved the company's $4.8 billion purchase of TV station group Chris-Craft. The deal gave News Corp. an additional 10 TV stations.

News Corp. in 2003 finally realized its dream of owning a chunk of DIRECTV when it bought 34% of Hughes Electronics the satellite television company's parent from General Motors. News Corp. transferred its interest in Hughes (which changed its name to The DIRECTV Group) to its Fox Entertainment subsidiary. The following year in an effort to make its stock more attractive to US investors News Corp. shifted its incorporation from Australia to the US. It also purchased the rest of Fox Entertainment that it didn't already own for $6.2 billion.

In 2005 News Corp. made its push into online and digital entertainment. Anchoring the new operations it acquired MySpace.com operator Intermix Media for about $580 million. (Other assets owned by Intermix were later sold to Demand Media.) The deal was an about-face for a company that eschewed the World Wide Web during the dotcom boom of the 1990s.

The company made another splash in the television industry when it launched MyNetworkTV in 2006. The startup network was established in response to rivals WB and UPN merging to form The CW Television Network.

The following year News Corp. expanded its holdings significantly when it acquired newspaper giant Dow Jones along with its flagship paper The Wall Street Journal for $5.6 billion. A newspaper man at heart Murdoch doggedly pursued Dow Jones and its controlling Bancroft family through a lengthy —and at times contested —negotiation process primarily to get his hands on the flagship title.

In 2008 the company exchanged its 40% stake in DIRECTV along with some regional sports networks and $625 million in cash for Liberty Media's 19% stake in News Corp.

Looking to still expand its interests in television broadcasting in 2011 News Corp acquired UK TV production company Shine Group in a stock swap deal valued at $670 million. Shine which was founded and is managed by Elisabeth Murdoch the daughter of Rupert has operations in 10 territories. The deal gave News Corp. a stronger presence in the increasingly crucial international TV production market.

In 2011 the company finally decided that its Myspace investment failed to pay off as growth in online ad revenue significantly slowed and the social network site decisively lost the battle to attract users against the reigning social media champion Facebook. As a result News Corp. sold Myspace to digital advertising network provider Specific Media for a paltry $35 million. (It also obtained a minority equity stake in Specific Media.)

Also during this time News Corp. was faced with troubles at its News International UK newspaper unit when it became embroiled in scandal. In the summer of 2011 its News of the World was accused of hiring private investigators to hack into citizens' and public officials' voice mails. The paper was eventually shut down after 168 years of publication. In addition several senior executives resigned and the company dropped plans to acquire the remaining 61% of BSkyB that it didn't already own for about #7.8 billion ($12.5 billion).

EXECUTIVES

CTO; President Technology Digital Media Group, John A. McKinley Jr.

Deputy COO and Director; Chairman and CEO International, James R. Murdoch, age 39, $3,147,236 total compensation

Chairman and CEO, K. Rupert Murdoch, age 81, $8,100,000 total compensation

Senior Advisor to the Chairman and Director, Arthur M. Siskind, age 73, $1,715,427 total compensation

SEVP CFO and Director, David F. DeVoe, age 65, $2,853,750 total compensation

Deputy Chairman President and COO, Chase Carey, age 58, $8,100,000 total compensation

SVP Investor Relations, Reed Nolte

VP Corporate Communications Fox Cable Networks, Brian Peterson

EVP Office of the Chairman and Director, Joel T. Klein, age 65

EVP and Deputy CFO, John P. Nallen

CEO News International, Thomas (Tom) Mockridge, age 57

SVP Media Relations FOX Sports Net and FSN, Lou D'Ermilio

SVP Communications FOX Cable Networks, Scott Grogin

EVP Government Affairs, Michael Regan

Chairman and CEO FOX News Channel and FOX Business Network; Chairman Fox Television Stations and Twentieth Television, Roger Ailes, age 72, $5,000,000 total compensation

EVP Corporate Communications FOX TV Stations FOX Business Network and FOX News Network, Brian Lewis

SVP Corporate Affairs and Chief Communications Officer, Julie Henderson

EVP and Chief Human Resources Officer, Jeff Mook

SVP Public Relations FX Networks, John Solberg

SVP Media Relations FOX Business Network and FOX News Network, Irena Briganti

SVP Deputy General Counsel and Chief Compliance and Ethics Officer, Genie Gavenchak

CEO MySpace.com, Michael (Mike) Jones

VP Corporate Affairs and Communications, Jack Horner

VP Investor Relations, Joe Dorrego

Director Corporate Communications and Public Relations Fox International Channels, Alexandra Marinescu

SVP and Deputy General Counsel, Janet Nova

COO Education Division, Kristen Kane

SVP Education Division, Peter Gorman

SVP Strategy Education, Diana Rhoten

SEVP and Group General Counsel, Gerson Zweifach, age 58

Deputy COO and Director; Chairman and CEO International, James R. Murdoch, age 39

Director, Lachlan K. Murdoch, age 40

Director, John L. Thornton, age 58

Senior Advisor to the Chairman and Director, Arthur M. Siskind, age 73

SEVP CFO and Director, David F. DeVoe, age 65

Deputy Chairman President and COO, Chase Carey, age 58

Director, Sir Roderick I. (Rod) Eddington, age 62

Director, Stanley S. (Stan) Shuman, age 74

EVP Office of the Chairman and Director, Joel T. Klein, age 65

Director, Kenneth E. Cowley, age 77

Director, Andrew S. B. Knight, age 73

Director, Peter L. Barnes, age 69

Director, Jose Maria Aznar, age 59

Director, Viet D. Dinh, age 44

Director, Natalie Bancroft, age 32

Auditors: Ernst&YoungLLP

LOCATIONS

HQ: News Corporation
1211 Avenue of the Americas, New York NY 10036
Phone: 212-852-7000 **Fax:** 212-852-7145
Web: www.newscorp.com

2012 Sales

US & Canada	18,927	56
Australasia & other regions	6,091	18

PRODUCTS/OPERATIONS

2012 Sales

	$ mil.	% of total
Cable network programming	9,132	27
Publishing	8,248	24
Filmed entertainment	7,302	22
Direct broadcast satellite television	3,672	11
Total	**33,706**	**100**

Selected Operations

Filmed entertainment
- Feature film production and distribution
  - Fox Filmed EntertainmentFox 2000Fox AtomicFox Searchlight PicturesTwentieth Century FoxTwentieth Century Fox Animation
  - Twentieth Century Fox Home Entertainment
- Television production and distribution
  - Fox Television Studios
  - Twentieth Century Fox Television
  - Twentieth Television

Newspapers
- Dow Jones
  - Barron's (magazine)
  - Dow Jones Licensing Services
  - Dow Jones Local Media Group (local newspapers)
  - Dow Jones Newswires
  - Factiva (online news and business research)
  - The Wall Street Journal
  - The Wall Street Journal Digital NetworkAll Things DigitalBigCharts (stock market information)FINS (financial services employment listings)MarketWatchWSJ.com
- New York Post
- News International Limited (UK)
  - The Sun
  - The Sunday Times
  - The Times
- News Limited (Australia)
  - The Advertiser (Adelaide)
  - The Australian (national daily)
  - The Courier-Mail (Brisbane)
  - The Daily Telegraph (Sydney)
  - Herald Sun (Melbourne)
  - The Mercury (Hobart)
  - Northern Territory News (Darwin)
  - Sunday Herald Sun (Melbourne)
  - Sunday Mail (Adelaide)
  - The Sunday Mail (Brisbane)
  - Sunday Tasmanian (Hobart)
  - The Sunday Telegraph (Sydney)
  - The Sunday Times (Perth)

Cable network programming
- Big Ten Network (49%)
- Fox Business Network
- Fox College Sports
- Fox International Channels
  - LAPTV (32% Latin American pay television)
- Fox Movie Channel
- Fox News Channel
- Fox Pan American Sports (33%)
  - Fox Sports en Espa?ol
  - Fox Sports Latin America
- Fox Reality
- Fox Soccer Channel
- Fox Sports Net
- FUEL TV
- FX
- National Geographic Channel (67% cable channel)
- NGC Network Latin America (67% National Geographic Channel)
- NGC Network International (75% National Geographic Channel International)
- SPEED

Television
- FOX Broadcasting
- Fox Television Stations
  - KCOP (MyNetworkTV Los Angeles)
  - KDFI (MyNetworkTV Dallas)
  - KDFW (FOX Dallas)
  - KMSP (FOX Minneapolis)
  - KRIV (FOX Houston)
  - KSAZ (FOX Phoenix)
  - KTBC (FOX; Austin TX)
  - KTTV (FOX Los Angeles)
  - KTXH (MyNetworkTV Houston)
  - KUTP (MyNetworkTV Phoenix)
  - WAGA (FOX Atlanta)
  - WDCA (MyNetworkTV; Washington DC)
  - WFLD (FOX Chicago)
  - WFTC (MyNetworkTV Minneapolis)
  - WFXT (FOX Boston)
  - WHBQ (FOX Memphis)
  - WJBK (FOX Detroit)
  - WNYW (FOX New York City)
  - WOFL (FOX; Orlando FL)
  - WOGX (FOX; Gainesville FL)
  - WPWR (MyNetworkTV Chicago)
  - WTTG (FOX; Washington DC)
  - WTVT (FOX Tampa)
  - WTXF (FOX Philadelphia)
  - WUTB (MyNetworkTV Baltimore)
  - WWOR (MyNetworkTV New York City)
- MyNetworkTV
- Shine Ltd. (television production UK)
- Star Group (international television broadcasting Asia)

Direct broadcast satellite
- British Sky Broadcasting (39% UK)
- Sky Deutschland (45% Germany)
- SKY Italia

Magazines and inserts
- Magazine publishing
  - News Magazines (Australia)ALPHA (men's sports and lifestyle)donna hay (food and lifestyle)INSIDEout (home and lifestyle)Sunday Magazine (newspaper insert)
- News America Marketing Group (insert publications and in-store marketing)

Book publishing

HarperCollins Publishers
Other operations and investments
AskMen.com
Fox.com
FoxSports.com
FOXTEL (25% cable television system Australia)
Hulu (32% online video)
IGN.com
NDS Group (49% pay-TV technology and software UK)
News Outdoor Group (outdoor advertising)
Scout.com
SkyNZ (44% direct broadcast satellite service New Zealand)

COMPETITORS

Advance Publications
Bertelsmann
Bloomberg L.P.
CBS Corp
Disney
Gannett
Hearst Corporation
MGM
NBCUniversal
New York Times
Pearson plc
Reed Elsevier Group
Sony Pictures Entertainment
Thomson Reuters
Time Warner
Tribune Company
Viacom
Washington Post

HISTORICAL FINANCIALS

Company Type: Public

Income Statement FYE: June 30

	REVENUE ($ mil.)	NET INCOME ($ mil.)	NET PROFIT MARGIN	EMPLOYEES
06/12	33,706	1,179	3.5%	48,000
06/11	33,405	2,739	8.2%	51,000
06/10	32,778	2,539	7.7%	51,000
06/09	30,423	(3,378)	—	55,000
06/08	32,996	5,387	16.3%	64,000
Annual Growth	0.5%	(31.6%)	—	(6.9%)

2012 Year-End Financials

Debt ratio: 27.28%—
Return on equity: 4.78%
Cash ($ mil.): 9,626
Current ratio: 202.23
Long-term debt ($ mil.): 15,182
Dividends
Yield: —
Payout: 38.30%
Market value ($ mil.): —

	STOCK PRICE ($) FY Close	P/E High/Low	PER SHARE ($) Earnings	Dividends	Book Value
06/12	22.29	47 29	0.47	0.00	10.36
06/11	17.70	18 11	1.04	0.15	11.23
06/10	11.96	17 8	0.97	0.14	9.58
06/09	9.11	— —	(1.29)	0.12	8.89
06/08	15.04	13 8	1.81	0.12	10.97
Annual Growth	10.3%	— —	(28.6%)	—	(1.4%)

NextEra Energy Inc

For a Florida company without any oranges NextEra Energy produces a lot of juice. Its operations across the US and Canada include an independent power production business but most of its revenues come from utility Florida Power & Light (FPL). The unit distributes electricity to 4.6 million customers. Subsidiary FPL Group Capital owns nonutility businesses including NextEra Energy Resources an independent power producer and energy marketer. Overall NextEra Energy has more than 41000 MW of generating capacity. Subsidiary FPL FiberNet leases wholesale fiber-optic capacity to telephone cable and Internet providers; it operates a 7800 mile network.

Geographic Reach

Utility FPL serves customers across Florida. Energy wholesaler NextEra Energy Resources operates 100-plus facilities in more than two dozen states and Canada and it is expanding its generation portfolio.

Operations

NextEra Energy has two principal subsidiaries FPL one of the largest rate-regulated electric utilities in the US (with 24500 MW of capacity) and NextEra Energy Resources (with more than 16500 MW of capacity) which is the largest generator in the US of renewable energy from wind and solar sources. It also operates a fiber network business through FPL FiberNet.

Financial Analysis

In 2011 NextEra Energy reported flat sales. While FPL posted a 1% jump in revenues thanks to higher rates and an increase in cost recovery Next Era's total revenue was dragged down by a weaker performance by NextEra Energy Resources (due to softer market conditions and extended outages at its Seabrook nuclear facility). The flat revenues and higher interest and income tax expense costs resulted in the company posting a 2% dip in net income for the year. To raise cash in 2011 the company sold a 583-MW power plant in Rhode Island to Entergy for about $346 million.

Strategy

NextEra Energy's 10-year strategic plan (2008-2017) for meeting Florida's energy needs combines additions in generating capacity while using renewable energy sources and energy efficiency programs to avoid the need to build four previously proposed midsized power plants.

In 2011 the company signed nearly 2200 MW of long-term wind and solar contracts in 2011. Growing its solar portfolio it acquired the 550 MW Desert Sunlight Solar Farm near Desert Center California from First Solar in 2011. In 2010 NextEra Energy acquired four small solar photovoltaic projects located in Ontario from First Solar.

In 2009 its Lone Star Transmission subsidiary was allocated $565 million of a $4.9 billion transmission grid improvement program to deliver wind power to West Texas and the Texas Panhandle. Lone Star will build and operate 250 miles of the 2300-mile project which is expected to begin operating in 2014.

Company Background

In 2010 the company changed its corporate name from FPL Energy to NextEra Energy in order to better reflect its strategic focus on green energy and to differentiate it from subsidiary Florida Power & Light.

HISTORY

During Florida's land boom of the early 1920s new homes and businesses were going up fast. But electric utilities were sparse and no transmission lines linked systems.

In 1925 American Power & Light Company (AP&L) which operated utilities throughout the Americas set up Florida Power & Light (FPL) to consolidate the state's electric assets. AP&L built transmission lines linking 58 communities from Miami to Stuart on the Atlantic Coast and from Arcadia to Punta Gorda on the Gulf.

FPL accumulated many holdings including a limestone quarry streetcars phone companies and water utilities and purchases in 1926 and 1927 nearly doubled its electric properties. In 1927 the company used an electric pump to demonstrate how swamplands could be drained and cultivated.

During the 1940s and 1950s FPL sold its non-electric properties. The Public Utility Holding Company Act of 1935 forced AP&L to spin off FPL in 1950. The company was listed on the NYSE that year.

FPL grew with Florida's booming population. In 1972 its first nuclear plant (Turkey Point south of Miami) went on line. In the 1980s it began to diversify with the purchase of real estate firm W. Flagler Investment in 1981 and FPL Group was created in 1984 as a holding company. It subsequently acquired Telesat Cablevision (1985) Colonial Penn Group (1985 insurance) and Turner Foods (1988 citrus groves). FPL Group formed ESI Energy in 1985 to develop nonutility energy projects.

Diversification efforts didn't pan out and in 1990 the firm wrote off about $750 million. That year sticking to electricity the utility snagged its first out-of-state power plant in Georgia acquiring a 76% stake (over five years). FPL Group sold its ailing Colonial Penn unit in 1991; two years later it sold its real estate holdings and some of its cable TV businesses.

The utility gave environmentalists cause to complain in 1995. First the St. Lucie nuclear plant was fined by the Nuclear Regulatory Commission for a series of problems. FPL also wanted to burn orimulsion a cheap tar-like fuel. (Barred by the governor the utility gave up the plan in 1998.)

In 1997 FPL Group created FPL Energy an independent power producer (IPP) out of its ESI Energy and international operations; FPL Energy teamed up with Belgium-based Tractebel the next year to buy two gas-fired plants in Boston and Newark New Jersey.

FPL Energy built wind-power facilities in Iowa in 1998 and in Wisconsin and Texas in 1999; it also bought 35 generating plants in Maine in 1999. That year FPL Group sold its Turner Foods citrus unit and the rest of its cable TV holdings. By 2000 FPL Energy owned interests in plants in 12 states.

Out of its fiber-optic operations FPL Group in 2000 created subsidiary FPL FiberNet to market wholesale capacity. That year talks of Spanish utility giant Iberdrola purchasing FPL Group ended when Iberdrola's shareholders objected; in 2001 plans to merge with New Orleans-based Entergy fell through after a series of disagreements. The deal would have created one of the US's largest power companies.

In 2002 FPL Group purchased an 88% interest in the Seabrook Nuclear Generating Station in New Hampshire for $837 million from a consortium of US utilities including Northeast Utilities and BayCorp Holdings. In 2005 FPL Group acquired Gexa Corp. a Houston-based electric utility.

Late in 2005 FPL agreed to buy rival power concern Constellation Energy Group Inc. in an $11 billion stock deal. However the companies called the deal off in 2006 citing uncertainty about regulatory approvals.

FPL Energy had agreed to purchase British Energy's 50% stake in nuclear power generation firm AmerGen Energy in 2003; however Exelon which owns the other half of AmerGen exercised its right of first refusal and purchased the remainder of AmerGen.

The company purchased the Point Beach Nuclear Plant in Two Rivers from Wisconsin Energy for $924 million in 2007.

In 2009 the company acquired three wind power developments in South Dakota Texas and Wisconsin from Babcock & Brown for about $350 million

EXECUTIVES

VP Tax, James P. Higgins
President Gexa Energy GP LLC, Brian Landrum, age 50
Chairman and CEO; Chairman Florida Power & Light, Lewis (Lew) Hay III, age 56, $1,255,800 total compensation
EVP Engineering Construction and Corporate Services NextEra and Florida Power & Light, Robert L. (Bob) McGrath, age 58
EVP Power Generation Division NextEra and Florida Power & Light, Antonio Rodriguez, age 69
VP Controller and Chief Accounting Officer, Chris N. Froggatt, age 54
President and COO, James L. (Jim) Robo, age 49, $831,600 total compensation
Vice Chairman EVP Finance and CFO; EVP Finance and CFO Florida Power & Light, Moray P. Dewhurst, age 56, $204,162 total compensation
EVP and Chief Strategy Policy and Business Process Improvement Officer, Christopher A. (Chris) Bennett, age 53
SVP Development NextEra Energy Resources, Michael O'Sullivan
President Commodities and Retail Markets NextEra Energy Resources, Mark Maisto
SVP Finance and CFO NextEra Energy Resources, Mark R. Sorensen
Treasurer, Paul I. Cutler, age 52
EVP Nuclear Division and Chief Nuclear Officer NextEra and Florida Power & Light, Manoochehr K. Nazar, age 57
EVP Federal Regulatory Affairs, Joseph T. Kelliher
VP Customer Service, Marlene M. Santos
COO NextEra Energy Resources, T. J. Tuscai
Media Relations NextEra Energy Resources, Steve Stengel
VP and Corporate Secretary, Alissa E. Ballot
EVP General Counsel and Assistant Secretary; EVP Florida Power & Light, Charles E. Sieving, age 39
President FPL FiberNet LLC, Carmen M. Perez
VP Governmental Affairs - Federal, Michael M. Wilson
VP Environmental Services Florida Power & Light, Randall R. (Randy) LaBauve
President and CEO NextEra Energy Resources, Armando Pimentel Jr., age 49, $556,500 total compensation
VP and CIO Florida Power & Light, Lakshman Charanjiva
President and CEO Florida Power & Light, Eric E. Silagy
VP Marketing and Communications Florida Power & Light, Timothy (Tim) Fitzpatrick
VP Development and External Affairs, Pamela M. Rauch
VP and General Counsel Florida Power & Light, R. Wade Litchfield
Media Relations, Mark Bubriski
Media Relations Nuclear Communications, Michael Waldron
VP Distribution Florida Power & Light, G. Keith Hardy
EVP Human Resources NextEra and Florida Power & Light, Shaun J. Francis
Director, Michael H. (Mike) Thaman, age 48
Director, William H. Swanson, age 63
Director, Rudy E. Schupp, age 61
Director, James L. Camaren, age 57
Director, Hansel E. Tookes II, age 64
Director, J. Brian Ferguson, age 57
Director, Oliver D. Kingsley Jr., age 69
Director, Toni Jennings, age 62
Director, Sherry S. Barrat, age 62
Vice Chairman EVP Finance and CFO; EVP Finance and CFO Florida Power & Light, Moray P. Dewhurst, age 56
Director, Robert M. Beall II, age 68
Director, J. Hyatt Brown, age 74
Director, Kenneth B. Dunn, age 60
Auditors: Deloitte&ToucheLLP

LOCATIONS

HQ: NextEra Energy Inc.
700 Universe Blvd., Juno Beach FL 33408-0420
Phone: 561-694-4000 **Fax:** 330-463-6760
Web: www.joann.com

PRODUCTS/OPERATIONS

2011 Sales

	$ mil.	% of total
Florida Power & Light	10,613	69
NextEra Energy Resources	4,502	29
Corporate & other	226	2
Total	**15,341**	**100**

Selected Subsidiaries and Divisions

Florida Power & Light Company
Energy Marketing and Trading
FPL Group Capital Inc.
NextEra Energy Resources LLC
FPL FiberNet LLC
Lone Star Transmission

COMPETITORS

AES
Bangor Hydro-Electric
Calpine
Chesapeake Utilities
CMS Energy
Delmarva Power
Duke Energy
Edison International
Entergy
Exelon
Florida Public Utilities
GenOnEnergy
JEA
MidAmerican Energy
Oglethorpe Power
Progress Energy
Public Service Enterprise Group
SCANA
Seminole Electric
Sempra Energy
Southern Company
TECO Energy

HISTORICAL FINANCIALS

Company Type: Public

Income Statement FYE: December 31

	REVENUE ($ mil.)	NET INCOME ($ mil.)	NET PROFIT MARGIN	EMPLOYEES
12/11	15,341	1,923	12.5%	14,800
12/10	15,317	1,957	12.8%	15,000
12/09	15,643	1,615	10.3%	10,500
12/08	16,410	1,639	10.0%	10,700
12/07	15,263	1,312	8.6%	10,500
Annual Growth	0.1%	10.0%	—	9.0%

2011 Year-End Financials

Debt ratio: 40.16%
Return on equity: 12.87%
Cash ($ mil.): 377
Current ratio: 72.51
Long-term debt ($ mil.): 20,810
No. of shares (mil.): 416
Dividends
Yield: —
Payout: 47.93%
Market value ($ mil.): 25,326

	STOCK PRICE ($) FY Close	P/E High/Low		PER SHARE ($) Earnings	Dividends	Book Value
12/11	60.88	13	11	4.59	0.00	35.92
12/10	51.99	12	10	4.74	2.00	34.36
12/09	52.82	15	10	3.97	1.89	31.35
12/08	50.33	18	9	4.07	1.78	28.57
12/07	67.78	22	16	3.27	1.64	26.35
Annual Growth	(2.6%)	—	—	8.8%	—	8.1%

NII Holdings Inc.

NII Holdings spreads its former parent's version of wireless communications beyond US borders. NII brings the Nextel brand to Latin America serving customers in Brazil and Mexico (together about three-quarters of sales) as well as Argentina Chile and Peru. Based on Motorola Mobility's iDEN technology NII's service supports cellular phone numeric and text messaging two-way radio and Internet access. The company also sells mobile handsets most of which it buys from Motorola Mobility. It also offers BlackBerry devices from Research In Motion. NII maintains a subscriber base of more than 11 million users targeting small to large business customers and consumers with medium to high usage patterns.

While Brazil and Mexico vie for the largest share of NII's revenues the remaining quarter of sales is about evenly split between Argentina and Peru. The company has only about 80000 handsets (less than 1% of NII's total) in service in Chile.

NII's 20% increase in sales to $6.7 billion for 2011 was due to an increase in subscribers as its average revenue per user remained relatively unchanged. Despite the growth the company saw net income drop more than 40% to less than $200 million due to the near-doubling of other non-income non-operating expenses and a loss on foreign currency transactions. That left NII with its lowest profit margin less than 3% of the past decade.

Traditionally the company's competitors have focused on retail customers motivated primarily by price but NII has begun to feel more pressure as those companies have begun to enhance their services and support. NII continues to focus on enterprise clients and higher usage consumers as well as emphasize quality of customer service.

The company's continues to invest in upgrading its network from the previous iDEN technology to the more prevalent wideband code division multiple access (WCDMA). Its growth strategy also includes adding cell sites to improve its network performance and support WCDMA service working with partners to develop new handsets and implementing incentive programs to encourage third-party distribution sales.

Formerly known as Nextel International the mobile carrier was formed in 1995 as a subsidiary of Nextel Communications (now Sprint Nextel). The company changed its name from Nextel International to NII Holdings in 2001. It emerged as a separately traded company after undergoing Chapter 11 bankruptcy proceedings in 2002.

EXECUTIVES

CEO and Director, Steven P. (Steve) Dussek, age 55, $725,000 total compensation
EVP and General Counsel, Gary D. Begeman, age 53, $376,635 total compensation
Chairman, Steven M. (Steve) Shindler, age 49, $720,000 total compensation
EVP and COO, Gokul V. Hemmady, age 51, $418,000 total compensation
President Nextel Mexico, Peter A. (Pete) Foyo, age 46, $394,701 total compensation
President Nextel Peru, Miguel E. Rivera, age 59
President Nextel Chile, Claudio A. Hidalgo
EVP Business Operations, John McMahon, age 47, $350,819 total compensation
EVP and CTO, Alan Strauss, age 52
Media Relations, Claudia E. Restrepo
VP Treasurer and Controller, Daniel E. (Dan) Freiman, age 40

EVP Human Resources, Alfonso Martinez, age 50
VP and CIO, Dave P. Truzinski
Investor Relations, Tim Perrott
Media Relations Mexico, Carlos E. Ortega Leal
Media Contact Argentina, Veronica Alvarez Puente
EVP and CFO, Juan R. Figuereo, age 56
EVP and Chief Strategy and Marketing Officer, Greg Santoro, age 49, $352,767 total compensation
President and CEO Nextel Brazil, Sergio Borges Chaia, age 46, $637,500 total compensation
President Nextel Argentina, Ruben Butvilofsky, age 59
Media Relations Peru, Rosa Bonilla
Media Relations Brazil, Marcello Pimental
Media Relations Chile, Leonardo A. Cerda Cortes
CEO and Director, Steven P. (Steve) Dussek, age 55
Director, Charles M. Herington, age 52
Director, Kevin L. Beebe, age 52
Director, Rosendo G. (Ro) Parra, age 52
Director, Donald Guthrie, age 56
Director, Raymond P. (Ray) Dolan, age 54
Director, Carolyn F. Katz, age 50
Director, John W. Risner, age 52
Auditors: PricewaterhouseCoopersLLP

LOCATIONS

HQ: NII Holdings Inc.
1875 Explorer St. Ste. 1000, Reston VA 20190
Phone: 703-390-5100 **Fax:** 703-547-5269
Web: www.nii.com

2011 Sales

	$ mil.	% of total
Brazil	3,441	51
Mexico	2,249	34
Argentina	648	10
Peru	354	5
Corporate & other	30	-
Adjustments	(4.5)	-
Total	**6,719**	**100**

2011 No. of Handsets & Devices in Service

	In thou.	% of total
Brazil	4,115	38
Mexico	3,696	35
Peru	1,435	13
Argentina	1,388	13
Chile	78	1
Total	**10,712**	**100**

PRODUCTS/OPERATIONS

2011 Sales

	$ mil.	% of total
Service & other	6,403	95
Digital handset & accessory	316	5
Total	**6,719**	**100**

COMPETITORS

America Movil
Iusacell
Tele Norte Celular
Telecom Argentina
Telecom Italia
Telefonica
Telefonica del Peru
Telemar Norte Leste
Telemig Celular

HISTORICAL FINANCIALS

Company Type: Public

Income Statement FYE: December 31

	REVENUE ($ mil.)	NET INCOME ($ mil.)	NET PROFIT MARGIN	EMPLOYEES
12/11	6,719	198	3.0%	15,300
12/10	5,601	341	6.1%	13,500
12/09	4,397	381	8.7%	13,673
12/08	4,269	369	8.6%	12,299
12/07	3,296	378	11.5%	9,873
Annual Growth	19.5%	(14.9%)	—	11.6%

2011 Year-End Financials

Debt ratio: 49.22%
Return on equity: 6.35%
Cash ($ mil.): 2,322
Current ratio: 204.74
Long-term debt ($ mil.): 4,253
No. of shares (mil.): 171
Dividends
Yield: —
Payout: —
Market value ($ mil.): 3,646

	STOCK PRICE ($) FY Close	P/E High	P/E Low	PER SHARE ($) Earnings	Dividends	Book Value
12/11	21.30	38	17	1.15	0.00	18.29
12/10	44.66	22	15	1.99	0.00	19.57
12/09	33.58	15	5	2.30	0.00	16.47
12/08	18.18	26	6	2.14	0.00	10.78
12/07	48.32	40	19	2.11	0.00	12.76
Annual Growth	(18.5%)	—	—	(14.1%)	—	9.4%

NIKE, Inc

Fleet-of-footwear NIKE named for the Greek goddess of victory is the world's #1 shoe and apparel company. NIKE designs develops and sells a slew of products and services to help in playing basketball and soccer (football) as well as in running men's and women's training and other action sports. Under its namesake brand NIKE also markets sports-inspired products for children and various competitive and recreational activities such as golf tennis and walking and sportswear by Converse and Hurley. NIKE sells through more than 800-owned retail stores worldwide an e-commerce site and to thousands of retail accounts independent distributors and licensees. Chairman Philip Knight controls the company.

HISTORY

Phil Knight a good miler and Bill Bowerman a track coach who tinkered with shoe designs met at the University of Oregon in 1957. The two men formed Blue Ribbon Sports in 1962 in an effort to make quality American running shoes. The next year they began selling Tiger shoes manufactured by Japanese shoe manufacturer Onitsuka Tiger. They sold the running shoes out of cars at track meets.

The company became NIKE in 1972 named for the Greek goddess of victory. The NIKE "Swoosh" logo was designed by a graduate student named Carolyn Davidson who was paid $35. The same year NIKE broke with Onitsuka in a dispute over distribution rights.

At the 1972 Olympic Trials in Oregon Knight and Bowerman persuaded some of the marathoners to wear NIKE shoes. When some of these runners placed the two advertised that NIKEs were worn by "four of the top seven finishers."

Bowerman tested a new sole in 1974 by stuffing a piece of rubber into a waffle iron. The result was the waffle sole which NIKE added to its running shoes. NIKE grew as running's popularity surged in the 1970s. (NIKE even offered a red-and-silver shoe for disco dancing.) By 1979 it had 50% of the US running shoe market. NIKE went public the next year.

NIKE expanded with shoes for other sports introducing the Air Jordan basketball shoe in 1985 (named for basketball star Michael Jordan) and the Cross Trainer two years later. NIKE's famous "Just Do It" slogan was introduced in 1988 the same year it bought dress-shoe maker Cole Haan.

In 1992 NIKE opened its first NIKETOWN store. It acquired Canstar Sports which included hockey equipment maker Bauer in 1995 (now Bauer NIKE Hockey). NIKE signed 20-year-old golf phenom Tiger Woods to a $40 million endorsement contract that year. Also in 1995 NIKE acquired a license to place its logo on NFL uniforms. (Reebok took over this license in 2002.)

NIKE launched a Jordan-branded athletic footwear and apparel division in 1997. Prompted by falling sales in Asia NIKE cut 1200 jobs in 1998 (about 5% of its workforce) to cut costs. With demand for athletic shoes weakening in 1999 NIKE reported its first drop in sales since 1994. Also in 1999 the company began opening JORDAN store-within-a-store boutiques. Bowerman died in 1999; NIKE released a line of running shoes in his honor.

In 2000 the company launched a line of athletic electronics including MP3 players heart monitors and two-way radios. A full year before Tiger Woods' contract expired NIKE in 2000 signed the golfer to a five-year contract. The company said the new contract represented a "substantial raise" from his previous $40 million deal.

NIKE opened its first NIKEgoddess store in Newport Beach California in October 2001. The company acquired Hurley International a distributor of action sports apparel in April 2002.

In September 2003 NIKE acquired competitor Converse and left it as a separate operating unit to keep the Converse name intact. In October Bauer NIKE Hockey announced the closing of its hockey stick factory in Ontario and a staff reduction at its Quebec facilities.

NIKE purchased athletic apparel and footwear makers Official Starter Properties and Official Starter LLC in 2004 for $43 million then bundled the brands into a unit called Exeter Brands Group based in New York City. Knight stepped down as president and CEO of the company in December 2004 but remained chairman. He was succeeded by Bill Perez former S.C. Johnson & Son chief executive.

In January 2006 NIKE veteran Mark Parker succeeded Perez as president and CEO.

The company announced a partnership in 2007 with Foot Locker to launch a new store focused purely on basketball called "House of Hoops by Foot Locker." The stores sell only NIKE products and about 50 are planned over the next three years. NIKE in December 2007 also sold off its Exeter Brands Group including the Starter brand to Iconix Brand Group for $60 million in cash as part of a strategy to divest lagging brands in its portfolio.

In March 2008 NIKE acquired UK-based global soccer brand Umbro for about $576 million. The deal provided NIKE with a foundation in soccer in the US and England and positioned the company to enter emerging soccer markets such as China Russia and Brazil. Moreover Umbro which sells directly and through licensees brought high-profile sports marketing agreements with soccer players teams and leagues and its own global reach.

To help fund its soccer purchase NIKE shed its hockey business. More than a dozen years after acquiring Bauer NIKE Hockey NIKE sold the hockey unit in early 2008 to a group of investors including Kohlberg & Company and W. Graeme Roustan for $200 million. It divested its hockey unit after a strategic review of subsidiaries that didn't reach the $2 billion mark in sales a long-term growth strategy for the company.

NIKE has paid Tiger Woods millions of dollars in endorsements each year as one of his major sponsors since signing him in the 1990s. The company stood by the famed golfer in late 2009 when it was alleged that the athlete had been party to marital infidelity.

EXECUTIVES

VP Apparel Sports Categories, John J. Notar, age 55
VP Commerce Affiliates, Clare L. Hamill, age 57
President Global Operations, Gary M. DeStefano, age 55, $1,000,000 total compensation
VP Global Human Resources Infrastructure and Shared Services, Oscar Cardona, age 52
President CEO and Director, Mark G. Parker, age 54, $1,475,000 total compensation
President New Business Development, Thomas E. Clarke, age 60, $1,107,051 total compensation
Chairman, Philip H. Knight, age 72, $1,392,308 total compensation
VP and CFO, Donald W. Blair, age 54, $810,000 total compensation
President Direct to Consumer, Jeanne P. Jackson, age 60
VP Global Sales, Roland P. Wolfram, age 53
President NIKE Brand, Charles D. (Charlie) Denson, age 56, $1,260,000 total compensation
VP Merchandising and Product, Eric D. Sprunk, age 48, $810,000 total compensation
Corporate Secretary, John F. Coburn III
VP Global Brand and Category Management, Trevor Edwards, age 50, $804,615 total compensation
President NIKE Foundation, Maria S. Eitel, age 50
VP Creative Design, Tinker Hatfield, age 60
VP and General Manager Emerging Markets, Joaquin Hidalgo, age 51
VP and General Manager North America, Elliott Hill, age 49
VP Sports Marketing Jordan Brand, Howard White, age 62
VP North America Running, Amy White
VP Global Design, John R. Hoke III, age 47
VP Category Project Leader, Shelley K. Dewey, age 60
VP Global Category Basketball, Craig Zanon
Presidentand Chief Executive Officer Umbro, Michael Spillane, age 49
VP North America Women's Training, Pamela Catlett, age 47
VP and General Manager Western Europe, Brent Scrimshaw
VP and Corporate Controller, Bernard F. (Bernie) Pliska, age 50
VP Marketing North America, Ken Dice
VP Global Operations and Technology, Hans van Alebeek, age 47
VP Global Category Football, Hubertus (Bert) Hoyt, age 57
Chairman Hurley International, Robert (Bob) Hurley, age 57
VP; President NIKE Golf, Cindy Davis, age 50
VP Sustainable Business and Innovation, Hannah Jones, age 45
VP Global Sourcing and Manufacturing, Nicholas (Nick) Athanasakos, age 49
VP and General Manager Greater China, Craig Cheek, age 46
VP E-Commerce, Chris Shimojima
Director Investor Relations, Lance Allega
VP Lean Business Solutions and CIO, Roland Paanakker
CFO Affiliates, Bob Woodruff
VP Western Europe Retail, Martin Brok
VP General Counsel and Corporate Affairs, Hilary K. Krane, age 48
VP NIKE Global Design and Action Sports, Sandy Bodecker, age 56
President Nike Affiliates; Interim CEO Hurley, Roger Wyett, age 55
VP Global Brand Creative, Greg Hoffman
VP Global Category Women's Training, Heidi O'Neill, age 46
VP and General Manager Converse EMEA (Europe Middle East and Africa), Willem Haitink
VP Global Brand Marketing, Davide Grasso
VP Global Sports Marketing, John F. Slusher, age 43
VP Nike Foundation, Leslie Lane, age 44
VP Global Diversity and Inclusion, Gina A. Warren
VP Global Category NSW, Dermott Cleary
VP Apparel Product Creation, Diana Crist
VP and General Manager Brasil, Chris Kypriotis
VP and General Manager Category Kids, Pat Zeedick
VP Global Human Resources, David J. Ayre
VP; CEO Cole Haan, Dave McTague, age 49
VP North America Merchandising, Joe Serino
VP Global Category Running, Jayme Martin
VP Footwear Design, Peter Hudson
President Jordan Brand, Keith Houlemard, age 47
VP North America Basketball, Dan Jones
VP Global Apparel, Jan Singer, age 48
VP Global Category Athletic Training and Field Sports, Kris Aman, age 43
VP and General Manager UK and Ireland, Marc Van Pappelendam
VP and General Manager Central and Eastern Europe, Michaela (Michi) Stitz
President and CEO Converse, Jim Calhoun, age 45
VP Apparel Sportswear, Brian Zappitello
VP Corporate Audit, Carol L. Welch
VP Global Merchandising, Dennis van Oossanen
VP Western Europe Marketing, Dirk-Jan van Hameren
VP Manufacturing and Sourcing, Ernie Rose
VP Logistics and Geography Operations, Gerry Rogers
VP North America Athletic Training, Mark Riley
VP Western Europe Merchandising, Fiona Reekie
VP GlobalCommunications, Nigel Powell
VP Digital Sport, Stefan Olander
VP Global Basketball Sports Marketing, Lynn Merritt
VP North America Human Resources, Monique Matheson
Assistant Secretary, Peter Koehler
VP North America Sports Marketing, Tommy Kain
VP North America Retail, Tim Hershey
VP Global Footwear, Andrea Correani, age 45
VP Brand Human Resources, Steve Conroy
VP Global Football and Western Europe Sports Marketing, Riccardo Colombini
VP Western Europe Sales, Simon Clark
VP and CFO NIKE Brand, Andy Campion
VP North America Supply Chain Operations, Mike Brewer
VP Global Footwear Product Creation and Operations, Mark Allen
VP and General Manager Japan, Carl Grebert, age 43
CFO NIKE EMEA, Greg Brink
VP Global Planning and Development, Chris Clipper
VP Footwear Sports Performance, Bruce Connelly
VP North America NSW, Jamie Jeffries
VP North America Sales, Tom Peddie
VP and COO Direct to Consumer, Christiana Shi
VP Europe Operations, Bert Stevens
VP Footwear Sportswear, Greg Thompson
Seniro Director Investor Relations, Kelley Hall
Manager Investor Relations, Kathy Strege
Director, John G. Connors, age 52
Director, John C. Lechleiter, age 58
Director, Alan B. Graf Jr., age 56
Director, Timothy D. (Tim) Cook, age 51
President CEO and Director, Mark G. Parker, age 54
Director, Orin C. Smith, age 68
Director, Johnathan A. Rodgers, age 66
Director, Elizabeth J. (Beth) Comstock, age 51
Director, Douglas G. Houser, age 75
Director, Jill K. Conway, age 76
Director, John R. Thompson Jr., age 68
Director, Ralph D. DeNunzio, age 78
Director, Phyllis M. Wise, age 65
Auditors: PricewaterhouseCoopersLLP

LOCATIONS

HQ: NIKE Inc.
1 Bowerman Dr., Beaverton OR 97005-6453
Phone: 503-671-6453 **Fax:** 503-671-6300
Web: www.nikebiz.com

2012 Sales

	$ mil.	% of total
North America	8,839	37
Western Europe	4,144	17
Greater China	2,539	10
Central & Eastern Europe	1,200	5
Japan	829	3
Emerging markets	3,410	14
Global brand divisions	111	1
Other businesses	3,056	13
Total	**24,128**	**100**

PRODUCTS/OPERATIONS

2012 Sales

	$ mil.	% of total
NIKE brand		
Footwear	13,426	55
Apparel	6,333	26
Equipment	1,202	5
Global brand divisions	111	1
Other	3,056	13
Total	**24,128**	**100**

Selected Products

Athletic Shoes
- Aquatic
- Auto racing
- Baseball
- Basketball
- Bicycling
- Cheerleading
- Cross-training
- Fitness
- Football
- Golf
- Running
- Soccer
- Tennis
- Volleyball
- Wrestling

Athletic Wear and Equipment
- Accessories
- Athletic bags
- Bats
- Caps
- Digital devices
- Eyewear

Fitness wear
Gloves
Golf clubs
Headwear
Jackets
Pants
Protective equipment
Running clothes
Shirts
Shorts
Skirts
Snowboards and snowboard apparel
Socks
Sport balls
Timepieces
Uniforms

Selected Subsidiaries

Converse Inc. (athletic and casual footwear apparel and accessories)
Hurley International LLC (action sports apparel and accessories)
Umbro International Limited (athletic and casual footwear apparel and soccer equipment)

COMPETITORS

Acushnet	PUMA SE
adidas	Quiksilver
Amer Sports	R. Griggs
ASICS	Ralph Lauren
Brown Shoe	Rawlings Sporting Goods
Callaway Golf	Rollerblade
Columbia Sportswear	Russell Brands
Deckers Outdoor	Saucony
Fila Korea	Skechers U.S.A.
Fruit of the Loom	Stride Rite
FUBU	Timberland
Hanesbrands	
Juicy Couture	Timex
K-Swiss	Tommy Hilfiger
Levi Strauss	Under Armour
Mizuno	VF Corporation
New Balance	Victoria' s Secret Stores
Oakley	
Phoenix Footwear	Wolverine World Wide

HISTORICAL FINANCIALS

Company Type: Public

Income Statement

FYE: May 31

	REVENUE ($ mil.)	NET INCOME ($ mil.)	NET PROFIT MARGIN	EMPLOYEES
05/12	24,128	2,223	9.2%	44,000
05/11	20,862	2,133	10.2%	38,000
05/10	19,014	1,906	10.0%	34,400
05/09	19,176	1,486	7.8%	34,300
05/08	18,627	1,883	10.1%	32,500
Annual Growth	6.7%	4.2%	—	7.9%

2012 Year-End Financials

Debt ratio: 2.49%
Return on equity: 21.41%
Cash ($ mil.): 2,317
Current ratio: 298.34
Long-term debt ($ mil.): 228
No. of shares (mil.): 916
Dividends
Yield: —
Payout: 71.88%
Market value ($ mil.): 99,093

	STOCK PRICE ($) FY Close	P/E High/Low		PER SHARE ($) Earnings	Dividends	Book Value
05/12	108.18	47	33	2.37	0.00	11.33
05/11	84.45	41	30	2.20	0.00	10.52
05/10	72.38	40	26	1.93	0.00	10.08
05/09	57.05	46	25	1.52	0.00	8.95
05/08	68.37	37	28	1.87	0.00	7.97
Annual Growth	12.2%	—	—	6.1%	—	9.2%

NiSource Inc. (Holding Co.)

NiSource is the main energy source for resourceful Americans living in the Midwest the South and New England. The company's utility subsidiaries distribute natural gas to about 3.8 million customers in seven states via 58000 miles of pipeline. NiSource also generates transmits and distributes power to some 458000 customers in 20 counties in its home state through its largest subsidiary Northern Indiana Public Service Company (NIPSCO). NiSource owns one of the largest natural gas transmission and underground storage systems in the US (capable of storing 639 billion cu. ft. of natural gas) including a 15000-mile interstate pipeline system.

Geographic Reach

Through subsidiary Columbia Energy NiSource owns and operates five distribution subsidiaries that provide natural gas to 2.2 million residential commercial and industrial customers in Ohio Pennsylvania Virginia Kentucky and Maryland. NiSource also distributes natural gas to 795000 in Indiana. Columbia Gas of Massachusetts distributes natural gas to 298000 end users in Massachusetts. Several of NiSource's utilities participate in customer choice programs in states with deregulated energy markets. CNS Microwave operates 75 microwave towers in Kentucky Louisiana Maryland Mississippi Ohio Pennsylvania Tennessee Virginia and West Virginia.

Operations

The energy holding company operates in three major business areas: gas distribution; gas transmission and storage; and electric generation transmission and distribution. It also provides retail services as well as telecommunications infrastructure for wireless applications.

Financial Analysis

NiSource's gross revenues dropped by almost 4% in 2011 primarily due lower gas distribution sales which were dragged down by lower gas commodity prices. However net income was up 6% thanks to lower depreciation and amortization costs and lower interest and other debt charges.

Strategy

NiSource believes that its long-term success lies in developing a portfolio that balances creating more efficiencies in its regulated utility operations while expanding its higher-growth gas transmission and storage businesses.

To boost its gas transmission and storage assets and take advantage of the burgeoning shale gas market in 2012 the company formed joint ventures with Hilcorp Energy to develop gas production and midstream infrastructure in the Utica shale in Northeastern Ohio and Western Pennsylvania. In 2010 the company initiated three separate projects (for a total of $80 million) in the Majorsville Pennsylvania area to aggregate Marcellus Shale gas production for downstream transmission.

HISTORY

NiSource's earliest ancestor was the South Bend (Indiana) Gas Light Company founded in 1868 by the Studebaker brothers (of later auto fame) to supply gas. In 1886 a natural-gas discovery near Kokomo Indiana led to a boom in northern Indiana's use of the fuel. By 1900 steel plants and other industries had set up shop along Lake Michigan in northwestern Indiana and in Illinois.

Another NiSource ancestor was formed in 1901 as Hammond Illuminating but it changed its name to South Shore Gas and Electric. In 1909 Northern Indiana Gas and Electric was founded by merging South Shore with other regional utilities. The next year Northern Indiana acquired South Bend.

A third NiSource predecessor Calumet Electric (founded in 1912) had acquired several utilities by the early 1920s when utility magnate Samuel Insull bought it to add to his huge Midland Utilities holding company. In 1923 Insull bought Northern Indiana Gas and Electric which merged three years later with Calumet to form Northern Indiana Public Service Company (NIPSCO). NIPSCO acquired its current service territory in 1930 when it swapped some areas with another Midland subsidiary.

The Public Utility Holding Company Act of 1935 beginning the regulation of regional monopolies forced Midland to divest NIPSCO in 1947. In the 1950s and 1960s NIPSCO built two power plants and tripled its natural gas supply through a contract with a Houston gas company.

Responding to rising demand NIPSCO in 1970 applied to build a nuclear unit at its Bailly plant estimated to cost $180 million. In 1981 the nuke was abandoned after its cost rose to $2.1 billion. Reorganizing in 1987 NIPSCO became part of holding company NIPSCO Industries.

The Energy Policy Act of 1992 ushered in wholesale-power competition. That year NIPSCO acquired Kokomo Gas and Fuel and in 1993 it picked up Northern Indiana Fuel and Light and Crossroads Pipeline.

To prepare for oncoming retail competition NIPSCO in 1993 divided the electric and gas utilities into competing units and increased NIPSCO's marketing force. In 1997 NIPSCO branched out buying water utility holding company IWC Resources and the next year it began a customer choice program for its natural gas customers (all gas was delivered through its distribution lines however).

The company changed its name to NiSource in 1999 but did not alter its acquisition strategy. NiSource entered the US Northeast's gas market where deregulation plans were under way by purchasing New England utility Bay State Gas. A unit of Bay State Gas EnergyUSA bought natural gas marketer TPC and NiSource began integrating its nonregulated operations into EnergyUSA.

After launching a hostile takeover which it later withdrew NiSource purchased natural gas giant Columbia Energy Group for $6 billion in 2000. NiSource then sold its salt cavern gas storage and pipeline construction subsidiaries as well as certain Columbia electric generation and LNG facilities. In 2001 NiSource sold its Columbia Propane unit to AmeriGas Partners; it also agreed to sell water company IWC Resources (and its utility subsidiary Indianapolis Water) to the City of Indianapolis (the sale was completed in 2002).

In 2002 NiSource teamed up with the merchant services unit of Aquila (formerly UtiliCorp) to form an energy marketing and trading joint venture; however NiSource later backed out of the partnership due to instability in the energy trading industry. It also shut down its coal-fired Mitchell Generating Station and sold its SM&P Utility Resources subsidiary to The Laclede Group.

The following year NiSource sold its Columbia Transmission Communications (Transcom) subsidiary to Neon Communications (which itself was acquired by Globix in 2005).

To pay down debt and focus on its core operations in 2008 NiSource sold Northern Utilities and

Granite State Gas Transmission to Unitil for about $202 million. It also sold its Whiting Clean Energy facility to BP Alternative Energy North America for $217 million.

EXECUTIVES

President CEO and Director, Robert C. (Bob) Skaggs Jr., age 57, $800,000 total compensation
EVP; Group CEO Gas Transmission & Storage, Jimmy D. Staton, age 51, $440,000 total compensation
EVP and CFO, Stephen P. (Steve) Smith, age 50, $500,000 total compensation
VP Ethics and Compliance and Corporate Secretary, Gary W. Pottorff
Chairman, Ian M. Rolland, age 78
SVP Corporate Affairs, Glen L. Kettering, age 57
EVP and Chief Legal Officer, Carrie J. Hightman, age 54
VP Chief Risk Officer and Treasurer, David J. (Dave) Vajda, $215,000 total compensation
EVP; Group CEO Gas Distribution Segment, Joseph (Joe) Hamrock, age 48
SVP and CIO, Violet G. Sistovaris
VP Audit, Larry J. Francisco
VP Controller and Chief Accounting Officer, Jon D. Veurink, age 47
SVP Human Resources, Robert D. (Rob) Campbell, age 52, $270,000 total compensation
EVP; Group CEO Northern Indiana Public Service Co., Jim L. Stanley, age 57
Manager Communications, Mike Banas
Co-Owner Vice President of Sales and Marketing, Renee Coll
Director, Richard L. (Rich) Thompson, age 72
President CEO and Director, Robert C. (Bob) Skaggs Jr., age 57
Director, W. Lee Nutter, age 68
Director, Marty R. Kittrell, age 55
Director, Carolyn Y. Woo, age 57
Director, Steven C. Beering, age 79
Independent Director, Richard A. Abdoo, age 68
Independent Director, Michael E. Jesanis, age 55
Director, Deborah S. Parker, age 58
Independent Director, Sigmund Cornelius
Auditors: Deloitte&ToucheLLP

LOCATIONS

HQ: NiSource Inc.
801 E. 86th Ave., Merrillville IN 46410
Phone: 219-647-5990 **Fax:** 219-647-5589
Web: www.nisource.com

PRODUCTS/OPERATIONS

2011 Sales

	$ mil.	% of total
Gas distribution	2,917	49
Electric	1,427	24
Gas transmission & storage	1,354	22
Other	318	5
Total	**6,019**	**100**

Selected Subsidiaries

Utility operations
- Bay State Gas Company (natural gas utility)
- Colombia Gas of Kentucky Inc. (natural gas utility)
- Columbia Gas of Maryland Inc. (natural gas utility)
- Columbia Gas of Ohio Inc. (natural gas utility)
- Columbia Gas of Pennsylvania Inc. (natural gas utility)
- Columbia Gas of Virginia Inc. (natural gas utility)
- Kokomo Gas and Fuel Company (natural gas utility)
- Northern Indiana Fuel and Light Company Inc. (NIFL natural gas utility)
- Northern Indiana Public Service Company (NIPSCO electric and natural gas utility electric generation)

Gas transmission and storage operations
- Columbia Gas Transmission Corporation
- Columbia Gulf Transmission Company
- Crossroads Pipeline Company

Other operations
- CNS Microwave (telecommunications infrastructure)
- EnergyUSA-TPC (energy marketing and asset management)
- NiSource Energy Technologies (distributed power generation technologies)

COMPETITORS

AEP
Atmos Energy
Baltimore Gas and Electric
Constellation Energy Group
Dominion Resources
Duke Energy
El Paso Corporation
EQT Corporation
FirstEnergy
IPALCO Enterprises
National Grid USA
New Jersey Resources
Nicor Gas
Northeast Utilities
NSTAR
RGC Resources
Southern Union
Unitil
Vectren

HISTORICAL FINANCIALS

Company Type: Public

Income Statement FYE: December 31

	REVENUE ($ mil.)	NET INCOME ($ mil.)	NET PROFIT MARGIN	EMPLOYEES
12/11	6,019	299	5.0%	7,957
12/10	6,422	292	4.5%	7,604
12/09	6,649	217	3.3%	7,616
12/08	8,874	79	0.9%	7,981
12/07	7,939	321	4.0%	7,607
Annual Growth	(6.7%)	(1.8%)	—	1.1%

2011 Year-End Financials

Debt ratio: 38.41%
Return on equity: 5.99%
Cash ($ mil.): 11
Current ratio: 61.66
Long-term debt ($ mil.): 6,267
No. of shares (mil.): 281
Dividends
Yield: —
Payout: 89.32%
Market value ($ mil.): 6,711

	STOCK PRICE ($) FY Close	P/E High/Low	PER SHARE ($) Earnings	Dividends	Book Value
12/11	23.81	23 17	1.03	0.00	17.73
12/10	17.62	17 14	1.04	0.92	17.66
12/09	15.38	20 10	0.79	0.92	17.55
12/08	10.97	68 36	0.29	0.92	17.24
12/07	18.89	22 15	1.17	0.92	18.52
Annual Growth	6.0%	— —	(3.1%)	—	(1.1%)

Nordstrom, Inc.

Service with a smile is a part of Nordstrom's corporate culture. One of the nation's largest upscale apparel and shoe retailers Nordstrom sells clothes shoes and accessories through more than 115 Nordstrom department stores about 110 off-price outlet stores (Nordstrom Rack) in more than 30 states and online. It also operates a pair of Jeffrey luxury boutiques a "Last Chance" clearance store and newly-acquired online private sale site HauteLook. With its easy-return policy and touches such as thank-you notes from employees Nordstrom has earned a reputation for top-notch customer service. Members of the Nordstrom family who own nearly 25% of the company's stock closely supervise the chain.

Financial Analysis

Buoyed by the improving economy Nordstrom's fiscal 2012 (ends January) sales topped $10.8 billion (including credit card revenues) an increase of about 12% vs. the prior year. Net income increased more than 11% over the same period. The double-digit sales and income growth followed a strong fiscal 2011 signaling that the ill effects of the deep recession are behind it. In what is perhaps another indicator of better economic times full-line Nordstrom stores outperformed their off-price sister chain Nordstrom Rack for the second year in a row. Same-store sales at Nordstrom and Nordstrom Rack stores increased by more than 8% and 3% respectively in fiscal 2012. Going forward the company plans to open one full-line Nordstrom store and a dozen new Rack stores in fiscal 2013 one of which will be a 38000-sq.-ft. two-level store in Boston's Back Bay neighborhood.

Strategy

Extending its reach to the private-sales arena the company acquired e-tailer HauteLook for $180 million in stock in 2011. HauteLook launched in 2007 offers discounted apparel accessories and home decor to registered Web shoppers in the US and Canada. As part of the deal HauteLook became a subsidiary of Nordstrom and it continues to be based in Los Angeles and led by founder Adam Bernhard. Nordstrom took notice of HauteLook amid the rising popularity of (and sales generated through) private-sale sites during the recession; also referred to as flash sales sites such as HauteLook provide steep discounts on name-brand merchandise for short periods of time (generally 24 to 48 hours). Like other primarily brick-and-mortar retailers (such as ANN and Saks) Nordstrom is placing increased emphasis on e-commerce a channel known for pulling in profits that (unlike retail stores) are not as restricted by overhead.

Operations

The family-run company has consolidated its catalog and Internet businesses into one unit called Nordstrom Direct. The direct channel is outpacing the rest of Nordstrom in terms of growth with a net sales increase of nearly 30% in fiscal 2012 vs. 2011. The firm also owns a federal savings bank Nordstrom fsb through which it offers a private-label credit card as well as two co-branded Nordstrom VISA cards.

HISTORY

In 1901 John Nordstrom a lumberjack and successful gold miner used his Alaska Gold Rush money to open Wallin & Nordstrom shoe store in Seattle with shoemaker Carl Wallin. Nordstrom retired in 1928 and sold his half of the business which included a second store to his sons Everett and Elmer. Wallin sold his share to the brothers after retiring the following year. A third Nordstrom son Lloyd joined in 1933. The shoe chain thrived and incorporated as Nordstrom's in 1946.

By 1963 Nordstrom's was the largest independent shoe chain in the country. The company diversified by acquiring Best Apparel's stores in Seattle and Portland Oregon. Three years later Nordstrom's bought Portland's Nicholas Ungar a fashion retailer and merged it with one of its shoe stores in Portland under the name Nordstrom Best.

Renaming itself Nordstrom Best in 1966 the company went public in 1971 and changed its name again in 1973 to Nordstrom. The retailer grew steadily throughout the 1970s opening new stores boosting sales in existing stores and diversifying. In 1976 Nordstrom started Place Two featuring apparel and shoes in smaller stores than its traditional department layouts. It moved into Southern California (Orange County) two years later. Buoyed by almost $300 million in new sales Nordstrom executives planned an aggressive expansion.

Nordstrom opened its first store on the East Coast in 1988 in Virginia. The chain continued to expand opening stores in Northern California and in the affluent Washington DC suburbs.

The 1989 San Francisco earthquake along with a national downturn hurt retail sales significantly. Nordstrom's much-touted focus on customer service had a downside: The company was investigated in 1990 for not paying employees for customer services they performed including delivery of merchandise on their own time. (Three years later Nordstrom set aside $15 million to pay back wages to employees who had performed off-the-clock services.)

The company continued to expand in the East and Midwest opening its first store in the New York City area in 1991. In 1993 the retailer opened a men's boutique in New York (Faconnable). Looking for new ways to attract customers Nordstrom introduced a mail-order catalog the next year.

Following the family's business tradition six members of Nordstrom's fourth generation began running the company in 1995. Third-generation members James Nordstrom John Nordstrom Bruce Nordstrom and Jack McMillan retired as co-chairmen and were replaced by non-family members Ray Johnson and John Whitacre. (Johnson retired in 1996.)

Nordstrom created Nordstrom.com a partnership with Benchmark Capital and Madrona Investment Group in 1999 to consolidate its catalog and Internet operations.

In early 2000 amid slumping sales the company dissolved the co-presidency. Less than a year later however the Nordstroms were back in charge. Chairman and CEO Whitacre resigned and Blake Nordstrom took over running the company as president. His father Bruce came out of retirement to take the chairman's role. Later the company bought the French design company Faconnable which supplies the products for its Faconnable boutiques.

In May 2002 the company bought out Benchmark's and Madrona's minority stake in Nordstrom.com.

Nordstrom bought a majority interest in August 2005 in luxury specialty stores Jeffrey New York and Jeffrey Atlanta. Terms of the agreement were not disclosed. The Jeffrey stores had about $35 million in sales in 2004. Also in 2005 the company opened stores in Atlanta; Dallas; Irvine California; and San Antonio.

In late 2007 Nordstrom sold its four US Faconnable boutiques and 37 European locations to Lebanon-based M1 Group for about $210 million. Overall in 2007 Nordstrom opened three full-line department stores and a single Rack store.

Nordstrom opened its first full-line department store in Hawaii in early 2008. That October amid economic gloom the retailer opened a store in Pittsburgh. Overall the retailer opened eight new Nordstrom stores and half a dozen Rack outlets in 2008. In 2009 it added three full-line Nordstrom locations and 13 Rack outlets.

Nordstrom acquired e-tailer HauteLook for $180 million in stock in March 2011. Based in Los Angeles HauteLook is a leader in online private sales.

EXECUTIVES

President and Director, Blake W. Nordstrom, age 51, $700,000 total compensation
EVP and CFO, Michael G. Koppel, age 55, $480,000 total compensation
EVP and Director; President Merchandising, Peter E. (Pete) Nordstrom, age 50, $650,000 total compensation
Chairman, Enrique (Rick) Hernandez Jr., age 56
EVP and Director; President Stores, Erik B. Nordstrom, age 48, $650,000 total compensation
EVP and CIO, R. Michael Richardson, age 55
EVP General Counsel and Corporate Secretary, Robert B. Sari, age 56
VP Investor Relations and Treasurer, Robert E. (Rob) Campbell, age 56
EVP; Chairman and CEO Nordstrom fsb; President Nordstrom Credit, Kevin T. Knight, age 56
EVP and Regional Manager Orange County and Los Angeles, Robert J. Middlemas, age 55
VP and Director New Rack Stores, Karen C. (K. C.) Shaffer
EVP Human Resources and Diversity Affairs, Delena M. Sunday, age 51
EVP; President Nordstrom Rack, Geevy S. K. Thomas, age 47
EVP and Chief Marketing Officer, Anne Martin-Vachon, age 50
Senior Financial Analyst Investor Relations, Lacy Fitzpatrick
EVP and Chief Administrative Officer, Daniel F. (Dan) Little, age 50, $420,000 total compensation
VP and Regional Manager Southern States, Karen McKibbin
VP Marketing, Michael Crotty
EVP and General Merchandise Manager Cosmetics Division, Laurie M. Black, age 53
VP and Regional Manager San Diego and Mountain, Nora Cummings
EVP; President Nordstrom Direct, James F. (Jamie) Nordstrom Jr., age 39
VP Store Planning, David P. Lindsey, age 55
EVP Designer Merchandising, Jeffrey Kalinsky
EVP and General Merchandise Manager Men's Apparel, David M. Witman, age 53
EVP and General Merchandise Manager Accessories and Women's Specialized Divisions, Margaret Myers, age 65
VP CMM Women's Designer Apparel, Jennifer Wheeler
EVP and General Merchandise Manager Shoe Division, Scott A. Meden, age 49
VP Corporate Communications, Brooke White
VP Finance and Principal Accounting Officer, James A. Howell, age 46
EVP and General Merchandise Manager Women?s Apparel Division, Loretta Soffe, age 45
VP and Regional Manager Midwest, Brent Harris
Manager National Merchandise Kids' Wear, Gary Flynn
EVP; President Nordstrom Product Group, Mark J. Tritton, age 48
Director Business Public Relations, Colin Johnson
Manager Investor Relations, Sandy Fabre
VP and Regional Manager Northern California, Jim O'Neal
EVP Strategy and Development, Ken Worzel, age 47
VP and Regional Manager Northwest, Leslie Martin
Public Relations, Aubrie Corey
President and Director, Blake W. Nordstrom, age 51
Director, Robert G. (Bob) Miller, age 67
Director, Robert D. (Bob) Walter, age 66
Director, Philip G. (Phil) Satre, age 62
Director, Phyllis J. Campbell, age 60
EVP and Director; President Merchandising, Peter E. (Pete) Nordstrom, age 50
Director, B. Kevin Turner, age 47
EVP and Director; President Stores, Erik B. Nordstrom, age 48
Director, Alison A. Winter, age 65
Director, Felicia Thornton, age 48
Director, Michelle M. Ebanks
Auditors: Deloitte&ToucheLLP

LOCATIONS

HQ: Nordstrom Inc.
1617 6th Ave., Seattle WA 98101-1707
Phone: 206-628-2111 **Fax:** 206-628-1795
Web: www.nordstrom.com

PRODUCTS/OPERATIONS

2012 Stores

	No.
Full-line	117
Rack &	108
Total	**225**

2012 Sales

	$ mil.	% of total
Retail	10,497	97
Credit card	380	3
Total	**10,877**	**100**

2012 Sales

	% of total
Women's	33
Shoes	23
Men's	15
Women's	12
Cosmetics	11
Children's	3
Other	3
Total	**100**

Selected Retail Operations

HauteLook (private-sale website for apparel and home decor)
Jeffrey (boutiques)
Last Chance (clearance store)
Nordstrom (specialty stores selling apparel shoes and accessories for women men and children)
Nordstrom Direct (catalogs and online ordering)
Nordstrom Rack (outlets selling merchandise from Nordstrom specialty stores and manufacturers)

COMPETITORS

Ann Taylor
Astor & Black
Barneys
Benetton
Bloomingdale' s
Bluefly
Brooks Brothers
Brown Shoe
Cache
Dillard' s
Donna Karan
Eddie Bauer LLC
J. C. Penney
J. Crew
Jones Group
Lands' End
Loehmann' s
Macy' s
Men' s Wearhouse
Neiman Marcus
Saks Fifth Avenue
Talbots
The Gap
Tiffany & Co.
Von Maur
Wayfair

HISTORICAL FINANCIALS

Company Type: Public

Income Statement FYE: January 28

	REVENUE ($ mil.)	NET INCOME ($ mil.)	NET PROFIT MARGIN	EMPLOYEES
01/12	10,877	683	6.3%	56,500
01/11	9,700	613	6.3%	52,000
01/10	8,627	441	5.1%	48,000
01/09*	8,573	401	4.7%	51,000
02/08	8,828	715	8.1%	56,500
Annual Growth	5.4%	(1.1%)	—	0.0%

*Fiscal year change

2012 Year-End Financials

Debt ratio: 42.94%
Return on equity: 34.92%
Cash ($ mil.): 1,877
Current ratio: 215.92
Long-term debt ($ mil.): 3,140

No. of shares (mil.): 207
Dividends
Yield: —
Payout: 29.30%
Market value ($ mil.): 10,079

	STOCK PRICE ($) FY Close	P/E High/Low		PER SHARE ($) Earnings	Dividends	Book Value
01/12	48.55	16	12	3.14	0.00	9.43
01/11	40.91	16	10	2.75	0.00	9.27
01/10	34.54	19	6	2.01	0.00	7.22
01/09*	12.69	21	4	1.83	0.00	5.62
02/08	39.74	20	10	2.88	0.00	5.05
Annual Growth	5.1%	—	—	2.2%	—	16.9%

*Fiscal year change

Norfolk Southern Corp.

Transportation titan Norfolk Southern is the one big train that could. Its main subsidiary Norfolk Southern Railway transports freight over a network consisting of about 20000 route miles in 20+ states in the eastern southeastern and Midwestern US and in Ontario and Quebec. The rail system is made up of more than 15000 route miles owned by Norfolk Southern and nearly 5000 route miles of trackage rights which allow the company to use tracks owned by other railroads. Norfolk Southern transports coal and general merchandise including automotive products and chemicals. It also offers intermodal services (freight transportation by a combination of train and truck) through its Triple Crown Services unit.

Operations

Norfolk Southern reports through three segments: General Merchandise Coal and Intermodal. General Merchandise accounts for 50% of the company's revenue. The segment is subdivided into five commodity groups: Agriculture/Consumer/Government (such commodities and products as soybeans wheat beverages canned goods ethanol and military items); Chemicals (sulfur petroleum products plastics among others); Metals/Construction (steel aluminum cement bricks etc); Automotive (finished vehicles from and auto parts for such auto OEMs as Ford General Motors and Toyota); and Paper/Clay/Forest (lumber and wood products pulp board and paper products wood fibers wood pulp scrap paper and clay). The General Merchandise segment carried about 120 million tons on more than 2 million railroad carloads in 2011.

Coal is Norfolk Southern's single largest commodity group accounting for 31% of revenue. The company carried about 178 million tons of coal in 2011 originating from major coal basins and destined for more than 100 coal generation plants as well as export metallurgical and industrial facilities. Operating in the eastern US Intermodal carried more than 3 million units in 2011 for such clients as intermodal marketing companies international steamship lines and truckers.

Financial Analysis

Norfolk Southern's revenue rose 17% in 2011 compared with 2010 thanks mainly to higher revenue per unit in response to more consumer demand. General Merchandise revenue increased 12% in 2011 compared with 2010 as the result of higher rates and fuel surcharges. Within General Merchandise the commodity group of Agriculture/Consumer Products/Government headed up 9% in 2011 compared with 2010. Chemicals increased 5%. Metals/Construction soared 23%. Paper/Clay/Forest Products headed up 6%. These commodity groups did well mainly as a result of increased rates and fuel surcharges. Automotive surged 20% in response to more output of light vehicles in North America.

Coal rose 27% in 2011 vs. 2010 to meet more demand from the domestic and global steel production market. Intermodal revenues went up 19% in 2011 compared with 2010 behind more traffic volume and higher rates and fuel surcharges. Net income for the company as a whole surged 28% in 2011 compared with 2010 thanks mainly to a 20% jump in railway operations income and lower taxes.

Strategy

Looking ahead Coal is expected to do well in response to more exports of coal for steel production and a tight supply in Australia after flooding. Among other forecasts: Domestic metallurgical coal will struggle with less demand. Industrial coal shipments will to rise in 2012 and 2013 to meet demand from new business. Demand for utility coal will decrease as a mild winter and low natural gas prices divert need for it. Agriculture/Consumer/Government's revenues will rise in response to more demand for ethanol and animal feed.

Chemicals are expected to enjoy a healthy next few years thanks to more shipments of crude oil from the Midwest to Eastern refineries and more demand for liquefied petroleum. Metals/Construction is forecast to respond to growth in the natural gas drilling market and higher metal-related traffic volumes. Automotive is also expected to respond to higher production of light vehicles in North America.

Thanks in part to $267 million of capital funding from several states and the federal government Norfolk Southern will continue to work on the Crescent Corridor an intermodal route spanning 11 states from New Jersey to Louisiana. Norfolk Southern is heralding the railroad as a solution to highway congestion relief. Other expansion efforts have included the Pan Am Southern joint venture between Norfolk Southern and Pan Am Railways that is responsible for a 155-mile track between New York and Massachusetts and the MidAmerica Corridor a partnership between NS and Canadian National Railway for sharing track between the Midwest and Southeast.

HISTORY

Norfolk Southern Corporation resulted from the 1982 merger of two US rail giants –Norfolk & Western Railway Company (N&W) and Southern Railway Company –which had emerged from more than 200 and 150 previous mergers respectively.

N&W dates to 1838 when one track connected Petersburg Virginia to City Point (now Hopewell). This eight-miler became part of the Atlantic Mississippi & Ohio (AM&O) which was created by consolidating three Virginia railways in 1870.

In 1881 Philadelphia banker E.W. Clark bought the AM&O and renamed it the Norfolk & Western. N&W rolled into Ohio by purchasing two other railroads (1892 1901).

The company took over the Virginian Railway a coal carrier with track paralleling much of its own in 1959. In 1964 N&W became a key railroad in the Midwest by acquiring the New York Chicago & St. Louis Railroad and the Pennsylvania Railroad's line between Columbus and Sandusky Ohio. It also leased the Wabash Railroad with lines from Detroit and Chicago to Kansas City and St. Louis.

Southern Railway can be traced back to the South Carolina Canal & Rail Road a nine-mile line chartered in 1827 and built by Horatio Allen to win trade for Charleston's port. It began operating the US's first regularly scheduled passenger train in 1830 and became the world's longest railway when it opened a 136-mile line to Hamburg South Carolina (1833).

Soon other railroads sprang up in the South including the Richmond & Danville (Virginia 1847) and the East Tennessee Virginia & Georgia (1869) which were combined to form the Southern Railway System in 1894. Southern eventually controlled more than 100 railroads forging a system from Washington DC to St. Louis and New Orleans.

The 1982 merger of Southern and N&W created an extensive rail system throughout the East South and Midwest. Norfolk Southern (a holding company created for the two railroads) also bought North American Van Lines in 1985. Triple Crown Services the company's intermodal subsidiary was started in 1986. The company also made a failed attempt to take over Piedmont Aviation the next year.

Norfolk Southern revived North American Van Lines by selling its refrigerator truck operation Tran-star (1993) and suspending its commercial trucking line. But it later sold the rest of the motor carrier (1998) to focus on rail operations.

When CSX announced its plans to buy Conrail in 1997 Norfolk Southern's counteroffer led to a split of the former Northeastern monopoly between Norfolk Southern (58%) and CSX (42%). Problems with integrating Conrail's assets hurt Norfolk Southern's results. But by 2000 it had regained some of the traffic it had lost to service problems and its intermodal shipping business also gained speed. In 2004 Norfolk Southern and CSX reorganized Conrail to give each parent company direct ownership of the portion of Conrail's assets that it operates. Conrail still operates switching facilities and terminals used by both Norfolk Southern and CSX.

Norfolk Southern got hit in the wallet in 2001: The company agreed to pay $28 million to settle a racial discrimination lawsuit brought by black employees in 1993. Norfolk Southern began rounds of layoffs and closed redundant depots and facilities in 2001.

In 2005 nine people died in South Carolina when chlorine gas leaked from a ruptured car on a Norfolk Southern freight train. The car was breached when the train crashed into a company-owned locomotive and two train cars that were parked on a siding.

The company opened the Heartland Corridor in 2010 between Chicago and Norfolk Virginia.

EXECUTIVES

EVP and Chief Marketing Officer, Donald W. (Don) Seale, age 59, $500,000 total compensation
EVP and COO, Mark D. Manion, age 59, $500,000 total compensation
EVP Law and Corporate Relations, James A. (Jim) Hixon, age 58, $500,000 total compensation
EVP Finance and CFO, John P. Rathbone, age 59, $500,000 total compensation
VP Industrial Products, David T. Lawson
Chairman President and CEO, Charles W. (Wick) Moorman IV, age 59, $950,000 total compensation
VP Human Resources, Cindy C. Earhart
VP Law, William A. Galanko
VP Intermodal Operations, Robert E. (Bob) Huffman
VP Government Relations, Bruno Maestri
VP Business Development, Robert E. Martinez
SVP Energy and Properties, Daniel D. (Danny) Smith, age 59
VP Intermodal and Automotive Marketing, Michael R. (Mike) McClellan
President Triple Crown Services, James A. (Jim) Newton
VP Transportation, Michael J. Wheeler
EVP Administration, James A. (Jim) Squires, age 50, $465,000 total compensation
VP Real Estate and Corporate Sustainability Officer, F. Blair Wimbush
EVP Planning and CIO, Deborah H. (Debbie) Butler, age 57, $465,000 total compensation
VP Process Engineering, Terry N. Evans
Director Investor Relations, Leanne D. Marilley
VP and Treasurer, Marta R. Stewart, age 54
VP Operations Planning and Support, Gerhard A. Thelen
VP Taxation, Robert M. Kesler Jr.
VP Mechanical, Tim A. Heilig
VP Information Technology, Thomas G. Werner
VP Engineering, Timothy J. Drake
VP Customer Service, Fredric M. Ehlers
VP Labor Relations, Harold R. Mobley
Corporate Secretary, Howard D. McFadden
VP Strategic Planning, John H. Friedmann
Director Government Relations, Frank Voyack
Assistant VP Government Relations, Marque Ledoux
VP and Controller, Clyde H. (Jake) Allison Jr., age 48
Assistant VP Government Relations Mid-West States, George J. Camille
Assistant VP Government Relations Mid-Atlantic States, C. Scott Muir
VP Safety and Environmental, David F. Julian
Assistant VP Corporate Communications, Frank Brown
VP Audit and Compliance, Thomas E. Hurlbut
Manager Corporate Communications, Robin Chapman
Resident VP Government Relations, Rudy Husband
Director Corporate Communications, Susan Terpay
Assistant VP Government Relations, Darrell Wilson
Manager Government Relations Alabama Mississippi Lousiana and Tennessee, Elizabeth Lawlor
Resident VP Government Relations Georgia and Florida, Joel E. Harrell III
Resident VP Government Relations North Carolina, Durwood S. Laughinghouse
Resident VP Government Relations South Carolina, Frank R. Macchiaverna
Resident VP Government Relations Indiana and Michigan, Paul A. Gilley
Resident VP Government Relations Ohio and Kentucky, William J. (Bill) Harris III
Resident VP Government Relations Pennsylvania and New York, Michael R. (Mike) Fesen
Resident VP Government Relations Virginia, W. Bruce Wingo
Resident VP Government Relations West Virginia, William G. (Bill) Carper Jr.
Director Investor Relations, Michael Hostutler
Director, Steven F. Leer, age 59
Director, Daniel A. (Dan) Carp, age 63
Director, Alston D. (Pete) Correll Jr., age 70
Director, Burton M. (Burt) Joyce, age 70
Director, Erskine B. Bowles, age 66
Director, Michael D. (Mike) Lockhart, age 62
Director, Thomas D. (Tom) Bell Jr., age 62
Director, Karen N. Horn, age 68
Director, Gerald L. Baliles, age 72
Director, Adm. J. Paul Reason, age 71
Director, Robert (Bob) Bradway, age 49
Independent Director, Wesley Bush
Auditors: KPMGLLP

LOCATIONS

HQ: Norfolk Southern Corporation
3 Commercial Place, Norfolk VA 23510-2191
Phone: 757-629-2680 **Fax:** 757-664-5069
Web: www.nscorp.com

PRODUCTS/OPERATIONS

2011 Sales

	$ mil.	% of total
Coal	3,458	31
Intermodal	2,130	19
General merchandis		
Agriculture consumer government	1,439	13
Chemicals	1,368	12
Metals and construction	1,241	11
Automotive	780	7
Paper clay and forest	756	7
Total	**11,172**	**100**

Selected Facilities Served

Active coal-loading facilities
Auto assembly plants
Auto distribution facilities
Bulk transfer facilities
Coal and iron ore transload facilities
General warehouses/distribution centers
Intermodal terminals
Just-in-time rail auto parts center
Lumber reload centers
Metals distribution centers
Paper distribution centers
Paper mills
Power generation plants served
Steel mills and processing facilities
Triple Crown Service terminals
Vehicle mixing centers

COMPETITORS

American Commercial Lines
APL Logistics
Burlington Northern Santa Fe
Canadian National Railway
Canadian Pacific Railway
CSX
Genesee & Wyoming
Hub Group
Ingram Industries
J.B. Hunt
Kansas City Southern
Kirby Corporation
Landstar System
Pacer International
Piedmont Natural Gas
Pier 1 Imports
Pilgrim' s Pride
Pinnacle West
Pitney Bowes
Plum Creek Timber
Portec
PVH
Schneider National
Union Pacific
Werner Enterprises

HISTORICAL FINANCIALS

Company Type: Public

Income Statement

FYE: December 31

	REVENUE ($ mil.)	NET INCOME ($ mil.)	NET PROFIT MARGIN	EMPLOYEES
12/11	11,172	1,916	17.2%	30,329
12/10	9,516	1,496	15.7%	28,559
12/09	7,969	1,034	13.0%	28,593
12/08	10,661	1,716	16.1%	30,709
12/07	9,432	1,464	15.5%	30,806
Annual Growth	4.3%	7.0%	—	(0.4%)

2011 Year-End Financials

Debt ratio: 26.42%
Return on equity: 19.33%
Cash ($ mil.): 276
Current ratio: 102.94
Long-term debt ($ mil.): 7,390
No. of shares (mil.): 330
Dividends
Yield: —
Payout: 30.46%
Market value ($ mil.): 24,072

	STOCK PRICE ($) FY Close	P/E High	P/E Low	PER SHARE ($) Earnings	Dividends	Book Value
12/11	72.86	14	11	5.45	0.00	30.00
12/10	62.82	16	11	4.00	1.40	29.85
12/09	52.42	19	10	2.76	1.36	28.06
12/08	47.05	16	9	4.52	1.22	26.23
12/07	50.44	16	12	3.68	0.96	25.64
Annual Growth	9.6%	—	—	10.3%	—	4.0%

Northeast Utilities

Northeast Utilities (NU) uses Yankee ingenuity power and gas to keep customers happy. The largest utility in New England NU operates six electric and gas utilities in Connecticut Massachusetts and New Hampshire and serves nearly 3.5 million electric and gas customers. It has 4500 miles of power transmission lines 72000 miles electric distribution lines and 6000 miles of gas distribution lines. Subsidiaries include Connecticut Light and Power Public Service Company of New Hampshire and Western Massachusetts Electric. NU's Yankee Gas supplies natural gas to 200000 customers in Connecticut. In 2012 NU bought regional rival NSTAR (which has 1.1 million power and 300000 gas customers) for $4.2 billion.

The "merger of equals" created a major energy player in the US Northeast which serves more than half the total utility customers in New England. NSTAR shareholders hold about 44% of the expanded company.

The acquisition boosts the financial resources of NU to pay for $9 billion of planned transmission projects aimed at bringing cleaner power from Northern New England and Canada to population centers in Southern New England.

NU's competitive businesses (under the NU Enterprises umbrella) consist of a few wholesale energy marketing contracts Northeast Generation Services (which is being wound down) and an electrical contracting business.

The company's operating strategy has been focused on increasing the scope and efficiency of its regulated operations by upgrading its infrastructure and by using new technologies (such as automated meters and other smart grid technologies) that enable customers to better manage their energy usage.

To give better access and service to its customers in 2009 NU relocated its headquarters from Berlin Connecticut to a larger building in downtown Hartford.

Northeast Utilities reported lower revenues in 2010 as the result of lower power generation service and related congestion charges (the costs of producing power that is passed on to customers) and lower gas prices.

HISTORY

In 1966 three old intertwined New England utilities merged. One was The Hartford Electric Light Company (HELCO) founded in 1883 by Austin Dunham in Hartford Connecticut. In 1915 the company signed the first power exchange agreement in the US with Connecticut Power (CP) which HELCO acquired in 1920.

The second founded in 1886 was Western Massachusetts Electric (WMECO) which merged with Western Counties in the 1930s to become WMECO. The third was Connecticut Light and Power (CL&P). Founded as Rocky River Power in 1905 it took the CL&P name in 1917. In 1929 it built the US's first large-scale pumped-storage hydroelectric plant.

In the 1950s HELCO formed Yankee Atomic Electric with CL&P WMECO and others to build an experimental nuclear reactor. In 1965 members of the group began jointly building the Connecticut Yankee nuke (on line in 1968). After years of cooperation CL&P HELCO and WMECO merged in 1966 and Northeast Utilities (NU) was born. It was the first multistate utility holding company created since the Public Utility Holding Company Act of 1935 had broken up the old utility giants. Holyoke Water Power joined NU the following year.

The 1970s energy crisis spurred NU to continue building nukes including Maine Yankee Vermont Yankee and two Millstone units. But by the 1980s construction delays had raised the cost of the final unit Millstone 3.

Regulators forced CL&P to spin off its gas utility Yankee Energy System in 1989. The next year NU acquired bankrupt utility Public Service Company of New Hampshire (PSNH) and its new Seabrook nuke. (PSNH emerged from bankruptcy in 1991.)

The 1995 shutdown of Millstone 1 began NU's nuclear troubles. In 1996 regulators closed all of its nukes except Seabrook because of safety concerns and NU mothballed Connecticut Yankee. The next year Michael Morris replaced CEO Bernard Fox who left after federal regulators ordered NU to comply with regulations and fix management problems –NU managers had routinely retaliated against whistleblowers –the first time a utility had been given such an order. New managers came in including a former whistleblower but NU couldn't avoid a record-setting $2.1 million fine. NU received permission to restart the Millstone units in 1998-99. But it had to absorb the $1 billion in power replacement associated with the shutdown.

Meanwhile as deregulation loomed NU created a retail marketer (now Select Energy) and a telecommunications arm (Mode 1 Communications) in 1996. Two years later retail competition began in Massachusetts and deregulation legislation was passed in Connecticut (deregulation went into effect there in 2000).

In 1999 NU sold its Massachusetts plants to New York's Consolidated Edison and auctioned off its non-nuclear plants in Connecticut to its subsidiary Northeast Generation and Northern States Power (now Xcel Energy). NU agreed to plead guilty to 25 federal felony counts and pay $10 million in penalties for polluting water near Millstone and lying to regulators.

That year Consolidated Edison agreed to buy NU for $3.3 billion in cash and stock and $3.9 billion in assumed debt. The deal broke down in 2001 however; Con Edison charged NU with misrepresenting information about power-supply contracts and NU charged Con Edison with improperly attempting to renegotiate the terms of the acquisition.

Bringing an old family member home NU bought Yankee Energy System for $679 million in 2000. Later that year Dominion Resources which had helped NU restart Millstone 2 and Millstone 3 (Millstone 1 had been taken out of service) agreed to buy the Millstone complex for $1.3 billion. The sale closed in 2001.

Also in 2001 NU subsidiary Select Energy bought Niagara Mohawk's energy marketing unit NU sold the distribution business of its Holyoke Water Power utility to the City of Holyoke for $18 million and retail electric competition began in New Hampshire. The company agreed to sell CL&P's 10% stake in the Vermont Yankee nuclear facility to Entergy in 2001; the deal was completed the following year.

NU sold its 40% interest in the Seabrook Nuclear Generating facility in 2002 to FPL Group.

In 2006 NU sold nonregulated subsidiary Select Energy which marketed and traded energy to wholesale and retail customers to Hess Corporation. That year the company also sold its competitive generation assets in Connecticut and Massachusetts to Energy Capital Partners for $1.34 billion.

In 2007 Connecticut Light and Power Company completed the installation of electric service to Yankee Gas Services Company's new liquefied natural gas facility in Waterbury.

EXECUTIVES

Chairman, Charles W. (Chuck) Shivery, age 66, $1,035,000 total compensation
VP Human Resources Northeast Utilities Service Company, Jean M. LaVecchia, age 60, $304,019 total compensation
SVP General Counsel and Secretary, Gregory B. Butler, age 54, $406,988 total compensation
EVP and CFO, James J. (Jim) Judge, age 55
President; Chief Executive Officer; Trustee, Thomas J. (Tom) May, age 64
Assistant Secretary, O. Kay Comendul
EVP and COO; CEO CL&P PSNH WMECO and Yankee Gas, Leon J. (Lee) Olivier, age 63, $550,000 total compensation
EVP and Chief Administrative Officer, David R. McHale, age 51, $524,520 total compensation
VP and Treasurer, Randall A. (Randy) Shoop
President and COO CL&P, William P. (Bill) Herdegen III, age 56
President and COO Connecticut Light and Power, Jeffrey D. (Jeff) Butler, age 55
President and COO Yankee Gas, Rodney O. (Rod) Powell, age 60
VP Accounting and Controller, Jay S. Buth, age 42
President and COO Western Massachusetts Electric Co., Peter J. Clarke, age 50
Senior Vice President - Enterprise Planning and Development of NUSCO., James B. Robb, age 51
Media Relations, Deborah Beauchamp
Secretary Chief Compliance Officer and Deputy General Counsel, Samuel K. (Sam) Lee
Assistant Treasurer Finance, Susan B. Weber
VP Customer Operations WMECO, Robert S. Coates Jr.
IR Contact Officer, Barbara Nieman
Independent Trustee, Charles Gifford
Independent Trustee, Francis Doyle
Independent Trustee, Frederica Williams
Independent Trustee, James DiStasio
Independent Trustee, Paul Camera
Independent Trustee, William Faasen
Trustee, John S. Clarkeson, age 69
Director, Dennis R. Wraase, age 68
Trustee, Richard H. Booth, age 65
Director, E. Gail de Planque, age 67
Trustee, Cotton M. Cleveland, age 59
Trustee, Sanford (Sandy) Cloud Jr., age 67
Trustee, Elizabeth T. Kennan, age 74
Trustee, Robert E. Patricelli, age 72
Trustee, John F. Swope, age 73
Trustee, John G. Graham, age 73
Trustee, Kenneth R. Leibler, age 62
Auditors: Deloitte&ToucheLLP

LOCATIONS

HQ: Northeast Utilities
56 Propect St., Hartford CT 06103
Phone: 860-665-5000 **Fax:** 732-741-3140
Web: www.neort.com

PRODUCTS/OPERATIONS

2010 Sales

	$ mil.	% of total
Utilities		
Distribution		
Electric	3,802	77
Gas	434	9
Transmission	625	13
Competitive businesses	80	1
Adjustments	(44.0)	-
Total	**4,898**	**100**

Selected Subsidiaries

The Northeast Utilities System (regulated utilities)
- Connecticut Light and Power Company (CL&P electric utility)
- Public Service Company of New Hampshire (PSNH electric utility)
- Western Massachusetts Electric Company (WMECO electric utility)
- Yankee Energy System Inc. (natural gas utility Connecticut)
  - Yankee Gas Services Company (retail natural gas service)

Other Operations
- Northeast Utilities Service Company (administrative services for NU subsidiaries)
- NU Enterprises Inc. (nonutility operations)

COMPETITORS

AEP
Bangor Hydro-Electric
Central Vermont Public Service
Con Edison
Green Mountain Power
Iberdrola USA
Massachusetts Municipal Wholesale Electric
National Grid USA
NiSource
PG&E Corporation
Public Service Enterprise Group
Southern Company
UIL Holdings
Unitil
USPowerGen

HISTORICAL FINANCIALS

Company Type: Public

Income Statement FYE: December 31

	REVENUE ($ mil.)	NET INCOME ($ mil.)	NET PROFIT MARGIN	EMPLOYEES
12/11	4,465	394	8.8%	6,063
12/10	4,898	387	7.9%	6,182
12/09	5,439	330	6.1%	6,078
12/08	5,800	260	4.5%	6,189
12/07	5,822	246	4.2%	5,869
Annual Growth	(6.4%)	12.5%	—	0.8%

2011 Year-End Financials

Debt ratio: 33.64%
Return on equity: 9.84%
Cash ($ mil.): 77
Current ratio: 69.70
Long-term debt ($ mil.): 4,614

No. of shares (mil.): 177
Dividends
Yield: —
Payout: 49.55%
Market value ($ mil.): 6,390

	STOCK PRICE ($) FY Close	P/E High	P/E Low	PER SHARE ($) Earnings	Dividends	Book Value
12/11	36.07	16	14	2.22	0.00	22.65
12/10	31.88	15	11	2.19	1.03	22.26
12/09	25.79	14	10	1.91	0.95	21.03
12/08	24.06	19	11	1.67	0.83	20.13
12/07	31.31	21	17	1.59	0.78	19.54
Annual Growth	3.6%	—	—	8.7%	—	3.8%

Northern Tier Energy LP

LOCATIONS

HQ: Northern Tier Energy LP
38C Grove Street, Suite 100, Ridgefield, CT 06877
Phone: 203 244-6550
Web: www.ntenergy.com

HISTORICAL FINANCIALS

Company Type:

Income Statement FYE: December 31

	REVENUE ($ mil.)	NET INCOME ($ mil.)	NET PROFIT MARGIN	EMPLOYEES
12/11	4,280	28	0.7%	2,667
12/10*	344	24	7.2%	0
11/10	3,195	61	1.9%	0
12/09	2,940	54	1.9%	0
Annual Growth	13.3%	(19.7%)	—	—

*Fiscal year change

2011 Year-End Financials

Debt ratio: 30.23%—
Return on equity: 9.07%
Cash ($ mil.): 123
Current ratio: 122.27
Long-term debt ($ mil.): 301

Dividends
Yield: —
Payout: —
Market value ($ mil.): —

Northern Trust Corp.

Northern Trust Corporation works to keep its clients' trust. Founded in 1889 flagship subsidiary The Northern Trust Company and other units bearing the Northern Trust name offer banking and trust services brokerage asset servicing securities lending and proprietary mutual funds (the Northern Funds) to institutional clients and the affluent from more than 90 offices in nearly 20 states and more than 15 countries. Operating in two main segments Corporate and Institutional Services and Personal Financial Services Northern Trust has more than $4.2 trillion of assets under custody and some $670 billion under management.

The Corporate and Institutional Services division provides global master trust and custody services trade settlement and reporting fund administration banking brokerage and investment operations outsourcing and analysis asset management and servicing brokerage and banking services. Clients include retirement funds fund managers foundations and endowments insurance companies and government entities. The company added hedge fund services to its activities through the 2011 purchase of fund administrator Omnium (now Northern Trust Hedge Fund Services) from Citadel in a deal that added more than $70 billion in assets under administration.

Northern Trust's Personal Financial Services segment offers trust and investment management custody philanthropic consulting estate administration private banking and brokerage services to high-net-worth individuals and families executives and professionals retirees and privately held businesses and their owners. In 2010 Northern Trust added to the business with the acquisition of Los Angeles-based investment advisory Waterline Partners. Northern Trust's wealth management group serves individuals and family offices that have more than $200 million of assets.

The company's foreign operations include branches in Australia Canada the Cayman Islands Ireland Luxembourg the Netherlands Sweden and the UK. The company is targeting Asia for growth where it has offices in China Hong Kong India Japan and Singapore. In 2011 Northern Trust expanded in Europe with the purchase of Bank of Ireland's fund administration investment operations outsourcing and custody business. The acquisition was combined with Northern Trust's existing operations in Ireland which is a European hub for cross-border fund administration.

Northern Trust recorded net income of more than $600 million in 2011 but that figure represents a decline from each of the last two years though its revenues have remained steady. The company attributes the decrease in profits to higher restructuring and acquisition-related charges. It has seen growth however in its assets under management and custody both organically and from acquisitions.

HISTORY

When banker Byron Smith took time off to handle family concerns in 1885 friends turned to him for advice on trust and estate matters. It occurred to him that there was a market for such services within a banking framework.

Smith tested new Illinois banking and trust laws by arranging for state banking authorities to reject his charter application for Northern Trust. As Smith had hoped the charter was upheld by the Illinois Supreme Court.

Northern Trust opened in 1889 in one of Chicago's new skyscrapers the Rookery. With $1 million in capital –about 40% from Smith and the rest from the likes of Marshall Field (retailing) Martin Ryerson (steel) and Philip Armour (meatpacking) –the bank attracted $138000 in deposits its first day.

By 1896 the bank was firmly established; Smith began taking a salary and the company issued its first dividend. Ten years later the firm built its solid granite edifice the "Gray Lady of LaSalle Street" where it still resides.

The bank began buying commercial paper in 1912 joined the Federal Reserve System in 1917 and became a custodian for expropriated German assets during WWI. Byron Smith died in 1914 and was succeeded by his son Solomon.

Northern Trust rejected the get-rich-quick ethos of the 1920s. It was so strong during the Depression that after the 1933 bank holiday people actually clamored to make deposits and the bank administered the Depression-era scholarship fund that helped Ronald Reagan attend college. By 1941 almost half of Northern Trust's commercial deposits originated outside the Chicago area. The bank kept growing during and after WWII.

Solomon Smith retired in 1963; his son Edward took over and launched the company's expansion overseas (Northern Trust International was formed in 1968) and out of state (Florida in 1971 Arizona in 1974). The firm's business was helped by the 1974 passage by Congress of ERISA which required company retirement plans to be overseen by an outside custodian. Edward retired in 1979.

Northern Trust expanded locally when Illinois legalized intrastate branch banking in 1981. In 1987 the company lost money due in part to defaults on loans made to developing countries. It moved into California in 1988 and Texas in 1989.

Northern Trust navigated the early 1990s recession expanded geographically in the mid-1990s and added services through acquisitions. In 1995 the company became the first foreign trust company to operate throughout Canada. That year it bought investment management service RCB International (now Northern Trust Global Advisors). It expanded in the Sun Belt with such acquisitions as Dallas' Metroplex Bancshares and was made first custodian for the Teacher Retirement System of Texas (1997).

In 1998 the company expanded into Michigan and broke into the Cleveland and Seattle markets in 1999. Northern Trust entered cyberspace as well launching a website for its mutual funds. In 2000 the company opened locations in Nevada and Missouri and bought Florida-based investment adviser Carl Domino Associates (renamed Northern Trust Value Investors). Also that year the bank bought Ireland's Ulster Bank Investment Services.

In 2004 Northern Trust bought the fund management custody and trust operations of Baring Asset Management from Amsterdam-based ING Groep.

EXECUTIVES

EVP and General Auditor, Dan E. Phelps
EVP and Treasurer, William R. Dodds Jr., age 59
EVP and Head Human Resources and Administration, Timothy P. Moen, age 59
EVP General Counsel and Assistant Secretary, Kelly R. Welsh, age 59
Vice Chairman and EVP, Sherry S. Barrat, age 62, $550,000 total compensation

President and COO, William L. (Bill) Morrison, age 61, $550,000 total compensation
SVP and Director Investor Relations, Beverly J. (Bev) Fleming
Head Americas Global Fund Services, Dan Houlihan
Corporate Secretary and Assistant General Counsel, Rose A. Ellis
EVP; President Corporate and Institutional Services, Steven L. (Steve) Fradkin, age 50, $550,000 total compensation
EVP and CFO, Michael G. O'Grady
Chairman and CEO, Frederick H. (Rick) Waddell, age 58, $900,000 total compensation
CEO Western Region U.S. Personal Financial Services, Steven R. (Steve) Bell
EVP Northern Trust Company; President Wealth Management Group Northern Trust Company, Douglas P. (Doug) Regan
EVP and Head of Corporate Risk Management; EVP Northern Trust Company, Jeffery D. Cohodes, age 51
EVP Banking and Treasury Management and Corporate Banking Northern Trust Company, Arthur J. Fogel, age 49
EVP Foreign Exchange and Cash Management Northern Trust Company, Patrick J. McDougal
EVP; President Personal Financial Services, Jana R. Schreuder, age 53, $550,000 total compensation
EVP Northern Trust Company, Jean E. Sheridan
EVP Northern Trust Company; CEO Asia Pacific region for Northern Trust, Teresa A. Parker
EVP; President Northern Trust Global Investments, Stephen N. Potter, age 55, $500,000 total compensation
EVP and Head Corporate Risk Management; President Operations and Technology, Joyce St. Clair, age 53
EVP Northern Trust Company, Lloyd A. Wennlund
CEO Midwest Region U.S. Personal Financial Services, David C. (Dave) Blowers
EVP and Controller, Aileen B. Blake, age 44
EVP; Head Global Fund Services, Peter B. Cherecwich
SVP and Director Public Affairs, Kelly King Dibble
EVP Corporate Social Responsibility, Connie L. Lindsey
EVP Northern Trust Company, Penelope J. Biggs
EVP Northern Trust Company; Chief Fiduciary Officer and National Director Trust Services, R. Hugh Magill
EVP Northern Trust Company, Lyle L. Logan, age 53
EVP Northern Trust Company, Marianne G. Doan
EVP Northern Trust Company, Brian P. Ovaert
President and CEO Northern Trust Company Canada, Robert J. (Rob) Baillie
CEO Southwest Region U.S. Personal Financial Services, Steve MacLellan
CEO Europe Middle East and Africa; EVP Northern Trust Company, Wilson Leech
Director Institutional Public Relations, John O'Connell
Second VP and Media Relations Specialist EMEA, Camilla Greene
EVP Northern Trust Company; Head Americas Region for Corporate and Institutional Services, Stephen B. (Biff) Bowman
EVP, Alan W. Robertson
EVP and Chief Investment Officer, Robert P. (Bob) Browne, age 46
SVP and Chief Investment Strategist, James D. (Jim) McDonald
SVP and Head Global Corporate Communications, Douglas A. (Doug) Holt
SVP and Chief Investment Officer Personal Financial Services West, Richard K. Barnett
Head Sales and Client Services Asia-Pacific ex-Japan Northern Trust Global Investments, Fifi Ting
EVP Northern Trust Company, Darrell B. Jackson
CEO Channel Islands Global Fund Services, Vic Holmes
Public Relations Officer, Cathryn Raia
Managing Director Washington D.C., Joanne C. (Joanie) Stringer
SVP and Head Corporate Strategy, Caroline E. Devlin
SVP and Chief Compliance and Ethics Officer, Saverio Mirarchi
EVP Credit Policy, Mark J. Van Grinsven
EVP Northern Trust Company; Head Asia Pacific and COO Global Fund Services, Jennifer L. Driscoll
EVP Northern Trust Company, Peter A. Gloyne
EVP Northern Trust Company; COO Northern Trust Global Investments, Mark C. Gossett
EVP Northern Trust Company, Peter A. Magrini
EVP Northern Trust Company, Michael A. Vardas
EVP Northern Trust Company, K. Kelly Mannard
EVP Northern Trust Company, John D. Skjervem
SVP and Relationship Manager London Securities Lending, Mark Snowdon
SVP and Head Global Securities Lending Northern Trust Company, Andrew R. (Andy) Clayton
Managing Director EMEA Northern Trust Global Investment, John Krieg
CEO Northeast Region U.S. Personal Financial Services, Jeff Kauffman
Head Global Fund Services Europe, Toby Glaysher
Director Investment Sales Northern Trust Global Investments, Kristina Ilar
President New York Financial Services, John F. Hoffman
Managing Director Stamford Connecticut, Brian P. Donovan
VP and Media Relations Specialist EMEA, Sara Murshed
SVP and Head EMEA Corporate Marketing and Corporate Communications, Mark Lacey
Media Relations Specialist Personal Financial Services Media Relations, Sophia Venetos
VP and Director Personal Financial Services Media Relations, Amy Bickers
Media Relations Specialist Americas and Asia-Pacific, Newton Sears
CEO Southeast Region U.S. Personal Financial Services, Sheldon T. Anderson
Head Global Fund Services UK, Laurence Everitt
Chief Investment Officer Personal Financial Services, Katherine Ellis Nixon
Director, Enrique J. Sosa, age 71
Director, Robert W. (Bob) Lane, age 62
Director, Nicholas D. (Nick) Chabraja, age 69
Director, Martin P. Slark, age 57
Director, John W. Rowe, age 66
Director, Susan M. Crown, age 53
Director, Edward J. (Ted) Mooney, age 70
Director, Linda Walker Bynoe, age 59
Vice Chairman and EVP, Sherry S. Barrat, age 62
Director, Robert C. (Bob) McCormack, age 72
Director, Prof Dipak C. Jain, age 54
Director, Charles A. Tribbett III, age 56
Director, David B. Smith Jr., age 45
Auditors: KPMGLLP

LOCATIONS

HQ: Northern Trust Corporation
50 S. La Salle St., Chicago IL 60603
Phone: 312-630-6000 **Fax:** 312-630-1512
Web: www.northerntrust.com

Selected Operations

US
- Arizona
- California
- Colorado
- Connecticut
- Delaware
- Florida
- Georgia
- Illinois
- Massachusetts
- Michigan
- Minnesota
- Missouri
- Nevada
- New York
- Ohio
- Texas
- Washington
- Wisconsin

International
- Australia
- Canada
- China
- Hong Kong
- India
- Ireland
- Japan
- Luxembourg
- the Netherlands
- Singapore
- Sweden
- UK

PRODUCTS/OPERATIONS

2010 Sales

	$ mil.	% of total
Trust investment & other servicing fees	2,081	52
Interest income	1,296	32
Foreign exchange trading	382	9
Treasury management fees	78	2
Security commissions & trading income	60	2
Other	125	3
Total	**4,025**	**100**

2011 Sales

	$ mil.	% of total
Trust investment & other servicing fees	2,169	52
Interest income	1,408	34
Foreign exchange trading	324	8
Treasury management fees	72	2
Security commissions & trading income	60	1
Other	134	3
Total	**4,025**	**100**

Selected Subsidiaries

Northern Investment Corporation
Northern Investment Management Company
Northern Trust Bank FSB
The Northern Trust Company
- MFC Company Inc.
- Norlease Inc.
- The Northern Trust Company Canada
- Northern Trust Holdings Limited (UK)
  - Northern Trust Global Services Limited (UK)
- The Northern Trust International Banking Corporation
  - Northern Trust Cayman International Ltd. (Cayman Islands)
  - The Northern Trust Company of Hong Kong Limited
  - Northern Trust Fund Managers (Ireland) Limited
  - Northern Trust (Ireland) LimitedNorthern Trust Custodial Services (Ireland) LimitedNorthern Trust Fund Services (Ireland) LimitedNorthern Trust Investor Services (Ireland) LimitedNorthern Trust Property Services (Ireland) Limited
  - Northern Trust Management Services Limited (UK)
  - Northern Trust Partners Scotland Limited (UK)
  - Northern Trust Scottish Limited Partnership (99% UK)Northern Trust Luxembourg Capital S.A.R.L.
- Northern Trust Investments Inc.
- NTG Services LLCNT Mortgage Holdings LLC

The Northern Trust Company of Delaware
The Northern Trust Company of New York
Northern Trust Global Advisors Inc.
- The Northern Trust Company of Connecticut

NT Global Advisors Inc. (Canada)
Northern Trust Global Investments Japan K.K.
Northern Trust Holdings L.L.C.
Northern Trust NA
Northern Annuity Sales Inc.
Realnor Properties Inc.
Waterline Partners LLC
Northern Trust Securities Inc.
Northern Trust Services Inc.
Nortrust Holding Corporation
Northern Trust Bank N.A.
Nortrust Realty Management Inc.

COMPETITORS

Bank of America
Bank of New York Mellon
Barclays
Bessemer Trust
Brown Brothers Harriman
Citigroup
Deutsche Bank
Fifth Third
FMR
Harris
JPMorgan Chase
Morgan Stanley
State Street
Wells Fargo

HISTORICAL FINANCIALS

Company Type: Public

Income Statement FYE: December 31

	ASSETS ($ mil.)	NET INCOME ($ mil.)	INCOME AS % OF ASSETS	EMPLOYEES
12/11	100,223	603	0.6%	14,100
12/10	83,843	669	0.8%	12,800
12/09	82,141	864	1.1%	12,400
12/08	82,053	794	1.0%	12,200
12/07	67,611	726	1.1%	10,918
Annual Growth	10.3%	(4.5%)	—	6.6%

2011 Year-End Financials

Debt ratio: 4.53%
Return on equity: 8.48%
Cash ($ mil.): 34,460
Current ratio: —
Long-term debt ($ mil.): 4,536
No. of shares (mil.): 241
Dividends
Yield: —
Payout: 45.34%
Market value ($ mil.): 9,558

	STOCK PRICE ($) FY Close	P/E High/Low		PER SHARE ($) Earnings	Dividends	Book Value
12/11	39.66	23	14	2.47	0.00	29.53
12/10	55.41	22	17	2.74	1.12	28.19
12/09	52.40	21	14	3.16	1.12	26.12
12/08	52.14	25	10	3.47	1.12	28.62
12/07	76.58	24	17	3.24	1.03	20.44
Annual Growth	(15.2%)	—	—	(6.6%)	—	9.6%

Northrop Grumman Corp

Northrop Grumman defends its high place in the defense sector. As one of the world's top military contractors (behind Lockheed Martin and Boeing) the company operates through four business sectors: Aerospace Systems (aircraft spacecraft laser systems electronic subsystems); Electronic Systems (radar sensors chemical detection countermeasure systems); Information Systems (C4ISR or command control communications computers intelligence surveillance reconnaissance); and Technical Services (systems support training and simulation). It spun off its Shipbuilding sector (ships nuclear submarines aircraft carriers) in 2011. The US government represents most of Northrop Grumman's sales.

HISTORY

Jack Northrop co-founded Lockheed Aircraft in 1927 and designed its record-setting Vega monoplane. He founded two more companies —Avion Corporation (formed in 1928 and bought by United Aircraft and Transportation) and Northrop Corporation (formed in 1932 with Douglas Aircraft which absorbed it in 1938) —before founding Northrop Aircraft in California in 1939.

During WWII Northrop produced the P-61 fighter and the famous Flying Wing bomber which failed to win a production contract. In the 1950s Northrop depended heavily on F-89 fighter and Snark missile sales. When Thomas Jones succeeded Jack Northrop as president (1959) he moved the company away from risky prime contracts in favor of numerous subcontracts and bought Page Communications Engineers (telecommunications 1959) and Hallicrafters (electronics 1966) to reduce its dependence on government contracts.

In the early 1970s Northrop was hit with a bribery scandal and the disclosure of illegal payments to Richard Nixon's 1972 campaign fund; Jones was eventually fined for an illegal contribution. As a result a shareholder lawsuit forced Jones to resign as president (he was allowed to remain as chairman). In 1981 the company won the B-2 bomber contract. Jones retired as chairman in late 1990 and under the leadership of Kent Kresa (who became CEO in early 1990 and chairman when Jones retired) Northrop pleaded guilty to 34 counts related to fudging test results on some government projects; it was fined $17 million. In a related shareholders' suit Northrop paid $18 million in damages in 1991.

Northrop and The Carlyle Group bought LTV's Vought Aircraft Industries (now named Triumph Aerostructures - Vought Aircraft Division) in 1992. In 1994 it paid $2.1 billion for Grumman Corporation a premier electronic systems firm and manufacturer of fighter aircraft for the US Navy and changed its name to Northrop Grumman.

In 1929 Roy Grumman Jake Swirbul and Bill Schwendler founded Grumman; within three months it had a contract to design a Navy fighter. Grumman completed its first commercial aircraft (the Grumman Goose) in 1937 and went public in 1938. It soared during WWII on the wings of its Wildcat and Hellcat fighter planes.

Grumman built its first corporate jet (Gulfstream) in 1958 and began work on the Lunar Module for the Apollo space program in 1963. It was near bankruptcy during the 1970s due to costs related to its F-14 Tomcat fighter. Grumman rebuilt its military business in the 1980s and achieved its greatest success in electronic systems.

The UK Ministry of Defence awarded a $279 million contract to Northrop Grumman in 1995 to develop and produce a system to counter infrared missiles. In 1997 Northrop Grumman bought Logicon (information and battle-management systems). It then agreed to an $11.6 billion purchase by Lockheed Martin but the US government citing concerns about increased lack of competition in the defense industry blocked the deal in 1998. As a result Northrop Grumman began a restructuring that cut 10500 defense and aircraft jobs and added 2500 positions to its Logicon subsidiary.

In 1999 Northrop Grumman bought the information systems division of California Microwave for $93 million and Allegheny Teledyne's Ryan Aeronautical (aerial drones) for $140 million. The next year Northrop Grumman sold its underperforming commercial aerostructures business to The Carlyle Group in a $1.2 billion transaction in order to focus on its growing defense electronics and information technology segments. Later in 2000 Northrop Grumman acquired Comptek Research and bought Federal Data (information systems for the US government) from Carlyle in a transaction valued at $302 million. Pension income that year accounted for more than $500 million (about 55%) of the company's pre-tax profit.

In 2001 the company completed the deal to acquire Litton Industries for $3.8 billion plus $1.3 billion in debt. In the fall Northrop Grumman acquired the electronics and information unit of Aerojet-General Corp. a subsidiary of GenCorp for about $300 million (it became Grumman's Space Systems Division). While its wallet was open the company agreed to match the $2.6 billion that General Dynamics had agreed to pay for submarine and aircraft carrier builder Newport News —a move that the US Defense Department endorsed. In December Honeywell agreed to pay Northrop Grumman $440 million to settle an antitrust and patent infringement lawsuit that Litton had filed against Honeywell in 1990.

The deal to buy Newport News was completed in early 2002. Northrop Grumman then made a hostile $6 billion bid for conglomerate TRW when TRW's stock plunged following the sudden departure of its CEO David Cote to Honeywell. In the wake of Northrop Grumman's spurned initial bid Raytheon General Dynamics and BAE SYSTEMS made offers for TRW's aerospace and defense assets. Finally though TRW accepted a sweetened $7.8 billion offer from Northrop Grumman in July 2002.

The acquisition fortified Northrop Grumman's position in military satellites missile systems and systems integration. In fact Northrop signed a consent decree with the US Justice Department in which the company agreed (under pain of fines) that it wouldn't take unfair advantage of its exclusive position when selling certain components — such as satellite sensors —to competitors.

TRW's Systems unit became Northrop Grumman Mission Systems; TRW's Space and Electronics unit was later known as Northrop Grumman Space Technology. As for TRW's car parts business Northrop sold all but 19.6% of the unit to Blackstone Group for about $4.7 billion to pay down debt; by early 2005 Northrop reduced its stake to 9.9%.

In April 2003 Kresa stepped down as president and CEO and Ronald Sugar took over those roles; Sugar added the chairmanship to his title when Kresa retired in October.

Among Northrop's 2004 contracts were $1.04 billion for X-47B Joint Unmanned Combat Air Systems $1.2 billion (preferred bidder) for E-3D AWACS contract support and $1.4 billion for the CVN 21 generation aircraft carrier. The company also split an $8.4 billion submarine contract with General Dynamics.

Early in 2005 Northrop sold 7.2 million shares of its TRW Automotive stake raising more than $142 million and reducing its stake to 9.9%. It also acquired Integic Corporation an IT company that specialized in business process management and enterprise health applications.

In 2006 Northrop Grumman established Northrop Grumman Technical Services (NGTS) as a separate sector; it was tasked with consolidating Northrop's logistics operations across its various sectors.

Late that same year Northrop Grumman agreed to buy Essex Corporation —a provider of signal image and information processing for defense and intelligence customers in the US. The deal was valued at about $580 million including the assumption of debt. The deal was completed early in 2007 and Essex became a part of Northrop Grumman Mission Systems (now Northrop Grumman Information Systems).

In 2008 the company shed its Electro-Optical Systems business (night vision and applied optics products) to L-3 Communications for $175 million.

In 2009 Northrop Grumman sold its Advisory Services Division comprising subsidiary TASC (engineering and consulting services to the US military and state governments) to private equities General Atlantic LLC and KKR for $1.65 billion. The sale brings Northrop Grumman into compliance with a new federal law that strengthens conflict of interest rules for defense contractors that both sell to and provide consulting for the US military.

Expanding its aerospace and information capabilities the company purchased Sonoma Photonics and assets from Swift Engineering's Killer Bee Unmanned Air Systems lineup for its Aerospace Systems sector (2009). The deal followed its acquisition of 3001 International for $92 million (a nearly three times larger investment) in 2008. The Virginia-based geospatial data collection and analysis provider not only bolstered Northrop Grumman's military offerings but it also reeled in a host of new civilian customers.

Also in 2009 Northrop Grumman settled two decade-old lawsuits with the US government. It agreed to pay $325 million to resolve allegations that it provided defective military satellite parts to the National Reconnaissance Office. The second lawsuit was filed by Northrop Grumman against the US government for uncompensated costs incurred as a result of the cancellation of the Tri-Service Standoff Attack Missile program.

EXECUTIVES

Corporate VP and CFO, James F. (Jim) Palmer, age 63, $800,001 total compensation
Corporate VP and Secretary, Jennifer C. McGarey
Chairman President and CEO, Wesley G. (Wes) Bush, age 51, $950,000 total compensation
Corporate VP and General Counsel, Sheila C. Cheston, age 53
Corporate VP and CTO, Alexis C. Livanos, age 63
VP Advanced Technology Northrop Grumman Information Systems, Robert F. (Bob) Brammer
Corporate VP Communications, Darryl M. Fraser, age 53
Corporate Vice President - Operations, Linda A. Mills, age 62
Corporate VP; President Aerospace Systems Sector, Gary W. Ervin, age 54, $598,077 total compensation
Corporate VP; President Electronic Systems Sector, James F. (Jim) Pitts, age 60, $600,001 total compensation
Corporate VP Finance, Mark A. Rabinowitz, age 50
UK Chairman; CEO Information Systems Europe, Sir Nigel Essenhigh, age 67
Corporate VP; President Technical Services Sector, Thomas E. (Tom) Vice, age 49
Corporate Lead Executive US Air Force Space and Missile Systems Center, Edward T. (Ed) Alexander
Corporate VP and Chief Human Resources Officer, Denise M. Peppard, age 55
VP and CIO, Bernard P. (Bernie) McVey Jr.
Corporate Lead Executive Boston, Joseph B (Joe) Magnone
Corporate Lead Executive Dayton Ohio, William J. (Jay) Jabour
Army Corporate Lead Executive Fort Huachuca Ariz., Walter (Steve) Pedigo
Director Business Development Integrated Product Team Leader and Corporate Lead Executive Hampton Roads Va., Tim Peppe
Corporate Lead Executive U.S. Training and Doctrine Command, Donald G. Lisenbee
Corporate Lead Executive Orlando, Lee R. Barnes Jr.
Corporate Lead Executive Naval Air Systems Command, Scott D. Stewart
Corporate Lead Executive San Diego, John Pettitt
Corporate Lead Executive Scott Air Force Base Ill., John Becker
Corporate Lead Executive Tampa, Harry B. Axson
Corporate VP; President Enterprise Shared Services, Gloria A. Flach, age 53
Corporate VP Government Relations, M. Sidney (Sid) Ashworth, age 61
VP Compensation Benefits & International, Debora L. (Debbie) Catsavas
Corporate Lead Executive Nebraska Region; Sector VP and Deputy General Manager Defense Mission Systems Division, Robert C. (Bob) Hinson
Lead Executive Colorado Springs, Russ Anarde
VP Engineering, Nicholas g. Paraskevopoulo
VP Electro Optical/Infra Red Trageting Systems Electronic Systems, James B. Mocarski
VP and Chief Compliance Officer, Judy Perry Martinez
Company Lead Cybersecurity; VP Cyber Initiatives, Mike Papay
VP James Webb Space Telescope Program, Scott P. Willoughby
Sector VP and General Manager Northrop Grumman Aerospace Systems Sector Space Systems Division, Jeff Grant
VP and General Manager Cyber Intelligence Division, Kathy Warden
Corporate VP and Treasurer, Mark A. Caylor
VP and Controller Technical Services, Timothy (Tim) Harrington
VP Radio Frequency Combat and Information Systems Land and Self Protection Systems, Janine Nyre
VP Business Development Information Systems, Gary Salisbury
VP and Program Manager Virginia Information Technologies Agency (VITA), Jim Kane
Corporate VP Controller and Chief Accounting Officer, Kenneth L. Bedingfield, age 39
Vice President Strategic Communications, Randy Belote
Corporate Vice President President, Thomas E. E.
Corporate Vice President; Chief Global Business Development Officer, David Perry
Vice President - High-Altitude; Long-Endurance Enterprise, James Culmo
Director, Bruce S. Gordon, age 66
Director, Madeleine A. Kleiner, age 60
Director, Stephen E. Frank, age 70
Director, Karl J. Krapek, age 63
Director, Kevin W. Sharer, age 64
Director, Lewis W. (Lew) Coleman, age 70
Director, Donald E. Felsinger, age 65
Director, Aulana L. Peters, age 70
Director, Victor H. (Vic) Fazio, age 69
Director, Richard B. (Dick) Myers, age 70
Independent Director, Gary Roughead
Independent Director, Thomas Schoewe
Auditors: Deloitte&ToucheLLP

LOCATIONS

HQ: Northrop Grumman Corporation
2980 Fairview Park Dr., Falls Church VA 22042
Phone: 703-280-2900 **Fax:** 704-362-4208
Web: www.nucor.com

PRODUCTS/OPERATIONS

2011 Sales

	$ mil.	% of total
Business Sector $ mil. % of total		
Aerospace systems	10,458	37
Information systems	7,921	28
Electronic systems	7,372	26
Technical services	2,699	9
Intersegment eliminations	(2038)	-
Total	**26,412**	**100**

2011 Sales

Customer $ mil. % of total		
US government	23,905	91
Other customers	2,507	9
Total	**26,412**	**100**

2011 Sales

	$ mil.	% of total
Product sales	15,073	57
Service revenues	11,339	43
Total	**26,412**	**100**

COMPETITORS

Aerojet
BAE SYSTEMS
Boeing
Cubic Corp.
EADS
Elbit Systems
Exelis
Finmeccanica
GE
GenCorp
General Dynamics
Hamilton Sundstrand
Hanjin Heavy Industries & Construction
Herley Industries
Honeywell Aerospace
Lockheed Martin
Meggitt
Raytheon
Rockwell Collins
ThalesRaytheonSystems

HISTORICAL FINANCIALS

Company Type: Public

Income Statement FYE: December 31

	REVENUE ($ mil.)	NET INCOME ($ mil.)	NET PROFIT MARGIN	EMPLOYEES
12/11	26,412	2,118	8.0%	72,500
12/10	34,757	2,053	5.9%	117,100
12/09	33,755	1,686	5.0%	120,700
12/08	33,887	(1,262)	—	123,600
12/07	32,018	1,790	5.6%	122,600
Annual Growth	(4.7%)	4.3%	—	(12.3%)

2011 Year-End Financials

Debt ratio: 15.54%
Return on equity: 20.49%
Cash ($ mil.): 3,002
Current ratio: 126.26
Long-term debt ($ mil.): 3,935
No. of shares (mil.): 253
Dividends
Yield: —
Payout: 26.20%
Market value ($ mil.): 14,847

STOCK PRICE ($) FY Close	P/E High/Low		PER SHARE ($) Earnings	Dividends	Book Value
12/11 58.48	9	6	7.52	0.00	40.71
12/10 64.78	10	8	6.82	1.84	46.59
12/09 55.85	11	7	5.21	1.69	41.34
12/08 45.04	—	—	(3.77)	1.57	36.45
12/07 78.64	16	13	5.12	1.48	52.35
Annual Growth (7.1%)	—	—	10.1%	—	(6.1%)

Northwest Bancshares, Inc. (MD)

LOCATIONS

HQ: Northwest Bancshares, Inc. (MD)
100 Liberty Street, Warren, PA 16365
Phone: 814 726-2140
Web: www.northwestsavingsbank.com

HISTORICAL FINANCIALS

Company Type:

Income Statement FYE: December 31

	ASSETS ($ mil.)	NET INCOME ($ mil.)	INCOME AS % OF ASSETS	EMPLOYEES
12/11	7,957	64	0.8%	2,121
12/10	8,148	57	0.7%	2,040
12/09	8,025	32	0.4%	2,023
12/08	6,930	48	0.7%	2,013
12/07	6,663	49	0.7%	0
Annual Growth	4.5%	6.9%	—	—

2011 Year-End Financials

Debt ratio: 10.04%
Return on equity: 5.56%
Cash ($ mil.): 687
Current ratio: —
Long-term debt ($ mil.): 798
No. of shares (mil.): 97
Dividends
Yield: —
Payout: 67.19%
Market value ($ mil.): 1,213

STOCK PRICE ($) FY Close	P/E High/Low		PER SHARE ($) Earnings	Dividends	Book Value
12/11 12.44	21	17	0.64	0.00	11.85
12/10 11.78	24	19	0.53	0.40	11.85
12/09 11.27	38	37	0.30	0.00	11.90
Annual Growth 5.1%	—	—	46.1%	—	(0.2%)

Northwestern Mutual Life Insurance Co. (Milwaukee, WI)

From its birthplace on the Wisconsin frontier Northwestern Mutual Life Insurance writes policies for members across the US. One of the largest US life insurers the firm has some $1 trillion worth of life insurance policies in force. Its network of representatives sell life disability long-term care and employee benefits (health dental and retirement) products. It also offers retirement products including annuities and mutual funds to a clientele of small businesses and prosperous individuals. Its institutional asset manager Russell Investments is known for the Russell 2000 stock index. Northwestern Mutual also offers brokerage and trust services through its investment and wealth management subsidiaries.

Geographic Reach

Northwestern Mutual operates from 350 offices throughout the US. Subsidiary The Frank Russell Company (known as Russell Investments) has 24 global offices.

Operations

While life insurance is generally not a glitzy industry Northwestern Mutual formed in 1857 takes staid and steady to another level through its cautious investment and cost management strategies. As its former chairman and CEO James Ericson (who retired in mid-2001) stated the company would "enter the 21st century as we left the 19th."

While the company has reorganized over time to bring more emphasis to its wealth management products life insurance still accounts for the majority of its revenues. Northwestern Mutual also paid scant attention to an industry trend of demutualizing and remains committed to ownership by its 3.5 million policyholders. Being cautious and deliberate by nature has served the company well during the economic turmoil of recent years. With no debt and plenty of premiums squirreled away in low-risk investments it spent the months of crisis calmly dusting off its triple-A ratings paying out dividends and attracting new agents.

Sales & Marketing

Northwestern Mutual administers its life policies from its 350 offices across the US. Its network of registered sales representatives provide access to products from all of the company's business divisions. Russell Investments has some 1900 associates who work with more than 580 independent distribution partners.

Financial Analysis

As more people began taking measures to prepare for their financial security Northwestern Mutual kicked off its largest recruiting effort to date in 2011 to meet the increasing demand for its planning services. As a result the company added more new clients and gained a 3% increase in premiums in part from the addition of 350000 new policies added to its more than 5 million life insurance policies in force that year. The company saw its revenues rise 2% over 2010 to $23.6 billion also aided by modest investment income gains; its net income fell about 15% from 2010 to $645 million attributable to increased benefit payments (more than $7 billion paid out) and higher expenses. Overall the company's financial position remained strong with a 5% increase in total assets to $190 billion and a 3% increase in its surplus and asset valuation reserve to more than $18 billion.

Strategy

Northwestern Mutual's strategy for stability and growth is based on its keen attention to managing its operating expenses and maintaining its diversified general account investment portfolio along with prudently managing product risk. Other elements include differentiating itself from competitors by promoting the strength of its brand and by continuing to invest in technology as with the addition of its retirement planning tool to meet client needs and expectations.

HISTORY

In 1854 at age 72 John Johnston a successful New York insurance agent moved to Wisconsin to become a farmer. Three years later Johnston returned to the insurance business when he and 36 others formed Mutual Life Insurance (changed to Northwestern Mutual Life Insurance in 1865). From the beginning the company's goal was to become better not just bigger.

The company continued to offer level-premium life insurance in the 1920s while competitors offered new types of products. This failure to rise to new demands brought a decline in market share that lasted into the 1940s.

Northwestern Mutual automated in the late 1950s. In 1962 it introduced the Insurance Service Account whereby all policies owned by a family or business could be consolidated into one monthly premium and paid with pre-authorized checks. In 1968 Northwestern Mutual inaugurated Extra Ordinary Life (EOL) which combined whole and term life insurance using dividends to convert term to paid-up whole life each year. EOL soon became the company's most popular product.

Suffering from a low profile in 1972 the insurer kicked off its "The Quiet Company" ad campaign during the summer Olympics. Public awareness of Northwestern Mutual jumped. But even in advertising the company was staid; a revamped Quiet Company campaign made a return Olympic appearance 24 years later in another effort to raise the public's consciousness.

In the 1980s Northwestern Mutual began financing leveraged buyouts gaining direct ownership of companies. Investments included two-thirds of flooring maker Congoleum (with other investors); it also bought majority interests in Milwaukee securities firm Robert W. Baird (1982) and mortgage guarantee insurer MGIC Investment (1985; later divested).

The firm stayed out of the 1980s mania for fast money and high-risk diversification. Instead it devoted itself almost religiously to its core business despite indications that it was a shrinking market.

In the early 1990s new life policy purchases slowed and the agency force declined —ominous signs since insurers make their premium income on retained policies and continued sales are crucial to growth. Northwestern Mutual reversed the trend adding administrative support for its agents using database marketing to target new customers and increasing the cross-selling of products among existing customers. The result was a record-setting 1996.

With the financial services industry consolidating Northwestern Mutual in 1997 moved into the mutual fund business by setting up its Mason Street Funds.

In the 1990s many large mutuals sought to demutualize and in 1998 Northwestern Mutual politically influential in Wisconsin successfully lobbied for legislation to permit demutualization citing the need to be able to move quickly in shifting markets. However despite that effort and victory the company chose not to demutualize.

To expand its wealth management services in 1999 the company acquired Frank Russell Company a pension management firm. The acquisition gave Northwestern Mutual a foothold in global investment management and analytical services (the Russell 2000 index). In 2001 the firm opened Northwestern Mutual Trust a wholly owned personal trust services subsidiary.

In 2004 the employees of Robert W. Baird completed a buyback of Northwestern Mutual's stake in the firm.

While Northwestern Mutual remained calm during the stormy economy in late 2008 the company agreed to pay as much as $92 million to settle a class action lawsuit filed in 2004. The plaintiffs alleged that the company's sales materials were misleading regarding certain term life and disability insurance policies. Northwestern Mutual maintained that it had acted fairly but settled the case to limit its exposure to additional litigation expenses.

EXECUTIVES

SVP Product Distribution, Meridee J. Maynard, age 56
EVP and Chief Investment Officer, Mark G. Doll, age 62
EVP Insurance and Investment Products, Gregory C. Oberland, age 54
Chairman and CEO, John E. Schlifske, age 53
EVP Enterprise Operations and Technology, Jean M. Maier, age 57
SVP Agency Services, Christina H. Fiasca, age 57
President Chief Risk Officer and Trustee, Gary A. (Skip) Poliner, age 58
EVP Chief Compliance Officer and Chief Administrative Officer, Marcia Rimai, age 56
VP and CFO, Michael G. Carter, age 50
SVP Real Estate, David D. Clark, age 60
SVP Financial Planning and Product Delivery, John M. Grogan, age 48
VP and Controller, J. Chris Kelly, age 52
SVP Securities, Jeffrey J. Lueken, age 51
Chief Investment Officer, Ronald P. Joelson, age 53
VP Disability Income, John L. Kordsmeier, age 57
VP Wealth Management, Eric P. Christophersen, age 50
General Counsel and Secretary, Raymond J. Manista, age 46
VP Life Product, David W. Simbro, age 50
VP Investment Product Operations, Calvin R. Schmidt, age 49
VP Human Resources, Joann M. (Jo) Eisenhart
SVP Public Markets, Jefferson V. DeAngelis
VP Compliance and Best Practices, Timothy J. Gerend
VP Communications and Corporate Affairs, Kimberley Goode
VP Information Systems, Karl G. Gouverneur
VP New Business, Thomas C. Guay
VP and Treasurer, Gary M. Hewitt
VP Policyowner Services, Kathleen A. Oman
VP Corporate Planning, Bethany M. Rodenhuis
CIO and Head Information Systems, Timothy G. (Tim) Schaefer
EVP Agencies, Todd M. Schoon
VP Agencies, Paul J. Steffen
VP Marketing, Conrad C. York
VP and Chief Actuary, David R. Remstad
Director Media Relations, Darryll Fortune
Assistant Director Media Relations, Jean Towell
Public Relations Specialist, Meredyth Naramore
Public Relations Specialist, Shawn Rolland
VP Enterprise Risk Assurance, Sandra L. Botcher
VP Government Relations, Steven M. Radke
VP Enterprise Solutions, Todd O. Zinkgraf
VP Long-Term Care, Steve P. Sperka
Trustee, Hans Helmerich, age 53
Trustee, Edward J. Zore, age 67
Trustee, James P. Hackett, age 57
Trustee, P. Russell Hardin
Trustee, David J. Lubar, age 57
Trustee, Timothy W. Sullivan, age 58
Trustee, John N. Balboni, age 63
Trustee, Ulice Payne Jr., age 56
Trustee, Peter M. Sommerhauser, age 69
Trustee, David J. Drury, age 63
Trustee, Mary Ellen Stanek, age 55
President Chief Risk Officer and Trustee, Gary A. (Skip) Poliner, age 58
Trustee, Margery Kraus, age 65
Trustee, Barry L. Williams, age 67
Trustee, S. Scott Voynich
Trustee, Connie K. Duckworth, age 58
Trustee, David A. Erne, age 68
Trustee, Dale E. Jones, age 52
Trustee, Benjamin F. (Ben) Wilson
Trustee, Ralph A. Weber
Auditors: PricewaterhouseCoopersLLP

LOCATIONS

HQ: The Northwestern Mutual Life Insurance Company Inc.
720 E. Wisconsin Ave., Milwaukee WI 53202-4797
Phone: 414-271-1444 **Fax:** 508-946-7704
Web: www.oceanspray.com

PRODUCTS/OPERATIONS

2011 Revenues

Premiums	14,618	62
Other income	538	2

2011 Investment Portfolio (excluding policy loans)

	% of total
Bonds &	71
Mortgage	15
Stocks & other	14
Total	**100**

Selected Subsidiaries

Northwestern Long Term Care Insurance Company
Northwestern Mutual Investment Services LLC (brokerage and advisory services for individuals and businesses)
Northwestern Mutual Wealth Management Company (federal savings bank that provides financial planning investment management and trust services)
Russell Investment Group (registered trade name of The Frank Russell Company; global asset management and investment services to institutional and individual investors)

COMPETITORS

AEGON USA
Ameritas
CIGNA
Citigroup
FMR
Genworth Financial
Guardian Life
ING
John Hancock Financial Services
MassMutual
MetLife
Mutual of Omaha
Nationwide
New York Life
Pacific Mutual
Principal Financial
Prudential
Sun Life
SunAmerica Financial Group
T. Rowe Price
The Hartford
TIAA-CREF

HISTORICAL FINANCIALS

Company Type: Private - Mutual Company

Income Statement FYE: December 31

	REVENUE ($ mil.)	NET INCOME ($ mil.)	NET PROFIT MARGIN	EMPLOYEES
12/11	23,595	645	2.7%	0
12/10	23,109	756	3.3%	0
12/04	17	0	4.7%	1,100
12/03	16	0	4.2%	0
Annual Growth	1025.6%	876.8%	—	—

NRG Energy Inc

A company so nice they named it twice is doubling its efforts to deliver power. NRG Energy a leading power producer with a generating capacity of about 25540 MW (including 1405 MW of renewable energy assets) is getting more greener as it invests in wind and solar power. The vast majority of NRG's power plants are in North America but it also has one in Australia and one in Germany. Its portfolio includes more than 190 generation units at 45 power plants. It also markets natural gas oil and other commodities NRG's retail units (Reliant Energy and Green Mountain Energy) distribute power to 1.9 million customers in Texas. In 2012 the company bought rival GenOn Energy in a $1.7 billion stock deal.

The deal creates the largest competitive generator in the US with 47000 MW of capacity in the East Gulf Coast and West and an enterprise value of $18 billion. The parties hope that synergies balance sheet efficiencies increased economies of scale and geographic diversity will save the expanded company $300 million a year in free cash flow.

Geographic Reach

NRG Energy has generation plants assets in more than a dozen US states and in Australia and Germany. Its NGR Thermal unit provides third-party steam to downtown heating and cooling systems in cities such as Pittsburgh San Diego San Francisco and Harrisburg Pennsylvania.

Financial Analysis

In 2011 NRG's revenues grew by about 3% thanks to a spike in retail sales due to a really hot summer spurring demand and favorable hedging results. However net income dropped by 59% primarily because of lower wholesale generation prices and margins the negative impact of a heat wave in Texas on margins and high impairment charges.

Strategy

NRG has pulled back on international exposure looking to grow its position in the fragmented but less risky North American market. In 2010 NRG agreed to acquire about 3900 MW of generating power in a deal with the Blackstone Group which had planned to buy Dynegy for some $4.7 billion. However the Dynegy deal fell through prompting NRG to restrategize. (It subsequently acquired 1300 MW plant in East Texas for $525 million from the Kelson Limited Partnership in a move to fill in some of the gaps in its combined-cycle gas portfolio).

Expanding its retail presence in the US Northeast in 2011 the company bought Philadelphia-based electricity and natural gas provider Energy Plus Holdings for $190 million. In 2010 in a move to boost its retail presence in Texas and beef up its alternative energy resources the company acquired Green Mountain Energy a leading retailer of green energy services and products for $350 million.

In 2009 in a move to expand its share of the Texas retail market NRG acquired the Texas retail business of Reliant Energy (now GenOn Energy) for about $285 million. NRG also acquired the Reliant Energy trade name in the deal.

Further responding to government demands for utilities to increase their use of renewables in 2011 it bought the 290-MW Agua Caliente solar project in Arizona from First Solar. When completed in 2014 it will be the largest operational photovoltaic site in the world producing enough energy to power more than 225000 homes. Its electricity will be sold to Pacific Gas and Electric in California through 2039.

In 2010 the company acquired the South Trent wind farm near Sweetwater Texas boosting the company's wind power portfolio to 450 MW. Also that year subsidiary NRG Solar agreed to buy nine solar development projects in California and Arizona from US Solar an affiliate of Arclight Capital Partners. The deal doubles NRG Solar's products under development to about 1150 MW.

That year NRG also acquired alternative energy provider Northwind Phoenix which operates a district cooling system providing chilled water to commercial buildings in the central business district of Phoenix. That year it also annouced that it will create the US's first privately funded network of electric vehicle charging stations. Based in Houston the chain opened its first charging station in 2011 and plans to open about 60 more under the eVgo brand.

EXECUTIVES

Chairman, Howard E. Cosgrove, age 69
President Green Mountain Energy Company, Paul D. Thomas
President CEO and Director, David W. Crane, age 53, $1,100,000 total compensation
Media Relations, Meredith Moore
Media Relations, David Gaier
EVP and President Alternative Energy Services, Denise M. Wilson, age 52, $400,000 total compensation
SVP Business Operations, Bob Henry
EVP and Regional President Gulf Coast, John W. Ragan, age 52, $350,000 total compensation
SVP Investor Relations, Nahla A. Azmy
SVP and Regional President East, Lee Davis
SVP and Chief Accounting Officer, James J. (Jim) Ingoldsby
President Nuclear Innovation North America (NINA), Steven C. (Steve) Winn, age 46, $350,000 total compensation
EVP Strategy and M&A, Andrew J. (Drew) Murphy, age 51, $400,000 total compensation
SVP; President West, M. Stephen (Steve) Hoffmann, age 58
Deputy General Counsel and Corporate Secretary, Tanuja M. Dehne
Media Relations, Lori Neuman
EVP; Chief Customer Officer; and President Reliant Energy, Jason Few, age 46
EVP and COO, Mauricio Gutierrez, $398,462 total compensation
VP and Treasurer, Christopher S. (Chris) Sotos
Plant Manager NRG Energy Center Dover LLC, William Grow
SVP; President NRG EV Services, Arun Banskota
EVP and General Counsel, Michael Bramnick
Media Relations, Dave Knox
Analyst Investor Relations, Erin Gilli
President Bluewater Wind, Peter Mandelstam
Senior Analyst Investor Relations, Stefan Kimball
EVP; President NRG Solar and Regional President West, Tom Doyle
Senior Director IT Enterprise Services, Gregory (Greg) Flay
SVP Informaton Technology, Steve Wilburn
SVP; President South Central, Doug Pedigo
EVP and CFO, Kirkland Andrews
SVP and Chief Administrative Officer, Patti Helfer
President Reliant, Elizabeth Killinger
SVP and Regional President West, John Chillemi
Director, Gerald (Gerry) Luterman, age 68
Director, Walter R. Young Jr., age 67
Director, Thomas H. (Tom) Weidemeyer, age 64
Director, Paul W. Hobby, age 51
Director, William E. Hantke, age 64
President CEO and Director, David W. Crane, age 53
Director, Stephen L. Cropper, age 62
Director, Herbert H. (Herb) Tate Jr., age 59
Director, Kirbyjon H. Caldwell, age 58
Director, Anne C. Schaumburg, age 62
Director, Kathleen A. McGinty, age 49
Auditors: KPMGLLP

LOCATIONS

HQ: NRG Energy Inc.
211 Carnegie Center, Princeton NJ 08540-6213
Phone: 609-524-4500 **Fax:** 609-524-4501
Web: www.nrgenergy.com

2011 Sales

	$ mil.	% of total
Retail	5,807	60
Wholesale		
Texas	2,561	26
Northeast	579	6
South Central	548	6
West	42	-
Other	58	-
Thermal	143	2
Adjustments	(659)	-
Total	**9,079**	**100**

PRODUCTS/OPERATIONS

2011 Sales

	$ mil.	% of total
Retail	5,807	64
Energy	2,069	23
Capacity	736	8
Mark-to-market activities	325	4
Thermal and other	142	1
Total	**9,079**	**100**

Selected Subsidiaries

Green Mountain Energy Company (retail power)
NEO Corporation (distributed generation; landfill gas hydroelectric and other renewable generation)
NRG Power Marketing Inc. (power sales)
NRG Resource Recovery (waste-to-energy facilities)
NRG Texas LLC (power generation)
NRG Thermal Corporation (district heating and cooling combined heat and power facilities)
Reliant Energy Texas Retail LLC
Texas Genco LP (power generation)
West Coast Power LLC (power generation)

Selected Mergers & Acquisitions

2011
Energy Plus Holdings LLC ($190 million; Philadelphia PA; electricity and natural gas provider)
Agua Caliente (Arizona; solar power project)
2010
Green Mountain Energy Company ($350 million; Austin TX; green energy retail services and products provider)

COMPETITORS

Accent Energy
AEP
AES
Alliant Energy
Avista
Calpine
Cogentrix
Community Energy
Direct Energy
Duke Energy
Dynegy
Edison International
El Paso Corporation
Energy Future
Entergy
FirstEnergy
GenOnEnergy
Gexa Energy
Integrys Energy Services
MidAmerican Energy
Nicor Gas
PG&E Corporation
PPL Corporation
Preferred Energy Services
PSEG Power
SCANA
Sempra Generation
Tenaska

HISTORICAL FINANCIALS

Company Type: Public

Income Statement FYE: December 31

	REVENUE ($ mil.)	NET INCOME ($ mil.)	NET PROFIT MARGIN	EMPLOYEES
12/11	9,079	197	2.2%	5,193
12/10	8,849	477	5.4%	4,964
12/09	8,952	942	10.5%	4,607
12/08	6,885	1,188	17.3%	3,526
12/07	5,989	586	9.8%	3,412
Annual Growth	11.0%	(23.9%)	—	11.1%

2011 Year-End Financials

Debt ratio: 36.80%
Return on equity: 2.55%
Cash ($ mil.): 1,363
Current ratio: 133.96
Long-term debt ($ mil.): 9,745
No. of shares (mil.): 227
Dividends
Yield: —
Payout: —
Market value ($ mil.): 4,123

	STOCK PRICE ($) FY Close	P/E High/Low		PER SHARE ($) Earnings	Dividends	Book Value
12/11	18.12	33	23	0.78	0.00	34.00
12/10	19.54	14	10	1.84	0.00	33.59
12/09	23.61	8	4	3.44	0.00	31.23
12/08	23.33	9	3	4.29	0.00	31.39
12/07	43.34	40	17	2.01	0.00	24.29
Annual Growth	(19.6%)	—	—	(21.1%)	—	8.8%

Nucor Corp.

Nucor takes a minimillist approach to succeeding in the steel industry. At its various minimills Nucor produces hot- and cold-rolled steel steel joists and metal buildings. It has the capacity to produce more than 26 million tons of steel per year. North America's largest recycler of scrap metal it produces steel by melting scrap in electric arc furnaces. Most of its products are sold to steel service centers manufacturers and fabricators. Subsidiary Harris Steel fabricates rebar for highways and bridges and other construction projects. Its David J. Joseph Company unit processes and brokers ferrous and nonferrous metals pig iron hot briquetted iron and direct reduced iron (DRI).

HISTORY

Nucor started as the second carmaking venture of Ransom Olds who built his first gasoline-powered car in 1897. Two years later Samuel Smith a Detroit copper and lumber magnate put up $199600 to finance Olds Motor Works. A fire destroyed the company's Detroit plant in 1901 so Olds moved production to Lansing Michigan where he built America's first mass-produced car —the Oldsmobile. In 1904 Olds left Olds Motor Works which was bought by General Motors (GM) in 1908 and formed Reo Car Company (renamed Reo Motor Car in 1906). In addition to cars it eventually made trucks and buses.

By the end of the Depression Ford GM and Chrysler commanded over 85% of the US passenger car market. Reo stopped making cars in 1936 and sold its truck manufacturing operations in 1957. Meanwhile it had formed Reo Holding which in 1955 merged with Nuclear Consultants to form Nuclear Corporation of America. The new company offered services such as radiation studies and made nuclear instruments and electronics.

In 1962 Nuclear bought steel joist maker Vulcraft and gained the services of Kenneth Iverson. The diverse company was unprofitable losing $2 million on $22 million in sales in 1965. That year Iverson took over as CEO moved headquarters to Charlotte North Carolina and shut down or sold about half of the company's businesses. By focusing on its profitable steel joist operations the firm ended 1966 in the black. Because the company depended on imports for 80% of its steel needs Iverson decided to move into steel production. Nuclear Corporation built its first minimill in 1969.

The company was renamed Nucor in 1972. It started making steel deck (1977) and cold-finished steel bars (1979). Production tripled and sales more than doubled between 1974 and 1979.

Nucor began to diversify adding grinding balls (used in the mining industry to process ores 1981); steel bolts steel bearings and machined steel parts (1986); and metal buildings and components (1987). Nucor and Japanese steelmaker Yamato Kogyo formed Nucor-Yamato and built a mill in 1988 to produce wide-flange beams (for heavy construction). The following year Nucor opened a state-of-the-art mill in Crawfordsville Indiana and another mill near Hickman Arkansas in 1992.

Iverson turned over his CEO duties to company veteran John Correnti in 1996. The next year Nucor began building a steel beam mill in South Carolina and added a galvanizing facility to its Hickman mill.

In 1998 Nucor announced plans to build its first steel plate mill which became operational in 2000. The company slashed prices twice in 1998 to compete against low-cost imports from Russia Japan and Brazil. Both sales and earnings declined that year due to low metal prices reduced shipments and start-up costs for new plants. The company raised its prices in 1999 and continued its expansion plans. Differences with the board prompted Correnti to resign in 1999; chairman David Aycock assumed his duties. In September 2000 Aycock resigned from the company and Daniel DiMicco formerly an EVP moved up to the rank of CEO.

Nucor along with Australia's Broken Hill Proprietary Corporation and Japan's Ishikawajima-Harima Heavy Industries began a joint venture in 2000 for its technology strip casting. The new technology allows steel production in smaller cheaper plants. In 2001 Nucor purchased a significant amount of assets of Auburn Steel a producer of merchant steel bar for $115 million.

In 2002 Nucor teamed up with Companhia Vale do Rio Doce (Vale) a Brazilian producer and exporter of iron-ore pellets to develop low-cost iron based products. That year Nucor purchased Alabama-based Trico Steel a steel sheet producer for approximately $116 million. In late 2002 Nucor bought financially troubled Birmingham Steel for $615 million in cash and debt.

Nucor Steel Kingman LLC a subsidiary of Nucor Corporation purchased the Kingman Arizona rebar and wire rod rolling unit of North Star Steel for around $35 million in 2003.

Its Vulcraft unit saw an increase in non-residential building construction in 2004 which boosted sales of joist girders steel deck and steel joists. Nucor bought Nucor Tuscaloosa in mid-2004 a producer of coiled plate with an annual capacity of around 700000 tons. The following year saw the company purchase Ohio's Marion Steel for approximately $110 million. The mill was added to Nucor's bar products line.

Record high prices in the industry (led by high demand throughout the world) led to record high sales in 2004. As a matter of fact Nucor's first half of the year outpaced previous annual highs and the company achieved that feat again in the second half.

The company named CEO DiMicco chairman in 2006.

In the latter half of the last decade it started a program of rapid external growth. It acquired the former Connecticut Steel Verco Manufacturing and Canadian steel products maker Harris Steel which like Connecticut Steel had been a customer and partner of Nucor for years. Harris itself made an acquisition in 2008 when it bought rebar fabricator and distributor Ambassador Steel. Nucor also expanded its downstream operations with the 2007 acquisition of building systems maker MAGNATRAX for $280 million. Its largest acquisition was that of the David J. Joseph Company a scrap metal broker that had supplied Nucor's minimills for 40 years.

The company has always operated primarily in the US but in 2008 it moved into the international market with the formation of a European joint venture with Duferco. The JV produces steel beams and merchant bar products from manufacturing locations in Italy and serves the European and North African markets. Nucor put about $650 million into the new venture called Nucor S.r.l. Duferdofin.

That year it also expanded considerably in the US by spending $1 billion to buy ferrous and nonferrous metals group The David J. Joseph Company.

In 2010 Nucor formed a US-based joint venture with Mitsui & Co. Nucor paid $225 million for its half of the venture named Steel Technologies.

EXECUTIVES

EVP, Ladd R. Hall, age 56
CEO and Director, John J. Ferriola, age 60, $434,900 total compensation
VP; EVP The David J. Joseph Company, Craig Feldman
EVP Bar Products, James R. Darsey
Chairman, Daniel R. (Dan) DiMicco, age 61, $800,000 total compensation
VP; President Nucor Buildings Group, Harry R. Lowe
EVP Fabricated Construction Products, Hamilton Lott Jr., age 63, $395,300 total compensation
EVP; President and CEO DJJ, Keith B. Grass, age 55, $312,500 total compensation
VP; EVP The David J. Joseph Company, Robert L. (Rob) Angotti
VP; General Manager Vulcraft Division Florence South Carolina, James R. Beard
EVP Beam and Plate Products, R. Joseph Stratman, age 56
VP; EVP The David J. Joseph Company, James H. (Jim) Goetz
General Manager; SVP; Employee Services The David J. Joseph Company, Judith G. (Judy) Smith
General Manager Taxes, Elizabeth W. Bowers
EVP CFO and Treasurer, James D. (Jim) Frias, age 55
General Manager Construction, Norman L. Maero
General Manager Environmental Affairs, Steven J. Rowlan
General Manager and Secretary, A. Rae Eagle
VP; President Nucor Building Systems, Jeffrey B. (Jeff) Carmean
VP; General Manager Sheet Mill Division Hickman Arkansas, Samuel E. Commella Jr.
VP; General Manager Sheet Mill and Beam Mill Division Berkeley County South Carolina, Giffin F. Daughtridge
VP; General Manager Sheet Mill Division Crawfordsville Indiana, Ronald L. Dickerson
VP; General Manager Bar Mill and Cold Finish Division Darlington South Carolina, Michael S. Gurley
VP; General Manager Vulcraft Division Grapeland Texas, James R. Landrum
VP; General Manager Nucor Steel Decatur Decatur Alabama, Michael D. Lee
General Manager NUCONSTEEL Denton Texas, Donald R. Moody
VP; President American Buildings Company, Raymond S. Napolitan Jr.
VP; President Nucor Europe, K. Rex Query
General Manager International Business Development, Richard L. Wechsler
General Manager Business Development and Strategic Planning, Stephen D. Laxton
VP; General Manager Nucor Steel Birmingham Inc. Birmingham Alabama, Francis W. Griggs
VP; General Manager Nucor-Yamato Steel Blytheville Arkansas, Douglas J. Jellison
VP; General Manager Nucor Steel Kankakee Inc. Kankakee Illinois, John R Ohm
VP; General Manager Bar Mill Division Norfolk Nebraska, Dirk A. Petersen
VP; General Manager Nucor Steel Jackson Inc. Jackson Mississippi, James A. Sheble
President and CEO Harris Steel Group, John Harris
VP; General Manager Nucor Steel Tuscaloosa Inc. Tuscaloosa Alabama, Randy C. Skagen
General Manager Building Systems Division Waterloo Indiana, Ronald K. Kuenkler
VP; General Manager Fastener Division St. Joe Indiana and Nucor Cold Finish Wisconsion Oak Creek Wisconsin, Tomas A. Miller
VP; General Manager Bar Mill Division Plymouth Utah, David R. Smith
VP; General Manager Vulcraft and Cold Finish Division Brighan City Utah, Stanley L. Walker
VP; General Manager Vulcraft Division St. Joe Indiana, Shannon L. Phillips
VP; General Manager Nucor Steel Marion Inc. Marion Ohio, John C. Farris
General Manager Corporate Legal Affairs, Douglas R. Gunson
Director Metallics Strategies, Bradford G. True
General Manager Nu-Iron Unlimited Point Lisas Trinidad, Lester L. Hart
General Manager Nucor Building Systems Utah Brigham City Utah, Edmund R. Aller
General Manager Nucor Building Systems Division Terrell Texas, Thomas J. Batterbee
General Manager Nucor Building Systems Division Swansea South Carolina, Allen C. Behr
VP and General Manager Nucor Steel Conneticut Inc. Wallingford Connecticut and Nucor Wire Products Inc. Pennsylvania New Salem Pennsylvania, Mark M. Brandon
VP and General Manager Nucor Steel Seattle Seattle Washington, Matthew J. Lyons
General Manager Plate Mill Division Hertford County North Carolina, Robert W. McCracken
General Manager Verco Decking Phoenix Arizona, Mark Miller
VP; General Manager Vulcraft Division Fort Payne Alabama, D. Edward Ryan
General Manager Nucor Steel Memphis Inc. Memphis Tennessee, B. Thad Solomon
General Manager Bar Mill Division Jewett Texas, D. Chad Utermark
VP and General Manager Vulcraft New York, J. Michael Heine
VP and General Manager Vulcraft Division Cold Finish Division, Doyle G. Hopper Jr.

VP and General Manager Nucor Steel Auburn Auburn New York, Michael D. Keller
VP and General Manager Nucor Steel Marion Marion Ohio, David A. Sumoski
General Manager Nucor LMP Steel Maryville Missouri, Kevin Van de Ven
CEO and Director, John J. Ferriola, age 60
Director, Bernard L.M. Kasriel, age 65
Director, Clayton C. Daley Jr., age 60
Director, Christopher J. (Chris) Kearney, age 57
Director, John H. Walker, age 54
Director, Victoria F. Haynes, age 64
Director, Peter C. Browning, age 70
Director, Harvey B. Gantt, age 69
Director, James D. Hlavacek, age 68
Auditors: PricewaterhouseCoopersLLP

LOCATIONS

HQ: Nucor Corp.
1915 Rexford Road, Charlotte, NC 28211
Phone: 704 366-7000 **Fax:** 704 362-4208
Web: www.nucor.com

PRODUCTS/OPERATIONS

2011 Sales

	$ mil.	% of total
Steel Mills	13,960	70
Raw Materials	2,128	11

Selected Products

Alloy steel
- Cold-drawn steel bars
- Finished hex caps
- Hex-head cap screws
- Locknuts
- Structural bolts and nuts

Carbon steel
- Angles
- Beams
- Channels
- Cold-drawn steel bars
- Finished hex nuts
- Flats
- Floor plate
- Galvanized sheet
- Grinding balls
- Hexagons
- Hot-rolled sheet
- Reinforcing bars
- Structural bolts and nuts
- Wide-range beams

Engineered products
- Composite floor joists
- Floor deck
- Joists
- Joist girders
- Pre-engineered metal buildings
- Roof deck
- Special-profile steel trusses

Stainless steel
- Cold-rolled steel
- Hot-rolled steel
- Pickled sheet

Selected Subsidiaries

Harris Steel Inc.
Harris Steel ULC (Canada)
The David J. Joseph Company
Magnatrax Corporation
Nucor Castrip Arkansas LLC
Nucor Energy Holdings Inc.
Nucor-Yamato Steel Company

COMPETITORS

AK Steel Holding Corporation
ArcelorMittal USA
BlueScope Steel
Commercial Metals
Gerdau Ameristeel
Harsco
Renco
Schnitzer Steel
Steel Dynamics
Tata Europe
United States Steel

HISTORICAL FINANCIALS

Company Type: Public

Income Statement FYE: December 31

	REVENUE ($ mil.)	NET INCOME ($ mil.)	NET PROFIT MARGIN	EMPLOYEES
12/11	20,023	778	3.9%	20,800
12/10	15,844	134	0.8%	20,500
12/09	11,190	(293)	—	20,400
12/08	23,663	1,830	7.7%	21,700
12/07	16,592	1,471	8.9%	18,000
Annual Growth	4.8%	(14.7%)	—	3.7%

2011 Year-End Financials

Debt ratio: 29.39%
Return on equity: 10.41%
Cash ($ mil.): 1,200
Current ratio: 279.96
Long-term debt ($ mil.): 3,630
No. of shares (mil.): 316
Dividends
Yield: —
Payout: 59.29%
Market value ($ mil.): 12,534

	STOCK PRICE ($) FY Close	P/E High	P/E Low	PER SHARE ($) Earnings	Dividends	Book Value
12/11	39.57	20	13	2.45	0.00	23.60
12/10	43.82	119	87	0.42	1.44	22.55
12/09	46.65	—	—	(0.94)	1.41	23.47
12/08	46.20	14	4	5.98	1.91	25.25
12/07	59.22	14	9	4.94	2.44	17.75
Annual Growth	(9.6%)	—	—	(16.1%)	—	7.4%

NuStar Energy L.P.

NuStar Energy is following its own star in pursuit of energy profits through terminalling and storing petroleum products transporting petroleum products and anhydrous ammonia and via asphalt and fuels marketing. The independent company (operating primarily in the US) manages 5480 miles of refined product pipelines 2000 miles of ammonia pipelines 940 miles of crude oil pipelines 84 refined product terminal facilities and one crude oil storage facility. It has more than 96 million barrels of storage capacity and operates product terminals in Canada Mexico the Netherlands St. Eustatius Turkey and the UK as well as the US. NuStar Energy operates two asphalt refineries and a number of terminals.

Financial Analysis

The expansion of its assets coupled with high oil prices lifted NuStar Energy's revenues in 2011 by 49% despite a decline in pipeline revenues due to maintenance delays at some refineries. However the company also reported a 7% drop in net income largely due to higher operating costs and weaker "other income" (including $5 million in costs associated with the early termination of a third-party storage agreement at NuStar Energy's Paulsboro refinery and a contingent loss adjustment of $3.3 million related to a litigation settlement).

To pay down debt in 2012 the company created a joint venture with investment firm Lindsay Goldberg to own and operate NuStar's asphalt refining assets. The deal helped reduce NuStar Energy's debt load by about $500 million.

Strategy

The company is pursuing a strategy of internal growth and strategic complementary acquisitions. It has targeted oil and gas assets as well as asphalt which is used to make road surfaces and roofing materials. Asphalt is particularly attractive as a key growth business for the company largely because of the traditionally strong margins the product yields during normal economic cycles.

In 2012 the company agreed to buy crude oil pipeline gathering and storage assets and natural gas liquids assets in the Eagle Ford Shale play in Texas from TexStar Midstream Services LP for $425 million.

In 2010 NuStar Energy spent $44.1 million to buy Denham Capital's stake in Asphalt Holdings an Alabama-based company with three storage terminals with a collective capacity of 1.8 million barrels. (In 2008 NuStar Energy dramatically boosted its asphalt business acquiring CITGO Asphalt Refining Company's asphalt operations including a 74000 barrel-per-day asphalt refinery in Paulsboro New Jersey a 30000 barrel-per-day asphalt refinery in Savannah Georgia and three asphalt terminals in a $838.5 million deal.)

The company is also eyeing international growth and in February 2011 it spent $54 million to acquire 75% of a joint venture partnered by Turkish companies S-Oil and Aves) that operates two oil terminals in Turkey and with storage capacity of 930000 barrels.

That year in the US it also took advantage of an opportunity to exploit the growing oil production from the Eagle Ford Shale play in South Texas by acquiring bankrupt AGE Refining which has refinery assets in Elmendorf and San Antonio for $62 million.

Ownership

NuStar GP Holdings holds about 17% of NuStar Energy.

EXECUTIVES

Chairman, William E. (Bill) Greehey, age 75
President CEO and Director, Curtis V. (Curt) Anastasio, age 55, $466,900 total compensation
EVP CFO and Treasurer, Steven A. (Steve) Blank, age 57, $335,950 total compensation
EVP Administration, Mary Rose Brown, age 55, $301,350 total compensation
EVP Operations, James R. (Rick) Bluntzer, age 57, $301,350 total compensation
EVP and General Counsel, Bradley C. (Brad) Barron, age 46, $221,167 total compensation
SVP European Operations, Mary F. Morgan, age 59, $320,000 total compensation
SVP and Controller, Thomas R. (Tom) Shoaf, age 53
VP and Corporate Secretary, Amy L. Perry
VP Operations Product Movement, Mark Meador
SVP Marketing and Business Development, Daniel S. (Danny) Oliver, age 45
SVP Trading and Supply, Paul W. Brattlof, age 50, $285,392 total compensation
SVP Corporate Development, Mike Hoeltzel
VP Human Resources, Bob Grimes
VP Corporate Communications, Joanna Weidman
VP Investor Relations, Chris Russell
VP Tax, Audra Fahey
SVP Information Services, Manish Kapoor
VP and Assistant Secretary, Karen Thompson
Director, J. Dan Bates, age 67
President CEO and Director, Curtis V. (Curt) Anastasio, age 55
Director, Rodman D. Patton, age 68
Director, Dan J. Hill, age 71
Director, Stan L. McLelland, age 66
Auditors: Ernst&YoungLLP

LOCATIONS

HQ: NuStar Energy L.P.
2330 N.Loop 1604 W., San Antonio TX 78248
Phone: 210-918-2000 **Fax:** 210-918-5057
Web: www.nustarenergy.com

2011 Sales

	$ mil.	% of total
US	4,834	73
Netherlands	1,564	24
Other countries	176	3
Total	**6,575**	**100**

PRODUCTS/OPERATIONS

2011 Sales

	$ mil.	% of total
Asphalt & fuels marketing	5,757	87
Storage	566	8
Transportation	311	5
Adjustments	(60.1)	-
Total	**6,575**	**100**

COMPETITORS

BP
Enbridge (U.S.)
Ergon
Marathon Petroleum
Martin Resource Management
Shell Pipeline
Transammonia
TransCanada

HISTORICAL FINANCIALS

Company Type: Public

Income Statement FYE: December 31

	REVENUE ($ mil.)	NET INCOME ($ mil.)	NET PROFIT MARGIN	EMPLOYEES
12/11	6,575	221	3.4%	1,508
12/10	4,403	238	5.4%	1,413
12/09	3,855	224	5.8%	1,379
12/08	4,828	254	5.3%	344
12/07	1,475	150	10.2%	332
Annual Growth	45.3%	10.2%	—	46.0%

2011 Year-End Financials

Debt ratio: 39.24%
Return on equity: 7.77%
Cash ($ mil.): 17
Current ratio: 127.24
Long-term debt ($ mil.): 1,942
No. of shares (mil.): 70
Dividends
Yield: —
Payout: 156.12%
Market value ($ mil.): 4,009

	STOCK PRICE ($) FY Close	P/E High/Low		PER SHARE ($) Earnings	Dividends	Book Value
12/11	56.66	25	18	2.78	0.00	40.31
12/10	69.48	22	17	3.19	4.27	41.83
12/09	56.09	17	12	3.47	4.24	41.27
12/08	41.06	13	7	4.22	4.01	40.52
12/07	53.30	26	19	2.74	3.77	40.37
Annual Growth	1.5%	—	—	0.4%	—	(0.0%)

NYSE Euronext

NYSE Euronext is one of the world's largest exchange groups boasting trades totaling about one-third of the global cash equities volume. It operates esteemed exchanges in the US and Europe including the New York Stock Exchange (NYSE) Euronext NYSE Liffe and NYSE Amex formerly the American Stock Exchange. The exchanges have about 8000 listed companies and offer products and services such as cash equities futures options swaps carbon trading clearing market data technology services and more. The NYSE (the world's largest) lists some 2800 companies including most of the most powerful US corporations; it also recruits foreign firms seeking the greater liquidity available in US markets.

HISTORY

To prevent a monopoly on stock sales by securities auctioneers 24 New York stockbrokers and businessmen agreed in 1792 to avoid "public auctions" to charge a commission on sales of stock and to "give preference to each other" in their transactions. The Buttonwood Agreement named after a tree on Wall Street under which they met established the first organized stock market in New York. The Bank of New York was the first corporate stock traded under the Buttonwood tree.

Excluded traders continued dealing on the streets of New York until 1921 and later formed the American Stock Exchange.

In 1817 the brokers created the New York Stock & Exchange Board a stock market with set meeting times. The NYS&EB began to require companies to qualify for trading (listing) by furnishing financial statements in 1853. Ten years later the board became the New York Stock Exchange.

Stock tickers began recording trades in 1867 and two years later the NYSE consolidated with competitors the Open Board of Brokers and the Government Bond Department. Despite repeated panics and recessions in the late 1800s the stock market remained unregulated until well into the 20th century.

In the 1920s the NYSE installed a centralized stock quote service. Postwar euphoria brought a stock mania that fizzled in the crash of October 1929. The subsequent Depression brought investigation and federal regulation to the securities industry.

The NYSE registered as an exchange in 1934. In 1938 it reorganized with a board of directors representing member firms nonmember brokers and the public; it also hired its first full-time president member William McChesney Martin. As a self-regulating body the NYSE policed the activities of its members.

The NYSE began electronic trading in the 1960s; in 1968 it broke 1929's one-day record for trading volume (16 million shares). It became a not-for-profit corporation in 1971. Despite upgrades technology was at least partly to blame for the crash of 1987: A cascade of large sales triggered by computer programs fueled the market's fall.

In 1995 Richard Grasso became the first NYSE staff employee named chairman. The NYSE followed other US stock markets in 1997 by switching trade increments from one-eighth point to one-sixteenth point (known as a "teenie" by arbitrageurs). New circuit-breaker rules halted trading on October 27 when the Dow Jones Industrial Average dropped 550 points in a day (the NYSE increased the trigger to 1050 points in 1999).

The NYSE used a veiled threat to move to New Jersey to win itself the promise of some growing space. In 1999 the exchange named Karen Nelson Hackett as its first woman governor.

The Big Board in 2000 announced plans to go public but the move stalled then died. It also extended its official pricing until 6:30 p.m. (Eastern). In the wake of the terrorism attacks that shook Wall Street and the nation the NYSE and Nasdaq in 2001 began discussing a disaster plan that would see the two cooperating should a future incident cripple either market. Also that year the NYSE moved entirely to decimal pricing in accordance with SEC mandates.

Grasso who earned a reputation as something of a hero in the months following the 2001 terrorist attacks on New York City resigned under fire two years later when his $187 million pay package was revealed. During the furor over Grasso's pay the SEC launched an investigation and many officials –including the heads of top pension funds –called for his resignation.

Former Citigroup chairman John Reed was named interim chairman and CEO following Grasso's departure; former Goldman Sachs president John Thain was subsequently tapped for the CEO role in 2004.

The company acquired ECN Archipelago in 2006 and finally went public. The marriage wasn't entirely painless though. To reduce costs and eliminate redundant positions created by the merger NYSE cut more than 500 jobs (nearly 20% of employees) including some floor specialists.

Also that year the group acquired the approximately one-third stake it didn't already own in Securities Industry Automation Corporation (now SIFMA) which provided communications data processing and clearing services for the exchange.

To better compete with electronic exchanges such as archrival NASDAQ OMX the NYSE broke from its tradition of operating as an auction exchange in 2006 and adopted a hybrid system permitting automated trading. To fuel the transformation it bought electronic communications network Archipelago. Through the acquisition the NYSE added stock options and fixed-income products and took control of the Archipelago Exchange now NYSE Arca.

Member-owned and not-for-profit for more than 200 years the NYSE became a publicly traded company as part of the $10 billion transaction. NYSE stockholders got about 70% of the firm while Archipelago shareholders got the rest. However some traders became wary that the combination might lead to the extinction of the open-outcry floor auctions (where stock prices are set largely by a throng of traders on the exchange floor) that characterize the NYSE.

Less than three months after that transaction closed the NYSE announced the deal for Euronext which had also been courted by Deutsche Borse. Euronext rejected a larger $11 billion bid from the German exchange claiming it carried too much debt.

Continuing its international aspirations NYSE Euronext in 2007 purchased a 5% stake in India's largest stock exchange Mumbai-based National Stock Exchange. Additionally NYSE Euronext bought 20% of the Qatar Exchange (formerly Doha Securities Market) for $200 million.

NYSE Euronext acquired domestic rival AMEX in 2008; the unit became the group's market for emerging growth companies. The following year the cmopany bought trading systems designer NYFIX for $144 million strengthening its technological capabilities to provide faster trades in addition to cost savings.

EXECUTIVES

Group EVP and CFO, Michael S. Geltzeiler, age 53, $750,000 total compensation
Director; Chairman Euronext N.V., Rijnhard W. F. van Tets, age 64

Chairman, Jan-Michiel Hessels, age 70
Group EVP and Head European Execution, Roland Gaston-Bellegarde, age 50, $695,006 total compensation
Chairman and CEO Euronext Brussels, Vincent Van Dessel
Deputy Chairman, Marshall N. Carter, age 71
EVP and General Auditor, Mary L. Brienza, age 54
VP Member Firm Regulation, William J. Wollman, age 42
CEO and Director, Duncan L. Niederauer, age 52, $1,000,000 total compensation
CEO NYSE Regulation, Claudia O. Crowley, age 56
Group EVP and Global Head Human Resources, Philippe Duranton, age 51
Executive Legal Director and General Counsel Euronext N.V., Catherine Langlais
Group EVP and Head Global Derivatives, Garry P. Jones, age 53
COO, Lawrence E. (Larry) Leibowitz, age 51
Group EVP and General Counsel, John K. Halvey, age 51, $750,000 total compensation
President Deputy CEO and Director, Dominique Cerutti, age 51, $46,911 total compensation
EVP Global OTC Services, Finbarr Hutcheson
CEO NYSE Euronext Amsterdam, Cees Vermaas
Chairman and CEO NYSE Euronext Lisbon, Luis Laginha de Sousa
Director, James J. (Jim) McNulty, age 61
Director, Robert G. (Bob) Scott, age 66
Director, Sylvain Hefes, age 59
Director, Patricia M. (Pat) Cloherty, age 69
Director, Duncan M. McFarland, age 68
Director; Chairman Euronext N.V., Rijnhard W. F. van Tets, age 64
Director, Jackson P. Tai, age 61
Deputy Chairman, Marshall N. Carter, age 71
Director, Sir Brian Williamson, age 67
Director, Sir George Cox, age 71
CEO and Director, Duncan L. Niederauer, age 52
Director, Ellyn L. Brown, age 62
Director, Ricardo Salgado, age 67
President Deputy CEO and Director, Dominique Cerutti, age 51
Auditors: PricewaterhouseCoopersLLP

LOCATIONS

HQ: NYSE Euronext
11 Wall Street, New York, NY 10005
Phone: 212 656-3000
Web: www.nyse.com

2011 Sales

	$ mil.	% of total
US	3,101	68
Continental Europe	762	17
UK	689	15
Total	**4,552**	**100**

PRODUCTS/OPERATIONS

2011 Sales

	$ mil.	% of total
Transaction & clearing fees	3,162	69
Listing	446	10
Market data	371	8
Technology services	358	8
Other	215	5
Total	**4,552**	**100**

2011 Sales by Segment

	$ mil.	% of total
Cash trading & listings	2,929	64
Derivatives	1,135	25
Services & technology solutions	490	11
Adjustments	(2)	-
Total	**4,552**	**100**

COMPETITORS

BATS
CBOE
CME
Deutsche Borse
E*TRADE Financial
Hong Kong Exchanges
Investment Technology
Knight Capital
Liquidnet
London Stock Exchange
MarketAxess
NASDAQ OMX
NYMEX Holdings
Singapore Exchange
TRADEBOOK

HISTORICAL FINANCIALS

Company Type: Public

Income Statement FYE: December 31

	REVENUE ($ mil.)	NET INCOME ($ mil.)	NET PROFIT MARGIN	EMPLOYEES
12/11	4,552	619	13.6%	3,077
12/10	4,425	577	13.0%	2,968
12/09	4,687	219	4.7%	3,367
12/08	4,703	(738)	—	3,757
12/07	4,158	643	15.5%	3,083
Annual Growth	2.3%	(0.9%)	—	(0.0%)

2011 Year-End Financials

Debt ratio: 15.87%
Return on equity: 9.41%
Cash ($ mil.): 396
Current ratio: 100.44
Long-term debt ($ mil.): 2,036
No. of shares (mil.): 258
Dividends
Yield: —
Payout: 50.85%
Market value ($ mil.): 6,734

	STOCK PRICE ($) FY Close	P/E High	P/E Low	PER SHARE ($) Earnings	Dividends	Book Value
12/11	26.10	18	9	2.36	0.00	25.51
12/10	29.98	16	10	2.21	1.20	26.04
12/09	25.30	37	18	0.84	1.20	26.43
12/08	27.38	—	—	(2.78)	1.15	25.31
12/07	87.77	40	25	2.70	0.75	35.41
Annual Growth	(26.2%)	—	—	(3.3%)	—	(7.9%)

O'Reilly Automotive, Inc.

No need to jump O'Reilly Automotive's battery. The fast-growing company sells automotive aftermarket parts (both new and remanufactured) maintenance supplies professional service equipment tools and accessories through more than 3700 stores in some three dozen states and online. Many O'Reilly stores also offer a range of services including oil and battery recycling battery testing paint mixing and tool rental. The company wheels and deals with automotive professionals as well as do-it-yourself customers. Founded in 1957 by Charles F. O'Reilly and his son "Chub" O'Reilly Automotive is still family run.

Sales and Marketing

O'Reilly Automotive calls attention to itself by way of television and radio ads direct mail and newspaper distribution in-store and online promotions and sports and event sponsorships. The firm spent nearly $74 million on advertising in 2011 vs. $70 million and nearly $73 million in 2010 and 2009 respectively.

Financial Analysis

Like other retailers in the automotive aftermarket category O'Reilly fared quite well during the recession posting higher sales and profits and revving up its retail presence through acquisitions (most notably CSK Auto on the West Coast). High unemployment rates and weak credit markets prompted more Americans to maintain their vehicles and drive them longer instead of purchase new cars. As a result O'Reilly saw its sales and profits accelerate as professional mechanics experienced an uptick in their business and do-it-yourselfers became more hands-on. Indeed O'Reilly's sales more than doubled between 2007 and 2011. Most recently sales rose about 7% in 2011 vs. 2010 to about $5.8 billion while net income rose 21% over the same period. The uptick was driven by the opening of about 170 new stores and a 4.6% rise in sales at existing stores. Improved efficiency at CSK stores helped drive the increase in same-store sales and profits.

Strategy

In late 2010 O'Reilly finished integrating the roughly 1300-store CSK Auto chain. The $500 million purchase which was completed in 2008 created the third-largest auto parts retailer in the nation behind rivals AutoZone and Advance Auto Parts. CSK operated stores in 22 states including a dozen that O'Reilly had not previously operated in under the Checker Auto Parts Schuck's Auto Supply Kragen and Murray's Discount names. Most the stores were converted to the O'Reilly banner however nearly 20 were closed and about 40 CSK locations merged with existing O'Reilly stores. While acquisitions are key to extending O'Reilly's reach to new markets so too are new store openings which have primarily bolstered the chain's presence in existing markets in recent years. In 2011 the company added about 170 new stores; including its first in West Virginia.

O'Reilly is looking to capture additional revenues from race fans who are believed to spend more on automotive parts than the general public. To this end the retailer partnered with NASCAR in 2008 to be its official auto parts store and has sponsored numerous races since then including the Checker O'Reilly Auto Parts 500 NASCAR Sprint Cup race. In 2009 it also backed more than 1500 local and regional motorsports events.

Ownership

T. Rowe Price owns more than 10% of O'Reilly Automotive's shares.

EXECUTIVES

COO and Co-President, Ted F. Wise, age 61, $576,154 total compensation
Vice Chairman, Lawrence P. (Larry) O'Reilly, age 65, $210,000 total compensation
Vice Chairman, Charles H. O'Reilly Jr., age 72
Chairman, David E. O'Reilly, age 62, $500,000 total compensation
CEO and Co-President, Gregory L. (Greg) Henslee, age 51, $784,615 total compensation
VP and Corporate Secretary, Tricia Headley
VP Western Division, Larry Ellis, age 57
VP Advanced Technology, Mike Williams
SVP Sales and Operations, Jeff M. Shaw, age 49, $187,692 total compensation
EVP Finance and CFO, Thomas G. (Tom) McFall, age 41, $342,308 total compensation
VP Human Resources, Phillip Thompson
SVP Merchandise, Michael D. (Mike) Swearengin, age 51
VP Southwest Division, Greg Langdon, age 63
SVP Distribution Operations, Gregory D. Johnson, age 46
VP Sales, Tony Bartholowmew

VP Advertising and Marketing, Doug Ruble
VP Store Acquisitions and Expansion, Alan Fears
VP Information Systems, Steve Jasinski
VP Loss Prevention, Barry Sabor
VP Store Administration, Phyllis Evans
VP Merchandise, Tom Seboldt
SVP Inventory Management, Randy Johnson, age 56
VP Real Estate, Charlie Downs
VP Risk Management, Wayne Price
VP Purchasing, Greg Beck
VP Retail Systems, Brett Heintz
VP Central Division, Ken Cope
VP Southern Region, Jaime Hinojosa
VP Eastern Division, Brad Beckham
VP Northern Division, Kenny Martin
VP Northwest Division, Ro Salazar
VP CSK Store Integration, Keith Childers
VP Distribution Eastern Division, Tom Connor
VP Legal Claim Services, Jeff Groves
VP Pricing, Brad Knight
VP Finance and Controller, Jeremy Fletcher
Director, Rosalie O'Reilly-Wooten, age 70
Vice Chairman, Lawrence P. (Larry) O'Reilly, age 65
Vice Chairman, Charles H. O'Reilly Jr., age 72
Director, Thomas T. Hendrickson, age 57
Director, Paul R. Lederer, age 72
Director, Jay D. Burchfield, age 65
Director, Ronald Rashkow, age 71
Director, John R. Murphy, age 60
Auditors: Ernst&YoungLLP

LOCATIONS

HQ: O' Reilly Automotive Inc.
233 S. Patterson, Springfield MO 65802-2298
Phone: 417-862-6708 **Fax:** 417-874-7242
Web: www.oreillyauto.com

2011 Locations

	No.
Texas	563
California	474
Missouri	181
Georgia	161
Illinois	141
Washington	141
Tennessee	138
Arizona	128
North	120
Alabama	112
Oklahoma	112
Minnesota	106
Ohio	101
Arkansas	99
Michigan	94
Indiana	89
Louisiana	87
Colorado	84
Wisconsin	78
Kansas	71
Mississippi	71
Iowa	66
Kentucky	62
South	61
Utah	55
Florida	46
Nevada	44
Oregon	44
New	39
Idaho	30
Nebraska	30
Virginia	25
Montana	23
Wyoming	16
North	13
Alaska	12
Hawaii	11
South	11
West	1
Total	**3,740**

PRODUCTS/OPERATIONS

COMPETITORS

Acheeve Inc.
Advance Auto Parts
AutoZone
CARQUEST
Genuine Parts
Pep Boys
Sears
Target Corporation
U.S. Auto Parts
VIP
Wal-Mart
Whitney Automotive Group

HISTORICAL FINANCIALS

Company Type: Public

Income Statement FYE: December 31

	REVENUE ($ mil.)	NET INCOME ($ mil.)	NET PROFIT MARGIN	EMPLOYEES
12/11	5,788	507	8.8%	49,148
12/10	5,397	419	7.8%	47,142
12/09	4,847	307	6.3%	44,822
12/08	3,576	186	5.2%	40,735
12/07	2,522	193	7.7%	23,576
Annual Growth	23.1%	27.2%	—	20.2%

2011 Year-End Financials

Debt ratio: 14.50%
Return on equity: 17.85%
Cash ($ mil.): 361
Current ratio: 165.04
Long-term debt ($ mil.): 796
No. of shares (mil.): 127
Dividends
Yield: —
Payout: —
Market value ($ mil.): 10,168

	STOCK PRICE ($) FY Close	P/E High	P/E Low	PER SHARE ($) Earnings	Dividends	Book Value
12/11	79.95	22	14	3.71	0.00	22.37
12/10	60.42	21	12	2.95	0.00	22.76
12/09	38.12	19	12	2.23	0.00	19.54
12/08	30.74	22	14	1.48	0.00	16.93
12/07	32.43	23	18	1.67	0.00	13.82
Annual Growth	25.3%	—	—	22.1%	—	12.8%

Occidental Petroleum Corp

Harnessing its heritage of Western technical know-how Occidental Petroleum engages in oil and gas exploration and production and makes basic chemicals plastics and petrochemicals. In 2011 it reported proved reserves of 3.2 billion barrels of oil equivalent primarily from assets in the US the Middle East North Africa and Latin America. Subsidiary Occidental Chemical (OxyChem) produces acids chlorine and specialty products and owns Oxy Vinyls the #1 maker of polyvinyl chloride (PVC) resin in North America. Occidental Petroleum's midstream and marketing units gather treat process transport store trade and market crude oil natural gas NGLs condensate and CO2 and generate and market power.

Geographic Reach

The company is investing heavily in the US (California the Mid-Continent and the Permian Basin) the Middle East and North Africa (Bahrain Iraq Libya Oman Qatar UAE and Yemen) and Latin America (Bolivia and Colombia.)

Operations

Occidental operates a global oil and gas exploration and production business and a significant midstream and marketing enterprise. It also controls Occidental Chemical (OxyChem) a major North America-based chemical manufacturer. Oil and gas exploration and production accounts for about 3/4 of the company's total revenues.

Financial Analysis

After seeing revenues fall during the global recession stronger commodity prices and increased production helped to lift the company's revenues and income in 2010 and 2011. In 2011 Occidental reported a 26% jump in revenues thanks to robust oil and refined product prices and increased demand for its petroleum and chemical products. Net income rose by more the 49% thanks to higher revenues outpacing increased costs coupled with lower exploration expenses and impairment charges.

Strategy

Occidental is focusing on large mature oil and gas assets with long-term growth potential.

In addition to its existing assets in Qatar and Yemen the company is developing new fields in Oman and Abu Dhabi. In 2010 Occidental signed a deal to develop an oil field in Iraq and in early 2011 it teamed up with ADNOC to develop the major Shah gas field in the UAE.

However unrest across the Arab world in 2011 particularly in Bahrain Libya and Yemen confronted the company with a great deal of uncertainty about the short-term protection of its assets and its long term strategy in the region.

To raise cash to pay down debt in 2011 the company sold its Argentina-based assets to China Petrochemical for $2.45 billion. The deal helped cover some of the costs of Occidental's $3.4 billion acquisition (in late 2010 and early 2011) of safer US-based assets –oil and gas properties in South Texas and North Dakota.

In North America it has been building core assets. To finance its purchase of the US government's 78% interest in California's historic and underdeveloped Elk Hills oil field (in 2008) the company divested its natural gas pipeline and marketing operation MidCon and sold off noncore oil and gas properties in the US Venezuela and the Netherlands. It also acquired $1.2 billion of assets in the Permian and Piceance basins in the US from Plains Exploration & Production. By the end of 2011 about half of Occidental's total oil and gas production came from the US primarily from its Elk Hills and Permian Basin assets.

HISTORY

Founded in 1920 Occidental Petroleum struggled until 1956 when billionaire industrialist Dr. Armand Hammer sank $100000 into the company then worth $34000. It drilled two wells and both came in. Hammer eventually gained control of the company.

Occidental's discovery of California's second-largest gas field (1959) was followed by a concession from Libya's King Idris (1966) and the discovery of a billion-barrel Libyan oil field. In 1968 Occidental bought Signal Oil's European refining and marketing business as an outlet for the Libyan oil. It also diversified buying Island Creek Coal and Hooker Chemical.

In 1969 Occidental sold 51% of its Libyan production to the Libyan government under duress after Idris was ousted. (It suspended operations there in 1986). It soon began oil exploration in Latin America (1971) and in the North Sea (1972-73) where it discovered the lucrative Piper field.

Other projects included a 20-year fertilizer-for-ammonia deal with the USSR (1974) and a coal joint venture with China (1985).

During the 1980s Occidental sold some foreign assets and bought US natural gas pipeline firm MidCon (1986). It also bought Iowa Beef Processors (IBP) for stock worth $750 million (1981) and then spun off 49% of it in 1987 for $960 million.

In 1983 Hammer hired Ray Irani to revive Occidental's ailing chemicals business (losses that year: $38 million). Irani integrated operations to ensure higher margins during industry downturns and purchased Diamond Shamrock Chemicals (1986) Shell's vinyl chloride monomer unit (1987) a DuPont chloralkali facility (1987) and Cain Chemical (1988). OxyChem's profits reached almost $1.1 billion by 1989.

Hammer died in 1990 and Irani became CEO. In 1991 to reduce debt Occidental exited the Chinese coal business and sold the North Sea oil properties. Occidental also spun off IBP the largest US red-meat producer to its shareholders.

Occidental paid Irani $95 million in 1997 to buy out his employment contract; instead his compensation (a minimum of $1.2 million a year) was tied to the company's fortunes. That year Occidental's $3.65 billion bid won the US government's auction of its 78% stake in California's Elk Hills petroleum reserve one of the largest in the continental US.

To help pay for Elk Hills the company sold MidCon to K N Energy for $3.1 billion in 1998. Occidental traded its petrochemical operations to Equistar Chemicals a partnership between Lyondell (now LyondellBasell) and Millennium Chemicals for $425 million and a 29.5% stake.

In a venture with The Geon Company Occidental in 1999 formed Oxy Vinyls the #1 producer of polyvinyl chloride (PVC) resin in North America. That year also brought a windfall: Chevron agreed to pay Occidental $775 million to settle a lawsuit stemming from the 1982 withdrawal by Gulf (later acquired by Chevron) of an offer to buy Cities Service (later acquired by Occidental).

In 2000 Occidental sold its 29% stake in Canadian Occidental back to the company for $828 million to help fund the purchase of oil and gas producer Altura Energy a partnership of BP and Shell Oil for $3.6 billion. Later that year the company sold some Gulf of Mexico properties to Apache for $385 million.

Occidental acquired a new exploration block in Yemen in 2001. The next year it sold its 30% of Equistar Chemicals to Lyondell in exchange for a 21% stake in Lyondell. In 2005 it acquired a stake in a gas and oil production site located in Texas' Permian Basin from ExxonMobil for a reported $972 million. Occidental closed the acquisition of Vintage Petroleum for a reported $3.8 billion in early 2006.

The government of Ecuador seized Occidental Petroleum's Ecuadorian assets in 2006 as part of a nationalization drive. That year Plains Exploration and Production sold non-core oil and gas properties to Occidental for $865 million.

Also in 2006 Occidental reduced its stake in Lyondell from 12% to 8%. The following year Occidental sold its remaining Lyondell shares on the open market.

In North America in 2008 the company bought a 15% stake in the Joslyn Oil Sands project for nearly $500 million. That project is based in Alberta Canada and is operated by Total.

The company re-entered Libya in 2008.

Beefing up its investment vehicles in 2009 the company purchased Citigroup's commodities trading unit (Philbro LLC).

EXECUTIVES

EVP General Counsel and Secretary, Donald P. de Brier, age 71, $495,900 total compensation
President CEO and Director, Stephen I. (Steve) Chazen, age 65, $720,000 total compensation
Chairman, Ray R. Irani, age 77, $1,170,000 total compensation
VP and CIO, Donald L. Moore Jr.
VP Tax, Michael S. Stutts
EVP Business Support, James M. Lienert, age 59
VP Acquisitions and Corporate Finance; VP Oil and Gas California Operations, Todd A. Stevens
President Occidental Chemical, B. Chuck Anderson, age 52
VP Investor Relations, Christopher G. (Chris) Stavros
VP Controller and Principal Accounting Officer, Roy Pineci, age 49
VP Communications and Public Affairs, Richard S. Kline
VP Government Relations, Ian M. Davis
VP Internal Audit, Gary L. Daugherty
VP Health Environment and Safety, Charles F. Weiss
EVP Human Resources, Martin A. Cozyn, age 51
VP; President Oxy Oil & Gas Americas, William E. Albrecht, age 60, $400,000 total compensation
VP and Treasurer, Robert J. Williams Jr., age 53
VP; President International Production Oil and Gas, Edward A. (Sandy) Lowe, age 60
VP; EVP Worldwide Exploration Oil and Gas, Anita M. Powers
EVP Oil and Gas, John M. Winterman
EVP and CFO, Cynthia L. Walker, age 35
Director, Carlos M. Gutierrez, age 58
President CEO and Director, Stephen I. (Steve) Chazen, age 65
Director, Howard I. Atkins, age 61
Director, Edward P. Djerejian, age 73
Director, Rodolfo Segovia, age 75
Director, Margaret M. (Peggy) Foran, age 57
Director, Walter L. (Wally) Weisman, age 76
Director, Avedick B. (Dick) Poladian, age 60
Director, Spencer Abraham, age 59
Auditors: KPMGLLP

LOCATIONS

HQ: Occidental Petroleum Corporation
10889 Wilshire Blvd., Los Angeles CA 90024-4201
Phone: 310-208-8800 **Fax:** 310-443-6690
Web: www.oxy.com

2011 Sales

	% of total
US	63
Qatar	14
Oman	10
Colombia	4
Yemen	4
UAE	1
Other	4
Total	**100**

PRODUCTS/OPERATIONS

2011 Sales

	$ mil.	% of total
Oil & gas	18,419	74
Chemicals	4,915	20
Midstream marketing & other	1,447	6
Adjustments	(652)	-
Total	**24,119**	**100**

Selected Subsidiaries

Occidental Chemical Corp. (OxyChem; chemicals polymers and plastics)
Oxy Vinyls LP (76% polyvinyl chloride)
Occidental Energy Marketing Inc. (energy marketing)
Occidental Exploration and Production Company (exploration and production)

COMPETITORS

Apache
Ashland Inc.
BP
ConocoPhillips
Devon Energy
Dow Chemical
DuPont
Eastman Chemical
Exxon Mobil
Hess Corporation
Huntsman International
Imperial Oil
J.M. Huber
Koch Industries Inc.
Marathon Oil
Olin
PEMEX
Royal Dutch Shell
Sunoco
TOTAL

HISTORICAL FINANCIALS

Company Type: Public

Income Statement FYE: December 31

	REVENUE ($ mil.)	NET INCOME ($ mil.)	NET PROFIT MARGIN	EMPLOYEES
12/11	24,119	6,771	28.1%	11,300
12/10	19,157	4,530	23.6%	11,000
12/09	15,531	2,915	18.8%	10,100
12/08	24,480	6,857	28.0%	10,400
12/07	20,013	5,400	27.0%	9,700
Annual Growth	4.8%	5.8%	—	3.9%

2011 Year-End Financials

Debt ratio: 9.78%
Return on equity: 18.00%
Cash ($ mil.): 3,781
Current ratio: 145.24
Long-term debt ($ mil.): 5,871
No. of shares (mil.): 811
Dividends
Yield: —
Payout: 22.12%
Market value ($ mil.): 75,992

	STOCK PRICE ($) FY Close	P/E High/Low		PER SHARE ($) Earnings	Dividends	Book Value
12/11	93.70	14	8	8.32	0.00	46.39
12/10	98.10	18	13	5.56	1.47	39.97
12/09	81.35	24	13	3.58	1.31	35.82
12/08	59.99	12	5	8.35	1.21	33.69
12/07	76.99	12	7	6.44	0.94	27.64
Annual Growth	5.0%	—	—	6.6%	—	13.8%

Office Depot, Inc.

Paper clips add up to big money for Office Depot. The world's #2 office supply chain (behind Staples) Office Depot sells office supplies through about 1130 company-owned and licensed locations throughout North America and 130 locations overseas. The big-box retail stores sell to both consumers and small- and medium-sized businesses. In addition to general office supplies (about two-thirds of sales) its stores offer computer hardware and software office furniture art and school supplies and printing and copying services. Office Depot also sells goods through catalogs and call centers the Internet and a contract sales force. Amid the weak economy the company is closing stores and exiting markets.

HISTORY

Pat Scher Stephen Dougherty and Jack Kopkin opened the first Office Depot one of the first office supply superstores in Lauderdale Lakes Florida in 1986. Scher was selected as chairman. By the end of the year the fledgling company had opened two more stores (both in Florida).

Office Depot opened seven more stores in 1987. When Scher died of leukemia that year the company recruited David Fuente former president of Sherwin-Williams' Paint Store Division as chairman and CEO. Office Depot continued its breakneck expansion under Fuente. In 1988 –the year the company went public –it opened 16 stores and broke into new markets in four states.

The chain stepped up its pace and by 1990 it had expanded into several other areas including the South and Midwest. Office Depot also added computers and peripherals and opened its first delivery center.

In 1991 the company became North America's #1 office products retailer and expanded its presence in the West through the acquisition of Office Club another warehouse-type office supply chain with 59 stores (most in California). Fuente remained chairman and CEO while former Office Club CEO Mark Begelman became president and COO. (Begelman who left in 1995 and eventually formed the MARS music chain had founded the first Office Club in 1987 in Concord California; he took it public in 1989.)

The company entered the international market with its 1992 purchase of Canada's H. Q. Office International and through licensing agreements in 1993 (in Colombia and Israel). Office Depot created its business services division by acquiring various contract stationers including Eastman Office Products (the West Coast's #1 contract office supplier) in the mid-1990s and added locations in Mexico and Poland; it established a joint venture in France with retailer Carrefour in 1996.

Also in 1996 Office Depot announced a $3.4 billion agreement to be acquired by Staples which would have created a company with more than 1100 stores. However the government blocked the purchase on antitrust grounds in 1997 and the agreement dissolved. Unfettered by merger distractions Office Depot resumed opening stores at a rapid pace including two in Thailand and took its catalog and delivery services online. It then established a joint venture with Japanese retailer Deo Deo.

In 1998 Office Depot acquired Viking Office Products in a $2.7 billion deal. With more than 60% of its sales coming from outside the US Viking augmented Office Depot's already strong delivery network and international expansion. Office Depot acquired the remaining 50% of its French operations from Carrefour in 1998 and the remaining 50% of its Japanese operations from Deo Deo in 1999.

Office Depot started putting Internet kiosks in its US stores in 2000 allowing customers to browse and shop company Web sites. In July 2000 Bruce Nelson CEO of Viking replaced Fuente as CEO of Office Depot. Citing weak computer sales and high warehouse prices the company closed about 70 stores and cut its workforce. In early 2002 Nelson was named chairman as well as CEO after Fuente stepped down.

Office Depot sold its Australian operations to Officeworks a unit of Coles Myer in January 2003. Office Depot used the proceeds to expand its faster-growing European operations. Also that year the company acquired the retail operations of French office supplier Guilbert from Pinault-Printemps-Redoute a move that doubled the company's business in Europe. (Staples had acquired Guilbert's mail-order business the previous year.)

In 2004 the company acquired about 125 retail locations from troubled toy seller Toys "R" Us converting 50 of those into Office Depot locations and selling off the remainder.

Nelson left the company and Neil Austrian served as interim head. Office Depot named AutoZone leader Steve Odland as CEO and chairman in 2005. That year the company shuttered its Viking Office Products brand in the US consolidating its catalog sales under the Office Depot banner. (It still markets products through Viking in international markets.) The business services division also sells technology products through Tech Depot (formerly 4SURE.com).

The company acquired privately held Allied Office Products (AOP) the largest independent dealer of office products and services in the US in 2006. AOP became part of Office Depot's North American Business Solutions Division.

Office Depot opened 70 new stores in 2007 (vs. 115 the previous year).

In mid-2008 the company acquired 13 stores in Sweden through the acquisition of AGE Kontor & Data AB a contract and retail office supply company operating there.

In 2009 the company closed about 125 stores in North America and exited the Japanese market.

CEO Steve Odland resigned in November 2010. In late 2010 Israeli department store operator New Hamashbir Lazarchan acquired Office Depot's operations in Israel for $50 million. New Hamashbir Lazarchan also agreed to pay royalties on revenues generated by Office Depot Israel which has about 45 stores.

Office Depot appointed new leadership in mid-2011 naming interim leader Neil Austrian as the company's permanent replacement for chief executive and chairman. Austrian has served as a director at Office Depot since 1998. He stepped in to lead the office products retailer on a temporary basis following the resignation of Steve Odland in late 2010. Odland's resignation came soon after Office Depot settled Securities and Exchange Commission charges that the company selectively informed analysts and institutional investors that its earnings would fall short of estimates. Office Depot agreed to pay $1 million while Odland and the firm's former CFO agreed to pay $50000.

EXECUTIVES

President International, Steven M. (Steve) Schmidt, age 57, $625,000 total compensation
President International, Charles E. Brown, age 58, $625,000 total compensation
EVP and CFO, Michael D. (Mike) Newman, age 55, $625,000 total compensation
Chairman and CEO, Neil R. Austrian, age 72, $526,615 total compensation
VP Investor Relations, Brian Turcotte
President North America, Kevin A. Peters, age 54
Director Public Relations, Brian Levine
SVP and Chief Compliance Officer, Robert Brewer
EVP General Counsel and Corporate Secretary, Elisa D. Garcia C., age 54
SVP and Controller, Mark E. Hutchens, age 46
Senior Director Loyalty and Direct Marketing, Larry Wadford
VP Merchandising, Randy Wick
VP and Associate General Counsel, Steve Calkins
VP HR, Michele Henderson
VP Legal Counsel Europe, Boubacar Diarra
EVP and Chief Merchandising Officer, Farla Efros
EVP and Chief Marketing Officer, Robert Moore
EVP Human Resources, Michael Allison
Director, Marsha J. (Marty) Evans, age 64
Director, Kathleen Mason, age 63
Director, W. Scott Hedrick, age 66
Director, Brenda J. Gaines, age 62
Director, Myra M. Hart, age 71
Director, Thomas J. (Tom) Colligan, age 68
Director, Raymond Svider, age 49
Director, Justin M. Bateman, age 38
Director, James S. Rubin, age 44
Auditors: Deloitte&ToucheLLP

LOCATIONS

HQ: Office Depot, Inc.
6600 North Military Trail, Boca Raton, FL 33496
Phone: 561 438-4800 **Fax:** 561 265-4406
Web: www.officedepot.com

2012 Stores

	No.
US	1,112
International	
France	54
Sweden	51
South	18
Total	**1,235**

PRODUCTS/OPERATIONS

2012 Sales

	% of total
Office	65
Technology	21
Furniture &	14
Total	**100**

2012 Sales

	$ mil.	% of total
North American Retail	4,457	42
North American Business Solutions	3,214	30
International	3,022	28
Total	**10,695**	**100**

Selected Products

Office supplies
- Basic supplies and labels
- Binders and accessories
- Breakroom and janitorial supplies
- Business cases
- Calendars and planners
- Desk accessories
- Executive gifts
- Filing and storage
- Paper and envelopes
- Pens pencils and markers
- School supplies

Technology products
- Audio-visual equipment and supplies
- Cameras
- Computers and related accessories (including monitors and printers)
- Copiers
- Data storage supplies
- Fax machines
- Networking supplies
- PDAs
- Software

Office furniture
- Armoires
- Bookcases
- Carts and stands
- Chair mats and floor mats
- Chairs
- Desks
- Filing cabinets
- Lamps and light bulbs
- Office furnishings
- Panel systems
- Tables
- Workstations

COMPETITORS

Amazon.com
Apple Inc.
Best Buy
BJ' s Wholesale Club
CDW
Costco Wholesale
FedEx Office
Fry' s Electronics
Insight Enterprises
Lyreco
Mail Boxes Etc.
OfficeMax
RadioShack
Ricoh USA
School Specialty
Staples
Systemax
Unisource
United Stationers
Wal-Mart

HISTORICAL FINANCIALS

Company Type: Public

Income Statement FYE: December 31

	REVENUE ($ mil.)	NET INCOME ($ mil.)	NET PROFIT MARGIN	EMPLOYEES
12/11	11,489	95	0.8%	39,000
12/10	11,633	34	0.3%	40,000
12/09	12,144	(596)	—	41,000
12/08	14,495	(1,478)	—	43,000
12/07	15,527	395	2.5%	49,000
Annual Growth	(7.3%)	(29.9%)	—	(5.5%)

2011 Year-End Financials

Debt ratio: 16.11%
Return on equity: 8.68%
Cash ($ mil.): 570
Current ratio: 134.03
Long-term debt ($ mil.): 648
No. of shares (mil.): 286
Dividends
Yield: —
Payout: —
Market value ($ mil.): 616

	STOCK PRICE ($) FY Close	P/E High/Low		PER SHARE ($) Earnings	Dividends	Book Value
12/11	2.15	28	8	0.22	0.00	3.85
12/10	5.45	—	—	(0.01)	0.00	4.09
12/09	7.05	—	—	(2.30)	0.00	4.16
12/08	2.93	—	—	(5.42)	0.00	4.96
12/07	13.65	27	9	1.43	0.00	11.30
Annual Growth	(37.0%)	—	—	(37.4%)	—	(23.6%)

OfficeMax Inc (DE)

This company is taking the office supply business to the max. OfficeMax is the #3 office products retailer in North America (far behind Staples and Office Depot) with more than 900 superstores across the US Puerto Rico the Virgin Islands and Mexico. The stores offer about 10000 name-brand and OfficeMax-branded products including paper pens forms and organizers as well as office furniture and a wide range of technology products. OfficeMax also provides printing and document services through its ImPress store-within-a-store. In addition to its retail outlets the company's contract division (51% of sales) sells directly to business and government customers by phone catalogs and the Internet.

HISTORY

Boise Cascade got its start in 1957 with the merger of two small lumber companies –Boise Payette Lumber Company (based in Boise Idaho) and Cascade Lumber Company (Yakima Washington). The business diversified in the 1960s under the leadership of Robert Hansberger moving into office-products distribution in 1964. A number of acquisitions followed including Ebasco Industries (1969) a consulting engineering and construction firm. By 1970 Boise Cascade had made more than 30 buys to diversify into building materials paper products real estate recreational vehicles (RVs) and publishing.

In the early 1970s the company suffered a timber shortage as its access to public timberlands dwindled. Its plans to develop recreational communities in California Hawaii and Washington met opposition from residents causing Boise Cascade to scrap all but six of the 29 projects.

High costs related to the remaining projects left the company in debt in 1972. John Fery replaced Hansberger as president that year and sold companies not directly related to the business's core forest-product operations.

In the late 1980s and early 1990s Boise Cascade sold more nonstrategic operations including its Specialty Paperboard Division in 1989. It sold more than half of its corrugated-container plants in 1992 to focus on manufacturing forest products and distributing building materials and office supplies.

Boise Cascade also sold its wholesale office-product business in 1992 to focus on direct sales to big buyers such as IBM and Boeing. The company sold off its Canadian subsidiary Rainy River Forest Products during 1994 and 1995. Resurgent paper prices resulted in a profit in 1995 Boise Cascade's first since 1990.

Also in 1995 in a move into the international paper market Boise Cascade signed a joint venture agreement with Shenzhen Leasing to form Zhuhai Hiwin Boise Cascade a Chinese manufacturer of carbonless paper. That year it sold a minority stake in Boise Cascade Office Products (BCOP) to the public.

The company sold its coated-papers business to paper and packaging heavyweight Mead in 1996 for $639 million. The following year Boise began harvesting its first quick-growth cottonwood trees (specially grown to cut the cost of harvesting from traditional slow-growth hardwood plantations). Also in 1997 BCOP bought Jean-Paul Guisset an office-products direct marketer in France. Although this acquisition boosted sales and increased the company's European presence company profits suffered that year because of weak paper prices.

The low price of paper in 1998 prompted the company to close four sawmills and a research and development center. Restructuring costs associated with the closures and a fire at the company's Medford Oregon plywood plant led to a net income loss for the year.

In 1999 Boise bought Wallace Computer Services a contract stationer business and broadened its building-supply distribution network nationwide by acquiring Furman Lumber a building-supplies distributor. In 2000 Boise Cascade completed the purchase of the 19% of Boise Office Solutions that it didn't already own. The company also sold its European office products operations for $335 million and then turned around and purchased the Blue Star Business Supplies Group of US Office Products in Australia and New Zealand for about $115 million.

Because of the decline in federal timber sales in 2001 the company closed its plywood mill and lumber operations in Emmett Idaho and a sawmill in Cascade Idaho. In 2002 lagging profits prompted Boise to implement cost-cutting procedures. In 2003 the company pinned its hopes for growth on the office product segment with the acquisition of OfficeMax for nearly $1.2 billion in cash and stock. The deal put Boise Cascade's office products business on par with industry leaders Staples and Office Depot.

The company sold its paper forest products and timberland assets to investment firm Madison Dearborn Partners for $3.7 billion in October 2004. That year it changed its name to OfficeMax and tagged Christopher Milliken a former Boise Cascade executive as CEO but he resigned after only four months on the job. Former ShopKo Stores CEO Sam Duncan was tapped as his replacement.

OfficeMax opened its first new prototype store in Macedonia Ohio in 2005.

The company moved its headquarters in 2006 from Itasca Illinois to nearby Naperville. Looking to improve its balance sheet OfficeMax announced a major restructuring effort that year that saw the company close about 110 underperforming locations in the US. Meanwhile it opened about 60 new locations during the year. In 2007 the company opened about another 60 locations in the US and 15 in Mexico through a partnership.

In 2008 OfficeMax opened 43 new stores in the US and 17 in Mexico including three Ink-Paper-Scissors stores (the firm's new small-format store).

Years later in November 2010 Duncan stepped down as the company's chairman president and CEO with Ravi Saligram taking over as OfficeMax's president and CEO. Lead director Rakesh Gangwal assumed the title of non-executive chairman to backfill Duncan's responsibilities on the board.

EXECUTIVES

SVP Finance and Chief Accounting Officer, Deborah A. (Deb) O'Connor, age 49, $300,000 total compensation

Chairman, Rakesh Gangwal, age 58

President CEO and Director, Ravichandra K. (Ravi) Saligram, age 55

EVP and Chief Merchandising Officer, Ryan T. Vero, age 42, $533,540 total compensation

EVP CFO and Chief Administrative Officer, Bruce H. Besanko, age 54, $480,192 total compensation

EVP and Chief Marketing and Strategy Officer, Kimberly L. (Kim) Feil, age 53

EVP and CIO, Randy G. Burdick

VP and Chief Diversity Officer, Carolynn Brooks

VP Global Loss Prevention, John Voytilla

Senior Director External Relations, William (Bill) Bonner

VP Investor Relations and Treasurer, Tony Giuliano, age 53

EVP General Counsel and Chief Compliance Officer, Matthew R. (Matt) Broad, age 52

EVP Supply Chain and General Manager Services, Reuben E. Slone

SVP Corporate Secretary and Associate General Counsel, Susan Wagner-Fleming

SVP Marketing and Advertising, Bob Thacker

EVP and Chief Digital Officer, Jim Barr

EVP and Chief Human Resources Officer, Steve Parsons, age 47

EVP; President Retail, Michael J. Lewis

SVP E-Commerce and Direct Marketing, Julie Krueger

SVP; Managing Director Australasian Operations, David Armstrong

EVP and Chief Merchandising Officer, Ronald Lalla

SVP Supply Chain, Larry Hartley

EVP; President Contract, John Kenning

Director, Warren F. Bryant, age 66

Director, Dorrit J. Bern, age 61

Director, Francesca Ruiz de Luzuriaga, age 57

President CEO and Director, Ravichandra K. (Ravi) Saligram, age 55

Director, Joseph M. (Joe) DePinto, age 49
Director, William J. Montgoris, age 65
Director, David M. Szymanski, age 55
Auditors: KPMGLLP

LOCATIONS

HQ: OfficeMax Inc (DE)
263 Shuman Boulevard, Naperville, IL 60563
Phone: 630 438-7800
Web: www.officemax.com

2012 Sales

	$ mil.	% of total
US	5,492	79
Other countries	1,428	21
Total	**6,920**	**100**

PRODUCTS/OPERATIONS

2012 Sales

	$ mil.	% of total
Contract	3,605	52
Retail	3,314	48
Total	**6,920**	**100**

2012 Contract Sales

	% of total
Office supplies &	58
Technology	31
Office	11
Total	**100**

2012 Retail Sales

	% of total
Technology	50
Office supplies &	43
Office	7
Total	**100**

COMPETITORS

Amazon.com
Best Buy
BJ' s Wholesale Club
CDW
Container Store
Costco Wholesale
FedEx Office
Insight Enterprises
Mail Boxes Etc.
Newegg
Office Depot
Office Solutions
Quill Corporation
RadioShack
Ricoh USA
Sam' s Club
Staples
Systemax
Target Corporation
Unisource
United Stationers
Wal-Mart

HISTORICAL FINANCIALS

Company Type: Public

Income Statement FYE: December 31

	REVENUE ($ mil.)	NET INCOME ($ mil.)	NET PROFIT MARGIN	EMPLOYEES
12/11	7,121	34	0.5%	29,000
12/10	7,150	71	1.0%	30,000
12/09	7,212	0	0.0%	31,000
12/08	8,267	(1,657)	—	33,000
12/07	9,081	207	2.3%	36,000
Annual Growth	(5.9%)	(36.0%)	—	(5.3%)

2011 Year-End Financials

Debt ratio: 42.71%
Return on equity: 6.13%
Cash ($ mil.): 427
Current ratio: 191.35
Long-term debt ($ mil.): 1,699
No. of shares (mil.): 86
Dividends
Yield: —
Payout: —
Market value ($ mil.): 391

	STOCK PRICE ($) FY Close	P/E High/Low		PER SHARE ($) Earnings	Dividends	Book Value
12/11	4.54	49	11	0.38	0.00	6.60
12/10	17.98	24	12	0.79	0.00	7.06
12/09	13.56	—	—	(0.03)	0.00	5.95
12/08	7.44	—	—	(21.90)	0.00	3.82
12/07	20.54	20	8	2.66	0.00	30.22
Annual Growth	(31.4%)	—	—	(38.5%)	—	(31.6%)

Ohio Power Company

To access electricity across the state of Ohio 706000 retail customers turn to Ohio Power (which does business as part of AEP Ohio along with Columbus Southern Power and Wheeling Power). The company one of American Electric Power's largest utility subsidiaries operates more than 31260 miles of transmission and distribution lines. The utility also generates more than 8500 MW of capacity from primarily hydroelectric and fossil-fueled power plants (the bulk from coal-fired plants) and it sells wholesale electricity to other power companies.

Ohio Power provides power to a number of industries including iron and steel rubber and plastic products stone clay glass and concrete products petroleum refining and chemicals. The company's top customers include Ormet Premcor Refining Republic Engineered Products Timken and Wheeling Pittsburgh.

About 3% of AEP Ohio's power was generated from renewable sources in 2008 but the company is committed to ramp that up to meet state and federal emission goals. In 2009 it agreed to a 20-year solar energy purchasing deal with Wyandot Solar. The 10 MW Wyandot Solar plant is located next to AEP Ohio's North Upper Sandusky substation. In 2010 the company teamed up with with Turning Point Solar to announce plans to develop the largest commercial solar plant east of the Rockies. The 50 MW solar generating facility is to be built on 500 acres in southeastern Ohio is expected to come on line in 2012.

The company reported a rise in revenues and income in 2010 primarily as the result of increased weather-related usage by residential and commercial customers and an increase in capacity settlements under the Interconnection Agreement (a cost-sharing agreement among AEP utilities).

In 2011 the parent company announced plans to merge sister Ohio utility Columbus Southern Power into Ohio Power to improve AEP's operating efficiencies.

EXECUTIVES

VP and Director, Carl L. English, age 65, $552,115 total compensation
VP and Director, Robert P. (Bob) Powers, age 57, $511,961 total compensation
Vice Chairman VP and Director, Venita McCellon-Allen, age 52
Chairman CEO and Director, Michael G. (Mike) Morris, age 65, $1,254,808 total compensation
VP and Director, Susan Tomasky, age 58, $511,961 total compensation
VP and Director, John B. (Jack) Keane, age 65
President and COO, Joseph (Joe) Hamrock, age 48
EVP, Charles R. Patton, age 53
VP and Director, Brian X. Tierney, age 45
VP and Director, Nicholas K. (Nick) Akins, age 51
Director Customer Services and Marketing, Karen L. Sloneker
Director Business Operations Support, Matthew D. (Matt) Kyle
VP Regulatory and Finance, Selwyn J. Dias
Director Corporate Communications, Terri Flora
Media Relations Central and Southern Ohio (including Columbus Delaware Chillicothe Chesapeake Portsmouth Hillsboro Ironton and Seaman areas), Vikki Michalski
Media Relations Eastern Ohio (including Guernsey Knox Licking Morgan Muskingum Noble Perry southern Richland Belmont Jefferson Columbiana and Harrison Counties) and Northern Panhandle of West Virginia (Marshall and Ohio Counties), Carmen Prati-Miller
Manager Safety and Health, David A. (Dave) Varwig
Media Relations Northern Ohio (including Canton Wooster and New Philadelphia), Shelly Haugh
Media Relations Northwest Ohio (including Lima Findlay Tiffin and other portions of Northwest Ohio), Shelly Clark
Media Relations Southeastern Ohio (including Athens Gallipolis Lancaster Marietta Pomeroy and Wellston), Jeff Rennie
VP and Director, Carl L. English, age 65
VP and Director, Robert P. (Bob) Powers, age 57
Vice Chairman VP and Director, Venita McCellon-Allen, age 52
VP and Director, Susan Tomasky, age 58
VP and Director, John B. (Jack) Keane, age 65
VP and Director, Brian X. Tierney, age 45
VP and Director, Nicholas K. (Nick) Akins, age 51
Auditors: Deloitte&ToucheLLP

LOCATIONS

HQ: Ohio Power Company
1 Riverside Plaza, Columbus OH 43215-2373
Phone: 614-716-1000 **Fax:** 614-716-1823
Web: www.aepohio.com

PRODUCTS/OPERATIONS

2011 Sales

	$ mil.	% of total
Electric generation transmission & distribution	4,406	81
Sales to AEP affiliates	978	17
Other - affiliated	27	1
Other - nonaffiliated	18	1
Total	**5,431**	**100**

COMPETITORS

Columbia Gas of Ohio
Dominion East Ohio
DPL
Duke Energy Ohio
Ohio Edison
The Illuminating Company
Toledo Edison
Vectren Energy Delivery of Ohio

HISTORICAL FINANCIALS

Company Type: Subsidiary

Income Statement FYE: December 31

	REVENUE ($ mil.)	NET INCOME ($ mil.)	NET PROFIT MARGIN	EMPLOYEES
12/10	5,431	464	8.6%	3,256
12/09	3,223	311	9.7%	2,100
12/08	3,011	306	10.2%	2,391
12/07	3,096	231	7.5%	2,434
Annual Growth	20.6%	26.2%	—	10.2%

2010 Year-End Financials

Debt ratio: 31.13%
Return on equity: 10.45%
Cash ($ mil.): 2
Current ratio: 74.99
Long-term debt ($ mil.): 3,809
No. of shares (mil.): 27
Dividends
Yield: —
Payout: 140.17%
Market value ($ mil.): 2,152

	STOCK PRICE ($) FY Close	P/E High/Low		PER SHARE ($) Earnings	Dividends	Book Value
12/10	77.00	—	—	(0.00)	0.00	159.21
12/09	77.00	—	—	(0.00)	4.50	113.94
12/08	66.00	—	—	(0.00)	0.00	116.32
12/07	66.00	—	—	(0.00)	0.00	87.24
Annual Growth	5.3%	—	—	—	—	22.2%

OLAM AMERICAS INC

LOCATIONS

HQ: OLAM AMERICAS INC
25 UNION PL STE 3, SUMMIT, NJ 079013603
Phone: 9089881960
Web: WWW.OLAMONLINE.COM

HISTORICAL FINANCIALS

Company Type:

Income Statement

FYE: June 30

	REVENUE ($ mil.)	NET INCOME ($ mil.)	NET PROFIT MARGIN	EMPLOYEES
06/11	9,870	171	1.7%	0
Annual Growth	—	—	—	—

2011 Year-End Financials

Debt ratio: —
Return on equity: 1.70%
Cash ($ mil.): 502
Current ratio: 0.20
Long-term debt ($ mil.): —
Dividends
Yield: —
Payout: —
Market value ($ mil.): —

Old National Bancorp (Evansville, IN)

Old National Bank is old but it's not quite national. Founded in 1834 the main subsidiary of Old National Bancorp operates about 200 offices in Indiana Kentucky and Illinois. Serving consumers and business customers the bank offers standard fare such as checking and savings accounts credit cards and loans. Its treasury segment manages investments for the bank as well as for commercial clients. Business loans commercial and residential mortgages and consumer loans account for most of Old National's lending activity. The company also sells insurance manages wealth for high-networth clients and offers investment and retirement services through third-party provider LPL Financial.

Old National has identified metropolitan areas within its market such as Indianapolis; Louisville Kentucky; and Lafayette Indiana for growth within its core community banking segment; that growth has largely been fueled by acquisitions. The company's latest was the 2012 purchase of Indiana Community Bancorp which added 17 branches in the southeastern part of the state. The transaction was valued at nearly $80 million.

In 2011 Old National bought Monroe Bancorp for some $83 million bringing in about 10 branches in central and southern Indiana. Later that year it added more than 50 additional branches through the acquisition of the failed Integra Bank in an FDIC-assisted transaction. The company had previously acquired Integra Wealth Management and Trust from the bank adding clients in Indiana Kentucky and Illinois.

Old National continues to seek out additional mergers and acquisitions including branch purchases whole bank acquisitions and FDIC-assisted deals in midsized markets within or contiguous to its existing footprint. The company is pursuing internal growth by increasing its focus on commercial banking and cross-selling its insurance and wealth management offerings.

Meanwhile Old National is also reigning in expenses. It cut more than 10% of its workforce in 2010. The company also eliminated free checking and is concentrating on lower-cost deposits. In 2012 Old National announced it would sell or consolidate nearly 30 branches but no job eliminations were included in the plan.

The company's strategies paid off in 2011 as revenues increased nearly 10% to more than $500 million and net income almost doubled to some $72.4 million. Its results were boosted by the Monroe and Integra acquisitions as well as a decrease in its provisions for credit losses and a reduction in long-term debt.

HISTORY

Old National bought 65 Charter One bank branches in Indiana from Citizens Financial Group for nearly $16 million in 2009. The acquisition strengthened its presence in Indianapolis and Lafayette as well as in the Indiana cities of Anderson Bloomington and Fort Wayne.

EXECUTIVES

President CEO and Director, Robert G. (Bob) Jones, age 55, $650,000 total compensation
EVP and Chief Legal Counsel, Jeffrey L. (Jeff) Knight, age 52, $236,023 total compensation
EVP and Chief Credit Officer, Daryl D. Moore, age 54, $299,059 total compensation
Chairman, Larry E. Dunigan, age 69
EVP and Chief Client Services Officer, Annette W. Hudgions, age 54, $250,016 total compensation
EVP; CEO Old National Trust and President Old National Wealth Management, Caroline J. Ellspermann, age 44
Eastern Regional CEO, Dennis P. Heishman
SEVP and CFO, Christopher A. (Chris) Wolking, age 52, $309,016 total compensation
VP Investor Relations, Lynell J. Walton
Central Regional CEO, Donald A. Schroeder
President and CEO ONB Insurance Group, Tom Flynn
Director Public Relations Old National Bank, Kathy Schoettlin
SEVP and Chief Banking Officer, Barbara A. Murphy, age 61, $342,000 total compensation
EVP and Chief Risk Officer, Candice J. Rickard, age 48
Regional CEO Southern, James Sandgren
Northern Regional CEO, Dan L. Doan
EVP and Director Corporate Strategy, James C. Ryan III, age 40
Public Relations Contact, Kate Miller
EVP and CIO, John R. Kamin
President CEO and Director, Robert G. (Bob) Jones, age 55
Director, Niel C. Ellerbrook, age 63
Director, Andrew E. Goebel, age 64
Director, James T. Morris, age 68
Director, Alan W. Braun, age 67
Director, Phelps L. Lambert, age 64
Director, Marjorie Z. Soyugenc, age 71
Director, Kelly N. Stanley, age 68
Director, Linda E. White, age 62
Director, Arthur H. McElwee Jr., age 69
Director, Joseph D. Barnette Jr., age 72
Auditors: CroweHorwathLLP

LOCATIONS

HQ: Old National Bancorp
One Main Street, Evansville IN 47708
Phone: 812-464-1294 **Fax:** 812-464-1567
Web: www.oldnational.com

PRODUCTS/OPERATIONS

2011 Sales

	$ mil.	% of total
Interest		
Loans including fees	237	47
Investment securities	88	18
Other	0	-
Noninterest		
Service charges on deposit accounts	51	10
Insurance premiums & commissions	37	7
ATM fees	25	5
Wealth management fees	20	4
Investment product fees	11	2
Other	37	7
Total	**509**	**100**

COMPETITORS

Fifth Third
First Financial (IN)
German American Bancorp
Huntington Bancshares
JPMorgan Chase
MainSource Financial
Peoples Bancorp (IN)
PNC Financial
U.S. Bancorp

HISTORICAL FINANCIALS

Company Type: Public

Income Statement

FYE: December 31

	ASSETS ($ mil.)	NET INCOME ($ mil.)	INCOME AS % OF ASSETS	EMPLOYEES
12/11	8,609	72	0.8%	2,551
12/10	7,263	38	0.5%	2,491
12/09	8,005	13	0.2%	2,812
12/08	7,873	62	0.8%	2,507
12/07	7,846	74	1.0%	2,494
Annual Growth	2.3%	(0.8%)	—	0.6%

2011 Year-End Financials

Debt ratio: 3.38%
Return on equity: 7.01%
Cash ($ mil.): 222
Current ratio: —
Long-term debt ($ mil.): 290
No. of shares (mil.): 94
Dividends
Yield: —
Payout: 36.84%
Market value ($ mil.): 1,103

	STOCK PRICE ($) FY Close	P/E High/Low		PER SHARE ($) Earnings	Dividends	Book Value
12/11	11.65	16	11	0.76	0.00	10.92
12/10	11.89	32	21	0.44	0.28	10.08
12/09	12.43	130	64	0.14	0.44	9.68
12/08	18.16	26	13	0.95	0.92	11.02
12/07	14.96	17	12	1.14	0.88	9.86
Annual Growth	(6.1%)	—	—	(9.6%)	—	2.6%

Old Republic International Corp.

Old Republic International keeps pace with changing financial times. With more than 100 subsidiaries across North America Old Republic International's primary operations are conducted through the Old Republic General Insurance division which offers commercial liability and property/casualty insurance (mostly commercial trucking workers' compensation and general liability policies). In addition the company's Title Insurance group specializes in naturally issuing title insurance to property owners and lenders. Its Old Republic National Title subsidiary is one of the US's oldest and largest title insurance companies with offices throughout the US.

While Old Republic does sell some of its property/casualty and specialty products directly it relies on independent agencies brokers and financial institutions to distribute the majority. Commercial property/casualty policies account for more than half of the company's sales. Title insurance accounts for some 30% of revenues while the smaller mortgage guaranty business (currently in runoff) brings in about 10% of sales. The company also maintains a small life and health insurance business.

The mortgage guaranty division stopped actively writing and selling new policies in 2011 when a waiver allowing it to operate with reduced capital requirements expired. The division which failed to recover from the collapse of the residential real estate market in 2008 is operating under the supervision of the North Carolina Department of Insurance. It is servicing its existing mortgage guaranty policies on a "runoff" basis. In 2012 Old Republic made a strategic decision to recapitalize its business by combining its mortgage guaranty and consumer credit indemnity lines as a first step in preparing its Republic Financial Indemnity Group (RFIG) for a partial leveraged buyout to be followed by its spin-off to its shareholders. Certain shareholders objected to the plan however and the company quickly withdrew its registration statement for the spin-off.

In response to the souring real estate market Old Republic has been increasing its focus on its commercial liability and property/casualty operations. In 2010 the company strengthened the general insurance division by acquiring commercial insurance provider PMA Capital through a stock-and-debt merger transaction worth some $365 million. The acquisition expanded and diversified Old Republic's general insurance business and allows for greater future growth opportunities and operational synergies.

Increased sales in the general insurance segment and the title insurance segment (which actually benefitted from the real estate crisis due to a decrease in competition in the title insurance sector) have allowed Old Republic's annual revenues to climb in recent years including a 13% increase in 2011 to some $4.6 billion.

The company's net income dropped that year when it posted a loss of some $140 million (largely tied to the troubled mortgage guaranty division); however the company's public filings clearly state that it looks at its business in five-to-10-year intervals and therefore isn't bothered by the ups and downs in shorter cycles. The health of its general insurance business and the fact that it carries very little debt make it easier to take that view.

EXECUTIVES

Director; Chairman Republic Mortgage Insurance, William A. (Bill) Simpson, age 70, $310,858 total compensation
SVP Secretary and General Counsel, Spencer LeRoy III, age 65, $408,496 total compensation
Chairman and CEO, Aldo C. (Al) Zucaro, age 73, $776,146 total compensation
SVP Investments and Treasurer, Charles S. Boone, age 58, $163,333 total compensation
Vice Chairman, James A. (Jim) Kellogg, age 60, $476,034 total compensation
President and CEO Bituminous Insurance, R. Gregory Ator, age 59
President and COO; President Old Republic General Insurance and Old Republic Life Insurance, R. Scott Rager, age 63, $433,667 total compensation
President and CEO Republic Financial Indemnity Group Inc., Christopher S. Nard, age 48, $395,000 total compensation
SVP Title Insurance; Chairman and CEO Old Republic National Title Insurance, Rande K. Yeager, age 63, $357,167 total compensation
SVP and CFO, Karl W. Mueller, age 52, $385,000 total compensation
Regional VP Old Republic Home Protection, Terry Toole
Director; Chairman Republic Mortgage Insurance, William A. (Bill) Simpson, age 70
Director, Harrington Bischof, age 77
Director, Arnold L. Steiner, age 74
Director, Jimmy A. Dew, age 71
Director, John M. Dixon, age 72
Vice Chairman, James A. (Jim) Kellogg, age 60
Director, Leo E. Knight Jr., age 66
Director, Fredricka Taubitz, age 68
Director, Charles F. Titterton, age 70
Director, Dennis P. Van Mieghem, age 71
Director, Steven R. Walker, age 66
Auditors: KPMGLLP

LOCATIONS

HQ: Old Republic International Corporation
307 N. Michigan Ave., Chicago IL 60601
Phone: 312-346-8100 **Fax:** 312-726-0309
Web: www.oldrepublic.com

PRODUCTS/OPERATIONS

2011 Sales

	$ mil.	% of total
General insurance	2,547	54
Title insurance	1,391	30
Mortgage guaranty	506	11
Corporate & Other	143	3
Consolidated realized investment gains	115	2
Adjustments	(58.7)	-
Total	**4,645**	**100**

Selected Subsidiaries

Old Republic General Insurance Group Inc.
- Bitco Corporation
- Chicago Underwriting Group Inc.
- Employers General Insurance Group Inc.
- International Business & Mercantile Insurance Holdings Ltd.
- Old Republic Home Protection Company Inc.
- Old Republic Insurance Company
- Old Republic Insured Credit Services Inc.
- Old Republic Lloyds of Texas
- Old Republic Risk Management Inc.
- Old Republic Security Holdings Inc.
- Old Republic Surety Group Inc.
- Old Republic Union Insurance Company
- Phoenix Aviation Managers Inc.
- PMA Companies Inc.
- Reliable Canadian Holdings Inc. (Canada)

Old Republic Mortgage Guaranty Group Inc.
- Republic Mortgage Insurance Company
- Republic Mortgage Insurance Company of Florida
- Republic Mortgage Insurance Company of North Carolina
- RMIC Corporation

Old Republic Title Insurance Group Inc.
- Old Republic National Title Holding Company
- Asset Discovery Inc.
- Kasparnet Inc.
- L.T. Service Corporation
- Lex Terrae Ltd.
- Lex Terrae National Title Services Inc.
- Old Republic Exchange Facilitator Company
- Old Republic National Title Insurance Company
- Old Republic Title Holding Company Inc.

COMPETITORS

ACE Limited
AEGON
AIG
Allianz
AXA
Berkshire Hathaway
Chubb Corp
CNA Financial
Farmers Group
Fidelity National Financial
First American
ING
Investors Title
Kingsway
PMI Group
Progressive Corporation
Radian Group
Stewart Information Services
The Hartford
Travelers Companies
Unum Group
W. R. Berkley

HISTORICAL FINANCIALS

Company Type: Public

Income Statement FYE: December 31

	ASSETS ($ mil.)	NET INCOME ($ mil.)	INCOME AS % OF ASSETS	EMPLOYEES
12/11	16,050	(140)	—	7,900
12/10	15,882	30	0.2%	8,000
12/09	14,190	(99)	—	5,900
12/08	13,266	(558)	—	5,600
12/07	13,290	272	2.0%	5,700
Annual Growth	4.8%	—	—	8.5%

2011 Year-End Financials

Debt ratio: 5.69%
Return on equity: (-3.72)%
Cash ($ mil.): 93
Current ratio: —
Long-term debt ($ mil.): 912
No. of shares (mil.): 259
Dividends
Yield: —
Payout: —
Market value ($ mil.): 2,404

	STOCK PRICE ($) FY Close	P/E High/Low		PER SHARE ($) Earnings	Dividends	Book Value
12/11	9.27	—	—	(0.55)	0.00	14.55
12/10	13.63	118	77	0.13	0.69	15.90
12/09	10.04	—	—	(0.42)	0.68	16.17
12/08	11.92	—	—	(2.41)	0.67	15.55
12/07	15.41	20	12	1.17	0.63	19.71
Annual Growth	(11.9%)	—	—	—	—	(7.3%)

Omnicare Inc.

Omnicare strives to be omnipresent in US nursing homes. The firm is the country's largest institutional pharmacy services provider dispensing drugs to nursing homes assisted-living centers and other long-term care (LTC) facilities in the US and parts of Canada. In addition it provides clinical and financial software consulting and billing services to LTC facilities as well as infusion respiratory and chronic disease therapy products and services for nursing home residents and hospice patients. It also provides some services to drugmakers. The company has pharmacy and distribution locations across the US and it serves LTC facility customers with a combined capacity of more than 1 million patient beds.

Operations

The company's operations are organized into a "hub-and-spoke" model. Its pharmacy service administrative activities as well as some routine prescription refilling operations are located at some 30 regional hubs where scale centralization and automation can produce greater efficiency. More than 100 smaller local pharmacies (the "spokes") in turn focus on activities requiring direct customer interaction.

Omnicare divides its operations into two business categories. The long-term care (LTC) group handles the company's primary institutional pharmacy service operations for nursing retirement and other care facilities. This segment which accounts for more than 80% of annual revenues also provides compliance and efficiency consulting services and technology programs such as the Omniview online prescription management platform.

The company's other division the specialty care group is a growing supplier of specialty pharmaceuticals (medications for chronic conditions that require special handling) and chronic disease management services to long-term care facilities hospice organizations and other health care centers. It also provides branding commercialization and logistics support services to drugmakers.

Financials

Omnicare returned its operations to profitability in fiscal 2011 reporting some $87 million in net income. Omnicare's net income loss in 2010 was primarily attributed to the devaluation of its former CRO business which was suffering from adverse market conditions. Omnicare also reported a 1% increase in revenues to some $6.2 billion in 2011.

Over the years Omnicare has struggled to keep its earnings and revenue levels climbing due to lower reimbursements on drugs from health insurers including Medicare and Medicaid policies which together account for about two-thirds of sales. Economic and competitive factors have also impeded the company's growth progress. Though it hopes to overcome these elements with its new strategic priorities changes in federal health legislation could lead to further challenges in the future.

Strategy

The highly acquisitive Omnicare has expanded its long-term care operations over the years by purchasing small independent institutional pharmacies and integrating them into its organization. However in mid-2010 the company announced plans to pull in and focus on organic growth measures within its existing operations with a focus on increasing the number of beds (facilities) its LTC segment serves through customer satisfaction and retention efforts; promoting the specialty care unit's services to drugmakers; and streamlining its organization through technology enhancements in areas such as billing and dispensing automation. The change in strategic priorities led to a number of operational restructuring programs including some layoffs and noncore asset sales.

In addition to divesting its noncore home infusion operations through an asset-swap arrangement with Walgreen in 2010 the company's restructuring efforts included the sale of its remaining durable goods operations and its Tidewater group purchasing operation in 2011. Omnicare also sold its former CRO Services division Omnicare Clinical Research (now known as Theorem Clinical Research) to private equity firm Nautic Partners for an undisclosed sum in 2011. Following the asset sale Omnicare divided its remaining operations (previously lumped into the pharmacy services segment) into two business divisions: long-term care and specialty care.

Mergers and Acquisitions

Regardless of its shift in strategies Omnicare still completed about a half dozen small pharmacy acquisitions in 2010 and 2011. The company also completed a larger-than-usual deal with Walgreen in late 2010; the asset swap transaction allowed Omnicare to take over Walgreen's long-term care pharmacy operations in five states while Walgreen took control of Omnicare's home infusion service operations. The swap fit in with Omnicare's strategy of focusing on and growing its LTC business. And in 2012 the firm reached a $40 million deal to purchase the institutional pharmacy business of Five Star Quality Care. The acquisition will add eight pharmacies serving LTC facilities in 13 states.

The company attempted to complete a large-scale acquisition in 2011 by making an offer to acquire rival institutional pharmacy operator PharMerica in a $716 million cash-and-debt deal in 2011. However after PharMerica rejected the bid as undervalued and the FTC frowned upon Omnicare's hostile tender offer attempt Omnicare dropped the acquisition efforts in early 2011.

HISTORY

cIn 1981 W. R. Grace subsidiaries Daylin and Chemed merged some health care units to form Omnicare which was then spun off. Omnicare began a restructuring process in 1985 that reshaped the firm around pharmacy services for long-term care facilities. It acquired 17 long-term care pharmacies in 1993 alone.

As the baby boomers age the company will continue to have a growing market for the long run. Using economies of scale to keep costs down Omnicare began pursuing an aggressive acquisition strategy.

In 1994 the company teamed with Health Care and Retirement Corp. one of the US's largest nursing home operators. It acquired 17 pharmacy units in 1996 including those of Revco and several other retailers. In 1997 Omnicare expanded its operations by targeting assisted living providers and small rural hospitals. It continued acquiring pharmacy service providers (20 in 1997 –including its largest deal up to that time American Medserve – and CompScript in 1998) and it leveraged its treatment outcomes database with the addition of contract research organizations (Coromed 1997; IBAH 1998).

Also in 1998 Omnicare settled a lawsuit that alleged a company pharmacy had repackaged and resold unused medications originally sold to nursing homes (and paid for by Medicaid). That year the company acquired Extendicare's pharmacy operations. In 1999 Omnicare expanded its services for the drug development industry with the purchase of a German clinical research organization; the company also acquired the pharmaceutical division of nursing home operator Life Care Services of America.

Omnicare consolidated its three clinical research organizations into Omnicare Clinical Research in 2000 and it acquired NCS HealthCare and Sun Healthcare's SunScript Pharmacy business in 2003; the move was designed to strengthen its position as the largest supplier of pharmacy services to long-term care facilities in the US.

After a year-long pursuit the company acquired NeighborCare in a hostile takeover in 2005. The deal valued at nearly $2 billion brought with it 300000 patient beds and took Omnicare's annual revenue to more than $6 billion. Following the acquisition Omnicare consolidated about 30 pharmacy locations. It also lost some nursing home customers who complained about bad service.

The same it year it won NeighborCare Omnicare also bought RxCrossroads a mail-order specialty pharmaceutical company that specializes in providing pricey drugs used to treat chronic conditions and excelleRx a distributor of pharmaceuticals and related products to hospice agencies in 47 states.

To keep its operations nimble after its many acquisitions the company launched a reorganization program in 2006 that included restructuring its pharmacy service business into the hub-and-spoke model to centralize some administration and technology functions. The program which was completed in 2010 also included some workforce reductions. As part its restructuring initiatives Omnicare integrated its Clinimetrics unit a CRO focused on biotechnology clients into the broader CRO division Omnicare Clinical Research.

In late 2009 the company agreed to pay $98 million to settle allegations from the US Department of Justice that it had accepted kickback payments from drug manufacturers and nursing homes. Omnicare settled the charges without admitting any wrongdoing.

EXECUTIVES

SVP Professional Services; Long Term Care Operations, W. Gary Erwin, age 59

President and CFO, John L. Workman, age 60, $79,615 total compensation

SVP Operations Finance, Robert E. Dries

SVP Finance, Robert (Rocky) Kraft

Chairman, James D. (Denny) Shelton, age 58

EVP; President Long-Term Care Operations, Jeffrey M. Stamps, age 52, $395,211 total compensation

President Central Division Long Term Care Operations, Michael J. (Mike) Arnold

President West Division Long Term Care Operations, Thomas A. (Tom) Schleigh Jr.

President Southeast Division Long Term Care Operations, David H. (Dave) West

CEO and Director, John G. Figueroa, age 49

SVP Sales and Customer Development Long Term Care Operations, Beth A. Kinerk, age 43, $350,292 total compensation

VP Investor Relations, Patrick Lee

President Northeast Division Long Term Care Operations, Patrick F. Downing

SVP and CIO, Randy Carpenter

SVP Operations Long Term Care Operations, Melinda J. (Mindy) Ferris

President Mideast Division Long Term Care Operations, Mark J. Schroder

SVP and Chief Marketing Officer, Tim Canning

SVP Trade Relations, Timothy J. (Tim) Hopkins

VP Specialty Care Group Operations, Amit Jain

SVP General Counsel and Secretary, Alexander M. (Aly) Kayne
EVP; President Specialty Care Group, Nitin Sahney, age 49
EVP Human Resources, Priscilla Stewart-Jones
SVP and Chief Compliance Officer, Kathleen McGuan
Chief Audit Officer, Tim Downard
SVP Purchasing, Dan Maloney
CFO Long Term Care Operations, John Gould
VP Operations Specialty Care Group Operations, John Doster
SVP Specialty Care Group Operations, David Hileman
SVP and General Manager excelleRx, Tom Stieritz
SVP and General Manager RxCrossroads, Dan Thomas
VP Access Solutions Specialty Care Group Operations, Denise Von Dohren
General Manager ACS, Dennis Wilson
Director, Steven J. (Steve) Heyer, age 60
Director, Andrea R. Lindell, age 68
Director, Barry P. Schochet, age 60
Director, Mark A. Emmert, age 59
Director, Amy Wallman, age 62
CEO and Director, John G. Figueroa, age 49
Auditors: PricewaterhouseCoopersLLP

LOCATIONS

HQ: Omnicare Inc.
1600 RiverCenter II 100 E. RiverCenter Blvd., Covington KY 41011
Phone: 859-392-3300 **Fax:** 859-392-3333
Web: www.omnicare.com

PRODUCTS/OPERATIONS

2012 Sales

Long-term care	4,848	83
Specialty care	1,301	17
Total	**6,160**	**100**

2012 Sales by Payer Source

Federal Medicare programs (Part B & Part D)		50
Private pay third-party & facilities (includes Medicare Part A)		39
Total	**0**	**100**

COMPETITORS

Accredo Health	Maxor
AmerisourceBergen	McKesson
Cardinal Health	NHC
Catamaran	Novation
Covenant Care	PharMerica
Diamond Drugs Inc.	Standard Management
Express Scripts	The Harvard Drug Group
Five Star Quality Care	Walgreen
Kinney Drugs Inc.	

HISTORICAL FINANCIALS

Company Type: Public

Income Statement FYE: December 31

	REVENUE ($ mil.)	NET INCOME ($ mil.)	NET PROFIT MARGIN	EMPLOYEES
12/11	6,182	86	1.4%	14,600
12/10	6,146	(106)	—	15,200
12/09	6,166	211	3.4%	15,200
12/08	6,310	156	2.5%	17,200
12/07	6,220	114	1.8%	17,800
Annual Growth	(0.1%)	(6.6%)	—	(4.8%)

2011 Year-End Financials

Debt ratio: 27.73%
Return on equity: 2.29%
Cash ($ mil.): 580
Current ratio: 425.39
Long-term debt ($ mil.): 1,968
No. of shares (mil.): 113
Dividends
Yield: —
Payout: 20.07%
Market value ($ mil.): 3,914

	STOCK PRICE ($) FY Close	P/E High/Low		PER SHARE ($) Earnings	Dividends	Book Value
12/11	34.45	46	28	0.76	0.00	33.40
12/10	25.39	—	—	(0.91)	0.11	32.72
12/09	24.18	16	12	1.80	0.09	32.22
12/08	27.76	25	12	1.32	0.09	28.89
12/07	22.81	46	23	0.94	0.09	27.03
Annual Growth	10.9%	—	—	(5.2%)	—	5.4%

Omnicom Group, Inc.

While it might not be omnipotent Omnicom Group can create advertising that is omnipresent. The company ranks as the world's #1 corporate media services conglomerate with advertising marketing and public relations operations serving some 5000 clients in more than 100 countries. It serves global advertising clients through its agency networks BBDO Worldwide DDB Worldwide and TBWA Worldwide while such firms as GSD&M's Idea City Merkley + Partners and Zimmerman Advertising provide services for regional and national clients. More than 190 other firms in its Diversified Agency Services division including Fleishman-Hillard Integer and Rapp provide public relations and other marketing services.

Financials

Omnicom Group saw its revenues increase by more than 10% and net income increase by 15% in 2011 thanks to a recovering market that saw companies boost their advertising budgets. Acquisitions also contributed to a growth in earnings.

Mergers & Acquisitions

Throughout the year the firm bought 12 companies including Nancy Bailey & Associates a corporate licensing and consulting firm. Nancy Bailey is working closely with Beanstalk another licensing specialist owned by Omnicom. Also in 2011 Omnicom bought Marina Maher Communications (MMC) for an undisclosed amount. MMC adds expertise in consumer products food and beverage and prescription and OTC drugs marketing from a female customer perspective.

In addition to adding subsidiaries that expand its advertising and marketing service offerings the company also makes acquisitions to grow its geographic presence. In 2012 its Diversified Agency Services bought a majority stake in Medical Collective Intelligence a Japanese online medical communications agency based in Tokyo.

Geographic Reach

Omnicom has US offices in New York Connecticut and Florida while it has international offices in London Shanghai and Singapore.

Strategy

Omnicom's fortunes have been buoyed in part by its agency networks and their consistently strong creative work (traditional media advertising accounts for more than 45% of revenue) but the bulk of its growth has traditionally come from such areas as customer relationship management (CRM) and specialty communications. Omnicom sees continued growth being tied to its ability to provide an ever-expanding menu of services to its largest clients especially in the digital and social media arenas.

The company has also been focused on expanding its media planning and buying operations. OMD Worldwide is a leading media specialist firm (behind Publicis' Starcom MediaVest) but Omnicom still trails WPP Group Publicis and Interpublic in total media services billings. To help close the gap OMD launched Full Circle Entertainment a branded entertainment production unit that works with clients like DIRECTV and Pier 1. In addition Omnicom's Prometheus Media Services unit is its third media specialist alongside OMD Worldwide and PHD Media Limited.

HISTORY

Omnicom Group was created in 1986 to combine three leading ad agencies into a single group capable of competing in the worldwide market. BBDO Worldwide founded in New York in 1928 as Batten Barton Durstine & Osborn had a huge PepsiCo account and developed the Pepsi Generation campaign. Doyle Dane Bernbach Group (DDB) which had created the "fahrvergnugen" ads for Volkswagen had strong ties in Europe. And Needham Harper Worldwide which had served up the "You Deserve a Break Today" commercials for McDonald's had connections in Asia. BBDO remained separate but DDB and Needham Harper were merged to form DDB Needham Worldwide. The business services units (public relations firms and direct marketers) of each of these companies were tucked under the Diversified Agency Services (DAS) umbrella.

Bruce Crawford a previous chairman of BBDO who had just finished a stint running New York's Metropolitan Opera became chairman and CEO in 1989. He transformed DAS from a chaotic group of shops into an integrated marketing giant and ran Omnicom as a holding company of independent operating units working together through cross-referrals. By keeping costs low especially interest expenses Omnicom survived the 1990-91 recession with little pain. The company acquired Goodby Berlin & Silverstein (now Goodby Silverstein & Partners) in 1992. The next year TBWA Advertising (founded in Paris in 1970 by American Bill Tragos) was added to Omnicom's roster.

The merger spree continued in 1994 when Omnicom purchased WWAV Group the largest direct-marketing agency in the UK. In 1995 Omnicom fused TBWA with Chiat/Day (founded in 1968 by Jay Chiat and Guy Day) to form TBWA International Network. Omnicom also acquired Michigan-based Ross Roy Communications (later Interone Marketing Group). In 1997 DDB Needham won back its McDonald's account after a 15-year hiatus. That year Crawford stepped down as CEO (though he remained chairman) and John Wren took control of Omnicom.

In 1998 the company acquired PR firm Fleishman-Hillard adding to the PR clout it established with the acquisition of Ketchum Communications (now Ketchum) in 1996. Omnicom also acquired GGT Group of London for $235 million. (GGT's New York office Wells BDDP had lost a large Procter & Gamble account that year.) It merged GGT's BDDP Worldwide with TBWA to form TBWA Worldwide. BBDO landed a $200 million account with PepsiCo's Frito-Lay that year.

Omnicom's position in Europe was boosted in 1999 when it bought the Abbot Mead Vickers (now Abbot Mead Vickers BBDO) shares it didn't already own. That year TBWA founder William

Tragos retired from the company (replaced by Lee Clow) and DDB Needham changed its moniker to DDB Worldwide Communications Group. Omnicom also bought market research firm M/A/R/C for about $95 million and invested $20 million in pharmaceutical clinical trials company SCIREX. In 2000 BBDO scored a major coup over rival FCB Worldwide (now part of Interpublic) by landing the $1.8 billion DaimlerChrysler account. The next year it formed Seneca Investments to hold its stakes in several i-services shops including Agency.com and Organic. (Omnicom acquired the interactive agencies outright in 2003.)

After years of acquisitions and fine-tuning its operating structure Omnicom encountered the effects of the global recession in late 2008. Like most players in the media communications and advertising industries Omnicom experienced declines in revenue and net income at the end of 2009. It attributed the crisis within the automotive industry and declines in the demand for its sports and event marketing services as major reasons for the drops.

In 2010 the company acquired seven companies including Sales Power an in-store promotion company catering to South China and Maslov PR a public relations firm based in Moscow. Among the twelve companies it acquired in 2011 was Nancy Bailey & Associates a corporate licensing and consulting firm.

EXECUTIVES

EVP, Bruce Redditt
EVP and CFO, Randall J. Weisenburger, age 53, $975,000 total compensation
CEO Organic, Marita C. Scarfi
Vice Chairman and CFO BBDO Worldwide, James A. (Jim) Cannon, age 73
SVP Finance and Controller, Philip J. Angelastro, age 47
Treasurer, Dennis E. Hewitt
President CEO and Director, John D. Wren, age 59, $1,000,000 total compensation
Chairman, Bruce Crawford, age 83
President and CEO TBWA Worldwide, Thomas (Tom) Carroll, age 56
Chairman TBWA Worldwide, Jean-Marie Dru, $1,007,560 total compensation
CEO Omnicom Digital, Jonathan Nelson
Chairman GSD&M's Idea City, Roy M. Spence Jr., age 63
President and CEO BBDO Worldwide, Andrew Robertson, age 51, $900,000 total compensation
Vice Chairman, Peter W. Mead, age 72, $815,000 total compensation
Chairman and CEO Diversified Agency Services, Thomas L. Harrison, age 64, $900,000 total compensation
President and CEO Singer Direct, Thomas (Tom) Rocco
Chairman India, Keki B. Dadiseth, age 66
CIO Omincom Media Group, Kenneth Corriveau
SVP and Corporate Director of Public Affairs, Pat Sloan
Tax Counsel, Philip J. George
CEO Doremus, Carl Anderson
CEO Porter Novelli, Gary Stockman
President Sales Novus Print Media Network Media Group, David P. (Dave) Murphy, age 58
CEO Omnicom Media Group UK and PHD Media, Philippa Brown
VP Omnicom Digital Asia Pacific India Middle East & Africa (APIMA), Jason Kuperman
CFO Omnicom Media Group, Mark Amabile
President and CEO DDB Worldwide, Chuck E. Brymer, age 52, $850,000 total compensation
SVP General Counsel and Secretary, Michael J. O'Brien, age 50
Chairman and Chief Creative Officer DDB Worldwide, Bob Scarpelli
Vice Chairman; CEO Omnicom Asia-Pacific India Middle East and Africa, William T. (Tim) Love, age 62
Chairman and CEO Omnicom Media Group, Daryl D. Simm, age 51
CEO PHD Worldwide, Mike Cooper
CEO Omnicom Media Group Europe Middle East and Africa, Colin Gottlieb
Vice Chairman; Chairman Asia Pacific, Serge Dumont
President DAS Healthcare, Rabin K. (Rob) Dhoble, age 50
VP Sales National In-Store, Pat Lockridge
CFO Omnicom Media Group UK, Martin Telling
Director New Business and Marketing Omnicom Media Group UK, Sam Phillips
Chief Executive Central and Eastern Europe Omnicom Media Group, Ian Clarke
EVP, Asit Mehra
EVP, Janet Riccio
CEO OMG Digital, Matt Spiegel
SVP and Chief Diversity Officer, Tiffany R. Warren
Chief Creative Officer TPN, Sharon Love
CEO Novus Print Media Network Media Group, Brian Burke
Director Business Development US DDB Worldwide, Brandon Snow
CEO EVB, Daniel Stein
Director Corporate Communications Asia Pacific India Middle East and Africa (APIMA), Clara So
SVP; CFO Asia Pacific India Middle East and Africa (APIMA), Dara Akbarian
EVP, Rita E. Rodriguez
CEO Omnicom Media Group Latin America, Julian Porras
President CEO and Director, John D. Wren, age 59
Director, Linda Johnson Rice, age 54
Director, John R. (Reg) Murphy, age 78
Director, Gary L. Roubos, age 75
Director, Alan R. Batkin, age 67
Director, Leonard S. Coleman Jr., age 63
Director, Susan S. Denison, age 66
Director, John R. (Jack) Purcell, age 80
Director, Errol M. Cook, age 72
Director, Mary C. Choksi, age 61
Director, Michael A. Henning, age 71
Director, Robert C. Clark, age 68
Auditors: KPMGLLP

LOCATIONS

HQ: Omnicom Group, Inc.
437 Madison Avenue, New York, NY 10022
Phone: 212 415-3600 **Fax:** 212 415-3393
Web: www.omnicomgroup.com

2011 Sales

	$ mil.	% of total
US	7,048	51
UK	1,227	9
Other regions	3,017	22

PRODUCTS/OPERATIONS

2011 Sales

	$ mil.	% of total
Advertising	6,401	46
Public relations	1,215	9
Specialty communications	1,189	8
Total	13,872	100

Selected Operations

Global advertising networks
- BBDO Worldwide
- DDB Worldwide
- TBWA Worldwide

National advertising agencies
- Goodby Silverstein & Partners (San Francisco)
- GSD&M' s Idea City (Austin TX)
- MartinWilliams (Minneapolis)
- Merkley + Partners (New York City)
- Zimmerman Partners Advertising (Fort Lauderdale FL)

Marketing and consulting agencies

Direct response
- Interbrand (brand identity)
- M/A/R/C Research (market research)
- Rapp (direct marketing)
- Targetbase (direct marketing)

Promotional marketing
- The Beanstalk Group (brand licensing and consulting)
- CPM (field marketing)
- The Integer Group (retail marketing)
- Kaleidoscope (sports and event marketing)
- Millsport (sports and event marketing)

Public relations
- Clark & Weinstock
- Cone
- Fleishman-Hillard
- Gavin Anderson & Company
- GPC International
- Ketchum
- Porter Novelli International
- Smythe Dorward Lambert

Specialty communications
- Adelphi Group (health care)
- Corbett Accel Healthcare (health care)
- Dieste (multicultural marketing)
- Doremus (business-to-business advertising)
- SafirRosetti (security and intelligence)

Media services
- Icon International
- Novus Print Media
- OMD Worldwide
- PHD Network

COMPETITORS

Aegis Group
Dentsu
Hakuhodo
Havas
Interpublic Group
Publicis Groupe
WPP

HISTORICAL FINANCIALS

Company Type: Public

Income Statement

FYE: December 31

	REVENUE ($ mil.)	NET INCOME ($ mil.)	NET PROFIT MARGIN	EMPLOYEES
12/11	13,872	952	6.9%	70,600
12/10	12,542	827	6.6%	65,500
12/09	11,720	793	6.8%	63,000
12/08	13,359	1,000	7.5%	68,000
12/07	12,694	975	7.7%	70,000
Annual Growth	2.2%	(0.6%)	—	0.2%

2011 Year-End Financials

Debt ratio: 15.57%
Return on equity: 27.18%
Cash ($ mil.): 1,781
Current ratio: 89.29
Long-term debt ($ mil.): 3,182
No. of shares (mil.): 273
Dividends
Yield: —
Payout: 30.03%
Market value ($ mil.): 12,188

	STOCK PRICE ($) FY Close	P/E High	P/E Low	PER SHARE ($) Earnings	Dividends	Book Value
12/11	44.58	15	11	3.33	0.00	12.82
12/10	45.80	17	12	2.70	0.80	12.54
12/09	39.15	16	9	2.53	0.60	13.60
12/08	26.92	16	7	3.17	0.60	11.46
12/07	47.53	36	15	2.95	0.58	12.67
Annual Growth	(1.6%)	—	—	3.1%	—	0.3%

Oneok Inc.

ONEOK ("one oak") is OK with its singled-minded pursuit of profits from natural gas activities. Through its 43%-owned ONEOK Partners (of which it is the general partner) it operates more than 15900 miles of gas-gathering pipeline and 7100 miles of transportation pipeline as well as gas processing plants and storage facilities. The unit also owns one of the US's top natural gas liquids (NGL) systems. ONEOK's energy services unit focuses on marketing natural gas across the US. The company's regulated utilities –Oklahoma Natural Gas Kansas Gas Service and Texas Gas Service – distribute natural gas to more than 2 million customers. ONEOK also has a parking garage and leases office space in Tulsa.

HISTORY

In 1906 Oklahoma Natural Gas (ONG) was founded to pipe natural gas from northeastern Oklahoma to Oklahoma City. A 100-mile pipeline was completed the next year. In 1921 ONG created two oil companies to pump out the oil it found as a result of its natural gas exploration.

ONG changed hands many times in the 1920s ending up with utility financier G. L. Ohrstrom and Company which milked it dry by brokering acquisitions (purchasing gas properties and then selling them to ONG) and collecting fees. Stock sales drove revenues inflating the stock's price and the inflated price triggered more stock sales. The bubble burst on October 29 1929. A series of leadership changes ensued and in 1932 the company was dissolved and reincorporated. Under president Joseph Bowes ONG recovered wooing back dissatisfied customers and upgrading its pipelines.

In the late 1930s the company pioneered a type of underground storage that injected gas into depleted gas reservoirs in the summer and withdrew it during winter's peak use times.

The 1950s and 1960s saw the company expand. In 1962 it created its first subsidiary Oklahoma Natural Gas Gathering Company selling gas out of state and therefore subject to federal regulation.

ONG was not affected in the lean 1970s by federal laws that kept wellhead prices low for gas transported across state lines because its main operations were confined to Oklahoma. Congress deregulated wellhead prices in 1978 spurring exploration but causing great price fluctuations in the 1980s. In 1980 ONG changed its name to ONEOK.

In the 1980s ONEOK signed take-or-pay contracts which forced it to pay for gas offered by its suppliers even if it had no customers. When recession in the 1980s caused demand to drop ONEOK had to pay for high-priced natural gas it couldn't sell. In 1988 the company was ordered to pay some $50 million to supplier Forest Oil of Denver. A year later ONEOK was sued for allegedly failing to tell stockholders about the take-or-pay agreements (settled in 1993 for $5.5 million). It later sold more than half of its oil and gas reserves to Mustang Energy for $52 million to finance the Forest Oil court award. The company was still settling lawsuits over the agreements into the 1990s; it settled the last of the claims by 1998.

ONEOK began buying gas transmission and production facilities in Oklahoma and creating drilling alliances in the 1990s. In 1997 ONEOK bought the natural gas assets of Westar Energy formerly Western Resources for $660 million and ONEOK stock worth $800 million. The acquisition doubled the number of ONEOK's customers and increased its gas marketing gathering and transmission operations.

In 1998 the company sold oil and gas reserves processing plants and gathering systems in Kansas Louisiana and Oklahoma to Duke Energy. With gas utility deregulation looming ONEOK purchased producing oil and gas properties primarily in Oklahoma and Texas.

That year it agreed to buy Southwest Gas of Las Vegas for $863.6 million. Southern Union offered $976 million for Southwest Gas in 1999 but Southwest Gas agreed instead to a $912.3 million deal with ONEOK. Southern Union sued Southwest Gas alleging that it had conspired with ONEOK to block the Southern Union bid. In 2000 the legal action made ONEOK cancel the Southwest Gas deal.

In 1999 ONEOK bought a 31% stake (later reduced) in exploration and production company Magnum Hunter Resources for $50 million. The next year the company expanded its natural gas gathering and processing operations in the US mid-continent region by buying assets from Dynegy ($308 million) and Kinder Morgan ($108 million).

President and COO David Kyle took over as chairman and CEO in 2000 after Larry Brummett died of cancer. In 2001 the company established a new unit ONEOK Power with the startup of a new power plant northwest of Oklahoma City. In 2002 ONEOK sold several processing facilities to Mustang Fuel for $93 million.

Westar Energy reduced its stake to approximately 15% by selling shares back to ONEOK and to the public in mid-2003; it sold its remaining shares to Cantor Fitzgerald later that year.

ONEOK has been juggling assets to focus on profitable businesses. The firm which gets a large slice of its revenues from its gas distribution gathering and processing operations sold about 70% of its oil and gas production assets in Kansas Oklahoma and Texas to Chesapeake Energy for $300 million in 2003. Later that year shifting its production focus to the Texas market (and focusing on development rather than exploration) it acquired oil and gas reserves and related gathering systems in East Texas from Wagner & Brown for about $240 million.

The company also acquired Southern Union's Texas natural gas distribution business (540000 customers) as well as Southern Union's stake in a Mexican gas utility and its propane distribution gas marketing and gas transmission operations in the southwestern US for $420 million.

ONEOK acquired Northern Plains Natural Gas a general partner of pipeline operator Northern Border Partners (later renamed ONEOK Partners) from CCE Holdings (a joint venture of Southern Union and GE Commercial Finance) for $175 million in 2004. The transaction followed CCE Holdings' acquisition of Enron's CrossCountry Energy unit.

Also in 2004 ONEOK changed the name of its wholesale energy unit from ONEOK Energy Marketing and Trading to ONEOK Energy Services.

The company bought Koch Industries' natural gas liquids assets in 2005 for $1.35 billion. That year ONEOK sold properties to TXOK Acquisition Inc. for $645 million and some Texas natural gas assets to Eagle Rock Energy for $528 million to help pay down debt.

To generate cash and increase shareholder return in 2006 ONEOK sold its gathering and processing natural gas liquids pipelines and storage businesses to Northern Border Partners (renamed ONEOK Partners) for $3 billion and became that company's general partner.

EXECUTIVES

SVP Administrative Services, David E. Roth, age 57
EVP CFO and Treasurer ONEOK and ONEOK Partners, Robert F. (Rob) Martinovich, age 54
Chairman and CEO; Chairman and CEO ONEOK Partners, John W. Gibson, age 59, $825,000 total compensation
VP and Controller Oklahoma Natural Gas Kansas Gas Service and Texas Gas Service, Beverly C. Monnet, age 52
VP Customer Services ONEOK Distribution Companies, David D. (Dave) Arnold, age 54
President Kansas Gas Service, Bradley O. (Brad) Dixon, age 59
VP Operations and Engineering ONEOK Distribution Companies, Daniel C. (Dan) Walker, age 59
President Oklahoma Natural Gas, Gregory A. (Greg) Phillips, age 49
VP ONEOK Energy Services, John L. Sommer, age 56
President ONEOK Energy Services, Patrick J. (Pat) McDonie, age 51
VP ONEOK Energy Services, Scott E. Gentry, age 51
VP Retail Marketing ONEOK Energy Services, Greg Ingenthron, age 51
VP Associate General Counsel and Corporate Secretary, Eric Grimshaw, age 60
Regional VP Kansas Gas Service, Teryl C. Rose, age 50
President Natural Gas ONEOK Partners, Curtis L. Dinan, age 44, $400,000 total compensation
EVP and COO, Pierce H. Norton II, age 52, $357,000 total compensation
President ONEOK Distribution Companies, Caron A. Lawhorn, age 51
COO and Director ONEOK Partners, Terry K. Spencer, age 53, $365,250 total compensation
SVP General Counsel and Assistant Secretary; SVP General Counsel and Secretary ONEOK Partners, John R. Barker, age 64, $375,000 total compensation
Regional VP Texas Gas Service, James Paul Wilson, age 49
VP Investor Relations and Public Affairs ONEOK and ONEOK Partners, Dandridge (Dan) Harrison, age 57
Media Contact, Megan Washbourne, age 36
President Natural Gas Pipelines ONEOK Partners, W. Kent Shortridge, age 45
Regional VP Operations Kansas Gas Service, Ronald D. Bridgewater, age 46
President Texas Gas Service, Kari L. French, age 54
SVP Corporate Planning and Development ONEOK and ONEOK Partners, Robert S. (Bob) Mareburger, age 50
VP ONEOK Energy Services, Mark J. Quinlan
SVP General Counsel and Assistant Secretary ONEOK and ONEOK Partners, Stephen W. (Steve) Lake, age 48
VP Administration Texas Gas Service, Eric A. Grundman, age 48
SVP ONEOK Energy Services, Charles M. (Chuck) Kelley
VP ONEOK Energy Services, John O'Dell
SVP and Chief Accounting Officer ONEOK and ONEOK Partners, Derek S. Reiners, age 41
VP Administration Oklahoma Natural Gas, Ronnie W. Brown
Regional VP Oklahoma Natural Gas, Steven P. Wood

Regional VP Eastern Region Oklahoma Natural Gas, Scott D. Shepherd
VP Compliance and Ethics, Neal F. Lehman
Director, Jim W. (Jimmy) Mogg, age 63
Director, Julie H. Edwards, age 53
Director, Pattye L. Moore, age 54
Director, James C. (Jim) Day, age 69
Director, Gerald B. Smith, age 61
Chairman and CEO; Chairman and CEO ONEOK Partners, John W. Gibson, age 59
Director, William L. Ford, age 69
Director, Gary D. Parker, age 66
Director, Eduardo A. (Eddie) Rodriguez, age 56
Director, David J. Tippeconnic, age 72
Auditors: PricewaterhouseCoopersLLP

LOCATIONS

HQ: ONEOK Inc.
100 W. 5th St., Tulsa OK 74103
Phone: 918-588-7000 **Fax:** 918-588-7960
Web: www.oneok.com

PRODUCTS/OPERATIONS

2011 Sales

	$ mil.	% of total
ONEOK Partners	10,919	74
Energy Services	2,274	15
Distribution	1,609	11
Adjustments	2	-
Total	**14,805**	**100**

COMPETITORS

Adams Resources
AEP
Atmos Energy
BP
CenterPoint Energy
CMS Energy
Duncan Energy
Dynegy
Energen
Energy Future
Enterprise Products
EQT Corporation
Exxon Mobil
FirstEnergy
Hess Corporation
National Fuel Gas
OGE Energy
Southern Union
Southwest Gas
Williams Companies

HISTORICAL FINANCIALS

Company Type: Public

Income Statement FYE: December 31

	REVENUE ($ mil.)	NET INCOME ($ mil.)	NET PROFIT MARGIN	EMPLOYEES
12/11	14,805	360	2.4%	4,795
12/10	13,030	334	2.6%	4,839
12/09	11,111	305	2.7%	4,758
12/08	16,157	311	1.9%	4,742
12/07	13,477	304	2.3%	4,555
Annual Growth	2.4%	4.3%	—	1.3%

2011 Year-End Financials

Debt ratio: 35.73%
Return on equity: 16.11%
Cash ($ mil.): 65
Current ratio: 71.43
Long-term debt ($ mil.): 4,529
No. of shares (mil.): 206
Dividends
Yield: —
Payout: 64.29%
Market value ($ mil.): 17,902

	STOCK PRICE ($) FY Close	P/E High/Low		PER SHARE ($) Earnings	Dividends	Book Value
12/11	86.69	50	32	1.68	0.00	10.84
12/10	55.47	35	26	1.55	0.91	11.46
12/09	44.57	31	13	1.44	0.82	10.42
12/08	29.12	34	16	1.48	0.78	9.96
12/07	44.77	39	28	1.40	0.70	9.47
Annual Growth	18.0%	—	—	4.7%	—	3.4%

ONEOK Partners LP

For ONEOK Partners it's OK to have three businesses: natural gas pipelines; gas gathering and processing; and natural gas liquids (NGLs). Its pipelines include Midwestern Gas Transmission Guardian Pipeline Viking Gas Transmission and OkTex Pipeline. It operates 15200 miles of gas-gathering pipeline and 7100 miles of transportation pipeline as well as gas processing plants and storage facilities (with 51.7 billion cu. ft. of capacity). It also owns one of the US's top natural NGL systems (more than 6900 miles of pipeline). Energy services company ONEOK holds a 42% stake in ONEOK Partners and 100% of its general partner.

The company pursues a strategy of building up its fee-based earnings coupled with organic growth and complementary acquisitions in both conventional oil and gas and unconventional (shale plays).

Expanding its NGL capacity by 25000 barrels per day in 2009 ONEOK Partners completed a NGL gathering pipeline connecting two natural gas processing plants in the Woodford Shale play (Oklahoma) to its natural gas liquids gathering system in the Mid-Continent. In 2010 the company also invested heavily in another growth area the Williston Basin in North Dakota where it is the largest independent gatherer and processor of natural gas. That year it announced plans to build three new Williston Basin natural gas processing plants to meet the growing demand of exploration and prodcution companies.

To pay down debt in 2010 the company sold a 49% stake in its Kansas-based natural gas liquids pipeline (Overland Pass Pipeline Company) to Williams Partners (which already held a 1% stake) for $424 million.

The company reported a 34% increase in revenues in 2010 thanks to higher volumes and high commodity prices. The higher costs of product sales and fuel trimmed operating income growth to 7%.

In 2012 the company announced plans to invest up to $360 million to grow its projects in the Woodford Shale formation.

ONEOK Partners was formed in 2006 when ONEOK spun off its gathering and processing NGLs pipelines and storage businesses for $3 billion following that company's acquisition of Northern Border Partners. Building out its assets in 2007 the company acquired an interstate pipeline system from Kinder Morgan Energy Partners for $300 million.

EXECUTIVES

SVP CFO Treasurer and Director, Robert F. (Rob) Martinovich, age 54
Chairman President and CEO, John W. Gibson, age 59, $295,926 total compensation
VP Natural Gas Liquids Gathering and Fractionation, Michael L. (Mike) Turner, age 38
SVP Natural Gas Pipelines Natural Gas, Michel E. (Mike) Nelson, age 64
SVP Technical and Corporate Services, Stephan R. (Steve) Guy, age 57
President Natural Gas, Curtis L. Dinan, age 44, $143,190 total compensation
VP Market Services, Raymond D. (Ray) Neppl, age 64
COO and Director, Terry K. Spencer, age 53
SVP General Counsel and Secretary, John R. Barker, age 64
VP Commercial Intrastate Natural Gas Pipelines, Wesley R. Dunbar
VP Commercial Interstate Natural Gas Pipelines, J. Philip May
President Natural Gas Pipelines, W. Kent Shortridge, age 45
SVP Corporate Planning and Development, Robert S. (Bob) Mareburger, age 50
VP Natural Gas Gathering and Processing Operations Natural Gas, Craig Forsander, age 47
President Natural Gas Liquids, Sheridan C. Swords, age 43
President Natural Gas Liquid Pipelines Natural Gas Liquids, Roger G. Thorpe, age 45
SVP Natural Gas Liquids Operations Natural Gas Liquids, Wesley J. Christensen, age 58
Media Relations, Tom Droege
VP and Associate General Counsel, Stephen B. Allen, age 38
VP and Associate General Counsel, Joseph L. McCormick, age 52
Manager Investor Relations, Christy Williamson
SVP and Chief Accounting Officer, Derek S. Reiners, age 41
President Natural Gas Gathering and Processing, David R. (Dave) Scharf, age 55
Director, Jim W. (Jimmy) Mogg, age 63
Director, Gary N. Petersen, age 61
Director, Julie H. Edwards, age 53
SVP CFO Treasurer and Director, Robert F. (Rob) Martinovich, age 54
Director, Gerald B. Smith, age 61
Director, Gil J. Van Lunsen, age 70
COO and Director, Terry K. Spencer, age 53
Director, Craig F. Strehl, age 54
Director, Shelby E. Odell, age 72
Auditors: KPMGLLP

LOCATIONS

HQ: ONEOK Partners LP
100 West Fifth Street, Tulsa, OK 74103
Phone: 918 588-7000
Web: www.oneokpartners.com

PRODUCTS/OPERATIONS

2012 Sales

	$ mil.	% of total
Natural gas liquids	9,176	90
Natural gas gathering & processing	689	7
Natural gas pipelines	316	3
Total	**10,182**	**100**

Natural Gas Pipelines
Midwestern Gas Transmission Company
Viking Gas Transmission Company
Guardian Pipeline
OkTex Pipeline Company
ONEOK Gas Transporta
ONEOK Gas Gathering
ONEOK Gas Storage
ONEOK WesTex Transmissi
ONEOK Texas Gas Storage
Mid Continent Market Center
ONEOK Transmission Company
Natural Gas Gathering & Processing
Crestone Energy Ventures
ONEOK Field Services
ONEOK Rockies Midstream

COMPETITORS

Dynegy
El Paso Corporation
Enbridge
Kinder Morgan Energy Partners
Panhandle Eastern Pipe Line
TransCanada

HISTORICAL FINANCIALS

Company Type: Public

Income Statement FYE: December 31

	REVENUE ($ mil.)	NET INCOME ($ mil.)	NET PROFIT MARGIN	EMPLOYEES
12/11	11,322	830	7.3%	4,795
12/10	8,675	472	5.4%	1,275
12/09	6,474	434	6.7%	1,273
12/08	7,720	625	8.1%	1,232
12/07	5,831	407	7.0%	1,136
Annual Growth	18.0%	19.5%	—	43.3%

2011 Year-End Financials

Debt ratio: 43.33%
Return on equity: 24.13%
Cash ($ mil.): 35
Current ratio: 69.14
Long-term debt ($ mil.): 3,515
No. of shares (mil.): 203
Dividends
Yield: —
Payout: 69.40%
Market value ($ mil.): 11,768

	STOCK PRICE ($) FY Close	P/E High/Low		PER SHARE ($) Earnings	Dividends	Book Value
12/11	57.74	26	11	3.35	0.00	16.88
12/10	79.50	47	32	1.75	2.23	16.05
12/09	62.30	35	19	1.80	2.17	15.58
12/08	45.55	21	13	3.01	2.10	16.00
12/07	61.25	34	28	2.11	1.99	13.24
Annual Growth	(1.5%)	—	—	12.3%	—	6.3%

Oracle Corp.

Oracle wants to proclaim it far and wide: it knows all about supporting business operations. The leader in enterprise software (70% of its sales) it also provides hardware and services to help companies improve their processes. Best known for its focus on databases it offers aid in areas such as managing business data collaboration and application development customer relationship management and supply chain management. In recent years the company has aggressively used acquisitions to expand such as its entry into the hardware business with the purchase of Sun Microsystems. No single country outside the US accounts for more than 10% of sales but combined international customers represent nearly 60% of sales.

HISTORY

Larry Ellison Robert Miner Bruce Scott and Edward Oates founded System Development Laboratories in 1977 to create a database management system according to theoretical specifications published by IBM. Ellison had studied physics at the University of Chicago but dropped out in the 1960s to seek his fortune in Silicon Valley. He was part of the team that developed the first IBM-compatible mainframe. Miner an experienced programmer was the main developer of Oracle's database manager which was able to run on many computer brands and was introduced in 1979. The company also changed its name that year to Relational Software.

In 1983 the company changed its name again this time to Oracle in order to more closely align itself with its primary product. Oracle went public in 1986 and within two years had a 36% share of Uncle Sam's PC database market. It also added financial management graphics and human resource management software.

Oracle's rapid growth came at a great cost. It gained notoriety as a leader in vaporware –that is announced products that actually had not yet been developed. When the company's software was released it was sometimes bug-ridden and lacked promised features. Duplicate billings and the booking of unconsummated sales inflated revenues.

Oracle recorded a loss for fiscal 1991 accompanied by a downward restatement of earnings for past years. Its stock nosedived. The company laid off 400 employees and revised its growth estimates. Ellison stabilized the company with $80 million in financing from Nippon Steel.

Thanks to Oracle7 (launched in 1992) the company within two years became the #1 database management software maker. Sales for fiscal 1994 hit $2 billion. Ellison by that time had developed a reputation as an extravagant adventurer (his hobbies included yacht racing and piloting disarmed fighter planes).

Oracle formed affiliate Network Computer Inc. in 1997 to market Internet appliances (with no disk drive and local memory) that Ellison envisioned would strip Microsoft of its operating system ubiquity. Oracle and Netscape (now owned by Time Warner) merged joint venture Navio Communications one year later into Network Computer (renamed Liberate Technologies) redesigned around interactive software and spun off in 1999.

Also in 1999 the company bought three niche front-office software specialists and took its Oracle Japan subsidiary public. The next year it partnered with rival Commerce One to provide software and support for a giant online venture merging the Web-based procurement exchanges of General Motors Ford Motor and Daimler.

Oracle continued to expand its portfolio of business applications in 2001 introducing warehouse supply chain and customer relationship management software as well as software suites targeted at small businesses.

The company launched a hostile takeover bid for PeopleSoft in 2003 just days after the rival software maker had disclosed plans to acquire J.D. Edwards. PeopleSoft's board unanimously rejected the initial all-cash offer of $5.1 billion deeming the unsolicited bid inadequate and citing antitrust concerns. After bitter negotiations that included a number of rejected bids Oracle finally reached an agreement to acquire PeopleSoft for $10.3 billion in late 2004; the deal closed in early 2005.

Soon after the PeopleSoft deal closed Oracle again pursued a takeover. Rival SAP had announced plans to acquire retail software developer Retek for about $500 million. After a brief bidding war Oracle purchased Retek for about $670 million. The company followed that acquisition with a host of smaller deals in 2005 including identity management software developer Oblix; data management software maker TimesTen; retail inventory management software developer ProfitLogic; and logistics software provider Global Logistics Technologies.

Not content to rest on its acquisitive laurels Oracle initiated another blockbuster deal in 2006 purchasing Siebel Systems for $5.85 billion. The company also added Portal Software to its fold in 2006. The following year Oracle bought business intelligence software provider Hyperion Solutions for about $3.3 billion and Agile Software for about $495 million.

In 2008 Oracle completed another big deal the purchase of application server software and middleware maker BEA Systems in a transaction valued at $8.5 billion. An offer of a mere $6.7 billion in late 2007 was rejected by BEA which was formed by veterans of Sun Microsystems to address the need to adapt mainframe systems to a network computing platform.

Oracle next set its sights on what would become one of its most ambitious acquisitions to date. In 2009 it announced plans to buy Sun Microsystems for about $7.4 million. The deal which was Oracle's first significant entry into the market for hardware and chips was completed in early 2010. The company used the Sun purchase it made in 2010 to extend its software expertise to Sun's servers Solaris operating system and SPARC chips enabling it to offer customers integrated hardware and software systems (much like rivals IBM and Hewlett-Packard). The company also bought Passlogix a provider of single sign-on products for the enterprise market late in 2010.

Also in 2010 the company acquired Phase Forward for about $685 million. The deal expanded Oracle's presence in the health care and life sciences market. Phase Forward's clinical drug trial management software has been used by clients such as AstraZeneca Eli Lilly and Boston Scientific. Oracle further boosted its clinical trial management offerings with the 2012 acquisition of ClearTrial which offers its applications in the cloud.

Oracle paid about $1 billion in 2011 for e-commerce software developer Art Technology Group (ATG) to complement its customer relationship management retail and supply chain product lines. ATG's software is used by businesses to unify and streamline the automation and management of online merchandising marketing and content management efforts. It enables personalization of shopper content automated product recommendations and live customer contact via browser chat windows. The deal let Oracle extend its Oracle Retail platform to include online in-store and mobile channels.

The company followed the ATG acquisition with the 2011 purchase of network storage system maker Pillar Data Systems to expand its data storage holdings. Before that acquisition Oracle founder and CEO Larry Ellison had owned 55% of Pillar through his Tako Ventures investment firm. Also in 2011 Oracle bought Web experience management software maker FatWire. That deal further extended Oracle's reach into the world of unified multichannel Web communications marketing and e-commerce customer engagement.

In 2012 Oracle acquired human capital software maker Taleo in a transaction valued at around $1.9 billion. The purchase added a cloud-based talent management product to Oracle's product line. Talent management –encompassing recruitment performance management learning and development and compensation functions –is in demand as organizations look to manage and engage employees in career development via a single system. With the deal Oracle added a recruitment function lacking in its HR product and proved its willingness to spend cash to keep up with top competitor SAP.

The Taleo deal came on the heels of Oracle's purchase of RightNow Technologies a provider of hosted customer support software. The $1.5 billion acquisition was intended to help Oracle offer a consistent customer experience management across its sales channels. RightNow's software enables the management of customer interactions via mobile Web chat social media and call centers.

Oracle also bought knowledge management software developer InQuira and data management and Web commerce software developer Endeca that year.

EXECUTIVES

Chairman, Jeffrey O. (Jeff) Henley, age 67, $693,750 total compensation
CEO and Director, Lawrence J. (Larry) Ellison, age 67, $250,001 total compensation
EVP and Head Oracle Japan, Derek H. Williams, age 67
SVP Oracle University, John L. Hall
EVP Oracle Customer Support Services, Charles A. (Chuck) Rozwat, age 64, $600,000 total compensation
Chief Corporate Architect, Edward Screven
SVP Customers Primavera Global Business Unit, Richard K. (Dick) Faris
Co-President and Director, Mark V. Hurd, age 55
VP Product Management Oracle Business Intelligence, Paul Rodwick
EVP Global Business Units, Robert K. (Bob) Weiler, age 61
Co-President CFO and Director, Safra A. Catz, age 50, $800,000 total compensation
SVP Human Resources, Joyce Westerdahl
EVP Product Development, Thomas Kurian, age 45, $780,114 total compensation
EVP North America Sales and Consulting, Keith G. Block, age 51, $800,000 total compensation
SVP North America Support Services, Juan C. Jones
SVP Applications Development, Cliff Godwin
SVP Application Development, Steve Miranda
SVP and General Manager Communications Global Business Unit, Bhaskar M. Gorti
SVP European Union Enlargement and Commonwealth of Independent Stages Region, Alfonso Di Ianni
Chief Security Officer, Mary Ann Davidson
SVP Tools and Middleware and Chief Architect, Ted Farrell
SVP and General Manager Oracle Retail, Mike Webster
SVP Oracle Database Server Technologies, Andrew Mendelsohn
EVP Microelectronics Group, Michael E. (Mike) Splain, age 55
CTO Oracle Asia Research And Development Centers, Kevin Walsh
SVP Applications Development, Rick Jewell
SVP Oracle Consulting Services Asia Pacific, Casey Poon
EVP Oracle Latin America, Luiz Meisler, age 59
United States and Canada Public Relations Industries, Katie Barron
SVP and CIO, Mark E. Sunday, age 57
SVP Hardware Sales Asia Pacific and Japan, Adrian Jones
EVP Systems, John F. Fowler, age 51
United States and Canada Public Relations Corporate Finance and Corporate Citizenship, Kimberly (Kim) Pineda
SVP Linux and Virtualization Engineering, Wim A. Coekaerts
VP Supply Chain Execution and Product Lifecycle Management Strategy, Jon S. Chorley
VP Human Resources Asia Pacific, Alison Sibree
EVP Oracle Asia Pacific, Steve Au Yeung, age 46
Chief Marketing Officer, Judith Sim
SVP Applications Asia Pacific, Tan Yen Yen
SVP Corporate Controller and Chief Accounting Officer, William Corey West, age 50
Group VP Oracle Fusion and GRC Applications Development, Chris Leone
SVP Oracle Fusion Middleware and Java, Hasan Rizvi
VP Platform Technology Solutions, John Gawkowski
VP Enterprise Performance Management Global Business Unit, Rich Clayton
SVP Oracle CRM, Anthony Lye
SVP Worldwide Alliances and Channels and Embedded Sales, Judson Althoff
CEO and Managing Director Oracle Financial Services Software, Chet Kamat
SVP General Counsel and Secretary; President and CEO Art Technology, Dorian E. Daley, age 53
United States and Canada Public Relations Products, Carol Sato
VP Development Identity Management and Security Products, Amit Jasuja
SVP; President and CEO Oracle Corporation Japan, Takao Endo
EVP Oracle Europe Middle East and Africa, Loic le Guisquet, age 50
SVP North America Alliances and Channels, Ted Bereswill
VP Standards Strategy and Architecture, Donald R. Deutsch
VP Database Product Marketing, William (Willie) Hardie
SVP Systems Technologies, Juan R. Loaiza
VP Oracle Technology Product Marketing, Rick Schultz
Group VP Product Marketing, Robert G. Shimp
VP Database Product Management, Mark Townsend
VP Oracle Fusion Middleware Product Management, Amit Zavery
VP Human Capital Management Strategy, Gretchen Alarcon
VP PeopleSoft Enterprise Development, Paco Aubrejuan
VP Applications Marketing, Folia Grace
VP Public Sector Industry Solutions Oracle U.S.A., Wayne S. Bobby
Senior Director Life Sciences Industry and Marketing, Dennis Constantinou
VP and CTO Oracle Public Sector, Peter Doolan
SVP Oracle Public Sector, Mark Johnson
VP Public Sector North America, Bud Langston
VP Consumer Sector And Energy Industries Oracle Product Industries, Thomas E. (Tom) Madigan
VP Oracle Higher Education, Jim McGlothlin
Industry Director Transportation, Ralph Menzano
SVP Public Sector and Education Global Business Unit, Juan F. Rada
United States and Canada Public Relations Applications, Susanne Penner
United States and Canada Public Relations Oracle Services On Demand Support Consulting Education and Technology, Letty Ledbetter
VP Technology Oracle Corporation European Enlargement and Commonwealth of Independent States Region, Alain Ozan
VP Oracle Corporation South East Europe, Atilla Kiral, age 59
VP Applications European Enlargement and Commonwealth of Independent States Region, Hans Peter Kipfer
SVP Alliances and Channels Oracle Europe Middle East and Africa, Stein Surlien
SVP Worldwide Operations, Cindy Reese
SVP Industries Business Unit, Sonny Singh
Industry Director K-12 Education, Diana Richie
SVP and General Manager Oracle's Financial Services, Frank Brienzi
VP Logistics Product Strategy, Derek Gittoes
Group VP and General Manager JD Edwards, Lyle Ekdahl
VP Product Management Oracle Enterprise 2.0, Andy MacMillan
Group VP Alliances and Channels Oracle Asia Pacific and Japan, George Wong
VP Oracle University, Damien Carey
SVP Oracle Customer Services Asia Pacific and Japan, Chon-Phung Lim
Group VP Server and Storage Systems Asia Pacific, George Or
SVP Oracle Fusion Middleware and Acting Head Technology Business Unit Asia Pacific, Roger Li
SVP EMEA Technology Oracle Europe Middle East and Africa, Andrew Sutherland
SVP NAS Applications and Cloud Services, Joanne Olsen
SVP Corporate Development and Strategic Planning, Douglas Kehring
VP Oracle Accelerate Applications Marketing and Business Development, Mark S. Johnson
VP Oracle Corporate Communications EMEA, Val Russell
SVP Technology Hardware and Public Sector, Matthew Mills
Director, Bruce R. Chizen, age 56
Director, H. Raymond (Ray) Bingham, age 66
CEO and Director, Lawrence J. (Larry) Ellison, age 67
Co-President and Director, Mark V. Hurd, age 55
Director, George H. Conrades, age 73
Co-President CFO and Director, Safra A. Catz, age 50
Director, Naomi O. Seligman, age 74
Director, Jeffrey S. Berg, age 65
Director, Michael J. Boskin, age 67
Director, Hector Garcia-Molina, age 58
Director, Donald L. (Don) Lucas, age 82
Auditors: Ernst&YoungLLP

LOCATIONS

HQ: Oracle Corporation
500 Oracle Pkwy., Redwood City CA 94065
Phone: 650-506-7000 **Fax:** 650-506-7200
Web: www.oracle.com

2012 Sales

	$ mil.	% of total
United States	15,767	43
United Kingdom	2,302	6
Japan	1,865	5
Germany	1,484	4
Canada	1,234	3
Australia	1,163	3
France	1,162	3
Other countries	12,144	33
Total	**35,622**	**100**

2012 Sales by Segment

	$ mil.	% of total
Software license updates & product support		
Americas	8,672	24
Europe the Middle East & Africa	5,194	14
Asia/Pacific	2,344	6
New software license		
Americas	5,107	14
Europe the Middle East & Africa	2,884	8
Asia/Pacific	1,915	5
Services		
Americas	2,420	7
Europe the Middle East & Africa	1,473	4
Asia/Pacific	810	2
Hardware systems products		
Americas	1,880	5
Europe the Middle East & Africa	1,140	3
Asia/Pacific	807	2
Hardware systems support		
Americas	1,157	3
Europe the Middle East & Africa	870	2
Asia/Pacific	448	1
Total	**37,121**	**100**

PRODUCTS/OPERATIONS

2012 Sales

	$ mil.	% of total
Software		
License updates and product support	16,210	44
New licenses	9,906	27
Hardware systems		

Products	3,827	10
Support	2,475	7
Services	4,703	12
Total	**37,121**	**100**

Selected Mergers and Acquisitions

2012
- ClearTrial (Chicago; cloud-based clinical trial operations software)
- DataRaker (cloud-based analytics platform)
- RightNow Technologies ($1.5 billion; Montana; hosted customer support software)
- Taleo ($2 billion; San Francisco; cloud-based human capital software)
- Vitrue ($300 million; Atlanta; cloud-based social marketing campaign application)

2011
- Art Technology Group ($1 billion; e-commerce software)
- FatWire Software (undisclosed price; New York; Web experience management solutions)
- Ksplice (undisclosed price; Cambridge MA; zero-downtime update technology for Linux)
- Pillar Data Systems (undisclosed price; San Jose CA; SAN Block I/O storage systems)

2010
- Convergin (undisclosed price; Israel; network integration software)
- Phase Forward ($685 million; clinical drug trial management software)
- Secerno (undisclosed price; Oxford UK; database firewall solutions)
- Sun Microsystems ($7.4 billion; UNIX-based servers)

Selected Products

Software
- Business applications
  - Business intelligence
  - Customer experience
  - Customer relationship
  - Enterprise content
  - Financial
  - Governance risk & compliance
  - Human capital
  - Supply chain
- Databases
- Enterprise application integration
- Middleware

Services
- Consulting
  - Cloud computing
  - Enterprise architecture
  - Systems integration
- Education/training

Hardware
- Servers (SPARC servers x86 servers)
- Solaris operating system (hardware-related software)
- Storage & tape

COMPETITORS

Accenture
ADP
Autonomy
BMC Software
CA Inc.
CDC Software
Ceridian
Cisco Systems
Courion
EMC
Fujitsu Technology Solutions
Hewlett-Packard
Hitachi
IBM
Infor Global
Informatica
Intel
JasperSoft
JDA Software
Manhattan Associates
Microsoft
MicroStrategy
NCR
Novell
Open Text
Pegasystems
Progress Software
Quest Software
Red Hat
Sage Group
salesforce.com
SAP
SAS Institute
SOA Software
Software AG
SuccessFactors
Taleo
Teradata
TIBCO Software
Workday Inc.

HISTORICAL FINANCIALS

Company Type: Public

Income Statement FYE: May 31

	REVENUE ($ mil.)	NET INCOME ($ mil.)	NET PROFIT MARGIN	EMPLOYEES
05/12	37,121	9,981	26.9%	115,000
05/11	35,622	8,547	24.0%	108,000
05/10	26,820	6,135	22.9%	105,000
05/09	23,252	5,593	24.1%	86,000
05/08	22,430	5,521	24.6%	84,233
Annual Growth	13.4%	16.0%	—	8.1%

2012 Year-End Financials

Debt ratio: 21.03%—
Return on equity: 22.85%
Cash ($ mil.): 14,955
Current ratio: 260.09
Long-term debt ($ mil.): 13,524
Dividends
Yield: 0.91%
Payout: 12.24%
Market value ($ mil.): —

	STOCK PRICE ($) FY Close	P/E High	P/E Low	PER SHARE ($) Earnings	Dividends	Book Value
05/12	26.47	17	12	1.96	0.24	8.91
05/11	34.22	22	13	1.67	0.21	7.85
05/10	22.57	22	16	1.21	0.00	6.13
05/09	19.59	21	13	1.09	0.00	5.01
05/08	22.84	21	17	1.06	0.00	4.47
Annual Growth	3.8%	—	—	16.6%	—	18.8%

Oriental Financial Group, Inc.

LOCATIONS

HQ: Oriental Financial Group, Inc.
997 San Roberto Street, Oriental Center 10th Floor, Professional Offices Park,
Phone: (787) 771 6800
Web: www.orientalfg.com

HISTORICAL FINANCIALS

Company Type:

Income Statement FYE: December 31

	ASSETS ($ mil.)	NET INCOME ($ mil.)	INCOME AS % OF ASSETS	EMPLOYEES
12/11	6,693	34	0.5%	725
12/10	7,312	9	0.1%	717
12/09	6,550	22	0.4%	526
12/08	6,205	26	0.4%	539
12/07	5,999	41	0.7%	518
Annual Growth	2.8%	(4.4%)	—	8.8%

2011 Year-End Financials

Debt ratio: 6.33%
Return on equity: 4.95%
Cash ($ mil.): 605
Current ratio: —
Long-term debt ($ mil.): 423
No. of shares (mil.): 41
Dividends
Yield: —
Payout: 31.34%
Market value ($ mil.): 499

	STOCK PRICE ($) FY Close	P/E High	P/E Low	PER SHARE ($) Earnings	Dividends	Book Value
12/11	12.11	19	14	0.67	0.00	16.86
12/10	12.49	—	—	(0.50)	0.17	15.80
12/09	10.80	21	1	0.75	0.16	13.62
12/08	6.05	26	6	0.90	0.56	10.76
12/07	13.41	10	6	1.50	0.56	14.90
Annual Growth	(2.5%)	—	—	(18.2%)	—	3.1%

Oshkosh Corp

Need to plow through Sahara sands or Buffalo snow? Oshkosh has your ride. The company makes and sells heavy-duty vehicles and vehicle bodies for commercial access fire and emergency and defense work. Commercial and access lines include concrete batch plants refuse vehicle bodies (McNeilus brand) tow trucks (Jerr-Dan) and aerial work platforms (JLG). Its emergency offerings range from snow blowers to aircraft rescue and firefighting vehicles (Pierce). More than 40 plants build the lineup. Vehicles are sold via dealers to global airport institutional construction and municipal markets. Oshkosh also makes tactical trucks and other equipment for the US DoD; the US government represents about 56% of sales.

Year-over-year consolidated net sales fell about 23% in 2011 mainly because of lower sales under the MRAP All Terrain Vehicle (M-ATV) contract though the company enjoyed strong sales in its access equipment segment and newly established Family of Medium Tactical Vehicles (FMTV) program.

By segment the defense segment's net sales fell 39% behind the conclusion of initial M-ATV production. FMTV provided some compensation. This segment supplies the US and foreign militaries as well as law-enforcement agencies with military tactical wheeled vehicles. The company expects the FMTV program to account for some 40% of this segment's sales in fiscal 2012 compared with about 13% the previous year. During the same period it expects to roll out more than 400 M-ATVs.

The access equipment segment's net sales decreased about 32% as a result of lower intersegment M-ATV-related sales though this segment did benefit from stronger demand for equipment replacement. This segment was formed primarily by the 2007 acquisition of a maker of aerial work platform and telehandlers JLG. Besides supplying equipment rental companies construction contractors manufacturing companies home improvement stores and the military JLG provides Jerr-Dan tow trucks and vehicle carriers for the towing industry. Oshkosh is optimistic that this segment will enjoy growth of about 20% in fiscal 2012 to meet replacement demand.

Challenged by lower municipal spending in the US the fire & emergency segment was down about 13%. This segment supplies commercial and custom firefighting vehicles and equipment vehicles for aircraft rescue snow removal and broadcasting ambulances and mobile medical trailers.

The commercial segment's net sales declined 9% caused mainly by less demand for refuse collection vehicles. Commercial makes rear- and front-discharge concrete mixers refuse collection vehicles portable and stationary concrete batch plants for ready-mix companies and waste haulers. Despite previously poor sales the company has been hopeful about more demand for refuse collection vehicles.

Challenged by customer markets that have been down variously from 40% to 90% and especially by a lower US defense budget Oshkosh has been implementing a lean strategy of cutting non-value added labor that has included reducing its manufacturing operations by 20% and unifying its purchasing operations into a single global unit. These measures are included under a plan called MOVE. Other prongs in the strategy include using new technologies to expand the functions of its products and developing business in the emerging markets of Asia Eastern Europe the Middle East and Latin America. The company is looking ahead to fiscal 2013 for the beginning of MOVE's stronger benefits.

In the meantime tie ups with big brands including Caterpillar have proven beneficial. In 2009 Oshkosh inked a 20-year lease to build CAT-branded telehandlers routed to market through Caterpillar's global dealer network.

To reflect its more diverse operations Oshkosh changed its name from Oshkosh Truck Corporation to Oshkosh Corporation in 2008.

HISTORY

Bernhard Mosling and William Besserdich founded Oshkosh Truck in 1917 attracting investors with "Old Betsy" a four-wheel-drive 3000-pound truck. Over the next few decades the company developed a range of heavy-duty vehicles. Sales took off when the US Army gave truck contracts to Oshkosh during WWII. Commercial sales increased after the war the result of demand from mining and plantation companies. Oshkosh Truck went public in 1985.

Defense cutbacks prompted the company to diversify. It acquired Deere & Company's motorhome chassis business in 1989 and Miller Trailers the next year.

In 1995 Oshkosh formed a strategic alliance with Daimler-Benz's (now Daimler AG) Freightliner Corporation (now Daimler Trucks North America) although the transfer of Oshkosh's chassis business caused the company's sales to drop by more than $100 million in fiscal 1995. The following year Oshkosh bought fire truck maker Pierce Manufacturing for $158 million. Robert Bohn became CEO in 1997 succeeding Eugene Goodson who quit in a disagreement with the board. Oshkosh also bought Quebec-based Nova Quintech's firefighting ladder technology that year.

The company acquired McNeilus Companies a leading maker of concrete mixers and bodies for refuse trucks for $250 million in 1998. It also won the initial contract for the US Marine Corps' Medium Tactical Truck Replacement program potentially worth up to $1.2 billion. In 1999 Oshkosh bought Kewaunee Engineering which made parts for aerial devices for $6.3 million. The next year Oshkosh picked up Viking Truck and Equipment (concrete mixer sales and service). Later in 2000 Oshkosh diversified into ambulances with the purchase of Medtec Ambulance Corporation.

Oshkosh expanded its European presence in 2001 when it bought the Geesink Norba Group (refuse collection truck bodies mobile and stationary compactors and transfer stations) from Powell Duffryn Ltd. for $137 million. In 2004 Oshkosh acquired Jerr-Dan a towing equipment manufacturer from Littlejohn & Co. for about $80 million. Later that year the company acquired 75% of two Italy-based firefighting equipment manufacturers BAI Brescia Antcendi International and BAI Tecnica.

The following year Oshkosh bought Canadian concrete mixer truck company London Machinery Inc.

Oshkosh acquired access equipment manufacturer JLG Industries in 2006.

2006 was a record year for Oshkosh's sales and profits but thanks to its acquisition of JLG Industries Oshkosh's 2007 sales and profits were lifted to even greater heights. The addition of JLG was largely responsible for Oshkosh increasing sales by 84% compared with the previous year.

The acquisition of JLG marked Oshkosh's expansion into the aerial platform market and JLG instantly became Oshkosh's largest product segment. The move also gave Oshkosh purchasing leverage and gave the company exposure to complementary markets.

Not surprisingly the company's defense products also enjoyed brisk sales of parts and services for the thousands of Oshkosh trucks currently in service in Iraq. Oshkosh also won market share for its line of emergency vehicles including response vehicles used in homeland security applications.

Also in 2006 Oshkosh acquired AK Specialty Vehicles (since renamed Oshkosh Specialty Vehicles) from HealthTronics for about $140 million. Oshkosh Specialty Vehicles makes mobile medical broadcast and homeland-security command and control vehicles —new specialty vehicle markets for Oshkosh. Buying AK Specialty Vehicles also increased Oshkosh's presence in Europe. Later that year Oshkosh bought Iowa Mold Tooling a maker of tire service general mechanics and lubrication trucks. The purchase boosted Oshkosh's market presence for trucks serving the construction tire service and mining industries.

In 2008 Oshkosh changed its name from Oshkosh Truck Corporation to Oshkosh Corporation. The move highlights the company's more diverse operations.

Among Oshkosh's disappointments has been its European refuse collection vehicle operation Geesink. After three years of restructuring this business continued to perform poorly. In 2009 Oshkosh sold Geesink to Platinum Equity retaining only Geesink's plant in Romania which fabricates parts for Oshkosh's JLG business. Oshkosh's European fire apparatus and equipment company BAI also failed to meet expectations. Oshkosh sold off its 75% stake to BAI management the same year.

EXECUTIVES

President CEO and Director, Charles L. (Charlie) Szews, age 55, $583,377 total compensation
Chairman, Richard M. Donnelly, age 68
EVP General Counsel and Secretary, Bryan J. Blankfield, age 51, $376,300 total compensation
VP and Managing Director Oshkosh Capital, Kevin S. Ramsburg
VP Investor Relations, Patrick N. Davidson
EVP Government Operations and Industry Relations, Joseph H. (Jay) Kimmitt, age 62, $361,265 total compensation
EVP Chief Administration Officer and Human Resources Officer, Michael K. Rohrkaste, age 54
EVP and President Access Equipment, Wilson R. Jones, age 51
SVP Finance and Controller, Thomas J. Polnaszek
EVP and CFO, David M. Sagehorn, age 49, $411,021 total compensation
EVP and Chief Procurement Officer, Gregory L. (Greg) Fredericksen, age 51
SVP Business Development, Mark M. Radue
VP Tax, David L. (Dave) Moskol
Assistant Treasurer, Corey R. Braun
SVP and Treasurer, R. Scott Grennier
EVP; President Commercial, Frank R. Nerenhausen, age 48
Senior Executive Assistant and Corporate Assistant Secretary, Virginia K. Abel
VP Global Procurement and Supply Chain, Matteo R. Pisciotta
EVP and President Fire and Emergency, James W. (Jim) Johnson, age 47
VP Communications, John Daggett
EVP Technology, Gary W. Schmidel
SVP Total Quality Management, Colleen Moynihan
EVP and President Defense, John M. Urias
VP and Deputy General Counsel, Pamela Patzke
VP Global Information Technology, Dave Schecklman
VP Ethics and Compliance, Robin Schroeder
Senior Executive Assistant and Paralegal and Corporate Assistant Secretary, Lori R. Mackey
SVP and President Commercial, Todd S. Fierro
Director, Craig P. Omtvedt, age 62
Director, Harvey N. Medvin, age 76
Director, John S. Shiely, age 59
Director, Peter B. Hamilton, age 65
President CEO and Director, Charles L. (Charlie) Szews, age 55
Director, Michael W. Grebe, age 72
Director, Kathleen J. Hempel, age 62
Director, J. Peter Mosling Jr., age 68
Director, Richard G. Sim, age 68
Director, Leslie F. Kenne, age 64
Director, Duncan J. Palmer, age 47
Auditors: Deloitte&ToucheLLP

LOCATIONS

HQ: Oshkosh Corporation
2307 Oregon St., Oshkosh WI 54902
Phone: 920-235-9150 **Fax:** 920-233-9268
Web: www.oshkoshcorporation.com

2011 Sales

	$ mil.	% of total
North America		
US	6,281	83
Other North America	179	2
Europe Africa & the Middle East	706	9
Rest of the world	417	6
Total	**7,584**	**100**

PRODUCTS/OPERATIONS

2011 Sales

	$ mil.	% of total
Defense	4,365	57
Access equipment	2,052	26
Fire & emergency	800	10
Commercial	564	7
Adjustments	(197.8)	-
Total	**7,584**	**100**

Selected Products

Access equipment
- Aerial work platforms
- Boom lifts
- Scissor lifts
- Stock pickers
- Telehandlers
- Towing & recovery equipment
- Trailers
- Vertical mast lifts

Commercial
- All-make parts
- Automated mobile & stationary compactors
- Concrete batch plants
- Container handling equipment
- Demountable containers
- Rear- & front-discharge mixers

Rear front & side loaders
Refuse collection vehicle bodies
Revolution mixer drums
Defense
Armored wheeled vehicles
Heavy equipment transporters (HET)
Heavy expanded mobility tactical trucks (HEMTT)
High-mobility trailers
Logistic vehicle system replacements (LVSR)
Medium tactical trucks (MTT)
Medium tactical vehicle replacements (MTVR)
Off road tractor/trailers
Palletized load system (PLS) trucks & trailers
Urban assault vehicles
Fire & emergency
Aircraft rescue & fire fighting (ARFF) vehicles
Ambulances
Custom & commercial fire apparatus
Rescue & homeland security apparatus
Snow blowers & plow trucks

COMPETITORS

AM General
American LaFrance
BAE Systems Land & Armaments
Collins Industries
Daimler
Daimler Trucks North America
Dover Corp.
E-ONE
Federal Signal
Force Protection
General Dynamics Land Systems
Haulotte
Heil Environmental
Hyundai Motor
Iveco S.p.A.
J C Bamford Excavators
L-3 Communications
Leyland Trucks
Mack Trucks
MAN
MANITOU BF
Miller Industries
Navistar
Navistar International
PACCAR
Skyjack
Spartan Motors
Terex
Trinity Industries
UD Trucks
Volvo

HISTORICAL FINANCIALS

Company Type: Public

Income Statement FYE: September 30

	REVENUE ($ mil.)	NET INCOME ($ mil.)	NET PROFIT MARGIN	EMPLOYEES
09/12	8,180	230	2.8%	13,200
09/11	7,584	273	3.6%	13,100
09/10	9,842	790	8.0%	12,400
09/09	5,295	(1,098)	—	12,300
09/08	7,138	79	1.1%	14,000
Annual Growth	3.5%	30.6%	—	(1.5%)

2012 Year-End Financials

Debt ratio: 19.30%
Return on equity: 12.45%
Cash ($ mil.): 540
Current ratio: 158.08
Long-term debt ($ mil.): 955
No. of shares (mil.): 91
Dividends
Yield: —
Payout: —
Market value ($ mil.): 2,511

	STOCK PRICE ($) FY Close	P/E High	P/E Low	PER SHARE ($) Earnings	Dividends	Book Value
09/12	27.43	12	6	2.51	0.00	20.24
09/11	15.74	13	5	2.99	0.00	17.48
09/10	27.50	5	3	8.69	0.00	14.63
09/09	30.93	—	—	(14.37)	0.30	5.75
09/08	13.16	58	9	1.06	0.40	18.66
Annual Growth	20.2%	—	—	24.0%	—	2.1%

Owens & Minor, Inc.

Owens & Minor (O&M) makes sure surgeons aren't left empty handed after shouting "Scalpel stat!" A leading distributor of medical and surgical supplies the company carries more than 200000 products from about 1200 manufacturers. Products distributed by O&M include surgical dressings endoscopic and intravenous products needles syringes sterile procedure trays gowns gloves and sutures. The firm also offers software consulting and other services to help customers manage their supplies. O&M's customers are primarily hospitals and health systems and the purchasing organizations that serve them. It delivers products to roughly 4000 health care providers from about 50 distribution centers across the US.

Geographic Reach

Though US operations account for most of O&M's sales the company is working to branch out into international medical distribution markets including Europe.

Operations

About 95% of O&M's sales come from the distribution of medical supplies. The company's major product suppliers include Covidien and Johnson & Johnson whose products account for almost 15% and about 10% of O&M's revenues respectively. In addition to delivering products made by its supply partners the distributor sells some 2900 value products under its own MediChoice label.

Sales & Marketing

Most of O&M's sales are attributed to contracts with acute-care hospitals which are often represented by group purchasing organizations (GPOs) or integrated healthcare networks (IHNs). GPO Novation is the largest client accounting for around 35% of the company's earnings with GPOs MedAssets (including its recently acquired Broadlane unit) accounting for more than 20% of sales and Premier accounting for 20%. The company also has an ongoing exclusive supplier agreement with the US Department of Defense. Additional clients include other government agencies and alternate health care locations such as physician clinics nursing homes and surgery centers.

Strategy

As the health care industry has consolidated so have the industries that serve it and O&M works to remain competitive by providing supply chain management tools and services in addition to supplies to help its customers control costs. Its OMSolutions business unit provides outsourcing and resource management services to acute care providers including fee-based one-on-one consultations and physical inventory reviews as well as inventory tracking and purchasing software. Many of the company's information technology and infrastructure operations are managed by third party Dell Perot Systems the IT outsourcing unit of Dell. (The company's agreement with Dell expires at the end of 2014.)

While the company experiences a successful level of revenue and income growth from greater product and service sales to existing customers as well as the addition of new clients O&M doesn't shy away from partnerships and acquisitions as other ways to help boost sales and services. For example in 2012 O&M entered a seven-year lease and technology services deal valued at $68 million with Penske Truck Leasing and its Penske Logistics unit to consolidate its delivery fleet with one vendor.

Mergers & Acquisitions

O&M forged moved to expand its third-party logistics presence and scale into the European health care market in 2012 when it paid some E130 million ($158 million) to purchase a majority of the Movianto Group from Celesio AG. Movianto Group brought with it 23 facilities in 11 European countries and gave O&M a firm global platform to expand upon.

Ownership

Investment firms own more than a third of the company with T. Rowe Price Associates and BlackRock at the top of the list respectively owning 10% and 7% of the company.

HISTORY

George Gilmer Minor Jr.'s great-grandfather was an apothecary and surgeon in colonial Williamsburg Virginia. His grandfather was Thomas Jefferson's personal physician. Minor himself worked as a wholesale drug salesman in Richmond after the Civil War. In 1882 he and rival wholesaler Otho Owens partnered to form the Owens & Minor Drug Company. The company was both a retail and wholesale business with a storefront that filled prescriptions and sold sundries paints oils and window glass. When Owens died in 1906 Minor became the company's president.

During the 1920s the Owens family sold their stake in the firm. George Gilmer Minor III served briefly as the company's president in the early 1940s; his son George Gilmer Minor IV (called Mr. Minor Jr. to differentiate him from his father) became president in 1947.

In 1954 Owens & Minor installed its first computerized order fulfillment system. The following year the firm became Owens Minor & Bodeker when it bought the Bodeker Drug Company which was both older and larger than Owens & Minor.

After 84 years in the drug wholesale business the company entered the medical and surgical distribution business after buying A&J Hospital Supply in 1966 and Powers & Anderson in 1968. In 1971 Owens Minor & Bodeker went public. By the end of the decade the company had operations in 10 states.

The fourth Minor to run the firm G. Gilmer Minor III (Mr. Minor Jr.'s son) was named president in 1981 (he became CEO in 1984). Under his direction Owens Minor & Bodeker would complete the transition from a drug wholesaler to a medical supplies distributor. In 1981 it purchased the Will Ross subsidiary of G.D. Searle (then the country's #2 medical and surgical supplies distributor).

The company reverted to its original name on its 100th anniversary in 1982. By 1984 medical supplies supplanted wholesale drugs as its primary source of income. In 1988 Owens & Minor listed on the NYSE.

The company passed the $1 billion revenue mark in 1990 and later sold its wholesale drug business. It extended its reach with the purchase of Lyons Physician Supply in 1993 and Stuart Medical (the #3 national distributor) in 1994.

The company consolidated its warehouse operations and upgraded its computer system in 1995. To make up for losses attributed to restructuring costs and discounting prices for large accounts Owens & Minor eliminated or reassigned jobs at several distribution centers.

In 1998 it lost its biggest customer when embattled Columbia/HCA (now HCA) canceled its contract. Owens & Minor replaced this business by contracting with such providers as Sutter Health.

In 1999 the company formed an alliance with drug distributor AmeriSource Health (now

AmerisourceBergen) to streamline transactions with Sutter Health. In 2002 Owens & Minor launched an initiative to offer automated supply chain management services to its clients.

Chairman and CEO G. Gilmer Minor III stepped down from the CEO post after 21 years in July 2005 but remained the company's chairman; Craig R. Smith the company's former COO was named CEO.

Also in 2005 the company expanded into the diabetic direct-to-consumer supply business by acquiring Access Diabetic Supply. (That division however was divested in 2009.)

The company acquired the acute care medical and surgical supply business of McKesson Medical-Surgical a subsidiary of McKesson Corporation for $165 million in 2006.

In 2009 in a move designed to focus on its core acute-care distribution operations it sold its direct-to-consumer (DTC) diabetes supply business Access Diabetic Supply to Liberty Medical (a division of Medco Health Solutions) for $63 million. O&M has exited its other DTC operations as well.

In 2010 O&M launched a new division OM Healthcare Logistics (OM HCL) to offer third-party logistics services to suppliers seeking to lower costs by outsourcing all of their supply chain processes including warehousing repackaging sample management and data management.

EXECUTIVES

SVP Human Resources, Erika T. Davis, age 48
VP Quality and Communications, Hugh F. Gouldthorpe Jr., age 73
SVP Operations, Charles C. Colpo, age 54, $406,750 total compensation
President CEO and Director, Craig R. Smith, age 60, $810,462 total compensation
Chairman, G. Gilmer Minor III, age 71, $656,184 total compensation
Interim CFO, D. Andrew (Drew) Edwards, age 53
EVP and COO, James L. (Jim) Bierman, age 60, $506,538 total compensation
SVP General Counsel and Corporate Secretary, Grace R. den Hartog, age 60, $350,766 total compensation
SVP Strategic Planning and Business Development, Mark A. Van Sumeren, age 54, $450,819 total compensation
Director Investor and Media Relations, Truitt (Trudi) Allcott
SVP and CIO, Richard W. (Rick) Mears, age 51
EVP Distribution, E. V. Clarke, age 51, $359,642 total compensation
SVP Sales and Operations, W. Marshall Simpson, age 43
VP Corporate Development, Robert K. Snead
SVP Specialty Services, Brian J. Shotto, age 48
President CEO and Director, Craig R. Smith, age 60
Director, Robert C. Sledd, age 59
Director, James E. (Jim) Ukrop, age 74
Director, John W. Gerdelman, age 60
Director, John T. Crotty, age 74
Director, James E. Rogers, age 66
Director, Anne Marie Whittemore, age 65
Director, A. Marshall Acuff Jr., age 72
Director, Peter S. Redding, age 73
Director, Eddie N. Moore Jr., age 64
Director, J. Alfred Broaddus Jr., age 73
Director, Richard E. Fogg, age 71
Auditors: KPMGLLP

LOCATIONS

HQ: Owens & Minor Inc.
9120 Lockwood Blvd., Mechanicsville VA 23116
Phone: 804-723-7000 **Fax:** 804-723-7100
Web: www.owens-minor.com

PRODUCTS/OPERATIONS

Selected Products

Clinical Supply Solutions (inventory and contract management service)
Implant Purchase Manager (utilization contract compliance and billing)OMDirect (Internet order fulfillment)
PANDAC system (helps track and control operating room inventories)
QSight (clinical inventory management system)
SurgiTrack (customizable surgical supply service)
WISDOM Gold (allows customers to track inventory usage and other information to keep costs down)

COMPETITORS

AmerisourceBergen
Buffalo Supply
Cardinal Health
Henry Schein
Invacare Supply Group
Johnson and Johnson Health Care Systems
Kerma Medical Products
McKesson
Medline Industries
Metro Medical Supply
Patterson Companies
PSS World Medical
SourceOne
Surgical Express
Tri-anim

HISTORICAL FINANCIALS

Company Type: Public

Income Statement FYE: December 31

	REVENUE ($ mil.)	NET INCOME ($ mil.)	NET PROFIT MARGIN	EMPLOYEES
12/11	8,627	115	1.3%	4,800
12/10	8,123	110	1.4%	4,800
12/09	8,037	104	1.3%	4,800
12/08	7,243	93	1.3%	5,300
12/07	6,800	72	1.1%	4,800
Annual Growth	6.1%	12.2%	—	0.0%

2011 Year-End Financials

Debt ratio: 10.92%
Return on equity: 12.55%
Cash ($ mil.): 135
Current ratio: 208.34
Long-term debt ($ mil.): 212
No. of shares (mil.): 63
Dividends
Yield: —
Payout: 44.20%
Market value ($ mil.): 1,763

	STOCK PRICE ($) FY Close	P/E High/Low		PER SHARE ($) Earnings	Dividends	Book Value
12/11	27.79	19	15	1.81	0.00	14.47
12/10	29.43	27	15	1.75	0.71	13.52
12/09	42.93	28	18	1.67	0.61	12.23
12/08	37.65	32	24	1.50	0.53	11.08
12/07	42.43	36	25	1.19	0.45	10.02
Annual Growth	(10.0%)	—	—	11.1%	—	9.6%

Owens Corning

Owens Corning operates in the PINK. Famous for its Pink Panther mascot and its trademarked PINK glass fiber insulation the company is a top global maker of building and composite material systems. Its building materials segment which accounts for more than 60% of sales makes insulation roofing and asphalt and other materials for the residential and commercial markets. Its composite products segment makes glass fiber reinforcement materials for the transportation industrial infrastructure marine wind energy and consumer markets. Owens Corning has operations in about 30 countries in the Americas Europe Africa and the Asia/Pacific region.

HISTORY

In the 1930s Corning Glass Works and Owens-Illinois Glass independently found that glass fiber has special resilience and strength. Realizing the potential market they formed joint venture Owens-Corning Fiberglas in 1938. The companies expanded rapidly in the 1940s and 1950s establishing several US plants and one in Canada. Their products included fine fibers thermal wool textiles and continuous filaments.

A US antitrust decree in 1949 denied the two founding firms any control over Owens-Corning. Each retained one-third ownership when the company went public in 1952. During the 1950s Owens-Corning developed new uses for fiberglass in automobile bodies shingles and insulation. In the 1960s the company expanded overseas. Fiberglass uses multiplied as applications developed in aerospace tires and underground tanks.

By 1980 the company had invested more than $700 million in acquisitions and made the Pink Panther its mascot. Owens-Corning introduced a rolled insulation in 1982.

The company successfully fended off a takeover attempt by Wickes Companies in 1986 but the effort left Owens-Corning with $2.6 billion in debt. It sold 10 businesses halved its research budget and laid off or lost to divestitures 46% of its workforce.

The company bought Fiberglas Canada that country's largest fiberglass-insulation maker in 1989. To expand globally Owens-Corning formed alliances in 1990 with BASF Lucky-Goldstar and Siam Cement.

Owens-Corning spent $65 million in 1991 on restructuring and took an $800 million charge to cover its liability to asbestos-exposure lawsuits (the company stopped making asbestos in 1972). That year it exchanged its commercial roofing business for the residential roofing business of Schuller International.

In 1994 Owens-Corning acquired UC Industries a maker of foam board insulation and bought Pilkington's insulation and industrial supply business. It also formed joint venture Alpha/Owens-Corning the largest producer of polyester resin in North America.

The company bought Western Fiberglass Group in 1995. That year Owens-Corning Fiberglas changed its name to Owens Corning and recouped part of its asbestos-related charge when it received a $330 million arbitration settlement from one of its insurers. Owens Corning formed a joint venture in India in 1995. Asbestos-litigation charges led to another loss in 1996.

In 1997 Owens Corning made several acquisitions including vinyl-siding maker Fibreboard and Amerimark Building Products a maker of vinyl and aluminum materials. In 1998 falling insulation prices led the company to announce layoffs and a restructuring plan that included plant closures. To pay off debt the company sold its half of Alpha/Owens-Corning to Alpha Corporation marking its exit from polyester-resin manufacturing. The company also agreed to take $550 million in a deal with France's Groupe Porcher Industries to form a joint venture for its fiberglass yarns and specialty materials businesses.

Seeking to end a liability issue that had dogged the company for a quarter of a century Owens Corning agreed in 1998 to pay out $1.2 billion to settle 176000 asbestos-related lawsuits. However the deal dissolved in 1999 when the US Supreme Court disallowed the settlement. Owens Corning then set up a $2.6 billion reserve fund to settle the claims. Also that year the company formed a joint venture (Decillion) with Geon to make fiberglass and PVC composites. In 2000 Owens Corning added to its acoustic panel business with the acquisition of Conwed Designscape. Still dogged by lawsuits that could eventually cost the company billions the company filed for bankruptcy protection late in 2000.

In 2001 Owens Corning sold its engineered pipe systems business to joint venture partner Saudi Arabian Amiantit Company. Seeking a foothold in the growing acoustic ceiling market the restructured company bought Wall Technology later that year.

Owens Corning increased its loose fill and thermacube insulation products line and capacity in 2002 in response to growing demand. It also acquired Woodbridge Virginia-based Certified Basements a basement finishing systems franchise and strengthened its position in Europe through a distribution contract with an Ashland Inc. subsidiary Ashland Finland OY to distribute its composite products through Ashland Specialty Chemical Company. Also that year Owens Corning's HOMExperts Home Repair and Improvements business expanded its service to Los Angeles San Francisco and Sacramento by acquiring assets of California-based Home Finishes LLC. (HOMExperts also operates in Atlanta Boston Chicago Denver Indianapolis Minneapolis/St. Paul and Washington DC.)

Following a period of falling stock prices for the company the New York Stock Exchange suspended its trading in December 2002. In early 2003 the company filed a bankruptcy reorganization plan to settle asbestos litigation. Under the plan Owens Corning provided partial payments to its creditors (mainly through distributing common stock and notes of the new reorganized company) and its existing common stock was canceled.

In 2004 Owens Corning Automotive (UK) Ltd. acquired the automotive assets of long-time customer Lancaster Fibre Technology Ltd. (UK). Lancaster Fibre Technology bases its automotive solutions on Owens Corning's Silentex Noise Control automotive silencer technology. It also purchased full ownership of Vitro Fibras (Mexico) a venture it had begun with Vitro (glass products Mexico) in 1957 to make light-density fiberglass products; molded pipe; board; and composite reinforcements. Owens Corning paid $71.5 million for Vitro's 60% stake.

The company emerged from bankruptcy in 2006. As part of the bankruptcy reorganization the company's paid some $5 billion in asbestos claims along with an additional $2.4 billion earmarked for debt holders.

After shedding the ponderous weight of bankruptcy the company didn't stand still. Owens Corning strengthened its composite operations in late 2007 when it acquired the reinforcements and composite fabrics business of materials giant Saint-Gobain.

While the company focused growth on its composites business it began trimming off other operations. Saint-Gobain acquired Owens Corning's vinyl siding business Norandex in 2007. Also that year it sold its continuous filament mat business to AGY and its Fabwel composite panels business to Crane.

EXECUTIVES

Chairman President and CEO, Michael H. (Mike) Thaman, age 48, $950,000 total compensation
VP Controller and Principal Accounting Officer, Kelly J. Schmidt, age 46
SVP CIO and Chief Shared Services Officer, David L. Johns, age 53, $367,500 total compensation
Group President Building Materials, Charles E. (Chuck) Dana, age 57, $450,001 total compensation
VP External Affairs, Brian McPeak
SVP and CFO, Duncan J. Palmer, age 47, $512,500 total compensation
VP and Chief Sustainability Officer, Frank C. O'Brien-Bernini, age 55
VP and Chief Innovation Officer, John Hillenbrand
SVP Human Resources, Daniel T. (Dan) Smith, age 47
Director Sustainability, Achilles Karagiozis
Group President Composite Solutions, Arnaud Genis, age 48
SVP and CFO, Michael C. McMurray
VP and Assistant General Counsel, Jeffrey S. Wilke
Leader Investor Relations, George Rosche
SVP General Counsel and Secretary, John W. Christy
Corporate Communications Leader, Matt Schroder
Director Corporate Communications, Todd Romain
Director, Ralph F. Hake, age 63
Director, Norman P. (Norm) Blake Jr., age 70
Director, F. Philip Handy, age 67
Director, J. Brian Ferguson, age 57
Director, Ann Iverson, age 67
Director, Landon Hilliard, age 72
Director, W. Gaston Caperton III, age 72
Director, Joseph F. Neely, age 71
Director, John D. Williams, age 57
Director, James J. McMonagle, age 67
Director, W. Howard Morris, age 51
Auditors: PricewaterhouseCoopersLLP

LOCATIONS

HQ: Owens Corning
One Owens Corning Parkway, Toledo, OH 43659
Phone: 419 248-8000
Web: www.owenscorning.com

2011 Sales

	$ mil.	% of total
US	3,552	67
Asia/Pacific	674	12
Europe	619	11
Canada & other	490	9
Total	**5,335**	**100**

PRODUCTS/OPERATIONS

2011 Sales by Segment

	$ mil.	% of total
Building Materials	3,537	64
Composites	1,976	36
Corporate eliminations	(178)	-
Total	**5,335**	**100**

COMPETITORS

Associated Materials
CertainTeed
Champion Window
Deceuninck
Dow Chemical
GAF Materials
Johns Manville
Knauf Insulation
PPG Industries
Saint-Gobain
SIG plc
TAMKO

HISTORICAL FINANCIALS

Company Type: Public

Income Statement

FYE: December 31

	REVENUE ($ mil.)	NET INCOME ($ mil.)	NET PROFIT MARGIN	EMPLOYEES
12/11	5,335	276	5.2%	15,000
12/10	4,997	933	18.7%	15,000
12/09	4,803	64	1.3%	16,000
12/08	5,847	(839)	—	18,000
12/07	4,978	96	1.9%	20,000
Annual Growth	1.7%	30.2%	—	(6.9%)

2011 Year-End Financials

Debt ratio: 26.07%
Return on equity: 7.46%
Cash ($ mil.): 52
Current ratio: 180.18
Long-term debt ($ mil.): 1,930
No. of shares (mil.): 120
Dividends
Yield: —
Payout: —
Market value ($ mil.): 3,472

	STOCK PRICE ($) FY Close	P/E High	P/E Low	PER SHARE ($) Earnings	Dividends	Book Value
12/11	28.72	17	9	2.23	0.00	30.61
12/10	31.15	5	3	7.37	0.00	29.40
12/09	25.64	52	10	0.50	0.00	22.07
12/08	17.30	—	—	(6.56)	0.00	21.52
12/07	20.22	48	27	0.74	0.00	30.49
Annual Growth	9.2%	—	—	31.8%	—	0.1%

Owens-Illinois, Inc.

Owens-Illinois (O-I) is involved in more toasts than Dick Clark and all Irish writers combined. The world's largest maker of glass containers it touts a leading market presence in the regions in which it operates —North and South America Europe and the Asia/Pacific. O-I's glass containers include bottles in a wide range of shapes sizes and colors used to hold beer wine liquor as well as soft drinks juice and other beverages. It also makes glass containers for foods such as soups salad dressings and dairy products and for pharmaceuticals. Major customers include Anheuser-Busch H.J. Heinz and SABMiller. Some 80 plants dot 21 countries; Europe and North America represent about 70% of O-I sales.

Despite its depth of operations and industry dominance the recession's impact on consumer end-markets coupled with the loss of certain beer contracts continues to chip away O-I's sales. In 2010 sales decreased more than 12% since their peak in 2008. The giant glass-maker suffered a loss in 2010 following two consecutive years of declining earnings. The dismal results however are not attributable to earnings from continuing operations which remain strong fueled by growth from O-I's higher-margin business in South America.

Among several ongoing issues denting profits O-I discontinued its plastic packaging business (2007) and the Venezuelan government took over of O-I operations in that country (2010). The company is hit with an energy bill that accounts for a whopping 15%-25% of production costs a rising transportation tab and a hefty asbestos-liability payment. In addition performance is rattled by fluctuating raw material prices and seasonal demand for glass products; these are partially offset by higher selling prices passed through to customers of premium products.

More significant O-I's bottom line is eroded by interest expense to service its $4.3 billion in corporate debt. In 2010 interest expense consumed more than 25% of net sales. An additional $3.6 billion in debt was taken on in 2010 to fund acquisitions.

Since 1990 O-I has acquired more than two dozen glass container businesses. In mid-2011 the company completed its acquisition of Verrerie du Languedoc a France-based bottle manufacturer. Verrerie du Languedoc is best known as the bottle supplier for both Perrier and San Pellegrino sparkling waters (by Nestle Waters). The deal which garners a plant near a Perrier bottler supports a new strategic tie-up between the world's premium water company and glass maker. Targeting the Asia/Pacific region O-I in 2010 purchased the glass container making business of Northern China's Hebei Rixin Glass Group. The deal more than doubles O-I's production capacity in China propelling it to the #2 spot in the country's glass manufacturing industry.

On its heels O-I partnered with Thailand-based Berli Jucker Public Co. to score four beverage and food container manufacturing plants located in China and Southeast Asia. Malaysian and Vietnamese plants are held as 50-50 joint ventures and the Chinese facility is managed as part of O-I's China operations. Berli Jucker holds majority ownership of the Thai plant.

O-I also expanded its presence in South America in 2010 with the acquisition of Brazil-based glassmaker Companhia Industrial de Vidros (CIV) for $594 million. CIV is expected to increase O-I sales in the region by about $200 million within a year of the acquisition.

O-I's expansion into developing operationally less-costly regions is accompanied by a consolidation of its more expensive manufacturing facilities due to their older and less efficient equipment located in markets where demand is maturing. In 2010 the company closed plants in Pennsylvania Michigan and California cumulatively eliminating 760 jobs. The company shuttered a plant in Finland in 2009 cutting 100 jobs. In 2008 the company closed a glass container plant in New Brunswick transferring production to other facilities in Canada.

Simultaneously O-I is placing a priority on winning over customers that have shied away from glass packaging as well as encouraging existing ones to use more. To this end its marketing efforts piggyback on the wave toward sustainable packaging. Along with developing a variety of container features and functions the company highlights the benefits of glass recyclability. The company is shrinking its own environmental footprint as well. In 2007 O-I initiated a 10-year plan to cut its energy use by 50% and its carbon dioxide-equivalent emissions by 65% in tandem with boosting its use of post-consumer recycled glass to 60%.

HISTORY

The Owens Bottle Machine Corp. was incorporated in Toledo Ohio in 1907 as the successor to a four-year-old New Jersey company of the same name. It initially grew by acquiring small glass companies. In 1929 Owens bought the Illinois Glass Co. (medical and pharmaceutical glass) and became Owens-Illinois Glass.

The company bought Libbey Glass (tableware) in 1935. Three years later Owens-Illinois and Corning Glass which were both studying uses for glass fiber began Owens-Corning Fiberglass a joint venture with a virtual industry monopoly.

After WWII Owens-Illinois (O-I) started to diversify beyond glass. The company went public in 1952. In 1956 it bought National Container (cardboard boxes). It also created a semi-rigid plastic container that was adopted by bleach and detergent companies.

The introduction of the non-returnable bottle in the 1960s gave new life to the glass industry. During the late 1960s the company bought Lily Tulip Cups (sold in 1981). In the 1970s the company started producing specialty optical and TV glass.

With the glass industry foundering at the beginning of the 1980s O-I invested over $600 million in its glass operations. In 1986 O-I refused an initial purchase offer by the buyout firm of Kohlberg Kravis Roberts (now KKR) but KKR raised the offer; O-I was sold and went private. Total debt after the LBO was $4.4 billion.

In the years following the LBO the company sold its forest products mortgage banking and health care businesses. O-I went public again in 1991 and expanded its plastics business with the purchase of Specialty Packaging Products in 1992 which added trigger sprayers and finger pumps to its line. The next year the company expanded its South American operations. O-I spun off Libbey Glass as a separate public firm and sold 51% of its interest in Kimble Glass (specialty packaging and laboratory ware; the rest was sold in 1997). The company acquired a majority stake in Ballarpur Industries one of India's largest makers of glass containers.

O-I bought Avir S.p.A. a European glass container maker in 1997. It also acquired assets of a bankrupt competitor Anchor Glass which gave it more than a 40% share of the US glass container market. O-I purchased the packaging unit of UK-based BTR (now called Invensys) in 1998. The next year the company sold its UK-based glass container maker Rockware Group (formerly part of BTR) to Ireland-based container maker Ardagh and its Chicago Heights pharmaceutical glass business to German glassmaker Gerresheimer Glas AG.

In 2000 following a short-lived victory for the company in asbestos-related litigation a US district judge in Texas overturned a $1.6 billion default judgment to be awarded the company by former asbestos maker T&N Ltd.

Charges related to asbestos litigation and restructuring fees cost the company dearly in 2000 as it posted a $270 million loss for the year. In 2001 O-I sold its Harbor Capital Advisors business to the Netherlands-based Robeco Groep for an estimated $490 million.

From 1998 to the end of 2002 O-I acquired 18 glass container businesses in as many countries (including businesses in the Americas Europe and the Asia/Pacific region) and seven plastics packaging businesses that operated in 12 countries. In 2002 one of the company's businesses Owens-Brockway Glass Container Inc. sold $1 billion worth of secured notes to pull the subsidiary out of debt a plan intended to improve the health of the entire company.

In 2003 Joseph Lemieux stepped down as CEO of the company. Steven McCracken was named president and CEO. McCracken replaced Lemieux as chairman in 2004.

O-I completed its acquisition of BSN Glasspack Europe's #2 glass container maker for about $1.3 billion the same year. The deal made O-I Europe's largest container company. Late in 2004 O-I sold its American and European blow-molded plastics operations to Graham Packaging Company. The company's asbestos-related cash payments in 2005 were $171 million (down from $190 million in 2004). The company announced in 2005 that it would begin doing business as O-I.

Steven McCracken resigned as chairman and CEO late in 2006. Board member Albert Stroucken who held similar leadership roles at H.B. Fuller succeeded McCracken. That year O-I shuttered a factory that made machine parts and closed a small recycling facility as part of its effort to focus on its core glass business and reduce costs.

In 2007 the company sold its plastics packaging business (O-I Plastics) which manufactured prescription bottles tamper-proof closures and injection-molded containers to Rexam for $1.8 billion. The sale included nearly 20 plants in the Americas Asia and Europe and an interest in two Mexican joint ventures formed in 2007. Before it was divested O-I Plastics accounted for a little more than 10% of sales.

EXECUTIVES

SVP Strategic Planning and General Counsel, James W. Baehren, age 61, $408,275 total compensation
VP and General Counsel, Philip McWeeny, $340,000 total compensation
Chairman President and CEO, Albert P. L. (Al) Stroucken, age 64, $1,024,000 total compensation
SVP and CFO, Edward C. (Ed) White, age 64, $438,046 total compensation
VP and Treasurer, Catherine E. Neel, age 51
VP Global Environment Health and Safety, Deborah C. Hockman, age 55
VP Sales and Marketing O-I North America, Abbott Wolfe
VP Glass Container Research and Development, Robert E. Lachmiller
CFO, Stephen P. Bramlage Jr.
VP Investor Relations, John Haudrich
VP Distribution Drug and Chemicals, Paul F. Butts
President O-I Europe, Jose A. Lorente, $393,949 total compensation
SVP and Chief Human Resources Officer, Paul Jarrell
VP and Chief Strategy Officer, Gregory T. (Greg) Sipla, age 45
President O-I North America, Miguel Escobar
President O-I Latin America, Andres Lopez
VP and Chief Process Improvement Officer, Ron White
Managing Director China, Paul Wang
VP and Chief Communications Officer, Barbara Owens
VP and Chief Procurement Officer, Radhika Batra
VP Sustainability, Jay Scripter
SVP Integrated Supply Chain, Ed Snyder
VP Global Quality, Shaun McMackin
VP Global Product Innovation, Michael Lonsway
VP Global Accounts, Anthony (Tony) Caracciolo
Corporate Controller Financial Reporting, John Reynolds
Director Corporate Development, Joe Juarez
VP and CTO, Giancarlo Currarino
SVP and Chief Commercial Officer, Tony Gardner
President Asia/Pacific, Sergio Galindo
President O-I China, Robert McGuire
Director, Gary F. Colter, age 66
Director, Corbin A. McNeill Jr., age 72
Director, Anastasia D. (Stasia) Kelly, age 62
Director, Peter S. Hellman, age 62
Director, Helge H. Wehmeier, age 69
Director, Dennis K. Williams, age 67
Director, Hugh H. Roberts, age 60
Director, Thomas L. Young, age 67

Director, John J. McMackin Jr., age 60
Director, Jay L. Geldmacher, age 57
Director, David H. Y. Ho, age 52
Auditors: Ernst&YoungLLP

LOCATIONS

HQ: Owens-Illinois, Inc.
One Michael Owens Way, Perrysburg, OH 43551
Phone: 567 336-5000
Web: www.o-i.com

2011 Sales

Regions		
North America	1,929	26
South America	1,226	17
Total	**7,358**	**100**

PRODUCTS/OPERATIONS

Selected Customers

Brown Forman
Constellation
Heineken
H.J. Heinz
Lion
MillerCoors
Molson/Coors
Nestle
PepsiCo
Pernod Ricard
Saxco International
Yuengling

Selected Glass Container Applications

Beer
Food
Juice
Other non-alcoholic beverages (returnable/refillable)
Pharmaceuticals
Ready-to-drink low-alcohol refreshers
Soft drinks
Spirits
Tea
Wine

COMPETITORS

Alcoa
Amcor
Anchor Glass
AptarGroup
Ball Corp.
Bemis
Berry Plastics
BWAY
Consolidated Container
Constar International
Crown Holdings
Graham Packaging
Jarden
Newell Rubbermaid
Plastipak
Rexam
Saint-Gobain
Saint-Gobain Containers
Sealed Air Corp.
Silgan
Sonoco Products
Tetra Pak
Tupperware Brands
Vitro

HISTORICAL FINANCIALS

Company Type: Public

Income Statement

FYE: December 31

	REVENUE ($ mil.)	NET INCOME ($ mil.)	NET PROFIT MARGIN	EMPLOYEES
12/11	7,358	(510)	—	24,000
12/10	6,633	(47)	—	24,000
12/09	7,066	161	2.3%	22,000
12/08	7,884	258	3.3%	23,000
12/07	7,679	1,340	17.5%	24,000
Annual Growth	(1.1%)	—	—	0.0%

2011 Year-End Financials

Debt ratio: 45.18%
Return on equity: (-60.79)%
Cash ($ mil.): 400
Current ratio: 120.00
Long-term debt ($ mil.): 3,627
No. of shares (mil.): 164
Dividends
Yield: —
Payout: —
Market value ($ mil.): 3,186

	STOCK PRICE ($) FY Close	P/E High/Low		PER SHARE ($) Earnings	Dividends	Book Value
12/11	19.38	—	—	(3.11)	0.00	5.10
12/10	30.70	—	—	(0.28)	0.00	11.09
12/09	32.87	40	10	0.95	0.00	9.12
12/08	27.33	39	11	1.52	0.00	6.23
12/07	49.50	6	2	7.99	0.00	13.90
Annual Growth	(20.9%)	—	—	—	—	(22.2%)

PACCAR Inc.

Old PACCARs never die they just get a new Peterbilt. PACCAR is one of the world's largest designers and manufacturers of big rig diesel trucks. Its lineup of light- medium- and heavy-duty trucks includes the Kenworth Peterbilt and DAF nameplates. The company also manufactures and distributes aftermarket truck parts for these brands. PACCAR's other products include Braden Carco and Gearmatic industrial winches. With the exception of a few company-owned branches PACCAR's trucks and parts are sold through independent dealers. Its PACCAR Financial Services and PacLease subsidiaries offer financing and truck leasing respectively.

Geographic Reach

The company owns manufacturing plants in five US states three countries in Europe and a facility in each of Australia Canada and Mexico. PACCAR Financial Services operates through three continents spanning around 20 countries.

In the European light/medium market PACCAR competes with DAF cab-over-engine trucks assembled in the UK by Leyland. About 55% of PACCAR's revenues are generated outside the US.

Financial Analysis

PACCAR's balance sheet has made a milestone comeback after the painful effects of the recession. From 2010 to 2011 total revenue surged by almost 60% toppling out at roughly $16.4 billion the second-highest in the company's history. Net income also skyrocketed over 100% from $457 million to more than $1 billion.

The sizable growth was primarily due to a major uptick in truck segment income which accounted for 93% of total 2011 revenues. Truck deliveries increased by over 100% in the US and 72% in Canada for 2011. Internationally total sales increased in Australia Mexico and South America primarily due to higher new truck deliveries in Mexico and the Andean region of South America. Overall it sold 138000 units in 2011 compared to 79000 units in 2010. The company was also helped by record aftermarket parts sales.

Strategy

PACCAR continues to examine business opportunities in Asia with a primary focus on Brazil China and India. In 2011 it opened a new technical center in Pune India focused on providing engineering information technology and component sourcing services across the emerging region.

The company's strategy is also focused on building and releasing new aerodynamic vehicles to broaden its product line. In 2012 it launched the new Kenworth T680 and the Peterbilt Model 579 line of aerodynamic vehicles.

HISTORY

William Pigott founded the Seattle Car Manufacturing Company in 1905 to produce railroad cars for timber transport. Finding immediate success Pigott began to make other kinds of railcars in 1906. When the Seattle plant burned the next year the company moved near Renton Washington. In 1911 Pigott renamed the company Seattle Car & Foundry.

In 1917 Seattle Car merged with the Twohy Brothers of Portland. The new company Pacific Car & Foundry was sold to American Car & Foundry in 1924. Pacific Car then diversified into bus manufacturing structural steel fabrications and metal technology.

Pacific Car was in decline by 1934 when William's son Paul bought it; since then the company has remained under family management. Paul Pigott added Hofius Steel and Equipment and Tricoach a bus manufacturer in 1936. The company entered the truck-making business with the 1945 purchase of Seattle-based Kenworth.

In the 1950s Pacific Car became the industry leader in mechanical refrigerator car production. It began producing off-road heavy trucks and acquired Peterbilt Trucks of Oakland (1958). To augment its winch business Pacific Car bought Canada's Gearmatic in 1963.

The company moved its headquarters to Bellevue Washington in 1969 and changed its name to PACCAR in 1971. Acquisitions in the 1970s included Wagner Mining Equipment (1973); International Car the largest US caboose producer (1975); and Braden Winch (1977). In 1980 PACCAR acquired UK-based Foden Trucks.

Demand for smaller trucks caused heavy-truck sales to drop 35% between 1979 and 1986 leading PACCAR to close two factories its first closures in 41 years. In 1987 PACCAR bought Trico Industries (oil-drilling equipment). Also that year PACCAR entered the auto parts sales market buying Al's Auto Supply; in 1988 it bought Grand Auto.

Truck demand hit a nine-year low in 1990. PACCAR responded by cutting its workforce by 11% that year and withdrawing from the auto parts wholesale market in 1991. The following year PACCAR acquired an interest in Wood Group ESP a maker and servicer of oil-field equipment. In 1993 PACCAR bought Caterpillar's line of winches.

In 1995 PACCAR opened a truck assembly plant in South Africa and bought the rest of VILPAC its truck-making joint venture in Mexico. When workers in Quebec went on strike the company closed the plant after eight months and shifted production to Mexico.

PACCAR expanded in Europe in 1996 by acquiring medium- and heavy-duty truck maker DAF Trucks (the Netherlands). Charles Pigott retired in 1996 and his son Mark became chairman and CEO. In 1997 PACCAR sold Trico Industries to EVI. The next year PACCAR bought light- and medium-duty truck maker Leyland Trucks (UK). After an $80 million renovation the company began producing medium-duty trucks in 1999 at its Quebec plant which was idled after the strike. That year the company started Paccar.com a venture capital fund for e-commerce startups and ePaccar an e-commerce marketplace for the trucking industry. It also sold its Al's Auto Supply and

Grand Auto parts retail operations to CSK Auto for $143 million.

Slow sales of large trucks prompted the company to lay off about one-third of its hourly –and almost one-fifth of its salaried –Peterbilt workers in 2000. In 2001 PACCAR entered a long-term contract with Cummins for the supply of heavy-duty engines. Later that year in order to bring production in line with worldwide demand PACCAR closed two truck manufacturing facilities –the Seattle Kenworth plant and a Foden plant in the UK (the entire Foden line was retired in 2006). The Peterbilt Motors Company plant in Nashville signed a five-year labor agreement with the UAW labor union in 2003.

Although the demand for PACCAR trucks in the US and Canada (primarily the Kenworth and Peterbilt brands) dipped in 2007 it was offset to a degree by a rise in both European truck sales and aftermarket products. In 2007 truck deliveries in Europe were up 8% over 2006 figures. In an effort to dedicate production efforts of its DAF branded trucks PACCAR retired the Foden Trucks line of trucks in 2006. Unit deliveries to Australia Mexico and other areas not deemed primary regions were up 35%.

In 2008 the company unveiled an enhanced engine research and development facility at PACCAR's Technical Center opened a new parts distribution center in Budapest and achieved a 20% capacity improvement at its Leyland manufacturing facility in the UK.

While PACCAR expected sales to drop in 2009 by approximately 40000 –the reality is they decreased by 61000 or about 55% over 2008. With the onslaught of the 2008 economic recession the company responded by reducing its headcount by 14%. The company welcomed a new president at the beginning of 2011. Jim Cardillo who served PACCAR for more than 20 years retired at the end of 2010. Ron Armstrong who counts 17 years with the company –most recently as executive VP –was elected to fill the position.

EXECUTIVES

Secretary, Janice M. D'Amato
VP, Richard E. Bangert II
VP, George E. West Jr.
Chairman and CEO, Mark C. Pigott, age 58, $1,350,000 total compensation
VP and General Counsel, David C. Anderson, age 58
EVP, Robert J. (Bob) Christensen, age 55
VP, Helene N. Mawyer
President, Ronald E. (Ron) Armstrong, age 57, $389,385 total compensation
VP, William D. (Bill) Jackson
VP, Thomas A. Lundahl
EVP, Daniel D. (Dan) Sobic, age 58, $460,000 total compensation
VP and Controller, Michael T. Barkley, age 56
VP, Jack LeVier
Treasurer, Robin E. Easton
VP, William R. Kozek
VP and CIO, T. Kyle Quinn, age 50
VP, Samuel Means III
VP; President DAF Trucks, Harrie C.A.M. Schippers
Director, Charles R. (Chuck) Williamson, age 63
Director, Stephen F. (Steve) Page, age 72
Director, Warren R. Staley, age 69
Director, Gregory M. E. (Greg) Spierkel, age 55
Director, John M. Fluke Jr., age 69
Director, Alison J. Carnwath, age 59
Director, Kirk S. Hachigian, age 52
Director, Robert T. Parry, age 72
Director, William G. (Gary) Reed Jr., age 73
Director, John M. Pigott, age 48
Auditors: Ernst&YoungLLP

LOCATIONS

HQ: PACCAR Inc
777 106th Ave. NE, Bellevue WA 98004
Phone: 425-468-7400 **Fax:** 425-468-8216
Web: www.paccar.com

2011 Sales

	$ mil.	% of total
US	7,389	45
Other regions	3,861	24

PRODUCTS/OPERATIONS

2011 Sales

	$ mil.	% of total
Trucks & other	15,325	93
Total	**16,355**	**100**

Selected Divisions and Subsidiaries

DAF Trucks N.V. (The Netherlands)
Dynacraft (battery cables hose assemblies and air conditioning hardlines)
Kenworth
Kenworth Mexicana S.A. de C.V.
Leyland Trucks Limited (UK)
PACCAR Australia Pty. Ltd.
PACCAR Engines
PACCAR Financial Corp.
PACCAR Mexico S.A. de C.V.
PACCAR of Canada Ltd.
 Canadian Kenworth Co.
 Peterbilt of Canada
PACCAR Parts
PACCAR Sales North America Inc.
PACCAR Winch
 Braden Winches & Hoists
 Carco Winches
 Gearmatic Winches

COMPETITORS

AGCO
Caterpillar
Cummins
Daimler
Dana Holding
Deere
Eaton
Fiat
Ford Motor
General Motors
Hino Motors
Isuzu
Iveco S.p.A.
Mack Trucks
MAN
Meritor
Morris Material Handling
Navistar International
Oshkosh Truck
Scania
UD Trucks
Volvo

HISTORICAL FINANCIALS

Company Type: Public

Income Statement FYE: December 31

	REVENUE ($ mil.)	NET INCOME ($ mil.)	NET PROFIT MARGIN	EMPLOYEES
12/11	16,355	1,042	6.4%	23,400
12/10	10,292	457	4.4%	17,700
12/09	8,086	111	1.4%	15,200
12/08	14,972	1,017	6.8%	18,700
12/07	15,221	1,227	8.1%	21,800
Annual Growth	1.8%	(4.0%)	—	1.8%

2011 Year-End Financials

Debt ratio: 38.76%
Return on equity: 19.43%
Cash ($ mil.): 1,990
Current ratio: 184.12
Long-term debt ($ mil.): 6,655
No. of shares (mil.): 356
Dividends
 Yield: —
 Payout: 45.45%
Market value ($ mil.): 13,369

	STOCK PRICE ($) FY Close	P/E High/Low		PER SHARE ($) Earnings	Dividends	Book Value
12/11	37.47	20	11	2.86	0.00	15.03
12/10	57.34	46	27	1.25	0.69	14.67
12/09	36.27	128	67	0.31	0.64	14.02
12/08	28.60	20	8	2.78	0.82	13.36
12/07	54.48	29	14	3.29	1.65	13.66
Annual Growth	(8.9%)	—	—	(3.4%)	—	2.4%

Pacific Mutual Holding Co.

While the breaching whale logo used by Pacific Life Insurance evokes the West Coast the company operates all across the US. As the primary operating subsidiary of Pacific Mutual Holding Company Pacific Life offers a wide range of life insurance asset management and financial services products including individual annuities and mutual funds. It also offers a variety of investment products and services for individuals businesses and pension plans. Subsidiary Pacific Life & Annuity offers the same mix of life insurance and investment products and services for individuals and businesses in New York. Pacific Life was founded in 1868.

Operations

Pacific Life policyholders are members of parent Pacific Mutual Holding Company which was created in 1997 following a conversion to the mutual holding company structure. Pacific LifeCorp is the intermediate stock holding company.

While life insurance is the company's bread and butter it has brought in other operations for variety. Pacific Life's Aviation Capital Group subsidiary leases commercial jets to 90 airlines in more than 40 countries. It also manages aircraft assets for third parties such as commercial airlines aircraft manufacturers and financial institutions. Other subsidiaries include Pacific Asset Management which provides third-party institutional asset management.

Sales & Marketing

Pacific Life's insurance policies are sold through independent distributors and through dealer/broker subsidiary Pacific Select Distributors.

Financial Analysis

The company's growth strategies helped Pacific Life achieve strong results in 2011 with revenues increasing 15% over 2010 to almost 6.7 billion and net income increasing 29% to $679 million. Its operating income climbed a whopping 40% over 2010 to reach $823 million. The gains achieved were attributed to enhanced service offerings expanded life insurance annuity and mutual fund product offerings and the two acquisitions made that year.

Strategy

Being a mutual company Pacific Life operates with a long-term focus to serve in the best interests of its policyholders and clients. in doing so the company navigated the chilly economic waters of the 2008-2009 recession by steadily introducing new products and building up its capital reserves. By 2010 its net income had grown as risk-weary customers squirreled more of their savings and retirement monies into life insurance and mutual funds.

Mergers Acquisitions & Divestitures

In 2008 the company added international reinsurance to its portfolio when it acquired the former London-based specialty reinsurance operations of Scottish Re and renamed the business as Pacific Life Re. It then added life retrocession (reinsurance of a reinsurer) to its line-up in 2011 by acquiring that business from Manulife and expanded its business to include the Toronto Boston Barbados and Cologne markets.

Also in 2011 Pacific life bought JPMorgan Chase's pension risk advisory business to form Pacific Global Advisors. The unit offers risk management solutions and advisory services to pension plan sponsors.

The firm divested a noncore business College Savings Bank in 2012 to a syndicate of investors for an undisclosed price. The banking unit managed two state-sponsored 529 college savings plans.

EXECUTIVES

EVP Retirement Solutions Division, Dewey P. Bushaw
EVP Real Estate Division, Michael S. Robb
Chairman and CEO, James T. (Jim) Morris, age 52
EVP Life Insurance Division, Michael A. Bell
President, Khanh T. Tran, age 56
SVP Brand Management and Public Affairs, Robert G. Haskell
SVP Business Development, Andrew Oleksiw
Group Managing Director and CEO Aviation Capital Group, R. Stephen Hannahs
EVP and Chief Investment Officer Investment Management Division; President Pacific Life Funds and Pacific Select Fund, Mark W. Holmlund
SVP and Chief Risk Officer, Henry M. (Hank) McMillan
EVP Corporate Development; CEO Pacific Select Fund and Pacific Life Funds, Mary Ann Brown
Assistant VP Pacific Life Academy Corporate Division, Greg Cleveland
President and CEO College Savings Bank, Gilbert S. Johnson
SVP Operations Life Insurance Division, Martha A. Gates
SVP and Treasurer, Denis P. Kalscheur
SVP Tax, Thomas (Tom) Gibbons
SVP and Chief Accounting Officer, Edward R. Byrd
SVP Enterprise Risk Management, Joseph E. Celentano
SVP and Chief Marketing Officer Life Insurance Division, Richard J. Schindler
VP Sales, John White
Chief Marketing Officer College Savings Bank, Dan Davenport
SVP General Counsel and Director, Sharon A. Cheever
VP Marketing, Christine Tucker
SVP Sales and Chief Marketing Officer Retirement Solutions Division, Chris van Mierlo
Sales Manager Regional/Wirehouse, Jack Hunter
Sales Manager Independent Planner, Stuart Holland
Sales Manager Bank/Financial Institutions, George Paulik
EVP and CFO, Adrian S. Griggs
SVP Investment Management, Todd Nasser
CFO College Savings Bank, Cheyanne Li
CEO Pacific Life Re, David R. Howell
Chief Marketing Officer UK and Ireland Pacific Life Re, David Heeney
Principal Officer and Director Asia Pacific Life Re, Andrew Linfoot
Assistant VP Public Affairs, Tennyson Oyler
SVP Technology and Operations Retirement Solutions Division, Philip A. Teeter
SVP Information Technology and Strategic Planning Life Insurance, Dawn M. Trautman
VP Finance Retirement Solutions Division; CFO Pacific Select Distributors, Gregory Keeling
VP Valuation and Risk Management Life Insurance Division, Katharine B. Young
Assistant VP Risk Management Retirement Solutions Division, David Chang
Assistant VP Program Management Real Estate Division, Lisa Fields
Assistant VP and Product Leader Life Insurance Division, Kenneth Fisher
Assistant VP Information Technology Investment Management Division, Darlene Goodwin
Assistant VP IT Operations Life Insurance Division, Matthew Hansberger
Assistant VP Tax Corporate Division, Kevin Hendra
Assistant VP Accounting and Reporting Investment Management Division, Jennifer Krumm
Assistant VP Information Technology Services Corporate Division, Dean Lagerborg
Assistant VP Application Development Life Insurance Division, Bill Martineau
Assistant VP Tax Counsel Corporate Division, Christian Phanco
Assistant VP Corporate Finance Corporate Division, Brian Reeves
Assistant VP Information Security and Business Continuity Planning Corporate Division, Scott Reynolds
Assistant VP Marketing and Distribution Life Insurance Division, Janice Sutton
Assistant VP Credit Analysis Investment Management Division, Jason Todd
SVP Human Resources and Facilities, Carol R. Sudbeck
Media Relations, Milda Goodman
VP Secretary and Director, Jane Guon
Director, Lawrence F. Harr
SVP General Counsel and Director, Sharon A. Cheever
VP Secretary and Director, Jane Guon
Auditors: Deloitte&ToucheLLP

LOCATIONS

HQ: Pacific Life Insurance Company
700 Newport Center Dr., Newport Beach CA 92660-6397
Phone: 949-219-3011 **Fax:** 949-219-7614
Web: www.pacificlife.com

PRODUCTS/OPERATIONS

2011 Revenues

	% of total
Retirement	44
Life	33
Aviation Capital	10
Reinsurance	7
Other	6
Total	**100**

Selected Subsidiaries

Aviation Capital Group Corp.
Pacific Asset Management
Pacific Global Advisors LLC
Pacific Life Re Limited (UK)
Pacific Select Distributors Inc.

COMPETITORS

Guardian Life
John Hancock Financial Services
Liberty Mutual
Mutual of Omaha
Nationwide
New York Life
Northwestern Mutual
Lincoln Financial Group
MassMutual
MetLife
Penn Mutual
Principal Financial
Prudential

HISTORICAL FINANCIALS

Company Type: Subsidiary

Income Statement

FYE: December 31

	ASSETS ($ mil.)	NET INCOME ($ mil.)	INCOME AS % OF ASSETS	EMPLOYEES
12/11	116,811	679	0.6%	0
12/10	115,992	480	0.4%	0
12/09	109,954	434	0.4%	0
12/08	96,983	(289)	—	0
12/07	0	647****************%		0
Annual Growth	—	1.2%	—	—

2011 Year-End Financials

Debt ratio: 6.86%—
Return on equity: 7.87%
Cash ($ mil.): 2,966
Current ratio: —
Long-term debt ($ mil.): 8,011
Dividends
Yield: —
Payout: —
Market value ($ mil.): —

Pacificorp

PacifiCorp has refocused on its core businesses: regulated utilities Pacific Power and Rocky Mountain Power which together provide electricity to 1.7 million customers in six western states. The subsidiaries operate 16200 miles of transmission lines and 62800 miles of distribution lines. PacifiCorp owns or has stakes in almost 70 thermal hydroelectric and renewable generation facilities that supply its utilities with more than 10400 MW of net capacity. Its PacifiCorp Energy unit purchases power from other generators and it sells excess power to wholesale customers in the western US. The company is a unit of MidAmerican Energy Holdings.

Operations

PacifiCorp consists of three business units: PacifiCorp Energy (electric generation commercial energy trading and coal mining) headquartered in Salt Lake City Utah; Pacific Power (electricity distribution to customers in Oregon Washington and California) headquartered in Portland; and Rocky Mountain Power (power distribution to customers in Utah Wyoming and Idaho) headquartered in Salt Lake City. PacifiCorp is headquartered in Portland.

Financial Analysis

PacifiCorp's 2011 revenues increased by 3.5% thanks in part to rate increases a higher commercial customer load primarily in Utah and Oregon an increase in industrial customer load in Utah and the impacts of colder weather on increasing residential customer load in Oregon.

However the company's net income dropped by 2% in 2011 due to lower wholesale sales prices and volumes higher volumes of purchased electricity an increase in coal prices and higher depreciation and property tax expenses. Other factors included lower sales of renewable energy credits partially offset by higher retail prices approved by regulators higher retail customer load and the net impact of general rate case settlement in Utah.

Strategy

Growing its generating capacity in 2011 PacifiCorp began building the 637-MW Lake Side 2 combined-cycle combustion turbine natural gas-fueled generating facility which is expected to be placed in service in 2014. In 2011 to secure fuel supply the company's Fossil Rock unit acquired the Cottonwood coal reserve lease in Emery County Utah. Cottonwood has 47 million tons of recoverable coal.

Ownership

PacifiCorp is an indirect subsidiary of MidAmerican Energy Holdings itself a consolidated subsidiary of Berkshire Hathaway.

HISTORY

Utility holding company Electric Bond and Share bought several small West Coast utilities and formed Pacific Power & Light (PP&L) in 1910 then expanded its service area through acquisitions and by building transmission lines. The Public Utility Holding Company Act of 1935 forced Electric Bond and Share to unload PP&L in 1950. Uncertainty over government power contracts spurred PP&L to build its own hydroelectric dams. In 1953 PP&L merged with Mountain States Power (which had two small phone companies) expanding into Idaho Montana and Wyoming.

In 1961 the utility merged with California Oregon Power and began operating coal-fired plants and acquiring some 1.5 billion tons of Montana and Wyoming coal reserves.

PP&L acquired Telephone Utilities (Washington) and long-distance company Alascom (Alaska) in the 1970s. It also formed the Northern Energy Resources Company (NERCO) to manage its coal-mining units.

The firm reorganized in 1982 becoming PacifiCorp. PP&L became a subsidiary and the phone services were renamed Pacific Telecom. In the mid-1980s PacifiCorp bought a financial service firm and explored for oil and gas through NERCO. In 1987 PacifiCorp merged with Utah Power and opened its grid to independent power producers.

By the early 1990s PacifiCorp was dropping poor performers. It entered wholesale power marketing in 1994 the year Fred Buckman became CEO. Under Buckman PacifiCorp bought Australian utility company Powercor in 1995 split Pacific Telecom into a separate subsidiary sold Alascom to AT&T and split its utility operations into generation transmission and retail sales units.

PacifiCorp bought natural gas marketer TPC in 1997 but sold TPC's gas pipeline to El Paso Natural Gas (now El Paso Energy). That year PacifiCorp agreed to buy the UK's Energy Group for about $9.6 billion including debt and sold Pacific Telecom to Century Telephone (now CenturyTel) and Pacific Generation an independent power producer developer to NRG Energy.

But in 1998 Buckman's plans began to unravel. Rival suitor Texas Utilities (which became TXU which in turn became Energy Future Holdings) for example cost the company $67 million by outbidding it for Energy Group. And PacifiCorp's power trading arm lost $151 million when its suppliers couldn't meet the energy demands of a sweltering hot summer in the western US. Buckman resigned replaced by chairman Keith McKennon and PacifiCorp was forced to reorganize. Later it agreed to be bought by UK-based Scottish Power.

In 1999 PacifiCorp sold TPC to NIPSCO (now called NiSource) for $132.5 million. It also sold its Montana service area to Flathead Electric Cooperative and exited most of its power-trading operations.

Scottish Power completed its purchase of PacifiCorp in 1999 and Alan Richardson replaced McKennon as CEO. The next year PacifiCorp sold its Centralia Washington coal-fired power plant and an adjacent coal mine to Canada's TransAlta for $554 million and it sold Powercor for $2.14 billion to Cheung Kong Infrastructure.

PacifiCorp experienced an unscheduled outage at one of its Utah power plants for about six months in 2000-01 which coupled with unusually high-priced wholesale electricity in the region caused losses for the company and led it to request rate increases for its service territories in 2001. That year PacifiCorp's interest in PacifiCorp Power Marketing (now PPM Energy) its remaining energy trading unit was transferred to another Scottish Power unit.

Growing its national market share MidAmerican Energy Holdings acquired PacifiCorp in 2006 from Scottish Power for a reported $5.1 billion.

EXECUTIVES

Chairman and CEO, Gregory E. (Greg) Abel, age 49
Director; President Rocky Mountain Power, A. Richard (Rich) Walje, age 60, $351,900 total compensation
SVP General Counsel and Director, Mark C. Moench, age 56
Director; President Pacific Power, R. Patrick (Pat) Reiten, age 50, $265,740 total compensation
SVP and CFO, Douglas K. (Doug) Stuver, age 48, $228,800 total compensation
President PacifiCorp Energy, Michael G. Dunn, age 46
Director, Patrick J. Goodman, age 45
Director; President Rocky Mountain Power, A. Richard (Rich) Walje, age 60
Director, Douglas L. Anderson, age 54
Director, Brent E. Gale, age 60
SVP General Counsel and Director, Mark C. Moench, age 56
Director; President Pacific Power, R. Patrick (Pat) Reiten, age 50
Director, Natalie L. Hocken, age 42
Auditors: Deloitte&ToucheLLP

LOCATIONS

HQ: PacifiCorp
825 NE Multnomah St. Ste. 2000, Portland OR 97232
Phone: 503-813-5000 **Fax:** 415-267-7268
Web: www.pgecorp.com

PRODUCTS/OPERATIONS

Selected Subsidiaries

PacificCorp Energy
Pacific Power
Rocky Mountain Power

Selected Services

Generating Facilities and Fuel Supply
- Coal
- Natural Gas
- Hydroelectric
- Wind and Other Renewable Resources
- Wholesale Activities

Transmission and Distribution

COMPETITORS

AES Wind Generation
Avista
Bonneville Power
Cascade Natural Gas
Chelan County PUD
Edison International
First Wind Holdings
IDACORP
Idaho Power
NV Energy
NW Natural
Pacific Gas and Electric
PG&E Corporation
Pinnacle West
Portland General Electric
PPL Montana
Public Utility District No. 1 of Clark County
Puget Energy
Questar
Questar Gas
Riverside Electric Utility
San Diego Gas & Electric
Seattle City Light
Sempra Energy
Sierra Pacific Power

HISTORICAL FINANCIALS

Company Type: Subsidiary

Income Statement

FYE: December 31

	REVENUE ($ mil.)	NET INCOME ($ mil.)	NET PROFIT MARGIN	EMPLOYEES
12/11	4,586	555	12.1%	6,400
12/10	4,432	566	12.8%	6,300
12/09	4,457	542	12.2%	6,447
12/08	4,498	458	10.2%	6,596
12/07	4,258	439	10.3%	6,470
Annual Growth	1.9%	6.0%	—	(0.3%)

2011 Year-End Financials

Debt ratio: 32.70%
Return on equity: 7.59%
Cash ($ mil.): 47
Current ratio: 81.75
Long-term debt ($ mil.): 6,194
No. of shares (mil.): 357
Dividends
Yield: —
Payout: 99.10%
Market value ($ mil.): 35,621

	STOCK PRICE ($) FY Close	P/E High/Low	PER SHARE ($) Earnings	Dividends	Book Value
12/11	99.78	— —	(0.00)	0.00	20.48
12/10	89.00	— —	(0.00)	5.00	20.48
12/09	84.50	— —	(0.00)	5.00	18.62
12/08	85.50	— —	(0.00)	5.00	16.77
12/07	90.00	— —	(0.00)	0.00	14.23
Annual Growth	2.6%	— —	—	—	9.5%

PacWest Bancorp

PacWest Bancorp is the holding company for Pacific Western Bank which operates about 65 branches in Southern California plus three in the San Francisco Bay Area. The bank caters to small and midsized businesses and their owners and employees offering traditional deposit and loan products and services. Commercial real estate mortgages business loans (including Small Business Administration loans) and construction loans account for most of the bank's lending activities. It also originates residential mortgage consumer and other loans. The bank offers investment services and international banking through agreements with correspondent banks.

The company's BFI Business Finance subsidiary and Financial Pacific Western division provides asset-based lending and factoring of accounts receivable to small businesses in Arizona California and the Pacific Northwest. PacWest added to its commercial lending operations with the acquisition of Utah-based Marquette Equipment Finance (renamed Pacific Western Equipment Finance) in early 2012. The unit has lease receivables in 45 states.

After spending several years in the red PacWest returned to profitability in 2011. Net income reached $50 million that year which was up from a $62 million loss reported the year before. Its a considerable improvement after losing more than $700 million in 2008. The company was hampered by the dismal California economy.

PacWest has grown through acquisitions of California community banks and other companies. It has made more than 20 acquisitions since 1999. During the economic downturn PacWest took advantage of a rash of bank failures through FDIC-assisted transactions. The acquired institutions were merged into Pacific Western Bank. Under the loss-sharing deals the FDIC agreed to reimburse PacWest for future losses tied to the acquisitions.

PacWest is focused on profitability and strategic growth. In a 2012 non-FDIC-assisted deal it bought American Perspective Bank adding two branches and a loan office in the Central Coast area. Also in 2012 PacWest continued its effort to strengthen its position in the California market and announced plans to acquire First California Financial Group in $212 million all-stock deal. However First California turned down the offer.

Later in 2012 PacWest sold 10 branches to Opus Bank an Irvine California-based bank. The sale is part of PacWest's ongoing effort to improve efficiency and profitability. Cutting loose the 10 branches will save the company about $2 million each year.

EXECUTIVES

Director; EVP Special Assets, Daniel B. Platt, age 65, $52,500 total compensation
CEO and Director; Chairman and CEO Pacific Western Bank, Matthew P. (Matt) Wagner, age 55, $750,000 total compensation
EVP and Chief Credit Officer; EVP and Chief Credit Officer Pacific Western Bank, Robert G. Dyck, age 55
Chairman, John M. Eggemeyer III, age 66
President Desert Region Pacific Western Bank, William T. Powers, age 71, $136,000 total compensation
EVP and Corporate Secretary; EVP CFO and Corporate Secretary Pacific Western Bank, Lynn M. Hopkins, age 44
EVP Human Resources; EVP Human Resources Pacific Western Bank, Michael L. Thompson, age 66, $162,500 total compensation
President Inland Empire Region Pacific Western Bank, Casey J. (Joe) Cecala III, age 56
President Eastern Region Pacific Western Bank, Christopher D. Blake, age 52
EVP and General Counsel and Assistant Secretary; President Los Angeles and Ventura Regions Pacific Western Bank, Jared M. Wolff, age 42, $343,750 total compensation
President; President and Director Pacific Western Bank, Michael J. (Mike) Perdue, age 57, $387,508 total compensation
EVP and CFO; EVP and Director Pacific Western Bank, Victor R. Santoro, age 63, $456,250 total compensation
EVP and Manager Operations and Systems; EVP and Manager Operations and Systems Pacific Western Bank, Mark Christian
Director, Susan E. Lester, age 55
Director; EVP Special Assets, Daniel B. Platt, age 65
Director, Robert A. (Bob) Stine, age 65
Director, George E. Langley, age 71
Director, Mark N. Baker, age 65
CEO and Director; Chairman and CEO Pacific Western Bank, Matthew P. (Matt) Wagner, age 55
Director, Barry C. Fitzpatrick, age 65
Director, Stephen M. Dunn, age 64
Director, John W. Rose, age 62
Director, Timothy B. Matz, age 67
Director, Arnold W. Messer, age 66
Director, Craig A. Carlson, age 62
Auditors: KPMGLLP

LOCATIONS

HQ: PacWest Bancorp
401 W. "A" St., San Diego CA 92101-7917
Phone: 619-233-5588 **Fax:** 619-235-1268
Web: www.pacwestbancorp.com

PRODUCTS/OPERATIONS

2011 Sales

	$ mil.	% of total
Interest		
Loans	260	80
Investment securities	34	11
Deposits in financial institutions	0	-
Noninterest		
Service charges on deposit accounts	13	4
FDIC loss sharing income net	7	2
Other commissions & fees	7	2
Other	2	1
Total	**326**	**100**

Selected Mergers & Acquisitions

2012
Maquette Equipment Finance ($35 million; Midvale Utah; equipment leasing)
2010
Los Padres Bank (FDIC-assisted deal; Solvang California; community bank)
2009
Affinity Bank (FDIC-assisted deal; Ventura California; community bank)

COMPETITORS

Bank of America
California Bank & Trust
City National
CVB Financial
JPMorgan Chase
Pacific Capital Bancorp
Rabobank America
San Diego County Credit Union
U.S. Bancorp
UnionBanCal
Wells Fargo
Westamerica

HISTORICAL FINANCIALS

Company Type: Public

Income Statement

FYE: December 31

	ASSETS ($ mil.)	NET INCOME ($ mil.)	INCOME AS % OF ASSETS	EMPLOYEES
12/11	5,528	50	0.9%	982
12/10	5,529	(62)	—	929
12/09	5,324	(9)	—	915
12/08	4,495	(728)	—	865
12/07	5,179	90	1.7%	881
Annual Growth	1.6%	(13.4%)	—	2.8%

2011 Year-End Financials

Debt ratio: 6.41%
Return on equity: 9.28%
Cash ($ mil.): 295
Current ratio: —
Long-term debt ($ mil.): 354
No. of shares (mil.): 37
Dividends
Yield: —
Payout: 15.33%
Market value ($ mil.): 706

	STOCK PRICE ($) FY Close	P/E High/Low		PER SHARE ($) Earnings	Dividends	Book Value
12/11	18.95	17	10	1.37	0.00	14.66
12/10	21.38	—	—	(1.77)	0.04	13.06
12/09	20.15	—	—	(0.30)	0.35	14.43
12/08	26.90	—	—	(26.79)	1.28	13.17
12/07	41.24	18	13	3.15	1.28	40.65
Annual Growth	(17.7%)	—	—	(18.8%)	—	(22.5%)

Pantry Inc. (The)

If you've ever passed through the Carolinas on business or made the drive to Disney World chances are The Pantry has provided fuel for your car and body. The company is the leading convenience store operator in the southeastern US with more than 1650 shops in about a dozen states. (Florida accounts for more than a quarter of the company's sales.) Most of the company's stores do business under the Kangaroo Express banner. Other store names include Golden Gallon Lil' Champ The Pantry (naturally) and Petro Express. The stores sell beverages candy gasoline magazines and tobacco products among other items. Fuel accounts for about three-quarters of the company's sales.

HISTORY

North Carolina businessmen Sam Wornom and Truby Proctor (president of Lee Moore Oil Co.) founded The Pantry in 1967 in Sanford North Carolina. The chain added new stores by borrowing against its existing stores paying the debt with new sales.

The Pantry had grown to about 480 outlets in 1987 when investment firm Montrose Capital bought Wornom's stake. Founded by former Duke University business professor Clay Hamner Montrose's shareholders included J. B. Fuqua (after whom the Duke business school is named) the late Dave Thomas (the Wendy's fast-food chain founder) and Wayne Rogers (Trapper John in the TV series M*A*S*H). Montrose gained control of The Pantry when it acquired half of Proctor's shares in 1990. Proctor remained as CEO.

With poor sales the company restructured during the early 1990s closing unprofitable stores and cutting costs. After struggling in 1991 and 1992 The Pantry made a slim profit in 1993. However burdened by debt the company was without the cash to make further substantive acquisitions and it resumed its annual losses the following year.

In 1995 Proctor sold his remaining shares to Freeman Spogli & Co. a California-based investment firm specializing in management-led buyouts and Chase Manhattan Capital. The next year Freeman Spogli and Chase Manhattan acquired the rest of the company from Montrose. Freeman Spogli owned 76% of The Pantry and Chase Manhattan owned 23% until more shares were issued to management and directors. Peter Sodini a former CEO with supermarket chain Purity Supreme (acquired by Stop & Shop) became CEO that year.

After a string of small acquisitions in early 1997 The Pantry more than doubled in size by paying about $135 million to Docks U.S.A. for the Lil' Champ Food Stores convenience store chain. Lil'

Champ –named for founder Julian Jackson a bantamweight boxing champion in the 1930s –had 489 outlets including 150 in Jacksonville Florida.

The Pantry continued to bulk up in 1998 acquiring nearly 155 stores through seven separate purchases of small chains. The biggest purchases among them included Quick Stop a 75-store chain in the Carolinas and 41 Zip Mart stores in North Carolina and eastern Virginia. The company exited the Georgia market that year.

In early 1999 The Pantry acquired 121 Handy Way stores in central Florida many of which operated fast-food outlets such as Hardee's and Subway. The Pantry went public that year to raise money to pay nearly $450 million in debt stemming from its acquisitions. Shortly thereafter the company bought 53 Depot Food Store outlets in Georgia and South Carolina from R & H Maxxon.

Late that year The Pantry added the 49-store Kangaroo chain in Georgia and in early 2000 it purchased the On-The-Way Foods Stores chain of 12 stores in Virginia and North Carolina. Other purchases in 2000 furthering the company's southeastern US expansion included 33 MiniMart and Big K chain stores and 26 Fast Lane convenience stores in Louisiana and Mississippi from R.R. Morrison and Son. In 2001 The Pantry bought 11 stores from East Coast Oil in North Carolina and Virginia.

In March 2003 The Pantry reached agreements with BP Products and Citgo Petroleum to brand and supply most of its gasoline for the next five years. In October the company completed the acquisition of the 138-store Golden Gallon chain from Ahold USA for about $187 million.

A secondary offering of 5 million shares of common stock in February 2004 reduced Freeman Spogli's holdings in The Pantry to about 42% from 60%.

The Pantry acquired D & D Oil Co. (operator of 53 convenience stores under the Cowboys banner in Alabama Georgia and Mississippi) in April 2005. In August it purchased 23 convenience stores in Virginia (operating under the Sentry Food Mart banner) from Angus I. Hines.

In May 2006 the company acquired the 38-store Shop-A-Snak Food Mart convenience store chain in Alabama doubling its store count in the state. In August it completed the acquisition of six Fuel Mate convenience stores in North Carolina. In late 2006 the company bought seven convenience stores in Florida from Rousseau Enterprises for an undisclosed sum.

Continuing its buying spree in 2007 The Pantry acquired 16 Angler's Mini-Mart stores in Charleston South Carolina and a single convenience store in Sanford North Carolina in mid-January. In April the company closed on 66 Petro Express convenience stores in North and South Carolina for $275 million (plus inventory costs) and its affiliated wholesale fuels business Carolina Petroleum Distributors. Also in April it purchased about a dozen Fast Phil's convenience stores in the Spartanburg South Carolina market from Willard Oil Co. Overall in 2007 the fast-growing chain acquired about 150 stores.

In June 2009 the company acquired 38 convenience stores from Herndon Oil Co. The terms of the cash purchase were not disclosed. Also that summer the company moved its corporate headquarters from Sanford to Cary North Carolina. In September CEO Peter Sondini retired after 10 years at the helm.

EXECUTIVES

SVP Human Resources, Keith A. Oreson, age 55
President and CEO, Dennis G. Hatchell
SVP General Counsel and Secretary, Thomas D. (Tom) Carney, age 65
Director Total Rewards, Diana King
Chairman, Edwin J. (Ed) Holman, age 65
VP Interim CFO and Corporate Controller, Berry Epley
President CEO and Director, Terrance M. (Terry) Marks, age 51
SVP Marketing, John J. Fisher, age 48
SVP Fuels, Keith S. Bell, age 48, $297,362 total compensation
VP Food Service, Brandon Frampton
SVP and CFO, Mark R. Bierley, age 45
SVP and CIO, Paul M. Lemerise, age 66
Director, Robert F. Bernstock, age 61
Director, Terry L. McElroy, age 63
Director, Thomas M. Murnane, age 65
Director, Paul L. Brunswick, age 72
President CEO and Director, Terrance M. (Terry) Marks, age 51
Director, Wilfred A. (Bill) Finnegan, age 53
Director, Bryan E. Monkhouse, age 67
Director, Maria C. Richter, age 58
Director, Mark D. Miles, age 58
Auditors: Deloitte&ToucheLLP

LOCATIONS

HQ: Pantry Inc. (The)
P.O. Box 8019, 305 Gregson Drive, Cary, NC 27511
Phone: 919 774-6700
Web: www.thepantry.com

2011 Stores

	No.
Florida	399
North	378
South	276
Georgia	128
Alabama	112
Tennessee	100
Mississippi	97
Virginia	50
Kansas	43
Kentucky	27
Louisiana	27
Indiana	9
Missouri	3
Total	**1,649**

PRODUCTS/OPERATIONS

2011 Merchandise Sales

	% of total
Grocery & other tobacco	29
Cigarettes	28
Packaged	16
Beer &	15
Food	9
Services	3
Total	**100**

2011 Sales

	$ mil.	% of total
Gasoline	6,359	78
Merchandise	1,778	22
Total	**8,138**	**100**

Selected Banners and Trademarks

Aunt M' s
Bean Street Coffee Company
Big Chill
Celeste
Cowboys
Golden Gallon
Kangaroo
Kangaroo Express
Market Express
Mini Mart
The Chill Zone
The Pantry
Petro Express
Quickstop
Sprint
Worth

COMPETITORS

7-Eleven
BI-LO
Couche-Tard
Crown Central
Cumberland Farms
Delhaize America
Exxon Mobil
Gate Petroleum
Publix
Racetrac Petroleum
Spinx
VPS Convenience Store Group
Winn-Dixie

HISTORICAL FINANCIALS

Company Type: Public

Income Statement FYE: September 27

	REVENUE ($ mil.)	NET INCOME ($ mil.)	NET PROFIT MARGIN	EMPLOYEES
09/12	8,253	(2)	—	13,709
09/11	8,138	9	0.1%	13,928
09/10	7,265	(165)	—	14,419
09/09	6,390	59	0.9%	13,694
09/08	8,995	31	0.4%	14,221
Annual Growth	(2.1%)	—	—	(0.9%)

2012 Year-End Financials

Debt ratio: 56.54%
Return on equity: (-0.78)%
Cash ($ mil.): 89
Current ratio: 98.61
Long-term debt ($ mil.): 943
No. of shares (mil.): 23
Dividends
Yield: —
Payout: —
Market value ($ mil.): 344

	STOCK PRICE ($) FY Close	P/E High/Low		PER SHARE ($) Earnings	Dividends	Book Value
09/12	14.77	—	—	(0.11)	0.00	13.95
09/11	12.82	55	25	0.44	0.00	14.06
09/10	24.11	—	—	(7.42)	0.00	13.55
09/09	16.07	9	5	2.65	0.00	20.26
09/08	18.67	22	6	1.43	0.00	17.55
Annual Growth	(5.7%)	—	—	—	—	(5.6%)

Park National Corp. (Newark, OH)

Customers can park their money with Park National. The holding company owns Park National Bank which operates more than 120 branches in Ohio and northern Kentucky through 11 community banking divisions. The banks provide an array of consumer and business banking services including traditional savings and checking accounts and CDs. Business loans including commercial leases and mortgages operating loans and agricultural loans account for about 35% of Park National's loan portfolio. The banks also originate consumer residential real estate and construction loans. Park National's nonbank units include consumer finance outfit Guardian Finance Scope Aircraft Finance and Park Title Agency.

Each of Park National Corporation's bank affiliates specialize in serving specific geographic locations. It's bank divisions include: Century National Bank; Fairfield National Bank; Farmers Bank;

First-Knox National Bank; Park National Bank; Richland Bank; Security National Bank; Second National Bank; Unity National Bank; and United Bank.

Park National Corporation and its subsidiaries operate in Ohio and northern Kentucky.

In 2011 Park National Corporation pulled out of Florida and the Gulf Coast region when it sold Vision Bancshares to Home Bancshares and its Centennial Bank subsidiary. The $28 million deal to sell Vision Bank should help boost Park National's capital ratios. The 2007 acquisition of Vision Bank which operated in Florida and Alabama expanded the company geographic reach but the deal quickly turned sour as Vision was plagued by bad loans and other troubles during the economic recession. Park National Corporation was forced to write off an increasing number of defaulted loans which cut into its net income. Vision Bank reported net losses from 2007 through 2011. To offset losses Park National also sold some of its securities portfolio in 2010 and 2011. The sale of Vision helped boost Park National's earnings and cut expenses. The deal also allowed the company to focus on its more profitable businesses in Ohio.

Amidst the sale of Vision Park National worked to correct accounting errors that dated back to 2010. The company restated its earnings in order to fix several mistakes tied to cash flow and expenses. Its revised earnings statement for 2011 reported a more than 45% jump in net income. The results were boosted by the company's performance in Ohio.

EXECUTIVES

CFO; SVP and CFO Park National Bank, John W. Kozak, age 56, $214,455 total compensation
Chairman and CEO Park National Corporation and Park National Bank, C. Daniel (Dan) DeLawder, age 62, $473,525 total compensation
President First-Knox National Bank, Gordon E. Yance
President Secretary and Director; President Park National Bank, David L. Trautman, age 50, $313,250 total compensation
Director; Chairman Century National Bank, William A. Phillips, age 79
Vice Chairman; Chairman Security National Bank, Harry O. Egger, age 72, $202,500 total compensation
SVP Park National Bank, Thomas J. Button
SVP Park National Bank, Cheryl L. Snyder
SVP Park National Bank, William R. Wilson
VP Park National Bank, Peter G. Cassanos
President Park National Bank of Southwest Ohio and Northern Kentucky, K. Douglas (Doug) Compton
VP Park National Bank, Cynthia H. Crane
SVP and Trust Officer Park National Bank, Thomas M. Cummiskey
SVP Park National Bank, Lynn B. Fawcett
VP Park National Bank, Daniel L. Hunt
VP Park National Bank, Steven J. Klein
SVP Park National Bank, Laura B. Lewis
VP and Trust Officer Park National Bank, Terry C. Myers
VP Park National Bank, Karen K. Rice
VP Park National Bank, David J. Rohde
VP Park National Bank, Alan C. Rothweiler
VP Park National Bank, R. Michael Shannon
VP Park National Bank, Robert G. Springer
VP and Trust Officer Park National Bank, Julie L. Strohacker
VP Park National Bank, Paul E. Turner
VP Park National Bank, Joan L. Franks
VP Security National Bank, Timothy L. (Tim) Bunnell
President Century National Bank, Thomas M. Lyall
SVP Century National Bank, Barbara A. Gibbs
SVP Century National Bank, Jack W. Imes
EVP Century National Bank, Patrick L. Nash
SVP Century National Bank, Michael F. Whiteman
VP Century National Bank, Jeffrey C. Jordan
VP Century National Bank, Bruce D. Kolopajlo
VP Century National Bank, Mark A. Longstreth
VP Century National Bank, James R. Merry
VP and Trust Officer Century National Bank, Jody D. Spencer
VP Century National Bank, Thomas N. Sulens
President Fairfield National Bank, Stephen G. (Steve) Wells
SVP and Trust Officer Fairfield National Bank, Thomas L. Kokensparger
VP Fairfield National Bank, Richard E. Baker II
VP Fairfield National Bank, Daniel R. Bates
SVP Fairfield National Bank, Timothy D. Hall
VP Fairfield National Bank, Linda M. Harris
President Farmers and Saving Bank, James S. Lingenfelter
SVP Farmers and Saving Bank, Kenneth G. Gosche
VP Farmers and Saving Bank, Sharon E. Blubaugh
VP Farmers and Saving Bank, Hal D. Sheaffer
VP Farmers and Savings Bank, Wayne D. Young
VP Park National Bank, Thomas A. Underwood
SVP First-Knox National Bank, W. Douglas Leonard
EVP First-Knox National Bank, Vickie A. Sant
VP First-Knox National Bank, James E. Brinker
VP and Trust Officer First-Knox National Bank, Cheri L. Butcher
SVP First-Knox National Bank, Mark P. Leonard
VP First-Knox National Bank, Jesse L. Marlow
President Guardian Financial, Earl W. Osborne
VP Guardian Financial Services, Matthew R. Marsh
VP and Auditor Park National Bank, Kathleen O. Crowley
VP and Trust Officer Park National Bank, John S. Gard
VP and Trust Officer Park National Bank, Teresa M. Kroll
VP and Trust Officer Park National Bank, John B. Uible
SVP Park National Bank, Timothy J. Lehman
President Richland Bank, David J. Gooch
VP and Trust Officer Richland Bank, Charla A. Irvin
VP Richland Bank, Michael A. Jefferson
President Scope Aircraft Finance, Robert N. (Bob) Kent Jr.
VP Scope Aircraft Finance, Charles W. Sauter
President Second National Bank, John E. Swallow
EVP Second National Bank, Steven C. Badgett
VP Second National Bank, Marie A. Boas
VP Second National Bank, Thomas J. Lawson
VP Second National Bank, Gene A. Rismiller
VP and Trust Officer Second National Bank, D. Todd Durham
President Security National Bank, William C. (Bill) Fralick
SVP Security National Bank, Andrew J. Irick
VP and Trust Officer Security National Bank, Mary L. Goddard
SVP Security National Bank, Thomas A. Goodfellow
VP and Trust Officer Security National Bank, James A. Kreckman
VP Security National Bank, Thomas C. Ruetenik
VP Security National Bank, Michael B. Warnecke
VP Security National Bank, James E. Leathley
President United Bank, Donald R. Stone
President Unity National Bank, John A. Brown
VP Unity National Bank, Stephen W. Vallo
VP Unity National Bank, David S. Frey
SVP Unity National Bank, Brett A. Baumeister
VP Unity National Bank, G. Dwayne Cooper
VP and Trust Officer Park National Bank of Southwest Ohio and Northern Kentucky, John F. Winkler II
VP Second National Bank, Daniel G. Schmitz
VP Century National Bank, Janice A. Hutchison
VP Century National Bank, Brian G. Kaufman
VP First-Knox National Bank, Cynthia L. Higgs
VP First-Knox National Bank, Julie A. Leonard
VP First-Knox National Bank, Jerry D. Simon
VP First-Knox National Bank, Todd P. Vermilya
SVP Richland Bank, Donald R. Harris Jr.
VP Park National Bank of Southwest Ohio and Northern Kentucky, Jason D. Hughes
VP Park National Bank, Lydia E. Miller
VP Park National Bank, Ralph H. Root III
VP Park National Bank, Christine S. Schneider
VP Park National Bank, Barbara A. Wilson
VP Park National Bank, Christa D. Wright
VP Park National Bank, Alice M. Browning
VP and Trust Officer Park National Bank, Damon P. Howarth
VP Park National Bank, Adam T. Stypula
VP Richland Bank, Katharine J. Barre
VP Richland Bank, Rebecca J. Toomey
VP and Trust Officer Security National Bank, Margaret L. Foley
VP and Chief Accounting Officer Park National Bank, Brady T. Burt, age 37
EVP Vision Bank Alabama, Andrew W. Braswell, age 46
EVP Security National Bank, Jeffrey A. (Jeff) Darding
VP Security National Bank, David A. Snyder
SVP Park National Bank of Southwest Ohio and Northern Kentucky, Michael J. Jacunski
VP Park National Bank of Southwest Ohio and Northern Kentucky, Joseph A. Wagner
SVP and Auditor Park National Bank, Jeffrey A. Wilson
VP First-Knox National Bank, Robert E. Boss
VP and Trust Officer Park National Bank, James M. Buskirk
VP Park National Bank, Jeffrey C. Gluntz
VP Park National Bank, Scott C. Green
VP Park National Bank, David F. Romes
VP Park National Bank, Erin E. Tschanen
VP Park National Bank, Stanley A. Uchida
VP Park National Bank, Brian S. Urquhart
VP Park National Bank, Bradden E. Waltz
VP and Trust Officer Park National Bank, Charles Wigton III
SVP Park National Bank of Southwest Ohio and Northern Kentucky, Edward L. Brady
SVP Park National Bank of Southwest Ohio and Northern Kentucky, Jennifer K. Fischer
SVP Park National Bank of Southwest Ohio and Northern Kentucky, Erick K. Harback
VP Park National Bank of Southwest Ohio and Northern Kentucky, John R. Nienaber
VP Park National Bank, Daniel H. Turben
VP Park National Bank of Southwest Ohio and Northern Kentucky, Ginger L. Vining
VP Richland Bank, Michael D. Volz
SVP United Bank, James A. Carr
VP Unity National Bank, Frank W. Wagner II
President Vision Bank Alabama, Diane C. Anderson
EVP Vision Bank Alabama, Darrell W. Melton
SVP Vision Bank Florida, Diane E. Floyd
SVP Vision Bank Alabama, Karen J. Harmon
SVP Vision Bank Alabama, George L. Hawthorne
SVP Vision Bank Alabama, Lyndsay P. Job
SVP Vision Bank Alabama, James E. Kirkland
SVP and Trust Officer Vision Bank Alabama, Julie H. Ralph
SVP Vision Bank Alabama, Debra M. Schmidt
SVP Vision Bank Alabama, Christie G. Barkley
VP Vision Bank Alabama, Patricia H. Campbell

VP Vision Bank Alabama, Robin B. Fly
VP Vision Bank Alabama, Bernard A. Fogarty
VP Vision Bank Alabama, Gregory G. Gontarski
VP Vision Bank Alabama, William Legrone
VP Vision Bank Alabama, Geneie S. Scheer
VP Vision Bank Alabama, Doug J. Sizemore
VP Vision Bank Alabama, Judy R. Smith
VP Vision Bank Alabama, Elizabeth O. Stone
VP Vision Bank Alabama, Laura E. Welch
VP Vision Bank Alabama, Rhonda L. Willis
President Vision Bank Florida, John D. Whitlock
EVP Vision Bank Florida, Jerry D. Gaskin
EVP Vision Bank Florida, Carolyn M. Husband
EVP Vision Bank Florida, William P. (Bill) Lloyd
SVP Vision Bank Florida, Colleen Y. Friesen
SVP Vision Bank Florida, Anita M. Mayer
SVP and Trust Officer Vision Bank Florida, Jim P. Norton
SVP Vision Bank Florida, John S. Robbins
VP Vision Bank Florida, Owen W. Ayers III
VP Vision Bank Florida, Jeremy S. Bennett
VP Vision Bank Florida, Joan A. Cleckley
VP Vision Bank Florida, Debbie H. Driskell
VP Vision Bank Florida, Laura V. Helms
VP Vision Bank Florida, Jim L. Hood
VP Vision Bank Florida, Terri A. Hugghins
VP Vision Bank Florida, Joseph M. Pelter II
VP Vision Bank Florida, Scott R. Robertson
VP Vision Bank Florida, Cindy L. Stephens
VP Vision Bank Florida, Leslie L. Welsch
VP Vision Bank Florida, Johanna L. White
VP Vision Bank Florida, Jennifer J. Woods
SVP Century National Bank, James C. Blythe
VP Century National Bank, Brian E. Hall
VP Century National Bank, Rebecca R. Porteus
VP and Auditor Park National Bank, Lynne F. Karla
VP Park National Bank, Carl H. Mayer
VP Park National Corporation, Matthew R. Miller
VP Park National Bank, Robin L. Stein
VP Park National Bank of Southwest Ohio and Northern Kentucky, Kim J. Cunningham
VP and Trust Officer Second National Bank, Eric J. McKee
VP United Bank, Anne K. Spreng
VP Vision Bank Alabama, Patricia R. Burrell
VP Vision Bank Alabama, Michelle L. Kinne
VP Vision Bank Alabama, Ken N. Neyman
SVP Vision Bank Florida, Emory R. Singletary
VP Vision Bank Florida, Jim M. Haag
Director, William T. (Bill) McConnell, age 78
President Secretary and Director; President Park National Bank, David L. Trautman, age 50
Director, Maureen Buchwald, age 80
Director, Rick R. Taylor, age 63
Director, James J. Cullers, age 81
Director, John J. O'Neill, age 91
Director; Chairman Century National Bank, William A. Phillips, age 79
Vice Chairman; Chairman Security National Bank, Harry O. Egger, age 72
Director, Leon Zazworsky, age 63
Director, F. William Englefield IV, age 57
Director, Sarah Reese Wallace, age 57
Director, Timothy L. (Tim) McLain, age 50
Director, Stephen Kambeitz, age 53
Auditors: CroweHorwathLLP

LOCATIONS

HQ: Park National Corporation
50 N. 3rd St., Newark OH 43058-3500
Phone: 740-349-8451 **Fax:** 740-349-3765
Web: www.parknationalcorp.com

PRODUCTS/OPERATIONS

2011 Sales

	$ mil.	% of total
Interest		
Loans including fees	262	60
Securities including dividends	68	16
Other	0	-
Noninterest		
Net gains on sales of securities	28	7
Service charges on deposit accounts	18	45
Fiduciary activities	15	3
Checkcard fee income	12	3
Other service income	10	2
Bank owned life insurance income	5	1
Other	12	3
Adjustments	(8.2)	-
Total	**426**	**100**

Selected Affiliates

Century National Bank
Fairfield National Bank
Farmers Bank
First-Knox National Bank
Guardian Finance Company
Park National Bank
Richland Bank
Scope Aircraft Finance
Second National Bank
Security National Bank
United bank
Unity National Bank

COMPETITORS

Bank of America
Camco Financial
Fifth Third
First Place Financial
FirstMerit
Huntington Bancshares
JPMorgan Chase
PNC Financial
U.S. Bancorp
Wayne Savings Bancshares
Wells Fargo

HISTORICAL FINANCIALS

Company Type: Public

Income Statement FYE: December 31

	ASSETS ($ mil.)	NET INCOME ($ mil.)	INCOME AS % OF ASSETS	EMPLOYEES
12/11	6,972	82	1.2%	1,920
12/10	7,298	74	1.0%	1,969
12/09	7,040	74	1.1%	2,024
12/08	7,070	13	0.2%	2,051
12/07	6,501	22	0.3%	2,066
Annual Growth	1.8%	37.9%	—	(1.8%)

2011 Year-End Financials

Debt ratio: 12.89%
Return on equity: 11.06%
Cash ($ mil.): 157
Current ratio: —
Long-term debt ($ mil.): 898
No. of shares (mil.): 15
Dividends
Yield: —
Payout: 75.96%
Market value ($ mil.): 1,002

	STOCK PRICE ($) FY Close	P/E High	P/E Low	PER SHARE ($) Earnings	Dividends	Book Value
12/11	65.06	15	10	4.95	0.00	48.19
12/10	72.67	16	12	4.51	3.76	48.43
12/09	58.88	15	8	4.82	3.76	48.19
12/08	71.75	85	46	0.97	4.71	46.00
12/07	64.50	63	41	1.60	3.73	41.53
Annual Growth	0.2%	—	—	32.6%	—	3.8%

Parker Hannifin Corp.

Parker-Hannifin operates on a big scale (motion control equipment made by helped sink a replica of the Titanic in the Academy Award-winning film.) Operating through three business segments –Industrial Aerospace and Climate & Industrial Controls –Parker-Hannifin is a leading global manufacturer of motion and control technologies including fluid power systems for the manufacturing and processing industries; hydraulic fuel pneumatic and electromechanical systems and components for the aerospace/defense industry; and motion and control systems for the heating ventilation air conditioning and refrigeration (HVACR) and transportation industries.

HISTORY

Entrepreneurial engineer Arthur Parker founded the Parker Appliance Company in 1918 to make pneumatic brake boosters. Its products were designed to help trucks and buses stop more easily. Unfortunately Parker's own truck slid off an icy road and over a cliff in 1919 destroying the company's inventory and ending that line of business.

Undeterred Parker started a hydraulics and pneumatic components business in 1924 to serve automotive and industrial clients. In 1927 the fuel-linkage system the company developed for the "Spirit of St. Louis" helped Lindbergh cross the Atlantic. The company prospered during the Depression; sales reached $2 million in 1934. Two of Parker's long-term clients were Douglas Aircraft and Lockheed.

The company went public in 1938. It employed 5000 defense workers during WWII. After Parker died in 1945 his wife Helen hired new management to focus on the automation market. The firm bought cylinder maker Hannifin in 1957 and became Parker-Hannifin.

In 1960 Parker-Hannifin formed an international unit in Amsterdam and it set up a German subsidiary in 1962. Overseas acquisitions and increased demand from the space program and the aviation market spurred growth in the 1960s. Patrick Parker the founder's son became president in 1968 and chairman in 1977. Parker-Hannifin expanded its aerospace business in 1978 with the purchase of Bertea (electrohydraulic flight controls). Patrick Parker continued as CEO until 1983 and as chairman until 1999.

During the 1980s Parker-Hannifin bought several smaller companies in niche markets including Schrader Bellows (pneumatics 1985) Compumotor (electromechanical applications 1986) and Stratoflex and Gull Corp. (hoses and fittings and aerospace electronics respectively 1988).

The company again pushed into Europe during the 1990s buying Sweden-based Trelleborg (hydraulic hoses) in 1992 and Atlas Automation (pneumatic components for automation equipment) in 1993. Parker-Hannifin made six major purchases in 1994 including Finn-Filter Oy Scandinavia's largest filter maker and Polyflex Europe's leading maker of thermoplastic hoses. The company added Abex NWL the aerospace business of Germany's Pneumo Abex in 1996.

US purchases in 1997 included the aircraft components business of XAR Industries SAES-Parker UHP Components (a gas-valve-making joint venture with Italy's SAES Getter Group) and Honeywell's solenoid valve unit. Parker-Hannifin expanded into the medical petrochemical and semiconductor markets in 1998 by purchasing Veriflo (high-purity valves and regulators) and into mobile equipment makers with Fluid Power Systems (hydraulic valves and electrohydraulic systems). Overseas expansion included the 1998 purchase of Sempress Pneumatics (pneumatic cylinders the Netherlands) and the purchases of Cougar Valves and Fittings (Australia) and Jinyoung Electric Machinery (automation components South Korea) in 1999.

In 2000 Parker-Hannifin acquired motion control maker Commercial Intertech in a deal worth around $473 million. It also bought Whatman's industrial business (purification products and gas generators) and Wynn's International (industrial sealing products in a $498 million deal). The company agreed to buy Dana Corp.'s Gresen Hydraulic business (pumps control valves and other parts for on- and off-road vehicles).

President and COO Donald Washkewicz succeeded Duane Collins as CEO in 2001. Collins remained chairman until his retirement in 2004 when Washkewicz replaced him in that role too. Parker-Hannifin acquired Eaton's air conditioning unit Aeroquip the same year. Near the end of 2001 the company acquired the Dayco hydraulic and industrial hose operations of Mark IV Industries.

In early 2002 Parker-Hannifin acquired ITR SpA an Italy-based hose and fittings manufacturer from the SAIAG Group for $68 million. The company acquired MTS Automation (analog and digital amplifiers brushless motors digital and servo controllers linear motors) from MTS Systems Corporation in 2003; MTS Automation became part of Parker-Hannifin's Compumotor Division. Later in the year the company acquired Control By Light Systems' aircraft business (fiber-optic communication and control electronics); the Massachusetts-based company became part of Parker-Hannifin's Electronic Systems Division.

Parker-Hannifin completed the acquisition of Denison International early in 2004 for about $2.4 billion. Later that year it purchased Mead Fluid Dynamics Ltd. the European operations of Mead Fluid Dynamics Inc. Also in 2004 Parker-Hannifin sold the automatic flight inspection system product line of its aerospace group to NXT LLC acquired privately held valve maker Sporlan Valve Co. and purchased sealant maker Acadia Elastomers Corporation.

Early in 2005 Parker-Hannifin sold Wynn Oil (chemical car care products) to Illinois Tool Works. It continued to grow internationally through acquisitions such as India's Markwel Hose Products which it bought in early 2005 a move that expanded its operations in the Asian motion and control markets. Wanting to secure its foothold in the water filtration market Parker-Hannifin acquired UK-based domnick hunter group after winning a bidding war with Eaton Corporation. domnick hunter drew such avid interest in part because it had developed products designed to protect against nuclear biological and chemical weapons.

Parker-Hannifin actively sought feedback from customers suppliers and employees as part of its product development program. The effort led to several new products in 2007. Examples include self-cleaning regenerative filtration systems that neutralize contaminants microfluidic process controllers that use pressure to control a variety of instrumentation and data-carrying seals that can help find oil and gas reservoirs more quickly.

Between 2007 and 2008 the company acquired more than 20 companies but its acquisition strategy has become more focused than in years past. The company made a number of acquisitions in 2008 to build on its international presence. Some examples include buying Legris SA division from Groupe Legris Industries for a well-established distribution network and presence in the European market; Origa Group which has operations in Germany and Austria; Malaysian firm EmiTherm; and the remaining 51% in Parker Seal de Mexico it did not already own.

Parker-Hannifin also bought Titan Industries in 2008 which makes rubber products and custom-made and composite hoses. The hose products let the company enter the marine and aircraft refueling markets. Titan was integrated into Parker-Hannifin's Industrial Hose Products division.

Separate from its acquisition activity 2008 proved to be a lucrative year for contracts in Parker-Hannifin's Aerospace segment. The company inked a major deal with French aircraft maker Airbus. The deal which is worth more than $2 billion calls for Parker Hannifin to provide the fuel system equipment and hydraulic systems for Airbus' A350 aircraft. The deal helped Parker Hannifin brace for anticipated slowdowns in some of its major industries including automotive and construction. The Aerospace segment designs and manufactures aircraft wheels and brakes for military and general aviation markets; centers throughout the world distribute the company's original and replacement equipment.

Parker-Hannifin treated 2009 quite differently from 2008 when it was seeking international expansion. largely through acquisitions. It bought Legris SA division from Groupe Legris Industries (fluid command and control systems) which brought a well-established distribution network and presence in the European market. Origa Group which makes actuators cylinders and valves has operations in Germany and Austria. The company acquired the 51% stake in Parker Seal de Mexico it did not already own to strengthen its foothold in Mexico. Also in 2008 the company bought Malaysian firm EmiTherm which makes shielding materials used by electronics manufacturers. Vansco Electronics gave the company additional global distribution capacity and Nexgen Hose brought an expanded presence in Canada for hose and tubing.

In 2010 it acquired SprayCool (formerly Isothermal Systems Research) a developer/supplier of thermal management electronics that are used in the aerospace and defense market. Mid-year it acquired Canada-based Micro Thermo Technologies from Carrier Corporation to add to its Climate & Industrial Controls segment. Micro Thermo extends the company's presence in the supermarket refrigeration and HVAC systems industry. Late in 2010 it acquired Houston-based Gulf Coast Seal Limited (GCS) a provider of elastomeric and plastic sealing components for offshore oil and gas applications. GCS has additional facilities located in Scotland.

Although 2009 and 2010 were tough for many of the industries that Parker-Hannifin serves the company managed to post all-time record sales net income and earnings per share for fiscal 2011. Sales reached $12.3 billion an increase of about 24% over the prior fiscal year. Net income for the year was a record $1.1 billion an increase of about 90% compared to 2010. Three acquisitions in fiscal 2011 contributed approximately $54 million in sales. The company also saw an increase in its Industrial segment sales. Its gross profit margin increased in 2011 primarily due to a combination of higher sales volumes and lower business realignment expenses compared to 2010.

Sales in 2011 for the Industrial North American operations increased about 25% mainly because of greater demand from distributors and end users particularly in the construction equipment agriculture and farm equipment heavy duty truck mining and machine tools markets. Meanwhile sales in the Industrial International operations increased 29% in 2011 due to higher volumes with the largest increases experienced in Europe and Asia/Pacific.

EXECUTIVES

VP; President Fluid Connectors Group, Robert W. (Bob) Bond, age 54
Chairman President and CEO, Donald E. (Don) Washkewicz, age 62, $1,097,250 total compensation
VP General Counsel and Secretary, Thomas A. Piraino Jr., age 63
EVP and Operating Officer, Lee C. Banks, age 49, $504,925 total compensation
VP and CIO, William G. (Bill) Eline, age 56
VP; President Instrumentation Group, John R. Greco, age 58
VP Corporate Communications, Christopher M. Farage
EVP and Operating Officer, Robert P. (Bob) Barker, age 62, $472,000 total compensation
VP and Treasurer, Pamela J. (Pam) Huggins, age 58
VP Technology and Innovation, M. Craig Maxwell, age 54
VP; President Automation Group, Roger S. Sherrard, age 46
EVP Corporate Human Resources, Daniel S. (Dan) Serbin, age 58
EVP and Operating Officer, Thomas L. (Tom) Williams, age 53, $504,925 total compensation
Director Corporate Communications, Aidan Gormley
VP; President Latin America Group, A. Ricardo Machado, age 64
VP Global Supply Chain and Procurement, John G. Dedinsky Jr., age 55
VP; President Climate and Industrial Controls Group, Thomas F. Healy, age 52
VP; President Hydraulics Group, Jeffrey A. Cullman, age 57
VP Tax, William R. Hoelting, age 55
VP; President Filtration Group, Peter Popoff, age 60
EVP Finance and Administration and CFO, Jon P. Marten, age 56
VP; President Asia Pacific Group, Yoon (Michael) Chung, age 49
VP; President Seal Group, Kurt A. Keller, age 54
VP; President Europe Middle East and Africa Group, Charly Saulnier
VP and Controller, Catherine A. (Cathy) Suever, age 53
Director, Candy M. Obourn, age 62
Director, Markos I. Tambakeras, age 61
Director, Robert J. (Bob) Kohlhepp, age 68
Director, Robert G. (Bob) Bohn, age 59
Director, James L. (Jim) Wainscott, age 55
Director, William E. Kassling, age 68
Director, Giulio Mazzalupi, age 71
Director, Klaus-Peter Muller, age 67
Director, Linda S. Harty, age 52
Director, Wolfgang R. Schmitt, age 68
Director, ?ke Svensson, age 60
Director, Joseph M. (Joe) Scaminace, age 59
Auditors: Deloitte&ToucheLLP

LOCATIONS

HQ: Parker-Hannifin Corporation
6035 Parkland Blvd., Cleveland OH 44124-4141
Phone: 216-896-3000 **Fax:** 216-896-4000
Web: www.parker.com

2012 Sales

	$ mil.	% of total
North America	7,830	60
International	5,315	40
Total	**13,145**	**100**

PRODUCTS/OPERATIONS

2012 Sales

	$ mil.	% of total
Industrial		
North America	5,041	38
International	5,034	38
Aerospace	2,102	16
Climate & Industrial Controls	967	8
Total	**13,145**	**100**

Selected Brand Names

Atlas Cylinders
Balston
Bayside
Bellows
Cabett
Calzoni
Chelsea
Chomerics
Compumotor
croloop
CTC
Ermeto
Fluid Power
Gold Ring
Greer
Gresen
Hiross
IPS
Jet-Pipe
Lucifer
Miller
Ross
Schrader
Sempress
Skinner
Sporlan
STC

Operating Groups & Selected Products

Aerospace
- Aircraft wheels and brakes
- Flight control components
- Fuel systems
- Pneumatic pumps and valves

Climate and industrial controls
- Expansion valves
- Filter-dryers
- Hose assemblies
- Pressure regulators
- Solenoid valves

Industrial
- Automation
  - Air preparation units
  - Electric actuators
  - Human/machine interface hardware and software
  - Indexers
  - Multi-axis positioning tables
  - Pneumatic valves
  - Stepper and servo drives
  - Structural extrusions
  - Vacuum products
- Filtration
  - Cabin air filters
  - Compressed-air and gas-purification filters
  - Fuel conditioning filters
  - Fuel filters/water separators
  - Gas generators
  - Gas generators
  - Hydraulic lubrication and coolant filters
  - Lube oil and fuel filters
  - Monitoring devices
  - Nitrogen and hydrogen generators
  - Process chemical and microfiltration filters
  - Water desalinization and purification
- Fluid Connectors
  - Couplers
  - Diagnostic equipment
  - Hoses and hose fittings
  - Tube fittings
  - Valves
- Hydraulics
  - Accumulators
  - Cylinders
  - Electrohydraulic systems
  - Hydrostatic steering units
  - Metering pumps
  - Motors and pumps
  - Power units
  - Rotary actuators
  - Sensors
  - Valves
- Instrumentation
  - Ball plug and needle valves
  - Cylinder connections
  - Fluoropolymer fittings
  - Miniature solenoid valves
  - Multi-solenoid manifolds
  - Packless ultra-high-purity valves
  - Quick connects
  - Regulators
  - Spray guns
  - Transducers
  - Tubing
  - Ultra-high-purity tube fittings
- Seals
  - Gaskets and packings
  - Metal and plastic composite seals
  - Medical devices seals and instruments
  - O-rings
  - O-seals
  - Thermal management products

COMPETITORS

Actuant
Applied Industrial Technologies
Atlas Copco
Bosch Rexroth
Colfax
Crane Co.
Curtiss-Wright
Danfoss
Donaldson Company
Eaton
Emerson Electric
Festo
Freudenberg-NOK
GE Aviation
Goodrich Corp.
Hamilton Sundstrand
Honeywell International
IMI plc
Invensys
ITT Corp.
Mark IV
Meggitt (North Hollywood)
Moog
Numatics
Pall Corporation
Roper Industries
Senior plc
SMC Corp.
SPX
Swagelok
TI Automotive
TSI Incorporated
Tyco
United Technologies
Visteon
Watts Water Technologies
Woodward Governor
Zodiac Aerospace

HISTORICAL FINANCIALS

Company Type: Public

Income Statement FYE: June 30

	REVENUE ($ mil.)	NET INCOME ($ mil.)	NET PROFIT MARGIN	EMPLOYEES
06/12	13,145	1,155	8.8%	59,300
06/11	12,345	1,057	8.6%	58,400
06/10	9,993	556	5.6%	54,800
06/09	10,309	508	4.9%	51,639
06/08	12,145	949	7.8%	61,722
Annual Growth	2.0%	5.0%	—	(1.0%)

2012 Year-End Financials

Debt ratio: 15.48%
Return on equity: 23.60%
Cash ($ mil.): 838
Current ratio: 180.94
Long-term debt ($ mil.): 1,503
No. of shares (mil.): 149
Dividends
Yield: —
Payout: 20.67%
Market value ($ mil.): 11,504

	STOCK PRICE ($) FY Close	P/E High	P/E Low	PER SHARE ($) Earnings	Dividends	Book Value
06/12	76.88	12	8	7.45	0.00	32.72
06/11	89.74	15	8	6.37	1.25	34.71
06/10	55.46	21	12	3.40	1.01	27.09
06/09	42.96	23	9	3.13	1.00	26.67
06/08	71.32	20	11	5.53	0.84	31.36
Annual Growth	1.9%	—	—	7.7%	—	1.1%

Peabody Energy Corp

In a time in which people still get most of their power from coal-fired plants Peabody Energy is king. The world's largest private-sector coal producer Peabody operates some 30 mines and processing facilities in the US and Australia. It sells about 251 million tons of coal annually and maintains more than 9 billion tons in reserve. US customers primarily power companies account for most of Peabody's sales and its coal fuels almost 50% of US power. Its operations include coal trading and brokering coalbed methane production transportation-related services and development of coal-based generating plants. The company has also begun investing in carbon capture technology.

Operations

The company operates three mining segments (Western US Mining Midwestern US Mining and Australian Mining) and a Trading and Brokerage segment. A fifth segment Corporate and Other includes mining and export/transportation joint ventures energy-related commercial activities as well as the management of coal reserve and real estate holdings.

Sales and Marketing

The bulk of Peabody's sales are to US electricity generating plants. The remaining sales are in Australia and to US manufacturing facilities. The company also has a 48% stake in a Venezuelan joint venture which produces thermal coal for export..

Financial Analysis

Peaboby saw it revenues grow by 18% in 2011 thanks to a 28% increase in the Australian mining segment due to higher prices and due to increased pricing for seaborne metallurgical and thermal coal thanks to stronger global coal demand. Other factors included coal supply constraints resulting from weather impacts in early 2011 a 7% increase in Western US Mining segment sales due to increase in volumes and the weighted average sales price and increased shipments in the Powder River Basin region due to increased customer demand and a 12% increase in Midwestern US Mining sales due to higher sales prices and contracts. It also saw a 63% increase in its Trading and Brokerage results due to increased in export volumes and higher coal market pricing on brokerage activity.

Net income declined by almost 24% primarily due to the increase in depreciation depletion and amortization expenses stemming from the company's acquisition of Macarthur Coal (Australia).

Strategy

Peabody focuses on organic growth projects in Australia and the US including expanding and extending existing mines and developing new ones. It is also working to grow its global Trading and Brokerage platform including sourcing coal from third-parties via purchases and joint venture arrangements and expanding its presence in the Asia-Pacific region through strategic partnerships and joint ventures.

In 2011 Peabody joined with the world's largest steel producer ArcelorMittal to make an offer to jointly acquire Macarthur Coal and its extensive holdings in Australia's Bowen Basin (270 million tons of coal reserves and mines that produced about 4 million metric tons in 2010). Under terms of the deal Peabody was to hold a 60% stake in Macarthur and ArcelorMittal 40%. Their joint venture was called PEAMCoal. Macarthur's largest shareholder China-based Citic Resources which owned 25% agreed to an offer of A$16 a share. Shortly after PEAMCoal took a majority stake in Macarthur ArcelorMittal backed out of the deal and sold its stake in the joint venture back to Peabody. Through its subsidiary PEAMCOAL Peabody acquired full control of Macarthur at a cost of about $5 billion.

Ownership

In 2012 BlackRock Inc. owned 11% of Peabody T. Rowe Proce Associates 9.5%.

Company Background

Peabody was founded in 1883 as a coal supplier but began coal mining in earnest in 1926.

EXECUTIVES

President and Chief Commercial Officer, Richard A. (Rick) Navarre, age 51, $730,000 total compensation
EVP and Chief Administrative Officer, Sharon D. Fiehler, age 55, $450,000 total compensation
SVP Government Relations, Fredrick D. (Fred) Palmer, age 67, $364,500 total compensation
Chairman and CEO, Gregory H. (Greg) Boyce, age 57, $1,075,000 total compensation
President Australia, Charles F. Meintjes, age 49
EVP Law Chief Legal Officer and Secretary, Alexander C. (Alex) Schoch, age 57
SVP Investor Relations and Corporate Communications, Vic Svec, age 46
President Americas, Kemal Williamson, age 52
SVP Continuous Improvement, Richard D. Robison, age 54
EVP and CFO, Michael C. (Mike) Crews, age 45, $425,000 total compensation
SVP Global Safety, Charles A. (Chuck) Burggraf
SVP Transition Services Australia, Bradley E. (Brad) Phillips
Chairman Australian Business, Eric Ford, age 57, $675,000 total compensation
EVP Technical Services, Jeane L. Hull
VP Office of the CEO, L. Cartan Sumner Jr.
Group Executive Powder River Basin and Southwest, George J. Schuller Jr.
VP International Government Relations, Michael J. Flannigan
President Asia, Zhenchun Shi
VP International Government Relations Asia, T. Layton Croft
General Manager Colorado Operations, E. Jason Davis
Superintendent Operations, Patrick Sollars
President Sales Marketing and Trading, Erik L. Ludtke
SVP Engineering Services, Scott P. Lawson
VP Information Technology Services, Randall M (Randy) Tucker
Director, William A. (Bill) Coley, age 68
Director, William C. (Bill) Rusnack, age 67
Director, Sandra A. Van Trease, age 51
Director, Alan H. Washkowitz, age 71
Director, Henry E. (Jack) Lentz Jr., age 67
Director, William E. James, age 66
Director, Robert B. Karn III, age 70
Director, M. Frances (Fran) Keeth, age 65
Director, John F. Turner, age 70
Director, Robert A. (Bob) Malone, age 60
Auditors: Ernst&YoungLLP

LOCATIONS

HQ: Peabody Energy Corp
701 Market Street, St. Louis, MO 63101-1826
Phone: 314 342-3400
Web: www.peabodyenergy.com

2011 Sales

	% of total
US	62
Japan	10
Korea	6
India	5
Other	17
Total	**100**

COMPETITORS

Alliance Resource
Alpha Natural Resources
Anglo American
Arch Coal
BHP Billiton
Cloud Peak Energy
CONSOL Energy
North American Coal
RAG AG

HISTORICAL FINANCIALS

Company Type: Public

Income Statement FYE: December 31

	REVENUE ($ mil.)	NET INCOME ($ mil.)	NET PROFIT MARGIN	EMPLOYEES
12/11	7,974	957	12.0%	8,300
12/10	6,860	774	11.3%	7,200
12/09	6,012	448	7.5%	7,300
12/08	6,593	953	14.5%	7,200
12/07	4,574	264	5.8%	7,000
Annual Growth	14.9%	38.0%	—	4.4%

2011 Year-End Financials

Debt ratio: 39.79%
Return on equity: 17.46%
Cash ($ mil.): 799
Current ratio: 164.82
Long-term debt ($ mil.): 6,556
No. of shares (mil.): 271
Dividends
Yield: —
Payout: 9.66%
Market value ($ mil.): 8,976

	STOCK PRICE ($) FY Close	P/E High/Low		PER SHARE ($) Earnings	Dividends	Book Value
12/11	33.11	21	9	3.52	0.00	20.23
12/10	63.98	22	12	2.85	0.30	17.25
12/09	45.21	28	12	1.66	0.25	13.98
12/08	22.75	25	5	3.51	0.24	10.89
12/07	61.64	62	37	0.98	0.24	9.33
Annual Growth	(14.4%)	—	—	37.7%	—	21.3%

Penney (J.C.) Co.,Inc. (Holding Co.)

J. C. Penney Company is a holding company for struggling department store operator J. C. Penney Corporation. One of the largest department store and e-commerce retailers in the US J. C. Penney Corp. operates some 1100 JCPenney department stores in 49 states and Puerto Rico and about 10 Foundry Big & Tall Supply Co. stores (launched in 2011). J. C. Penney Corp. its only subsidiary was founded in 1902 by James Cash Penney. In a bid to revive shoppers' and investors' interest in the aging chain Penney recruited former Apple stores chief Ron Johnson as CEO in 2011 and charged him with returning the business to retail relevancy. J. C. Penney Co. was formed in 2002 and is the publicly traded entity.

EXECUTIVES

Chairman, Thomas J. (Tom) Engibous, age 59
President Growth Brands Digital Ventures, Anne Sutherland Fuchs, age 64
CEO and Director, Ronald B. (Ron) Johnson, age 53
SVP and Controller, Dennis P. Miller, age 59
President, Michael R. Francis, age 49
SVP and CIO, Ed Robben, age 51
VP Corporate Communications and Community Relations, Darcie M. Brossart
SVP and Director Brand Marketing, Ruby Anik, age 55
EVP General Counsel and Secretary, Janet L. Dhillon, age 50, $468,750 total compensation
SVP Property Development, Thomas A. (Tom) Clerkin
EVP Product Development and Sourcing, Peter M. McGrath, age 61
Chief Merchant, Elizabeth H. (Liz) Sweney, age 57
EVP and Director JCPenney Stores, Michael W. Taxter
EVP jcpenney Stores, Tim Nichols
COO, Michael W. Kramer, age 48
President Gifting Grace, Mary Drolet
CFO, Kenneth H. (Ken) Hannah, age 44
EVP and Director Planning and Allocation, Clarence Kelley
EVP and Senior General Merchandise Manager Men's Home and Children's, Steven (Steve) Lawrence, age 44
SVP and General Merchandise Manager Children?s, Clark McNaught
SVP and Director Supply Chain Management; President JCP Logistics LP, Marie Lacertosa
VP Investor Relations, Kristin Hays
SVP and General Merchandise Manager Fine Jewelry, Pam Mortensen, age 57
SVP and General Merchandise Manager Handbags and Shoes, Lorraine Hitch
SVP Corporate Strategy, James (Jim) Kenney
SVP and General Merchandise Manager Women's Accessories, Jan Hodges
SVP and General Merchandise Manager Home, John J. Tighe, age 43
President CLAD, Will Swillie
EVP Product Development Design and Sourcing, Ken Mangone, age 52
EVP and CTO, Kristen E. Blum, age 46
Chief Talent Officer, Daniel E. (Dan) Walker
EVP The Square, Laurie Beja Miller, age 54
Director, Javier G. Teruel, age 61
Director, Colleen C. Barrett, age 67
Director, Leonard H. (Len) Roberts, age 63
Director, Steven Roth, age 70
Director, R. Gerald Turner, age 66
Director, Geraldine B. (Gerry) Laybourne, age 65
Director, Kent B. Foster, age 68
CEO and Director, Ronald B. (Ron) Johnson, age 53
Director, Mary Beth West, age 49
Director, Burl Osborne, age 74
Director, William A. Ackman, age 45
Auditors: KPMGLLP

LOCATIONS

HQ: J. C. Penney Company Inc.
6501 Legacy Dr., Plano TX 75024-3698
Phone: 972-431-1000 **Fax:** 469-791-3313
Web: www.benefitmall.com

PRODUCTS/OPERATIONS

COMPETITORS

Ascena Retail	Kohl' s
Bed Bath & Beyond	Macy' s
Belk	Men' s Wearhouse
Bon-Ton Stores	Nine West
Brown Shoe	Nordstrom
Casual Male Retail Group	Ross Stores
Costco Wholesale	Sears
Dillard' s	Stage Stores
Eddie Bauer LLC	Target Corporation
Foot Locker	The Gap
J. Crew	TJX Companies
Kmart	Wal-Mart
	Zale

HISTORICAL FINANCIALS

Company Type: Public

Income Statement

FYE: January 28

	REVENUE ($ mil.)	NET INCOME ($ mil.)	NET PROFIT MARGIN	EMPLOYEES
01/12	17,260	(152)	—	159,000
01/11	17,759	389	2.2%	156,000
01/10	17,556	251	1.4%	154,000
01/09*	18,486	572	3.1%	147,000
02/08	19,860	1,111	5.6%	155,000
Annual Growth	(3.4%)	—	—	0.6%

*Fiscal year change

2012 Year-End Financials

Debt ratio: 27.15%
Return on equity: (-3.79)%
Cash ($ mil.): 1,507
Current ratio: 184.36
Long-term debt ($ mil.): 2,871
No. of shares (mil.): 215
Dividends
Yield: —
Payout: —
Market value ($ mil.): 8,943

	STOCK PRICE ($) FY Close	P/E High/Low		PER SHARE ($) Earnings	Dividends	Book Value
01/12	41.42	—	—	(0.70)	0.00	18.57
01/11	32.29	21	12	1.63	0.00	23.04
01/10	24.83	34	13	1.08	0.00	20.25
01/09*	16.75	20	6	2.57	0.00	18.72
02/08	48.50	17	7	4.93	0.00	23.93
Annual Growth	(3.9%)	—	—	—	—	(6.1%)

*Fiscal year change

Penske Automotive Group Inc

Penske Automotive Group (PAG) has lots of lots. The #2 publicly traded auto dealer in the US behind AutoNation PAG operates 320 auto franchises from California to New York and Puerto Rico and abroad mainly in the UK. The company sells cars made by more than a dozen automakers. Non-US brands including AUDI BMW and Honda generate roughly 95% of sales. PAG also sells used vehicles and provides collision repair services and financing. UK subsidiary Sytner Group operates some 140 franchises selling more than 20 brands of mostly high-end models. Additionally PAG holds a 9% stake in Penske Truck Leasing (PTL) known for commercial leasing rental and contract maintenance. Chairman Roger Penske leads PAG.

The global financial crisis tight credit environment and uncertain economy have impacted automotive sales at PAG. After tumbling more than 25% between 2007 and 2009 year-over-year sales rebounded roughly 10% in 2010 and again in 2011. The rise was driven by an uptick in unit sales attributable to dealership acquisitions coupled with higher selling prices. Correspondingly earnings which dipped into the red in 2008 soared approximately 40% and 60% in 2010 and 2011 respectively over their prior year results.

Sales in the US which account for more than 60% of PAG's revenue however remain below the average level rung up in the last 10 years. PAG's long-term strategy focuses on offering a mix of mainly premium-brand vehicles and related services that stay apace with the continued recovery in the US automotive market. During 2011 premium brands accounted for nearly 70% of sales foreign brands accounted for more than 25% and US brands less than 5%.

Growth is further targeted through acquisitions and alliances. In 2012 the company entered the Madison Wisconsin market by buying the Jon Lancaster Toyota Scion and Lexus of Madison dealerships. PAG also acquired Savage BMW/MINI of Ontario California to strengthen its presence in Orange County and contribute some $125 million in annualized revenue. In 2011 PAG acquired seven US franchises estimated to deliver about $500 million in annual revenue. Outside of the US PAG expanded by purchasing 13 dealerships from the Isaac Agnew Group in the UK the third largest retail automotive market in Western Europe. Like the US acquisitions the group is anticipated to contribute around $500 million in revenues. Eyeing operations that fell outside of the company's goals PAG also disposed of 16 franchises most of which were in the US. Mid-year PAG's subsidiary smart USA the distributor of the smart fortwo vehicle in the US and Puerto Rico was sold to Daimler Vehicle Innovations part of Mercedes Benz USA.

PAG is simultaneously taking steps to diversify its international presence beyond the UK and Germany. To this end the company struck up a joint venture in 2012 with Andrea Mantellini; the Mantellini family owns a BMW/MINI group of dealers in Bologna Italy. The venture which marks PAG's first step into Italy paves the way for taking over and operating dealerships across northern Italy. The venture was jumped started by the purchase of a BMW/MINI dealership in Monza a Milan suburb. Its location is integral to the venture's momentum; Milan is among Europe's top 10 business and financial centers and the top 20 worldwide. Earlier in 2011 PAG agreed to acquire 50% of Alliance Motor Tyumen a Russia-based Lexus car dealer. Alliance Motor Tyumen is owned by Japan's Mitsui & Co. Penske's second-largest shareholder.

Penske Corporation through various affiliates is PAG's largest shareholder owning about a third of the company. Mitsui holds about a 17% stake in the company. Together they control slightly more than 50% of the shares and consequently control the composition of the board of directors and the direction of the business.

EXECUTIVES

Chairman and CEO, Roger S. Penske, age 75, $1,000,000 total compensation
President and Director, Robert H. Kurnick Jr., age 50, $600,000 total compensation
Managing Director Sytner Group, Gerard Nieuwenhuys, age 50
EVP Investor Relations and Corporate Development, Anthony R. (Tony) Pordon, age 47
EVP Marketing, Bud Denker
EVP Human Resources, Calvin C. Sharp, age 60, $350,000 total compensation
EVP East Operations, Bernie Wolfe, age 56
EVP West Operations, George Brochick, age 63
EVP Central Operations and Financial Services, R. Whitfield Ramonat, age 50
EVP. General Counsel and Secretary, Shane M. Spradlin, age 42, $250,000 total compensation
CIO, Steven Pickett
SVP International Business Development and Director, Yoshimi Namba, age 46
EVP and CFO, David K. Jones
SVP and Corporate Controller, J. D. Carlson, age 42
Director, Ronald G. (Ron) Steinhart, age 71
Director, Lucio A. Noto, age 73
Director, John D. Barr, age 64
President and Director, Robert H. Kurnick Jr., age 50
Director, H. Brian Thompson, age 72
Director, William J. (Bill) Lovejoy, age 71
Director, Michael R. Eisenson, age 56
Director, Richard J. Peters, age 64
Director, Kimberly J. (Kim) McWaters, age 47
SVP International Business Development and Director, Yoshimi Namba, age 46
Auditors: Deloitte&ToucheLLP

LOCATIONS

HQ: Penske Automotive Group Inc
2555 Telegraph Road, Bloomfield Hills, MI 48302-0954
Phone: 248 648-2500 **Fax:** 248 648-2525
Web: www.penskeautomotive.com

2011 Stores

	No.
US	166
UK	142
Germany	12
Total	**320**

2011 Sales

	% of total
US	63
International	37
Total	**100**

PRODUCTS/OPERATIONS

2011 Sales

	% of total
New	53
Used	31
Service &	13
Finance &	3
Total	**100**

2011 Sales by Brand

	% of total
BMW	25
Audi	12
Toyota	11
Honda	11
Mercedes	10
Porsche	5
Ferrari/Maserati	5
Chrysler Ford &	4
Land	4
Lexus	4
Nissan	2

Acura	2
Jaguar	1
Bentley	1
Other	3
Total	**100**

COMPETITORS

Asbury Automotive
Autobytel
AutoNation
CarMax
Ed Morse Auto
Fletcher Jones
Group 1 Automotive
Hendrick Automotive
Holman Enterprises
JM Family Enterprises
Jordan Automotive
Larry H. Miller Group
Lithia Motors
Lookers
Microsoft
Pendragon
Potamkin Automotive
Serra Automotive
Sonic Automotive

HISTORICAL FINANCIALS

Company Type: Public

Income Statement

FYE: December 31

	REVENUE ($ mil.)	NET INCOME ($ mil.)	NET PROFIT MARGIN	EMPLOYEES
12/11	11,556	176	1.5%	15,600
12/10	10,713	108	1.0%	14,800
12/09	9,523	76	0.8%	13,950
12/08	11,646	(411)	—	14,300
12/07	12,957	127	1.0%	15,800
Annual Growth	(2.8%)	8.5%	—	(0.3%)

2011 Year-End Financials

Debt ratio: 56.69%
Return on equity: 15.57%
Cash ($ mil.): 29
Current ratio: 102.00
Long-term debt ($ mil.): 846
No. of shares (mil.): 90
Dividends
Yield: —
Payout: 12.37%
Market value ($ mil.): 1,738

	STOCK PRICE ($) FY Close	P/E High/Low		PER SHARE ($) Earnings	Dividends	Book Value
12/11	19.25	12	8	1.94	0.00	12.58
12/10	17.42	15	9	1.18	0.00	11.31
12/09	15.18	25	6	0.83	0.27	10.29
12/08	7.68	—	—	(4.42)	0.36	8.57
12/07	17.46	18	13	1.35	0.30	14.96
Annual Growth	2.5%	—	—	9.5%	—	(4.2%)

Penson Worldwide Inc

Penson Worldwide clears the way for brokers to do their thing. The company is a third-party provider of clearing-related services including trade execution and settlement custody and technology support in the US and Canada. It operates mostly through Apex Clearing technoly arm Nexa Technologies and Penson Financial Services Canada. A majority of Penson's 230 correspondents (clients) are retail brokers but the company also provides services for banks institutional brokerages financial technology companies and securities exchanges.

The past several years have been a struggle for Penson Worldwide as net income and revenues have been falling steadily since 2007. Stagnant trading volumes brought on by the global economic downturn coupled with low interest rates cut into Penson's income. Net income fell for the third year in a row in 2011 as Penson reported a loss of $225 million. The hit to net income was a result of a $140 million good will and impairment charge which resulted from lowering the company's revenue potential. Revenue also has declined falling by more than 23% in 2011. An ill-timed acquisition and the disclosure that Penson held more than $42 million in illiquid bonds issued by a horse-racing track operator further injured Penson.

In efforts to raise capital and scale down its business the company sold off assets including its Australian unit to Bank of New York Mellon for about $33 million. Penson also shut down other international operations in the UK and Asia.

Probably the boldest move to retool operations came in 2012 when Penson and Peak6 Investment formed a new clearing services firm. The new firm Apex Clearing Corp. took on accounts from Penson's broker-dealer subsidiary Penson Financial Services. In exchange Penson Worldwide received a 94% ownership stake in Apex. Peak6 will provide capital and a management team to run Apex Clearing. The restructuring move happened only a few days after Penson sold its futures commission merchant Penson Futures to Knight Capital Group for $5 million.

EXECUTIVES

EVP and CFO, Kevin W. McAleer, age 61, $300,000 total compensation
Chairman, Roger J. Engemoen Jr., age 58, $287,500 total compensation
Vice Chairman and Interim CEO, Daniel P. (Dan) Son, age 73, $525,000 total compensation
CEO and Director, Philip A. (Phil) Pendergraft, age 52, $600,000 total compensation
Co-Head of Business Development Penson GHCO, Richard Anspacher
EVP General Counsel and Secretary, Andrew B. Koslow, age 51, $446,208 total compensation
President and COO, Bryce B. Engel, age 40, $239,611 total compensation
President and CEO Penson Financial Services Ltd., C. William (Bill) Yancey, $425,000 total compensation
Manager Corporate Communication Penson Financial Services Inc., Amanda McCutcheon
SVP and Head of Business Development Penson Financial Services Canada, Kevin Vanderheyden
President and CEO Penson Asia, Mark Munoz
SVP and Global Head of Foreign Exchange, David Faller
CEO Penson Financial Services Inc., Clive Triance, age 45
Head Sales Pension Financial Services Ltd., David Mudie, age 35
President and CEO Penson Financial Services Canada, John Skain
President and CEO Penson Futures, John Streich
Managing Director and CEO Asia Pacific Region, Craig Mason
President Nexa Technologies, Todd Boppell
COO Penson Financial Services Ltd., Darryl Wims
Managing Director Business Development Penson GHCO, Mike O'Callaghan
VP and Associate General Counsel Penson Financial Services Canada, Charles B. Piroli
Director Operations Penson Financial Services Ltd., Tyrone Conybear, age 44
CIO Penson Financial Services Inc., Andrew Konchan, age 41
SVP and Head of Global Securities Lending, Michael H. Johnson
COO Penson Futures, Steve Leone
CIO; President Nexa Technologies, Bruce Ferguson
Director, David Johnson, age 64
Vice Chairman and Interim CEO, Daniel P. (Dan) Son, age 73
CEO and Director, Philip A. (Phil) Pendergraft, age 52
Director, James S. Dyer, age 68
Director, David M. Kelly, age 73
Director, Thomas R. Johnson, age 44
Director, David A. Reed, age 64
Auditors: BDOSeidmanLLP

LOCATIONS

HQ: Penson Worldwide Inc.
1700 Pacific Ave. Ste. 1400, Dallas TX 75201
Phone: 214-765-1100 **Fax:** 214-217-4978
Web: www.penson.com

PRODUCTS/OPERATIONS

2011 Sales

	$ mil.	% of total
Clearing & commission fees	104	44
Interest	81	34
Technology	22	9
Other	30	13
Total	**238**	**100**

Selected Subsidiaries

Nexa Technologies Inc.
Penson Execution Services Inc.
Penson Financial Services Canada Inc.

COMPETITORS

BGC Partners
Fidelity National Information Services
FMR
GSEC
Knight Capital
MF Global
Pershing LLC
R.J. O' Brien
SWS Group

HISTORICAL FINANCIALS

Company Type: Public

Income Statement

FYE: December 31

	ASSETS ($ mil.)	NET INCOME ($ mil.)	INCOME AS % OF ASSETS	EMPLOYEES
12/11	6,197	(225)	—	815
12/10	10,254	(19)	—	985
12/09	7,251	16	0.2%	1,031
12/08	5,539	10	0.2%	1,058
12/07	7,846	26	0.3%	942
Annual Growth	(5.7%)	—	—	(3.6%)

2011 Year-End Financials

Debt ratio: 4.38%
Return on equity: (-298.35)%
Cash ($ mil.): 2,572
Current ratio: —
Long-term debt ($ mil.): 271
No. of shares (mil.): 27
Dividends
Yield: —
Payout: —
Market value ($ mil.): 32

	STOCK PRICE ($) FY Close	P/E High/Low		PER SHARE ($) Earnings	Dividends	Book Value
12/11	1.16	—	—	(8.01)	0.00	2.73
12/10	4.89	—	—	(0.73)	0.00	10.58
12/09	9.06	19	6	0.63	0.00	11.70
12/08	7.62	46	12	0.42	0.00	10.49
12/07	14.35	33	13	1.00	0.00	10.39
Annual Growth	(46.7%)	—	—	—	—	(28.4%)

People's United Financial, Inc.

People's United Financial is the holding company for People's United Bank (formerly People's Bank) which was founded in 1842. The bank has more than 400 locations including traditional branches supermarket branches commercial banking offices investment and brokerage offices and equipment leasing offices in New England and eastern New York. In addition to retail and commercial banking services the bank offers trust wealth management brokerage and insurance services. Its lending activities consist mainly of commercial mortgages (more than a third of its loan portfolio) commercial and industrial loans (more than a quarter) equipment financing residential mortgages and home equity loans

Other divisions of People's United Financial include People's United Insurance Agency and People's Securities which provides brokerage and investment services. In 2010 People's United Financial expanded its offerings by acquiring commercial lender Financial Federal Corporation (now People's United Equipment Finance) which provides financing and leasing to small and midsized business nationwide. People's Capital and Leasing which also operates throughout the US specializes in the packaging printing and health care industries; it added business aircraft financing to its capabilities in 2011.

People's United Financial has undergone significant transformation in recent years. The company demutualized and converted to a stock holding company in 2007 and early the following year acquired multibank holding company Chittenden Corporation. The deal added some 140 branches doubling People's United Bank's branch network and expanding its reach beyond Connecticut and New York and into the rest of New England.

People's United's growth was reflected in its 2011 results. Revenues were up more than 20% from some $1.1 billion to nearly $1.36 billion and net income more than doubled ($85.7 million to nearly $200 million). The company atttributed its improved performance in part to greater loan volume tighter expense controls and an increase in fee-based income such as service charges investment management fees and insurance and brokerage commissions.

People's United emphasizes cross-selling financial products by developing client relationships and has increasingly tied employee compensation to this ability. The company is particularly focused on building its small business lending wealth management and insurance business. It also continues to open new branches and seeks acquisition targets for further growth.

One of the main goals of People's United is to build its presence in the two largest metropolitan areas in its market New York City and Boston. Since 2010 the company has acquired three banks in the Boston area. The largest Danvers Bancorp added some 30 branches and carried a price tag of approximately $493 million. People's United also acquired LSB Corporation and Butler Bank the latter in an FDIC-assisted transaction that included a loss-sharing agreement with the regulator covering all acquired loans and foreclosed real estate of the failed bank. Those deals brought in about 10 branches in the Boston area. In 2010 People's United bought Bank of Smithtown which had about 30 branches primarily on Long Island in New York.

The company acquired nearly 60 branches many of which are located within Stop & Shop supermarkets in the New York metro area from RBS Citizens in 2012. People's United already had more than 80 Stop & Shop branches in Connecticut so the deal strengthened its relationship with the retailer and expanded its presence in the New York market.

EXECUTIVES

President and CEO, John P. (Jack) Barnes, age 56, $407,077 total compensation
SEVP CFO and Director, Kirk W. Walters, age 56
EVP; President and CEO Financial Federal Credit, Paul R. Sinsheimer, age 64
SVP and President Merrill Bank, William P. (Bill) Lucy, age 53
SVP and Treasurer, R. David Rosato, age 50
SEVP Retail and Business Banking, Robert R. (Bob) D'Amore, age 59, $407,077 total compensation
Chairman, George P. Carter, age 75
SVP and President R.C. Knox and Co., John F. Byrnes
SVP and Controller, Jeffrey A. Hoyt, age 42
SVP and President Chittenden Bank, Michael L. Seaver
SEVP Wealth Management, Louise T. Sandberg, age 60
SVP and President The Bank of Western Massachusetts and Flagship Bank, Timothy P. Crimmins Jr.
SVP Commercial Lending, Daniel M. Flynn
SVP and Division President Maine Bank & Trust, Samuel A. Ladd III
SVP Senior Corporate Counsel and Corporate Secretary, Susan D. Stanley
EVP and President People's Capital and Leasing, Vincent R. Cianciolo
Director External Communications, Brent Di Giorgio
First VP Corporate Communications, Valerie C. Carlson
SVP Customer Relationship Development, Sara M. Longobardi
SVP and President People's United Bank North Connecticut, Michael J. Casparino
SEVP Human Resources, David K. Norton, age 56
SEVP Commercial Banking, Jeffrey J. (Jeff) Tengel, age 49
SVP and CTO, David S. Marsh
EVP and Chief Credit Officer People's United Bank, David A. Bodor, age 65
SVP and Division President People's United Bank Southern Connecticut, Armando F. Goncalves
SEVP and General Counsel, Robert E. Trautmann, age 58
SVP Commercial Banking, David P. Berey
SVP Financial Planning and Analysis, Christina M. Bliven
SVP Real Estate Services, Peter Brestovan
SVP and President Chittenden Insurance, Daniel F. Casey
SVP Finance, Linda Cheever
SVP Commercial Lending, Harold F. Geissler
SVP and President People's Securities, Michael E. Harkins
SVP Loan and Wealth Management Operations, Florence F. Izzo
SVP Commercial Underwriting, Walter Kaercher
SVP Deposit Operations and Direct Banking, Patricia A. Manion
SVP and Chief Investment Officer, Matthew C. O'Reilly
SVP Commercial Real Estate, Thomas J. Pantello
SEVP and Chief Administrative Officer, Lee C. Powlus
SVP and Senior Corporate Counsel, Frances Ricci
SVP Consumer Deposit Products, Peter J. Scotch
SVP Investor Relations and Mergers and Acquisitions, Jared D. Shaw
SVP Business Services, Linda M. Stempek
SVP Human Resources, Maria A. Stolfi
SVP Residential and Consumer Lending, Wayne Walker
EVP and Chief Risk Officer, Chantal D. Simon, age 47
EVP Retail Service Delivery, Chris Sakaguchi
SVP Wealth Management, Manuel A. Andrade
SVP and Regional Manager Wealth Management, Sylvia MacKinnon
SVP Small Business and Marketing, William M. Samuelson
SVP; President Ocean Bank Division, Dianne M. Mercier
SVP and Chief Auditor, Marie A. Thresher
VP and Assistant Secretary, Eric J. Appellof
Director, Janet M. Hansen, age 69
SEVP CFO and Director, Kirk W. Walters, age 56
Director, Philip R. Sherringham, age 58
Director, John K. Dwight, age 67
Director, Mark W. Richards, age 66
Director, Jerry Franklin, age 64
Director, Eunice S. Groark, age 74
Director, James A. (Jim) Thomas, age 73
Director, Collin P. Baron, age 64
Director, Richard M. Hoyt, age 69
Auditors: KPMGLLP

LOCATIONS

HQ: People' s United Financial Inc.
850 Main St., Bridgeport CT 06604
Phone: 203-338-7171 **Fax:** 203-338-2310
Web: www.peoples.com

PRODUCTS/OPERATIONS

2011 Sales

	$ mil.	% of total
Interest & dividends		
Loans		
Commercial real estate	392	29
Commercial	358	26
Residential mortgage	129	10
Consumer	84	6
Securities	83	6
Other	4	-
Noninterest		
Bank service charges	131	10
Investment management fees	33	3
Insurance	30	2
Brokerage commissions	11	1
Other	100	7
Total	**1,359**	**100**

COMPETITORS

Bank of America
Citibank
Fairfield County Bank
KeyCorp
Liberty Bank
RBS Citizens Financial Group
Sovereign Bank
TD Bank USA
Webster Financial

HISTORICAL FINANCIALS

Company Type: Public

Income Statement FYE: December 31

	ASSETS ($ mil.)	NET INCOME ($ mil.)	INCOME AS % OF ASSETS	EMPLOYEES
12/11	27,567	198	0.7%	5,477
12/10	25,037	85	0.3%	5,198
12/09	21,257	101	0.5%	4,534
12/08	20,167	139	0.7%	4,754
12/07	13,554	150	1.1%	2,856
Annual Growth	19.4%	7.2%	—	17.7%

2011 Year-End Financials

Debt ratio: 1.88%
Return on equity: 3.81%
Cash ($ mil.): 748
Current ratio: —
Long-term debt ($ mil.): 519
No. of shares (mil.): 357
Dividends
Yield: —
Payout: 110.09%
Market value ($ mil.): 4,594

	STOCK PRICE ($) FY Close	P/E High/Low		PER SHARE ($) Earnings	Dividends	Book Value
12/11	12.85	25	19	0.57	0.00	14.62
12/10	14.01	71	51	0.24	0.62	14.53
12/09	16.70	61	50	0.30	0.61	14.78
12/08	17.83	52	35	0.42	0.58	15.01
12/07	17.80	40	29	0.52	0.40	14.90
Annual Growth	(7.8%)	—	—	2.3%	—	(0.5%)

Pepco Holdings Inc.

Pepco Holdings arguably has more power in the US capital than any politician. The holding company distributes electricity and natural gas through its Potomac Electric Power (Pepco) Delmarva Power & Light and Atlantic City Electric utilities to about 2 million customers in Delaware Maryland New Jersey and Washington DC. None of the company's three utilities have power generation plants. Nonregulated operations include energy efficiency consultation and renewable energy services for institutional and government clients through the company's Pepco Energy Services unit.

Geographic Reach

Pepco Holdings primarily serves customers in Delaware Maryland New Jersey and Washington DC.

Operations

PHI subsidiaries provide regulated power delivery and non-regulated energy and other services through its subsidiaries. Pepco Delmarva Power and Atlantic City Electric provide regulated electricity services (Delmarva Power also provides natural gas service). Pepco Energy Services provides energy efficiency and renewable energy services.

Financial Analysis

A $489 million drop in default electricity supply revenues (due mainly to customer migration to competitive suppliers and lower supply rates) led to a 16% drop in Pepco Holding's overall revenues in 2012. However net income jumped by more the 700% thanks largely to lower fuel and purchased energy costs and the absence of the debt-related losses that it carried in 2010.

Strategy

Pepco Holdings' flexible business strategy allows it to develop opportunities for growth or operational streamlining in both its regulated and unregulated segments.

Growing its renewable portfolio to meet tightening carbon emission regulations in 2012 Delmarva Power announced that it will get 38 MW of wind energy and associated renewable energy credits from enXco's Chestnut Flats wind farm in Pennsylvania.

In 2010 Pepco Holdings sold its Conectiv Energy power plant assets to Calpine for about $1.7 billion. The deal moved Pepco Holdings out of the merchant power business to free up cash and allowed the company to focus on its core regulated energy distribution businesses.

Company Background

Pepco Holdings formerly named Potomac Electric Power changed its name by forming a holding company in 2002; the name change took effect upon the completion of Pepco's acquisition of rival utility Conectiv (now Delmarva Power & Light).

EXECUTIVES

VP and CIO, Kenneth P. Cohn, age 58
EVP and Chief Regulatory Officer, Anthony J. (Tony) Kamerick, age 64, $383,874 total compensation
SVP and General Counsel, Kirk J. Emge, age 62, $350,000 total compensation
SVP External Affairs, Beverly L. Perry, age 64
Chairman President and CEO, Joseph M. (Joe) Rigby, age 55, $796,669 total compensation
VP Corporate Governance Secretary and Assistant Treasurer, Ellen Sheriff Rogers
Assistant Treasurer and Assistant Secretary, Karen G. Almquist
VP and Controller, Ronald K. Clark, age 56
VP Investor Relations, Donna J. Kinzel
Assistant Controller Pepco Energy Services, Kathy A. White
VP People Strategy and Human Resources, Ernest L. Jenkins, age 57
VP Public Policy, Kenneth J. (Ken) Parker
President and CEO Pepco Energy Services, John U. Huffman, age 52
EVP Power Delivery, David M. (Dave) Velazquez, age 52, $423,729 total compensation
VP PHI Service Company, Hallie M. Reese, age 48
SVP and CFO, Frederick J. (Fred) Boyle, age 54
VP Corporate Communications, Laura L. Monica, age 55
VP Corporate Citizenship and Social Responsibility, Debbi Jarvis
VP and General Auditor, Paul W. Friel, age 63
VP and Treasurer, Kevin M. McGowan
Media Relations, Bill Yingling
Media Relations, Bob Hainey
Director, Frank O. Heintz, age 68
Director, Terence C. Golden, age 67
Director, Lawrence C. Nussdorf, age 65
Director, Jack B. Dunn IV, age 61
Director, Pauline A. Schneider, age 69
Director, George F. MacCormack, age 68
Director, Barbara J. Krumsiek, age 59
Director, Frank K. Ross, age 68
Director, Lester P. Silverman, age 65
Director, Patrick T. Harker, age 53
Director, Patricia A. Oelrich, age 58
Auditors: PricewaterhouseCoopersLLP

LOCATIONS

HQ: Pepco Holdings Inc.
701 9th St. NW, Washington DC 20068
Phone: 202-872-2000 **Fax:** 202-331-6750
Web: www.pepcoholdings.com

PRODUCTS/OPERATIONS

2011 Sales

	$ mil.	% of total
Power delivery	4,650	78
Pepco Energy Services	1,238	21
Other non-regulated	48	1
Adjustments	(16)	-
Total	**5,920**	**100**

Selected Subsidiaries

Conectiv
- Atlantic City Electric Company (operates as Conectiv Power Delivery electric utility)
- Delmarva Power & Light Company (operates as Conectiv Power Delivery electric and gas utility)

Pepco Energy Services Inc. (power generation retail and wholesale energy marketing and management services)
PHI Service Company (support services)
Potomac Capital Investment Corporation (investments)
Potomac Electric Power Company (Pepco electric utility)

COMPETITORS

AEP
Appalachian Power
Baltimore Gas and Electric
Chesapeake Utilities
Con Edison
Constellation Energy Group
Dominion Resources
Exelon
FirstEnergy
New Jersey Resources
Northern Virginia Electric Cooperative
PPL Corporation
Public Service Enterprise Group
Virginia Electric and Power
WGL Holdings

HISTORICAL FINANCIALS

Company Type: Public

Income Statement FYE: December 31

	REVENUE ($ mil.)	NET INCOME ($ mil.)	NET PROFIT MARGIN	EMPLOYEES
12/11	5,920	257	4.3%	5,104
12/10	7,039	32	0.5%	5,014
12/09	9,259	235	2.5%	5,110
12/08	10,700	300	2.8%	5,474
12/07	9,366	334	3.6%	5,131
Annual Growth	(10.8%)	(6.4%)	—	(0.1%)

2011 Year-End Financials

Debt ratio: 33.75%
Return on equity: 5.93%
Cash ($ mil.): 109
Current ratio: 77.32
Long-term debt ($ mil.): 4,180
No. of shares (mil.): 227
Dividends
Yield: —
Payout: 94.74%
Market value ($ mil.): 4,618

	STOCK PRICE ($) FY Close	P/E High/Low		PER SHARE ($) Earnings	Dividends	Book Value
12/11	20.30	18	15	1.14	0.00	19.06
12/10	18.25	141	110	0.14	1.08	18.79
12/09	16.85	18	10	1.06	1.08	19.15
12/08	17.76	20	11	1.47	1.08	19.14
12/07	29.33	18	15	1.72	1.04	20.04
Annual Growth	(8.8%)	—	—	(9.8%)	—	(1.2%)

PepsiCo Inc.

The PepsiCo challenge (to archrival Coca-Cola) never loses its fizz for the world's #2-carbonated soft-drink maker. Its soft drink brands include

Pepsi Mountain Dew and their diet alternatives. Cola is not the company's only beverage: Pepsi sells Tropicana orange juice Gatorade sports drink SoBe tea and Aquafina water. The company also owns Frito-Lay the world's #1 snack maker with offerings such as Lay's Ruffles Doritos and Cheetos. The Quaker Foods unit makes breakfast cereals (Life Quaker oatmeal) Rice-A-Roni rice and Near East side dishes. Pepsi products are available in 200-plus countries; the US generates 50% of sales. The company operates its own bottling plants and distribution facilities.

HISTORY

Pharmacist Caleb Bradham invented Pepsi in 1898 in New Bern North Carolina. He named his new drink Pepsi-Cola (claiming it cured dyspepsia or indigestion) and registered the trademark in 1903. Following The Coca-Cola Company's example Bradham developed a bottling franchise system. By WWI 300 bottlers had signed up. After the war Bradham stockpiled sugar to safeguard against rising costs but in 1920 sugar prices plunged forcing him into bankruptcy in 1923.

Pepsi existed on the brink of ruin under various owners until Loft Candy bought it in 1931. Its fortunes improved in 1933 when in the midst of the Depression it doubled the size of its bottles to 12 ounces without raising the five-cent price. In 1939 Pepsi introduced the world's first radio jingle. Two years later Loft Candy merged with its Pepsi subsidiary and became The Pepsi-Cola Company.

Donald Kendall who became Pepsi-Cola's president in 1963 turned the firm's attention to young people ("The Pepsi Generation"). It acquired Mountain Dew in 1964 and became PepsiCo in 1965 when it acquired Frito-Lay.

In 1972 PepsiCo agreed to distribute Stolichnaya vodka in the US in exchange for being the only Western firm allowed to bottle soft drinks in the USSR. With the purchases of Pizza Hut (1977) Taco Bell (1978) and Kentucky Fried Chicken (1986) it became a major force in the fast-food industry.

When Coca-Cola changed its formula in 1985 Pepsi had a short-lived victory in the cola wars (until the return of Coca-Cola classic the new formula having been a dismal failure). The rivalry was extended to ready-to-drink tea in 1991 when in response to Coca-Cola's Nestea venture with Nestle PepsiCo teamed up with Lipton.

Between 1991 and 1996 PepsiCo aggressively expanded its overseas bottling operations. However its efforts contrasted markedly with Coca-Cola's well-oiled international distribution machine. The firm then shifted its attention to the organization of its overseas network. Roger Enrico became CEO in 1996.

A year later PepsiCo spun off its $10 billion fast-food unit as TRICON Global Restaurants (now known as YUM! Brands Inc.) putting itself in a better position to sell its soft drinks at other restaurants. Also in 1997 it bought Borden's Cracker Jack snack and Smith's snacks from the UK's United Biscuits.

In 1998 it bought Seagram's market-leading Tropicana juices (rival of Coca-Cola's Minute Maid) for $3.3 billion. The firm sold a 65% stake in its new Pepsi Bottling Group to the public in 1999.

Its more than $13 billion purchase of The Quaker Oats Company in 2001 added the dominant Gatorade sports drink brand to its lineup. To make room for Gatorade PepsiCo sold its competing All Sport energy drink to The Monarch Beverage Company an Atlanta-based soda company later that year.

Also in 2001 PepsiCo bought a majority of South Beach Beverage Co. maker of SoBe drinks (fruit blends energy drinks teas sports drinks). Later that year the company named president and COO Steve Reinemund as chairman and CEO Enrico as vice chairman (where he remained through 2002) and CFO Indra Nooyi as president. On the product side the company launched Pepsi Blue new berry-flavored cola in 2002 and Pepsi Vanilla in 2003 targeting thirsty teenagers in an attempt to energize its flat fizzy-drinks segment. (Both have since been discontinued.)

PepsiCo began a major restructuring of its PepsiCo Beverages & Foods division in 2003. The restructuring resulted in four company divisions: PepsiCo International PepsiCo Beverages North America Frito-Lay North America and Quaker Foods North America.

Like Coca-Cola PepsiCo also found opportunities for growth overseas in 2003. However claims surfaced that year that both Coke and Pepsi products bottled in India contained traces of DDT malathion and other pesticides that exceeded government limits. Coke and Pepsi denied the reports in a rare joint press conference. Government labs cleared the colas saying the drinks were safe but not before both soft-drink companies saw sales dip by as much as 50% in a two-week period.

In 2004 PepsiCo approached juice maker Ocean Spray about a joint venture but was turned away by the cranberry farmers who own the juice manufacturer. The company bought General Mills' stake of their joint venture Snack Ventures Europe (SVE) in 2005 for $750 million. The deal gave Pepsi control of Europe's largest snack food company.

Later that year the company revealed it was subject to an SEC investigation involving transactions it had with Kmart. Allegedly lower-level employees within its cola and snack divisions signed documents that Kmart used to improperly record nearly $6 million in revenue. PepsiCo cooperated with the investigation which led to the resignations of a PepsiCo national account manager and a sales director.

Venturing into the non-cola category PepsiCo acquired sparkling juice companies IZZE and Naked Juice in 2006. It also began selling Fuelosophy a smoothie drink at organic grocery store chain Whole Foods and struck a deal to develop products with Ocean Spray.

Bowing to the public's growing concern about childhood obesity in 2006 Pepsi along with Coca-Cola Cadbury Schweppes (which later spun off its North American beverage operation as Dr Pepper Snapple Group) and the American Beverage Association agreed to sell only water unsweetened juice and low-fat milk to public elementary and middle schools in the US. As for high schools the agreement called for no sugary sodas to be sold and one-half of the offered drinks to be water diet sodas lemonade or iced tea. The agreement was facilitated by former president Bill Clinton.

Reinemund stepped down as CEO in 2006 in order to spend more time with his family. Indra Nooyi was named as his replacement. Indian-born Nooyi the 11th female CEO of a FORTUNE 500 company was instrumental in strategic decisions at the company such as the acquisition of Tropicana and merger with Quaker Oats.

Shortly after her appointment Nooyi restructured the top level of power at the company. She appointed John Compton previously head of the Quaker-Tropicana-Gatorade unit to the newly created position of CEO for PepsiCo North America reporting directly to her. The company also appointed Albert Carey as president and CEO of Frito-Lay North America replacing Irene Rosenfeld who had left the company to become head of Kraft Foods.

In 2010 the company acquired its two largest bottlers: Pepsi Bottling Group and PepsiAmericas. After rejecting PepsiCo's initial bid as insufficient PepsiCo submitted another offer some months later this time upping its cash and stock proposal in a revised deal valued at $7.8 billion which was accepted by both companies.

In 2011 PepsiCo acquired all of the outstanding shares of Russia's Wimm-Bill-Dann Foods –maker of juice value-added dairy products and baby food –via a tender offer completed in May.

EXECUTIVES

CEO PepsiCo Americas Beverages, Albert P. (Al) Carey, age 60, $764,000 total compensation
Chairman and CEO, Indra K. Nooyi, age 56, $1,300,000 total compensation
EVP Public Policy Government Affairs General Counsel and Corporate Secretary, Maura Abeln Smith, age 56
SVP and General Auditor; Leader Global Financial Shared Services, Peter A. Bridgman, age 59
CEO Pepsi Beverages Company (PBC), Eric J. Foss, age 53
EVP Human Resources and Chief HR Officer, Cynthia M. Trudell, age 58
CEO PepsiCo Americas Beverages, Massimo F. d'Amore, age 55
President, John C. Compton, age 50, $860,000 total compensation
EVP Global Corporate Affairs, Timothy P. (Tim) Cost, age 52
Chief Scientific Officer; CEO Global Nutrition Group, Mehmood Khan, age 53
President Frito-Lay North America, Thomas R. (Tom) Greco
EVP Government Affairs General Counsel and Corporate Secretary, Larry D. Thompson, age 66
President Tropicana Beverages North America, Neil Campbell
CEO PepsiCo Americas Foods, Brian C. Cornell, age 53
EVP Sales and Marketing, A. Salman Amin, age 52
President Global Nutrition Platforms PepsiCo Global Nutrition Group, Jaya Kumar
SVP and Chief Procurement Officer, Grace M. Puma
CFO, Hugh F. Johnston, age 50
SVP Investor Relations, Jamie Caulfield
Chief Creative Officer and President Global Enjoyment, Brad Jakeman
SVP and Chief Communications Officer, Julie A. Hamp
SVP Deputy General Counsel and Assistant Secretary, Thomas H. Tamoney Jr.
President PepsiCo Foods Mexico Central America and Caribbean, Pedro Padierna
President Quaker Foods and Snacks North America, Jose Luis Prado
President South America Foods, Olivier Weber
President Latin America Beverages, Luis Montoya
Chairman PepsiCo China, Tim Minges
CEO PepsiCo Europe, Zein Abdalla, age 54
CEO PepsiCo Asia Middle East and Africa, Saad Abdul-Latif, age 59
SVP and CIO, Robert L. Dixon Jr.
President Global Operations, Enderson Guimaraes, age 52
SVP Global Supply Chain Operations, Richard (Rich) Beck
EVP Communications, Jim Wilkinson

President Gatorade North America and Global Chief Marketing Officer Sports Nutrition, Sarah Robb O'Hagan
SVP and Controller, Marie T. Gallagher, age 52
VP Global Hydration, Lorraine Hansen
Chief Marketing Officer Pepsi International; Chief Marketing Officer PepsiCo Beverages, Simon Lowden
Director, Ian M. Cook, age 59
Director, Lloyd G. Trotter, age 66
Director, Dina Dublon, age 59
Director, Ray L. Hunt, age 68
Director, James J. (Jim) Schiro, age 66
Director, Daniel L. Vasella, age 58
Director, Alberto Weisser, age 56
Director, Arthur C. Martinez, age 72
Director, Sharon Percy Rockefeller, age 67
Director, Victor J. Dzau, age 66
Director, Shona L. Brown, age 46
Director, Alberto Ibarguen, age 68
Auditors: KPMGLLP

LOCATIONS

HQ: PepsiCo Inc.
700 Anderson Hill Rd., Purchase NY 10577-1444
Phone: 914-253-2000 **Fax:** 914-253-2070
Web: www.pepsico.com

2011 Sales

	$ bil.	% of total
US	33	50
Russia	4	7
Mexico	4	7
Canada	3	5
UK	2	3
Other	18	28
Total	**66**	**100**

PRODUCTS/OPERATIONS

2011 Sales

	$ bil.	% of total
PepsiCo Americas Foods		
Frito-Lay North America	13	20
Latin America Foods	7	11
Quaker Foods North America	2	4
PepsiCo Americas Beverages	22	34
Europe	13	20
Asia Middle East & Africa	7	11
Total	**66**	**100**

Selected Brands

Asia Middle East and Africa
- 7UP
- Aquafina
- Cheetos
- Chipsy
- Doritos
- Kurkure
- Lay' s
- Mirinda
- Mountain Dew
- Pepsi
- Quaker
- Smith' s
- Tropicana

Europe
- 7UP
- Cheetos
- Chudo
- Diet Pepsi
- Doritos
- Lay' s
- Pepsi
- Pepsi Max
- Quaker
- Ruffles
- Tropicana
- Walkers

Frito-Lay North America
- Cheetos
- Doritos
- Fritos
- Lay' s
- Ruffles
- Sabra (joint venture)
- Santitas
- SunChips
- Tostitos

Latin America Foods
- Cheetos
- Doritos
- Marias Gamesa
- Quaker
- Ruffles
- Saladitas

PepsiCo Americas Beverages
- 7UP and Diet 7UP (outside the US)
- Aquafina
- Diet Mountain Dew
- Diet Pepsi
- Gatorade
- Mirinda
- Mountain Dew
- Pepsi
- Sierra Mist
- Tropicana Pure Premium

Quaker Foods North America
- Aunt Jemima
- Cap' n Crunch
- Life
- Near East
- Pasta Roni
- Quaker
- Quaker Chewy
- Rice-A-Roni

Selected Subsidiaries

Alimentos Quaker Oats y Compania Limitada (Guatemala)
Aradhana Convenience Foods Private Limited (India)
Beaman Bottling Company (US)
Bluebird Foods Limited (New Zealand)
Boquitas Fiestas LLC (US)
Bosso Holdings LLC (US)
Bramshaw (Ireland)
BUG de Mexico S.A. de C.V.
China Bottlers (Hong Kong) Limited
Chipiga S. de R. L. de C.V. (Mexico)
Chipsy for Food Industries S.A.E. (Egypt)
Copella Fruit Juices Limited (UK)
Corina Snacks Limited (Cyprus)
Dark Green Australia Pty Limited
Duo Juice Company (US)
Duyvis Production B.V. (The Netherlands)
Elaboradora Argentina de Cereales S.R.L.
Euro Juice G.m.b.H. Import and Vertrieb (Germany)
Far East Bottlers (Hong Kong) Limited
Frito-Lay North America Inc.
Froooties Limited (UK)
Gatorade Ltd. (UK)
Golden Grain Company (US)
Green Hemlock International LLC (US)
Heathland LP (US)
Holland Snacks S.A. de C. V. (Mexico)
Integrated Beverage Services (Bangladesh) Ltd.
International Bottlers Almaty Ltd. (Kazakhstan)
International Kas AG (Liechtenstein)
International Refreshments Co. Ltd. (Saudi Arabia)
Inversiones PFI Chile Limitada
Inversiones Santa Coloma S.A. (Venezuela)
IZZE Beverage Co. (US)
Jordan Ice & Aerated Water Ltd. (Jordan)
Jungla Mar del Sur (Costa Rica)
Larragana S.L. (Spain)
Latvian Snacks SIA (Latvia)
Lithuania Snacks Ltd.
Lotta Good LLC (US)
Naked Juice Co. (US)
New Century Beverage Company (US)
The Original Pretzel Company Pty. Ltd. (Australia)
Papas Chips (Uruguay)
Punch N.V. (Curacao)
Punica Getranke GmbH (Germany)
Quaker Foods (UK)
Quaker Manufacturing LLC (US)
S.C. Star Foods E.M. S.R.L. (Romania)
Sabra Dipping Company LLC (US)
Sakata Rice Snacks Australia Proprietary Limited
Seven-Up Asia Inc. (US)
Shoebill LLC (US)
Smartfoods Inc. (IS)
Smiths Crisps Limited (UK)
The Smiths Snackfood Company Ltd. (Australia)
South Beach Veverage company Inc. (US)
Sportmex Internacional S.A. De C.V. (Mexico)
Stacy' s Pita Chip Company Inc. (US)
Stokely-Van Camp Inc. (US)
Tastes of Adventures Pty. Ltd. (Australia)
Tasty Foods S.A. (Greece)
Tobago Snack Holdings LLC (US)
Tropicana Manufacturing Co. Inc. (US)
Twisties Australia One Pty Limited
Veurne Snackfoods BVBA (Belgium)
Vitamin Brands Ltd. (UK)
Walkers Snack Foods Limited (UK)
Wotsits Brands Limited (UK)
Zhanjiang Pepsi Cola Beverage Co. Ltd. (China)

COMPETITORS

American Beverage
Anadolu Efes
Arla Foods
Asahi Breweries
Bazi
Big Red
Bongrain
Britvic
Campbell Soup
Carolina Beverage
Celestial Seasonings
Chiquita Brands
Clearly Canadian
Coca-Cola
Coca-Cola FEMSA
ConAgra
Cott
Danone Water
Diamond Foods
Dr Pepper Snapple Group
DS Waters
Energy Brands
Fraser & Neave
FrieslandCampina
General Mills
Golden Enterprises
Grupo Bimbo
Hawaiian Springs
Inventure foods
Jones Soda
Kellogg
Lactalis
Merisant
Monarch Beverage
Monarch Beverage (GA)
Mondelez International
Monster Beverage
Mountain Valley
National Beverage
National Grape Cooperative
Nestle
New Leaf
Odwalla
Parmalat
Polar Beverages
Princes Limited
Procter & Gamble
Ralcorp
Red Bull
Reed' s
Snapple
Snyder' s-Lance
Sunny Delight
Tree Top
Weaver Popcorn Company
Wet Planet Beverages

HISTORICAL FINANCIALS

Company Type: Public

Income Statement FYE: December 31

	REVENUE ($ mil.)	NET INCOME ($ mil.)	NET PROFIT MARGIN	EMPLOYEES
12/11	66,504	6,443	9.7%	297,000
12/10	57,838	6,320	10.9%	294,000
12/09	43,232	5,946	13.8%	203,000
12/08	43,251	5,142	11.9%	198,000
12/07	39,474	5,658	14.3%	185,000
Annual Growth	13.9%	3.3%	—	12.6%

2011 Year-End Financials

Debt ratio: 36.73%
Return on equity: 31.29%
Cash ($ mil.): 4,067
Current ratio: 96.07
Long-term debt ($ mil.): 20,568
No. of shares (mil.): 1,564
Dividends
Yield: —
Payout: 50.25%
Market value ($ mil.): 103,771

	STOCK PRICE ($) FY Close	P/E High/Low		PER SHARE ($) Earnings	Dividends	Book Value
12/11	66.35	18	15	4.03	0.00	13.16
12/10	65.69	17	15	3.91	0.00	13.39
12/09	60.96	17	12	3.77	0.00	10.74
12/08	54.56	24	15	3.21	0.00	7.80
12/07	77.03	23	18	3.41	0.00	10.74
Annual Growth	(3.7%)	—	—	4.3%	—	5.2%

PETsMART, Inc.

PetSmart is the top dog and the cat's meow in its industry. The #1 US specialty retailer of pet food and supplies has 1200-plus stores in the US and Canada. Both pets and their masters may lay paws claws or hands on its 10000 products which range from scratching posts to iguana harnesses and are sold under national brands and PetSmart's own private labels. (The retailer also sells products through its PetSmart website.) Stores provide in-store boarding facilities (PetsHotels) grooming services and obedience training. Veterinary services are available as well in about 800 shops through pet hospital operator Medical Management International (known as Banfield) of which PetSmart owns about 20%.

Financial Analysis

PetSmart's sales topped $6.1 billion in fiscal 2012 (ends January) up 7% vs. the prior year. The gain was driven by the addition of some 45 new stores and increases in same-store sales (up 5.4%). Net income rose by 21% over the same period. Indeed as the love affairs between pets and their "pet parents" (company lingo for its customers) intensify the company has seen its sales grow by upwards of 30% during the past four years.

Strategy

Going forward the company is concentrating on the service side of small animal care. Grooming pet training boarding and day camp services cater to a growing industry niche and diversify PetSmart's revenue stream. Indeed sales of pet services grew by 9% to account for 11% of net sales in fiscal 2012. The retail chain operates about 190 in-store PetsHotels boarding facilities and Doggie Day Camps used primarily by upper-income consumers. The company estimates that there is enough demand to support some 400 PetsHotels; it opens about a dozen each year. As for its bricks-and-mortar retail business more than 85% of PetSmart's sales come from pet food and supplies. Surprisingly less than 2% of its sales are generated through selling pets such as fresh-water tropical fish birds reptiles and small animals. Indeed this part of its business has been shrinking albeit slightly. (PetSmart does not sell dogs or cats but instead encourages adoption by sponsoring in-store and front-of-store adoption programs with local humane organizations.) The retailer plans to launch at least 1400 of its PetSmart stores throughout North America. During the past two years the chain has opened more than 80 locations with another 45 to 50 stores slated to open in fiscal 2013.

HISTORY

In the mid-1980s the owner of a California pet supply wholesaler had an idea: If the company opened its own retail stores it could make a bundle supplying itself. Not wanting to compete with its own retail customers in California the company hired Jim and Janice Dougherty to run the first store in Las Vegas called Pet Food Supermarket. In response to customer requests the store began offering a broader range of products and soon business was booming. The store moved to a larger location and four more stores were eventually opened in Phoenix.

While managing the Pet Food Supermarkets the Doughertys met Ford Smith a retailer who had developed a plan for giant pet-supply stores while in business school. Together they agreed to give the Toys "R" Us superstore format a try for pet supplies. They opened two PetFood Warehouse stores in Arizona in 1987. The next year there were seven stores in Arizona Colorado and Texas.

In 1989 PetFood Warehouse officially became PETsMART Jim left the company due to health reasons (Janice followed shortly thereafter) and supermarket executive Sam Parker came on as CEO. His management team recrafted the PETsMART business strategy and gave the store a new look: brightly lit low shelves with various pet supplies in the front of the store and high warehouse-style shelves with bulk pet food in the back.

The 1990s saw PETsMART adding services such as in-store grooming obedience training veterinary exams and adoption programs; it also began selling birds and fish. In 1991 the company added 15 new stores. The following year 32 stores were opened.

PETsMART went public in 1993. The company added more than 40 stores that year. In 1994 PETsMART bought the Weisheimer Companies which operated about 30 pet superstores in the Midwest under the name Petzazz.

A year later the company went on an acquisition spree buying two pet superstore operators (56-store Georgia-based Petstuff and 10-store New Jersey-based Pet Food Giant) and two specialty-catalog retailers of pet and animal supplies. Some 80 stores were added in 1995 and Mark Hansen replaced Parker as CEO; Parker remained chairman.

Hansen took PETsMART overseas in 1996 through the acquisition of Pet City Holdings which operated more than 50 stores in the UK. The company also entered Canada that year. But the aggressive expansion campaign diverted the company's attention from daily operations and inventory management eroding PETsMART's earnings in fiscal year 1998. In response the company instituted a back-to-basics strategy of improved customer service and lower prices. Phil Francis formerly with Shaw's Supermarkets became CEO in 1998.

In 1999 PETsMART launched PETsMART.com in conjunction with PetJungle.com an online pet retailer backed by Internet incubator idealab!. The move intensified a catfight with several lavishly funded online pet supply stores including now-defunct Pets.com which was backed by dominant e-tailer Amazon.com. Soon thereafter the company bought AcmePet.com an online community oriented to pets.

The company sold its 92 UK stores to Pets At Home for more than $40 million in late 1999. In 2000 PETsMART increased its stake in PETsMART.com to 81%. (The remaining shares were acquired in 2002.) Carrefour sold its 9.9% stake in PETsMART for $194.3 million through a public offering that year.

In 2003 PETsMART finished remodeling its stores; the company replaced the traditional warehouse feel with a specialty-store shopping atmosphere. The company added 100 new stores in 2005. In line with those changes in 2006 PETsMART changed how its name is styled to PetSmart with the emphasis on "smart" rather than "mart."

PetSmart boosted its Canadian presence in 2007 with the acquisition of 19 stores from the Super Pet chain. (Super Pet plans to keep seven stores which it will rebrand.) It exited the equine products business in May 2007 when it sold State Line Tack to PetsUnited.

PetSmart temporarily suspended sales of birds in its stores nationwide in 2008 after discovering that birds with the bacterial infection psittacosis could spread the disease to humans.

In June 2009 PetSmart promoted president and COO Robert Moran to CEO of the company. He retained his title as president. Phil Francis who led the company for more than a decade was named executive chairman of PetSmart.

EXECUTIVES

Chairman and CEO, Robert F. (Bob) Moran, age 61, $903,365 total compensation

VP Deputy General Counsel and Assistant Secretary, J. Dale Brunk

President and COO, David K. Lenhardt, age 42, $475,573 total compensation

SVP Store Operations and Services, Bruce K. Thorn, age 44

EVP Merchandising Marketing Supply Chain and Strategic Planning, Joseph D. (Joe) O'Leary, age 53, $460,738 total compensation

SVP and CIO, Donald E. (Don) Beaver, age 53

SVP, Kenneth T. (Ken) Hall, age 43

SVP General Counsel and Secretary, Emily D. Dickinson, age 52

EVP and CFO, Lawrence P. (Chip) Molloy, age 50, $424,340 total compensation

SVP Real Estate and Development, Jaye D. Perricone, age 53

SVP Human Resources, Neil H. Stacey, age 58

Director Corporate Planning and Reporting, Christina Vance

Senior Marketing Manager Promotions, Jessica Case

SVP and Chief Marketing Officer, John Alpaugh

Manager Investor Relations, April Lenhard

VP Investor Relations, David (Dave) Cone

SVP Supply Chain, Eddie Burt

SVP Merchandising, Matt McAdam

SVP Finance, Mel Tucker

Director, Amin I. Khalifa, age 58

Director, Rita V. Foley, age 59

Director, Thomas G. (Tom) Stemberg, age 63

Director, Philip L. (Phil) Francis, age 65

Director, Gregory P. Josefowicz, age 58

Director, Richard K. Lochridge, age 68

Director, Barbara A. Munder, age 66

Director, Joseph S. Hardin Jr., age 67

Director, Angel Cabrera

Auditors: Deloitte&ToucheLLP

LOCATIONS

HQ: PetSmart Inc.
19601 N. 27th Ave., Phoenix AZ 85027
Phone: 623-580-6100 **Fax:** 678-566-9188
Web: www.exide.com

2012 Stores

	No.
US	1,159
Canada	73
Total	**1,232**

PRODUCTS/OPERATIONS

2012 Sales

	$ mil.	% of total
Merchandise	5,401	88
Pet services	674	11
Other	36	1
Total	**6,113**	**100**

Selected Merchandise

Animal carriers
Aquariums
Bedding
Bird cages
Books
Cat furniture
Collars
Dog houses
Freshwater tropical fish
Greeting cards
Health aids
Leashes
Litter
Magazines
Medications
Pet food
Reptiles
Shampoos
Toys
Treats

Selected Services

Boarding
Doggie day camp
Grooming
Obedience training
Veterinary services
Private Labels
Pet Food
- Authority (cat and dog food treats)
- Grreat Choice (dog treats)
- SophistaCat (cat food)

Pet Supplies
- Top Fin
- Top Paw
- Top Wing

COMPETITORS

Ahold U.S.A.
Costco Wholesale
Drs. Foster & Smith
Fat Cat
J&J Commerce
Pet Supermarket
Pet Valu
PetCareRx
PETCO
Petland
PetMed
Sears Holdings
Target Corporation
United Pharmacal
VCA Antech
Wal-Mart
Weis Markets

HISTORICAL FINANCIALS

Company Type: Public

Income Statement FYE: January 29

	REVENUE ($ mil.)	NET INCOME ($ mil.)	NET PROFIT MARGIN	EMPLOYEES
01/12	6,113	290	4.7%	50,000
01/11	5,693	239	4.2%	47,000
01/10*	5,336	198	3.7%	45,000
02/09	5,065	192	3.8%	46,000
02/08	4,672	258	5.5%	43,000
Annual Growth	6.9%	2.9%	—	3.8%

*Fiscal year change

2012 Year-End Financials

Debt ratio: 21.99%
Return on equity: 25.15%
Cash ($ mil.): 342
Current ratio: 185.51
Long-term debt ($ mil.): 505
No. of shares (mil.): 110
Dividends
Yield: —
Payout: 21.37%
Market value ($ mil.): 5,893

	STOCK PRICE ($) FY Close	P/E High/Low		PER SHARE ($) Earnings	Dividends	Book Value
01/12	53.52	21	15	2.55	0.00	10.48
01/11	40.17	20	12	2.01	0.00	10.14
01/10*	25.75	17	10	1.59	0.00	9.71
02/09	18.77	18	9	1.52	0.00	8.98
02/08	23.98	18	10	1.95	0.00	7.71
Annual Growth	22.2%	—	—	6.9%	—	8.0%

*Fiscal year change

Pfizer Inc

Pfizer pfabricates pfarmaceuticals pfor quite a pfew inpfirmities. The company is the world's largest research-based pharmaceuticals firm. Its top prescription products include cholesterol-lowering Lipitor pain management drugs Celebrex and Lyrica pneumonia vaccine Prevnar and erectile dysfunction treatment Viagra as well as arthritis drug Enbrel antibiotic Zyvox and high-blood-pressure therapy Norvasc. Consumer health products include such leading brands as Advil Centrum and Robitussin. Pfizer also sells Promil and Promise baby formula and keeps Pfluffy and Pfido in mind with its animal health products including Revolution (antiparasitic) and Convenia (anti-infective).

HISTORY

Charles Pfizer and his cousin confectioner Charles Erhart began making chemicals in Brooklyn in 1849. Products included camphor citric acid and santonin (an early antiparasitic). The company incorporated in 1900 as Chas. Pfizer & Co. was propelled into the modern drug business when it was asked to mass-produce penicillin for the war effort in 1941.

Pfizer discovered Terramycin and introduced it in 1950. Three years later it bought drugmaker Roerig its first major acquisition. In the 1950s the company opened branches in Belgium Canada Cuba Mexico and the UK and began manufacturing in Asia Europe and South America. By the mid-1960s Pfizer had worldwide sales of more than $200 million.

Beginning in the late 1950s Pfizer made Salk and Sabin polio vaccines and added new drugs such as Diabinese (antidiabetic 1958) and Vibramycin (antibiotic 1967). It moved into consumer products in the early 1960s buying BenGay Desitin and cosmetics maker Coty (sold 1992). It bought hospital products company Howmedica in 1972 (sold 1998) and heart-valve maker Shiley in 1979.

When growth slowed in the 1970s new chairman Edmund Pratt increased R&D expenditures resulting in Minipress (antihypertensive 1975) Feldene (arthritis pain reliever 1980) and Glucotrol (antidiabetic 1984). Licensing agreements with foreign companies let Pfizer sell antihypertensive Procardia XL and antibiotic Cefobid. In the 1980s Pfizer expanded its hospital products division buying 18 product lines and companies.

Lawsuits over the failure of about 500 heart valves and the alleged falsification of records led Pfizer to divest most of Shiley's operations in 1992. Drugs released that year included antidepressant Zoloft antibiotic Zithromax and cardiovascular agent Norvasc.

In 1995 Pfizer bought SmithKline Beecham's animal health business and Procter & Gamble's Bain de Soleil skin care line (sold 1999).

In 1997 Pfizer began promoting Lipitor the cholesterol-lowering drug discovered by partner Warner-Lambert; it grabbed nearly 13% of the market in its first four months. Pfizer also launched Aricept Eisai's treatment for Alzheimer's disease.

Pfizer made headlines (and lots of men happy) when the company won FDA approval for Viagra in 1998. The little blue pill became a pop icon and made the company a household name.

When Warner-Lambert said in 1999 that it would merge with American Home Products (now Wyeth) Pfizer sued to prevent the union and eventually succeeded with its own hostile bid. The merger with Warner-Lambert was completed and CEO William Steere retired. Pfizer also sold its animal feed additive business.

Pfizer IBM and Microsoft in 2001 formed a joint venture to sell software to automate prescription writing and other administrative procedures in physicians' offices. Determined to narrow its focus on pharmaceuticals the company in 2002 sold its Tetra fish care then sold its Adams confectionery and Schick-Wilkinson Sword shaving products businesses in 2003.

That year Pfizer purchased rival Pharmacia for $54 billion making it the world's largest research-based pharmaceutical company. Following its two giant acquisitions the company trimmed some 20000 people. In 2004 Pfizer acquired the research divisions of QuoreX which develops antibacterial drugs targeting hospital infections. It also purchased Esperion Therapeutics a developer of cholesterol drugs headed by Lipitor discoverer Roger Newton for $1.2 billion. (Pfizer eventually spun Esperion back off into a private independent entity in 2008 after its development drugs didn't pan out as planned although Pfizer retained some assets and a minority stake in the spinoff.)

In the wake of revelations that Merck's Vioxx increased the risk for cardiovascular diseases in 2004 Pfizer reviewed its own COX-2 pain medication Celebrex. Preliminary studies showed Celebrex increased the risk of heart attack; Pfizer didn't pull Celebrex off the market but did add a "black box" warning of possible cardiovascular and gastrointestinal risks. (In 2008 Pfizer reached an agreement in principle to settle for $894 million most of its pending patient lawsuits alleging that Celebrex caused heart attacks and strokes.)

Acquisitions in 2005 included the purchase of Angiosyn a private biotech working on an anti-angiogenesis therapy for macular degeneration (which can lead to blindness) and Idun Pharmaceuticals which was developing apoptosis (programmed cell death) inhibitors to treat liver disease cancer and other diseases.

That year the company scooped up research partner Vicuron Pharmaceuticals which had two anti-infective (anidulafungin and dalbavancin) drugs under review by the FDA and Bioren which has developed a technology that helps drugs last longer through antibody optimization. (Pfizer divested Vicuron as part of its cost-cutting efforts in 2009.)

While acquiring new holdings on the pharmaceutical front Pfizer trimmed its non-pharmaceutical businesses between 2003 and 2005 including operations it acquired with Pharmacia and its European generics portfolio. The company's animal health division sold off its diagnostics products division (which manufactured tests for bovine tuberculosis and paratuberculosis) to Swiss firm Prionics.

On the consumer health care front the population's increased germaphobia translated into high dollars for Pfizer following the acquisition of Purell. However Pfizer later unloaded its consumer unit altogether refocusing efforts onto its core pharmaceutical business. Johnson & Johnson in 2006 acquired the whole consumer caboodle including such brands as Benadryl Listerine Nicorette Rolaids and Sudafed for $16.6 billion. To comply with regulatory requirements for the deal the companies sold Zantac marketing rights in the US to Boehringer Ingelheim for $510 million; they sold the Cortizone Kaopectate and Unisom brands to Chattem.

As part of its ongoing acquisition strategy Pfizer bought biotech firm Rinat Neuroscience which was developing drugs for pain Alzheimer's disease and other neurological disorders in 2006. Pfizer also acquired vaccine technology firm PowderMed that year and it spent $1.4 billion acquiring Sanofi's joint rights to inhaled insulin drug Exubera. (Pfizer dropped Exubera from its product list in late 2007 however due to lukewarm response from physicians and patients. The company took a $2.8 billion charge as a result.)

Cancer medicine Sutent received FDA approval in 2006 and pain medication Celebrex was expanded to treat arthritic children. One R&D failure came when cholesterol candidate Torcetrapib once touted as the company's latest breakthrough was yanked from trials in late 2006 after the drug was found to raise blood pressure levels.

Pfizer's board in mid-2006 decided to shake things up and dismissed Hank McKinnell as its CEO. McKinnell retained his seat at the head of the company's board until stepping down in early 2007. Though McKinnell originally intended to stay on as CEO for another year past his retirement from the board he was instead abruptly replaced by the company's general counsel Jeffrey Kindler. Kindler almost immediately began restructuring the company including layoffs of a fifth of Pfizer's inflated sales force. By the end of 2007 about 12% of Pfizer's workforce had been cut.

Bestsellers Norvasc and antidepressant Zoloft lost patent protection in 2007. New products launched in 2007 included AIDS drug Selzentry and smoking-cessation aid Chantix. Former bestselling allergy medication Zyrtec (which the company later divested) and cancer treatment Camptosar faced generic competition starting in 2008. In 2008 the company released a new drug with overactive-bladder treatment Toviaz.

Pfizer also purchased Coley Pharmaceutical in early 2008 to gain access to Coley's vaccine technologies. Through additional 2008 purchases Pfizer expanded in key growth areas including oncology (Serenex) cardiovascular therapies (Encysive Pharmaceuticals) and animal health (Embrex and several European products of the former Schering-Plough which is now part of Merck).

A years-long court battle over a proposed Lipitor generic equivalent release by Ranbaxy was settled in 2008. Pfizer reached a settlement agreement with the generics maker allowing Ranbaxy to sell a generic Lipitor version in the US after November 30 2011.

A major program to tighten Pfizer financially and operationally was launched in early 2007; the program cut costs by about $2.8 billion by the end of 2008.

The company made a whopping $68 billion acquisition of fellow drugmaker Wyeth in 2009. The combination of the two drug giants was the largest pharmaceuticals merger in nearly a decade and the acquisition of Wyeth greatly broadened Pfizer's traditional and biological product offerings in areas including vaccines antibiotics women's health inflammatory and cardiovascular conditions and gastroenterology as well as consumer health and animal health.

The acquisition of Wyeth also brought Pfizer back into the consumer health arena which it had previously exited by adding products such as analgesic Advil and cough medicine Robitussin. The purchase added a stable of animal health products as well though Pfizer and Wyeth were both required to sell some animal health assets (primarily from Wyeth's Fort Dodge Animal Health unit) to Boehringer Ingelheim and Eli Lilly to meet regulatory approval requirements for the deal.

Following the merger Pfizer cut costs by integrating overlapping operations between the two organizations including administration sales research and development and manufacturing. The company reduced its workforce by 10% to prepare for the transaction and it estimated that the integration efforts would result in an overall 15% reduction of the combined workforce. The company also closed or sold a number of manufacturing plants including facilities in New York Virginia Puerto Rico and Ireland.

In 2009 schizophrenia drug Geodon received FDA approval for the treatment of bipolar mania.

Pfizer took a financial hit in 2009 when it agreed to pay $2.3 billion to settle allegations that it improperly marketed several drugs including discontinued painkiller Bextra. In a crackdown effort against pharmaceutical marketing fraud (promoting drugs for unapproved uses) the federal government reached several settlement agreements with large pharmaceutical companies (including smaller deals with Pfizer); however Pfizer's 2009 settlement was the largest to date.

In late 2010 Kindler resigned as CEO. He was replaced by Ian Read Pfizer's head of the global biopharmaceutical operations.

EXECUTIVES

SVP Chief Accounting Officer and Controller, Loretta V. Cangialosi
EVP Policy External Affairs and Communications, Sally Susman, age 50
Chairman Emeritus, M. Anthony Burns, age 69
EVP Business Operations and CFO, Frank A. D'Amelio, age 54, $1,060,000 total compensation
SVP and CIO, Jeffrey E. (Jeff) Keisling, age 55
SVP; President Pfizer Global Supply, Natale S. (Nat) Ricciardi, age 63
Chairman and CEO, Ian C. Read, age 58, $1,139,500 total compensation
SVP Investor Relations, Charles E. (Chuck) Triano
SVP and Chief Talent Officer, Tanya Clemons
President and General Manager Primary Care, Olivier Brandicourt, age 56
Group President Animal Health Consumer Healthcare and Corporate Strategy, Cavan M. Redmond, age 51
President and General Manager Specialty Care and Oncology, Geno J. Germano, age 51
VP Corporate Communications, Ray Kerins
EVP and General Counsel; President and General Manager Nutrition, Amy W. Schulman, age 51
SVP Clinical Development and Medical Affairs Oncology, Mace L. Rothenberg
EVP and Chief Medical Officer, Freda C. Lewis-Hall, age 56, $503,030 total compensation
President Worldwide Research and Development, Mikael Dolsten, age 53
President and General Manager Emerging Markets and Established Products, David Simmons, age 47
Chief Marketing Officer Pfizer Primary Care, Paul Levesque
EVP Worldwide Business Development and Innovation, Kristin C. Peck, age 40
Head Media Relations US, Chris Loder
EVP Chief Compliance and Risk Officer, Douglas M. (Doug) Lankler, age 46
VP and Corporate Secretary, Matthew Lepore
EVP Worldwide Human Resources, Charles H. (Chuck) Hill III, age 56
President Pfizer Canada Inc., John Helou
Director, George A. Lorch, age 70
Director, Stephen W. (Steve) Sanger, age 66
Director, W. Don Cornwell, age 64
Director, James M. (Jim) Kilts Jr., age 64
Director, Constance J. (Connie) Horner, age 70
Director, Michael S. Brown, age 71
Director, William H. (Bill) Gray III, age 70
Chairman and CEO, Ian C. Read, age 58
Director, Frances D. Fergusson, age 67
Director, Dennis A. Ausiello, age 66
Director, Suzanne Nora Johnson, age 54
Director, John P. Mascotte, age 72
Auditors: KPMGLLP

LOCATIONS

HQ: Pfizer Inc.
235 E. 42nd St., New York NY 10017-5755
Phone: 212-733-2323 **Fax:** 312-394-8941
Web: www.exeloncorp.com

2011 Sales

	$ mil.	% of total
US	26,933	40
Developed Europe	16,297	24
Emerging markets	13,104	20
Other developed regions	11,091	16
Total	**67,425**	**100**

PRODUCTS/OPERATIONS

2011 Sales

	$ mil.	% of total
Biopharmaceuticals		
Lipitor	9,577	14
Lyrica	3,693	6
Prevnar/Prevenar 13	3,657	5
Enbrel	3,666	5
Celebrex	2,523	4
Viagra	1,981	3
Norvasc	1,445	2
Zyvox	1,283	2
Xalatan/Xalacom	1,250	2
Sutent	1,187	2
Geodon/Zeldox	1,022	2
Premarin family	1,013	2
Genotropin	889	1
Detrol/Detrol LA	883	1
Vfend	747	1
Chantix/Champix	720	1
BeneFIX	693	1
Effexor	678	1
Zosyn/Tazocin	636	1
Pristiq	577	1
Other biopharmaceuticals	15,997	24
Biopharmaceutical alliance revenues	3,630	5
Animal health	4,184	6
Consumer health	3,057	5
Nutrition	2,138	3
Corporate & other (Pfizer CentreSource)	299	-
Total	**67,425**	**100**

Selected Products

Pharmaceuticals
Aricept (Alzheimer' s disease)
Aromasin (breast cancer)
+Arthrotec (osteoarthritis and rheumatoid arthritis)
BeneFIX (hemophilia)

BMP2 (bone and cartilage development)
Caduet (high cholesterol and blood pressure dual therapy)
Camptosar (colorectal cancer)
Cardura (hypertension and enlarged prostate disease)
Celebrex (arthritis pain)
Chantix/Champix (smoking cessation)
Dalacin/Cleocin (antibiotic for bacterial infections)
Detrol/Detrol LA (overactive bladder)
Diflucan (antifungal)
Effexor (antidepressant and anxiety disorder treatment)
Enbrel (arthritis treatment)
Fragmin (anticoagulant)
Genotropin (growth hormone deficiency)
Geodon/Zeldox (schizophrenia and bipolar disorder)
Inspra (high blood pressure)
Lipitor (cholesterol)
Lyrica (nerve pain)
Medrol (inflammation)
Methotrexate (severe psoriasis)
Neurontin (epilepsy)
Norvasc (hypertension)
Premarin (hormone replacement therapy)
Prevnar (pneumococcus vaccine)
Pristiq (antidepressant)
Protonix (protein pump inhibitor)
Rapamune (organ rejection preventative)
Rebif (multiple sclerosis)
ReFacto AF/Xyntha (hemophilia)
Relpax (migraines)
Revatio (hypertension)
Selzentry (HIV)
Skelaxin (muscle relaxant)
Somavert (acromegaly)
Spiriva (chronic obstructive pulmonary disease)
Sulperazon (antibiotic)
Sutent (carcinoma and tumors)
Toviaz (overactive bladder)
Tygacil (anti-infective)
Unasyn (injectable antibacterial)
Vfend (fungal infections)
Viagra (impotence)
Xalatan/Xalacom (glaucoma)
Xanax XR (anti-anxiety treatment)
Zithromax/Zmax (antibiotic)
Zoloft (depression)
Zosyn/Tazocin (anti-infective)
Zyvox (antibiotic)

Animal Health
Cerenia (nausia treatment for canines)
Convenia (canine and feline antibiotics)
Draxxin (cattle antibiotic)
Excede (cattle antibiotic)
Improvac (swine vaccine for boar taint)
Palladia (dog cancer treatment)
Revolution/Stronghold (antiparasitic for dogs and cats)
Rimadyl (canine osteoarthritis treatment)
Suvaxyn (swine vaccine)

Consumer Health
Advil (analgesic)
Anbesol (oral pain relief)
Caltrate (nutritional supplement)
Centrum (vitamins)
ChapStick (lip care)
Dimetapp (cough/cold remedy)
FiberCon (laxative)
Preparation H (hemorrhoid treatment)
Robitussin (cough/cold remedy)
ThermaCare (aches and pains)

Nutrition
Progress Gold (nutritional formula)
Promil Gold (nutritional formula)
S-26 Gold (nutritional formula)

Selected Mergers & Acquisitions

2012
Alacer Corp. (Foothill Ranch California; consumer health Emergen-C supplement drinks)
NextWave Pharmaceuticals (up to $680 million; ADHD liquid medication Quillivant)

2011
Consumer Health Unit of Ferrosan (Denmark; Multi-tabs multivitamins Bifiform probiotics Fri Flyt/Active Omega-3 supplements and IMEDEEN oral skin care)
Icagen Inc. ($60 million; Durham North Carolina; pain management biopharmaceuticals)

2010
FoldRx Pharmaceuticals ($400 million; neurodegenerative disease treatments including Vyndaquel)
King Pharmaceuticals Inc. ($3.6 billion; Bristol Tennessee; pain products including Avinza)
Synbiotics Corporation (veterinary diagnostic products)

2009
Wyeth ($68 billion; pharmaceuticals including Effexor and Enbrel animal health consumer health)

COMPETITORS

Abbott Labs
Amgen
Apotex
Astellas
AstraZeneca
Baxter International
Bayer AG
Biogen Idec
Boehringer Ingelheim
Bristol-Myers Squibb
Carma Laboratories
Chattem
Crucell
Eli Lilly
Forest Labs
GlaxoSmithKline
Johnson & Johnson
Merck
Merck KGaA
Mylan
Novartis
Novo Nordisk
Perrigo
Prestige Brands
Procter & Gamble
Ranbaxy Laboratories
Roche Holding
Sanofi
Sun Pharmaceutical
Teva
Watson Pharmaceuticals

HISTORICAL FINANCIALS

Company Type: Public

Income Statement

FYE: December 31

	REVENUE ($ mil.)	NET INCOME ($ mil.)	NET PROFIT MARGIN	EMPLOYEES
12/11	67,425	10,009	14.8%	103,700
12/10	67,809	8,257	12.2%	110,600
12/09	50,009	8,635	17.3%	116,500
12/08	48,296	8,104	16.8%	81,800
12/07	48,418	8,144	16.8%	86,600
Annual Growth	8.6%	5.3%	—	4.6%

2011 Year-End Financials

Debt ratio: 20.72%—
Return on equity: 12.18%
Cash ($ mil.): 3,539
Current ratio: 205.66
Long-term debt ($ mil.): 34,931

Dividends
Yield: —
Payout: 62.99%
Market value ($ mil.): —

	STOCK PRICE ($) FY Close	P/E High	P/E Low	PER SHARE ($) Earnings	Dividends	Book Value
12/11	21.64	17	13	1.27	0.00	10.85
12/10	17.51	19	14	1.02	0.72	10.96
12/09	18.19	15	9	1.23	0.80	11.15
12/08	17.71	20	12	1.20	1.28	8.53
12/07	22.73	23	19	1.17	1.16	9.62
Annual Growth	(1.2%)	—	—	2.1%	—	3.1%

PG&E Corp. (Holding Co.)

To a lot of Californians utility holding company PG&E Corporation is synonymous with power and gas. The company's venerable Pacific Gas and Electric unit serves about 5.2 million electric customers and almost 4.3 million natural gas customers in Northern and Central California.The utility is also engaged in electricity generation; procurement and transmission; and natural gas procurement transportation and storage. In September 2010 one of the PG&E utility's major gas transmission lines ruptured in San Bruno near San Francisco causing a major fire loss of life and destruction of or damage to scores of homes.

The incident resulted in the company taking a third quarter 2010 charge of $238 million and having to face federal investigations into the safety of its aging natural gas infrastructure. By early 2012 it was also facing more than 100 lawsuits filed by or on behalf of local residents.

Financial Analysis

The utility's revenues picked up in 2011 (electricity sales by 9% natural gas by 5%) thanks to increased demand spurred by a recovering economy and an electricity rate increase. However costs related to the San Bruno incident and expenses related to subsequent infrastructure upgrades pulled down PG&E's net income by 25% that year.

Strategy

On the electricity side of the ledger to help comply with the State of California's long-term carbon emission requirements PG&E has been pushing energy efficiency (both at its plants and its customers' facilities). In 2008 it announced a 15-year purchase agreement with Canada's Finavera Renewables to use wave power captured off the Northern California coastline. PG&E is the first US utility company that has committed to purchasing wave-generated power. The company is committed to meet California's carbon reductions requirements by which utilities are required to produce 33% of their total power from renewable sources by 2020.

PG&E also operates the Diablo Canyon nuclear power plant which underwent a lot of public scrutiny in 2011 following the nuclear power plant disaster near Sendai Japan.

HISTORY

Peter Donahue founded the first gas company in the western US San Francisco Gas in 1852 which merged with Edison Light & Power to become San Francisco Gas & Electric (SFG&E) in 1896. Meanwhile also in San Francisco money broker George Roe and other investors founded California Electric Light (1879). The first electric utility in the US it predated Edison's New York Pearl Street Station by three years. California Electric and SFG&E consolidated in 1905 to form Pacific Gas and Electric (PG&E).

In 1928 PG&E discovered natural gas in California and in 1930 it began converting more than 2.5 million appliances to burn this fuel. The company started exploring for out-of-state gas supplies in the 1950s first in Texas and New Mexico and then in western Canada.

The utility opened the world's first private atomic power plant (Vallecitos) in 1957 and in 1960 it developed the first geothermal plant (The Geysers) in North America. Its Humboldt Bay facility (completed 1963) was one of the first nukes to produce electricity at a cost comparable to that of conventional plants. Stanley Skinner began his 33-year career at PG&E in 1964 (he became CEO in 1995).

By the late 1970s PG&E had acquired some 500 electric gas and water utilities but it left the water business in the 1980s. That year Unit 1 of the Diablo Canyon nuclear facility went on line despite protests over its earthquake-fault location.

Unit 2 was operating by 1986. PG&E fell on hard times in the mid-1980s as industrial customers began to generate their own electricity or buy gas directly from suppliers. In response PG&E cut 2500 jobs in 1987 and formed an independent power producer which became U.S. Generating with construction giant Bechtel. In 1995 as deregulation accelerated in California the company formed an energy services division to serve large customers.

In 1996 PG&E was hit by an outage originating in the Pacific Northwest that affected nine western states and raised doubts over the power grid's stability. That year PG&E's gas unit bought a pipeline in Australia.

PG&E Corporation was formed as a holding company in 1997 and utility Pacific Gas and Electric became a subsidiary. The company also bought Bechtel's 50% stake in U.S. Generating. That year Skinner retired and president Robert Glynn became CEO. PG&E also settled a lawsuit filed in 1993 that claimed it had polluted groundwater by discharging toxic wastewater. (The case was the subject of a movie "Erin Brockovich" released in 2000.)

As its home state deregulated in 1998 PG&E was required to sell off most of its California power plants. The company auctioned off some of its hydro plants and Duke Energy picked up three of the utility's fossil-fuel plants in California and its Australian pipeline. (The divestiture requirement was reversed by regulatory agencies in 2000.) PG&E also bought 18 power plants (4800 MW) from New England Electric System.

In 1999 the company sold its Texas gas operations to El Paso Corporation agreed to sell most of its retail marketing arm (PG&E Services) to Enron and moved the headquarters of its nonregulated operations (PG&E National Energy Group) to Bethesda Maryland. PG&E suffered a loss that fiscal year.

A price squeeze brought on in part by deregulation battered Pacific Gas and Electric in 2000. Prices on the wholesale power market soared but a California rate freeze prevented the utility from passing along increasing costs to customers. In 2001 it suspended payments to creditors and suppliers to conserve cash but gained some prospect of relief when California's governor signed legislation to allow a state agency to buy power from wholesalers under long-term contracts. Also that year PG&E sold its nonregulated energy services unit and its natural gas liquids businesses.

Later in 2001 the California Public Utilities Commission (CPUC) approved a significant increase in retail electricity rates and the Federal Energy Regulatory Commission (FERC) approved a plan to limit wholesale energy prices during periods of severe shortage in 11 western states. The moves didn't come quickly enough for Pacific Gas and Electric which filed for bankruptcy protection. The unit completed its reorganization in 2004.

Poor conditions in the wholesale power market drove PG&E National Energy Group into bankruptcy in 2003; the unit changed its name to National Energy & Gas Transmission shortly after to signify separation from PG&E following its emergence from bankruptcy.

EXECUTIVES

SVP Corporate Affairs PG&E Corporation and Pacific Gas and Electric Company, Greg S. Pruett, age 54
Director; President Pacific Gas and Electric Company, Christopher P. (Chris) Johns, age 51, $593,866 total compensation
Chairman President and CEO, Anthony F. Earley Jr., age 63
VP Corporate Development, Brian Steel
VP Corporate Environmental and Federal Affairs and Chief Sustainability Officer, Steven L. (Steve) Kline, age 57
SVP and CFO; SVP Financial Services Pacific Gas and Electric Company, Kent M. Harvey, age 53, $454,106 total compensation
SVP and General Counsel, Hyun Park, age 50, $524,493 total compensation
VP Investor Relations, Gabriel B. (Gabe) Togneri, age 56
VP Corporate Governance and Secretary PG&E Corporation and Pacific Gas and Electric Company, Linda Y. H. Cheng, age 52
VP and Controller PG&E Corporation; VP CFO and Controller Pacific Gas and Electric Company, Dinyar B. Mistry, age 49
EVP Gas Operations, Nickolas (Nick) Stavropoulos, age 53
SVP Human Resources PG&E Corporation and Pacific Gas and Electric Company, John R. Simon, age 47
VP Internal Audit and Compliance PG&E Corporation and Pacific Gas and Electric Company, Stephen J. Cairns
VP and Chief Risk and Audit Officer PG&E Corporation and Pacific Gas and Electric Company, Anil K. Suri
Manager Investor Relations, Margaret Murphy
Director; President Pacific Gas and Electric Company, Christopher P. (Chris) Johns, age 51
Director, Lewis Chew, age 49
Director, Rosendo G. (Ro) Parra, age 52
Director, Roger H. Kimmel, age 65
Director, Forrest E. Miller, age 59
Director, Barbara L. Rambo, age 59
Director, David R. Andrews, age 70
Director, C. Lee Cox, age 71
Director, Maryellen C. Herringer, age 68
Director, Barry L. Williams, age 67
Director, Richard A. Meserve, age 67
Auditors: Deloitte&ToucheLLP

LOCATIONS

HQ: PG&E Corp. (Holding Co.)
77 Beale Street, P.O. Box 770000, San Francisco, CA 94177
Phone: 415 267-7000 **Fax:** 415 267-7265
Web: www.pgecorp.com

PRODUCTS/OPERATIONS

2011 Sales

	$ mil.	% of total
Electric	11,601	78
Natural gas	3,350	22
Total	**14,951**	**100**

COMPETITORS

AEP
AES
Avista
Calpine
Constellation Energy Group
Duke Energy
Edison International
Entergy
Exelon
FirstEnergy
GenOnEnergy
Modesto Irrigation District
North Baja Pipeline
Northern California Power Agency
NV Energy
PacifiCorp
Sacramento Municipal Utility
Sempra Energy
Southern Company
Tractebel Engineering
Turlock Irrigation District
Western Area Power Administration

HISTORICAL FINANCIALS

Company Type: Public

Income Statement FYE: December 31

	REVENUE ($ mil.)	NET INCOME ($ mil.)	NET PROFIT MARGIN	EMPLOYEES
12/11	14,956	858	5.7%	19,274
12/10	13,841	1,113	8.0%	19,424
12/09	13,399	1,234	9.2%	19,425
12/08	14,628	1,338	9.1%	21,667
12/07	13,237	1,006	7.6%	20,050
Annual Growth	3.1%	(3.9%)	—	(1.0%)

2011 Year-End Financials

Debt ratio: 27.91%
Return on equity: 7.09%
Cash ($ mil.): 893
Current ratio: 83.62
Long-term debt ($ mil.): 11,766
No. of shares (mil.): 412
Dividends
Yield: —
Payout: 86.67%
Market value ($ mil.): 16,993

	STOCK PRICE ($) FY Close	P/E High/Low		PER SHARE ($) Earnings	Dividends	Book Value
12/11	41.22	23	18	2.10	0.00	29.35
12/10	47.84	17	14	2.82	1.82	28.55
12/09	44.65	14	11	3.20	1.68	27.83
12/08	38.71	12	8	3.63	1.56	26.57
12/07	43.09	19	15	2.78	1.44	23.19
Annual Growth	(1.1%)	—	—	(6.8%)	—	6.1%

Philip Morris International Inc

Philip Morris International (PMI) knows how to light up a room. The company makes seven of the world's top 15 tobacco brands laying claim to at least 15% of the international cigarette market outside the US. The company's brands by sales volume are Marlboro (the world's #1-selling cigarette) L&M Bond Street Philip Morris Chesterfield and Parliament. Top local brands include Fortune Morven Gold and Dji Sam Soe. PMI's portfolio spans the price spectrum with premium mid-priced and value-priced products. Formerly part of Altria PMI has grown through acquisitions and alliances with cigarette and smokeless tobacco makers.

Geographic Reach

PMI's products are sold in 180 countries. Asia accounts for about a third of all sales.

Financial Analysis

Despite the uncertain global economy along with increasing government scrutiny and consumer awareness of the risks of smoking PMI's performance has continued to strengthen. In 2011 the company posted record high earnings and revenue soaring more than 18% and almost 15% respectively over the prior year. Its momentum is fueled primarily by higher pricing and favorable currency exchange rates. It further benefits from higher volume sales from each of its top ten brands marketed Asia (particularly in Indonesia and Korea) and Eastern Europe the Middle East and Africa.

Nonetheless growth in 2011 was modestly offset by declining market share in parts of Europe and Latin America coupled with higher marketing and manufacturing costs. Sales in the European Union notably Germany (PMI's largest market) have continued to decline. The softening market is in part due to the economic crisis that has hurt volumes as well as increased competition by rivals that avoid using "light" "mild" or "low tar" when selling cigarettes terms outlawed by the EU. Although PMI no longer sells the popular Marlboro Lights there Marlboro continues to account for more than 30% of PMI's total shipment volume.

Mergers & Acquisitions

PMI's consolidated results are also bolstered by a number of acquisitions that enhance its brand-rich portfolio and geographic presence. In mid-2011 PMI took over a cigarette manufacturer in Jordan. The purchase followed PMI's acquisition of a cigar business comprising trademarks in Australia and New Zealand. During 2011 PMI also revised its joint venture with Vietnam National Tobacco Corp. (Vinataba) in Vietnam opening the door to licensing the Marlboro label as PMI establishes a local branch to build its brands.

Other deals include combining business efforts in the Philippines with Fortune Tobacco and securing separate agreements with Alliance One Brasil and Universal Leaf to source tobacco from Brazilian farmers. The leaf suppliers provide roughly 10% of PMI's tobacco needs strengthening its control over its supply chain.

Most significant PMI acquired the South African tobacco branch of Swedish Match for 1.93 billion ZAR (about $256 million). The investment gives PMI a leg up in producing smokeless tobacco products and builds upon a joint venture between PMI and Swedish Match to market Swedish style snus and other smokeless tobacco lines outside of Scandinavia and the US. (Altria moved to dominate the rapidly rising niche by taking over UST a leader in the US market for smokeless products including the Copenhagen Husky and Skoal brands.) In the same month PMI purchased the Petter?es tobacco business for $209 million pocketing fine-cut brands popular in Sweden and Norway.

Company Background

PMI is a result of a spinoff from Altria in 2008. The separation positioned PMI as an independent publicly traded company free from its US branch Philip Morris USA. Altria simultaneously avoided an entanglement in various US legal and regulatory issues.

EXECUTIVES

Chairman and CEO, Louis C. Camilleri, age 57, $1,567,308 total compensation
COO, Andre Calantzopoulos, age 54, $1,207,377 total compensation
SVP Operations, Martin G. King, age 48
SVP and General Counsel, Marc S. Firestone, age 52
President Asia, Matteo L. Pellegrini, age 50
SVP Human Resources, Daniele Regorda, age 54
VP Investor Relations and Financial Communications, Nicholas Rolli
CFO, Hermann G. Waldemer, age 54, $930,249 total compensation
President Eastern Europe the Middle East Africa (EEMA) and PMI Duty Free, Miroslaw Zielinski, age 50
SVP Corporate Affairs, Even Hurwitz, age 50
VP and Controller, Joachim Psotta, age 54
VP Finance and Treasurer, Marco Kuepfer, age 54
President European Union, Jacek Olczak, age 47
VP Investor Relations, Julian Izant
Director Investor Relations and Financial Communications, Alex Williams
President Latin America and Canada, James R. (Jim) Mortensen, age 54
SVP Human Resources, Kevin Click, age 51
External Communications Executive, Monica Montero Lim
Manager Regulatory Affairs, Mauricio Saenz
Director Corporate Affairs West and Central Africa, Thierno Diallo
Supervisor Internal Controls, Mariusz Kubicki
Manager Accounting, Verena Oustin
Director Financial Analyses and Support, Hannah Yun
Managing Director Ukraine Caucasus Moldova, Elena Khomenko
Managing Director Brazil, Amancio Sampaio
General Manager Thailand, Tammy Chan
MOD Executive Training and Development, Kildine Pache
Country Lead Latin American Shared Services Center, Cecilia Selser
Project Leader Information Services, Joel Beetschen
Team Leader Information Services, Wojciech Nogalski
VP and Associate General Counsel EU, Emese Kiss
Senior Counsel Benelux, Katrien Verbiest
Brand Manager, Mayra Barros
Brand Executive, Oliver Plotek
Manager Marketing, Stephen Rajasigamany
Senior Analyst Market and Consumer Research, Deborah Sim
Brand Executive, Raymond van der Velden
Manager Events, Roxana Romanescu
Manager Quality and Processes Improvement, Simon Guay
Manager Secondary, Igor Kroshko
Director Operations Australia, Jodie Sandford
Scientist, Sam Ansari
Manager Quality System Projects, Yin Boll
Managing Director Next Generation Products and Adjacent Businesses, Ashok Rammohan
Region Subdirector Sales, Liliana Cabeza
Region General Manager Japan, Yoshifumi Kashiwagi
Manager Trade Marketing, Aydin Mizrahi
Manager Sales, Juan Ignacio Suarez
Deputy General Counsel and Corporate Secretary, Jerry E. Whitson, age 56
Director External Communications, Simone Piattelli Palmarini
Manager External Communications, Iro Antoniadou
Manager External Communications, Yuri Omelyanenko
SVP and CIO, Patrick Brunel
SVP Research and Development, Bertrand Bonvin
SVP Marketing & Sales, Frederic de Wilde
Director External Communications, Anne Edwards
Director, Mathis Cabiallavetta, age 67
Director, Sergio Marchionne, age 60
Director, Lucio A. Noto, age 73
Director, Harold Brown, age 84
Director, J. Dudley Fishburn, age 65
Director, Carlos Slim Helu, age 72
Director, Jennifer Li, age 44
Auditors: PricewaterhouseCoopersLLP

LOCATIONS

HQ: Philip Morris International Inc.
120 Park Ave., New York NY 10017-5592
Phone: 917-663-2000 **Fax:** -7125
Web: www.lge.com

2011 Sales

	% of total
Asia	34
European	30
Eastern Europe Middle East &	25
Latin America &	11
Total	**100**

2011 Manufacturing Facilities

	No.
Asia	17
Latin America &	17
European	11
Eastern Europe Middle East &	10
Total	**55**

PRODUCTS/OPERATIONS

2011 Shipment Volumes

	% of total
International	70
Local	30
Total	**100**

Selected Brands

Local brands
- Apollo-Soyuz (Russia)
- Assos (Greece)
- Belmont (Canada)
- Best (Serbia)
- Boston (Colombia)
- Canadian Classics (Canada)
- Champion (Philippines)
- Classic (Serbia)
- Delicados (Mexico)
- Diana (Italy)
- Dji Sam Soe (Indonesia)
- f6 (Germany)
- Fortune (Philippines)
- Hope (Philippines)
- Morven Gold (Pakistan)
- Number 7 (Canada)
- Optima (Russia)
- Petra (Czech Republic and Slovakia)
- Sampoema A (Indonesia)
- Sampoema Kretek (Indonesia)

Mid-price brands
- L&M
- Chesterfield

Other international brands
- Benson & Hedges
- Bond Street
- Lark
- Muratti
- Next
- Philip Morris
- Red & White

Premium-price
- Marlboro
- Merit
- Parliament
- Virginia Slims

Other tobacco products
- Interval (France)
- Petter?es (Norway and Sweden)
- Swedish Match snus smokefree tobacco

COMPETITORS

British American Tobacco
Gudang Garam
Imperial Tobacco
Japan Tobacco
Reemtsma Cigarettenfabriken

HISTORICAL FINANCIALS

Company Type: Public

Income Statement FYE: December 31

	REVENUE ($ mil.)	NET INCOME ($ mil.)	NET PROFIT MARGIN	EMPLOYEES
12/11	76,346	8,591	11.3%	78,100
12/10	67,713	7,259	10.7%	78,300
12/09	62,080	6,342	10.2%	77,300
12/08	63,640	6,890	10.8%	75,600
12/07	55,096	6,026	10.9%	75,500
Annual Growth	8.5%	9.3%	—	0.9%

2011 Year-End Financials

Debt ratio: 52.26%
Return on equity: 3751.53%
Cash ($ mil.): 2,550
Current ratio: 100.44
Long-term debt ($ mil.): 14,828
No. of shares (mil.): 1,725
Dividends
Yield: —
Payout: 58.14%
Market value ($ mil.): 135,449

	STOCK PRICE ($) FY Close	P/E High/Low		PER SHARE ($) Earnings	Dividends	Book Value
12/11	78.48	16	12	4.85	0.00	0.13
12/10	58.53	15	11	3.92	2.44	1.95
12/09	48.19	16	10	3.24	2.24	3.03
12/08	43.51	17	11	3.32	1.54	3.74
Annual Growth	21.7%	—	—	13.5%	—	(67.4%)

Phillips 66

LOCATIONS

HQ: Phillips 66
3010 Briarpark Drive, 3010 Briarpark Drive, Houston, TX 77042
Phone: 281 293-6600
Web: www.Phillips66.com

HISTORICAL FINANCIALS

Company Type:

Income Statement FYE: December 31

	REVENUE ($ mil.)	NET INCOME ($ mil.)	NET PROFIT MARGIN	EMPLOYEES
12/11	200,614	4,775	2.4%	12,400
12/10	148,656	735	0.5%	0
12/09	113,951	476	0.4%	0
Annual Growth	32.7%	216.7%	—	—

Pilgrims Pride Corp.

Pilgrim's Pride couldn't be blamed if it spread its tail feathers and did a barnyard strut. As one of the world's top chicken processors it boasts operations in breeding hatching raising processing and distributing chicken. The company sells prepared poultry products under the Pilgrim's Pride and EatWellStayHealthy labels to retail food outlets distributors and foodservice operators. It sells fresh frozen value-added prepared chicken and deli products. Pilgrim's Pride also produces table eggs and chicken by-products for use as animal feed. The company is majority owned by Brazil's JBS which acquired its stake after Pilgrim's Pride emerged from Chapter 11 bankruptcy.

HISTORY

Aubrey Pilgrim formed Pilgrim's Pride as Farmer's Feed and Seed Co. in 1946 with $1000 in cash and a $2500 note. Aubrey and brother Lonnie "Bo" Pilgrim (who joined the business in 1947) sold their first chicken from a pen behind their farm supply store and began to give away 100 baby chicks with each feed sack purchase. The Pilgrims bought back some of the grown birds to resell at a profit.

As demand for chickens grew Farmer's Feed and Seed took its first steps toward creating a vertically integrated chicken company. It opened its first processing plant in 1957 and entered the distribution business three years later delivering chicken to restaurants and grocery stores in northeastern Texas. Bo took over the business when Aubrey died of a heart attack in 1966.

The company was renamed Pilgrim's Industries in 1968 (and Pilgrim's Pride in 1985). Eggs became part of the product mix in 1969. That year Pilgrim's acquired Market Produce Co. a food distributor with facilities in Arlington Odessa and El Paso Texas. By 1979 the company was selling 1 million birds every week.

In the 1970s and 1980s Pilgrim grew through acquisitions and by using TV advertising to build a national brand. Its first TV commercial "The President Speaks" was a humorous 1983 spot featuring Bo in a wide-brimmed pilgrim's hat addressing his TV audience. To offset the wide swings in prices and profits in the highly cyclical commodity chicken industry Pilgrim moved into prepared foods in 1986 the year it went public. The firm expanded into the Mexican consumer market in 1988 through the purchase of several chicken producers there.

Bo caused an uproar the next year when he handed out campaign checks to Texas lawmakers during a senate session (a practice that is now illegal). The activity brought Bo before a grand jury although he was not indicted.

Between 1987 and 1991 Pilgrim's tripled the size of its Mexican operations and expanded its frozen retail and export businesses. Excess poultry production and low prices led to the company's $30 million loss in 1992. Debt restructuring that year forced it to seek outside capital. Pilgrim persuaded agricultural titan Archer Daniels Midland (ADM) to buy into the company but limited ADM's stake to 20%.

In 1993 the company took major steps toward arranging for a successor for the aging Bo by appointing his nephew Lindy "Buddy" Pilgrim as president. (Buddy formerly a marketing executive with Pilgrim had left the company in 1990 to lead a food industry consulting firm.)

Pilgrim bought Mexican chicken processor Union de Queretaro in 1995. Costs related to acquisitions nudged the company into the red that year and the next. Pilgrim's expanded its US processing capacity with the 1997 purchase of Green Acres Foods of Nacogdoches Texas. That year it also introduced EggsPlus an egg line with six times the vitamin E content of ordinary eggs and high levels of high-density lipoprotein.

ADM reduced its stake in Pilgrim from 20% to 4% in 1997 and eventually sold the rest in 1999. In 1998 Buddy resigned Bo took the title of senior chairman (though he later dropped "senior" from his title) and David Van Hoose who had ruled the roost in the company's Mexican operations became CEO.

Pilgrim opened a plant in Dallas in 1998 and bought one in Waco Texas from Cargill the next year. It bought poultry processor WLR Foods for about $280 million in 2001 and turned the business into its eastern division.

Challenges soon arose for the new division in 2002. Its flocks were struck with avian influenza which cost the company $26 million when it was forced to destroy 4.7 million birds. Later in the year Pilgrim was prompted to recall 27.4 million pounds of poultry deli meat after samples tested positive for Listeria bacteria. The recall was one of the largest in the US meat industry and covered five-and-a-half months' production from one plant near Philadelphia.

In 2003 Pilgrim plunked down nearly $550 million in stock cash and debt to acquire ConAgra's chicken processing business. Along with 16 plants and 15 distribution centers the deal included the Easy-Entree Country Pride and Pierce poultry brands. Through supplier agreements ConAgra became one of Pilgrim's largest customers. ConAgra in turn pocketed nearly 40% of the company's stock.

Van Hoose stepped down as CEO in late 2003; O.B. Goolsby was later named his replacement.

In its pursuit for higher-margin value-added products in 2004 Pilgrim sold off its whole-turkey and turkey breast processing plant in Hinton Virginia to the Virginia Poultry Growers Cooperative. In 2005 Pilgrim's Pride bought out ConAgra's stake in the company.

Due to poor performance during 2005 Pilgrim discontinued ground-turkey and cooked-turkey cold-cut production and began focusing on refrigerated salad production at its Franconia Pennsylvania plant; it limited turkey operations to fresh and frozen whole turkey processing at its New Oxford Pennsylvania plant. It also cut about 300 jobs in Pennsylvania.

Pilgrim acquired one of its largest rivals Gold Kist for $1.1 billion in 2007. The deal which came about after a hostile takeover bid and much legal wrangling between the two companies leapfrogged Pilgrim past Tyson Foods as the world's top poultry producer. (Tyson however is still the #1 chicken producer in the US.)

Goolsby died in 2007. He was replaced by J. Clinton Rivers formerly COO in 2008. Don Jackson was named the new CEO months later. New leader or not Pilgrim's Pride ran afoul of its shareholders in 2008 when they filed class action lawsuits claiming that the chicken processor concealed the impact of its capital problems on its current and future business. The suits further alleged that undisclosed material information contradicted the company's public statements.

Pilgrim's Pride filed for bankruptcy in 2008 and emerged from Chapter 11 the following year with JBS purchasing 64% of the company. At that time the company appointed Don Jackson the former CEO of Foster Farms as its new CEO.

In 2010 Jackson resigned to join JBS USA. He was succeeded by William Lovette in 2011. Lovette was formerly president and COO of Case Foods and spent 25 years with Tyson Foods in various senior management roles.

In March 2012 JBS through JBS USA increased its stake in Pilgrim's Pride to more than 75% through the purchase of nearly 19 million shares owned by Lonnie Bo Pilgrim a director for about $107 million.

EXECUTIVES

Executive Vice President of Sales & Operations, Walter F. Shafer
President CEO and Director, William W. (Bill) Lovette, age 52
Director, Don Jackson, age 61
President and Director General Mexico Operations, Alejandro M. Mann
EVP Sales and Marketing, Jerry D. Wilson
Director Corporate Communications, Ray Atkinson
SVP Consumer Sales and Marketing, Randall J. (Randy) Meyers
SVP Procurement, Timothy G. Thomas

VP Corporate Communications and Investor Relations, Gary L. Rhodes, age 49
SVP Commodity Risk Management Feed Ingredient Purchasing and Export Sales, Charles Von Der Heyde
SVP Live Production Technical Services, Randy Stroud
Chairman, Wesley Mendonca Batista
SVP Byproducts, Greg Tatum
SVP Corporate Accounts, Rick Grondin
SVP Prepared Foods Marketing, Andrew W. Seymour
CFO, Fabio Sandri, age 40
EVP Sales and Operations, Jayson Penn
SVP Food Safety and Quality Assurance, Kendra Waldbusser
SVP Human Resources, Doug Schult
Chairman of the Board, Wesley Batista

President CEO and Director, William W. (Bill) Lovette, age 52
Director, Lonnie (Bo) Pilgrim, age 54
Director, Joesley Mendonca Batista
Director, Jose Batista Junior
Director, Michael L. Cooper
Director, Wallim Cruz de Vasconcellos Junior
Director, Charles Macaluso
Director, Marcus Vinicius Pratini de Moraes
Independent Director, Marcus Moraes
Independent Director, Wallim Vasconcellos
Auditors: Ernst&YoungLLP

LOCATIONS

HQ: Pilgrim' s Pride Corporation
1770 Promontory Cir., Greeley CO 80634-9039
Phone: 970-506-8000 **Fax:** 602-250-2430
Web: www.pinnaclewest.com

2011 Sales

	% of total
US including Puerto Rico	90
Mexico	10
Total	**100**

PRODUCTS/OPERATIONS

2011 Sales

	% of total
US chicken	
Fresh	42
Prepared	28
Export & other chicken	11
Mexico	10
Other products	
US	9
Mexico —	
Total	**100**

COMPETITORS

Allen Family Foods
American Foods
Bachoco
Cagle' s
Cargill Meat Solutions
Clougherty Packing
Coleman Natural Foods
Cooper Farms
Eberly Poultry
Farmer' s Pride
Harvest Meat Company
Hormel
Jobbers Meat Packing
Keystone Foods
Perdue Incorporated
Rose Acre Farms
Sanderson Farms
Smithfield Foods
Tecumseh Poultry
Tyson Fresh Meats

HISTORICAL FINANCIALS

Company Type: Public

Income Statement FYE: December 25

	REVENUE ($ mil.)	NET INCOME ($ mil.)	NET PROFIT MARGIN	EMPLOYEES
12/11	7,535	(496)	—	39,500
12/10	6,881	87	1.3%	89,100
12/09*	1,602	33	2.1%	0
09/09	7,088	(151)	—	41,240
09/08	8,525	(998)	—	49,750
Annual Growth	(3.0%)	—	—	(5.6%)

*Fiscal year change

2011 Year-End Financials

Debt ratio: 51.18%
Return on equity: (-89.41)%
Cash ($ mil.): 41
Current ratio: 204.16
Long-term debt ($ mil.): 1,458
No. of shares (mil.): 214
Dividends
Yield: —
Payout: —
Market value ($ mil.): 1,284

	STOCK PRICE ($) FY Close	P/E High/Low		PER SHARE ($) Earnings	Dividends	Book Value
12/11	5.99	—	—	(2.32)	0.00	2.59
12/10	7.12	31	14	0.41	0.00	5.01
12/09*	8.40	19	1	0.44	0.00	(0.00)
09/09	7.06	—	—	(2.05)	0.00	1.96
09/08	3.55	—	—	(14.40)	0.00	4.75
Annual Growth	14.0%	—	—	—	—	(14.1%)

*Fiscal year change

Pinnacle Financial Partners Inc.

Pinnacle Financial Partners wants to be at the top of the community banking mountain in central Tennessee. It's the holding company for Pinnacle National Bank which has grown to nearly 35 branches in the Nashville and Knoxville areas since its founding in 2000. Serving consumers and small to midsized business the bank provides standard services such as checking and savings accounts CDs credit cards and loans and mortgages. The company offers investment and trust services through Pinnacle Asset Management. Insurance brokerage subsidiary Miller Loughry Beach specializes in property/casualty policies.

Business loans including commercial mortgages construction loans and commercial and industrial loans make up about three-quarters of its portfolio which also includes residential real estate and consumer loans. Like many other financial institutions Pinnacle Financial Partners was negatively impacted by the economic downturn. The deterioration of the residential real estate market in its market area left the bank with a heavy concentration of nonperforming residential mortgage and construction and development loans.

In response Pinnacle Financial Partners reduced its reliance on real estate and aggressively shed troubled assets. The moves helped the company reduce its credit losses and past-due loans. The company returned to profitability in 2011 reporting net income of some $37.1 million after two consecutive years in the red.

Pinnacle Financial Partners is focusing on organic growth and increasing deposits by targeting small businesses and individuals. The company has also grown by opening new branches particularly in the Knoxville area.

EXECUTIVES

President CEO and Board Member; President and CEO Pinnacle Bank, M. Terry Turner, age 56, $691,225 total compensation
Chief People Officer, Rachel West
SVP and Manager Client Advisory Group Rutherford County, R. Dale Floyd
Area Executive Rutherford County, William S. (Bill) Jones
Vice Chairman, Ed C. Loughry Jr., age 69
Chairman, Robert A. (Rob) McCabe Jr., age 61, $655,750 total compensation
EVP and Chief Administrative Officer, Hugh M. Queener, age 56, $322,500 total compensation
Senior Manager Product, James O. (Jamie) Sweeney III
EVP and Senior Lending Officer, J. Edward (Ed) White, age 62, $145,000 total compensation
EVP and Director WOW, Joanne B. Jackson, age 55, $117,000 total compensation
CFO, Harold R. Carpenter Jr., age 53, $322,500 total compensation
Manager Trust Services, Robert Newman
Risk and Performance Management Officer, Kim Jenny
SVP and Credit Officer, G. Glenn Layne
President Pinnacle Knoxville, Nathan Hunter
SVP and Manager Client Services Rutherford and Bedford, Ron Carter
EVP Pinnacle Knoxville, Mike DiStefano
Area Executive Wilson County, Scott McCormick
Head Special Assets, Jason K. West
SVP and Manager Client Services, Larry Whisenant
Chief Credit Officer, Harvey White, $115,000 total compensation
Manager Market West End Office, Karen Hargis
Senior Credit Officer Real Estate, Mike Hendren
SVP and Senior Credit Officer, Tim Huestis
Controller, Dan Stubblefield
Board Member, Hal N. Pennington, age 74
President CEO and Board Member; President and CEO Pinnacle Bank, M. Terry Turner, age 56
Board Member, Dale W. Polley, age 62
Vice Chairman, Ed C. Loughry Jr., age 69
Board Member, Colleen Conway-Welch, age 68
Board Member, James C. Cope, age 62
Board Member, William H. Huddleston IV, age 48
Board Member, Sue G. Atkinson, age 71
Board Member, Gregory L. Burns, age 56
Board Member, Wayne J. Riley, age 52
Board Member, Gary L. Scott, age 65
Board Member, Harold G. Bone, age 70
Auditors: KPMGLLP

LOCATIONS

HQ: Pinnacle Financial Partners Inc.
150 3rd Ave. S. Ste. 900, Nashville TN 37201
Phone: 615-744-3700 **Fax:** 615-744-3861
Web: www.mypinnacle.com

PRODUCTS/OPERATIONS

2011 Sales

	$ in mil.	% of total
Interest income		
Loans including fees	154	68
Securities	31	14
Federal funds sold and other	2	1
Noninterest income		
Service charges on deposit accounts	9	4

Investment services	6	3
Net gains on mortgage loans sold	4	2
Insurance sales commissions	4	2
Trust fees	3	1
Other	11	5
Total	**226**	**100**

Selected Subsidiaries

Pinnacle Advisory Services Inc.
Pinnacle Credit Enhancement Holdings Inc.
Pinnacle National Bank
- Miller & Loughry Inc. (dba Miller Loughry Beach)
- PFP Title Company
- Pinnacle Community Development Corporation
- Pinnacle Nashville Real Estate Inc.
- Pinnacle Rutherford Real Estate Inc.
- Pinnacle Rutherford Towers Inc.
- Pinnacle Service Company Inc.

PNFP Insurance Inc.

COMPETITORS

Bank of America
BB&T
Fifth Third
First Horizon
Regions Financial
SunTrust
U.S. Bancorp

HISTORICAL FINANCIALS

Company Type: Public

Income Statement FYE: December 31

	ASSETS ($ mil.)	NET INCOME ($ mil.)	INCOME AS % OF ASSETS	EMPLOYEES
12/11	4,863	43	0.9%	743
12/10	4,909	(24)	—	764
12/09	5,128	(35)	—	812
12/08	4,754	30	0.6%	729
12/07	3,794	23	0.6%	732
Annual Growth	6.4%	17.4%	—	0.4%

2011 Year-End Financials

Debt ratio: 6.65%
Return on equity: 6.16%
Cash ($ mil.): 172
Current ratio: —
Long-term debt ($ mil.): 323
No. of shares (mil.): 34
Dividends
Yield: —
Payout: —
Market value ($ mil.): 555

	STOCK PRICE ($) FY Close	P/E High/Low		PER SHARE ($) Earnings	Dividends	Book Value
12/11	16.15	15	9	1.09	0.00	20.67
12/10	13.58	—	—	(0.93)	0.00	20.00
12/09	14.22	—	—	(1.46)	0.00	21.22
12/08	29.81	24	15	1.27	0.00	26.40
12/07	25.42	24	15	1.34	0.00	20.96
Annual Growth	(10.7%)	—	—	(5.0%)	—	(0.3%)

Pitney Bowes Inc

Pitney Bowes has a measured approach to managing mail. The world's largest producer of postage meters the company also makes other mailing equipment and provides shipping and weighing systems. Pitney Bowes offers online postage services financing for office equipment purchases and facilities management services. It also develops software to create mailers and manage shipping transportation and logistics for government agencies and corporations. The company provides document management services through Pitney Bowes Management Services. Pitney Bowes gets about 70% of its sales in the US and all global revenues are split about evenly between small and medium-sized businesses (SMB) and large enterprises.

HISTORY

In 1912 Walter Bowes an address machine salesman gained control of Universal Stamping Machine which made stamp canceling machines. In 1920 Bowes joined with Arthur Pitney who had developed a postage metering machine. After creating a market by forcing through Congress legislation that outlawed the sale of meters the Pitney-Bowes Postage Meter Company began leasing new machines in 1921. During the 1920s Pitney-Bowes built a large service fleet with leasing and repair expertise; added mail handling machines including stampers and counters to its product line; and expanded into Canada Germany and the UK.

Pitney left in 1924 to start a competing company. Other competitors including IBM and NCR entered the market but they were never able to catch up with Pitney-Bowes. The company was so successful that almost no competitors remained. The US Justice Department investigated the business practices of the company which agreed to license its patents to potential competitors free of charge.

Facing the prospect of increased competition Pitney-Bowes began to diversify its operations. In 1967 the company took on Xerox with a line of copiers. In the late 1960s it moved into pricing and inventory control equipment and credit and ID card products. It also established a joint venture with Alpex for point-of-sale terminals that proved a flop. In 1973 the company wrote off its investment resulting in its first-ever loss.

But Pitney Bowes (the hyphen was dropped in 1970) continued to add operations. In 1979 it bought Dictaphone Corp. (voice processing). In 1981 the company consolidated Dictaphone subsidiary Grayarc with "The Drawing Board" (an office-supply catalog it acquired in 1980) to form Wheeler Group a direct-mail marketer of office supplies.

With its long history of meter leasing the company moved into the commercial arena eventually leasing such big-ticket items as airplanes and barges under the aegis of Pitney Bowes Financial Services. The company also continued to widen its product line with its 1981 introduction of Postage By Phone and a line of fax machines.

In the late 1980s the company began whittling its holdings selling its Dictaphone-related operations in pieces between 1988 and 1995. Meanwhile as its US markets matured Pitney Bowes added a variety of mailing services and electronic products and bolstered its overseas operations in 1994 with pacts to help China and Mexico update their postal systems. Vice chairman Michael Critelli was named CEO in 1996. The next year Pitney Bowes offloaded its nonoffice equipment leasing portfolio to GATX –a sale that let Pitney Bowes reduce its debt and focus on fewer interest-sensitive fee-based services.

In 1998 the company introduced a system that generated addressed and stuffed mass-mailing materials. The next year it filed a patent-infringement lawsuit against e-postage rivals Stamps.com and E-Stamp. Also in 1999 the Justice Department launched another antitrust investigation into the company's activities in the postage meter and online postage markets. In 2000 Pitney Bowes sold its mortgage servicing business Atlantic Mortgage & Investment Corporation to a subsidiary of ABN AMRO for about $490 million.

The next year Pitney Bowes bought the international operations of Bell & Howell's Mail and Messaging Technologies division for $51 million and it acquired Danka Business Systems' outsourcing unit Danka Services International for $290 million in an effort to strengthen its Pitney Bowes Management Services division. The company also received a $400 million settlement from a 1995 patent infringement suit against Hewlett-Packard (related to laser-jet printer technology). It then acquired Fimalac's mail systems subsidiary Secap. Pitney Bowes rounded out 2001 with the spinoff of its copier and fax business Pitney Bowes Office Systems. (The unit renamed Imagistics International was later acquired by Oce.)

In 2002 Pitney Bowes acquired privately held PSI Group a leading provider of mail pre-sort services for businesses for about $130 million. The company acquired government outsourcing service provider DDD Company (renamed Pitney Bowes Government Solutions) for almost $50 million in 2003. It purchased Groupe MAG a European distributor of finishing equipment and production mail equipment the following year. Also in 2004 Pitney Bowes acquired mail distributor International Mail Express (IMEX) for $29 million Group 1 Software for approximately $321 million mail processing services provider Ancora Capital & Management Group and the equipment service business of Standard Register.

In 2005 Pitney Bowes acquired Compulit a service company that provides litigation support to law firms and corporations; the purchase helped build a unit called Pitney Bowes Legal Solutions. The company also acquired Imagitas a mail marketing firm for approximately $230 million.

Pitney Bowes sold its Oce Imagistics lease portfolio to Rabobank Group subsidiary De Lage Landen for about $288 million in 2006. It also sold its Capital Services business (about 2% of sales in 2005) to an affiliate of Cerberus Capital Management for about $750 million.

Pitney Bowes also made a number of acquisitions in 2006. It acquired UK-based Emtex Software a provider of high-volume document production applications and services for about $41 million. Later in the year it bolstered its Pitney Bowes Management Services unit when it purchased Ibis Consulting for about $67 million. It acquired sister companies pmh Caramanning (marketing services) and Advertising Audit Service (promotional mail and marketing customization tools) in 2006. The company also acquired Print for about $47 million.

The company continued its acquisitive ways in 2007. It bought customer relationship services company Digital Cement ($52 million in cash) and France-based transactional print and document processor Asterion ($29 million in cash) that year bolstering its marketing and management services. It acquired location information and software provider MapInfo for $408 million in cash in 2007. It later purchased distributors in Australia and France that were both longtime providers of MapInfo products.

It later merged its MapInfo and Group 1 Software operations to form a single unit called Pitney Bowes Software. The company followed with the acquisition of mailing services provider Zipsort for $39 million in 2008.

Pitney Bowes president and COO Murray Martin was named CEO in 2007; Critelli assumed the role of executive chairman. Martin added the title of chairman in 2009.

EXECUTIVES

EVP; President Pitney Bowes Services Solutions, Vicki A. O'Meara, age 54, $500,000 total compensation
Chairman, Michael I. Roth, age 66
Chairman President and CEO, Murray D. Martin, age 64, $941,667 total compensation
EVP and Chief Human Resources Officer, Johnna G. Torsone, age 61
EVP and CIO, Gregory E. (Greg) Buoncontri, age 64
VP Corporate Secretary and Chief Governance Officer, Amy C. Corn
EVP and CFO, Michael (Mike) Monahan, age 51, $540,000 total compensation
VP Investor Relations, Charles F. McBride
VP Corporate Communications, Sheryl Y. Battles
Director External Communications, Carol Wallace
President Volly, Chuck L. Cordray
President Pitney Bowes Document Messaging Technologies, Ramesh A. Lakshmi-Ratan
President Pitney Bowes Government Solutions, Jon Love
VP External Communications Media and Industry Analyst Relations, Matthew (Matt) Broder
VP Finance and Chief Accounting Officer, Steven J. Green
VP; President U.S. Mailing Business, Patrick Brand
EVP; President Pitney Bowes Communications Solutions, Leslie R. Abi-Karam, age 53, $525,000 total compensation
VP Global Strategy and Business Development, John J. Schloff
VP and Treasurer, Helen Shan
EVP; President Pitney Bowes Software Solutions, John O'Hara, age 53
President Pitney Bowes Asia Pacific and Middle East, Eric Yves-Mahe
President Pitney Bowes Marketing Solutions, Art Fiordaliso
EVP and Chief Legal and Compliance Officer, Daniel J. (Dan) Goldstein, age 50
President and General Manager Pitney Bowes Management Services Americas, Jennifer Bonilla
Managing Director Pitney Bowes India, K. M. Nanaiah
EVP and Chief Strategy and Innovation Officer, Joseph H. (Joe) Timko, age 51
VP Marketing, Debra Thompson-Van
VP Pitney Bowes Foundation, Kathleen Ryan Mufson
VP E-commerce Solutions, Craig Reed
VP Business Development Multi-Vendor Services, Joanne Boyd
President and CEO, Marc B. Lautenbach
Director, Anne M. Busquet, age 62
Director, James H. (Jim) Keyes, age 71
Director, David L. Shedlarz, age 63
Director, Michael I. Roth, age 66
Director, Robert E. Weissman, age 71
Director, Rodney C. (Rod) Adkins, age 54
Director, Eduardo R. Menasce, age 66
Director, Anne Sutherland Fuchs, age 64
Director, Linda G. Alvarado, age 60
Director, David B. Snow Jr., age 57
Auditors: PricewaterhouseCoopersLLP

LOCATIONS

HQ: Pitney Bowes Inc.
1 Elmcroft Rd., Stamford CT 06926-0700
Phone: 203-356-5000 **Fax:** 312-751-2818
Web: www.playboyenterprises.com

2010 Sales

	$ mil.	% of total
US	3,804	70
Other countries	1,620	30
Total	**5,425**	**100**

2011 Sales

	$ mil.	% of total
US	3,588	68
Other countries	1,689	32
Total	**5,278**	**100**

PRODUCTS/OPERATIONS

2011 Sales

	$ mil.	% of total
Small & medium-sized business solutions		
North America mailing	1,961	37
International mailing	707	13
Enterprise business solutions		
Management services	949	18
Mail services	567	11
Production mail	544	10
Software	407	8
Marketing services	141	3
Total	**5,278**	**100**

2011 Sales

	$ mil.	% of total
Business services	1,684	32
Equipment sales	986	19
Support services	707	13
Financing	603	11
Rentals	563	11
Software	427	8
Supplies	308	6
Total	**5,278**	**100**

Selected Products

Global Mailing Equipment
- Address hygiene software
- Folders
- Letter and parcel scales
- Mail openers
- Mailing machines
- Mailroom furniture
- Manifest systems
- Paper handling systems
- Postage meters
- Shipping equipment
- Software-based shipping and logistics systems

Enterprise Systems
- Billing and payment systems
- Customer relationship management (CRM) software
- Electronic statement systems
- Incoming mail systems
- Mailing software
- Office mail systems
- Sorting equipment

Services
- Commercial and industrial financing
- Facilities maintenance
- Systems installation and support
- Training

COMPETITORS

Endicia
Gunther International
Neopost
salesforce.com
Siemens AG
Stamps.com
US Postal Service
Xerox

HISTORICAL FINANCIALS

Company Type: Public

Income Statement FYE: December 31

	REVENUE ($ mil.)	NET INCOME ($ mil.)	NET PROFIT MARGIN	EMPLOYEES
12/11	5,277	617	11.7%	28,700
12/10	5,425	292	5.4%	30,700
12/09	5,569	423	7.6%	33,004
12/08	6,262	419	6.7%	35,140
12/07	6,129	366	6.0%	36,165
Annual Growth	(3.7%)	13.9%	—	(5.6%)

2011 Year-End Financials

Debt ratio: 51.97%
Return on equity: 987650001000000.00%
Cash ($ mil.): 856
Current ratio: 105.43
Long-term debt ($ mil.): 3,683
No. of shares (mil.): 199
Dividends
Yield: —
Payout: 48.52%
Market value ($ mil.): 3,703

	STOCK PRICE ($) FY Close	P/E High	P/E Low	PER SHARE ($) Earnings	Dividends	Book Value
12/11	18.54	9	6	3.05	0.00	(0.20)
12/10	24.18	18	14	1.41	1.46	(0.47)
12/09	22.76	13	9	2.04	1.44	0.07
12/08	25.48	19	11	2.00	1.40	0.90
12/07	38.04	29	22	1.66	1.32	4.79
Annual Growth	(16.4%)	—	—	16.4%	—	—

PLACID REFINING COMPANY LLC

EXECUTIVES

President and CEO, Daniel R. (Dan) Robinson, age 64
VP and Secretary, Ronald D. (Ron) Hurst
Manager Marketing and Distribution, Matt Pfister
Refinery Manager Port Allen, Joey Hagmann
Contracts Administrator and Media Relations, Candace M. Weber
Sales Manager, Joe Hankins
Community Relations, Ron Hancock

LOCATIONS

HQ: PLACID REFINING COMPANY LLC
1601 ELM ST STE 3400, DALLAS, TX 752017201
Phone: 2148808479

PRODUCTS/OPERATIONS

COMPETITORS

CITGO Refining and Chemicals
NuStar Energy
United Refining
Valero Energy

HISTORICAL FINANCIALS

Company Type: Subsidiary

Income Statement FYE: December 31

	REVENUE ($ mil.)	NET INCOME ($ mil.)	NET PROFIT MARGIN	EMPLOYEES
12/11	4,699	4	0.1%	200
12/10	3,686	39	1.1%	0
12/06	2,925	128	4.4%	0
12/04	1,429	37	2.6%	0
Annual Growth	48.7%	(52.1%)	—	—

2011 Year-End Financials

Debt ratio: —
Return on equity: 0.10%
Cash ($ mil.): 58
Current ratio: 0.80
Long-term debt ($ mil.): —
Dividends
Yield: —
Payout: —
Market value ($ mil.): —

Plains All American Pipeline, L.P.

The term "All American" includes Canada for Plains All American Pipeline which has pipeline operations in the US and north of the border. The limited partnership is engaged in the transportation storage terminalling and marketing of crude oil refined products natural gas liquids (NGL) and liquefied petroleum gas (LPG) and owns extensive gathering terminal and storage facilities in across the US and in Canada. Plains All American Pipeline owns 18700 miles of gathering and mainline crude oil pipelines throughout the US and Canada operated a fleet of 70 trucks and 425 trailers 83 barges and 46 transport tugs and owned storage capacity of 20 million barrels.

Plains All American Pipeline handles more than 3 million barrels of crude oil refined products NGL and LPG per day through its extensive network based in key North American producing basins and transportation gateways.

The company has major gathering terminal and storage facilities in California Louisiana Oklahoma and Texas and in Alberta and Saskatchewan.

High oil and NGL prices plus the expansion of its capacity through nine acquisitions in 2011 boosted Plains All American Pipeline's revenues by 32% for the year. It reported a robust net income growth of 91% in 2011 as the increase in costs was eclipsed by the strong revenue growth fueled by acquisitions organic expansion high commodity prices and favorable market conditions. A recovering economy higher commodity prices and increased demand also lifted Plains All American Pipeline's revenue in 2010.

The company has steadily built its portfolio through acquisitions. In recent years Plains All American Pipeline has been pushing hard to expand its midstream operations in order to benefit from the revenue growth available through shipping storing and processing higher-priced NGL and LPG. In this context in 2012 the company bought BP's Canadian NGL operations for $1.7 billion. Canadian subsidiary Plains Midstream Canada acquired BP's Canadian NGL operations in 2012.

That year Plains All American Pipeline also agreed to buy four operating crude oil rail terminals one terminal under development and various contractual arrangements from U.S. Development Group for $500 million.

Boosting its US midstream assets in 2010 Plains All American Pipeline acquired oil gathering properties (which handle about 55000 barrels a day) and transportation assets (an 18000-barrels per day pipeline and eight truck terminals) from a unit of Nexen for $210 million. In 2011 it bought SG Resources Mississippi's salt-cavern natural-gas storage facility for $750 million.

In 2011 to further grow its midstream portfolio the company made a hostile $1.2 bid to acquire rival SemGroup. The deal would have significantly expanded Plains All American Pipeline's pipeline and storage assets. In 2012 the company withdrew its bid without comment.

Not neglecting its traditional business in 2011 it also bought Western Refining's 70000 barrels-per-day Yorktown refinery and an underused segment of its crude oil pipeline in southeast New Mexico for $220 million.

HISTORY

Goodyear Tire & Rubber subsidiary Celeron began designing the All American Pipeline in 1983 to bring heavy crude from California to the less-regulated refineries of Texas. It was completed in 1987 at a cost of $1.6 billion but by 1991 only a trickle of oil was dribbling through. The pipeline did not post a profit until 1994.

Prospects began to look up in the mid-1990s when Chevron Texaco and Exxon signed contracts to use the pipeline beginning in 1996. Plains Resources bought the pipeline in 1998 for $400 million; the company created Plains All American Pipeline to acquire and operate the pipeline then sold off a 43% stake in an IPO that raised $260 million. The next year Plains All American bought Scurlock Permian (2300 miles of pipeline) from Marathon Ashland Petroleum for $141 million and the West Texas Gathering System from Chevron (450 miles) for $36 million.

Shareholders sued Plains All American in 1999 after it reported that an employee's unauthorized crude-oil trading would cost the company about $160 million. (In 2000 the company agreed to pay $29.5 million plus interest to settle the cases.)

Plains All American announced plans to mothball all but the California section of the All American Pipeline in 1999. The next year El Paso Energy bought the 1088-mile section of the pipeline that was to be deactivated plus the right to run fiber-optic cable over the entire pipeline for $129 million.

Targeting Canada as part of its expansion strategy in 2001 Plains All American bought about 450 miles of oil pipeline and other midstream assets from Murphy Oil and acquired crude oil and LPG marketing firm CANPET Energy. Also that year Plains Resources reduced its stake in Plains All American from 44% to 29%.

In 2002 the company acquired the Wapella Pipeline System located in southeastern Saskatchewan and southwestern Manitoba. It also bought Shell Pipeline's West Texas crude oil pipeline assets for $315 million. Plains All American Pipeline continued its acquisition streak in 2003 with the acquisitions of the South Saskatchewan pipeline system in Canada and the ArkLaTex pipeline system originating in Sabine Texas.

In 2004 Plains All American continued its expansion with the acquisition of interests in the Capline and Capwood pipeline systems from Shell Pipeline Company for about $158 million. It also acquired the crude oil and pipeline operations of Link Energy for about $330 million and the Cal Ven pipeline system from Unocal Canada for about $19 million. Later that year the company continued its system expansion by acquiring the Schaefferstown propane storage facility from Koch Hydrocarbon for about $32 million.

In 2006 the company acquired Andrews Petroleum and Lone Star Trucking for $205 million. It also acquired stakes in a number of Gulf Coast crude oil pipeline systems from BP Oil Pipeline Company for $133.5 million. That year in a major deal the company acquired Pacific Energy Partners for $2.4 billion moving the company beyond crude oil and into the refined products and barging businesses.

In 2007 Plains All American Pipeline acquired LPG storage facilities in Arizona and South Carolina.

In 2008 Occidental Petroleum acquired 10% of the company's general partner boosting the amount of new capital available for Plains All American Pipeline to pay down debt and make further acquisitions. It also boosted its Canadian midstream assets with the acquisition of Rainbow Pipeline (crude oil gathering and pipelines).

Further expanding its asset base in 2009 the company acquired joint venture partner Vulcan Energy unit Vulcan Capital's 50% stake in PAA Natural Gas Storage which owns 40 billion cu. ft. of natural gas storage capacity in Michigan and Louisiana. It also acquired an additional 21% in the Capital Pipeline System (in which it held 22%) on the Gulf Coast.

EXECUTIVES

President and COO, Harry N. Pefanis, age 54, $300,000 total compensation
EVP, Phillip D. (Phil) Kramer, age 55, $250,000 total compensation
Chairman and CEO, Greg L. Armstrong, age 53, $375,000 total compensation
SVP Operations and Business Development, Mark J. Gorman, age 57
SVP Technology Process and Risk Management, Alfred A. (Al) Lindseth, age 42
VP, David E. Wright, age 66
VP Acquisitions, James G. (Jim) Hester, age 52
EVP and CFO, Al Swanson, age 48, $250,000 total compensation
VP General Counsel Commercial and Litigation and Assistant Secretary, Lawrence J. (Larry) Dreyfuss, age 57
VP, A. Patrick (Pat) Diamond, age 39
VP Environmental Health and Safety, Troy E. Valenzuela, age 50
President Plains Midstream Canada, W. David (Dave) Duckett, age 56, $251,058 total compensation
VP Corporate Development and Transportation Services Plains Midstream Canada, Ralph R. Cross, age 56
VP Crude Oil Plains Midstream Canada, Michael D. (Mike) Hallahan, age 51
SVP Commercial Activities, John P. vonBerg, age 57, $250,000 total compensation
VP Pipeline Business Development, Samuel N. Brown, age 55
VP West Coast Projects, John F. Russell, age 63
VP Refinery Supply, James B. (Jim) Fryfogle, age 60
VP Engineering, Daniel J. Nerbonne, age 54
EVP and CFO Plains Midstream Canada, David Craig, age 54
VP Lease Supply, Robert M. Sanford, age 62
VP Human Resources, Roger D. Everett, age 66
VP Terminals, John R. Keffer, age 52
VP Operations Plains Midstream Canada, Stephen L. Bart, age 51
EVP, John R. Rutherford, age 51
VP and Treasurer, Charles Kingswell-Smith, age 60
Director Investor Relations, Roy I. Lamoreaux
VP Internal Audit, Kevin L. Cantrell, age 51
VP Business Development Plains Midstream Canada, Mike Mikuska, age 43
VP Business Development?LPG Plains Midstream Canada, Gregg McClement, age 43
VP Accounting Plains Midstream Canada, Sandi Wingert, age 41
VP Accounting and Chief Accounting Officer, Chris Herbold, age 40
VP Operations, Phil Smith, age 53
Director, John T. Raymond, age 41
Director, Robert V. Sinnott, age 62
Director, J. Taft Symonds, age 72
Director, Gary R. Petersen, age 65
Director, Everardo Goyanes, age 67
Director, Christopher M. (Chris) Temple, age 44
Director, Vicky Sutil, age 47
Auditors: PricewaterhouseCoopersLLP

LOCATIONS

HQ: Plains All American Pipeline L.P.
333 Clay St. Ste. 1600, Houston TX 77002
Phone: 713-646-4100 **Fax:** 713-646-4572
Web: www.plainsallamerican.com

2011 Sales

	$ mil.	% of total
US	28,181	82
Canada	6,094	18
Total	**34,275**	**100**

PRODUCTS/OPERATIONS

2011 Sales

	$ mil.	% of total
Supply and logistics	33,065	96
Facilities	638	2
Transportation	572	2
Total	**34,275**	**100**

COMPETITORS

Buckeye Partners
Enbridge
Enterprise Products
NGL Energy Partners
ONEOK
Sunoco Logistics
TransMontaigne

HISTORICAL FINANCIALS

Company Type: Public

Income Statement FYE: December 31

	REVENUE ($ mil.)	NET INCOME ($ mil.)	NET PROFIT MARGIN	EMPLOYEES
12/11	34,275	966	2.8%	3,800
12/10	25,893	505	2.0%	3,500
12/09	18,520	579	3.1%	3,400
12/08	30,061	437	1.5%	3,302
12/07	20,394	365	1.8%	3,100
Annual Growth	13.9%	27.5%	—	5.2%

2011 Year-End Financials

Debt ratio: 33.80%
Return on equity: 17.72%
Cash ($ mil.): 26
Current ratio: 96.45
Long-term debt ($ mil.): 4,520
No. of shares (mil.): 310
Dividends
Yield: —
Payout: 80.02%
Market value ($ mil.): 22,825

	STOCK PRICE ($) FY Close	P/E High	P/E Low	PER SHARE ($) Earnings	Dividends	Book Value
12/11	73.45	30	23	2.44	0.00	17.54
12/10	62.79	54	43	1.20	1.88	15.38
12/09	52.85	32	21	1.66	1.81	15.04
12/08	34.69	39	19	1.34	1.75	14.45
12/07	52.00	51	39	1.26	1.64	14.76
Annual Growth	9.0%	—	—	18.0%	—	4.4%

PNC Financial Services Group (The)

PNC Financial Services has returned to its traditional banking roots. Its flagship PNC Bank subsidiary operates about 2500 branches in more than a dozen states in the mid-Atlantic the Midwest and Florida. In addition to retail and corporate banking the company offers insurance investments personal and institutional asset management and capital markets products and services. It owns boutique investment bank Harris Williams and about a quarter of money management giant BlackRock. PNC acquired RBC Bank (USA) from Royal Bank of Canada in 2012. The nearly $3.5 billion acquisition extended PNC's retail banking franchise in the Southeast and cemented its place among the five largest banks in the US.

HISTORY

First National Bank of Pittsburgh opened in 1863. In 1913 the bank consolidated with Second National Bank of Pittsburgh and in 1921 it bought Peoples National.

The company changed its name to Pittsburgh National after a long expansion following the Depression and WWII. The bank entered the credit card business in 1965 and joined the BankAmericard program (Visa's forerunner) four years later. In the inflationary 1970s Pittsburgh National diversified moving into commercial paper financing (1972) lease financing (1979) and credit life health and accident reinsurance (1979).

In 1983 Pittsburgh National merged with Provident National of Philadelphia (founded by Quakers in 1865) to form PNC Corp. The union combined Pittsburgh National's corporate lending strength with Provident's money management and trust operations. PNC expanded through the 1980s by buying more Pennsylvania banks and then moved into Kentucky in 1987. That year PNC with $37 billion in assets passed Mellon Bank as Pennsylvania's largest bank.

This growth was accompanied by investment in risky commercial mortgages so when the real estate market unraveled in 1989-90 PNC was stuck with millions of dollars in problem loans. It soon began selling its bad loans and property and tightening underwriting standards.

PNC reorganized in 1991 operating its several state-chartered banks as if they were a single entity. Acquisitions continued including BlackRock Financial Management Sears Mortgage 84 banking branches orphaned by the Chase Manhattan/Chemical Bank merger and New Jersey-based Midlantic Corp (founded in 1804 as Newark Banking and Insurance).

PNC's acquisitions focused more sharply on mortgages in 1997 and 1998; it bought Midland Loan Services as well as the mortgage origination offices of what became FleetBoston. The former purchase moved the company strongly into servicing and securitization to become a major buyer in the secondary commercial-mortgage market.

In addition to consolidating its asset management operations under the BlackRock subsidiary in 1998 (spun off the next year) PNC bought BTM Capital an asset-based lender headquartered in Boston. After rules separating banking from securities activities were relaxed in 1998 the firm bought Louisville Kentucky-based securities brokerage Hilliard Lyons. Also that year the company paid $30 million to attach its name to the Pittsburgh Pirates' baseball stadium for 20 years. Christened PNC Park it opened in 2001.

In 1999 PNC bought credit card processor First Data's Investor Services Group which it merged into PFPC. That year PNC agreed to pay $375000 to 31 women employees in response to a Labor Department charge that PNC had a "glass ceiling." Later in 1999 the company signed on as the exclusive banking services provider for iVillage.com an Internet site for women.

PNC exited the vehicle leasing and residential mortgage businesses in 2001. The following year the company sold BillingZone a joint venture with Perot Systems that provided electronic bill payment and presentment services; it was purchased by eONE Global a unit of First Data.

Belying speculation that it was a takeover target itself PNC bought United National Bancorp in 2004 and after much drama acquired Riggs National the following year.

PNC had originally agreed to buy Riggs in 2004 but lowered its bid after Riggs pleaded guilty to Bank Secrecy Act violations in early 2005. (Riggs also paid millions in fines and technology upgrades to comply with the anti-terrorism measure.) Riggs sued PNC for damages for backing out on the deal but dropped the charges after agreeing on a renegotiated sale price.

After the dust settled PNC wasted no time making its presence known in the coveted Washington DC market where Riggs had been the #1 bank. It quickly obliterated the vestiges of troubled Riggs removing that institution's signs and replacing them with its own during the weekend after the deal was finalized (most bank systems' conversions and name changes usually take place months after an acquisition closes). PNC also extended hours at former Riggs branches and added locations in and around the nation's capital.

In 2005 the company bought boutique investment bank Harris Williams which specializes in mergers and acquisitions advisory services. Harris Williams kept its name and became a subsidiary of PNC after the deal was completed.

PNC sold part of its 70% share in BlackRock to Merrill Lynch in 2006 netting some $1.6 billion from the transaction.

In 2007 PNC expanded its commercial mortgage operations with the acquisition of multifamily housing lender ARC Commercial Mortgage (now PNC ARCS). Increasingly focusing its brokerage business on input print activities PNC sold brokerage firm Hilliard Lyons to Houchens Industries in 2008.

Also in 2007 and 2008 PNC acquired bank holding companies Yardville National Bancorp Mercantile Bankshares and Sterling Financial. The deals brought in more than 300 branches in the mid-Atlantic region boosting PNC's banking leasing trust investment and brokerage operations.

EXECUTIVES

General Auditor, Samuel R. Patterson, age 53
Vice Chairman, Thomas K. (Tom) Whitford, age 55, $475,384 total compensation
EVP and General Counsel, Helen P. Pudlin, age 62
Senior Vice Chairman and Chief Risk Officer, Joseph C. (Joe) Guyaux, age 61, $1,385,000 total compensation
Chairman and CEO, James E. (Jim) Rohr, age 63, $2,750,000 total compensation
EVP and Chief Human Resources Officer, Joan L. Gulley, age 64
EVP and Chief Credit Officer, Michael J. Hannon, age 55
SVP Investor Relations, William H. Callihan
Senior Vice Chairman, William S. (Bill) Demchak, age 49, $2,250,000 total compensation
EVP and CFO, Richard J. Johnson, age 55, $862,500 total compensation
EVP and Chief Communications Officer, Donna C. Peterman
EVP Chief Investment Officer and Treasurer, E. William (Bill) Parsley III, age 46
SVP and Director External Communications, Brian Goerke

EVP and Chief Risk Officer, Enrico Dallavecchia, age 50
Chief Governance Counsel and Secretary, George P. Long III
SVP and Chief Economist, Stuart G. Hoffman
EVP Asset Management Group, Robert Q. Reilly, age 47
Chief Regulatory Affairs Officer, Robert F. Hoyt, age 47
CIO, Anuj Dhanda
VP Corporate Communications, Fred Solomon
Media Contact Retail Banking, Patrick McMahon
Media Contact Corporate and Institutional Banking, Amy Vargo
Media Contact Wealth Management, Alan Aldinger
Media Contact PNC Grow Up Great and Community Involvement, Joseph Balaban
SVP and Controller, Gregory H. Kozich, age 48
SVP and Manager Corporate Recruiting and Employee Inclusion, Kathleen C. D'Appolonia
EVP and Managing Executive Investments, James P. Dunigan
SVP and Director Payments and e-Business, Thomas S. Kunz
Assistant VP and Economist, Kurt J. Rankin
COO and Leader Technology and Corporate Services, John Ericksen
Head Corporate and Institutional Banking, Michael P. Lyons, age 41
Director, Richard B. (Rick) Kelson, age 65
Director, Paul W. Chellgren, age 69
Director, Dennis F. (Denny) Strigl, age 65
Vice Chairman, Thomas K. (Tom) Whitford, age 55
Senior Vice Chairman and Chief Risk Officer, Joseph C. (Joe) Guyaux, age 61
Director, Charles E. (Chuck) Bunch, age 63
Director, Thomas J. Usher, age 69
Director, Helge H. Wehmeier, age 69
Director, Anthony A. (Tony) Massaro, age 67
Director, Donald J. Shepard, age 65
Director, Richard O. Berndt, age 69
Director, Bruce C. Lindsay, age 70
Director, Jane G. Pepper, age 66
Director, Lorene K. Steffes, age 66
Senior Vice Chairman, William S. (Bill) Demchak, age 49
Director, Gen. George H. Walls Jr., age 69
Director, Kay Coles James, age 62
Auditors: PricewaterhouseCoopersLLP

LOCATIONS

HQ: PNC Financial Services Group (The)
One PNC Plaza, 249 Fifth Avenue, Pittsburgh, PA 15222-2707
Phone: 412 762-2000 **Fax:** 412 762-5798
Web: www.pnc.com

Selected Banking Markets

Delaware
Florida
Georgia
Illinois
Indiana
Kentucky
Maryland
Michigan
Missouri
New Jersey
Ohio
Pennsylvania
Virginia
West Virginia
Wisconsin

PRODUCTS/OPERATIONS

2011 Sales

	$ mil.	% of total
Interest		
Loans	7,595	48
Investment securities	2,161	14
Other	438	3
Noninterest		
Consumer services	1,243	8
Asset management	1,088	7
Corporate services	898	6
Residential mortgage	713	4
Service charges on deposits	534	3
Other	1,150	7
Total	**15,820**	**100**

Selected Subsidiaries

PNC Bancorp Inc.
PNC Bank National AssociationPNC Bank Capital Securities LLCPNC Capital Leasing LLCPNC Preferred Funding LLCPNC REIT Corp.
PNC Holding LLC
PNC Funding Corp
PNC Investment Corp.
PNC Venture LLC

COMPETITORS

Bank of America
Capital One
Citigroup
Fifth Third
Harris
Huntington Bancshares
JPMorgan Chase
KeyCorp
M&T Bank
RBS Citizens Financial Group
Sovereign Bank
TD Bank USA
U.S. Bancorp
Wells Fargo

HISTORICAL FINANCIALS

Company Type: Public

Income Statement

FYE: December 31

	ASSETS ($ mil.)	NET INCOME ($ mil.)	INCOME AS % OF ASSETS	EMPLOYEES
12/11	271,205	3,071	1.1%	51,891
12/10	264,284	3,397	1.3%	50,769
12/09	269,863	2,403	0.9%	55,820
12/08	291,081	882	0.3%	59,595
12/07	138,920	1,467	1.1%	28,320
Annual Growth	18.2%	20.3%	—	16.3%

2011 Year-End Financials

Debt ratio: 12.43%
Return on equity: 9.02%
Cash ($ mil.): 5,274
Current ratio: —
Long-term debt ($ mil.): 33,720
No. of shares (mil.): 527
Dividends
Yield: —
Payout: 20.15%
Market value ($ mil.): 30,392

	STOCK PRICE ($) FY Close	P/E High	P/E Low	PER SHARE ($) Earnings	Dividends	Book Value
12/11	57.67	11	8	5.64	0.00	64.62
12/10	60.72	12	9	5.74	0.40	57.49
12/09	52.79	13	4	4.36	0.96	64.81
12/08	49.00	32	17	2.46	2.61	57.39
12/07	65.65	17	14	4.35	2.44	43.56
Annual Growth	(3.2%)	—	—	6.7%	—	10.4%

Popular Inc.

LOCATIONS

HQ: Popular Inc.
Popular Center Building, 209 Munoz Rivera Avenue, Hato Rey,
Phone: (787) 765 9800
Web: www.popular.com

PRODUCTS/OPERATIONS

2011 Sales

	$ mil.	% of total
Interest		
Loans	1,694	67
Investment securities	203	8
Trading account securities & other	39	2
Noninterest		
Service charges on deposit accounts	184	7
Other service fees	239	9
Other	168	7
Adjustments	(33.1)	-
Total	**2,497**	**100**

Selected Subsidiaries and Affiliates

Banco Popular de Puerto Rico
BP Sirenusa International LLC (US)
Popular Auto Inc.
Popular Mortgage Inc.
Popular Capital Trust I (US)
Popular Insurance Inc.
Popular International Bank Inc.
Banco Popular North America (US)
E-LOAN Inc.
Equity One Inc.
Popular Insurance V.I. Inc. (US Virgin Islands)
Popular Life RE
Popular Securities Inc.

HISTORICAL FINANCIALS

Company Type:

Income Statement

FYE: December 31

	ASSETS ($ mil.)	NET INCOME ($ mil.)	INCOME AS % OF ASSETS	EMPLOYEES
12/11	37,348	151	0.4%	8,329
12/10	38,722	137	0.4%	8,277
12/09	34,736	(573)	—	9,407
12/08	38,882	(1,243)	—	20,974
12/07	44,411	(64)	—	12,303
Annual Growth	(4.2%)	—	—	(9.3%)

2011 Year-End Financials

Debt ratio: 4.97%
Return on equity: 3.86%
Cash ($ mil.): 7,029
Current ratio: —
Long-term debt ($ mil.): 1,856
No. of shares (mil.): 102
Dividends
Yield: —
Payout: —
Market value ($ mil.): 143

	STOCK PRICE ($) FY Close	P/E High	P/E Low	PER SHARE ($) Earnings	Dividends	Book Value
12/11	1.39	3	1	1.40	0.00	38.20
12/10	3.14	—	—	(0.60)	0.00	37.16
12/09	2.26	2	0	2.40	0.00	39.70
12/08	5.16	—	—	(45.50)	0.00	115.90
12/07	10.60	—	—	(2.70)	0.00	127.91
Annual Growth	(39.8%)	—	—	—	—	(26.1%)

PPG Industries, Inc.

Thanks to its diversified product offerings you won't catch PPG Industries painting itself into a corner. Coatings –such as paints (Pittsburgh Paints Lucite and Monarch) stains (Olympic) and sealants —account for most of its sales; the remainder comes from glass chemicals and specialty materials. PPG's glass offerings include flat glass for buildings fabricated glass and continuous-strand fiberglass used in aircraft and buildings. Its chemicals segment makes chlor-alkali chemicals and the specialty materials unit provides silica products. The company also makes optical products like Transitions-brand lenses.

HISTORY

After the failure of his first two plate-glass manufacturing plants John Ford persuaded former railroad superintendent John Pitcairn to invest $200000 in a third factory in 1883 in Creighton Pennsylvania. The enterprise Pittsburgh Plate Glass (PPG) became the first commercially successful US plate-glass factory.

Ford left in 1896 after Pitcairn established a company distribution system replacing glass jobbers. Ford went on to found a predecessor of competitor Libbey-Owens-Ford (now owned by glass-maker Pilkington).

Pitcairn built a soda ash plant in 1899 bought a Milwaukee paint company the following year and began producing window glass in 1908. Pitcairn died in 1916 leaving his stock to his sons.

Strong automobile and construction markets in the early 20th century increased demand for the company's products. In 1924 PPG revolutionized glass production with the introduction of a straight-line conveyor manufacturing method. In the 1930s and 1940s PPG successfully promoted structural glass for use in the commercial construction industry.

PPG was listed on the NYSE in 1945. In 1952 it started making fiberglass and in 1968 the company adopted its present name.

Vincent Sarni (CEO 1984-93) recognized that 85% of the company's sales were to the maturing construction and automobile industries. Sarni decided to move the company into growing industries such as electronics.

In 1986 PPG spent $154 million on acquisitions including the medical electronics units of Litton Industries and Honeywell. It acquired the medical technology business of Allegheny International in 1987 and bought Casco Nobel a coatings distributor and the Olympic and Lucite paint lines from Clorox in 1989.

The company which owned one-third of Dutch fiberglass producer Silenka BV acquired the rest in 1991. In 1992 PPG acquired a silica plant in the Netherlands its first in Europe. Two years later it acquired the European automotive coatings business of Netherlands-based Akzo Nobel.

In the 1990s PPG backed away from Sarni's earlier strategies for greater diversification and unloaded a number of high-tech businesses. The firm refocused on its core coatings glass and chemicals operations. PPG acquired Matthews Paints a leading maker of paints for outdoor signs and the refinish coating business of Lilly Industries in 1995.

The company bolstered its chemical operations in 1997 with the addition of France's Sipsy Chime Fine. That same year President and COO Raymond LeBoeuf took over as CEO. In 1998 PPG sold its European flat and automotive glass business to Belgium-based Glaverbel. Acquisitions that year included Australia-based Orica's technical coatings unit and the US paint operations (Porter Paints) of Akzo Nobel.

In 1999 PPG expanded its European coatings business with the purchase of Belgium-based Sigma Coatings' commercial transport coatings unit and Akzo Nobel's aircraft coatings and sealants company PRC-DeSoto International. That year PPG also bought Imperial Chemical Industries' Germany-based coatings business for large commercial vehicles and its US-based auto refinish and industrial coatings businesses. PPG's acquisition spree continued in 2000 with architectural coating maker Monarch Paint.

Early in the new decade PPG suffered from flat or declining earnings from existing operations. Amid falling sales and lower prices for chemicals and glass PPG began to cut jobs and closed some facilities. Still the company recorded its first loss in more than 10 years in 2002 and its second straight year of declining sales.

Like many manufacturers in its industry PPG has been exposed to potentially costly asbestos litigation mainly because of its 50% stake in the bankrupt Pittsburgh Corning a joint venture with Corning that made insulation with asbestos. In 2002 PPG and its insurers agreed to pay roughly $2.7 billion to settle its asbestos claims.

LeBoeuf retired in 2005. He was replaced by president and COO Charles Bunch who had joined the company in 1979 and worked up through the ranks of first the finance department and then the coatings operations.

In 2008 PPG acquired SigmaKalon for $3 billion. SigmaKalon was among the top 10 paint manufacturers in the world and did business almost entirely outside the US. The company now operates as PPG's Architectural Coatings segment. That same year PPG sold its auto glass business to private equity group Kohlberg & Company which set the unit up as a stand-alone company called Pittsburgh Glass Works. PPG received $330 million plus a 40% interest in the company.

In 2011 PPG acquired Equa-Chlor a producer of chlorine caustic soda and muriatic acid for $27 million. Equa-Chlor produces about 220 tons of chlorine per day. In addition to its products PPG also bought Equa-Chlor's distribution system which includes a railcar fleet it integrated into its own. The deal for the Washington state-based company bolsters PPG's chlor-alkali business in the Northwest US and expands its overall supply chain.

EXECUTIVES

SVP Automotive OEM Coatings, Cynthia A. Niekamp, age 52
Chairman and CEO, Charles E. (Chuck) Bunch, age 63, $1,050,000 total compensation
EVP Architectural Coatings EMEA; President PPG Europe, Pierre-Marie de Leener, age 55, $577,466 total compensation
VP Flat Glass, Richard A. (Dick) Beuke
SVP Commodity Chemicals, Michael H. McGarry, age 53
SVP Optical and Specialty Materials, Richard C. (Rick) Elias, age 58
SVP Finance and CFO, David B. Navikas, age 61
VP and Treasurer, Aziz S. Giga
EVP Performance Coatings, J. Rich Alexander, age 56, $420,000 total compensation
VP Information Technology, Werner Baer
VP Aerospace Coatings and Sealants, David P. (Dave) Morris
VP Government and Community Affairs, Lynne D. Schmidt
VP Investor Relations, Vince Morales
VP Automotive Refinish, John R. Outcalt
VP Coatings Research and Development and Chief Technology, Charles F. Kahle II
SVP and General Counsel, Glenn E. Bost II
VP Architectural Coatings North America, Scott Sinetar
SVP Industrial Coatings; President PPG Asia/Pacific, Viktor R. Sekmakas
VP Protective and Marine Coatings, Thomas S. (Tom) Mauck
VP Automotive OEM Coatings Europe, Jean-Marie Greindl
VP Aerospace Products, Barry N. Gillespie
Supervisor Public Relations, K.C. McCrory
Manager Corporate Public Relations, Jeremy Neuhart
VP Chlor-Alkali Marketing Services and Cal-hypo, Sharon Piciacchio
VP Packaging Coatings, Douglas S. Pegg
VP Automotive Refinish EMEA, Gary Danowski
VP Fiber Glass, Thomas P. (Tom) Kerr
Assistant General Counsel and Corporate Secretary, Anne M. Foulkes
VP Automotive Refinish United States and Canada, Gregory Benckart
VP Asia/Pacific Coatings; General Manager Refinish Architectural and PMC Asia/Pacific, Michael Horton
VP Strategic Planning and Corporate Development, Anup Jain
VP Human Resources, J. Craig Jordan
VP Corporate Marketing, Patrick J. Kenny
VP Automotive OEM Coatings Americas, Timothy M. Knavish
VP Tax Administration, Johann F. (John) Kolling
VP Corporate Purchasing and Distribution, Stephen T. Lampe
VP Environment Health and Safety, John Richter
VP Automotive OEM Coatings Asia/Pacific, Vincent Robin
VP Architectural Coatings ? EMEA - Region Western Europe, Ram Vadlamannati
VP Industrial Coatings Asia/Pacific, Chunping (Willie) Wu
VP Refinish Coatings Asia and Architectural Coatings China, Pauline Yuen
Media Contact UK, Ken Armistead
Media Contact Asia Pacific, Hunter Lee
Director, James G. Berges, age 64
Director, David R. Whitwam, age 70
Director, Thomas J. Usher, age 69
Director, Michele J. Hooper, age 60
Director, Victoria F. Haynes, age 64
Director, Robert Ripp, age 70
Director, Robert Mehrabian, age 70
Director, Hugh Grant, age 53
Director, Stephen F. (Steve) Angel, age 56
Director, Martin H. Richenhagen, age 59
Auditors: Deloitte&ToucheLLP

LOCATIONS

HQ: PPG Industries Inc.
1 PPG Place, Pittsburgh PA 15272
Phone: 412-434-3131 **Fax:** 412-434-2011
Web: www.ppg.com

2011 Sales

	$ mil.	% of total
The Americas		
Other countries	1,121	7
Asia/Pacific	2,518	17

PRODUCTS/OPERATIONS

2011 Sales

	$ mil.	% of total
Performance Coatings	4,626	31
Architectural Coatings EMEA	2,104	14
Optical & Specialty Materials	1,204	8
Total	**14,885**	**100**

Selected Products

Performance Coatings
- Aerospace coatings
- Architectural coatings (Lucite paints Olympic stains)
- Refinish

Industrial Coatings
- Automotive coatings chemicals adhesives and sealants
- Industrial coatings
- Packaging coatings (food and beverage containers)

Commodity Chemicals
- Calcium hypochlorite
- Caustic soda
- Chlorine
- Chlorine derivatives
- Phosgene derivatives

Optical and Specialty Materials
- Optical products (Transitions variable-tint lenses)
- Silica products

Glass
- Aircraft transparencies
- Coated glass
- Continuous-strand fiberglass
- Flat glass

COMPETITORS

3M
Akzo Nobel
BASF Coatings AG
BEHR
Benjamin Moore
Dow Chemical
DuPont Performance Coatings
Ferro
Kelly-Moore
Nippon Paint
Nippon Sheet Glass
Pilkington Group
RPM International
Sherwin-Williams

HISTORICAL FINANCIALS

Company Type: Public

Income Statement FYE: December 31

	REVENUE ($ mil.)	NET INCOME ($ mil.)	NET PROFIT MARGIN	EMPLOYEES
12/11	14,885	1,095	7.4%	38,400
12/10	13,423	769	5.7%	38,300
12/09	12,239	336	2.7%	39,900
12/08	15,849	538	3.4%	44,900
12/07	11,206	834	7.4%	34,900
Annual Growth	7.4%	7.0%	—	2.4%

2011 Year-End Financials

Debt ratio: 25.60%
Return on equity: 33.70%
Cash ($ mil.): 1,457
Current ratio: 180.82
Long-term debt ($ mil.): 3,574
No. of shares (mil.): 151
Dividends
Yield: —
Payout: 32.90%
Market value ($ mil.): 12,681

	STOCK PRICE ($) FY Close	P/E High/Low		PER SHARE ($) Earnings	Dividends	Book Value
12/11	83.49	14	10	6.87	0.00	21.39
12/10	84.07	18	12	4.63	2.18	22.68
12/09	58.54	30	14	2.03	2.13	22.65
12/08	42.43	21	11	3.25	2.09	20.30
12/07	70.23	16	13	5.03	2.04	25.34
Annual Growth	4.4%	—	—	8.1%	—	(4.1%)

PPL Corp

PPL packs a powerful punch in Pennsylvania Kentucky and the UK where it distributes electricity to more than 10 million customers through regulated subsidiaries PPL Electric Utilities two utilities in Kentucky and Western Power Distribution Holdings. The company has 19000 MW of generating capacity and also sells energy wholesale in key US markets. Western Power Distribution operates two of the 15 distribution networks providing electricity service in the UK —WPD (South West) and WPD (South Wales). PPL's marketing unit PPL EnergyPlus buys and sells coal oil and natural gas as well as renewable energy credits.

Operations

PPL operates electricity distribution companies with more than 2.2 million customers in the US (PPL Electric Utilities Louisville Gas and Electric and Kentucky Utilities) and more than 7.8 million customers in the UK (Western Power Distribution). The utility operations have 200000 miles of electric lines. PPL also operates a major wholesale power energy marketing operation in the US (PPL EnergyPlus).

In the Northeastern and Northwestern US PPL generates 11000 MW of power and some 8000 MW in Kentucky. Its power generation comes primarily from coal-fired plants.

Financial Analysis

The company's revenues grew by almost 50% in 2011 largely as the result of an acquisition spree that added new utilities in the US and the UK to its energy portfolio. This expansion was reflected in a more than 59% jump in net income as higher revenues outpaced increased costs. (For 2011 2010 and 2009 was $1.5 billion $938 million and $407 million).

Strategy

Once a global power player with interests in distribution companies worldwide the company has opted for the UK as its non-US focus. PPL seeks long term stability in its regulated power distribution businesses through efficient operations and strong customer and regulatory relations while seeking growth opportunities in its competitive electricity generation and marketing businesses.

Growing its US power capacity in 2012 PPL acquired AES Ironwood and AES Prescott which together own and operate the 705 MW AES Ironwood natural gas-fired power plant in Lebanon Pennsylvania from a unit of AES Corporation for $302 million.

Expanding its regulated power operations in 2011 the company acquired the UK's #2 electric distribution business WPD Midlands Holdings (formerly Central Networks) for $5.7 billion. The deal gave the company greater market share in the UK and added to 2011 earnings and cash flow.

That year to raise cash PPL sold its stakes in some non-core generating stations in the US to an affiliate of LS Power Equity for $381 million. The company was also pursuing further rate increases across its service areas in order to defray costs.

Buoyed by a rebounding economy in 2010 PPL acquired E.ON U.S. the owner of Kentucky's two major utilities Louisville Gas & Electric and Kentucky Utilities for $7.6 billion. The utilities serve 1.2 million customers primarily in Kentucky. The deal made PPL stronger (with 19000 MW of generating capacity) and more geographically diverse.

HISTORY

PPL's wires reach back to Lehigh Coal & Navigation which was formed in 1822 to mine Pennsylvania coal and build a canal to deliver it to Philadelphia. Heavy industry and steel mills flourished in the Lehigh Valley and Thomas Edison formed small electric companies to serve the area in the early 1880s. Rivals soon followed and by 1900 there were 64 companies in what would become PPL's territory.

Lehigh formed Lehigh Navigation Electric in 1912 to provide power to its coal mines only to lose control of the company to conglomerate Electric Bond & Share in 1917. S. Z. Mitchell Electric Bond & Share's president merged the renamed Lehigh Valley Light & Power with six other utilities to form Pennsylvania Power & Light (PP&L) in Allentown in 1920. The next year PP&L became a subsidiary of National Power & Light.

PP&L bought more than 60 neighboring utilities in a decade and by 1930 industrial customers accounted for 70% of power sales. The company also built a 220000-volt transmission interconnection line with neighbors Philadelphia Electric (now PECO Energy a unit of Exelon) and Public Service Electric and Gas of New Jersey (now part of Public Service Enterprise Group). During the Depression the company offset falling industrial sales with residential sales.

The Public Utility Holding Company Act of 1935 forced large utility holding companies to streamline their businesses and by 1948 National Power & Light had unloaded PP&L.

To keep up with postwar demand PP&L built several coal-fired power plants. By 1964 industry still accounted for about a third of sales but suburbs assumed greater importance. PP&L began operating coal mines in the early 1970s and started building the Susquehanna nuclear plant.

Although its proprietary coal supply helped PP&L weather skyrocketing fuel costs in the 1970s huge construction delays endemic to nukes hit the utility for $4 billion by the time Susquehanna was completed in 1982. Flat sales in the late 1980s led to 2000 job cuts and to a reorganization by CEO William Hecht.

In 1992 the federal Energy Policy Act signaled the end of the monopoly era by promoting wholesale competition. PP&L formed Power Markets Development (now PPL Global) in 1994 to make energy investments worldwide. The next year it created holding company PP&L Resources to house both regulated and non-regulated businesses.

The Customer Choice Act was passed in Pennsylvania in 1996 ushering in competition and the utility formed its non-regulated retail power sales arm PP&L EnergyPlus. PP&L also bought 25% of Chile's Empresas Emel in 1997 (upped to 67% 1999). Fellow US utility Southern Company which bought UK utility SWEB in 1995 had turned over a 51% stake in SWEB to PP&L Resources by 1998.

PP&L Resources began buying mechanical contracting firms in 1998 to complement its electric business and it purchased natural gas and propane distributor Penn Fuel Gas.

In 1999 the company bought generating facilities with a total capacity of 1315 MW from Montana Power. Also that year PP&L Resources and Southern sold SWEB's supply business and the SWEB brand name to London Electricity a unit of Electricite de France. PP&L Resources and Southern retained their stakes in SWEB's distribution network which was renamed Western Power Distribution (later changed to WPD Holdings UK after it acquired British utility Hyder in 2000).

PP&L Resources changed its name to PPL Corporation in 2000 and reorganized into four major operating subsidiaries: PPL Utilities PPL EnergyPlus PPL Generation and PPL Global. PPL's restructuring efforts separated its regulated distribution operations from its non-regulated generation supply and services operations.

In 2002 PPL's Brazilian utility Companhia Energetica do Maranh?o (Cemar) filed for bankruptcy protection and fell under the control of the Brazilian government. (PPL divested its interest in Cemar in 2004.) Also in 2002 PPL purchased the remaining 49% stake in WPD Holdings UK (now Western Power Distribution Holdings) from Mirant (now GenOn Energy) for $235 million.

In 2007 the company sold its Latin American companies as well as its domestic telecommunications and synthetic fuels businesses.

In 2008 PPL sold its US propane and gas distribution unit.

EXECUTIVES

Chairman President and CEO Louisville Gas and Electric and Kentucky Utilities, Victor A. (Vic) Staffieri
SVP General Counsel and Secretary, Robert J. Grey, age 61, $425,110 total compensation
SVP Finance and Treasurer, James E. Abel, age 60
VP External Affairs, Joanne H. Raphael
President CEO and Director; President PPL Generation, William H. (Bill) Spence, age 55, $657,664 total compensation
President PPL Electric Utilities, Gregory N. (Greg) Dudkin, age 54
EVP and CFO, Paul A. Farr, age 44, $498,054 total compensation
President PPL Global and President PPL Energy Services Group, Rick L. Klingensmith, age 51
President PPL EnergyPlus, Robert D. (Rob) Gabbard
VP Customer Service PPL Gas Utilities, Robert M. Geneczko
General Manager Corporate Communications, Daniel J. (Dan) McCarthy
SVP PPL Fossil and Hydro Generation; President PPL Nuclear Development, Victor N. Lopiano, age 61
VP Risk Management and Chief Risk Officer, J. Matt Simmons Jr., age 46
VP and CIO, James E. (Jim) Schinski, age 52
President PPL Energy Supply and President PPL Generation, David G. (Dave) DeCampli, age 54
Senior Manager Corporate Communications, George Lewis
Manager Financial Communications, George E. Biechler
SVP Marketing EnergyPlus, Gene Alessandrini
VP and COO Western Fossil and Hydro PPL Generation, Pete Simonich
VP and Controller, Vincent (Vince) Sorgi, age 40
Manager Community Relations Susquehanna, Joseph J. Scopelliti
Director Investor Relations, Joseph P. Bergstein
Director, John W. Conway, age 66
Director, Steven G. (Steve) Elliott, age 65
President CEO and Director; President PPL Generation, William H. (Bill) Spence, age 55
Director, Louise K. Goeser, age 59
Director, Frederick M. Bernthal, age 69
Director, Stuart Heydt, age 72
Director, Stuart E. (Stu) Graham, age 66
Director, Natica von Althann, age 61
Director, Keith H. Williamson, age 59
Director, Venkata Raja Rajamannar Madabhushi, age 50
Auditors: Ernst&YoungLLP

LOCATIONS

HQ: PPL Corporation
2 N. 9th St., Allentown PA 18101-1179
Phone: 610-774-5151 **Fax:** 610-774-4198
Web: www.pplweb.com

2011 Sales

	$ mil.	% of total
US	11,084	87
UK	1,653	13
Total	**12,737**	**100**

PRODUCTS/OPERATIONS

2011 Sales

	$ mil.	% of total
Utility	6,292	49
Wholesale energy marketing	5,214	41
Unregulated retail electric & gas	726	6
Energy-related businesses	507	4
Net energy trading margins	(2)	-
Total	**12,737**	**100**

Selected Subsidiaries

PPL Development Corporation (acquisition and divestiture activities)
PPL Electric Utilities Corporation (electricity distribution)
PPL Energy Supply (nonregulated operations)
 PPL EnergyPlus LLC (wholesale and retail energy marketing)
 PPL Generation LLC (electricity generation)
  PPL Montana LLC (electricity generation)
 PPL Global LLC (international utility operations)
  Western Power Distribution Holdings Limited (formerly WPD Holdings UK electricity distribution)
PPL Services Corporation (shared services for PPL Corp. and other subsidiaries)

Selected Mergers & Acquisitions

2012
 AES Ironwood and AES Prescott ($302 million; Lebanon PA; natural gas-fired power plant)
2011
 WPD Midlands Holdings ($5.7 billion; UK; electric distribution)
2010
 E.ON.US ($7.6 billion; Kentucky; Louisville Gas & Electric and Kentucky Utilities)

COMPETITORS

ABB
AEP
Canadian Utilities
Centrica
Con Edison
Constellation Energy Group
Covanta
Delmarva Power
Dominion Resources
Duke Energy
Duquesne Light Holdings
EnergySolve
Exelon
FirstEnergy
Green Mountain Energy
HC Energia
Iberdrola USA
Maine & Maritimes
Midwest Generation
Ontario Power Generation
Orange & Rockland Utilities
Pepco Holdings
Public Service Enterprise Group
Scottish and Southern Energy
South Jersey Industries
Southern Company
TransAlta
UIL Holdings

HISTORICAL FINANCIALS

Company Type: Public

Income Statement

FYE: December 31

	REVENUE ($ mil.)	NET INCOME ($ mil.)	NET PROFIT MARGIN	EMPLOYEES
12/11	12,737	1,495	11.7%	17,722
12/10	8,521	938	11.0%	14,000
12/09	7,556	407	5.4%	10,489
12/08	8,044	930	11.6%	10,554
12/07	6,498	1,288	19.8%	11,149
Annual Growth	18.3%	3.8%	—	12.3%

2011 Year-End Financials

Debt ratio: 43.54%
Return on equity: 13.81%
Cash ($ mil.): 1,202
Current ratio: 122.28
Long-term debt ($ mil.): 17,993
No. of shares (mil.): 578
Dividends
 Yield: —
 Payout: 51.85%
Market value ($ mil.): 17,017

	STOCK PRICE ($) FY Close	P/E High	P/E Low	PER SHARE ($) Earnings	Dividends	Book Value
12/11	29.42	11	9	2.70	0.00	18.72
12/10	26.32	15	11	2.17	1.40	16.98
12/09	32.31	32	23	1.08	1.38	14.57
12/08	30.69	22	12	2.47	1.34	14.34
12/07	52.09	16	10	3.35	1.22	15.69
Annual Growth	(13.3%)	—	—	(5.2%)	—	4.5%

PPL Energy Supply, LLC

LOCATIONS

HQ: PPL Energy Supply, LLC
Two North Ninth Street, Allentown, PA 18101-1179
Phone: 610 774-5151
Web: www.pplweb.com

HISTORICAL FINANCIALS

Company Type:

Income Statement

FYE: December 31

	REVENUE ($ mil.)	NET INCOME ($ mil.)	NET PROFIT MARGIN	EMPLOYEES
12/10	6,429	768	11.9%	4,676
12/09	5,889	861	14.6%	7,128
12/08	6,132	246	4.0%	7,054
12/07	6,572	768	11.7%	6,950
Annual Growth	(0.7%)	(0.0%)	—	(12.4%)

2010 Year-End Financials

Debt ratio: 25.98%—
Return on equity: 19.11%
Cash ($ mil.): 379
Current ratio: 132.19
Long-term debt ($ mil.): 3,024
Dividends
 Yield: —
 Payout: —
Market value ($ mil.): —

	STOCK PRICE ($) FY Close	P/E High	P/E Low	PER SHARE ($) Earnings	Dividends	Book Value
12/10	25.98	—	—	(0.00)	0.00	(0.00)
12/09	26.41	—	—	(0.00)	1.75	(0.00)
12/08	24.80	—	—	(0.00)	1.75	(0.00)
12/07	24.80	—	—	(0.00)	1.75	(0.00)
Annual Growth	1.6%	—	—	—	—	—

Praxair, Inc.

Praxair makes lighter than air and heavier than air gases available for practical applications. The largest North American industrial gas supplier it produces and sells atmospheric gases (oxygen nitrogen argon and rare gases) as well as process and specialty gases (CO2 helium and hydrogen) for the chemicals food and beverage semiconductor and healthcare industries worldwide. Its Praxair Surface Technologies unit supplies high-temperature and corrosion-resistant metallic ceramic and powder coatings mainly to the aircraft plastics and primary metals markets. Depending on a customer's needs Praxair can build an on-site gas plant or provide gases by the cylinder.

HISTORY

The origins of Praxair date to the work of Karl von Linde a professor of mechanical engineering at the College of Technology in Munich Germany in the late 1800s. In 1895 he created the cryogenic air liquefier. Von Linde built his first oxygen-production plant in 1902 and a nitrogen plant in 1904 and in the first decade of the 20th century he built a number of air-separation plants throughout Europe.

By 1907 von Linde had moved to the US and founded Linde Air Products in Cleveland to extract oxygen from air. Linde Air Products joined rival Union Carbide in 1911 in experimenting with the production of acetylene; it became a unit of Union Carbide in 1917. America's war effort and economic expansion in the 1920s spurred the development of new uses for industrial gases. Union Carbide's Linde unit also contributed to the development of the atomic bomb in the 1940s when its scientists perfected a process for refining uranium.

As Union Carbide expanded worldwide over the next two decades Linde became America's #1 producer of industrial gases. In the 1960s Linde expanded into oxygen-fired furnaces for steel production and the use of nitrogen in refrigerators. By the early 1980s Linde accounted for 11% of Union Carbide's annual sales.

The disastrous 1984 chemical accident at Union Carbide's plant in Bhopal India coupled with heavy debt and falling sales forced Union Carbide to reorganize. In 1992 Linde was spun off as Praxair. William Lichtenberger former president of Union Carbide headed the new company and pushed global expansion. Two years later Praxair set up China's first helium transfill plants for medical magnetic resonance imaging. In 1995 the company began operations in India and Peru.

In 1996 Praxair Surface Technologies bought Miller Thermal (thermal spray coatings) and Maxima Air Separation Center (industrial and specialty gases Israel). Also that year the company picked up $60 million when it sold the Linde name and trademark to Linde a German engineering and industrial gas company. Praxair purchased and then spun off Chicago Bridge & Iron. The company kept only its Liquid Carbonic division the world's leading supplier of carbon dioxide for processing. The move opened up a new market in carbonated beverages for Praxair.

In 1997 and 1998 Praxair constructed plants and to control its own delivery systems acquired 20 packaged-gases distributors in the US and one in Germany. The company also formed a joint venture in China to produce high-purity nitrogen and other specialty gases for electronics and then teamed up with rival L'Air Liquide in a production joint venture.

Praxair supplied an argon-based protection system for the Shroud of Turin's public display in Italy in 1998. It also installed the industry's first small on-site hydrogen-generating system at an Indiana powdered-metals plant. In 1999 the company formed a global alliance with German pharmaceutical and chemicals company Merck KGaA to provide gases and chemicals to the semiconductor industry. The same year Praxair acquired Materials Research Corporation a maker of thin-film deposition materials for semiconductors and the TAFA Group which makes thermal-spray equipment and related products.

In 2001 Praxair underwent a restructuring that included layoffs in its surface technologies unit (hurt by the decline in jet orders) and Brazilian operations. The next year the company started work on a new plant to serve Singapore's high-tech industry. Praxair boosted its health care segment with the acquisition of Alpine Medicine.

In 2004 Praxair Healthcare Services bought Home Care Supply for $245 million. With Home Care Supply joining the company's existing operations the combined Healthcare Services unit grew its sales to $750 million worldwide slightly more than 10% of Praxair's total annual sales. The home care market became more important for Praxair as the company saw high growth potential in it (and high margins) and wanted to be able to compete with rivals L'Air Liquide and Air Products and Chemicals.

The company bought some of L'Air Liquide's German assets for about $650 million later that year. Due to antitrust requirements the French company needed to dispose of the businesses after buying much of Messer Group earlier in the year. The acquisition put Praxair's European sales over $1 billion annually.

In 2006 Praxair sold the aviation repair business of the Surface Technologies unit to Gridiron Capital and Skyview Capital. The firms created a new company called PAS Technologies to house operations that serve both the commercial and military sectors with the repair of aviation engine and airframe parts and the application of protective coatings to those parts. Also that year Praxair's distribution unit acquired Medical Gas of Illinois and Withrow Oxygen Service of California.

Praxair expanded its presence in the Middle East in 2010 by acquiring a 49% stake in the ROC Group's operations in Kuwait United Arab Emirates and Qatar.

EXECUTIVES

EVP and CFO, James S. (Jim) Sawyer, age 55, $550,000 total compensation
VP Communications and Public Relations; President The Praxair Foundation, Nigel D. Muir
VP Strategic Planning and Marketing, Sunil Mattoo
VP Marketing and Business Development North American Industrial Gases, Scott K. Sanderude
VP Human Resources, Sally A. Savoia
VP; President Praxair Distribution, George P. Ristevski, age 52
VP and Treasurer, Michael J. (Mike) Allan
Chairman President and CEO, Stephen F. (Steve) Angel, age 56, $1,035,000 total compensation
SVP; President White Martins Gases Industriais Ltda., Domingos H. G. Bulus, age 50
VP and Controller, Elizabeth T. (Liz) Hirsch
EVP; President North American Industrial Gases Mexico businesses and Praxair Distribution, Eduardo F. Menezes, age 48
President Global Hydrogen, Daniel H. (Dan) Yankowski
VP Global Supply Systems, Murray G. Covello
President Praxair Surface Technologies, Mark F. Gruninger, age 47
President Praxair Healthcare Services, Scott W. Kaltrider
President Praxair Mexico & Central America, Murilo Melo
President Praxair Distribution, John M. Panikar
SVP General Counsel and Corporate Secretary, James T. (Jim) Breedlove, age 64, $460,000 total compensation
President Praxair China, David H. Chow
SVP and CTO, Raymond P. (Ray) Roberge
VP Mergers and Acquisitions, Richard L. (Rick) Steinseifer
President Asia; President Electronica, Anne K. Roby
Media Contact, Susan Szita Gore
Media Contact, Ruthann Kidd
VP Global Procurement and Materials Management, Barry G. McGinley
EVP; President Praxair Asia Praxair Europe and Russia Praxair Surface Technologies Strategic Planning and Global Procurement and Materials Management, Scott E. Telesz
President Praxair Asia, Joseph S. (Joe) Cappello, age 46
VP Tax, Timothy S. (Tim) Heenan
Managing Director Praxair India, Gajanan Nabar
Director Investor Relations, Kelcey E. Hoyt
Director Global Information Security and Chief Security Officer, Ramachandra Hedge
Director, Raymond W. LeBoeuf, age 65
Director, Ira D. Hall, age 67
Director, Wayne T. Smith, age 66
Director, Edward G. (Ed) Galante, age 61
Director, Claire W. Gargalli, age 69
Director, Robert L. Wood, age 57
Director, Oscar de Paula Bernardes Neto, age 66
Director, Nance K. Dicciani, age 64
Director, Larry D. McVay, age 64
Auditors: PricewaterhouseCoopersLLP

LOCATIONS

HQ: Praxair Inc.
39 Old Ridgebury Rd., Danbury CT 06810-5113
Phone: 203-837-2000 **Fax:** 800-772-9985
Web: www.praxair.com

2011 Sales

	$ mil.	% of total
North America	5,531	49
Europe	1,448	13
Surface Technologies	648	6

PRODUCTS/OPERATIONS

2011 Sales by End Market

	$ mil.	% of total
Manufacturing	24	
Energy	11	
Electronics	9	
Food & Beverage	6	
Other	11	

2011 Sales by Distribution Method

Merchant (delivered liquids)	32	
On-site (includes noncryogenics)	25	
Total	**0**	**100**

Selected Products and Services

Atmospheric Gases
- Argon
- Nitrogen
- Oxygen
- Rare gases

Process Gases

Acetylene
Carbon dioxide
Carbon monoxide
Electronic gases
Helium
Hydrogen
Specialty gases

Surface Technologies

Ceramic coatings and powders
Electric arc plasma and high-velocity oxygen fuel spray equipment
Industrial gas-production equipment
Metallic coatings and powders

Selected Subsidiaries

Home Care Supply Inc.
Praxair Asia Inc. (China)
Praxair Canada Inc.
Praxair Europe Finance-Consultadoria e Projectos Lda. (Portugal)
Praxair Healthcare Services Inc.
Praxair Mexico Holdings S. de R.L. de C.V.
Praxair Puerto Rico LLC
Praxair Surface Technologies Inc.
White Martins Gases Industriais Ltda. (Brazil)

COMPETITORS

Air Products
Airgas
Balchem
Chromalloy Gas Turbine
GKN Aerospace
Chem-tronics
L' Air Liquide
Teleflex
The Linde Group

HISTORICAL FINANCIALS

Company Type: Public

Income Statement FYE: December 31

	REVENUE ($ mil.)	NET INCOME ($ mil.)	NET PROFIT MARGIN	EMPLOYEES
12/11	11,252	1,672	14.9%	26,184
12/10	10,116	1,195	11.8%	26,261
12/09	8,956	1,254	14.0%	26,164
12/08	10,796	1,211	11.2%	26,936
12/07	9,402	1,177	12.5%	27,992
Annual Growth	4.6%	9.2%	—	(1.7%)

2011 Year-End Financials

Debt ratio: 40.12%
Return on equity: 30.47%
Cash ($ mil.): 90
Current ratio: 102.84
Long-term debt ($ mil.): 5,838
No. of shares (mil.): 298
Dividends
Yield: —
Payout: 36.70%
Market value ($ mil.): 31,913

	STOCK PRICE ($) FY Close	P/E High/Low		PER SHARE ($) Earnings	Dividends	Book Value
12/11	106.90	20	16	5.45	0.00	18.38
12/10	95.47	25	19	3.84	1.80	19.05
12/09	80.31	21	13	4.01	1.60	17.34
12/08	59.36	26	12	3.80	1.50	13.06
12/07	88.71	25	16	3.62	1.20	16.30
Annual Growth	4.8%	—	—	10.8%	—	3.0%

Precision Castparts Corp.

Though it has expertise in casting you won't find Precision Castparts Corp. (PCC) offering Hollywood stars any movie roles. The company is a maker of investment castings used in jet aircraft satellite launches armaments and medical applications (prostheses). Its Investment Cast products segment makes jet engine parts fluid management valves and deep-hole boring tools. Forged Products and Fastener Products round out the company's three segments and cover the power generation and paper and pulp industries as well as general industry. PCC traces its history back to the 1950s.

HISTORY

The history of Precision Castparts Corp. (PCC) is not as precise as its castings. The Oregon Saw Company was founded in 1949 and sold in 1953; its buyer wanted neither the future PCC nor a power tools unit so the two became Omark Industries. In 1956 a buyer purchased the power tool business but wasn't interested in castings; that operation was spun off as Precision Castparts Corp.

In the early 1950s a group of Oregon Saw's casting employees developed a process for producing parts as large as 60 inches by use of investment casting making products that rivaled the strength of forged and machined parts at a fraction of the cost. After a two-year search they landed their first aerospace customer –Air Research Corp. –with many to follow. The higher operating temperatures generated by aircraft engines led the company to buy a vacuum furnace in 1959 to fabricate parts that could tolerate greater heat; two more vacuum furnaces were added and sales vaulted toward $10 million by 1967. PCC went public in 1968 and continued to grow. In 1976 the company acquired Centaur Cast Alloys (small investment castings UK) to make parts for the European aerospace industry. By that time General Electric (GE) and Pratt & Whitney accounted for most of PCC's business. Edward Cooley who had masterminded the company's growth since incorporation forged ahead with plans to double production capacity.

In 1980 the airline industry crashed but PCC's sales held at about $90 million. Structural airplane products soon picked up and in 1984 the company bought two titanium foundries in France. To diversify it added TRW's cast airfoils (used in aircraft engines and industrial gas turbines) division in 1986. That acquisition renamed PCC Airfoils increased PCC's annual sales by about 80%; sales reached $443 million by 1989.

The company broadened its offerings again in 1991 when it acquired Advanced Forming Technology which made small complex metal-injection molded parts used in everything from adding machines to military ordnance. The early 1990s recession hit the airline industry and sales dropped. Cooley retired as chairman in 1994 and GE veteran William McCormick replaced him. The next year PCC acquired Quamco Inc. (industrial tools and machines). In 1996 PCC flowed into the fluid management market with the acquisition of NEWFLO for about $300 million.

In 1997 PCC spent $437 million to acquire seven more companies that helped boost sales 75% from 1996 levels. The next year it purchased four metalworking companies that served industries other than aerospace. Having reduced dependence on sales to the aerospace industry to just over 50% PCC began consolidating operations and closing plants to reduce costs.

The company continued to diversify through acquisitions in 1999 but it also expanded its aerospace operations with the purchase of Wyman-Gordon a leading maker of advanced metal forgings for the aerospace market. PCC's 2000 acquisitions included the aerospace division of United Engineering Forgings and Germany-based Convey Engineering (heavy-duty valves). The next year the company bought the assets of Netherlands-based Wouter Witzel and the US's Drop Dies and Forgings Company (renamed Wyman-Gordon Cleveland). In 2002 PCC bought the rest of Western Australian Specialty Alloys (casting and forging alloys) for $27.6 million in cash and PCC shares.

In 2003 Precision Castparts' PCC Structurals unit reached a $400 million agreement with Rolls-Royce to supply large titanium and steel castings. That year the company acquired SPS Technologies a producer of fasteners and other metal components for the aerospace automotive and industrial markets. In 2004 subsidiary SPS Aerospace Fasteners signed a four-year deal with Airbus worth about $72 million to supply collars nuts studs and titanium pins to Airbus plants across Europe.

PCC acquired Air Industries Corporation in early 2005. In 2006 PCC bought Special Metals Corporation (SMC) a maker of nickel alloys and super alloys for $295 million in cash and the assumption of $245 million in SMC debt. PCC intended to use SMC's product as raw materials for its own aircraft engine components. SMC also served the automotive chemical and power generation industries.

Later in 2006 PCC bought Shur-Lok Corporation a manufacturer of aerospace fasteners for about $110 million. The acquisition combined with the 2005 purchase of Air Industries Corporation helped to further PCC's desire to grow its airframe fasteners business.

Early in 2007 PCC completed the purchase of GSC a leading maker of aluminum and steel structural investment casting for the aerospace energy and medical markets. It also acquired Cherry Aerospace which expanded its fastener products portfolio.

In 2009 the company acquired Carlton Forge Works which makes aircraft engines for Boeing and Airbus; California-based Arcturus Manufacturing (hammer forging operations) was included in the transaction. PCC also picked up Airdrome Holdings (fluid fittings) Fatigue Technology (cold expansion technology) and Hackney Ladish (forged pipe fittings) in 2009.

EXECUTIVES

SVP CFO and Assistant Secretary, Shawn R. Hagel, age 46, $510,000 total compensation
Chairman and CEO, Mark Donegan, age 55, $1,366,875 total compensation
SVP General Counsel and Secretary, Roger A. Cooke, age 64, $460,000 total compensation
VP and CIO, Byron J. Gaddis, age 55
SVP Corporate Training and Organizational Development, John W. Ericksen, age 50
SVP New Business Integration, Steven G. (Steve) Hackett, age 55, $510,000 total compensation
Director Communications, Dwight E. Weber
EVP; President Forged Products, Kenneth D. (Ken) Buck, age 52, $527,497 total compensation

SVP; President Structurals Casting Operations, Ross M. Lienhart, age 58, $327,512 total compensation
VP Strategic Planning and Corporate Development, Kirk G. Pulley, age 43
VP Corporate Controller and Assistant Secretary, Russell S. Pattee, age 48
SVP, Joseph I. Snowden, age 55, $356,347 total compensation
VP Treasurer and Assistant Secretary, Steven C. Blackmore, age 50
VP Corporate Taxes and Assistant Secretary, Roger P. Becker, age 58
EVP; President Fastener Products, Kevin M. Stein, age 46, $436,250 total compensation
VP Internal Audit, Mark E. Ellis, age 52
President PCC Airfoils, John P. O'Neill
VP Chief Compliance Officer and Deputy General Counsel, Emi A. Donis
Director, Don R. Graber, age 68
Director, Vernon E. Oechsle, age 69
Director, Richard L. Wambold, age 60
Director, Steven G. (Steve) Rothmeier, age 65
Director, Gen. Lester L. Lyles, age 65
Director, Ulrich R. (Rick) Schmidt, age 62
Director, Timothy A. (Tim) Wicks, age 46
Director, Daniel J. Murphy, age 64
Auditors: Deloitte&ToucheLLP

LOCATIONS

HQ: Precision Castparts Corp.
4650 SW Macadam Ave. Ste. 300, Portland OR 97239-4262
Phone: 503-417-4800 **Fax:** 503-417-4817
Web: www.precast.com

2012 Sales

	$ mil.	% of total
US	5,952	83
Other countries	465	6

PRODUCTS/OPERATIONS

2012 Sales

	$ mil.	% of total
Forged products	3,189	44
Fastener products	1,698	24

Selected Mergers and Acquisitions

FY2012
- Titanium Metals Corporation ($2.9 billion; Dallas; maker of melted mill and fabricated titanium products)
- Klune Industries (North Hollywood California; maker of aluminum nickel titanium and steel aerostructures)
- RathGibson (Lincolnshire Illinois; maker of welded finished stainless steel and special alloy pipe and tubing)
- Heroux-Devtek ($296 million; Quebec Canada; supplier of landing gears and landing gear products)

FY2011
- Primus International ($900 million; Algona Washington; maker of complex metal industrial parts and assemblies)
- Unison Engine Components operating as Tru-Form Rings (maker of flash-weld and cold-rolled rings used in jet/gas turbine engines)

Selected Products and Services

Fasteners
- Advanced forming technology
- E/One (for the disposal of residential sanitary waste)
- J&L fiber services (for pulp and paper industry)
- PCC Precision Tool Group
- SPS aerospace fasteners (for commercial/military aircraft)
- SPS engineered fasteners (high strength for automotive and construction applications)

Forged products
- Special Metals Corporation
- Wyman-Gordon Forgings

Investment Cast Products
- PCC Airfoils (high-temperature blades and vanes)
- PCC Structurals (structural investment castings)
- Specialty materials and alloys (alloys waxes and metal processing for investment casting)

COMPETITORS

Alcoa
Allegheny Technologies
ATI Ladish
Carpenter Technology
Chicago Rivet
Crane Co.
Curtiss-Wright
ESCO
Farwest Steel Corporation
Federal Screw Works
Georg Fischer
Goodrich Corp.
Haynes International
Hitachi Metals
Kennametal
LISI
Mettis Aerospace
SOURIAU PA&E
Sumitomo Metal Industries
Swagelok
Teleflex
ThyssenKrupp
United Technologies
Universal Stainless
V & M Tubes (USA)
Volvo Aero

HISTORICAL FINANCIALS

Company Type: Public

Income Statement FYE: April 1

	REVENUE ($ mil.)	NET INCOME ($ mil.)	NET PROFIT MARGIN	EMPLOYEES
04/12	7,214	1,224	17.0%	21,500
04/11*	6,220	1,013	16.3%	18,308
03/10	5,486	921	16.8%	18,064
03/09	6,827	1,044	15.3%	20,611
03/08	6,852	987	14.4%	21,400
Annual Growth	1.3%	5.5%	—	0.1%

*Fiscal year change

2012 Year-End Financials

Debt ratio: 1.97%
Return on equity: 14.64%
Cash ($ mil.): 698
Current ratio: 353.52
Long-term debt ($ mil.): 207
No. of shares (mil.): 145
Dividends
Yield: —
Payout: 1.43%
Market value ($ mil.): 25,115

	STOCK PRICE ($) FY Close	P/E High/Low		PER SHARE ($) Earnings	Dividends	Book Value
04/12	172.90	21	16	8.41	0.00	57.56
04/11*	149.61	21	14	7.04	0.00	49.83
03/10	123.82	19	9	6.49	0.00	41.50
03/09	63.12	17	6	7.43	0.00	34.74
03/08	101.35	22	13	7.04	0.00	29.09
Annual Growth	14.3%	—	—	4.5%	—	18.6%

*Fiscal year change

Priceline.com, Inc.

riceline.com would like to name itself the king of online travel. At priceline.com buyers can "name their own price" for airline tickets hotel rooms rental cars cruises and vacation packages. Customers can also choose set-price options. With its patented business model priceline.com generates most of its revenue from travel-related services. In the case of airline tickets and hotel reservations priceline.com generates sales on the margin keeping the difference between the price paid by the individual and what priceline.com shelled out for the ticket or hotel room. Founded in 1997 the company operates its business through the Booking.com priceline.com rentalcars.com and Agoda brand names.

Adding to its operations priceline has agreed to acquire its smaller rival Kayak Software for $1.8 billion in cash and stock. The deal which is expected to close in early 2013 is the largest in priceline's history and could provide a new source of revenue (advertising) for the company. Kayak Software is an online travel comparison and booking site that makes most of its money from referrals and advertising.

Like many companies focused on travel priceline.com saw fewer customers hit the road and take to the skies when the economy took a dive. But based on the company's business model its profit margins rise when travel partners discount their rates. Post-recession however the threat of slimmer profit margins as travel picks up has the company banking on international markets for growth. The move has enabled priceline.com to build on its global offering and boost its main metric: the number of room nights booked. Most of this business comes from commissions earned from hotel reservations. The online travel retailer which offers hotel room reservations at more than 210000 hotels worldwide attributes its international success to the hotel market which isn't as consolidated as it is in the US and to the company's strategy of targeting smaller independent hotels and chains with set prices.

The strategy has worked so far. While priceline.com generated 40% of its 2011 revenue in the US that's down significantly from 64% in 2009. priceline.com is seeing more success in its international business (primarily driven by its Booking.com unit) which represented about 78% of its 2011 gross bookings (the total dollar value typically including all taxes and fees of travel services purchased by customers) and some 88% of operating income. Its businesses in the Netherlands the UK and Asia have boosted its bottom line. Looking to invest further in its international effort priceline.com purchased TravelJigsaw an international car rental reservation service that it later renamed rentalcars.com.

In the cut-throat travel industry the company keeps an eye on its rivals and its marketing strategy as more consumers book their own travel online. When priceline.com in 2007 eliminated processing fees for certain airline tickets and reduced processing fees for some merchant hotel room services competitors Expedia Travelocity and Orbitz followed suit with similar deals in 2008 and 2009.

Not everyone who hooks up with priceline.com gets his or her ticket to ride however. The company limits how it accepts offers. priceline.com considers an individual's named price for a plane ticket "reasonable" if it's no more than 30% lower than the lowest fare for the route.

HISTORY

riceline.com founder Jay Walker launched a string of ventures before making the leap into e-commerce. In 1994 he founded Walker Digital an entrepreneurial think tank formed to develop business models that could germinate into new companies.

In 1996 Walker Digital found the impetus that would drive priceline.com: Each day major airlines have more than 500000 empty seats. Walker's team reasoned that if the airlines were offered even a discounted price for these empty seats they'd jump at the chance to cut their losses. Based on that premise Walker Digital developed a "name your price" system and founded priceline.com in 1997.

The company launched its airfare service in 1998 and obtained financing from General Atlantic Partners and Paul Allen's Vulcan Ventures (now called Vulcan Northwest). That year it expanded into hotel reservations and added a car-buying service. Richard Braddock became chairman and CEO in 1998.

priceline.com added home financing services to its offerings in 1999. The company went public with a chart-busting IPO later that year. priceline.com also launched a rental car service. Branching into the retail arena it licensed its technology to WebHouse Club for use in selling grocery products. The company sued Microsoft in 1999 claiming that company's Expedia unit's name-your-own-price hotel reservation service violated priceline.com's patent.

In 2000 the company licensed its business model to several international ventures including General Atlantic Partners' Priceline.com Europe (headed by Dennis Malamatinas former Burger King CEO) SOFTBANK's Priceline.com Japan (a deal that was later cancelled) MyPrice in Australia and New Zealand (also cancelled) and Asian conglomerate Hutchinson Whampoa. In collaboration with Alliance Capital (now AllianceBernstein) priceline.com created subsidiary pricelinemortgage to act as mortgage broker.

Daniel Schulman became CEO later that year. Jay Walker resigned as vice chairman at the end of 2000 after taking on the role of CEO at Walker Digital. After deciding it would probably never be profitable WebHouse Club shut down ending priceline.com's foray into grocery sales. Known for its splashy ads priceline.com dumped pop icon William Shatner as its TV spokesperson in favor of "Sex and the City" star Sarah Jessica Parker. (Shatner returned in 2002.) Later that year the company fired Schulman and reappointed Braddock as CEO.

In 2002 the company joined with National Leisure Group to offer cruises from its website. Later that year priceline.com purchased the assets of discount travel site Lowestfare.com. It also announced plans to sell cars under a marketing agreement with Autobytel. In late 2002 Braddock passed his CEO responsibilities to president Jeffery Boyd. (Braddock remained as chairman.)

A handful of new international destinations (Australia Japan Indonesia Malaysia South Korea Taiwan) was added in 2003 to priceline.com's hotel reservation service. In April 2004 chairman Richard Braddock (former president of Citicorp and one of the last remaining high-profile board members resigned from the company. Director Ralph Bahna was then named chairman. The following month priceline.com acquired most of Travelweb.com. That September it bought Active Hotels of Britain for about $161 million in cash. In December 2004 priceline.com acquired the remaining stake in Travelweb for about $4 million.

EXECUTIVES

President CEO and Director, Jeffery H. (Jeff) Boyd, age 55, $550,000 total compensation
CEO priceline.com North America; President North American Travel, Christopher L. (Chris) Soder, age 52, $330,000 total compensation
CIO North America, Michael Diliberto
Chairman, Ralph M. Bahna, age 69
Chief Marketing Officer, Brett Keller, age 44
EVP General Counsel and Corporate Secretary, Peter J. Millones Jr., age 42, $320,000 total compensation
EVP Corporate Development; Head Worldwide Strategy and Planning, Glenn D. Fogel, age 50
SVP Hotels, Tim Gordon
SVP CFO and Chief Accounting Officer, Daniel J. Finnegan, age 50, $315,000 total compensation
Chairman Agoda; Managing Director Australia and New Zealand Booking.com B.V., Adrian Currie
Chairman Booking.com B.V., Kees Koolen, age 46, $362,297 total compensation
SVP Finance and Investor Relations, Matthew N. Tynan, age 36
CEO Agoda, Robert Rosenstein, age 45
Director, Craig W. Rydin, age 60
Director, James M. Guyette
Director, Jeffrey E. (Jeff) Epstein, age 55
President CEO and Director, Jeffery H. (Jeff) Boyd, age 55
Director, Jan L. Docter, age 62
Director, Nancy B. Peretsman, age 58
Director, Howard W. (Skip) Barker Jr., age 65
Auditors: Deloitte&ToucheLLP

LOCATIONS

HQ: priceline.com Incorporated
800 Connecticut Ave., Norwalk CT 06854-9998
Phone: 203-299-8000 **Fax:** 203-299-8948
Web: www.priceline.com

2011 Sales

US	1,761	40
UK	709	16

PRODUCTS/OPERATIONS

2011 Sales

	$ mil.	% of total
Agency	2,339	54
Other	11	—

Selected Products

Airline tickets
Cruises
Hotel rooms
Rental cars
Vacation packages

COMPETITORS

Amadeus IT
American Express
Autobytel
AutoNation
AutoTrader
BCD Travel
Carlson Wagonlit
Expedia
Facebook
GetThere
Google
Groupon
Hotels.com
Hotwire Inc.
Internet Brands
Intuit
Kayak Software
last minute network
Microsoft
Orbitz Worldwide
Prestige Travel
Sabre Holdings
Travelocity
Travelport
Travelzoo
TripAdvisor
TUI Travel
Yahoo!

HISTORICAL FINANCIALS

Company Type: Public

Income Statement FYE: December 31

	REVENUE ($ mil.)	NET INCOME ($ mil.)	NET PROFIT MARGIN	EMPLOYEES
12/11	4,355	1,059	24.3%	5,000
12/10	3,084	528	17.1%	3,400
12/09	2,338	489	20.9%	2,010
12/08	1,884	193	10.3%	1,780
12/07	1,409	157	11.1%	1,324
Annual Growth	32.6%	61.1%	—	39.4%

2011 Year-End Financials

Debt ratio: 12.53%
Return on equity: 41.14%
Cash ($ mil.): 632
Current ratio: 277.34
Long-term debt ($ mil.): —
No. of shares (mil.): 49
Dividends
Yield: —
Payout: —
Market value ($ mil.): 23,291

	STOCK PRICE ($) FY Close	P/E High	P/E Low	PER SHARE ($) Earnings	Dividends	Book Value
12/11	467.71	26	19	20.63	0.00	51.69
12/10	399.55	38	16	10.38	0.00	36.90
12/09	218.41	20	6	9.88	0.00	29.00
12/08	73.65	28	10	3.98	0.00	17.82
12/07	114.86	29	10	3.42	0.00	15.05
Annual Growth	42.1%	—	—	56.7%	—	36.1%

Principal Financial Group, Inc.

Ah the circle of life. For a child in elementary school avoiding the principal is paramount. However folks looking toward retirement may actually seek out The Principal. Founded in 1879 Principal Financial Group (or The Principal) is a top administrator of employer-sponsored retirement plans offering pension products and services as well as mutual funds annuities asset management trust services and investment advice. Its insurance segment provides group and individual life and disability insurance and group dental and vision coverage. To compete with banks encroaching on the company's territory and to maximize customer asset retention subsidiary Principal Bank offers online banking.

The Principal boasts more than 18 million customers and about $367 billion of assets under management. Its products are offered through a network of about 11600 independent brokers consultants and agents as well as through its own sales force at more than 40 offices nationwide.

With operations in about a dozen countries The Principal aims to become a global player in retirement services targeting countries in Asia and Latin America that rely on private-sector defined-contribution pension plans to accommodate their growing number of retirees. The company typically builds its international business through startups acquisitions and joint ventures. In 2012 the company made plans to acquire Chilean pension management firm AFP Cuprum S.A. for $1.5 billion. Pending regulatory hurdles The Principal hopes to close the deal during the first quarter of 2013. It has been lured by the attractive emerging retirement and long-term savings markets such as Chile Mexico and Brazil that AFP Cuprum serves. Also in 2012 the company bought 60% of Brazilian asset manager Claritas which has some $1.8 billion in assets under management. Prior to 2012 The Principal acquired pension fund manager AFORE in 2011 from HSBC; the deal added some 1.6 million customers and nearly $3 billion of assets under management in Mexico.

In the UK the company acquired hedge fund Finisterre Capital enhancing its emerging market investment capabilities in 2011. Also that year it bought a majority stake of Origin Asset Management a UK firm with some $2.6 billion in assets under management. Additionally The Principal has offices in Australia and Southeast Asia and a joint venture in China.

In the US The Principal courts firms with fewer than 1000 employees for its insurance and pension products; that market is primed for growth as a relatively low percentage of small to midsized businesses currently offer these products. Its strategy for growth also includes targeting large institutional clients for its asset management operations which include Principal Global Investors. The company serves approximately 650 institutional investors.

A rebound in the markets in 2010 and 2011 helped to boost The Principal's retirement and investor services segments and increase Principal Global Investors' assets under management leading to an uptick in profits. However the growth has been partially offset by the company's decision to exit the group medical insurance business.

It stopped selling medical insurance and entered into an agreement with UnitedHealthcare to renew medical insurance for existing customers. The Principal decided to cut the segment after it began to shrink in size compared to its other lines of business. The move allowed the company to sharpen its focus on asset management in the US and abroad.

In 2012 The Principal announced plans to buy First Dental Health a California-based preferred provider organization with more than 11000 dentists operating in the West.

HISTORY

Principal Financial was founded as the Bankers Life Association in 1879 by Edward Temple a Civil War veteran and banker. Life insurance became popular after the war but some dishonest insurers canceled customers' policies before they had to pay out benefits. Bankers Life an assessable association (members shared the cost of death benefits as the claims arose) was intended to provide low-cost protection to bankers and their families. The company soon began offering life insurance to non-bankers but it refused to insure women because of the high mortality rate among mothers during childbirth.

Bankers Life relied on volunteer workers until 1893. By 1900 it was operating in 21 states. Temple died in 1909 and two years later the company converted to a legal reserve mutual life insurance company with a new name: the Bankers Life Company. The conversion scared many customers away however. About 50000 policies were lost over the next three years. In 1915 Bankers Life began insuring women.

WWI slowed growth and the 1918-1919 influenza epidemic which killed many policyholders hit the company hard. The Depression also stunted growth. In 1941 the firm started offering group life insurance and during WWII it became a major force in that area.

Bankers Life grew through the 1950s and 1960s adding individual accident and health insurance (1952) and other products. In 1968 it began offering variable annuities for profit-sharing plans and mutual funds forming what are now Princor Financial Services and Principal Management. In 1977 Bankers Life introduced an adjustable life insurance product that allowed policyholders to change both premium costs and coverage.

In 1986 the company made a few name changes becoming The Principal Financial Group and renaming its largest unit Principal Mutual Life Insurance (now Principal Life Insurance). That year Principal Financial acquired Eppler Guerin & Turner the largest independent stock brokerage firm in the Southwest.

In 1993 Principal Financial was issued Mexico's first new insurance license in 50 years; subsequent expansion included Argentina China and Spain.

In 1996 Principal Financial expanded its health care operations purchasing third-party administrator The Admar Group. The next year the company bought the 76000-member FHP of Illinois health plan. Despite this fast buildup Principal Financial decided to exit the direct provision of health care; in 1997 it sold these operations to what is now Coventry Health Care for a 40% stake in the firm which it also later sold.

Continuing to refocus the company in 1998 sold its Principal Financial Securities brokerage and bought ReliaStar Mortgage to build a mortgage banking franchise. The company also launched online banking services. Also that year Principal Financial converted to a mutual holding structure. It formed joint ventures in such countries as Chile Mexico and India as part of its move into asset management overseas.

Principal Financial went public in 2001 when it started trading on the New York Stock Exchange.

As with its health care operations Principal Financial made a hasty exit from the mortgage business after building that part of its business through acquisitions. Amid rising interest rates and an industry-wide decrease in loan volume the company sold its retail mortgage branches to American Home Mortgage in 2003 then sold its remaining mortgage banking business to Citigroup the following year. Also in 2004 the company bolstered its core operations by purchasing health care claims processor J.F. Molloy & Associates and the US trust operations of Dutch banking giant ABN AMRO.

At the end of 2006 The Principal finalized its purchase of WM Advisors the former mutual fund operations of Washington Mutual.

EXECUTIVES

SVP and Chief Marketing Officer, Mary A. O'Keefe, age 55

President Retirement Insurance and Financial Services, Daniel J. (Dan) Houston, age 50, $427,312 total compensation

EVP and General Counsel, Karen E. Shaff, age 57

Chairman President and CEO, Larry D. Zimpleman, age 60, $741,539 total compensation

SVP and Chief Investment Officer, Julia M. Lawler, age 52

SVP and Secretary, Joyce Nixson Hoffman

President Global Asset Management; CEO Principal Global Investors, James P. (Jim) McCaughan, age 58, $523,712 total compensation

SVP and CIO, Gary P. Scholten, age 54

SVP Insurance Solutions, Deanna D. Strable

SVP Retirement and Investor Services; President Principal Funds, Nora M. Everett

SVP Retirement Distribution, Timothy J. (Tim) Minard

SVP Retirement and Investor Services, Gregory J. Burrows

SVP Human Resources and Corporate Services, Ralph C. Eucher

SVP and CFO, Terrance J. (Terry) Lillis, age 59, $295,689 total compensation

SVP and Chief Risk Officer, Gregory B. (Greg) Elming

President Principal Financial Group Latin America, Luis Valdes

SVP; President Principal International Asia, Rex Auyeung

SVP; COO Principal International, Ned A. Burmeister

SVP Strategy and Finance, Timothy N. (Tim) Dunbar

Director, Gary E. Costley, age 68

Director, Betsy J. Bernard, age 56

Director, Richard L. (Dick) Keyser, age 69

Director, Sandra L. (Sandy) Helton, age 62

Director, Michael T. Dan, age 61

Director, Elizabeth E. Tallett, age 63

Director, Jocelyn E. Carter-Miller, age 54

Director, C. Daniel Gelatt, age 64

Director, Arjun K. Mathrani, age 67

Director, Dennis H. Ferro, age 66

Auditors: Ernst&YoungLLP

LOCATIONS

HQ: Principal Financial Group Inc.
711 High St., Des Moines IA 50392
Phone: 515-247-5111 **Fax:** 515-246-5475
Web: www.principal.com

Selected Operations

Australia
Brazil
Chile
China
Hong Kong
India
Indonesia
Japan
Malaysia
Mexico
Singapore
Thailand
UK
US

PRODUCTS/OPERATIONS

2011 Sales

	$ mil.	% of total
Net investment income	3,375	38
Premiums & other considerations	2,891	32
Fees & other revenues	2,565	29
Net realized capital gains	75	1
Adjustments	(197.3)	-
Total	**8,709**	**100**

2011 Sales by Segment

	$ mil.	% of total
Retirement & Investor Services	4,074	45
US Insurance Solutions		
Specialty benefits insurance	1,507	16
Individual life insurance	1,476	16
Principal International	909	10
Exited group medical insurance business	606	7
Principal Global Investors	546	6
Adjustments	(411.0)	-
Total	**8,709**	**100**

COMPETITORS

Aetna
AIG
Allianz
AXA
BlackRock
FMR
ING
John Hancock Financial Services
JPMorgan Chase
Lincoln Financial Group
MassMutual
MetLife
Morgan Stanley Investment Management
PIMCO
T. Rowe Price
The Vanguard Group
Unum Group

HISTORICAL FINANCIALS

Company Type: Public

Income Statement FYE: December 31

	ASSETS ($ mil.)	NET INCOME ($ mil.)	INCOME AS % OF ASSETS	EMPLOYEES
12/11	148,298	715	0.5%	13,527
12/10	145,631	699	0.5%	13,627
12/09	137,759	622	0.5%	14,487
12/08	128,182	458	0.4%	16,234
12/07	154,520	860	0.6%	16,585
Annual Growth	(1.0%)	(4.5%)	—	(5.0%)

2011 Year-End Financials

Debt ratio: 1.06%
Return on equity: 7.42%
Cash ($ mil.): 2,833
Current ratio: —
Long-term debt ($ mil.): 1,564
No. of shares (mil.): 301
Dividends
Yield: —
Payout: 32.56%
Market value ($ mil.): 7,407

	STOCK PRICE ($) FY Close	P/E High	P/E Low	PER SHARE ($) Earnings	Dividends	Book Value
12/11	24.60	16	10	2.15	0.00	32.01
12/10	32.56	16	10	2.06	0.55	30.36
12/09	24.04	16	3	1.97	0.50	24.74
12/08	22.57	42	6	1.63	0.45	9.54
12/07	68.84	23	17	3.09	0.90	28.64
Annual Growth	(22.7%)	—	—	(8.7%)	—	2.8%

PrivateBancorp, Inc.

It's your private banker a banker for money and any old teller won't do. PrivateBancorp is the holding company for The PrivateBank and Trust which provides commercial and community banking business and real estate lending investments and money management services to middle-market companies commercial real estate professionals small business owners executives and wealthy individuals and their families. The bank has some 20 offices in the Chicago area and more than a dozen more than in the Atlanta Cleveland Denver Des Moines Detroit Milwaukee Minneapolis Kansas City St. Louis markets. Subsidiary The PrivateBank Mortgage Company originates residential mortgages.

PrivateBancorp's Lodestar Investment Counsel subsidiary provides trust and investment management services to families foundations and high-net-worth individuals with more than $500000 to invest. PrivateBancorp cross-sells its wealth management services to executives who have commercial banking relationships with the company.

Formerly modeled after a traditional European private bank PrivateBancorp launched a strategic plan in late 2007 in response to Bank of America's acquisition of Chicago-based LaSalle Bank hoping to capitalize on area consumers and middle-market firms alienated by the sale. Former LaSalle Bank CEO Larry Richman was named president and CEO of PrivateBancorp and PrivateBank that year. PrivateBancorp also recruited several other LaSalle executives.

As part of its effort to court midsized businesses PrivateBank has specialty banking groups devoted to the architecture construction and engineering health care and security alarm financing sectors. Targeting firms with up to $2 billion in annual revenues the bank has expanded its fee-based activities such as treasury management and capital markets services. Since the shift in focus to commercial lending PrivateBancorp has more than doubled its assets and loan portfolio and has nearly tripled its deposit base. Despite the growth which also includes increased revenues the company's bottom line has suffered however. PrivateBancorp has reported three consecutive years of losses largely due to sour real estate loans.

In 2009 the company grew by acquiring the deposits and assets of the failed Founders Bank in an FDIC-assisted transaction. The acquisition added 10 locations in Chicago's southwest suburbs to The PrivateBank and Trust's network. The company hopes is using the acquisition as a platform to build its community banking services for consumers and small businesses.

Chicago-based investment firm GTCR Golder Rauner owns nearly 15% of PrivateBancorp.

EXECUTIVES

Chairman, James M. Guyette
Controller, Paul R. Carey
Director External Reporting and Accounting Policy, Barbara E. Briick, age 48
CEO PrivateBank Milwaukee, Mark N. Lemke
Managing Director and Director Human Resources PrivateBank, Marcia A. Bowden
Managing Director; Head Business Banking, Thomas (Tom) Doherty
Managing Director and Senior Trust Officer PrivateBank, Ann Blickensderfer
Managing Director; Head Community Banking, Alan S. (Al) Adams
CEO Private Bank Georgia, Brian D. Schmitt, age 50
Executive Managing Director; President Commercial Real Estate, Karen B. Case, age 53, $56,435 total compensation
Executive Managing Director; President National Commercial Banking, Bruce R. Hague, age 57, $435,000 total compensation
Executive Managing Director; President Illinois Commercial and Specialty Banking, Bruce S. Lubin, age 58, $385,000 total compensation
CEO PrivateBank Michigan, Daniel Pehrson
Commercial Banking Officer PrivateBank Minneapolis, Seth E. Hove
Managing Director and CFO, Kevin M. Killips, age 56, $339,564 total compensation
Managing Director and Chief Credit Officer, Kevin J. Van Solkema, age 51, $246,333 total compensation
Managing Director and Chief Risk Officer, Leonard E. Wiatr
Managing Director and CIO PrivateBank, Elizabeth M. (Bess) Cummings, age 55
Managing Director; President Personal Client Services, C. Brant Ahrens, age 41
Managing Director and Chief Human Resources Officer PrivateBank, Joan A. Schellhorn, age 63
Director Communications, Amy K. Yuhn
Managing Director Commercial Banking PrivateBank, Michael T. Hopton
Managing Director General Counsel and Corporate Secretary, Jennifer R. Evans, age 53
Managing Director and Corporate Treasurer, Hammad Pirzada
CTO, James (Chip) Bennett
Managing Director; Head Private Wealth Group, Kristine R. (Kris) Garrett
Managing Director; Head Mortgage Banking, Richard (Rick) Bechtel
Managing Director Investor Relations, Beth Coronelli
Managing Director Compliance, Kimberly Adams-Ekwemoha
Managing Director; Head Retail Banking, Tom Bugielski
Director, Edward W. (Ed) Rabin Jr., age 65
Director, James C. Tyree, age 54
Director, Cheryl E. Mayberry McKissack, age 56
Director, William R. Rybak, age 61
Director, Robert F. Coleman, age 67
Director; Chairman PrivateBank and Trust, Norman R. (Norm) Bobins, age 69
Director, James B. (Jim) Nicholson, age 68
Director, Alejandro (Alex) Silva, age 64
Director, Collin E. Roche, age 41
Auditors: Ernst&YoungLLP

LOCATIONS

HQ: PrivateBancorp Inc.
120 S. LaSalle St., Chicago IL 60603
Phone: 312-564-2000 **Fax:** -10746
Web: www.infineum.com

PRODUCTS/OPERATIONS

2011 Sales

	$ mil.	% of total
Interest		
Loans including fees	413	72
Taxable securities	61	11
Other	6	1
Noninterest		
Loan and credit-related fees	22	4
Treasury management	19	3
Capital markets products	19	3
Trust and investments	17	3
Mortgage banking	6	1
Net securities gains	5	1
Other	6	1
Total	579	100

Selected Subsidiaries

The PrivateBank and Trust Company
BBH Financial Advisors Inc.
Lodestar Investment Counsel LLC
PB Real Estate LLC
PBTC & Company LLC
PRIVATESTAR LLC
TPB Title Agency LLC

COMPETITORS

Bank of America
CFS Bancorp
Citizens Republic Bancorp
First Midwest Bancorp
Harris
MB Financial
Northern Trust
Park Bancorp
Wintrust Financial

HISTORICAL FINANCIALS

Company Type: Public

Income Statement FYE: December 31

	ASSETS ($ mil.)	NET INCOME ($ mil.)	INCOME AS % OF ASSETS	EMPLOYEES
12/11	12,416	44	0.4%	1,045
12/10	12,465	1	0.0%	1,060
12/09	12,059	(30)	—	1,040
12/08	10,040	(92)	—	773
12/07	4,990	11	0.2%	597
Annual Growth	25.6%	39.2%	—	15.0%

2011 Year-End Financials

Debt ratio: 3.06%
Return on equity: 3.42%
Cash ($ mil.): 361
Current ratio: —
Long-term debt ($ mil.): 379
No. of shares (mil.): 71
Dividends
Yield: —
Payout: 9.30%
Market value ($ mil.): 788

	STOCK PRICE ($) FY Close	P/E High/Low		PER SHARE ($) Earnings	Dividends	Book Value
12/11	10.98	38	16	0.43	0.00	18.07
12/10	14.38	—	—	(0.17)	0.04	17.21
12/09	8.97	—	—	(0.95)	0.04	17.31
12/08	32.46	—	—	(3.13)	0.30	18.03
12/07	32.65	78	47	0.53	0.30	17.61
Annual Growth	(23.8%)	—	—	(5.1%)	—	0.6%

ProAssurance Corp.

ProAssurance protects professional health associates –the doctors dentists and nurses of the US. One of the largest medical liability insurance providers in the nation ProAssurance is the holding company for ProAssurance Indemnity ProAssurance Casualty and other subsidiaries that sell liability coverage for health care providers primarily in the South and Midwest. Its customers include individual doctors in private practice as well as large physician groups clinics and hospitals. Its ProAssurance Specialty Insurance subsidiary writes excess and surplus (higher risk) lines of medical professional liability insurance. The ProAssurance Casualty unit also provides some coverage for legal professionals.

Although the company is licensed throughout the US its operations are concentrated in about half a dozen states with Alabama Texas and Ohio accounting for a third of the company's premiums and Florida Michigan and Indiana bringing in about 20%. The company has more than 20 regional sales and support offices that provide marketing underwriting and claims management services; however almost two-thirds of its products are sold through independent agents.

ProAssurance's plans for long-term growth are based on the controlled expansion of its existing operations and by acquiring other specialty insurance companies or books of business. In 2012 the company moved to expand when it agreed to acquire Medmarc Insurance Group a liability underwriter for medical technology and life science policies in a $154 million transaction. The purchase also adds some legal professional coverage operations. Also that year ProAssurance agreed to acquire the Independent Nevada Doctors Insurance Exchange (IND) a medical professional liability insurer in Nevada in a public stock conversion transaction. IND will merge with ProAssurance's existing Nevada division following the transaction.

Regional expansion has been a key part of the company's growth strategy in previous years as well. For instance in 2010 ProAssurance plunked down about $230 million to buy American Physicians Service Group (APS) and its American Physicians Insurance (API) subsidiary launching itself into the top ranks of medical professional liability insurance providers in Texas. ProAssurance had targeted Texas as a key growth market and API became one of ProAssurance's main operating units following the purchase.

ProAssurance had already expanded in Texas through the 2009 acquisition of Houston-based Mid-Continent General Agency (now ProAssurance Mid-Continent Underwriters) a provider of professional liability insurance to ancillary health care providers and others. The company also expanded its specialty services coverage through the $120 million purchase of Podiatry Insurance Company of America (PICA) in a demutualization transaction; PICA serves podiatrists chiropractors and other specialists.

ProAssurance is also testing the waters in fields outside of the medical professionals customer base. In 2009 the company purchased Georgia Lawyers Insurance Company to add coverage for legal professionals. Georgia Lawyers was then merged into the ProAssurance Casualty division.

The company's aggressive acquisitions are part of its strategy to better compete against larger property/casualty insurance firms as well as smaller niche providers. ProAssurance works to provide local services that cater to the liability climates of its core geographies; it also focuses on targeted customer segments (medical and legal) to allow for a deep understanding of the industries' needs. The firm touts its conservative pricing and investment strategies as the means to navigate through times of rough economic and market conditions.

ProAssurance has been able to sustain financial stability during difficult market conditions through disciplined underwriting and prudent pricing and loss reserving practices and by investing conservatively. Utilizing these practices the company achieved an increase of about $46 million or almost 9% growth over 2010 in net premiums earned which included an increase of roughly $53 million attributable to the APS business. Revenues increased by about 3.5% and net income jumped 19% for the year.

EXECUTIVES

President and Director, Victor T. Adamo, age 64, $526,885 total compensation
Chairman and CEO, W. Stancil (Stan) Starnes, age 63, $798,000 total compensation
SVP Chief Underwriting Officer and Chief Actuary; Co-President Professional Liability Group, Howard H. Friedman, age 53, $445,038 total compensation
SVP Corporate Communications and Investor Relations, Frank B. O'Neil, age 58
SVP and CFO, Edward L. (Ned) Rand Jr., age 45, $414,346 total compensation
SVP and Chief Claims Officer; Co-President Professional Liability Group, Darryl K. Thomas, age 54, $390,384 total compensation
SVP Corporate Secretary and General Counsel, Jeffrey P. Lisenby, age 43
Director; President CEO and Director Podiatry Insurance Company of America, Jerry D. Brant, age 73, $358,155 total compensation
SVP Risk Management and Chief Medical Officer, Hayes V. Whiteside
Director, Drayton Nabers Jr., age 71
Director, John J. McMahon Jr., age 69
Director, William H. Woodhams, age 74
Director, Ann F. Putallaz, age 66
President and Director, Victor T. Adamo, age 64
Director, Robert E. Flowers, age 62
Director, Lucian F. Bloodworth, age 71
Director, Wilfred W. Yeargan, age 72
Director, William J. Listwan, age 69
Director; President CEO and Director Podiatry Insurance Company of America, Jerry D. Brant, age 73
Auditors: Ernst&YoungLLP

LOCATIONS

HQ: ProAssurance Corp.
100 Brookwood Place, Birmingham, AL 35209
Phone: 205 877-4400 **Fax:** 205 802-4799
Web: www.proassurance.com

2011 Gross Premiums Written by State

	% of total
Alabama	14
Texas	10
Ohio	9
Florida	7
Michigan	6
Indiana	5
Other	49
Total	**100**

PRODUCTS/OPERATIONS

2011 Gross Premiums Written by Type

	% of total
Physicians	80
Other health	8
Health care	5
Legal	3
Others	4
Total	**100**

Selected Subsidiaries

PACO Assurance Company Inc.
Podiatry Insurance Company of America (PICA)
ProAssurance Casualty Co.
ProAssurance Group Services Corporation
ProAssurance Indemnity Company Inc.
ProAssurance National Capital Insurance Co.
ProAssurance Specialty Insurance Company Inc.

COMPETITORS

Berkshire Hathaway
CNA Financial
COPIC
Coverys
Dentists Insurance Company
EDIC
FPIC Insurance
Markel
Medical Liability Mutual Insurance
Monitor Liability Managers Inc.
NCMIC
Physicians' Reciprocal Insurers
Princeton Insurance Company
State Volunteer Mutual Insurance
The Doctors Company
Travelers Companies
White Mountains Insurance Group

HISTORICAL FINANCIALS

Company Type: Public

Income Statement FYE: December 31

	ASSETS ($ mil.)	NET INCOME ($ mil.)	INCOME AS % OF ASSETS	EMPLOYEES
12/11	4,998	287	5.7%	652
12/10	4,875	231	4.8%	739
12/09	4,647	222	4.8%	689
12/08	4,280	177	4.2%	551
12/07	4,439	168	3.8%	587
Annual Growth	3.0%	14.3%	—	2.7%

2011 Year-End Financials

Debt ratio: 0.99%
Return on equity: 13.26%
Cash ($ mil.): 130
Current ratio: —
Long-term debt ($ mil.): 49
No. of shares (mil.): 61
Dividends
Yield: —
Payout: 10.74%
Market value ($ mil.): 4,878

	STOCK PRICE ($) FY Close	P/E High/Low		PER SHARE ($) Earnings	Dividends	Book Value
12/11	79.82	17	12	4.66	0.00	35.42
12/10	60.60	17	14	3.60	0.00	30.17
12/09	53.71	16	12	3.35	0.00	26.30
12/08	52.78	24	15	2.61	0.00	21.35
12/07	54.92	22	19	2.39	0.00	19.34
Annual Growth	9.8%	—	—	18.2%	—	16.3%

Procter & Gamble Co.

The Procter & Gamble Company (P&G) boasts dozens of billion-dollar brands for home hair and health. The world's largest maker of consumer packaged goods divides its business into two global units: Beauty and Grooming and Household Care. The company also makes pet food water filters and over-the-counter acid-reflux medication. About two dozen of P&G's brands are billion-dollar sellers including Always Braun Crest Fusion Gillette Head & Shoulders Mach3 Olay Oral-B Pantene and Wella in the beauty and grooming segment as well as Bounty Charmin Dawn Downy Duracell Gain Iams Pampers and Tide in the household care segment. P&G's hundreds of brands are available in more than 180 countries.

HISTORY

Candle maker William Procter and soap maker James Gamble merged their small Cincinnati businesses in 1837 creating The Procter & Gamble Company (P&G) which incorporated in 1890. By 1859 P&G had become one of the largest companies in Cincinnati with sales of $1 million. It introduced Ivory a floating soap in 1879 and Crisco shortening in 1911.

The Ivory campaign was one of the first to advertise directly to the consumer. Other advertising innovations included sponsorship of daytime radio dramas in 1932. P&G's first TV commercial for Ivory aired in 1939.

Family members headed the company until 1930 when William Deupree became president. In the 29 years that Deupree served as president and then chairman P&G became the largest US seller of packaged goods.

After years of researching cleansers for use in hard water P&G introduced Tide detergent in 1947. It began a string of acquisitions when it picked up Spic and Span (1945; sold 2001) Duncan Hines (1956; sold 1998) Charmin Paper Mills (1957) and Folgers Coffee (1963 sold 2008). P&G launched Crest toothpaste in 1955 and Head & Shoulders shampoo and Pampers disposable diapers in 1961.

Rely tampons were pulled from shelves in 1980 when investigators linked them to toxic shock syndrome. In 1985 P&G moved into health care when it purchased Richardson-Vicks (NyQuil Vicks) and G.D. Searle's nonprescription drug division (Metamucil). The acquisitions of Noxell (1989; CoverGirl Noxzema) and Max Factor (1991) made it a top cosmetics company in the US. (It sold Noxzema in 2008.)

P&G began a major restructuring in 1993 cutting 13000 jobs and closing 30 plants. The firm acquired Eagle Snacks from Anheuser-Busch in 1996 and sued rival Amway over rumors connecting P&G and its moon-and-stars logo to Satanism. (The suit was dismissed in 1999.) Also in 1996 the FDA approved the use of olestra a controversial fat substitute developed by P&G.

In 1997 it acquired Tambrands (Tampax tampons) making P&G #1 in feminine sanitary protection. Impatient with progress on its sales goals in 1998 P&G began restructuring to focus on global business units rather than geographic regions. Chairman John Pepper handed over his chairman and CEO title in 1999 to president Durk Jager who promised five new products a year and a shakeup of the corporate culture.

In 1999 the company announced further reorganization plans including 15000 job cuts worldwide by 2005. That same year P&G bought The Iams Company (maker of Eukanuba- and Iams-brand dog and cat foods).

With earnings flat Jager resigned in 2000. P&G insider Alan G. Lafley immediately assumed the president and CEO duties and Pepper returned to succeed Jager as chairman.

In 2001 P&G announced job cuts for 9600 employees to further reduce costs. It also sold its Comet cleaner business. That year P&G completed its purchase of the Clairol hair care company from Bristol-Myers Squibb for nearly $5 billion.

In 2002 P&G closed three Clairol plants one warehouse and one distribution center —eliminating about 750 jobs. Production of Clairol products was moved to existing P&G plants. It also sold its olestra plant in Cincinnati to Twin Rivers Technologies but retained ownership of the Olean brand and technology. Additionally it sold its Jif peanut butter and Crisco shortening brands to J.M. Smucker and several personal care brands (including Sea Breeze and Vitalis) to Helen of Troy.

In 2002 P&G branched out in a joint venture with Clorox to help it improve the Glad-brand plastic bags and wraps. P&G held a 10% stake in the Glad venture until late 2004 when the company invested another $133 million to boost its stake to 20% the limit allowed by the agreement.

Also that year Lafley announced that P&G had completed its multiyear restructuring and would stop reporting two sets of results (one with restructuring charges and one without).

Further expanding its hair care segment and building on its successes with Clairol P&G purchased the first of several stakes in Wella in 2003 (it now owns the entire company). That year P&G also entered the premium pet food market with its purchase of The Iams Company for $2.3 billion. And to secure its foothold in China P&G bought the remaining 20% stake in its joint venture with partner Hutchison Whampoa China Ltd. in 2004 for $1.8 billion.

P&G bought four brands to sell in Southeast Asia in its effort to erode market share from Unilever. In 2005 P&G purchased Fab Trojan Dynamo and Paic laundry brands sold in Hong Kong Singapore Thailand and Malaysia from Colgate-Palmolive.

In 2006 P&G paired up with ARYx Therapeutics to develop that company's gastrointestinal disorder treatment.

In 2007 P&G paired its marketing savvy with the diagnostics expertise of Inverness Medical Innovations to form a joint venture company called SPD Swiss Precision Diagnostics. The joint venture makes and markets in-home diagnostic products including pregnancy tests and ovulation/fertility monitoring products under the Clearblue PERSONA Accu-Clear and other names. P&G paid $325 million for its 50% stake in the venture.

Further expanding its luxury hair-care portfolio in 2008 P&G purchased Frederic Fekkai & Co. from Chrysallis a management company of private equity firm Catterton Partners. The acquisition gave P&G a foothold in department store hair care which for Fekkai had generated double-digit gains each year. Fekkai caters to prestige stores located in the US such as Neiman Marcus Nordstrom and Sephora. Later that year P&G purchased NIOXIN Research Laboratories to add volume to its hair-care business.

In early 2009 P&G formed a new subsidiary — Agile Pursuits Franchising —to oversee its franchising efforts after purchasing Atlanta-based car wash firm Carnett's in February.

Alan G. Lafley resigned from his posts as CEO in July 2009 and chairman in January 2010. Former COO Robert McDonald took over for Lafley as president CEO and chairman. In August P&G sold Iams Pet Imaging (IPI) to AnimalScan LLC. IPI fell under the company's P&G Pet Care North America division.

EXECUTIVES

External Relations Family Care (Puffs Bounty Charmin), Laura Lewis
President Duracell, Mark S. Bertolami, age 50
Group President Global Fabric Care, Jorge S. Mesquita, age 51
Group President Central and Eastern Europe Middle East and Africa and Global High Frequency Store Channel, Laurent L. Philippe, age 61
Group President Asia and Global Specialty Channel, Deborah A. (Deb) Henretta, age 51
Chairman President and CEO, Robert A. (Bob) McDonald, age 59, $1,400,000 total compensation
Global Marketing and Brand Building Officer, Marc S. Pritchard, age 52
Vice Chairman Global Operations, Werner Geissler, age 58, $907,500 total compensation
Vice Chairman Global Business Units, E. Dimitri Panayotopoulos, age 59, $947,500 total compensation
Group President Global Oral Care, Charles E. Pierce, age 56
President Global Business Services and CIO, Filippo Passerini, age 55
Director Investor Relations, John T. Chevalier
Group President Global Baby Care, Martin Riant, age 53
President Global Braun Beauty and Grooming, John P. Goodwin, age 48
President Special Assignment, Robert Jongstra, age 56
Global Human Resources Officer, Moheet Nagrath, age 53
Global Marketing-Design External Relations, Martha Depenbrock
Group President Latin America and Global Club Cash and Carry Channel, Jorge A. Uribe, age 56
Male Grooming, Damon Jones
President Global Male Grooming, Patrice Louvet, age 47
SVP and Comptroller, Valarie L. Sheppard, age 48
Director Children's Safe Drinking Water (PUR), Greg Allgood
CTO, Bruce Brown, age 54
External Relations Global Oral Care, Michelle Vaeth
Group President Global Female Beauty, Virginia C. (Gina) Drosos, age 49
Group President North America and Global Hyper Super Mass Channel, Melanie Liddle Healey, age 51
Group President Global Home Care, David S. Taylor, age 54
Global Braun Corporate and Household, Lars Atorf

External Relations Snacks (Pringles), Kay Puryear
External Relations Global Pantene Global Herbal Essences, Randall Chinchilla
Director External Relations North America MDO, Marie-Laure Salvado
Baby Care External Relations Pampers, Bryan McCleary
External Relations Health Care (Vicks), Crystal Harrell
External Relations Family Care (Puffs Bounty Charmin), Lisa H. Jester
External Relations Global Retail Hair Color (Nice ?n Easy Koleston), Tracey Long
Global Skin Care, Anitra C. Marsh
Baby Care External Relations Pampers and Luvs, Tricia P. Higgins
Associate Director External Relations Global Health Care, Tom M. Millikin
External Relations Health Care (Global PUR), Suzette J. Middleton
External Relations Duracell (Global), Kurt Iverson
U.S. Hispanic Brand External Relations Multi-Cultural Marketing Public Relations, Anelsie Ramos
P&G Fund Live Learn and Thrive Global Social Investments, Brian J. Sasson
Chief Legal Officer and Secretary, Deborah P. Majoras, age 48
SVP Global Beauty/Grooming and Corporate Innovation Fragrances and Flavors, Shekhar Mitra
President Global Wal-Mart Team, Jeffery K. Schomburger, age 50
Corporate Sustainable Development, Peter White
Group President Global Feminine Care, Steven D. (Steve) Bishop, age 48
Group President Western Europe and Global Discounter and Pharmaceutical Channels, Giovanni Ciserani, age 50
Group President Global Family Care, Mary Lynn Ferguson-McHugh, age 53
President Global Health Care, Thomas M. Finn, age 50
Corporate External Relations and Financial Communications, Jennifer Chelune
CFO, Jon R. Moeller, age 48, $675,000 total compensation
Global Design Officer, Philip J Duncan, age 47
Vice Chairman on Special Assignment, Edward D. (Ed) Shirley, age 55, $907,500 total compensation
SVP Global Consumer and Market Knowledge Officer, Joan M. Lewis
Corporate External Relations, Paul Fox
Global Customer Business Development Officer, Robert L. Fregolle Jr., age 55
SVP and Treasurer, Teri L. List, age 49
VP; General Manager UK and Ireland, Irwin Lee
Professional External Relations and Overall Global Home Care Family Care, Lee Bansil
Global External Relations Officer, Christopher D. (Chris) Hassall, age 58
VP Corporate, Nancy Swanson
North America Retail Hair Care (Herbal Essences and Aussie), Rotha Penn
External Relations Procter Gamble Productions, Jeannie Tharrington
Global Marketing-Design External Relations, Barbara Hauser
Consumer and Market Knowledge External Relations, Ivanette Bonilla
Disaster and Humanitarian Relief, Keith Zook
Cincinnati Community Relations, Sean T. Parker
External Relations North America Market Development Organization (MDO), Dave McCracken
Multicultural External Relations Multi-Cultural Marketing Public Relations, Felisa Insignares
SVP Global Business Services and Chief Diversity Officer, Linda W. Clement-Holmes, age 50
NA Olay Secret and Personal Cleansing, Wendy S. Kennedy
SVP Global Snacks and Pet Care, Daniel S. Rajczak
President Greater China, Shannan Stevenson
Associate Director Investor Relations, Katie Kool
Corporate Exernal Relations, Mandy Wagner
Corporate External Relations, Mary Ralles
Global Marketing External Relations, Tressie Rose
General Beauty and Grooming Queries, Julie de Stefano
Beauty Print and TV/Film Clearances/Licensing, Abby Remley
North America Gillette Old Spice Tag and Sports-Related Activities, Michael (Mike) Norton
Global Grooming General Inquiries, Racheal Hummel
North Amierca Braun, Kristen Gugliotta
Global Gillette Emerging Markets, Kara Buckley
Global Body Care and Venus/Hair Removal, Jay Gooch
North America Hair and Female Beauty, Brent Miller
Global Venus NA Braun Female Satin Care Pure Divine, Laura Brinker
North America Hair Care & Color (Pantene Pantene Ethnic), Cheri McMaster
North America Head and Shoulders, Mary Woods
P&G Salon Professional - North America, Jessica Shih
North America Aussie, Teca Gillespie
P&G Salon Professional - North America Salon Professional (Corporate) Wella Professionals, Mary Atherton
Cover Girl and Max Factor Cosmetics Print & TV/Film Clearances/Licensing, Paige Cali
Global ER Fine Fragrances and Prestige Beaute, Michela Ratti
External Relations and Advertising North America Fine Fragrances, Shane English
External Relations and Advertising North America Fine Fragrances, Lisa Kessler
External Relations and Advertising North America Fine Fragrances, Rica Roman
General Health Care Queries Print & TV/Film Clearances/Licensing, Lisa Van Skaik
Health Care Digestive Wellness (Align Pepto Bismol Metamucil POTC), Liz Ming
General Resource Feminine Care External Relations, Jenny Haralamos
Always & Tampax Feminine Care, Velvet Gogol Bennett
Associate Director Global Feminine Care, David Bernens
Kids: Crest Pro-Health FOR ME Oral-B Stages; Social Media, Laura Dressman
Crest Pro-Health Toothpaste & Mouthwash, Kristopher Parlett
Global Oral Care Scientific Communications Professional, Veronica Sanchez
Crest Whitestrips Crest 3D White Scope Mouthwash Branded Entertainment, Alissa Fitzgibbons
Floss Fixodent Oral-B Toothbrushes, Tricia Gottlieb
General Oral Care Queries; Oral Care Print & TV/Film Clearances/Licensing, Dorothy Daniel
Pet Care (Eukanuba Iams & Natura), Jason Taylor
General Resource Pet Care External Relations, Dalynn Sours
NA Fabric Care (Downy Bounce Gain SWASH) Digital ER, Sarah Pasquinucci
NA P&G Professional (Influencer Marketing), Renee Buchanan
Home Care (Procter & Gamble Professional Procter & Gamble Chemicals), Chris Vuturo
Home Care Technical ER, Ian Tholking
General HC Queries Home Care Print & TV/Film Clearances/Licensing, Tia Rochelle
Director Ohio Government & Community Relations, Brian Hodgett
Global Product Supply Officer, Yannis Skoufalos, age 54
President Global Prestige, Joanne Crewes
Corporate External Relations, Jeff LeRoy
Consumer and Market Knowledge External Relations, David Schottelkotte
President Duracell, Stassi Anastassov, age 51
President Global Female Beauty, Colleen E. Jay, age 50
Global Beauty and Grooming, Kelly Vanasse
Group Manager Investor Relations, Brian Boutchard
NA MDO External Relations, Gerri Cunnigan
Pet Care, Gricelly Vargas
External Relations NA Fabric Care (Tide), My Anh Nghiem
External Relations NA Fabric Care (Tide Tide Additives Cheer Era Dreft) General Fabric Care, Mandy Treeby
NA Fabric Care External Relations Environmental Sustainability General Fabric Care, Petra Stovickova
External Relations NA Home Care (Dawn Gain Cascade), Michelle Lohman
External Relations NA Home Care (Febreze Mr. Clean Swiffer), Jeff Pierce
Director, Patricia A. (Pat) Woertz, age 59
Director, Susan Desmond-Hellmann, age 54
Director, Kenneth I. (Ken) Chenault, age 61
Director, Angela F. Braly, age 50
Director, Johnathan A. Rodgers, age 66
Director, Mary Agnes (Maggie) Wilderotter, age 57
Director, Margaret C. (Meg) Whitman, age 55
Director, Scott D. Cook, age 59
Director, W. James (Jim) McNerney Jr., age 62
Director, Ernesto Zedillo, age 60
Auditors: Deloitte&ToucheLLP

LOCATIONS

HQ: The Procter & Gamble Company
One Procter & Gamble Plaza, Cincinnati OH 45202
Phone: 513-983-1100 **Fax:** 513-983-9369
Web: www.pg.com

2012 Sales

	% of total
North	39
Western	19
Asia	18
Central & Eastern Europe Middle East &	14
Latin	10
Total	**100**

PRODUCTS/OPERATIONS

2012 Sales

	% of total
Fabric care & home care (includes pet care after May	32
Beauty	24
Baby care & family	19
Health	15
Grooming	10
Total	**100**

Selected Mergers & Acquisitions

FY2010
Natura Pet Products (California holistic and natural pet foods)
Sara Lee European air-freshener business ($470 million plug-in and stand-by air fresheners aerosol sprays and toilet cleaners)
FY2009
The Art of Shaving (high-end men' s shaving and skin care products)

FY2005
The Gillette Company ($57 billion Boston maker of razors blades batteries and oral care items)

Selected Divestitures

FY2012
Pringles ($2.7 billion to Kellogg Company)
FY2011
PUR water purification business (to Helen of Troy)
Zest (to High Ridge Brands P&G retaining the rights to sell Zest in the Philippines the Middle East and Latin America)
FY2009
Prescription drug unit ($3 billion to Warner Chilcott)
FY2008
Folger Coffee Company ($3 billion to The J. M. Smucker Company)
Infusium 23 (to Helen of Troy)
Noxzema (to Alberto-Culver P&G retaining business in parts of Western Europe)
FY2006
SpinBrush ($75 million to Church & Dwight)

Selected Segments & Their Billion Dollar Brands

Fabric Care & Home Care
- Ace
- Ariel
- Dawn
- Downy
- Duracell
- Febreze
- Gain
- Iams
- Tide

Beauty
- Head & Shoulders
- Olay
- Pantene
- SK-II
- Wella

Baby Care & Family Care
- Bounty
- Charmin
- Pampers

Health Care
- Always
- Crest
- Oral-B
- Vicks

Grooming
- Braun
- Fusion
- Gillette
- Mach3

COMPETITORS

Alticor	L' Oreal
Amway	Mary Kay
Avon	Meda Pharmaceuticals
Bath & Body Works	Mondelez International
Baxter of California	Nestle
BIC	PepsiCo
Body Shop	Pfizer
Bristol-Myers Squibb	Philips Electronics
Church & Dwight	Revlon
Clorox	Russell Hobbs
Colgate-Palmolive	S.C. Johnson
Discus Dental	Sanofi
Dr. Bronner' s	SANYO
Energizer Holdings	Scott' s Liquid Gold
Estee Lauder	SEB
Frito-Lay	Shiseido
Hain Celestial	Spectrum Brands
Heinz	Tom' s of Maine
Henkel	Turtle Wax
Johnson & Johnson	Unilever
Kimberly-Clark	VIVUS

HISTORICAL FINANCIALS

Company Type: Public

Income Statement FYE: June 30

	REVENUE ($ mil.)	NET INCOME ($ mil.)	NET PROFIT MARGIN	EMPLOYEES
06/12	83,680	10,756	12.9%	126,000
06/11	82,559	11,797	14.3%	129,000
06/10	78,938	12,736	16.1%	127,000
06/09	79,029	13,436	17.0%	135,000
06/08	83,503	12,075	14.5%	138,000
Annual Growth	0.1%	(2.9%)	—	(2.2%)

2012 Year-End Financials

Debt ratio: 22.52%—
Return on equity: 16.95%
Cash ($ mil.): 4,436
Current ratio: 87.97
Long-term debt ($ mil.): 21,080
Dividends
Yield: —
Payout: 58.39%
Market value ($ mil.): —

	STOCK PRICE ($) FY Close	P/E High/Low		PER SHARE ($) Earnings	Dividends	Book Value
06/12	61.25	18	15	3.66	0.00	23.09
06/11	63.57	16	14	3.93	1.97	24.46
06/10	59.98	15	12	4.11	1.80	21.49
06/09	51.10	16	10	4.26	1.64	21.63
06/08	60.81	19	16	3.64	1.45	22.91
Annual Growth	0.2%	—	—	0.1%	—	0.2%

Progressive Corp. (OH)

It's risky business and Progressive loves it. Long a leader in nonstandard high-risk personal auto insurance The Progressive Corporation has motored beyond its traditional business into standard-risk and preferred auto insurance as well as other personal-use vehicle coverage (motorcycles recreational vehicles and snowmobiles). Progressive also offers commercial policies for heavy trucks vans and lighter trucks. It writes a bit of professional liability insurance for directors and officers insurance of community banks. The company markets directly to consumers online and by phone and through more than 35000 independent agents who account for roughly 60% of the company's business.

Operations

Personal insurance accounts for 90% of the company's net premiums while commercial auto represents the remainder. Other indemnity and service business accounts for less than 1% of the company's revenues. In 2010 Progressive sold off its small professional liability insurance business but arranged to continue writing such policies through a third-party.

Progressive stopped writing homeowners insurance years ago but it continues to offer coverage to its auto insurance customers underwritten by third party insurance carriers. Progressive also offers personal umbrella insurance that provides coverage for the extras in life such as personal injury and legal defense.

Financial Analysis

Unlike some insurers who in fat markets earn more from their investments than their premiums more than 90% of Progressive's revenues have historically come from policy premiums. This quirk allowed the company to maintain a bit more serenity than its competitors during most market fluctuations. However it loaded up on subprime investments in 2007 which proved a regrettable strategy. Subsequently in 2008 Progressive experienced its first loss in 26 years. By 2009 the company's income had bounced back sufficiently to afford expansion efforts but have since remained relatively flat. The company reported increased revenues through 2011 when sales increased 4% to some $15.5 billion.

Strategy

The company's actual insurance operations have remained profitable and grown as it has entered into new geographic markets and expanded distribution of its personal auto products online. Already among the leading US auto insurers based on premiums (just behind State Farm and Allstate) Progressive is aiming to be on top.

Because it is fairly easy for customers to switch auto insurers Progressive competes on price and accessibility. To attract new customers the company's television ads featuring its perky spokesperson "Flo" have shot up the company's brand recognition. Operating on the premise that a few drivers are responsible for the majority of claims and that previous risk models were incomplete Progressive is now also offering rates that are tied to actual usage. In 2011 it launched its Snapshot program to offer usage-based discounts. Snapshot customers plug a tracking device into their cars for a month; data collected by the device are used to determine the customer's discounted premium rates. While the product didn't take the market by storm in its first year Progressive is betting that it will be a big part of its future.

To retain customers Progressive is promoting its non-auto personal products through bundled packages with lower auto rates. Once a customer has bought a bundled package of home/auto/umbrella coverage they are also much less likely to switch insurance providers.

The company took a bold international expansion measure in 2009: Launching personal auto insurance online in Australia. International expansion has not been a key strategy for Progressive but apparently the time was right for such growth. And apparently the company is prepared to give the new operation time to grow which is good considering that it has not yet made significant contributions to overall revenues.

Ownership

Colorful chairman Peter Lewis is the son of one of the insurer's founders. He built Progressive up from a regional operation to a national player and controls more than 5% of the company.

HISTORY

Attorneys Jack Green and Joseph Lewis founded Progressive Mutual Insurance in Cleveland in 1937. Initially offering standard auto insurance the company attracted customers through such innovations as installment plans for premiums (a payment method popularized during the Depression) and drive-in claims services (the company was headquartered in a garage). Progressive's early years were uncertain –at one point the founders were even advised to go out of business –but the advent of WWII bolstered business: Car and insurance purchases were up but accidents were down as gas rationing limited driving.

Then came the suburbs and cars of the 1950s. While most competitors sought low-risk drivers Progressive exploited the high-risk niche through careful underwriting and statistical analysis. Subsidiary Progressive Casualty was founded in 1956 (the year after Joseph Lewis died) to insure the best of the worst. Lewis' son Peter joined the company in 1955 and helped engineer its early-1960s expansion outside Ohio. After Green retired in 1965 Peter gained control of the company through a leveraged buyout and renamed it The Progressive Corporation. Six years later Lewis took it public and formed subsidiary Progressive American in Florida.

In the mid-1970s the industry went into a funk as it was hit by a wave of consolidations and rising interest rates. Lewis set a goal for the company to always earn an underwriting profit instead of depending on investments to make a profit. Progressive achieved stellar results during the 1970s especially after states began requiring drivers to be insured and other insurers began weeding out higher risks.

Competition in nonstandard insurance grew in the 1980s as major insurers such as Allstate and State Farm joined the fray with their larger sales forces and deeper pockets. In 1988 California's Proposition 103 retroactively reduced rates; Progressive fought California's demand for refunds but set aside reserves to pay them.

That year Lewis hired Cleveland financier Alfred Lerner to guide company investments. Lerner invested $75 million in Progressive via a convertible debenture; five years later he converted it to stock half of which he sold for $122 million. Soon after he was asked to resign. In 1993 Progressive settled with California for $51 million and applied to earnings the remaining $100 million in refund reserves. (Company soul-searching related to Proposition 103 led to the launch of Progressive's now-famous "Immediate Response" vehicles which provide 24-hour claims service at accident sites.)

In 1995 Progressive's practice of using consumer credit information to make underwriting decisions drew the attention of Arkansas and Vermont insurance regulators who said the company might be discriminating against people who didn't have the credit cards Progressive used to evaluate creditworthiness. In 1996 insurance regulators in Alaska Maryland and Texas also began probing Progressive's credit information practices.

In 1997 Progressive bought nonstandard auto insurer Midland Financial Group. As competition grew in 1999 the company cut rates and said it would write no new policies in Canada. In 2000 – with underwriting margins dropping industrywide –the company continued advertising aggressively. Progressive stopped writing new homeowners insurance in 2002 instead concentrating on its core operations. In 2006 the company began offering personal umbrella coverage.

EXECUTIVES

President CEO and Director, Glenn M. Renwick, age 56, $750,000 total compensation
Chairman, Peter B. Lewis, age 78, $511,538 total compensation
VP and Chief Accounting Officer, Jeffrey W. Basch, age 54
VP and Treasurer, Thomas A. King, age 52
Product Manager Boat, Rick Stern
Chief Marketing Officer, M. Jeffrey (Jeff) Charney
VP Chief Legal Officer and Secretary, Charles E. Jarrett, age 55, $424,038 total compensation
CIO, Raymond M. Voelker, age 49, $377,307 total compensation
Chief Investment Officer, William M. Cody, age 50, $380,000 total compensation
Claims Group President, Susan P. Griffith, age 47, $380,000 total compensation
President Commercial Lines Group, John A. Barbagello, age 53
Director Special Projects, Brian A. Silva, age 58
Group President Personal Lines, John P. Sauerland, age 47, $380,000 total compensation
VP and CFO, Brian C. Domeck, age 53, $380,000 total compensation
Media Relations, Leah Knapp
Media Relations, Katherine M. (Kathy) Bell
General Manager Personal Lines, David J. Skove
Chief Human Resource Officer, Valerie Krasowski, age 46
Director Accounting and Assistant Secretary, Mariann Wojtkun Marshall, age 50
Media Contact, Linda J. Harris
Business Leader Mobile, Matthew (Matt) Lehman
General Manager Usage-Based Insurance, Richard Hutchinson
Director Internal and External Communications, Mari Pumarejo
Director Web Experience, Andy Fulford
Business Leader Central Services, Mike Capuzzi
General Manager Personal Lines, Mark Niehaus
General Manager Personal Lines, Dan Mascaro
Director, Stuart B. Burgdoerfer, age 49
Director, Heidi G. Miller, age 57
President CEO and Director, Glenn M. Renwick, age 56
Director, Lawton W. Fitt, age 58
Director, Patrick H. Nettles, age 68
Director, Roger N. Farah, age 59
Director, Charles A. (Chuck) Davis, age 63
Director, Norman S. Matthews, age 79
Director, Bradley T. Sheares, age 55
Auditors: PricewaterhouseCoopersLLP

LOCATIONS

HQ: The Progressive Corporation
6300 Wilson Mills Rd., Mayfield Village OH 44143
Phone: 440-461-5000 **Fax:** 800-456-6590
Web: www.progressive.com

PRODUCTS/OPERATIONS

COMPETITORS

21st Century Insurance
Allstate
American Family Insurance
Cincinnati Financial
Farmers Group
GEICO
Infinity Property & Casualty
Liberty Mutual
Nationwide
Ohio Casualty
Old Republic
State Auto Financial
State Farm
Travelers Companies
USAA
White Mountains Insurance Group

HISTORICAL FINANCIALS

Company Type: Public

Income Statement FYE: December 31

	ASSETS ($ mil.)	NET INCOME ($ mil.)	INCOME AS % OF ASSETS	EMPLOYEES
12/11	21,844	1,015	4.6%	25,007
12/10	21,150	1,068	5.1%	24,638
12/09	20,049	1,057	5.3%	24,661
12/08	18,250	(70)	—	25,929
12/07	18,843	1,182	6.3%	26,851
Annual Growth	3.8%	(3.7%)	—	(1.8%)

2011 Year-End Financials

Debt ratio: 11.18%
Return on equity: 17.49%
Cash ($ mil.): 155
Current ratio: —
Long-term debt ($ mil.): 2,442
No. of shares (mil.): 613
Dividends
Yield: —
Payout: 25.08%
Market value ($ mil.): 11,960

	STOCK PRICE ($) FY Close	P/E High/Low		PER SHARE ($) Earnings	Dividends	Book Value
12/11	19.51	14	11	1.59	0.00	9.47
12/10	19.87	14	10	1.61	1.16	9.13
12/09	17.99	11	6	1.57	0.00	8.55
12/08	14.81	—	—	(0.10)	0.00	6.23
12/07	19.16	15	10	1.65	2.01	7.26
Annual Growth	0.5%	—	—	(0.9%)	—	6.9%

Prosperity Bancshares Inc.

Prosperity Bancshares reaches banking customers across the Lone Star State. The holding company for Prosperity Bank operates 213 branches in and around the Texas cities of Dallas Houston Austin Corpus Christi Lubbock and San Antonio. Serving consumers and small to midsized businesses the bank offers traditional deposit and loan services in addition to investment services through third-party provider LPL Financial. Prosperity Bank focuses on real estate lending: Commercial mortgages make up the largest segment of the company's loan portfolio (35%) followed by residential mortgages (27%). Business construction consumer home equity and agricultural loans round out its lending activities.

Prosperity Bancshares operates banking locations in Houston South Texas the Dallas/Fort Worth metroplex East Texas Bryan/College Station Central Texas and West Texas.

Prosperity Bancshares bases its growth strategy on three key elements: Internal growth; cost controls; and acquisitions. Net income has climbed steadily since 2008 due to an increase in net interest income. The increase in net interest income is a result of balance sheet growth from a slew of recent acquisitions. Net income grew by 10% in 2011. Assets deposits and loans also have seen an uptick thanks to those acquisitions.

The acquisitive Prosperity Bancshares has been buying up small banks in Texas as it hopes to hit a sweet spot in the market between the national giants that dominate the Texas banking scene and smaller community banks. Compared to many of its peers elsewhere in the country the company has remained prosperous (and profitable) during the economic downturn thanks in part to its presence in the relatively stable Texas market its conservative loan underwriting standards and growth through acquisitions.

In 2010 it bought some 20 locations from First Bank and acquired three branches that U.S. Bancorp divested from its acquisition of the failed FBOP Corporation. The deals strengthened Prosperity Bank's presence in the Dallas and Houston areas.

In early 2012 Prosperity acquired Texas Bankers a three-branch Austin bank with some $72 million in assets. The merger increased Prosperity's number of Central Texas branches to 34 banking locations. It followed that deal with the purchase of The Bank Arlington a single-branch bank operating in the Dallas/Ft. Worth area. The company also plans to buy East Texas Financial Services adding another handful of branches to its network. It acquired single-branch Community National Bank of Bellaire Texas in late 2012.

Also in 2012 Prosperity expanded into West Texas after it merged American State Financial Corporation and its American State Bank subsidiary into its operations. The deal added 37 West Texas banking offices in Lubbock Midland/Odessa and Abilene. The deal added about $3 billion in assets to Prosperity's roster.

Prosperity Bancshares was founded in 1983

EXECUTIVES

Chairman and CEO; Senior Chairman and CEO Prosperity Bank, David Zalman, age 55, $606,107 total compensation
CFO; EVP and CFO Prosperity Bank, David Hollaway, age 56, $277,083 total compensation
Vice Chairman; Chairman and COO Prosperity Bank, H. E. (Tim) Timanus Jr., age 67, $352,623 total compensation
Chairman Central Texas Centers, Edward Z. (Eddie) Safady
President COO and Director; President Prosperity Bank, James D. (Dan) Rollins III, age 53, $430,725 total compensation
Chairman South Texas Area Banking Centers, Steve Hipes
President South Texas Area Banking Centers, Bob Kuhn
General Counsel; Vice Chairman and General Counsel Prosperity Bank, Peter E. Fisher, age 65, $242,208 total compensation
Chief Credit Officer Prosperity Bank, Chris Bagley
Chief Lending Officer Prosperity Bank, Randy D. Hester
Chairman Houston Area Banking Centers, Robert L. Benter
President Houston Area, Chris J. Delaup
President Dallas/Fort Worth and East Texas Area, Deke Hayes
Chairman Bryan/College Station Area, Mark D. Humphrey
President Houston Area Banking Center, Randall Reeves
General Counsel, Charlotte Rasche
Chairman West Texas, Mike Epps
Director, Ned S. Holmes, age 67
Vice Chairman; Chairman and COO Prosperity Bank, H. E. (Tim) Timanus Jr., age 67
Director, Robert Steelhammer, age 71
Director, James A. Bouligny, age 76
Director, Harrison Stafford II, age 70
Director, Ervan E. Zouzalik, age 75
President COO and Director; President Prosperity Bank, James D. (Dan) Rollins III, age 53
Director, William H. Fagan, age 82
Director, Perry Mueller Jr., age 78
Director, Leah Henderson, age 45
Auditors: Deloitte&ToucheLLP

LOCATIONS

HQ: Prosperity Bancshares Inc.
4295 San Felipe, Houston TX 77027
Phone: 281-269-7199 **Fax:** 281-269-7222
Web: www.prosperitybanktx.com

PRODUCTS/OPERATIONS

2011 Sales

	$ mil.	% of total
Interest		
Loans including fees	214	50
Securities	157	37
Federal funds sold	0	-
Noninterest		
Non-sufficient funds fees	24	6
Debit card and ATM card income	15	4
Service charges on deposit accounts	10	2
Other	6	1
Total	**428**	**100**

COMPETITORS

Amegy
Bank of America
Citibank
Comerica
Compass Bancshares
Cullen/Frost Bankers
Encore Bancshares
JPMorgan Chase
MetroCorp Bancshares
North Dallas Bank
Texas Capital Bancshares
Wells Fargo
Woodforest Financial

HISTORICAL FINANCIALS

Company Type: Public

Income Statement FYE: December 31

	ASSETS ($ mil.)	NET INCOME ($ mil.)	INCOME AS % OF ASSETS	EMPLOYEES
12/11	9,822	141	1.4%	1,664
12/10	9,476	127	1.3%	1,708
12/09	8,850	111	1.3%	1,594
12/08	9,072	84	0.9%	1,734
12/07	6,372	84	1.3%	1,359
Annual Growth	11.4%	13.9%	—	5.2%

2011 Year-End Financials

Debt ratio: 1.00%
Return on equity: 9.04%
Cash ($ mil.): 212
Current ratio: —
Long-term debt ($ mil.): 97
No. of shares (mil.): 46
Dividends
Yield: —
Payout: 23.92%
Market value ($ mil.): 1,893

	STOCK PRICE ($) FY Close	P/E High/Low		PER SHARE ($) Earnings	Dividends	Book Value
12/11	40.35	15	10	3.01	0.00	33.41
12/10	39.28	16	10	2.73	0.64	31.11
12/09	40.47	17	8	2.41	0.57	29.03
12/08	29.59	21	12	1.86	0.51	27.24
12/07	29.39	19	14	1.94	0.46	25.51
Annual Growth	8.2%	—	—	11.6%	—	7.0%

Protective Life Corp.

Protective Life wants to cushion its customers from the nasty blows of life and death. The company primarily sells life insurance products through its Life Marketing business segment including universal term and bank-owned life insurance coverage; Protective Life also brings in and manages blocks of life insurance policies sold elsewhere through its Acquisitions segment. The firm's Asset Protection unit sells extended service contracts and credit life insurance while its Annuities division offers fixed and variable annuities. The Stable Value Products unit sells guaranteed funding agreements for financial instruments such as municipal bonds and the ProEquities brokerage serves independent financial advisors.

Operations

Protective Life sells its life and annuity products across out the US through its Protective Life Insurance Company subsidiary. That subsidiary in turn operates Protective Life and Annuity Insurance Company which writes business in New York and subsidiary West Coast Life which sells to customers out West. The company's combined life insurance operations (Life Marketing Acquisitions and Annuities) account for 80% of its revenue.

Sales and Marketing

The Life Marketing division's products are sold through independent agents worksite plans and financial institutions. Meanwhile Protective Life's Asset Protection unit distributes polices through auto and marine dealers and its Annuities division sells through brokers and independent dealers.

Financial Analysis

Revenues at Protective Life increased 15% to $3.6 billion in 2011 due to increased premiums and policy fees within the Life Marketing division as well as an increase of business within the Acquisitions segment due to purchases of new blocks of insurance policies. Net income also rose in 2011 by 30% to $339 million. Protective Life has experienced financial growth over the last few years following a dip in revenues and profits during the credit crisis of 2008.

Strategy

Protective Life has aggressively capitalized on the industry trend of consolidation carefully selecting small and midsized firms that complement its existing operations. It has acquired more than 40 insurance companies or blocks of policies in the past three decades allowing the company to gain premiums without expensive commissions.

Mergers and Acquisitions

Though acquisitions slowed during the economic recession Protective Life closed a $340 million purchase of United Investors Life from Torchmark subsidiary Liberty National Life at the end of 2010. The purchase bolstered its Annuities division by adding variable annuity offerings as well as some closed books of policies in runoff (non-marketed) stages that were added to the Acquisitions segment.

HISTORY

In 1907 —when former Alabama governor William Jelks founded Protective Life in Birmingham —the South had not yet risen again and most insurance business was controlled by northern companies. Protective Life survived the financial panic that year and grew steadily paying its first dividends in 1916. It was sorely tested in 1918 as were most insurance companies when the influenza pandemic took thousands of lives particularly in large cities.

Protective Life merged in 1927 with another Birmingham-based insurance company Alabama National Insurance founded in 1908 as Great Southern Life Insurance. Alabama National's Samuel Clabaugh a former banker was appointed president and under his guidance the company passed through the Depression intact having cautiously conserved its capital. Another Alabama National alumnus William Rushton whose family name would become synonymous with Protective Life in Birmingham took over as CEO in 1937. Colonel Rushton as he became known after his stint in WWII continued to lead the company for the next 20 years investing in southern economic development.

In 1963 Protective Life formulated a new strategy concentrating on the upper-income market advanced underwriting business insurance and estate planning. The company planned to expand geographically with hopes of going nationwide. Protective Life was operating in 14 states by 1969 the year that Rushton's son William Rushton III assumed command from the colonel.

Under the younger Rushton Protective expanded its operations to all 50 states. The firm purchased 39 companies and numerous blocks of policies between 1970 and 1997.

In 1992 Rushton was named chairman and Drayton Nabers was appointed CEO. In 1994 Protective teamed with Indonesia's Lippo Group (which has interests in securities banking and insurance) to form Hong Kong-based Lippo Protective Life Insurance now CRC Protective Life Insurance. The joint venture introduced US-style universal life insurance to Hong Kong. Denomination of policies in US dollars attracted clients wary of unstable Asian currencies.

In the early 1990s Protective pioneered the concept of selling indemnity dental insurance on a voluntary payroll-deduction basis. In 1995 the company purchased National Health Care Systems of Florida operating under the trade name Denti-Care and entered the managed dental care business.

In 1997 Protective acquired West Coast Life Insurance and Western Diversified Group. It also continued to build its dental care operations through the 1997 acquisitions of three more small managed dental care companies and its 1998 purchase of United Dental Care making it the third-largest managed dental care company in the US. In 1999 Nabers took on the additional role of chairman taking over after William Rushton resigned. That year the company began distributing term life insurance over the Internet through agreements with HomeCom Communications and Matrix Direct Insurance Services. (Matrix was sold to American International Group in 2007.)

Protective bought specialty insurer Lyndon Insurance Group in 2000 from Frontier Insurance Group. Then Protective's subsidiary Protective Life Insurance acquired 70000 life insurance policies from Standard Insurance. Nabers stepped down as CEO at the end of 2001.

The company sold its dental benefits division to Fortis Inc. in 2002. The following year Nabers resigned as chairman to become Alabama's finance director and Protective CEO John Johns was named chairman.

During the economic recession Protective briefly considered acquiring The Bank of Bonifay a small Florida bank in early 2009. The purchase would have helped it obtain status as a bank holding company potentially allowing it to tap into the US Treasury's Troubled Asset Relief Program (TARP). However after observing the glacial speed with which the Treasury was considering such applications Protective scrapped the plan and stuck with insurance.

Another response to the recession: during 2009 the company stopped marketing its Stable Value Products and for that one year it simply maintained its existing agreements. By 2010 Protective Life was back to marketing its guaranteed funding agreements for financial instruments such as municipal bonds and money market funds and guaranteed investment contracts (GICs) for 401(k) plans.

EXECUTIVES

SVP Stable Value Products, Judy Wilson, age 53
EVP General Counsel and Secretary, Deborah J. Long, age 58, $388,333 total compensation
SVP Acquisitions and Corporate Development, Carolyn King, age 62
Vice Chairman and CFO, Richard J. (Rich) Bielen, age 51, $437,500 total compensation
Chairman President and CEO, John D. Johns, age 59, $845,833 total compensation
EVP and Chief Investment Officer, Carl S. Thigpen, age 55, $396,667 total compensation
SVP Asset Protection, Brent E. Griggs, age 56
SVP Controller and Chief Accounting Officer, Steven G. Walker, age 52
SVP and Chief Human Resources Officer, D. Scott Adams, age 47
EVP and COO, Carolyn M. Johnson, age 51, $396,667 total compensation
EVP and Chief Risk Officer, Edward M. Berko, age 54
EVP and Chief Risk Officer, Michael (Mike) Temple
Director, Charles D. McCrary, age 60
Director, C. Dowd Ritter, age 65
Vice Chairman and CFO, Richard J. (Rich) Bielen, age 51
Director, John J. McMahon Jr., age 69
Director, Thomas L. (Tom) Hamby, age 62
Director, Jesse J. Spikes
Director, Malcolm Portera, age 65
Director, James S. M. (Jamie) French, age 71
Director, Elaine L. Chao, age 59
Director, W. Michael Warren Jr., age 64
Director, Robert O. (Rob) Burton
Director, Vanessa Leonard, age 51
Director, William A. Terry, age 54
Director, Vanessa Wilson, age 53
Director, Hans H. Miller
Auditors: PricewaterhouseCoopersLLP

LOCATIONS

HQ: Protective Life Corporation
2801 Hwy. 280 South, Birmingham AL 35223
Phone: 205-268-1000 **Fax:** 508-753-5548
Web: www.pwrr.com

PRODUCTS/OPERATIONS

2011 Revenues

	$ mil.	% of total
Life Marketing	1,301	36
Annuities	634	18
Stable Value Products	170	5
Total	**3,566**	**100**

COMPETITORS

AEGON USA
AIG
Ameritas
APCO
C.A.R.S. Protection Plus
CNO Financial
ING Americas
Interstate National Dealer Services
MassMutual
MetLife
Nationwide
New York Life
Northwestern Mutual
Pacific Mutual
Principal Financial
Prudential
Warrantech

HISTORICAL FINANCIALS

Company Type: Public

Income Statement FYE: December 31

	ASSETS ($ mil.)	NET INCOME ($ mil.)	INCOME AS % OF ASSETS	EMPLOYEES
12/11	52,932	339	0.6%	2,332
12/10	47,562	260	0.5%	2,315
12/09	42,311	271	0.6%	2,317
12/08	39,572	(41)	—	2,372
12/07	41,786	289	0.7%	2,406
Annual Growth	6.1%	4.0%	—	(0.8%)

2011 Year-End Financials

Debt ratio: 4.67%
Return on equity: 8.03%
Cash ($ mil.): 267
Current ratio: —
Long-term debt ($ mil.): 2,472
No. of shares (mil.): 81
Dividends
Yield: —
Payout: 15.82%
Market value ($ mil.): 1,842

	STOCK PRICE ($) FY Close	P/E High/Low		PER SHARE ($) Earnings	Dividends	Book Value
12/11	22.56	7	4	3.92	0.00	51.68
12/10	26.64	9	6	2.97	0.54	38.88
12/09	16.55	7	1	3.34	0.48	28.96
12/08	14.35	—	—	(0.59)	0.82	10.89
12/07	41.02	12	10	4.05	0.89	35.02
Annual Growth	(13.9%)	—	—	(0.8%)	—	10.2%

Protective Life Insurance Co

Need protection in New York? Hire a body guard. Need to protect your assets? Protective Life & Annuity Insurance would like to help. Protective Life and Annuity Insurance markets and sells financial security in the form of term and universal life insurance and annuity products. Although the company is based in Alabama and licensed to sell insurance throughout the US it exclusively serves clients in New York. The company sells coverage through independent agents in partnership with employer groups and through its own sales division. Protective Life and Annuity Insurance is a subsidiary of Protective Life Insurance Company which is part of Protective Life Corporation.

Every state has unique requirements that insurance companies must meet in order to gain permission to operate there. New York's insurance code has the stiffest requirements and many small companies simply choose not to operate in that market. However the market is so large and tempting that other companies opt to maintain separate subsidiaries that exclusively serve New York. In this instance parent company Protective Life Insurance Company serves the rest of the US while Protective Life & Annuity is strictly focused on New York.

EXECUTIVES

President and Chief Actuary, Wayne E. Stuenkel, age 58
SVP Controller and Chief Accounting Officer, Steven G. Walker, age 52
CFO, Richard Bielen

VP Marketing, Elizabeth Bell
SVP Human Resources, Scott Adams
Auditors: PricewaterhouseCoopersLLP

LOCATIONS

HQ: Protective Life and Annuity Insurance Company
2801 Hwy. 280 South, Birmingham AL 35223
Phone: 205-268-1000 **Fax:** 203-821-5790
Web: www.sargentlock.com

PRODUCTS/OPERATIONS

COMPETITORS

Guardian Insurance and Annuity
MetLife
New York Life
Penn Mutual
Prudential
The Hartford

HISTORICAL FINANCIALS

Company Type: Subsidiary

Income Statement FYE: December 31

	ASSETS ($ mil.)	NET INCOME ($ mil.)	INCOME AS % OF ASSETS	EMPLOYEES
12/11	52,791	347	0.7%	2,058
12/10	47,476	258	0.5%	1,840
12/09	42,229	277	0.7%	1,935
12/08	39,501	(54)	—	1,957
12/07	41,145	252	0.6%	1,694
Annual Growth	6.4%	8.3%	—	5.0%

2011 Year-End Financials

Debt ratio: 2.37%
Return on equity: 6.45%
Cash ($ mil.): 169
Current ratio: —
Long-term debt ($ mil.): 1,248
No. of shares (mil.): 5
Dividends
Yield: —
Payout: 61.88%
Market value ($ mil.): —

Provident Financial Services Inc

Provident wants to be a prominent force in the New Jersey banking scene. Provident Financial Services owns The Provident Bank which serves individuals businesses and families in about 10 northern and central New Jersey counties. Founded in 1839 the bank offers traditional deposit and lending products as well as wealth management and trust services through more than 80 branches. Commercial real estate loans and residential mortgages each make up more a quarter of the bank's loan portfolio. Business consumer and construction loans help to round out its lending activities. The company's Provident Investment Services subsidiary sells life and health insurance and investment products.

The Provident Bank has no subprime loans on its books but has not been totally immune to the credit crisis either as it has seen its percentage of nonperforming assets increase each year since 2005. The company however also remained profitable each of those years except for 2009 when it recognized a goodwill impairment charge. Although 2011 revnues were down more than $10 million to some $308 million Provident Financial reported record earnings of more than $57 million for the year an increase of some 15% thanks in part to decreased funding costs and higher interest-related income.

Provident Financial remains focused on its conservative lending practices and is seeking to diversify its portfolio and reduce risk by placing more emphasis on commercial real estate multifamily residential and business loans.

In 2011 the company acquired Beacon Trust Company an asset manager for individuals municipalities corporations pension funds and not-for-profit organizations. The deal significantly expanded its wealth management business and boosted its assets under management to some $1.5 billion. It is part of Provident Financial's initiative to grow its fee-based business. The company continues to evaluate additional acquisition opportunities of banks and other financial services providers.

EXECUTIVES

Chairman President and CEO Provident and The Provident Bank, Christopher P. Martin, age 56, $474,308 total compensation
SVP and Chief Accounting Officer, Frank S. Muzio, age 59
EVP and CFO Provident and The Provident Bank, Thomas M. Lyons, age 48, $219,639 total compensation
EVP and Director Retail Banking The Provident Bank, Michael A. Raimonde, age 60, $238,347 total compensation
General Counsel and Corporate Secretary; EVP Chief Administrative Officer and General Counsel The Provident Bank, John F. Kuntz, age 57, $269,500 total compensation
EVP and Chief Lending Officer The Provident Bank, Donald W. Blum, age 56, $282,356 total compensation
EVP and CIO The Provident Bank, Giacomo Novielli, age 53
SVP and Chief Human Resources Officer The Provident Bank, Janet D. Krasowski, age 59
EVP and Chief Credit Officer The Provident Bank, Brian Giovinazzi, age 58, $161,138 total compensation
SVP and Chief Wealth Management Officer The Provident Bank, James D. Nesci, age 40
Director, Jeffries Shein, age 73
Director, Geoffrey M. Connor, age 66
Director, Frank L. Fekete, age 61
Director, Carlos Hernandez, age 63
Board Member, William T. Jackson, age 74
Board Member, Arthur R. McConnell, age 74
Director, Edward O'Donnell, age 62
Director, Terence (Terry) Gallagher
Director, Thomas W. Berry, age 65
Director, Laura L. Brooks, age 60
Director, Katharine Laud, age 54
Director, Thomas B. (Tom) Hogan Jr., age 67
Auditors: KPMGLLP

LOCATIONS

HQ: Provident Financial Services Inc.
239 Washington St., Jersey City NJ 07302
Phone: 732-590-9200 **Fax:** -10852
Web: www.intertek.com

PRODUCTS/OPERATIONS

2011 Sales

	$ mil.	% of total
Interest		
Real estate secured loans	158	52
Commercial loans	42	14
Consumer loans	25	8
Securities & other	48	16
Noninterest		
Fees	25	8
Other	7	2
Total	308	100

COMPETITORS

Bank of America
Capital One
Citibank
Hudson City Bancorp
JPMorgan Chase
New York Community Bancorp
PNC Financial
TD Bank USA
Valley National Bancorp

HISTORICAL FINANCIALS

Company Type: Public

Income Statement FYE: December 31

	ASSETS ($ mil.)	NET INCOME ($ mil.)	INCOME AS % OF ASSETS	EMPLOYEES
12/11	7,097	57	0.8%	963
12/10	6,824	49	0.7%	957
12/09	6,836	(121)	—	998
12/08	6,548	41	0.6%	1,027
12/07	6,359	37	0.6%	1,019
Annual Growth	2.8%	11.3%	—	(1.4%)

2011 Year-End Financials

Debt ratio: 12.97%
Return on equity: 6.02%
Cash ($ mil.): 69
Current ratio: —
Long-term debt ($ mil.): 920
No. of shares (mil.): 59
Dividends
Yield: —
Payout: 46.53%
Market value ($ mil.): 803

	STOCK PRICE ($) FY Close	P/E High/Low		PER SHARE ($) Earnings	Dividends	Book Value
12/11	13.39	15	10	1.01	0.00	15.88
12/10	15.13	18	12	0.88	0.44	15.38
12/09	10.65			(2.16)	0.44	14.79
12/08	15.30	26	15	0.74	0.44	17.09
12/07	14.42	29	22	0.63	0.42	16.78
Annual Growth	(1.8%)	—	—	12.5%	—	(1.4%)

Provident New York Bancorp

Provident New York Bancorp is the holding company for Provident Bank a community-based thrift operating some 35 offices in New York's Hudson Valley region and another in New Jersey operating as Towncenter Bank. Founded in 1888 the bank attracts consumers and business clients by offering traditional deposit products such as checking and savings accounts and CDs; its Provident Municipal Bank subsidiary provides deposit services to area municipalities. The bank uses funds from deposits to originate primarily real estate loans and mortgages. Subsidiary Hudson Valley Investment Advisors provides money management services for institutional and individual investors.

Commercial mortgages business loans and construction loans combined make up more than half of the bank's loan portfolio; residential mortgages make up another quarter. The company has increased its commercial lending activities while maintaining a balanced loan portfolio. However it has experienced an increase in delinquencies since the onset of the credit crisis particularly in loans to small businesses. The company's income and revenue levels dipped as a result. The company has begun implementing cost-cutting measures including layoffs.

Provident Bank was mutually owned until 2004 when the company converted to stock ownership. In a simultaneous transaction Provident New York Bancorp acquired E.N.B. Holding Company which owned Ellenville National Bank and its nine branches. Also that year the company acquired Warwick Community Bancorp which operated in New York and New Jersey. The latter deal brought in Hardenbaugh Abstract Agency which offers title insurance policies and abstracts.

Provident New York's growth strategy also includes building market share on its home turf. Wealthy Westchester County a bedroom community of New York City has been a target area for expansion. In 2012 the company agreed to buy Gotham Bank of New York a single-branch entity in mid-Manhattan.

EXECUTIVES

EVP and CFO, Paul A. Maisch, age 56, $246,993 total compensation
VP and Deputy Auditor, Donna M. Lyons
Vice Chairman, Dennis L. Coyle, age 75
Chairman, William F. Helmer, age 77
President and CEO Provident New York Bancorp and Provident New York Bank, Jack L. Kopnisky, age 56
VP and Accounting Operations Manager, Richard E. Rooney
EVP Strategic Planning and Commercial Lending, Stephen G. Dormer Sr., age 61, $246,993 total compensation
SVP and Director Finance and Management Information Systems, John J. Fitzpatrick, age 55, $144,800 total compensation
SVP Municipal Affairs and Not-for-Profits, Harold J. Peterson
VP and Special Assets, Clarence G. Hartwick
EVP Business Services, Richard O. Jones, age 62, $249,131 total compensation
SVP and Director Commercial Lending, Carl Capuano
SVP and Commercial Loan Team Leader Southern Region, William J. Lamadore
VP and Manager Human Resources, Angelo Agrafiotis
VP and Corporate Services Officer, Barbara S. Boggan
VP and Manager Professional Services Group, Steven T. Breen
VP and Community Business Loan Senior Underwriter, Paul L. Cambreleng
SVP and Chief Credit Officer, John Carothers
SVP and Manager Regional Commercial Loan, Vincent L. DeLucia
SVP and Compliance and Ethics Officer, Gerald D. Filandro
VP and Community Business Loan Officer Southern Region, Carol A. Fitzgerald
VP and Community Business Loan Specialist, Katherine Fitzgerald
SVP and Chief Auditor, Alfred E. Friedman
VP and Credit Group Team Leader, George R. Gallant
SVP and Corporate and Deposit Services, Linda K. LeMond
VP and Manager Administrative Services, Dominic P. Mazza
VP and Manager Purchasing, Vincent G. Mazzillo
VP and Commercial Market Specialist, Thomas A. McGorry
VP and Information Technology Risk Analyst, Irene McManus-Zeig
VP and Assistant Director Sales and Service Support, Mary Ann More
VP and Manager Consumer Loan Administration, Vasco Pereira
VP and Senior Auditor, John R. Retherford
VP and Branch Administration Officer, Jennifer A. Rundle
SVP and Director Human Resources, Jean Strella
VP and Manager Telecommunications Applications, Patricia Sullivan
SVP and Retail Banking Community Business Lending, William Vacca
VP and Commercial Loan Team Leader, Rebecca Brenda Wiener
VP and Director Information Technology, Pamela A. Bariou
VP and Associate General Counsel, Katherine B. Brown
VP and Airmont Business Manager, Steven R. Clenin
VP and Manager Loan Origination, John R. Anderson
VP and Manager Procedures and Special Projects, Susan Barrett-Casement
VP and Manager Commercial Relationship, Suzanne Boyko
VP and Financial and Manager Regulatory Reporting, Holly A. Cavagnolo
VP and Corporate Services Officer, Mary Curley
VP and Community Business Loan Team Leader, Steven D. Drobysh
VP and Manager Business Nanuet and Pearl River, Jane Euell
VP and Mortgage and Consumer Loan Officer, Patricia K. Felipe
VP and Manager Senior Commercial Relationship, Christopher J. Fiorello
VP and Community Business Loan Specialist, David Garlinghouse
VP and Manager Benefits, Anna M. Goas
VP and Controller, Miranda Grimm
VP and District Manager Southern Region, Robert Jiminez
VP Commercial Business Development, Rita L. Kokkoris
VP and Manager Operational Risk, James F. Lee
VP and Manager Loan Origination Department, Jeannie Lynch-O'Connor
VP and Business Manager Warwick, Mary McClurg
VP Municipal Affairs and Not-for-Profits, Thomas M. Nash
VP and Manager Security/BSA/Branch Operations, Edward Sciarabba
VP and District Manager Central Region, Robin Seidman
SVP and Director Sales and Service Support, Barbara A. Shea
VP and Business Manager Kerhonkson, Robin G. Tischmacher
VP and Commercial Relationship Manager, Lawrence Frank Zema
EVP Chief Risk Officer General Counsel and Corporate Secretary, Daniel G. Rothstein, age 64, $273,189 total compensation
SVP and Chief Credit Officer, John Oliver
VP and Manager Commercial Relationship, Peter K. Abt
VP and Manager Commercial Relationship Center, Aloysius F. Colligan
VP and Community Business Loan Officer, Frank W. Armstrong
VP and Manager Commercial Loan Administration, Kathryn A. Tiedemann
VP and Manager Commercial Relationship, Nicole J. Bartuccelli
VP Treasury Operations, John Sillings
VP Portfolio Management, Rachael Bauco
VP and Manager Business Stony Point, Kathleen Alyce Rodriguez
VP and Manager Business Airmont, Steven R. Clenin
VP and Director Marketing, Suzanne M. Copeland
VP and Head Commercial Loan Northern Region, Patrick J. Doulin
VP and Manager Commercial Loan Administration, Brenda C. Edwards
VP and Assistant Controller, Carl J. Ferraro
VP and Manager Business Ellenville and Kerhonkson, William C. Gettel
VP and Executive Plans and Controls Officer, Jerome D. Goldberg
VP and Corporate Services Officer, Juliana M. Rhinefield
VP and Manager Commercial Relationship Center, Michael P. Goldrick
VP and Manager Commercial Real Estate Administration, Carolyn T. Katz
VP and Manager District Northern Region, Michelle L. Mabee-Loughren
VP and Manager Commercial Relationship, John Jameson
VP and Manager Business Hillcrest, Rose M. Johnson
VP Special Assets, Stuart Kratter
VP and Manager Compensation, Jaya Madan Lund
VP and Manager Alternate Delivery Channel, Jennifer A. Myers
Vice Chairman, Dennis L. Coyle, age 75
Director, R. Michael Kennedy, age 60
Director, Thomas G. Kahn, age 69
Director, Judith Hershaft, age 71
Director, Thomas F. Jauntig Jr., age 67
Director, Donald T. McNelis, age 79
Director, William R. Sichol Jr., age 71
Director, Burt Steinberg, age 66
Director, Victoria Kossover, age 56
Director, Carl J. Rosenstock, age 58
Director, Navy E. Djonovic, age 46
Auditors: CroweHorwathLLP

LOCATIONS

HQ: Provident New York Bancorp
400 Rella Blvd., Montebello NY 10901
Phone: 845-369-8040 **Fax:** 845-369-8255
Web: www.providentbanking.com

PRODUCTS/OPERATIONS

2012 Sales

	$ mil.	% of total
Interest		
Loans including fees	91	62
Securities	23	16
Other	1	-
Noninterest		
Deposit fees & service charges	11	8
Net gain on sale of securities	10	7
Investment management fees	3	2
Other	7	5
Adjustments	(0.5)	-
Total	**147**	**100**

Selected Subsidiaries

Hardenburgh Abstract Company Inc.
Provest Services Corp.

Provident Bank
Provident Municipal Bank
Provident REIT Inc. (real estate investment trust)

COMPETITORS

Capital One
Citibank
HSBC USA
JPMorgan Chase
KeyCorp
M&T Bank

HISTORICAL FINANCIALS

Company Type: Public

Income Statement FYE: September 30

	ASSETS ($ mil.)	NET INCOME ($ mil.)	INCOME AS % OF ASSETS	EMPLOYEES
09/12	4,022	19	0.5%	522
09/11	3,137	11	0.4%	550
09/10	3,021	20	0.7%	603
09/09	3,021	25	0.9%	578
09/08	2,984	23	0.8%	593
Annual Growth	7.8%	(4.4%)	—	(3.1%)

2012 Year-End Financials

Debt ratio: 8.58%
Return on equity: 4.05%
Cash ($ mil.): 437
Current ratio: —
Long-term debt ($ mil.): 345
No. of shares (mil.): 44
Dividends
Yield: —
Payout: 46.15%
Market value ($ mil.): 416

	STOCK PRICE ($) FY Close	P/E High	P/E Low	PER SHARE ($) Earnings	Dividends	Book Value
09/12	9.41	19	11	0.52	0.00	11.12
09/11	5.82	35	19	0.31	0.24	11.39
09/10	8.39	19	15	0.54	0.24	11.26
09/09	9.55	20	11	0.67	0.24	10.81
09/08	13.22	24	17	0.61	0.24	10.03
Annual Growth	(8.1%)	—	—	(3.9%)	—	2.6%

Prudential Annuities Life Assurance Corp

LOCATIONS

HQ: Prudential Annuities Life Assurance Corp
One Corporate Drive, Shelton, CT 06484
Phone: 203 926-1888

HISTORICAL FINANCIALS

Company Type:

Income Statement FYE: December 31

	ASSETS ($ mil.)	NET INCOME ($ mil.)	INCOME AS % OF ASSETS	EMPLOYEES
12/11	52,313	(212)	—	0
12/10	57,266	421	0.7%	0
12/09	51,956	83	0.2%	0
12/08	39,551	19	0.1%	501
12/07	45,299	294	0.7%	501
Annual Growth	3.7%	—	—	—

2011 Year-End Financials

Debt ratio: 1.15%
Return on equity: (-19.68)%
Cash ($ mil.): 285
Current ratio: —
Long-term debt ($ mil.): 600
No. of shares (mil.): 0
Dividends
Yield: —
Payout: —
Market value ($ mil.): —

Prudential Financial, Inc.

Prudential Financial wants to make sure its position near the top of the life insurance summit is set in stone. Prudential known for its Rock of Gibraltar logo is one of the top US life insurers and also one of the largest insurance companies worldwide. The firm is perhaps best known for its individual life insurance though it also sells group life and disability insurance as well as annuities. Prudential also offers investment products and services including asset management services mutual funds and retirement planning. In Asia the company operates through its Gibraltar Life Insurance unit.

HISTORY

In 1873 John Dryden founded the Widows and Orphans Friendly Society in New Jersey to sell workers industrial insurance (low-face-value weekly premium life insurance). In 1875 it became The Prudential Friendly Society taking the name from England's Prudential Assurance Co. The next year Dryden visited the English company and copied some of its methods such as recruiting agents from its targeted neighborhoods.

Prudential added ordinary whole life insurance in 1886. By 1900 the firm was selling more than 2000 such policies annually and had 3000 agents in eight states. In 1896 the J. Walter Thompson advertising agency (now the WPP Group) designed Prudential's Rock of Gibraltar logo.

The firm issued its first group life policy in 1916 (Prudential became a major group life insurer in the 1940s). In 1928 it introduced an Accidental Death Benefit which cost it an extra $3 million in benefits the next year alone (death claims rose drastically early in the Depression).

In 1943 Prudential mutualized. The company began decentralizing operations in the 1940s. Later it introduced a Property Investment Separate Account (PRISA) which gave pension plans a real estate investment option. By 1974 the firm was the US's group pension leader.

The insurer bought securities brokerage The Bache Group to form Pru Bache (now Prudential Securities) in 1981. Bache's forte was retail investments an area expected to blend well with Prudential's insurance business. Under George Ball Pru Bache tried to become a major investment banker —but failed. In 1991 Ball resigned leaving losses of almost $260 million and numerous lawsuits involving real estate limited partnerships.

Despite the 1992 settlement of the real estate partnership suits Prudential remained under scrutiny by several states because of "churning" a process in which agents generated commissions by inducing policyholders to trade up to more expensive policies. In 1995 new management led by former Chase Manhattanite Arthur Ryan brought sales under control sold such units as reinsurance and mortgage servicing and put its $6 billion real estate portfolio on the block. (In 1997 it sold its property management unit and Canadian commercial real estate unit; in 1998 it sold its landmark Prudential Center complex in Boston.)

In 1996 regulators from 30 states found that Prudential knew about the churning earlier than it had admitted had not stopped the perpetrators and had even promoted them. A 1997 settlement called for the company to pay restitution but the more than $2 billion estimated cost was thought to be less than the losses customers had suffered.

As the financial services industry continued to restructure Prudential in 1998 announced plans to demutualize. To focus on life insurance the company sold its health care unit to Aetna in 1999. The same year Prudential paid $62 million to resolve more churning claims revamped itself into international institutional and retail divisions and trimmed jobs. Ending its attempts to originate business the company cut 75% of its investment banking staff in 2000.

Demutualized Prudential Financial's 2001 IPO —one of the largest ever in the insurance industry —raised more than $3 billion. Prudential Financial became the holding company name for all operations making Prudential Insurance (the company's former name) a subsidiary and pure life insurer.

Following the IPO Prudential got busy at rearranging its portfolio. It sold off its property/casualty insurance businesses to Liberty Mutual in 2003. Prudential also sold its brokerage division to banking powerhouse Wachovia in 2003 turning Wachovia Securities (38% owned by Prudential) into the third-largest brokerage firm in the US. (Prudential later sold its 38% interest in Wachovia Securities which was renamed Wells Fargo Advisors).

Variable annuities and retirement held a special allure for the company. It bought Swedish insurer Skandia's US annuities operations in 2003 and during 2004 it bought CIGNA's retirement business. It then acquired Allstate's variable annuity business in 2006 and purchased some retirement assets from Union Bank of California for $103 million in 2007.

Prudential agreed to pay NASD a $2 million fine and to reimburse customers nearly $10 million in 2004 because of alleged rules violations regarding the sale of annuities. In late 2006 the company agreed to pay $19 million ($16.5 million in restitution and $2.5 million as penalty) after the New York Attorney General determined that certain payments to insurance brokers amounted to collusion.

The company added to its substantial Japanese operations (which include subsidiary Gibraltar Life) by acquiring Aoba Life Insurance Company in 2004. Its acquired South Korean asset management firm Hyundai Investment and Securities in 2004 and renamed it Prudential Investment Securities. To keep all things in balance the company shuttered its Philippine insurance operations in 2006 and its Dryden Wealth Management business which operated in Europe and Asia in 2005.

Like many in the insurance industry the company took a hit financially in 2008 due to its investments in asset- and mortgage-backed securities. As the global credit markets deteriorated Prudential suffered losses. However revenues and income recovered nicely after market conditions improved in 2009.

Up until late 2009 Prudential's 38% ownership of Wells Fargo Advisors (formerly Wachovia Securities) allowed its customers access to securities brokerage and financial advice; however the company sold its holdings in Wells Fargo Advisors to Wells Fargo for some $4.5 billion in cash. The sale was part a "lookback" transaction agreed upon when Wells Fargo acquired Wachovia in late 2008.

During 2011 the company shed a few operations. It sold its Prudential Bache Global Commodities Group to Jeffries Group for $430 million and offloaded its real estate and relocation services group to Brookfield Asset Management for some $110 million. While that business was placed under Brookfield's Global Relocation Services the business was granted use of the Prudential brand under a licensing agreement.

EXECUTIVES

Vice Chairman, Mark B. Grier, age 59, $882,692 total compensation
Chairman President and CEO, John R. Strangfeld Jr., age 58, $1,038,462 total compensation
EVP and CFO, Richard J. Carbone, age 64, $519,231 total compensation
SVP Corporate Human Resources, Sharon C. Taylor, age 57
EVP; COO U.S. Businesses, Charles F. (Charlie) Lowrey, age 54
EVP; COO International Businesses, Edward P. (Ed) Baird, age 63, $467,308 total compensation
SVP Operations and Systems and CIO, Barbara G. Koster, age 57
SVP Company Actuary and Chief Risk Officer, Helen M. Galt, age 64
SVP and General Counsel, Susan L. Blount, age 54
Chief Communications Officer, Robert (Bob) DeFillippo
Chief Investment Officer, Scott G. Sleyster
Managing Director and CEO DLF Pramerica Life Insurance Company Limited (DPLI), Pavan Dhamija
Vice Chairman, Mark B. Grier, age 59
Director, Karl J. Krapek, age 63
Director, Gordon M. Bethune, age 70
Director, Martina Hund-Mejean, age 51
Director, Constance J. (Connie) Horner, age 70
Director, William H. (Bill) Gray III, age 70
Director, James G. Cullen, age 69
Director, Gilbert F. (Gil) Casellas, age 59
Director, James A. Unruh, age 70
Director, Christine A. (Chris) Poon, age 59
Director, W. Gaston Caperton III, age 72
Director, Thomas J. Baltimore Jr., age 48
Auditors: PricewaterhouseCoopersLLP

LOCATIONS

HQ: Prudential Financial Inc.
751 Broad St., Newark NJ 07102-3777
Phone: 973-802-6000 **Fax:** 863-284-5532
Web: www.publix.com

PRODUCTS/OPERATIONS

2011 Revenues

	$ mil.	% of total
International insurance	19,788	40
US Retirement solutions & investment management	10,820	22
US Individual Life & group insurance	8,968	18
Closed block business	7,015	15
Corporate & adjustments	2,454	5
Total	**49,045**	**100**

Selected Acquisitions

2011
AIG Edison Life Insurance
AIG Star Life Insurance
2009
Yamato Life ($72 million Japan)

COMPETITORS

AEGON
Aetna
Aflac
AIG
Allianz
American Financial Group
American Life Insurance
Aviva
AXA
Berkshire Hathaway
Charles Schwab
Citigroup
COUNTRY Financial
Dai-ichi Life
FMR
Great-West Lifeco
ING
John Hancock Financial Services
MassMutual
Meiji Yasuda Life
Merrill Lynch
MetLife
Nationwide Life Insurance
Nippon Life Insurance
Northwestern Mutual
Principal Financial
Prudential plc
The Hartford
The Vanguard Group
Zurich Financial Services

HISTORICAL FINANCIALS

Company Type: Public

Income Statement FYE: December 31

	ASSETS ($ mil.)	NET INCOME ($ mil.)	INCOME AS % OF ASSETS	EMPLOYEES
12/11	624,521	3,666	0.6%	50,104
12/10	539,854	3,195	0.6%	41,044
12/09	480,203	3,124	0.7%	41,943
12/08	445,011	(1,073)	—	41,844
12/07	485,814	3,704	0.8%	40,703
Annual Growth	6.5%	(0.3%)	—	5.3%

2011 Year-End Financials

Debt ratio: 4.13%
Return on equity: 9.85%
Cash ($ mil.): 14,251
Current ratio: —
Long-term debt ($ mil.): 25,792
No. of shares (mil.): 470
Dividends
Yield: —
Payout: 20.08%
Market value ($ mil.): 23,558

	STOCK PRICE ($) FY Close	P/E High	P/E Low	PER SHARE ($) Earnings	Dividends	Book Value
12/11	50.12	9	6	7.22	0.00	79.19
12/10	58.71	11	8	5.75	1.15	66.73
12/09	49.76	7	1	7.63	0.70	54.29
12/08	30.26	—	—	(2.42)	0.58	31.71
12/07	93.04	13	11	7.61	1.15	52.20
Annual Growth	(14.3%)	—	—	(1.3%)	—	11.0%

PSEG Power LLC

Power player PSEG Power does not play with power it markets it for profit. The company is the independent power production and energy marketing subsidiary of Public Service Enterprise Group (PSEG). The unit owns and/or manages about 25 power stations in Connecticut New Jersey New York and Pennsylvania. It oversees PSEG Nuclear LLC (which operates the Salem and Hope Creek generating stations in New Jersey and owns 50% of the Peach Bottom plant in Pennsylvania) and PSEG Fossil LLC (which has gas oil coal and natural gas power plants). PSEG Power has installed capacity of more than 13000 MW. Its PSEG Energy Resources and Trade unit buys and sells wholesale power natural gas and other energy commodities.

The company oversees the operations of 25 power stations. It operates through three principal direct wholly owned subsidiaries: PSEG Nuclear LLCPSEG Fossil LLC and PSEG Energy Resources and Trade.

PSEG Power operates in Connecticut New Jersey New York and Pennsylvania.

In 2011 the company reported a 8% dip in revenues. That year it also posted a 12% drop in net income due to lower revenues and higher operation and maintenance and depreciation and amortization costs.

PSEG Power integrates its generating assets and gas supply business with its wholesale energy fuel supply energy trading and marketing and risk management operations. PSEG redistributes properties between its units as a way to pay down debt and streamline operations.

In 2011 PSEG Power sold generating assets (two 1000 MW gas-fired plants) in Texas in two separate transactions in order to raise $686 million. The company closed the sale of the Guadalupe plant for $351 million in March 2011 and the Odessa plant for $335 million in July 2011. The proceeds from the sale of the facilities in West Texas and South Texas were used for general corporate purposes.

(In 2009 PSEG transferred to PSEG Power some 2000 MW of traditional generating capacity in Texas from PSEG Energy Holdings as part of a reorganization to focus the latter company on renewable energy development).

EXECUTIVES

EVP CFO and Director, Caroline Dorsa, age 52
VP and Controller, Derek M. Di Risio, age 47
Chairman and CEO, Ralph Izzo, age 54
SVP Fossil Operations, John P. Cowan
Director Corporate Communications, Paul Rosengren
President COO and Director, William (Bill) Levis, age 55
President PSEG Energy Resources & Trade, Clarence J. (Joe) Hopf Jr., age 55
President PSEG Fossil, Richard P. Lopriore, age 62
President and Chief Nuclear Officer PSEG Nuclear, Thomas P. Joyce, age 59
SVP PSEG Nuclear, Robert C. Braun
SVP Power Technology Development and Construction PSEG Fossil, George P. Barnes Jr.
VP Finance Power PSEG Services, Daniel J. (Dan) Cregg
VP Power Operations and Asset Management PSEG Energy Resources and Trade, Raymond V. DePillo
Manager External Affairs, Neil Brown
Media Relations Nuclear, Joe Delmar
VP Salem Generating Station PSEG Nuclear, Carl J. Fricker
Media Relations Fossil, Nancy Tucker-Datrio
Media Relations Fossil, Michael Jennings
Media Relations Fossil and Nuclear, Joseph (Skip) Sindoni
Media Relations, Jennifer (Jenn) Kramer
Director Nuclear Oversight, Brian C. Booth
VP Operations Support PSEG Nuclear, Paul J. Davison
VP Hope Creek PSEG Nuclear, John F. Perry
VP Gas Supply PSEG Energy Resources and Trade, John P. Scarlata
Salem Plant Manager PSEG Nuclear, Ed Eilola
EVP CFO and Director, Caroline Dorsa, age 52
Director, Eileen A. Moran, age 56
Director, Randall E. (Randy) Mehrberg, age 56
President COO and Director, William (Bill) Levis, age 55

Director, Jacob A. (Lon) Bouknight Jr., age 68
Director Nuclear Oversight, Brian C. Booth
Auditors: Deloitte&ToucheLLP

LOCATIONS

HQ: PSEG Power LLC
80 Park Plaza - T25, Newark NJ 07102-4194
Phone: 973-430-7000 **Fax:** 973-623-5389
Web: www.pseg.com

PRODUCTS/OPERATIONS

2011 Fuel Mix

	% of total
Nuclear	56
Oil & natural	29
Coal	15
Total	**100**

Subsidiaries
PSEG Energy Resources and Trade LLC marketing)
PSEG Fossil LLC (gas oil and coal-fired plants)
PSEG Nuclear LLC (nuclear plants)

COMPETITORS

AEP
AES
Calpine
Constellation Generation
Duke Energy
Edison Mission Energy
Exelon
Exelon Energy
GenOnEnergy
InterGen
International Power
NRG Energy
Sempra Generation

HISTORICAL FINANCIALS

Company Type: Subsidiary

Income Statement FYE: December 31

	REVENUE ($ mil.)	NET INCOME ($ mil.)	NET PROFIT MARGIN	EMPLOYEES
12/11	6,143	1,098	17.9%	2,699
12/10	6,558	1,143	17.4%	2,803
12/09	7,143	1,189	16.6%	2,906
12/08	7,770	1,050	13.5%	2,538
12/07	6,796	941	13.8%	2,538
Annual Growth	(2.5%)	3.9%	—	1.5%

2011 Year-End Financials

Debt ratio: 24.81%—
Return on equity: 20.17%
Cash ($ mil.): 12
Current ratio: 297.89
Long-term debt ($ mil.): 2,685
Dividends
Yield: —
Payout: 45.54%
Market value ($ mil.): —

Public Service Enterprise Group Inc.

In the Garden State Public Service Enterprise Group's (PSEG) diversified business model has it smelling like a rose. Regulated subsidiary Public Service Electric and Gas (PSE&G) transmits and distributes electricity to 2.2 million customers and natural gas to 1.8 million customers in New Jersey. Nonregulated subsidiary PSEG Power operates PSEG's generating plants. PSEG Power's 13500-MW generating capacity comes mostly from nuclear and fossil-fueled plants in the US Northeast. Other operations (under PSEG Energy Holdings) include energy infrastructure investments solar and other renewable plant development.

Geographic Reach

Once a major global power player PSEG has sold most of its overseas independent power plant interests in order to focus on its core North American power businesses. In 2011 PSEG Global's international generation portfolio consisted only of three plants in Venezuela with a collective capacity of 160 MW.

Operations

In 2011 PSEG Global (a unit of PSEG Energy Holdings) owned stakes in 14 power plants (545 MW of capacity from fossil fuel and renewable energy sources) primarily in Texas and California.

Financial Analysis

Commodity revenues made up more than 59% of the company's revenues in 2010 although the company made no profit on the supply of energy as the costs were passed through to its customers. On the regulated side of its portfolio lower wholesale power prices and lower gas volumes due to weather conditions dragged down the company's revenues and net income further that year.

To raise cash the company sold its two 1000 MW combined-cycle generation facilities in Texas in separate deals for about $687 million.

HISTORY

Tragedy struck Newark New Jersey in 1903 when a trolley slid down an icy hill and collided with a train killing more than 30 people. While investigating the accident state attorney general Thomas McCarter discovered the mismanagement of the trolley company and many of New Jersey's other transportation gas and electric companies. Planning to buy and consolidate these companies McCarter resigned and established the Public Service Corporation in 1903 with several colleagues.

The company formed divisions for gas utilities electric utilities and transportation companies. The trolley company generated almost half of Public Service's sales during its first year.

In 1924 the gas and electric companies consolidated as Public Service Electric and Gas (PSE&G). A new company was formed that year to operate buses and in 1928 it merged with the trolley company to form Public Service Coordinated Transport (later Transport of New Jersey). PSE&G signed interconnection agreements with two Pennsylvania electric companies in 1928 to form the first integrated power pool —later known as the Pennsylvania-New Jersey-Maryland Interconnection. The Public Utility Holding Company Act of 1935 ushered in the era of regulated regional monopolies ensuring PSE&G a captive market.

During the 1960s PSE&G joined Philadelphia Electric to build its first nuclear plant at Peach Bottom Pennsylvania. The company completed a second nuke in 1977 at Salem New Jersey. Its third one went on line at Hope Creek New Jersey. However plant mismanagement earned PSE&G a slew of fines in the 1980s and 1990s.

The company sold its transportation system to the State of New Jersey in 1980. Five years later PSE&G formed holding company Public Service Enterprise Group (PSEG) to move into nonutility enterprises and created Community Energy Alternatives (CEA now PSEG Global) to invest in independent power projects. In 1989 Enterprise Diversified Holdings (now PSEG Energy Holdings) was formed to handle activities ranging from real estate to oil and gas production.

CEA and three partners acquired a Buenos Aires power plant in 1993. Taking advantage of overseas privatization in the late 1990s it expanded into Asia and with AES purchased two Argentine electric companies.

PSE&G's nuclear problems resurfaced when the Salem plant was shut down in 1995 to rectify equipment breakdowns. In 1997 PSEG paid Salem partners Delmarva Power & Light and PECO Energy $82 million to settle their lawsuits charging mismanagement of Salem; both units were back on line by 1998.

Continuing to diversify in the late 1990s PSEG formed PSEG Energy Technologies in 1997 to market power and acquired five mechanical services companies in 1998 and 1999.

In 1999 PSEG Global teamed up with Panda Energy International to build three merchant plants in Texas (to be completed by 2001). It also planned plants in India and Venezuela and joined Sempra Energy to buy 90% of Chilquinta Energia an energy distributor in Chile and Peru. In 2000 it bought 90% of a distributor serving Argentina and Brazil.

New Jersey's electricity markets were deregulated in 1999; a year later the company transferred PSE&G's generation assets to nonregulated unit PSEG Power. PSEG Power also took charge of PSEG Global's plants under development in Illinois Indiana and Ohio; announced plans for new plants in New Jersey; and acquired an Albany New York plant from Niagara Mohawk.

PSEG Global completed a power plant in Texas in 2001. It also bought 94% of generator and distributor Saesa from Chile's largest conglomerate Copec for $460 million; it later acquired the rest of Saesa through a tender offer. It also purchased a Peruvian generation firm ElectroAndes for $227 million.

In 2002 PSEG Power acquired two Connecticut plants from Wisconsin Energy for approximately $270 million.

PSEG had agreed to be acquired by Exelon but both New Jersey and Pennsylvania opposed the merger and the deal fell through in 2006.

In 2006 PSEG Global sold its 32% stake in RGE a Brazilian electric distribution company with approximately 1.1 million customers to Companhia Paulista de Forca e Luz. In 2008 it sold the SAESA Group of Companies (a power distribution group) in southern Chile to a consortium formed by Morgan Stanley Infrastructure and the Ontario Teachers' Pension Plan for $887 million.

The company's revenues took a hit in 2009 when the global recession and an unusually cool summer in its service region conspired to suppress power demand.

EXECUTIVES

EVP and CFO, Caroline Dorsa, age 52, $386,589 total compensation
EVP Strategy and Development, Randall E. (Randy) Mehrberg, age 56, $542,963 total compensation
SVP Human Resources and Chief Human Resources Officer PSEG Services, Margaret M. Pego
President and COO PSE&G, Ralph A. LaRossa, age 48, $464,728 total compensation
VP and Controller, Derek M. Di Risio, age 47
Chairman President and CEO, Ralph Izzo, age 54, $946,450 total compensation
President and COO PSEG Power, William (Bill) Levis, age 55, $543,960 total compensation
EVP and General Counsel, Jacob A. (Lon) Bouknight Jr., age 68
VP Electric Operations PSE&G, John R. Latka
VP Corporate Planning PSEG Services, Kevin J. Quinn, age 55

VP State Governmental Affairs PSEG Services, Richard T. Thigpen
President PSEG Fossil, Richard P. Lopriore, age 62
President and Chief Nuclear Officer PSEG Power, Thomas P. Joyce, age 59
SVP PSEG Nuclear, Robert C. Braun
VP Mergers Acquisitions and Development and President PSEG Global, Scott S. Jennings
VP Renewables and Energy Solutions PSE&G, Alfredo Z. (Al) Matos
VP Finance Power PSEG Services, Daniel J. (Dan) Cregg
VP Power Operations and Asset Management PSEG Energy Resources and Trade, Raymond V. DePillo
VP Investor Relations, Kathleen A. Lally
VP IT and CIO PSEG Services, Manoj S. Chouthai
VP Policy and Environmental Health and Safety, Eric B. Svenson Jr.
VP Organizational Effectiveness PSEG Services, Michelle Hallerdin
VP Business Assurance and Resilience, Michael S. Paszynsky
VP Business Operations PSEG Services, Patricia R. McLaughlin
VP Customer Operations PSE&G, Joseph A. Forline
VP Human Resources Client Services PSEG Services, Cora Brina
VP Asset Management and Centralized Services PSE&G, David M. Daly
VP and Assistant Controller PSEG Services, Stuart J. Black
SVP Public Affairs and Sustainability PSEG Services Corporation, Anne E. Hoskins
VP Corporate and Commercial PSEG Services, Shawn P. Leyden
VP Regulatory PSEG Services, Tamara L. Linde
VP and Assistant Controller Tax PSEG Services, Robert C. Krueger Jr.
VP Internal Audit Services PSEG Services, William J. Metzger
VP Communications and Advertising PSEG Services, J. Brian Smith
VP Gas Operations PSE&G, Jorge L. Cardenas
VP Salem Generating Station PSEG Nuclear, Carl J. Fricker
VP Fossil Operations PSEG Fossil, John Paul Cowan
VP Operations Support PSEG Nuclear, Paul J. Davison
VP Hope Creek PSEG Nuclear, John F. Perry
VP Federal Affairs PSEG Services Corporation, Kristen Ludecke
VP Compensation and Benefits PSEG Services, Christine M. De Stefano
President PSEG Foundation, Sheila Rostiac
Director, Thomas A. Renyi, age 66
Director, Richard J. (Dick) Swift, age 67
Director, William V. Hickey, age 67
Director, David Lilley, age 65
Director, Albert R. Gamper Jr., age 70
Director, Shirley Ann Jackson, age 64
Director, Conrad K. Harper, age 71
Director, Hak Cheol (H. C.) Shin, age 55
Auditors: Deloitte&ToucheLLP

LOCATIONS

HQ: Public Service Enterprise Group Incorporated
80 Park Plaza, Newark NJ 07101-1171
Phone: 973-430-7000 **Fax:** 973-824-7056
Web: www.pseg.com

PRODUCTS/OPERATIONS

2010 Sales

	$ mil.	% of total
PSE&G	7,869	54
Power	6,558	45
Energy Holdings	137	1
Adjustments	(2771)	-
Total	**11,793**	**100**

Selected Subsidiaries

PSEG Energy Holdings Inc. (nonutility companies)
PSEG Global Inc. (solar plants and other alternative energy investments)
PSEG Resources Inc. (energy infrastructure investments)
PSEG Power LLC
PSEG Fossil LLC (operator of PSEG' s fossil fuel plants)
PSEG Nuclear LLC (operator of PSEG' s nuclear plants)
PSEG Energy Resources and Trade LLC (energy marketing)
PSEG Services Corporation (management and administrative services for PSEG)
Public Service Electric and Gas Company (PSE&G distribution of electricity and gas)

COMPETITORS

AES
CenterPoint Energy
Con Edison
Constellation Energy Group
Delmarva Power
Exelon
FirstEnergy
GenOnEnergy
National Grid USA
New Jersey Resources
NextEra Energy
Northeast Utilities
NRG Energy
PPL Corporation
Sempra Energy
South Jersey Industries
Tractebel Engineering

HISTORICAL FINANCIALS

Company Type: Public

Income Statement FYE: December 31

	REVENUE ($ mil.)	NET INCOME ($ mil.)	NET PROFIT MARGIN	EMPLOYEES
12/11	11,079	1,503	13.6%	9,784
12/10	11,793	1,564	13.3%	9,965
12/09	12,406	1,592	12.8%	10,352
12/08	13,322	1,188	8.9%	9,849
12/07	12,853	1,335	10.4%	9,905
Annual Growth	(3.6%)	3.0%	—	(0.3%)

2011 Year-End Financials

Debt ratio: 27.14%
Return on equity: 14.63%
Cash ($ mil.): 834
Current ratio: 132.26
Long-term debt ($ mil.): 7,461
No. of shares (mil.): 505
Dividends
Yield: —
Payout: 46.28%
Market value ($ mil.): 16,701

	STOCK PRICE ($) FY Close	P/E High/Low		PER SHARE ($) Earnings	Dividends	Book Value
12/11	33.01	12	10	2.96	0.00	20.30
12/10	31.81	11	9	3.08	1.37	19.04
12/09	33.25	11	8	3.14	1.33	17.53
12/08	29.17	44	11	2.34	1.29	15.52
12/07	98.24	38	25	2.62	1.17	14.51
Annual Growth	(23.9%)	—	—	3.1%	—	8.8%

Publix Super Markets, Inc.

Publix Super Markets tops the list of privately owned grocery operators in the US. By emphasizing service and a family-friendly image over price Publix has grown faster and been more profitable than Winn-Dixie Stores and other supermarket rivals. More than two-thirds of its 1040-plus stores are in Florida but it also operates in Alabama Georgia South Carolina and Tennessee. Publix makes some of its own bakery deli dairy goods and fresh prepared foods at its own manufacturing plants in Florida and Georgia. Also many stores house pharmacies and banks. Founder George Jenkins began offering stock to Publix employees in 1930. Employees own about 31% of Publix which is still run by the Jenkins family.

HISTORY

George Jenkins age 22 resigned as manager of the Piggly Wiggly grocery in Winter Haven Florida in 1930. With money he had saved to buy a car he opened his own grocery store Publix next door to his old employer. The small store (named after a chain of movie theaters) prospered despite the Depression and in 1935 Jenkins opened another Publix in the same town.

Five years later after the supermarket format had become popular Jenkins closed his two smaller locations and opened a new more modern Publix Market. With pastel colors and electric-eye doors it was also the first US store to feature air conditioning.

Publix Super Markets bought the All-American chain of Lakeland Florida (19 stores) in 1944 and moved its corporate headquarters to that city. The company began offering S&H Green Stamps in 1953 and in 1956 it replaced its original supermarket with a mall featuring an enlarged Publix and a Green Stamp redemption center. Publix expanded into South Florida in the late 1950s.

As Florida's population grew Publix continued to expand opening its 100th store in 1964. Publix was the first grocery chain in the state to use barcode scanners; all its stores had the technology by 1981. The company beat Florida banks in providing ATMs and during the 1980s opened debit card stations.

Publix continued to grow in the 1980s safe from takeover attempts because of its employee ownership. In 1988 it installed the first automated checkout systems in South Florida giving patrons an always-open checkout lane.

The chain stopped offering Green Stamps in 1989 and most of the $19 million decrease in Publix advertising expenditures was attributed to the end of the 36-year promotion. That year after almost six decades "Mr. George" —as founder Jenkins was known —stepped down as chairman in favor of his son Howard. (George died in 1996.)

In 1991 Publix opened its first store outside Florida in Georgia as part of its plan to become a major player in the Southeast. Publix entered South Carolina in 1993 with one supermarket; it also tripled its presence in Georgia to 15 stores.

The United Food and Commercial Workers Union began a campaign in 1994 against alleged gender and racial discrimination in Publix's hiring promotion and compensation policies.

Publix opened its first store in Alabama in 1996. That year a federal judge allowed about 150000 women to join a class-action suit filed in 1995 by 12 women who had sued Publix charging that the company consistently channeled female employees into low-paying jobs with little chance for good promotions. The case which at the time was said to be the biggest sex discrimination lawsuit ever was set to go to trial but in 1997 the company paid $82.5 million to settle and another $3.5 million to settle a complaint of discrimination against black applicants and employees.

Publix promised to change its promotion policies but two more lawsuits alleging discrimination against women and blacks were filed in 1997 and 1998. The suit filed on behalf of the women was denied class-action status in 2000. Later that year the company settled the racial discrimination lawsuit for $10.5 million. Howard Jenkins stepped down as CEO in mid-2001; his cousin Charlie Jenkins took the helm.

In mid-2002 Publix made an equity investment in Florida-based Crispers a chain of 13 quick-serve restaurants targeting health-conscious diners. Also that year Publix entered the Nashville Tennessee market with the purchase of seven Albertsons supermarkets a convenience store and a fuel center.

Publix pulled the plug in 2003 on its online store PublixDirect which offered delivery service in parts of Florida citing disappointing sales. However it added 78 bricks-and-mortar stores in 2003.

In 2004 Publix acquired three Florida stores from Kash n' Karry a subsidiary of Belgium's Delhaize Group. Also that year it became the majority owner of Crispers.

Publix introduced the Hispanic-themed Sabor format in 2005 in Kissimmee Florida.

In 2007 the chain began offering seven popular antibiotics free at some 685 Publix Pharmacies. The drugs account for almost 50% of the generic pediatric prescriptions filled at Publix. That year Publix opened its first GreenWise Market in Palm Beach Gardens Florida. Also in 2007 the company launched a new store format called GreenWise Market (the name Publix has already given to its store-within-a-store natural/organic sections and private-label line of specialty foods) to court more health-conscious consumers and compete with national organic chains such as Whole Foods.

CEO Charlie Jenkins retired in 2008 and was succeeded by his cousin and Publix president Ed Crenshaw. The company completed the roughly $500 million acquisition of 49 Albertsons stores in Florida the same year.

In May 2011 Publix sold its 36 Crispers restaurants in Florida (acquired in 2007) to Healthy Food Concepts LLC an affiliate of a Florida-based investment group thereby exiting the restaurant business.

EXECUTIVES

VP, Thomas M. McLaughlin, age 61
VP, Mark R. Irby, age 56
CFO and Treasurer, David P. Phillips, age 52, $610,870 total compensation
VP, William V. (Bill) Fauerbach, age 65
Vice Chairman, Hoyt R. (Barney) Barnett, age 68, $309,000 total compensation
CEO and Director, William E. (Ed) Crenshaw, age 61, $777,400 total compensation
VP, M. Clayton Hollis Jr., age 55
Chairman, Charles H. (Charlie) Jenkins Jr., age 68, $213,957 total compensation
SVP General Counsel and Secretary, John A. Attaway Jr., age 53, $416,000 total compensation
VP, David E. Bornmann, age 54
VP, David S. (Dave) Duncan, age 58
VP, David E. Bridges, age 62
VP and Controller, G. Gino DiGrazia, age 49
VP and Controller, Sandra J. (Sandy) Estep, age 52
VP and Assistant Secretary, Linda S. Kane, age 46
VP, Linda S. Hall, age 52
VP, Dale S. Myers, age 59
Director Media and Community Relations, Maria Brous
VP, Alfred J. Ottolino, age 46
President, Randall T. Jones Sr., age 49, $622,193 total compensation
SVP, John T. Hrabusa, age 56
VP, Michael R. (Mike) Smith, age 52
VP, Scott E. Brubaker, age 53
SVP and CIO, Laurie Z. Douglas, age 48, $517,400 total compensation
Director Marketing and Advertising, Kevin Lang
VP Risk Management, Marc H. Salm, age 51
SVP, Charles B. Roskovich Jr., age 50
VP, Joseph (Joe) DiBenedetto Jr., age 52
VP Real Estate, Jeffrey G. Chamberlain, age 55
Vice Chairman, Hoyt R. (Barney) Barnett, age 68
CEO and Director, William E. (Ed) Crenshaw, age 61
Director, Howard M. Jenkins, age 60
Director, Carol Jenkins Barnett, age 55
Director, E. Vane McClurg, age 70
Director, Maria A. Sastre, age 57
Director, Sherrill W. Hudson, age 69
Director, Jane B. Finley, age 65
Auditors: KPMGLLP

LOCATIONS

HQ: Publix Super Markets, Inc.
3300 Publix Corporate Parkway, Lakeland, FL 33811
Phone: 863 688-1188
Web: www.publix.com

2011 Supermarkets

	No.
Florida	743
Georgia	179
Alabama	49
South	45
Tennessee	30
Total	**1,046**

PRODUCTS/OPERATIONS

2011 Sales

	% of total
Grocery	86
Other	14
Total	**100**

Selected Supermarket Departments

Bakery
Banking
Dairy
Deli
Ethnic foods
Floral
Groceries
Health and beauty care
Housewares
Meat
Pharmacy
Photo processing
Produce
Seafood
Foods Processed
Baked goods
Dairy products
Deli items

COMPETITORS

ALDI
BI-LO
Costco Wholesale
CVS Caremark
Harris Teeter Supermarkets
IGA
Ingles Markets
Kerr Drug
Kmart
Kroger
Nash-Finch
Rite Aid
Sedano' s
Sweetbay
The Pantry
Wal-Mart
Walgreen
Whole Foods
Winn-Dixie

HISTORICAL FINANCIALS

Company Type: Private

Income Statement FYE: December 31

	REVENUE ($ mil.)	NET INCOME ($ mil.)	NET PROFIT MARGIN	EMPLOYEES
12/11	27,178	1,491	5.5%	152,000
12/10	25,328	1,338	5.3%	148,000
12/09	24,514	1,161	4.7%	142,000
12/08	24,109	1,089	4.5%	144,000
12/07	23,193	1,183	5.1%	144,000
Annual Growth	4.0%	6.0%	—	1.4%

2011 Year-End Financials

Debt ratio: 1.19%
Return on equity: 24.22%
Cash ($ mil.): 366
Current ratio: 136.69
Long-term debt ($ mil.): 119
No. of shares (mil.): 779
Dividends
Yield: —
Payout: 27.89%
Market value ($ mil.): —

	STOCK PRICE ($) FY Close	P/E High/Low	PER SHARE ($) Earnings	Dividends	Book Value
12/11	0.00	— —	1.90	0.00	10.64
12/10	0.00	15 9	1.70	0.00	9.30
12/09	105.00	75 71	1.47	0.00	8.07
Annual Growth	—	— —	13.7%	—	14.8%

PulteGroup, Inc.

PulteGroup pulls its weight in providing homes for American families. The company became the top homebuilder in the US when it merged with rival Centex in 2009. The company which targets a cross-section of homebuyers around the country buys land to build single-family houses duplexes townhouses and condominiums. Its Centex brand is marketed to entry-level buyers while Pulte Homes are targeted towards customers looking to trade up. PulteGroup also builds Del Webb retiree communities mostly in Sun Belt locales for the growing number of buyers in the 55-plus age range. The company sells its homes in some 70 markets across 30 states. In 2011 its homes sold for an average price of $259000.

HISTORY

William Pulte built his first home in Detroit in 1950 and incorporated his business in 1956 as William J. Pulte Inc.

In 1961 the company built its first subdivision in Detroit. During that decade Pulte moved into Washington DC (1964) Chicago (1966) and Atlanta (1968). In 1969 Pulte merged with Colorado's American Builders to form the Pulte Home Corporation a publicly traded company.

Originally a builder of high-priced single-family homes Pulte began expanding into affordable and midrange housing markets. To lower costs it pioneered modular designs and prebuilt components. Pulte architects designed the Quadrominium a large structure with four separate two-bedroom units each with its own entrance and garage (priced at a mere $20000 per unit in the 1970s).

Pulte formed Intercontinental Mortgage (later renamed ICM Mortgage) and began making home loans in 1972. The company ran into trouble in 1988 when it was accused of forcing Pulte homebuyers in Baltimore to use ICM financing instead of cheaper loans from the county. Pulte settled by repaying the difference in loan costs.

By the mid-1980s Pulte was one of the US's largest on-site homebuilders. PHM Corporation was created in 1987 as a holding company for the Pulte group of companies. That year PHM entered the thrift business by assisting the Federal Savings and Loan Insurance Corp.'s S&L bailout. It acquired five Texas S&Ls (with assets of $1.3 billion) for $45 million and eventually combined them to form First Heights (finally discontinuing the business in 1994).

Pulte Homes' Quality Leadership customer satisfaction program introduced in the early 1990s paid off in 1991 as Pulte enjoyed record sales despite a depressed home market. Renamed Pulte Corporation in 1993 the company soon faced rising interest rates which dampened the US housing market and affected the Mexican peso. Pulte recorded a $2 million foreign-currency loss on an affordable-housing venture in Mexico in 1994. Nonetheless it began a second joint venture in that country in 1995 and helped form mortgage bank Su Casita with nine Mexican homebuilders to finance home construction on its border. That year it also started developing retirement communities when it bought the Ponds at Clearbrook in New Jersey.

In 1996 its Mexican joint venture Condake-Pulte began building thousands of affordable homes for General Motors and Sony employees in "maquiladora" residential areas near the US-Mexico border. The company also bought Rhode Island's top homebuilder LeBlanc.

Pulte restructured in 1997 and a year later shed its manufactured housing and building supply business. It also acquired DiVosta one of Florida's largest homebuilders and Tennessee-based Radnor Homes.

The company's 1988 foray into S&Ls came back to haunt it in 1998: The Federal Deposit Insurance Corp. won a lawsuit that accused the builder of abusing tax benefits associated with the S&Ls. (Pulte settled the case in 2001 by paying $41.5 million.) In 1999 Pulte bought the interest held by investment firm Blackstone Group its partner in active-adult homebuilding.

The next year Pulte joined other builders in an Internet-based building materials cooperative. Also in 2000 the company began dealings to expand its homebuilding operations into Argentina.

The company changed its name to Pulte Homes in 2001. That year Mark O'Brien became the company's CEO. He directed Pulte through the major acquisition of retirement community developer Del Webb for about $800 million in stock and $950 million in assumed debt. The combined company became the largest US homebuilder. In 2002 Pulte reorganized the structure of its operations in Mexico and created Pulte Mexico S. de R.L. de C.V. one of the largest builders in that country.

Adding to its portfolio of accolades Pulte was named 2002 "Builder of the Year" by "Professional Builder" magazine and in 2003 Pulte ranked 19th among the "Top 50 Best-Performing Companies" in Business Week's performance rankings of the Standard & Poor's 500-stock index.

Pulte expanded its operations in the fast-growing San Diego area in 2003 by purchasing assets of ColRich Communities which included about 500 entitled lots in five communities in the South Bay and Coastal North areas of San Diego. It boosted its presence in the Albuquerque Phoenix and Tucson markets by acquiring Sivage-Thomas Homes (Albuquerque) with about 7000 lots in the region and Del Webb entered the Reno Nevada market with its Sierra Canyon active adult community. O'Brien left the company in June 2003 after having served in senior management positions for six years (and 21 total years) within the company. EVP and COO Richard Dugas stepped up to become the company's president and CEO at that time.

In September 2003 the US Court of Federal Claims awarded Pulte and related parties $48.7 million as a result of a breach of contract by the US government related to Pulte's acquisition of five savings and loans in 1988.

J.D. Power and Associates recognized Pulte as a top performer for its fifth consecutive year in its "2004 New Home Builder Customer Satisfaction Study." Out of the 25 markets it surveyed Pulte ranked highest in 14 markets #2 in nine markets and #3 in six markets.

At the close of 2004 Pulte sold some operations in Argentina to real estate developer Grupo Farallon. The next year it sold its Mexican and remaining Argentine homebuilding enterprises to focus exclusively on US operations.

The downturn in the US housing market —due to a toxic cocktail of higher home prices increased foreclosures high unemployment and constraints on mortgage lending —led to weakened demand for new homes and higher cancellation rates. For Pulte this trend meant decreased profitability and a decline in homebuilding activity. Pulte responded to the downturn and adjusted its operations by cutting jobs and shuttering plants to meet lower demand levels.

The company bought rival Centex in 2009. The acquisition made Pulte the largest homebuilder in the US and also strengthened Pulte's offerings in the lower-priced home segment.

A year following the Centex merger founder William Pulte retired from the company and from its board of directors. He was named chairman emeritus.

EXECUTIVES

Vice Chairman, Timothy R. (Tim) Eller, age 63
VP and Treasurer, Bruce E. Robinson, age 50
VP Tax and Assistant Secretary, Gregory M. Nelson, age 56
Chairman President and CEO, Richard J. Dugas Jr., age 46, $1,000,000 total compensation
President North Florida Division, Peter J. Keane, age 46, $615,010 total compensation
Manager Corporate Communications, Jacque Petroulakis
President Gulf Coast Area, Harmon D. Smith
President Central Area, Patrick J. Beirne
VP and CIO, Jerry R. Batt, age 61
President and CEO Pulte Mortgage, Debra W. (Deb) Still
President Illinois and Michigan Division, Steven S. (Steve) Atchison, age 42
SVP and Chief Marketing Officer, Deborah W. Meyer, age 49
EVP Human Resources, James R. (Jim) Ellinghausen, age 53, $475,000 total compensation
SVP General Counsel and Secretary, Steven M. Cook, age 53, $355,000 total compensation
VP Merchandising, Janice M. Jones
President East Area, John B. Bertero III
President Pacific Northwest Division, R. John Ochsner
EVP and CFO, Robert T. O'Shaughnessy, age 46
VP Investor Communications, James P. (Jim) Zeumer
President Indianapolis and Cleveland Division, Anthony W. (Tony) Barbee Jr.
VP Strategic Planning, Stephen P. (Steve) Schlageter
VP Sales and Marketing Austin, Lance Gunn
President Southern California Division, Christopher S. (Chris) Haines
President West Area, J. Steven (Steve) Kalmbach
President Sacramento and Reno Division, Christopher B. (Chris) Cady
President Colorado Division, Matthew W. (Matt) Mandino
President Arizona Division, John J. Chadwick
President St. Louis Division, Curtis H. VanHyfte
President Tennessee Division, Charles A. (Charlie) Coleman
President San Antonio Division, Laurin J. Darnell
President Houston Division, James A. (Jim) Rorison
President New England Division, James R. (Jim) McCabe
President Northeast Corridor Division, Paul Schneier
President Georgia Division, Andrew C. (Casey) Hill
President Charlotte Division, Jon Cherry
President Central Texas Division, Jay A. Thompson
President South Florida Division, Ryan Marshall
VP and Controller, Michael J. Schweninger, age 43
Manager Corporate Communications, Valerie Dolenga
Manager Corporate Communications, Eric Younan
President Dallas/Ft. Worth Division, Bryan Swindell
President Las Vegas Division, Scott Wright
President Mid Atlantic Division, Lewis Birnbaum
President Minnesota Division, Marv McDaris
President New Mexico Division, Jay Gillilan
President South Carolina Coastal Division, Will Cutler
VP Finance and Homebuilding Operations, James L. Ossowski
President Raleigh Division, Lawrence Lane
VP Corporate Communications, Travis M. Parman
VP National Homebuilding Operations, Michael P. Wyatt
President Bay Area Division, Dan Carroll
Director, Brian P. Anderson, age 61
Vice Chairman, Timothy R. (Tim) Eller, age 63
Director, Cheryl W. Grise, age 60
Director, Patrick J. O'Leary, age 54
Director, Bryce Blair, age 53
Director, David N. McCammon, age 77
Director, James J. Postl, age 66
Director, Debra J. Kelly-Ennis, age 55
Director, Bernard W. (Bernie) Reznicek, age 75
Auditors: Ernst&YoungLLP

LOCATIONS

HQ: PulteGroup, Inc.
100 Bloomfield Hills Parkway, Suite 300, Bloomfield Hills, MI 48304
Phone: 248 647-2750 **Fax:** 248 433-4598
Web: www.pulte.com

2011 Sales

	$ mil.	% of total
North	740	18
Northeast	717	17
Southwest	697	17
Southeast	675	16
Texas	631	15
Florida	571	14
Financial services	103	3
Total	**4,136**	**100**

Homebuilding Regions
Florida
North (IL IN MI MN MO Northern CA OH OR WA)
Northeast (CT DE MD MA NJ NY PA RI VA)
Southeast (GA NC SC TN)
Southwest (AZ CO HI NV NM Southern CA)
Texas

PRODUCTS/OPERATIONS

2011 Sales

	$ mil.	% of total
Homebuilding		
Home sales	3950.7	96
Land sales	82.9	2
Financial services	103	2
Total	**4,136**	**100**

Selected Brands

Centex
Del Webb
DiVosta Homes
Fox & Jacobs
Pulte Homes

COMPETITORS

Beazer Homes
D.R. Horton
Hovnanian Enterprises
KB Home
Lennar
M.D.C.
Meritage Homes
NVR
Pardee Homes
Standard Pacific
The Ryland Group
Toll Brothers

HISTORICAL FINANCIALS

Company Type: Public

Income Statement FYE: December 31

	REVENUE ($ mil.)	NET INCOME ($ mil.)	NET PROFIT MARGIN	EMPLOYEES
12/11	4,136	(210)	—	3,579
12/10	4,569	(1,096)	—	4,363
12/09	4,084	(1,182)	—	5,700
12/08	6,289	(1,473)	—	5,300
12/07	9,263	(2,255)	—	8,500
Annual Growth	(18.3%)	—	—	(19.4%)

2011 Year-End Financials

Debt ratio: 44.85%
Return on equity: (-10.85)%
Cash ($ mil.): 1,083
Current ratio: 1239.78
Long-term debt ($ mil.): 3,088
No. of shares (mil.): 382
Dividends
Yield: —
Payout: —
Market value ($ mil.): 2,414

	STOCK PRICE ($) FY Close	P/E High/Low	PER SHARE ($) Earnings	Dividends	Book Value
12/11	6.31	— —	(0.55)	0.00	5.07
12/10	7.52	— —	(2.90)	0.00	5.59
12/09	10.00	— —	(3.94)	0.12	8.39
12/08	10.93	— —	(5.81)	0.16	10.98
12/07	10.54	— —	(8.94)	0.16	16.80
Annual Growth	(12.0%)	— —	—	—	(25.9%)

PVH Corp

PVH has the buttoned-down look all sewn up. A top apparel firm worldwide and key US dress-shirt maker PVH sells clothes accessories and shoes for men women and children under its own brands such as Calvin Klein Van Heusen Tommy Hilfiger IZOD and ARROW. It sells other brands under license including Geoffrey Beene CHAPS DKNY and Nautica and offers private-label goods. PVH distributes to department stores; it generates nearly a third of its revenue from wholesale clients Macy's Kohl's JCPenney and Wal-Mart. The apparel manufacturer also peddles its products through some 650 outlet stores in the US. In mid-2011 the company dropped the Phillips-Van Heusen name in favor of a simpler moniker PVH.

The name change reflects the company's emphasis over the past decade on its diversified portfolio of brands. PVH said its transformation into one of the world's largest apparel firms started with the acquisition of Calvin Klein in 2003 and carried through to its purchase of Tommy Hilfiger Group (THG) in 2010. The deals were monumental for PVH; the Calvin Klein and Tommy Hilfiger brands generate more than 75% of the company's sales and profits. The two lifestyle and apparel labels are also central to PVH's future growth initiatives.

Boosting its business further PVH in late 2012 agreed to acquire The Warnaco Group which holds the Calvin Klein jeans and underwear licensing agreements in a deal valued at $2.9 billion. The purchase which offers PVH global control of the Calvin Klein brand gives Warnaco shareholders a combined 10% stake in the larger company.

Previously the company's purchase of THG had capped off several years of brand building. The company which already had been selling the Tommy Hilfiger brand under license wrote a check to London-based private equity firm Apax Partners for E2.2 billion (about $3 billion) in cash to fold the brand into its bulging portfolio. As part of the agreement PVH forked over about E276 million ($378 million) worth of its stock and assumed E100 million ($137 million) in debt. Both companies which boast well-known iconic brands create an international apparel powerhouse with an expected annual revenue of about $4.6 billion (about E3.4 billion). Buying THG gave PVH greater access to higher-margin overseas markets; THG generates about 60% of its sales in international markets.

Part of PVH's long-standing strategy has been to grow its Calvin Klein brands globally. The firm has three brand tiers that cater to different markets positioning and channels. Its Calvin Klein business comprises brand names Calvin Klein Collection ck Calvin Klein and Calvin Klein (white label) to capture several marketing opportunities. To give it greater control PVH in 2008 acquired CMI the licensee of the high-end collection of apparel and accessories for men and women. It's using its bridge brand ck Calvin Klein to help PVH extend its reach into Europe and Asia which supports the brand's upper-moderate price range. The company's also opening stores in China Southeast Asia Japan Europe and the Middle East under the ck Calvin Klein banner. It operates more than 60 freestanding stores in those regions with some 30 more expected to be opened by licensees by the end of 2010. PVH believes its white-label Calvin Klein brand offers it the most growth opportunities in North America by showcasing its men's sportswear business licensing men's and women's apparel and accessories adding new fragrances and underwear brands and pursuing licensing deals for new products.

To extend its reach into niche markets PVH bought privately held necktie maker Superba for more than $110 million in 2007 to market Calvin Klein and IZOD neckwear. The company offers men's and women's sunglasses through a licensing agreement with Marchon Eyewear. Other licensing deals include watches footwear and handbags. (In a new marketing idea the company won the bid to put its name on a New Jersey sports arena home of the New Jersey Nets basketball team which was renamed the IZOD Center in October 2007.)

While PVH is entering new markets the company has been fine-tuning its licensing and international strategies. In 2008 PVH partnered with Timberland in a licensing agreement to make men's apparel (in 2008) and women's apparel (in 2009). PVH also partnered with G-III Apparel Group in December 2007 to manufacture and distribute Calvin Klein Performance-branded clothing for women. The line targets active sporting goods and specialty stores in the US Canada and Mexico.

PVH has made several moves in recent years in an effort to gain global control of the Van Heusen brand. PVH acquired the Van Heusen label for Europe and Asia from UK-based Coats Viyella. PVH licensed the brand back to the previous owner giving the company distribution rights in the UK and Ireland. PVH extended the reach for IZOD's European unit as well by partnering with Rousseau SAS in mid-2006. Rousseau markets and distributes an IZOD-branded men's sportswear line sold in France Belgium Andorra Luxembourg and Monaco.

While PVH is expanding its business it's keeping an eye on expenses. Looking to stay ahead of the US economic downturn and lower its operating costs PVH in 2009 shuttered some 175 stores and shed about 400 employees –comprising 250 salaried positions and 150 people from its neckwear unit.

FMR owns about 10% of the company while Earnest Partners holds a more than 7% stake in PVH. In mid-2005 chairman Bruce Klatsky passed his CEO title to Mark Weber. Weber left within a year and was replaced by president and COO Emanuel Chirico. Klatsky retired in 2007 after nearly 36 years with the firm. Chirico who assumed the title of chairman and Klatsky had worked together for about two decades.

HISTORY

Moses Phillips came to America from Poland in 1881. While living in a one-room apartment in Pottsville Pennsylvania he sold flannel shirts (which his wife sewed) to coal miners from a pushcart. He soon brought the rest of his family to the US and upgraded the pushcart to a horse and buggy. Business continued to grow and the Phillips-Jones Corporation was formed in 1907.

The company moved to New York in 1914 and control passed from father to son for four generations. Isaac followed Moses then Seymour took over in 1941 until he handed the reins to Lawrence who joined the company in 1948 and became president and CEO in 1969. Ads in the 1950s featured such actors as Anthony Quinn Burt Lancaster and Ronald Reagan in Van Heusen shirts. In 1957 the company received its present name. Phillips-Van Heusen (PVH) grew via acquisitions throughout the 1970s and began selling its merchandise at its own outlet stores in 1979 but it didn't want its products sold at the off-price outlets that became popular in the early 1980s. The company stopped doing business with stores and distributors that allowed PVH merchandise to reach cut-price vendors.

In 1987 PVH acquired G. H. Bass & Co. maker of Bass and Weejun shoes for $79 million. It also bought back over 5 million shares of stock in order to fend off an acquisition bid by the Hunt family of Texas. Lawrence stepped down in 1993 ending the unbroken chain of Phillipses at the helm. Bruce Klatsky a human rights supporter who had started work at the company 22 years earlier as a merchandising trainee took over as CEO. In 1995 the Phillips family sold its stake in the business. PVH acquired the Gant and IZOD brands (and about 90 outlet stores) from Crystal Brands that year for about $115 million.

The company's retail outlet stores had driven its growth between 1985 and 1995 but a weakening in outlet store sales caused a downturn in 1994. During 1995 and 1996 PVH closed 218 of its poorest performing stores. Klatsky also closed three US shirt factories in 1995 as the company moved more of its production overseas.

PVH decided to close 150 more outlet stores (affecting 700 jobs) reposition Gant as a premium brand and exit the private-label sweater manufacturing business in 1997. A major marketing push that year earmarked nearly $40 million for advertising (compared to the $1.2 million advertising budget in 1996). Klatsky ended an organized labor controversy at PVH's Guatemala operation in 1997 by meeting with union officials and ratifying a union contract.

After a repositioning attempt failed to move Bass upscale (but resulted in a $54 million charge) the company in 1998 cited the expense of doing business in the US when it closed its Bass shoe manufacturing plant in Wilton Maine (where Bass had been founded in 1876). PVH then shifted the manufacturing to plants in Puerto Rico and the Dominican Republic.

In 1999 PVH sold Gant to the brand's international licensee Pyramid Partners (in which PVH has a minority stake) for $71 million. In 2000 the company purchased Cluett Designer Group (a licensee for Kenneth Cole dress shirts) from Cluett American; it also licensed the Arrow shirts and sportswear brand from Cluett American. Coats Viyella the UK-based owner of the Van Heusen brand in Europe and Asia sold the label to PVH in February 2001 for $17.5 million. PVH then licensed the brand to Coats Viyella for use in the UK and Ireland. That November the company announced it would lay off 1200 employees due to a sluggish retail environment.

PVH bought most of fashion design giant Calvin Klein in 2003 renewing its commitment to apparel and divesting of its footwear endeavors.

Bruce Klatsky stepped down as CEO of the company (but remained chairman) in mid-2005. Former president and COO Mark Weber was tapped as his replacement. He lasted about eight months in that position. Emanuel Chirico was named to the top spot in 2006 when Weber left the company.

PVH has made several moves in recent years in an effort to gain global control of the Van Heusen brand. PVH acquired the Van Heusen label for Europe and Asia from UK-based Coats Viyella. PVH licensed the brand back to the previous owner giving the company distribution rights in the UK and Ireland. PVH extended the reach for IZOD's European unit as well by partnering with Rousseau SAS in mid-2006. Rousseau markets and distributes an IZOD-branded men's sportswear line sold in France Belgium Andorra Luxembourg and Monaco.

In 2008 PVH acquired the rights to produce neckwear under the Kenneth Cole New York and Liz Claiborne brands among others from privately held Mulberry Thai Silks for about $10 million. A couple years later in 2010 PVH purchased iconic brand Tommy Hilfiger Group from investor Apax Partners for the equivalent of about $3 billion.

In June 2011 the company renamed itself PVH Corp. officially dropping the Phillips-Van Heusen moniker.

EXECUTIVES

EVP Logistics and Technology, Jon D. Peters
President Van Heusen Retail, Margaret P. Lachance
COO Global Supply Chain, Ellen Constantinides
Chairman and CEO, Emanuel (Manny) Chirico, age 54, $1,000,000 total compensation
President, Allen E. Sirkin, age 69, $936,667 total compensation
President and CEO Calvin Klein, Paul Thomas (Tom) Murry III, age 61, $850,000 total compensation
SVP Human Resources, David F. Kozel
SVP General Counsel and Secretary, Mark D. Fischer
President Tommy Hilfiger Sportswear North America, Molly Yearick
EVP; Chief Operating and Financial Officer, Michael A. (Mike) Shaffer, age 49, $475,000 total compensation
CEO Wholesale Apparel, Francis Kenneth (Ken) Duane, age 55, $800,000 total compensation
President Dress Furnishings, Marc Schneider
Group President Wholesale Sportswear, Malcolm Robinson
President Bass Retail, Scott H. Orenstein
President IZOD Retail, Donna Patrick
President Licensing, Kenneth L. (Ken) Wyse
CEO Tommy Hilfiger; CEO International Operations, Fred Gehring, age 57
EVP Marketing, Michael Kelly
SVP and Controller, Bruce Goldstein
President and COO Calvin Klein Retail, Steven B. Shiffman
President PVH Dress Shirts, Mitchell Lechner
President Van Heusen and Arrow Sportswear, Geoffrey Barrett
President IZOD and Timberland Sportswear, Cheryl Dapolito
EVP and General Counsel Calvin Klein, Pamela Bradford
EVP Logistics Services, Kevin Urban
VP and General Manager Canadian Retail Operations, Andrea Elliott
SVP Business Development and Investor Relations and Treasurer, Dana Perlman
President Calvin Klein Men's Sportswear, Alexander Cannon
VP and Assistant Corporate Controller, James Holmes
Director, Craig W. Rydin, age 60
Director, David A. Landau, age 46
Director, Henry J. Nasella, age 65
Director, Mary Baglivo, age 54
Director, Joseph B. (Joe) Fuller, age 55
Director, Bruce Maggin, age 69
Director, Margaret L. Jenkins, age 60
Director, V. James Marino, age 61
Director, Rita M. Rodriguez, age 69
Director, Christian Stahl, age 41
Auditors: Ernst&YoungLLP

LOCATIONS

HQ: PVH Corp.
200 Madison Ave., New York NY 10016
Phone: 212-381-3500 **Fax:** 212-381-3950
Web: www.pvh.com

2010 Sales

	$ mil.	% of total
US	2,129	89
Other countries	269	11
Total	**2,398**	**100**

PRODUCTS/OPERATIONS

2010 Sales

	$ mil.	% of total
Net sales	2,070	86
Royalty revenue	245	10
Advertising & other revenue	82	4
Total	**2,398**	**100**

Selected Brands

Arrow (owned)
Bass/GH Bass (owned)
BCBG Max Azria (licensed)
Calvin Klein (owned)
DKNY (licensed)
Geoffrey Beene (licensed)
IZOD (owned)
Reaction by Kenneth Cole (licensed)
Tommy Hilfiger (owned)
Van Heusen (owned)

COMPETITORS

Allen-Edmonds
Armani
Berkshire Hathaway
Brown Shoe
Capital Mercury Apparel
Donna Karan
Eddie Bauer LLC
Genesco
Gucci
Haggar
Hugo Boss
J. Crew
Jones Group
Kellwood
Kenneth Cole
Levi Strauss
Luxottica
Oxford Industries
Perry Ellis International
Prada
Ralph Lauren
Reebok
Stride Rite
The Gap
Timberland
VF Corporation
Warnaco Group

HISTORICAL FINANCIALS

Company Type: Public

Income Statement FYE: January 29

	REVENUE ($ mil.)	NET INCOME ($ mil.)	NET PROFIT MARGIN	EMPLOYEES
01/12	5,890	317	5.4%	25,700
01/11	4,636	53	1.2%	22,700
01/10*	2,398	161	6.7%	10,800
02/09	2,491	91	3.7%	11,100
02/08	2,425	183	7.6%	11,600
Annual Growth	24.8%	14.8%	—	22.0%

*Fiscal year change

2012 Year-End Financials

Debt ratio: 28.37%
Return on equity: 11.71%
Cash ($ mil.): 233
Current ratio: 166.61
Long-term debt ($ mil.): 1,832
No. of shares (mil.): 68
Dividends
Yield: —
Payout: 3.44%
Market value ($ mil.): 5,219

	STOCK PRICE ($) FY Close	P/E High/Low		PER SHARE ($) Earnings	Dividends	Book Value
01/12	76.70	17	12	4.36	0.00	39.90
01/11	58.05	87	47	0.80	0.00	36.42
01/10*	39.29	14	5	3.08	0.00	22.51
02/09	19.02	27	8	1.76	0.00	19.40
02/08	43.15	19	10	3.21	0.00	18.65
Annual Growth	15.5%	—	—	8.0%	—	20.9%

*Fiscal year change

Quad/Graphics, Inc.

Your mailbox may be filled with Quad/Graphics' handiwork. A leading US printing company Quad/Graphics produces catalogs magazines books direct mail and other commercial material. Services include production design photography binding wrapping and distribution. It has produced catalogs for Bloomingdale's books for National Geographic and magazines such as Time Inc.'s People. The company owns some 140 facilities in about 20 countries throughout North America Latin America and Europe. Quad/Graphics was founded in 1971 by the late Harry Quadracci.

HISTORY

Ink runs in the Quadracci family. Harry R. Quadracci founded Standard Printing in Racine Wisconsin in 1930 when he was 16. Four years later Quadracci sold out to William A. Krueger. Though he worked to build Krueger into a major regional printer Quadracci had little equity in the company.

In the 1960s Harry R. Quadracci's son Harry V. Quadracci joined Krueger as a company lawyer. Within a few years he had worked his way up to plant manager. Krueger was a union shop and in those days unions dictated the work rules and often salary levels. In 1970 there was a three-and-a-half-month strike. At odds with new management and reportedly dissatisfied with the way Krueger caved in to union demands and the adversarial relationship between company and union the younger Quadracci left.

After 18 months of unemployment in 1971 Quadracci formed a limited partnership with 12 others to get a loan to buy a press which was installed in a building in Pewaukee Wisconsin. The next year his father joined the company as chairman. Within two years the partners had recouped their initial investment but the business' future remained in question until about 1976. One of its most innovative moves was to make its delivery fleet drivers into entrepreneurs by requiring them to find cargo to haul on their return trips.

Working on a shoestring Quadracci hired inexperienced workers and trained them moving them up as the company grew. The need to improvise fostered a flexibility that Quadracci institutionalized by keeping management layers flat and remaining accessible to his employees. Beginning in 1974 Quadracci rewarded his workers with equity in the company.

In the 1980s Quad/Graphics' commitment to technology enabled it to offer better service than many of its competitors. It was also immune to the merger-and-acquisition fever of the time. Free of acquisition debt the company had excellent credit and was able to finance equipment upgrades with bank loans. Quad/Graphics expanded by opening a plant in Saratoga Springs New York (1985) and buying a plant in Thomaston Georgia (1989).

But there were missteps such as its 1985 attempt to break into the newspaper coupon insert business dominated by Treasure Chest Advertising. Quad/Graphics sold that operation three years later. The company could not avoid the national economic downturn that began about that time which forced it to lay off employees in the late 1980s and early 1990s and prompted it to reduce weekend overtime pay (from double time to time-and-a-half). The firm was also hit when a major customer consolidated its printing outside the Midwest. In response Quad/Graphics increased its capacity in other regions of the US during the 1990s.

In 1996 the company bought 40% of Argentine printer Anselmo L. Morvillo. Benefiting from the UPS strike and changes in the postal regulations in 1997 Quad/Graphics expanded its shipping services with Parcel Direct targeting parcels for large shippers such as catalog merchants in cooperation with the US Postal Service. Also that year it created a joint venture color printing firm with Brazil's Folha Group.

In 1998 Quad/Graphics expanded its international reach agreeing to a joint venture in Poland. The next year the company was awarded the prepress business of Conde Nast magazines. In 2000 it launched a business-to-business portal called Smart Tools.

The company was shocked in 2002 when Harry V. Quadracci drowned at age 66. His brother Tom was then appointed president. In 2004 Tom Quadracci assumed the role of chairman and CEO while Harry's son Joel took over as president.

Quad/Graphics sold its package delivery business Parcel Direct to FedEx for $120 million in 2004.

In 2006 the company acquired Openfirst in a deal that was projected to double the printing firm's direct mail division QuadDirect. Later that year the firm acquired a printing plant in Reno Nevada expanding its distribution capacity on the West Coast. Tom Quadracci stepped down as CEO in late 2006 and Joel Quadracci succeeded him. Tom Quadracci remained executive chairman through the end of 2006 before retiring.

In 2007 the company bought Poland-based Winkowski a leading commercial printer. Quad/Graphics later renamed the unit Quad-Winkowski and appointed Tom Frankowski a veteran of its US manufacturing operations as the unit's president.

In order to strengthen its international presence the company extended its reach into Europe by acquiring Ireland-based Vigitek in 2008. Vigitek whose scanners and inspection systems detect printing defects was renamed Quad/Tech following the purchase.

Focusing on diversifying beyond its core catalog and magazine printing services in 2008 Quad/Graphics invested $25 million to expand its direct mail division which had previously been a smaller contributor. The move helped the company to acquire digital presses and envelope inserters and to update other features of its production center.

As demand fell for printing services in 2009 Quad/Graphics laid off about 550 plant workers nationwide. The company linked the workforce reduction to dwindling sales of catalogs and other media.

In 2010 Quad/Graphics made a significant move to expand when it acquired one of its biggest rivals World Color Press for about $1.2 billion. It also became a publicly traded company at that time listing on the New York Stock Exchange. Later that year the company closed eight plants and cut more than 4000 jobs.

Next in 2010 it purchased specialty products printer HGI Company. Quad/Graphics made the acquisition to bolster its commercial and specialty products offerings. HGI's specialty products include retail point-of-purchase (POP) displays and materials through its Tempt brand which produces in-store signage and promotional programs for retail customers.

In 2011 and 2012 the company swapped several assets with Montreal-based print company Transcontinental . As part of the exchange Quad/Graphics acquired three of Transcontinental's facilities in Mexico and sold all but one of its eight Canadian facilities to Transcontinental (Quad/Graphics retained its Vancouver facility).

EXECUTIVES

President Latin America, Guy Trahan
EVP and CFO, John C. Fowler
Sales Boynton Beach Florida, Scott Kaczmarek
Sales Atlanta, Ralph Herrmann
Sales Boston, Jason Sawtelle
Sales Detroit, John Stano
Sales Washington DC, Jeff Button
Chairman President and CEO, J. Joel Quadracci
Director; President QuadCreative; President and Publisher Milwaukee Magazine, Betty Ewens Quadracci, age 73
Sales Seattle, Beth Danielson
VP Information Systems and Infrastructure; President QuadDirect, Steve Jaeger
President Quad/Tech, Karl Fritchen
EVP Manufacturing and Operations; President Europe, Thomas J. (Tom) Frankowski
Sales Denver, Scott Ingram
President Retail Inserts Directories Books and Canada, Brian Freschi
VP and General Counsel, Andy Schiesl
EVP; President Magazines and Catalogs, David A. Blais
VP Human Resources, Gregg Bolt
Director Photography QuadPhoto, Mark Kozlowski
President Logistics and Distribution, David (Dave) Riebe
Sales Los Angeles, Dana Brown
Imaging Operations Manager Boston Imaging, Terry Shean
Imaging Operations Manager Dallas Imaging, Larry Hediger
Imaging Operations Manager Hartford (WI) Imaging, Troy Holappa
Gravure Imaging Operations Manager Lomira (WI) Gravure Imaging, Chris Olson
Gravure Imaging Operations Manager Martinsburg (WV) Gravure Imaging, Kevin Haught
Imaging Operations Manager Minneapolis Imaging, Sharon Pohlman
Imaging Operations Manager Saratoga Springs (NY) Imaging, Mark Wheeler
Imaging Operations Manager Sussex (WI) Imaging, Dean McFadden
Imaging Operations Manager Washington DC Imaging, Gary Spesard
Imaging Operations Manager West Allis (WI) Imaging, Kelly Paolo
Sales New York City, Brian Hickey
Sales San Francisco, Paul Schroeder
Imaging Operations Manager Atlanta Imaging, Duane Harrell
Sales Dallas, Dave Carpenter
VP Marketing and Communications, Maura Packham
President QuadMed, Ray Zastrow
President Latin America, Tony Scarinqi
Director, John S. Shiely, age 59
Director, Thomas O. (Tom) Ryder, age 67
Director, William J. Abraham Jr., age 64
Director; President QuadCreative; President and Publisher Milwaukee Magazine, Betty Ewens Quadracci, age 73
Director, Christopher B. (Chris) Harned, age 49
Director, Douglas P. Buth
Auditors: Deloitte&ToucheLLP

LOCATIONS

HQ: Quad/Graphics Inc.
N61 W23044 Harry' s Way, Sussex WI 53089-3995
Phone: 414-566-6000 **Fax:** 414-566-4650
Web: www.qg.com

2011 Sales

	$ mil.	% of total
US	3,798	88
Latin America	303	7
Europe	209	5
Other	12	-
Total	**4,324**	**100**

PRODUCTS/OPERATIONS

2011 Sales

	$ mil.	% of total
Products		
Catalog magazines & retail inserts	2,826	65
Direct mail directories & other printed products	964	22
Other	35	1
Services		
Logistics services	370	9
Imaging & other services	128	3
Total	**4,324**	**100**

Selected Services

Binding and finishing
Color correction
Defect detection
Design
Desktop production
Direct mailing
Imaging and photography
Ink jetting
Integrated circulation
Mailing and distribution
Mailing list management
Printing
Scanning

Selected Clients

Magazines
- Conde Nast
- Hearst Magazines
- Meredith Corporation
- The National Geographic Society
- Rodale Inc.
- The Reader' s Digest Association
- Time Inc.
- Wenner Media

Retail Newspaper Inserts
- J.C. Penney Company
- Target Corporation

Catalogs
- Coldwater Creek
- J.Crew Group
- L.L. Bean
- Williams-Sonoma

Direct Mail Products
- Guthy-Renker
- Publishers Clearing House
- Weight Watchers International

Book Publishing
- Harlequin Enterprises Limited
- The McGraw-Hill Companies
- The Reader' s Digest Association
- Simon & Schuster

Directories
- Dex One Corporation
- Yellow Book USA
- Yellow Pages Group Limited

COMPETITORS

Angstrom Graphics
Arandell
Brown Printing
Cenveo
Consolidated Graphics
Dai Nippon Printing
Merrill
R.R. Donnelley
Toppan Printing

HISTORICAL FINANCIALS

Company Type: Public

Income Statement FYE: December 31

	REVENUE ($ mil.)	NET INCOME ($ mil.)	NET PROFIT MARGIN	EMPLOYEES
12/11	4,324	(46)	—	24,300
12/10	3,391	(250)	—	25,000
12/09	1,788	52	3.0%	11,600
12/08	2,266	109	4.8%	0
12/07	2,048	178	8.7%	0
Annual Growth	20.5%	—	—	—

2011 Year-End Financials

Debt ratio: 31.87%	No. of shares (mil.): 46
Return on equity: (-3.59)%	Dividends
Cash ($ mil.): 25	Yield: —
Current ratio: 133.63	Payout: —
Long-term debt ($ mil.): 1,406	Market value ($ mil.): 668

	STOCK PRICE ($) FY Close	P/E High/Low	PER SHARE ($) Earnings	Dividends	Book Value
12/11	14.34	— —	(1.00)	0.00	28.03
12/10	41.26	— —	(6.67)	0.00	31.88
Annual Growth	(65.2%)	— —	—	—	(12.1%)

Qualcomm, Inc.

Cell phone makers wireless carriers and governments worldwide call on QUALCOMM to engineer a quality conversation. The company pioneered the commercialization of the code-division multiple access (CDMA) technology used in digital wireless communications equipment and satellite ground stations mainly in North America. It licenses CDMA semiconductor technology and system software to equipment and cell phone makers. QUALCOMM's OmniTRACS satellite vehicle tracking system is used by the trucking industry to manage vehicle fleets while QUALCOMM Ventures invests in wireless communications and Internet startups. Samsung Electronics accounts for more than 10% of annual sales.

HISTORY

Professors Irwin Mark Jacobs and Andrew Viterbi founded digital signal processing equipment company Linkabit in 1968. M/A-COM acquired the company in 1980. Led by Jacobs Viterbi and five other executives left M/A-COM Linkabit in 1985 to start engineer-focused QUALCOMM (for "quality communications") to provide contract R&D services. The company's first home was located above a strip mall pizza parlor in San Diego. CEO Jacobs dreamed of modifying code-division multiple access (CDMA) –a secure wireless transmission system developed during WWII –for commercial use.

In 1988 QUALCOMM introduced OmniTRACS a satellite-based system that tracks the location of long-haul truckers. By 1989 when QUALCOMM unveiled its version of CDMA the company was working on military contracts worth $15 million.

In 1990 the company interrupted the Cellular Telecommunications Industry Association's (CTIA) plans to adopt a rival technology called time-division multiple access when communications service providers NYNEX (now part of Verizon) and Ameritech (later part of SBC Communications and now part of AT&T) adopted QUALCOMM's maverick technology. QUALCOMM initiated a CDMA public relations blitz and by 1991 Motorola AT&T Clarion and Nokia had signed product development and testing agreements.

The company went public in 1991 and introduced the Eudora e-mail software program (named for "Why I Live at the P.O." author Eudora Welty) which it licensed from the University of Illinois. That year QUALCOMM and Loral Corporation unveiled plans for Globalstar a satellite telecommunications system similar to the Iridium system. The CTIA adopted CDMA as a North American standard for wireless communications in 1993.

In 1996 most of the major US cellular carriers upgraded to CDMA. However QUALCOMM's earnings fell due to manufacturing startup expenses and R&D and marketing costs. Earnings bounced back the next year and the company signed a contract to supply wireless ground stations for Globalstar. Also in 1997 Russia charged a QUALCOMM technician with espionage but allowed him to return to the US.

The company spun off its wireless phone service operations in 1998 as Leap Wireless International. It also formed Wireless Knowledge a joint venture with Microsoft to develop software and services for Internet access from portable computing devices.

In 1999 QUALCOMM and rival Ericsson settled a bitter dispute over the use of CDMA as an industry standard when they signed a cross-licensing deal. QUALCOMM sold its cell phone operations to Kyocera in 2000. The company also bought SnapTrack (cell phone location software) and signed a potentially huge deal with China Unicom. The latter was a step forward for Chinese carriers and equipment makers itching to use CDMA in a region where the Global System for Mobile Communication (GSM) rules.

Later that year rivals Nokia and Motorola teamed up to push for the standardization of Motorola's 1Xtreme technology over QUALCOMM's high-data-rate (HDR) format for 3G networks. (However 1Xtreme is based on QUALCOMM's CDMA patents.) By mid-2000 the company made plans to spin off its semiconductor subsidiary to the public. QUALCOMM cancelled the IPO a year later.

In 2001 the Chinese government after years of balking at CDMA in favor of 3G granted QUALCOMM and China Unicom permission to install a CDMA-based network. That year Microsoft sold its stake in Wireless Knowledge; the joint venture became a subsidiary of QUALCOMM.

In 2003 the company shut down Wireless Knowledge and absorbed its operations. It also augmented its OmniTRACS offerings by acquiring fleet management operations from a subsidiary of Alcatel (now Alcatel-Lucent). The following year QUALCOMM bought UK-based user interface designer Trigenix.

QUALCOMM purchased content delivery software specialist Elata in 2005. EVP Paul Jacobs son of co-founder Irwin Mark Jacobs took over as CEO in mid-2005; his father remained chairman of the company. Early the following year QUALCOMM acquired semiconductor designer Berkana Wireless for about $56 million in cash. It also closed on its acquisition of Flarion Technologies a developer of a proprietary version of OFDM (orthogonal frequency-division multiplexing) technology called FLASH-OFDM. An alternative to WiMAX FLASH-OFDM is a cellular broadband technology used to connect mobile devices to networks. QUALCOMM paid about $600 million in cash and stock for Flarion and the deal included milestone incentives that could add another $205 million to the price.

In 2006 QUALCOMM paid a $1.8 million fine to the federal government for exercising operational control over Flarion before actually closing the transaction to acquire the chipset company. The fine was part of an agreement with the US Department of Justice; QUALCOMM officially denied any wrongdoing saying it disagreed with the Justice Department that its acquisition agreement with Flarion violated any federal laws or regulations.

In late 2006 QUALCOMM acquired Airgo Networks which specialized in Wi-Fi networking gear and paid $39 million for the Bluetooth assets of RF Micro Devices.

The Eudora e-mail program became an open-source product in May 2007 with QUALCOMM ceasing commercial sales of the product. In late 2006 the company released the final commercial versions of Eudora for Macintosh and Windows computers and cut the price to less than $20. Future versions of Eudora were to be based on the Thunderbird e-mail software platform developed by The Mozilla Foundation.

At the end of 2007 QUALCOMM acquired Firethorn Holdings for about $210 million in cash. Firethorn previously a unit of ITC Holding is a developer of software for mobile banking services on cell phones and other wireless devices. Its products are implemented by such financial institutions as Regions Financial SunTrust Banks and Wachovia and by wireless services providers like AT&T Mobility and Verizon Wireless.

Taking a leaf from such competitors as Intel and Nokia with their corporate venture capital operations (Intel Capital and BlueRun Ventures respectively) QUALCOMM put $500 million into QUALCOMM Ventures to make equity investments in a variety of start-up ventures. Portfolio companies include A123 Systems (rechargeable batteries for portable devices) AirPlay (interactive games for cell phones) Airvana (radio access network infrastructure) Bitfone (mobile device management software) Obopay (mobile payment service) and China Techfaith Wireless Communication Technology (mobile design house).

In 2007 QUALCOMM Ventures said it would invest E100 million in European companies developing mobile application or platform software handset components network infrastructure and core technologies for 3G (WCDMA) wireless communications. Its first investment went to Paris-based Streamezzo a developer of rich-media software platforms and services for mobile communications.

QUALCOMM and rival Broadcom have been embroiled in patent battles for over two years. The International Trade Commission (ITC) ruled in 2007 that new mobile phones being imported into the US with certain QUALCOMM chipsets were barred from sale because they infringed on a Broadcom patent. QUALCOMM appealed the ruling to no avail. Three months later a federal appeals judge stayed the import ban and in 2008 the US Court of Appeals for the Federal Circuit vacated the ITC ban and asked it to reconsider the case. The following year Broadcom and QUALCOMM reached a legal settlement dismissing all patent claims against each other and granting each certain rights under their patent portfolios. The company agreed to pay Broadcom $891 million in cash over four years under the settlement with $200 million due in mid-2009.

Perhaps piling on in the wake of the ITC ruling against QUALCOMM Nokia not only filed a patent infringement claim against the company but it also joined with other vendors to nudge the European Commission the European Union's antitrust regulator to upgrade its investigation into QUALCOMM's royalty practices. The two companies reached a legal settlement on patents in 2008 agreeing to dismiss all litigation. Nokia also agreed to withdraw its complaint with the European Commission. The settlement called for Nokia to assign certain patents related to the GSM OFDMA and WCDMA wireless standards to QUALCOMM and for the handset giant to pay a lump sum and royalties to QUALCOMM under a 15-year licensing agreement. Nokia later reported the lump-sum payment made before the end of 2008 totaled E1.7 billion (about $2.5 billion). In November 2009 the European Commission closed the formal antitrust case against the company based on the inability to draw any conclusions; all complaints were withdrawn.

In early 2009 QUALCOMM acquired graphics and multimedia assets from Advanced Micro Devices (AMD) for $65 million in cash. The company previously licensed graphics cores from AMD's handheld business. QUALCOMM hired about 170 engineers from AMD's handheld business in connection with the deal.

In 2010 the Qualcomm Innovation Center subsidiary bought San Francisco-based iSkoot a provider of service that enable cell phone makers to include social networking features on their smartphones.

EXECUTIVES

SVP; President Firethorn, Rocco J. Fabiano, age 55
Chairman and CEO, Paul E. Jacobs, age 49, $964,427 total compensation
SVP and CIO, Norm Fjeldheim
Vice Chairman, Steven R. (Steve) Altman, age 51, $708,045 total compensation
EVP Human Resources, Daniel L. Sullivan, age 61
EVP; President Global Market Development, Margaret L. (Peggy) Johnson, age 50
SVP Worldwide Sales; President Qualcomm CDMA Technologies (QCT) Asia, Jim Doh
EVP, Roberto Padovani, age 57, $459,235 total compensation
SVP; President QUALCOMM Government Technologies, Kimberly M. Koro
EVP and CFO, William E. Keitel, age 59, $684,004 total compensation
SVP Programming and Advertising FLO TV, Jonathan Barzilay
EVP; President Global Business Operations, Jing Wang, age 50
President nPhase, Steve Pazol
SVP Global Marketing and Investor Relations, William F. (Bill) Davidson Jr.
SVP; President Qualcomm MEMS Technologies, John Batey
EVP General Counsel and Corporate Secretary, Donald J. Rosenberg, age 61, $576,940 total compensation
EVP European Innovation Development, Andrew M. Gilbert, age 49
SVP Government Affairs, William (Bill) Bold
Investor Relations, Garrett Ponder
Public Relations, Emily Kilpatrick
President and COO, Steven M. (Steve) Mollenkopf, age 43, $637,123 total compensation
Senior Director Investor Relations, John Sinnott
EVP; President Qualcomm Technology Licensing, Derek K. Aberle, age 42
EVP; General Manager Qualcomm CDMA Technologies (QCT), James Lederer, age 52
Senior Director Marketing, Pete Lancia
Senior Manager Investor Relations, Amy Berguson
VP Sales Services and Marketing Qualcomm Enterprise Services, Norm Ellis
VP Marketing and Product Management Qualcomm Enterprise Services, Rick Roesler
VP Business Development, Al St. George
VP Operations QES, Steve Yamamoto
President Qualcomm Internet Services (QIS) and Innovation Center, Rob Chandhok
VP Investor Relations, Warren Kneeshaw
President and CEO Qualcomm Enterprise Services, Rich Sulpizio
Senior Manager Investor Relations, Todd Schak
Public Relations, Bertha Agia
Public Affairs Legal Public Relations, Christie Thoene
Europe Publlic Relations, Richard Tinkler
Press Contact South Korea, Seungsoo Kim
Press Contact China, Mingjuan Hou
Press Contact Latin America, Yennie Rautenberg
PR and Communications Qualcomm India, Meena Nichani
Press Contact Southeast Asia, Adrian Fu
Press Contact Japan, Takayuki Nozaki
Press Contact Middle East and Africa, Dan Album
Press Contact Qualcomm MEMS Technologies, Cheryl Goodman
Press Contact Qualcomm Enterprise Services, Anita Gomes
SVP; President Greater China, Xiang Wang
Senior Director Information Technology, Matt Clark
Managing Director Qualcom Enterprise Services Europe B.V., Mark Warner
EVP and CTO, Matt Grob
EVP Engineering Qualcomm Technologies, James H. (Jim) Thompson, age 48
Vice Chairman, Steven R. (Steve) Altman, age 51
Director, Stephen M. (Steve) Bennett, age 58
Director, Marc I. Stern, age 67
Director, Thomas W. (Tom) Horton, age 51
Director, Brent Scowcroft, age 86
Director, Barbara T. Alexander, age 63
Director, Duane A. Nelles, age 68
Director, Sherry Lansing, age 66
Director, Robert E. Kahn, age 73
Director, Raymond V. (Ray) Dittamore, age 68
Director, Irwin M. Jacobs, age 78
Director, Susan Hockfield, age 60
Director, Sir Donald G. (Don) Cruickshank, age 69
Director, Francisco Ros, age 60
Auditors: PricewaterhouseCoopersLLP

LOCATIONS

HQ: QUALCOMM Incorporated
5775 Morehouse Dr., San Diego CA 92121-1714
Phone: 858-587-1121 **Fax:** 817-415-2647
Web: www.radioshack.com

2012 Sales

	$ mil.	% of total
China	7,971	42
South Korea	4,203	22
Taiwan	2,648	14
US	967	5
Other Countries	3,332	17
Total	19,121	100

PRODUCTS/OPERATIONS

2012 Sales

	$ mil.	% of total
QCT (Qualcomm CDMA Technologies)	12,141	64
QTL (Qualcomm Technology Licensing)	6,327	33
QWI (Qualcomm Wireless & Internet)	633	3
Other	20	-
Total	19,121	100

Selected Operations and Products

Code-Division Multiple Access (CDMA) Technologies Group
- Integrated circuits
  - Baseband
  - Intermediate-frequency
  - Power management
  - Radio-frequency
- Systems software

Engineering Services Group
Enterprise Services
Firethorn Holdings
Flarion Technologies
Government Technologies
Innovation Center
Internet Services
MediaFLO Technologies
MEMS Technologies
Qualcomm Ventures
Strategic Initiatives
Technology Licensing Group
- CDMA technologies and patents (cdmaOne CDMA2000 WCDMA TD-SCDMA)
- Royalties from products incorporating CDMA technology

Wireless and Internet Group
- Digital Media
  - Digital motion picture delivery systems (under development)
  - Government systems (development and analysis services; wireless base stations and phones)
- Internet Services
  - Applications development software for wireless devices (BREW)
- Wireless Systems
  - Low-Earth-orbit satellite-based telecommunications system (Globalstar)
  - Satellite and terrestrial two-way data messaging and position reporting systems and services (OmniTRACS OmniExpress TruckMAIL)

COMPETITORS

Apple Inc.
Broadcom
CSR plc
Freescale Semiconductor
Fujitsu
IBM Microelectronics
Icera
Infineon Technologies
Intel
InterDigital
Marvell Technology
Maxim Integrated Products
MediaTek
Motorola Mobility
NAVTEQ
NEC
Nokia
NVIDIA
NXP Semiconductors
Panasonic Corp
Renesas Electronics
Samsung Electronics
Spreadtrum
ST-Ericsson
STMicroelectronics
Texas Instruments
Trimble Navigation

HISTORICAL FINANCIALS

Company Type: Public

Income Statement FYE: September 30

	REVENUE ($ mil.)	NET INCOME ($ mil.)	NET PROFIT MARGIN	EMPLOYEES
09/12	19,121	6,109	31.9%	26,600
09/11	14,957	4,260	28.5%	21,200
09/10	10,991	3,247	29.5%	17,500
09/09	10,416	1,592	15.3%	16,100
09/08	11,142	3,160	28.4%	15,400
Annual Growth	14.5%	17.9%	—	14.6%

2012 Year-End Financials

Debt ratio: —
Return on equity: 18.22%
Cash ($ mil.): 3,807
Current ratio: 295.08
Long-term debt ($ mil.): —
No. of shares (mil.): 1,706
Dividends
Yield: —
Payout: 26.50%
Market value ($ mil.): 106,574

	STOCK PRICE ($) FY Close	P/E High/Low		PER SHARE ($) Earnings	Dividends	Book Value
09/12	62.47	19	13	3.51	0.00	19.65
09/11	50.29	23	17	2.52	0.00	16.03
09/10	44.55	25	16	1.96	0.00	12.94
09/09	44.70	50	30	0.95	0.00	12.17
09/08	45.84	29	19	1.90	0.00	10.84
Annual Growth	8.0%	—	—	16.6%	—	16.0%

Quanta Services, Inc.

To quickly quantify Quanta's services: This specialty contractor designs installs repairs and maintains network infrastructure in the US and Canada. The company serves the electric natural gas oil pipeline renewable energy and telecommunications industries. Quanta which was founded in 1997 also owns fiber optic telecommunications infrastructure. Quanta's other services include outsource management and other specialty work such as installing traffic and light rail control systems directional drilling and constructing wind and solar power facilities. More than 65% of the company's revenues come from its electric power infrastructure segment. It is exiting telecommunications infrastructure services.

Quanta typically expands through acquisitions. Most recently the company has been focusing on expanding its capabilities and growing internationally. In 2011 Quanta acquired Coe Drilling a horizontal directional drilling company in Australia. Canada also has been a target for growth for Quanta. In another 2011 deal Quanta bought McGregor Construction an electric power infrastructure services company in Canada. Also that year Quanta acquired two other smaller businesses based in British Columbia. Both mainly provided electric power infrastructure services. The deals enhanced Quanta's previous electric power acquisition of Valard Construction in Canada. In a retreat from telecommunications infrastructure services business Quanta sold substantially all of its domestic telecommunications infrastructure services operations to Dycom Industries for $275 million. The sale allows Quanta to better focus on energy infrastructure.

Also in 2011 Quanta expanded its electric power infrastructure services in the US when it acquired Utilimap a provider of geographic information system utility asset management services.

Several trends in the market place present Quanta with opportunities to grow. Demand for electricity in North America continues to increase. However the electric power grid system is aging. Quanta is positioned to make system upgrades and demand for its services should increase.

Renewable energy such as wind and solar also presents opportunities for Quanta. As demand for those energy sources increases so will demand for services such as transmission line installation and project management.

Quanta also sees potential for growth in the natural gas segment. Development of gas shale formations in North America has provided in an increase in supply of natural gas. More natural gas-fired power plants are expected to be built during the next two decades.

Quanta made an effort to grow in the natural gas sector when it acquired a 39% stake in Howard Midstream Energy Partners in 2011. The company owns operates and constructs midstream oil and gas plant and pipeline facilities. The acquisition was made in order to position Quanta for more opportunities in the development of the Texas Eagle Ford shale region.

Quanta has experienced a steady increase in demand for its services as the economy slowly recovers. As more clients began to increase spending on infrastructure projects the company's revenues also grew. In 2011 Quanta reported more than $4.6 billion in revenues (an increase of about 18%). Net income fell in 2011 due to a charge related to a pension plan withdrawal and other tax-related settlements.

EXECUTIVES

Chief Financial Officer; Chief Accounting Officer, Derrick A. Jensen, age 41, $251,463 total compensation
EVP, James H. Haddox, age 63, $494,400 total compensation
Executive Chairman, John R. Colson, age 64, $824,006 total compensation
Vice President - Finance; Treasurer, Nicholas M. (Nick) Grindstaff, age 49
Director of Communications, Reba Reid
COO, Earl C. (Duke) Austin Jr., age 43
Senior Vice President - Business Development and Outsourcing, Benadetto G. Bosco, age 54
President Telecommunications and Cable Television, Kenneth W. (Ken) Trawick, age 64, $453,206 total compensation
Vice President; General Counsel, Tana L. Pool, age 52
President and CEO, James F. (Jim) O'Neil III, age 53, $411,994 total compensation
Senior Vice President, Max Thomas
Senior Vice President Sales, Dean Strickland
Director Business Development, James Blackman
President; Chief Executive Officer; Director, James Neil
Vice President Operations, Larry Baker
Senior Vice President - Business Development, Lonnie Hamilton
EVP Business Development, Rob Marchetti
Vice President Strategic Accounts, Tony Broccolo
President Vice President, William Rowe
President; Chief Executive Officer; Director, James ONeil
Independent Director, Vincent D. Foster, age 54
Director, John R. Wilson, age 62
Director, James R. Ball, age 69
Director, Louis C. Golm, age 70
Director, Bruce E. Ranck, age 63
Director, Bernard Fried, age 55
Director, Patrick Henry (Pat) Wood III, age 49
Director, Worthing F. Jackman, age 47
Director, J. Michal Conaway, age 63
Auditors: PricewaterhouseCoopersLLP

LOCATIONS

HQ: Quanta Services Inc.
2800 Post Oak Blvd. Ste. 2600, Houston TX 77056-3023
Phone: 713-629-7600 **Fax:** 713-629-7676
Web: www.quantaservices.com

2011 Sales

	$ mil.	% of total
$ in mil. % of toal		
US	4,088	88
Canada & other	535	12
Total	4,623	100

PRODUCTS/OPERATIONS

2011 Sales

	$ mil.	% of total
Electric Power Services	3,029	66
Natural gas & pipeline	1,024	22
Telecommunications	457	10
Fiber optic licensing	112	2
Total	**4,623**	**100**

Selected Subsidiaries

Allteck Line Contractors
Blair Park Services
Bradford Brothers
Can-Fer Utility Services
Computapole
Dacon Corporation
Dashiell Corporation
Dillard Smith Construction Company
Driftwood Electrical
EHV Power
Engineering Associates
Fiber Technologies
Golden State Utility Co.
H.L. Chapman Pipeline Construction
InfraSource Telecommunications Services
InfraSource Services
InfraSource Pipeline Facilities
InfraSource Telecommunications Services
Intermountain Electric
Irby Construction Company
Longfellow Drilling Services
Manuel Brothers
Mears Group Inc.
M.J. Electric
North Houston Pole Line
North Sky Communications
PAR Electrical Contractors
Parkside Utility Construction
Pauley Construction Company
Potleco
Price Gregory Services
Professional Teleconcepts
Quanta Energized Services
Quanta Government Solutions
Quanta Pipeline Services Engineering
Quanta Power Generation
Quanta Technology
Quanta Wireless Solutions
Realtime Engineers Inc.
Ryan Company
Spalj Construction Company
Sumter Utilities
Sunesys
Trawick Construction Company
Underground Construction Company
Valard Construction
VCI Telecom
W.C. Communications
Winco Powerline Services

COMPETITORS

Cable Com
Comm-Works
Dycom
EMCOR
Goldfield
Henkels & McCoy
Integrated Electrical Services
Mass Electric
MasTec
MDU Construction Services
MYR Group
Pike Electric Corporation
Tetra Tech

HISTORICAL FINANCIALS

Company Type: Public

Income Statement FYE: December 31

	REVENUE ($ mil.)	NET INCOME ($ mil.)	NET PROFIT MARGIN	EMPLOYEES
12/11	4,623	132	2.9%	17,500
12/10	3,931	153	3.9%	13,751
12/09	3,318	162	4.9%	14,673
12/08	3,780	166	4.4%	14,751
12/07	2,656	135	5.1%	15,261
Annual Growth	14.9%	(0.6%)	—	3.5%

2011 Year-End Financials

Debt ratio: —
Return on equity: 3.92%
Cash ($ mil.): 315
Current ratio: 225.99
Long-term debt ($ mil.): —
No. of shares (mil.): 206
Dividends
Yield: —
Payout: —
Market value ($ mil.): 4,442

	STOCK PRICE ($) FY Close	P/E High/Low		PER SHARE ($) Earnings	Dividends	Book Value
12/11	21.54	39	25	0.62	0.00	16.40
12/10	19.92	32	23	0.72	0.00	15.91
12/09	20.84	31	20	0.81	0.00	14.80
12/08	19.80	37	11	0.88	0.00	13.45
12/07	26.24	33	19	0.89	0.00	12.78
Annual Growth	(4.8%)	—	—	(8.6%)	—	6.4%

Quest Diagnostics, Inc.

Quest Diagnostics is testing its ability to be the world's leading clinical lab. The company performs diagnostics on some 146 million specimens each year including routine clinical tests such as cholesterol checks Pap smears HIV screenings and drug tests. Quest Diagnostics also performs esoteric testing (such as genetic screening) and anatomic pathology testing (such as tissue biopsies for cancer testing). In all the company serves half of the physicians and hospitals in the US as well as government agencies and other clinical labs. Quest Diagnostics has more than 2000 patient service centers where samples are collected and the Quest Diagnostic Nichols Institute where new diagnostics are developed.

Geographic Reach

While more than 95% of sales come from the US market Quest aims for its international operations to eventually account for more than 10% of revenues. The firm is especially focused on expanding in the developing world where the diagnostic testing market is more fragmented. Key growth markets outside the US include India Ireland Mexico Puerto Rico and the UK.

Operations

Quest strives to make itself ubiquitous with a comprehensive menu of tests (more than 3000) and a network of labs and collection sites that blanket the US. In addition to its own patient service centers where samples are collected the company maintains a staff of 3000 field phlebotomists who collect blood samples in physicians' offices. It also provides pathology testing services and staffing within hospitals. Other workers include the contracted paramedical examiners who conduct examinations for life insurance applicants.

While more than 90% of Quest's revenue comes from its testing services the company also offers a number of other products and services. Its online data management system the Care360 physician portal lets doctors order diagnostic tests review results prescribe medication and manage patient files while its Care360EHR is an electronic health record product. Quest also offers software that helps patients schedule tests and assess their results. A small portion of sales comes from providing testing services to drug companies' clinical trials. Additionally Quest provides global testing and risk assessment services for the life insurance industry.

Financial Analysis

Despite its lofty position in the clinical testing market Quest has been conducting cost-cutting measures to keep its competitive edge. Programs launched in 2010 streamlined processes and reduced the workforce slightly in response to reduced testing volumes. Settlement of a civil lawsuit in early 2011 pulled down the net income for the year and acquisitions tied up some of the company's cash flow.

Strategy

Quest keeps looking to grow its reach by acquiring firms with complementary locations or testing capabilities. However it is also working to build up its specialized testing products and diagnostic development efforts. Quest is especially focused on growing its product line in the esoteric and gene-based testing markets which are experiencing increasing product demand in areas such as cancer diagnostics and personalized medicine (using genetic tests to determine the most effective medication regimens).

Quest has also been working to enhance its line of point-of-care diagnostics. Such point-of-care tests are increasing in popularity because they can be performed at the bedside or in the doctor's office and produce results more quickly.

Mergers & Acquisitions

Towards that end the company has made a number of acquisitions that have increased its presence in specific testing categories such as cancer biopsy tests. In 2011 Quest expanded into another specialist category with the acquisition of genetic testing firm Athena Diagnostics from Thermo Fisher Scientific for $740 million. Offering some 350 esoteric diagnostics for neurological conditions including Alzheimer's disease and spinal muscular atrophy Athena became Quest's base for neurology diagnostics.

To bring genetic diagnostics development closer in-house Quest acquired Celera for $327 million in 2011. The purchase included Celera's Berkeley HeartLab (cardiovascular tests) a pipeline of diagnostic products a handful of marketed specialty test products and a vault full of discovered genetic biomarkers that have the potential to be used as diagnostics.

HISTORY

Quest Diagnostics began as one man's quest to make clinical tests more affordable. Pathologist Paul Brown started Metropolitan Pathological Laboratory (MetPath) in his Manhattan apartment in 1967. To help his business take off in 1969 he bought two $55000 blood analyzers that could automatically perform a dozen common tests; the machines allowed him to charge patients $5.50 while hospitals and other labs were charging upwards of $40. Investments in emerging lab technology helped MetPath continue to beat competitors' prices and grow its business. It made its first profit in 1971 and eventually attracted the attention of Corning Glass Works which bought 10% of the company in 1973.

MetPath's growth was due in part to investments in technology. The company built a state-of-the-art central lab in New Jersey in 1978 that could process some 30000 specimens daily; it also went on an acquisition spree to expand across the US. These investments left the firm swamped with debt and Corning bought the company in 1982.

An autonomous unit of Corning MetPath continued to grow as Medicare reimbursement for lab tests went up and more doctors ordered more tests to catch and prevent disease before it happened. To cut costs in the mid-1980s the company reorganized its facilities to create a regional lab network. A reorganization in 1990 at its parent placed MetPath in the Corning Lab Services subsidiary.

Corning Lab Services strengthened its operations in the early 1990s by buying labs from regional operators. In 1994 MetPath became Corning Clinical Laboratories. Around the same time the company found itself besieged with demands from HMOs and other managed care providers to lower its costs. Also during this time the company settled a handful of federal suits accusing it of fraudulent Medicare billing. In the face of increasing pressure parent Corning spun off its lab testing business to the public as Quest Diagnostics in 1996.

On its own Quest aimed to grow through acquisitions. In 1999 it bought rival SmithKline Beecham Clinical Laboratories from GlaxoSmithKline. (GSK gained a minority stake in Quest through the deal; it gradually sold off all shares in Quest by 2011.) Continuing its growth strategy in the 21st century it bought American Medical Laboratories to expand its esoteric testing operations in 2002. The company was finally able to close its acquisition of Unilab in early 2003 after the deal ran into delays with the FTC. Quest sold some labs and service contracts in northern California to LabCorp to appease FTC regulators.

Quest Diagnostics acquired LabOne a provider of risk assessment services for life insurance companies in 2005. The following year it purchased point-of-care test makers Enterix (colorectal cancer screens) and Focus Diagnostics (infectious disease and esoteric testing). In 2007 the company purchased another point-of-care testing provider Sweden-based HemoCue for $344 million.

In 2007 the company acquired laboratory services firm AmeriPath in a deal worth about $2 billion. The purchase strengthened Quest's operations in a number of areas including anatomic pathology (especially cancer testing) and molecular diagnostics.

To expand internationally the company began providing testing services in India in 2008 including esoteric testing for hospitals tests for the life insurance industry and diagnostics for global clinical trials.

EXECUTIVES

President CEO and Director, Stephen H. (Steve) Rusckowski, age 55
SVP and Chief Human Resources Officer, Jeffrey S. (Jeff) Shuman, age 58
VP Human Resources, David W. Norgard
SVP and CFO, Robert A. Hagemann, age 55, $541,009 total compensation
SVP and General Counsel, Michael E. Prevoznik, age 50, $466,552 total compensation
Chairman, Daniel C. (Dan) Stanzione, age 66
SVP Discovery and Development; President Celera, Kathy P. Ordo?ez, age 62
VP and General Manager Focus Diagnostics, John G. R. Hurrell, age 62
SVP and Chief Medical Officer, Jon R. Cohen, age 57, $412,500 total compensation
SVP Physician Services Business, Catherine T. Doherty
SVP Oncology and Neurology Services, Joan E. Miller, age 57, $464,068 total compensation
VP Communications and Investor Relations, Laure E. Park
VP Office of the Chairman, Dermot Shorten
VP Operations, Wayne R. Simmons, age 56, $403,649 total compensation
VP Compliance, Timothy (Tim) Sharpe
VP Insurer and Employer Services, Rich Bevan
VP and Chief Laboratory Officer, Stephen Suffin
Director Investor Relations, Kathleen Valentine
SVP Commercial, Everett V. Cunningham
SVP Operations, John B. Haydon
President CEO and Director, Stephen H. (Steve) Rusckowski, age 55
Director, Gary M. Pfeiffer, age 62
Director, John B. (Jack) Ziegler, age 66
Director, Gail R. Wilensky, age 68
Director, William F. Buehler, age 72
Director, Jenne K. Britell, age 69
Director, John C. Baldwin, age 63
Auditors: PricewaterhouseCoopersLLP

LOCATIONS

HQ: Quest Diagnostics Incorporated
3 Giralda Farms, Madison NJ 07940
Phone: 973-520-2700 **Fax:** 212-660-3878
Web: www.mktg.com

PRODUCTS/OPERATIONS

2011 Revenues

Clinical testing	6,814	91
Total	**7,510**	**100**

2011 Revenues

	% of total
Clinical testing	
Routine clinical	50
Gene-based & esoteric	25
Anatomic pathology	13
Drugs of abuse testing (employer	3
Healthcare IT clinical trials testing insurance services & diagnostic	9
Total	**100**

Selected Acquisitions

S.E.D. Medical Laboratories (2012 testing labs patient service centers)
Athena Diagnostics (2011 specialized genetic & neurology diagnostics)
Celera (2011 diagnostic products diagnostic development)
AmeriPath (2007 laboratory services)
HemoCue (2007 point-of-care tests)
Enterix (2006 point-of-care colorectal cancer screening)
LabOne (2005 life insurance risk assessment services)

Selected Products and Services

Clincial laboratory testing
- Routine clinical testing (body fluid testing)
  - Alcohol and other substance-abuse tests
  - Allergy tests (ImmunoCap)
  - Blood cholesterol
  - Complete blood cell counts
  - Pap smears
  - Pregnancy testing
  - Urinalyses
- Gene-based and esoteric testing
  - Endocrinology
  - Cancer monitoring (gene-based)
  - Cellular immunology
  - Genetics
  - Hematology
  - Microbiology
  - Molecular diagnostics
  - Oncology
  - Protein chemistry
  - Serology
  - Toxicology
- Anatomic pathology testing (AmeriPath Dermpath Diagnostics and Quest Diagnostics brands)
  - Cancer biopsies
  - Tissue and cell testing

Other products and services
- Clinical trials testing
- Diagnostic products
- Medical data management systems
- Life insurance risk assessment services

Selected Subsidiaries

American Medical Laboratories Incorporated
AmeriPath Inc.
Celera Corporation
Enterix Inc.
Focus Diagnostics Inc.
HemoCue Inc.
LabOne Inc.
MedPlus Inc.
OralDNA Labs Inc.
Quest Diagnostics Nichols Institute

COMPETITORS

Alere
Arup Laboratories
Bio-Reference Labs
Genomic Health
LabCorp
Medtox Scientific
Oncolab
Pathology Associates Medical Laboratories
Psychemedics
Solstas
Sonic Healthcare

HISTORICAL FINANCIALS

Company Type: Public

Income Statement FYE: December 31

	REVENUE ($ mil.)	NET INCOME ($ mil.)	NET PROFIT MARGIN	EMPLOYEES
12/11	7,510	470	6.3%	42,000
12/10	7,368	720	9.8%	42,000
12/09	7,455	729	9.8%	43,000
12/08	7,249	581	8.0%	42,800
12/07	6,704	339	5.1%	43,500
Annual Growth	2.9%	8.5%	—	(0.9%)

2011 Year-End Financials

Debt ratio: 43.22%
Return on equity: 12.74%
Cash ($ mil.): 164
Current ratio: 89.76
Long-term debt ($ mil.): 3,370
No. of shares (mil.): 157
Dividends
Yield: —
Payout: 13.70%
Market value ($ mil.): 9,140

	STOCK PRICE ($) FY Close	P/E High	P/E Low	PER SHARE ($) Earnings	Dividends	Book Value
12/11	58.06	21	16	2.92	0.00	23.46
12/10	53.97	15	11	4.05	0.40	23.63
12/09	60.38	16	11	3.87	0.40	21.77
12/08	51.91	19	13	2.97	0.40	18.94
12/07	52.90	33	27	1.74	0.40	17.13
Annual Growth	2.4%	—	—	13.8%	—	8.2%

Qwest Corp

LOCATIONS

HQ: Qwest Corp
100 CenturyLink Drive, Monroe, LA 71203
Phone: 318 388-9000
Web: www.qwest.com

HISTORICAL FINANCIALS

Company Type:

Income Statement FYE: December 31

	REVENUE ($ mil.)	NET INCOME ($ mil.)	NET PROFIT MARGIN	EMPLOYEES
12/11*	6,635	543	8.2%	25,000
03/11	2,268	299	13.2%	0
12/10	9,271	1,082	11.7%	26,050
12/09	9,731	1,197	12.3%	27,805
12/08	10,388	1,438	13.8%	30,549
Annual Growth	(10.6%)	(21.6%)	—	(4.9%)

*Fiscal year change

2011 Year-End Financials

Debt ratio: 33.39%	No. of shares (mil.): 1
Return on equity: 5.49%	Dividends
Cash ($ mil.): 3	Yield: —
Current ratio: 56.22	Payout: 115.65%
Long-term debt ($ mil.): 8,261	Market value ($ mil.): —

Radian Group, Inc.

Radian Group is glowing from a conflagration of private mortgage insurance claims. Through subsidiaries Radian Guaranty Radian Mortgage Assurance and Radian Insurance Radian Group provides traditional private mortgage insurance coverage to protect lenders from defaults by borrowers who put down a deposit of less than 20% when buying a home. Such coverage provides protection on individual loans and covers unpaid loan principal and delinquent interest. Its pool insurance covers limited exposure on groups of loans. Radian still insures municipal bonds written before 2008 through its financial guaranty business. Radian Group's customers include mortgage bankers commercial banks and savings institutions.

During headier days the government encouraged lenders to turn more Americans into homeowners and Radian made a steady diet of insuring subprime mortgages. However that strategy meant that it was among the first to be hit and hit hard when the housing market imploded and mortgage defaults piled up. The company began pulling back on the riskiest of bonds (such as second-liens) by mid-2007 but by early 2008 its ratings had been lowered.

In response to the market troubles Radian stopped insuring certain types of higher-risk home loans and began working with existing mortgage services to help distressed borrowers modify their loan terms. The company's Radian Asset Assurance operations in the US and UK also stopped accepting new business as part of its general hunkering down to ride out the storm.

While Radian's net premiums earned from mortgage insurance have remained fairly steady the company's revenues plummeted in 2010 due to the ongoing degradation of the credit default swaps in its financial guaranty segment. That year it put Radian Asset Assurance's UK operations into liquidation. However despite the $537.5 million in losses pinned on financial guaranty in 2010 the company is carefully laying out a phoenix-type strategy for the segment. In 2011 it purchased an inactive US financial guaranty company in the hopes of using it to start out fresh writing public finance insurance once the markets pick up.

As the credit environment slowly stabilizes the company is working to capture more high-quality mortgage insurance business and diversify its customer base. As a result it has seen a drop in primary delinquent loans which declined by 12% in 2011 from the previous year. In 2011 Radian's revenue jumped 79% from 2010 (this included $822 million combined net gains from the change in fair value of derivatives and other financial instruments) and its net income soared to $302 million an 83% increase from its net loss in 2010 of $1.8 billion.

What will finally make Radian's future a little brighter? An improved economy with steady jobs and stabilized real estate market will go a long way to reducing the number of mortgage defaults the company might cover. In the meantime it does have a back-up plan: if its primary operating subsidiary Radian Guaranty's risk-to-capital ratio gets too far out of whack sister subsidiary Radian Mortgage Assurance is being groomed to take over writing new business.

HISTORY

Radian Group was born from the ashes of the 1987 stock crash and the rubble of the natural disasters of the early 1990s. Parent insurance company Reliance Group was deep in debt and desperately in need of cash. To raise money Reliance separated CMAC Investment (and operating subsidiary Commonwealth Mortgage Assurance) from subsidiary Commonwealth Land Title and took the company public in 1992.

In 1994 after two years of lackluster stock performance the board promoted CFO Frank Filipps (an American International Group veteran) to CEO. Filipps limited commissions to new policies rather than retained business. The pokey stock nosed up with some help from low interest rates and high numbers of new mortgage loans. Despite a raise in interest rates in 1995 the company continued to expand its market share.

In 1996 the company launched Prophet Score a new risk-assessment model that allowed CMAC to expand its coverage to include subprime loans. These measures jump-started sales to new highs in 1997 and 1998. Nevertheless CMAC (and its competitors) suffered in the market because of negative publicity: private mortgage (PMI) insurers were slammed for keeping quiet when borrowers' equity rose to 20% the point when PMI is usually considered unnecessary. In 1999 CMAC bought former rival Amerin and changed the name of the combined company to Radian Group.

Radian diversified its operations through the 2001 acquisition of credit-based insurance and financial services provider Enhance Financial (renamed Radian Reinsurance and later merged into Radian Asset Assurance Inc.) In 2002 Radian sold off the Enhance Consumer Services subsidiary.

In 2005 Filipps departed to join Clayton Holdings. Sanford Ibrahim was then named CEO.

The company expanded into Asia in 2005 through a partnership with Standard Chartered Bank (Hong Kong) with Radian as the exclusive provider of residential mortgage insurance to the lender. However the deal did not take root and Standard Chartered Bank yanked their contract in early 2008.

When the real estate industry was booming Radian establisted two joint ventures with fellow mortgage insurer MGIC Investment Corporation: subprime mortgage investor C-BASS and Sherman Financial a purchaser of distressed consumer debt. Following the subprime meltdown C-BASS' investors opened the escape hatch in 2007 and executed their "what if" plans leaving the JV in runoff. C-BASS ultimately filed for Chapter 11 bankruptcy protection in 2010. Radian held fast to its investment in Sherman for a while; however the company finally broke down and divested its stake in the debt management firm for $172 million in 2010 to focus fully on its mortgage insurance operations.

EXECUTIVES

EVP and CFO, C. Robert (Bob) Quint, age 52, $370,000 total compensation
President Radian Guaranty, Teresa A. Bryce Bazemore, age 52, $400,000 total compensation
EVP and COO Radian Guaranty, Robert H. (Bob) Griffith, age 54
Chairman, Herbert Wender, age 74
President Radian Asset Assurance, David J. (Dave) Beidler
SVP Corporate Communications and Marketing, Richard A. Gillespie
CEO and Director, Sanford A. Ibrahim, age 60, $800,000 total compensation
EVP and CIO Radian Group and Radian Guaranty, Lawrence C. DelGatto, $300,000 total compensation
EVP and Chief Risk Officer Radian Guaranty, H. Scott Theobald, age 51, $260,000 total compensation
Chief Risk Officer, Richard I. (Rick) Altman, age 45
SVP Account Management, Marshall G. Gayden
SVP and Corporate Controller, Catherine M. Jackson, age 49
EVP General Counsel and Corporate Secretary, Edward J. Hoffman, age 38
SVP Field Sales, Michael Dziuba
Director, David C. Carney, age 74
Director, Ronald W. Moore, age 67
Director, Jan Nicholson, age 67
Director, James W. Jennings, age 75
Director, Howard B. Culang, age 65
Director, Stephen T. Hopkins, age 61
Director, Robert W. Richards, age 69
Director, Anthony W. (Tony) Schweiger, age 70
CEO and Director, Sanford A. Ibrahim, age 60
Director, Noel J. Spiegel
Director, Lisa W. Hess, age 55
Auditors: Deloitte&ToucheLLP

LOCATIONS

HQ: Radian Group Inc.
1601 Market St., Philadelphia PA 19103
Phone: 215-231-1000 **Fax:** 215-854-1457
Web: www.radiangroupinc.com

PRODUCTS/OPERATIONS

2011 Revenues

Financial guaranty	1,039	53
Mortgage insurance	908	47

Selected Subsidiaries

Enhance Financial Services Group Inc.

Commonwealth Mortgage Assurance Company of Texas
Enhance C-BASS Residual Finance Corporation
Residual Interest Investments LP (99%/1%-owned by Commonwealth Mortgage Assurance Company of Texas and Enhance C-BASS Residual Finance Corporation respectively)
Guaranty Risk Services Inc.
Lottery Receivables Series 1998A Corporation
Radian Reinsurance (Bermuda) Limited
Radian Asset Securities Inc.
Radian Guaranty Inc.
Radian Asset Assurance Inc.
Asset Recovery Solutions Group Inc.Windsor Management Inc.
MAAC Holdings (Bermuda) LimitedMunicipal and Infrastructure Assurance Corporation
Van-American Insurance Agency Inc.
Radian Insurance Inc.
Radian Mauritius Holdings Limited
Radian Mortgage Assurance Inc.
Radian Mortgage Insurance Inc.
Radian Mortgage Services (Hong Kong) Ltd.
Radian Services LLC
Radian MI Services Inc.
Radian Insurance Services LLC
Radian Mortgage Reinsurance Company

COMPETITORS

Assured Guaranty
Genworth Financial
MGIC Investment
Old Republic
PMI Group
Republic Mortgage Insurance
Triad Guaranty
United Guaranty
US Department of Veterans Affairs

HISTORICAL FINANCIALS

Company Type: Public

Income Statement FYE: December 31

	ASSETS ($ mil.)	NET INCOME ($ mil.)	INCOME AS % OF ASSETS	EMPLOYEES
12/11	6,656	302	4.5%	650
12/10	7,620	(1,805)	—	767
12/09	8,076	(147)	—	803
12/08	8,116	(410)	—	835
12/07	8,210	(1,290)	—	832
Annual Growth	(5.1%)	—	—	(6.0%)

2011 Year-End Financials

Debt ratio: 12.30%
Return on equity: 25.56%
Cash ($ mil.): 35
Current ratio: —
Long-term debt ($ mil.): 818
No. of shares (mil.): 133
Dividends
Yield: —
Payout: 0.44%
Market value ($ mil.): 312

	STOCK PRICE ($) FY Close	P/E High	P/E Low	PER SHARE ($) Earnings	Dividends	Book Value
12/11	2.34	4	1	2.26	0.00	8.88
12/10	8.07	—	—	(15.74)	0.01	6.46
12/09	7.31	—	—	(1.80)	0.01	24.22
12/08	3.68	—	—	(5.12)	0.05	25.06
12/07	11.68	—	—	(16.22)	0.08	33.83
Annual Growth	(33.1%)	—	—	—	—	(28.4%)

RadioShack Corp.

LOCATIONS

HQ: RadioShack Corp.
Mail Stop CF3-201, 300 RadioShack Circle, Fort Worth, TX 76102
Phone: 817 415-3011 **Fax:** 817 415-6808
Web: www.radioshack.com

HISTORICAL FINANCIALS

Company Type:

Income Statement FYE: December 31

	REVENUE ($ mil.)	NET INCOME ($ mil.)	NET PROFIT MARGIN	EMPLOYEES
12/11	4,378	72	1.6%	34,000
12/10	4,472	206	4.6%	36,400
12/09	4,276	205	4.8%	36,700
12/08	4,224	192	4.6%	36,800
12/07	4,251	236	5.6%	35,800
Annual Growth	0.7%	(25.7%)	—	(1.3%)

2011 Year-End Financials

Debt ratio: 30.83%
Return on equity: 9.58%
Cash ($ mil.): 591
Current ratio: 273.18
Long-term debt ($ mil.): 670
No. of shares (mil.): 99
Dividends
Yield: —
Payout: 71.43%
Market value ($ mil.): 964

	STOCK PRICE ($) FY Close	P/E High	P/E Low	PER SHARE ($) Earnings	Dividends	Book Value
12/11	9.71	27	13	0.70	0.00	7.59
12/10	18.49	14	11	1.68	0.25	7.97
12/09	19.50	12	4	1.63	0.25	8.37
12/08	11.94	13	5	1.49	0.25	6.53
12/07	16.86	20	10	1.74	0.25	5.87
Annual Growth	(12.9%)	—	—	(20.4%)	—	6.6%

Ralcorp Holdings, Inc.

You can't judge a food by its cover: Ralcorp Holdings is the largest US maker of private label or store brand products and a major player in the food service market. Ralcorp's portfolio includes Ralston ready-to-eat and hot breakfast cereals as well as Bremner crackers and cookies Nutcracker trail mixes Medallion corn snacks and Linette chocolates. Carriage House produces dressings jellies and sauces and a frozen bakery business frozen cookies and in-store baked goods under the Krusteaz and other labels. Ralcorp also makes dry pasta for retail and food service customers through American Italian Pasta Co. Ralcorp has agreed to be acquired by ConAgra Foods in a deal valued at $6.8 billion.

Looking to beef up its private-label business ConAgra Foods offered $90 per share in cash for Ralcorp representing about a 28% premium to Ralcorp's closing share price on the day before the deal was announced. The sale is slated to close by the end of March 2013.

In 2012 Ralcorp spun off its Post Foods cereal business to further strengthen its private-brand position. The spinoff gives Ralcorp shareholders a stake in two stand-alone publicly-traded companies. The deal is intended to spur a turnaround for Ralcorp as well as help write a new chapter for Post. Although Ralcorp's sales in 2011 marked five years of growth earnings tumbled to a loss. The company's loss was in part anticipated given the charges taken for goodwill and brand impairment merger and integrations costs (from acquisitions) and interest expense. Moreover Ralcorp's footing going into 2011 was undermined by more than 25% decline in profitability during the previous year from 2009's record high (attributable to a gain made on selling its stake in Vail Resorts). As of late 2012 Ralcorp began to explore the sale of its 6.8 million shares –representing its remaining stake –in Post's common stock.

The spinoff is a departure from Ralcorp's tradition of growth through acquisition. Indeed Ralcorp has purchased more than 25 companies since 1997. Most recently the company in mid-2012 acquired Gelit S.r.l. a maker of private-brand frozen ready meals in Italy. Gelit will operate as part of Ralcorp's American Italian Pasta Co. division. Earlier in the year it expanded its portfolio of private brands by acquiring wire-cut cookie maker Petri Baking Products; it plans to fold the cookie company into its Snacks Sauces & Spreads division. Among the more significant Ralcorp took over Post Foods from Kraft Foods in a deal valued at approximately $2.7 billion in 2008. The Post brand is the #3 US breakfast cereal (behind Kellogg and General Mills) comprising such well-known brands as Honey Bunches of Oats (the third-best selling breakfast cereal in the US) Pebbles Shredded Wheat Grape-Nuts and Honeycomb. Ralcorp's expectations for the name brand cereal maker however failed to materialize. Following a spike of more 400% in 2009 year-over-year branded cereal sales have slumped due to soft demand and lower selling prices coupled with higher promotion spending.

The impact of Post Foods on Ralcorp's performance reflects the difficulty in selling a strong-branded food business alongside of a value-priced private label portfolio during a slow moving economy. Ralcorp's customers range from highly competitive retail grocery store chains to mass merchandisers warehouse club stores supercenters drugstores restaurant chains and foodservice distributors in the US and Canada. Retail giant Wal-Mart known for attracting bargain shoppers accounts for slightly less than 20% of Ralcorp's sales.

Other acquisitions appear to be a better fit. Ralcorp bought out of Sara Lee's refrigerated dough business for about $545 million in fall 2011. (Proceeds from the Post spin off are earmarked to pay down the debt incurrent in the Sara Lee deal.) The Sara Lee unit which includes private label toaster pastries crescent rolls pizza and pie crusts and other specialty items swells Ralcorp's private brand offerings and boosts its share of the refrigerated dough market. The refrigerated dough addition joins Ralcorp's frozen bakery products division.

Ralcorp's $1.2 billion acquisition of American Italian Pasta Co. (AIPC) in 2010 scooped up an 85% stake in one of the largest US dry pasta manufacturers. AIPC operating as an independent division of Ralcorp brings an array of branded and private label products as well as strategically located production facilities and a hefty roster of top-tier customers. On its heels in 2010 Ralcorp bought out and absorbed Sepp's Gourmet Foods a maker of frozen breakfast foods marketed to the retail food and foodservice sectors. Sepp's had operations in British Columbia and Ontario Canada.

Long accustomed to being the acquirer Ralcorp became an acquisition target of food giant ConAgra in 2011. Ralcorp rejected ConAgra's more than $5 billion unsolicited takeover bid for the third time. ConAgra a persistent suitor initially offered $82 per share for Ralcorp and later raised its offer to $94 a share. Ralcorp rejected ConAgra noting that its cash offers failed to provide an adequate premium to shareholders.

HISTORY

Ralston Purina spun off Ralcorp Holdings then a maker of name-brand and private-label foods in 1994 under co-CEOs Richard Pearce and Joe Micheletto. Ralston was concerned that its huge pet food and Eveready battery interests had overshadowed its smaller consumer foods and ski resort businesses.

A cereal price war in 1996 ate at Ralcorp's price advantage and devoured margins. To focus on its core private-label business in 1997 the firm sold its branded snack and cereal businesses (which included Cookie Crisp and Chex) to General Mills for about $570 million and its ski resort holdings to Vail Resorts for $310 million (it received a 22% stake in Vail; shares were gradually reduced until by 2009 Ralcorp owned less than 5%). Pearce resigned while the sales were in progress; Micheletto stayed on as CEO.

The company expanded its cookie and cracker division by adding the Wortz Company (the #2 US private-label cracker and cookie maker) for about $46 million in 1997 and Sugar Kake Cookie the following year. In 1998 Ralcorp entered a new private-label category snack nuts by purchasing nut makers Flavor House and Nutcracker Brands. Faced with price competition and decreasing demand it sold its Beech-Nut baby food business that year for $68 million to the Milnot company.

To broaden its private-label portfolio further in early 1999 Ralcorp bought Martin Gillet (mayonnaise and salad dressings) and Southern Roasted Nuts of Georgia. In late 1999 the company bought Ripon Foods (cookies sugar wafers breakfast bars). And seeing breakfast cereal sales shrinking Ralcorp purchased Ripon Foods in 1999 in part for its ability to make private-label breakfast bars.

In 2000 Ralcorp purchased private-label chocolate candy maker James P. Linette and the Cascade Cookie Company. That same year it bought Red Wing (syrups peanut butter jelly barbecue sauce) from Tomkins for about $132 million. Also in 2000 Ralcorp said it would merge with animal feed company Agribrands International but the agreement fell through. Additionally that year the company said it would buy Genesee Corporation's Ontario Foods business (powdered drinks soups prepared meals) for $50 million but called off that deal too.

Ralcorp purchased cookie-maker Lofthouse Foods during 2002. Early in 2003 the company sold off its industrial tomato-paste facility. Later that year Ralcorp purchased frozen breakfast foods company Bakery Chef for $287.5 million.

In 2004 the company acquired Concept 2 Bakers (C2B) a frozen par-baked artisan bread maker from McGlynn Bakeries. In 2005 it purchased private-label corn-snack (corn and tortilla chips) manufacturer Medallion Foods and Canadian private-label griddle-product maker Western Waffles.

It purchased Parco Foods a Chicago-based cookie maker for in-store bakeries and Cottage Bakeries a frozen bread dough maker in 2006. Its 2007 purchase of Bakery Chef (frozen foodservice pancakes and waffles) allowed Ralcorp to reach people eating breakfast at restaurants. It bought Bloomfield Bakers for about $140 million in 2007 as well. The deal included Bloomfield affiliate Lovin Oven. Bloomfield makes nutritional and cereal bars.

Ralcorp purchased Harvest Manor Farms a Cedar Rapids Iowa-based maker of private-label and Hoody's-branded nuts in 2009. Harvest Manor products strengthened Ralcorp's snack food portfolio. Also that year Ralcorp divested itself from its earlier days selling off its approximate 19% interest in popular ski destination Vail Resorts. In mid-2010 Ralcorp acquired American Italian Pasta Company a leading US manufacturer of dry pasta. In October 2011 it completed the $545 million purchase of Sara Lee's North American private brand refrigerated dought business which includes distribution facilities in Carrollton Texas and Forest Park Georgia.

EXECUTIVES

Corporate VP; President Cereal Products, Ronald D. (Ron) Wilkinson, age 62, $315,000 total compensation

CEO President and Director, Kevin J. Hunt, age 61, $575,000 total compensation

Co-CEO President and Director, David P. Skarie, age 65, $575,000 total compensation

VP and Director Human Resources, Jack Owczarczak

Chairman, William P. (Bill) Stiritz, age 77

Corporate VP and Chief Accounting Officer, Thomas G. Granneman, age 63, $295,000 total compensation

Chairman, J. Patrick (Pat) Mulcahy, age 67

Corporate VP Treasurer Corporate Development Officer, Scott D. Monette, age 51

VP; President American Italian Pasta, Walter N. (Walt) George, age 56

VP; President Ralcorp Frozen Bakery Products, Charles G. (Chuck) Huber Jr., age 47

VP; President Ralcorp Snacks Sauces and Spreads, Richard R. Koulouris, age 56, $300,000 total compensation

VP General Counsel and Secretary, Gregory A. (Greg) Billhartz

Director Business Development, Matt Pudlowski

Director, David R. Banks, age 75

Director, David W. Kemper, age 61

Director, Jack W. Goodall, age 74

CEO President and Director, Kevin J. Hunt, age 61

Co-CEO President and Director, David P. Skarie, age 65

Director, Bill G. Armstrong, age 63

Vice Chairman, J. Patrick (Pat) Mulcahy, age 66

Director, Jonathan E. Baum, age 51

Director, David R. Wenzel, age 49

Director, Benjamin Akande

Auditors: PricewaterhouseCoopersLLP

LOCATIONS

HQ: Ralcorp Holdings Inc.
800 Market St., St. Louis MO 63101
Phone: 314-877-7000 **Fax:** 314-877-7900
Web: www.ralcorp.com

PRODUCTS/OPERATIONS

2011 Sales

	$ mil.	% of total
Snacks sauces & spreads	1,602	34
Branded cereal products	953	20
Other cereal products	838	18
Frozen bakery products	768	16
Pasta	577	12
Total	**4,741**	**100**

Selected Branded Products

3 Minute Brand (hot breakfast cereal)
Anthony' s
Bremner (snacks)
Cascade (cookies)
Champagne (crackers)
Flavor House (snack nuts)
Golden Grain (pasta)
Heartland (pasta)
Hoody' s (snack nuts)
JERO (bottled non-alcoholic cocktail mixes)
Linette (snack)
Lofthouse (cookies)
Krusteaz (frozen breakfast foods)
Major Peters' (bottled non-alcoholic cocktail mixes)
Medallion (corn and tortilla chips)
Mrs. Grass (pasta)
Muellers (pasta)
Nutcracker (snack nuts)
Panne Provincio (in-store bakery bread)
Parco (cookies)
Pasta Lensi (pasta)
Pennsylvania Dutch (pasta)
Ralson (hot breakfast cereal)
Rippin' Good (cookies)
Ry Krisp (crackers)

Selected Subsidiaries

American Italian Pasta Company
Bloomfield Bakers LP
Bremner Food Group Inc.
The Bun Basket Inc.
The Carriage House Companies Inc.
Cottage Bakery Inc.
Flavor House Products Inc.
Harvest Manor Farms LLC
Heritage Wafers LLC
J.T. Bakeries Inc.
Lofthouse Bakery Products Inc.
Lovin Oven LLC
Medallion Foods Inc.
National Oats Company
North American Baking Ltd.
Nutcracker Brands Inc.
Parco Foods L.L.C.
Ralcorp Frozen Bakery Products Inc.
Ripon Foods Inc.
Sugar Kake Cookie Inc.
Western Waffles Corp. (Canada)

COMPETITORS

ak-mak Bakeries
Annie' s Inc.
Barilla
Campbell Soup
Cento
Colavita
Dakota Growers
Eden Foods
Fehr Foods
Frito-Lay
General Mills
Gilster-Mary Lee
Heinz
Interbake Foods
John Sanfilippo & Son
Kellogg
Marzetti
McKee Foods
MOM Brands
Mondelez International
National Grape Cooperative
New World Pasta
NORPAC
Otis Spunkmeyer
Pepperidge Farm
PepsiCo
Renee' s Gourmet Foods
Rossi Pasta
Silver Lake Cookie
Smucker
Snyder' s-Lance
Unilever PLC
Voortman Cookies
Welch' s

HISTORICAL FINANCIALS

Company Type: Public

Income Statement FYE: September 30

	REVENUE ($ mil.)	NET INCOME ($ mil.)	NET PROFIT MARGIN	EMPLOYEES
09/12	4,322	73	1.7%	10,300
09/11	4,741	(187)	—	11,000
09/10	4,048	208	5.2%	10,800
09/09	3,891	290	7.5%	9,350
09/08	2,824	167	5.9%	9,000
Annual Growth	11.2%	(18.7%)	—	3.4%

2012 Year-End Financials

Debt ratio: 44.54%
Return on equity: 4.46%
Cash ($ mil.): 307
Current ratio: 200.00
Long-term debt ($ mil.): 1,894
No. of shares (mil.): 55
Dividends
Yield: —
Payout: —
Market value ($ mil.): 4,018

	STOCK PRICE ($) FY Close	P/E High	P/E Low	PER SHARE ($) Earnings	Dividends	Book Value
09/12	73.00	67	45	1.31	0.00	29.93
09/11	76.71	—	—	(3.41)	0.00	47.46
09/10	58.48	18	14	3.74	0.00	51.51
09/09	58.47	14	10	5.09	0.00	47.77
09/08	67.41	12	9	5.38	0.00	42.85
Annual Growth	2.0%	—	—	(29.8%)	—	(8.6%)

Raytheon Co.

Raytheon ("light of the gods") took a shine to its place in the upper pantheon of US military contractors; the company regularly places among the Pentagon's top 10 prime contractors. Its air/land/sea/space/cyber defense offerings include reconnaissance targeting and navigation systems as well as missile systems (Patriot Sidewinder and Tomahawk) unmanned ground and aerial systems sensing and radars. Additionally Raytheon makes systems for communications (satellite) and intelligence radios cybersecurity and air traffic control. It also offers commercial electronics products and services as well as food safety processing technologies. The US government accounts for about 75% of sales.

HISTORY

In 1922 Laurence Marshall and several others founded American Appliance Company to produce home refrigerators. When their invention failed Marshall began making Raytheon (meaning "light of/from the gods") radio tubes. Raytheon was adopted as the company's name in 1925. It bought the radio division of Chicago's Q. R. S. Company in 1928 and formed Raytheon Production Company with National Carbon Company (makers of the Eveready battery) to market Eveready Raytheon tubes in 1929.

Growing rapidly in WWII Raytheon became the first producer of magnetrons (tubes used in radar and later in microwave ovens). Wartime sales peaked at $173 million but dwindled by 1947. Amid rumors of bankruptcy Charles Adams became Raytheon's president. He sold Raytheon's unprofitable radio and TV business in 1956.

In 1964 Adams (then chairman) named missile engineer Thomas Phillips president. Phillips oversaw several purchases designed to balance Raytheon's commercial and military earnings beginning with Amana Refrigeration (1965) D.C. Heath (textbooks 1966) Caloric (stoves 1967) and three petrochemical firms (1966-69).

Raytheon began making computer terminals in 1971 (exited 1984). In 1980 it bought Grumman's Beech Aircraft division. Despite efforts to diversify Raytheon still relied on missiles radar and communications systems for most of its sales in 1987. In 1991 it won an $800 million US Army contract to upgrade Patriot missiles used in the Persian Gulf War. After 43 years with Raytheon Phillips retired that year and president Dennis Picard became chairman.

Raytheon expanded as it bought the business jet division of British Aerospace (1993) E-Systems (advanced electronics and surveillance equipment 1995) and most of Chrysler's aerospace and defense holdings (1996).

By 1997 Raytheon doubled in size and became the #1 US missile maker after buying Texas Instruments' missile and defense electronics holdings for about $3 billion and Hughes Electronics' (now The DIRECTV Group) defense business for $9.5 billion. It consolidated those and other electronics units into Raytheon Systems Company (dismantled 2000). Raytheon sold its analog chip-making business to Fairchild Semiconductor (1997); its home appliance heating and air-conditioning and commercial cooking units to Goodman Holding (1997); and its flight controls business to Moog (1998).

Weak sales in Asia hurt Raytheon in 1998 and it announced cuts of some 14000 defense jobs (16% of the unit's workforce) and the closure of 28 plants over two years. Former AlliedSignal VC Daniel Burnham became CEO in 1998 succeeding Picard. Raytheon also began a legal battle with Hughes claiming it had been overcharged $1 billion in 1997 for Hughes' defense unit (the suit was settled for about $650 million in 2001).

In 1999 Raytheon cut more jobs made plans to close or combine 10 facilities and took a $668 million charge to correct financial problems in its defense electronics business. The company also sold its road construction equipment business to Terex and its hybrid microelectronics business to Imrex Microelectronics.

Raytheon sold its flight simulation and training business to L-3 Communications for $160 million in 2000 and its engineering and construction unit to Washington Group International (formerly Morrison Knudsen) for about $500 million. That year Raytheon sold $800 million in aircraft loans and leases to Debis Capital Services and began trying to sell its aircraft business for a reported price tag of about $4 billion. Raytheon was awarded a $1.4 billion contract that ran through 2008 from Lockheed Martin to develop three radar systems for the US's Theater High Altitude Area Defense (THAAD) program. Raytheon also sold its optical systems business to BFGoodrich (now Goodrich) and agreed to a joint venture with France-based Thales (formerly Thomson-CSF) to form a joint air defense venture ThalesRaytheonSystems.

In 2002 Raytheon sold its aircraft integration unit to L-3 Communications for over $1 billion in cash and made a bid for TRW's satellite and missile defense operations. The company shelved plans to sell its Raytheon Aircraft unit in 2003 but continued to sell non-core units including its commercial infrared unit (to L-3 Communications) in 2004.

Raytheon agreed to team up in 2005 with EADS North America to bid on the Army's $1 billion Future Cargo Aircraft program. Under the agreement Raytheon would be prime contractor; EADS would assemble and deliver the medium cargo transport planes.

Spending on homeland security and the wars in Iraq and Afghanistan was extremely beneficial to Raytheon's fortunes. In 2001 and 2002 the company lost $763 million and $640 million respectively. Profits recovered in 2003 to the tune of $365 million as the conflict in Afghanistan continued and Iraq ramped up. Since then profits climbed every year with 2007 bringing a bonanza of more than $2.3 billion in profits.

As 2006 wound to a close Raytheon announced it would sell Raytheon Aircraft to a new company Hawker Beechcraft formed by Goldman Sachs and Onex Corporation for $3.3 billion. The deal was completed in 2007. In late 2007 Raytheon sold Flight Options which provided fractional jet ownership services to H.I.G. Capital.

Raytheon picked up Telemus Solutions a provider of information security and intelligence services and support for military customers in 2008. Adding to its Network Centric Systems business Raytheon purchased BBN Technologies for $350 million in 2009. The deal scored BBN's array of advanced networking and technologies for processing speech and language and information as well as sensor systems and cyber security.

Raytheon continued to make a slew of acquisitions throughout 2010 and 2011. Notable purchases included Applied Signal Technology Trusted Computer Solutions Technology Associates Henggeler Computer Consultants Pikewerks Corporation and Ktech Corporation.

EXECUTIVES

VP and Treasurer, Richard A. Goglia, age 60
VP Global Marketing Communications, Lucy A. Flynn, age 58
Chairman and CEO, William H. Swanson, age 63, $1,297,920 total compensation
SVP and CFO, David C. Wajsgras, age 52, $790,203 total compensation
SVP Human Resources, Keith J. Peden, age 61
SVP Business Development; CEO Raytheon International, Thomas M. Culligan, $384,808 total compensation
VP and CIO, Rebecca B. Rhoads
VP and Chief Accounting Officer, Michael J. Wood, age 43
VP Corporate Affairs and Communications, Pamela A. (Pam) Wickham
Acting VP Homeland Security, Timothy W. Josiah
SVP General Counsel and Secretary, Jay B. Stephens, age 65, $690,825 total compensation
VP; President Technical Systems, John D. Harris II, age 50
VP Internal Audit, Lawrence J. Harrington
VP; Deputy General Manager Missile Systems, Edward Miyashiro
VP; President Raytheon Network Centric Systems, Daniel J. (Dan) Crowley, age 49
VP Contracts and Supply Chain, David Wilkins
VP Raytheon Company Evaluation Team, Michael M. Hoeffler
VP; President Space and Airborne Systems (SAS), Richard R. (Rick) Yuse, age 60
VP Engineering Technology and Mission Assurance, Mark E. Russell, age 50
VP; President Integrated Defense Systems, Thomas A. (Tom) Kennedy, age 57
President Asia Raytheon International, Walter F. Doran
VP; President Missile Systems, Taylor W. Lawrence, age 48, $383,237 total compensation

VP National Intelligence Programs Business Development, Garnett Stowe
Intelligence and Information Systems (IIS), Michael P. (Mike) Morgan
Director Raytheon Virtual Technology, Patrick Fines
Director Talent Acquisition, Paul Clegg
Media Contact Global Headquarters, Jonathan D. (Jon) Kasle
VP; President Intelligence and Information Systems, Lynn A. Dugle, age 52
VP Communications and Public Affairs Space and Airborne Systems, Catherine H. Blades
VP Army Programs US Business Development, Galen B. Jackman
Director Investor Relations, Jim Singer
VP Strategy, Mitch Kugler
Managing Director Australia, Michael Ward
Business Development Executive ISS Business, Chris Foster
VP ISS, Steve Hawkins
VP Mission Assurance, James W. Wade
VP Government Relations, Mark T. Esper
VP Investor Relations, Todd Ernst
VP Mission Operations Solutions Intelligence and Information Systems, Ron Stefano
VP Radar Sensor Systems (RSS), Charles Marinello
Director, Ronald L. Skates, age 70
Director, Michael C. Ruettgers, age 69
Director, Frederic M. (Fred) Poses, age 69
Director, William R. Spivey, age 65
Director, John M. Deutch, age 73
Director, Linda G. Stuntz, age 57
Director, Adm. Vernon E. (Vern) Clark, age 67
Director, Stephen J. (Steve) Hadley, age 65
Auditors: PricewaterhouseCoopersLLP

LOCATIONS

HQ: Raytheon Company
870 Winter St., Waltham MA 02451-1449
Phone: 781-522-3000 **Fax:** 781-522-3001
Web: www.raytheon.com

2011 Sales

US	18,690	75
Middle East & North Africa	2,216	9
Total	**24,857**	**100**

PRODUCTS/OPERATIONS

2011 Sales

Missile Systems	5,590	21
Space & Airborne Systems	5,255	20
Network Centric Systems	4,497	17
Technical Services	3,353	13
Adjustments	(1811)	-

Selected Products

Integrated Defense Systems (IDS)
- Aegis Weapon Systems radar equipment
- AN/AQS Minehunting Sonar System
- Joint Land Attack Cruise Missile Defense Elevated Netted Sensor (JLENS)
- Landing Platform Dock Amphibious Ship LPD-17
- Patriot Air and Missile Defense System
- Sea-Based X-Band Radar (SBX)
- Ship Self-Defense System (SSDS)
- Surface-Launched AMRAAM (SLAMRAAM)
- Terminal High Altitude Area Defense (THAAD) Radar

Intelligence and Information Systems (IIS)
- Army Research Lab
- Communications systems
- Department of Education programs
- Distributed Common Ground System
- Emergency Patient Tracking System
- Global Broadcast Service
- Global Hawk Ground Segment
- Information solutions programs
- Managed data storage solutions
- Mobile Very Small Aperture Satellite Terminal
- National Polar-Orbiting Operational Environmental Satellite System Program
- RedWolf telecommunications surveillance
- Signal and imagery intelligence programs
- Supercomputing
- U-2 (field support)
- UAV systems and ground stations

Missile Systems (MS)
- Advanced Medium-Range Air-to-Air missile (AMRAAM)
- AIM-9X Sidewinder
- Evolved SeaSparrow (ESSM)
- Excalibur long-range artillery system
- Exoatmospheric Kill Vehicle
- Extended Range Guided Munition (ERGM)
- High-Speed Anti-Radiation Missile Targeting System
- Paveway laser-guided bombs
- Maverick AGM-65 missiles
- Tomahawk and Tactical Tomahawk cruise missiles
- TOW Javelin Phalanx Standard and SeaRAM missiles

Network Centric Systems (NCS)
- Airspace management and homeland security
- Command and control systems
- Combat systems
- Integrated communications systems
- Precision technologies and components

Space and Airborne Systems (SAS)
- Active electronically scanned array radars
- Airborne radars and processors
- Electronic warfare systems
- Electro-optic/infrared sensors
- Intelligence surveillance and reconnaissance systems
- Space and missile defense technology

Technical Services (TS)
- Base operations
- Logistics support
- Maintenance support
- Professional services
- Treaty compliance monitoring
- Weapons security and destruction

Selected Markets

Command Control Communication and Intelligence (C3I)
- Systems provide integrated real-time support for on- and off-battlefield and transform raw data into actionable intelligence

Cybersecurity
- Provides cyber capabilities to the Intelligence DoD and DHS markets as well as embedding cybersecurity in Raytheon' s products and IT infrastructure

Effects
- Achieves specific military actions or outcomes from force protection to theater/national missile defense

Homeland Security
- Domestic and international homeland security markets especially transportation security immigration control/identity management critical infrastructure protection maritime security energy security intelligence program support law enforcement solutio

Mission Support
- Provides total life-cycle and training system engineering logistics and maintenance support to customer

Sensing
- Acquires precise situational data across air space ground and underwater domains and generates information needed for effective battlespace decisions

COMPETITORS

BAE Systems Inc.
Boeing
Crane Aerospace & Electronics
DRS Technologies
Emerson Electric
Exelis
Fluor
GE
Harris Corp.
Herley Industries
Honeywell Aerospace
Interstate Electronics
L-3 Avionics
Lockheed Martin
MBDA
Meggitt-USA
Northrop Grumman
Rockwell Collins
Saab AB
Sierra Nevada Corp

HISTORICAL FINANCIALS

Company Type: Public

Income Statement FYE: December 31

	REVENUE ($ mil.)	NET INCOME ($ mil.)	NET PROFIT MARGIN	EMPLOYEES
12/11	24,857	1,866	7.5%	71,000
12/10	25,183	1,840	7.3%	72,000
12/09	24,881	1,935	7.8%	75,000
12/08	23,174	1,672	7.2%	73,000
12/07	21,301	2,578	12.1%	72,100
Annual Growth	3.9%	(7.8%)	—	(0.4%)

2011 Year-End Financials

Debt ratio: 17.81%
Return on equity: 22.81%
Cash ($ mil.): 4,000
Current ratio: 151.86
Long-term debt ($ mil.): 4,605
No. of shares (mil.): 339
Dividends
Yield: —
Payout: 39.68%
Market value ($ mil.): 16,401

	STOCK PRICE ($) FY Close	P/E High/Low		PER SHARE ($) Earnings	Dividends	Book Value
12/11	48.38	10	7	5.28	0.00	24.13
12/10	46.34	12	9	4.88	1.44	27.17
12/09	51.52	11	7	4.89	1.24	26.00
12/08	51.04	17	11	3.95	1.12	22.72
12/07	60.70	11	9	5.79	1.02	29.43
Annual Growth	(5.5%)	—	—	(2.3%)	—	(4.8%)

Realogy Holdings Corp

Realogy Holdings (formerly Domus Holdings) has the goods for domestic bliss for a lot of people. It is the largest franchisor of residential real estate offices in the world through its Realogy unit which has about 13800 offices in more than 100 countries. Its brands include Century 21 Coldwell Banker ERA Better Homes and Gardens Real Estate and Sotheby's. In addition to franchising the company owns and operates more than 725 offices under the already mentioned brands along with the Corcoran Group and CitiHabitats labels. It also provides relocation title and settlement services and mortgages. The residential real estate giant changed its name in September 2012 and went public in October.

IPO

The initial public offering of 40 million shares priced at $27 (the top of its price range) was a vote of confidence of sorts in the recovery of the residential real estate market in the US. Realogy will use the IPO proceeds to reduce its more than $7 billion in debt. Despite losing $99 million in 2010 and $440 million in 2011 the firm believes the real estate market is poised for recovery. Its strategy includes growing all segments of its business though it offers no specifics on that front.

Ownership

Post-IPO the investment firms Apollo Management and Paulson & Co. own 48% and 15% of Realogy's shares respectively.

EXECUTIVES

EVP General Counsel and Corporate Secretary, Marilyn J. Wasser, age 56
Chairman President and CEO, Richard A. Smith, age 58

President and CEO Realogy Franchise Group, Alexander E. (Alex) Perriello III, age 64
CEO Sotheby's International Realty Affiliates LLC, Michael R. Good
President and CEO NRT LLC, Bruce G. Zipf, age 55
President and CEO Cartus Corporation, Kevin J. Kelleher, age 57
CEO Coldwell Banker Real Estate LLC, James R. (Jim) Gillespie
EVP CFO and Treasurer, Anthony E. (Tony) Hull, age 53
EVP and Chief Administrative Officer, David J. (Dave) Weaving, age 45
President and COO Sotheby's International Realty Affiliates LLC, Philip A. White Jr., age 59
President and COO Coldwell Banker Commercial Affiliates LLC and President ONCOR International LLC, Fred Schmidt
President and CEO ERA Franchise Systems LLC, Charlie Young
President and CEO Title Resource Group (TRG), Donald J. (Don) Casey, age 50
President and COO Coldwell Banker Real Estate LLC, Budge Huskey
President and CEO Century 21 Real Estate LLC, Richard W. (Rick) Davidson
SVP Chief Accounting Officer and Controller, Dea Benson, age 56
President and CEO Better Homes and Gardens Real Estate LLC, Sherry Cris
Director, V. Ann Hailey, age 60
Director, Marc E. Becker, age 39
Director, Scott M. Kleinman, age 39
Director, M. Ali Rashid, age 35
Auditors: PricewaterhouseCoopersLLP

LOCATIONS

HQ: Realogy Holdings Corp
One Campus Drive, Parsippany, NJ 07054
Phone: 973 407-2000
Web: www.realogy.com

PRODUCTS/OPERATIONS

2011 Sales

	$ mil.	% of total
Company-owned real estate brokerage services	2,970	69
Real estate franchise services	557	13
Relocation services	423	10
Title and settlement services	359	8
Adjustments	(216)	-
Total	**4,093**	**100**

COMPETITORS

Baird & Warner
Brookfield Global Relocation
Brookfield Residential Properties
CBRE Group
Corky McMillin
Counselor Realty
Cushman & Wakefield
Draper and Kramer
Ebby Halliday Realtors
First American
Fortune International Realty
HomeServices
HomeVestors of America
Investors Title
Jones Lang LaSalle
Keller Williams
Move Inc.
New Valley
NRT LLC
RE/MAX
SIRVA
Weichert Realtors
ZipRealty

HISTORICAL FINANCIALS

Company Type: Private

Income Statement

FYE: December 31

	REVENUE ($ mil.)	NET INCOME ($ mil.)	NET PROFIT MARGIN	EMPLOYEES
12/11	4,093	(441)	—	10,400
12/10	4,090	(99)	—	13,500
12/09	3,932	(262)	—	0
12/08	4,725	(1,912)	—	0
Annual Growth	(4.7%)	—	—	—

2011 Year-End Financials

Debt ratio: 95.74%
Return on equity: 987650001000000.00%
Cash ($ mil.): 143
Current ratio: 56.13
Long-term debt ($ mil.): 6,825
No. of shares (mil.): 8
Dividends
Yield: —
Payout: —
Market value ($ mil.): —

Regions Financial Corp

Regions Financial ain't just whistling Dixie anymore. The holding company for Regions Bank which sprouted in the South has grown by acquiring other financial services firms over the years. The bank has some 1730 branches in 16 states roughly stretching from the Southeast and Texas northward through the Mississippi River Valley. It offers standard consumer and business services like deposit accounts loans and mortgages credit cards trust services and private banking. Another unit provides equipment financing for commercial clients. Regions Financial sold the investment banking and brokerage business of Morgan Keegan to Raymond James for some $1.2 billion in 2012.

HISTORY

Regions Financial was created out of three venerable Alabama banks. The oldest First National Bank of Huntsville was founded in 1855. When 10 years later the bank was besieged by Union troops a loyal cashier hid securities in the chimney and refused to tell the soldiers where they were. A few years later it was robbed by Jesse James (for years the bank kept in its vaults a gun purported to belong to a James gang member). First National Bank of Montgomery was founded in 1871 and Exchange Security Bank in 1928.

Banking veteran Frank Plummer consolidated the three banks to form Alabama's first multibank holding company First Alabama Bancshares in 1971. The combined firm then became the bank that ate Alabama. But even as it gobbled up other banks its diet remained bland: Its lending programs were modest and focused on a narrow range of business.

The bank's growth in the 1980s was solid if unexciting as it picked up community banks in Alabama (Anniston National Bank and South Baldwin Bank among others) and Georgia (Georgia Co. a mortgage subsidiary of Columbus Bank and Trust). Before he died in 1987 Plummer brought in Willard Hurley as chairman. Hurley put the brakes on acquisitions when they overloaded the bank's data-processing systems. He also put the company up for sale igniting its stock price for a while but there were no serious suitors.

When Hurley passed the baton to Stanley Mackin in 1990 the bank was still rumored to be for sale. But Mackin had other ideas. He put the bank back on its acquisition track and raised the bar on profitability expectations for each department. In 1993 Mackin orchestrated First Alabama's purchase of Secor a failed New Orleans thrift outbidding rival AmSouth Bancorporation. The Secor purchase raised eyebrows but First Alabama sold some branches and folded other operations into its organization.

In 1994 First Alabama changed its name to Regions Financial in order to reflect its out-of-state operations. The next year Regions rolled into Georgia in a big way leaping from a few banks to holdings with approximately $4 billion in assets. Rumors of a merger with either Wachovia or SunTrust Banks popped up in 1996 but the bank continued on its independent course. The next year the company's tank-like progress was halted when it was outbid for Mississippi's Deposit Guaranty Corp. by First American.

By way of consolation Regions in 1998 bought First Commercial Corp. of Little Rock paying a premium price for its 26 banks mortgage company and investment company. Regions also acquired 13 other companies that year and began a major overhaul of its systems concurrently with the assimilation of these operations. This effort included the consolidation of the back-office aspects of its retail and indirect lending operations.

Mackin retired in 1998 and banking veteran Carl Jones Jr. became CEO. Under his direction the bank continued its geographic infill strategy with acquisitions of banks and branches in Arkansas Florida Louisiana Tennessee and Texas in 1999 and 2000. The company also sold its credit card portfolio to MBNA (since acquired by Bank of America) and in 2001 acquired Memphis-based investment bank Morgan Keegan.

Regions Financial has looked for acquisitions in order to grow geographically and diversify its product and services mix. It fortified its foothold in the South and expanded into the Midwest with its blockbuster merger with Union Planters in 2004. Roughly two years later the company acquired fellow Birmingham-based bank AmSouth for nearly $10 billion in stock. The latter deal created one of the 10 largest banks in the US and helped Regions Financial keep pace with other megabanks in its markets such as Bank of America and SunTrust. The deals also helped entrench the company in states such as Alabama Arkansas Mississippi and Tennessee where it is a market leader.

Former CEO Jones helped mastermind the $6 billion acquisition of Union Planters in 2004; he stepped down as CEO after the merger but remained Regions' chairman until 2006. Jackson Moore chairman and CEO of Union Planters took over the reins of Regions as president and CEO.The company's acquisition of AmSouth for $10 billion in 2006 saw yet another change in leadership with Moore becoming executive chairman and AmSouth's top executive C. Dowd Ritter becoming chairman president and CEO.

In 2009 Ritter stepped down as CEO. He was succeeded by former company president Grayson Hall who initially joined Regions Financial's management trainee program in 1980. Ritter will continue to provide consulting services to the company until 2015.

After the mortgage sector got battered by the housing bust and rising interest rates Regions in 2007 sold its subprime mortgage origination unit EquiFirst to Barclays Bank (the flagship subsidiary of UK-based Barclays).

Market turmoil provided some opportunities. In 2008 Regions Financial assumed control of the branches and deposits of failed Atlanta-area financial institution Integrity Bank in an FDIC-assisted transaction; it did the same with another failed Georgia bank FirstBank Financial Services in 2009.

EXECUTIVES

President CEO and Director, O. B. Grayson Hall Jr., age 55, $730,000 total compensation
SEVP and Chief Administrative Officer, David B. Edmonds, age 58, $475,000 total compensation
Chairman, Earnest W. (Earnie) Deavenport Jr., age 74
CEO Morgan Keegan, John C. Carson Jr., age 55
SEVP; President Central Region, John M. Turner Jr., age 50
Director Investor Relations, M. List Underwood Jr.
SEVP Consumer Services Group, John B. Owen, age 51
SEVP General Counsel and Corporate Secretary, Fournier J. (Boots) Gale III, age 67
SEVP; President Southwest Region, Ronald G. (Ronnie) Smith
Manager Corporate Communications, Tim Deighton
EVP Controller and Chief Accounting Officer, Brad Kimbrough, age 48
SEVP; President Midsouth Region, C. Keith Herron, age 48
SEVP; President Florida Region, Brett D. Couch, age 49
SEVP and Chief Marketing Officer, Scott M. Peters
SEVP; Head Business Services Group, John C. Asbury
SEVP; President Wealth Management Group, William D. (Bill) Ritter, age 41
SEVP and CFO, David J. Turner Jr., age 48
SEVP Operations and Technology, Cynthia M. (Cindy) Rogers
SEVP and Director Human Resources, David R. (Dave) Keenan
SEVP Chief Credit Officer and Head Credit Operations, Barbara (Barb) Godin
SEVP and Chief Risk Officr, C. Matthew Lusco, age 54
SEVP and CFO Business Operations and Support, Ellen Jones
Associate Director Investor Relations, Dana Nolan
Manager Shareholder Services, Helen Johnson
Manager Media Relations, Mel Campbell
Director, Charles D. McCrary, age 60
President CEO and Director, O. B. Grayson Hall Jr., age 55
Director, Eric C. Fast, age 63
Director, James R. (Jim) Malone, age 69
Director, Donald (Don) DeFosset, age 63
Director, George W. Bryan, age 68
Director, John R. Roberts, age 70
Director, Carolyn H. Byrd, age 63
Director, John E. Maupin Jr., age 65
Director, Samuel W. Bartholomew Jr., age 67
Director, Susan W. Matlock, age 65
Director, Baron David J. Cooper Sr., age 66
Director, Lee J. Styslinger III, age 51
Auditors: Ernst&YoungLLP

LOCATIONS

HQ: Regions Financial Corp
1900 Fifth Avenue North, Birmingham, AL 35203
Phone: 800 734-4667

PRODUCTS/OPERATIONS

2011 Sales

	$ mil.	% of total
Interest income		
Loans including fees	3,444	54
Taxable securities	758	12
Other	50	1
Noninterest		
Service charges on deposit accounts	1,168	18
Mortgage income	220	3
Trust department income	199	3
Net securities gains	112	2
Other	444	7
Total	**6,395**	**100**

COMPETITORS

Arvest Bank
Bank of America
BB&T
Capital One
Citigroup
Compass Bancshares
First Citizens BancShares
First Horizon
JPMorgan Chase
SunTrust
Synovus
Trustmark
Wells Fargo
Woodforest Financial

HISTORICAL FINANCIALS

Company Type: Public

Income Statement FYE: December 31

	ASSETS ($ mil.)	NET INCOME ($ mil.)	INCOME AS % OF ASSETS	EMPLOYEES
12/11	127,050	(215)	—	26,813
12/10	132,351	(539)	—	27,829
12/09	142,318	(1,031)	—	28,509
12/08	146,247	(5,595)	—	30,784
12/07	141,041	1,251	0.9%	33,161
Annual Growth	(2.6%)	—	—	(5.2%)

2011 Year-End Financials

Debt ratio: 6.38%
Return on equity: (-1.30)%
Cash ($ mil.): 7,045
Current ratio: —
Long-term debt ($ mil.): 8,110
No. of shares (mil.): 1,258
Dividends
Yield: —
Payout: —
Market value ($ mil.): 5,413

	STOCK PRICE ($) FY Close	P/E High/Low		PER SHARE ($) Earnings	Dividends	Book Value
12/11	4.30	—	—	(0.34)	0.00	13.11
12/10	7.00	—	—	(0.62)	0.04	13.32
12/09	5.29	—	—	(1.27)	0.13	14.99
12/08	7.96	—	—	(8.09)	0.96	24.32
12/07	23.65	21	13	1.76	1.46	28.58
Annual Growth	(34.7%)	—	—	—	—	(17.7%)

Reinsurance Group of America, Inc.

Just what is reinsurance? Here hold this pile of insurance risk while we explain that holding company Reinsurance Group of America (RGA) is one of the largest life reinsurers in the US. RGA provides insurance companies with reinsurance on the risks they've taken on allowing them to reduce their liability and increase their business volume. Its operations are organized into three large groups: Global Mortality which covers individual life insurance policies; Global Group Health and Long-Term Care including critical illness coverage; and Global Financial Markets for annuities and financial coverage. Although RGA has operations in 25 countries North America accounts for about 70% of its revenue.

Geographic Reach

Although the company supports clients in 70 countries and is expanding internationally particularly in such emerging markets as China India Mexico and the Middle East its North American operations still account for more than 65% of its net premium with the US alone bringing 55%.

Operations

The company's US operating unit RGA Reinsurance provides both traditional life reinsurance and reinsurance on investment assets such as annuities and corporate-owned life insurance policies. Its customers are generally large US-based life insurance companies. In addition to its traditional mortality-risk and asset reinsurance the US operations also offer financial reinsurance to help its customers meet regulatory requirements.

Financial Analysis

The company's financial position remained strong in 2011. RGA achieved total revenue of $8.8 billion a 7% increase over 2010 and net income of almost $600 million (a 5% increase over 2010) continuing a trend of revenue and income growth. This is mainly due to increased net premiums across all geographic segments including double-digit increases in Europe and South Africa and in the Asia/Pacific region. In fact net income over the past five years has grown at a compound rate of 16% with net premiums growing at a compound 11%. At the close of 2011 RGA had life reinsurance in force valued at about $2.7 trillion and $32 billion in consolidated assets.

Strategy

RGA's strategy for growth has positioned the company well for harsh economic times and industry challenges. To achieve profitable results the company relies on its strong underwriting capabilities and disciplined pricing as well as geographic expansion and diversification in the products and services it offers.

Mergers & Acquisitions

In 2009 the company acquired the US and Canadian group reinsurance operations of ING Groep. ING chose to jettison the business during a restructuring and RGA was happy to build up its group reinsurance niche.

EXECUTIVES

SEVP and Chief Marketing Officer; CEO RGA International Corporation, Graham S. Watson, age 62, $522,652 total compensation
SEVP Global Group Health and Long-Term Care and Global Financial Solutions, Paul A. Schuster, age 57, $461,942 total compensation
EVP; Vice Chairman and EVP RGA Reinsurance Company, David B. Atkinson, age 58, $419,077 total compensation
SEVP and CFO, Jack B. Lay, age 57, $461,942 total compensation
President CEO and Director, A. Greig Woodring, age 60, $872,558 total compensation
Executive Vice President General Counsel Secretary, William L. (Bill) Hutton

Executive Vice President - Corporate Finance; Treasurer, Todd C. Larson, age 48
Chairman, J. Cliff Eason, age 64
SVP Investor Relations and Controller, John Hayden
EVP and Chief of Staff, Robert M. (Bob) Musen
EVP International Business Development, Brendan J. Galligan
EVP Global Major Accounts, Paul Nitsou, age 50, $394,782 total compensation
Executive Vice President, Gary M. Comerford
President and CEO RGA Life Reinsurance Company Canada, Alain Neemeh, $336,131 total compensation
EVP RGA Financial Markets, John Laughlin
EVP and Chief Risk Officer, Mike Stein
Executive Director Corporate Communications, Sally Smith
Chief Operating Officer, Donna H. Kinnaird
EVP, Joni Wood Lehman
Director Communications, John Stewart
Executive Vice President, Mark E. Showers
EVP U.S. Group Reinsurance, Michael (Mik) Emerson
Chief Actuary U.S. Group Reinsurance, Dean Abbott
SVP Healthcare Reinsurance U.S. Group Reinsurance, Steve Abood
SVP Operations U.S. Group Reinsurance, Jeffrey (Jeff) Birkholz
SVP Healthcare Reinsurance U.S. Group Reinsurance, Michelle Fallahi
SVP Group Life Accident and Disability Reinsurance U.S. Group Reinsurance, Jim Rathburn
Senior Vice President, Gay Burns
President and CEO RGA Life Reinsurance Company of Canada and Head Global Mortality Products, Alain P. Neemeh
Head of Business Development, Jason Hurley
Chief Financial Officer, Mark Stew
Head of Underwriting Operations, Mick Jones
Vice President, Nadine Gooderick
Senior Vice President and Chief Pricing Actuary, Jonathan Porter
Executive Vice President, Anna Manning
General Manager, Ashraf Azzouni
Managing Director, Amit Punchhi
Chief Marketing Officer, Shih-Nin Low
Senior Vice President Chief Marketing Officer, Greg Goodfliesh
Executive Vice President, Allan E. OBryant
Executive Vice President, Allan E. E.
Managing Director, Klaus Mattar
Executive Vice President, Scott Cochran
Assistant Vice President RGA Reinsurance Company, Ray Jeon
Senior Vice President Business Development, Paul Sauv+
Senior Vice President, Olav Cuiper
Senior Vice President, Yuko Oshima
President; Chief Executive Officer of RGA Life Reinsurance Company of Canada; Head - Global Mortality Products, Alain Neemeh
Director, Alan C. Henderson, age 66
President CEO and Director, A. Greig Woodring, age 60
Director, Frederick J. (Fred) Sievert, age 64
Director, Stuart I. Greenbaum, age 75
Director, John F. Danahy, age 65
Director, J. Cliff Eason, age 64
Director, Rachel Lomax, age 66
Director, William J. Bartlett, age 62
Director, Arnoud W. A. Boot, age 52
Independent Director, Stanley Tulin
Auditors: Deloitte&ToucheLLP

LOCATIONS

HQ: Reinsurance Group of America Incorporated
1370 Timberlake Manor Pkwy., Chesterfield MO 63017-6039
Phone: 636-736-7000 **Fax:** 636-736-7100
Web: www.rgare.com

2011 Revenues

	$ mil.	% of total
US	4,910	56
Europe & South Africa	1,247	14
Canada	1,051	12
Corporate & other	191	2

2011 Net Premiums

	$ mil.	% of total
US	3,992	55
Europe & South Africa	1,194	16
Canada	835	11
Corporate & other	8	-

PRODUCTS/OPERATIONS

2011 Revenues

	$ mil.	% of total
Net premiums	7,335	83
Investment losses	(36.1)	-
Total	**8,829**	**100**

Selected Products and Services

e-Underwriting solutions
Facultative and underwriting expertise
Financial solutions
Group reinsurance
Individual life reinsurance
Individual living benefits reinsurance
Product development

Selected Subsidiaries

Reinsurance Company of Missouri Incorporated (RCM)
RGA Americas Reinsurance Company Ltd. (RGA Americas)
RGA Atlantic Reinsurance Company Ltd. (RGA Atlantic)
RGA International Reinsurance Company (RGA International)
RGA Life Reinsurance Company of Canada (RGA Canada)
RGA Reinsurance Company (Barbados) Ltd. (RGA Barbados)
RGA Reinsurance Company (RGA Reinsurance)
RGA Reinsurance Company of Australia Limited (RGA Australia)

COMPETITORS

AEGON USA
Berkshire Hathaway
General Re
Generali
Hannover Re
Munich Re America
Munich Re Group
SCOR Reinsurance
Swiss Re
Swiss Re Life

HISTORICAL FINANCIALS

Company Type: Public

Income Statement FYE: December 31

	ASSETS ($ mil.)	NET INCOME ($ mil.)	INCOME AS % OF ASSETS	EMPLOYEES
12/11	32,104	599	1.9%	1,655
12/10	29,081	574	2.0%	1,535
12/09	25,249	407	1.6%	1,367
12/08	21,658	176	0.8%	1,222
12/07	21,598	293	1.4%	1,066
Annual Growth	10.4%	19.5%	—	11.6%

2011 Year-End Financials

Debt ratio: 6.44%
Return on equity: 9.77%
Cash ($ mil.): 962
Current ratio: —
Long-term debt ($ mil.): 2,066
No. of shares (mil.): 73
Dividends
Yield: —
Payout: 7.42%
Market value ($ mil.): 3,833

	STOCK PRICE ($) FY Close	P/E High/Low		PER SHARE ($) Earnings	Dividends	Book Value
12/11	52.25	8	6	8.09	0.00	83.65
12/10	53.71	7	6	7.69	0.48	68.71
12/09	47.65	9	4	5.55	0.45	52.99
12/08	42.82	15	13	2.71	0.09	36.03
Annual Growth	6.9%	—	—	44.0%	—	32.4%

Reliance Steel & Aluminum Co.

Reliance Steel & Aluminum shows its mettle as North America's largest metals service center company. Through a network of 220-plus service and distribution centers (many dealing only in specialty metals) it processes and distributes more than 100000 metal products worldwide to some 125000 customers in a broad range of industries. It markets carbon alloy stainless steel and specialty steel products as well as aluminum brass copper and titanium products. Markets include the aerospace construction manufacturing semiconductor and electronics and transportation industries. Founded in 1939 Reliance operates in 38 US states as well as in Canada and Mexico. It also has sites in Asia and Europe.

Financial Analysis

Reliance achieved net sales of $8.13 billion in 2011 a 29% jump over the previous year. Demand in such markets as energy and agricultural and mining equipment industries led the growth. Sales were up in almost all of the company's end markets with the exception of nonresidential construction its largest which continued to lag behind pre-recession levels. Although pricing volatility and weakened demand affected the company's gross profit margins its net income soared 77% over the previous year reaching $343.8 million as the company tightened cost controls.

Strategy

In the past few years Reliance has shifted its focus to internal growth including opening new plants and adding to its processing capabilities or relocating centers to new facilities. It also continues to expand the types of metals it sells and the processing services it offers. The company expects to continue to grow through strategic acquisitions and internal initiatives that broaden its product offerings geographic reach and customer base.

To further expand in the perforated metals market in 2012 Reliance acquired McKey Perforating (New Berlin Wisconsin) and its subsidiary McKey Perforated Products (Manchester Tennessee) which are metal perforating and fabrication service centers. The price was undisclosed. It also bought special alloy steel bar and heavy-wall tubing distributor Sunbelt Steel Texas which had $48 million in sales in 2011.

That year it moved to expand its operations in Tennessee again when subsidiary Precision Strip acquired the Worthington Steel Vonore plant part of Worthington Industries for an undisclosed price. The plant processes and distributes carbon steel aluminum and stainless steel products on a toll basis (processing the metal for a fee without taking ownership of it).

Mergers & Acquisition

Still on a buying spree in 2012 Reliance acquired Texas-based National Specialty Alloys (NSA). NSA is a global specialty alloy processor and distributor of stainless steel and nickel alloy bars and shapes. It also ventured abroad that year to acquire the assets of Airport Metals (Australia) Pty Ltd a subsidiary of Samuel Son & Co. for an undisclosed sum. The purchase gives the company's new subsidiary Bralco Metals (Australia) Pty Ltd entry into the Australian market to service aircraft and other customers.

In 2012 the company also acquired through subsidiary Feralloy Corporation Alabama-based GH Metal Solutions for an undisclosed price. GH Metal is a carbon steel products processor and fabricator with about $44 million in annual sales.

A key addition for serving energy companies came in 2011 when Reliance acquired Houston-based Continental Alloys & Services for about $200 million. Continental is a materials management company that supplies steel and alloy pipe tube and bar products and manufactures various tools designed for energy service companies. It has 12 locations in seven countries.

Company Background

In the last decade Reliance has been on something of a spending binge buying up a number of smaller rivals. The company has grown significantly over the years through a series of acquisitions both large and small. After its IPO in 1994 Reliance picked up more than 45 businesses although the economy in 2009 slowed its pace.

EXECUTIVES

President Valex Corp., Daniel A. Mangan
President Service Steel Aerospace Corp., Terry L. Wilson
President Phoenix Corporation, Stephen E. Almond
President Chatman Steel Corporation, Bert M. Tenenbaum
President CCC Steel Inc., Bernd D. Hildebrandt
President American Metals Corporation, Craig A. Schwartz
VP Human Resources, Donna Newton, age 58
EVP and CFO, Karla R. Lewis, age 46, $375,000 total compensation
Chairman and CEO, David H. Hannah, age 61, $700,000 total compensation
SVP Operations, William K. Sales Jr., age 54, $330,000 total compensation
President COO and Director, Gregg J. Mollins, age 57, $520,000 total compensation
President AMI Metals Inc., Scott A. Smith
SVP Operations, James D. Hoffman, age 53, $330,000 total compensation
President Earle M. Jorgensen Company, R. Neil McCaffery
VP General Counsel and Secretary, Kay Rustand, age 64
President Viking Materials Inc., Craig Sauer
President PDM Steel Service Centers, Derek A. Halecky
Director Investor Contact, Kim P. Feazle
President Delta Steel, Robert A. (Bob) Embry, age 69
President Allegheny Steel Distributors, Bernie J. Herrmann
President Precision Strip, Joseph B. Wolf
President Pacific Metal Company, John S. Nosler
President Liebovich Bros., Michael J. Tulley
President Toma Metals Inc., Daniel T. Yunetz
President Infra-Metals, Mark Haight, age 53
President Infra-Metals, John E. Lusdyk, age 59
VP and Corporate Controller, Brenda S. Miyamoto, age 39
SVP Operations, Stephen P. (Steve) Koch, age 45
President Siskin Steel & Supply Company, Paul Loftin
President Crest Steel Corporation, Randall Putnam
President Yarde Metals, Matt Smith
President Sugar Steel, Robert Sugar
Managing Director MetalWeb, Derek Webb
President Metals Supply Company, John Hess
SVP Supplier Development, Sheldon Tenenbaum, age 66
President Chapel Steel, Stanley (Stan) Altman
President Clayton Metals, Brian Cleveland
CIO, Susan C. Borchers, age 51
President Feralloy, Carlos Rodriguez-Borjas
President COO and Director, Gregg J. Mollins, age 57
Director, Mark V. Kaminski, age 56
Director, Thomas W. Gimbel, age 60
Director, Douglas M. Hayes, age 68
Director, Leslie A. Waite, age 66
Director, Franklin R. Johnson, age 75
Director, Andrew G. Sharkey III, age 65
Director, John G. Figueroa, age 49
Auditors: KPMGLLP

LOCATIONS

HQ: Reliance Steel & Aluminum Co.
350 South Grand Avenue, Suite 5100, Los Angeles, CA 90071
Phone: 213 687-7700
Web: www.rsac.com

2011 Sales by Region

	$ mil.	% of total
US		
Southeast		17
California		11
Northeast		7
Pacific Northwest		5
Mountain		4
Total	0	100

PRODUCTS/OPERATIONS

2011 Sales by Commodity

	% of total
Carbon	53
Aluminum	15
Stainless	15
Alloy	10
Toll	2
Other	5
Total	100

Selected Processing Services

Bending
Blanking
Cutting-to-length
Electropolishing
Fabricating
Pipe Threading
Precision plate sawing
Shape cutting/burning
Skin milling
Slitting
Tee splitting and straightening
Welding

COMPETITORS

A. M. Castle
Balli
Metals USA
O' Neal Steel
Olympic Steel
Russel Metals
Ryerson
Steel Technologies
Ternium Mexico
Worthington Industries

HISTORICAL FINANCIALS

Company Type: Public

Income Statement FYE: December 31

	REVENUE ($ mil.)	NET INCOME ($ mil.)	NET PROFIT MARGIN	EMPLOYEES
12/11	8,134	343	4.2%	10,650
12/10	6,312	194	3.1%	9,610
12/09	5,318	148	2.8%	8,870
12/08	8,718	482	5.5%	10,230
12/07	7,265	407	5.6%	9,260
Annual Growth	2.9%	(4.2%)	—	3.6%

2011 Year-End Financials

Debt ratio: 23.75%
Return on equity: 10.94%
Cash ($ mil.): 84
Current ratio: 394.64
Long-term debt ($ mil.): 1,319
No. of shares (mil.): 75
Dividends
Yield: —
Payout: 10.48%
Market value ($ mil.): 3,652

	STOCK PRICE ($) FY Close	P/E High/Low		PER SHARE ($) Earnings	Dividends	Book Value
12/11	48.69	13	7	4.58	0.00	41.91
12/10	51.10	21	13	2.61	0.40	37.83
12/09	43.22	22	9	2.01	0.40	35.34
12/08	19.94	12	2	6.56	0.40	33.17
12/07	54.20	12	7	5.36	0.32	28.12
Annual Growth	(2.6%)	—	—	(3.9%)	—	10.5%

Renasant Corp

Those who are cognizant of their finances may want to do business with Renasant Corporation. The holding company owns Renasant Bank which serves consumers and local business through about 80 locations in Alabama Georgia Mississippi and Tennessee. The bank offers standard products such as checking and savings accounts CDs credit cards and loans and mortgages as well as trust retail brokerage and retirement plan services. Its loan portfolio is dominated by residential and commercial real estate loans. The bank also offers agricultural business construction and consumer loans and lease financing. Subsidiary Renasant Insurance sells personal and business coverage.

Renasant entered Georgia in 2010 with the FDIC-assisted acquisition of Crescent Bank & Trust after that institution was shut down by regulators. The deal added about a dozen branches to Renasant's network. The company made a similar acquisition the following year when it assumed much of the assets of American Trust Bank another failed Georgia bank.

Renasant is poised to make additional purchases; urban areas in the South such as Birmingham and Huntsville Alabama; Oxford and Tupelo Mississippi; Nashville and Memphis Tennessee; and northern Georgia are target markets. The company utilizes a decentralized approach that allows local bank presidents to execute their own business plans based on their knowledge of their markets. In 2011 it expanded into Montgomery and Tuscaloosa Alabama as well as Starkville Mississippi. Renasant also bought the Birmingham-based trust division of RBC Bank.

Amid the economic downturn Renasant has looked to diversify its loan portfolio. The bank has reduced its amount of loans for construction and land development –a sector that has been hit particularly hard –by tightening its underwriting standards. The company has remained profitable and its net income increased in 2010 and 2011 buoyed by more favorable interest rate spreads and its Georgia acquisitions.

EXECUTIVES

EVP and CFO; SEVP CFO and Cashier Renasant Bank, Stuart R. Johnson, age 58, $250,000 total compensation
Chairman President and CEO; President and CEO Renasant Bank, E. Robinson (Robin) McGraw, age 65, $410,000 total compensation
EVP; SEVP and CIO Renasant Bank, James W. Gray, age 55, $230,000 total compensation
EVP; SEVP and Chief Credit Officer Renasant Bank, Harold H. Livingston, age 63
EVP; SEVP and Chief Credit Policy Officer Renasant Bank, Claude H. Springfield III, age 64
EVP; SEVP and Chief Administrative Officer Renasant Bank, C. Mitchell (Mitch) Waycaster, age 53, $258,000 total compensation
Vice Chairman, J. Larry Young, age 73
EVP and Director; President Tennessee Division and Middle Tennessee Renasant Bank, R. Rick Hart, age 63, $355,950 total compensation
EVP and General Counsel; SEVP and General Counsel Renasant Bank, Stephen M. Corban, age 56, $75,000 total compensation
EVP; President Alabama Division, Michael D. Ross, age 47
EVP; President Mississippi Division Renasant Bank, J. Scott Cochran, age 48
Director, Theodore S. (Ted) Moll, age 69
Director, John T. (Tom) Foy, age 64
Director, William M. Beasley, age 60
Director, George H. Booth II, age 57
Director, Frank B. Brooks, age 68
Director, John M. Creekmore, age 56
Director, J. Niles McNeel, age 65
Vice Chairman, J. Larry Young, age 73
Director, Richard L. Heyer Jr., age 55
Director, Neal A. Holland Jr., age 55
EVP and Director; President Tennessee Division and Middle Tennessee Renasant Bank, R. Rick Hart, age 63
Director, Albert J. Dale III, age 61
Director, Jack C. Johnson, age 69
Director, T. Michael Glenn, age 56
Director, Michael D. Shmerling, age 56
Director, Jill V. Deer
Auditors: HorneLLP

LOCATIONS

HQ: Renasant Corporation
209 Troy St., Tupelo MS 38802-4827
Phone: 662-680-1001 **Fax:** 662-680-1234
Web: www.renasantbank.com

PRODUCTS/OPERATIONS

2011 Sales

	$ mil.	% of total
Interest		
Loans	141	59
Securities	28	12
Other	0	.
Noninterest		
Service charges on deposit accounts	19	8
Fees & commissions	17	7
Gain on acquisition	9	4
Gains on sales of securities	5	2
Wealth management	4	2
Other	13	6
Total	**239**	**100**

COMPETITORS

BancorpSouth
Citizens Holding
Citizens National Bank of Meridian
Compass Bancshares
First Horizon
First M&F
Hancock Holding
Regions Financial
Trustmark

HISTORICAL FINANCIALS

Company Type: Public

Income Statement FYE: December 31

	ASSETS ($ mil.)	NET INCOME ($ mil.)	INCOME AS % OF ASSETS	EMPLOYEES
12/11	4,202	25	0.6%	1,030
12/10	4,297	31	0.7%	996
12/09	3,641	18	0.5%	816
12/08	3,715	24	0.6%	866
12/07	3,612	31	0.9%	880
Annual Growth	3.9%	(4.7%)	—	4.0%

2011 Year-End Financials

Debt ratio: 5.79%
Return on equity: 5.26%
Cash ($ mil.): 209
Current ratio: —
Long-term debt ($ mil.): 243
No. of shares (mil.): 25
Dividends
Yield: —
Payout: 66.67%
Market value ($ mil.): 376

	STOCK PRICE ($) FY Close	P/E High/Low		PER SHARE ($) Earnings	Dividends	Book Value
12/11	15.00	17	12	1.02	0.00	19.44
12/10	16.91	13	9	1.38	0.68	18.75
12/09	13.60	19	9	0.87	0.68	19.45
12/08	17.03	21	12	1.14	0.68	19.00
12/07	21.57	18	11	1.64	0.66	19.15
Annual Growth	(8.7%)	—	—	(11.2%)	—	0.4%

Republic Bancorp, Inc. (KY)

The second-largest bank holding company based in Kentucky Republic Bancorp is the parent of Republic Bank & Trust which has about 40 branches in central Kentucky and southern Indiana. It also owns Republic Bank a thrift with a handful of branches in metropolitan Tampa and a single location in the Cincinnati area. In 2012 Republic Bancorp entered the Nashville and Minneapolis market through the FDIC-assisted acquisitions of the failed Tennessee Commerce Bank and First Commercial Bank respectively. The company's banks offer deposit accounts loans and mortgages credit cards private banking and trust services.

Republic Bancorp's lending activities mainly consist of residential mortgages and commercial real estate loans which together account for some three-fourths of the company's loan book. The company also offered loans secured by income tax refunds throughout the US. The segment provided refund anticipation loans to more than 3 million customers in 2010 but came under fire from regulators. That year the Internal Revenue Service announced it would stop supplying Debt Indicator information (used to determine whether a taxpayer is creditworthy) to institutions that issue such loans. As a result the FDIC in 2011 announced that Republic Bank & Trust's origination of refund anticipation loans without Debt Indication information was unsafe and issued a cease-and-desist order; the tax season of 2012 was the final season the company offered the loans.

Income tax refund loans are typically offered to unbanked and underbanked customers. Republic Bancorp hopes to otherwise tap into that market which includes some 30 million US households by offering nontraditional banking products. To that end the company is also offering prepaid cards. In addition Republic also offers electronic refund checks and deposits which carry no risk to the company.

In 2011 the company entered the warehouse lending business through which it offers short-term credit facilities secured by single-family residences to mortgage bankers nationwide. The move follows somewhat of a trend of community banks adding to their commercial loan operations by offering warehouse lending. Within a year Republic had committed lines of credit totaling some $108 million.

Republic Bancorp's revenues grew 12% in 2011 from $281 million in 2010 to $314 million. Profits grew even more from $65 million in 2010 to $94 million in 2011 (an increase of 45%). The growth was largely driven by an increase in net interest and noninterest income in the company's tax refund solutions segment. Republic also decreased its provision for loan losses in 2011. To offset declines in net interest income from its traditional banking segment the company has tweaked its investment strategy as well as boosted its loan portfolio through acquisitions. Republic has also cut its operating expenses.

The Trager family including the estate of founder Bernard his son Steven (chairman and CEO) and nephew Scott (president) controls a majority of Republic Bancorp.

EXECUTIVES

President; President and Director Republic Bank & Trust; Director Republic Bank, A. Scott Trager, age 59, $325,000 total compensation
Chairman and CEO; Chairman and CEO Republic Bank & Trust; Chairman Republic Bank, Steven E. (Steve) Trager, age 51, $330,000 total compensation
EVP CFO Chief Accounting Officer and Treasurer Republic Bancorp and Republic Bank & Trust, Kevin Sipes, age 40, $260,000 total compensation
SVP and Regional Manager Republic Bank & Trust, Kathy Potts
VP and Chief Market Officer Bowling Green Kentucky Republic Bank & Trust, Gary Pierce
VP and Banking Center Manager Georgetown Kentucky Republic Bank & Trust, Susan Smith
VP and COO Louisville Kentucky Republic Bank & Trust, Barb Cutter
VP and Business Banking Officer Crestwood Kentucky Republic Bank & Trust, Melissa Lyons
VP and Regional Manager Republic Bank & Trust, Beau Baird
VP and Regional Manager Republic Bank & Trust, David Jett
VP and Chief Market Officer Owensboro Kentucky Republic Bank & Trust, Shirley Cecil
SVP and Regional Manager Republic Bank & Trust, Tucker Ballinger
President Northern Kentucky Market Republic Bank & Trust, Steve Brunson
VP and Business Development Officer Shelbyville Kentucky Republic Bank & Trust, Michael Tipton

SVP Secretary and General Counsel Republic Bank & Trust, Michael A. (Mike) Ringswald
EVP and Managing Director Retail Banking Republic Bank & Trust, Steven E. (Steve) DeWeese, age 43
SVP Collections Republic Bank & Trust, Duane Wilson
VP Community Relations Republic Bank & Trust, Carolle Jones Clay
VP Facilities Republic Bank & Trust, Carol James
SVP Human Resources Republic Bank & Trust, Margaret Wendler
SVP Information Technology Republic Bank & Trust, Roger Batsel
VP Internal Audit Republic Bank & Trust, Ann Bauer
SVP Marketing Republic Bank & Trust, Michael Sadofsky
President Central Kentucky Market Republic Bank & Trust, Bo Henry
President Florida Market Republic Bank & Trust, Doug Winton
SVP Operations Republic Bank & Trust, Shannon Reid
SVP Chief Legal and Compliance Officer Republic Bank, John Rippy
SVP and Chief Investment Officer Republic Bank & Trust, Greg Williams
VP and Chief Market Officer Shepherdsville Kentucky Republic Bank & Trust, Dan Cline
President Tax Refund Solutions Republic Bank & Trust, William R. (Bill) Nelson, age 48, $247,917 total compensation
SVP Treasury Management Republic Bank & Trust, Jeff Nelson
SVP and COO Commercial Lending and Head Treasury Management Group Republic Bank & Trust; Executive Director Republic Bank, Robert J. Arnold, age 53
SVP Retail Operations Republic Bank & Trust, Barbara Trager
SVP CRA/Compliance Republic Bank & Trust, Nancy Presnell
VP and Controller Republic Bank & Trust, Mike Newton
SVP Finance Republic Bank & Trust, Juan Montano
VP Purchasing Republic Bank & Trust, Brian Sizemore
Manager Security Republic Bank & Trust, Mark Speevack
VP Trust Republic Bank & Trust, Joe Sutter
Director, R. Wayne Stratton, age 64
Director, Sandra Metts Snowden, age 66
Director, Susan Stout Tamme, age 61
Director, Michael T. Rust, age 60
Director, Craig A. Greenberg, age 38
Auditors: CroweHorwathLLP

LOCATIONS

HQ: Republic Bancorp, Inc. (KY)
601 West Market Street, Louisville, KY 40202
Phone: 502 584-3600
Web: www.republicbank.com

PRODUCTS/OPERATIONS

2011 Sales

	$ mil.	% of total
Interest		
Loans including fees	177	56
Taxable investment securities	15	5
Other	2	1
Noninterest		
Electronic refund check fees	88	28
Service charges on deposit accounts	14	4
Debit card interchange fees	5	2
Mortgage banking	3	1
Gain on sale of banking center & other	7	3
Adjustments	(0.3)	-
Total	**314**	**100**

COMPETITORS

Bank of America
BB&T
Citizens First
Community Trust
Farmers Capital Bank
Fifth Third
Home Federal
KeyCorp
PNC Financial
S.Y. Bancorp
U.S. Bancorp

HISTORICAL FINANCIALS

Company Type: Public

Income Statement FYE: December 31

	ASSETS ($ mil.)	NET INCOME ($ mil.)	INCOME AS % OF ASSETS	EMPLOYEES
12/11	3,419	94	2.8%	728
12/10	3,622	64	1.8%	766
12/09	3,918	42	1.1%	747
12/08	3,939	33	0.9%	756
12/07	3,165	24	0.8%	761
Annual Growth	2.0%	39.4%	—	(1.1%)

2011 Year-End Financials

Debt ratio: 28.53%
Return on equity: 20.81%
Cash ($ mil.): 362
Current ratio: —
Long-term debt ($ mil.): 975
No. of shares (mil.): 20
Dividends
Yield: —
Payout: 13.47%
Market value ($ mil.): 480

	STOCK PRICE ($) FY Close	P/E High	P/E Low	PER SHARE ($) Earnings	Dividends	Book Value
12/11	22.90	5	4	4.49	0.00	21.59
12/10	23.75	8	5	3.10	0.56	17.74
12/09	20.60	13	7	2.02	0.52	15.19
12/08	27.20	21	9	1.62	0.47	13.38
12/07	16.53	21	12	1.20	0.42	12.26
Annual Growth	8.5%	—	—	39.1%	—	15.2%

Republic Services, Inc.

Homeowners and businesses in 39 states in the US and Puerto Rico pledge allegiance to Republic Services and the trash collection for which it stands. The company is the second-largest nonhazardous waste management provider in the US behind leader Waste Management in terms of revenues and geographic coverage. Republic provides waste disposal services for commercial industrial municipal and residential customers through its network of 334 collection companies. The company owns or operates 191 solid waste landfills 194 transfer stations and 74 recycling centers. It also has 69 landfill-to-gas and two solar energy landfill cover operations.

Operations

To better address the local variables of the waste collection business Republic organizes its operations into three regions. Each region is further divided into several operating areas which provide collection transfer disposal and recycling services. Regional and area managers are given considerable authority under the company's decentralized management structure. In 2012 the company restructured its field and corporate operations consolidating field regions from four to three and areas from 28 to 20 relocating office space and reducing administrative staffing levels in order to create more efficiencies.

Financial Analysis

In 2011 the company posted revenues of $8.2 billion edging out its 2010 revenues of $8.1 billion by a little more than 1% due to slight increases in prices and fuel recovery fees. However the company's net income that year of $589.2 million jumped 16% over the previous year associated with a number of recoveries and other expenses that favorably impacted the company's results. Republic also did not incur any additional restructuring charges in 2011 related to its Allied Waste acquisition in 2008.

Strategy

Republic had grown by buying smaller waste management operations in its existing service areas and in new regions. Likely candidates included assets of municipalities that were privatizing their waste management services. Since swallowing the large national business of Allied Waste in 2008 the company has focused on growing organically by integrating and streamlining its operations to increase efficiency. It is also implementing higher pricing and investing in such growth strategies as recycling infrastructure national accounts and acquisitions.

Ownership

Republic's largest shareholder is Microsoft chairman Bill Gates who owns about 18% of the company through his investment vehicle Cascade Investment.

HISTORY

Republic Services began in 1980 as Republic Resources an oil exploration and production company. In 1989 after a stockholder group tried to force Republic into liquidation Browning-Ferris (BFI) founder Thomas Fatjo stepped in gained control of Republic Resources and refocused it on a field he knew well –solid waste. Renamed Republic Waste the company began making acquisitions.

In 1990 Michael DeGroote founder of BFI competitor Laidlaw bought into Republic Waste. In 1995 Wayne Huizenga –who co-founded Waste Management in 1971 and was beginning to develop a national auto sales organization in the mid-1990s after his tenure as chairman and CEO of Blockbuster Entertainment –approached DeGroote about a deal. They rejected an immediate merger of the waste and auto businesses because the latter was not well-enough developed and would drag down Republic's numbers. Instead they agreed to merge Republic and the Hudson Companies (a trash business owned by Huizenga's brother-in-law Harris Hudson) to sell Huizenga a large interest in Republic through a private offering and to give him control of the board (in 1995). The company became Republic Industries.

Huizenga's investment brought a flood of new investors. With new resources Republic Industries became a driving force in the garbage industry's consolidation binge and the company bought more than 100 smaller waste haulers between 1995 and 1998. Republic Industries spun off about 30% of its waste business as Republic Services in 1998; the IPO raised $1.3 billion. Republic's acquisition trend continued as it agreed to buy 16 landfills 136 commercial collection routes and 11 transfer stations from Waste Management for $500 million. Later that year Waste Management veteran James O'Connor succeeded Huizenga as CEO although Huizenga continued as chairman.

Investors filed class-action lawsuits against Republic in 1999 claiming the Waste Management purchases held far more integration problems than the company admitted. In 2000 Republic swapped nine of its solid-waste operations for eight Allied Waste businesses which Allied needed to divest in order to gain federal approval for its merger with BFI.

While many firms in the industry were selling off assets in 2001 Republic was expanding its operations in the Northern California market by acquiring Richmond Sanitary Services. Huizenga retired as chairman at the end of 2002 and was once again succeeded by O'Connor. Huizenga stayed on the board as a director until May 2004.

In 2007 the company sold Living Earth Technology Company (a noncore stand-alone business in Texas) for about $37 million. In 2008 prior to its megadeal with Allied Waste Republic rebuffed a takeover bid by industry leader Waste Management.

In late 2008 Republic Services the once #3 industry player acquired #2 company Allied Waste for $6 billion to place it closer to industry leader Waste Management in terms of revenues and geographic coverage. Following the acquisition Republic divested assets in seven markets (six municipal solid waste landfills six collection businesses and three transfer stations) in order to meet US antitrust regulations.

EXECUTIVES

President CEO and Director, Donald W. (Don) Slager, age 50, $858,173 total compensation
SVP Treasury and Risk Management, Edward A. Lang III
EVP and CFO, Tod C. Holmes, age 63, $575,000 total compensation
Chairman, James W. Crownover, age 68
SVP and Chief Accounting Officer, Charles F. Serianni
EVP Business Development, Brian A. Bales
SVP Operations Midwest Region, Jack Perko
SVP Corporate Communications, William C. (Will) Flower
SVP National Accounts, Gary L. Sova
SVP Operations East Region, Ronald R. (Ron) Krall
SVP Operations South Region, Robert Boucher
SVP Human Resources, Catharine D. Ellingsen
SVP and CIO, William G. (Bill) Halnon
EVP Human Resources, Jeffrey A. Hughes
SVP Operations West Region, Jeffrey D. (Jeff) Andrews
EVP Sales and Marketing, Christopher R. Synek
EVP General Counsel and Corporate Secretary, Michael P. Rissman, age 51, $319,353 total compensation
SVP Operations and Controller, Jerome S. Clark
SVP Environmental Development and Compliance, James G. VanWeelden
Manager Media Relations, Peg Mulloy
SVP Pricing Management, Scott H. Russeth
SVP Integration and Process Improvement, Christopher P. Melocik
Director, John M. Trani, age 67
Director, John W. Croghan, age 81
President CEO and Director, Donald W. (Don) Slager, age 50
Director, W. Lee Nutter, age 68
Director, Michael W. (Mike) Wickham, age 65
Director, William J. (Bill) Flynn, age 58
Director, Michael Larson, age 52
Director, Nolan Lehmann, age 67
Director, Ramon A. Rodriguez, age 66
Director, Allan C. (Al) Sorensen, age 73
Auditors: Ernst&YoungLLP

LOCATIONS

HQ: Republic Services Inc.
18500 N. Allied Way, Phoenix AZ 82054
Phone: 480-627-2700 **Fax:** 713-381-8200
Web: www.enterpriseproducts.com

2011 Sales

	$ mil.	% of total
Western	2,155	26
Southern	2,029	25
Total	**8,192**	**100**

PRODUCTS/OPERATIONS

2011 Sales

	$ mil.	% of total
Collection		
Commercial	2,487	30
Residential	2,135	26
Industrial	1,515	19
Other	32	-
Landfill Operations		
Landfill	1,020	13
Recyclable Materials	438	5
Other Noncore	140	2
Transfer	421	5
Total	**8,192**	**100**

COMPETITORS

Casella Waste Systems
Progressive Waste
Recology
Rumpke
Veolia ES Solid Waste
Waste Connections
Waste Industries USA
Waste Management

HISTORICAL FINANCIALS

Company Type: Public

Income Statement FYE: December 31

	REVENUE ($ mil.)	NET INCOME ($ mil.)	NET PROFIT MARGIN	EMPLOYEES
12/11	8,192	589	7.2%	30,000
12/10	8,106	506	6.2%	30,000
12/09	8,199	495	6.0%	31,000
12/08	3,685	73	2.0%	35,000
12/07	3,176	290	9.1%	13,000
Annual Growth	26.7%	19.4%	—	23.3%

2011 Year-End Financials

Debt ratio: 35.40%
Return on equity: 7.67%
Cash ($ mil.): 66
Current ratio: 66.70
Long-term debt ($ mil.): 6,887
No. of shares (mil.): 369
Dividends
Yield: —
Payout: 53.85%
Market value ($ mil.): 10,191

	STOCK PRICE ($) FY Close	P/E High/Low		PER SHARE ($) Earnings	Dividends	Book Value
12/11	27.55	21	16	1.56	0.00	20.77
12/10	29.86	25	19	1.32	0.78	20.45
12/09	28.31	23	12	1.30	0.76	19.86
12/08	24.79	92	49	0.37	0.72	19.24
12/07	31.35	29	18	1.51	0.55	7.03
Annual Growth	(3.2%)	—	—	0.8%	—	31.1%

Resolute Forest Products Inc

Like many sturdy trees Resolute Forest Products formerly AbitibiBowater is a product of grafting. Formed by the combination of two of the world's largest newsprint makers —Abitibi-Consolidated and Bowater Resolute makes newsprint commercial printing paper mechanical paper pulp and wood products. It relies on 18 pulp and paper mills and 24 wood products plants in Canada South Korea and the US to distribute its products to about 90 countries; it is one of the world's largest recyclers of newspapers and magazines. Resolute owns or has cutting rights to more than 40 million acres of forestland in North America. In early 2009 the company filed for bankruptcy in the US and Canada and emerged in 2010.

HISTORY

The roots of Bowater can be traced to the founders of its British parent Bowater PLC (renamed Rexam plc in 1995). After several years with a papermaking firm William Bowater set up his own business in London in 1881. Cashing in on a booming newspaper readership W. V. Bowater & Sons secured contracts as a paper wholesaler with two leading newspaper publishers: Alfred Harmsworth (of the "Daily Mail" and the "Daily Mirror") and Edward Lloyd (of the "Daily Chronicle").

In 1914 Bowater set up a US marketing subsidiary Hudson Packaging & Paper Co. and in 1919 it opened an Australian office in Sydney. Eric Bowater the founder's grandson took over as chairman at the age of 32 and led the company in a major expansion. By 1936 Bowater accounted for 60% of Britain's newsprint output up from just 22% only six years before. Bowater began manufacturing in North America in 1938 when it purchased a pulp and newsprint mill in Corner Brook Newfoundland.

WWII had a devastating impact on the company's UK newsprint business and output fell by 80%. Bowater PLC diversified into paper packaging in 1944 buying Acme Corrugated Cases. Bowater PLC expanded its presence in the US in 1954 with the opening of Bowater Southern a newsprint mill in Tennessee. That year Eric Bowater died. Christopher Chancellor formerly with Reuters became CEO.

In 1964 Bowater formed Bowater United States Corp. to manage its US operations. Bowater moved away from paper production in the 1970s diversifying into such areas as packaging tissue products building products commodity trading and foodstuffs. In 1984 Bowater exited the paper and pulp business spinning off its US operations as Bowater Incorporated.

After the spinoff the new US-based Bowater expanded its range of products. In 1991 the company acquired an 80% interest in Great Northern Paper (GNP); it acquired the remaining 20% in 1992. The next year Bowater started up the GNP recycling facilities; completed the consolidation of its corporate headquarters in Greenville South Carolina; and sold 70000 acres of nonstrategic timberlands.

Arnold Nemirow former CEO of Wausau Paper Mills (Wisconsin) became Bowater's COO in 1994; subsequently he became CEO and chairman. After three years of losses (largely due to a slump in paper prices) the company turned around in 1995 aided by cost-reduction programs the sale of timberlands and higher paper prices. In 1996 Bowater sold its Star Forms subsidiary.

Bowater bought Montreal-based Avenor in 1998 for $2.4 billion which was 25% more than the hostile takeover bid from rival Abitibi-Consolidated. Although the cost contributed to a loss that year Bowater became the world's #2 newsprint maker with the acquisition.

A slump in newsprint prices occurred in 1999 and the company sold GNP (exiting the directory paper business) and more than 1.5 million acres of timberlands in Maine and the Carolinas. Also that year Bowater bought a South Korean paper mill.

In 2000 Bowater implemented several price increases as the market for newsprint began to improve. The company bought Canada's Alliance Forest Products in 2001 in a deal worth $770 million. The acquisition added three paper mills and 10 sawmill facilities. Later Bowater combined its Canadian subsidiaries Bowater Pulp and Paper Canada and Bowater Canadian Forest Products (formerly Alliance Forest Products) into a new Canadian forest products unit.

Bowater announced job cuts in 2002 (up to 500) and in 2003 announced the closing of a specialty paper machine in Quebec a move that reduced production capacity by 100000 metric tons annually.

CEO Arnold Nemirow retired in 2006; Georgia-Pacific veteran David Paterson succeeded him in the position. In addition Paterson began serving as chairman at the beginning of 2007 (he resigned in early 2011). That year the company merged with rival Abitibi-Consolidated to form North America's largest newsprint producer.

The company faced financial challenges early on and received a $350 million investment from Fairfax Financial in 2008. The investment was part of a $1.4 billion refinancing plan. Early in 2008 the company sold its mill in Snowflake Arizona to Catalyst Paper Corporation for $161 million in cash. The sale of the mill which has an annual capacity of 375000 tons was part of a deal to satisfy antitrust regulators in light of the merger.

Greenpeace activists blockaded the world headquarters of AbitibiBowater in 2008 to protest the company's alleged continued destruction of the last remaining intact areas of the Boreal Forest. The company manages the largest tract of publicly owned forest in Canada (about 55 million acres). Greenpeace's outreach to major AbitibiBowater customers has resulted in a loss of several million dollars in purchase contracts because of environmental concerns.

In 2009 the company filed for Chapter 11 in US Bankruptcy Court as well as bankruptcy protection in Canada. It had a debt of almost $9 billion –just shy of the value of its total listed assets. Citing various reasons –a decline in advertising credit crunch and decreased newsprint demand –the company set about to restructure its operations. AbitibiBowater cut jobs shuttered underperforming mills and sold non-core assets. In early 2009 the company sold more than 189000 acres of timberland in Quebec for C$70 million. AbitibiBowater subsequently shed another 300000 acres of Quebec timberland for C$53 million. It sold its 60% interest in the hydroelectric dam on the Manicouagan River to Hydro-Quebec for C$615 million.

With approval from the Quebec Superior Court the company struck a deal in 2009 with Fairfax Financial Holdings a major shareholder and other investors for about $350 million in emergency debtor-in-possession financing for some of its subsidiaries. Subsequently AbitibiBowater won court approval for more financing. AbitibiBowater also proposed a debt-for-equity swap transaction to its noteholders a move intended to trim its debt by $2.4 billion. The company was allowed to enter into a loan agreement with Bank of Montreal for $100 million debtor-in-possession financing. It continued an existing securitization program for its accounts receivable providing another $210 million in financing.

In order to save as many jobs as possible AbitibiBowater asked workers for concessions to help the company through its restructuring. Of the company's 15000 active employees around the world approximately 11600 employees were represented by the CEP (Communications Energy and Paperworkers Union of Canada) and the United Steelworkers in the US. (A tentative agreement was reached in spring 2010 with the CEP with the proposal to terminate pension plans stricken from the deal.)

AbitibiBowater emerged from bankruptcy in late 2010. Credited with getting the company out of bankruptcy CEO Danny Paterson resigned at the end of 2010 to return to the US. He was succeeded by veteran forestry executive Dick Garneau on the first day of 2011.

EXECUTIVES

SVP Corporate Affairs and Chief Legal Officer, Jacques P. Vachon, age 52, $340,000 total compensation
Chairman, Richard B. (Dick) Evans, age 63
SVP and CFO, William G. Harvey, age 54, $425,000 total compensation
SVP Human Resources and Public Affairs, Alain Grandmont, age 56, $425,000 total compensation
President CEO and Director, Richard Garneau, age 63
Manager Newsprint Thorold, Gordon Cole
General Manager ACH Limited Partnership, Jim Gartshore
VP Corporate Communications Sustainability and Government Affairs, Seth Kursman
SVP Wood Products Global Supply Chain and Information Technology, Yves Laflamme, age 56
VP Finance, Duane A. Owens, age 40
SVP and CFO, Jo-Ann Longworth, age 50
Director Canadian Public Affairs, Pierre Choquette
Manager Newsprint Clermont, Claude Potvin
Manager Newsprint Augusta, Jay Backus
Manager Market Pulp Newsprint and Commercial Printing Products Calhoun, Joe Vaughn
Manager Market Pulp and Commercial Printing Products Catawba, Mike Forrest
Manager Newsprint and Market Pulp Coosa Pines, Allen Sanders
Manager Commercial Printing Papers Alma, Carl Dahl
Manager Newsprint Baie-Comeau, Christian Gelinas
Manager Commercial Printing Papers and Market Pulp Fort Frances, Derrick Lindgren
Manager Newsprint Grenada Mississippi, Wade Taylor
Manager Newsprint and Commercial Printing Papers Iroquois Falls, Jean-Francois Guillot
Manager Commercial Printing Papers Kenogami, Jean Descoteaux
Manager Commercial Printing Papers Laurentide, Daniel Laberge
Manager Newsprint Mokpo, JeongHoon (Joseph) Cho
Manager Newsprint Ponderay (Usk WA), Paul Machtolf
SVP Pulp and Paper Operations, Alain Boivin
SVP Pulp and Paper Sales and Marketing, John Lafave
Director U.S. Public Affairs, Debbie Johnston
Manager Newsprint Amos, Daniel Marcoux
Manager Technical Services, Rick Gruttner
Manager Newsprint and Commercial Printing Papers Mersey, Brad Pelley
Manager Market Pulp Newsprint and Commercial Printing Papers Thunder Bay, Doug Murray
General Manager Hydro-Saguenay, Michel Desjardins
Manager Comtois and Senneterre Sawmills, Maxime Langlais
Manager Produits Forestiers Saguenay - Petit-Saguenay and Saint-Hilarion Sawmills, Jose Bouchard
Manager Outardes Sawmill, Pierre Cormier
Manager Girardville La Dore Mistassini Roberval Saint-Felicien and Saint-Thomas Sawmills, Michel C. Ouellet
Manager Oakhill Sawmill, Hans Pedersen
Manager Laurentide Mill and Produits Forestiers Mauricie Sawmill, Fernand Potvin
Manager Fort Frances Iroquois Falls and Thunder Bay Mills; Thunder Bay Sawmill, Rick Groves
Manager Maniwaki Sawmill, Paul Grondin
Manager Produits Forestiers Saguenay ? Saint-Fulgence Sawmill, Joseph Fortin
Manager Augusta Calhoun Catawba Coosa Pines Grenada and Ponderay Mills, Kent Cumberton
SVP Human Resources, Pierre Laberge
Director, Jeffrey A. Hearn, age 58
Director, Alain Rheaume
Director, Pierre Dupuis, age 67
Director, Michael S. (Mike) Rousseau
President CEO and Director, Richard Garneau, age 63
Director, Paul C. Rivett, age 43
Director, Sarah E. Nash, age 58
Director, David H. Wilkins
Director, Richard Falconer
Auditors: PricewaterhouseCoopersLLP

LOCATIONS

HQ: Resolute Forest Products Inc.
1155 Metcalfe St. Ste. 800, Montreal Quebec H3B 5H2 Canada
Phone: 514-875-2160 **Fax:** 864-2829482
Web: www.abitibibowater.com

2010 Sales

	$ mil.	% of total
US	2,775	59
Canada	703	15
Mexico	166	3
Brazil	156	3
Italy	128	2
India	96	2
UK	73	2
Korea	36	1
Other countries	613	13
Total	**4,746**	**100**

PRODUCTS/OPERATIONS

2010 Sales

	$ mil.	% of total
Newsprint	1,804	38
Specialty papers	1,321	28
Market pulp	715	15
Coated papers	482	10
Wood products	424	9
Total	**4,746**	**100**

Selected Operations

Energy
Pulp and paper
Recycling
Woodlands
Wood products

COMPETITORS

Bio Pappel
Brant Industries
Buckeye Technologies
Canfor
Catalyst Paper
Georgia-Pacific
Horizon Paper
International Paper
Neenah Paper
NewPage
Norske Skog
North Pacific Paper
RockTenn CP
SP Newsprint
West Fraser Timber
Weyerhaeuser

HISTORICAL FINANCIALS

Company Type: Public

Income Statement

FYE: December 31

	REVENUE ($ mil.)	NET INCOME ($ mil.)	NET PROFIT MARGIN	EMPLOYEES
12/11	4,756	41	0.9%	10,400
12/10	4,746	2,614	55.1%	10,500
12/09	4,366	(1,553)	—	12,100
12/08	6,771	(2,234)	—	15,900
12/07	3,876	(490)	—	18,000
Annual Growth	5.2%	—	—	(12.8%)

2011 Year-End Financials

Debt ratio: 9.86%
Return on equity: 1.20%
Cash ($ mil.): 369
Current ratio: 325.18
Long-term debt ($ mil.): 621
No. of shares (mil.): 97
Dividends
Yield: —
Payout: —
Market value ($ mil.): 1,413

	STOCK PRICE ($) FY Close	P/E High	P/E Low	PER SHARE ($) Earnings	Dividends	Book Value
12/11	14.55	71	33	0.42	0.00	35.19
12/10	23.67	1	1	27.63	0.00	38.18
Annual Growth	(38.5%)	—	—	(98.5%)	—	(7.8%)

Reynolds American Inc

Hot does not begin to describe Reynolds American Inc. (RAI). The holding company holds the #2 spot among US makers of cigarettes and smokeless tobacco through subsidiaries RJR Tobacco and American Snuff. RJR Tobacco produces many of the top-selling cigarette brands: Camel Doral Kool Pall Mall Salem and Winston. It also makes and markets smoke-free Camel tobacco products. American Snuff offers moist snuff under the value-priced Grizzly and the premium Kodiak brands. RAI businesses include cigarette maker Santa Fe Natural Tobacco and nicotine gum maker Niconovum. RAI is the result of a merger of R.J. Reynolds Tobacco and Brown & Williamson a subsidiary of British American Tobacco that owns 42% of RAI.

HISTORY

R. J. Reynolds formed the R.J. Reynolds Tobacco Company in 1875 in Winston North Carolina to produce chewing tobacco. In the late 1890s Reynolds lost two-thirds of the company to the American Tobacco Trust but he regained control in 1911 after the trust was dismantled by the government. Two years later the company introduced Camel.

After Reynolds died in 1918 leadership passed to Bowman Gray whose family ran the company for the next 50 years. Camel held the #1 or #2 cigarette position throughout the 1930s and 1940s and Reynolds became the largest domestic cigarette company. In response to growing health concerns in the 1950s the company introduced its filtered Winston (1954) and Salem (1956) brands.

In response to growing antismoking sentiment Reynolds Tobacco began diversifying into foods and other nontobacco businesses beginning in the 1960s. Acquisitions included Chun King Patio Foods American Independent Oil Del Monte Inglenook wines Smirnoff vodka Kentucky Fried Chicken Sunkist beverages and Canada Dry all of which it had sold by 1991. In September 1985 Reynolds acquired Nabisco Brands (Newtons Oreo Planters nuts) for $4.9 billion. In 1986 the parent company was re-named RJR Nabisco Inc.

In November 1988 RJR Nabisco agreed to be acquired by Kohlberg Kravis Roberts (KKR). The deal valued in excess of $25 billion closed in April 1989. After being privately held for a period KKR took RJR Nabisco Holdings public in 1991. In early 1995 KKR divested its remaining holdings in RJR Nabisco. Also that year Andrew Schindler was promoted to CEO of the firm.

The tobacco business ended the much-criticized Joe Camel campaign in the US in 1997 and cut its tobacco workforce by 10%. The big US tobacco companies reached a $206 billion settlement in 1998 covering 46 states (four states had already settled for $40 billion) and began hiking cigarette prices by 45 cents a pack.

Prior to 1999 RJR was a subsidiary of RJR Nabisco Holdings Corp. (RJRN). In 1999 following the sale of the company's international tobacco business to Japan Tobacco for $8 billion the remaining tobacco and food businesses were separated and RJRN was renamed Nabisco Group Holdings Corp. (NGH). In June the former parent company RJRN was renamed RJ Reynolds Tobacco Holdings Inc. and became an independent publicly traded company again with RJ Reynolds Tobacco Company as its wholly owned subsidiary. (The separation was accomplished through a spinoff of the domestic tobacco business to RJR Nabisco stockholders.)

A Florida jury rendered a $35 billion punitive damages verdict against RJRT in 2000. The company filed an appeal as it and four other Big Tobacco firms claimed the verdict –totaling $145 billion —would put them out of business (which violates Florida tort law). A state appeals court later threw out the verdict saying the thousands of Florida smokers named in the case could not lump their complaints into one lawsuit. That decision is now under review by the Florida Supreme Court.

RJRT spun off its Targacept subsidiary (created in 1999) in August 2000 retaining a 43% stake. In December RJRT acquired its former parent company Nabisco Group Holdings Corp. for $9.8 billion.

In January 2002 RJRT acquired the Santa Fe Natural Tobacco Company maker of the Natural American Spirit additive-free cigarette brand for $340 million in cash. That year RJR also formed a joint venture with UK-based Gallaher to sell American blend cigarettes in Europe particularly in France Spain Italy and the Canary Islands. In early 2008 RJR terminated its Gallaher joint venture.

While pursuing new markets overseas RJRT scaled back marketing efforts at home –in part because of the agreement it signed with US states in 1998. In June 2003 NASCAR and RJRT parted ways signaling the end to NASCAR's Winston Cup series. The race circuit is now called the Sprint Cup.

In September 2003 the company said it would focus marketing activities on its Camel and Salem brands. It also launched a two-year plan to cut costs by $1 billion which included cutting jobs by 40%. By the end of 2003 RJRT had cut 1400 jobs. Shortly thereafter the company announced merger plans with Brown & Williamson.

Before combining with RJRT to create Reynolds American in July 2004 Brown & Williamson had been ordered to cut back on promoting its Kool brand which was associated with hip-hop music. The issue carried over to Reynolds American which agreed in October 2004 to settle several related lawsuits in New York Illinois and Maryland by paying $1.5 million toward antismoking campaigns and severely restricting Kool promotions that critics said targeted black youths.

In 2006 Lane Limited sold its Dr. Grabow line of pipes and filters Dill's pipe cleaners and Sparta North Carolina manufacturing facility to International Pipes & Accessories LLC for about $4.3 million. Lane Limited sold the brands and plant to focus on making and marketing its premium tobacco products.

In June 2009 the passage of the Family Smoking and Tobacco Control Act by the US Congress gave the FDA unprecedented authority to regulate tobacco products including the authority to regulate marketing ban candy flavorings and reduce nicotine in tobacco products. In December RAI Niconovum AB a Swedish maker of smoking cessation products for about $44 million. The newly-acquired firm will operate as a separate company of RAI.

In early 2011 RAI sold off its roll-your-own and pipe tobacco Lane Limited subsidiary for some $205 million to Scandinavian Tobacco Group so that it could concentrate on its cigarettes and smokeless tobacco segments. Also Susan Ivey stepped down as the company's chairman president and CEO replaced by Netherlands-born Daniel Delen who had risen to be chairman president and CEO of RAI's largest subsidiary RJR Tobacco.

EXECUTIVES

EVP and CFO, Thomas R. (Tom) Adams, age 61, $533,882 total compensation
Chairman, Thomas C. (Tom) Wajnert, age 69
President. Niconovum USA, Tommy J. Payne, age 54, $399,275 total compensation
SVP Deputy General Counsel and Secretary Reynolds American and Reynolds American Services, McDara P. Folan III, age 53
President CEO and Director, Daniel M. (Daan) Delen, age 46, $814,600 total compensation
President Santa Fe Natural Tobacco Company, Michael A. (Mike) Little
SVP Risk and Compliance Services, Susan B. Wilson
CFO R.J. Reynolds Tobacco Company; SVP Decision Support RAI Services Company, Mark A. Peters
SVP Strategy and Business Development, E. Kenan (Ken) Whitehurst, age 55
SVP and Treasurer, Daniel A. Fawley, age 54
EVP Operations and Chief Scientific Officer R.J. Reynolds Tobacco Company, Jeffery S. (Jeff) Gentry, age 54, $450,418 total compensation
Media Relations, Maura Payne
EVP Consumer Marketing R.J. Reynolds Tobacco Company, J. Brice O'Brien, age 43
EVP Trade Marketing R.J. Reynolds Tobacco Company, Robert D. Stowe, age 54
SVP Strategy and Planning R.J. Reynolds Tobacco Company, Walton T. Carpenter, age 58

EVP and Chief Human Resources Officer Reynolds America and Reynolds American Services, Lisa J. Caldwell, age 51
President and Chief Commercial Officer R.J. Reynolds Tobacco Company, Andrew D. Gilchrist, age 39
SVP Research and Development R.J. Reynolds Tobacco Company, Daniel J. Herko, age 51
EVP General Counsel and Secretary Reynolds American and RAI Services Company; EVP and General Counsel R.J. Reynolds Tobacco, Martin L. (Mark) Holton III
SVP Operations R.J. Reynolds Tobacco Company, Tommy L. Hickman
SVP Research and Development American Snuff Company LLC, R.H. (Bobby) Krauch Jr.
SVP and Chief Accounting Officer Reynolds American and Reynolds American Services, Frederick W. Smothers, age 48
VP and Managing Director SFR Tobacco International, Bill Morachnick
EVP Public Affairs Reynolds American R.J. Reynolds Tobacco Company and RAI Services Company, Robert H. Dunham
Managing Director Niconovum AB, Nils Siegbahn
President American Snuff Company LLC, Randall M. (Mick) Spach
Director, Martin D. (Marty) Feinstein, age 63
Director, John J. Zillmer, age 56
Director, Nana Mensah, age 59
Director, Lionel L. Nowell III, age 57
President CEO and Director, Daniel M. (Daan) Delen, age 46
Director, Holly K. Koeppel, age 53
Director, Luc Jobin, age 53
Director, John P. Daly, age 55
Director, H.G.L. (Hugo) Powell, age 67
Director, Neil R. Withington, age 55
Auditors: KPMGLLP

LOCATIONS

HQ: Reynolds American Inc.
401 N. Main St., Winston-Salem NC 27101-2990
Phone: 336-741-2000 **Fax:** 336-741-4238
Web: www.reynoldsamerican.com

PRODUCTS/OPERATIONS

2011 Sales

	$ mil.	% of total
RJR Tobacco	7,297	85
American Snuff	648	8
Santa Fe	436	5
Other	160	2
Total	**8,541**	**100**

Selected Brands

American Snuff (smokeless tobacco)
- Grizzly
- Kodiak

RJR Tobacco (cigarettes)
- Camel
- Camel Dissolvables (smoke-free tobacco)
  - Orbs
  - Sticks
  - Strips
- Camel Snus (smoke-free pouch)
- Capri
- Doral
- Dunhill (RJR' s super-premium cigarette licensed from British American Tobacco)
- Kool
- Misty
- Pall Mall
- Salem
- State Express 555 (RJR' s super-premium cigarette licensed from British American Tobacco)
- Winston

Santa Fe Natural Tobacco
- Natural American Spirit

Other
- Niconovum (nicotine replacement therapies)

COMPETITORS

Auri
Commonwealth Brands
GSK Italy
JT International
Lorillard
Nat Sherman
Philip Morris USA
Smokin Joes
Star Scientific
Swisher International
UST llc
Vector Group

HISTORICAL FINANCIALS

Company Type: Public

Income Statement FYE: December 31

	REVENUE ($ mil.)	NET INCOME ($ mil.)	NET PROFIT MARGIN	EMPLOYEES
12/11	8,541	1,406	16.5%	5,450
12/10	8,551	1,113	13.0%	5,750
12/09	8,419	962	11.4%	6,550
12/08	8,845	1,338	15.1%	6,900
12/07	9,023	1,308	14.5%	7,300
Annual Growth	(1.4%)	1.8%	—	(7.0%)

2011 Year-End Financials

Debt ratio: 22.54%
Return on equity: 22.49%
Cash ($ mil.): 1,956
Current ratio: 100.72
Long-term debt ($ mil.): 3,206
No. of shares (mil.): 576
Dividends
Yield: —
Payout: 89.58%
Market value ($ mil.): 23,864

	STOCK PRICE ($) FY Close	P/E High/Low		PER SHARE ($) Earnings	Dividends	Book Value
12/11	41.42	17	13	2.40	0.00	10.85
12/10	32.62	35	16	1.91	1.84	11.17
12/09	52.97	33	19	1.65	1.73	11.15
12/08	40.31	31	17	2.29	1.70	10.70
12/07	65.96	32	26	2.22	1.60	12.65
Annual Growth	(11.0%)	—	—	2.0%	—	(3.8%)

Rite Aid Corp.

Rite Aid is clinging to its position as a distant third (behind Walgreen and CVS) in the US retail drugstore business. The struggling company runs some 4665 drugstores in about 30 states and the District of Columbia. Rite Aid stores fill prescriptions (more than two-thirds of sales) and sell health and beauty aids convenience foods greeting cards and other items including some 3000 Rite Aid brand private-label products. About 60% of all Rite Aid stores are freestanding and 50% have drive-through pharmacies. Rite Aid acquired more than 1850 Brooks and Eckerd drugstores from Canada's Jean Coutu Group for about $4 billion which saddled the company with plenty of debt and redundant stores in some areas.

HISTORY

Wholesale grocer Alex Grass founded Rack Rite Distributors in Harrisburg Pennsylvania in 1958 to provide health and beauty aids and other sundries to grocery stores. He offered the same products at his first discount drugstore Thrif D Discount Center opened in 1962 in Scranton Pennsylvania. Four years later the company began placing pharmacies in its 36 stores. Rite Aid went public and adopted its current name in 1968 and the next year it made the first of many diverse acquisitions: Daw Drug Blue Ridge Nursing Homes and plasma suppliers Immuno Serums and Sero Genics.

Purchases in the 1970s included Sera-Tec Biologicals of New Jersey (blood plasma) and nearly 300 stores. By 1981 Rite Aid was the #3 drugstore chain and sales exceeded $1 billion. In 1984 it bought the American Discount Auto Parts chain and Encore Books discount chain and spun off its wholesale grocery operation in 1984 as Super Rite retaining a 47% stake (sold 1989).

Acquisitions added almost 900 stores during the 1980s. Expansion costs eroded Rite Aid's profit margins and the company focused on integrating its buys in 1990.

As part of a major restructuring in 1994 the company began selling its non-drugstore assets. Also in 1994 Rite Aid acquired Pharmacy Card and Intell-Rx and merged the two to form Eagle Managed Care.

Martin Grass took Rite Aid's reins from his dad in 1995. That year the company agreed to buy Revco at the time the #2 drugstore operator but the deal was derailed by FTC and Department of Justice objections in 1996. Rite Aid bounced back and acquired Thrifty PayLess (with more than 1000 stores) for about $2.3 billion in 1996. The deal gave the company more than 3600 stores and a presence in the western US. Also in 1996 Rite Aid exited several markets. In 1998 it closed many smaller stores and bought PCS Health Systems (the #1 US pharmacy benefits manager) from drug maker Eli Lilly and merged its Eagle Managed Care division into PCS.

In 1999 after a "Wall Street Journal" investigation Rite Aid revealed that Martin Grass Alex Grass and other family members held stakes in several suppliers and real estate interests doing business with the company. That year Rite Aid partnered with General Nutrition Companies Inc. (GNC) and took a 25% stake in the Internet retailer drugstore.com. Later in 1999 Rite Aid began slashing its $5.1 billion debt by cutting corporate staff and selling off some stores in California and the Pacific Northwest. CEO Martin Grass resigned and a team of former Fred Meyer officers –led by Robert Miller –took over.

In 2000 the company secured $1 billion from Citibank to reduce debt and provide capital. In July 2000 the company announced it would restate profits that over the past two years had been inflated in excess of $1 billion. Later that year Rite Aid sold PCS Health Systems to pharmacy benefits manager Advance Paradigm for more than $1 billion (about $500 million less than what Rite Aid originally paid for it). Rite Aid announced plans in 2001 to expand GNC concessions to additional stores.

To raise cash Rite Aid sold large blocks of its drugstore.com stock trimming its original 25% stake to less than 10% by April 2002. Former chairman and CEO Martin Grass former general counsel and vice chairman Franklin Brown and former CFO Frank Bergonzi among others were indicted in June 2002 for allegedly falsifying Rite Aid's books.

In April 2003 former chairman and CEO Martin Grass agreed to pay nearly $1.5 million to settle a lawsuit in which shareholders alleged that Rite Aid's books were falsified inflating the stock's value. In June Grass and former CFO Franklyn Bergonzi both pleaded guilty to conspiracy to defraud shareholders. Eric Sorkin Rite Aid's former VP of pharmacy services pleaded guilty to conspiring to obstruct justice. The following month Rite Aid began mailing checks totaling nearly $140 million to thousands of its current and former shareholders damaged by the accounting scandal at the company. In October former chief counsel Franklin Brown was convicted of conspiracy and lying to the Securities and Exchange Commission among other charges.

Despite its high debt load Rite Aid reportedly made a $4 billion cash-and-stock offer for struggling rival Eckerd but lost out to CVS and Canada's Jean Coutu Group who divvied up Eckerd in mid-2004.

In May 2004 Grass whose father founded Rite Aid struck a plea deal with prosecutors under which he was sentenced to eight years in prison. Also in May several other former company executives including Sorkin and ex-CFO Frank Bergonzi were sentenced in the accounting scandal. In June Rite Aid agreed to pay the US government $5.6 million (plus another $1.4 million to more than 20 states) to settle a federal lawsuit alleging the drugstore chain submitted false prescription claims to government insurance programs. In October former vice chairman Brown was sentenced to 10 years in prison the longest sentence of six Rite Aid officials charged in the accounting scandal.

CFO John Standley resigned in 2005 to join supermarket operator Pathmark Stores as its CEO. Standley joined Rite Aid as its CFO in 1999.

In April 2007 the company agreed to a store swap with California-based Longs Drug Stores. Under the terms of the agreement Rite Aid acquired six Longs stores in Northern California Oregon and Washington in exchange for giving Longs six of its stores in Nevada.

In its first major deal since its brush with bankruptcy in 1999 Rite Aid acquired more than 1850 Brooks and Eckerd drugstores and six distribution centers from Canada's Jean Coutu Group in a cash-and-stock deal valued at about $4 billion in June 2007.

Rite Aid exited the Las Vegas market in 2008 saying it was not a core market and had not contributed to overall results. It sold 27 of its Las Vegas stores to Walgreens. It March 2009 Rite Aid made a similar disposal of all seven of its stores in San Francisco and five locations in eastern Idaho when it sold them to Walgreen. Rite Aid said the stores were in areas with too light a store presence to operate efficiently. In July Rite Aid agreed to pay $500000 in consumer refunds to settle charges by the FTC that the company falsely advertised its Germ Defense line of cold-and-flu remedies as preventing illness or reducing the severity and duration of symptoms. The FTC said Rite Aid did not have evidence to support its Germ Defense product claims. Rite Aid founder Alex Grass died in August 2009 at the age of 82.

President and CEO John Standley added the title of chairman in mid-2012.

EXECUTIVES

Chairman President and CEO, John T. Standley, age 49, $900,000 total compensation
Co-Chairman, Mary F. Sammons, age 65, $1,000,000 total compensation
SVP Pharmacy Services, Christopher S. (Chris) Hall, age 47, $420,192 total compensation
SVP Supply Chain, Wilson A. Lester Jr., age 53
EVP General Counsel and Secretary, Marc A. Strassler, age 64
SEVP CFO and Chief Administrative Officer, Frank G. Vitrano, age 57, $700,000 total compensation
Co-Chairman, Michel Coutu, age 58
SVP and CIO, Don P. Davis, age 59
EVP Merchandising, Enio Anthony (Tony) Montini Jr., age 59
SVP Marketing, John Learish, age 46
SVP Merchandising, Bryan Shirtliff, age 51
SVP Corporate Communications, Karen Rugen
SVP and Chief Accounting Officer, Douglas E. (Doug) Donley, age 49
Group VP Real Estate, Karen Smith
SVP Indirect Procurement, Gerald P. (Jerry) Cardinale
Group VP Category Management, Bill Bergin
SVP and Chief Compliance Officer, Anthony J. (Tony) Bellezza, age 45
SVP and Chief Communications Officer, Susan Henderson, age 59
SVP Store Development, David N. Kelly
EVP Store Operations, Robert K. (Bob) Thompson, age 55
EVP Human Resources, Brian R. Fiala, age 51, $457,600 total compensation
SEVP and COO, Kenneth A. (Ken) Martindale, age 51, $600,000 total compensation
SVP Mid-Atlantic Division, Jon Olson
EVP Pharmacy, Robert I. Thompson, age 58
SVP Southern Division, Scott Bernard
SVP Managed Care and Government Affairs, William (Bill) Wolfe, age 48
Group VP Pharmaceutical Purchasing and Clinical Services, Ernie Richardsen, age 44
SVP Pharmacy Operations, Dan Miller, age 56
Group VP Strategy and Investor Relations, Matt Schroeder, age 42
Group VP Compensation Benefits and Shared Services, Ken Black
SVP Western Division, Bill Romine
SVP Northeast Division, Derek Griffith
Group VP Loss Prevention, Bob Oberosler
President CEO and Director, John T. Standley, age 48
Director, Michael N. Regan, age 64
Director, David R. (Dave) Jessick, age 59
Director, Mary F. Sammons, age 65
Director, Marcy Syms, age 61
Director, James L. (Jim) Donald, age 58
Director, Michel Coutu, age 58
Director, Francois J. Coutu, age 57
Director, John M. Baumer, age 44
Director, Joseph B. Anderson Jr., age 69
Director, Andre Belzile, age 50
Auditors: Deloitte&ToucheLLP

LOCATIONS

HQ: Rite Aid Corporation
30 Hunter Ln., Camp Hill PA 17011
Phone: 717-761-2633 **Fax:** 717-975-5871
Web: www.riteaid.com

2012 Stores

	No.
New	630
California	588
Pennsylvania	548
Michigan	282
New	264
North	228
Ohio	227
Virginia	192
Georgia	191
Massachusetts	155
Maryland	144
Washington	139
Kentucky	116
West	104
South	96
Alabama	94
Tennessee	83
Maine	79
Connecticut	77
Oregon	71
New	68
Louisiana	65
Rhode	45
Delaware	43
Vermont	38
Mississippi	27
Utah	22
Colorado	20
Idaho	13
Indiana	10
District of	7
Nevada	1
Total	**4,667**

PRODUCTS/OPERATIONS

2012 Sales

	% of total
Prescription	68
General merchandise &	17
Over-the-counter medications & personal	10
Health & beauty	5
Total	**100**

2012 Sales

	$ mil.	% of total
Pharmacy	17,725	68
Front-end	8,293	32
Other	101	-
Total	**26,121**	**100**

Selected Merchandise and Services

Beverages
Convenience foods
Cosmetics
Designer fragrances
Greeting cards
Health and personal care products
Household items
Over-the-counter drugs
Photo processing
Prescription drugs
Private-label products
Seasonal merchandise
Vitamins and minerals

COMPETITORS

A&P
Ahold U.S.A.
BJ' s Wholesale Club
Costco Wholesale
CVS Caremark
Discount Drug
Dollar General
Family Dollar Stores
Kmart
Kroger
Marc Glassman
Medicine Shoppe
Publix
Safeway
Target Corporation
Wal-Mart
Walgreen

HISTORICAL FINANCIALS

Company Type: Public

Income Statement FYE: March 3

	REVENUE ($ mil.)	NET INCOME ($ mil.)	NET PROFIT MARGIN	EMPLOYEES
03/12*	26,121	(368)	—	90,000
02/11	25,214	(555)	—	91,800
02/10	25,669	(506)	—	97,500
02/09	26,289	(2,915)	—	103,000
03/08	24,326	(1,078)	—	112,800
Annual Growth	1.8%	—	—	(5.5%)

*Fiscal year change

2012 Year-End Financials

Debt ratio: 85.93%
Return on equity: 987650001000000.00%
Cash ($ mil.): 162
Current ratio: 175.25
Long-term debt ($ mil.): 6,248
No. of shares (mil.): 898
Dividends
Yield: —
Payout: —
Market value ($ mil.): 1,501

STOCK PRICE ($) FY Close		P/E High/Low	PER SHARE ($) Earnings	Dividends	Book Value
03/12*	1.67	— —	(0.43)	0.00	(2.88)
02/11	1.28	— —	(0.64)	0.00	(2.48)
02/10	1.52	— —	(0.59)	0.00	(1.89)
02/09	0.28	— —	(3.49)	0.00	(1.35)
03/08	2.67	— —	(1.54)	0.00	2.06
Annual Growth	(11.1%)	— —	—	—	—

*Fiscal year change

RiverSource Life Insurance Co

LOCATIONS

HQ: RiverSource Life Insurance Co
1099 Ameriprise Financial Center, Minneapolis, MN 55474
Phone: 612 671-3131
Web: www.riversource.com

HISTORICAL FINANCIALS

Company Type:

Income Statement FYE: December 31

	ASSETS ($ mil.)	NET INCOME ($ mil.)	INCOME AS % OF ASSETS	EMPLOYEES
12/11	105,380	779	0.7%	0
12/10	102,626	796	0.8%	0
12/09	92,972	740	0.8%	0
12/08	77,223	71	0.1%	0
12/07	90,782	421	0.5%	0
Annual Growth	3.8%	16.6%	—	—

2011 Year-End Financials

Debt ratio: 0.28%
Return on equity: 13.27%
Cash ($ mil.): 828
Current ratio: —
Long-term debt ($ mil.): 300
No. of shares (mil.): 0
Dividends
Yield: —
Payout: 96.28%
Market value ($ mil.): —

RLI Corp.

You might wonder what folks in Illinois know about earthquake insurance but as a specialty property/casualty insurer Peoria-based RLI knows how to write such policies. Through its subsidiaries the company mainly offers coverage for US niche markets –risks that are hard to place in the standard market and are otherwise underserved. It focuses on public and private companies as well as non-profit organizations. RLI's commercial property/casualty lines include products liability property damage marine cargo directors and officers liability medical malpractice and general liability. It also writes commercial surety bonds and a smattering of specialty personal insurance.

Geographic Reach

While the company operates in all 50 US states California is RLI's largest market accounting for about 20% of the company's premiums.

Operations

RLI's specialty commercial property/casualty operations are conducted through its RLI Insurance Mt. Hawley Insurance and RLI Indemnity subsidiaries. Personal offerings account for small portion of RLI's revenues and include homeowners insurance in Hawaii home business coverage pet insurance and personal umbrella (supplemental property/casualty) policies.

Sales and Marketing

RLI markets its products to brokers and independent agents through branch offices scattered across the US.

Financial Analysis

Like many insurers RLI's finances took a negative hit from the economic turmoil of 2008 and 2009. The company improved its returns in both 2010 and 2011 reporting a 6% increase in revenues to $619 million and a 2% rise in net income to some $131 million. Growth in 2011 was attributed to increased premiums from RLI's commercial property business including operations acquired during the year.

Strategy

The company has gradually expanded its range of products with an emphasis on property insurance. In 2010 it began providing reinsurance to a major US crop insurer and it expanded its reinsurance operations in 2011 through the formation of a new property treaty reinsurance unit. In addition RLI entered a new personal specialty market in 2010 when it partnered with Embrace Pet Insurance Agency to underwrite pet insurance policies. In 2012 the company entered the recreational vehicle (RV) insurance market by forming an underwriting partnership with Recreation Insurance Specialists.

Mergers and Acquisitions

To broaden its geographic footprint RLI acquired Seattle-based Contractors Bonding Insurance a niche provider of property/casualty insurance products and surety bonds in 2011 for some $136 million. Then in 2012 it moved into the field of medical malpractice coverage through the acquisition of Rockbridge Underwriting Agency.

Company Background

Gerald Stephens founded the company in 1961 and served as its chairman from 2001 until his retirement in 2011.

EXECUTIVES

President and COO RLI Insurance and Mt. Hawley Insurance, Michael J. (Mike) Stone, age 63, $485,250 total compensation
Chairman President and CEO, Jonathan E. Michael, age 58, $728,000 total compensation
SVP and CFO, Joseph E. Dondanville, age 55, $362,400 total compensation
VP Human Resources, Jeffrey D. Fick, age 51, $236,333 total compensation
VP Claims, Donald J. Driscoll
VP Corporate Development, Aaron H. Jacoby, age 41
Treasurer and Chief Investment Officer, John E. Robison, age 44
VP and CIO, Carol J. Denzer, age 49
VP Executive Products Group, Chad Berberich
Producer Licensing, Jackie Sweeter
VP Internal Audit, Seth A. Davis
VP General Counsel and Corporate Secretary, Daniel O. Kennedy, age 47, $296,000 total compensation
Assistant VP Technology and Cyber Liability Executive Products Group, Betty Shepherd
VP MLP Executive Products Group, Brian Flynn
SVP Risk Services, Craig W. Kliethermes, age 47, $315,000 total compensation
Southeast Regional Manager Executive Products Group, Mike Robinson
Senior Human Resources Generalist and Lead Recruiter, Wendy Bass
VP and Controller, Todd W. Bryant
Manager Human Resources, Stacy Clubb
VP Underwriting Design Professionals, L. Lenny Waldhauser
SVP Underwriting E and S Property, Jeff Wefer
VP Underwriting Fidelity, Mike Beranek
VP Underwriting Reinsurance, Kevin Brawley
VP Underwriting Surety, Roy Die
VP Underwriting Transportation, Dave Dunn
VP Underwriting E and S Property, Kevin McDonough
VP Underwriting Specialty Markets, Dick Quehl
VP Underwriting Surety, Dave Sandoz
VP Underwriting Marine, Bob Schauer
VP Underwriting Casualty, Paul Simoneau
VP and Chief Investment Officer, Aaron P. Diefenthaler
VP and CFO, Thomas L. Brown
VP Information Technology, Murali Natarajan
Director, F. Lynn McPheeters, age 69
Director, Barbara R. Allen, age 59
Director, Gerald I. Lenrow, age 84
Director, Robert O. Viets, age 68
Director, Kaj Ahlmann, age 61
Director, John T. Baily, age 68
Director, Charles M. Linke, age 74
Director, Jordan W. Graham, age 51
Auditors: KPMGLLP

LOCATIONS

HQ: RLI Corp.
9025 N. Lindbergh Dr., Peoria IL 61615-1499
Phone: 309-692-1000 **Fax:** 404-321-5483
Web: www.rpc.net

PRODUCTS/OPERATIONS

2011 Revenues

	$ mil.	% of total
Net premiums earned		
Property	203	33
Net investment income	63	10
Total	**619**	**100**

Selected Products

Commercial
- Casualty
- Contractors bonding and insurance
- Executive products liability
- Marine
- Professional services
- Property
- Reinsurance
- Specialty programs
- Transportation

Personal
- Homeowners (Hawaii)
- Home business owners
- Personal umbrella

Surety Bonds

COMPETITORS

ACE Limited
Arch Insurance Group
Baldwin & Lyons
Chubb Corp
CNA Financial
Crum & Forster
Endurance Specialty
Great American Insurance Company

Great West Casualty
HCC Insurance
James River Group
Lancer Insurance
Lexington Insurance
Markel
Meadowbrook Insurance
Navigators
Philadelphia Insurance Companies
Safeco
The Hartford
Travelers Companies
United States Liability Insurance Group

HISTORICAL FINANCIALS

Company Type: Public

Income Statement — FYE: December 31

	ASSETS ($ mil.)	NET INCOME ($ mil.)	INCOME AS % OF ASSETS	EMPLOYEES
12/11	2,695	130	4.8%	862
12/10	2,514	127	5.1%	734
12/09	2,538	93	3.7%	747
12/08	2,419	78	3.3%	783
12/07	2,626	175	6.7%	763
Annual Growth	0.6%	(7.2%)	—	3.1%

2011 Year-End Financials

Debt ratio: 3.71%
Return on equity: 15.95%
Cash ($ mil.): 81
Current ratio: —
Long-term debt ($ mil.): 100
No. of shares (mil.): 21
Dividends
Yield: —
Payout: 101.64%
Market value ($ mil.): 1,542

	STOCK PRICE ($) FY Close	P/E High/Low	PER SHARE ($) Earnings	Dividends	Book Value
12/11	72.86	12 8	6.09	0.00	38.69
12/10	52.57	10 8	6.00	8.15	37.75
12/09	53.25	14 10	4.32	1.08	39.14
12/08	61.16	18 12	3.60	0.99	32.98
12/07	56.79	8 7	7.30	0.87	34.95
Annual Growth	6.4%	— —	(4.4%)	—	2.6%

Robinson (C.H.) Worldwide, Inc.

C.H. Robinson Worldwide (CHRW) keeps merchandise moving. A third-party logistics (3PL) provider the company arranges freight transportation using trucks trains ships and airplanes belonging to other companies. It contracts with some 53000 carriers. CHRW handles about 10 million shipments per year for its 37000-plus customers that include companies in the food and beverage manufacturing and retail industries. Besides transportation the company also offers logistics for supply chain management services through more than 230 offices. In addition CHRW buys sells and transports fresh produce throughout the US. Its T-Chek unit provides such services as funds transfer and fuel purchasing management.

HISTORY

In the early 1900s Charles H. Robinson began a produce brokerage in Grand Forks North Dakota. Robinson entered a partnership in 1905 with Nash Brothers the leading wholesaler in North Dakota and the company C.H. Robinson was born.

Robinson became president but soon relinquished control under mysterious circumstances (rumor had it he ran off with Annie Oakley). H. B. Finch took charge and by 1913 a new company Nash Finch became C.H. Robinson's sole owner.

As a subsidiary C.H. Robinson primarily procured produce for Nash Finch which helped it expand into Illinois Minnesota Texas and Wisconsin. To avoid FTC scrutiny over preferential treatment Nash Finch split CHR in two: C.H. Robinson Co. owned by C.H. Robinson employees which sold produce to Nash Finch warehouses; and C.H. Robinson Inc. owned by Nash Finch.

After WWII the interstate highway system and refrigerated trucks changed the industry. No longer dependent on railroads C.H. Robinson began charging for truck brokerage of perishables. The two companies formed by the 1940s split reunited under the C.H. Robinson name in the mid-1960s; Nash Finch kept a 25% stake in the company and sold the rest to employees. Not surprisingly Nash Finch wanted to divert C.H. Robinson profits to its other businesses so in 1976 C.H. Robinson employees bought out Nash Finch.

The next year D. R. "Sid" Verdoorn was named president and Looe Baker became chairman. They focused on increasing C.H. Robinson's data-processing capability and adding branch offices. In 1980 the Motor Carrier Act deregulated the transportation industry and C.H. Robinson entered the freight-contracting business acting as a middleman for all types of goods. The company grew rapidly from about 30 offices in 1980 to more than 60 in 1990.

As part of its overall effort to become a full-service provider C.H. Robinson formed its Intermodal Division (more than one mode of transport) in 1988. It also established an information services division (1991) and bought fruit juice concentrate distributor Daystar International (1993). By this time the company was working with more than 14000 shippers and moving more than 500000 shipments a year.

Meanwhile C.H. Robinson had ventured overseas with the launch of its international division in 1989. It entered Mexico in 1990 and added airfreight operations and international freight forwarding through the 1992 purchase of C.S. Green International. In 1993 C.H. Robinson picked up a 30% stake in French motor carrier Transeco (acquiring the rest later) and opened offices in Mexico Chile and Venezuela.

The company went public in 1997 and became C.H. Robinson Worldwide (CHRW). The next year Verdoorn who was CEO assumed the additional role of chairman. The following year the company acquired Argentina's Comexter transportation group to gain market share in South America and it expanded its European operation in 1999 through the purchase of Norminter a French third-party logistics provider. Much closer to home CHRW bought Eden Prairie-based Preferred Translocation Systems a logistics provider to LTL carriers and Chicago-based transportation provider American Backhaulers.

In 2000 CHRW partnered with PaperExchange.com Inc. the global e-business marketplace for the pulp and paper industry to provide an exclusive logistics service to PaperExchange.com members. CHRW continued to expand in 2002 with the purchase of Miami-based Smith Terminal Transportation Services. Verdoorn stepped down as CEO that year and company president John Wiehoff was promoted to replace him. Verdoorn retired at the end of 2006 and Wiehoff succeeded him as chairman.

The company acquired three US-based produce sourcing and marketing companies –FoodSource Inc. FoodSource Procurement and Epic Roots –in 2004 for a reported $270 million. That year CHRW added seven offices in China by acquiring a Dalian-based freight forwarder and in 2005 it gained operations in Germany Italy and the US by buying two freight forwarding companies Hirdes Group Worldwide and Bussini Transport. Also in 2005 CHRW bought US-based freight broker Payne Lynch & Associates as well as an India-based freight forwarder Triune. The following year (2006) the company acquired US-based LXSI Services a specialist in domestic airfreight and expedited ground transportation management that had gross revenue of about $25 million.

In mid-2008 CHRW acquired Transera International Holdings a project forwarding business based in Canada. Transera has office locations in Canada Dubai Singapore and the US and has annual revenues of about $125 million.

In 2009 the company purchased London-based Walker Logistics Overseas an international freight forwarder serving primarily the electronics telecommunications medical sporting goods and military industries. The acquisition expanded its capabilities in Asia-to-Europe trade and brought two key distribution gateways –London and Amsterdam. CHRW then expanded its produce distribution business even further in 2009 by opening a European-based produce sourcing company in France which will focus on bringing fresh produce from France Italy and Spain to North and South America Europe Asia and Middle Eastern countries. That same year CHRW acquired certain assets of International Trade & Commerce (ITC) a US customs brokerage company that specializes in warehousing distribution and services between the US and Mexico. Also in 2009 the company bought Rosemont Farms as well as Quality Logistics which provides logistics for produce transportation; both companies are based in Florida.

In 2010 CHRW expanded its transportation management services to India by building a new facility and control tower operations. The India-based facility was established to serve customers in South and Southeast Asia as well as in Pakistan and the Middle East.

EXECUTIVES

Treasurer Tax Director and Assistant Secretary, Troy A. Renner, age 47
SVP and CFO, Chad M. Lindbloom, age 47, $260,000 total compensation
Chairman President and CEO, John P. Wiehoff, age 50, $400,000 total compensation
VP and CIO, Thomas K. (Tom) Mahlke, age 40
VP, Timothy P. (Tim) Manning, age 47
SVP Transportation, Mark A. Walker, age 54, $200,000 total compensation
SVP Transportation, Scott A. Satterlee, age 43, $200,000 total compensation
VP, Molly M. DuBois, age 41
VP Investor Relations and Public Affairs, Angela K. (Angie) Freeman, age 44
SVP Produce, James P. (Jim) Lemke, age 45, $200,000 total compensation
VP Human Resources, Laura Gillund, age 51
SVP Transportation, James E. (Jim) Butts, age 56, $200,000 total compensation
VP, Steven M. (Steve) Weiby, age 45
Director, David W. (Dave) MacLennan, age 53
VP, Christopher J. (Chris) O'Brien, age 44
President T-Chek, Bryan D. Foe, age 44

VP, Daniel W. Ryan, age 39
VP General Counsel and Secretary, Ben G. Campbell, age 46
Manager Public Relations, Mike Wilken
VP, Scott A Shannon
VP, Mac S. Pinkerton
Director, Wayne M. Fortun, age 63
Director, Michael W. (Mike) Wickham, age 65
Director, Robert (Bob) Ezrilov, age 67
Director, James B. (Jim) Stake, age 59
Director, Brian P. Short, age 62
Director, David W. (Dave) MacLennan, age 53
Director, ReBecca (Becky) Koenig Roloff, age 57
Director, Scott P. Anderson, age 46
Auditors: Deloitte&ToucheLLP

LOCATIONS

HQ: C.H. Robinson Worldwide Inc.
14701 Charlson Rd., Eden Prairie MN 55347-5088
Phone: 952-937-8500 **Fax:** 952-937-6714
Web: www.chrobinson.com

2011 Sales

	$ mil.	% of total
US	9,488	92
Other countries	848	8
Total	**10,336**	**100**

PRODUCTS/OPERATIONS

2011 Sales

	$ mil.	% of total
Transportation	8,740	85
Sourcing	1,535	15
Payment services	60	-
Total	**10,336**	**100**

Selected Services

Air
Intermodal
Less-than-truckload
Logistics
- Customs brokerage
- Transportation management services
- Warehousing services

Ocean
Truckload

COMPETITORS

ALC
APL Logistics
BNSF Logistics
Cass Information Systems
CEVA Logistics
Chiquita Brands
Comdata
CorTrans Logistics
DHL
Dole Food
Exel
Expeditors
FedEx Trade Networks
Fresh Del Monte Produce
Greatwide Logistics
Hub Group
J.B. Hunt
Kuehne + Nagel International
Landstar Inway
Menlo Worldwide
MIQ Logistics
Pacer Transportation Solutions
Panalpina
Penske Truck Leasing
Ryder System
Schneider Logistics
TLC
Transplace
UPS Supply Chain Solutions

HISTORICAL FINANCIALS

Company Type: Public

Income Statement

FYE: December 31

	REVENUE ($ mil.)	NET INCOME ($ mil.)	NET PROFIT MARGIN	EMPLOYEES
12/11	10,336	431	4.2%	8,353
12/10	9,274	387	4.2%	7,628
12/09	7,577	360	4.8%	7,347
12/08	8,578	359	4.2%	7,961
12/07	7,316	324	4.4%	7,332
Annual Growth	9.0%	7.4%	—	3.3%

2011 Year-End Financials

Debt ratio: —
Return on equity: 34.57%
Cash ($ mil.): 373
Current ratio: 183.83
Long-term debt ($ mil.): —
No. of shares (mil.): 163
Dividends
Yield: —
Payout: 45.80%
Market value ($ mil.): 11,405

	STOCK PRICE ($) FY Close	P/E High/Low		PER SHARE ($) Earnings	Dividends	Book Value
12/11	69.78	31	24	2.62	0.00	7.64
12/10	80.19	34	22	2.33	1.04	7.25
12/09	58.73	29	18	2.13	0.97	6.46
12/08	55.03	32	19	2.08	0.90	6.50
12/07	54.12	30	23	1.86	0.76	6.10
Annual Growth	6.6%	—	—	8.9%	—	5.8%

Rock-Tenn Co.

A rock-solid reputation? You betcha. One of North America's containerboard giants Rock-Tenn produces packaging for food hardware apparel and other consumer goods. Its lineup includes recycled and bleached paperboard containerboard consumer and corrugated packaging and point-of-purchase displays. Specialty paperboard is also converted into book cover and laminated paperboard and sold to other manufacturers for such applications as furniture storage and automotive components. Rock-Tenn in mid-2011 significantly expanded when it acquired former corrugated packaging and paperboard competitor Smurfit-Stone now known as RockTenn CP LLC.

Rock-Tenn has realigned its operations into three business segments: Corrugated Packaging (50% of total sales); Consumer Packaging (43%); and Recycling and Waste Solutions (7%). This last segment consists of Rock-Tenn's recycled fiber brokerage and collection operations.

The company owns about 160 facilities and leases about 75 worldwide. These facilities are located in Argentina Canada Chile China Puerto Rico and 38 US states.

Rock-Tenn's landmark purchase of rival Smurfit-Stone was valued at almost $5 billion in a deal that included cash stock and Smurfit-Stone debt. The transaction positioned Rock-Tenn as the second largest producer of containerboard (used to make shipping boxes) in North America. With approximately 9.4 million tons of mill capacity it ranks second behind International Paper. Moreover Smurfit-Stone's operations extended Rock-Tenn's reached to the Midwest and West Coast enabling it to capitalize on demand for containerboard as the recession's hangover diminished.

Purchasing Smurfit-Stone also skyrocketed Rock-Tenn's 2011 revenues to historic levels. From 2010 to 2011 the company's total sales surged by almost 80% from $3 billion to $5.4 billion —a milestone high. On the flip side Rock-Tenn's profits declined by around 37% from $225 million to $141 million. The company also assumed about $1.2 billion in Smurfit-Stone's debt and as of September 2011 Rock-Tenn's total debt hovered at around $3.4 billion.

Rock-Tenn previously purchased Innerpac Holding Company for $23.9 million in fall 2010. The deal gave Rock-Tenn a larger piece of the corrugated and specialty partition market as well as greater control over its own supply chain.

HISTORY

Former preacher Arthur Morris founded Rock-Tenn in 1936 as Southern Box Co. a folding carton maker. Acquisitions fueled the company's growth in the following years. During WWII it became Rock City Box Co. Morris' son-in-law Worley Brown was appointed CEO in 1967.

The company adopted its current name in 1973 after merging with Tennessee Paper Mills. Rock-Tenn bought Mead's recycled products unit in 1988 and began book cover production. Brad Currey a banker who was recruited by Brown in 1976 became CEO in 1989.

Rock-Tenn bought a folding carton plant in Canada in 1993 and in 1994 the company went public. It acquired Olympic Packaging (folding cartons) and Alliance Display & Packaging (corrugated displays) in 1995. The company boosted its position as a leading maker of folding cartons in 1997 with its $414 million purchase of Waldorf Corporation its largest acquisition to date. That year Rock-Tenn also bought two paperboard companies and formed RTS Packaging its 65%-owned joint venture with Sonoco Products.

To cut costs and compensate for stagnant demand Rock-Tenn closed several US plants in 1999. The following year CEO Brad Currey retired and was replaced by Jim Rubright formerly an EVP at energy firm Sonat (El Paso Energy). Also in 2000 Rock-Tenn entered the gypsum paperboard liner business through a joint venture with Lafarge. In 2001 the company announced additional plant closings as demand for its products bottomed out.

In 2002 in a rebounding market Rock-Tenn bought point-of-purchase display and fixture maker Athena Industries increasing annual sales by an estimated $12 million.

Pactiv purchased Rock-Tenn's packaging business in 2003 for about $60 million. The next year Rock-Tenn acquired a corrugated sheet facility located in Athens Alabama from Menasha Packaging Company. That move was part of an effort to expand its geographic reach. In 2005 the company acquired pulp and packaging assets from Gulf States Paper (now The Westervelt Company).

In 2007 the consumer packaging segment grew when Rock-Tenn picked up its remaining 40% interest in Fold-Pak (formerly GSD Packaging) giving Rock-Tenn a 100% stake in the food container maker a relatively recession-proof business. In 2008 Rock-Tenn obtained Southern Container for around $850 million. The New York-based private containerboard and corrugated packaging manufacturer operated one mill eight corrugated box plants two sheet plants and four graphics facilities. Its capacity boosted Rock-Tenn's annual bleached and recycled paperboard production to some 2.4 million tons.

During the recession Rock-Tenn cut costs by consolidating its operations into large plants that capitalize on economies of scale via optimized equipment and capacity usage. From 2007 to 2010 three folding carton plants were shuttered two sheet plants and certain assets at a corrugated graphics subsidiary a laminated paperboard converting facility a drum manufacturing operation and two interior packaging plants.

The company made perhaps the most important acquisition in its history in May 2011 when it purchased rival Smurfit-Stone later rebranding it as RockTenn CP. Rock-Tenn shelled out almost $5 billion (which included cash stock and Smurfit-Stone debt) for the deal.

EXECUTIVES

President Corrugated Packaging and Recycling, James B. (Jim) Porter III, age 61, $521,375 total compensation
EVP Specialty Paperboard Products, Richard E. (Dick) Steed
EVP CFO and Chief Administrative Officer, Steven C. (Steve) Voorhees, age 57, $407,500 total compensation
EVP General Counsel and Secretary, Robert B. (Bob) McIntosh, age 54, $305,000 total compensation
Chairman and CEO, James A. (Jim) Rubright, age 65, $981,250 total compensation
Chief Accounting Officer, A. Stephen (Steve) Meadows, age 62
SVP Coated Mill Operations, Thomas M. (Tom) Stigers
President Consumer Packaging, Michael E. (Mike) Kiepura, age 55, $450,000 total compensation
SVP and Senior Environmental Counsel, Nina E. Butler
SVP and General Manager Corrugated Container, Steven C. (Steve) Strickland, age 60
EVP and General Manager Recycled Fiber Division, Erik Deadwyler
SVP Employee Services, Jennifer Graham-Johnson
SVP Six Sigma, George W. Turner
SVP and Treasurer, John D. Stakel
SVP and CIO, Paul W. Stecher
SVP and General Manager Containerboard Mills, Michael P. (Mike) Exner, age 58
EVP and General Manager Merchandising Displays, Craig A. Gunckel
President and CEO RTS Packaging, Alan P. Bosma
VP Procurement Safety and Health, Gregory L. (Greg) King
SVP Engineering, John O. Telesca
Director, Robert M. (Bob) Chapman, age 59
Director, Ralph F. Hake, age 63
Director, John W. Spiegel, age 70
Director, Bettina M. Whyte, age 63
Director, G. Stephen Felker, age 61
Director, Timothy J. Bernlohr, age 53
Director, Terrell K. (Terry) Crews, age 57
Director, Lawrence L. Gellerstedt III, age 56
Director, Robert B. Currey, age 71
Director, J. Powell Brown, age 44
Director, James E. Young, age 62
Director, Russell M. Currey, age 50
Auditors: Ernst&YoungLLP

LOCATIONS

HQ: Rock-Tenn Company
504 Thrasher St., Norcross GA 30071
Phone: 770-448-2193 **Fax:** 678-291-7666
Web: www.rocktenn.com

PRODUCTS/OPERATIONS

2011 Sales

Corrugated Packaging	2,687	50
Total	**5,399**	**100**

Selected Products

Packaging products
- Folding cartons (for food items hardware products paper goods and other items)
- Protective packaging (solid fiber partitions)

Paperboard
- 100% recycled coated and uncoated grades
- Laminated paperboard (for book covers book binders and furniture products)

Specialty corrugated packaging and displays
- Corrugated packaging and sheet
- Point-of-purchase displays

COMPETITORS

Caraustar
Clearwater Paper
Georgia-Pacific
Graphic Packaging Holding
Green Bay Packaging
International Paper
Kapstone Paper and Packaging
Shorewood Packaging
Sonoco Products
Temple-Inland

HISTORICAL FINANCIALS

Company Type: Public

Income Statement FYE: September 30

	REVENUE ($ mil.)	NET INCOME ($ mil.)	NET PROFIT MARGIN	EMPLOYEES
09/12	9,207	249	2.7%	26,300
09/11	5,399	141	2.6%	26,600
09/10	3,001	225	7.5%	10,400
09/09	2,812	222	7.9%	10,300
09/08	2,838	81	2.9%	10,700
Annual Growth	34.2%	32.1%	—	25.2%

2012 Year-End Financials

Debt ratio: 31.93%
Return on equity: 7.31%
Cash ($ mil.): 37
Current ratio: 155.49
Long-term debt ($ mil.): 3,151
No. of shares (mil.): 70
Dividends
Yield: —
Payout: 23.19%
Market value ($ mil.): 5,116

	STOCK PRICE ($) FY Close	P/E High/Low		PER SHARE ($) Earnings	Dividends	Book Value
09/12	72.18	21	13	3.45	0.00	48.05
09/11	48.68	28	17	2.77	0.80	47.85
09/10	49.81	10	7	5.70	0.60	26.00
09/09	47.11	9	4	5.75	0.40	20.07
09/08	39.98	21	10	2.14	0.40	16.75
Annual Growth	15.9%	—	—	12.7%	—	30.1%

Rockwell Automation, Inc.

Rockwell Automation only rocks to the scintillating sounds of its control products. The company is one of the world's largest industrial automation companies serving automotive food and beverage (including dairy) personal care life sciences oil and gas mining and paper and pulp markets. Rockwell's control products & solutions unit makes industrial automation products such as motor starters and contactors relays timers signaling devices and variable-speed drives. To complement its automation product offerings its architecture & software unit offers factory management software and motion control sensors and machine safety components. Rockwell Automation makes about half of its sales in the US.

HISTORY

Rockwell Automation is the legacy of two early-20th-century entrepreneurs: Willard Rockwell and Clement Melville Keys. Rockwell gained control in 1919 of Wisconsin Parts Company an Oshkosh Wisconsin maker of automotive axles. He went on to buy a number of industrial manufacturers merging them in 1953 to create Rockwell Spring & Axle. Renamed Rockwell-Standard in 1958 it led the world in the production of mechanical automotive parts by 1967.

In 1928 Keys founded North American Aviation (NAA) as a holding company for his aviation interests. General Motors bought NAA in 1934 and named James Kindelberger as its president. The company moved in 1935 from Maryland to Inglewood California where it built military training planes.

NAA made more than 15000 AT-6 trainers during WWII and it produced the B-25 bomber and the P-51 fighter planes. By the end of the war NAA had built almost 43000 aircraft more than any other US manufacturer. NAA's sales plunged at the end of WWII. In 1948 GM took its subsidiary public; Kindelberger revitalized the company with new factories in California and Ohio. Major products included the F-86 (1948) and its successor the F-100 (1953). NAA also produced the X-15 rocket plane (1959).

In the 1960s NAA built rocket engines and spacecraft for the Apollo program. NAA merged with Rockwell-Standard creating North American Rockwell in 1967. The company adopted the Rockwell International name in 1973.

Rockwell won the contract for the B-1 bomber in 1970 and the space shuttle orbiter in 1972. The following year it bought Collins Radio the backbone of its avionics segment. Rockwell briefly ventured into consumer goods buying Admiral (appliances) in 1974 and selling it in 1979.

The company bought Allen-Bradley (industrial electronics) in 1985. Facing declining military-related revenues as B-1 production ended Don Beall who became CEO in 1988 spent billions on modernizing plants and research and development for Rockwell's electronics and graphics units. In 1989 Rockwell sold its Measurement & Flow Control Division and bought the Baker Perkins printing machinery business in the UK.

Rockwell sold its fiber-optic transmission equipment unit to Alcatel (now Alcatel-Lucent) in 1991. It acquired industrial automation supplier Sprecher + Schuh in 1993 and Reliance Electric (which was merged with Allen-Bradley) in 1995. The next year Rockwell sold its aerospace and defense divisions to Boeing for $3.2 billion and its Graphic Systems business to investment firm Stonington Partners. It also acquired integrated circuit maker Brooktree Corp. in 1996.

A 1997 federal court order forced Rockwell to pay Celeritas Technologies nearly $58 million for breaching patent protections and misappropriating trade secrets related to computer and cell phone communication technology. That year Rockwell acquired Hughes Electronics' airline passenger communications and entertainment systems unit (now The DIRECTV Group) and it spun off its automotive unit as Meritor Automotive (now ArvinMeritor). President Don Davis also became CEO in 1997.

Rockwell spun off its sluggish semiconductor business to shareholders (as Conexant Systems) in 1998 in a move to cut losses and focus on its faster-growing industrial automation operations. The company recorded a fiscal 1998 loss in part from restructuring costs.

In 1999 Rockwell moved its headquarters from California to Milwaukee the base of its automation division. That year the company's Rockwell Collins unit bought out Kaiser Aerospace and Electronics' interest in their avionics joint venture Flight Dynamics. Rockwell also sold its business that made large power transformers for electric utilities to SPX. Rockwell agreed in 2000 to buy K Systems for about $300 million. Later that year it announced plans to spin off its Rockwell Collins avionics and communications unit to its shareholders. The spinoff was completed in July 2001. Concurrently Rockwell International changed its name to Rockwell Automation to reflect its new focus.

Rockwell parted company with its computer telephony (FirstPoint) and its large power transformer operations. Rockwell's journey from a defense company to an automation specialist was completed when it spun off its avionics and communications unit Rockwell Collins to shareholders.

Davis stepped down as CEO in 2004 and was replaced by Keith Nosbusch who also took on the chairman's role the following year. Nosbusch was in charge of Control Systems from 1998 until he was named president and CEO.

In 2007 the company sold most of the operations of its former power systems unit which offered motors and motor repair services as well as bearings bushings clutches and brakes. Rockwell sold its Dodge mechanical power transmission division as well as the industrial motors unit of its Reliance Electric subsidiary to Baldor Electric (now a part of ABB) for $1.8 billion. (Rockwell retained the rest of Reliance which makes electrical drives.) These units made up most of the company's power systems business segment which previously accounted for about a fifth of Rockwell's revenue — that is about a billion dollars.

Internationally Rockwell Automation bought UK firm Industrial Control Services (ICS Triplex) in 2007 to help expand its control products & solutions unit. The following year it purchased three companies that helped strengthen its product portfolio in automation and enterprise intelligence software.

Additionally it purchased CEDES Safety & Automation (machine safety products) as well as software makers Incuity Software (factory control systems) and Pavilion Technologies (process control systems) in 2008. All three deals helped strengthen its product portfolio in automation and enterprise intelligence software.

Rockwell Automation acquired certain assets and liabilities in 2009 of Xi'an Hengsheng Science & Technology to advance its global footprint and to better serve its customers in China. That same year Rockwell bought a majority stake in the North American assets of Rutter Hinz a Canadian engineering firm and a subsidiary of Rutter Inc. The deal adds engineering expertise in industrial automation process control and power distribution specifically for the oil and gas industry.

In 2010 the company teamed up with FANUC subsidiary Fanuc FA (factory automation) a programmable automation controller (PAC) to integrate CNC and PAC systems.

EXECUTIVES

Chairman CEO and President, Keith D. Nosbusch, age 61, $993,962 total compensation
VP and General Tax Counsel, Kent G. Coppins, age 58
SVP General Counsel and Secretary, Douglas M. Hagerman, age 50, $484,093 total compensation
SVP Global Sales and Marketing, John P. McDermott, age 53, $436,699 total compensation
President Asia Pacific, Robert A. (Bob) Ruff, age 63, $499,425 total compensation
VP and General Auditor, A. Lawrence Stuever, age 59
SVP and CFO, Theodore D. (Ted) Crandall, age 57, $532,544 total compensation
SVP Strategic Development, Steven A. (Steve) Eisenbrown, age 58, $526,673 total compensation
SVP Human Resources, Susan J. Schmitt, age 48
Director External Communications, John A. Bernaden
VP and General Manager Power Control Business, Michael (Mike) Laszkiewicz
VP and General Manager Manufacturing and Process Solutions Business, Terry Gebert
SVP Advanced Technology and CTO, Sujeet Chand, age 53
VP and Treasurer, Steven W. Etzel, age 51
SVP Operations and Engineering Services, Martin (Marty) Thomas, age 53
Director Marketing Rockwell Automation America, Ninveh Neuman
President Europe Middle East and Africa, Hedwig Maes
President Latin American Region, Bob Becker
VP North America Sales Global Sales and Marketing, Lee Tschanz
SVP Control Products and Solutions, Blake Moret
SVP Architecture and Software, Frank Kulaszewicz
Director, Steven R. Kalmanson, age 59
Director, James P. (Jim) Keane, age 52
Director, Donald R. Parfet, age 59
Director, William T. McCormick Jr., age 67
Director, Betty C. Alewine, age 63
Director, Verne G. Istock, age 71
Director, David B. Speer, age 60
Director, Barry C. Johnson, age 68
Auditors: Deloitte&ToucheLLP

LOCATIONS

HQ: Rockwell Automation, Inc.
1201 South Second Street, Milwaukee, WI 53204
Phone: 414 382-2000
Web: www.rockwellautomation.com

2011 Sales

	$ mil.	% of total
US	2,917	49
Europe Middle East & Africa	1,267	21
Asia/Pacific	910	15
Latin America	508	8
Canada	396	7
Total	**6,000**	**100**

PRODUCTS/OPERATIONS

2011 Sales

	$ mil.	% of total
Control products & solutions	3,406	57
Architecture & software	2,594	43
Total	**6,000**	**100**

Selected Mergers & Acquisitions

FY2012
SoftSwitching Technologies (Middleton Wisconsin; provider of industrial power quality detection and protection systems)

FY2011
Lektronix (Cannock UK; provider of electric motor drives industrial computers and computerized numerical control equipment
Hiprom (Johannesburg South Africa; global mining equipment)

Selected Products and Services

Condition sensors
Drive systems
Motion control systems
Motor control centers
Motor starters
PlantPAx Process Automation System
Push buttons
Relays
Signaling devices
Software (Rockwell Software)
Termination and protection devices
Timers

COMPETITORS

ABB
Danaher
Dematic GmbH
Eaton
Emerson Electric
FANUC
Hitachi
Honeywell ACS
Invensys
Metso
Mitsubishi Corp.
OMRON
Schneider Electric
Select Business Solutions
Siemens AG
Toshiba
Weiss Instrument
Wonderware
Yokogawa Electric

HISTORICAL FINANCIALS

Company Type: Public

Income Statement — FYE: September 30

	REVENUE ($ mil.)	NET INCOME ($ mil.)	NET PROFIT MARGIN	EMPLOYEES
09/12	6,259	737	11.8%	22,000
09/11	6,000	697	11.6%	21,000
09/10	4,857	464	9.6%	19,000
09/09	4,332	220	5.1%	19,000
09/08	5,697	577	10.1%	21,000
Annual Growth	2.4%	6.3%	—	1.2%

2012 Year-End Financials

Debt ratio: 18.84%
Return on equity: 39.80%
Cash ($ mil.): 903
Current ratio: 221.17
Long-term debt ($ mil.): 905
No. of shares (mil.): 139
Dividends
Yield: —
Payout: 34.02%
Market value ($ mil.): 9,723

	STOCK PRICE ($) FY Close	P/E High	P/E Low	PER SHARE ($) Earnings	Dividends	Book Value
09/12	69.55	16	10	5.13	0.00	13.25
09/11	56.00	20	11	4.80	1.48	12.32
09/10	61.73	19	12	3.22	1.22	10.31
09/09	42.60	29	11	1.55	1.16	9.26
09/08	37.34	19	9	3.90	1.16	11.79
Annual Growth	16.8%	—	—	7.1%	—	3.0%

Rockwell Collins, Inc.

Rockwell Collins a spinoff of Rockwell Automation makes aviation electronics and communication equipment for commercial and military aircraft. The company boasts that nearly every commercial cockpit contains something made by Rockwell Collins. It also provides flight simulation and training MRO services navigation and surveillance systems. The company has two primary segments: Commercial Systems (avionics and in-flight entertainment systems for commercial aircraft) and government systems (airborne/ground/shipboard communication systems with military applications and overhaul services). Serving more than two dozen countries Rockwell Collins makes about 70% of its sales in the US.

Geographic Reach

Rockwell Collins has some 20 plants in the US as well as plants in France Germany Mexico and the UK. The company operates engineering facilities sales offices warehouses and service outlets in about 20 countries.

Operations

The government systems segment provides products for a variety of uses but they all have the common theme of design for use under rugged conditions constrained by challenges in relation to size weight and power. These products include satellite communications systems handheld navigation devices flight controls helmet-mounted displays and training systems.

The company's commercial systems segment provides systems and products for the original manufacturing retrofitting and upgrading of aircraft. Products include the Pro Line Fusion integrated avionics system cabin management systems head-up guidance systems primary actuation systems and simulators for crew training. The segment serves a range of customers from the biggest aircraft makers in the world to owners of individual aircraft. Aftermarket products are sold through distributors and to regional airline operators.

Both segments use an internal sales force to market products worldwide. The US government accounts for 43% of sales. Though these segments serve a diverse base of customers with a varied portfolio of products the company uses a shared services operating platform that consolidates resources to develop products in both of its segments.

Financial Analysis

Year-over-year 2011 sales increased 4% thanks mainly to a surge in sales for commercial systems which was enough to compensate for a decline in sales for government systems. Net income was up 13%. The company as a whole enjoyed an operating cash flow of $657 million from sales of more than $4.8 billion.

Government systems' year-over-year sales decreased 2%. Sales for the segment's avionics business went up 3% thanks to healthy sales of the E-6 special mission aircraft program the KC-46A Tanker program and rotary wing avionics. Communications products sales fell 7% due to less demand for satellite communication products as the US government delayed funding and an upgrade program was completed. Struggling with lower demand for iForce public safety vehicle systems and soldier system optronics products surface solutions went down 8%. Navigation products slipped 3% amid lower demand for GPS-based products. The segment accounts for 59% of sales.

Year-over-year 2011 sales rose 13% for commercial systems. Air transport aviation electronics sales soared 9% thanks in part to strong demand from Boeing for the 787 and 747-8 aircraft. Business and regional aviation electronics surged 17% supported by sales to Bombardier and Cessna.

The company is leveraging its research development engineering and product design expertise. Its investment in R&D was more than 18% of sales in 2011. R&D is expected again to be about 18% of sales in 2012.

Strategy

Joint ventures are an important element of the company's strategy for growth. It maintains 50-50 JVs with BAE Systems for Data Link Solutions (serving the worldwide data link market); Elbit Systems for Vision Systems International (helmet-mounted cueing systems for the military fixed-wing market); Honeywell International for Integrated Guidance Systems (weapons guidance and navigation products); Quadrant Group for Quest Flight Training (aircrew training for the UK Ministry of Defense).

The company anticipates a slight decline for its government systems segment but is more optimistic about commercial systems in 2012 when a year-over-year increase of 2% to 4% is expected. Compensating for the decline in sales for government systems that is attributable to cuts in the US defense budget Rockwell Collins has initiated cost-savings measures and a restructuring plan that matches resources more optimally for the new defense landscape.

One advantage and risk of the company's standard operating procedure is the fixed-price contract which accounts for about 90% of sales. This practice creates costs savings but it can also bring cost overruns if initial cost estimates prove to be wrong.

HISTORY

From 2008 to 2010 Rockwell Collins made four acquisitions that helped preserve its technological leadership. SEOS a display system designer for commercial/military simulators was picked up late 2008 to augment the flight training segment. Earlier in the year Rockwell Collins expanded its unmanned aerial vehicles (UAVs) lineup by purchasing Athena Technologies a provider of flight control and navigation systems for UAVs for $107 million. Mid-2009 Rockwell Collins ramped up its networked communications offerings by acquiring DataPath. The $130 million deal garnered experience in developing satellite-based communications systems for military and commercial customers. In 2010 the company purchased Houston-based AR (Air Routing) Group and its related companies. A business aircraft trip support-company Air Routing offers Rockwell Collins' customers a single hub for weather information flight planning services and fuel preparations; it also enhances the company's aftermarket services.

The company purchased Computing Technologies for Aviation (CTA) in early 2011. CTA which provides flight operations management for corporate and other aviation customers bolsters the Commercial Systems' flight information offerings. Hard on its heels Rockwell Collins acquired Blue Ridge Simulation. Blue Ridge Simulation specializes in advanced sensor simulation for US defense agencies and commercial and international training exercises. The lineup which runs from weather radar simulators to complex simulators for surveillance and fire control adds a sensor simulation capability to Rockwell Collins' slate of training services.

EXECUTIVES

Chairman and CEO, Clayton M. (Clay) Jones, age 62, $1,022,538 total compensation

VP; General Manager Communications Products Government Systems, Robert P. (Bob) Haag, age 44

SVP e-Business, John-Paul E. (J. P.) Besong, age 59

EVP and COO Commercial Systems, Kent L. Statler, age 46, $480,278 total compensation

EVP International and Service Solutions, Gregory S. (Greg) Churchill, age 54, $540,777 total compensation

President, Robert K. (Kelly) Ortberg, age 51, $521,101 total compensation

SVP Corporate Development, Barry M. Abzug, age 60

SVP and CFO, Patrick E. Allen, age 48, $492,020 total compensation

SVP General Counsel and Secretary, Gary R. Chadick, age 51, $397,115 total compensation

SVP Washington Operations, Robert A. (Bobby) Sturgell, age 53

SVP Human Resources, Ronald W. (Ron) Kirchenbauer, age 65

SVP Operations, Bruce M. King

VP; General Manager Surface Solutions Government Systems, Glen T. (Tommy) Dodson

VP Media Relations, Pam J. Tvrdy

SVP Engineering and Technology, Nan Mattai, age 60

VP; General Manager Air Transport Systems Commercial Systems, Jeffrey A. (Jeff) Standerski

VP; General Manager Business and Regional Systems Commercial Systems, Greg Irmen

VP; General Manager Information Management Systems Commercial Systems, Stephen J. (Steve) Timm

VP; Managing Director Asia Pacific International and Service Solutions, Thud Chee (TC) Chan

VP; General Manager Service Solutions International and Service Solutions, Scott R. Gunnufson

VP; General Manager Simulation and Training Solutions Government Systems, LeAnn Ridgeway

VP; Managing Director Americas International and Service Solutions, Thierry Tosi

VP Investor Relations, Steve Buesing

VP; General Manager Mobility and Rotary Wing Solutions Government Systems, David J. (Dave) Nieuwsma

VP; General Manager Cabin and ElectroMechanical Systems Commercial Systems, David S. Austin

VP; Managing Director Europe Middle East and Africa International and Service Solutions, Claude Alber

EVP and COO Government Systems, Philip J. Jasper

Director, Anthony J. Carbone, age 70

Director, David Lilley, age 65

Director, Andrew J. Policano, age 62

Director, Chris A. Davis, age 61

Director, Donald R. Beall, age 73

Director, Gen. Ralph E. (Ed) Eberhart, age 65

Director, Cheryl L. Shavers, age 57

Director, Jeffrey L. (Jeff) Turner, age 60

Auditors: Deloitte&ToucheLLP

LOCATIONS

HQ: Rockwell Collins Inc.
400 Collins Rd. NE, Cedar Rapids IA 52498
Phone: 319-295-1000 **Fax:** 319-295-1523
Web: www.rockwellcollins.com

2011 Sales

	$ mil.	% of total
US	3,356	70
Europe	848	18
Asia/Pacific	267	5
Canada	241	5
Africa/Middle East	54	1
Latin America	40	1
Total	4,806	100

PRODUCTS/OPERATIONS

2011 Sales

	$ mil.	% of total
Government systems		
Avionics	1,434	30
Communication products	698	15
Surface solutions	377	8
Navigation products	304	6
Commercial systems		
Air transport aviation electronics	1,049	22
Business & regional aviation electronics	944	19
Total	**4,806**	**100**

2011 Sales by Product

	$ mil.	% of total
Products	4,223	88
Services	583	12
Total	**4,806**	**100**

Selected Products and Services

Government/Defense (airborne and surface)
- Cockpit display
- Communications
- Engineering services
- Flight deck subsystems
- Maintenance repair parts and after-sales support
- Military data link
- Navigation (including radio navigation)
- Simulation and training

Commercial (air transport aviation electronics and business and regional aviation electronics)
- Communications
- Electro-mechanical
- Information management
- Integrated avionics (Pro Line Fusion)
- Integrated cabin electronics
- Maintenance repair parts and after-sales support services
- Navigation
- Simulation and training
- Surveillance

COMPETITORS

BAE SYSTEMS
Ball Corp.
Boeing
CAE Inc.
Chemring
DRS Technologies
Esterline
Exelis
General Dynamics
Harris Corp.
Honeywell Aerospace
L-3 Communications
Meggitt
Northrop Grumman
Panasonic Avionics
Radiall
Raytheon
Smiths Group
Thales
Trimble Navigation
ViaSat

HISTORICAL FINANCIALS

Company Type: Public

Income Statement

FYE: September 30

	REVENUE ($ mil.)	NET INCOME ($ mil.)	NET PROFIT MARGIN	EMPLOYEES
09/12	4,726	609	12.9%	19,000
09/11	4,806	634	13.2%	20,500
09/10	4,665	561	12.0%	20,000
09/09	4,470	594	13.3%	19,300
09/08	4,769	678	14.2%	20,300
Annual Growth	(0.2%)	(2.6%)	—	(1.6%)

2012 Year-End Financials

Debt ratio: 14.66%
Return on equity: 48.37%
Cash ($ mil.): 335
Current ratio: 193.54
Long-term debt ($ mil.): 779
No. of shares (mil.): 142
Dividends
Yield: —
Payout: 26.02%
Market value ($ mil.): 7,628

	STOCK PRICE ($) FY Close	P/E High/Low		PER SHARE ($) Earnings	Dividends	Book Value
09/12	53.64	14	11	4.15	0.00	8.85
09/11	52.76	16	11	4.06	0.96	9.94
09/10	58.25	19	13	3.52	0.96	9.45
09/09	50.80	14	7	3.73	0.96	8.22
09/08	48.09	18	11	4.16	0.80	8.88
Annual Growth	2.8%	—	—	(0.1%)	—	(0.1%)

Ross Stores, Inc.

Ross wants to let you dress (and lots more) for less. A leading off-price apparel retailer (behind TJX Cos. and Kohl's) Ross operates about 1125 Ross Dress for Less and dd's DISCOUNTS stores that sell mostly closeout merchandise including men's women's and children's clothing at prices well below those of department and specialty stores. While apparel accounts for about 50% of sales Ross also sells small furnishings toys and games luggage and jewelry. Featuring the Ross "Dress for Less" trademark the chain targets 18- to 54-year-old white-collar shoppers from primarily middle-income households. Ross and dd's stores are located in strip malls in some 30 states mostly in the western US and Guam.

Operations

dd's DISCOUNTS (launched in 2004) serves one of the fastest-growing demographic markets in the US. The ultra-low-price spinoff which offers brand-name apparel at a 20%-70% discount has grown to number about 90 locations in seven states including big ones such as California Florida and Texas. The stores which average 22700 square feet are located in strip shopping centers in urban and suburban neighborhoods.

Geographic Reach

More than a quarter of Ross Stores are in California where discount department store operator Kohl's is expanding rapidly after acquiring about 30 stores that once belonged to defunct discount retailer Mervyn's. On the East Coast Ross opened a new 1.3-million-sq.-ft. distribution center in South Carolina to support its growth in the southeastern US.

Financial Analysis

The fast-growing chain saw its fiscal 2012 (ends January) sales increase more than 9% vs. the prior year while net income grew by 18% over the same period. Same-store sales increased 5% following 5% and 6% increases in fiscal 2011 and 2010 respectively. Ross has seen its sales jump a robust 44% to $8.6 billion in fiscal 2012 from $5.9 billion in fiscal 2008.

Strategy

Ross Stores' off-price business model appears to be just the right fit for both during and after the recession. Amid strong sales the retailer is adding stores. Over the past four years the company has added about 235 new locations including many dd's DISCOUNTS shops. New markets for the retailer include Illinois and the District of Columbia. Indeed it entered Illinois in a big way in October 2011 with 12 stores in the Chicago area. Going forward the company plans to continue adding stores in existing markets while opening Ross and dd's stores in new markets. To boost its relationships with suppliers Ross does not require them to provide markdown/promotional allowances or return privileges. This combined with opportunistic purchases (closeouts such as manufacturer overruns and canceled orders) allows the company to obtain large discounts on merchandise. As a result Ross Stores' customers typically pay 20% to 60% less than department and specialty store prices. Ross holds down costs by offering minimal service and few frills inside its stores.

Ownership

The investment firm FMR LLC owns about 14% of the company's shares.

HISTORY

In 1957 the Ross family founded Ross Stores and opened its first junior department store; by 1982 there were six of the stores in the San Francisco area. That year two retailing veterans Stuart Moldaw (founder of Country Casuals and The Athletic Shoe Factory) and Donald Rowlett (creator of Woolworth's off-price subsidiary J. Brannam) led the acquisition of the company. Moldaw (chairman) and Rowlett (president) wanted to create an off-price chain in California where –despite the success such endeavors were having in the rest of the country –such stores were largely absent. The duo intended to establish a foothold by saturating California markets before competitors muddied the waters.

They restocked the stores with brand-name men's women's and children's apparel shoes accessories and domestics merchandise at reduced prices. Before the end of 1982 they opened two more Ross "Dress for Less" stores; the next year 18 more were added including the chain's first non-California store in Reno Nevada (much of the chain's expansion came through the acquisition of existing strip mall stores). Another 40 stores were added in 1984.

The company went public in 1985 to help fund its expansion and extended its reach to include Colorado Florida Georgia New Mexico and Oregon; that year it opened 41 stores. In 1986 39 new stores were opened including locations in Maryland North Carolina and Virginia though the company was forced to close 25 unprofitable stores primarily in recession-hammered Texas and Oklahoma. Ross lost more than $41 million for the year and the honeymoon was over.

Rowlett resigned in 1987 and company veteran Norman Ferber was soon named CEO. Ross opened only 11 stores that year all of which were located in markets the company had already broached. It also decided to focus its expansion efforts in three markets: the West Coast; the Washington DC area; and Florida. On the merchandise side housewares were dropped and cosmetics fragrances and high-end clothing were added. Ross returned to the black in 1987 posting an $11 million profit. The company continued refining its merchandising strategy and by 1989 it had more than 150 stores making it one of the largest off-price retailers.

Ross opened 72 stores between 1990 and 1992 bringing its total to more than 220 stores as sales passed the $1 billion mark. Ferber became chairman in 1993 and continued to focus the company on existing markets. The chain grew to more than 290 stores by the end of 1995. VP Michael Balmuth was named CEO the next year.

The company's buying department had more than tripled in size by 1998 allowing it to have buyers in the right place at the right time to take advantage of buying opportunities. The non-apparel business tripled during the same time both keys to the retailer's success. That year Ross added fine jewelry maternity wear sporting goods small furnishings and educational toys to its list of product offerings. With its stock price sagging in late 1998 Ross began a $120 million stock repurchase program in 1999. After repurchasing 5.4 million shares of its stock the company pledged to continue the program through 2001. Ross opened 30 stores in 1999; its 34 openings in 2000 included its first non-US store in Guam.

In 2001 the company entered new markets in Georgia Montana North Carolina South Carolina and Wyoming and opened new stores in existing markets for a total of 45 new stores.

Ross opened 60 new stores in 2002 and closed five others followed in 2003 by 61 new stores some of which were in new markets such as Louisiana and Tennessee.

In August 2004 Ross opened its first three dd's DISCOUNTS stores in Vallejo San Leandro and Fresno California. The retailer moved its headquarters from Newark California to Pleasanton in mid-2004 and then sold the Newark property for about $17 million.

The company opened 10 dd's DISCOUNTS stores and about 75 Ross stores in 2005. Ross Stores also purchased a 685000-sq. ft. warehouse in Moreno Valley California that year.

The retailer's deal with supermarket operator Albertsons inked in late 2006 fueled its 2007 expansion plans and secured 46 Albertsons stores located in Arizona California Colorado Florida Oklahoma and Texas. dd's DISCOUNTS expanded beyond California in 2007 with its first stores in Arizona Florida and Texas.

dd's Discounts entered two new markets –Georgia and Nevada –in 2010. In fiscal 2012 the chain entered Arkansas Illinois and the District of Columbia.

EXECUTIVES

SVP Supply Chain, Michael L. Wilson
President and Chief Development Officer, James S. Fassio, age 57, $600,259 total compensation
Group SVP and CFO, John G. Call, age 53, $493,787 total compensation
Chairman, Norman A. Ferber, age 63
Vice Chairman and CEO, Michael A. Balmuth, age 61, $1,054,614 total compensation
President and Chief Merchandising Officer Ross Dress for Less, Barbara Rentler, age 54, $818,334 total compensation
SVP Human Resources, D. Jane Marvin
EVP Stores and Loss Prevention, Gary L. Cribb, age 47
SVP General Counsel and Corporate Secretary, Mark LeHocky
President and Chief Merchandising Officer dd?s DISCOUNTS, Douglas (Doug) Baker, age 53
SVP and General Merchandise Manager, Carl Matteo
President and COO, Michael B. O'Sullivan, age 48, $711,944 total compensation
Group EVP Merchandising Ross Home Men's and Children's, Lisa Panattoni, age 49, $748,420 total compensation
EVP Supply Chain and Allocation and CIO, Michael K. (Mike) Kobayashi
SVP Merchandise Control, Art Roth
EVP Strategy Marketing and Human Resources, Ken Caruana
EVP Merchandising, Jennifer Vecchio, age 47
SVP and General Merchandise Manager, Robert J. Bernard, age 57
SVP Stores, Mary Walter
EVP Merchandising, Bernie Brautigan
SVP and General Merchandise Manager, Anthony J. DiElsi
Senior Director Investor Relations, Bobbi Chaville
SVP Planning, Lisa Albani
SVP and General Merchandise Manager, Pamela Smith
SVP and General Merchandise Manager, Angela Culhane
SVP and General Merchandise Manager, Susanne DeMarco
SVP Property Development, Gregg McGillis
SVP and General Merchandise Manager, Joyce Pearson
EVP Merchandising, Dan Cline
SVP and General Merchandise Manager, Debra Branco
SVP and General Merchandise Manager, Meg Newhouse-Sealove
Director, Gregory L. (Greg) Quesnel, age 63
Director, George P. Orban, age 66
Vice Chairman and CEO, Michael A. Balmuth, age 61
Director, Sharon D. Garrett, age 63
Director, Donald H. (Don) Seiler, age 83
Director, Michael J. Bush, age 51
Director, K. Gunnar Bjorklund, age 52
Auditors: Deloitte&ToucheLLP

LOCATIONS

HQ: Ross Stores, Inc.
4440 Rosewood Drive, Pleasanton, CA 94588-3050
Phone: 925 965-4400
Web: www.rossstores.com

2012 Stores

	No.
US	
California	290
Texas	173
Florida	138
Arizona	59
Georgia	46
Pennsylvania	37
Washington	37
North	33
Virginia	33
Colorado	29
Nevada	26
Oregon	26
Tennessee	25
South	20
Maryland	19
Oklahoma	19
Alabama	18
Utah	15
Hawaii	13
Illinois	12
Louisiana	12
New	10
Idaho	9
New	8
Montana	6
Mississippi	5
Arkansas	2
Wyoming	2
Delaware	1
District of	1
Guam	1
Total	**1,125**

PRODUCTS/OPERATIONS

2012 Stores

	No.
Ross Dress for	1,037
dd's	88
Total	**1,125**

2012 Sales

	% of total
Women's	29
Home accents bed &	25
Accessories lingerie fine jewelry &	13
Men's	13
Shoes	12
Children's	8
Total	**100**

Selected Merchandise

Bed and bath
Children' s apparel
Cookware
Educational toys
Fine jewelry
Fragrances
Gourmet foods
Home accents
Ladies' apparel
- Accessories
- Dresses
- Junior
- Lingerie
- Maternity
- Misses sportswear
- Petites
- Women' s World

Luggage
Men' s apparel
- Traditional men' s
- Young men' s

Shoes
Small electronics
Small furnishings
Sporting goods and exercise equipment

COMPETITORS

Ascena Retail
Big Lots
Burlington Coat Factory
Cato
Charming Shoppes
Family Dollar Stores
Fred' s
J. C. Penney
Kmart
Kohl' s
Men' s Wearhouse
Sears
Target Corporation
TJX Companies
Wal-Mart

HISTORICAL FINANCIALS

Company Type: Public

Income Statement

FYE: January 28

	REVENUE ($ mil.)	NET INCOME ($ mil.)	NET PROFIT MARGIN	EMPLOYEES
01/12	8,608	657	7.6%	53,900
01/11	7,866	554	7.1%	49,500
01/10	7,184	442	6.2%	45,600
01/09*	6,486	305	4.7%	40,000
02/08	5,975	261	4.4%	39,100
Annual Growth	9.6%	26.0%	—	8.4%

*Fiscal year change

2012 Year-End Financials

Debt ratio: 4.54%
Return on equity: 44.02%
Cash ($ mil.): 649
Current ratio: 142.96
Long-term debt ($ mil.): 150
No. of shares (mil.): 226
Dividends
Yield: —
Payout: 15.38%
Market value ($ mil.): 11,590

	STOCK PRICE ($) FY Close	P/E High/Low		PER SHARE ($) Earnings	Dividends	Book Value
01/12	51.09	32	16	2.86	0.00	6.58
01/11	65.46	28	19	2.32	0.00	5.64
01/10	45.93	27	16	1.77	0.00	4.71
01/09*	29.42	35	19	1.17	0.00	3.91
02/08	29.89	36	22	0.95	0.00	3.62
Annual Growth	14.3%	—	—	31.7%	—	16.1%

*Fiscal year change

Ryder System, Inc.

When it comes to commercial vehicles and distribution Ryder System wants to be the designated driver. The company's Fleet Management Solutions segment acquires manages maintains and disposes of fleet vehicles for commercial customers. Similarly the Supply Chain Solutions segment provides logistics and supply chain services from industrial start (raw material supply) to finish (product distribution). Ryder also offers Dedicated Contract Carriage service by supplying trucks drivers and management and administrative services to customers on a contract basis. Ryder's worldwide fleet of more than 195900 vehicles ranges from tractor-trailers to light-duty trucks.

HISTORY

Ryder Truck Rental founded in Miami by Jim Ryder in 1933 was the first truck leasing company in the US. It rented trucks in four southern states until 1952 when it bought Great Southern Trucking (renamed Ryder Truck Lines) doubling its size. In 1955 the year it went public as Ryder System Ryder bought Carolina Fleets (a South Carolina trucking company) and Yellow Rental (a northeastern leasing service). More purchases over the next decade extended its truck rental business across the US and into Canada. Ryder Truck Lines was sold to International Utilities in 1965.

After establishing One-Way truck rental services for self-movers in 1968 the company entered several new markets including new automobile transport (1968) truck driver and heavy-equipment operator training (1969) temporary services (1969) insurance (1970) truck stops (1971) and oil refining (1974).

Leslie Barnes the former president of Allegheny Airlines (later part of US Airways) replaced Jim Ryder as CEO in 1975 and sold the oil refinery and other company assets by the end of the year.

Anthony Burns Ryder's president became CEO in 1983. Burns sold Ryder's truck stops (1984) and through 65 acquisitions moved the firm into aviation sales and service (1982) freight hauling (1983) aircraft leasing (1984) aircraft engine overhauling (1985) and school busing (1985). By 1987 Ryder was the US leader in truck leasing and automobile hauling the world's #1 non-airline provider of aviation maintenance and parts and second only to Canada's Laidlaw in school bus fleet management.

Ryder sold its freight hauling business and most of its insurance interests in 1989. Responding to the weak economy and financial turmoil in the airline industry the company began withdrawing from its aircraft operations in 1991 with the discontinuation of its leasing business. Unfortunately the company's name was linked to two tragedies in the 1990s: Ryder trucks were used in the 1993 World Trade Center terrorist bombing in New York and the 1995 bombing of the Oklahoma City federal building.

To expand its logistics capabilities Ryder acquired LogiCorp in 1994 and bought two UK logistics businesses from FedEx. But the consumer truck rental unit once a bright spot on the balance sheet was dragging down earnings. Ryder sold its bright yellow trucks in 1996 to investor group Questor Partners. (Budget Group which bought the business in 1998 was licensed to use the "Ryder" brand. However Ryder and Budget reached an agreement in 2002 to terminate the license.)

In 1997 Ryder sold its faltering automotive carrier business to industry leader Allied Holdings. The next year Ryder bought Companhia Transportadora e Comercial Translor a leading logistics company in Brazil.

Burlington Northern Santa Fe SVP Gregory Swienton became Ryder's president and COO in 1999; Burns remained chairman and CEO. That year as part of the long restructuring initiative Ryder sold its school-bus unit to UK-based FirstGroup for $940 million.

Burns retired as CEO in 2000 remaining chairman and Swienton took over. Also that year Ryder established TTR Logistics a joint venture with Toyota Tsusho America to provide Toyota and other Japanese auto companies with logistics and transportation services.

In 2001 the company established an Asia/Pacific headquarters with its acquisition of Singapore-based Ascent Logistics.

In 2003 Ryder added to its fleet support services operations when it acquired Vertex Services a Houston-based fuel storage tank management company.

Early in 2004 Ryder strengthened its rental fleet with the acquisition of privately owned General Car and Truck Leasing System based in Davenport Iowa; the acquisition included 4200 vehicles and 15 service locations. Later that year Ryder acquired Ruan Leasing Company a truck rental and service company located in Des Moines Iowa.

It purchased Canadian transportation and supply chain management provider Pollock NationaLease in 2007. Among its purchases in 2008 Ryder bought Lily Transportation and Pennsylvania-based Gordon Truck Leasing; both are regional full-service truck leasing firms. Also in 2008 Ryder picked up Gator Leasing and its fleet of approximately 2300 vehicles thereby extending its network service in Florida.

In late 2008 Ryder added Transpacific Container Terminal Ltd. and CRSA Logistics Ltd. which included CRSA Logistics' operations in Hong Kong and Shanghai China. These investments strengthened Ryder's role in moving commerce to and from North America and Asia. To further its role in import/export services Ryder entered into a joint venture with Cargo Services Far East Limited a logistics solutions provider based in Asia. Also in 2008 the company launched its RydeGreen Hybrid medium-duty straight truck line which offers reduced fuel consumption and emissions. In addition to the lease offering a limited supply of RydeGreen trucks are made available to commercial customers in the US.

Looking to the Northeast US for growth Ryder purchased Connecticut-based Edart Leasing in early 2009; the deal gives Ryder coverage throughout Connecticut Massachusetts and New Jersey.

EXECUTIVES

President Global Supply Chain Solutions, John H. Williford, age 55, $525,000 total compensation
Chairman and CEO, Gregory T. (Greg) Swienton, age 62, $900,000 total compensation
EVP and CFO, Art A. Garcia, age 51
President and COO, Robert E. Sanchez, age 46, $410,000 total compensation
VP Corporate Communications, David Bruce
EVP and Chief Adminsitrative Officer, Gregory F. (Greg) Greene, age 52
Director Corporate Communications, Lisa B. Hagen
EVP Chief Legal Officer and Secretary, Robert D. (Bob) Fatovic, age 46, $337,000 total compensation
President Global Fleet Management Solutions, Dennis C. Cooke, age 48
VP Investor Relations and Public Affairs, Robert (Bob) Brunn
Senior Analyst Corporate Communications, Marilu Del Toro
Director, James S. (Jim) Beard, age 71
Director, John M. Berra, age 64
Director, Eugene A. (Gene) Renna, age 67
Director, Hansel E. Tookes II, age 64
Director, Lynn M. Martin, age 72
Director, Abbie J. Smith, age 58
Director, L. Patrick (Pat) Hassey, age 66
Director, Luis P. (Lou) Nieto Jr., age 57
Director, E. Follin Smith, age 52
Director, Robert J. Eck, age 54
Auditors: PricewaterhouseCoopersLLP

LOCATIONS

HQ: Ryder System Inc.
11690 NW 105th St., Miami FL 33178
Phone: 305-500-3726 **Fax:** 305-500-3203
Web: www.ryder.com

2011 Sales

	$ mil.	% of total
US	5,075	84
Canada	481	8
UK/Germany	324	5
Mexico	147	3
Asia	21	-
Total	**6,050**	**100**

PRODUCTS/OPERATIONS

2011 Sales

	$ mil.	% of total
Fleet management solutions	4,218	66
Supply chain solutions	1,605	25
Dedicated contract carriage	600	9
Adjustments	(373.9)	-
Total	**6,050**	**100**

Selected Services

Fleet Management Solutions
- Commercial rental
- Contract maintenance
- Full service leasing
- Used vehicles

Supply Chain Solutions
- Distribution management
- Transportation management

Dedicated Contract Carriage

COMPETITORS

Arkansas Best
Barloworld Handling
C.H. Robinson Worldwide
Con-way Inc.
FedEx
J.B. Hunt
Landstar System
Penske Truck Leasing
Schenker Inc.
Schneider National
Trailer Fleet Services
UniGroup
UPS
YRC Worldwide

HISTORICAL FINANCIALS

Company Type: Public

Income Statement FYE: December 31

	REVENUE ($ mil.)	NET INCOME ($ mil.)	NET PROFIT MARGIN	EMPLOYEES
12/11	6,050	169	2.8%	27,500
12/10	5,136	118	2.3%	25,900
12/09	4,887	61	1.3%	22,900
12/08	6,203	199	3.2%	28,000
12/07	6,566	253	3.9%	28,800
Annual Growth	(2.0%)	(9.6%)	—	(1.1%)

2011 Year-End Financials

Debt ratio: 44.40%
Return on equity: 12.88%
Cash ($ mil.): 104
Current ratio: 92.70
Long-term debt ($ mil.): 3,107
No. of shares (mil.): 51
Dividends
Yield: —
Payout: 34.15%
Market value ($ mil.): 2,718

	STOCK PRICE ($) FY Close	P/E High/Low	PER SHARE ($) Earnings	Dividends	Book Value
12/11	53.14	18 11	3.28	0.00	25.77
12/10	52.64	23 14	2.25	1.04	27.44
12/09	41.17	42 17	1.11	0.96	26.71
12/08	38.78	21 8	3.52	0.92	24.17
12/07	47.01	13 9	4.24	0.84	32.52
Annual Growth	3.1%	— —	(6.2%)	—	(5.7%)

Ryerson Holding Corp

LOCATIONS

HQ: Ryerson Holding Corp
227 W. Monroe, 27th Floor, Chicago, IL 60606
Phone: 312 292-5000

HISTORICAL FINANCIALS

Company Type:

Income Statement

FYE: December 31

	REVENUE ($ mil.)	NET INCOME ($ mil.)	NET PROFIT MARGIN	EMPLOYEES
12/11	4,729	(8)	—	4,000
12/10	3,895	(104)	—	4,200
12/09	3,066	(190)	—	0
12/08	5,309	32	0.6%	0
Annual Growth	(3.8%)	—	—	—

2011 Year-End Financials

Debt ratio: 64.68%
Return on equity: 987650001000000.00%
Cash ($ mil.): 61
Current ratio: 247.27
Long-term debt ($ mil.): 1,264
No. of shares (mil.): 5
Dividends
Yield: —
Payout: —
Market value ($ mil.): —

S & T Bancorp, Inc. (Indiana, PA.)

S&T Bancorp is the bank holding company for S&T Bank which serves customers from some 60 branch offices in western Pennsylvania. Targeting individuals and local businesses the bank offers such standard retail products as checking savings and money market accounts; CDs; and credit cards. Business loans including commercial mortgages make up about three-fourths of the company's loan portfolio; the bank also originates residential mortgages construction loans and consumer loans. Through subsidiaries S&T Bank sells life disability and property/casualty insurance; provides investment management services; and manages the Stewart Capital Mid Cap Fund.

The company's greater dependence on commercial real estate loans (nearly half of its loan portfolio) during the recession exposed it to larger credit risks loan charge-offs and nonperforming loans. Although revenues remained rather steady net income plummeted some 97% in 2009. As the economy began showing signs of recovery the following year though so did S&T Bancorp. A substantial drop in loan loss provisions and net charge-offs helped the company improve results. However a smaller loan portfolio and new regulations limiting service fees cut into the company's earnings overall in 2011. Although both interest and noninterest revenues shrunk 8% that year to $209.1 million net income grew 9% to $47.3 million (though still short of the $60.2 million it netted in 2008).

Its rebound has been not only attributable to the strengthening economy but also to a new strategy which was designed to return the company to higher performance levels. S&T refocused its efforts on all of its main business lines: banking credit insurance and investments. The company also also began to focus on market-specific needs by creating six geographic divisions. By introducing new mobile banking products and pushing for increased electronic delivery of its services the bank has also saved a significant amount of money.

Retaining customers and attracting new ones is another way S&T has grown deposits. The company seeks to expand organically and through acquisitions. It added some 10 offices to its network when it bought fellow western Pennsylvania bank IBT Bancorp in 2008 and added another eight branches in central Pennsylvania through the 2012 acquisition of Mainline Bancorp. S&T now plans to acquire Gateway Bank which will add two branches in the greater Pittsburgh area.

EXECUTIVES

SEVP and Chief Administrative Officer Market Sales Bank Operations and Corporate Technology, David P. Ruddock, age 50
SEVP and COO, Edward C. Hauck, age 59, $275,000 total compensation
Chairman S&T Bancorp and S&T Bank, James C. Miller, age 66, $178,004 total compensation
Manager Employee Services, D. Kathleen (Kathi) Greenwell
President CEO and Director S&T Bancorp and S&T Bank, Todd D. Brice, age 49, $375,000 total compensation
SVP Retail Banking, Richard A. (Rich) Fiscus
SEVP and CFO, Mark Kochvar, age 51
SEVP and Chief Lending Officer, David G. Antolik, age 45, $240,000 total compensation
EVP; Managing Director S&T Insurance Group, Thomas E. Kiral, age 51
President and Chief Investment Officer Stewart Capital Advisors, Malcolm E. Polley, age 49
VP and Sr. Financial Officer, Tim McKee
EVP Commercial Lending, Michelle Petrovsky, age 45
SVP Marketing, G. Robert (Rob) Jorgenson Jr.
SVP Banking Operations, Robert E. Werner
VP and Relationship Manager Wealth Management Group, Dennis E. Hunt
EVP Chief Risk Officer and Secretary, Ernest J. Draganza
SVP Commercial Lending, Stephen A. (Steve) Drahnak
SVP Commercial Lending, Michael J. (Mike) Settimio
SVP Commercial Lending S&T Bank, Richard J. (Dick) Scholton
SVP, Wendy Bell, age 48
SVP Commercial Lending, Richard C. Black
VP and Senior Portfolio Manager Wealth Management, Charles G. Frank
VP and Wealth Management Adviser S&T Bank, Shannon Rummell
SVP and Deputy Chief Credit Officer, William (Bill) Kametz
SVP and Manager Consumer and Business Suport Center, William C. (Bill) Jones
Director, David L. Krieger, age 68
President CEO and Director S&T Bancorp and S&T Bank, Todd D. Brice, age 49
Director, Thomas A. Brice, age 72
Director, James L. Carino, age 79
Director, Jeffrey D. Grube, age 58
Director, Joseph A. Kirk, age 72
Director, William J. Gatti, age 70
Director, Ruth M. Grant, age 80
Director, Charles A. Spadafora, age 70
Director, John J. Delaney, age 70
Director, Michael J. Donnelly, age 54
Director, Frank W. Jones, age 67
Director, Alan Papernick, age 74
Director, Charles G. Urtin II, age 65
Director, Robert Rebich Jr., age 70
Director, James V. Milano, age 52
Director, John N. Brenzia
Director, Christine J. Toretti
Auditors: KPMGLLP

LOCATIONS

HQ: S&T Bancorp Inc.
800 Philadelphia St., Indiana PA 15701
Phone: 724-349-1800 **Fax:** 724-465-6874
Web: www.stbank.com

PRODUCTS/OPERATIONS

2011 Sales

	$ mil.	% of total
Interest		
Loans including fees	154	74
Investment securities & other	11	5
Noninterest		
Debit & credit card fees	10	5
Service charges on deposit accounts	9	5
Insurance fees	8	4
Wealth management fees	8	4
Other	6	3
Adjustments	(0.1)	-
Total	**209**	**100**

Selected Subsidiaries

9th Street Holdings Inc.
Commonwealth Trust Credit Life Insurance Company (50%)
S&T Bank
  S&T Insurance Group LLC
    S&T-Evergreen Insurance LLC
  S&T Bancholdings Inc.
  S&T Professional Resources Group LLC
  S&T Settlement Services LLC
  Stewart Capital Advisors LLC

COMPETITORS

AmeriServ Financial
F.N.B. (PA)
Fidelity Bancorp (PA)
First Commonwealth Financial
Northwest Bancshares
PNC Financial
RBS Citizens Financial Group

HISTORICAL FINANCIALS

Company Type: Public

Income Statement FYE: December 31

	ASSETS ($ mil.)	NET INCOME ($ mil.)	INCOME AS % OF ASSETS	EMPLOYEES
12/11	4,119	47	1.1%	909
12/10	4,114	43	1.1%	936
12/09	4,170	7	0.2%	937
12/08	4,438	60	1.4%	963
12/07	3,421	56	1.6%	806
Annual Growth	4.8%	(4.2%)	—	3.1%

2011 Year-End Financials

Debt ratio: 2.97%
Return on equity: 9.64%
Cash ($ mil.): 270
Current ratio: —
Long-term debt ($ mil.): 122
No. of shares (mil.): 28
Dividends
Yield: —
Payout: 42.55%
Market value ($ mil.): 550

	STOCK PRICE ($) FY Close	P/E High/Low		PER SHARE ($) Earnings	Dividends	Book Value
12/11	19.55	17	11	1.41	0.00	17.44
12/10	22.59	19	12	1.34	0.60	20.70
12/09	17.01	507	154	0.07	0.92	19.94
12/08	35.50	17	11	2.28	1.24	16.24
12/07	27.64	16	12	2.26	1.21	13.75
Annual Growth	(8.3%)	—	—	(11.1%)	—	6.1%

Safeway Inc.

For many Americans "going to Safeway" is synonymous with "going to the grocery store." Safeway is one of North America's largest food retailers with some 1675 stores located mostly in the western Midwestern and mid-Atlantic regions of the US as well as western Canada. It also operates regional supermarket companies including The Vons Companies (primarily in Southern California) Dominick's Finer Foods (Chicago) Carr-Gottstein Foods (Alaska's largest retailer) Genuardi's Family Markets (eastern US) and Randall's Food Markets (Texas). Safeway owns grocery e-retailer GroceryWorks.com. Outside the US Safeway owns 49% of Casa Ley which operates about 185 food and variety stores in western Mexico.

HISTORY

Founded in 1914 by Sam Seelig Safeway had grown to about 300 stores in California and Hawaii by 1926. That year investment banker Charles Merrill one of the founders of Merrill Lynch bought Safeway. Merrill convinced M. B. Skaggs –of the famous grocery retailing Skaggs family –to become president and his brother L. S. Skaggs (founder of what became American Stores) became VP. M. B. merged his 430 or so Skaggs stores with Safeway and took the Safeway name.

Safeway bought Arizona Grocery Piggly Wiggly Pacific and Eastern Stores in 1928 and Piggly Wiggly Western States a grocer operating in California Texas and Nevada in 1929. Two years later the chain had its greatest number of stores (3527); this number was reduced as smaller stores were converted into larger supermarkets. In addition the company expanded internationally into western Canada the UK and Australia. Peter Magowan grandson of Merrill became chairman and CEO in 1980. (His father Robert Magowan ran the chain for about 15 years.) The company acquired 49% of Mexican retailer Casa Ley in 1981. Safeway sold its Australian and German operations four years later.

In 1986 Safeway received an unsolicited buyout bid from the Dart Group. In response Peter and takeover specialist Kohlberg Kravis Roberts (KKR) took Safeway private in a leveraged deal; Dart made a $159 million profit on its shares. Saddled with debt in 1987 and 1988 the company sold more than 1350 stores. Included in that number were 162 Southern California stores (sold to The Vons Companies in exchange for stock) and about 120 stores in the UK to food and beverage company Argyll Group (now Safeway plc). A slimmer Safeway reemerged as a public company in 1990.

Steven Burd became president in 1992 and CEO the next year. He has played hardball with the unions representing about 90% of Safeway's employees. In 1995 with 87 stores in Alberta Canada he replaced 4000 full-time union employees with part-time workers a move that saved the company $40 million. Burd also reduced corporate and store staff consolidated distribution centers and restructured the debt left over from the 1986 LBO.

The cost-cutting moves enabled Safeway to cut prices which in turn reversed declines in the chain's market share. However labor disputes including strikes and lockouts in Colorado and Canada (which closed 86 stores for 40 days) cut into the company's improving sales and earnings numbers during 1996 and 1997.

Safeway acquired the rest of Vons it didn't already own in 1997. Burd took over the title of chairman from the retiring Peter the next year. Late in 1998 Safeway acquired the Dominick's Supermarkets chain. The acquisitions continued in 1999 when the grocer bought Alaska's top food retailer Carr-Gottstein Foods. It also acquired the Texas-based 115-store Randall's Food Markets (largely owned by KKR).

In 2000 Safeway bought a majority stake in GroceryWorks.com. Also that year KKR reduced its stake in Safeway to less than 5%.

The grocer completed its acquisition of Genuardi's Family Markets a chain of about 40 supermarkets in Pennsylvania Delaware and New Jersey in February 2001. Later that month Safeway purchased 11 ABCO Desert Markets in Arizona. In June its GroceryWorks subsidiary got a $22 million infusion when Tesco the world leader in online grocery sales acquired a 35% stake in it. Safeway announced ambitious expansion plans in October; it said it would build 80-85 new stores in 2002 and complete some 250 remodels.

In January 2002 Safeway launched Safeway.com its Internet grocery shopping and delivery service to consumers in the Portland and Vancouver Washington areas. In November Safeway decided to sell its 113-store Dominick's grocery store chain and exit the Chicago market. Safeway booked a net loss of about $828 million in 2002 thanks to write downs at Dominick's and its faltering Texas division Randall's.

The retailer expanded Safeway.com in July 2003 to the Seattle metro area its eighth online market in the western US. In September the company launched Rancher's Reserve its store-brand beef in Safeway's biggest product launch in some 20 years.

A four-and-a-half month strike by grocery workers in Safeway's second-largest market Southern California affecting nearly 300 Safeway-owned Vons and Pavilions stores ended in March 2004. The dispute pitted workers' demands for generous health care benefits against Safeway's drive to cut costs and remain profitable in the face of mounting competition particularly from non-unionized Wal-Mart. The strike took its toll on Safeway's bottom line causing a $103 million loss during the fourth quarter. However Safeway achieved a key goal: the establishment of a two-tier pay and benefits scheme under which new hires will receive substantially less in wages and benefits than veteran employees. Later in the month Safeway named Robert L. Edward as its new CFO succeeding Vasant Prabhu who left the company to become CFO at Starwood Hotels & Resorts Worldwide.

Several public pension funds including the nation's two largest (California Public Employees' Retirement System and the New York State fund) agitated for the ouster of Burd citing the purchase of Dominick's and steep losses from the five-month Southern California grocery strike among Burd's missteps. Yielding to pressure from shareholders Safeway shook up its board of directors to include more (eight of nine) independent members. Soon after Burd survived a shareholder vote attempting to uncouple his dual roles of chairman and CEO.

The grocery chain separated the non-perishables side of marketing in November 2004 into five distinct business groups (with full financial accountability for sales profit promotion and product strategy) and named Frank Calfas president of Safeway's marketing operations. In December the grocery chain settled a lawsuit filed in June 2004 by the California attorney general alleging that Safeway sold tobacco products to minors at its Pack N' Save Pavilions Safeway and Vons stores. Safeway agreed to pay $245000 and instruct cashiers to ask for proof of age among other measures.

In 2005 Safeway launched the "O Organics" line of more than 150 organic products including bread cereal coffee frozen foods milk and more. In Texas where Safeway stores are struggling the company closed 26 stores –including 16 Randall's locations –in 2005. Safeway ended the year with 458 Lifestyle stores accounting for 26% of its total store count.

Safeway purchased the rest of GroceryWorks from its partner in the online venture UK-based Tesco in October 2006 boosting its stake from 56% in the online grocery seller to 100% ownership. The move anticipated Tesco's entry into the Southern California and Phoenix markets.

In June 2007 Safeway opened its first freestanding restaurant called Citrine in Redwood City California. Also that year Safeway's Blackhawk subsidiary acquired San Diego-based EWI Holdings a provider of prepaid payment processing technology and services.

The grocery chain announced the formation in April 2008 of the Better Living Brands Alliance a vehicle managed by Safeway subsidiary Lucerne Foods to market its in-house O Organics and Eating Right brands across all retail channels including foodservice operators and overseas.

2009 was "very difficult year" for Safeway according to CEO Burd. Indeed the chain posted a $1 billion loss following a $1.8 billion goodwill impairment charge. Sales fell 7.4%.

EXECUTIVES

SVP Finance and Control and Chief Accounting Officer, David F. Bond, age 58

SVP Real Estate and Engineering, Donald P. Wright, age 59, $351,000 total compensation

SVP Finance and Investor Relations, Melissa C. Plaisance, age 52

SVP and CIO, David T. Ching, age 59
EVP; President Safeway Health, Larree M. Renda, age 53, $670,465 total compensation
SVP Secretary General Counsel and Chief Governance Officer, Robert A. Gordon, age 60, $526,860 total compensation
Chairman and CEO, Steven A. (Steve) Burd, age 62, $1,449,000 total compensation
President and CFO, Robert L. Edwards, age 56, $638,305 total compensation
SVP Strategic Initiatives Health Initiatives and Reengineering, Kenneth M. Shachmut, age 63
SVP Human Resources, Russell M. Jackson, age 54
EVP Retail Operations, Bruce L. Everette, age 60, $638,471 total compensation
President Denver Division, Scott Grimmett
VP Lifestyle, Anthony Gilmore, age 50
President Marketing, Michael R. (Mike) Minasi
President Non-Perishables, David M. Lee
President Lifestyle, Rojon D. Hasker, $354,000 total compensation
President Seattle Division, Gregory A. (Greg) Sparks
President The Vons Companies, Thomas C. (Tom) Keller
President Canada Safeway, Chuck Mulvenna
President Portland and Seattle Divisions, Steven R. (Steve) Frisby
President Northern California Division, Karl Schroeder
COO Safeway.com, Dave Lauffer
SVP Planning and Business Development, David R. Stern, age 57
VP Investor Relations, Julie Hong
EVP and Chief Marketing Officer, Diane M. Dietz, age 45, $670,001 total compensation
SVP Pharmacy, David J. (Dave) Fong
SVP Meat and Seafood, Mike McGinnis
President Phoenix Division, Daniel J. (Dan) Valenzuela
SVP Supply Operations, Jerry Tidwell, age 60
Director Supplier Diversity, Tim Williams
Corporate VP Public Affairs, Brian Dowling
Group VP Retail Initiatives, Henry A. (Hank) Cominiello
VP and Treasurer, Brad Fox
Manager Diversity Initiatives and Community Relations Eastern Division, Clarence Lewis
SVP and Group General Manager Meals and Dry Grocery, Jim Lewis
SVP and Group General Manager Dairy Refrigerated and Frozen Foods, Henry Michon
SVP and Group General Manager Home Care and General Merchandise, Bob Shelton
SVP Marketing Planning, Carl Graziani
Chairman Casa Ley S.A. De C.V. (Mexico), Juan Manuel Ley Lopez
SVP Internal Audit, John A. Lewis
President Merchandising, Kelly Griffith
President Eastern Division, Steve Neibergall
President and General Manager Perishables, Thomas L. (Tom) Schwilke
Director Risk Management Strategies, Roy Franco
VP, Rick Pickering
SVP Consumer Brands, Joseph (Joe) Ennen
Director Corporate Public Affairs, Teena Massingill
SVP Government Relations Public Affairs Corporate Social Responsibility and Philanthropy, Jonathan Mayes, age 54
President Texas Division, Paul McTavish
President Customer Loyalty and Digital Technologies, Mir Aamir
SVP Pharmacy Health and Wellness, Darren Singer
Assistant VP Legal, Valerie D. Lewis
Acting President Dominick's Finer Foods, Brian Baer
Director, Frank C. Herringer, age 69
Director, T. Gary Rogers, age 70
Director, William Y. (Bill) Tauscher, age 62
Director, Paul M. Hazen, age 70
Director, Mohanbir S. Gyani, age 60
Director, Arun Sarin, age 57
Director, Michael S. Shannon, age 53
Director, Janet E. Grove, age 61
Director, Kenneth Oder, age 64
Auditors: Deloitte&ToucheLLP

LOCATIONS

HQ: Safeway Inc.
5918 Stoneridge Mall Rd., Pleasanton CA 94588-3229
Phone: 925-467-3000 **Fax:** 925-467-3323
Web: www.safeway.com

2011 Sales

	$ mil.	% of total
US	36,923	85
Canada	6,707	15
Total	**43,630**	**100**

2011 Stores by Division

	No.
Southern California	277
Northern	268
Canada	225
Seattle (includes	199
Eastern	155
Denver	137
Phoenix	114
Portland	113
Texas (Randall's & Tom	111
Chicago	76
Total	**1,678**

2011 Manufacturing & Processing Plants

	US	Canada
Milk	6	3
Bakery	6	2
Soft drink bottling	4	
Ice cream	2	2
Fruit & vegetable processing	1	3
Cake commissary	1	-
Cheese & meat packaging -	1	
Sandwich commissary -	1	
Total	**20**	**12**

PRODUCTS/OPERATIONS

2011 Sales

	$ mil.	% of total
Non-perishables	17,512	40
Perishables	15,899	36
Pharmacy	3,874	9
Fuel	4,596	11
Other	1,746	4
Total	**43,630**	**100**

COMPETITORS

Acme Markets
Ahold U.S.A.
Albertsons
Bashas'
BJ' s Wholesale Club
Comerci
Costco Wholesale
CVS Caremark
Fiesta Mart
Giant Food
GNC
H-E-B
IGA
Katz Group
Kroger
Loblaw
Meijer
Overwaitea
PETCO
Raley' s
Rite Aid
Sam' s Club
Save Mart
Smart & Final
Sobeys
Soriana
Stater Bros.
SUPERVALU
Target Corporation
Tesco
Trader Joe' s
Unified Grocers
Wal-Mart
Wal-Mart de Mexico
Walgreen
Wegmans
Whole Foods
WinCo Foods

HISTORICAL FINANCIALS

Company Type: Public

Income Statement

FYE: December 31

	REVENUE ($ mil.)	NET INCOME ($ mil.)	NET PROFIT MARGIN	EMPLOYEES
12/11*	43,630	516	1.2%	178,000
01/11	41,050	589	1.4%	180,000
01/10	40,850	(1,097)	—	186,000
01/09	44,104	965	2.2%	197,000
12/07	42,286	888	2.1%	201,000
Annual Growth	0.8%	(12.7%)	—	(3.0%)

*Fiscal year change

2011 Year-End Financials

Debt ratio: 35.89%
Return on equity: 14.03%
Cash ($ mil.): 729
Current ratio: 83.10
Long-term debt ($ mil.): 4,569
No. of shares (mil.): 296
Dividends
Yield: —
Payout: 37.25%
Market value ($ mil.): 6,240

	STOCK PRICE ($) FY Close	P/E High	P/E Low	PER SHARE ($) Earnings	Dividends	Book Value
12/11*	21.04	17	11	1.49	0.00	12.42
01/11	22.49	17	12	1.55	0.00	13.57
01/10	21.29	—	—	(2.66)	0.00	12.74
01/09	24.05	15	8	2.21	0.00	15.82
12/07	34.95	19	15	1.99	0.00	15.23
Annual Growth	(11.9%)	—	—	(7.0%)	—	(5.0%)

*Fiscal year change

SAIC Inc

SAIC pledges its allegiance to the US government. A leading government services contractor the company provides a wide range of information technology services including systems engineering and project management to federal and state agencies including all branches of the US military. It specializes in such areas as consulting and technical support related to defense systems custom software development network security management intelligence gathering and logistics. While SAIC does serve some commercial customers the US government accounts for over 90% of its revenues with the Army and Navy accounting for 26% and 13% respectively. The company serves as both a prime contractor and subcontractor.

SAIC's defense related business is its largest single segment with the US Department of Defense accounting for three-quarters of sales in fiscal 2012. The company's intelligence and cybersecurity and its health energy and civil units each account for roughly 30% of sales. SAIC's intelligence and cybersecurity division focuses on systems and services related to intelligence surveillance reconnaissance and digital security. The unit specializes in airborne maritime space and ground-based surveillance systems and it provides intelligence collection processing exploitation and dissemination systems to speed decision-making in based on complex data sets.

The company's health energy and civil solutions division offers services and software for critical infrastructure homeland security safety and mission assurance training environmental assessments and restoration engineering design and construction purposes as well as sophisticated IT services. Areas of specialty include engineering design and construction services energy management renewables and energy distribution healthcare IT data management and analytics health infrastructure and biomedical support and research.

SAIC's revenues have more than doubled in the past decade thanks to robust federal spending on homeland security military and defense programs. In 2012 however the company's sales dipped 3%. Meanwhile its net income dropped by more than half a billion dollars due to decreased operating income and increased interest expense resulting from 2010 debt issuance; this was partially offset by a decrease in the provision for income taxes. SAIC's operating expenses were also higher for the year particularly in the area of general and administrative costs.

In response to lagging commercial sales SAIC sold its oil and gas technology services business to top tier Indian software services provider Wipro in 2011 for $150 million to focus on its core government services segment. The following year the company sold it test and evaluation business to fellow government services provider American Systems Corporation (ASC) for an undisclosed amount.

The sale to ASC closely followed SAIC's announcement of plans to split into two publicly traded companies one focused on government technical services and the other tasked with providing products and services for the national security engineering and health care markets. SAIC touts the split as expanding the addressable market for each company by removing potential conflicts of interest within the organization as well as providing a more clearly defined growth strategy for each business. The split is expected to occur in the latter half of SAIC's 2013 fiscal year.

Though sales have largely increased organically SAIC also fuels growth with the purchase of complementary businesses. The company has a long history of expansion through acquisition buying more than 20 companies in the past six years.

In 2012 the company paid nearly $475 million to acquire maxIT Healthcare a leading healthcare IT consultancy mainly that served commercial hospital groups ambulatory clinics and other health care providers. Its services included IT strategy planning electronic health record implementation and management consulting in such areas as accountable care transformation revenue cycle improvement and regulatory compliance. The deal extended SAIC's health care customer base for its Vitalize Consulting Solutions unit.

The previous year SAIC acquired Vitalize Consulting Solutions a provider of clinical business and IT services to the health care industry to expand its selection of services particularly related to electronic health record implementation. The previous year the company bought the transmission and distribution engineering operations of Chicago-based Patrick Energy Services a developer of power transmission and distribution power systems applications to extend its reach into the energy and smart grid services market.

SAIC's 2010 acquisitions supported its security products and services business. It bought x-ray security scanning systems maker Spectrum San Diego; data security specialist CloudShield; data analysis and surveillance systems maker Science Engineering and Technology Associates Corporation; and business engineering and energy consultancy R.W. Beck Group. Also that year the company boosted its homeland security business when it acquired Reveal Imaging Technologies a specialist in explosives detection equipment for airport baggage scanning used by the Transportation Security Administration.

Examples of the company's contracts in this area include support of command control and communications programs for the Department of Defense and integration of vehicle and cargo inspections systems used for border security. SAIC added the Department of Energy to its customer roster in 2010 when it was awarded a contract to provide technical and managerial support services for the agency's statistical analysis and modeling efforts.

HISTORY

Physicist Robert Beyster who worked at Los Alamos National Laboratory in the 1950s was hired by General Atomics in 1957 to establish and manage its traveling wave linear accelerator. When the company was sold to Gulf Oil in 1968 research priorities changed and Beyster left. He founded Science Applications Inc. (SAI) the following year and built his business from consulting contracts with Los Alamos and Brookhaven National Laboratory. During the first year Beyster instituted an employee-ownership plan that rewarded workers who brought on board new business with stock in SAI. Beyster's idea was to share the success of SAI and to raise capital.

In 1970 the company established an office in Washington DC to court government contracts. Despite a recession SAI continued to grow during the 1970s and by 1979 sales topped $100 million. The following year SAI restructured becoming a subsidiary of Science Applications International Corporation (SAIC) a new holding company.

During the 1980s defense buildup an emphasis on high-tech weaponry and SAIC's high-level Pentagon connections (directors have included former defense secretaries William Perry and Melvin Laird and former CIA director John Deutch) brought in contracts for submarine warfare systems and technical development for the Strategic Defense Initiative ("Star Wars"). As defense spending slowed with the end of the Cold War though SAIC began casting a wider net. By 1991 computer systems integration and consulting accounted for 25% of sales which surpassed the $1 billion mark.

SAIC made several purchases during the mid-1990s including transportation communications firm Syntonic and Internet domain name registrar Network Solutions Inc. (NSI). It also began merger talks with The Aerospace Corporation a government-funded research center in 1996 until the Air Force scotched the deal a few months later. In 1997 SAIC acquired Bellcore (the research lab of the regional Bells later renamed Telcordia Technologies) and reduced its stake in NSI through a public offering. SAIC formed several alliances in 1998 including a joint venture with Rolls-Royce to service the aerospace energy and defense industries.

The next year SAIC expanded its IT expertise with the acquisition of Boeing's Information Services unit. It also acquired the call center software operations of Elite Information Group. SAIC in 2000 realized a significant gain on its $5 million purchase of NSI when e-commerce software maker VeriSign bought the minority-owned (23%) subsidiary for about $20 billion in stock. SAIC signed a variety of large contracts the next year including an outsourcing agreement with BP to manage that company's North American application and hosting services as well as a $3 billion deal to provide support (in conjunction with Bechtel Group) for the US Department of Energy's civilian radioactive waste management program.

The omnipresent and self-described workaholic Beyster retired as CEO in 2003 turning the position over to Kenneth Dahlberg a former executive of General Dynamics. (Dahlberg became chairman of SAIC the following year.) In 2005 the company sold its Telcordia subsidiary to investment firms Warburg Pincus and Providence Equity Partners for $1.3 billion.

SAIC's IPO in 2006 ended the company's reign as the largest employee-owned research and engineering firm.

SAIC acquired Applied Marine Technology –a company with expertise in special operations special mission units and other areas of special warfare operations as well as in homeland security and terrorism –in 2006. Other 2006 acquisitions included AETC a San Diego-based provider of remote sensing systems for the Department of Defense; Varec a provider of measurement control and automation systems; aerospace engineering and IT services firm bd Systems; and Applied Ordnance Technology a provider of technical products and services catering to weapons systems.

In 2007 SAIC acquired Benham Investment Holdings a provider of consulting engineering architecture design/build and other related services as well as Scicom Technologies. It also split its joint venture Amsec with Northrop Grumman in 2007. SAIC inherited the aviation combat systems and strike force integration businesses while Northrop Grumman received the ship engineering logistics and technical services components of the venture. The company bought IT services provider SM Consulting in 2008. It also purchased Icon Systems a developer of laser-based systems for military training and testing. SAIC purchased technical and business consulting firm R.W. Beck Group and cyber security product testing services provider Atlan in 2009. Atlan validated hardware and software components using US government security standards.

Kenneth Dahlberg stepped down as CEO in 2009 and was succeeded by Walter Ravenstein a former top executive of BAE Systems. Dahlberg remained chairman.

EXECUTIVES

Secretary, Douglas E. Scott, age 55, $464,423 total compensation

EVP General Counsel and Audit, Vincent A. Maffeo, age 61

President Defense Solutions Group, Deborah H. (Deb) Alderson, age 55, $479,519 total compensation

EVP and CFO, Mark W. Sopp, age 46, $547,115 total compensation

Chairman, A. Thomas Young, age 74

President CEO and Director, Gen. John P. Jumper, age 67

VP Media Relations, Laura Luke

President Health Energy and Civil Solutions Group, Joseph W. (Joe) Craver III, age 53, $455,192 total compensation

CEO SAIC-Frederick, David Heimbrook

COO, K. Stuart (Stu) Shea, age 55, $455,192 total compensation

General Manager Intelligence and Information Solutions (Cyber) Business Unit, Larry D. Cox

SVP and Corporate Controller, John R. Hartley, age 51

Media Relations, Melissa Koskovich

EVP Human Resources, Brian F. Keenan, age 55

SVP and CTO, Amy E. Alving, age 49

SVP and Treasurer, Steven P. Fisher, age 51

EVP Corporate Development, James E. (Jim) Cuff

EVP Communications and Government Affairs, Deborah L. (Debbie) James

President Intelligence Surveillance and Reconnaissance Group, Anthony J. (Tony) Moraco
SVP Investor Relations, Paul E. Levi
Chief Scientist SAIC-Frederick, Larry Arthur
Acting President Defense Solutions Group, Thomas G. Baybrook
Chief Ethics and Compliance Officer, Laura Kennedy
Director, Harry M. J. Kraemer Jr., age 57
Director, Jere A. Drummond, age 72
Director, Edward J. (Sandy) Sanderson Jr., age 63
Director, Lawrence C. Nussdorf, age 65
Director, Louis A. Simpson, age 75
Director, John J. Hamre, age 61
President CEO and Director, Gen. John P. Jumper, age 67
Director, France A. Cordova, age 64
Director, Miriam E. (Mim) John, age 63
Director, Anita K. Jones, age 70
Director, Thomas F. Frist III, age 44
Auditors: Deloitte&ToucheLLP

LOCATIONS

HQ: SAIC Inc.
1710 SAIC Dr., McLean VA 22102
Phone: 703-676-4300 **Fax:** -8560
Web: www.foxconntech.com.tw

PRODUCTS/OPERATIONS

2012 Sales

	$ mil.	% of total
Defense	4,191	40
Intelligence & cybersecurity	3,540	33
Health energy & civil solutions	2,858	27
Adjustments	(2)	-
Total	**10,587**	**100**

COMPETITORS

Accenture
Affiliated Computer Services
American Science and Engineering
BAE Systems Technology Solutions
Battelle Memorial
Booz Allen
CACI International
CH2M HILL
Computer Sciences Corp.
Exelis
General Dynamics
Honeywell Technology Solutions
HP Enterprise Services
IBM Global Services
KBR
KEYW
Kratos Defense & Security Solutions
L-3 Communications
Lockheed Martin Information Systems
ManTech
Northrop Grumman Info Systems
OSI Systems
Raytheon Technical Services
Serco
SRA International
Unisys

HISTORICAL FINANCIALS

Company Type: Public

Income Statement FYE: January 31

	REVENUE ($ mil.)	NET INCOME ($ mil.)	NET PROFIT MARGIN	EMPLOYEES
01/12	10,587	59	0.6%	41,100
01/11	11,117	618	5.6%	43,400
01/10	10,846	497	4.6%	46,200
01/09	10,070	452	4.5%	45,400
01/08	8,935	415	4.6%	43,800
Annual Growth	4.3%	(38.6%)	—	(1.6%)

2012 Year-End Financials

Debt ratio: 27.78%
Return on equity: 2.71%
Cash ($ mil.): 1,592
Current ratio: 139.01
Long-term debt ($ mil.): 1,299
No. of shares (mil.): 341
Dividends
Yield: —
Payout: —
Market value ($ mil.): 4,385

	STOCK PRICE ($) FY Close	P/E High/Low		PER SHARE ($) Earnings	Dividends	Book Value
01/12	12.86	98	63	0.18	0.00	6.40
01/11	16.57	12	9	1.63	0.00	6.88
01/10	18.33	16	14	1.24	0.00	5.91
01/09	19.74	19	15	1.12	0.00	9.92
01/08	18.90	20	16	1.00	0.00	10.62
Annual Growth	(9.2%)	—	—	(34.9%)	—	(11.9%)

SanDisk Corp.

If forgetting things drives you crazy SanDisk's products might help preserve your sanity. The company is a top producer of data storage products based on flash memory which retains data even when power is interrupted. Its products include removable and embedded memory cards used in digital cameras mobile phones digital audio/video players USB drives solid-state drives (SSDs) GPS devices tablets and other electronic gear. The company sells to such manufacturers as Samsung Electronics and Canon as well as through retailers including Amazon.com and Best Buy. Nearly 70% of sales come from the Asia/Pacific region.

Revenue rose 17% in 2011 after an increase of 35% in 2010 on a year-over-year basis. Net income for the year was down slightly though SanDisk remained profitable. Sales of products which represent more than 90% of sales recorded an uptick of 18% thanks mainly to strong sales of memory devices for mobile (smartphones and tablets) and gaming applications. The company also saw a slight increase in sales to the retail market primarily due to higher sales of cards for mobile phones and USB drives.

Also because the company has reduced the costs of its manufacturing operations product gross margins as a percent of product revenue rose to 42% in 2010 from 27% in 2009 falling slightly in 2011 to 39% as average selling price reductions exceeded cost reductions for the year. The cost reductions come in part from the use of specialized manufacturing equipment and new technology platforms.

At the end of fiscal 2011 SanDisk held more than 2000 US patents and 1700 foreign patents. The company licenses its technology to such customers as Intel Lexar Media Sony and Toshiba. The company's top 10 customers and licensees represent more than 48% of sales; Samsung is its largest single customer. SanDisk is branching out into other product areas that use flash memory such as SSDs (a smaller high-performance alternative to traditional hard-disk drives). The company once relied heavily on retailers and distributors to move its products but most of its sales are now to OEMs.

In 2012 the company bought SSD caching software company FlashSoft. SanDisk will sell FlashSoft software by itself but also use it to improve the performance of SanDisk SSDs. Also that year it bought Silicon Valley-based Schooner Information Technology which develops flash-optimized database and storage software. In 2011 SanDisk paid more than $325 million for Pliant Technology extending its reach into the fast-growing market for SSDs and adding enterprise-level storage systems to its product line-up.

The company has also become a leading competitor in the market for digital audio/video players with its Sansa brand. SSDs and digital music are just a two of the markets where SanDisk has expanded. The company's strategy for growth is focused on increasing overall revenue by lowering the cost of the NAND flash memory that powers its technology and by working with other companies to develop new NAND applications and products. To cushion itself against possible limits to the development of NAND SanDisk also invests in alternative technologies including bit-cost scalable 3-dimensional NAND (BiCS) and 3-dimensional resistive RAM (3D ReRAM).

SanDisk outsources all of its controller component manufacturing and much of its assembly and test operations to foundries (contract semiconductor manufacturers). Its flash memory wafers primarily come from manufacturing joint ventures with Toshiba which produce finished wafers in Japan that are sold to SanDisk and Toshiba. SanDisk also has in-house assembly and test operations in China.

The company has additional sales marketing and support facilities in China France Germany India Ireland Israel Japan Russia Singapore Scotland South Korea Spain Sweden Taiwan the United Arab Emirates and the US.

HISTORY

SanDisk was co-founded as SunDisk in 1988 by Eli Harari an expert on nonvolatile memory technology. SunDisk's first product based on a four-megabit flash chip was developed with AT&T Bell Labs and released in 1991. In 1992 the company formed a development partnership with disk drive maker Seagate Technology; as part of the pact Seagate acquired 25% of SunDisk.

Because SunDisk was being confused with Sun Microsystems in 1995 the company changed its name to SanDisk. It went public that year and introduced the industry's smallest Type II (a PC card slot size designation) flash storage card –the CompactFlash. Sales increased by nearly 80% in 1995 SanDisk's first profitable year. The next year SanDisk and Matsushita (now Panasonic) developed double-density flash a breakthrough technology that doubled the capacity of flash storage products.

In 1997 SanDisk started production of its double-density flash series investing $40 million in a semiconductor plant in Taiwan with United Microelectronics. In 1999 SanDisk said it would move about 75% of its production to China partly through a partnership with Celestica.

Seagate divested the last of its ownership stake in SanDisk in 2000. Also that year SanDisk and Toshiba formed a joint venture FlashVision to produce advanced flash memory at a Toshiba semiconductor plant in Virginia. FlashVision commenced production the following year. (The joint venture's operations were moved to one of Toshiba's Japanese plants after Toshiba announced the sale of the Virginia factory –which primarily made DRAM chips –to Micron Technology in 2001.) SanDisk and Toshiba consolidated manufacturing at Toshiba's Yokkaichi memory fab in 2002.

In 2004 SanDisk opened a retail distribution center in China and formed a new joint venture with Toshiba Flash Partners for the purpose of adding manufacturing capacity. The following year Toshiba began operation of a new fab in Yokkaichi for making NAND flash memory devices. The semiconductors were produced on silicon wafers measuring 300mm (12 inches) across.

In 2006 SanDisk acquired Matrix Semiconductor a developer of 3-D one-time programmable (OTP) chip technology for about $300 million in stock and cash. The companies began working together on integrating the Matrix technology into SanDisk's product line.

SanDisk purchased rival msystems in 2006 for about $1.5 billion in stock. After passing on an opportunity to acquire competitor Lexar Media (which went to chip maker Micron Technology earlier that year) SanDisk pursued msystems instead widening its portfolio of flash memory-based data storage products.

Responding to the dramatic collapse of prices in the NAND flash memory market SanDisk set a number of cost-cutting measures in 2007. These included the layoff of up to 10% of the worldwide staff (approximately 250 employees) salary cuts for senior executives salary freezes for all other employees and a hiring freeze for most areas.

In 2008 Samsung Electronics made a hostile takeover bid for SanDisk. The unsolicited acquisition offer valued at $5.85 billion in cash came amid turbulent business conditions in the memory device industry with oversupply in the DRAM and NAND flash memory markets continually driving down prices and causing red ink for several memory chip makers. SanDisk quickly rejected the unsolicited bid saying it undervalued the company and was not in the best interests of its shareholders. Samsung withdrew the offer in late 2008 citing growing uncertainties in SanDisk's business and the worldwide financial crisis. Samsung and SanDisk had discussed a possible combination earlier in 2008 but after nearly four months of negotiations Samsung grew impatient.

During the year SanDisk did some acquiring of its own strengthening its Sansa media player product with MusicGremlin a developer of digital content distribution technologies which had previously marketed the Gremlin portable audio player. The Gremlin used a Wi-Fi connection to update and share musical playlists.

Harari retired in 2010 after 22 years as CEO of the company he co-founded handing the reins to co-founder and president Sanjay Mehrotra as part of a planned succession. The chairman position was filled by director Michael Marks president of private equity firm Riverwood Capital and former CEO of contract manufacturer Flextronics.

EXECUTIVES

President CEO and Director, Sanjay Mehrotra, age 53, $561,000 total compensation
Vice Chairman, Irwin Federman, age 76
Chairman, Michael E. Marks, age 61
EVP Administration and CFO, Judy Bruner, age 53, $486,000 total compensation
SVP and General Manager OEM and Country Manager SanDisk Israel, Dan Inbar
SVP OEM Marketing, Drew Henry
EVP and CTO, Yoram Cedar, age 59, $404,693 total compensation
EVP and Chief Strategy Officer, Sumit Sadana, age 43
Senior Director Corporate Communications Brand and Web, Ryan Donovan
Chief Intellectual Property Counsel, E. Earle Thompson, age 55
SVP IP Licensing and Chief Legal Officer, James F. (Jim) Brelsford, age 56
SVP Memory Technology Design and Product Development, Khandker Nazrul Quader
SVP Finance, Milo Azarmsa
SVP Human Resources, Tom Baker
SVP Technology and Fab Operations; President SanDisk Japan, Atsuyoshi Koike, age 59
Director Public Relations, Mike Wong
Director Regional Sales Africa and Middle East Retail Sales, Tareq Husseini
Director Regional Sales UK Ireland and Nordics Retail Sales, Keith Norman
Director Regional Sales Central and Eastern Europe Retail Sales, Sascha Bohmer
Director Regional Sales Southern Europe Retail Sales, Frederic Descombe
Director Investor Relations, Jay Iyer
Public Relations Coordinator, Emilie Johnson
CIO, Ravi Naik
SVP Worldwide Operations, Manish Bhatia
SVP and General Manager Client Storage Solutions, Kevin Conley
SVP and General Manager Retail, Shuki Nir
SVP and GeneralManager Storage Group, Thomas Rampone
SVP Corporate Engineering, Jeff VerHeul
President CEO and Director, Sanjay Mehrotra, age 53
Director, Steven J. (Steve) Gomo, age 60
Director, Eddy W. Hartenstein, age 61
Vice Chairman, Irwin Federman, age 76
Director, Kevin A. DeNuccio, age 52
Director, Catherine P. (Cathy) Lego, age 55
Director, Chenming (Calvin) Hu, age 64
Auditors: Ernst&YoungLLP

LOCATIONS

HQ: SanDisk Corporation
601 McCarthy Blvd., Milpitas CA 95035
Phone: 408-801-1000 **Fax:** 408-801-8657
Web: www.sandisk.com

2011 Sales

	$ mil.	% of total
Asia/Pacific		
Taiwan	1,419	25
South Korea	374	7
Other countries	2,102	37
US	853	15
Europe Middle East & Africa	688	12
Other regions	223	4
Total	**5,662**	**100**

PRODUCTS/OPERATIONS

2011 Sales

	$ mil.	% of total
Products		
OEM	3,458	61
Retail	1,829	32
Licensing & royalty	374	7
Total	**5,662**	**100**

Selected Products

Embedded data storage devices (FlashDrive)
MP3 music players (Sansa)
Portable storage devices (Cruzer)
Removable storage cards (used in cellular phones digital cameras digital music players digital voice recorders and personal digital assistants)
- CompactFlash
- Memory Stick
- MultiMedia
- Secure Digital
- SmartMedia

COMPETITORS

Apple Inc.
Archos
Atmel
Buffalo Technology
Creative Technology
Eastman Kodak
FUJIFILM
Fusion-io
Gemalto
IM Flash Technologies
Imation
Intel
Iomega
Iriver
Kingston Technology
Lexar
Macronix International
Micron Technology
Microsoft
Netlist
OCZ Technology
Panasonic Corp
Philips Electronics
PNY Technologies
Samsung Electronics
Seagate Technology
Silicon Motion
Silicon Storage
SK Hynix
SMART Modular Technologies
SMDK
Sony
STEC
STMicroelectronics
Toshiba Semiconductor & Storage Products
Verbatim Corp.
Viking Modular Solutions
Western Digital

HISTORICAL FINANCIALS

Company Type: Public

Income Statement FYE: January 1

	REVENUE ($ mil.)	NET INCOME ($ mil.)	NET PROFIT MARGIN	EMPLOYEES
01/12	5,662	986	17.4%	3,939
01/11	4,826	1,300	26.9%	3,469
01/10*	3,566	415	11.6%	3,267
12/08	3,351	(2,056)	—	3,565
12/07	3,896	218	5.6%	3,172
Annual Growth	9.8%	45.8%	—	5.6%

*Fiscal year change

2012 Year-End Financials

Debt ratio: 15.77%
Return on equity: 13.97%
Cash ($ mil.): 1,167
Current ratio: 398.40
Long-term debt ($ mil.): 1,604
No. of shares (mil.): 242
Dividends
Yield: —
Payout: —
Market value ($ mil.): 11,936

	STOCK PRICE ($) FY Close	P/E High	P/E Low	PER SHARE ($) Earnings	Dividends	Book Value
01/12	49.21	13	8	4.04	0.00	29.13
01/11	49.86	9	5	5.44	0.00	24.45
01/10*	28.99	16	4	1.79	0.00	17.10
12/08	9.18	—	—	(9.13)	0.00	14.04
12/07	33.54	61	35	0.93	0.00	22.12
Annual Growth	10.1%	—	—	44.4%	—	7.1%

*Fiscal year change

Sandy Spring Bancorp Inc

Sandy Spring Bancorp is the holding company for Sandy Spring Bank which operates around 50 branches in the Baltimore and Washington DC metropolitan areas. Founded in 1868 the bank is one of the largest and oldest headquartered in Maryland. It provides standard deposit services including checking and savings accounts money market accounts and CDs. Commercial and residential real estate loans account for nearly three-quarters of the company's loan portfolio; the remainder is a mix of consumer loans business loans and equipment leases. The company also offers personal investing services wealth management trust services insurance and retirement planning.

Sandy Spring Bancorp's nonbank subsidiaries include money manager West Financial Services and Sandy Spring Insurance which sells annuities and operates insurance agencies Chesapeake Insurance Group and Neff & Associates.

As with many of its peers Sandy Spring Bancorp felt the sting of the recession and reported a nearly $20 million loss in 2009 as loan demand weakened and provisions to cover loan losses ballooned. The decrease in loan demand however helped the company to focus on its existing portfolio and reduce its nonperforming loans and provisions for loan losses. As the economy showed signs of a slow turnaround and the company's credit management efforts took hold Sandy Spring Bancorp returned to profitability in 2010 reporting net income of more than $17 million. The company kept the momentum going into 2011 when charged-off loans and provisions for loan losses continued to decline and profits nearly doubled (net income of more than $34 million on revenues of nearly $183 million). Loan demand began to rebound as well.

In 2012 Sandy Spring Bancorp acquired CommerceFirst Bancorp a small Maryland bank with a strong Small Business Administration lending practice. The $25.4 million transaction added five branches to Sandy Spring Bank's network.

EXECUTIVES

EVP General Counsel and Corporate Secretary Sandy Spring Bancorp and Sandy Spring Bank, Ronald E. Kuykendall, age 59, $190,000 total compensation
Chairman Sandy Spring Bancorp and Sandy Spring Bank, Robert L. Orndorff Jr., age 56
EVP Sandy Spring Bank, R. Louis (Lou) Caceres, age 49, $257,900 total compensation
SVP and Information Security Officer Sandy Spring Bank, Frank L. Bentz III, age 53
President CEO and Director Sandy Spring Bancorp and Sandy Spring Bank, Daniel J. (Dan) Schrider, age 47, $269,324 total compensation
VP Public and Community Relations Sandy Spring Bank, Kulley A.W. Bancroft
SVP Human Resources Sandy Spring Bank, Dawn Weglein
EVP and CFO Sandy Spring Bancorp and Sandy Spring Bank, Philip J. Mantua, age 53, $237,335 total compensation
SVP Financial Reporting, Daniel A. Russo
SVP and Director Corporate Development, Michael A. Bateman
President Sandy Spring Insurance Corporation Sandy Spring Bank, R. Stephan (Steve) Geoffray
VP and Assistant Corporate Secretary Sandy Spring Bank, Janet Replogle
EVP and Chief Credit Officer Sandy Spring Bank, Jeffrey A. (Jeff) Welch
EVP Commercial Banking Group Sandy Spring Bank, William W. (Bill) Hill, age 59
EVP and President Potomac Bank Division Sandy Spring Bank, Joseph J. O'Brien Jr.
EVP and CIO, John D. Sadowski, age 48
Director, Susan D. Goff, age 66
Director, Dennis A. Starliper, age 65
Director, Solomon Graham, age 69
Director, Gilbert L. Hardesty, age 71
Director, Charles F. Mess, age 73
Director, David E. Rippeon, age 63
Director, Craig A. Ruppert, age 58
President CEO and Director Sandy Spring Bancorp and Sandy Spring Bank, Daniel J. (Dan) Schrider, age 47
Director, Mark E. Friis, age 56
Director, Pamela A. Little, age 58
Director, Marshall H. Groom, age 73
Auditors: GrantThorntonLLP

LOCATIONS

HQ: Sandy Spring Bancorp Inc.
17801 Georgia Ave., Olney MD 20832
Phone: 301-774-6400 **Fax:** 301-260-0044
Web: www.sandyspringbank.com

PRODUCTS/OPERATIONS

2011 Sales by Segment

	$ mil.	% of total
Community banking	173	94
Investment management	5	3
Insurance	5	3
Inter-segment elimination	(0.8)	-
Total	**183**	**100**

2011 Sales

	$ mil.	% of total
Interest		
Loans & leases	107	59
Investment securities	31	17
Other	0	-
Noninterest		
Trust & investment management fees	11	6
Service charges on deposit accounts	9	5
Insurance agency commissions	4	3
Fees on sales of investment products	3	2
Visa check fees	3	2
Mortgage banking	3	2
Other	6	4
Total	**183**	**100**

COMPETITORS

Bank of America
BB&T
Capital One
Carrollton Bancorp
Citizens Republic Bancorp
Fulton Financial
OBA Financial Services
PNC Financial
SunTrust

HISTORICAL FINANCIALS

Company Type: Public

Income Statement

FYE: December 31

	ASSETS ($ mil.)	NET INCOME ($ mil.)	INCOME AS % OF ASSETS	EMPLOYEES
12/11	3,711	34	0.9%	713
12/10	3,519	23	0.7%	711
12/09	3,630	(14)	—	703
12/08	3,313	15	0.5%	717
12/07	3,043	32	1.1%	749
Annual Growth	5.1%	1.4%	—	(1.2%)

2011 Year-End Financials

Debt ratio: 11.87%
Return on equity: 7.64%
Cash ($ mil.): 71
Current ratio: —
Long-term debt ($ mil.): 440
No. of shares (mil.): 24
Dividends
Yield: —
Payout: 24.11%
Market value ($ mil.): 423

	STOCK PRICE ($) FY Close	P/E High/Low		PER SHARE ($) Earnings	Dividends	Book Value
12/11	17.55	14	10	1.41	0.00	18.52
12/10	18.43	18	8	1.05	0.05	16.95
12/09	8.89	—	—	(0.90)	0.37	22.66
12/08	21.83	31	14	0.96	0.96	23.90
12/07	27.82	19	13	2.01	0.92	19.31
Annual Growth	(10.9%)	—	—	(8.5%)	—	(1.0%)

Sanmina Corp

Sanmina (formerly Sanmina-SCI) is a top contract manufacturer of sophisticated electronic components including printed circuit boards and board assemblies backplanes and backplane assemblies enclosures cable assemblies optical components and modules and memory modules. In addition the company provides services such as design and engineering materials management order fulfillment and in-circuit testing. It serves OEMs in the health care aerospace telecommunications and technology industries among others. Sanmina has manufacturing facilities in 18 countries on four continents. Because its customers base production in lower-cost regions more than 80% of sales come from outside the US.

HISTORY

Bosnian immigrants Jure Sola (chairman and CEO) and Milan Mandaric founded Sanmina in 1980 to provide just-in-time manufacturing of printed circuit boards (PCBs). The name Sanmina comes from the names of Mandaric's children.

During the late 1980s and early 1990s Sanmina shifted production to higher-margin components such as backplane assemblies and subassemblies. Mandaric an entrepreneur with other interests left in 1989. The company went public in 1993.

Like other contract manufacturers Sanmina began bolstering its operations through acquisitions. The company bought manufacturing plants from Comptronix (1994) Assembly Solutions (1995) Golden Eagle Systems (1996) and Lucent Technologies (1996). In 1997 the company bought contract electronics maker Elexsys International which was headed by Milan Mandaric. Sanmina also opened a plant in Ireland.

Sanmina's 1998 acquisitions included Massachusetts-based Altron its #1 competitor in backplane manufacturing. In 1999 the company acquired assets from Nortel Networks and Devtek Electronics Enclosure a designer of enclosure systems for the telecommunications and networking industries.

In 2000 Sanmina acquired PCB maker Hadco in a $1.3 billion deal expanding its global presence. That year the company also purchased Swedish contract manufacturer Essex AB entered into a joint venture with Siemens to manufacture complex PCBs and acquired some plants from Nortel and Lucent.

In mid-2001 Sanmina agreed to buy rival SCI Systems one of the world's largest contract manufacturers for about $4.5 billion. (Sanmina also assumed $1.5 billion of SCI's debt.) Later that year it also acquired a facility in Texas from (and signed a multiyear supplier agreement with) French telecom titan Alcatel (now Alcatel-Lucent). When its acquisition of SCI Systems closed late in the year Sanmina changed its name to Sanmina-SCI. (Sola and SCI Systems chairman and CEO Eugene Sapp became co-chairmen; Sola remained CEO of the combined company.)

The acquisition of SCI vaulted Sanmina-SCI into the top ranks of contract manufacturers such as Flextronics and Celestica. The deal also capped a buying spree that expanded the company into Europe and Asia. In several instances Sanmina-SCI acquired manufacturing facilities from major customers such as IBM and Elscint; these deals included long-term contracts for Sanmina-SCI to supply products back to those same customers.

Sanmina-SCI forged several deals in early 2002. The company announced a three-year $5 billion agreement with IBM to produce desktop PCs. As part of the deal Sanmina-SCI acquired two US plants from IBM. In addition Sanmina-SCI and HP penned a deal whereby the company produces some HP products and acquired HP's manufacturing operations in France for $65.8 million. Also that year Sanmina-SCI acquired plants in France Germany and Spain from Alcatel for $129.9 million as part of a multiyear supply agreement. All three deals were completed by mid-year.

Also in 2002 Sanmina-SCI acquired privately held Viking Components (custom memory modules and modems) for $11 million. It later combined the company with its InterWorks subsidiary to form Viking InterWorks (now Viking Modular Solutions).

After a year as co-chairman Eugene Sapp stepped down from that post in late 2002 while remaining a director of the company.

In 2003 Sanmina-SCI acquired privately held Newisys a developer of enterprise-class servers. The following year Sanmina-SCI acquired Singapore-based Pentex-Schweizer Circuits (printed circuit board fabrication services) for about $80 million.

In mid-2006 the company opened a new enclosures manufacturing facility measuring 347000 sq. ft. in Guadalajara Mexico.

Like dozens of other tech companies Sanmina-SCI found problems in 2006 with its past practices in granting stock options to executives and other employees. An internal investigation by a special board committee going back to the beginning of 1997 found that most grants in the prior decade were not correctly dated or accounted for requiring the company to restate financial results and record non-cash compensation charges.

Among other changes recommended by the special committee the board adopted a policy of establishing fixed dates for granting equity-based awards reducing or eliminating the possibility of backdating or springloading options. The company stated that an executive had resigned as a result of the options investigation. Carmine Renzulli the EVP for global human resources left Sanmina-SCI about that time.

Sanmina-SCI shuttered Newisys in 2007 laying off 87 employees.

In 2008 Sanmina-SCI sold its PC manufacturing business saying the barely profitable business was no longer integral to the company's long-term strategy. The company transferred its PC plant in Monterrey Mexico to Lenovo Group and sold certain assets to the giant Chinese PC maker. Other assets of the PC business in Hungary Mexico and the US were sold to Foxteq Holdings a unit of Foxconn Technology Group which is part of Hon Hai Precision Industry the world's largest contract electronics manufacturer. The PC business previously represented nearly a third of Sanmina-SCI's revenues.

In early 2009 Sanmina-SCI scored JDS Uniphase's Shenzhen China optical facility. Subsequently Sanmina-SCI inked an agreement with OneChip Photonics to manufacture Photonic Integrated Circuit (PIC)-based Fiber-to-the-Premises (FTTP) transceivers. Management plans to manufacture the FTTP transceivers in China but launch them from Sanmina-SCI's domestic new product introduction and gateway centers.

In 2012 Sanmina-SCI changed its name back to Sanmina but continued to offer SCI-branded products.

EXECUTIVES

EVP Global Human Resources, David L. Pulatie, age 70
Chairman and CEO, Jure Sola, age 60, $804,385 total compensation
VP Business Development, John Naismith
EVP and CFO, Robert K. (Bob) Eulau, age 50, $398,585 total compensation
EVP Worldwide Sales and Marketing, Dennis Young, age 60, $325,506 total compensation
Financial Information and Investor Relations, Paige Bombino
EVP General Counsel and Corporate Secretary, Michael R. (Mike) Tyler, age 56, $354,615 total compensation
VP Enterprise Services and CIO, Manesh Patel
Senior Director Corporate Marketing, Michael Kovacs
Director Corporate Compliance, Michael Delgado
VP Industrial Markets, Tom Clawson
VP Business Development, Randy Thomas
Director, Mario M. Rosati, age 66
Director, A. Eugene Sapp Jr., age 75
Director, Jacquelyn M. (Jackie) Ward, age 74
Director, Neil R. Bonke, age 70
Director, John P. Goldsberry, age 57
Director, Jean Manas, age 47
Auditors: KPMGLLP

LOCATIONS

HQ: Sanmina Corporation
2700 N. 1st St., San Jose CA 95134
Phone: 408-964-3500 **Fax:** 408-964-3344
Web: www.sanmina-sci.com

2011 Sales

	$ mil.	% of total
China	1,792	27
Mexico	1,274	19
US	1,199	18
Other countries	2,337	36
Total	**6,602**	**100**

PRODUCTS/OPERATIONS

2011 Sales

	$ mil.	% of total
Communications	3,135	48
Industrial defense & medical	1,609	24
Multimedia	945	14
Enterprise computing & storage	913	14
Total	**6,602**	**100**

Selected Services

Backplane assembly
Cable assembly
Circuit assembly
Circuit fabrication
Configuration
Distribution
Enclosures
Engineering
Forward logistics
In-circuit testing
Inventory management
Materials management
Order fulfillment
Printed circuit board design
Reverse engineering
Sustaining engineering
System assembly and testing

COMPETITORS

Benchmark Electronics	Nam Tai
BenQ	Plexus
Cal-Comp Electronics	SMTC Corp.
Celestica	Suntron
CTS Corp.	SYNNEX
Flextronics	TTM Technologies
Hon Hai	Universal Scientific
IBM Canada	Venture Corp.
Inventec	Viasystems
Jabil	Wistron

HISTORICAL FINANCIALS

Company Type: Public

Income Statement

FYE: September 29

	REVENUE ($ mil.)	NET INCOME ($ mil.)	NET PROFIT MARGIN	EMPLOYEES
09/12*	6,093	180	3.0%	44,879
10/11	6,602	68	1.0%	45,505
10/10	6,318	122	1.9%	44,199
10/09	5,177	(136)	—	38,602
09/08	7,202	(486)	—	45,610
Annual Growth	(4.1%)	—	—	(0.4%)

*Fiscal year change

2012 Year-End Financials

Debt ratio: 28.33%
Return on equity: 18.70%
Cash ($ mil.): 409
Current ratio: 190.75
Long-term debt ($ mil.): 837
No. of shares (mil.): 81
Dividends
Yield: —
Payout: —
Market value ($ mil.): 695

	STOCK PRICE ($) FY Close	P/E High	P/E Low	PER SHARE ($) Earnings	Dividends	Book Value
09/12*	8.51	6	3	2.16	0.00	11.81
10/11	6.68	20	8	0.83	0.00	9.54
10/10	12.01	12	4	1.48	0.00	8.30
10/09	8.18	—	—	(1.65)	0.00	6.91
09/08	1.64	—	—	(5.52)	0.00	7.86
Annual Growth	50.9%	—	—	—	—	10.7%

*Fiscal year change

Santander Holdings USA Inc.

Santander Holdings USA is the parent company of Sovereign Bank which reigns in the Northeast with more than 700 branch locations. The bank caters to individuals and small to midsized businesses offering deposits credit cards insurance and investments as well as commercial loans and mortgages (which together account for nearly half of its total portfolio) and residential mortgages and home equity loans (more than a quarter). Santander Holdings also owns a majority of Santander Consumer USA which purchases and services subprime car loans made by auto dealerships and other companies. Spain-based banking giant Banco Santander acquired the rest of Sovereign Bancorp it didn't already own in 2009.

Founded in 1902 Sovereign Bank has grown by making some 30 acquisitions since 1990. Its acquisitive ways have brought the company new markets and sometimes new headaches. For example its 2006 purchase of Independence Community Bank and its 125 branches gave the bank a foothold in the New York metro area and linked the bank's mid-Atlantic and New England operations. The deal was fraught with difficulties including shareholder concern over where power of the company would end up if the company sold shares to fund the acquisition. In the ensuing tumultous years three CEOs were replaced as Sovereign tried to overcome its exposure to bad loans.

Streamlining back-office operations were among the cost-cutting efforts utilized to stop the company's losses. The bank transferred its loan servicing operations to Santander Consumer USA and stopped originating indirect auto loans in the Southeast and Southwest after that business performed poorly.

Santander Holdings returned to profitability in 2009 after Sovereign Bancorp suffered more than $3 billion in (mainly investment- and credit-related) losses in 2007 and 2008 combined as the company ramped up its focus on risk management and collections. It continued its momentum into 2010 and 2011 as the economy showed signs of improvement. In 2011 the company reported revenue growth of 23% (some $7.2 billion) and net income growth of some 19% (some $1.3 billion) as both interest and noninterest earnings increased. Santander Holdings has stabilized the credit quality of its loan portfolio and experienced fewer net charge-offs and lowered its provisions for loan losses. Improved performance from investments an uptick in net interest margins and acquisitions by Santander Consumer helped the company's results as well.

As Santander Holdings continues to keep a close eye on credit quality its strategies for growth include courting large corporate clients and strengthening its core retail business by adding new products. In early 2012 Sovereign Bank changed its charter from a thrift to a national commercial bank which provides it with more flexibility to target corporate clients in particular. The company is also focused on specialized business lines such as lending for multifamily housing in Brooklyn New York.

In 2011 the company sold a 35% stake in Santander Consumer to an investment group and its management team. The deal brought Santander nearly $1 billion enough to account for its biggest noninterest earnings of the year.

HISTORY

Sovereign which had built itself into a regional powerhouse appealed to the Spanish bank as it pursued growth in the US. Santander acquired its initial stake in the company of about 20% in 2006 later upped that to about 25% then bought the rest for nearly $2 billion in early 2009.

The deal was fraught with difficulties though. Sovereign planned to fund the acquisition by selling an additional stake to Santander a move that was opposed by some shareholders concerned about control of the company. Sovereign and the opposing shareholders launched a volley of lawsuits and countersuits. Ultimately the disputes were settled with Sovereign adding independent directors (including one from lead shareholder Relational Investors) to its board and with Relational Investors agreeing to back Sovereign's board nominees for a number of years.

There was more turmoil to come though. Later in 2006 Sovereign's longtime CEO Jay Sidhu was forced to resign under criticism over the company's stock price and performance. A few weeks later the president and COO of the bank resigned after being passed over for Sidhu's position which went to former vice chairman Joe Campanelli.

Campanelli consolidated senior leadership in his home base of Boston (instead of in the Philadelphia headquarters) and centralized the company's decision-making process to address inefficiencies in the organization. The bank's new leadership closed branches cut jobs and ceased its wholesale mortgage business in order to concentrate on its core retail banking operations.

However turmoil in the financial industry affected banks throughout the world including smaller banks that didn't receive government support. Sovereign stock value fell more than 70% in 2008 and the board elected to replace Campanelli as CEO. (His strategy of expanding into new loan areas beyond the Northeast was called into question for increasing the bank's exposure to risk.) Paul Perrault formerly CEO of Chittenden Corporation took the helm of the company in early 2009 but was replaced after less than a month on the job by Gabriel Jaramillo when Santander completed its acquisition of Sovereign.

After the deal was complete Santander implemented its own cost-saving efforts such as streamlining its back-office operations. The bank transferred its loan servicing operations to Santander Consumer USA and stopped originating indirect auto loans in the Southeast and Southwest after that business performed poorly.

EXECUTIVES

Chairman Santander Holdings USA and Sovereign Bank, Jerry A. Grundhofer, age 67
Country Head Santander USA; Chief Executive Sovereign Bank, Jorge Moran, age 48
VP Corporate Communications Sovereign Bank, Ellen Molle
Chief Risk Management Officer, Juan Davila, age 42
General Counsel, Richard A Toomey Jr., age 67
Chief of Staff to the CEO Sovereign Bank, Edvaldo A. Catalani Morata, age 48
Managing Director Retail Business Development and and SME Banking, Nuno Goncalo de Macedo e Santana de Almeida Matos, age 44, $359,476 total compensation
CFO, Guillermo Sabater, age 43, $224,036 total compensation
Managing Director Human Resources, Francisco Simon, age 41
Managing Director Manufacturing Group, Eduardo J. Stock, age 50
Managing Director Global Banking and Markets, Jose Castello Orta, age 50
Director, John P. Hamill, age 71
Director, Wolfgang Schoellkopf, age 79
Director, Marian L. Heard, age 72
Director, Gonzalo de Las Heras, age 72
Director, Alberto Sanchez, age 48
Director, Juan Andres Yanes, age 50
Auditors: Deloitte&ToucheLLP

LOCATIONS

HQ: Santander Holdings USA Inc.
75 State St., Boston MA 02109
Phone: 617-346-7200 **Fax:** 864-288-8692
Web: www.spanamerica.com

Selected Locations

Connecticut
Delaware
Maryland
Massachusetts
New Hampshire
New Jersey
New York
Pennsylvania
Rhode Island

PRODUCTS/OPERATIONS

2011 Sales

	$ mil.	% of total
Interest		
Loans	4,834	67
Investment securities	412	6
Deposits	6	-
Noninterest		
SCUSA transaction	987	14
Consumer banking fees	637	9
Commercial banking fees	175	2
Other	124	2
Adjustments	(2.8)	-
Total	**7,175**	**100**

COMPETITORS

Bank of America
Citibank
Fulton Financial
HSBC USA
JPMorgan Chase
KeyCorp
M&T Bank
People' s United Financial
PNC Financial
RBS Citizens Financial Group
Susquehanna Bancshares
TD Bank USA
Webster Financial
Wells Fargo

HISTORICAL FINANCIALS

Company Type: Subsidiary

Income Statement

FYE: December 31

	REVENUE ($ mil.)	NET INCOME ($ mil.)	NET PROFIT MARGIN	EMPLOYEES
12/11	7,249	1,172	16.2%	8,557
12/10	5,813	1,022	17.6%	11,714
12/09	4,765	161	3.4%	10,596
12/08	3,104	(2,357)	—	0
12/07	5,010	(1,349)	—	0
Annual Growth	9.7%	—	—	—

2011 Year-End Financials

Debt ratio: 19.96%
Return on equity: 9.31%
Cash ($ mil.): 2,623
Current ratio: 8.03
Long-term debt ($ mil.): 16,064
No. of shares (mil.): 520
Dividends
Yield: —
Payout: 63.58%
Market value ($ mil.): 13,008

	STOCK PRICE ($) FY Close	P/E High/Low	PER SHARE ($) Earnings	Dividends	Book Value
12/11	25.00	— —	(0.00)	0.00	24.21
12/10	25.15	— —	(0.00)	1.83	21.73
12/09	25.40	— —	(0.00)	1.83	18.37
12/08	16.10	— —	(0.00)	1.83	8.43
12/07	20.74	— —	(0.00)	1.83	(0.00)
Annual Growth	4.8%	— —	—	—	—

SCANA Corp

SCANA is cooking with (natural) gas and electricity all over South and North Carolina and Georgia. The holding company serves 668000 electricity customers and 1.2 million gas customers in the neighboring states through utilities South Carolina Electric & Gas (SCE&G) Public Service Company of North Carolina and SCANA Energy (in Georgia). SCANA has an electric generating capacity of about 5270 MW derived from fossil-fueled power plants and hydroelectric and nuclear generation facilities. Unregulated operations include retail and wholesale energy marketing and trading gas transportation power plant management fiber-optic telecommunications services and appliance and HVAC maintenance.

SCANA (which derives its name from the letters in "South CAroliNA") has a strong market position in three states. It also has the advantage of a deregulated segment to offset the limited growth curve of its regulated utilities. The company operates in Georgia's deregulated gas market where it has emerged as a distribution leader with 455000 customers (a 30% market share).

On the regulated side of the ledger in 2009 SCANA won a competitive bid to continue serving as Georgia's sole regulated provider of natural gas a role the company has had since the Georgia Public Service Commission launched the regulated provider program in 2002.

In 2010 an improving economy and increased rate adjustments (in both the electric and gas segments) and colder-than-normal weather and higher consumption (which lifted retail gas sales) boosted the company's overall revenues and income. Higher electric rates and revenues could not prevent SCANA seeing its revenues drop by 4% in 2011 dragged down by low gas prices and the effects of a mild winter crimping demand. However net income improved by almost 3% in 2011 thanks to lower fuel costs for power generation and lower expenses for natural gas purchased for resale.

Looking to expand its generation base in 2012 South Carolina Electric & Gas Company and Santee Cooper received approval from the Nuclear Regulatory Commission for combined construction and operating licenses for two new nuclear units at the V. C. Summer Station in Jenkinsville South Carolina.

HISTORY

SCANA's earliest ancestors include Charleston Gas Light Company (1846) and Columbia Gas Light Company (1852) formed to light those cities' streets. After barely surviving the Civil War the companies rebuilt only to face the greater challenge posed by Thomas Edison's lightbulb in 1879.

Electric utilities such as Charleston Electric Light Company (1886) began to emerge and they also introduced electric trolleys which were commonly operated by electric utilities to boost power consumption. After a series of mergers among utilities in South Carolina the Columbia Electric Street Railway Light and Power Company (1892) and Charleston Consolidated Railway Gas and Electric Company (1897) were formed to handle energy and transit needs in their respective cities.

The 1920s brought another wave of utility mergers and consolidation in South Carolina. Columbia Electric Street Railway became part of the Broad River Power Company in 1925 and Charleston Consolidated Railway became a part of South Carolina Power Company the next year. In 1937 Broad River was renamed South Carolina Electric & Gas (SCE&G).

SCE&G went public in 1948. After a two-year fight with the South Carolina Public Service Authority SCE&G finally gained approval to purchase South Carolina Power Company in 1950. During the 1950s it built several power plants and natural gas distribution lines and joined other utilities to build the Southeast's first nuclear plant prototype in 1959.

A dozen years later SCE&G and the South Carolina Public Service Authority began building a nuke near the pilot plant. Because of delays related to the Three Mile Island accident and stricter regulations the plant cost $1.3 billion by the time it was completed in 1984.

SCE&G and Carolina Energies merged in 1982 under the SCE&G name. SCANA Corporation was formed two years later to allow the company to separate its utility business from nonregulated activities. The company formed an energy marketing subsidiary in 1988.

In 1989 Hurricane Hugo wiped out power to 300000 customers. SCE&G's efforts to quickly restore power in its storm-ravaged territory won it industry praise.

Moving into telecommunications SCANA in 1994 joined ITC Holding (now ITC^DeltaCom) to build a fiber-optic network in the Southeast. In 1996 SCANA invested in Powertel which launched PCS wireless phone service in the Southeast later that year.

Meanwhile in 1995 SCANA and Westvaco formed a joint venture Cogen South to build a cogeneration plant to provide power to a Westvaco paper mill in Charleston. SCANA sold its oil and gas subsidiary Petroleum Resources to Kelley Oil in 1997.

As deregulation overtures became stronger in 1998 SCANA expanded its natural gas business by entering Georgia's deregulated market where it quickly became a leader. In 1999 it began planning to extend its gas pipeline into North Carolina sold its propane assets to Suburban Propane to reduce debt and agreed to buy natural gas distributor Public Service Company of North Carolina in a $900 million deal which closed in 2000.

Also in 2000 SCANA sold its home security business and swapped its 27% stake in Powertel for stock in Deutsche Telekom which took control of the PCS provider. The following year SCANA agreed to sell its 800 MHz emergency radio network to Motorola; the deal was completed in 2002. Also that year SCANA sold its Deutsche Telecom interest.

SCANA purchased 50000 retail customer accounts in Georgia from Energy America a unit of UK utility Centrica in 2004.

SCANA in 2006 merged its two gas transportation units (SCG Pipeline and South Carolina Pipeline) as Carolina Gas Transmission.

The global recession with the resulting low commodity prices and demand pulled down SCANA's revenues and income in 2009.

EXECUTIVES

SVP; President and COO SCANA Energy Marketing SCANA Energy SCANA Communications and ServiceCare; Senior Executive Oversight PSNC Energy and South Carolina Electric & Gas Powering Marketing, George J. Bullwinkel Jr., age 63, $465,000 total compensation
Chairman and CEO, Kevin B. Marsh, age 56, $580,000 total compensation
Risk Management Officer and Treasurer, Mark R. Cannon
Corporate Secretary Associate General Counsel and Director Corporate Governance, Gina S. Champion
COO, Stephen A. Byrne, age 52
SVP Fuel Procurement and Asset Management, Sarena D. Burch, age 54
SVP and CFO, James E. (Jimmy) Addison, age 51, $412,500 total compensation
SVP Governmental Affairs and Economic Development, Charles B. McFadden, age 67
Controller, James E. Swan IV
VP Communications and Planning, Cathy Love
SVP; President and COO Carolina Gas Transmission, Paul V. Fant Sr., age 58
Manager Public Affairs, Eric Boomhower
Manager Media and Community Relations, Simone McKinney
SVP and Chief Nuclear Officer South Carolina Electric & Gas, Jeffrey B. (Jeff) Archie, age 54
SVP General Counsel and Assistant Secretary, Ronald T. (Ron) Lindsay, age 61
Director, James M. (Jim) Micali, age 64
Director, Harold C. Stowe, age 65
Director, James A. Bennett, age 51
Director, Lynne M. Miller, age 60
Director, Maceo K. Sloan, age 61
Director, Bill L. Amick, age 68
Director, D. Maybank Hagood, age 50
Director, Sharon Allred Decker, age 55
Director, James W. Roquemore, age 57
Director, Joshua W. Martin III, age 67
Auditors: Deloitte&ToucheLLP

LOCATIONS

HQ: SCANA Corporation
100 SCANA Pkwy., Cayce SC 29033
Phone: 803-217-9000 **Fax:** 803-217-8119
Web: www.scana.com

PRODUCTS/OPERATIONS

2011 Sales

	$ mil.	% of total
Electric operations	2,424	55
Gas (nonregulated)	1,136	26
Gas (regulated)	849	19
Total	**4,409**	**100**

Selected Operations

Carolina Gas Transmission Corp. (gas transportation and natural gas purchase transmission and sale; LNG liquefaction storage and regasification plants)
Public Service Company of North Carolina Incorporated (dba PSNC Energy natural gas distribution)
SCANA Communications Inc. (fiber-optic telecommunications tower construction and investments)

SCANA Energy Marketing Inc. (electricity and natural gas marketing)
SCANA Energy (retail natural gas marketing)
SCANA Services Inc. (support services)
ServiceCare Inc. (maintenance for home appliances)
South Carolina Electric & Gas Company (SCE&G electric and gas utility)
South Carolina Fuel Company Inc. (financing for SCE&G' s nuclear fuel fossil fuel and sulfur dioxide emission allowances)
South Carolina Generating Company Inc. (GENCO owns and operates Williams power plant and sells electricity to SCE&G)

COMPETITORS

AEP
AGL Resources
CenterPoint Energy
Dominion Resources
Duke Energy
Dynegy
El Paso Corporation
Entergy
Green Mountain Energy
Laclede Group
NextEra Energy
North Carolina Electric Membership
Piedmont Natural Gas
Progress Energy
PS Energy
Santee Cooper
Sempra Energy
Southern Company
TVA

HISTORICAL FINANCIALS

Company Type: Public

Income Statement FYE: December 31

	REVENUE ($ mil.)	NET INCOME ($ mil.)	NET PROFIT MARGIN	EMPLOYEES
12/11	4,409	387	8.8%	5,889
12/10	4,601	376	8.2%	5,877
12/09	4,237	357	8.4%	5,828
12/08	5,319	346	6.5%	5,786
12/07	4,621	320	6.9%	5,703
Annual Growth	(1.2%)	4.9%	—	0.8%

2011 Year-End Financials

Debt ratio: 39.20%
Return on equity: 9.95%
Cash ($ mil.): 29
Current ratio: 90.80
Long-term debt ($ mil.): 4,622
No. of shares (mil.): 130
Dividends
Yield: —
Payout: 65.32%
Market value ($ mil.): 5,858

	STOCK PRICE ($) FY Close	P/E High/Low		PER SHARE ($) Earnings	Dividends	Book Value
12/11	45.06	15	12	2.97	0.00	29.92
12/10	40.60	14	12	2.98	1.90	29.15
12/09	37.68	13	9	2.85	1.88	27.71
12/08	35.60	14	10	2.95	1.84	26.76
12/07	42.15	17	13	2.74	1.76	26.26
Annual Growth	1.7%	—	—	2.0%	—	3.3%

SCBT Financial Corp

SCBT Financial is the holding company for South Carolina Bank and Trust and South Carolina Bank and Trust of the Piedmont (both banks are also known as SCBT) which operate about 90 branches throughout the Palmetto state. The company also owns North Carolina Bank and Trust or NCBT which has three locations in the Charlotte area. Serving retail and business customers the banks provide deposit accounts loans and mortgages as well as trust and investment planning services. More than half of the company's loan portfolio is devoted to commercial mortgages; consumer real estate loans are more than a quarter. SCBT Financial is buying The Savannah Bancorp for $67.1 million.

The Savannah Bancorp also owns two bank subsidiaries: The Savannah Bank and Bryan Bank & Trust. The purchase will add 11 branches to the company's network. Previously in 2012 SCBT acquired Peoples Bancorporation in South Carolina. That deal added about 10 branches. The company is also growing by opening new branches and loan production offices.

SCBT Financial entered northern Georgia in 2010 when it acquired the failed Community Bank & Trust; the deal added more than 30 locations most of them inside supermarkets. SCBT acquired two other failed banks the following year Habersham Bank in Georgia and South Carolina-based BankMeridian. All three transactions were made with assistance from the FDIC. The Community Bank & Trust acquisition helped SCBT achieve record net income in 2010 (nearly $52 million) though the company's nonperforming assets nearly tripled.

Earnings were down by more than half in 2011 as SCBT recorded smaller acquisition gains from the Habersham and BankMeridian transactions and nonperforming assets continued to rise (though not nearly as much as the previous year).

EXECUTIVES

President CEO and Director; CEO South Carolina Bank and Trust, Robert R. Hill Jr., age 45, $400,000 total compensation
SEVP Manager Retail Banking and Division Head Lowcountry and Orangeburg Regions, Dane H. Murray, age 62
Chairman SCBT Financial and South Carolina Bank and Trust, Robert R. Horger, age 61
Vice Chairman SCBT Financial and South Carolina Bank and Trust, Dwight W. Frierson, age 55
EVP and Treasurer, Richard C. Mathis, age 61, $190,000 total compensation
SEVP and COO, John C. Pollok, age 46, $256,000 total compensation
SEVP and Chief Risk Officer, Joe E. Burns, age 57, $175,000 total compensation
President Northern Banking Group, Thomas S. Camp, age 60, $202,500 total compensation
President South Carolina Bank and Trust, John F. Windley, age 59, $215,000 total compensation
President Wealth Management Group, Todd Harward
Secretary, Renee R. Brooks
President Western Banking Group, Greg A. Lapointe
EVP and CFO, Donald E. (Donnie) Pickett
President CEO and Director; CEO South Carolina Bank and Trust, Robert R. Hill Jr., age 45
Vice Chairman SCBT Financial and South Carolina Bank and Trust, Dwight W. Frierson, age 55
Director, Harry M. Mims Jr., age 70
Director, James W. Roquemore, age 57
Director, John W. Williamson III, age 63
Director, M. Oswald Fogle, age 67
Director, Thomas E. Suggs, age 62
Director, Luther J. Battiste III, age 62
Director, Ralph W. Norman Jr., age 58
Director, James E. (Jimmy) Addison, age 51
Director, Susie H. VanHuss, age 72
Director, Alton C. (Al) Phillips, age 48
Director, Herbert G. (Herb) Gray
Director, Kevin P. Walker, age 62
Auditors: DixonHughesGoodmanLLP

LOCATIONS

HQ: SCBT Financial Corporation
520 Gervais St., Columbia SC 29201
Phone: 803-771-2265 **Fax:** 803-531-0524
Web: www.scbandt.com

PRODUCTS/OPERATIONS

2011 Sales

	$ mil.	% of total
Interest		
Loans including fees	162	68
Investment securities	8	4
Other	1	-
Noninterest		
Service charges on deposit accounts	22	10
Gain on acquisitions	16	7
Bankcard services	11	5
Mortgage banking	6	3
Securities gains net	5	2
Amortization of FDIC indemnification asset	(10.1)	-
Other	2	1
Total	**293**	**100**

COMPETITORS

Bank of America
Bank of South Carolina
BB&T
First Citizens Bancorporation
First Financial Holdings
Regions Financial
Security Federal

HISTORICAL FINANCIALS

Company Type: Public

Income Statement FYE: December 31

	ASSETS ($ mil.)	NET INCOME ($ mil.)	INCOME AS % OF ASSETS	EMPLOYEES
12/11	3,896	22	0.6%	1,071
12/10	3,594	51	1.4%	1,015
12/09	2,702	13	0.5%	700
12/08	2,766	15	0.6%	692
12/07	2,597	21	0.8%	701
Annual Growth	10.7%	1.2%	—	11.2%

2011 Year-End Financials

Debt ratio: 1.20%
Return on equity: 5.92%
Cash ($ mil.): 131
Current ratio: —
Long-term debt ($ mil.): 46
No. of shares (mil.): 14
Dividends
Yield: —
Payout: 41.72%
Market value ($ mil.): 407

	STOCK PRICE ($) FY Close	P/E High/Low		PER SHARE ($) Earnings	Dividends	Book Value
12/11	29.01	22	15	1.63	0.00	27.19
12/10	32.75	10	7	4.08	0.68	25.79
12/09	27.69	47	23	0.74	0.68	22.20
12/08	34.50	25	17	1.52	0.68	21.77
12/07	31.67	18	12	2.32	0.67	21.17
Annual Growth	(2.2%)	—	—	(8.4%)	—	6.5%

Schein (Henry), Inc.

From Poughkeepsie to Prague Henry Schein outfits dental offices around the world with everything they need. The company is a leading global distributor of dental supplies equipment and pharmaceuticals. Henry Schein provides everything from the delicate hand held tools up to the X-ray equipment and patient chairs as well as office supplies and anesthetics. But the company isn't only interested in teeth: It also supplies doctors' offices veterinarians and other office-based health care providers with diagnostic kits surgical tools drugs vaccines and animal health products. Other offerings include practice management software repair services and financing.

Operations

Henry Schein's health care distribution segment accounts for nearly all of the company's sales and is divided into four smaller divisions: dental (US and Canada) medical (US) animal health (US) and international (dental medical and animal health products sold in Europe Australia and New Zealand). The company also has a health care technology segment that provides practice management software and related services worldwide.

Geographic Reach

Henry Schein operates about 65 distribution centers throughout the US Canada the Asia/Pacific region and Europe. It also distributes through affiliates in some areas including the Middle East and Iceland.

Strategy

Henry Schein is a leader the North American dental supply market. One root of its success is its distribution strategy: it operates about 65 distribution centers throughout the globe that can quickly fill and deliver orders to nearby customers. In areas without distribution centers it delivers products through direct air package service. It also distributes through affiliates in certain areas.

Its overall growth strategy is counting on an aging US population that requires more dental care a steady increase in cosmetic dentistry and a migration of care from acute care settings (hospitals) to physician offices.

While still focusing on increasing sales of its core dental product lines the company has significantly widened its presence in the medical and animal health markets both through acquisitions and by introducing new products and services.

Sales & Marketing

The company sells its products via direct mail telephone sales and a field sales force.

Mergers & Acquisitions

Not content with its market leading position in North America the company aggressively pursues acquisitions to expand its geographic reach.

In 2012 Henry Schein targeted the European animal health market when it paid some $40 million to acquire AUV Veterinary Services from Dutch firm AUV Group. The purchase secured Henry Schein the leading distributor of veterinary supplies in Belgium and the Netherlands. It also moved to expand in Ireland that year when it purchased animal health products distributor C&M Vetlink.

Also in 2012 the firm increased its ownership interest in Butler Schein Animal Health which distributes companion animal health supplies to vets in the US to about 72%. (Henry Schein had acquired a majority stake in Butler Schein Animal Health then known as Butler Animal Health in 2009 effectively trippling the tripled the size of its domestic animal health division).

In 2011 the company entered the veterinary market in Australia and New Zealand with the $92 million buy of Provet Holdings. The purchase helped Henry Schein cement its strategy to expand its international health care distribution unit which grew from some $2.5 billion in sales in 2010 to some $3 billion in sales in 2011.

Henry Schein expanded its health care technology segment through the acquisition of majority ownership of ImproMed and McAllister Software Systems both developers of veterinary practice management systems in the US.

Financial Analysis

Henry Schein's international health care distribution unit grew from some $2.5 billion in sales in 2010 to some $3 billion in sales in 2011. Coupled with increases in its other segments the company achieved overall revenue growth of 13% in 2011 from $7.5 billion to $8.5 billion; net income also grew 13% to $367 million.

Henry Schein's mix of consumable basics (filling amalgam cement polish) and big-ticket equipment (imaging systems lasers nitrous oxide systems) helped it ride out the economic recession with no dips in revenue.

HISTORY

For more than 50 years Henry Schein distributed drugs made by Schein Pharmaceuticals. In 1992 management spun off the drug business and led by former accountant Stanley Bergman began acquiring other dental supply companies at a terrific rate: 34 between 1994 and 1996 alone.

The company went public in 1995 and bought more than a dozen businesses. These purchases which included product marketer Vertex Corporation's distribution unit moved Henry Schein into the medical and veterinary supply fields. The purchase of Schein Dental Equipment (founded by Marvin Schein) boosted per-customer sales by adding big-ticket merchandise to the product mix.

Acquisitions continued hot and heavy as the company boosted operations abroad. The purchases hit the bottom line; Schein avoided bloat by restructuring operations closing facilities and developing new systems. The company consolidated 13 distribution centers into five in 1997. The following year the firm expanded into Canada and bought a controlling stake in UK direct marketer Porter Nash.

To boost profits the company announced in 2000 that it would cut 5% of its workforce. It also shut down some facilities and sold its software development business as part of its overall restructuring plan. In 2001 the firm resumed its acquisitions when it bought the dental supply business of drug maker Zila. Over the next few years it expanded internationally when it bought up firms in the Czech Republic Germany Italy New Zealand and the UK.

Choosing to focus on supplying office-based health care practitioners in 2006 it sold its hospital supply business for $36.5 million. Other dispositions have included the sale of its oncology and specialty pharmaceutical businesses (2007) and a dental products wholesaler (2009).

EXECUTIVES

EVP Global Corporate Strategy and Director, Mark E. Mlotek, age 56, $475,000 total compensation

EVP Chief Administrative Officer and Director, Gerald A. Benjamin, age 59, $296,207 total compensation

President COO and Director, James P. Breslawski, age 58, $600,000 total compensation

SVP and Chief Compliance Officer, Leonard A. David, age 63

EVP CFO and Director, Steven Paladino, age 55, $475,000 total compensation

Chairman and CEO, Stanley M. Bergman, age 62, $1,150,000 total compensation

SVP and Chief Merchandising Officer, Michael Racioppi, age 57, $340,275 total compensation

President International Group, Michael Zack, age 59

VP Corporate Communications, Susan Vassallo

Senior Advisor, Stanley Komaroff, age 76, $475,000 total compensation

SVP and CTO, James A. (Jim) Harding, age 56

President Global Healthcare Specialties Group, Lonnie Shoff, age 53

VP Investor Relations, Neal Goldner

SVP and General Counsel, Michael S. Ettinger

Director, Philip A. (Phil) Laskawy, age 71

Director, Paul K. Brons, age 70

EVP Global Corporate Strategy and Director, Mark E. Mlotek, age 56

EVP Chief Administrative Officer and Director, Gerald A. Benjamin, age 59

President COO and Director, James P. Breslawski, age 58

EVP CFO and Director, Steven Paladino, age 55

Director, Karyn Mashima, age 58

Director, Norman S. Matthews, age 79

Director, Louis W. Sullivan, age 77

Director, Bradley T. Sheares, age 55

Director, Barry J. Alperin, age 72

Director, Donald J. Kabat, age 76

Auditors: BDOUSALLP

LOCATIONS

HQ: Henry Schein Inc.
135 Duryea Rd., Melville NY 11747
Phone: 631-843-5500 **Fax:** 631-843-5676
Web: www.henryschein.com

2011 Sales

	$ mil.	% of total
US	5,212	61
Other countries	2,573	30

PRODUCTS/OPERATIONS

2011 Sales

	$ mil.	% of total
Health care distributi		
International	3,012	35
Dental	2,861	33
Medical	1,412	17
Animal health	993	12
Technology	250	3
Total	**8,530**	**100**

Selected Acquisitions

2012
- Accord (75% full-service dental distribution Thailand)
- Modern Laboratory Services (medical and clinical lab supply distribution California)
- Ortho Technology Inc. (orthodontics distributor Florida)

COMPETITORS

Allscripts
athenahealth
Benco Dental
Burkhart Dental
Cardinal Health
Carestream Health
Darby Dental
IDEXX Labs
McKesson
MWI Veterinary Supply
NextGen
Omega Pharma
Patterson Companies
PSS World Medical
Sybron Dental

HISTORICAL FINANCIALS

Company Type: Public

Income Statement FYE: December 31

	REVENUE ($ mil.)	NET INCOME ($ mil.)	NET PROFIT MARGIN	EMPLOYEES
12/11	8,530	367	4.3%	15,000
12/10	7,526	325	4.3%	13,500
12/09	6,538	311	4.8%	12,500
12/08	6,394	243	3.8%	12,500
12/07	5,920	215	3.6%	12,000
Annual Growth	9.6%	14.3%	—	5.7%

2011 Year-End Financials

Debt ratio: 9.31%
Return on equity: 15.12%
Cash ($ mil.): 147
Current ratio: 178.71
Long-term debt ($ mil.): 363
No. of shares (mil.): 89
Dividends
Yield: —
Payout: —
Market value ($ mil.): 5,794

	STOCK PRICE ($) FY Close	P/E High/Low		PER SHARE ($) Earnings	Dividends	Book Value
12/11	64.43	18	15	3.97	0.00	27.05
12/10	62.16	17	14	3.49	0.00	26.23
12/09	53.01	16	10	3.44	0.00	23.85
12/08	35.38	23	12	2.67	0.00	21.62
12/07	62.05	26	19	2.36	0.00	19.87
Annual Growth	0.9%	—	—	13.9%	—	8.0%

Schwab (Charles) Corp.

The once-rebellious Charles Schwab is all grown up. The discount broker now offers the same traditional brokerage services it shunned some three decades ago. Schwab manages nearly $1.9 trillion in assets for approximately 10 million individual and institutional clients. Traders can access its services via telephone wireless device the Internet and through more than 300 offices in some 45 states plus London and Hong Kong. Besides discount brokerage the firm offers financial research advice and planning; investment management; retirement and employee compensation plans; and about 70 proprietary Schwab and Laudus mutual funds.

Though its Charles Schwab Bank unit which provides mortgages CDs and other banking products the company remains in step with the industrywide movement toward one-stop shopping for financial services. This strategy as well as its ongoing pursuit of technological innovations and product expansion helps the company meet the evolving financial services needs of its diverse client base.

The company's OneSource service offers investors access to more than 2000 no-load funds. Schwab also provides access to nearly 28000 bonds bond funds and other fixed income investment products from more than 300 dealers. Additional services include futures and commodities trading access to IPOs and educational investment materials including ratings of more than 3000 stocks. Schwab provides trading and support services to independent investment advisors as well.

Schwab's assets under management continue to balloon though its income levels have slipped as clients make fewer equity trades due to the shaky investment environment. Historically low interest rates negatively impact the company and the Federal Reserve has said that rates are expected to remain low until at least 2014. One-time charges in 2010 related to litigation and regulatory matters exiting the credit card business and losses in money market funds have also impacted the company's bottom line. Trading revenues picked up the following year as did asset management and administration fees. Although revenues grew some 9% in 2011 (to $4.9 billion) and net income rose 90% (to $864 million) the company hasn't yet recovered to the earning levels of 2007 and 2008.

That year portfolio manager AXA Rosenberg disclosed that it had discovered a coding glitch in its computer-driven investment models. The firm helped run funds for various asset managers and pension plans including Charles Schwab's four Laudus Rosenberg funds. Charles Schwab liquidated the funds in the aftermath of the disclosure.

Charles Schwab continues to grow via acquisitions. To that end it has agreed to acquire Massachusetts-based ThomasPartners a dividend income-focused asset management firm with some $2.3 billion in assets under management. The deal which is expected to close by the end of 2012 includes an upfront payment of $85 million in cash and potential performance-dependent payments later on. In 2011 Charles Schwab acquired retail brokerage optionsXpress. The $1 billion deal helps expand its client base and online equity options and futures trading business and it has already boosted the company's trading revenues. In another 2011 transaction Charles Schwab acquired Compliance11. The deal helped expand Charles Schwab's abilities to offer compliance monitoring and reporting.

PrevioAlso in 2010 Charles Schwab purchased investment advisory firm Windward Investment Management for some $150 million in cash and stock. The deal broadened Charles Schwab's presence in the growing exchange-traded funds (ETF) market. ETFs which trade like stocks have gained popularity as investment tools because of their flexibility and they often have lower costs than other products. Schwab changed the acquired firm's name to Windhaven Investment Management after the transaction was complete.

Chairman Charles Schwab owns approximately 16% of his namesake firm.

HISTORY

During the 1960s Stanford graduate Charles Schwab founded First Commander Corp. which managed investments and published a newsletter. But he failed to properly register with the SEC and after a hiatus he returned to the business under the name Charles Schwab & Co. in 1971. Initially a full-service broker Schwab moved into discount brokerage after the SEC outlawed fixed commissions in 1975. While most brokers defiantly raised commissions Schwab cut its rates steeply.

From 1977 to 1983 Schwab's client list increased thirtyfold and revenues grew from $4.6 million to $126.5 million enabling the firm to automate its operations and develop cash-management account systems. To gain capital Charles sold the company to BankAmerica (now Bank of America) in 1983. Schwab grew but federal regulations prevented expansion into such services as mutual funds and telephone trading. Charles bought his company back in 1987 and took it public. When the stock market crashed later that year trading volume fell by nearly half from 17900 per day. Stung Schwab diversified further offering new fee-based services. Commission revenues fell from 64% of sales in 1987 to 39% in 1990 but by 1995 the long bull market had pushed commissions to more than 50%.

In 1989 Schwab introduced TeleBroker a 24-hour Touch-Tone telephone trading service available in English Spanish Mandarin or Cantonese.

Schwab continued to diversify courting independent financial advisors. Other buys included Mayer & Schweitzer (1991 now Schwab Capital Markets) an OTC market maker that accounted for about 7% of all NASDAQ trades. In 1993 the firm opened its first overseas office in London but traded only in dollar-denominated stocks until it bought Share-Link (later Charles Schwab Europe) the UK's largest discount brokerage in 1995. It subsequently sold the British pound sterling brokerage business to Barclays PLC although it has maintained its US dollar business in the UK.

During the next year Schwab made a concerted effort to build its retirement services by creating a 401(k) administration and investment services unit. In 1997 Schwab allied with J.P. Morgan Hambrecht & Quist and Credit Suisse First Boston (CSFB) to give its customers access to IPOs; the next year the relationship with CSFB deepened to give Schwab access to debt offerings. In late 1997 and early 1998 Schwab reorganized to reflect its new business lines. The firm also began recruiting talent rather than promoting from within.

Expansion was key at the turn of the century. In 1999 Schwab moved toward more broker-advised investing: It inked a deal (geared toward its retirement products customers) with online financial advice firm Financial Engines and introduced Velocity a desktop system designed to make trading easier for fiscally endowed investors. In 2000 Schwab bought online broker CyBerCorp (later CyberTrader) as well as U.S. Trust which markets to affluent clients.

While Schwab's World Trade Center offices were destroyed by the September 11 terrorist attacks the company did not lose any of its New York staff.

To pare expenses Schwab reduced its workforce by about 35% between 2000 and 2003. Founder and chairman Charles Schwab relinquished his role of co-CEO in early 2003 only to move back into the driver's seat in mid-2004 when former CEO David Pottruck was asked to step down by the company's board.

One of Schwab's first orders of business was to reexamine the company's 2004 acquisition of SoundView Technology Group which was combined with its Capital Markets operations to form Schwab SoundView Capital Markets. While the purchase was intended to help the company beef up its services for institutional investors Schwab said that SoundView lacked "synergy" with the company's tradition of supporting the individual investor and sold the business to Swiss bank UBS.

Schwab acquired The 401(k) Companies from Nationwide Financial Services in 2007. The addition became part of the company's existing Charles Schwab Trust subsidiary which serves as a trustee for employee benefit plans. Also that year Schwab sold U.S. Trust to Bank of America for some $3.3 billion in cash and shut down its CyberTrader day trading arm merging the direct-access brokerage's business with its own.

EXECUTIVES

EVP General Counsel and Secretary, Carrie E. Dwyer, age 61, $500,000 total compensation

Chairman, Charles R. (Chuck) Schwab, age 74, $500,000 total compensation

EVP Branch Network, Jeffrey R. (Jeff) Carney

SVP and Chief Investment Strategist Charles Schwab and Company, Elizabeth (Liz Ann) Sonders
SVP Investor Relations, Richard G. Fowler
President CEO and Director; CEO Charles Schwab Bank, Walter W. (Walt) Bettinger II, age 51, $900,000 total compensation
EVP; President Charles Schwab Bank, Paul V. Woolway
EVP and COO Schwab Investor Services, G. Andrew Gill
EVP and Chief Marketing Officer, Laurine M. Garrity, age 50
SVP Corporate Public Relations, Greg Gable
EVP Shared Strategic Services, John S. Clendening
EVP and CFO, Joseph R. Martinetto, age 49, $450,000 total compensation
EVP Institutional Services, James D. McCool, age 53, $475,000 total compensation
EVP Investor Services, Benjamin L. Brigeman, age 49, $475,000 total compensation
President and CEO Charles Schwab Investment Management, Marie A. Chandoha
EVP Human Resources and Employee Services, Jay L. Allen, age 55
EVP Schwab Investor Development, Lisa Kidd Hunt
VP Participant Services, Catherine Golladay
Public Relations, Sarah Bulgatz
Public Relations, Mike Cianfrocca
Public Relations, Lindsay Tiles
Public Relations, Alison Wertheim
SVP Corporate Brokerage Services, Trish Cox
SVP Schwab Equity Ratings, Greg Forsythe
Director Trading and Derivatives Charles Schwab and Company, Randy Frederick
Managing Director ETF Research Charles Schwab Investment Advisory, Michael Iachini
SVP Shared Strategic Services Charles Schwab and Company, Rene L. Kim
SVP Windhaven Investment Management, Bryan Olson
VP and Chief Investment Officer Charles Schwab Investment Advisory, James D. Peterson
SVP Schwab Center for Financial Research; President Charles Schwab Investment Advisory, Mark W. Riepe
SVP Schwab Community Services Charles Schwab and Company; President Charles Schwab Foundation, Carrie Schwab-Pomerantz
Director Market Sector Research Schwab Center for Financial Research, Brad Sorensen
VP Financial Planning Schwab Center for Financial Research, Rande Spiegelman
EVP Advisor Services, Bernard J. Clark
Public Relations, Dan Mahoney
Public Relations, Alyson Nikulicz
Public Relations, Anita Fox
Public Relations, Susan Forman
Public Relations, Jennifer Davis
EVP and CIO, Bradley J. (Brad) Peterson, age 53
EVP Operational Services, Ron Carter
EVP and Chief Marketing Officer, Jonathan M. Craig
EVP Corporate Risk, Nigel J. Murtagh
Director, Robert N. Wilson, age 71
Director, Frank C. Herringer, age 69
Director, Roger O. Walther, age 76
Director, Paula A. Sneed, age 64
Director, Arun Sarin, age 57
Director, Nancy H. Bechtle, age 74
Director, C. Preston Butcher, age 73
Director, Stephen T. McLin, age 65
President CEO and Director; CEO Charles Schwab Bank, Walter W. (Walt) Bettinger II, age 51
Auditors: Deloitte&ToucheLLP

LOCATIONS

HQ: Schwab (Charles) Corp.
211 Main Street, San Francisco, CA 94105
Phone: 415 667-7000 **Fax:** 415 627-8894
Web: www.aboutschwab.com

PRODUCTS/OPERATIONS

2011 Sales

	$ mil.	% of total
Asset management & administration fees		
Mutual funds	1,095	22
Advice solutions	522	11
Other	311	6
Interest	1,900	39
Trading revenue		
Commissions	866	17
Principal transactions	61	1
Other	129	3
Total	**4,884**	**100**

Selected Subsidiaries

Charles Schwab Bank
Charles Schwab Investment Management Inc. (mutual fund investment adviser)
Schwab Holdings Inc.
Charles Schwab & Co. Inc. (securities broker-dealer)

COMPETITORS

Ameriprise
Bank of America
E*TRADE Financial
Edward Jones
FMR
Franklin Templeton
John Hancock Financial Services
Legg Mason
Morgan Stanley
Principal Financial
Raymond James Financial
Scottrade
ShareBuilder
TD Ameritrade
The Vanguard Group

HISTORICAL FINANCIALS

Company Type: Public

Income Statement FYE: December 31

	REVENUE ($ mil.)	NET INCOME ($ mil.)	NET PROFIT MARGIN	EMPLOYEES
12/11	4,691	864	18.4%	14,100
12/10	4,248	454	10.7%	12,800
12/09	4,193	787	18.8%	12,400
12/08	5,150	1,212	23.5%	13,400
12/07	4,994	2,407	48.2%	13,300
Annual Growth	(1.6%)	(22.6%)	—	1.5%

2011 Year-End Financials

Debt ratio: 1.84%
Return on equity: 11.20%
Cash ($ mil.): 34,713
Current ratio: 47.83
Long-term debt ($ mil.): 2,001
No. of shares (mil.): 1,271
Dividends
Yield: —
Payout: 34.29%
Market value ($ mil.): 14,313

	STOCK PRICE ($) FY Close	P/E High	P/E Low	PER SHARE ($) Earnings	Dividends	Book Value
12/11	11.26	28	15	0.70	0.00	6.07
12/10	17.11	52	34	0.38	0.24	5.18
12/09	18.82	29	17	0.68	0.24	4.37
12/08	16.17	25	14	1.05	0.22	3.51
12/07	25.55	13	9	1.97	1.20	3.22
Annual Growth	(18.5%)	—	—	(22.8%)	—	17.2%

Science Applications International Corp.

LOCATIONS

HQ: Science Applications International Corp.
1710 SAIC Drive, McLean, VA 22102
Phone: 703 676-4300

HISTORICAL FINANCIALS

Company Type:

Income Statement FYE: January 31

	REVENUE ($ mil.)	NET INCOME ($ mil.)	NET PROFIT MARGIN	EMPLOYEES
01/12	10,587	56	0.5%	41,000
01/11	10,921	611	5.6%	0
01/10	10,580	482	4.6%	0
01/07	8,294	391	4.7%	44,100
01/06	7,792	927	11.9%	43,600
Annual Growth	8.0%	(50.4%)	—	(1.5%)

2012 Year-End Financials

Debt ratio: 29.58%
Return on equity: 2.72%
Cash ($ mil.): 1,635
Current ratio: 139.01
Long-term debt ($ mil.): 1,419
No. of shares (mil.): 0
Dividends
Yield: —
Payout: —
Market value ($ mil.): —

Seaboard Corp.

With pork and turkey from the US flour from Haiti and sugar from Argentina Seaboard has a lot on its plate. The diversified agribusiness and transportation firm has operations in some 40 countries in the Americas the Caribbean and Africa. Seaboard sells its pork and poultry in the US and abroad. Overseas it trades grain (wheat soya) operates power plants and feed and flour mills and grows and refines sugar cane. Seaboard owns a shipping service for containerized cargo between the US the Caribbean and South America; it has shipping terminals in Miami and Houston and a fleet of 40 vessels (12 owned others chartered) and ships to ports worldwide. Seaboard is run by descendants of founder Otto Bresky.

Operations

In the US Seaboard is a leading producer and processor of pork (with about a 9% market share of all pork processed in the US) with operations in Oklahoma Kansas Texas and Colorado. (It has the capacity to produce about 4 million hogs annually.) Despite what some consider to be an industry oversupply of pork Seaboard has significantly expanded its pork business with an emphasis on private-label preseasoned pork products. It markets some of its pork products under the Prairie Fresh (in the US) Seaboard Farms (international) and Daily's brands. The company has an agreement with Missouri-Based Triumph Foods to process and market all of Triumph's pork products. Looking to add poultry to its lineup Seaboard in December 2010 acquired a 50% stake in the US's largest turkey producer Butterball from Maxwell Farms for $177 million. (Maxwell previously bought out 49%-owner Smithfield)

As its name suggests Seaboard is engaged in ocean transportation which is sensitive to the global economy. (In 2009 demand for its transportation services dipped as global trade contracted.) Year-over-year unit volume fell for the first time in more than a decade. Also service to Port-au-Prince was interrupted by the earthquake.

Overseas the company operates mainly commodity merchandising grain processing sugar production and electric power generation. In addition to shipping and the trading of sugar pork and commodities Seaboard grows and processes citrus and sugar and has distillery operations in Argentina; it manufactures ethanol and has trucking transportation operations in the US. It also owns jalape?o farms in Texas and Honduras.

Financial Analysis

Following a dropoff in 2009 caused by the global financial crisis Seaboard has posted two years of robust sales and earnings growth. In 2011 sales increased 31% vs. 2010 and net income rose nearly 22% over the same period. (In the previous annual comparison sales rose 22% while net income tripled.) The company credited the increase in sales in 2011 vs. 2010 to higher prices and volumes of commodities traded and also an increase in overall sale prices for pork products.

Ownership

CEO and director Steven Bresky owns nearly 75% of Seaboard's shares.

HISTORY

Otto Bresky founded his company as a flour broker in 1916. He acquired his first flour mill in Atchison Kansas in 1918 and the following year purchased the Imperial Brewery Co. in Kansas City and converted it to a flour mill. Over the next four decades Bresky ground out a series of acquisitions of milling companies. In 1928 he purchased Rodney Milling Co. and retained the name as the identity for the family business. The company then purchased Ismert-Hincke Milling Co. (1938) and the Consolidated Flour Mills Co. (1950). In 1959 Rodney Milling merged with publicly traded Hathaway Industries and changed its name to Seaboard Allied Milling Corp.

In the 1960s Seaboard Allied became one of the first millers to shift flour milling from the source of the raw materials (the wheat fields of the Great Plains) to the population centers in the Southeast and on the East Coast. In 1962 Seaboard Allied built a flour mill in Chattanooga Tennessee. It then purchased George Urban Milling Company in Buffalo New York (1965) and built a flour mill in Jacksonville Florida (1966). But Bresky's expansionist strategy did not stop at the Atlantic Seaboard. The company acquired a flour mill in Guayaquil Ecuador in 1966 (a joint venture with Continental Grain Co.) then constructed flour mills in Freetown Sierra Leone (1968) and Georgetown Guyana (1969).

Bresky retired in 1973 and was succeeded by his son Harry. A chip off the old block Harry acquired a flour mill in Cleveland Tennessee and built flour mills in Buchanan Liberia and in Sapele Nigeria that year. In 1978 Seaboard Allied acquired Mochasa Ecuador's leading producer of animal feed and launched Top Feeds a mixed-feed plant in Sapele.

Facing stiff competition in the mill business from agribusiness giants in 1982 Seaboard Allied sold all its US flour mills to Cargill. The company changed its name to Seaboard that year and began expanding outside the US. In 1983 the company formed Seaboard Marine a shipping business in Florida to serve its increasingly far-flung enterprises.

In addition to geographic diversification the company expanded into new agribusiness areas. Seaboard acquired Central Soya's poultry unit in 1984 and it bought the Elberton Poultry Company the next year. Seaboard commenced shrimp farming operations in Ecuador in 1986 and in Honduras in 1987. Two years later Transcontinental Capital Corporation (Bermuda) a subsidiary began supplying power from a floating power barge to the Dominican Republic.

Seaboard entered the hog business in 1990 by acquiring a pork-processing plant in Albert Lea Minnesota. It opened a hog-processing facility in Guymon Oklahoma in 1996 and closed the Minnesota plant. That year the company bought a stake in Ingenio y Refinerio San Martin del Tabacal an Argentina-based sugar cane and citrus company. It then acquired flour-mill pasta-plant and cookie operations in Beira Mozambique.

During 1998 Seaboard bought a controlling interest in the Argentine sugar business purchased a Bulgarian winery and acquired a flour and feed milling business in Zambia.

In 2000 Seaboard sold its poultry division to ConAgra for $375 million. Also that year the company acquired a 35% stake in Unga Group (feed milling Kenya) and the JacintoPort marine terminal in Houston.

During 2001 the company traded its non-controlling interest in a joint-venture salmon processor (ContiSea LLC) to Norway's Fjord Seafood ASA for stock and swapped its majority ownership of one Bulgarian winery for minority ownership in a larger one. That same year it ceased production at its Honduran shrimp farms and jalape?o pickling operations.

Seaboard purchased more of Fjord Seafood in 2002; with 20% of the company it became the largest shareholder. However by the end of 2003 Seaboard sold off its entire investment in Fjord Seafood for $37 million. That same year the company sold its closed shrimp businesses. In 2004 the company acquired a controlling stake in a Mozambique grain milling business.

Seaboard acquired Daily's Foods for $45 million in 2005; the bacon processor and foodservice supplier has been added to the company's Seaboard Foods (formerly Seaboard Farms) unit.

After serving as CEO for more than 30 years in 2006 Harry Bresky stepped down as CEO (but remained as chairman) and turned over the company's reins to his son Steven. Harry Bresky died in 2007.

In 2010 Seaboard acquired a 50% stake in Butterball LLC.

EXECUTIVES

SVP Engineering, James L. (Jim) Gutsch, age 58
SVP General Counsel and Secretary, David M. Becker, age 50
SVP and CFO, Robert L. Steer, age 52, $655,631 total compensation
President CEO and Director, Steven J. Bresky, age 58, $858,985 total compensation
President Seaboard Foods, Rodney K. (Rod) Brenneman, age 47, $515,592 total compensation
SVP Corporate Controller and Chief Accounting Officer, John A. Virgo, age 51
President Seaboard Foods LLC, Terry J. Holton
SVP Finance and Treasurer, Barry E. Gum, age 45
SVP Governmental Affairs, Ralph L. Moss, age 66
SVP Taxation and Business Development, David S. Oswalt, age 44
President Seaboard Marine, Edward A. (Eddie) Gonzalez, age 46, $403,531 total compensation
President Seaboard Overseas Trading Group, David M. Dannov, age 50, $349,592 total compensation
VP Audit Services, Ty Tywater
Assistant Treasurer, Adriana N. Hoskins
President CEO and Director, Steven J. Bresky, age 58
Director, Joseph E. (Joe) Rodrigues, age 75
Director, David A. Adamsen, age 60
Director, Douglas W. Baena, age 69
Auditors: KPMGLLP

LOCATIONS

HQ: Seaboard Corporation
9000 W. 67th St., Shawnee Mission KS 66202
Phone: 913-676-8800 **Fax:** 913-676-8872
Web: www.seaboardcorp.com

2011 Sales

	$ mil.	% of total
Caribbean Central & South America	2,225	39
Africa	1,489	26
North America		
US	1,328	23
Canada & Mexico	407	7
Pacific Basin & Far East	238	4
Eastern Mediterranean	49	1
Europe	8	-
Total	**5,746**	**100**

PRODUCTS/OPERATIONS

2011 Sales

	$ mil.	% of total
Commodity trading & milling	2,689	47
Pork	1,744	30
Marine	928	16
Sugar	259	5
Power	111	2
Turkey	12	-
Total	**5,746**	**100**

Selected Operations

Cargo shipping
Citrus production and processing
Commodity merchandising (wheat corn and soybean meal)
Domestic trucking transportation
Electric power generation
Flour maize and feed milling
Jalape?o-pepper processing
Pork production and processing
Sugar production and refining

COMPETITORS

ADM
American Crystal Sugar
APL
Bay State Milling
Bunge Limited
Cargill
Carr' s Milling
CGC
Chelsea Milling
Chiquita Brands
CHS
Colonial Group
Crowley Maritime
CSX
Della Natura Commodities
Dole Food
Evergreen Marine
Evergreen Mills
Farmers Rice Milling
Fresh Del Monte Produce
Genco Shipping and
Jennie-O
Johnsonville Sausage
Louis Dreyfus Group
M. A. Patout
Makino
Mondelez International
Neptune Orient
Nicor Gas
Nutreco
NYK Line
Organic Milling
Overseas Shipholding Group
Sara Lee North American Retail
Smithfield Foods
Southern States
Star of the West
Sudzucker
Sunkist
Tate & Lyle
Tyson Foods
U.S. Sugar

Trading
Horizon Milling
Hormel
Imperial Sugar
Viterra Inc.
Western Sugar Cooperative
Zacky Farms

HISTORICAL FINANCIALS

Company Type: Public

Income Statement

FYE: December 31

	REVENUE ($ mil.)	NET INCOME ($ mil.)	NET PROFIT MARGIN	EMPLOYEES
12/11	5,746	345	6.0%	10,573
12/10	4,385	283	6.5%	10,865
12/09	3,601	92	2.6%	10,957
12/08	4,267	146	3.4%	10,734
12/07	3,213	181	5.6%	10,663
Annual Growth	15.6%	17.5%	—	(0.2%)

2011 Year-End Financials

Debt ratio: 5.77%
Return on equity: 16.64%
Cash ($ mil.): 71
Current ratio: 290.70
Long-term debt ($ mil.): 116

No. of shares (mil.): 1
Dividends
Yield: —
Payout: —
Market value ($ mil.): 2,465

	STOCK PRICE ($) FY Close	P/E High	P/E Low	PER SHARE ($) Earnings	Dividends	Book Value
12/11	2,036.00	10	6	284.66	0.001,717.27	
12/10	1,991.00	9	5	231.69	9.001,460.02	
12/09	1,349.00	21	11	74.74	3.001,246.54	
12/08	1,194.00	16	7	118.19	3.001,176.50	
12/07	1,470.00	19	10	144.15	3.001,088.36	
Annual Growth	8.5%	—	—	18.5%	—	12.1%

Sealed Air Corp.

Pop-Pop-Pop sounds like cha-ching for Sealed Air. Best known as the company that created Bubble Wrap Sealed Air also makes Instapak foam Jiffy mailers and Fill-Air inflatable packaging systems through its Protective Packing segment. Its largest segment Food Packaging makes Cryovac bags trays and absorbent pads for use by food processors and supermarkets to protect meat and poultry. Other products include shrink packaging for consumer goods such as toys and CDs; medical packaging for pacemakers and IV fluid; and specialty packaging for fabricators and the manufacturing industry. Sealed Air serves customers in 175 countries and operates through three subsidiaries: Sealed Air Cryovac and Diversey.

HISTORY

In the late 1950s after US engineer Al Fielding and Swiss inventor Marc Chavannes found no takers for their plastic air-bubble-embossed wallpaper they looked for another use for the material. They came up with Bubble Wrap the first product of Sealed Air which they founded in 1960 and took public soon after. AirCap as the material was first known didn't just protect products from damage; it also reduced storage and shipping costs.

Sealed Air expanded in the early 1970s into bubble-lined mailers and adhesive products with subsidiary PolyMask. With the $5 million company in the doldrums Dublin-born packaging veteran Dermot Dunphy was brought in as CEO in 1971. New products followed Dunphy's entrance including the Bubble Wrap-based Solar Pool Blanket. Sealed Air's sales moved beyond the US in the 1970s into Canada Japan and Western Europe. The company bought Instapak in 1977.

The purchase in 1983 of the Dri-Loc product line moved Sealed Air into food packaging. The company began selling static-control packaging in 1984 and in 1987 it bought padded-mailer maker Jiffy Packaging. Fielding and Chavannes both retired in 1987. Sealed Air pleaded guilty in 1989 to making illegal chemical shipments to Libya (made by a division the company has since sold).

By 1989 Sealed Air had plenty of cash on hand but with no appealing acquisitions to spend it on the company was a potential takeover target. It had also grown complacent. To provide greater incentive to the company's rank and file while warding off any buyout overtures Dunphy and CFO Bill Hickey took Sealed Air through a risky recapitalization. This plunged the company into debt but more than doubled its employees' ownership stake. The newly inspired packaging maker became more efficient the cost of Sealed Air's raw materials dropped and the company brought its debt back down over the next several years.

The acquisition of Korrvu in 1991 gave Sealed Air a gateway to innovative packaging for electronics manufacturers. The company made a host of mostly small purchases in Asia Australia Europe and North America between 1993 and 1996. When Sealed Air bought New Zealand-based Trigon Industries in 1995 its food-packaging business nearly doubled in size along with sales outside the US.

In 1998 Sealed Air made an Instapak-like expansion when it combined with W. R. Grace's packaging business (including the Cryovac Formpac and Omicron lines). Grace structured a deal with Sealed Air that gave Grace's shareholders about two-thirds of the resulting packaging-only company. Sealed Air tripled its sales and number of employees with the purchase.

The company restructured its operations in 1999 to integrate its newly acquired businesses. It closed facilities with overlapping operations and eliminated 750 jobs (5% of its workforce). Dunphy retired in 2000 (although he remains a director) and president William Hickey became CEO. That year Sealed Air acquired Dolphin Packaging (plastic packaging products) and Shanklin (high-performance shrink-film packaging equipment) to complement its shrink films.

In 2001 more than three years after the company combined its operations with W. R. Grace's packaging business Sealed Air continued to defend itself against asbestos lawsuits related to Grace's past operations. (In 2005 the company's definitive settlement agreement was accepted by the bankruptcy court.)

Another lawsuit was prompted by a 2003 fire in a New Jersey nightclub that killed 100 people. The fire occurred during a concert by the rock band Great White. Their pyrotechnics set fire to soundproofing material on the walls inside the club. The material was allegedly supplied by Sealed Air which did not admit to any wrongdoing. However the company agreed to pay $25 million to the victims' families in 2008.

Sealed Air restructured its reporting system in 2004 bringing its medical films connectors and tubing under its Food Packaging segment. It also cut nearly 400 employees and consolidated some of its operations.

Early in 2006 Sealed Air acquired Nelipak Holdings a Netherlands-based rigid packaging company. The company sold its security bag business (Trigon) to Ampac in 2007 and it sold its interest in joint venture PolyMask (surface protection films) to partner 3M.

To diversify its offerings the company bought selected assets in 2007 of The Dow Chemical Company's Ethafoam HRC (High Recycled Content) polyethylene foam product line which contains at least 65% recycled content. The acquisition gave Sealed Air all the rights to technologies customer contracts and trademarks as well as production equipment for Ethafoam Synergy Equifoam and Envision branded foam products. Dow made the products until 2009 at which time Sealed Air took over the manufacturing. The company opened a new manufacturing facility in Louisville Kentucky in November 2009 where it will manufacture Ethafoam and its Cell-Aire polyethylene foam packaging products.

With the realization that more than half of the company's were generated by international sales the company initiated a multi-year global manufacturing strategy starting in 2006 to better serve emerging high-growth regions. It streamlined current facilities and opened new ones in China Mexico and Poland; the initiative was completed in 2009.

Sealed Air made one of the most important acquisitions in its history in late 2011 when it acquired Diversey one of the largest industrial and institutional cleaning products manufacturer for around $2.6 billion.

EXECUTIVES

VP, Manuel Mondragon, age 62, $243,667 total compensation
VP General Counsel and Secretary, H. Katherine White, age 66, $261,667 total compensation
Controller, Jeffrey S. Warren, age 58
VP, James P. Mix, age 60
VP, Mary A. Coventry, age 58
VP, Jonathan B. Baker, age 58, $290,000 total compensation
President CEO and Director, William V. Hickey, age 67, $637,500 total compensation
VP, Hugh L. Sargant, age 63
Treasurer and Interim CFO, Tod S. Christie, age 53
VP, James Donald Tate, age 60
VP, J. Ryan Flanagan, age 48
VP, Ruth Roper, age 57
VP, Christopher C. Woodbridge, age 60
VP, Cheryl Fells Davis, age 59
VP, Karl R. Deily, age 54
VP, Jean-Marie Demeautis, age 61, $415,890 total compensation
Director Investor Relations, Amanda Butler
VP, Ann C. Savoca, age 53
SVP, Emile Z. Chammas, age 43
VP, Pedro Chidichimo, age 53
VP, Yagmar Sagnak, age 45
VP, Warren J. Kudman, age 49
VP, Larry Pillote, age 57
President CEO and Director, William V. Hickey, age 67
Director, Kenneth P. Manning, age 70
Director, George H. (Hank) Brown, age 72
Director, Lawrence R. (Larry) Codey, age 67
Director, T. J. Dermot Dunphy, age 79
Director, William J. (Bill) Marino, age 68
Director, Michael Chu, age 63
Director, Jacqueline B. (Jackie) Kosecoff, age 63
Auditors: KPMGLLP

LOCATIONS

HQ: Sealed Air Corp.
200 Riverfront Boulvard, Elmwood Park, NJ 07407-1033
Phone: 201 791-7600

2011 Sales

	$ mil.	% of total
US	2,305	41
Europe Middle East & Africa	1,676	29
Asia Pacific	940	17
Latin America	545	10
Total	**5,640**	**100**

PRODUCTS/OPERATIONS

2011 Sales

	$ mil.	% of total
Food packaging	2,053	36
Food solutions	1,015	18
Diversey	795	14
Total	**5,640**	**100**

Selected Brands

Bubble Wrap
CRYOVAC
Ethafoam
Fill-Air
Instapak
Jiffy Mailer
Korrvu
Shanklin

Selected Products

Food Packaging
- Absorbent pads and case liners
- Bulk packaging
- Foam trays
- Laminates
- Lidstock
- Pouches
- Rollstock
- Vacuum bags

Medical Packaging
- Cleanroom blisters
- Films (Nexcel and Nelipak brands)
- Lidding material
- Medical device packaging
- Sealing machines

Protective Packaging
- Air cushioning (Bubble Wrap)
- Cushioned mailing bags (Jiffy Mailer)
- Foam packaging (Instapak)
- Inflatable packaging and cushioning (Fill-Air and FillTeck)
- Paper cushioning (PackTiger)
- Paper packaging (Kushion Kraft and Custom Wrap)
- Polyethylene fabrication foam (Cellu-Cushion CelluPlank Stratocell)
- Polyethylene foam (Cell-Aire)
- Suspension and retention packaging (Korrvu)

Shrink Packaging
- Equipment
- Films

Specialty Materials
- Foams
- Solar pool heating
- TurboTag RF Temperature Monitoring system
- Vacuum insulated panels

COMPETITORS

3M
AEP Industries
Bemis
Clorox
Curwood
Ecolab
Huhtamaki
Intertape Polymer
Packaging Dynamics
Pactiv
Pliant Corporation
Polyair Inter Pack
Printpack
Procter & Gamble
Reynolds Food Packaging
Sonoco Products
Tekni-Plex
Winpak

HISTORICAL FINANCIALS

Company Type: Public

Income Statement FYE: December 31

	REVENUE ($ mil.)	NET INCOME ($ mil.)	NET PROFIT MARGIN	EMPLOYEES
12/11	5,640	149	2.6%	26,300
12/10	4,490	255	5.7%	16,100
12/09	4,242	244	5.8%	16,200
12/08	4,843	179	3.7%	17,000
12/07	4,651	353	7.6%	17,700
Annual Growth	4.9%	(19.4%)	—	10.4%

2011 Year-End Financials

Debt ratio: 43.90%
Return on equity: 5.04%
Cash ($ mil.): 722
Current ratio: 136.88
Long-term debt ($ mil.): 5,010
No. of shares (mil.): 192
Dividends
Yield: —
Payout: 65.00%
Market value ($ mil.): 3,305

	STOCK PRICE ($) FY Close	P/E High/Low		PER SHARE ($) Earnings	Dividends	Book Value
12/11	17.21	32	18	0.80	0.00	15.40
12/10	25.45	16	12	1.44	0.50	15.09
12/09	21.86	15	7	1.35	0.48	13.84
12/08	14.94	25	11	0.99	0.48	12.19
12/07	23.14	31	10	1.89	0.40	12.50
Annual Growth	(7.1%)	—	—	(19.3%)	—	5.4%

Sears Holdings Corp

In the world of retail Sears Holdings is an appliance giant. In addition to home appliances the company is a leading retailer of tools as well as lawn and garden fitness and automotive repair equipment. With more than 2600 retail stores in the US and Canada Sears Holdings operates through subsidiaries including Sears Roebuck and Co. and Kmart. Sears Holdings also owns a 51% stake in Sears Canada after it completed a spinoff of a portion of its interest in 2012. Sears Holdings was created in 2005 as a result of the $11.9 billion mega-merger of Sears and struggling Kmart.

Geographic Reach

Sears Holdings subsidiary Sears Roebuck and Co. has Sears-branded and affiliated stores in all 50 states and Puerto Rico. Sears Canada operates about 500 full-line and specialty stores throughout Canada. Subsidiary Kmart boasts Kmart-branded stores in 49 states Guam Puerto Rico and the US Virgin Islands.

Operations

Sears Holdings operates through three segments: Kmart Sears Domestic and Sears Canada. Sears Domestic is its largest segment raking in a little more than half of Sears Holdings' total sales. In 2012 the company's stake in Sears Canada dropped from 95% to 51% as a result of a spinoff of part of its ownership interest. Sears Holdings believes the spinoff allows investors to more easily target growth opportunities at Sears Canada directly.

Outside of retail Sears Holdings has a real estate business unit called SHC Realty one of the largest corporate real estate organizations in the world. It offers for sale or lease closed Kmart and Sears stores. It also leases empty space inside and outside of the stores.

Financial Analysis

Sales continued to fall at Sears and Kmart stores in fiscal 2012 (ends January) as the chains shuttered stores and continued to shed business to competitors including Wal-Mart and Target. Indeed Sears Holdings' fiscal 2012 sales declined 4% vs. the prior year and the company was unprofitable. It was the fifth consecutive year that Sears Holdings posted a negative annual sales comparison. (Sales have tumbled more than 20% over the past five years.) Same-store sales at Kmart Sears and Sears Canada stores declined by 1.4% 3% and nearly 8% respectively in fiscal 2012. Cash flow from operations continued its two-year plunge. The spinoff of Orchard Supply Hardware in late 2011 real estate sales and pending separation of the Sears Hometown and Outlet businesses along with certain hardware stores via a rights offering have or are intended to raise money and boost liquidity for the parent company.

Strategy

The pairing of Sears and Kmart was intended to leverage the strengths of both chains by making their products brands (Kenmore Craftsman DieHard) and services (including auto and appliance repair) available through more locations and distribution channels. That strategy has utterly failed to translate into an increase in sales for either retailer. Indeed Sears Holdings has struggled since its formation in 2005 while investors initially wowed by the financial prowess of chairman Edward Lampert have grown disenchanted and confused regarding his long-term vision for the company.

Lampert has not invested much in improving the stores themselves focusing instead on growing the company's online properties. Part of that strategy is paying off as the number of visitors to the Sears.com and Kmart.com websites is actually growing; its online presence is also complemented by the PartsDirect.com (DIY repair parts) and LandsEnd.com (casual apparel) websites. Still some analysts point out that without more capital improvements to existing store locations especially those stores in older malls it will be hard to woo shoppers from such rivals as Wal-Mart Target and Home Depot among others.

Ownership

ESL Investments owns 62% of Sears Holdings' shares while Fairholme Capital Management owns about 15%.

EXECUTIVES

EVP and CFO, Robert A. (Rob) Schriesheim, age 52
EVP Off-Mall Businesses, W. Bruce Johnson, age 60, $850,000 total compensation
President CEO and Director, Louis J. (Lou) D'Ambrosio, age 48
Chairman, Edward S. (Eddie) Lampert, age 49
President and CEO Lands' End, Edgar O. Huber
EVP Apparel and Home, John D. Goodman, age 47, $183,333 total compensation
SVP; President Food and Consumables & Health and Wellness, Robin S. Michel
EVP and Chief Merchandising Officer; President Dears and Kmart Formats, Ronald D. (Ron) Boire, age 51
VP and Chief Marketing Officer, Monica L. Woo, age 56
President Home Fashions, Chris Capuano
VP Corporate Communications, Chris Brathwaite
SVP Finance, William K. Phelan, age 49
SVP; President Tools, Sam A. Solomon
SVP, William R. Harker, age 39

EVP; President Kenmore Craftsman and DieHard, Scott J. Freidheim, age 45, $800,000 total compensation
SVP; President Retail Services, Deidra C. Merriwether, age 43
SVP; President Apparel, Lana C. Krauter
SVP General Counsel and Corporate Secretary, Dane A. Drobny, age 44
VP Information Technology, Keith Sherwell
VP Deputy General Counsel and Assistant Secretary, Dorian R. Williams
President Marketing, Imran Jooma
VP Controller and Chief Accounting Officer, Robert A. Riecker, age 47
Director, Ann N. Reese, age 59
President CEO and Director, Louis J. (Lou) D'Ambrosio, age 48
Director, Steven T. (Steve) Mnuchin, age 49
Director, Thomas J. Tisch, age 57
Director, Emily Scott, age 50
Director, William C. (Bill) Kunkler III, age 55
Auditors: Deloitte&ToucheLLP

LOCATIONS

HQ: Sears Holdings Corporation
3333 Beverly Rd., Hoffman Estates IL 60179
Phone: 847-286-2500 **Fax:** -10790
Web: www.groupnbt.com

PRODUCTS/OPERATIONS

2012 Sales

	$ mil.	% of total
Sears Domestic	21,649	52
Kmart	15,285	37
Sears Canada	4,633	11
Total	**41,567**	**100**

2011 US Stores

	No.
Sears	
Mall	834
Dealer	986
Sears Hardware	96
Sears Essentials/Sears	33
Outlet	116
Sears Home Appliance	75
The Great	9
Lands'	14
Other	42
Total	**2,205**
Kmart	1,305
Sears	500
Total	**4,010**

Selected Subsidiaries

Kmart Corporation
Kmart Holding Corporation
Lands' End Inc.
Sears Canada Inc.
Sears Home Improvement Products Inc.
Sears Outlet Stores LLC
Sears Roebuck Acceptance Corp.
Sears Roebuck and Co.
Sears Roebuck de Puerto Rico Inc.
SRC Real Estate Holdings (TX) LLC

COMPETITORS

Ace Hardware
Amazon.com
AutoZone
Bed Bath & Beyond
Best Buy
Dillard' s
Home Depot
Hudson' s Bay
J. C. Penney
Kohl' s
Lowe' s
Macy' s
Menard
Office Depot
Pep Boys
ServiceMaster
Target Corporation
The Gap
Wal-Mart
Whirlpool
Zale

HISTORICAL FINANCIALS

Company Type: Public

Income Statement

FYE: January 28

	REVENUE ($ mil.)	NET INCOME ($ mil.)	NET PROFIT MARGIN	EMPLOYEES
01/12	41,567	(3,140)	—	293,000
01/11	43,326	133	0.3%	280,000
01/10	44,043	235	0.5%	322,000
01/09*	46,770	53	0.1%	324,000
02/08	50,703	826	1.6%	337,000
Annual Growth	(4.8%)	—	—	(3.4%)

*Fiscal year change

2012 Year-End Financials

Debt ratio: 16.34%
Return on equity: (-73.35)%
Cash ($ mil.): 747
Current ratio: 111.20
Long-term debt ($ mil.): 2,088
No. of shares (mil.): 106
Dividends
Yield: —
Payout: —
Market value ($ mil.): 4,670

	STOCK PRICE ($) FY Close	P/E High/Low		PER SHARE ($) Earnings	Dividends	Book Value
01/12	44.06	—	—	(29.40)	0.00	40.39
01/11	76.08	104	51	1.19	0.00	78.08
01/10	93.28	53	18	1.99	0.00	79.10
01/09*	40.92	266	68	0.42	0.00	76.89
02/08	108.31	34	15	5.70	0.00	80.81
Annual Growth	(20.1%)	—	—	—	—	(15.9%)

*Fiscal year change

Selective Insurance Group Inc

Selective Insurance Group is trying to be more accepting –without becoming indiscriminate. Since the early 1990s the property/casualty insurance holding company has been expanding its service area beyond its native New Jersey to reach the entire eastern US seaboard and much of the Midwest. Commercial policies sold by its seven subsidiaries include workers' compensation and commercial automobile property and liability insurance. Personal lines include homeowners and automobile insurance. The company also offers federal flood insurance administration services and some excess and surplus insurance. Some 1000 independent agencies market Selective Insurance products.

The company targets small and midsized businesses and government entities; in 2011 commercial lines accounted for 80% of net premiums written. Personal lines brought in 18% and and excess and surplus (E&S) products brought in the slim remainder. (E&S insurance covers more unusual risks than standard insurance.) Selective has invested in technology to speed up the process of writing new business.

While New Jersey still accounts for 25% of Selective Insurance's net written premiums it writes business in 22 states and intends to become a "super-regional" insurer. By doing business in a wider geographic range the company hopes to spread out its catastrophic risk exposure. It maintains its headquarters in New Jersey and regional branch offices in five other states.

Following an initial drop in revenues during the early days of the recession and the sale of its human resources business Selective Insurance has remained stable with modest (2%) revenue growth amounting to $1597 million in 2011. Hurricane Irene and more than 20 other storms in 2011 brought catastrophe losses of $118.8 million and pulled Selective Insurance's net income down 70% from 2010 to $19.9 million.

Selective is hoping to build up its portfolio of personal and commercial E&S insurance products. To meet that goal in 2011 the company bought up the renewal rights to a block of E&S products from Alterra Capital and Montpelier U.S. Insurance Company the E&S business of Montpelier Re.

EXECUTIVES

Chairman President and CEO, Gregory E. Murphy, age 56, $934,616 total compensation
EVP and Chief Actuary, Ronald J. Zaleski Sr., age 57, $415,385 total compensation
EVP General Counsel Corporate Secretary and Chief Compliance Officer, Michael H. Lanza, age 50, $451,731 total compensation
EVP and CFO, Dale A. Thatcher, age 50, $493,269 total compensation
EVP and Chief Investment Officer, Kerry A. Guthrie, age 54, $421,154 total compensation
SVP Bonds and Agency Development Selective Insurance Company of America, Antonio C. Albanese
SVP and Regional Manager Southern Region Selective Insurance Company of America, James McLain
SVP Workers Compensation Selective Insurance Company of America, Kathleen A. Muedder
SVP and Regional Manager Northeast Region and Agency Development Selective Insurance Company of America, Charles A. (Chuck) Musilli III
SVP Application Delivery and Business Practices Selective Insurance Company of America, Jeffrey F. Kamrowski
SVP Investor Relations and Treasurer; SVP Investor Relations Selective Insurance Company of America, Jennifer DiBerardino
EVP Insurance Operations, John J. Marchioni, age 42
SVP and Controller; Controller Selective Insurance Company of America, Anthony D. Harnett
SVP and Regional Manager Heartland Region Selective Insurance Company of America, Erik A. Reidenbach
SVP Investments Fixed Income Selective Insurance Group and Selective Insurance Company of America, Diederik Olijslager
SVP and Regional Manager Mid-Atlantic Region Selective Insurance Company of America, Charles C. Adams
SVP and Regional Manager New Jersey Region Selective Insurance Company of America, Edward F. Drag II
SVP and Chief Underwriting Officer Personal Lines Selective Insurance Company of America, Allen H. Anderson
SVP and Director Commercial Lines Pricing and Research Selective Insurance Company of America, Andrew S. Becker
EVP and Chief Human Resources Officer, Kimberly Burnett, age 54
Corporate Secretary, Robyn P. Turner
VP and Director Communications, Gail L. Petersen
SVP Application Delivery Services Selective Insurance Company of America, Bradford S. Allen

SVP Commercial Lines Small Business Selective Insurance Company of America, William S. Becker
SVP Information Technology Infrastructure and Facilities Management Selective Insurance Company of America, Kevin L. Jenkins
SVP Enterprise Technology Services Selective Insurance Company of America, Richard W. Mohr
VP Tax and Treasury, Sarita Chakravarthi
VP Infrastructure Services and Operations Information Technology Services Selective Insurance Company of America, John P. Bresney
VP Commercial Lines Underwriting Selective Insurance Company of America, Darryl P. Holmes
VP Infrastructure Architecture and Engineering Information Technology Services Selective Insurance Company of America, Robert McKenna
Assistant VP Billing Services Selective Insurance Company of America, Raymond J. Farinella
SVP and Chief Claims Officer Selective Insurance Company of America, Douglas H. Holbrook
SVP and Chief Investment Officer Selective Insurance Company of America, Susan B. Sweeney
Assistant VP and Manager Field Operations Selective Insurance Company of America, Scott C. Betlesky
Assistant VP Flood Operations Selective Insurance Company of America, Cassie S. Masone
SVP and Chief Underwriting Officer Commercial Lines Selective Insurance Company of America, Dennis L. Barger
SVP Claims General Counsel Selective Insurance Company of America, Thomas M. Clark
SVP Field Underwriting and Information Strategy Selective Insurance Company of America, Brenda Hall
SVP Claims Strategic Program Selective Insurance Company of America, Debra J. Wilber
Assistant VP and Manager Safety Operations Southern Region Selective Insurance Company of America, Gwendolyn Chisolm
EVP and CIO, Ronald St. Clair, age 47
EVP and Chief Human Resources Officer, Amy R. Carver
Director, Ronald L. O'Kelley, age 67
Director, William M. Rue, age 64
Director, Paul D. Bauer, age 68
Director, A. David Brown, age 69
Director, Joan M. Lamm-Tennant, age 59
Director, S. Griffin McClellan III, age 74
Director, J. Brian Thebault, age 60
Director, Cynthia S. (Cie) Nicholson, age 47
Director, John C. Burville, age 64
Director, Michael J. Morrissey, age 64
Auditors: KPMGLLP

LOCATIONS

HQ: Selective Insurance Group Inc.
40 Wantage Ave., Branchville NJ 07890
Phone: 973-948-3000 **Fax:** 973-948-0292
Web: www.selective.com

PRODUCTS/OPERATIONS

2011 Revenues

Insurance operations		
Personal lines	264	17
Investments	150	9

Selected Acquisitions

2011

Commercial E&S business (from Alterra Excess & Surplus Insurance Co.)
Montpelier U.S. Insurance Company (Scottsdale AZ; Excess & Surplus insurance)

COMPETITORS

Cincinnati Financial
GEICO
Hanover Insurance Company
Harleysville Group
Liberty Mutual
Markel
NJM Insurance
Progressive Corporation
Scottsdale Insurance
State Farm
The Hartford
Travelers Companies
Zurich Financial Services

HISTORICAL FINANCIALS

Company Type: Public

Income Statement FYE: December 31

	ASSETS ($ mil.)	NET INCOME ($ mil.)	INCOME AS % OF ASSETS	EMPLOYEES
12/11	5,736	19	0.3%	2,000
12/10	5,231	65	1.3%	1,900
12/09	5,114	36	0.7%	1,900
12/08	4,941	43	0.9%	2,000
12/07	5,001	146	2.9%	2,200
Annual Growth	3.5%	(39.3%)	—	(2.4%)

2011 Year-End Financials

Debt ratio: 5.36%
Return on equity: 1.79%
Cash ($ mil.): 0
Current ratio: —
Long-term debt ($ mil.): 307
No. of shares (mil.): 54
Dividends
Yield: —
Payout: 144.44%
Market value ($ mil.): 965

	STOCK PRICE ($) FY Close	P/E High/Low		PER SHARE ($) Earnings	Dividends	Book Value
12/11	17.73	51	33	0.36	0.00	20.39
12/10	18.15	15	12	1.20	0.52	19.95
12/09	16.45	33	15	0.68	0.52	18.83
12/08	22.93	32	21	0.82	0.52	16.84
12/07	22.99	21	7	2.59	0.49	19.81
Annual Growth	(6.3%)	—	—	(38.9%)	—	0.7%

Sempra Energy

Sempra Energy isn't joining the Marines but it is faithful to making money in utility markets in the US and around the world. In the US Sempra distributes natural gas to more than 6.6 million customer meters and electricity to 1.4 million customer meters through its Southern California Gas (SoCalGas) and San Diego Gas & Electric (SDG&E) utilities. Other reporting segments include Sempra US Gas & Power (natural gas and renewables) and Sempra International (Sempra Mexico and Sempra South American Utilities) which were formerly known as Sempra Global. Sempra Energy companies serve more than 31 million consumers worldwide.

Geographic Reach

Boosting its international utility holdings in 2011 Sempra Energy acquired AEI's stakes in two jointly owned South American utilities (Chilquinta Energia and Luz del Sur) for $875 million.

Operations

The company develops and acquires merchant power plants (Sempra Generation formerly Sempra Energy Resources) liquefied natural gas (LNG) regasification facilities (Sempra LNG) and affordable housing properties.

Financial Analysis

Acquisitions plus higher power rates at SDG&E lifted electric revenues by more than $1.3 billion in 2011 and overall company revenues by 11% despite weaker revenue performances by its gas utility and energy-related businesses. The stronger performance and lower fuel and purchased power prices coupled with cost savings from reorganizing lifted Sempra Energy's 2011 net income by 82%.

Strategy

Building its midstream portfolio in 2010 the company acquired El Paso's Mexico-based pipeline and compression assets for $300 million.

In 2010 and 2011 Sempra Energy exited the commodities trading business. (In 2008 Sempra Energy had formed a partnership with The Royal Bank of Scotland to operate RBS Sempra Commodities including Sempra Energy Trading which traded and markets wholesale energy commodities in Asia Europe and North America. However to refocus its operations around its more financially reliable North American businesses to pay down debt and to meet EU antitrust requirements in 2010 the company sold the European and Asian segments of this partnership to JP Morgan Chase for about $1.6 billion. It also sold that unit's retail commodity operations to Noble Group for $318 million and eventually wound down its joint venture with The Royal Bank of Scotland).

In early 2012 the company consolidated Sempra Generation Sempra Pipelines & Storage and Sempra LNG (together formerly Sempra Global) into Sempra International and Sempra US Gas & Power to improve its management and pursue strategic initiatives. Sempra US Gas & Power includes natural gas and renewables while Sempra International includes subsidiaries Sempra Mexico and Sempra South American Utilities.

HISTORY

Sempra Energy is the latest incarnation of some of California's leading lights. Formed by the $6.2 billion merger between Enova and Pacific Enterprises the company traces its roots back to the 1880s.

Enova began as San Diego Gas which lit its first gaslights in 1881 and added electricity in 1887 (when it became San Diego Gas & Electric Light). Massive utility holding company Standard Gas & Electric bought the company in 1905 and renamed it San Diego Consolidated Gas & Electric. Over the next few decades San Diego Consolidated expanded through acquisitions and even stayed profitable during the Depression. But the 1935 Public Utilities Holding Company Act forced Standard to divest many of its widespread utilities and in 1940 San Diego Consolidated went public as San Diego Gas & Electric (SDG&E).

SDG&E grew quickly until the 1970s when new environmental laws slowed plans to build more power plants and rates soared because the company had to purchase power. The company finally added more generating capacity in the 1980s and the state of California allowed SDG&E to diversify into real estate software and oil and gas distribution. In 1995 it created Enova to serve as its holding company.

Meanwhile up the coast in San Francisco Pacific Enterprises began as gas lamp rental firm Pacific Lighting in 1886; it quickly moved into gas distribution to defend its market against electricity. The firm bought three Los Angeles gas and electric utilities in 1889 and continued to grow through acquisitions; it consolidated all of its utilities in the 1920s. Pacific Lighting sold its electric properties to the city of Los Angeles in 1937 in exchange for a long-term gas franchise.

The company entered oil and gas exploration in 1960. A decade later it merged its gas utility operations into Southern California Gas (SoCalGas). Pacific Lighting continued to diversify in the 1980s buying two oil and gas companies and three drugstore chains. Renamed Pacific Enterprises in 1988 the company launched an unsuccessful diversification effort that cost it $88 million in 1991. Over the next two years it sold off noncore businesses to focus on SoCalGas and in the mid-1990s it began moving into South and Central America. This included a joint venture with Enova and Mexico's Proxima SA to build and operate Mexico's first private utility.

Pacific Enterprises and Enova agreed in 1997 to a $6.2 billion merger; Sempra Energy was born in 1998. That year California began deregulating its retail power market. In response Sempra sold SDG&E's non-nuclear power plants (1900 MW) in 1999. It used the proceeds to eliminate its competitive transition charge and in turn lowered its electric rates.

But under deregulation rates tripled by mid-2000; that summer the California Public Utilities Commission (CPUC) implemented a rate freeze for electric customers. Wholesale power prices soared and rolling blackouts occurred in 2000 and 2001 as a result of the state's inadequate energy supply. In 2001 the CPUC began allowing utilities to increase their rates and SDG&E agreed to sell its transmission assets to the state for about $1 billion.

Sempra sold its 72.5% share in power marketing firm Energy America to British energy company Centrica in 2001. In 2002 the company purchased bankrupt utility Enron's London-based metals trading unit for about $145 million; later that year it purchased Enron's metals concentrates and metals warehousing businesses.

The company restructured its competitive energy business units in 2005 renaming several divisions and dividing the former Sempra Energy Solutions operations (retail energy marketing and services for commercial and industrial customers) under the Commodities and Generation divisions. That year Sempra sold one of its gas storage units to Vulcan's investment company for a reported $250 million; Vulcan is headed up by Microsoft cofounder Paul Allen

In 2006 the company settled class-action litigation that claimed that two of its subsidiaries Southern California Gas and San Diego Gas & Electric had helped to create the 2000-2001 energy crises in California by restricting the supply of natural gas to the state.

In 2007 Sempra was awarded a $172 million settlement arising from a 2002 dispute over the company's minority stakes in two Argentine natural gas holding companies.

In 2008 Sempra Energy formed a commodities marketing joint venture with The Royal Bank of Scotland RBS Sempra Commodities.

In a move to expand its midstream and distribution assets in the southeastern US in 2008 the company acquired EnergySouth for $510 million.

The company reported a jump in its revenues in 2010 thanks to a recovering global economy that drove up energy demand along with higher oil and gas prices and increased rates. Losses related to winding down its commodities unit trimmed Sempra Energy's net income for the year.

EXECUTIVES

President and CEO Sempra LNG, Darcel L. Hulse, age 59
Chairman, Donald E. Felsinger, age 65, $1,184,300 total compensation
Chairman President and CEO Pacific Enterprises and Southern California Gas Company, Michael W. Allman, age 51
CEO and Director, Debra L. (Debbie) Reed, age 56
President and CEO Southern California Gas Company, Anne S. Smith, age 58
VP Investor Relations and Corporate Communications, Steven D. Davis, age 56
President and COO San Diego Gas & Electric, Michael R. (Mike) Niggli, age 62
VP Global Information Technologies Sempra Pipelines & Storage, Matthias Beier
President, Mark A. Snell, age 55, $595,300 total compensation
Chairman and CEO San Diego Gas & Electric Company, Jessie J. Knight Jr., age 61
EVP and General Counsel, M. Javade Chaudhri, age 59, $517,300 total compensation
EVP and CFO, Joseph A. (Joe) Householder, age 56, $445,000 total compensation
VP CFO Chief Accounting Officer Treasurer and Controller Southern California Gas San Diego Gas & Electric and Pacific Enterprises, Robert M. Schlax, age 57
President and CEO Sempra Pipelines & Storage, George S. Liparidis
VP Tax and Chief Tax Counsel, Paul Yong
VP and Treasurer, Richard A. Vaccari
President and CEO Sempra Generation, Jeffery W. (Jeff) Martin, age 49
VP Audit Services, Patricia K. (Patti) Wagner
VP Corporate Relations and Corporate Secretary, Randall L. Clark
VP Risk Analysis and Management, Amy H. Chiu
SVP Human Resources Diversity and Inclusion, G. Joyce Rowland, age 57
VP Corporate Planning, Monica Haas
VP Audit Services, Lisa Urick
Director, Wilford D. Godbold Jr., age 73
Director, William C. (Bill) Rusnack, age 67
Director, Alan L. Boeckmann, age 64
CEO and Director, Debra L. (Debbie) Reed, age 56
Director, William D. Jones, age 56
Director, Lynn Schenk, age 67
Director, James G. Brocksmith Jr., age 71
Director, Carlos Ruiz, age 62
Director, Luis K. Tellez, age 53
Auditors: Deloitte&ToucheLLP

LOCATIONS

HQ: Sempra Energy
101 Ash St., San Diego CA 92101
Phone: 619-696-2000 **Fax:** -3372
Web: www.westernpower.co.uk

2011 Sales

	$ mil.	% of total
North America		
US	8,135	81
Mexico	821	8
South America	1,080	11
Total	**10,036**	**100**

PRODUCTS/OPERATIONS

2011 Sales

	$ mil.	% of total
Sempra Utilities		
Natural gas	4,489	45
Electric	3,833	38
Energy-related businesses	1,714	17
Total	**10,036**	**100**

COMPETITORS

AEP
AES
AT&T
Avista
Calpine
CenterPoint Energy
CMS Energy
Constellation Energy Group
Dominion Resources
Duke Energy
Edison International
El Paso Corporation
Endesa S.A.
Entergy
GenOnEnergy
IBERDROLA
Los Angeles Water and Power
NV Energy
PacifiCorp
PG&E Corporation
PSEG Global
Public Service Enterprise Group
Sacramento Municipal Utility
Southwest Gas
Tenaska
Williams Companies

HISTORICAL FINANCIALS

Company Type: Public

Income Statement FYE: December 31

	REVENUE ($ mil.)	NET INCOME ($ mil.)	NET PROFIT MARGIN	EMPLOYEES
12/11	10,036	1,407	14.0%	17,483
12/10	9,003	733	8.1%	13,504
12/09	8,106	1,122	13.8%	13,839
12/08	10,758	1,113	10.3%	13,673
12/07	11,438	1,099	9.6%	14,314
Annual Growth	(3.2%)	6.4%	—	5.1%

2011 Year-End Financials

Debt ratio: 32.57%
Return on equity: 14.30%
Cash ($ mil.): 252
Current ratio: 56.02
Long-term debt ($ mil.): 10,078
No. of shares (mil.): 239
Dividends
Yield: —
Payout: 34.16%
Market value ($ mil.): 13,196

	STOCK PRICE ($) FY Close	P/E High/Low		PER SHARE ($) Earnings	Dividends	Book Value
12/11	55.00	10	8	5.62	0.00	41.09
12/10	52.48	19	15	2.98	1.56	37.96
12/09	55.98	12	8	4.52	1.56	36.94
12/08	42.63	14	8	4.43	1.37	32.75
12/07	61.88	16	12	4.16	1.24	31.92
Annual Growth	(2.9%)	—	—	7.8%	—	6.5%

Shaw Group Inc.

The Shaw Group is one of the largest engineering and construction contractors for the power generation market as well as a top environmental services firm. Shaw designs engineers builds maintains and decommissions fossil fuel and nuclear power plants; provides consulting services to the chemical industry; performs environmental rehabilitation services; manages facilities; and manufactures piping systems. Shaw serves clients across the Americas Middle East Europe and Asia. Clients include multinational oil companies industrial corporations and manufacturers utilities and government agencies. Chicago Bridge & Iron (CB&I) is buying Shaw for some $3 billion.

The deal will create one of the world's largest construction and engineering firms specializing in the energy sector. Shaw's largest segments are Shaw Environmental & Infrastructure (Shaw E&I) and its power unit which includes work in the nuclear power generation industry. The company claims to have worked on 95% of the nuclear power facilities in the US. With rising oil prices and a growing focus on alternative energy sources interest in nuclear energy has seen a serious boost. Shaw has scaled up its operations to meet demand from companies that are restarting their nuclear construction programs. The company is mainly targeting new-build nuclear power plant projects outside of the US. The company also owns a 20% stake in nuclear reactor designer Westinghouse Electric. However Toshiba Corp. plans to buy Shaw's stake in Westinghouse for more than $1.6 billion. The deal will clear Shaw of most of its debt.

In addition to nuclear power plants Shaw also builds gas-fired power plants and clean coal-fired power plants. Gas-fired power generation has experienced an increase in demand as power producers look to diversify their assets and reduce carbon dioxide and greenhouse gas emissions. Meanwhile clean coal-fired power plants have experienced a recent slowdown in development as there is uncertainty about emissions regulations and low natural gas prices.

Shaw's plant services segment handles power plant maintenance. The company provides maintenance for 44 of the 104 nuclear power plants that operate in the US making it the largest provider in the country. Shaw is expanding its plant services arm to fossil and industrial markets such as the petrochemical chemical oil and gas steel and manufacturing industries.

The company's fabrication and manufacturing segment is one of the largest providers of piping systems in the US. It is focused on expanding internationally especially in Brazil and the Middle East. Shaw opened a new fabrication facility in the United Arab Emirates where it will provide pipes for the oil and gas power desalination refinery and nuclear industries. Shaw also is eyeing fabrication opportunities in the mining industry in the Dominican Republic and South America.

Shaw's environmental and infrastructure segment focuses on large-scale federal and state projects. In 2011 Shaw entered the coastal restoration services sector when it acquired Florida-based Coastal Planning & Engineering Inc. for $26 million. The deal strengthened Shaw's existing project management and ports and harbors expertise. The unit is part of Shaw E&I and works on projects along the US Gulf Coast as well as global offshore energy support. Shaw E&I is anticipating higher demand in the sector driven by the US government spends more to modernize infrastructure and improve aging facilities.

In an effort to focus on growth in its primary industries Shaw sold substantially all of its struggling energy and chemicals business to Technip for approximately $290 million. As part of the deal Shaw will retain some energy and chemical personnel at its Baton Rouge office as well as its Toronto-based operations.

Several factors hurt Shaw's financial results in 2011. Sales declined by 15% and the company posted a $175 million loss for the year. The company incurred a hefty $64 million charge related to a lawsuit in 2011. The earthquake and tsunami in Japan (which damaged a nuclear power plant) also hurt earnings for Shaw that year. Cost increases and schedule delays on a major ethylene project in Asia also contributed to a decrease in profits for the company.

HISTORY

James Bernhard formed National Fabricators in 1986. After visiting the Benjamin F. Shaw Company's plant in South Carolina to bid on its inventory he established The Shaw Group in 1987 and bought the 100-year-old maker of power-station piping systems. From 1988 to 1990 Shaw expanded its business by leasing three plants in Louisiana and Texas. The company bought a plant in 1992.

Shaw formed a joint venture with Venezuela-based Formiconi in 1993 to open a plant there. The company began making pipes for chemicals and oil refining with its purchase of Sunland Fabricators. Shaw also went public that year.

In 1994 Shaw acquired Fronek Company (pipe engineering and design services) bought out its Venezuelan partner and watched its domestic fiscal earnings bend south when its South Carolina plant had to repair a botched fabrication job.

Shaw expanded plant capacity and added more induction bending machines to its inventory in 1996 and 1997. It purchased NAPTech (industrial piping systems) in 1997. Company spending continued with the 1998 acquisitions of Lancas (construction Venezuela) Cojafex BV (induction bending equipment the Netherlands) and Bagwell Brothers (offshore platforms heliports and vessels for the petroleum industry). The Cojafex buy proved to be one of the company's best acquisitions because its pipe-bending machines eliminated much of the cost of welding. Also in 1998 Shaw sold its NAPTech Pressure Systems (pressure vessels) subsidiary and others that provided welding supplies boiler steam leak-detection devices and corrosion-resistant pipe systems.

In 1999 Shaw won a five-year contract to supply 90% of the piping for GE's gas turbines for power plants. In 2000 Shaw signed a letter of intent with a US power developer to build a $380 million power plant in central Texas. It also created EntergyShaw a joint venture with Entergy Corporation to build cookie-cutter power plants in North America and Europe in hopes of driving down costs and speeding construction time. That year the company purchased Stone & Webster Inc. for about $38 million and around 2.5 million shares of stock.

In 2002 Shaw acquired the assets of The IT Group (which was in bankruptcy) for about $105 million in cash and up to $95 million in assumed debt and made the environmental services firm a subsidiary Shaw Environmental & Infrastructure (Shaw E&I). It also entered into an agreement to buy industrial construction group Turner Industries but quickly terminated discussions with its hometown rival.

Shaw divested its hanger engineering and pipe support businesses in 2004 and its Roche consulting operations the following year. In 2006 it acquired a 20% stake in nuclear reactor designer Westinghouse Electric. It also established investment and transaction arm Shaw Capital to handle the group's growth and assets.

The company scaled back in the noncore areas of transmission and distribution in order to focus on engineering and construction. In 2008 it sold powerline services business Energy Delivery Services to Pike Electric for some $24 million.

EXECUTIVES

Chairman President and CEO, James M. Bernhard Jr., age 58, $1,972,768 total compensation
CEO Power Group, Clarence L. Ray Jr., age 65
EVP and COO, Gary P. Graphia, age 49, $853,679 total compensation
President Fabrication and Manufacturing (F & M) Group, David L. Chapman Sr., age 67, $645,935 total compensation
EVP and CFO, Brian K. Ferraioli, age 57, $645,935 total compensation
President Energy and Chemicals, Louis J. (Lou) Pucher, age 69
EVP General Counsel and Corporate Secretary, John Donofrio, age 50, $524,687 total compensation
President Nuclear Division Power, David P. (Dave) Barry, age 61, $475,000 total compensation
President and COO Power, Eli Smith
President Environmental and Infrastructure (E & I) Group, George P. Bevan, age 65
VP Investor Relations and Corporate Communications, Gentry Brann
President Commercial State and Local Division Shaw Environmental and Infrastructure Group, Vahid Ownjazayeri
President Fossil Division Power, Andy Dupuy
VP and CTO, Jeremy Turner
President Energy & Chemicals (E & C) Group, James Glass
SVP and Chief Accounting Officer, Timothy J. Poche
Interim Chief Accounting Officer; Vice President, James Wilems
Senior Vice President and Chief Financial Officer - Shaws Power Group, Timothy Poche
Director, Thomas E. (Tom) Capps, age 77
Director, Michael J. Mancuso, age 70
Director, David W. Hoyle, age 73
Director, Albert D. McAlister, age 61
Director, Stephen R. (Steve) Tritch, age 63
Director, James F. Barker, age 65
Director, Daniel A. Hoffler, age 64
Auditors: KPMGLLP

LOCATIONS

HQ: The Shaw Group Inc.
4171 Essen Ln., Baton Rouge LA 70809
Phone: 225-932-2500 **Fax:** 225-987-3328
Web: www.shawgrp.com

2012 Sales

	$ mil.	% of total
US	5,187	86
Asia/Pacific	489	8
Middle East	163	3
South America & Mexico	85	2
UK & other European countries	53	1
Canada	16	-
Other	12	-
Total	**6,008**	**100**

PRODUCTS/OPERATIONS

2012 Sales

	$ mil.	% of total
Power	1,973	33
Environmental & Infrastructure (E&I)	1,814	30
Plant Services	1,089	18
Energy & Chemicals (E&C)	579	10
Fabrication & Manufacturing (F&M)	551	9
Total	**6,008**	**100**

2012 Sales by Industry

	$ mil.	% of total
Power generation	2,872	48
Environmental & infrastructure	1,814	30
Chemicals	1,280	21
Other	41	1
Total	**6,008**	**100**

COMPETITORS

AECOM
Austin Industries
Bechtel
Black & Veatch
CH2M HILL
Chicago Bridge &
MRC Global
Parsons Corporation
Peter Kiewit Sons'
Senior plc
Siemens Water Technologies

Iron
Day & Zimmermann
Fluor
Foster Wheeler
Jacobs Engineering
KBR
Tetra Tech
The Linde Group
Turner Industries
URS
Willbros

HISTORICAL FINANCIALS

Company Type: Public

Income Statement FYE: August 31

	REVENUE ($ mil.)	NET INCOME ($ mil.)	NET PROFIT MARGIN	EMPLOYEES
08/12	6,008	198	3.3%	25,000
08/11	5,937	(175)	—	27,000
08/10	7,000	92	1.3%	27,000
08/09	7,279	15	0.2%	28,000
08/08	6,998	140	2.0%	26,000
Annual Growth	(3.7%)	9.0%	—	(1.0%)

2012 Year-End Financials

Debt ratio: 33.07%
Return on equity: 20.91%
Cash ($ mil.): 1,091
Current ratio: 101.93
Long-term debt ($ mil.): 5
No. of shares (mil.): 66
Dividends
Yield: —
Payout: —
Market value ($ mil.): 2,795

	STOCK PRICE ($) FY Close	P/E High/Low		PER SHARE ($) Earnings	Dividends	Book Value
08/12	42.08	14	7	2.90	0.00	14.32
08/11	23.31	—	—	(2.18)	0.00	12.69
08/10	32.40	36	23	1.08	0.00	18.14
08/09	29.33	250	67	0.18	0.00	17.02
08/08	49.54	45	28	1.67	0.00	17.83
Annual Growth	(4.0%)	—	—	14.8%	—	(5.3%)

Sherwin-Williams Co.

No matter how you coat it Sherwin-Williams is one of the largest paint manufacturers in the US and worldwide (along with Akzo-Nobel PPG Industries and Henkel). Sherwin-Williams' products include a variety of paints finishes coatings applicators and varnishes sold under brands such as Dutch Boy Krylon Sherwin-Williams Thompson's WaterSeal Ronseal Sayerlack and Minwax. The company operates more than 4000 paint stores worldwide. It sells automotive finishing and refinishing products through wholesale branches throughout the Americas as well as in Asia and Europe. Other outlets (and competitors) include mass merchandisers home centers independent dealers and automotive retailers.

Operations

Sherwin-Williams expanded its operating segments from three to four in 2011 because of growth in sales geographic reach and product lines. It added a Latin American Coatings Group to its Global Finishes Group Paint Stores Group and Consumer Group segments.

The Paints Stores Group it's largest segment operates the biggest network of specialty paint stores in North America serving painting contractors as well as do-it-yourself homeowners. In 2011 the company added 60 new stores and plans to add another 50 or 60 in 2012.

The Consumer Group supplies both branded and private-label products throughout North America and parts of Europe. It consists of a North American supply chain of 32 manufacturing plants and seven distribution centers and also supports the company's Paint Stores Group with new product development and research manufacturing and distribution.

The Global Finishes Group manufactures and sells automotive finishes industrial coatings and marine coatings worldwide. Acquisitions are pivotal to the growth of this segment bringing new technology in key areas.

Once operating within the Global Finishes Group is the newest segment the Latin America Coatings Group. The segment develops and produces a variety of architectural paint and coatings and related products throughout Latin America. It distributes its products through some 265 company-operated specialty paint stores as well as through direct and outside sales reps dealers and distributors.

Financial Analysis

In 2011 Sherwin-Williams realized record group sales of $8.77 billion an increase of about 13% over 2010. Sales increased in all segments except the Consumer Group whose new sales declined nearly 2% that year because of a decrease in architectural paint business with one of its large retail customers. Higher paint sales volumes increased prices and acquisitions all contributed to the hike in sales offsetting the higher costs in raw materials. However the company's net income decreased 5% in 2011 to $442 million from $462 million the previous year because of costs associated with an IRS settlement that year.

Strategy

Volume demand in the markets Sherwin-Williams serves has declined more than 20% since 2007 and raw material costs have spiked nearly 40%. To adjust to these conditions the company focuses on streamlining operations and growing market share. As part of its strategy Sherwin-Williams invests more than $100 million per year in research development and commercialization of new product technologies.

Acquisitions are also key to the company's strategy for growth and for addition of technologies. Among its acquisitions in 2011 was UK-based Leighs Paints a leader in fire-protectant (intumescent) coatings. Because the intumescent technology prolongs the structural integrity of steel and concrete in a catastrophic fire more people are able to evacuate. The company also is involved in developing more environmentally sustainable chemicals and processes. In 2012 it added another zero-VOC (Volatile Organic Compound) architectural paint line to its products.

In a major geographic expansion in 2012 the company agreed to acquire Grupo Comex a leader in the paint and coatings market in Mexico for $2.34 billion.

HISTORY

In 1870 Henry Sherwin bought out paint materials distributor Truman Dunham and joined Edward Williams and A. T. Osborn to form Sherwin Williams & Company in Cleveland. The business began making paints in 1871 and became the industry leader after improving the paint-grinding mill in the mid-1870s patenting a reclosable can in 1877 and improving liquid paint in 1880.

In 1874 Sherwin-Williams introduced a special paint for carriages beginning the concept of specific-purpose paint. (By 1900 the company had paints for floors roofs barns metal bridges railroad cars and automobiles.) Sherwin-Williams incorporated in 1884 and opened a dealership in Massachusetts in 1891 that was the forerunner of its company-run retail stores. The company obtained its "Cover the Earth" trademark in 1895.

Before the Depression Sherwin-Williams bought a number of smaller paint makers: Detroit White Lead (1910) Martin-Senour (1917) Acme Quality Paints (1920) and The Lowe Brothers (1929). Responding to wartime restrictions the company developed a fast-drying and water-reducible paint called Kem-Tone and the forerunner of the paint roller the Roller-Koater.

Sales doubled during the 1960s as the company made acquisitions including Sprayon (aerosol paint 1966) but rising expenses kept earnings flat. In 1972 the company expanded its stores to include carpeting draperies and other decorating items. But long-term debt ballooned from $80 million in 1974 to $196 million by 1977 when the company lost $8.2 million and suspended dividends for the first time since 1885.

John Breen became CEO in 1979 reinstated the dividend purged over half of the top management positions and closed inefficient plants. He also focused stores on paint and wallpaper merchandise and purchased Dutch Boy (1980).

In 1990 Sherwin-Williams began selling Dutch Boy in Sears stores and Kem-Tone in Wal-Marts. Acquisitions that year included Borden's Krylon and Illinois Bronze aerosol operations and DeSoto's architectural coatings segment which made private-label paints for Sears and Home Depot. In 1991 Sherwin-Williams bought two coatings business units from Cook Paint and Varnish and the Cuprinol brand of coatings.

Sherwin-Williams purchased paint manufacturer Pratt & Lambert in 1996. That year it introduced several new products including Low Temp 35 a paint for low temperatures; Healthspec a low-odor paint; and Ralph Lauren designer paints. Prep-Rite do-it-yourself interior primers debuted in 1997. Also that year Sherwin-Williams bought Thompson Minwax (Thompson's Water Seal Minwax Wood Products) from Forstmann Little and Chile-based Marson Chilena a spray paint maker.

The company streamlined some of its business segments and trimmed jobs in 1998. Christopher Connor president of the Paint Stores group replaced Breen as CEO in 1999 and chairman in 2000. Also in 2000 Sherwin-Williams moved into the European automotive coatings market by acquiring Italy-based ScottWarren.

In late 2001 the company acquired Wisconsin-based Mautz Paint Company.

After a rough but still profitable 2001 the company grew revenues and profits for its consumer units (consumer paints and paint stores) in 2002 thanks largely to a healthy do-it-yourself market. Sales for its automotive finishes and international units however were down because of a slow collision-repair market and currency-exchange effects.

In 2010 Sherwin-Williams bought Arch Chemicals' Sayerlack a leading Italian wood care coating company and acquired Becker Acroma Industrial Wood Coatings a Swedish manufacturer of industrial wood coatings. It also acquired all shares of AlSher Titania (a joint venture with Altair Nanotechnologies) it did not already own giving it a 100% stake in the technology company. AlSher Titania is developing a promising titanium dioxide technology that Sherwin-Williams plans to commercialize.

That same year the company also acquired Pinturas Condor an Ecuadorian diversified coatings supplier with $60 million in annual sales bolstering its market share in architectural paint in Latin America.

EXECUTIVES

President and COO, John G. Morikis, age 49, $732,703 total compensation
Chairman and CEO, Christopher M. (Chris) Connor, age 56, $1,268,986 total compensation
SVP General Counsel and Secretary, Louis E. Stellato, age 62, $384,514 total compensation
SVP Human Resources, Thomas E. Hopkins, age 55
SVP Finance and CFO, Sean P. Hennessy, age 55, $567,632 total compensation
President and General Manager Diversified Brands Division Consumer Group, Harvey P. Sass, age 55
SVP Corporate Planning and Development, Steven J. Oberfeld, age 60, $487,711 total compensation
President and General Manager Southeastern Division Paint Stores Group, Robert J. Davisson, age 52
VP and Treasurer, Cynthia D. Brogan, age 61
VP Administration, Richard M. Weaver, age 58
President and General Manager Latin American Coatings Group Global Finishes Group, Alexander Zalesky, age 53
SVP Corporate Communications and Public Affairs, Robert J. Wells, age 55
President and General Manager Eastern Division Paint Stores Group, Timothy J. Drouilhet, age 51
President and General Manager Chemical Coatings Division Global Finishes Group, Drew A. McCandless, age 52
President Global Finishes Group, George E. Heath, age 47
President and General Manager Mid Western Division Paint Stores Group, Monty J. Griffin, age 52
President and General Manager South Western Division Paint Stores Group, Cheri M. Phyfer, age 41
President and General Manager Automotive Division Global Finishes Group, Thomas C. Hablitzel, age 50
President and General Manager Paint and Coatings Division Consumer Group, Joel Baxter, age 52
President and General Manager Protective and Marine Coatings Division Global Finishes Group, Peter J. Ippolito, age 48
VP and Corporate Controller, Allen Mistysyn, age 44
Director, John M. Stropki Jr., age 62
Director, Susan J. Kropf, age 64
Director, Richard K. Smucker, age 64
Director, A. Malachi Mixon III, age 72
Director, David F. (Dave) Hodnik, age 65
Director, Curtis E. Moll, age 73
Director, Gary E. McCullough, age 54
Director, Arthur F. (Art) Anton, age 55
Director, Thomas G. (Tom) Kadien, age 56
Director, James C. (Jim) Boland, age 72
Auditors: Ernst&YoungLLP

LOCATIONS

HQ: The Sherwin-Williams Company
101 W. Prospect Ave., Cleveland OH 44115-1075
Phone: 216-566-2000 **Fax:** 216-566-2947
Web: www.sherwin-williams.com

PRODUCTS/OPERATIONS

2011 Sales

	$ mil.	% of total
Paint Stores Group	4,780	55
Consumer Group	1,274	15
Latin America Coatings Group	829	9
Total	**8,766**	**100**

Operations
Paint Stores
Products
Architectural coatings
Industrial maintenanc
Marine products
Brands
ArmorSeal
Brod-Dugan
Con-Lux
FlexBon Paints
Hi-Temp
Kem
Mautz
Mercury
Old Quaker
Powdura
Pro-Line
SeaGuard
Sherwin-Williams
Consumer
Products
Architectural paints
Industrial maintenanc
Paints
Private-label coatings
Stains
Wood finishings
Varnishes
Brands
Cuprinol
Dupli-color
Dura Clad
Dutch Boy
EverLast
Formby's
H&C
Krylon
Martin Senour
Maxwood Latex Stains
Minwax
Plastic Kote
Pratt & Lambert
Red Devil
Rubberset
Signature Select
Thompson's
White Lightning
Automotive Finishes
Products
Finishing refinishing and touch-up products for motor vehicles
Brands
Baco
Excelo
Lazzuril
Martin Senour
ScottWarren
Sherwin-Williams
Western
International Coatings
Products
Architectural paints
Industrial maintenance products
Stains
Varnishes
Wood finishing products
Brands
Andina
Colorgin
Dutch Boy
Globo
Kem-Tone
Krylon
Marson
Martin Senour
Minwax
Pratt & Lambert
Pulverlack
Ronseal
Sherwin-Williams
Sumare

COMPETITORS

Akzo Nobel
BASF SE
BEHR
Benjamin Moore
California Products
Comex Group
Coronado Paint
Diamond Vogel Paint
Dunn-Edwards
DuPont
Ferro
H.B. Fuller
Home Depot
Kelly-Moore
Lowe' s
PPG Industries
RPM International
True Value
Valspar
Wal-Mart

HISTORICAL FINANCIALS

Company Type: Public

Income Statement FYE: December 31

	REVENUE ($ mil.)	NET INCOME ($ mil.)	NET PROFIT MARGIN	EMPLOYEES
12/11	8,765	441	5.0%	32,988
12/10	7,776	462	5.9%	32,228
12/09	7,094	435	6.1%	29,220
12/08	7,979	476	6.0%	30,677
12/07	8,005	615	7.7%	31,572
Annual Growth	2.3%	(8.0%)	—	1.1%

2011 Year-End Financials

Debt ratio: 19.00%
Return on equity: 29.13%
Cash ($ mil.): 32
Current ratio: 104.57
Long-term debt ($ mil.): 639
No. of shares (mil.): 103
Dividends
Yield: —
Payout: 35.27%
Market value ($ mil.): 9,271

	STOCK PRICE ($) FY Close	P/E High/Low		PER SHARE ($) Earnings	Dividends	Book Value
12/11	89.27	21	16	4.14	0.00	14.61
12/10	83.75	20	14	4.21	1.44	15.04
12/09	61.65	17	11	3.78	1.42	13.62
12/08	59.75	16	11	4.00	1.40	13.72
12/07	58.04	15	12	4.70	1.26	14.54
Annual Growth	11.4%	—	—	(3.1%)	—	0.1%

Signature Bank (New York, NY)

Signature Bank marks the spot where some professional New Yorkers bank. The institution provides customized banking and financial services to smaller private businesses their owners and their top executives through about two dozen locations throughout the metropolitan area including all five boroughs Long Island and affluent Westchester County. It attracts deposits by offering personal and business checking and money market accounts. The bank's lending activities mainly entail real estate and business loans. Subsidiary Signature Securities offers wealth management financial planning brokerage services and life and disability insurance.

Mortgage loans including commercial real estate loans multifamily residential mortgages home loans and lines of credit and construction and land loans comprise the bulk of Signature Bank's loan portfolio (and much of its asset base as well). The bank branched out into specialty lending in 2012 forming subsidiary Signature Financial to offer equipment finance and leasing transportation financing and funding for taxi medallions.

Founded in 2001 as an alternative to megabanks Signature Bank has grown into an institution with nearly $15 billion in assets a figure that has more than doubled since the bank was spun off from Bank Hapoalim in 2004. It plans to continue to fill a service void created by industry consolidation. The bank targets businesses that have fewer than 1000 employees and revenues of less than $50 million. Representative clients include real estate companies law firms entertainment agencies and foundations. Signature Bank has also been building its private client business by adding banking teams and opening offices throughout the New York metro area.

The bank's emphasis on personal service helped it to grow its deposit base and loan portfolio in 2011. During a time when many other banks struggled under the weight of bad loans in a bad economy Signature Bank achieved record earnings for the fourth consecutive year. Its 2011 revenue exceeded $622 million and its net income approached $150 million.

EXECUTIVES

Vice Chairman, John Tamberlane, $259,616 total compensation
EVP Group Director and Chairman Commercial Real Estate Committee, George M. Klett
Chairman, Scott A. Shay, $288,710 total compensation
President CEO and Director, Joseph J. DePaolo, $328,750 total compensation
EVP and Group Director, Edwin J. Sirlin
EVP and COO, Mark T. Sigona
EVP and Chief Credit Officer, Michael J. Merlo, $223,269 total compensation
SVP and CTO, Michael Sharkey
EVP and CFO, Eric R. Howell
VP and Associate Group Director, Elizabeth R. Forgione
Media Contact, Susan Lewis
SVP and Treasurer, Peter S. Quinlan
EVP and Group Director, Randi Schneer
VP Loan and Operations and Residential Lending, Debra M. Eannel
SVP and Senior Lender, Steven P. Saporito
SVP and Group Director, John F. Brown
SVP and Group Director, Terry Marks
Group Director and SVP, Frances Tutone
VP and Associate Group Director, Deborah Squatrito
VP and Associate Group Director, Karen Rello
VP and Associate Group Director, Maureen Surette
VP and Associate Group Director, Terry Tarangelo
Group Director and SVP Private Client Banking, Sandra G. Sapperstein
Associate Group Director and VP Private Client Banking, Stephen Bucki
Associate Director and VP Private Client Banking, Mary Gioia
Group Director and Senior Vice President Private Client Banking Team, Thomas Murphy
Associate Group Director and Vice President Private Client Banking Team, Timothy Gilbert
Group Director and SVP Private Client Banking, Matthew R. Weltman
Associate Group Director and VP Private Client Banking, Lorraine Quinlan
Senior Client Associate Private Client Banking, Mayra Rios
Associate Group Director Private Client Banking, Scott A. Fenton
Group Director and SVP, Barbara von Borstel
SVP and Group Director, Ronald M. Berkowitz
SVP and Group Director, Gabrielle E. Stern
SVP and Group Director, Abidus S. Chowdhury
VP and Associate Group Director, Howard Green
SVP and Group Director, Norman Burak
Vice Chairman, John Tamberlane
Director, Alfonse M. (Al) D'Amato, age 74
President CEO and Director, Joseph J. DePaolo
Director, Alfred B. DelBello
Director, Yacov Levy
Director, Ann F. Kaplan, age 66
Director, Jeffrey W. (Jeff) Meshel
Director, Kathryn A. Byrne
Director, Alfonse M. D'Amato
Director, Frank R. Selvaggi
Auditors: KPMGLLP

LOCATIONS

HQ: Signature Bank
565 5th Ave., New York NY 10017
Phone: 646-822-1500 **Fax:** 817-465-5065
Web: www.lelandscott.com

PRODUCTS/OPERATIONS

2011 Sales

	$ mil.	% of total
Interest		
Loans net	333	54
Securities available for sale	223	36
Securities held to maturity	18	3
Other	5	1
Noninterest		
Fees & service charges	15	2
Net gains on sales of securities	14	2
Commissions	9	1
Other	3	1
Total	**622**	**100**

COMPETITORS

Apple Bank for Savings
Astoria Financial
Bank Leumi USA
Capital One
Citigroup
Herald National Bank
HSBC USA
JPMorgan Chase
New York Community Bancorp
Safra Bank
TD Bank USA

HISTORICAL FINANCIALS

Company Type: Public

Income Statement

FYE: December 31

	ASSETS ($ mil.)	NET INCOME ($ mil.)	INCOME AS % OF ASSETS	EMPLOYEES
12/11	14,666	149	1.0%	720
12/10	11,673	102	0.9%	660
12/09	9,146	62	0.7%	614
12/08	7,192	43	0.6%	553
12/07	5,845	27	0.5%	501
Annual Growth	25.9%	53.0%	—	9.5%

2011 Year-End Financials

Debt ratio: 4.60%
Return on equity: 10.62%
Cash ($ mil.): 40
Current ratio: —
Long-term debt ($ mil.): 675
No. of shares (mil.): 46
Dividends
Yield: —
Payout: —
Market value ($ mil.): 2,770

	STOCK PRICE ($) FY Close	P/E High/Low	PER SHARE ($) Earnings	Dividends	Book Value
12/11	59.99	18 13	3.37	0.00	30.49
12/10	50.06	21 13	2.46	0.00	22.84
12/09	31.90	25 15	1.30	0.00	19.79
12/08	28.69	27 17	1.35	0.00	19.81
12/07	33.75	41 32	0.91	0.00	14.34
Annual Growth	15.5%	— —	38.7%	—	20.8%

Simmons First National Corp.

Simmons First National thinks it's only natural it should be one of the largest financial institutions in The Natural State. The holding company owns Simmons First National Bank and seven other community banks that bear the Simmons First Bank name and maintain local identities; together they operate around 90 branches throughout Arkansas and in Kansas and Missouri. Serving consumers and area businesses the banks offer stardard deposit products like checking and savings accounts IRAs and CDs. Lending activities mainly consist of commercial real estate loans single-family mortgages and consumer loans such as credit card and student loans.

In addition to Simmons First National Bank the company owns Simmons First Bank of Jonesboro Simmons First Bank of South Arkansas Simmons First Bank of Northwest Arkansas Simmons First Bank of Russellville Simmons First Bank of Searcy Simmons First Bank of El Dorado and Simmons First Bank of Hot Springs. Simmons First Trust Company a subsidiary of Simmons First National Bank provides trust and fiduciary services; Simmons First Investment Group offers broker-dealer services.

Simmons has expanded throughout Arkansas in part by opening new branches as well as by acquisitions that extended the company's reach to such areas as Conway Hot Springs and northwestern Arkansas. After the economic environment began to deteriorate in 2007 Simmons changed course and focused inward. It tightened its lending standards and added new checking and savings account products to improve liquidity.

Simmons had been content to stay in its home state but in 2010 began considering a strategy it implemeted during the savings and loan crisis of the late 1980s and early 1990s buying troubled financial institutions through the government. It did just that and entered Missouri through the acquisition of the lone branch of the failed Southwest Community Bank in Springfield. Simmons First later entered Kansas and added nearly 10 branches with the acquisition of the failed Security Savings Bank. In 2012 Simmons acquired Clayton Missouri-based Truman Bank in a similar transaction adding four branches to its network. All three deals were facilitated by the FDIC and included loss-sharing agreements with the regulator.

The company's strategy paid off as revenues and net income increased in 2010 thanks in part to the acquisitions and efficiency initiatives implemented during the recession. Without the one-time gains related to the 2010 acquisitions however the company's 2011 revenue (more than $180 million) and net income (nearly $25 million) fell back to levels approximately the same as in 2009.

Simmons tries to differentiate itself from smaller competitors by offering a wider array of products while striving to provide more personalized service than larger regional banks.

EXECUTIVES

Secretary, John L. Rush, age 77
Chairman and CEO; Chairman and CEO Simmons First National Bank, J. Thomas May, age 65, $474,285 total compensation

EVP and CFO, Robert A. Fehlman, age 47, $225,300 total compensation
Chairman and CEO Simmons First Bank of El Dorado, John F. Dews
CEO Simmons First Bank of Jonesboro, Barry K. Ledbetter
Chairman and CEO Simmons First Bank of Russellville, Ronald B. (Ron) Jackson
President and CEO Simmons First Bank of Searcy, Brooks Davis
President Simmons First National Bank, H. Glenn Rambin
Chairman and CEO Simmons First Bank of South Arkansas, Freddie G. Black
President and CEO Simmons First Bank of Northwest Arkansas, Thomas W. Spillyards
President and COO; Chairman Simmons First Bank of Hot Springs, David L. Bartlett, age 60, $314,769 total compensation
EVP Administration, Marty D. Casteel, age 60, $225,300 total compensation
SVP Credit Policy and Risk Assessment, Kevin J. Archer, age 48, $92,915 total compensation
SVP and Controller, David W. Garner, age 42
EVP Marketing, Robert C. Dill, age 68, $179,393 total compensation
President and CEO Simmons First Bank of Hot Springs, Steven W. (Steve) Trusty
SVP and Director Human Resources, Sharon K. Burdine, age 46
SVP and Manager Corporate Audit and Compliance, Tina M. Groves, age 42
SVP and Corporate Sales Director Marketing Group, Amy Johnson
SVP Cash Management and e-Banking, Lisa W. Hunter
Director, Steven A. Cosse, age 64
Director, George A. Makris Jr., age 55
Director, Harry L. Ryburn, age 76
Director, William E. (Bill) Clark II, age 42
Director, Robert L. Shoptaw, age 65
Director, Edward (Eddie) Drilling, age 56
Director, W. Scott McGeorge, age 68
Director, Stanley E. Reed, age 60
Director, Eugene Hunt, age 66
Director, Sharon L. Gaber
Auditors: BKDLLP

LOCATIONS

HQ: Simmons First National Corporation
501 Main St., Pine Bluff AR 71601
Phone: 870-541-1000 **Fax:** 870-541-1154
Web: www.simmonsfirst.com

PRODUCTS/OPERATIONS

2011 Sales

	$ mil.	% of total
Interest		
Loans	113	62
Investment securities	14	8
Other	1	1
Noninterest		
Credit card fees	16	9
Service charges on deposit accounts	16	9
Trust income	5	3
Net gain on sale of mortgage loans	4	2
Other	10	6
Total	**182**	**100**

COMPETITORS

Arvest Bank
BancorpSouth
Bank of America
Bank of the Ozarks
BOK Financial
First Federal Bancshares of Arkansas
Home BancShares
IBERIABANK
Regions Financial
U.S. Bancorp

HISTORICAL FINANCIALS

Company Type: Public

Income Statement FYE: December 31

	ASSETS ($ mil.)	NET INCOME ($ mil.)	INCOME AS % OF ASSETS	EMPLOYEES
12/11	3,320	25	0.8%	1,075
12/10	3,316	37	1.1%	1,108
12/09	3,093	25	0.8%	1,096
12/08	2,923	26	0.9%	1,111
12/07	2,692	27	1.0%	1,103
Annual Growth	5.4%	(1.9%)	—	(0.6%)

2011 Year-End Financials

Debt ratio: 3.64%
Return on equity: 6.22%
Cash ($ mil.): 570
Current ratio: —
Long-term debt ($ mil.): 120
No. of shares (mil.): 17
Dividends
Yield: —
Payout: 51.70%
Market value ($ mil.): 468

	STOCK PRICE ($) FY Close	P/E High/Low		PER SHARE ($) Earnings	Dividends	Book Value
12/11	27.19	20	13	1.47	0.00	23.70
12/10	28.50	14	11	2.15	0.76	23.01
12/09	27.80	17	12	1.74	0.76	21.72
12/08	29.47	19	12	1.91	0.76	20.69
12/07	26.50	16	12	1.92	0.73	19.57
Annual Growth	0.6%	—	—	(6.5%)	—	4.9%

Simon Property Group, Inc.

Simon says: "Shop!" And millions do. Simon Property Group is the largest shopping mall and retail center owner in the US with a portfolio of some 340 retail properties totaling approximately 245 million sq. ft. of leasable space in more than 40 states and Puerto Rico. The self-managed self-administered real estate investment trust (REIT) owns develops and manages regional shopping malls outlet malls (under the Premium Outlet Prime Outlet and The Mills brands) boutique malls and shopping centers. Its portfolio is concentrated in the Southeast Midwest and Northeast US. The REIT also has stakes in outlet centers in Japan South Korea Malaysia and Mexico.

HISTORY

nSimon Property Group helped change the face of the US retail landscape from mom-and-pop stores to shopping malls. The original Simon Property Group (formed in 1993) was the offshoot of brothers Melvin and Herbert Simon's Melvin Simon & Associates (MSA founded in 1959). MSA's first project was Southgate Plaza a strip center in Bloomington Indiana consisting of a half-dozen small tenants anchored by a food store.

To get started the Simons sometimes borrowed cash from friends but during the 1960s and 1970s developers could usually borrow 100% of a shopping center's construction costs after securing an anchor tenant. Leases then provided money to repay debt and make a down payment on the next project. The Simons consistently retained equity developing a huge asset base that they used as collateral for larger projects.

The new strip malls lacked the prestige of big-city stores such as Macy's; they also lacked the personal touch of the neighborhood shops they put out of business. But they boasted retail's two most important virtues –price and convenience –and in time they developed into the modern mall. MSA built its first indoor mall in the mid-1960s in snowy Fort Collins Colorado. By the late 1960s MSA and other developers were consumed with mall projects.

Unlike many developers the Simons were genial honest negotiators appealing to merchants and bankers put off by city slickers or hucksters. Yet Mel and Herb were often compared to the Marx brothers for bickering between themselves. During one negotiation Mel allegedly took off his shoe and threw it at Herb.

In the mid-1970s Mel packed up and headed west to become a Hollywood producer. After a string of such Oscar noncontenders as "Porky's" and "Love at First Bite" Mel returned to the family company in the 1980s and in 1983 the brothers bought pro basketball's Indiana Pacers. Melvin Simon died in 2009.

As the 1989 real estate slump hit the Simons were busy building the largest mall in the country just outside Minneapolis. Completed in 1992 the Mall of America included a roller coaster a two-story miniature golf course and a walk-through aquarium. In 1993 Simon Property Group went public in one of the largest IPOs of its time.

In 1996 the company became the Simon DeBartolo Group after merging with DeBartolo Realty founded to hold the retail and residential properties of another sporting family the DeBartolos (San Francisco 49ers).

After its record-setting purchase of private paired-share REIT Corporate Property Investors in 1998 the company reverted to the Simon Property Group name (Edward DeBartolo's name had been soiled in a Louisiana casino scandal) and added more than 20 midwestern properties to its fold giving the company a firm lock on the top mall REIT spot.

In 1999 Simon bought stakes in 14 malls in the northeastern US and became 50%-owner of the Mall of America after buying a 27% stake in the development held by financing partner TIAA-CREF for $318 million. The following year it formed a joint venture with Kimco Realty to buy 250 stores from the bankrupt Montgomery Ward chain.

Simon seemed ready to embrace online shopping during the Internet craze by working on initiatives that combined the traditional shopping experience with the convenience of the Internet including its clixnmortar.com which developed high-tech shopping tools. However like other ambitious online concepts of the era Simon's was slow to catch on with consumers. The company wrote off losses related to its tech investments in 2001 and went back to focusing on food courts.

In 2002 the company bought part of the mall portfolio of Rodamco North America. That year Simon also pulled out of a much-ballyhooed project –building a family entertainment complex at Penn's Landing in Philadelphia's Center City – after a deadline to lease 50% of the center was not met. Later that year the company merged with

SPG Realty Consultants ending the companies' paired share corporate structure.

In 2003 the company bought out the 42% stake in The Forum Shops held by joint venture partner Sheldon Gordon after he exercised a provision in his deal with Simon that forced the company to buy out his share or sell him its 58% stake. That same year Simon dropped a bid with Westfield America (now Westfield Group) to acquire rival Taubman Centers after a legal battle was ended by the passage of an antitakeover bill in Michigan.

In 2004 the company was forced to sell a controlling interest in the Mall of America to Canadian real estate firm Triple Five an original partner in the development after a court ruled that Simon improperly acquired control of the mall from TIAA-CREF in 1999. (The case is still pending appeals.) Later that year Simon acquired outlet mall developer Chelsea Property Group for about $3.5 billion.

Also in 2004 the REIT acquired Chelsea Property Group allowing it to open its first Premium Outlet center in Mexico. Three years later it acquired The Mills Corporation giving it 37 additional properties across the country.

With property interests already established in Japan and South Korea the REIT pursued investments in China but decided to cut its losses there and sold those assets in late 2009. Elsewhere overseas Simon sold its interest in a joint venture that owned seven shopping centers in France and Poland to Unibail-Rodamco the following year.

In 2010 Simon lost its bid to acquire struggling General Growth Properties the nation's second-largest mall owner. If Simon had won the bid for General Growth the combined company would have far eclipsed its competitors with about a third of the US retail market. Antitrust concerns factored into General Growth's decision to accept an offer from Brookfield Asset Management.

Simon later had another takeover attempt rebuffed when it bid to acquire UK-based mall owner Capital Shopping Centres for some #3 billion ($4.7 million). The offer was decried as too low.

EXECUTIVES

President Premium Outlet Centers, John R. Klein
EVP and Treasurer, Andrew A. (Andy) Juster, age 59
Secretary and General Counsel, James M. Barkley, age 60, $519,231 total compensation
President COO and Director, Richard S. (Rick) Sokolov, age 62, $812,077 total compensation
EVP and CFO, Stephen E. Sterrett, age 56, $493,269 total compensation
SEVP and Chief Administrative Officer, John Rulli, age 56, $467,308 total compensation
Chairman Emeritus, Herbert (Herb) Simon, age 77
Chairman and CEO, David Simon, age 50, $1,038,462 total compensation
Assistant General Counsel and Assistant Secretary, Steven E. (Steve) Fivel, age 51
CIO, David Schacht
President The Mills, Gregg M. Goodman, age 48
EVP Development Operations Simon Malls, Michael E. McCarty
SEVP; President Leasing, Gary L. Lewis, age 53, $500,000 total compensation
SEVP Leasing Simon Malls, Bruce Tobin, age 58
EVP Leasing Premium Outlet Centers, Richard N. Lewis
EVP Real Estate Premium Outlet Centers, Mark J. Silvestri
SVP Energy and Procurement, George Caraghiaur
Chief Marketing Officer; President Simon Brand Ventures, Mikael Thygesen
EVP Leasing Simon Malls, Vicki Hanor
EVP Leasing Simon Malls, Barney Quinn
EVP Leasing The Mills, Gary Duncan
EVP Property Management The Mills, Paul C. Fickinger
President Community/Lifestyle Centers, Myles H. Minton
SVP Finance Operating Properties, David L. Campbell
EVP Simon Management Group, Timothy G. Earnest
EVP Leasing Simon Malls, Butch Knerr
SVP and Chief Accounting Officer, Steven K. (Steve) Broadwater, age 45
SEVP; President Simon Malls, David J. Contis, age 53
SVP Management Premium Outlet Centers, Gregory C. Link
SVP Leasing Community/Lifestyle Centers, Paul S. Ajdaharian
SVP Development Community/Lifestyle Centers, Kevin A. Sims
Assistant VP Business Development, Lisa Bennett
SVP Corporate Marketing, Shari Simon
Assistant VP Corporate Special Events, Jacque Ellis
EVP and Chief Investment Officer, Matthew Lentz
President COO and Director, Richard S. (Rick) Sokolov, age 62
Chairman and CEO, David Simon, age 50
Director, Larry C. Glasscock, age 63
Director, Melvyn E. (Mel) Bergstein, age 70
Director, Reuben S. Leibowitz, age 64
Director, Karen N. Horn, age 68
Director, J. Albert Smith Jr., age 71
Director, Linda Walker Bynoe, age 59
Director, Daniel C. (Dan) Smith, age 54
Director, Allan Hubbard, age 64
Auditors: Ernst&YoungLLP

LOCATIONS

HQ: Simon Property Group Inc.
225 W. Washington St., Indianapolis IN 46204
Phone: 317-636-1600 **Fax:** 317-263-2318
Web: www.simon.com

PRODUCTS/OPERATIONS

2011 Sales

	$ mil.	% of total
Minimum rent	2,664	62
Tenant reimbursements	1,177	27
Overage rent	140	3
Management fees & other	128	3
Other	195	5
Total	**4,306**	**100**

COMPETITORS

Belz
Cadillac Fairview
CBL & Associates Properties
General Growth Properties
Glimcher Realty
Horizon Group Properties
Kimco Realty
Lincoln Property
Macerich
Taubman Centers
Vornado Realty
Weingarten Realty

HISTORICAL FINANCIALS

Company Type: Public

Income Statement FYE: December 31

	REVENUE ($ mil.)	NET INCOME ($ mil.)	NET PROFIT MARGIN	EMPLOYEES
12/11	4,306	1,245	28.9%	5,500
12/10	3,957	753	19.0%	5,900
12/09	3,775	387	10.3%	5,200
12/08	3,783	463	12.3%	5,300
12/07	3,650	491	13.5%	5,100
Annual Growth	4.2%	26.2%	—	1.9%

2011 Year-End Financials

Debt ratio: 70.36%
Return on equity: 25.34%
Cash ($ mil.): 798
Current ratio: 71.92
Long-term debt ($ mil.): 18,446
No. of shares (mil.): 293
Dividends
Yield: —
Payout: 100.57%
Market value ($ mil.): 37,890

	STOCK PRICE ($) FY Close	P/E High	P/E Low	PER SHARE ($) Earnings	Dividends	Book Value
12/11	128.94	38	27	3.48	0.00	16.73
12/10	99.49	51	33	2.10	2.60	16.78
12/09	79.80	78	25	1.05	2.70	17.46
12/08	53.13	56	20	1.87	3.60	16.89
12/07	86.86	63	43	1.95	3.36	20.64
Annual Growth	10.4%	—	—	15.6%	—	(5.1%)

SLM Corp.

Those who graduated "magna cum payments" may not be familiar with SLM but they probably know its more common moniker Sallie Mae. The company which manages some 10 million student loans is one of the US's largest sources of funding and servicing for education loans. Formerly primarily a wholesale acquirer SLM now originates more than half its loans. The firm originates acquires finances and services private student loans which are not guaranteed by the government. In addition SLM earns fees for its servicing and collections services as well as processing and administrative offerings through various subsidiaries. The firm is one of four private entities providing servicing for the Department of Education.

HISTORY

The Student Loan Marketing Association was chartered in 1972 as a response to problems in the Guaranteed Student Loan Program of 1965. For years the GSL program had tinkered with rates to induce banks to make loans but servicing the small loans was expensive and troublesome. Sallie Mae began operations in 1973 buying loans from their originators; its size provided economies of scale in loan servicing.

Originally only institutions making educational or student loans were allowed to own stock in Sallie Mae. This was later changed so that anyone could buy nonvoting stock. In 1993 voting stock was listed on the NYSE.

Sallie Mae was always a political football altered again and again to reflect the education policies of the party in power. When it was founded during the Nixon administration its loans were restricted by a needs test which was repealed during the Carter years. The Reagan administration reimposed the needs test and at the same time sped up the schedule under which the company was to become self-supporting which it did by late 1981.

Forced to rely on its own resources Sallie Mae turned to creative financing. One of its traditional advantages was that its loan interest rates were linked to Treasury bills traditionally about 3% above the T-bill rate. The company became a master at riding the spread between its cost of funds and the interest rates it charged.

Between 1983 and 1992 Sallie Mae's assets swelled by more than 400% and its income rose by almost 500%. As the firm grew management became more visible with high pay and extravagant perks. Although salaries were not inconsistent with those of executives at comparable private corporations the remuneration level and perks irked Congress. But Sallie Mae kept growing –in 1992 it expanded its facilities and added 900 new staff members.

The 1993 Omnibus Budget Reconciliation Act with its transfer of the student loan program directly to the government and its surcharge on Sallie Mae began to adversely affect earnings in 1994. While awaiting permission to alter its charter the company stepped up its marketing efforts especially to school loan officers who advised students on loan options.

In 1995 then-COO Albert Lord led a group of stockholders in a push to cut operating expenses and repackage student loans as securities a la Freddie Mac and Fannie Mae. Lord and some of his supporters won seats on the board (as well as the enmity of Lawrence Hough who resigned as CEO in the midst of the melee). That year Sallie Mae bought HICA Holding one of two private insurers of education loans. In 1996 Congress passed legislation forcing Sallie Mae's privatization.

Despite SLM's rising stock shareholders were unhappy with chairman William Arceneaux's status quo business plan. Lord gained control in 1997.

In 1998 the organization became SLM Holding. Assets and earnings were muted that year when unfavorable market conditions prevented Sallie Mae from securitizing its loans.

The firm the next year expanded its lending operations by buying Nellie Mae. Also in 1999 Sallie Mae teamed with Answer Financial to sell insurance. Growth continued in 2000 when the company bought loan servicer Student Loan Funding Resources as well as the marketing student loan servicing and administrative operations of USA Group; the company changed its name to USA Education following the acquisition. The company also cut some 1700 jobs approximately 25% of its workforce.

The following year Sallie Mae teamed with Intuit allowing the financial software company access to Sallie Mae's 7 million customers. It also launched online recruiting service TrueCareers that year.

In 2002 it bought Pioneer Credit Recovery and General Revenue Corporation two of the nation's largest student loan collection agencies. It also reverted to the SLM moniker to reconnect with the name by which it has so long been known.

The privatization plan put into place in the mid-'90s (orchestrated in large part by then-CEO Lord) came to fruition nearly four years ahead of schedule when SLM transitioned to a private organization in December 2004.

In 2007 SLM saw its stock values plummet to their lowest levels in about a decade. A number of industry-wide factors figured into the losses not the least of which was the downturn in the credit market. Also affecting the company was the signing into law of the College Cost Reduction and Access Act (CCRAA). Intended to reform student lending and cut costs for borrowers the act slashed subsidies for lenders participating in the Federal Family Education Loan Program (FFELP). The reform cut into the company's interest-earning operations. As a result SLM increased its focus on higher-yielding private education loans which carry a lower risk.

Additionally SLM that year became ensnared in a student-lending industry probe led by New York attorney general Andrew Cuomo. The company agreed to a $2 million settlement and to abide by a code of conduct regarding its dealings with college employees.

One of the most dramatic results of the troubles was the collapse of a planned acquisition by a consortium of investment firms. The planned $8.8 billion deal included buyers J.C. Flowers (which was to own about a half of SLM) Bank of America and JPMorgan Chase. In the midst of the industry probe J.C. Flowers sought a change in SLM's leadership in an effort to secure regulatory approval for the acquisition; Thomas J. (Tim) Fitzpatrick was ousted as CEO. Ultimately the buyers canceled the deal citing the reduced potential value of SLM. The student lender filed a lawsuit to challenge the termination but eventually dropped the suit. It later cut more than 10% of its workforce.

EXECUTIVES

Chairman, Anthony P. (Tony) Terracciano, age 73
EVP Administration, Joni J. Reich
Vice Chairman and CEO, Albert L. Lord, age 67, $1,298,076 total compensation
President and COO, John F. (Jack) Remondi, age 49, $1,038,461 total compensation
Corporate Secretary, Carol R. Rakatansky
SEVP and Chief Lending Officer, John (Jack) Hewes, age 63, $600,000 total compensation
SVP Technology, Timothy (Tim) Staley
EVP and General Counsel, Laurent C. Lutz, age 51
Director Capital Markets, Kenneth (Ken) Fischbach
EVP and CFO, Jonathan C. (Jon) Clark, age 53, $305,769 total compensation
EVP and Chief Marketing Officer, Joseph (Joe) DePaulo, age 46, $300,000 total compensation
President Sallie Mae Bank, Paul Thome
SVP Investor Relations, Steven McGarry
Vice Chairman and CEO, Albert L. Lord, age 67
Director, Barry A. Munitz, age 70
Director, Wolfgang Schoellkopf, age 79
Director, Howard H. Newman, age 64
Director, William M. Diefenderfer III, age 67
Director, A. Alexander Porter Jr., age 73
Director, Diane Suitt Gilleland, age 65
Director, Earl A. Goode, age 71
Director, Ann T. Bates, age 54
Director, Ronald F. Hunt, age 68
Director, Steven L. Shapiro, age 72
Director, Barry L. Williams, age 67
Director, J. Terry Strange, age 67
Director, Michael E. Martin, age 56
Director, Frank C. Puleo, age 66
Auditors: PricewaterhouseCoopersLLP

LOCATIONS

HQ: SLM Corporation
300 Continental Dr., Newark DE 19713
Phone: 302-283-8000 **Fax:** 215-977-3409
Web: www.sunocoinc.com

PRODUCTS/OPERATIONS

2011 Sales

	$ mil.	% of total
Interest		
FFELP loans	3,461	51
Private education loans	2,429	36
Other	40	1
Servicing	381	6
Contingency revenue	333	5
Gains on debt repurchases & other	106	1
Adjustments	(994)	-
Total	**5,756**	**100**

Selected Subsidiaries

HICA Holding
Sallie Mae Bank
Sallie Mae Inc.
SLM Education Credit Finance Corporation
  Bull Run I LLC
  SLM Education Credit Funding LLC
SLM Investment Corporation
Southwest Student Services Corporation

COMPETITORS

Bank of America
Brazos Higher Education Service Corp.
Educational Funding of The South
First Marblehead
FirstCity Financial
Great Lakes Higher Education
KeyCorp
Mohela
Nelnet
Pennsylvania Higher Education Assistance Agency
SunTrust
Texas Guaranteed

HISTORICAL FINANCIALS

Company Type: Public

Income Statement

FYE: December 31

	ASSETS ($ mil.)	NET INCOME ($ mil.)	INCOME AS % OF ASSETS	EMPLOYEES
12/11	193,345	633	0.3%	6,600
12/10	205,307	530	0.3%	7,600
12/09	169,985	324	0.2%	8,000
12/08	168,768	(212)	—	8,000
12/07	155,564	(896)	—	11,000
Annual Growth	5.6%	—	—	(12.0%)

2011 Year-End Financials

Debt ratio: 79.85%
Return on equity: 12.07%
Cash ($ mil.): 2,794
Current ratio: —
Long-term debt ($ mil.): 154,393
No. of shares (mil.): 509
Dividends
Yield: —
Payout: 25.42%
Market value ($ mil.): 6,821

	STOCK PRICE ($) FY Close	P/E High/Low		PER SHARE ($) Earnings	Dividends	Book Value
12/11	13.40	14	10	1.18	0.00	10.30
12/10	12.59	14	11	0.94	0.00	9.51
12/09	11.27	32	8	0.38	0.00	10.88
12/08	8.90	—	—	(0.69)	0.00	10.69
12/07	20.14	—	—	(2.26)	0.75	11.20
Annual Growth	(9.7%)	—	—	—	—	(2.1%)

Smithfield Foods, Inc.

When Smithfield Foods waddles up to the trough the other porkers stand back. Big from acquisitions the company is the world's largest hog producer and pork processor. Its products include more than 50 brands of fresh pork and processed value-added pork products. Smithfield Foods sells its products under such brand names as Armour Eckrich Cook's Farmland Foods John Morrell Patrick Cudahy Gwaltney and Healthy Ones. In addition to meat products the company's specialty foods division offers nuts desserts and dressings. Smithfield distributes its meats in the US and internationally mainly in Mexico Western Europe the UK Poland and Romania.

HISTORY

Joseph Luter's father and grandfather set up Smithfield Foods in 1936 and built it into a regional pork producer. Luter began to manage the business in 1962 after his father died. In 1969 he sold the company to conglomerate Liberty Equities for $20 million and was retained as its manager but he was soon dismissed.

Smithfield Foods foundered in his absence and grew weak from overexpansion and non-pork diversifications. Luter bought the business back in 1975 paying a fraction of what he had sold it for. At that time the company was a wholesaler of pork and fish products and was operating 27 seafood restaurants. Luter trimmed the fat to pay down debt leaving only the pork operations. He then began to expand in the pork business through acquisitions including Gwaltney Packing in 1982 thereby doubling its size. Other purchases included pork processors Patrick Cudahy (1985) and Esskay (1986).

The company formed a joint venture with pork producer Carroll's Foods in 1987 to help lessen its dependence on Midwestern hog farmers. To move toward higher-quality pork the joint venture acquired North American rights from National Pig Development (a UK-based family-owned firm) for a long and lean English breed –the NPD hog which became the basis for the company's flagship brand Smithfield Lean Generation Pork.

The company co-founded Circle Four Farms a giant hog farm in Utah in 1994 with partners Murphy's Family Farms Carroll's and Prestage Farms. (Two years later it bought out the other partners.) Smithfield Foods also bought regional processors Valleydale Foods (1993) and John Morrell (1995) and struggling Lykes Meat Group (1996) thereby transforming it into a company with a national presence. In 1997 the company was ticketed with $12.6 million in fines by the EPA for water violations. The fine was later lowered by $6 million by an appellate court.

Beginning in 1998 Smithfield Foods went shopping abroad starting with Canadian meat processor Canada's Schneider Corporation and Societe Bretonne de Salaisons France's largest private-label maker of hams and bacon. In 1999 Smithfield bought a controlling interest in Poland's largest meat and poultry processor Animex; purchased a 32% stake in one of Canada's largest pork processors Mitchell's Gourmet Foods; and formed a joint venture in Mexico.

In 2000 the company acquired Murphy Family Farms for about $460 million doubling its pig production. Later in 2000 Smithfield Foods entered a brisk bidding war to acquire beef and pork giant IBP Fresh Meats but lost out to Tyson Foods.

Now with a taste for beef in 2001 Smithfield acquired midsized beef processors Moyer Packing Company (MOPAC) and Packerland Holdings. The company bought neighboring country-ham maker The Smithfield Companies. Smithfield then bought 50% of case-ready meat company Pinnacle Foods later re-named it Pennexx. Later that year the company set to expanding its ready-to-eat and deli lineup by acquiring bankrupt Gorges/Quik-to-Fix Foods and RMH Foods. Smithfield began a joint venture in late 2001 with Artal Holland to distribute processed meat products in China.

Lower hog prices in 2002 caused Smithfield's first quarter profits to plummet by 80% despite gains from its newly acquired beef operations. To fatten up its deli offerings in 2002 the company purchased Italian foods maker Stefano Foods for $35.8 million.

By 2003 Smithfield owned 41% of Pennexx and stood as the company's largest lender. Mounting losses at Pennexx caused it to default on its loans from Smithfield. As part of the lending agreement Smithfield took possession of Pennexx's assets in June of 2003. It then renamed the company Showcase Foods Inc and rolled it into its beef operations. However the investment was deemed a money-losing failure and Smithfield shuttered the business in 2004.

Despite cries of anti-trust in late 2003 Smithfield spent $367 million to purchase the Farmland Foods pork production and processing businesses from ailing cooperative Farmland Industries. The purchase gave Smithfield control of 27% of the US pork industry.

With an eye on its overseas operations in early 2004 Smithfield spent $88 million to purchase Hormel's 15% share of Spanish meat processor Campofrio Alimentacion. Later in the year it went on to purchase additional shares bringing its ownership up to 22%. By the end of 2004 Smithfield had purchased Campofrio's Polish meat processing unit Morliny. When combined with its ownership of Animex the acquisition gave Smithfield control over 10% of Poland's domestic meat industry.

Elsewhere in the world during 2004 Smithfield acquired UK fresh and processed meat companies Norwich Food Company and Ridpath Pek then combined the two companies into Smithfield Foods Ltd. However after acquiring and merging several meat processors in Canada Smithfield sold all of its Canadian operations in the form of Schneider Corporation to Maple Leaf Foods for $378 million in 2004.

As part of a restructuring in 2004 Winn-Dixie Stores sold its Dixie Packers meat processing plant to Smithfield. Along with the purchase came an agreement to supply the grocery retailer with products from the plant.

Before Smithfield lost its 2000 bidding war for IBP to Tyson the company had snapped up shares of IBP as leverage. Even though all the shares were eventually sold off the Department of Justice took a dim view of a portion of the purchase and filed an anti-trust suit seeking $5.5 million. Admitting no wrongdoing Smithfield settled the suit in 2004 agreeing to pay $2 million.

In 2005 Smithfield acquired MF Cattle Feeding which has operations in Colorado and Idaho. Later that year MF and ContiGroup subsidiary ContiBeef formed a 50-50 joint venture cattle-feeding business named Five Rivers Ranch Cattle Feeding.

Extending its reach into Europe in 2005 Smithfield purchased French meat processor Jean Caby for $466 million. In 2006 it purchased Sara Lee's European meats business for $575 million and the assumption of about $39 million in pension liabilities. Smithfield financed the purchase through a 50-50 joint venture with Oaktree Capital Management. Smithfield combined the Sara Lee operations with Jean Caby and named the new joint venture Groupe Smithfield.

Back home the company added to its holdings as well. The company purchased Cook's Ham from ConAgra in 2006 for about $260 million. Later that year it purchased the bulk of ConAgra's refrigerated meats business for $571 million in cash.

The deal included the Eckrich Armour Lunch-Makers Margherita and Longmont brands. The Butterball brand was sold to Carolina Turkeys (now Butterball LLC) of which Smithfield owns 49%. Not part of the deal were the Brown 'N Serve Hebrew National Pemmican and Slim Jim brands which ConAgra retains.

After 31 years as Smithfield's CEO and chairman Joseph Luter stepped down as CEO in 2006. However he remained as non-executive chairman of the company. President and COO C. Larry Pope a 25-year veteran of Smithfield succeeded Luter as CEO.

Taking heed of the advancing Internet Smithfield's specialty foods group launched a Web site (smithfieldincentives.com) in 2006. Designed to appeal to corporate-gift-givers the site offers gourmet food products including Smithfield meat products as well as a line of sweets nuts desserts and chocolate. The same year company sold its subsidiary value-added meat-product company Quik-to-Fix Foods to foodservice supplier Advance Food for an undisclosed amount. Later that year Smithfield's subsidiary Smithfield Packing closed a pork packing plant in Virginia as it consolidated its East Coast processing operations.

The company paid $810 million (including $125 million in debt) for it in 2007. As the US's #1 pork processor and marketer Smithfield's takeover of Premium Standard (the nation's #2 pork producer) created a pig-production powerhouse. Premium Standard brought brands such as All Natural Fresh & Tender Lundy's Natural Excellence and Premium Farms to the Smithfield roster.

The company merged its Groupe Smithfield Holdings with Spanish meat processor Campofrio Alimentacion in 2008. The all-stock transaction created a leading European meat processor. Smithfield owns 37% of the combined companies which operate under the Campofrio Food Group name.

EXECUTIVES

CEO Campofrio Food Group, Robert A. Sharpe II
President CEO and Director, C. Larry Pope, age 57, $1,100,000 total compensation
President John Morrell, Joseph B. Sebring, age 64, $700,000 total compensation
Chairman, Joseph W. Luter III, age 73, $992,667 total compensation
President Murphy-Brown, Jerry H. Godwin, age 65, $750,000 total compensation
President North Side Foods, Robert G. Hofmann II, age 62
VP Operations Analysis, Bart Ellis, age 56
SVP and Chief Commodity Hedging Officer, Dhamu Thamodaran, age 56
VP Chief Legal Officer and Secretary, Michael H. Cole, age 52
VP and Corporate Controller, Jeffrey A. Deel, age 54
EVP, Joseph W. (Joe) Luter IV, age 47, $700,000 total compensation
SVP Corporate Affairs and Chief Sustainability Officer, Dennis H. Treacy, age 57
CIO, Mansour T. Zadeh, age 57

EVP and CFO, Robert W. (Bo) Manly IV, age 59, $600,000 total compensation
President and COO Pork Group, George H. Richter, age 67, $800,000 total compensation
CEO Smithfield Foods Ltd., John Alton Jones
President Patrick Cudahy, William G. (Bill) Otis, age 55
VP Finance and Chief Accounting Officer, Kenneth M. Sullivan, age 48
President Curly's Foods, John Pauley
President Stefano Foods, Enrico Piraino, age 64
Senior Corporate VP Operations and Engineering, Henry L. Morris, age 69
VP Investor Relations and Corporate Communications, Keira Lombardo
CFO Pork Group, Brian J. Hennessy
President Animex, Darek Nowakowski, age 58
VP and Senior Counsel, Michael D. Flemming, age 63
VP Corporate Tax, Vernon T. Turner, age 48
President Smithfield Packing, Timothy O. (Tim) Schellpeper, age 47, $500,000 total compensation
VP Internal Audit, Craig R. Harlow
VP and General Manager Smithfield Specialty Foods Group, William (Pete) Booker III
President Premium Standard Farms, Bill Homann
President Farmland Foods, Michael E. Brown
VP and Corporate Treasurer, Timothy Dykstra
President Cumberland Gap Provision, R. D. McGregor
President Armour-Eckrich Meats, Joe Sebring
President Smithfield Foods International Group, Jason Richter
President Smithfield Prod., Bogdan Mihail
President CEO and Director, C. Larry Pope, age 57
Director, Frank S. Royal, age 72
Director, John T. Schwieters, age 72
Director, Melvin O. Wright, age 84
Director, Robert L. Burrus Jr., age 77
Director, Carol T. Crawford, age 69
Director, Wendell H. Murphy, age 73
Director, Margaret G. Lewis, age 58
Director, Rt. Hon. Paul S. Trible Jr., age 65
Director, David C. Nelson, age 53
Director, Richard T. Crowder
Auditors: Ernst&YoungLLP

LOCATIONS

HQ: Smithfield Foods Inc.
200 Commerce St., Smithfield VA 23430
Phone: 757-365-3000 **Fax:** 757-365-3017
Web: www.smithfieldfoods.com

2011 Sales

	$ mil.	% of total
US	10,900	89
International	1,302	11
Total	**12,202**	**100**

PRODUCTS/OPERATIONS

2011 Pork Sales

	% of total
Packaged	56
Fresh by-products &	44
Total	**100**

Selected Brands

Aoste
Armour
Basse' s Choice
Big 8' s
Bistro
Campofrio
Carando
Casa Taraneasca
Cochonou
Comtim
Cook' s
Cumberland Gap
Curly' s Foods
Del Mare
Dinner Bell
El Mi?o
Ember Farms
Esskay
E-Z-Cut Hams
Farmland
Farmstead
Flavore
Genuine Smithfield Ham
Great
Gwaltney
Healthy Ones
Higueral
Hunter
Jean Caby
John Morrell
John Morrell Off the Bone
Justin Bridou
Krakus
Kretschmar Deli
Krey
La Abuelita
LunchMakers
Lundy' s
Lykes
Marcassou
Margherita
Maverick
Mayrose
Mazury
Milano' s Italian Grille
Morliny
Mosey' s Corned Beef
Nobre
Norson
Olde Kentucky
Party Dipper
Patrick Cudahy
Paula Deen Collection
Pavone
Peyton' s
Premium Standard Farms
Pure Farms
Quick-N-Easy
Rath Black Hawk
Ready Crisp
Realean
Riojano
Rip-n-Dip
Rodeo
Simply Natural
Sizzle & Serve

Selected Subsidiaries

Farmland Foods Inc.
Henry' s Hickory House LLC
Iowa Quality Meats Ltd.
John Morrell & Co.
Murphy-Brown LLC
Murphy Farms of Texahoma Inc.
North Side Foods Corp.
Patrick Cudahy Incorporated
Premium Pet Health LLC
Premium Standard Farms LLC

COMPETITORS

Boar' s Head
Cargill Meat Solutions
Clougherty Packing
Coleman Natural Foods
ConAgra
Hormel
Indiana Packers
JBS
Johnsonville Sausage
Mondelez International
Oberto Sausage Company
Pederson' s
Quality Pork Processors Inc.
Sadia
Sara Lee North American Retail
Seaboard Foods
Usinger' s

HISTORICAL FINANCIALS

Company Type: Public

Income Statement

FYE: April 29

	REVENUE ($ mil.)	NET INCOME ($ mil.)	NET PROFIT MARGIN	EMPLOYEES
04/12*	13,094	361	2.8%	46,050
05/11	12,202	521	4.3%	46,350
05/10	11,202	(101)	—	48,000
05/09	12,487	(190)	—	52,400
04/08	11,351	128	1.1%	52,300
Annual Growth	3.6%	29.4%	—	(3.1%)

*Fiscal year change

2012 Year-End Financials

Debt ratio: 26.47%
Return on equity: 10.67%
Cash ($ mil.): 324
Current ratio: 290.33
Long-term debt ($ mil.): 1,900
No. of shares (mil.): 157
Dividends
Yield: —
Payout: —
Market value ($ mil.): 3,340

	STOCK PRICE ($) FY Close	P/E High/Low		PER SHARE ($) Earnings	Dividends	Book Value
04/12*	21.22	11	8	2.21	0.00	21.52
05/11	23.56	8	4	3.12	0.00	21.35
05/10	18.74	—	—	(0.65)	0.00	16.60
05/09	8.61	—	—	(1.35)	0.00	17.84
04/08	28.48	36	25	0.96	0.00	22.68
Annual Growth	(7.1%)	—	—	23.2%	—	(1.3%)

*Fiscal year change

Smucker (J.M.) Co.

The J. M. Smucker Company gets its bread and butter from more than just making and marketing jelly. The company's known for manufacturing its namesake Smucker's fruit spread and for selling the ubiquitous Jif peanut butter brand. But Smucker's has expanded its products portfolio to include Folgers the #1-coffee brand in the US as well as market leaders in espresso (Cafe Bustelo) and premium java (Dunkin' Donuts licensed). Other top-shelf lines are Hungry Jack and Pillsbury baking mixes and frostings Eagle and Carnation canned milk and Crisco shortening and oils among many. Smucker's brands are sold to consumers through retail outlets in the US and Canada with some products exported.

HISTORY

Jerome Smucker began operating a steam-powered cider mill in 1897 for farmers in Orrville Ohio but he found that his biggest business was selling apple butter made using a secret Smucker family recipe. By the 1920s The J. M. Smucker Company had begun producing a full line of preserves and jellies and in 1935 it acquired its first fruit-processing operations.

Under Jerome's grandson Paul Smucker the company gained widespread national distribution by the mid-1960s. Tim Smucker succeeded his father Paul as president in 1981 then as chairman in 1987 when his brother Richard became president.

The company's growth has been enhanced through the development of its industrial fruit fillings business and acquisitions of domestic natural juice and peanut butter companies including Knudsen & Sons (1984) After the Fall (1994) and Laura Scudder's (from National Grape Co-op 1994). It has gradually expanded internationally through acquisitions. In 1993 it acquired the jam preserves and pie-filling unit of Canada's Culinar. In a 1998 deal Smucker purchased Australia's Allowrie jam and Lackersteens marmalade lines.

Smucker sold its flagging Mrs. Smith's frozen pie business to Flowers in 1997 less than two years after buying the unit from Kellogg. It bought Kraft's domestic fruit spread unit in 1997 and in 1999 purchased the northwestern Adams peanut butter business from Pro-Fac Cooperative. Smucker kept the Adams name but shifted packaging to its Pennsylvania peanut butter plant.

Spreading into retail the company opened a store in 1999 in its hometown of Orrville and then launched online and catalog sales. Also that year Smucker bought a fruit filling plant in Brazil from Groupe Danone a major customer. During 2000 the company's Henry Jones Foods subsidiary (Australia) purchased Taylor Foods (sauces marinades).

Smucker acquired International Flavors & Fragrances' formulated fruit and vegetable preparation businesses in 2001. Moving beyond its stronghold in natural peanut butter brands the next year Smucker purchased the Jif peanut butter and Crisco cooking oil and shortening brands from Procter & Gamble. The $670 million purchase price for Jif and Crisco included shifting 53% of Smucker stock into the hands of P&G shareholders.

A decision to concentrate on North America led to the $37 million sale of Australian subsidiary Henry Jones Foods in 2004. Also that year Smucker sold its operations in Brazil to Cargill and closed down two fruit processing plants in California and Oregon. Its purchase of International Multifoods that year added an array of US brands to the Smucker family including Pillsbury flour baking mixes and ready-to-spread frostings; Hungry Jack pancake mixes syrup and potato side dishes; Martha White baking mixes and ingredients; and PET evaporated milk brands. Canadian brands included Robin Hood flour and baking mixes Bick's pickles and condiments and Golden Temple flour and rice.

To further its strategy of concentrating on its core retail brands in 2005 Smucker sold its US foodservice and bakery business and the Canadian operations of Gourmet Baker (all part of its International Multifoods acquisition) to Value Creation Partners. The following year the company sold its Canadian grain-based foodservice operations and industrial businesses to Cargill and CHS Inc. The operations were integrated into leading US flour miller Horizon Milling (which is jointly owned by Cargill and CHS). Adding to its name-brand offerings in 2006 Smucker acquired the White Lily brand of flours baking mixes and frozen biscuits from C.H. Guenther.

The company extended its baking offerings with the 2007 acquisition of sweetened condensed and evaporated milk producer Eagle Family Foods Holdings. Smucker paid $133 million in cash and $115 million in assumed debt for it. Eagle is a good fit with Smucker's PET milk products. Given Smucker's size and subsequent bargaining power with food retailers (including Wal-Mart the giant in US food retailing) and Eagle's domination of the North American canned-milk sector (it is the largest producer of evaporated and sweetened condensed milk in the US and Canada) the pairing of the two companies was a sensible move for both.

Adding to its list of leading North American brands in 2007 Smucker also acquired the Carnation Milk brand in Canada from Nestle. The deal fit well with Smucker's Eagle Sweetened Condensed Milk brand. The next year it continued its growth strategy by acquiring Canadian company Europe's Best maker of the best-selling frozen fruit and vegetables in that country.

Boosting its namesake bread-and-butter business Smucker in 2008 acquired the jam and jelly operation Knott's Berry Farm from ConAgra.

Smucker boosted its coffee business through the purchases of Folger's in 2008 Rowland Coffee Roasters maker of Cuban coffee brands Cafe Bustelo and Cafe Pilon in 2011 and Sara Lee's North American Foodservice coffee and tea operations in 2012.

Smucker tempered its growth plans in 2010 by selling the Hungry Jack and Idaho Spuds frozen potato brands to Basic American Foods which had already been co-packing the products for Smucker. The Hungry Jack pancake mix and syrup products were not part of the transaction. The divestiture was part of a product and resource realignment by Smucker.

EXECUTIVES

SVP and CFO, Mark R. Belgya, age 51, $330,000 total compensation
President COO and Director, Vincent C. Byrd, age 57, $500,000 total compensation
CEO and Director, Richard K. Smucker, age 64, $820,000 total compensation
Chairman, Timothy P. (Tim) Smucker, age 68, $820,000 total compensation
President International Foodservice and Natural Foods, Steven T. Oakland, age 51, $400,000 total compensation
VP Industry and Government Affairs, Julia L. Sabin, age 52
SVP Corporate and Chief Administrative Officer, Barry C. Dunaway, age 49, $330,000 total compensation
Director; President U.S. Retail Coffee, Mark T. Smucker, age 42
Director; President U.S. Retail Consumer Foods, Paul Smucker Wagstaff, age 42
VP and Controller, John W. Denman, age 55
VP Information Services and CIO, Andrew G. (Andy) Platt, age 56
VP Industry and Government Affairs, Albert W. Yeagley, age 64
VP US Retail Sales, John F. Mayer, age 56
VP Marketing Communications, Christopher P. Resweber, age 50
SVP Logistics and Operations Support, Dennis J. Armstrong, age 57
VP and General Manager Foodservice, Kenneth A. Miller, age 63
VP General Counsel and Corporate Secretary, Jeannette L. Knudsen, age 42
VP US Grocery Sales, James A. Brown, age 51
Director, Kathryn W. (Kitty) Dindo, age 63
President COO and Director, Vincent C. Byrd, age 57
CEO and Director, Richard K. Smucker, age 64
Chairman and Co-CEO, Timothy P. (Tim) Smucker, age 67
Director, R. Douglas Cowan, age 71
Director, Paul J. Dolan, age 53
Director, Alex Shumate, age 62
Director, Nancy Lopez Knight, age 55
Director, Elizabeth Valk (Lisa) Long, age 62
Director, William H. Steinbrink, age 69
Director; President U.S. Retail Coffee, Mark T. Smucker, age 42
Director; President U.S. Retail Consumer Foods, Paul Smucker Wagstaff, age 42
Director, Gary A. Oatey, age 63
Auditors: Ernst&YoungLLP

LOCATIONS

HQ: The J. M. Smucker Company
1 Strawberry Ln., Orrville OH 44667-0280
Phone: 330-682-3000 **Fax:** 330-684-6410
Web: www.smucker.com

2012 Sales

	$ mil.	% of total
Domestic	5,014	91
International		
Canada	447	8
Other countries	64	1
Total	**5,525**	**100**

PRODUCTS/OPERATIONS

2012 Sales

	$ mil.	% of total
US retail coffee	2,297	42
US retail consumer foods	2,094	38
International foodservice & natural foods	1,133	20
Total	**5,525**	**100**

Selected Mergers & Acquisitions

FY2012
Sara Lee North American Foodservice coffee and tea operations ($420.6 million)
Guilin Seamild Biologic Technology Development Co. ($35.9 million for 25% stake Chinese oatmeal maker)
FY2011
Rowland Coffee Roasters ($360 million makes Hispanic coffee brands Cafe Bustelo and Cafe Pilon)
FY2008
The Folger Coffee Company ($3.7 billion coffee products)

Selected Products

Baking mixes and ready-to-spread frostings
Canned milk
Coffee
Flour and baking ingredients
Frozen sandwiches
Fruit spreads
Juices and beverages
Peanut butter
Pickles and condiments
Shortening and oils
Syrups
Toppings

Selected Brands by Segment

International foodservice and natural foods
- Bick's
- Cafe Bustelo
- Cafe Pilon
- Carnation (under license)
- Crisco
- Crosse & Blackwell
- Double Fruit
- Five Roses
- Folgers
- Golden Temple
- Jif
- Plate Scapers
- R.W. Knudsen
- Recharge
- Red River
- Robin Hood
- Santa Cruz Organic
- Smucker's

US retail coffee
- Cafe Bustelo
- Cafe Pilon
- Folgers
- Dunkin' Donuts (under license)
- Millstone

US retail consumer foods
- Adams
- Borden and Elsie design (under license)
- Crisco

Dickinson' s
Eagle Brand
Fungetti
Goober
Hungry Jack
Jif
Laura Scudder' s
Magic Shell
Magnolia
Martha White
Pillsbury (under license)
Smucker' s
Uncrustables
White Lily

COMPETITORS

B&G Foods
Boyd Coffee
Caribou Coffee
Chiquita Brands
Coca-Cola
Coca-Cola North America
Community Coffee
ConAgra
Cranberries Limited
Darigold Inc.
Dean Foods
Diedrich Coffee
Dole Food
E.D. Smith
General Mills
Goya
Green Mountain Coffee
H. J. Heinz Limited
Hershey
Mondelez International
Monster Beverage
National Grape Cooperative
Nestle
Ocean Spray
PepsiCo
Pinnacle Foods
Ralcorp
Spectrum Organic Products
Starbucks
Tata Global Beverages
Tree Top
Tropicana
Unilever
Welch' s

HISTORICAL FINANCIALS

Company Type: Public

Income Statement FYE: April 30

	REVENUE ($ mil.)	NET INCOME ($ mil.)	NET PROFIT MARGIN	EMPLOYEES
04/12	5,525	459	8.3%	4,850
04/11	4,825	479	9.9%	4,500
04/10	4,605	494	10.7%	4,850
04/09	3,757	265	7.1%	4,700
04/08	2,524	170	6.7%	3,250
Annual Growth	21.6%	28.2%	—	10.5%

2012 Year-End Financials

Debt ratio: 22.72%
Return on equity: 8.90%
Cash ($ mil.): 229
Current ratio: 266.38
Long-term debt ($ mil.): 2,020
No. of shares (mil.): 110
Dividends
Yield: 2.36%
Payout: 46.31%
Market value ($ mil.): 8,782

	STOCK PRICE ($) FY Close	P/E High/Low		PER SHARE ($) Earnings	Dividends	Book Value
04/12	79.63	20	17	4.06	1.88	46.82
04/11	75.07	18	13	4.05	0.00	46.35
04/10	61.07	15	9	4.15	1.40	44.71
04/09	39.40	18	11	3.12	6.28	41.71
04/08	49.88	21	15	3.00	1.20	32.95
Annual Growth	12.4%	—	—	7.9%	11.9%	9.2%

Sonic Automotive, Inc.

LOCATIONS

HQ: Sonic Automotive, Inc.
4401 Colwick Road, Charlotte, NC 28211
Phone: 704 566-2400 **Fax:** 704 536-5116
Web: www.sonicautomotive.com

HISTORICAL FINANCIALS

Company Type:

Income Statement FYE: December 31

	REVENUE ($ mil.)	NET INCOME ($ mil.)	NET PROFIT MARGIN	EMPLOYEES
12/11	7,871	76	1.0%	9,200
12/10	6,880	89	1.3%	9,200
12/09	6,131	31	0.5%	9,200
12/08	6,034	(685)	—	10,400
12/07	8,336	95	1.1%	11,400
Annual Growth	(1.4%)	(5.5%)	—	(5.2%)

2011 Year-End Financials

Debt ratio: 60.52%
Return on equity: 14.59%
Cash ($ mil.): 1
Current ratio: 102.08
Long-term debt ($ mil.): 536
No. of shares (mil.): 52
Dividends
Yield: —
Payout: 7.75%
Market value ($ mil.): 779

	STOCK PRICE ($) FY Close	P/E High/Low		PER SHARE ($) Earnings	Dividends	Book Value
12/11	14.81	11	7	1.29	0.00	9.93
12/10	13.24	8	5	1.49	0.03	8.80
12/09	10.39	21	1	0.62	0.36	7.07
12/08	3.98	—	—	(17.00)	0.48	4.73
12/07	19.36	15	9	2.13	0.48	22.52
Annual Growth	(6.5%)	—	—	(11.8%)	—	(18.5%)

Sonoco Products Co.

Sonoco Products believes you can judge a container by its packaging. The company is one of the world's largest makers of industrial and consumer packaging used by the food consumer goods construction and automotive industries. Its consumer packaging segment produces round and shaped composite cans for snack foods powdered beverages pet food and more. Sonoco makes flexible and rigid packaging (paper and plastic) for food personal care items and chemicals and it produces paperboard tubes and cores too for industrial protective packaging. The company's end-to-end packaging services include co-packing and fulfillment supply chain management and point-of-purchase display design/assembly.

HISTORY

Sonoco Products originated during the South's industrial renewal after the Civil War. Major James Coker and son James Jr. (who had been badly wounded at the Battle of Chickamauga) founded the Carolina Fiber company in Hartsville South Carolina to make pulp and paper from pine trees. The business was based on a thesis James Jr. wrote in 1884 at Stevens Institute of Technology in Hoboken New Jersey. The essay explained how to make paper pulp using the sulfite process.

After failing to sell the pulp commercially the Cokers decided to use it to make paper cones for the textile industry which was seeing rapid growth in the southern US. In 1899 Major Coker and investor W. F. Smith formed the Southern Novelty Company. Major Coker's son Charles became president in 1918. As sales neared $1 million in 1923 the company changed its name to Sonoco.

In the 1920s Sonoco formed a joint venture in the UK to make Sonoco-style textile carriers. The venture became the Textile Paper Tube Company which later set up plants in Germany India Ireland the Netherlands and South Africa.

When Charles died in 1931 his 27-year-old son James became president. James eventually set up eight plants in the US and established a Canadian subsidiary. With the introduction of man-made fibers the textile industry expanded dramatically and Sonoco kept pace with the technological changes. By the late 1940s it had eight paper machines in operation at its Hartsville mill.

In the 1950s Sonoco formed a Mexican subsidiary; began tube operations in California Indiana and Texas; and diversified into corrugated materials. The company forged a business relationship in 1964 with Showa Products Company of Japan.

Charles Coker great-grandson of the founder became president in 1970. Sonoco entered the wastepaper-packing business in 1972 and the folding-carton and fiber-partitions businesses in 1973. The company expanded rapidly and by 1986 Sonoco had 150 plants. The next year it acquired the consumer packaging division of Boise Cascade which was then the country's #1 producer of composite cans. By 1989 Sonoco was the world's top maker of uncoated recycled cylinder paperboard.

Charles became CEO in 1990. The company set up a Singapore office and a tube and core plant in Malaysia in 1992 and acquired specialty packager Engraph the following year. In 1995 Sonoco formed a joint venture to produce paperboard in China and bought a paper mill and a tube-making plant in France. The company acquired paper-mill assets in Brazil in 1996 and entered a joint venture in Indonesia to make composite cans.

The next year saw further expansion as Sonoco entered a joint venture in Chile and a second joint venture in Brazil. In 1997 packaging maker Greif Bros. bought most of Sonoco's industrial container division and in 1998 Sonoco sold its North American pressure-sensitive-labels business to CCL Industries. President Peter Browning also replaced Charles as CEO (Charles remained chairman). Also in 1998 the company cut about 13% of its workforce and closed five plants to trim costs and consolidate operations. It also bought the Burk group of companies a German plastics-molding organization.

In 1999 Sonoco bought the composite can assets of Crown Cork & Seal (now Crown Holdings) and doubled its flexible packaging business with the purchase of Graphic Packaging International's flexible packaging unit. CEO Peter Browning retired in 2000 and was replaced by company veteran Harris DeLoach. Sonoco announced several plant closures in 2001. It also acquired four packaging companies –U.S. Paper Mills Corp. Plywood Reel Co. Phoenix Packaging and Hayes Manufacturing Group –as well as the assets of Pac One Corporation's flexible packaging business. In 2002 Sonoco restructured its UK tube and core business by closing one factory and downsizing another.

In 2003 Sonoco purchased Australian Tube Company (ATC) a maker of paper-based tubes and cores; it also sold its high-density film business to an investment group for $119 million. In 2004 the company acquired CorrFlex Graphics which offers point-of-purchase displays and related products for about $250 million.

In 2006 Sonoco bought The Cin-Made Packaging Group which makes rigid composite containers. At the end of that year Sonoco bought privately held Clear Pack Company which makes rigid plastic containers.

Sonoco combined its European tube/core and coreboard operations with the similar operations of Helsinki-based Ahlstrom Corporation to form a joint venture company named Sonoco-Alcore. Sonoco owned 65% of the venture until mid-2006 when the company bought out Ahlstrom's minority stake. Later that year a unit of Sonoco-Alcore bought out a joint venture partner to take full ownership of Italy-based Demolli Industria Cartaria which makes tubes cores and recycled paperboard for customers in Italy and northern Europe.

In 2007 the company acquired private Canadian rigid plastic container maker Matrix Packaging for $210 million. It also acquired six manufacturing facilities from Caraustar Industries. The purchase included Caraustar's fiber container operations that make recycled paperboard containers and its plastics operations that make injection molding film packaging and adhesive products.

Continuing to expand in 2008 Sonoco picked up the industrial packaging business of Am-Tex Packaging International Inc. and Canada-based Void-Form International which makes fiber-based concrete forms. Totaling $5.5 million in cash the investments increase Sonoco's industrial segment adding fulfillment capacity and expertise in manufacturing structures used to form concrete as it poured.

Sonoco purchased Madem Reels USA a nailed wood and plywood reel maker in a deal valued at $11.2 million and in 2009 EconoReel Corporation a maker and distributor of small to midsized plastic and composite spools and reels for $7.2 million. Both reel businesses catered to an established base of wire and cable OEMs.

Sonoco aggressively restructured in 2009; its actions included shuttering one US paper mill and five tube and core plants (three in the US and one each in Europe and Canada). Its consumer packaging segment closed two US rigid paper packaging facilities and the packaging services segment a fulfillment center in Germany.

EXECUTIVES

Chairman and CEO, Harris E. DeLoach Jr., age 67, $1,023,600 total compensation
VP and CIO, Bernard W. (Bernie) Campbell, age 62
SVP Corporate Planning, Kevin P. Mahoney, age 56
President COO and Director, M. Jack Sanders, age 58, $500,004 total compensation
VP Protective Packaging; Integration Leader, Vicki B. Arthur, age 54
VP Global Rigid Plastics & Corporate Customers, Rodger D. Fuller, age 50
VP Operating Excellence, John M. Grups
VP Global Operating Excellence, Marty F. Pignone, age 55
VP Global Flexible Packaging, Robert L. Puechl, age 56
VP and CFO, Barry L. Saunders, age 53
VP Investor Relations and Corporate Affairs, Roger P. Schrum, age 56
VP; General Manager Nestle, Patrick B. Keese
VP Industrial Carriers North America, James A. Harrell III, age 50
VP Global Rigid Paper and Closures, R. Howard Coker Jr., age 49
VP; General Manager Protective Packaging, Jeffrey J. Stafford
VP Global Paper and Industrial Converted Products, John M. Colyer Jr., age 51
General Manager Paperboard Specialties, Beryl (Smitty) Thomas
VP Global Flexibles and Packaging Services, Robert C. (Rob) Tiede, age 53, $366,876 total compensation
VP Treasurer and Secretary, Ritchie L. Bond, age 55
VP; Managing Director Sonoco Asia, Brad Weller
VP Global Operations Consumer Sector, Alan Hutchins
Director Manufacturing Rigid Paper and Plastics North America, Jim Lassiter
VP; General Manager Unilever, James W. Morris
VP; General Manager Blowmolding, Steven C. (Steve) Gendreau
VP Rigid Paper and Closures North America, Marcy J. Thompson, age 50
VP; General Manager Rigid Paper and Closures Europe, Sean Carnes
VP; General Manager South America, Gerson Heidrich
VP Human Resources, Allan H. McLeland, age 45
VP Global Protective Packaging, Ronald G. Leach
Director, Thomas E. Whiddon, age 59
Director, Marc D. Oken, age 65
Director, James M. (Jim) Micali, age 64
President COO and Director, M. Jack Sanders, age 58
Director, Philippe R. Rollier, age 69
Director, John H. Mullin III, age 70
Director, James L. Coker, age 71
Director, Caleb C. Fort, age 50
Director, Edgar H Lawton III, age 51
Director, Gen. Lloyd W. Newton, age 69
Director, Pamela L. Davies, age 55
Director, John E. (Jack) Linville, age 66
Director, John Haley
Auditors: PricewaterhouseCoopersLLP

LOCATIONS

HQ: Sonoco Products Company
1 N. 2nd St., Hartsville SC 29550-3305
Phone: 843-383-7000 **Fax:** 843-383-7008
Web: www.sonoco.com

2011 Sales

US	2,821	63
Canada	385	9
Total	**4,498**	**100**

PRODUCTS/OPERATIONS

2011 Sales

Paper & Industrial Converted Products	1,996	43
Consumer Packaging	1,983	43
Packaging Services	472	10
Protective Packaging	158	4
Total	**4,498**	**100**

Selected Products & Services

Paper & Industrial Converted Products
- Tubes & cores
  - Concrete forms
  - Molded plugs
  - Pallets
  - Pallet components
  - Paperboard tubes cores
  - Roll packaging
  - Rotary die boards
  - Void forms
- Paper
  - Boxboard
  - Chipboard
  - Corrugating medium
  - Lightweight corestock
  - Linerboard
  - Recovered paper
  - Recycled paperboard
  - Specialty grades
  - Tubeboard
- Sonoco Recycling
  - Collection processing & recycling of old corrugated containers paper plastic metal glass other recyclable materials

Consumer Packaging
- Ends & closures
  - Aluminum steel & peelable membrane easy-open closures for composite metal & plastic containers
- Printed flexible packaging
  - Thin-gauge rotogravure flexographic & combination printed film (laminations & rotogravure cylinder engraving brand artwork management)
  - Thin-gauge packaging
- Rigid packaging - blow molded plastics
  - Monolayer & multilayer bottles & jars
- Rigid packaging - paper
  - Composite paperboard cans (round & shaped)
  - Fiber cartridges
  - Single-wrap paperboard packages
- Rigid packaging - thermoformed plastic
  - Mono coated & barrier & non-barrier laminated tubs cups spools consumer & institutional trays

Packaging Services
- Paperboard specialties
  - Rixie coasters
  - Stancap glass covers
  - Other paper amenities
- Point-of-purchase (P-O-P)
  - Contract packaging co-packing & fulfillment services
  - Designing manufacturing assembling packing & distributing temporary semi permanent & permanent P-O-P displays
- Service centers
  - Packaging supply chain management (custom packing fulfillment primary package filling scalable service centers)

Protective Packaging
- Molded & extruded plastics (product design tool design & fabrication; manufacturing in both injection molding & extrusion technologies)
- Protective packaging
  - Contract package testing
  - Sonopost technology
  - Sonobase carriers
  - Sonopop systems

COMPETITORS

Amcor
AptarGroup
Avery Dennison
Ball Corp.
Bemis
Caraustar
Crown Holdings
Graphic Packaging Holding
Greif
International Paper
MeadWestvaco
Owens-Illinois
Pactiv
Rock-Tenn
Sealed Air Corp.
Silgan
Temple-Inland
The Newark Group

HISTORICAL FINANCIALS

Company Type: Public

Income Statement FYE: December 31

	REVENUE ($ mil.)	NET INCOME ($ mil.)	NET PROFIT MARGIN	EMPLOYEES
12/11	4,498	217	4.8%	19,600
12/10	4,124	201	4.9%	17,300
12/09	3,597	151	4.2%	16,500
12/08	4,122	164	4.0%	17,500
12/07	4,039	214	5.3%	18,600
Annual Growth	2.7%	0.4%	—	1.3%

2011 Year-End Financials

Debt ratio: 32.28%
Return on equity: 15.41%
Cash ($ mil.): 175
Current ratio: 156.94
Long-term debt ($ mil.): 1,232
No. of shares (mil.): 100
Dividends
Yield: —
Payout: 53.99%
Market value ($ mil.): 3,303

	STOCK PRICE ($) FY Close	P/E High/Low		PER SHARE ($) Earnings	Dividends	Book Value
12/11	32.96	17	13	2.13	0.00	14.09
12/10	33.67	18	14	1.96	1.11	14.84
12/09	29.25	20	11	1.50	1.08	13.64
12/08	23.16	22	13	1.63	1.07	11.66
12/07	32.68	21	13	2.10	1.02	14.50
Annual Growth	0.2%	—	—	0.4%	—	(0.7%)

Southern California Edison Co.

One of the Golden State's largest utilities Southern California Edison (SCE) distributes power to a population of more than 14 million people (4.9 million customer accounts) in central coastal and southern California (excluding Los Angeles and some other cities). SCE has 5574 MW of net generating capacity from stakes in nuclear hydroelectric and fossil-fueled power plants (although it has sold a number of its fossil-fueled facilities in response to the state's deregulation legislation). The utility sells excess power to wholesale customers. SCE is a unit of utility and competitive power holding company Edison International.

The utility's system consists of about 12000 circuit miles of transmission lines more than 103500 circuit miles of distribution lines and more than 700 distribution substations.

SCE's 50000-square-mile service area includes more than 400 cities and communities in central coastal and southern California.

In 2011 a rate increase and a $95 million increase in FERC capital reimbursement revenue related to the Tehachapi Transmission Project (a major transmission project) helped to raise SCE's revenues by 6% compared to flat growth in 2010. However net income only grew by 5% in 2011 due to higher purchased power prices and an increase in operating expenses and depreciation costs.

In recent years the utility has been ramping up its green energy options in order to comply with the state of California's aggressive long term renewable energy goal (which in 2011 was boosted from 20% of power output to 33%). That year SCE generated 21% of its power from renewable sources.

In 2011 SCE had a purchased renewable energy capacity of 3720 MW including about 2060 MW from wind sources 960 MW from geothermal and more than 380 MW from solar. In late 2011 SCE reduced its development pipeline of potential wind projects to 1300 MW in order conserve cash.

The utility offers power contract options designed to help smaller biomass generators and is installing up to 150 solar photovoltaic installations on Southern California commercial rooftops. SCE is also installing smart electric meters –digital two-way communication devices which allow customers and the utility to better manage energy use than the older mechanical meters can. The company plans to have 5 million smart meters installed by the end of 2012.

EXECUTIVES

President, Ronald L. (Ron) Litzinger, age 52, $446,168 total compensation
SVP Business Integration and CIO, Mahvash Yazdi, age 60, $394,947 total compensation
VP Power Production, Russell W. (Russ) Krieger Jr.
EVP External Relations, Stephen E. Pickett, age 61
VP and Treasurer, Robert C. Boada
VP Customer Service Operations, Harry B. Hutchison
SVP Transmission and Distribution, James A. Kelly, age 54
VP and Associate General Counsel, Ann P. Cohn
SVP and CFO, Linda G. Sullivan, age 48
VP Associate General Counsel Chief Governance Officer and Corporate Secretary, Barbara E. Mathews
VP Regulatory Operations and Affiliates Officer, Akbar Jazayeri
VP Power Delivery, Walter J. Johnston
VP Business Integration, Kevin M. Payne
EVP Power Delivery Services, Lynda L. Ziegler, age 59
SVP Power Supply, Stuart R. Hemphill
VP and General Auditor, Megan E. Scott-Kakures
VP Local Public Affairs, Leslie E. (Les) Starck
VP Business Customer Division, Lisa D. Cagnolatti
VP Energy Supply and Management, Kevin R. Cini
VP Customer Programs and Services, Erwin G. Furukawa
VP Engineering and Technical Services, David L. Mead
VP Corporate Communications, Veronica Gutierrez
VP Public Affairs, Gaddi Vasquez
VP Human Resources, Patricia H. Miller
VP and Chief Ethics and Compliance Officer, Stacy Mines
VP and Controller, Chris C. Dominski
VP and Associate General Counsel, Russell C. Swartz
VP and Station Manager Nuclear Generation, Douglas R. Bauder
VP Renewable and Alternative Power, Marc L. Ullrich
SVP and Chief Nuclear Officer, Peter (Pete) Dietrich
Board Member, Theodore F. (Ted) Craver Jr., age 60
Director, Thomas C. Sutton, age 69
Board Member, Richard T. Schlosberg III, age 67
Board Member, Ronald L. (Ron) Olson, age 70
Board Member, Luis G. Nogales, age 68
Board Member, James M. Rosser, age 72
Board Member, Bradford M. Freeman, age 70
Board Member, Vanessa C. L. Chang, age 59
Board Member, Jagjeet S. (Jeet) Bindra, age 64
Board Member, Charles B. Curtis, age 71
Board Member, Brett White, age 52
Auditors: PricewaterhouseCoopersLLP

LOCATIONS

HQ: Southern California Edison Co.
2244 Walnut Grove Avenue, P.O. Box 800, Rosemead, CA 91770
Phone: 626 302-1212 **Fax:** 626 302-4815
Web: www.edison.com

PRODUCTS/OPERATIONS

2011 Sales

	% of total
Commercial	42
Residential	40
Industrial	6
Public	5
Resale	1
Agriculture & other	6
Total	**100**

2011 Fuel Sources

	% of total
SCE-owned	43
Purchased	36
California Department of Water	21
Total	**100**

COMPETITORS

American States Water
Avista
Bonneville Power
Calpine
Imperial Irrigation District
NV Energy
Pacific Gas and Electric
PacifiCorp
Portland General Electric
Sacramento Municipal Utility
San Diego Gas & Electric
SoCalGas

HISTORICAL FINANCIALS

Company Type: Subsidiary

Income Statement

FYE: December 31

	REVENUE ($ mil.)	NET INCOME ($ mil.)	NET PROFIT MARGIN	EMPLOYEES
12/11	10,577	1,144	10.8%	18,069
12/10	9,983	1,092	10.9%	18,230
12/09	9,965	1,371	13.8%	17,348
12/08	11,248	734	6.5%	16,344
12/07	10,478	758	7.2%	15,442
Annual Growth	0.2%	10.8%	—	4.0%

2011 Year-End Financials

Debt ratio: 21.95%
Return on equity: 11.49%
Cash ($ mil.): 57
Current ratio: 67.88
Long-term debt ($ mil.): 8,431
No. of shares (mil.): 434
Dividends
Yield: —
Payout: 42.49%
Market value ($ mil.): 9,176

	STOCK PRICE ($) FY Close	P/E High/Low		PER SHARE ($) Earnings	Dividends	Book Value
12/11	21.10	—	—	(0.00)	0.00	22.90
12/10	18.45	—	—	(0.00)	1.08	(0.00)
12/09	17.99	—	—	(0.00)	0.00	(0.00)
12/08	17.31	—	—	(0.00)	0.00	(0.00)
12/07	18.50	—	—	(0.00)	1.08	(0.00)
Annual Growth	3.3%	—	—	—	—	—

Southern Company (The)

The Southern Company isn't just whistling Dixie. The holding company is one of the largest electricity distributors in the US. It operates regulated utilities Alabama Power Georgia Power Gulf Power and Mississippi Power which combined have a generating capacity of more than 43550 MW and serve more than 4.4 million electricity customers in the southeastern US. Southern also has energy marketing operations and it provides energy consulting and management services for businesses and institutions. Through its Southern LINC Wireless unit it provides wireless communications services in its US utility territory; its Southern Telecom unit offers wholesale fiber-optic services.

Operations

The company's nonregulated energy sector activities include marketing excess energy from its retail plants. It is building competitive plants across the southeastern US through subsidiary Southern Power. In 2011 this unit had 7500 MW of generating capacity.

In 2011 Southern's transmission assets (valued at $6.2 billion) included more than 27000 miles of transmission lines 3700 electric substations and 300000 acres of right of way.

Financial Analysis

The recovering economy helped lift commercial and industrial retail revenues in 2011 contributing to Southern's 1% rise in overall revenues more than compensating for weak wholesale revenues and the mild weather which sapped residential power demand. The company posted an 11% jump in net income for the year thanks to lower fuel and operating costs.

Strategy

In keeping with the federal regulatory framework which demands that utilities cut back on carbon emissions Southern's Mississippi Power is building a 582-MW integrated gasification combined cycle power plant. One of the first advanced gasification generating facilities with carbon capture capabilities in the US it is expected to become operational in 2014.

Looking to grow its green generating capacity in 2012 Southern received government approval to begin construction on the first two new nuclear units in the US in 30 years at subsidiary Georgia Power's Plant Vogtle near Waynesboro.

Furthering its green energy strategy in 2010 Southern formed Southern Renewable Energy to build acquire own and manage renewable generation asset. This unit teamed up with Ted Turner's Turner Renewable Energy to bring online one of the largest solar photovoltaic power plants in the US. The 30 MW plant built by First Solar to supply electricity to 9000 homes in New Mexico began commercial operations in late 2010.

HISTORY

Steamboat captain W. P. Lay founded the Alabama Power Company in 1906 to develop electric power on the Coosa River. James Mitchell took over in 1912 moved headquarters from Montgomery to Birmingham and bought a number of Alabama's utilities consolidating them with Alabama Power under his Canadian holding company Alabama Traction Light & Power (ATL&P).

In 1920 ATL&P became Southeastern Power & Light forming Mississippi Power (1924) and Georgia Power (1927) to take over electric utilities in those states and Gulf Power to do the same in northern Florida (1925).

Southeastern merged with Penn-Ohio Edison to form Commonwealth & Southern in 1929. But by 1942 Commonwealth & Southern was dissolved under the Public Utilities Holding Company Act of 1935 since it owned 11 unrelated unconnected utilities. Alabama Power Georgia Power Gulf Power and Mississippi Power were placed under a new holding company The Southern Company which began full operations in 1949.

In 1975 amid an anti-utility political environment created by energy shortages Georgia Power was near bankruptcy; Alabama Power stopped work on new construction and laid off 4000 employees in 1978. That year when Alabama governor and utility critic George Wallace left office state regulators granted Southern long-sought rate relief.

The SEC allowed Southern to diversify into unregulated operations —a first in the US —with the 1981 formation of Southern Energy which began investing in independent power projects and companies. In 1988 Southern bought Savannah Electric and Power.

Meanwhile the industry was undergoing major changes and utilities were venturing outside their territories. Southern sold a Georgia power plant to two Florida utilities in 1990. Two years later it bought 50% of Bahamian utility Freeport Power and by 1994 Southern had a 49% stake in three power plants in Trinidad and Tobago. At home the company formed Southern LINC in 1995 to offer wireless telecom services in the southeastern US via specialized mobile radio (SMR) technology.

Also that year the company joined other US electric companies in raiding Britain's deregulated electricity larder. It bought UK utility South Western Electricity (SWEB) in 1995 though it later turned over a 51% stake to partner PP&L Resources. In 1996 it acquired 80% of Hong Kong's Consolidated Electric Power Asia buying the rest the next year.

The first US company to enter Germany's electric utility market Southern bought a 25% stake in Berlin's electric utility Bewag in 1997. That year and the next Southern expanded into the northeastern US and California buying power plants from Commonwealth Energy Eastern Utilities ConEd PG&E and Orange and Rockland Utilities.

Focusing on power transmission in the UK Southern and PP&L Resources (which became PPL in 2000) sold SWEB's power supply business and the SWEB brand name to London Electricity an Electricite de France unit in 1999. The former SWEB's distribution network was renamed Western Power Distribution.

In 2000 Southern sold a 20% stake in Southern Energy which included the company's merchant energy operations (excluding those in the southeastern US) and its overseas investments to the public. Southern Energy changed its name to Mirant (now GenOn Energy) in 2001 and that year Southern spun off its remaining stake in the unit to its shareholders. To improve operating efficiencies in 2006 the company merged its Savannah Electric unit into another subsidiary Georgia Power.

EXECUTIVES

EVP; President and CEO Alabama Power, Charles D. McCrary, age 60, $687,713 total compensation
EVP; President External Affairs, Christopher C. (Chris) Womack, age 53
Chairman President and CEO, Thomas A. (Tom) Fanning, age 55, $690,250 total compensation
EVP General Counsel and Corporate Secretary, G. Edison Holland Jr., age 59, $538,329 total compensation
EVP; President and CEO Georgia Power, W. Paul Bowers, age 55, $614,870 total compensation
EVP, Steven R. (Steve) Spencer, age 56
President and CEO Southern Company Services, Susan N. Story, age 52
EVP and COO, Anthony J. Topazi, age 62
EVP and Chief Transmission Officer, William O. (Billy) Ball
President and CEO Gulf Power, Mark A. Crosswhite, age 49
EVP and CFO, Art P. Beattie, age 58
SVP Human Resources, Marsha S. Johnson
EVP Engineering and Construction Services Generation, Penny M. Manuel, age 48
President and CEO SouthernLINC Wireless and Southern Telecom, Donald R. (Don) Horsley, age 57
VP CFO and Treasurer SouthernLINC Wireless, Craig Elder
SVP Chief Compliance Officer and General Counsel Georgia Power, Thomas P. Bishop, age 51
VP Technical Services Generation, Kimberly D. (Kim) Flowers, age 48
SVP Southern Company Services; SVP and Senior Production Officer Alabama Power, Theodore J. (Ted) McCullough, age 48
VP Sales and Distribution SouthernLINC Wireless, Rodney H. Johnson
SVP and CIO, Kenneth E. Coleman
Media Contact, Terri Cohilas
Director Business and Government Sales SouthernLINC Wireless, Michael S. Smith
Assistant Corporate Secretary, Melissa K. Caen
VP Marketing and Customer Support SouthernLINC Wireless, Julie T. Pigott
Director Legal and External Affairs SouthernLINC Wireless, Michael Rosenthal
Direct Sales Manager SouthernLINC Wireless, Scott Barrentine
SVP and General Counsel, John Pemberton
SVP Southern Company Services; President and CEO Southern Power, Oscar C. Harper
President and CEO Mississippi Power, Edward Day VI, age 52
Assistant Treasurer; VP Finance Southern Company Services, Xia Liu
VP Southern Wholesale Energy, Murry Weaver
VP and CFO Operations, William C. (Bill) Grantham
VP Governmental Affairs, Bryan Anderson
VP Human Resources, Stacy Kilcoyne
President and CEO Southern Nuclear, Stephen Kuczynski, age 49
Director Investor Relations and Financial Planning, Daniel S. Tucker
SVP and Chief Environmental Counsel, Karl Moor
Director, Jon A. Boscia, age 59
Director, Donald M. (Don) James, age 63
Director, William G. Smith Jr., age 58
Director, Steven R. Specker, age 66
Director, H. William (Bill) Habermeyer Jr., age 69
Director, Warren A. Hood Jr., age 60
Director, Juanita Powell Baranco, age 63
Director, Larry D. Thompson, age 66
Director, Dale E. Klein, age 64
Director, Henry A. Clark III, age 62
Auditors: Deloitte&ToucheLLP

LOCATIONS

HQ: The Southern Company
30 Ivan Allen Jr. Blvd. NW, Atlanta GA 30308
Phone: 404-506-5000 **Fax:** 404-506-0455
Web: www.southernco.com

PRODUCTS/OPERATIONS

2011 Sales

	$ mil.	% of total
Electric		
Retail	15,071	85
Wholesale	1,905	11
Other revenues	681	4
Total	**17,657**	**100**

2011 Fuel Mix

	% of total
Coal	52
Oil &	30
Nuclear	16
Hydro	2
Total	**100**

Selected Subsidiaries and Affiliates

Alabama Power Company (electric utility)
Georgia Power Company (electric utility)
Gulf Power Company (electric utility)
Mississippi Power Company (electric utility)
Southern Company Energy Solutions LLC (energy services)
Southern Company Services Inc. (administrative services limited energy trading)
SouthernLINC Wireless (wireless services)
Southern Telecom (fiber-optic telecommunications)
Southern Nuclear Operating Company Inc. (operates and maintains Alabama Power' s and Georgia Power' s nuclear plants)
Southern Power Company (independent power production)
Southern Renewable Energy Inc.(green energy activities)

COMPETITORS

AEP
AGL Resources
CenterPoint Energy
Cleco
Constellation Energy Group
Duke Energy
Energen
Entergy
FirstEnergy
Florida Public Utilities
JEA
MEAG Power
NextEra Energy
Oglethorpe Power
PacifiCorp
Progress Energy
SCANA
TECO Energy
TVA
Xcel Energy

HISTORICAL FINANCIALS

Company Type: Public

Income Statement FYE: December 31

	REVENUE ($ mil.)	NET INCOME ($ mil.)	NET PROFIT MARGIN	EMPLOYEES
12/11	17,657	2,268	12.8%	26,377
12/10	17,456	2,040	11.7%	25,940
12/09	15,743	1,708	10.8%	26,112
12/08	17,127	1,742	10.2%	27,276
12/07	15,353	1,734	11.3%	26,742
Annual Growth	3.6%	6.9%	—	(0.3%)

2011 Year-End Financials

Debt ratio: 34.36%
Return on equity: 12.15%
Cash ($ mil.): 1,315
Current ratio: 95.36
Long-term debt ($ mil.): 18,647
No. of shares (mil.): 865
Dividends
Yield: —
Payout: 73.43%
Market value ($ mil.): 40,047

	STOCK PRICE ($) FY Close	P/E High/Low		PER SHARE ($) Earnings	Dividends	Book Value
12/11	46.29	18	14	2.55	0.00	21.57
12/10	38.23	16	13	2.36	1.80	20.49
12/09	33.32	18	13	2.06	1.73	19.48
12/08	37.00	18	14	2.25	1.66	18.46
12/07	38.75	17	15	2.28	1.60	17.63
Annual Growth	4.5%	—	—	2.8%	—	5.2%

Southern Copper Corp

LOCATIONS

HQ: Southern Copper Corp
1440 East Missouri Avenue, Suite 160, Phoenix, AZ 85014
Phone: 602 264-1375
Web: www.southernperu.com

HISTORICAL FINANCIALS

Company Type:

Income Statement FYE: December 31

	REVENUE ($ mil.)	NET INCOME ($ mil.)	NET PROFIT MARGIN	EMPLOYEES
12/11	6,818	2,336	34.3%	12,145
12/10	5,149	1,554	30.2%	11,126
12/09	3,734	929	24.9%	11,523
12/08	4,850	1,406	29.0%	11,494
12/07	6,085	2,216	36.4%	12,134
Annual Growth	2.9%	1.3%	—	0.0%

2011 Year-End Financials

Debt ratio: 34.05%
Return on equity: 58.19%
Cash ($ mil.): 848
Current ratio: 312.38
Long-term debt ($ mil.): 2,735
No. of shares (mil.): 850
Dividends
Yield: —
Payout: 89.13%
Market value ($ mil.): 25,653

	STOCK PRICE ($) FY Close	P/E High/Low		PER SHARE ($) Earnings	Dividends	Book Value
12/11	30.18	18	9	2.76	0.00	4.72
12/10	48.74	27	14	1.83	1.68	4.58
12/09	32.91	33	12	1.09	0.44	4.56
12/08	16.06	78	6	1.60	1.94	3.96
12/07	105.13	56	20	2.51	2.27	4.36
Annual Growth	(26.8%)	—	—	2.4%	—	2.0%

Southside Bancshares, Inc.

Southside Bancshares operates deep in the heart of Texas. It's the holding company for Southside Bank which serves East Texas through about 35 branches with a concentration in the cities of Tyler and Longview. About half of its branches are located in supermarkets (including Albertsons and Brookshire stores) and many offer extended hours. The bank provides traditional services such as savings money market and checking accounts CDs and other deposit products as well as trust and investment services. Real estate loans primarily residential mortgages make up about half of the company's loan portfolio which also includes business consumer and municipal loans.

In 2011 the bank acquired the 50% it didn't already own in SFG Finance which acquires portfolios of high-yield subprime auto loans from other lenders around the country. Auto loans and municipal loans account for a large portion of the bank's growing loan portfolio.

Southside Bancshares' revenues have slipped for the past two years from $201.9 million in 2009 to $182.8 million in 2010 and $166.4 million in 2011. Its noninterest earnings took a hit in 2011 due to regulatory changes that limit overdraft fees as well as a decreased gain on sales of loans as a part of Southside's strategy of holding on to more loans. The company's loan portfolio grew by some 10% that year which helped increase its net income some 3% to $40.6 million. The company that year also benefited from growth in trust income as well as brokerage fees (as a result of the SFG Finance acquisition).

To grow its deposits and deepen its presence in the markets it serves the company has been expanding its network of banking locations –both in-store and full-service branches.

EXECUTIVES

SEVP; SEVP and Director Southside Bank, Jeryl W. Story, age 61, $330,250 total compensation
EVP and CFO; EVP CFO and Board Member Southside Bank, Lee R. Gibson, age 55, $330,250 total compensation
President Secretary and Board Member; President COO and Board Member Southside Bank, Sam Dawson, age 65, $350,065 total compensation
Vice Chairman; Vice Chairman and Chief Administrative Officer Southside Bank, Robbie N. Edmonson, age 81
Chairman and CEO Southside Bancshares and Southside Bank, B. G. Hartley, age 83, $505,050 total compensation
EVP and Treasurer Southside Bank, Michael L. Coogan, age 53, $222,769 total compensation
President Secretary and Board Member; President COO and Board Member Southside Bank, Sam Dawson, age 65
Vice Chairman; Vice Chairman and Chief Administrative Officer Southside Bank, Robbie N. Edmonson, age 81
Board Member, Paul W. Powell, age 79
Board Member, William Sheehy, age 71
Board Member, Herbert C. Buie, age 82
Board Member, Joe Norton, age 36
Board Member, Alton Cade, age 76
Board Member, Melvin B. Lovelady, age 76
Board Member, Preston Smith, age 56
Board Member, Donald W. Thedford, age 63
Board Member, Pierre de Wet
Board Member, Laurence Anderson
Auditors: PricewaterhouseCoopersLLP

LOCATIONS

HQ: Southside Bancshares Inc.
1201 S. Beckham Ave., Tyler TX 75701
Phone: 903-531-7111 **Fax:** 903-592-3692
Web: www.southside.com

PRODUCTS/OPERATIONS

2011 Sales

	$ mil.	% of total
Interest		
Loans	66	38
Mortgage-backed & related securities	51	29
Investment securities	12	7
Other	0	-
Noninterest		
Deposit services	15	9
Gain on sale of securities	12	7
Fair value gain - securities	6	4
Trust income	2	2
Other	6	4
Adjustments	(8.9)	
Total	166	100

COMPETITORS

Bank of America
Capital One
East Texas Financial
Jacksonville Bancorp of Illinois
Regions Financial

HISTORICAL FINANCIALS

Company Type: Public

Income Statement FYE: December 31

	ASSETS ($ mil.)	NET INCOME ($ mil.)	INCOME AS % OF ASSETS	EMPLOYEES
12/11	3,303	39	1.2%	557
12/10	2,999	39	1.3%	578
12/09	3,024	44	1.5%	560
12/08	2,700	30	1.1%	546
12/07	2,196	16	0.8%	530
Annual Growth	10.7%	23.8%	—	1.3%

2011 Year-End Financials

Debt ratio: 9.72%
Return on equity: 15.11%
Cash ($ mil.): 43
Current ratio: —
Long-term debt ($ mil.): 321
No. of shares (mil.): 17
Dividends
Yield: —
Payout: 37.47%
Market value ($ mil.): 375

	STOCK PRICE ($) FY Close	P/E High/Low		PER SHARE ($) Earnings	Dividends	Book Value
12/11	21.66	10	8	2.27	0.00	14.95
12/10	21.07	10	8	2.28	0.76	12.43
12/09	19.62	10	5	2.56	0.64	11.64
12/08	23.50	14	8	1.87	0.49	9.89
12/07	20.46	25	18	1.02	0.39	8.29
Annual Growth	1.4%	—	—	22.1%	—	15.9%

Southwest Airlines Co

Southwest Airlines will fly any plane as long as it's a Boeing and let passengers sit anywhere they like –as long as they get there first. Sticking with what has worked Southwest has expanded its low-cost no-frills no-reserved-seats approach to air travel throughout the US to serve 70+ cities in more than 35 states. Now the largest carrier of US domestic passengers Southwest still stands as an inspiration for scrappy low-fare upstarts the world over. The carrier has enjoyed 39 straight profitable years amid the airline industry's ups and downs. Southwest's fleet numbers about 700 aircraft. The company acquired AirTran Holdings the parent company of AirTran Airways in 2011 for about $3.2 billion.

HISTORY

Texas businessman Rollin King and lawyer Herb Kelleher founded Air Southwest in 1967 as an intrastate airline linking Dallas Houston and San Antonio. The now-defunct Braniff and Texas International sued questioning whether the region needed another airline but the Texas Supreme Court ruled in Southwest's favor. In 1971 the company renamed Southwest Airlines made its first scheduled flight.

Operating from Love Field in Dallas Southwest adopted "love" as the theme of its early ad campaigns serving love potions (drinks) and love bites (peanuts). When other airlines moved to the new Dallas/Fort Worth International Airport (DFW) in 1974 Kelleher insisted on staying at Love Field gaining a virtual monopoly there.

When Kelleher decided to fly outside Texas Congress passed the Wright Amendment in 1979. Designed to protect DFW the law restricted the states served directly from Love Field. (Arkansas Louisiana New Mexico and Oklahoma were on the original list; a 1997 amendment added Alabama Kansas and Mississippi. In 2000 a federal court removed the restrictions for planes with 56 or fewer seats. Later Missouri was added to the list of states eligible for direct service from Love Field.)

When Lamar Muse Southwest's president resigned in 1978 because of differences with King Kelleher assumed control. (Muse later took over his son Michael's nearly bankrupt airline Muse Air which was sold in 1985 to Southwest. The airline was liquidated in 1987.)

An industry maverick Kelleher introduced advance-purchase Fun Fares in 1986 and a frequent-flier program in 1987 based on the number of flights taken instead of mileage. He gained attention in 1992 for starring in Southwest's TV commercials and for arm wrestling Stevens Aviation chairman Kurt Herwald for the rights to the "Just Plane Smart" slogan. When Southwest became the official airline of SeaWorld in Texas Kelleher had a Boeing 737 painted as a killer whale.

Southwest took on the East Coast with service to Baltimore in 1993 and bought Salt Lake City-based Morris Air in 1994. That year it launched a ticketless system and adopted its own passenger reservation system to cut costs.

The airline expanded into Florida in 1996 and that year Southwest began selling tickets through its website. Agreements with Icelandair in 1996 and 1997 allowed Southwest passengers to connect from four US cities to Europe through Icelandair's Baltimore hub. In 1998 Southwest flew its first nonstop transcontinental flight from Oakland California to Baltimore. For the first time since DFW opened the carrier had to share Love Field with rivals including AMR's American Airlines.

Southwest added more routes in the East during 1999. Kelleher underwent treatment for prostate cancer that year. In 2000 the airline had its first major accident when a 737 overran the end of a runway in Burbank California and ground to a halt in a busy street –a mishap that caused only minor injuries.

Later that year Southwest placed its biggest aircraft order ever calling for delivery of another 94 Boeing 737s between 2002 and 2007. To mark the airline's 30th anniversary in 2001 Southwest changed its logo and added blue to its traditional color scheme of gold red and orange. Also that year Southwest experienced a rare labor dispute when stalled contract negotiations led to picketing by the airline's ground crew union.

Kelleher stepped down as president and CEO in 2001. General counsel Jim Parker took over as CEO and EVP Colleen Barrett –who first worked for Kelleher as his secretary and is given much of the credit for maintaining Southwest's corporate spirit –was named president and COO.

Parker would reign over the airline during one of the most tumultuous times in its history. Despite an industrywide downturn resulting from the lagging US economy and exacerbated by the September 11 terrorist attacks Southwest managed to post a profit for 2001 and 2002 but it did not come easily.

Increased Internet sales led the airline to close its call centers in Dallas Little Rock and Salt Lake City in 2003. Nearly 2000 workers were given the choice of relocating to another call center or accepting a severance package. By the beginning of the next year more than half had declined relocation.

Rising fuel costs and labor issues haunted the airline. Union negotiations with flight attendants began in 2002 and lasted for two years during which time Parker was publicly chastised for being uncooperative. A resolution was not reached until Kelleher and Barrett were asked to step in by Parker who resigned in 2004 after negotiations ended. He was replaced by former CFO Gary Kelly.

Southwest in 2005 launched its first code-share agreement with now-defunct ATA Airlines as part of a deal that gave Southwest some of ATA's gates at Chicago's Midway Airport. Also that year Southwest added service to Fort Myers Florida and to Pittsburgh.

After intense lobbying from both Southwest and American Airlines Congress revisited the Wright Amendment in 2006. A compromise measure signed into law that year allowed Southwest to offer direct one-stop service –meaning passengers need not change planes –from Love Field to states not covered by the original Wright law or its revisions.

Also in 2006 Southwest added service to Denver and to Dulles International Airport in Washington DC. The next year the carrier resumed flights to and from San Francisco International Airport which it had last served in 2001.

Marking a milestone for Southwest Kelleher and Barrett stepped down from the company's board in 2008 and Kelly replaced Kelleher as chairman. Also in 2008 a code-sharing deal with ATA Airlines allowed Southwest to sell tickets on ATA flights to Hawaii before ATA filed for Chapter 11 bankruptcy protection and shut down its operations in April of that year.

After a year of tense meetings with FAA officials Southwest agreed in early 2009 to pay a $7.5 million fine over required structural inspections in 2008 on 46 planes. The carrier removed the planes from service for inspection causing some canceled flights but went back to business as usual within a few days.

The airline industry was hit hard during the 2008/2009 recession. Southwest watched its profits fall some 44% from $178 million in net income in 2008 to $99 million in 2009. Despite the downturn Southwest launched service to four new destinations in 2009: Minneapolis/St. Paul New York (LaGuardia) Boston and Milwaukee.

The company made a move to expand westward in 2009 by placing a bid to acquire Denver-based bankrupt carrier Frontier Airlines for $170 million but the bid was rejected. Instead Republic Airways with its $109 million offer was declared the winning bidder. Another deciding factor was that Southwest planned to phase out the Frontier brand over a period of two years while Republic kept the Frontier brand alive after making the carrier a wholly owned subsidiary.

Southwest acquired AirTran Holdings in spring 2011 for about $3.2 billion in cash stock and the assumption of debt. AirTran Holdings was the parent company of AirTran Airways.

EXECUTIVES

SVP and Chief Marketing Officer, Davis S. (Dave) Ridley, age 58

EVP and Chief Commercial Officer; President AirTran Airways, Robert E. (Bob) Jordan, age 51, $340,000 total compensation

SVP Culture and Communications, Ginger C. Hardage

EVP and Chief People and Administrative Officer, A. Jeff Lamb III, age 49
EVP and Chief Legal & Regulatory Officer, Ron Ricks, age 62, $370,000 total compensation
Chairman President and CEO, Gary C. Kelly, age 56, $441,750 total compensation
VP Customer Relations and Rapid Rewards, James A. (Jim) Ruppel
VP Maintenance Operations, Jim Sokol
SVP Finance and CFO, Laura H. Wright, age 51, $309,000 total compensation
SVP Technical Operations, Brian K. Hirshman
VP Marketing Sales and Distribution, Kevin M. Krone
VP Diversity and Inclusion, Ellen Torbert
SVP Operations, Greg Wells
SVP Finance and CFO, Tammy Romo
VP Customer Support and Services, Alfred J. (Jack) Smith III, age 60
SVP Procurement, Daryl Krause
VP Properties Airport Affairs, Bob Montgomery
VP Procurement, Rob Myrben
SVP Labor Relations, J. Randolph (Randy) Babbitt, age 65
VP and General Counsel, Madeleine Johnson
EVP and COO, Michael G. (Mike) Van de Ven, age 50, $365,000 total compensation
VP Technical Services, Kirk Thornburg
VP Communications and Strategic Outreach, Linda B. Rutherford
VP Ground Operations, Chris Wahlenmaier
VP Safety and Security, Scott Halfmann
SVP Customers, Teresa Laraba
VP Cabin Services, Mike Hafner
VP Flight Operations, Chuck Magill
VP Operations Coordination Center, Matt Hafner
VP Labor Relations, Michael (Mike) Ryan
VP Technology Enterprise Management Applications and Testing Services Portfolio, Laurie Hulin
VP Revenue Management and Pricing, Kay Weatherford
VP Technology and CTO, Bob Young
VP and Controller, Leah Koontz
VP Cargo and Charters, Matt Buckley
VP Network Planning, John Jamotta
VP Governmental Affairs, Karen Lewis
VP and CIO, Randy Sloan
VP Technical Services, Trevor Stedke
VP Technology Aircraft Operations Portfolio, Jeff Buhr
VP Strategic Planning, Mike Delehant
VP People, Julie Weber
VP and General Counsel, Mark Shaw
Director, Douglas H. (Doug) Brooks, age 59
Director, William H. Cunningham, age 67
Director, John T. Montford, age 68
Director, Daniel D. Villanueva, age 74
Director, Nancy B. Loeffler, age 65
Director, Thomas M. Nealon, age 51
Auditors: Ernst&YoungLLP

LOCATIONS

HQ: Southwest Airlines Co.
2702 Love Field Dr., Dallas TX 75235
Phone: 214-792-4000 **Fax:** 214-792-5015
Web: www.southwest.com

PRODUCTS/OPERATIONS

2011 Sales

	$ mil.	% of total
Passenger	14,735	94
Freight	139	1
Other	784	5
Total	**15,658**	**100**

COMPETITORS

Alaska Air
AMR Corp.
Delta Air Lines
Frontier Airlines
JetBlue
United Continental
US Airways

HISTORICAL FINANCIALS

Company Type: Public

Income Statement FYE: December 31

	REVENUE ($ mil.)	NET INCOME ($ mil.)	NET PROFIT MARGIN	EMPLOYEES
12/11	15,658	178	1.1%	45,392
12/10	12,104	459	3.8%	34,901
12/09	10,350	99	1.0%	34,726
12/08	11,023	178	1.6%	35,499
12/07	9,861	645	6.5%	34,378
Annual Growth	12.3%	(27.5%)	—	7.2%

2011 Year-End Financials

Debt ratio: 20.76%
Return on equity: 2.59%
Cash ($ mil.): 829
Current ratio: 95.85
Long-term debt ($ mil.): 3,107
No. of shares (mil.): 772
Dividends
Yield: —
Payout: 7.83%
Market value ($ mil.): 6,613

	STOCK PRICE ($) FY Close	P/E High	P/E Low	PER SHARE ($) Earnings	Dividends	Book Value
12/11	8.56	58	32	0.23	0.00	8.90
12/10	12.98	23	17	0.61	0.02	8.35
12/09	11.43	89	39	0.13	0.02	7.36
12/08	8.62	69	30	0.24	0.02	6.69
12/07	12.20	20	14	0.84	0.02	9.45
Annual Growth	(8.5%)	—	—	(27.7%)	—	(1.5%)

Spectra Energy Corp

Spectra Energy covers a wide spectrum natural gas activities including gathering and processing transmission and storage and distribution. Spectra Energy operates 19100 miles of transmission pipeline and 305 billion cu. ft. of storage capacity in the US and Canada. Units include U.S. Gas Transmission Texas Eastern Transmission Algonquin Gas Transmission BC Pipeline Division Natural Gas Liquids Division and Market Hub Partners. It also has stakes in DCP Midstream (gas gathering and NGLs) Maritimes & Northeast Pipeline Gulfstream Natural Gas System Spectra Energy Income Fund and 69% of Spectra Energy Partners. Its Union Gas unit distributes gas to 1.3 million customers in 400 communities in Ontario.

Financial Analysis

The global recession hurt the company's revenues in 2009 as lower commodity prices and weakness in demand depressed sales.

In 2010 to raise cash it sold 24.5% of Gulfstream Natural Gas System to Spectra Energy Partners for $330 million.

That year the company reported higher revenues and net income thanks to an improving economy increased demand and higher commodity prices.

Strategy

The company's strategy is to solidify its position as a premier natural gas infrastructure enterprise by developing new opportunities and projects while enhancing its core customer service reliability cost management and compliance skills.

Expanding its role in the oil pipeline market in 2012 Spectra Energy agreed to buy the Express-Platte Pipeline System from Borealis Infrastructure the Ontario Teachers Pension Plan and Kinder Morgan Energy Partners for $1.5 billion. The Express-Platte System is one of just three major pipelines moving crude oil from Western Canada to the US Rockies and Midwest refineries and markets.

In 2012 Spectra Energy opened a new natural gas processing plant in Dawson Creek British Columbia part of its $1.5 billion investment strategy in infrastructure. That year it also signed a deal with BG Group to develop a pipeline from northeast British Columbia to serve BG Group's potential LNG export facility in Prince Rupert on the northwest coast of the province.

In a move to boost its Gulf Coast natural gas storage position in 2010 Spectra Energy acquired the Bobcat Gas Storage asset from Haddington Energy Partners and GE Energy Financial Service for about $540 million. The company plans to invest a further $450 million in the asset which by 2015 will have a total storage capacity of 46 billion cu. ft.

Spectra Energy invested in more than 40 pipeline expansion and upgrade projects between 2006 and 2010.

EXECUTIVES

CFO, John Patrick (Pat) Reddy, age 59, $500,000 total compensation
Chairman, William T. (Bill) Esrey, age 70
Chief Administrative Officer, Dorothy M. Ables, $370,500 total compensation
Chairman President and CEO DCP Midstream, Thomas C. (Tom) O'Connor, age 56
President CEO and Director, Gregory L. (Greg) Ebel, age 47, $850,000 total compensation
Chief Communications Officer, John R. Arensdorf, age 62
Group VP US Transmission and Storage Southeast, R. Mark Fiedorek
Chief Development and Operations Officer, Alan N. Harris, age 59, $500,000 total compensation
Group VP US Transmission Northeast, William T. (Bill) Yardley
VP Business Development Storage Transmission Union Gas, Allen Capps
President Spectra Energy Transmission West, Douglas P. Bloom
VP and Treasurer, Steve Baker
General Counsel, Reginald D. (Reggie) Hedgebeth, $358,077 total compensation
Director, Peter B. Hamilton, age 65
Director, Joseph H. Netherland, age 65
Director, Dennis R. Hendrix, age 72
Director, Michael McShane, age 58
Director, F. Anthony (Tony) Comper, age 66
Director, Michael E. J. Phelps, age 63
Director, Austin A. Adams, age 68
President CEO and Director, Gregory L. (Greg) Ebel, age 47
Director, Paul M. Anderson, age 66
Director, Joseph (Joe) Alvarado, age 59
Director, Pamela L. (Pam) Carter, age 62
Auditors: Deloitte&ToucheLLP

LOCATIONS

HQ: Spectra Energy Corp
5400 Westheimer Ct., Houston TX 77056
Phone: 713-627-5400 **Fax:** 713-627-4691
Web: www.spectraenergy.com

PRODUCTS/OPERATIONS

2010 Sales

	$ mil.	% of total
Transportation storage & processing of natural gas	2,870	58
Distribution of natural gas	1,450	29
Sales of natural gas liquids	459	9
Other	166	4
Total	**4,945**	**100**

COMPETITORS

Dynegy
El Paso Corporation
Entergy
Enterprise Products
Kinder Morgan
Koch Industries Inc.
Piedmont Natural Gas
TransMontaigne

HISTORICAL FINANCIALS

Company Type: Public

Income Statement FYE: December 31

	REVENUE ($ mil.)	NET INCOME ($ mil.)	NET PROFIT MARGIN	EMPLOYEES
12/11	5,351	1,184	22.1%	5,700
12/10	4,945	1,049	21.2%	550
12/09	4,552	848	18.6%	5,400
12/08	5,074	1,129	22.3%	5,200
12/07	4,742	957	20.2%	5,100
Annual Growth	3.1%	5.5%	—	2.8%

2011 Year-End Financials

Debt ratio: 41.66%
Return on equity: 14.68%
Cash ($ mil.): 174
Current ratio: 56.88
Long-term debt ($ mil.): 10,146
No. of shares (mil.): 651
Dividends
Yield: —
Payout: 58.56%
Market value ($ mil.): 20,018

	STOCK PRICE ($) FY Close	P/E High/Low		PER SHARE ($) Earnings	Dividends	Book Value
12/11	30.75	17	13	1.81	0.00	12.39
12/10	24.99	16	12	1.61	1.00	12.03
12/09	20.51	16	9	1.32	1.00	11.01
12/08	15.74	16	7	1.81	0.96	9.07
12/07	25.82	19	15	1.51	0.88	10.85
Annual Growth	4.5%	—	—	4.6%	—	3.4%

Spectrum Group International Inc

From stamps to antique arms to fine wine to baseball memorabilia one auction house operates across the spectrum of global collectible items. Spectrum Group International serves both collectors and dealers and operates in two primary areas: trading (the majority of its business) and collectibles (handled through both auctions and direct sales). Its trading business operates through A-Mark Precious Metals which sells coins and other precious metals on a wholesale basis. Spectrum Group has auction houses in the US Germany Hong Kong the Netherlands and Switzerland. The company was founded by Greg Manning who started collecting stamps at age 7 and opened an office to market stamps in 1971 at the age of 25.

Operations

Spectrum Group's trading business A-Mark Precious Metals and its subsidiaries (of which Spectrum Group owns an 80% interest) offers services such as financing leasing consignment hedging and customized financial deals. Operations of the collectibles business consist of a network of companies specializing in coins stamps and vintage wines. Auctions are traditional live events and also conducted via the Internet and telephone.

Strategy

Spectrum Group operates under the strategy of becoming a global leader in rare collectibles. Since 2003 it has made a number of acquisitions to expand its share in the collectibles market and its geographic footprint. To further build the trading business Spectrum Group concurrently targets new commodity products and entry into undeveloped countries.

Sales & Marketing

A-Mark Precious Metals and its subsidiaries account for approximately 97% of sales. Sales are driven by trading of gold silver platinum and palladium and distribution for government mints worldwide. The company's collectibles business accounts for the remaining 3% of total sales.

Geographic Reach

In addition to the US Spectrum Group has a growing presence in Europe and the Asia/Pacific region. In fiscal 2011 (ends June) the US represented about 98% of sales Europe 2% and the Asia/Pacific region a negligible percent. Although slight in comparison to the US international sales led by European demand multiplied more than 14 times in 2011 over the prior year.

Financial Analysis

In fiscal 2011 Spectrum Group's revenues maintained a four-year positive pace jumping almost 20% over 2010. Results comprised approximately a 19% increase in trading revenue and more than 28% bump in the collectibles business. Trading revenues were fueled by higher precious metal prices and increased demand for gold and silver worldwide. Collectibles' revenue benefited from an increase in numismatic (coin) trading and the addition of Stack's-Bowers Numismatics (acquired in January 2011) along with strong auction sales.

Spectrum Group also posted a modest profit in 2011 following a two-year tumble into the red in 2010. The rebound reflected improved trading and collectibles business coupled with decreased corporate expenses for goodwill and asset impairments and a litigation settlement. Less than stellar profits in 2011 were tarnished mainly by losses on foreign currency exchanges on loans by Spectrum Group to its international subsidiaries.

Ownership

Until 2012 Spanish collectibles company Afinsa Bienes Tangibles and its subsidiary Auctentia collectively owned 57% of Spectrum Group.

Spectrum Group in 2012 entered a securities purchase agreement with Afinsa. As part of the $51 million deal Spectrum Group purchased a majority of Afinsa's and Auctentia's ownership interest. The transaction reduced Afinsa's ownership in Spectrum to about 10%.

Company Background

Spectrum Group has seen its coffers most significantly eroded by an investigation of criminal wrongdoing by Spanish company Afinsa Bienes Tangibles. In addition Afinsa has been in insolvency proceedings in Spain since mid-2006; the Madrid bankruptcy court has ordered a liquidation of Afinsa's assets.

HISTORY

Greg Manning started collecting stamps at age 7 and was making a profit in mail-order stamps by the time he was 15. Manning held his first public auction in 1966 at the age of 20. Five years later he opened an office to market stamps and by 1981 his business had grown enough to warrant the construction of a 76000-sq.-ft. facility in Montville New Jersey from which Manning ran his auction business as a subsidiary.

The Greg Manning Company went public in 1993 changing its name to Greg Manning Auctions. That year it acquired Ivy Shreve & Mader Philatelic Auctions and made an agreement with Paul W. Schmid Inc. to market replicas of historical items mainly bank notes. The firm bought Harmer Rooke Galleries an auctioneer of antiquities rare coins and collectibles in 1994 and sold the Americana Division of Harmer Rooke the next year. The company acquired CEE JAY Auctions in 1997.

Greg Manning Auctions moved online in 1998 when it bought Internet auctioneer Teletrade and also added diamonds movie posters and fine art to its lineup. The company formed a joint venture with eBay's Butterfield & Butterfield subsidiary in 1999 to auction fine art and collectibles on eBay's Web site. It also established online auctions in China that year and is developing similar operations in Europe. The company bought Spectrum Numismatics a leading coin supplier in 2000. Also that year the company rejected a $138 million takeover offer from Take to Auction.com.

In 2001 the company shifted its Chinese operations away from the Internet with the launch of cybermall iAtoZ.com. It also bought a stake in a related retail cell phone chain which operates as iAtoZ.com/EBT. In 2003 the company acquired European auction houses Auctentia Subastas Corinphila Auktionen and Kohler. The following year Greg Manning purchased Bowers and Merena Kingswood Coin Auctions and Superior Sports Auctions from Collectors Universe for $2.5 million.

In 2005 Greg Manning Auctions changed its name to Escala Group as it grew into a global collectibles and precious metals trading company. Founder Manning stepped down as CEO that year and Jose Miguel Herrero was tapped to replace him. Herrero left the company in late 2006 and CFO Matthew Walsh was named president and acting CEO. Walsh stepped down in early 2008 and Greg Roberts previously head of several company divisions took the titles of president and CEO.

Escala came under investigation in 2006/2007 in connection with a stamp fraud scheme stemming from its partner firm Afinsa Bienes Tangibles.

In May 2009 Escala changed its name to Spectrum Group and centralized all of its US collectibles operations. The decision aimed in part to disassociate Spectrum Group from the investigations at Afinsa. In response to the Afinsa's alleged misconduct Spectrum Group conducted an internal investigation and eventually removed all of Afinsa's executives working at the company and on the board of directors. It also moved its stamp operations from Bethel Connecticut to its headquarters in Orange County California. In 2012 Afinsa's stake in Spectrum Group was reduced from 57% to about 10%.

EXECUTIVES

President CEO and Director, Gregory N. (Greg) Roberts, age 49, $450,000 total compensation

EVP Chief Administrative Officer General Counsel and Secretary, Carol Meltzer, age 52, $300,000 total compensation
President Bowers and Merena Galleries, Stephen (Steve) Deeds
CEO Philatelic Divisions North America and Asia; CEO H.R. Harmer, Laurence Gibson, age 53
Chairman, Antonio Arenas, age 55
COO Greg Martin Auctions, Carol Watson
Managing Director Heinrich Kohler, Dieter Michelson
President Hong Kong Operations John Bull Stamp Auctions, Sam Chiu
EVP and CFO, Paul Soth, age 53
VP and Chief Accounting Officer, Arthur Hamilton
Director, Jeffrey D. Benjamin, age 50
Director, Jay Moorhead, age 60
President CEO and Director, Gregory N. (Greg) Roberts, age 49
Director, James M. Davin, age 65
Director, Christopher W. (Chris) Nolan Sr., age 46
Director, George Lumby, age 66
Auditors: BDOSeidmanLLP

LOCATIONS

HQ: Spectrum Group International Inc.
18061 Fitch, Irvine CA 92614
Phone: 949-955-1250 **Fax:** 949-567-1360
Web: www.spectrumgi.com

2011 Sales

	$ mil.	% of total
US	7,051	98
Europe	149	2
Asia/Pacific	1	-
Total	7,202	100

PRODUCTS/OPERATIONS

2011 Sales

	$ mil.	% of total
Trading	6,962	97
Collectibles		
Coins	224	3
Stamps	11	-
Wine	4	-
Total	7,202	100

Selected Brands

A-Mark Precious Metals
Collateral Finance Corporation
Corinphila Auktionen
Corinphila Veilingen
HR Harmer
Heinrich Kohler
John Bull Stamp Auctions
Spectrum Numismatics International
Spectrum Wine auctions
Stack' s Bowers Galleries
Stack' s Bowers and Ponterio
Teletrade

COMPETITORS

Christie' s
Collectors Universe
eBay
Gallery of History
Heritage Auction Galleries
Leland' s Auctions
Paid Inc.
Phillips de Pury & Company
Sotheby' s
Superior Galleries

HISTORICAL FINANCIALS

Company Type: Public

Income Statement

FYE: June 30

	REVENUE ($ mil.)	NET INCOME ($ mil.)	NET PROFIT MARGIN	EMPLOYEES
06/12	7,974	4	0.1%	190
06/11	7,202	3	0.1%	177
06/10	6,012	(1)	—	143
06/09	4,293	7	0.2%	142
06/08	2,856	(14)	—	134
Annual Growth	29.3%	—	—	9.1%

2012 Year-End Financials

Debt ratio: 25.62%
Return on equity: 4.40%
Cash ($ mil.): 25
Current ratio: 133.13
Long-term debt ($ mil.): 6
No. of shares (mil.): 32
Dividends
Yield: —
Payout: —
Market value ($ mil.): 62

	STOCK PRICE ($) FY Close	P/E High	P/E Low	PER SHARE ($) Earnings	Dividends	Book Value
06/12	1.88	26	15	0.12	0.00	2.82
06/11	2.90	27	13	0.11	0.00	2.81
06/10	1.83	—	—	(0.03)	0.00	2.61
06/09	2.99	13	5	0.23	0.00	2.85
06/08	2.80	—	—	(0.52)	0.00	2.73
Annual Growth	(9.5%)	—	—	—	—	0.8%

Spirit AeroSystems Holdings Inc

Unlike the Wright Brothers modern aerospace designers and manufacturers like Spirit AeroSystems Holdings operate with more resources than a wing and a prayer. The company makes commercial and military airplane components such as fuselages propulsion systems wings and underwing parts. It designs and builds aerostructures for every Boeing aircraft currently in production and provides components to Boeing's chief rival Airbus. Spirit AeroSystems claims to be the largest supplier of wing parts for Airbus' A320 aircraft and produces the majority of aerostructures for Boeing's 737. Spirit AeroSystems maintains operations in the US the UK and Asia. Canadian investment firm Onex Corp. controls the company.

About 83% of Spirit AeroSystems' revenues come from Boeing and Airbus accounts for 11%. This risk gets offset by the fact that its the only source for most of its products and its contracts give it supplier rights for the life of the aircraft program for most models. Spirit AeroSystems began life as an internal supplier for Boeing aircraft.

To keep production up to snuff for its two main customers the company has been expanding its manufacturing capabilities with new facilities in North Carolina and abroad in Malaysia which is its first Asian facility and in France. The North Carolina facility which started operations in 2010 makes composite panels and wing components; the Malaysian plant (opened in 2009) performs the same operations. The French facility planned to commence operations in 2011 will assemble center fuselage sections. Along that same vein Spirit AeroSystems is rumored to be interested in acquiring Latecoere a France-based fuselage maker and Airbus supplier. Spirit AeroSystems also opened a repair facility in China in 2009 through a joint venture with Hong Kong Aircraft Engineering Company Limited and other Chinese aerospace manufacturers.

Like virtually every other business on the planet Spirit AeroSystems took a hit from the economic downturn. It showed up as a decreased demand for mid-size business jets a program it was just beginning for Gulfstream Aerospace. With Spirit AeroSystems carrying most of the development costs overspending on the engineering phase combined with the dip in demand combined to sap nearly $100 million off the books.

Onex Corporation has 91% of Class B shares which gives it 73% total voting power in Spirit AeroSystems.

EXECUTIVES

Chairman, Robert D. (Bob) Johnson, age 64
President CEO and Director, Jeffrey L. (Jeff) Turner, age 60, $263,390 total compensation
SVP CTO and Business Development, H. David Walker, age 60, $199,992 total compensation
SVP Corporate Administration and Human Resources, Gloria F. Flentje, age 68
SVP Corporate Strategy, John Lewelling, age 51, $375,003 total compensation
SVP Advanced Projects, Richard (Buck) Buchanan, age 61
SVP and COO, Michael G. (Mike) King, age 56, $77,681 total compensation
VP and Managing Director Spirit AeroSystems (Europe), Neil McManus, age 46
SVP Oklahoma, Alexander K. (Alex) Kummant, age 50
SVP CFO and Treasurer, Philip D. Anderson, age 47, $180,003 total compensation
SVP and General Manager Propulsion Systems Segment, John Pilla, age 52
VP and Chief Scientist, Peter Wu
SVP; General Manager Fuselage, David Coleal
Assistant Controller, Hector F. Cortez
VP Controller and Treasurer, James S. Sharp
Investor Relations, Coleen Tabor
Corporate Communications, Debbie Gann
SVP Corporate Administration and Human Resources, Sam Marnick
Director, Ivor J. (Ike) Evans, age 69
Director, Paul E. Fulchino, age 65
Director, Charles L. Chadwell, age 71
Director, James L. Welch, age 57
Director, Richard A. (Dick) Gephardt, age 70
Director, Ronald T. (Ron) Kadish, age 63
President CEO and Director, Jeffrey L. (Jeff) Turner, age 60
Director, Francis Raborn, age 68
Director, Tawfiq Popatia, age 37
Auditors: PricewaterhouseCoopersLLP

LOCATIONS

HQ: Spirit AeroSystems Holdings Inc
3801 South Oliver, Wichita, KS 67210
Phone: 316 526-9000
Web: www.spiritaero.com

2010 Sales

	$ mil.	% of total
US	3,674	88
UK	400	10
Other	98	2
Total	4,172	100

PRODUCTS/OPERATIONS

2010 Sales

	$ mil.	% of total
Fuselage systems	2,035	49
Wing systems	1,067	26
Propulsion systems	1,061	25
Other	8	-
Total	**4,172**	**100**

2010 Sales by Customer

	$ mil.	% of total
Boeing	3,480	83
Airbus	465	11
Sikorsky	59	2
Other	166	4
Total	**4,172**	**100**

COMPETITORS

Airbus
Boeing
Bombardier
Dassault Aviation
Embraer
Finmeccanica
Fuji Heavy Industries
GKN
Goodrich Corp.
Gulfstream Aerospace
Hawker Beechcraft
Kawasaki Heavy Industries
Lockheed Martin
Mitsubishi Heavy Industries
Northrop Grumman
Saab AB
Snecma
Textron
Triumph Aerostructures - Vought Aircraft Division
Triumph Group

HISTORICAL FINANCIALS

Company Type: Public

Income Statement FYE: December 31

	REVENUE ($ mil.)	NET INCOME ($ mil.)	NET PROFIT MARGIN	EMPLOYEES
12/11	4,863	192	4.0%	13,932
12/10	4,172	218	5.2%	14,158
12/09	4,078	191	4.7%	13,982
12/08	3,771	265	7.0%	14,944
12/07	3,860	296	7.7%	13,987
Annual Growth	5.9%	(10.3%)	—	(0.1%)

2011 Year-End Financials

Debt ratio: 23.82%
Return on equity: 9.80%
Cash ($ mil.): 177
Current ratio: 345.46
Long-term debt ($ mil.): 1,152
No. of shares (mil.): 142
Dividends
Yield: —
Payout: —
Market value ($ mil.): 2,969

	STOCK PRICE ($) FY Close	P/E High/Low		PER SHARE ($) Earnings	Dividends	Book Value
12/11	20.78	19	11	1.35	0.00	13.75
12/10	20.81	15	11	1.55	0.00	12.74
12/09	19.86	15	6	1.37	0.00	11.18
12/08	10.17	18	4	1.91	0.00	9.27
12/07	34.50	18	13	2.13	0.00	9.08
Annual Growth	(11.9%)	—	—	(10.8%)	—	10.9%

Sprint Nextel Corp

In the US telecom race Sprint Nextel is the #3 wireless carrier behind Verizon and AT&T in terms of subscribers. The company serves more than 55 million customers with mobile voice data and Web services over a nationwide network. While the namesake brand is reserved for premium postpaid accounts Sprint also offers prepaid mobile access through its Virgin Mobile USA and Boost Mobile subsidiaries which target a younger demographic. It also provides cellular access to other carriers and resellers on a wholesale basis. The company's much smaller legacy wireline business provides long-distance voice Internet and data services primarily to corporate customers and other carriers. In 2012 Japan's SOFTBANK agreed to acquire 70% of Sprint.

HISTORY

sIn 1899 Jacob Brown and son Cleyson began operating the Brown Telephone Company one of the first non-Bell phone companies in the western US in Abilene Kansas. Cleyson later formed Union Electric (phone equipment 1905) and Home Telephone and Telegraph (long-distance 1910). In 1911 he consolidated his company with other Kansas independents as United Telephone then obtained capital from rival Missouri and Kansas Telephone (later Southwestern Bell) which bought 60% of United's stock.

Cleyson sold his electric utility to finance expansions in telephone services and in 1925 he incorporated United Telephone and Electric. Reorganized as United Utilities after the Depression United continued to buy local exchanges. A post-WWII order backlog halted United's acquisition activity until 1952 but the company soon began further expansion becoming the second largest non-Bell phone company in the US before 1960.

During the 1960s United focused on satellites nuclear power plants and cable TV and it bought North Electric (1965) the US's oldest independent phone equipment maker. The company was renamed United Telecommunications in 1972. Meanwhile Southern Pacific developed the telegraph system along its railroad tracks into a microwave long-distance network called Southern Pacific Communications (1970) and known as SPRINT (for Southern Pacific Railroad Internal Telecommunications). In 1983 GTE acquired the network and renamed it GTE Sprint Communications. The next year United acquired U.S. Telephone the Dallas-based reseller of long-distance services and the eighth-largest US long-distance company.

A year after the 1984 AT&T Corp. breakup United bought 50% of GTE Sprint (United bought another 30% in 1989 and the balance in 1992). United and GTE teamed up to combine their long-distance systems –GTE Sprint and US Telecom – to form US Sprint. The unit began offering long-distance in 1986 and completed a nationwide fiber-optic network the next year (the "US" was later dropped from the partnership's name leaving Sprint).

In the 1990s the company fought long-distance competition by focusing on residential users and small businesses. Renamed Sprint Corporation in 1992 it joined the Bellcore research consortium (later known as Telcordia Technologies) and acquired cellular provider Centel Corporation in 1993.

Deutsche Telekom and France Telecom together took a 20% stake in Sprint in 1996 giving it a $3.6 billion boost just as it began to pump money into its PCS network. The trio also launched Global One an international telecom provider. That year Sprint spun off its cellular unit (renamed 360 Communications later bought by ALLTEL) and bought Paranet a computer network services provider in 1997.

In 1998 Sprint and EarthLink combined their Internet units and Sprint took a minority stake in the ISP. Sprint Spectrum a wireless partnership with several cable firms was combined with PhillieCo (another cable partnership) and Sprint-Com (its PCS subsidiary) to form Sprint PCS Group. Selling a 10% stake in the PCS Group to the public Sprint split its stock into the FON Group (non-wireless operations) and the PCS Group.

Meanwhile in 1998 Sprint FON began rolling out Sprint ION (Integrated On-Demand Network) a service that combined voice video and data on a single phone connection (the service was discontinued in 2001). Planning to assemble a fixed-wireless broadband network Sprint Corporation bought several wireless cable TV providers in 1999 including American Telecasting and People's Choice TV.

That year Sprint and its groups were the objects of a takeover battle between MCI WorldCom (later MCI) and BellSouth. MCI prevailed and agreed to buy them for $115 billion in stock and $14 billion in assumed debt but the deal was canceled in 2000 because of opposition from regulators. Also in 2000 Sprint sold its Global One stake to France Telecom for $1.4 billion. The next year Deutsche Telekom and France Telecom sold their Sprint stock.

In 2003 news reports that chairman William Esrey was planning to step down were followed by reports that COO Ronald LeMay would also be leaving the company and that Gary Forsee a vice chairman at BellSouth would assume the position as CEO. BellSouth then obtained a restraining order keeping Forsee from accepting the position. In a statement Sprint said that Esrey and LeMay would stay in their current positions while management evaluated alternatives. Later reports indicated a rift in the Sprint boardroom over the use of a questionable form of tax shelter. After a favorable court decision Sprint named Forsee as its CEO. LeMay stepped down from the COO position and Esrey soon after stepped down as chairman.

Sprint was not immune to the economic despair that plagued the telecom industry. Its reorganization plans designed to cut expenses included deep job cuts –it eliminated more than 20000 jobs in two years. Sprint FON in 2003 completed the sale of its directory publishing unit to R. H. Donnelly (now Dex One) for $2.1 billion in a move to pay down its $21 billion debt. The company also sold its managed hosting business to VeriCenter. It contracted with outsiders for some software operations and the company outsourced the bulk of its wireless customer service operation to IBM. Also in 2003 it began a 12-year project to upgrade its local service network to packet-based technology.

Combating dwindling demand Sprint cut 22000 jobs in 2003-04. Sprint also sold much of its Paranet computer network services unit to Texas-based technology consulting firm Vivare. The company once held a small stake in Canadian telecom player Call-Net Enterprises now Rogers Telecom Holdings which it traded for shares in Rogers Communications when that company acquired Call-Net in 2005.

At that time ranked #3 in the US (behind the wireless units of AT&T and Verizon) in terms of subscribers Sprint acquired #5 carrier Nextel Communications in 2005 for $35 billion in cash and stock in hopes of putting more pressure on its larger rivals. The combined company was renamed Sprint Nextel.

One consequence of the merger was a series of battles the company had to fight with its affiliates. Chief among them was Nextel Partners which exercised its right to force an acquisition by Sprint Nextel then fought for months over the purchase price. The skirmish ended when Sprint Nextel purchased Nextel Partners in 2006 as part of a stock deal valued at about $6.5 billion.

Sprint Nextel also faced off against affiliate US Unwired which tried to block the Sprint-Nextel merger; it bought the company later in 2005 for $1.3 billion. The deal added 500000 subscribers to Sprint Nextel's customer base and expanded its network into 48 additional markets in nine states. In related deals Sprint Nextel later bought affiliate Alamosa Holdings for $3.4 billion and UbiquiTel for $1.3 billion. The company continued making acquisitions in 2007 purchasing midwestern affiliate Northern PCS for $312.5 million.

The expanded company also struggled with customer churn as it lost existing subscribers and had a hard time drumming up new business. Defections were not limited to its consumer and enterprise segments. Sprint Nextel historically a provider of telecom services to the US government suffered a notable setback in 2007 when it was excluded from bidding on government contracts worth billions. Technical snags emerged as well as Sprint Nextel tried to integrate the two networks which each employed somewhat different technology. The resulting call quality problems contributed to customer defections and that hurt the bottom line that year.

Chairman William Kennard resigned in 2007 stepping down from the seat he had held since the merger. CEO Gary Forsee (who was instrumental in orchestrating the purchase) added chairman to his title but was forced to resign by the board of directors later that year amid shrinking earnings and subscriber numbers. The company then named Terabeam chairman and CEO (and former Embarq chief) Daniel Hesse to the top spot. He began replacing Sprint Nextel's top finance sales and marketing executives shortly after in hopes that new blood would speed the revitalization of the business. Board member James Hance was named nonexecutive chairman.

As it struggled under its own weight to keep pace with rivals the company used layoffs during 2007-08 to cut costs. Additionally it closed about 10% of its 1400 retail shops and 20% of its 20000 distribution points to bring down expenses. Sprint Nextel spun off its Embarq local consumer wireline voice operations to focus on its wireless broadband services in 2008.

Further divestment of physical assets included the 2008 sale of more than 3000 of its cell towers to private-equity firm TowerCo in exchange for a $670 million. Sprint Nextel got a much-needed cash injection out of the deal and retained use of the towers through a lease agreement.

Sprint Nextel has used acquisitions to gain market share and extend the reach of its brand. The company paid about $483 million in stock for Virgin Mobile USA in late 2009; Sprint Nextel also paid off Virgin Mobile USA's debt (estimated to be greater than $200 million) as part of the deal. Prior to the acquisition Virgin Group owned about 30% of Virgin Mobile USA while Sprint Nextel held a 13% stake; Seoul-based carrier SK Telecom was also a key shareholder. The acquisition built up Sprint Nextel's prepaid business which previously comprised only its Boost subsidiary. Virgin Mobile USA's mobile services were already delivered over Sprint Nextel's network.

Also in 2009 Sprint Nextel paid $831 million in cash and debt for affiliate iPCS to expand its service area in the Midwest where iPCS served about 700000 customers with mobile service sold under the Sprint brand. The deal also ended ongoing legal friction between the two companies. The conflict was fueled by lawsuits brought against Sprint Nextel by iPCS as the smaller company tried to prevent Sprint Nextel from competing in its region.

EXECUTIVES

President Strategic Planning and Corporate Initiatives, Keith O. Cowan, age 56, $725,000 total compensation
Chairman, James H. (Jim) Hance Jr., age 67
President CEO and Director, Daniel R. (Dan) Hesse, age 58, $1,200,000 total compensation
President Consumer Business Unit, Robert H. (Bob) Johnson, age 58
Chief Marketing Officer, Bill Malloy
CFO, Joseph J. (Joe) Euteneuer, age 57
Chief Sales Officer, Paget L. Alves, age 57
SVP Corporate Communications and Corporate Social Responsibility, William (Bill) White
SVP Human Resources, Sandra J. (Sandy) Price
Chief Service and Information Technology Officer, Robert L. (Bob) Johnson, age 53, $460,000 total compensation
President Integrated Solutions Group, Danny L. Bowman, age 46
General Counsel and Secretary, Charles Wunsch, age 56
President Network Operations and Wholesale, Steven L. (Steve) Elfman, age 56, $650,000 total compensation
President Global Wholesale Solutions, Matthew (Matt) Carter, age 51
Director, Frank Ianna, age 63
Director, Rodney O'Neal, age 58
Director, Gordon M. Bethune, age 70
Director, Larry C. Glasscock, age 63
Director, William R. (Bill) Nuti, age 48
President CEO and Director, Daniel R. (Dan) Hesse, age 58
Director, V. Janet Hill, age 64
Director, Sven-Christer Nilsson, age 67
Director, Robert R. Bennett, age 53
Auditors: KPMGLLP

LOCATIONS

HQ: Sprint Nextel Corporation
6200 Sprint Pkwy., Overland Park KS 66251-4300
Phone: 800-829-0965 **Fax:** -4277
Web: www.drreddys.com

PRODUCTS/OPERATIONS

2012 Sales

	$ mil.	% of total
Wireless	30,301	90
Wireline	3,370	10
Other	8	-
Total	**33,679**	**100**

COMPETITORS

AT&T Mobility
Cellco
CenturyLink
Cincinnati Bell
Leap Wireless
Level 3 Communications
MetroPCS
T-Mobile USA
TracFone
U.S. Cellular
Verizon

HISTORICAL FINANCIALS

Company Type: Public

Income Statement

FYE: December 31

	REVENUE ($ mil.)	NET INCOME ($ mil.)	NET PROFIT MARGIN	EMPLOYEES
12/11	33,679	(2,890)	—	40,000
12/10	32,563	(3,465)	—	40,000
12/09	32,260	(2,436)	—	40,000
12/08	35,635	(2,796)	—	56,000
12/07	40,146	(29,580)	—	60,000
Annual Growth	(4.3%)	—	—	(9.6%)

2011 Year-End Financials

Debt ratio: 41.05%—
Return on equity: (-25.29)%
Cash ($ mil.): 5,447
Current ratio: 159.06
Long-term debt ($ mil.): 20,266
Dividends
Yield: —
Payout: —
Market value ($ mil.): —

	STOCK PRICE ($) FY Close	P/E High/Low	PER SHARE ($) Earnings	Dividends	Book Value
12/11	2.34	— —	(0.96)	0.00	3.81
12/10	4.23	— —	(1.16)	0.00	4.87
12/09	3.66	— —	(0.84)	0.00	6.09
12/08	1.83	— —	(0.98)	0.08	6.86
12/07	13.13	— —	(10.31)	0.10	7.73
Annual Growth	(35.0%)	— —	—	—	(16.2%)

SPX Corp.

SPX Corp. controls the ebb and flow of multiple industries. The company operates from four units: Flow Technology (pumps valves other fluid handling devices); Test and Measurement (diagnostic tools fare-collection cable/pipe locators); Thermal Equipment and Services (cooling heating ventilation); and Industrial Products and Services (compactors power systems broadcast antenna systems aerospace components). SPX serves core markets which include infrastructure processing equipment and diagnostic tools. In turn these markets support electricity processed foods and beverages and vehicle services. It operates in 35-plus countries with a sales presence in 150 countries.

HISTORY

Paul Beardsley and Charles Johnson founded SPX in 1911 as The Piston Ring Company. The company which had its start making piston rings for major automakers expanded through a series of acquisitions. In 1931 it changed its name to Sealed Power to reflect the increasing diversity of its products. Expansion continued after WWII and the company went public in 1955. By 1959 Sealed Power made half of its sales from replacement parts.

Following further diversification and international growth in the 1960s and 1970s the company moved its stock listing to the New York Stock Exchange in 1972 and changed its name to SPX Corporation in 1988.

SPX ran into trouble in the early 1990s when a US recession resulted in losses. The company restructured however and by the time the auto industry rebounded in 1994 it was focused on specialty service tools and components.

Flat sales and losses in 1995-96 prompted the ouster of Dale Johnson (CEO from 1991 to 1995). He was replaced by GE veteran John Blystone who set about streamlining the business selling inefficient units and beefing up profitable lines. In 1997 SPX sold the Sealed Power division (its original business) for $223 million and acquired A. R. Brasch Marketing (owner's manuals and technical service and training materials).

SPX made a bold hostile takeover bid for much-larger auto parts maker Echlin in 1998 prompting rival Dana to step in and buy Echlin. Also that year the company paid $2.3 billion for General Signal a company nearly twice its size that provided SPX the opportunity to expand its automotive offerings. SPX later announced it would cut 1000 jobs and close about two dozen factories and warehouses it had picked up in the deal. Other buys that year included Tecnotest Toledo Trans-Kit and Valley Forge Group. SPX also received EGS Electrical Group's Dual-Lite and Signaling businesses in partial rescission of a 1997 joint venture.

In 1999 SPX sold Dual-Lite (exit signs and emergency lighting) to diversified manufacturer U.S. Industries. It also sold Acutex (solenoid valves and transmission products) to Hilite International and Best Power (uninterruptible power supplies) to UK-based engineering group Invensys.

Through its various units SPX spent $225 million on acquisitions in 2000. SPX acquired Fenner Fluid Power a division of Fenner plc; SPX's Inrange Technologies subsidiary picked up Varcom Corporation (network management hardware software and services) and Computerm Corporation (channel extension products); and the DeZurik unit acquired Copes-Vulcan's US and UK assets (control valves and turbine bypass systems).

In 2001 SPX acquired United Dominion Industries Limited (flow technology machinery specialty engineered products and test instrumentation) in a deal valued at $1.83 billion including the assumption of $876 million in United Dominion debt. In August of that year SPX announced plans to close 49 facilities and cut 2000 jobs (about 7% of its workforce) by 2003. SPX acquired Daniel Valve Company from Emerson Electric in early 2002. Later in the year the company acquired Balcke Cooling Products a unit of financially troubled German engineering group Babcock Borsig AG and Vance International a US-based security firm.

In 2003 the company acquired more than a dozen companies for close to $300 million. Following the security trend SPX acquired the US-based IDenticard Systems in early 2003. SPX sold Inrange Technologies to Computer Network Technology (CNT) in 2003 for $190 million. The following year SPX acquired the Kline Towers division (broadcast tower design engineering and construction) of Kline Iron & Steel.

The company then bought McLeod Russel Holdings (now SPX Air Treatment Holdings) a UK-based maker of filtration products complementary to those of SPX's air treatment business. Its Kendro Laboratory Products business acquired Germany-based H+P Labortechnik (steam sterilizers and magnetic stirrers for the life and materials sciences markets) and UK-based Medical Air Technology (microbiological safety cabinets and ultraclean air environments for the life sciences and hospital markets).

SPX acquired Bill-Jay Machine Tool (rotor head components for helicopters) to augment its Fenn Technologies aerospace components business. It also acquired the assets of Actron Manufacturing a maker of automotive test equipment and instruments under the Actron KAL-EQUIP and Faze brand names among others. Late in 2004 SPX announced its Service Solutions business had acquired automotive diagnostic test equipment maker AutoXray. That same year chairman and CEO Blystone abruptly resigned. The company separated the board and officer positions naming director Charles Johnson as chairman and VP Christopher Kearney as president and CEO.

SPX sold its Kendro Laboratory Products unit to Thermo Electron (now Thermo Fisher Scientific) in 2005. That same year it sold its Germany-based BOMAG compaction equipment business to privately held Fayat for $446 million and its Cofimco axial fan business to a Madison Capital Partners affiliate for $28 million. It sold its Edwards Systems Technology unit (fire detection and building safety systems) to GE for close to $1.4 billion three of its valve product lines –Mueller Steam Febco and Polyjet –to Watts Water Technologies and its Vance International security consulting subsidiary to Garda World Security for approximately $67 million. In late 2006 SPX sold its Dock Products business to the unit's management and an affiliate of Wynnchurch Capital.

In late 2006 the company acquired AB Custos a Swedish manufacturer of pumps for industrial and marine markets and aerator filters and regulators for the HVAC heating and plumbing market. Custos was placed in the Flow Technology segment. The acquisition which was valued at $184 million increased SPX's presence in the European market.

Johnson retired from the board at the annual meeting in 2007. The board designated Kearney to succeed him as chairman reuniting the top board and management posts. The board named J. Kermit Campbell an SPX director since 1993 as lead director for a two-year term. Campbell was CEO of Herman Miller.

In 2007 the company made two European acquisitions to expand its service solutions segment. It purchased the regional diagnostics division of Johnson Controls as well as Matra-Werke the German vehicle-repair division of KION Group.

In late 2007 SPX acquired the APV division of Invensys for nearly $516 million (about #250 million) in cash. APV made pumps valves heat exchangers and homogenizers for the beverage dairy food and pharmaceutical industries. APV became part of SPX's Flow Technology segment.

In 2007 the company sold its Contech automotive components business to Marathon Automotive Group for about $146 million in cash. SPX saw the business as no longer strategic to its long-term interests. Marathon Automotive Group was an entity formed by private equity Marathon Asset Management. SPX used most of the proceeds from the sale to buy back its own stock. Further in late 2008 the company sold its LDS Test and Measurement business unit (discontinued earlier in the year) to Spectris for about $86 million. LDS makes vibration testing and data acquisition equipment.

SPX subsequently put its Air Filtration business unit (Filtran) on the sale block signaling the company's accelerated exit from the automotive industry. It sold the business in fall 2009 to Chicago-based investment firm Madison Capital Partners. Filtran was the last of SPX's auto parts manufacturing segment. On the acquisition front SPX snapped up Yuba Heat Transfer from holding company Connell Limited Partnership for about $125 million in late 2009. Yuba manufactured and serviced feedwater heaters and condensers under the Yuba and Ecolair brands.

The following year SPX sold its Premier Mill brand of grinding and dispersing equipment in 2010. Privately held NETZSCH Fine Particle Technology LLS acquired the assets.

EXECUTIVES

Chairman President and CEO, Christopher J. (Chris) Kearney, age 57, $1,050,000 total compensation
EVP Global Business Systems and Services; President Asia Pacific, Robert B. Foreman, age 55, $725,000 total compensation
EVP CFO and Treasurer, Patrick J. O'Leary, age 54, $845,000 total compensation
VP and CFO Flow Technology, Jeremy W. Smeltser, age 37
Segment President Test and Measurement, David A. (Dave) Kowalski, age 54, $386,034 total compensation
Segment President Flow Technology, Don L. Canterna, age 61, $525,000 total compensation
Segment President Thermal Equipment and Services, Drew T. Ladau, age 52
SVP Secretary and General Counsel, Kevin L. Lilly, age 59, $450,000 total compensation
VP Business Development, J. Michael Whitted, age 40
Director, Michael J. Mancuso, age 70
Director, Terry S. Lisenby, age 60
Director, Martha B. Wyrsch, age 54
Director, Emerson U. Fullwood, age 64
Director, J. Kermit Campbell, age 73
Director, Albert A. (Al) Koch, age 70
Auditors: Deloitte&ToucheLLP

LOCATIONS

HQ: SPX Corporation
13515 Ballantyne Corporate Place, Charlotte NC 28277
Phone: 704-752-4400 **Fax:** 704-752-4505
Web: www.spx.com

2011 Sales

	$ mil.	% of total
US	2,725	50
China	327	6
South Africa	281	5
Total	**5,461**	**100**

PRODUCTS/OPERATIONS

2011 Sales

	$ mil.	% of total
Flow technology	2,042	37
Test & measurement	1,067	20
Total	**5,461**	**100**

Selected Products

Analyzers
Bacon press
Closures and pipeline pigging
Dispersion equipment
Dehydration equipment
Fittings
Filtration equipment
Heat exchangers
HVAC
Mixers
Pumps
Strainers
Valves

Selected Markets

Food and beverage
- Beverage
- BioTech
- Dairy
- Food
- Health care
- Personal care
- Pharmaceutical

General industry
- Adhesives and sealants
- Chemical processing
- Compressed air
- Electronics
- Environmental protection

HVAC
Marine
Mining and minerals
Paint ink and coatings
Pulp and paper
Rubber and plastics
Shipbuilding
Water and wastewater
Power and Energy
Alternative energy
Oil and gas
Power

Selected Subsidiaries

Balcke-Durr
Flash Technology
GFI Genfare
Kayex
Marley Engineered Products
Radiodetection
SPX Communication Technology
SPX Cooling Technologies
SPX Flow Technology
SPX Hydraulic Technologies
SPX Precision Components
SPX Service Solutions
TCI International
Thermal Product solutions
Waukesha Electric Systems
Weil-McLain

COMPETITORS

ABB
Alfa Laval
ALSTOM
AMETEK
Baltimore Aircoil
BBT Thermotechnik
Broan-NuTone
Cubic Transportation Systems
Danaher
Dresser Inc.
Eaton
Emerson Electric
Endress + Hauser
Evapco
Franklin Electric
GE
GEA Group
Glen Dimplex
Hamon
Harbin Power Equipment
Harris Corp.
Harsco
Honeywell International
IDEX
Ingersoll-Rand
Interpump
ITT Corp.
Johnson Controls
Parker-Hannifin
Power Conversion
Robbins & Myers
Robert Bosch
Roper Industries
Siemens AG
Snap-on
Trippe Manufacturing

HISTORICAL FINANCIALS

Company Type: Public

Income Statement

FYE: December 31

	REVENUE ($ mil.)	NET INCOME ($ mil.)	NET PROFIT MARGIN	EMPLOYEES
12/11	5,461	180	3.3%	18,000
12/10	4,886	205	4.2%	15,500
12/09	4,850	31	0.7%	15,000
12/08	5,855	247	4.2%	17,800
12/07	4,822	294	6.1%	18,500
Annual Growth	3.2%	(11.5%)	—	(0.7%)

2011 Year-End Financials

Debt ratio: 27.07%
Return on equity: 8.11%
Cash ($ mil.): 551
Current ratio: 148.64
Long-term debt ($ mil.): 1,925
No. of shares (mil.): 51
Dividends
Yield: —
Payout: 28.25%
Market value ($ mil.): 3,078

	STOCK PRICE ($) FY Close	P/E High	P/E Low	PER SHARE ($) Earnings	Dividends	Book Value
12/11	60.27	24	12	3.54	0.00	43.61
12/10	71.49	17	12	4.08	1.00	41.71
12/09	54.70	101	61	0.64	1.00	38.30
12/08	40.55	30	6	4.59	1.00	39.33
12/07	102.85	21	11	5.22	1.00	38.00
Annual Growth	(12.5%)	—	—	(9.3%)	—	3.5%

ST. JOSEPH HEALTH SYSTEM

EXECUTIVES

President CEO and Trustee, Deborah A. Proctor
EVP System Services, William J. (Bill) Murin
President and CEO St. Joseph Hospital Orange, Steven C. (Steve) Moreau
EVP and COO, Joseph (Joe) Randolph
President and CEO St. Jude Medical Center, Lee Penrose
SVP and General Counsel, Shannon Dwyer
SVP Theology and Ethics, John (Jack) Glaser
EVP Southern California Region and CFO, Darrin Montalvo
SVP Community Health, Azhar Qureshi
EVP Wellness and Health Improvement, Elliot B. Sternberg
SVP and CIO, Larry Stofko
SVP, Susan Whittaker
EVP, Sister Jayne Helmlinger
President and CEO Redwood Memorial Hospital and St. Joseph Hospital Eureka, Joe Mark
SVP Physician Practice, C. R. Burke
President and CEO Queen of the Valley Medical Center, Walt Mickens
EVP West Texas and Southern New Mexico, Richard H. Parks
Director Marketing and Communications Queen of the Valley Medical Center, Jaime Penaherrera
SVP Ministry Integrity, Margaret Hambleton
EVP Strategic Services, Annette M. Walker
VP Leadership Institute and Governance Support; Interim EVP Mission Integration, Jeff Thies
Chief Medical Officer, Clyde Wesp Jr.
Chairman, Walter W. (Bill) Noce
EVP Northern California Region, Kevin Klockenga
Manager Marketing and Media Relations System Office, Kellie Todd Griffin
Manager Marketing and Media Relations Covenant Health System, Michell Stephens
Manager Marketing and Media Relations Mission Hospital, Kelsey Martinez
Manager Marketing and Media Relations St. Mary Medical Center, Randy Bevilacqua
Manager Marketing and Media Relations SJHS-Humboldt County, Laurie Watson-Stone
Manager Marketing and Media Relations SJHS-Sonoma County, Katy Hillenmeyer
Manager Marketing and Media Relations St. Joseph Hospital Orange, Cathy Semar
Manager Marketing and Media Relations St. Jude Medical Center, Dru Ann Copping
Chair St. Joseph Hospital Orange, Sister Theresa LaMetterey
President and CEO St. Mary Medical Center, Alan H. Garrett
President and CEO Mission Hospital, Kenneth (Kenn) McFarland
Trustee, Dan S. Wilford, age 71
Trustee, Paula L. Woods
President CEO and Trustee, Deborah A. Proctor
Trustee, Rev Thomas R. Kopfensteiner
Trustee, Sister Eileen McNerney
Trustee, Sister Mary Bernadette McNulty
Trustee, Dick Blair
Trustee, Ned Dolejsi
Trustee, Sister JoAnn Eannareno
Trustee, Hector Flores
Trustee, Sister Marie Jeanne Gaillac
Trustee, Sister Diane Hejna
Trustee, Sister Loraine Polacci
Trustee, Hank Walker

LOCATIONS

HQ: St. Joseph Health System
500 S. Main St. Ste. 1000, Orange CA 92868-4533
Phone: 714-347-7500 **Fax:** 714-347-7540
Web: www.stjhs.org

Selected Operations

Northern California
Petaluma Valley Hospital
Queen of the Valley Medical Center (Napa)
Redwood Memorial Hospital (Fortuna)
St. Joseph Home Care Network (Sonoma)
St. Joseph Hospital (Eureka)
Santa Rosa Memorial Hospital
Southern California
Mission Hospital (Mission Viejo)
Mission Hospital Laguna Beach
St. Joseph Hospital (Orange)
St. Jude Medical Center (Fullerton)
St. Mary Medical Center (Apple Valley)
West Texas/Eastern New Mexico
Covenant Health System
Artesia General Hospital (New Mexico)
Covenant Hospital Levelland (Texas)
Covenant Hospital Plainview (Texas)
Covenant Medical Center (Lubbock TX)
Nor-Lea General Hospital (Lovington NM)
Roosevelt General Hospital (Portales NM)

PRODUCTS/OPERATIONS

COMPETITORS

Adventist Health
Arrowhead Medical Center
Banner Health
Catholic Health Initiatives
Cedars-Sinai Medical Center
Citrus Valley Health Partners
City of Hope
Dignity Health
HCA
Kaiser Permanente
Loma Linda University Medical Center
Los Angeles County Health Department
Memorial Health Services
Pasadena Hospital Association
Prospect Medical
Scripps health
Sutter Health
Tenet Healthcare
Western Medical Center - Santa Ana

HISTORICAL FINANCIALS

Company Type: Private - Not-for-Profit

Income Statement FYE: June 30

	REVENUE ($ mil.)	NET INCOME ($ mil.)	NET PROFIT MARGIN	EMPLOYEES
06/11	4,223	348	8.3%	21,500
06/10	4,268	268	6.3%	0
06/08	3,943	53	1.3%	0
06/07	3,668	302	8.2%	0
Annual Growth	4.8%	4.8%	—	—

2011 Year-End Financials

Debt ratio: —
Return on equity: 8.30%
Cash ($ mil.): 250
Current ratio: 0.90
Long-term debt ($ mil.): —

Dividends
Yield: —
Payout: —
Market value ($ mil.): —

St. Jude Medical, Inc.

If your heart has trouble catching the beat St. Jude Medical's got rhythm to spare. The company operates through four segments: cardiac rhythm management (CRM) cardiovascular atrial fibrillation and neuromodulation. The CRM division its largest includes pacemakers and implantable cardioverter defibrillators (ICDs) both of which use electrical impulses to shock irregularly beating hearts back into rhythm. Offerings from the other divisions include vascular and structural heart products ablation systems and spinal cord and deep brain stimulation devices. St. Jude sells its products in more than 100 countries; the US is its largest market.

Operations St. Jude Medical started out making mechanical heart valves but some 55% of its revenue these days comes from pacemakers and ICDs developed and marketed through the CRM division. ICDs correct for tachycardia or overly fast heartbeats and the company aggressively introduces new ICD products in a bid to take market share from its larger competitors in the field Medtronic and Boston Scientific and become a leading industry supplier. Pacemakers in contrast to ICDs are used to treat patients whose hearts beat too slowly. St. Jude developed one of the industry's first pacemakers with wireless telemetry – which in this case allows the patient to be monitored by his physician from a distance from the time of implantation all the way through to his follow-up.

Geographic Reach The company generates nearly half its sales in the US with Europe accounting for 28% and the Asia-Pacific region (led by Japan) accounting for 18%. St. Jude Medical saw growth across all regions except the US which fell slightly in 2011.

Financial Analysis The company continued its strong and steady growth in 2011 with revenue up 9% to $5.6 billion. Flat sales from St. Jude Medical's primary CRM division (due to US market contraction) were offset by double-digit growth in each of the company's other divisions. Particularly strong was the cardiovascular division which saw growth of some 30% on increased structural heart product sales because of the 2010 acquisition of AGA Medical. St. Jude's atrial fibrillation and neuromodulation divisions grew 16% and 10% respectively. Net income that year fell 9% to $826 million as St. Jude dealt with after-tax charges of more than $150 million related to restructuring.

Strategy St. Jude Medical like most other companies operating in the health care industry is still working out how new health care laws will impact its operations. The company faces legislative challenges including proposed new excise taxes on all US medical device sales and potential reimbursement changes through Medicare provisions aimed at improving quality and decreasing costs. A recall in 2010 of some of Boston Scientific's defibrillators helped shuttle St. Jude into a top industry position and the company is counting on the continued introduction of new products (it invests more than 10% of its annual income in research and development of new products) and a vigorous marketing campaign to keep it there. Even as St. Jude has been busily introducing new products from the CRM division it hasn't forgotten about its other divisions all of which are growing. The company looks to strengthen all of its divisions through acquisitions and organic product development.

Mergers & Acquisitions St. Jude Medical's CRM unit acquired medical imaging developer LightLab Imaging in 2010. The $90 million deal brought in LightLab's FDA-approved coronary imaging technology. The company also began expanding its wireless CRM segment late in 2010 when it invested $60 million in CardioMEMS a maker of a wireless implant that helps physicians remotely manage chronic cardiovascular diseases such as heart failure and aneurysms. The investment gave St. Jude about a 20% stake in CardioMEMS and the option to buy the company outright for an additional $375 million. In a move that bolstered both its atrial fibrillation and cardiovascular units the company traded some $1.1 billion in cash and stock to acquire AGA Medical in late 2010. AGA Medical –which was integrated into St. Jude's operations –brought with it products used to correct structural heart defects. St. Jude's neuromodulation business got a boost when the company acquired the intellectual property and non-cash assets of Northstar Neuroscience in 2009. While Northstar's implanted neurostimulator device had fizzled in clinical trials St. Jude saw potential promise in the technology and paid $2 million for the portfolio. The company intends to grow the neuromodulation segment by introducing products to treat other indications in addition to pain including depression and Parkinson's disease.

HISTORY

Manuel Villafana who started Cardiac Pacemakers in 1972 founded St. Jude Medical four years later to develop the bileaflet heart valve. In 1977 patient Helen Heikkinen received the first St. Jude heart valve. The firm also went public that year.

Villafana left in 1981 and established competitor Helix Biocore. St. Jude expanded into tissue valves with its purchase of BioImplant in 1986.

In the mid-1980s St. Jude gained market share when devices from Pfizer and Baxter International had problems. Concerns that the company hadn't diversified led to a joint venture in 1992 with Hancock Jaffe Laboratories to develop a bioprosthetic (constructed of animal tissue) heart valve. In 1994 it bought Siemens' pacemaker unit doubling revenues and tripling its sales force.

The firm continued diversifying buying Daig (cardiac catheters) in 1996 and Ventritex (cardiac defibrillators) in 1997. In 1997 the FDA approved St. Jude's Toronto SPV tissue valve marking its entry into that market. In 1999 St. Jude landed on CalPERS's list of worst-performing companies as it lagged behind rivals Guidant and Medtronic. A management shake-up followed and the firm strengthened its product lines buying Tyco International's Angio-Seal subsidiary (cardiac sealant) and Vascular Science (artery connectors). The next year the FDA stepped up its regulatory oversight after the company and its competitors recalled or issued warnings regarding defective or potentially defective devices.

In 2002 St. Jude bought Getz Bros. its largest distributor in Japan. The firm scooped up two other firms Irvine Biomedical and Epicor Medical in 2004.

The company acquired both Endocardial Solutions which makes diagnostic and therapeutic catheters marketed under the EnSite System brand and Velocimed a privately owned maker of interventional cardiology devices in early 2005. Velocimed's products included the Venture catheter and the Premere system used to seal a tiny hole between the left and right upper chambers of the heart that fails to close in some babies.

Also in 2005 St. Jude spent more than $1.3 billion to acquire Advanced Neuromodulation Systems establishing its presence in the neurostimulation market. That year marked the beginning of a several years' long expansion effort that included the acquisition of a number of product lines as well as expansion through organic growth efforts. During the five years between 2005 and 2010 the company expanded its line of pacemakers and began marketing a unique line of pacemakers that operate via wireless telemetry.

St. Jude also bolstered both its Atrial Fibrillation and Cardiovascular units by trading some $1.3 billion in cash and stock to acquire AGA Medical in 2010.

EXECUTIVES

President Neuromodulation Division, Christopher G. (Chris) Chavez, age 56

Chairman President and CEO, Daniel J. Starks, age 57, $975,000 total compensation

EVP and CFO, John C. Heinmiller, age 57, $665,000 total compensation

Group President, Michael T. Rousseau, age 56, $600,000 total compensation

President Atrial Fibrillation, Jane J. Song, age 49

VP Information Technology and CIO, Thomas R. Northenscold, age 54

President Cardiac Rhythm Management Division, Eric S. Fain, age 51, $549,423 total compensation

President International, Denis M. Gestin, age 48, $658,720 total compensation

VP Corporate Relations and Human Resources, Angela D. Craig, age 40

VP General Counsel and Corporate Secretary, Pamela S. Krop, age 53

VP and Corporate Controller, Donald J. Zurbay, age 44

President Cardiovascular Division, Frank J. Callaghan, age 58

Chief Medical Officer and SVP Research and Clinical Affairs Cardiac Rhythm Management, Mark D. Carlson

VP Global Quality, Behzad (Ben) Khosravi, age 55

Senior Manager Investor and Corporate Relations, J. C. Weigelt

Manager Public Relations and Communications U.S. and Cardiac, Amy Jo Meyer

Manager International Public Relations and Communications, Marisa Bluestone

Director Public Relations Neuromodulation, Denise Landry

Senior Manager Public Relations Neuromodulation, Guy Davis

President U.S. Division, Joel D. Becker, age 44
President Medical Neuromodulation Division, Rohan J. Hoare, age 47
VP Global Quality, Jeffry A. (Jeff) Fecho, age 51
VP General Counsel and Corporate Secretary, Jason A. Zellers, age 46
Director, Wendy L. Yarno, age 57
Director, Michael A. Rocca, age 67
Director, John W. Brown, age 77
Director, Stuart M. Essig, age 50
Director, Richard R. (Rick) Devenuti, age 54
Director, Barbara B. Hill, age 59
Director, Thomas H. Garrett III, age 67
Auditors: Ernst&YoungLLP

LOCATIONS

HQ: St. Jude Medical Inc.
1 St. Jude Medical Dr., St. Paul MN 55117-9983
Phone: 651-756-2000 **Fax:** 651-756-3301
Web: www.sjm.com

2011 Sales

US	2,647	47
Japan	641	12

PRODUCTS/OPERATIONS

2011 Sales

Cardiac rhythm management	3,033	54
Atrial fibrillation	822	15
Total	**5,611**	**100**

COMPETITORS

Abbott Labs
Bard
Biosense Webster
Boston Scientific
Cyberonics
Edwards Lifesciences
Empi
Johnson & Johnson
Medtronic
Sorin
W.L. Gore

HISTORICAL FINANCIALS

Company Type: Public

Income Statement FYE: December 31

	REVENUE ($ mil.)	NET INCOME ($ mil.)	NET PROFIT MARGIN	EMPLOYEES
12/11*	5,611	825	14.7%	16,000
01/11	5,164	907	17.6%	15,000
01/10	4,681	777	16.6%	14,000
01/09	4,363	384	8.8%	14,000
12/07	3,779	559	14.8%	12,000
Annual Growth	10.4%	10.2%	—	7.5%

*Fiscal year change

2011 Year-End Financials

Debt ratio: 31.06%
Return on equity: 18.46%
Cash ($ mil.): 985
Current ratio: 319.34
Long-term debt ($ mil.): 2,713
No. of shares (mil.): 319
Dividends
Yield: —
Payout: 33.33%
Market value ($ mil.): 10,963

	STOCK PRICE ($) FY Close	P/E High/Low		PER SHARE ($) Earnings	Dividends	Book Value
12/11*	34.30	21	13	2.52	0.00	14.00
01/11	42.75	16	13	2.75	0.00	13.29
01/10	36.78	18	13	2.26	0.00	10.24
01/09	34.27	43	23	1.10	0.00	9.37
12/07	41.07	30	21	1.59	0.00	8.54
Annual Growth	(4.4%)	—	—	12.2%	—	13.2%

*Fiscal year change

ST. VINCENT RANDOLPH HOSPITAL INC

LOCATIONS

HQ: ST. VINCENT RANDOLPH HOSPITAL INC
473 E GREENVILLE AVE, WINCHESTER, IN 473949436
Phone: 7655840004

HISTORICAL FINANCIALS

Company Type:

Income Statement FYE: June 30

	REVENUE ($ mil.)	NET INCOME ($ mil.)	NET PROFIT MARGIN	EMPLOYEES
06/11	33,770	6,141	18.2%	251
06/10	30	0	2.5%	0
06/09	27	1	5.1%	0
06/08	22	1	6.7%	0
Annual Growth	1051.8%	1505.5%		

2011 Year-End Financials

Debt ratio: —
Return on equity: 18.20%
Cash ($ mil.): 1
Current ratio: 0.90
Long-term debt ($ mil.): —
Dividends
Yield: —
Payout: —
Market value ($ mil.): —

Stancorp Financial Group Inc

Providing insurance and related financial services is standard operating procedure at StanCorp Financial Group. Through Standard Insurance (aka The Standard) and other divisions the company offers a range of financial products nationwide including group and individual disability coverage life and accident insurance retirement plans and supplemental group benefit plans. The insurance services segment holds more than 31000 group policies covering 6.8 million employees throughout the US. The company's asset management segment provides investment advisory retirement planning mortgage lending and other financial services.

The insurance services segment which includes subsidiaries Standard Insurance and Standard Life Insurance of New York generates more than 85% of StanCorp Financial Group's revenues. Group long term disability accounts for 40% of its premiums while life and accidental death and dismemberment products together account for another 40%. The remaining premiums are collected from group short term disability individual disability and group dental and vision insurance products. The company's products are sold through its sales force and independent employee benefit brokerage and consulting firms.

StanCorp's asset management segment offers an array of retirement products including 401(k) and 403(b) plans and individual annuities. It pitches its retirement plans at businesses that have between $1 million and $10 million in plan assets. Its annuities are targeted at conservative investors. The company does a smidgen of commercial mortgage lending for small retail office and industrial properties.

EXECUTIVES

Chairman President and CEO, J. Gregory (Greg) Ness, age 54, $612,500 total compensation
Chairman, Eric E. Parsons, age 63, $362,500 total compensation
VP Asset Management Standard Insurance, Scott A. Hibbs, age 50, $310,000 total compensation
SVP and CFO StanCorp Financial and Standard Insurance, Floyd F. Chadee, age 54, $460,000 total compensation
Assistant VP Investor Relations, Jeffrey J. (Jeff) Hallin
Manager Shareholder Services, Jane Keister
VP and Controller StanCorp Financial and Standard Insurance Company, Robert M. (Rob) Erickson, age 43, $204,000 total compensation
Assistant VP Corporate Secretary and Assistant General Counsel StanCorp Financial and Standard Insurance, Holley Y. Franklin
SVP Information Technology Standard Insurance, David M. O'Brien, age 55, $285,000 total compensation
Corporate Information, Bob Speltz
VP Human Resources and Corporate Services Standard Insurance, Karen M. Weisz, age 44
VP Sales Equities, Dan Hall
Regional Pension Manager Equities, Niki Green
VP Marketing and Communications Standard Insurance, Katherine Durham
Director, Mary F. Sammons, age 65
Director, Duane C. McDougall, age 60
Director, E. Kay Stepp, age 66
President COO and Director StanCorp Financial and Standard Insurance, J. Gregory (Greg) Ness, age 54
Director, Eric E. Parsons, age 63
Director, Ronald E. Timpe, age 72
Director, Stanley R. (Stan) Fallis, age 71
Director, Michael G. Thorne, age 71
Director, Virginia L. Anderson, age 64
Director, Frederick W. (Fred) Buckman, age 64
Director, Peter O. Kohler, age 73
Director, George J. Puentes, age 64
Auditors: Deloitte&ToucheLLP

LOCATIONS

HQ: StanCorp Financial Group Inc.
1100 SW 6th Ave., Portland OR 97204
Phone: 971-321-7000 **Fax:** 971-321-7757
Web: www.stancorpfinancial.com

PRODUCTS/OPERATIONS

2011 Revenues

Insurance services	2,498	86
Other	(14.8)	-

Selected Subsidiaries

StanCorp Equities Inc.
StanCorp Investment Advisers Inc.
StanCorp Mortgage Investors LLC
StanCorp Real Estate LLC
StanCorp Retirement Services Inc.
Standard Insurance Company
The Standard Life Insurance Company of New York
Standard Management Inc.

COMPETITORS

Aetna
Guardian Life

Aflac	MassMutual
Ameritas	MetLife
Assurant Employee Benefits	Ohio National
CNA Financial	Pacific Mutual
Delphi Financial Group	Principal Financial
GatesMcDonald	Prudential
	Unum Group

HISTORICAL FINANCIALS

Company Type: Public

Income Statement FYE: December 31

	ASSETS ($ mil.)	NET INCOME ($ mil.)	INCOME AS % OF ASSETS	EMPLOYEES
12/11	18,433	139	0.8%	2,974
12/10	17,843	189	1.1%	3,091
12/09	16,569	208	1.3%	3,150
12/08	14,555	162	1.1%	3,436
12/07	14,982	227	1.5%	3,437
Annual Growth	5.3%	(11.5%)	—	(3.6%)

2011 Year-End Financials

Debt ratio: 1.63%	No. of shares (mil.): 44
Return on equity: 6.93%	Dividends
Cash ($ mil.): 138	Yield: —
Current ratio: —	Payout: 28.80%
Long-term debt ($ mil.): 300	Market value ($ mil.): 1,627

	STOCK PRICE ($) FY Close	P/E High/Low		PER SHARE ($) Earnings	Dividends	Book Value
12/11	36.75	16	8	3.09	0.00	45.42
12/10	45.14	12	9	4.02	0.86	41.42
12/09	40.02	10	3	4.26	0.80	36.35
12/08	41.77	17	7	3.30	0.75	28.18
12/07	50.38	13	9	4.35	0.72	29.07
Annual Growth	(7.6%)	—	—	(8.2%)	—	11.8%

Stanley Black & Decker, Inc.

Stanley Black & Decker has the tools that neighbors envy. As a top US toolmaker it markets hand tools mechanics' tools power tools pneumatic tools and hydraulic tools. Since the merger the company's tool shed is bulging with additional items such as garden tools plumbing products (Pfister) and cleaning items (Dustbuster) as well as security hardware (Kwikset) and door products. Besides the Stanley and Black & Decker names it sells such brands as Bostitch Mac Tools and DEWALT. Stanley Black & Decker the result of the merger of Stanley Works and rival Black & Decker in 2010 peddles its products through home centers and mass-merchant distributors as well as through third-party distributors.

HISTORY

In 1843 Frederick Stanley opened a bolt shop in a converted early-19th-century armory in New Britain Connecticut. In 1852 he teamed with his brother and five friends to form The Stanley Works to cast form and manufacture various types of metal.

The business prospered during the 1860s when the Civil War and westward migration created a need for hardware and tools. When Stanley turned his attention to political and civic affairs company management fell to William Hart. He engaged in a "knuckles-bared" fight with four bigger competitors (Stanley was the sole survivor) and led the firm into steel strapping production which would become a major element in the company's operations. Hart was named president in 1884.

During WWI the company produced belt buckles and rifle and gas mask parts. Along with making numerous domestic acquisitions it established operations in Canada (1914) and Germany (1926). In 1920 the company merged with Stanley Rule and Level (a local tool company formed in 1857 by a cousin of Frederick Stanley) and in 1925 it opened a new hydroelectric plant near Windsor Connecticut to provide power for all its operations.

Stanley struggled through the Depression but following WWII the toolmaker embarked on four decades of expansion. Staying within its traditional product line Stanley acquired a myriad of companies including Berry Industries (garage doors 1965) Ackley Manufacturing and Sales (hydraulic tools 1972) Mac Tools (1980) and National Hand Tool (1986). The company grew globally in the late 1980s by establishing high-tech plants in Europe and the Far East.

After twice fending off takeover attempts by rival Newell (now Newell Rubbermaid) in the early 1990s Stanley returned to acquisitions. In 1992 it acquired LaBounty Manufacturing (large hydraulic tools) American Brush (paintbrushes and decorator tools) Mail Media (Jensen Tools precision tool kits and Direct Safety safety equipment) Goldblatt Tool (masonry and dry-wall tools) and a controlling interest in Tona a.s. Pecky a major Czech maker of mechanics' tools. The following year the company sold its Taylor Rental subsidiary the largest system of general rental centers in the US to SERVISTAR.

When weak sales hit Stanley's primary markets in mid-1995 the company responded with a massive restructuring program including $150 million in expense cuts. That year it created the Stanley Home Decor division to make and market home decorating products.

As part of the restructuring Stanley sold the Creative Rivets division of Stanley-Bostitch to rival rivet maker Marson in 1996. That year Stanley's Mac Tools division formed an alliance with Automotive Diagnostics division to distribute SPX's specialized tools through more than 2000 Mac Tools distributors. In 1997 Stanley sold its garage-related products unit to radar-detector manufacturer Whistler;. That year continuing its corporate overhaul Stanley announced that it would cut 4500 jobs –almost a quarter of its workforce.

With its restructuring still in the works in 1998 Stanley paid $117 million for 90% of Israel's ZAG Industries a maker of plastic home-improvement products. While continuing to close plants in 1999 Stanley settled charges with the FTC for selling Made-in-USA tools that had foreign components. In 2001 Stanley acquired electrical tools distributor Contact East while still undergoing restructuring.

In 2002 the Stanley board voted to change its incorporation to Bermuda which would decrease the company's tax bill but Stanley withdrew the plan later that same year. Also that year Stanley acquired Best Lock Corporation. The company's restructuring resulted in the closing of about 90 facilities with about 4000 job cuts by December 2002.

In 2003 the company cut another 1000 jobs and discontinued MacDirect the Mac Tools retail channel.

Stanley in 2004 acquired Blick Cal-Dor Specialties CST/Berger (which makes laser and optical leveling and measuring equipment) Frisco Bay Industries and electronic-security integrator ISR Solutions. (Blick has since been folded into the Stanley Security Solutions - Europe Ltd. operation.) The same year John Lundgren a former executive with Georgia-Pacific became chairman and CEO. Also in 2004 Stanley sold its residential entry-door business to Masonite International and its Home Decor division to Wellspring Capital Management.

The company continued to lock on to the security segment in 2005 through its acquisition of Security Group for about $50 million. Also that year it bought National Manufacturing for $170 million.

In January 2006 the company acquired France's Facom a leading European maker of hand and mechanics tools for about $486 million. That July Stanley purchased a 67% stake in Besco Pneumatic Corp. a Taiwan-based maker of pneumatic tools for $42 million in cash. Stanley has the option to acquire an additional 15% stake in the company over the next five years. Stanley also created two new divisions in late 2006 to support its continued focus on electronic systems. Its Stanley Convergent Security Solutions houses its existing business specific to electronic access controls and systems integration as well as commercial monitoring. HSM was folded into the Stanley Convergent Security Solutions division in January 2008. Its Stanley Mechanical Access Solutions consists of its existing commercial lock operation and automatic doors as well as hardware-related business. Stanley sold its CST/berger business consisting of leveling and measuring devices to Robert Bosch Tool Corporation for $205 million in July 2008.

Partnering with fellow toolmaker Stanley Works merged its operations with Black & Decker in 2010 and renamed the new entity Stanley Black & Decker. The blended businesses are led by Stanley's Lundgren and Black & Decker's Nolan Archibald as executive chairman.

EXECUTIVES

Chairman, Nolan D. Archibald, age 68

President CEO and Director, John F. Lundgren, age 60, $1,050,000 total compensation

SVP Human Resources, Mark J. Mathieu, age 59, $340,000 total compensation

EVP and COO, James M. (Jim) Loree, age 53, $610,000 total compensation

SVP General Counsel and Secretary, Bruce H. Beatt, age 60

SVP; President Stanley Healthcare Solutions, Hubert W. (Bert) Davis Jr., age 64, $365,000 total compensation

President Construction and DIY North America, Les H. Ireland, age 47

CIO, Rhonda Gass

President Engineered Fastening Solutions, Michael A. (Mike) Tyll, age 55

SVP; Group Executive Mechanical Access Systems, Justin C. Boswell, age 44

VP; President Asia, Jeff H. T. Chen, age 54

SVP; Group Executive Construction and DIY, Jeffery D. (Jeff) Ansell, age 44, $400,000 total compensation

President Emerging Markets Group, Bhupinder S. (Ben) Sihota, age 53

Staff Executive Engineered Fastening Solutions, Denise Nemchev

President Americas Engineered Fastening Solutions, Christine Yingli Yan

SVP and CFO, Donald (Don) Allan Jr., age 47, $350,000 total compensation

President Asia Engineered Fastening Solutions, Giri Chakravarthi
President Stanley Security Solutions Europe, Massimo Grassi, age 50
President Europe Engineered Fastening Solutions, Manfred Mueller
VP Internal Audit, Greg Waybright
VP Corporate Business Development, Corbin B. Walburger
Director Investor Relations, Kathryn H. (Kate) White
Director Global Communications, Tim Perra
VP and Integration Co-Leader, Anthony W. (Tony) Milando, age 49
President Construction & DIY Latin America ANZ, Jaime A. Ramirez, age 44
President Construction and DIY EMEA, John H. A. Wyatt, age 53
President Professional Power Tools and Products, William S. (Bill) Taylor, age 56
SVP; Group Executive Stanley Security Solutions, D. Brett Bontrager, age 50
CFO Construction and DIY, Lee B. McChesney
VP Corporate Tax, Michael A. Bartone, age 52
VP and Treasurer, Craig A Douglas, age 57
VP Human Resources, Joe Voelker
President Consumer Power Tools and Products, Jeff Cooper
CIO Construction and DIY, Peter Dubois
President Accessory Products Construction and DIY, Beau Parker
VP Technology Construction and DIY, Robert (Bob) St. John
VP Operations Construction and DIY, Steve Strafstrom
President Infrastructure Solutions, Tim Jones
VP Brand Management and Licensing, Scott Bannell
VP Sourcing, Mike Prado
President Hardware and Home Improvement Group, Gregory J. (Greg) Gluchowski Jr.
President Hand Tools and Pneumatic Products, Kyle Dancho
VP Business Development Engineered Fastening Solutions, Martin Schnurr
COO and CFO Convergent Security, Brian Kaner
President CSS North America and UK Direct, Tony Byerly
CIO Convergent Security, Donald Young
Director, George W. Buckley, age 65
Director, Robert B. (Bob) Coutts, age 62
Director, Marianne Miller Parrs, age 68
President CEO and Director, John F. Lundgren, age 60
Director, Robert L. (Bob) Ryan, age 67
Director, John G. Breen, age 77
Director, Manuel A. (Manny) Fernandez, age 66
Director, Benjamin H. (Ben) Griswold IV, age 72
Director, Patrick D. (Pat) Campbell, age 59
Director, Carlos M. Cardoso, age 53
Director, Lawrence A. (Larry) Zimmerman, age 69
Auditors: Ernst&YoungLLP

LOCATIONS

HQ: Stanley Black & Decker Inc.
1000 Stanley Dr., New Britain CT 06053
Phone: 860-225-5111 **Fax:** 860-827-3895
Web: www.stanleyblackanddecker.com

2011 Sales

	$ mil.	% of total
US	5,240	51
Canada	655	6
Other Americas	837	8
France	706	7
Other Europe	2,208	21
Asia	727	7
Total	**10,376**	**100**

PRODUCTS/OPERATIONS

2011 Sales

	$ mil.	% of total
Construction & D-I-Y	5,236	51
Security	2,638	25
Industrial	2,501	24
Total	**10,376**	**100**

Selected Brand Names

Atro
Black & Decker
Blackhawk
Bostitch
DEWALT
Dustbuster
Facom
FatMax
Jensen
Kwikset
LaBounty
Mac Tools
Powerlock
Pfister
Proto
Scumbuster
Stanley
Vidmar
Virax
ZAG

COMPETITORS

ASSA ABLOY
Atlas Copco
Beam
Bosch
Cooper Industries
Danaher
Eastern Company
Eaton
Electrolux
Emerson Electric
Energizer Holdings
Hitachi
Illinois Tool Works
Ingersoll-Rand
Jacuzzi Brands
Klein Tools
Kohler
Makita
Masco
Panasonic Corp
Robert Bosch
Robert Bosch LLC
Royal Appliance
Sandvik
Snap-on
Textron
Toro Company
Trane Inc.

HISTORICAL FINANCIALS

Company Type: Public

Income Statement FYE: December 31

	REVENUE ($ mil.)	NET INCOME ($ mil.)	NET PROFIT MARGIN	EMPLOYEES
12/11*	10,376	674	6.5%	44,700
01/11	8,409	198	2.4%	36,700
01/10	3,737	224	6.0%	16,700
01/09	4,426	313	7.1%	18,225
12/07	4,483	336	7.5%	18,400
Annual Growth	23.3%	19.0%	—	24.8%

*Fiscal year change

2011 Year-End Financials

Debt ratio: 21.65%
Return on equity: 9.63%
Cash ($ mil.): 906
Current ratio: 132.25
Long-term debt ($ mil.): 2,925
No. of shares (mil.): 169
Dividends
Yield: —
Payout: 41.31%
Market value ($ mil.): 11,428

	STOCK PRICE ($) FY Close	P/E High	P/E Low	PER SHARE ($) Earnings	Dividends	Book Value
12/11*	67.60	19	12	3.97	0.00	41.43
01/11	66.87	50	37	1.32	0.00	42.18
01/10	51.51	19	8	2.79	0.00	24.68
01/09	35.47	13	6	3.92	0.00	21.40
12/07	48.39	16	12	4.00	0.00	21.50
Annual Growth	8.7%	—	—	(0.2%)	—	17.8%

*Fiscal year change

Staples Inc

Staples is clipping along as the #1 office supply superstore operator in the US and as a worldwide leader in the office category. It sells office products furniture computers and other supplies through some 2300 Staples stores in the Americas Europe Asia and Australia. (About 1915 of its stores are located in North America.) In addition to its retail outlets Staples sells office products via the Internet and through its catalog and direct sales operations including subsidiary Quill Corp. Staples also provides document management and copying services at its stores and some 25 stand-alone copy and print shops. After expanding in Europe Staples is growing in Asia and South America.

HISTORY

A veteran of the supermarket industry (and the man who developed the idea for generic food) Thomas Stemberg was fired from his executive position with Connecticut supermarket Edwards-Finast in 1985. Stemberg began searching for a niche retail market —he found one in office supplies which he estimated at $100 billion.

While large companies could buy in bulk from dealers smaller businesses were served by mom-and-pop office supply stores that charged much higher prices. Applying the supermarket model to office supply Stemberg founded Staples in late 1985 with Leo Kahn a former competitor in the supermarket business. With money from Kahn and venture capital firms Staples opened its first store in a Boston suburb the next year.

In 1987 the retailer moved into the New York City area and continued to expand throughout the Northeast. By early 1989 —the year it went public —it had 23 stores. The company introduced a line of low-priced private-label products in 1989.

Aggressive expansion began the following year when Staples opened three stores in Southern California and introduced two new concepts: Staples Direct (delivery operations for midsized businesses) and Staples Express (downtown stores offering smaller merchandise selections). International growth included buying a stake in Canada's Business Depot (1991) and 48% of MAXI-Papier a European office supply store chain (1992). It also paired up with Kingfisher to establish stores in the UK (Kingfisher sold its interest to Staples in 1996).

Additional acquisitions gave Staples more than 200 stores by the end of 1993. The next year Staples entered Arizona Virginia and Kentucky (by acquiring selected Office America stores); acquired the rest of Canada's Business Depot; and began expanding into the contract stationer business. It started Staples Business Advantage a regional stationer in 1995. The company agreed to buy Office Depot its biggest rival in 1996 but the FTC rejected the $4.3 billion deal on antitrust grounds.

Staples continued opening new stores and adding operations. It launched Staples.com its Internet sales operation in 1998. Acquisitions included the privately held Quill (to expand its direct-sales business 1998) and Claricom Holdings (telecommunications services to small businesses renamed Staples Communications 1999; sold 2001). Also in 1999 Staples invested in Register.com (a domain name registration service) and Point.com (a wireless phone retailer) and it began opening small airport stores. In addition the company continued its international expansion that year introducing its Quill catalog business in the UK and buying three European office supply companies (which added about 40 stores extending the company's presence in Germany and moving it into the Netherlands and Portugal).

In early 2001 the company shelved plans to take its Staples.com stock public saying it would convert Staples.com to its own stock. Also that year it merged its catalog and Staples.com operations into Staples Business Delivery. During 2002 Staples acquired Medical Arts Press (specialized medical software and forms to medical providers) and the mail-order business of Guilbert a subsidiary of French retailer PPR (formerly Pinault-Printempts-Redoute); the $815 million Guilbert deal provided entree for Staples in France Italy Spain and Belgium. (Office Depot bought Guilbert's retail operation the following year.) Company veteran Ron Sargent took over as CEO that same year.

The company continued to expand its international operations through acquisitions in 2004 buying Globus Office World (UK) Pressel Versand International (Austria) and Malling Beck (Denmark). Staples also expanded into China that year through a joint venture with Chinese office supply company OA365. CEO Sargent took on the added title of chairman when Stemberg resigned in 2005.

A 2006 joint venture with UB Office Systems brought the company into the Taiwanese market.

In 2007 Staples entered China and India through partnerships in both countries. In late 2007 the company reached a settlement in a California class-action lawsuit brought by store managers seeking overtime pay dating back to 1995. Staples agreed to pay $38 million. Again in early 2009 the firm was ordered to pay almost $2.5 million to 343 plaintiffs in a case brought under the Fair Labor Standards Act. A federal court jury ruled that Staples violated the law by classifying employees as exempt and failing to pay them overtime.

In July 2008 Staples acquired Netherlands-based business supply wholesaler Corporate Express NV in a deal valued at about $2.7 billion. The acquisition included about 60 stores in Europe and greatly expanded Staples' reach.

In 2010 Staples gained full control of Corporate Express Australia after bidding A$390 million for the roughly 40% it didn't already own. Adding Finland to its domain Staples acquired Oy Lindell with seven company-owned and two franchised office supply stores in Finland.

EXECUTIVES

Vice Chairman, John J. Mahoney, age 60, $673,400 total compensation
Chairman & CEO, Ronald L. (Ron) Sargent, age 56, $1,112,000 total compensation
CFO, Christine T. Komola, age 44
President & COO, Michael A. (Mike) Miles Jr., age 50, $673,400 total compensation
SVP and General Counsel, Cynthia L. Pevehouse, age 54
President North American Delivery, Joseph G. (Joe) Doody, age 60, $522,400 total compensation
EVP Human Resources, Shira D. Goodman, age 51
President US Stores, Demos Parneros, age 49, $522,400 total compensation
President Staples Europe, Rob Vale
President Staples Business Depot, Steven E. Matyas
EVP Staples Advantage, Neil E. Ringel
Director Technology and Services European Retail, Andrew Gabriel
Managing Director UK Retail and Direct, Amee Chande
VP Retail Marketing, Christine Mallon
Director Information Services, Neelima Sharma
CIO, Christine (Chris) Putur
Director, Basil L. Anderson, age 65
Director, Carol M. Meyrowitz, age 58
Vice Chairman, John J. Mahoney, age 60
Director, Robert E. (Bob) Sulentic, age 55
Director, Rowland T. (Row) Moriarty, age 65
Director, Arthur M. Blank, age 69
Director, Mary E. (Betsy) Burton, age 60
Director, Robert C. (Bob) Nakasone, age 64
Director, Paul F. Walsh, age 62
Director, Justin King, age 50
Director, Elizabeth A. Smith, age 48
Director, Vijay Vishwanath, age 52
Director, Drew G. Faust
Auditors: Ernst&YoungLLP

LOCATIONS

HQ: Staples Inc.
500 Staples Dr., Framingham MA 01702
Phone: 508-253-5000 **Fax:** 508-253-8989
Web: www.staples.com

2012 Stores

	No.
North	1,917
International	378
Total	**2,295**

2012 Sales

	$ mil.	% of total
US	16,643	67
Canada	3,073	12
Other countries	5,305	21
Total	**25,022**	**100**

2012 Locations

	No.
US	
California	221
New	142
Florida	101
Pennsylvania	95
New	89
Massachusetts	76
Ohio	63
Texas	60
Illinois	54
North	50
Virginia	45
Maryland	44
Arizona	43
Michigan	42
Connecticut	39
Georgia	39
Washington	31
Indiana	30
New	23
Tennessee	23
Colorado	20
Oregon	21
South	21
Oklahoma	18
Kentucky	17
Iowa	16
Utah	14
Alabama	12
Maine	12
Missouri	11
New	11
Wisconsin	11
Rhode	10
Arkansas	8
Idaho	8
Montana	8
Delaware	7
Minnesota	7
Nevada	7
Vermont	7
West	6
Nebraska	5
Wyoming	4
Kansas	4
Washington	2
Mississippi	2
North	2
Louisiana	1
South	1
Canada	334
UK	137
Germany	62
The	46
Portugal	35
China	28
Norway	21
Australia	17
Sweden	17
Finland	7
Belgium	6
Argentina	2
Total	**2,295**

PRODUCTS/OPERATIONS

2012 Sales

	$ mil.	% of total
North American delivery	10,056	40
North American retail	9,660	39
International	5,305	21
Total	**25,022**	**100**

2012 Sales

	% of total
Office	44
Office machines & related	30
Computers & related	15
Services	6
Office	5
Total	**100**

Selected Operations

Corporate Express (US Europe office products wholesale)
Office Centre (stores The Netherlands)
Quill Corporation (US catalog)
Staples (stores North America and Europe)
Staples Business Advantage (contract stationers for midsized to large businesses)
Staples Business Delivery
Staples Express (smaller-store format)
Staples National Advantage (contract stationers for large multiregional businesses)
Staples The Office Superstore (stores Canada)
Staples.com (Internet shopping site)

COMPETITORS

Amazon.com
Apple Inc.
Best Buy
BJ' s Wholesale Club
CDW
Costco Wholesale
Dell
FedEx Office
Fry' s Electronics
Hewlett-Packard
Insight Enterprises
Lyreco
Mail Boxes Etc.
Office Depot
OfficeMax
RadioShack
Ricoh USA
S.P. Richards
Systemax
Target Corporation
Tesco
Unisource
United Stationers
Wal-Mart

HISTORICAL FINANCIALS

Company Type: Public

Income Statement

FYE: January 28

	REVENUE ($ mil.)	NET INCOME ($ mil.)	NET PROFIT MARGIN	EMPLOYEES
01/12	25,022	984	3.9%	87,782
01/11	24,545	881	3.6%	89,019
01/10	24,275	738	3.0%	91,095
01/09*	23,083	805	3.5%	91,125
02/08	19,372	995	5.1%	75,578
Annual Growth	6.6%	(0.3%)	—	3.8%

*Fiscal year change

2012 Year-End Financials

Debt ratio: 15.18%
Return on equity: 14.04%
Cash ($ mil.): 1,264
Current ratio: 154.40
Long-term debt ($ mil.): 1,599

No. of shares (mil.): 695
Dividends
Yield: —
Payout: 28.57%
Market value ($ mil.): 11,139

	STOCK PRICE ($) FY Close	P/E High/Low		PER SHARE ($) Earnings	Dividends	Book Value
01/12	16.01	16	9	1.40	0.00	10.08
01/11	22.32	21	14	1.21	0.00	9.63
01/10	23.46	24	14	1.02	0.00	9.29
01/09*	15.94	23	12	1.13	0.00	7.78
02/08	23.93	20	14	1.38	0.00	8.12
Annual Growth	(9.6%)	—	—	0.4%	—	5.6%

*Fiscal year change

Starbucks Corp.

Wake up and smell the coffee —Starbucks is everywhere. The world's #1 specialty coffee retailer Starbucks has more than 17000 coffee shops in about 40 countries. The outlets offer coffee drinks and food items as well as roasted beans coffee accessories and teas. Starbucks operates more than 9000 of its shops which are located in about 10 countries (mostly in the US) while licensees and franchisees operate almost 8000 units worldwide (primarily in shopping centers and airports). The company also owns the Seattle's Best Coffee and Torrefazione Italia coffee brands. In addition Starbucks markets its coffee through grocery stores and licenses its brand for other food and beverage products.

HISTORY

Starbucks was founded in 1971 in Seattle by coffee aficionados Gordon Bowker Jerry Baldwin and Ziv Siegl who named the company for the coffee-loving first mate in Moby Dick and created its famous two-tailed siren logo. They aimed to sell the finest-quality whole bean and ground coffees. By 1982 Starbucks had five retail stores and was selling coffee to restaurants and espresso stands in Seattle. That year Howard Schultz joined Starbucks to manage retail sales and marketing. In 1983 Schultz traveled to Italy and was struck by the popularity of coffee bars. He convinced Starbucks' owners to open a downtown Seattle coffee bar in 1984. It was a success; Schultz left the company the following year to open his own coffee bar Il Giornale which served Starbucks coffee.

Frustrated by its inability to control quality Starbucks sold off its wholesale business in 1987. Later that year Il Giornale acquired Starbucks' retail operations for $4 million. (Starbucks' founders held on to their other coffee business Peet's Coffee & Tea.) Il Giornale changed its name to Starbucks Corporation prepared to expand nationally and opened locations in Chicago and Vancouver. In 1988 the company published its first mail-order catalog.

Starbucks lost money in the late 1980s as it focused on expansion (it tripled its number of stores to 55 between 1987 and 1989). Schultz brought in experienced managers to run Starbucks' stores. In 1991 it became the nation's first privately owned company to offer stock options to all employees.

In 1992 Starbucks went public and set up shops in Nordstrom's department stores. The following year it began operating cafes in Barnes & Noble bookstores. The company had nearly 275 locations by the end of 1993. Starbucks inked a deal in 1994 to provide coffee to ITT/Sheraton hotels (later acquired by Starwood Hotels & Resorts). The next year it capitalized on its popular in-house music selections by selling compact discs. Also in 1995 Starbucks joined with PepsiCo to develop a bottled coffee drink and agreed to produce a line of premium coffee ice cream with Dreyer's.

Starbucks expanded into Japan and Singapore in 1996. Also that year the company created Caffe Starbucks an online store located on AOL's marketplace. In 1997 Starbucks began testing sales of whole-bean and ground coffees in Chicago supermarkets.

In 1998 Starbucks expanded into the UK when it acquired that country's Seattle Coffee Company chain (founded in 1995) for about $86 million and converted its stores into Starbucks locations. It also announced plans to sell coffee in supermarkets nationwide through an agreement with Kraft Foods. In 1999 Starbucks bought Tazo an Oregon-based tea company as well as music retailer Hear Music and opened its first store in China. Schultz toned down his Internet plans in late 1999 after investors and analysts voiced skepticism.

In 2000 Schultz ceded the CEO post to president Orin Smith remaining chairman but focusing primarily on the company's global strategy. Starbucks jumpstarted its worldwide expansion the next year opening about 1100 stores worldwide including locations in a handful of new European countries such as Austria and Switzerland. It also spun off its Japanese operations as a public company. The following year the company opened its first shop in Spain and went on to open Starbucks locations in Greece and Germany. Later in 2002 it announced large-scale expansion plans in Mexico and Latin America.

The next year Starbucks acquired Seattle Coffee Company (and its Seattle's Best Coffee brand) from AFC Enterprises for $72 million. The deal gave Starbucks an additional 150 coffee shops (as if it needed them) but more importantly it gave the coffee giant the Seattle's Best Coffee brand and wholesale coffee business. It also got something new out of the deal: franchised locations.

Starbucks was one of the first national retailers to jump on the Wi-Fi bandwagon teaming with Hewlett-Packard and Deutsche Telekom's T-Mobile unit to offer high-speed wireless Internet access at 1200 of its locations in the US London and Berlin. In 2004 Starbucks and Hewlett-Packard unveiled their Hear Music service which allows Starbucks customers to create custom music CDs in some locations. It later premiered the Hear Music channel on XM Satellite Radio (later SIRIUS XM Radio) and launched a new Hear Music CD-burning media bar (co-developed with HP) in selected stores.

In 2005 the company began offering a hot chocolate in its US and Canada markets and in conjunction with Jim Beam Brands (now Beam) it introduced Starbucks Coffee Liqueur and Starbucks Cream Liqueur. That year Starbucks signed agreements with Suntory in Japan and Uni-President in Taiwan to sell its ready-to-drink coffees in those countries. Additionally Smith retired as president and CEO in 2005; he was replaced by Starbucks' North American president Jim Donald.

The company acquired full ownership of joint ventures Coffee Partners Hawaii and Cafe del Caribe (Puerto Rican outlets) in 2006. While Starbucks continued to dominate the coffee business traffic at its stores began to decline in 2007. The company brought Schultz back as CEO in 2008 replacing Donald.

Starbucks acquired fruit and vegetable juice maker Evolution Fresh in 2011 for $30 million in cash.

EXECUTIVES

Chairman President and CEO, Howard D. Schultz, age 59, $643,954 total compensation
SVP Northeast Division, James (Jim) McDermet
Starbucks Coffee Japan, Yuji Tsunoda
SVP Marketing, Terry Davenport, age 55
SVP Procurement, Jay Austin
SVP Partner Resources U.S., Marissa Andrada
EVP CFO and Chief Administrative Officer, Troy Alstead, age 49, $430,385 total compensation
President Channel Development and President Seattle's Best Coffee, Jeff Hansberry, age 47
SVP Culture and Leadership Development, Dave Olsen
Chief Digital Officer, Adam B. Brotman
SVP Coffee, Willard (Dub) Hay
SVP; President Canada and Latin America, Colin Moore
SVP Global Development EMEA, Mark Wesley
President Americas, Clifford (Cliff) Burrows, age 53, $595,000 total compensation
EVP Global Supply Chain Operations, Peter D. Gibbons, age 51
President Europe Middle East and Africa, Michelle Gass, age 44
President China and Asia Pacific, John Culver, age 51
SVP; President Starbucks Coffee Asia Pacific, Jinlong Wang, age 54
SVP and Deputy General Counsel, Michael Fink
SVP; Chief Retail Officer Starbucks Coffee Japan, Barbara Le Marrec
SVP Operations Starbucks Coffee International, Cosimo LaPorta
SVP and Chief Marketing Officer Seattle's Best Coffee, Chris Bruzzo, age 42
Chief Creative Officer; President Global Development and Evolution Fresh Retail, Arthur Rubinfeld, age 58, $450,000 total compensation
SVP; General Manager Starbucks Licensed Stores, Chris Carr
EVP General Counsel and Secretary, Lucy Lee Helm
SVP Finance International, Charles Jemley
SVP U.S. Store Development Global Strategy and Support Services, Michael Malanga
VP Corporate Social Responsibility, Ben Packard
EVP Public Affairs, Vivek Varma
Chief Community Officer, Blair H. Taylor
SVP Partner Resources International and Global Supply Chain Operations, James (Jim) Koster
SVP Finance U.S., Louis Jordan
Chief Marketing Officer and President Tazo Tea, Annie Young-Scrivner, age 43
EVP Partner Resources, Kalen Holmes
Partner Communications and Engagement, Valerie O'Neil
VP Assistant General Counsel and Assistant Secretary, Sophie Hager Hume
SVP Global Coffee, Craig Russell
SVP North Division, Clarice Turner
SVP South Division, Rossann Williams
VP Global Communications, Corey duBrowa
SVP Global Strategy, Mary Egan
CIO, Curtis Garner
SVP Global Logistics, Gregory Javor
SVP Supply Chain Operations, Stephen Lovejoy

SVP Global Development, William R. Transue
SVP Finance, Shannon Orr
Director, Javier G. Teruel, age 61
Director, Craig E. Weatherup, age 66
Director, William W. (Bill) Bradley, age 68
Director, Myron E. (Mike) Ullman III, age 65
Director, James G. (Jamie) Shennan Jr., age 70
Director, Mellody L. Hobson, age 43
Director, Sheryl K. Sandberg, age 42
Director, Olden Lee, age 70
Director, Kevin R. Johnson, age 51
Director, Joshua C. Ramo, age 43
Auditors: Deloitte&ToucheLLP

LOCATIONS

HQ: Starbucks Corporation
2401 Utah Ave. South, Seattle WA 98134
Phone: 206-447-1575 **Fax:** 206-447-0828
Web: www.starbucks.com

2011 Locations

US	10,787	
Total	**0**	**17,003**

PRODUCTS/OPERATIONS

2011 Sales

Company-operated retail	9,632	82
Foodservice & other	1,060	10

2011 Sales

	$ mil.	% of total
Beverage	7,217	62
Food	2,008	17
Whole beans and soluble coffees	1,451	12
Other	1,024	9
Total	**11,700**	**100**

2011 Locations

Company-owned	9,031	
Total	**0**	**17,003**

Selected Brands and Services

Starbucks Food Service
Ready-to-Drink Beverages
Packaged Coffee & Tea
Starbucks Ice Cream

Selected Mergers & Acquisitions

2012
Teavana Holdings Inc. ($620 million; Atlanta Georgia; tea & tea-related products retail)
Bay Bread (San Francisco; owner of La Boulange bakery)
2011
Evolution Fresh ($30 million; San Bernardino California; juices and smoothies)

COMPETITORS

Caffe Nero
Caribou Coffee
Cinnabon
Community Coffee
Dunkin
Einstein Noah Restaurant Group
Farmer Bros.
Green Mountain Coffee
Greggs
illy
Jamba
Lavazza
McDonald' s
Nestle
Panera Bread
The Coffee Bean
Tim Hortons
Whitbread

HISTORICAL FINANCIALS

Company Type: Public

Income Statement

FYE: September 30

	REVENUE ($ mil.)	NET INCOME ($ mil.)	NET PROFIT MARGIN	EMPLOYEES
09/12*	13,299	1,383	10.4%	160,000
10/11	11,700	1,245	10.6%	149,000
10/10	10,707	945	8.8%	137,000
09/09	9,774	390	4.0%	142,000
09/08	10,383	315	3.0%	176,000
Annual Growth	6.4%	44.7%	—	(2.4%)

*Fiscal year change

2012 Year-End Financials

Debt ratio: 6.69%
Return on equity: 27.09%
Cash ($ mil.): 1,188
Current ratio: 190.04
Long-term debt ($ mil.): 549
No. of shares (mil.): 749
Dividends
Yield: —
Payout: 37.99%
Market value ($ mil.): 37,997

	STOCK PRICE ($) FY Close	P/E High/Low		PER SHARE ($) Earnings	Dividends	Book Value
09/12*	50.71	34	20	1.79	0.00	6.82
10/11	37.29	25	15	1.62	0.00	5.89
10/10	25.94	22	15	1.24	0.00	4.95
09/09	19.83	39	14	0.52	0.00	4.10
09/08	14.96	62	32	0.43	0.00	3.39
Annual Growth	35.7%	—	—	42.8%	—	19.1%

*Fiscal year change

Starwood Hotels & Resorts Worldwide Inc

Starwood Hotels & Resorts Worldwide knows how to shine a light on hospitality. One of the world's largest hotel companies it has more than 1000 properties in about 100 countries. Starwood's hotel empire consists of upscale brands such as Sheraton and Westin. It operates about 100 luxury resorts and hotels through its St. Regis and Luxury Collection units while its 40 W Hotels offer ultra-modern style. Other brands include Four Points (value-oriented) Le Meridien (European-inspired) Aloft (select-service) and Element (extended stay). Starwood Vacation Ownership operates about 15 time-share resorts. Notable Starwood hotels include the St. Regis in New York and the Hotel Gritti Palace in Venice.

Financials

While the US economy continues to show signs of a recovery business travel is on the rise. As a result the company posted gains in revenue and net income in 2011 in response to a steady return in demand for hotel rooms. Starwood's revenue per available room a key indicator of business performance in the hotel industry increased by 7.4% in 2011 compared to 2010. The company also received an income tax benefit of approximately $92 million in 2011 primarily as a result of the favorable settlement of an IRS audit and tax benefits associated with asset sales.

Strategy

Starwood's strategy involves a reduction of its investment in owned real estate and an increased focus on its management and franchise operations a business model that is associated with lower costs. Since 2006 Starwood has sold 65 hotels for approximately $5.6 billion. Today the company owns leases or has a majority stake in about 60 properties. Some 500 of Starwood's hotels are owned and operated by franchisees while another 515 are managed on behalf of third parties or owned through joint ventures.

Development efforts include the newly constructed St. Regis Bal Harbour Resort the first luxury hotel to open in Miami in 2012. The Bal Harbour property also includes private residences for sale; in the fourth quarter of 2011 Bal Harbour closed on the sale of 36 units.

Geographic Reach

For international expansion Starwood is focused on Asia which it sees as a key emerging market. About 60% of its development pipeline consists of new properties in Asia/Pacific and 44% represents new growth in China specifically.

HISTORY

Barry Sternlicht earned his MBA from Harvard in 1986 and joined the fast track at JMB Realty bringing the company a UK real estate deal involving Randsworth Trust in 1989. He left two years later to start Starwood Capital Group with backers including the wealthy Burden and Ziff families. (JMB and its pension fund partners meanwhile lost their shirts when Randsworth went belly-up during the recession of the early 1990s.) In 1995 Starwood Capital joined Goldman Sachs and Nomura Securities to buy Westin Hotel (renamed Westin Hotels & Resorts) from Japanese construction firm Aoki. Founded in Washington State in 1930 Westin was acquired by UAL (now United Continental) in 1970 then Aoki bought it in 1988 during a boom in Japanese investments in US real estate.

Also in 1995 Sternlicht bought Hotel Investors Trust (a hotel REIT) and Hotel Investors Corp. (hotel management) two struggling firms whose chief attraction was their rare paired-share status allowing management company profits to flow through the REIT to investors exempt from corporate income tax. (The structure was banned in 1984 but four such entities were grandfathered in under the law.) The companies were renamed Starwood Lodging Trust and Starwood Lodging Corp. (together Starwood Lodging). Through more acquisitions Starwood amassed a collection of about 110 hotels by 1997.

Starwood's industry standing took a quantum leap in early 1998 when it acquired the 50% of the Westin hotel chain that Starwood Capital didn't already own and bought lodging giant ITT the former telephone industry conglomerate and owner of the Sheraton hotel chain. ITT –with more than 400 hotels and gaming properties (Desert Inn Caesars) –fought off a hostile takeover bid from Hilton Hotels (now Hilton Worldwide) and accepted Starwood Lodging's $14.6 billion offer. (Starwood Capital made $22 million in advising fees on the deal.) Later that year the firm changed its name to Starwood Hotels & Resorts bought four former Ritz-Carlton hotels and sold eight all-suite hotels to FelCor Suite Hotels (now FelCor Lodging Trust). Sternlicht then chose Walt Disney executive and Harvard classmate Richard Nanula to take the reins of Starwood's operating company. In late 1998 it launched W Hotels.

Before Congress closed the paired-share loophole for new acquisitions Starwood Hotels went on a shopping spree becoming a standard corporation in 1999. Nanula resigned that year apparently after repeated clashes with Sternlicht. The company bought time-share resort company Vistana –renamed Starwood Vacation Ownership (SVO) –and purchased the portion of European hotel operator Ciga (part of which Sheraton had acquired in 1994) that it didn't already own.

Gaming profits had begun to fall off in 1999 however as the Asian economic crisis stymied the flow of gambling-hungry tourists. The following year Starwood sold its Caesars unit to Park Place Entertainment for $3 billion and its Desert Inn hotel and casino to Mirage Resorts founder Steve Wynn for about $270 million. Tight economic conditions forced Starwood to cut costs and curtail discretionary spending. That year SVO began building new resorts in Arizona Colorado and Hawaii. Starwood saw its business begin to suffer following the September 11 2001 terrorist attacks which kept many potential travelers at home. As a result Starwood cut about 12000 jobs roughly 25% of its workforce.

To pay down its debt Starwood raised about $1.5 billion in capital by selling bonds (2002) and sold its Italian Ciga assets –including luxury hotels a golf club and other real estate interests –to Colony Capital (2003).

In 2004 Steven Heyer former president and COO of Coca-Cola was named CEO as Sternlicht began setting the stage for his retirement from the company. He stayed on for nearly another year as executive chairman however before leaving the company altogether.

The company's expansion efforts in 2005 included the acquisition of the Le Meridien brand for $225 million. (In a separate agreement Lehman Brothers and Starwood Capital Group by then an unaffiliated fund managed by Sternlicht jointly acquired the real estate properties.) In 2006 Starwood sold some 30 properties to Host Hotels & Resorts for about $4 billion. Heyer resigned from the company in 2007. Later that year Frits van Paasschen was named CEO.

Before the company's financials began improving in 2010 the company divested its Bliss spa and product business in order to focus on its core hospitality business. Starwood sold Bliss to spa company Steiner Leisure Limited in 2010 after consumer demand for luxury services fell during the weak economy in 2009 and 2008. Starwood raised some much-needed cash from the deal which was worth about $100 million. It continued to offer Bliss spas and amenities however in W Hotels and St. Regis Hotels.

EXECUTIVES

SVP and Corporate Controller, Alan M. Schnaid
President Latin America, Osvaldo V. Librizzi
Co-President Starwood Americas, Sergio D. Rivera, age 50
Chief Administrative Officer General Counsel and Secretary, Kenneth S. (Ken) Siegel, age 56, $615,039 total compensation
Chairman and President & CEO First Industrial Realty Trust Inc., Bruce W. Duncan, age 60, $479,167 total compensation
President Europe Africa and Middle East Division, Roeland Vos
SVP Brand Management; SVP Global Brand Management Sheraton Hotels & Resorts, Hoyt H. Harper II
President CEO and Director, Frits D. van Paasschen, age 51, $1,000,000 total compensation
Chairman and President Asia Pacific, Miguel Ko
Vice Chairman and CFO, Vasant M. Prabhu, age 52, $640,658 total compensation
EVP and Chief Brand Officer, Phil P. McAveety, age 45, $376,894 total compensation
President Global Development, Simon M. Turner, age 50, $625,000 total compensation
EVP and Chief Human Resources Officer, Jeffrey M. (Jeff) Cava, age 60
VP and Global Brand Leader Westin & Resorts, Brian Povinelli
SVP Global Sales, Christie Hicks
SVP Owner Relations and Franchise, Lynne Dougherty
President Hotel Group, Matthew E. (Matt) Avril, age 51, $725,000 total compensation
Senior Director Consumer Affairs, Helen Horsham-Bertels
President North America Division, Denise M. Coll
SVP Specialty Select Brands Aloft Element and Four Points by Sheraton, Brian McGuiness
SVP Distribution Loyalty and Partnership Marketing, Mark R. Vondrasek, age 43
Global Brand Leader W Hotels Worldwide and Le Meridien, Vincent Gillet
SVP & CIO, Roger Berry
EVP and Chief Brand Officer, Philip P. McAveety
Director, Eric Hippeau, age 60
Director, Clayton C. Daley Jr., age 60
Director, Thomas E. Clarke, age 60
Director, Thomas O. (Tom) Ryder, age 67
Director, Adam M. Aron, age 58
President CEO and Director, Frits D. van Paasschen, age 51
Director, Kneeland C. Youngblood, age 56
Director, Stephen R. Quazzo, age 52
Director, Charlene Barshefsky, age 61
Director, Lizanne Galbreath, age 54
Auditors: Ernst&YoungLLP

LOCATIONS

HQ: Starwood Hotels & Resorts Worldwide Inc.
One StarPoint, Stamford CT 06902
Phone: 203-964-6000 **Fax:** 713-207-3169
Web: www.centerpointenergy.com

2011 Sales

	$ mil.	% of total
US	3,561	63
International	2,063	37
Total	**5,624**	**100**

PRODUCTS/OPERATIONS

2011 Sales

	$ mil.	% of total
Owned leased & consolidated joint venture hotels	1,768	31
Management fees franchise fees & other income	814	14
Vacation ownership & residential	703	13
Other revenues from managed & franchise properties	2,339	42
Total	**5,624**	**100**

2011 Sales

	$ mil.	% of total
Hotel	4,756	85
Vacation ownership & residential	868	15
Total	**5,624**	**100**

Selected Brands

Aloft
Element
Four Points by Sheraton
Luxury Collection
Le Meridien
Sheraton
Westin

COMPETITORS

Accor
Bluegreen
Loews Hotels
LXR Luxury Resorts
Carlson Hotels
Diamond Resorts
Fairmont Raffles
Four Seasons Hotels
Hilton Worldwide
Hyatt
InterContinental Hotels
Marriott
Millennium & Copthorne Hotels
Omni Hotels
Silverleaf Resorts
Wyndham Worldwide

HISTORICAL FINANCIALS

Company Type: Public

Income Statement FYE: December 31

	REVENUE ($ mil.)	NET INCOME ($ mil.)	NET PROFIT MARGIN	EMPLOYEES
12/11	5,624	489	8.7%	154,000
12/10	5,071	477	9.4%	145,000
12/09	4,712	73	1.5%	145,000
12/08	5,907	329	5.6%	145,000
12/07	6,153	542	8.8%	155,000
Annual Growth	(2.2%)	(2.5%)	—	(0.2%)

2011 Year-End Financials

Debt ratio: 28.55%
Return on equity: 16.55%
Cash ($ mil.): 454
Current ratio: 127.21
Long-term debt ($ mil.): 2,596
No. of shares (mil.): 195
Dividends
Yield: —
Payout: 19.92%
Market value ($ mil.): 9,398

	STOCK PRICE ($) FY Close	P/E High/Low		PER SHARE ($) Earnings	Dividends	Book Value
12/11	47.97	25	14	2.51	0.00	15.08
12/10	60.78	24	13	2.51	0.30	12.81
12/09	36.57	91	23	0.41	0.20	9.77
12/08	17.90	31	6	1.77	0.90	8.87
12/07	44.03	28	16	2.57	0.90	10.87
Annual Growth	2.2%	—	—	(0.6%)	—	8.5%

State Auto Financial Corp.

Thanks to State Auto Financial the state of auto insurance is healthy in the Midwest. The company sells property/casualty policies through several subsidiaries writing personal commercial and specialty coverage including automobile homeowners multi-peril and workers' compensation insurance. It also participates in an insurance pool through its parent company State Auto Mutual Insurance which owns more than 60% of State Auto Financial and provides the offices for its headquarters. Subsidiary Stateco Financial Services manages the company's invested assets. State Auto Financial is the only part of State Auto Mutual that is publicly traded.

Operations

The company has four reportable segments: personal insurance business insurance specialty insurance and investment operations. The personal insurance segment provides primarily personal automobile and homeowners to the personal insurance market. The business insurance segment provides pcommercial automobile commercial multiperil fire and allied and general liability insurance covering small-to-medium sized commercial exposures in the business insurance market. The specialty insurance segment provides commercial coverages including workers' compensation that require specialized product underwriting claims handling or risk management services through a distribution channel of retail agents and wholesale brokers which may include program administrators and other specialty sources. The investment operations segment managed by Stateco provides investment services.

Geographic Reach

Through the mutual pool State Auto Financial and its sister companies known collectively as State Auto Group market products through independent insurance agencies in about 35 states. Ohio Kentucky and Texas are State Auto Financial's biggest markets accounting for almost 30% of its annual premiums. The company focuses its business insurance sales on small-to-medium-sized companies.

Financial Analysis

State Auto Financial's personal insurance products account for more than half of the company's revenues.

The company saw its revenues grow by 15% in 2011 thanks to an increase in premiums earned driven by the specialty insurance segment and by adding its RED unit to its pooling arrangement. It was also helped by an increase in net realized gain on investments driven by reducing equity holdings to manage risk parameters as well as by selling select securities in anticipation of cash transfers.

However State Auto Financial's net income plummeted by almost 700% in 2011 due to an increase in expenses. The company's 2011 net loss included a non-cash charge of $91.2 million related to a valuation allowance against its net deferred tax asset.

Strategy

While its revenues have grown steadily with just personal and standard commercial products State Auto Financial has made moves ot diversify its products. In 2010 the company jumped into writing new commercial specialty business through its RED subsidiary. It gained RED when it acquired Rockhill Holding in 2009. Writing new business through the RED subsidiary has allowed State Auto Financial to serve the alternative risk transfer market with such specialty business products as general liability auto liability workers' compensation property inland marine auto physical damage and miscellaneous professional liability.

To better focus on its existing standard auto business State Auto Financial decided to exit the non-standard auto insurance business. It sold its State Auto National business to Hallmark Financial Services for $14 million at the close of 2010.

EXECUTIVES

President and CEO BroadStreet Capital Partners, Richard L. Miley, age 55

VP and Investment Officer, James E. (Jim) Duemey

VP and Director Corporate Development, Cathy B. Miley, age 62, $183,000 total compensation

VP and Director Corporate Enterprise Risk Management, Steven R. Hazelbaker, age 56, $198,846 total compensation

Chairman President and CEO, Robert P. (Bob) Restrepo Jr., age 61, $753,462 total compensation

VP and Director Sales, John M. Petrucci

Chief Risk Officer, Cynthia A. Powell, age 51, $189,846 total compensation

VP and Director Business Insurance, Paul E. Nordman

VP and CFO, Steven E. English, age 51, $354,231 total compensation

VP and Director Operation Effectiveness, Lyle D. Rhodebeck, age 54

VP and Manager Data Center Construction Program, Terrence P. Higerd

VP and Director Information Technology, Doug E. Allen

VP and Director Internal Audit, David W. Dalton

VP Secretary and General Counsel, James A. (Jay) Yano, age 60, $306,923 total compensation

Director Media Relations, Kyle Anderson

VP Standard Lines, Joel E. Brown

VP and Chief Security and Continuity Plan Officer, Nancy D. Edwards

VP and Director Middle Market Operations, Larry D. Williams

SVP and Chief Sales Officer, Clyde H. Fitch Jr., age 61, $330,000 total compensation

VP and Director Budgeting and Planning, Jean Reynolds

VP and Director Strategy and Organization Effectiveness, Lorraine M. (Lori) Siegworth, age 44, $211,538 total compensation

VP and Director Specialty Lines, Jessica E. Buss

VP Personal Insurance Underwriting, Rick L. Holbein

VP and Dean State Auto University, Nelson McCants

VP and Chief Actuarial Officer, Matthew S. Mrozek

VP and Chief Claims Officer, Stephen P. Hunckler

Assistant VP and Director Treasury and Finance, Larry Adeleye

VP State Auto Financial State Automobile Mutual Insurance State Auto Property and Casualty Insurance, Timothy G. (Tim) Reik

Director, David R. Meuse, age 67

Director, David J. D'Antoni, age 67

Director, Thomas E. (Tom) Markert, age 54

Director, Eileen A. Mallesch, age 56

Auditors: Ernst&YoungLLP

LOCATIONS

HQ: State Auto Financial Corporation
518 E. Broad St., Columbus OH 43215-3976
Phone: 614-464-5000 **Fax:** 614-464-5325
Web: www.stateauto.com

2011 Direct Written Premiums

	% of total
Ohio	13
Texas	8
Kentucky	8
Indiana	6
Tennessee	5
Minnesota	5
Pennsylvania	4
Maryland	4
Illinois	3
Arkansas	3
West	3
Michigan	3
Other	35
Total	**100**

PRODUCTS/OPERATIONS

2011 Revenues

	$ mil.	% of total
Insurance premiums		
Personal insurance	800	52
Business insurance	379	24
Specialty insurance	249	16
Investment income & other	124	8
Total	**1,553**	**100**

COMPETITORS

AIG
Allstate
American Family
Kentucky Employers' Mutual
Nationwide
Insurance
American Southern
COUNTRY Financial
GEICO
GMAC Insurance
Progressive Corporation
State Farm
The Hartford
Travelers Companies

HISTORICAL FINANCIALS

Company Type: Public

Income Statement FYE: December 31

	ASSETS ($ mil.)	NET INCOME ($ mil.)	INCOME AS % OF ASSETS	EMPLOYEES
12/11	2,790	(146)	—	2,451
12/10	2,722	24	0.9%	2,483
12/09	2,564	10	0.4%	2,226
12/08	2,443	(31)	—	2,165
12/07	2,337	119	5.1%	2,185
Annual Growth	4.5%	—	—	2.9%

2011 Year-End Financials

Debt ratio: 4.17%
Return on equity: (-19.36)%
Cash ($ mil.): 356
Current ratio: —
Long-term debt ($ mil.): 116
No. of shares (mil.): 40
Dividends
Yield: —
Payout: —
Market value ($ mil.): 548

	STOCK PRICE ($) FY Close	P/E High/Low		PER SHARE ($) Earnings	Dividends	Book Value
12/11	13.59	—		(3.65)	0.00	18.82
12/10	17.42	33	22	0.62	0.60	21.24
12/09	18.50	116	56	0.26	0.60	21.34
12/08	30.06	—	—	(0.78)	0.60	19.27
12/07	26.30	12	8	2.86	0.50	23.10
Annual Growth	(15.2%)	—	—	—	—	(5.0%)

State Street Corp.

Ol' Blue Eyes sang about the State Street (that great street) in Chicago but investors may find Boston's State Street more melodious. Through its flagship State Street Bank and other subsidiaries the company provides investment management and servicing trading and research services. Its activities include trust and custody fund accounting foreign exchange shareholder services and other administrative services for institutional clients such as mutual and other investment funds pension plans insurance companies foundations endowments and investment managers. State Street has more than $21 trillion of assets under custody and administration in addition to some $2 trillion under management.

Other subsidiaries of State Street include asset manager State Street Global Advisors and State Street Alternative Investment Solutions. Boston Financial Data Services a joint venture with DST Systems provides shareholder services to mutual funds and other clients.

At the vanguard of financial services technology State Street banks on its computerized analytical and organizational tools to woo and retain clients and continues to enhance its systems. Among its offerings are foreign exchange trading platform FX Connect and Global Link which provides market research and portfolio analysis.

State Street which has operations in more than two dozen countries earns more than a third of its revenue outside of the US and has been investing in international growth. It expanded its global fund administration and alternative asset servicing capabilities in 2010 when it acquired Channel Islands-based Mourant International Finance Administration. Also that year the company bought the securities services business of Italian bank Intesa Sanpaolo. It acquired Bank of Ireland Asset Management and Swiss analytics firm Complementa in 2011 further increasing its presence in markets outside the US.

At home in the States the company acquired Boston-based agency brokerage firm Pulse Trading. The deal boosted State Street's electronic trading capabilities including block crossing and blotter-scraping for its transition management business. In 2012 the company arranged to buy hedge fund administrator Goldman Sachs Administration Services which has some $200 billion in assets from Goldman Sachs for $550 million.

After reporting more than $2 billion in losses in 2009 (in part due to lower equity market valuations and lending volumes plus an increase in bankruptcies) State Street returned to profitability in 2010. The company's acquisitions that year coupled with improved equity markets helped to boost transaction volumes and revenue. These same factors helped contribute to growth in 2011 too as revenues climbed some 7% to $10.3 billion. The company's assets under custody have also been climbing as the company adds new clients and new products like exchange-traded funds (ETFs). Cost-cutting initiatives including layoffs have helped State Street's bottom line as well.

But the company is not quite out of the woods yet as net losses from investment securities have been a drag on its earnings. In late 2010 State Street bit the bullet and sold some $11 billion in bad assets primarily mortgage-backed securities acquired during the frenzy for subprime lending at a $344 million loss.

HISTORY

The US's chaotic postrevolutionary era gave birth to the first ancestor of State Street Corporation. Union Bank was founded in 1792 by Boston businessmen breaking the eight-year monopoly held on Boston banking by Massachusetts Bank (a forerunner of FleetBoston which was acquired by Bank of America in 2004). Governor John Hancock's distinctive signature graced Union's charter; the bank set up shop at 40 State Street near the port and enjoyed the glory days of New England's shipping trade.

In the mid-19th century Boston's financial eminence faded as New York flexed its economic muscle. In 1865 the bank was nationally chartered and changed its name to National Union Bank of Boston. It got a new neighbor in 1891: Directors of Third National Bank set up State Street Deposit & Trust to engage in the newfangled business of trusts.

In 1925 National Union Bank merged with State Street and inherited its custodial business. The bank grew through the 1950s; acquisitions included the Second National Bank and the Rockland-Atlas National Bank.

In 1970 State Street converted to a holding company –the State Street Boston Financial Corp. (State Street Boston Corp. as of 1977). The company also went international that decade opening an office in Munich Germany.

Soaring inflation and the recession of the 1970s forced the company to radically rethink its mission. The 1974 passage of the Employee Retirement Income Security Act changed the laws governing the management of pension funds and created an opportunity. State Street was one of the first banks to move aggressively into high-tech information processing and affiliate Boston Financial Data Services began servicing pension assets in 1974.

Encouraged by that success in 1975 new CEO William Edgerly (who served until 1992) steered State Street away from branch banking and into investments trusts and securities processing. An early achievement was designing PepsiCo's retirement plan. Fee-based sales approached 50% of revenues; the company could now quit focusing on lending. In the 1980s and 1990s the company built its administration and investment management businesses overseas and moved into software.

Evolving in the late 1990s State Street left noncore businesses but expanded globally. In 1997 it formed European Direct Capital Management to invest in eastern and central Europe. State Street Global Advisors opened a London office in 1998 to serve wealthy individuals outside the US.

The company sold its commercial banking business to Royal Bank of Scotland in 1999 signaling an exit from that business and narrowing State Street's scope to the asset and investment management businesses. The company also bought Wachovia's custody and institutional trust business and teamed with Citigroup to sell 401(k) retirement products.

In 2000 State Street created FX Connect an electronic foreign exchange trading system. Also that year David Spina took over as CEO from the retiring Marshall Carter.

The firm bought Bel Air Investment Advisors and its broker/dealer affiliate Bel Air Securities in 2001 to cater to the ultrawealthy. In 2003 State Street sold its corporate trust business to U.S. Bancorp and its private asset management business to Charles Schwab's U.S. Trust. Spina retired in 2004; his protege Ron Logue stepped in as chairman and CEO.

In 2007 State Street added bulk by acquiring another Boston-based fund accounting and servicing provider Investors Financial Services. The company boosted its foreign exchange offerings with the acquisition of Currenex. The following year State Street and Citigroup sold their CitiStreet retirement and pension plan management joint venture to ING Groep for some $900 million.

The US Treasury invested some $2 billion in the company in 2008 as part of a broader bailout plan to restore confidence and increase liquidity. State Street was among eight other top banks that received a combined $250 billion; the company repaid the full amount within months.

In the distressed economic climate State Street's servicing and management revenues declined due to lower equity market valuations and lending volumes and an increase in bankruptcies. The company hit its nadir in 2009 when it reported more than $2 billion in losses.

EXECUTIVES

EVP and Chief Administrative Officer, David C. O'Leary, age 65
EVP; Chief Strategy Officer State Street Global Markets, Karen C. Keenan, age 42
EVP and CFO, Edward J. Resch, age 59, $700,000 total compensation
EVP and Global Head Alternative Investment Solutions, George E. Sullivan
EVP and Chief Investment Officer Global Cash Management State Street Global Advisors, Steven (Steve) Meier
President and CEO State Street Global Advisors, Scott F. Powers, age 52
Chairman President and CEO, Joseph L. (Jay) Hooley, age 55, $775,000 total compensation
EVP and Head Regulatory Industry and Government Affairs; President State Street International Holdings, Stefan M. Gavell
Vice Chairman and Head Europe and Asia-Pacific Global Services and Global Markets, Joseph C. Antonellis, age 57, $713,462 total compensation
EVP and General Manager Global Markets & Global Services (Asia Pacific) State Street Bank & Trust, Seck Wai Kwong
EVP Chief Innovation Officer and Technology Fellow, Madge M. Meyer
EVP and Head Global Operations Technology and Product Development, James S. Phalen, age 61, $550,000 total compensation
EVP Chief Legal Officer and Secretary, Jeffrey N. (Jeff) Carp, age 55, $550,000 total compensation
EVP Investment Services, Gunjan Kedia
EVP and Global Head Corporate Development and Global Relationship Management, John L. (Jack) Klinck Jr., age 48
EVP and Head Securities Finance; Chairman and President State Street Global Markets, Nicholas T. (Nick) Bonn
EVP and CIO, Christopher (Chris) Perretta
EVP and Director Community Affairs, George A. Russell Jr.
EVP; Head Global Sales and Marketing State Street Global Advisors, James (Jamie) Kase
EVP Corporate Finance, Maureen P. Corcoran
EVP; Chief Administrative Officer State Street Global Advisors, Marc P. Brown
EVP and Managing Director Corporate Advisory Services; Head of Multidimensional and Reporting and Analysis, James C. Caccivio Jr.
EVP and Head Global Services Sales and Business Development Europe Middle East and Africa, Timothy J. Caverly
EVP Global Realty and Global Procurement Services; President State Street Bank Realty, Donald E. (Don) Conover
EVP and Global Head Investment Manager Services, Jeff Conway
EVP and CTO; Chairman and General Manager State Street Zhejiang Technology, Albert J. (Jerry) Cristoforo
EVP and General Auditor, Jayne K. Donahue
EVP and COO Information Technology, Sharon E. Donovan Hart
EVP and Head Global Markets and Global Services Asia-Pacific, Peter O'Neill
EVP and Chief Human Resources and Citizenship Officer, Alison A. Quirk, age 49
EVP and Head Relationship Management and Client Strategy Alternative Investments Solutions, Gary E. Enos
EVP State Street Global Services' US Investor Services, Alan D. Greene
EVP and Head Global Operations, Robert Kaplan
EVP and Head Enterprise Risk Management, Nancy Loucks
EVP and Head Global Markets and Global Services, Michael F. (Mike) Rogers, age 54
EVP and Head Global Markets Europe and Investor Services UKMEA, Stephen Smit
EVP and Chief Investment Officer Multi Asset Class Solutions State Street Global Advisors, Alistair Lowe
EVP Treasurer and Head Global Treasury, David J. Gutschenritter, age 54
EVP Corporate Controller and Chief Accounting Officer, James J. Malerba, age 57

EVP State Street Corporation and State Street Bank and Trust; Managing Director State Street Bank Munich, Stefan Gmuer
EVP State Street Global Markets, Clifford M. (Cliff) Lewis
EVP; Head Global Program Office, Stephen J. (Steve) Reydel
EVP and Head Tax and Tax Advantaged Investments, Dennis E. Ross
EVP and Head European Offshore Domiciles, William Slattery
EVP and Head Global Markets? Sales and Trading and Research, Mark J. A. Snyder
EVP and Head Investor Services Technology, Brian J. Walsh
EVP and Head State Street Global Markets, David W. Puth, age 55
EVP General Counsel and Assistant Secretary, David C. Phelan, age 54
EVP, Michael J. Wilson
EVP, Tracy Atkinson
EVP and Manager Global Product Management, Patrick D. Centanni
EVP and Chief Administrative Officer Corporate Audit, Denise DeAmore
EVP and Chief Investment Officer Global Treasury, Paul J. Selian
EVP; Chief Risk Officer State Street Global Advisors, Jacques M. Longerstaey
EVP and Chief Marketing Officer, Hannah Grove
EVP and General Counsel State Street Global Advisors, Phillip S. Gillespie
SVP Investor Relations, S. Kelley MacDonald
EVP and Chief Risk Officer, Andrew Kuritzkes, age 51
Managing Director and Head Operations Kansas City, Tom Forrester
Global Head Sales Alternative Investment Solutions, Maria Cantillon
EVP; Chief Risk Officer State Street Global Markets, Robert (Bob) Baillargeon
EVP COO Investor Services Europe Middle East and Africa and Managing Director Poland Operations, Anthony Carey
EVP State Street Global Advisors and Head Europe Middle East and Africa, Greg Ehret
EVP and CIO State Street Global Services Europe Middle East and Africa, Ali ElAbboud
EVP; Global Chief Investment Officer State Street Global Advisors, Rick Lacaille
EVP; Head Portfolio Solutions State Street Global Markets, Ross McLellan
EVP Global Operations, Doreen Rigby
VP and Transition Manager Europe Middle East and Africa, Ben Mooney
Managing Director and Head Transition Management Europe Middle East and Africa, Rick Boomgaardt
Senior Managing Director and Head Alternative Investment Services Asia-Pacific, Carol Hall
Director, Gregory L. Summe, age 55
Director, Robert S. (Rob) Kaplan, age 54
Director, Kennett F. Burnes, age 69
Director, Ronald L. Skates, age 70
Director, Richard P. (Rick) Sergel, age 62
Director, David P. Gruber, age 70
Director, Robert E. Weissman, age 71
Director, Linda A. Hill, age 55
Director, Charles R. LaMantia, age 72
Vice Chairman and Head Europe and Asia-Pacific Global Services and Global Markets, Joseph C. Antonellis, age 57
Director, Dame Amelia C. Fawcett, age 55
Director, Peter Coym, age 70
Director, Patrick de Saint-Aignan, age 63
Auditors: Ernst&YoungLLP

LOCATIONS

HQ: State Street Corporation
One Lincoln St., Boston MA 02111
Phone: 617-786-3000 **Fax:** 617-664-4299
Web: www.statestreet.com

PRODUCTS/OPERATIONS

2011 Sales

	$ mil.	% of total
Fees		
Servicing	4,382	42
Trading	1,220	12
Management	917	9
Securities finance	378	4
Processing & other	297	3
Interest & other	3,080	30
Total	**10,274**	**100**

2011 Assets under Custody & Administration

	$ bil.	% of total
Mutual funds	5,265	24
Pension products	4,837	22
Collective funds	4,437	21
Insurance & other products	7,268	33
Total	**21,807**	**100**

COMPETITORS

Bank of New York Mellon
Citigroup
Credit Suisse (USA)
Deutsche Bank
First Data
Fiserv
JPMorgan Chase
Morgan Stanley
Northern Trust
Principal Financial
SEI Investments
UBS Financial Services

HISTORICAL FINANCIALS

Company Type: Public

Income Statement FYE: December 31

	ASSETS ($ mil.)	NET INCOME ($ mil.)	INCOME AS % OF ASSETS	EMPLOYEES
12/11	216,827	1,920	0.9%	29,740
12/10	160,505	1,556	1.0%	28,670
12/09	157,946	(1,881)	—	27,310
12/08	173,631	1,811	1.0%	28,475
12/07	142,543	1,261	0.9%	27,110
Annual Growth	11.1%	11.1%	—	2.3%

2011 Year-End Financials

Debt ratio: 3.75%
Return on equity: 9.90%
Cash ($ mil.): 61,786
Current ratio: —
Long-term debt ($ mil.): 8,131
No. of shares (mil.): 487
Dividends
Yield: —
Payout: 19.00%
Market value ($ mil.): 19,648

	STOCK PRICE ($) FY Close	P/E High	P/E Low	PER SHARE ($) Earnings	Dividends	Book Value
12/11	40.31	13	8	3.79	0.00	39.80
12/10	46.34	15	11	3.09	0.04	35.46
12/09	43.54	—	—	(4.31)	0.04	29.28
12/08	39.33	20	7	4.30	0.95	29.60
12/07	81.20	24	17	3.45	0.88	29.25
Annual Growth	(16.1%)	—	—	2.4%	—	8.0%

Steel Dynamics Inc.

Steel Dynamics may operate mini-mills but it produces big steel. Steel Dynamics Inc. (SDI) operates electric arc furnace mini-mills steel scrap processing and metals recycling centers and steel fabrication facilities. SDI sells to companies in the automotive construction and manufacturing industries as well as to steel processors and service centers primarily in the midwestern and eastern US. Among its mini-mill output are beams rails and other products used in the construction industrial machinery and transportation industries. It produces about 5 million tons of steel and recycles another 5 million tons annually. Wellington Management Company owns about 10% of Steel Dynamics.

Financial Analysis

The company's revenues grew about 59% in 2010 driven by improvements in the US economy resulting in increased customer demand and prices for its products. Steel operations grew 53% in 2010 with overall improved customer order volume and pricing; recycling was up 89% while steel fabrication gained 12%. Net income swung to a significant profit from a net loss on higher facility utilization and lower overall costs.

Strategy

The company's growth strategy is to expand existing facilities or build new one while also acquiring new businesses or entering joint ventures or alliances.

Steel Dynamics entered a joint venture in 2011 with Spain's Lafarga Group to construct a $39 million facility which will produce copper wire rod from recycled copper. The operation to be named SDI LaFarga LLC will be built in Indiana and utilize a source of copper scrap that had previously been diverted for export to China. The plant will be operational in 2013.

In 2010 the company acquired the steel-joist manufacturing business assets of Commercial Metals Company for about $17 million. The unit which Commercial Metals discontinued in early 2010 is being operated as a part of Steel Dynamics subsidiary New Millennium Building Systems and includes manufacturing plants in Hope Arkansas; Fallon Nevada; and Ciudad Juarez Mexico. The assets are expected to accelerate New Millennium's plans to expand into the southwestern and western US.

The company's Iron Dynamics unit produces direct reduced iron that serves as a lower-cost alternative to buying scrap metal for the company's mini-mills. SDI also has invested in a joint venture to produce iron nuggets another alternative raw material for the company's mills.

EXECUTIVES

VP and General Manager Roanoke Bar Division, Thomas J. (Joe) Crawford, age 56, $262,083 total compensation
VP Human Resources, Ben A. Eisbart, age 67
VP and General Manager Structural and Rail Division, John W. Nolan, $195,000 total compensation
EVP Steelmaking and Director; President and COO Steel Operations, Richard P. (Dick) Teets Jr., age 56, $490,000 total compensation
President and CEO, Mark D. Millett, age 52, $475,000 total compensation
Chairman, Keith E. Busse, age 69, $900,000 total compensation

Manager Investor Relations, Fredrick A. (Fred) Warner
Controller Structural and Rail Division, Bill Kautz
EVP Metals Recycling; President and COO OmniSource, Russell B. (Russ) Rinn, age 54
VP and General Manager Flat Roll Division, Glenn Pushis
Controller Steel of West Virginia, Dexter Childers Jr.
Manager Corporate Health and Safety, Janice E. (Jan) Conwell
VP and CIO, Robert E. (Bob) Francis
VP Treasurer and Risk Manager, Richard A. (Rick) Poinsatte, age 44
VP Internal Audit, Brent A. Ritenour, age 45
EVP and CFO, Theresa E. Wagler, age 41, $325,000 total compensation
EVP Strategic Planning and Business Development; President New Millennium Building Systems, Gary E. Heasley, age 47, $320,000 total compensation
Manager Sales Flat Roll Division, William T. (Tommy) Scruggs
Manager Sales Roanoke Bar Division, Parker Arthur
Controller Roanoke Bar Division, Bill Sarver
VP and General Manager Engineered Bar Products Division, Barry Schneider
VP; President Steel of West Virginia, Tim Duke
Sales Steel of West Virginia, Timothy Sizemore
General Manager New Millennium Building Systems Lake City Joist and Deck Plant and Salem Joist and Deck Plant, Chris Graham
General Manager New Millennium Building Systems Butler Joist and Deck Plant, Art Ullom
Manager Prepaint Product Flat Roll Division, Don Switzer
Controller Engineered Bar Products Division, Leon Waninger
EVP Steelmaking; President and COO Steel Operations, Richard P. Teets Jr., $490,000 total compensation
Manager Sales and Marketing Engineered Bar Products Division, Jeff Cordill
VP Iron Resources, Dave Bednarz
Manager Sales and Marketing Structural and Rail Division, Michael Busse
General Manager Sales and Marketing Long Products, Bill Brown
EVP Steelmaking and Director; President and COO Steel Operations, Richard P. (Dick) Teets Jr., age 56
Director, Paul B. Edgerley, age 56
Director, Frank D. Byrne, age 59
Director, John C. Bates, age 68
Director, Jurgen Kolb, age 69
Director, Joseph D. Ruffolo, age 70
Director, Richard J. Freeland, age 75
Director, James C. (Jim) Marcuccilli, age 61
Director, Gabriel L. Shaheen, age 58
Auditors: Ernst&YoungLLP

LOCATIONS

HQ: Steel Dynamics Inc.
7575 West Jefferson Blvd., Fort Wayne IN 46804
Phone: 260-969-3500 **Fax:** 260-969-3590
Web: www.steeldynamics.com

PRODUCTS/OPERATIONS

2011 Sales

Steel	5,070	53
Metals recycling/ferrous resources	4,152	43
Other	105	1
Total	**7,997**	**100**

Selected Products

Cold-rolled galvannealed
Cold-rolled hot-dipped galvanized
Direct reduced iron
Fully processed cold-rolled sheet
Hot-rolled galvannealed
Hot-rolled hot-dipped galvanized
Hot-rolled pickled and oiled
Liquid pig iron
Structural products (steel joists trusses)
Steel Operations
Sheet Products
  Hot rolled Products
  Cold Rolled Products
Long Products
  Structural
  Wide flange American Standard and miscellaneous beams
  H piling
  Channel sections
Rail Products
  Engineered Bar Products
  Merchant Bar Products
  Specialty Shapes
Metals Recycling and Ferrous Resources Operations
Steel Fabrication Operations

COMPETITORS

AK Steel Holding Corporation
ArcelorMittal USA
Canam Steel Corporation
Commercial Metals
Evraz
Gerdau Ameristeel
Nucor
Timken
United States Steel
Wheeling Corrugating

HISTORICAL FINANCIALS

Company Type: Public

Income Statement FYE: December 31

	REVENUE ($ mil.)	NET INCOME ($ mil.)	NET PROFIT MARGIN	EMPLOYEES
12/11	7,997	278	3.5%	6,530
12/10	6,300	140	2.2%	6,180
12/09	3,958	(8)	—	5,990
12/08	8,080	463	5.7%	6,650
12/07	4,384	394	9.0%	5,940
Annual Growth	16.2%	(8.4%)	—	2.4%

2011 Year-End Financials

Debt ratio: 39.81%
Return on equity: 12.01%
Cash ($ mil.): 390
Current ratio: 223.12
Long-term debt ($ mil.): 1,936
No. of shares (mil.): 218
Dividends
Yield: —
Payout: 32.79%
Market value ($ mil.): 2,878

	STOCK PRICE ($) FY Close	P/E High/Low		PER SHARE ($) Earnings	Dividends	Book Value
12/11	13.15	16	7	1.22	0.00	10.58
12/10	18.30	31	20	0.64	0.30	9.62
12/09	17.72	—	—	(0.04)	0.33	9.21
12/08	11.18	29	2	2.38	0.40	8.93
12/07	59.57	29	15	2.01	0.30	8.04
Annual Growth	(31.5%)	—	—	(11.7%)	—	7.1%

StellarOne Corp

StellarOne hopes to be a shining star in Virginia banking. StellarOne Corporation is the holding company for StellarOne Bank one of the largest community banks headquartered in the state. Through mpre than 50 locations the bank offers personal and commercial banking services such as checking savings and money market accounts CDs credit cards loans mortgages and wealth management services. Commercial real estate and construction loans account for the majority of its portfolio. StellarOne Bank also owns minority stakes in Banker's Insurance and Virginia Title Center through which the bank offers life property/casualty and title insurance.

Thanks in part to a slowly improving economy StellarOne reported nearly $16 million in net income for 2011 more than 60% more than the previous year even though revenues were down. Increased interest rate margins along with decreases in non-performing loans and charged-off loans contributed to the positive results.

StellarOne was not immune to the stresses of the economic crisis however. In 2012 the company announced a restructuring plan in which it would reduce headcount by some 4% in order to save on compensation and benefits costs. In 2009 it closed or combined eight underperforming branches.

StellarOne was created by the 2008 merger of Virginia Financial Group and FNB Corporation. In what the companies called a merger of equals Virginia Financial paid about $240 million in stock for FNB. The bank is headquartered in FNB's former hometown of Christenburg while the holding company is based in Virginia Financial Group's former hometown of Charlottesville.

EXECUTIVES

EVP and CFO, Jeffrey W. Farrar, age 51
President CEO and Director, O. R. (Ed) Barham Jr., age 61, $381,138 total compensation
EVP and COO, Litz H. Van Dyke, age 48, $222,777 total compensation
Chairman, Raymond D. (Ray) Smoot Jr., age 65, $24,800 total compensation
Director Wealth Management StellarOne Bank, Michael D. Williams
Director, Harold K. Neal, age 74
President CEO and Director, O. R. (Ed) Barham Jr., age 61
Director, Charles W. Steger, age 64
Director, Jon T. Wyatt, age 71
Director, Steven D. (Steve) Irvin, age 53
Director, Christopher M. Hallberg, age 62
Director, Gregory L. Fisher, age 62
Director, H. Wayne Parrish, age 68
Director, F. Courtney Hoge, age 71
Director, Jan S. Hoover, age 55
Director, Lee S. Baker, age 61
Director, Presley W. (William) Moore Jr., age 70
Director, Beverley E. Dalton, age 63
Director, Glen C. Combs, age 65
Director, H.C. Stuart Cochran
Director, Alan W. Myers
Director, Joe J. Thompson
Director, Keith L. Wampler
Auditors: GrantThorntonLLP

LOCATIONS

HQ: StellarOne Corporation
590 Peter Jefferson Pkwy. Ste. 250, Charlottesville VA 22911
Phone: 434-964-2211 **Fax:** 407-488-1505
Web: empowersoftware.com

PRODUCTS/OPERATIONS

2011 Sales

	$ mil.	% of total
Interest		
Loans including fees	108	71
Investment securities	12	8
Other	0	-
Noninterest		
Retail banking fees	15	10
Mortgage banking-related fees	8	6
Fiduciary commissions & fees	3	2
Other	4	3
Total	**152**	**100**

COMPETITORS

Bank of America
BB&T
First Citizens BancShares
First Community Bancshares
JPMorgan Chase
National Bankshares
SunTrust
Wells Fargo

HISTORICAL FINANCIALS

Company Type: Public

Income Statement FYE: December 31

	ASSETS ($ mil.)	NET INCOME ($ mil.)	INCOME AS % OF ASSETS	EMPLOYEES
12/11	2,917	15	0.5%	811
12/10	2,940	9	0.3%	838
12/09	3,033	(8)	—	827
12/08	2,956	9	0.3%	846
12/07	1,594	17	1.1%	496
Annual Growth	16.3%	(1.7%)	—	13.1%

2011 Year-End Financials

Debt ratio: 3.19%
Return on equity: 3.84%
Cash ($ mil.): 78
Current ratio: —
Long-term debt ($ mil.): 92
No. of shares (mil.): 22
Dividends
Yield: —
Payout: 27.12%
Market value ($ mil.): 260

	STOCK PRICE ($) FY Close	P/E High	P/E Low	PER SHARE ($) Earnings	Dividends	Book Value
12/11	11.38	26	16	0.59	0.00	18.15
12/10	14.54	45	27	0.35	0.16	18.75
12/09	9.96	—	—	(0.46)	0.28	18.57
12/08	16.90	49	28	0.45	0.64	17.46
12/07	14.85	18	9	1.57	0.64	15.08
Annual Growth	(6.4%)	—	—	(21.7%)	—	4.7%

Sterling Bancorp (N.Y.)

Sterling wants your silver. Sterling Bancorp is the holding company for Sterling National Bank which operates about a dozen branch locations in and around New York City. The bank offers such standard retail products as checking and savings accounts and CDs. Commercial industrial and residential mortgage warehouse loans account for more than half of the company's loan portfolio; other offerings include residential mortgages and equipment financing. Sterling also provides a variety of non-traditional banking offerings such as factoring (purchasing clients' accounts receivable) outsourced business support services for staffing agencies and trust administration. Sterling National Bank was founded in 1929.

Through an office in Hong Kong the company offers international trade services including financing for import and export transactions and issuing letters of credit. Factoring and trade finance unit Sterling Trade Capital primarily serves import-business clients offering such services as financing issuing letters of credit and creating bank acceptances.

Sterling Bank primarily serves clients in New York New Jersey and Connecticut but operates throughout the US.

In 2011 Sterling's revenues slipped 3% to $141.1 million but profits more than doubled to $17.6 million. The company cut its provision for loan losses that year by more than half as it experienced fewer net charge-offs. Also contributing to the growth net interest earnings rose as a result of larger loan and investment securities portfolios while interest expenses declined due to lower rates paid. Noninterest revenues fell slightly in 2011 largely due to lower securities gains as well as lower mortgage banking and service charge income.

Sterling has been focused on building its commercial loan portfolio. It has partially funded such growth through capital raising efforts including two stock offerings in the past couple of years. In 2010 it launched a residential mortgage warehouse lending business seeing opportunity in the market that many other lenders have exited. The company also sees lots of opportunity in its home market of metropolitan New York City which has hundreds of thousands of small to midsized companies it can potentially serve.

In late 2011 the company combined all of its operating segments into the single community banking segment. Subsequently Sterling National Bank absorbed the operations of former subsidiaries Sterling National Mortgage Company Sterling Factors Corporation and Sterling Resource Funding. The moves which reflect the interdependent nature of Sterling's various activities were designed to streamline the bank's operations and brand. The following year Sterling National Bank acquired residential mortgage broker Universal Mortgage expanding its presence into Brooklyn for the first time.

EXECUTIVES

SVP; EVP Sterling National Bank, Howard M. Applebaum, age 53, $300,600 total compensation
EVP Sterling National Bank, Eliot S. Robinson, age 69, $270,100 total compensation
President and Director; President and CEO Sterling National Bank, John C. Millman, age 69, $494,354 total compensation
VP and Treasurer; SVP Sterling National Bank, Joel M. Schprechman
EVP and CFO; EVP Sterling National Bank, John W. Tietjen, age 67, $264,500 total compensation
Chairman and CEO; Chairman Sterling National Bank, Louis J. Cappelli, age 81, $798,446 total compensation
SVP Sterling National Bank, John C. Gallo Jr.
SVP Sterling National Bank, Monica S. Lercher
SVP and Secretary; EVP Sterling National Bank, Dale C. Fredston
SVP Sterling National Bank, Michael J. Scheller
EVP Sterling National Bank, Michael Bizenov
SVP Sterling National Bank, Dixiana M. Berrios
SVP Sterling National Bank, Joseph L. Campbell
SVP Sterling National Bank, Jeffrey S. Fliegel
SVP Sterling National Bank, John B. McCormack
SVP Sterling National Bank, Thomas P. McGevna
SVP Sterling National Bank, Anthony V. Migliorino
SVP Sterling National Bank, Robert Nisi
SVP Sterling National Bank, Steven A. Orenstein
First VP Sterling National Bank, Thomas M. Braunstein
First VP Sterling National Bank, Salvatore F. Costa
First VP Sterling National Bank, Robert J. Formica
First VP Sterling National Bank, Thomas M. Frankel
First VP Sterling National Bank, Anthony M. Grosso
First VP Sterling National Bank, Steven W. Hebert
SVP Sterling National Bank, Leonard M. Imperiale
SVP Sterling National Bank, Benjamin S. Katz
SVP Sterling National Bank, Neal B. Krumper
First VP Sterling National Bank, Murray R. Markowitz
First VP Sterling National Bank, Robert A. Schnitzer
VP Sterling National Bank, Francis L. DeFranco
VP Sterling National Bank, Norka Del Rios
First VP Sterling National Bank, Dawn E. DeLuca
VP Sterling National Bank, Charles I. Derr
VP Sterling National Bank, John J. Howe
SVP Sterling National Bank, Irving Kahn
SVP Sterling National Bank, John P. LaLota
First VP Sterling National Bank, Kenneth A. Lee
First VP Sterling National Bank, Mary Anne E. Lindenbaum
First VP Sterling National Bank, Kenneth J. Marte
SVP Sterling National Bank, Wayne G. Miller
VP Sterling National Bank, George W. Moraitis
First VP Sterling National Bank, Samuel T. Nicoletti
VP Sterling National Bank, Robert E. Nuytkens
VP Sterling National Bank, Barbara A. Riordan
VP Sterling National Bank, Anna M. Roina
VP Sterling National Bank, John R. Rosado
First VP Sterling National Bank, Yvonne V. Shand
First VP Sterling National Bank, Vivian Tarnowski
VP Sterling National Bank, Ajay J. Timothy
SVP Sterling National Bank, Kenneth E. Cohen
SVP Sterling National Bank, Andrew Corsi
SVP Sterling National Bank, Allen J. Gershlak
SVP Sterling National Bank, Mindy F. Stern
SVP and Controller; SVP Sterling National Bank, Seth H. Ugelow
First VP Sterling National Bank, William H. Breitman
First VP Sterling National Bank, Marie T. Giunto
VP Sterling National Bank, Sadia Affrin
VP Sterling National Bank, Leszek Borysiak
VP Sterling National Bank, Anthony Cantone
VP Sterling National Bank, Anthony J. Colao
VP Sterling National Bank, Paul Colontino
VP Sterling National Bank, Peter E. Gardner
VP Sterling National Bank, Andrea Diaz
VP Sterling National Bank, Patrick Duffy
VP Sterling National Bank, Rosemarie Henry
VP Sterling National Bank, Paulette K. Johnson
VP Sterling National Bank, Richard J. Kruse
VP Sterling National Bank, Mary Jane G. Lerias
VP Sterling National Bank, Carol R. Lieber
VP Sterling National Bank, Michael J. Madeo
VP Sterling National Bank, Albert Salas
VP Sterling National Bank, Aimee Spennato
VP Sterling National Bank, Joan B. Stark
VP Sterling National Bank, Debra Washington
SVP Sterling National Bank, Joseph Costanza
SVP Sterling National Bank, Patricia Hrotko
SVP Sterling National Bank, David Minder
SVP Sterling National Bank, Paul A. Robinson
SVP Sterling National Bank, Leonard Rudolph
SVP Sterling National Bank, Gayle A. Surak
First VP Sterling National Bank, Richard Assaf
First VP Sterling National Bank, Ronald J. Bongiovanni

First VP Sterling National Bank, Mary Guitard
First VP Sterling National Bank, Edward Nugent
First VP Sterling National Bank, Angel Quinones
First VP Sterling National Bank, Keith Smith
First VP Sterling National Bank, Rick Zimmerman
VP Sterling National Bank, Paula Cappello
VP Sterling National Bank, Lidia L. Alarcon
VP Sterling National Bank, Patricia Cavallaro
VP Sterling National Bank, Anthony Daddezio
VP Sterling National Bank, Daniel J. Doody
VP Sterling National Bank, Ronald Ferraro
VP Sterling National Bank, Luz M. Figueroa
VP Sterling National Bank, Richard L. Friedman
VP Sterling National Bank, Helen Galpin
VP Sterling National Bank, Steven A. Georgeson
VP Sterling National Bank, Sonia A. Gordon
VP Sterling National Bank, Ross Harris
VP Sterling National Bank, John F. Henry
VP Sterling National Bank, David C. Johnson
VP Sterling National Bank, Sheila Kashkin
VP Sterling National Bank, John Lavin
VP Sterling National Bank, Connie M. Leardi
VP Sterling National Bank, Janie Y. L. Leung
VP Sterling National Bank, Joseph Mallozzi
VP Sterling National Bank, Kathleen L. McEntee
VP Sterling National Bank, Scott McGrath
VP Sterling National Bank, Mireya Mera
VP Sterling National Bank, Patricia O. Mungo
VP Sterling National Bank, John R. O'Toole
VP Sterling National Bank, Cynthia M. Paret
VP Sterling National Bank, Rodney O. Perry
VP Sterling National Bank, Ron A. Prezelmayer
VP Sterling National Bank, Diana M. Principe
VP Sterling National Bank, Steven Z. Reisner
VP Sterling National Bank, Peter Rippa
VP Sterling National Bank, Henri M. Rodrigues
VP Sterling National Bank, Robert S. Schepis
VP Sterling National Bank, Peter Sforzo
VP Sterling National Bank, Maribel Simancas
VP Sterling National Bank, Wing K. Siu
VP Sterling National Bank, Albert C. Snyder
VP Sterling National Bank, Anthony M. Spataro
VP Sterling National Bank, Alexander Van Den Essen
VP Sterling National Bank, Mary S. Winfield
VP Sterling National Bank, Edward Zekraus
SVP and Managing Director Sterling Warehouse Lending Group, Gary Timmerman
President and Director; President and CEO Sterling National Bank, John C. Millman, age 69
Director, Joseph M. Adamko, age 79
Director, Eugene T. Rossides, age 84
Director, Robert Abrams, age 73
Director, Allan F. Hershfield, age 80
Director, Henry J. Humphreys, age 83
Director, Fernando Ferrer, age 61
Director, Robert W. Lazar, age 68
Director, Carolyn Joy Lee
Auditors: CroweHorwathLLP

LOCATIONS

HQ: Sterling Bancorp
650 5th Ave., New York NY 10019-6108
Phone: 212-757-3300 **Fax:** 212-490-8852
Web: www.sterlingbancorp.com

PRODUCTS/OPERATIONS

2011 Sal

	$ mil.	% of total
Interest		
Loans	73	52
Investment securities	23	16
Other	0	-
Noninterest		
Accounts receivable management factoring commissions & other fees 17		24
Mortgage banking income	6	5
Service charges on deposit accounts	5	4
Other	7	6
Total	**141**	**100**

Selected Subsidiaries

Sterling Bancorp Trust I
Sterling Banking Corporation
Sterling Factors Corporation
Sterling National Bank
Sterling National Mortgage Company Inc.
Sterling Real Estate Holding Company Inc.
Sterling Resource Funding Corp.
Sterling Trade Services Inc.
Sterling National Asia Limited Hong Kong

COMPETITORS

Astoria Financial
Bank of America
Bank of New York Mellon
Citigroup
HSBC USA
Hudson Valley Holding
Israel Discount Bank of New York
JPMorgan Chase
New York Community Bancorp
Valley National Bancorp

HISTORICAL FINANCIALS

Company Type: Public

Income Statement FYE: December 31

	ASSETS ($ mil.)	NET INCOME ($ mil.)	INCOME AS % OF ASSETS	EMPLOYEES
12/11	2,493	17	0.7%	515
12/10	2,360	7	0.3%	558
12/09	2,165	9	0.4%	565
12/08	2,214	16	0.7%	562
12/07	2,012	14	0.7%	586
Annual Growth	5.5%	4.8%	—	(3.2%)

2011 Year-End Financials

Debt ratio: 5.96%
Return on equity: 7.97%
Cash ($ mil.): 157
Current ratio: —
Long-term debt ($ mil.): 148
No. of shares (mil.): 30
Dividends
Yield: —
Payout: 70.59%
Market value ($ mil.): 267

	STOCK PRICE ($) FY Close	P/E High	P/E Low	PER SHARE ($) Earnings	Dividends	Book Value
12/11	8.64	21	13	0.51	0.00	7.14
12/10	10.47	61	40	0.18	0.36	8.30
12/09	7.14	38	17	0.37	0.56	8.94
12/08	14.03	20	12	0.88	0.76	8.87
12/07	13.64	25	15	0.79	0.76	6.79
Annual Growth	(10.8%)	—	—	(10.4%)	—	1.3%

Sterling Financial Corp. (WA)

Sterling Financial Corporation is the holding company for Sterling Bank (formerly Sterling Savings Bank) one of the largest regional community banks in the Pacific Northwest. The bank operates about 190 branch locations in northern California Idaho Oregon and Washington and lends throughout the West from more than 30 loan origination offices. In California it does business under the name Sonoma Bank. Real estate and construction loans account for the majority of the bank's portfolio. Its wealth management division markets stocks bonds mutual funds annuities and other investments to bank customers. Sterling Financial is regaining its luster after being hard hit by the downturn in the housing market.

Operations

Sterling Financial Corp's. principal operating subsidiary is Sterling Bank. The bank operates three business segments: Commercial Real Estate; Community Banking; and a Home Loan division.

Financial Analysis

SFC's 2011 revenue declined 9% vs. 2010 while net income jumped 117% over the same period. 2011 marked the fourth consecutive year of falling revenue for the bank which is down about 38% vs. 2007 as the housing crisis pummeled California and SFC's other markets. On the plus side SFC returned to profitability in 2011 the first year since 2007. Indeed SFC's losses totaled nearly $1.4 billion between 2008 and 2010 largely as a result of a declining real estate asset portfolio.

Strategy

A new management team is seeking to return the bank to stable footing. Greg Seibly has replaced Harold Gilkey as Sterling's CEO; with more than 20 years in the financial industry Seibly previously served on the executive teams of such banks as U.S. Bancorp Wells Fargo and Bank of America. The company also named a new chairman COO and several new directors. Under Seibly the bank completed a $730 million recapitalization in 2010.

To further bolster its capital position SAFC is emphasizing sales and business development working on growing its fee income and streamlining operations. It sold bad loans and merged residential mortgage lender Golf Savings Bank into Sterling Savings. The bank has cut back on riskier construction and real estate lending to focus on writing loans for consumers small to midsized businesses and multifamily residences.

The adaptations seem to have helped Sterling as further growth is underway. The company expanded in 2012 through the acquisition of assets deposits and banking operations of in the Pacific Northwest.

Mergers Acquisitions and Divestments

Adding to its holdings the company in late 2012 agreed to buy California-based American Heritage Holdings the parent of Borrego Springs Bank for about $6.5 million. Borrego Springs Bank is a nationally chartered and federally insured commercial bank specializing in SBA and other government guaranteed lending through three branches and seven loan offices. The purchase will boost Sterling's government guaranteed lending and serving capabilities. Earlier in the year Sterling bought First Independent Bank from owner First Independent Investment Group thereby moving into the Portland/Vancouver market with 27 full-service branches. The deal included First Independent's wealth and asset management operations which allows Sterling to add trust services to its offerings.

In 2012 Sterling exited Montana with the sale of its operations there to Eagle Bancorp Montana. The $7.3 million deal included the divesture of seven retail branches and their non-depository investment services businesses.

Ownership

Thomas H. Lee Advisors and the private equity arm of Warburg Pincus each own nearly 23% of Sterling Financial's shares as a result of their $170 million capital infusions made in 2010 to avoid seizure of the company.

EXECUTIVES

EVP Investor and Corporate Relations, David A. Brukardt, age 54
Corporate Development Executive, Daniel G. Byrne, age 58, $276,000 total compensation
Chairman, Leslie S. (Les) Biller, age 64
Acting CFO, Patrick J. (Pat) Rusnak, age 48
Chief Credit Officer Sterling Savings Bank, David S. DePillo, age 51
EVP and Chief Production Officer, Deborah A. (Debbie) Meekins
SVP and Information Technology Director Sterling Savings Bank, Cindy Parker
President CEO and Director; President and CEO Sterling Savings Bank, J. Gregory (Greg) Seibly, age 49, $479,231 total compensation
EVP and CFO Sterling Savings Bank, Thomas W. Colosimo, age 60
COO; President and COO Sterling Savings Bank, Ezra A. Eckhardt, age 42, $449,923 total compensation
SVP Controller and Principal Accounting Officer; SVP and Controller Sterling Savings Bank, Robert G. Butterfield, age 43
Secretary, Andrew J. Schultheis
President INTERVEST, Larry A. Conley, age 60
EVP Golf Savings Bank, Donn C. Costa, age 51, $487,500 total compensation
SVP and Human Resources Executive, Karla Gehlen
SVP and Private Banking Director, Don Wood
SVP Real Estate Group Director, Cynthia Atheide
VP and Director Communication and Public Affairs, Cara Coon
Senior Credit Executive, Steve Hauschild
Director, C. Webb Edwards, age 64
Director, Ellen R.M. Boyer, age 52
Director, David A. (Dave) Coulter, age 65
Director, William L. (Ike) Eisenhart, age 60
Director, Robert C. (Bob) Donegan, age 58
Director, Scott L. Jaeckel, age 41
President CEO and Director; President and CEO Sterling Savings Bank, J. Gregory (Greg) Seibly, age 49
Director, Michael F. Reuling, age 66
Director, Robert H. (Bob) Hartheimer, age 55
Auditors: BDOSeidmanLLP

LOCATIONS

HQ: Sterling Financial Corporation
111 N. Wall St., Spokane WA 99201
Phone: 509-354-8186 **Fax:** 800-329-2733
Web: www.sedonline.com

PRODUCTS/OPERATIONS

2011 Sales

	$ mil.	% of total
Interest		
Loans	322	62
Mortgage-backed securities	71	13
Investments & cash equivalents	10	2
Noninterest		
Mortgage banking operations	52	10
Fees & service charges	50	9
Gains on sales of securities	16	3
BOLI	6	1
Other	1	-
Total	**530**	**100**

COMPETITORS

BancWest
Bank of America
Banner Corp
Columbia Banking
FS Bancorp
Glacier Bancorp
U.S. Bancorp
Washington Federal
Wells Fargo
Zions Bancorporation

HISTORICAL FINANCIALS

Company Type: Public

Income Statement FYE: December 31

	ASSETS ($ mil.)	NET INCOME ($ mil.)	INCOME AS % OF ASSETS	EMPLOYEES
12/11	9,193	39	0.4%	2,496
12/10	9,493	(224)	—	2,498
12/09	10,877	(838)	—	2,641
12/08	12,790	(335)	—	2,481
12/07	12,149	93	0.8%	2,571
Annual Growth	(6.7%)	(19.5%)	—	(0.7%)

2011 Year-End Financials

Debt ratio: 7.08%
Return on equity: 4.45%
Cash ($ mil.): 470
Current ratio: —
Long-term debt ($ mil.): 650
No. of shares (mil.): 62
Dividends
Yield: —
Payout: —
Market value ($ mil.): 1,036

	STOCK PRICE ($) FY Close	P/E High	P/E Low	PER SHARE ($) Earnings	Dividends	Book Value
12/11	16.70	35	19	0.63	0.00	14.16
12/10	18.97	—	—	(53.05)	0.00	12.45
12/09	0.62	—	—	(1,087.68)	0.00	408.62
12/08	8.80	—	—	(429.66)	0.00	1,444.51
12/07	16.79	0	0	122.76	0.00	1,520.35
Annual Growth	(0.1%)	—	—	(73.2%)	—	(68.9%)

Stifel Financial Corp.

Stifel Financial doesn't repress investors. The company serves individual corporate municipal and institutional clients through nearly 300 offices in the US with a concentration in the Midwest and mid-Atlantic regions. It also has locations in Canada and Europe. Through subsidiaries Stifel Nicolaus (founded 1890) Thomas Weisel (acquired in 2010) Century Securities Associates Stifel Bank & Trust and others the company provides asset management financial advice and banking services for private clients. Stifel also offers brokerage and mergers and acquisitions advisory services for corporate clients underwrites debt and equity and provides research on more than 1000 US and European equities.

Hoping to take advantage of the demise of bulge-bracket investment banks such as Bear Stearns and Lehman Brothers and turmoil in the industry in general Stifel Financial has been growing via acquisitions –nearly ten of them since 2005. In 2011 the company bought Stone & Youngberg which specializes in municipal bonds and fixed income securities.

The 2010 Thomas Weisel deal worth more than $300 million and one of Stifel Financial's largest to date boosted the company's investment banking capabilities in the technology health care and energy sectors. Thomas Weisel's Canadian operations took on the Stifel Nicolaus name.

Stifel Financial has also built up its asset management and brokerage operations through acquisition. In 2010 the company bought investment advisor Missouri Valley Partners from First Banks; the year before it acquired more than 50 wealth management branches in the US from UBS Financial Services.

The additions along with improved market conditions helped Stifel Financial achieve record revenues in 2011 the 16th consecutive year that the figure increased. Net income was up too rebounding from nearly $2 million in 2010 to more than $84 million thanks in part to increased commissions and fees related to brokerage and asset management services and a decline in compensation costs.

In addition to acquisitions Stifel Financial also has strategies to grow organically. These include establishing trust services at Stifel Bank & Trust and utilizing the bank to cross-sell mortgages and securities-based loans to wealth management clients. Stifel Financial also wants to extend the reach of its private client business in the US and its institutional equity operations globally.

EXECUTIVES

Vice Chairman, Richard J. Himelfarb, age 70, $250,000 total compensation
Co-Chairman President and CEO, Ronald J. (Ron) Kruszewski, age 53, $200,000 total compensation
SVP CFO and Director, James M. Zemlyak, age 52, $175,000 total compensation
Vice Chairman, Ben A. Plotkin, age 56, $250,000 total compensation
Co-Chairman, Thomas W. (Thom) Weisel, age 71
EVP and Director Capital Markets Stifel Nicolaus, Thomas P. Mulroy, age 50, $250,000 total compensation
SVP and Director Equity Research Stifel Nicolaus, Hugo J. (Hugh) Warns III
SVP, David D. Sliney, age 42, $150,000 total compensation
SVP and Managing Director Denver Municipal Trading Stifel Nicolaus, Michael F. Imhoff
SVP and Director Denver Public Finance Stifel Nicolaus, Stephen H. Bell
SVP and Director Syndicate Stifel Nicolaus, Thomas R. Kendrick IV
SVP and General Counsel, David M. Minnick, age 55, $125,000 total compensation
SVP and Director Private Markets Stifel Nicolaus, J. Joseph Schlafly III
SVP and Co-Head Institutional Group, Victor J. Nesi, age 52
Vice Chairman, Richard J. Himelfarb, age 70
Co-Chairman President and CEO, Ronald J. (Ron) Kruszewski, age 53
SVP CFO and Director, James M. Zemlyak, age 52
Vice Chairman, Ben A. Plotkin, age 56
Director, John P. Dubinsky, age 68
Co-Chairman, Thomas W. (Thom) Weisel, age 71
Director, Robert E. (Bob) Grady, age 54
Director, Charles A. Dill, age 72
Director, Richard F. (Dick) Ford, age 76
Director, Robert E. Lefton, age 80
Director, James M. Oates, age 65
Director, Bruce A. Beda, age 71
Director, Kelvin R. Westbrook, age 56
Director, Michael W. (Mike) Brown, age 66
Director, Alton F. Irby III, age 71
EVP and Director Capital Markets Stifel Nicolaus, Thomas P. Mulroy, age 50
Director, Frederick O. (Fred) Hanser, age 70
SVP and Co-Head Institutional Group, Victor J. Nesi, age 52
Auditors: Ernst&YoungLLP

LOCATIONS

HQ: Stifel Financial Corp.
501 N. Broadway, St. Louis MO 63102-2102
Phone: 314-342-2000 **Fax:** 818-553-2388
Web: www.publicstorage.com

PRODUCTS/OPERATIONS

2011 Sales

	$ mil.	% of total
Commissions	561	40
Principal transactions	343	24
Asset management & service fees	228	16
Investment banking	199	14
Interest	89	6
Total	**1,422**	**100**

Selected Subsidiaries

Broadway Air Corp.
Butler Wick & Co. Inc.
Century Securities Associates Inc.
  CSA Insurance Agency Incorporated
Choice Financial Partners Inc.
First Service Financial Company
  Stifel Bank & Trust
Hanifen Imhoff Inc.
Missouri Valley Partners
Stifel Asset Management Corp.
Stifel Nicolaus Limited (UK)
Stifel Nicolaus & Company Incorporated
  Ryan Beck Holdings LLC
  Stifel Nicolaus Insurance Agency Incorporated
Stifel Nicholas Limited (UK)
Thomas Weisel Partners Group Inc.

COMPETITORS

Bank of America
Cowen Group
Edward Jones
Goldman Sachs
Jefferies Group
JMP Group
Lazard
Morgan Stanley
Oppenheimer Holdings
Piper Jaffray
Raymond James Financial
Robert W. Baird & Co.
SWS Group
Wells Fargo Advisors

HISTORICAL FINANCIALS

Company Type: Public

Income Statement FYE: December 31

	ASSETS ($ mil.)	NET INCOME ($ mil.)	INCOME AS % OF ASSETS	EMPLOYEES
12/11	4,951	84	1.7%	5,097
12/10	4,213	1	0.0%	4,906
12/09	3,167	75	2.4%	4,434
12/08	1,558	55	3.6%	3,371
12/07	1,499	32	2.1%	2,834
Annual Growth	34.8%	27.2%	—	15.8%

2011 Year-End Financials

Debt ratio: 1.67%
Return on equity: 6.46%
Cash ($ mil.): 174
Current ratio: —
Long-term debt ($ mil.): 82
No. of shares (mil.): 51
Dividends
  Yield: —
  Payout: —
Market value ($ mil.): 1,660

	STOCK PRICE ($) FY Close	P/E High/Low	PER SHARE ($) Earnings	Dividends	Book Value
12/11	32.05	46 15	1.33	0.00	25.15
12/10	62.04	15711080	0.03	0.00	24.79
12/09	59.24	33 17	1.57	0.00	19.16
12/08	45.85	37 20	1.32	0.00	15.04
12/07	52.57	63 38	0.84	0.00	12.15
Annual Growth	(11.6%)	— —	12.2%	—	19.9%

Stryker Corp.

Is this an operating room or Dad's workshop? Stryker's surgical products include such instruments as drills saws and even cement mixers. The company's Reconstructive division makes artificial hip and knee joints trauma implants bone cement and other orthopedic supplies. The MedSurg Equipment segment houses microsurgery instruments endoscopy equipment and communications and patient handling tools. Stryker's Neurotechnology and Spine unit provides rods screws and artificial discs for spinal surgeries as well as coils and stents for cerebral vascular procedures. The firm's products are marketed globally to hospitals doctors and other health care facilities via direct sales personnel and distributors.

While Stryker operates manufacturing facilities in Asia and Europe and markets its products in more than 100 countries sales outside of the US make up only a third of its annual revenue. In the US Stryker uses its own sales and marketing force maintaining separate dedicated sales teams for each of its core product lines. By allowing for specialization each team can provide expertise and guidance directed specifically to customers in each of the medical specialties Stryker serves. In markets outside the US Stryker's products are peddled through company-owned subsidiaries as well as third-party distributors and medical device dealers.

Beginning in 2009 Stryker set out to diversify its operations through acquisitions. Purchases have brought the company new software and manufacturing technologies and entered it into new lines of business. Its $1.5 billion acquisition of Boston Scientific's neurovascular division in 2011 added minimally invasive devices (such as coils stents and balloon catheters) for the treatment of cerebral conditions such as brain aneurysms and hemorrhagic and ischemic strokes. Stryker further boosted its neurovascular operations later that year when it acquired Concentric Medical a maker of clot removal products for use in ischemic stroke procedures for some $135 million.

Following these acquisitions Stryker rearranged its operating structure from two divisions into three: Reconstructive MedSurg Equipment and Neurotechnology and Spine.

From hips to knees to spines the company has followed the implant strategy of staying on top of the latest technology by consistently upgrading and introducing new versions of its popular brands. Leading products include the Triathlon and Scorpio knee implant systems Simplex bone cement the VariAx and Hoffman systems and the Oasys spinal implant. During the lowest point in the economic recession sales of joint implants softened as patients put off non-critical joint replacements. By 2011 demand had perked up world wide.

Expansion efforts in the orthopedic segment have largely been focused on orthobiologics. During 2011 Stryker acquired synthetic bone graft material maker Orthovita for some $304 million in cash. It also spent $150 million to purchase France's Memometal Technologies for its in hand and foot device products.

Stryker's orthopedic division has also developed biological products to grow bone and cartilage. Its OP-1 bone growth product was so successful that in 2011 the company sold the product franchise to Olympus for $60 million. It then turned its attention onto another biological product BMP-7 which has applications in cartilage regeneration.

The MedSurg Equipment division includes surgical navigation systems endoscopic systems emergency medical equipment and other medical devices. Its biggest customers are hospitals and other care providers who have to invest a decent chunk of cash in order to upgrade their surgical equipment. MedSurg felt hospital expense cuts keenly during the recession and in response it sought diversification to increase sales. In 2010 Stryker purchased supportive surface maker (think: beds and tables) Gaymar Industries for approximately $150 million in cash. The two companies were already well-acquainted through a longstanding supply and sales agreement in the US.

Stryker was founded in 1941 by Dr. Homer Stryker; members of the Stryker family still own a minority portion of the company's stock.

EXECUTIVES

VP General Counsel and Secretary, Curtis E. Hall, age 55
VP Human Resources, Michael W. (Mike) Rude, age 50
Chairman, William U. (Bill) Parfet, age 65
VP Tax, Eric Lum
VP Finance Training Development and Internal Audit, James B. (Jim) Praeger
VP and Treasurer, Jeanne M. Blondia
VP Regulatory Affairs and Quality Assurance, Elizabeth A. (Beth) Staub
VP Strategy and Investor Relations, Katherine A. Owen, age 41
Group President Orthopaedics, Kevin A. Lobo
Group President International, Andrew G. Fox-Smith, age 46, $400,738 total compensation
Interim CEO; VP and CFO, Curt R. Hartman, age 48, $360,667 total compensation
VP and Chief Accounting Officer, Tony M. McKinney, age 42
Group President Global Quality and Operations, Lonny J. Carpenter, age 50
Group President MedSurg and Spine, Timothy J. (Tim) Scannell, age 47
VP and Chief Compliance Officer, Anne Mullally
Chairman Emeritus, John W. Brown, age 77
Director, Roch F. Doliveux, age 55
Director, Allan C. Golston
Director, Howard E. Cox Jr., age 68
Director, Louise L. Francesconi, age 59
Director, Ronda E. Stryker, age 57
Director, Howard L. Lance, age 56
Director, Srikant M. Datar, age 58
Auditors: Ernst&YoungLLP

LOCATIONS

HQ: Stryker Corporation
2825 Airview Blvd., Kalamazoo MI 49002-1802
Phone: 269-385-2600 **Fax:** 269-385-1062
Web: www.stryker.com

2011 Sales

	$ mil.	% of total
US	5,269	63
Total	**8,307**	**100**

PRODUCTS/OPERATIONS

2011 Sales

	$ mil.	% of total
Reconstructive	3,710	45
MedSurg Equipment	3,160	38
Neurotechnology & Spine	1,437	17
Total	**8,307**	**100**

Selected Acquisitions

MedSurg Equipment

Gaymar Industries (2010 support surfaces)
Sonopet (2010 ultrasonic aspirator control consoles)
Ascent Healthcare Solutions Inc. (2009 medical device reprocessing and remanufacturing)

Neurotechnology & Spine
Concentric Medical Inc. (2011 products to treat acute ischemic stroke)
Orthovita (2011 orthobiologic & biosurgery products)
OtisMed (2010 software technology)

Reconstructive
Memometal Technologies (2011 hand and foot products)
Porex Surgical Inc. (2010 facial implant products)

COMPETITORS

Arthrex
B. Braun Melsungen
Biomet
CONMED Corporation
Corin Group
Covidien
DePuy
DePuy Spine
DJO Global
Genzyme Biosurgery
Hill-Rom Holdings
Medtronic
Medtronic Sofamor Danek
Micrus
Midmark Corporation
Olympus
Orthofix
RTI Biologics
Smith & Nephew
STERIS
Synthes
Tornier
Wright Medical Group
Zimmer Holdings

HISTORICAL FINANCIALS

Company Type: Public

Income Statement FYE: December 31

	REVENUE ($ mil.)	NET INCOME ($ mil.)	NET PROFIT MARGIN	EMPLOYEES
12/11	8,307	1,345	16.2%	21,241
12/10	7,320	1,273	17.4%	20,036
12/09	6,723	1,107	16.5%	18,582
12/08	6,718	1,147	17.1%	17,594
12/07	6,000	1,017	17.0%	16,026
Annual Growth	8.5%	7.2%	—	7.3%

2011 Year-End Financials

Debt ratio: 14.25%
Return on equity: 17.51%
Cash ($ mil.): 905
Current ratio: 394.47
Long-term debt ($ mil.): 1,751
No. of shares (mil.): 381
Dividends
Yield: —
Payout: 21.81%
Market value ($ mil.): 18,940

	STOCK PRICE ($) FY Close	P/E High/Low		PER SHARE ($) Earnings	Dividends	Book Value
12/11	49.71	19	13	3.45	0.00	20.17
12/10	53.70	18	13	3.19	0.63	18.34
12/09	50.37	19	11	2.77	0.25	16.57
12/08	39.95	27	13	2.78	0.40	13.64
12/07	74.72	31	22	2.44	0.33	13.09
Annual Growth	(9.7%)	—	—	9.0%	—	11.4%

Sun Bancorp Inc. (NJ)

Sun Bancorp revolves around New Jersey. The holding company for Sun National Bank Sun Bancorp targets individuals and local businesses in central and southern New Jersey through some 65 branch locations. Sun National Bank offers standard retail services including savings accounts CDs and IRAs. The company's primary lending focus is originating industrial and commercial loans (including Small Business Administration (SBA) loans and lines of credit) which account for some 85% of its portfolio. Sun National Bank also makes home equity residential mortgage and other consumer loans. The company offers investment services through Sun Financial Services.

Sun Bancorp's geographic footprint includes midsize markets and select locations in metropolitan areas in New Jersey and into Pennsylvania.

Sun Bancorp suffered losses in 2010 and 2011 as provisions for loan losses and nonperforming assets took a bite out of profits. The challenges were brought on by a lingering recession marked by a depressed housing market and high unemployment levels. Demand for business and consumer credit remained low and evolving industry regulations created higher bank costs. In 2011 net income improved from the year before but was still in the red. Revenues fell 13% compared to the year before.

Sun Bancorp is focused on raising its capital position and expanding throughout its core New Jersey market. Sun Bancorp has grown its operations through acquisitions but it also has opened new branches. In 2012 Sun National Bank expanded its reach and opened a commercial lending office in Pennsylvania to serve the Philadelphia area. Sun Bancorp has an overall strategy to grow it commercial loan production.

In order to strengthen its balance sheet Sun Bancorp has sold loans to investors and it has offered common stock. In 2010 Chairman Bernard Brown and WL Ross & Co. invested $100 million in equity in the bank. As a result Brown and his family own about 10% of Sun Bancorp and director WL Ross owns about 25% of the company.

EXECUTIVES

Vice Chairman Treasurer and Secretary, Sidney R. (Sid) Brown, age 55, $185,054 total compensation
Chairman Sun Bancorp and Sun National Bank, Bernard A. Brown, age 87, $370,108 total compensation
EVP and Senior Lending Officer; Manager Wholesale Lending Sun National Bank, Bart A. Speziali, age 62, $257,964 total compensation
EVP and CFO, Thomas R. Brugger, age 45
EVP and COO; EVP and Chief Credit Policy Officer Sun National Bank, A. Bruce Dansbury, age 58, $320,000 total compensation
EVP and Chief Banking Officer Sun National Bank, Thomas J. Townsend
SVP, Robert C. Lemaire
EVP Consumer Banking Sun National Bank, Edward (Ed) Malandro
EVP and Director Wholesale Lending, Bradley (Brad) Fouss
VP Public Relations and Events, Christine Irving
President CEO and Director Sun Bancorp and Sun National Bank, Thomas X. Geisel, age 50, $490,384 total compensation
EVP and Chief Administrative Officer, Michele Estep
SVP and Director Marketing, Patricia McCrossan
President Sun Home Loans Sun National Bank, Steven J. Greenberg
SVP CIO; Head Bank Operations for Sun National Bank, Angelo J. Valletta
Vice Chairman Treasurer and Secretary, Sidney R. (Sid) Brown, age 55
Director, Alfonse M. Mattia, age 70
Director, Eli Kramer, age 57
Director, Anthony R. (Tony) Coscia
Director, Jeffrey S. Brown, age 52
Director, Peter Galetto Jr., age 58
Director, Anne E. Koons, age 59
Director, Wilbur L. Ross Jr., age 74
Director, William J. (Bill) Marino, age 68
Director, George A. Pruitt, age 65
Director, Anthony Russo III, age 69
Director, Edward H. Salmon, age 69
President CEO and Director Sun Bancorp and Sun National Bank, Thomas X. Geisel, age 50
Director, John A. Fallone, age 58
Auditors: Deloitte&ToucheLLP

LOCATIONS

HQ: Sun Bancorp Inc.
226 Landis Ave., Vineland NJ 08360
Phone: 856-691-7700 **Fax:** 856-691-9187
Web: www.sunnbnj.com

PRODUCTS/OPERATIONS

2011 Sales

	$ mil.	% of total
Interest		
Loans	112	73
Securities & other	13	9
Noninterest		
Service charges on deposit accounts	11	7
Gain on Sale of loans	3	2
BOLI income	3	2
Investment products income	2	2
Net gain on sales of investment securities	1	1
Losses	(12.8)	-
Other	4	4
Total	**140**	**100**

Selected Subsidiaries

Sun National Bank
2020 Properties L.L.C.
Sun Financial Services L.L.C.
Sun Home Loans Inc.

COMPETITORS

1st Constitution Bancorp
Bank of America
Cape Bancorp
Citigroup
Fulton Financial
Ocean Shore
PNC Financial
Provident Financial Services
Republic First Bank
Sovereign Bank
Susquehanna Bancshares
TF Financial
Valley National Bancorp

HISTORICAL FINANCIALS

Company Type: Public

Income Statement FYE: December 31

	ASSETS ($ mil.)	NET INCOME ($ mil.)	INCOME AS % OF ASSETS	EMPLOYEES
12/11	3,183	(67)	—	713
12/10	3,417	(185)	—	696
12/09	3,578	(17)	—	805
12/08	3,622	14	0.4%	781
12/07	3,338	19	0.6%	810
Annual Growth	(1.2%)	—	—	(3.1%)

2011 Year-End Financials

Debt ratio: 3.25%
Return on equity: (-21.84)%
Cash ($ mil.): 119
Current ratio: —
Long-term debt ($ mil.): 103
No. of shares (mil.): 85
Dividends
Yield: —
Payout: —
Market value ($ mil.): 207

STOCK PRICE ($) FY Close		P/E High/Low		PER SHARE ($) Earnings	Dividends	Book Value
12/11	2.42	—	—	(0.88)	0.00	3.61
12/10	4.64	—	—	(6.56)	0.00	5.33
12/09	3.75	—	—	(0.97)	0.00	15.29
12/08	7.49	25	11	0.62	0.00	15.57
12/07	15.78	26	17	0.78	0.00	15.13
Annual Growth	(37.4%)	—	—	—	—	(30.1%)

Sunoco Logistics Partners L.P.

Sunoco Logistics Partners acquires owns and operates a large swath of midstream and downstream assets primarily in tandem with former parent Sunoco. This includes ownership of more than 7400 miles of crude oil refined product and oil gathering pipelines and minority interests in four refined product pipelines (Explorer Pipeline Wolverine Pipe Line West Shore Pipe Line and Yellowstone Pipe Line) as well as more than 40 terminals and other storage assets related to Sunoco's refining and marketing operations in the Midwest Gulf Coast and Eastern states. Sunoco Logistics Partners also purchases domestic crude and resells it to Sunoco's refining and marketing unit.

The company pursues a strategy of growing its businesses organically and through complementary acquisitions (about 20 since 2002). In 2009 it acquired 52-mile Oklahoma crude oil pipeline Excel Pipeline LLC.

In 2009 Sunoco Logistics Partners reorganized its operations from geographical segments into more functional industry segments: refined products pipelines terminal facilities and crude oil pipeline. The company's refined products pipelines segment consists of 2200 miles of petroleum products pipeline and serves customers primarily in the Northeast and Midwest regions of the US. Through its terminal facilities unit Sunoco Logistics Partners is capable of storing 23 million barrels of crude oil and 10 million barrels of refined petroleum products. The crude oil pipeline segment consisting of about 3850 miles of crude oil pipelines primarily serves customers in Oklahoma and Texas.

In 2009 the company reported a major slump in revenues caused by the collapse of crude oil prices and a weaker demand for oil as the result of the global recession. However it also posted a very robust net income result primarily due to income from its its expanded operations lower oil costs and from increased fees across all of its segments.

In 2010 led by increased demand due to a rebounding economy and higher commodity prices the company reported a major jump in both revenues and net income. It was particularly buoyed by the strong performance (increased volumes and fees) of its terminals business.

In 2010 Sunoco Logistics Partners acquired the butane blending business of Texon L.P. for $140 million plus inventory. The business consists of technology for sophisticated blending of butane into gasoline contracts with several large terminal operators currently utilizing the technology butane inventories and other related assets.

Expanding its pipeline assets in 2011 the company acquired control of Inland Corp. (which has a 350-mile refined-products pipeline and related facilities) for $100 million. It also acquired the Eagle Point tank farm and related assets in Westville New Jersey from Sunoco for $100 million.

Lynn Elsenhans was named CEO of Sunoco Logistics in 2010. She replaced Deborah Fretz who announced her retirement.

Sunoco (which formed Sunoco Logistics Partners in 2002 to operate a major portion of its midstream and downstream assets) controlled about 31% of the company in 2011.

EXECUTIVES

VP Chief Human Resources Officer and Director, Dennis Zeleny, age 56
VP Operations, David A. Justin, age 59, $262,500 total compensation
Chairman and CEO, Lynn L. Elsenhans, age 54
President COO and Director, Michael J. (Mike) Hennigan, age 52
Controller, Michael D. Galtman, age 37
VP CFO and Director, Brian P. MacDonald, age 46
Media Contact, Thomas Golembeski
VP General Counsel and Secretary, Kathleen Shea-Ballay
VP Lease Acquisition and Marketing, Scott W. McCord
Director, Philip L. (Phil) Frederickson, age 56
Director, Stacy L. Fox, age 57
VP Chief Human Resources Officer and Director, Dennis Zeleny, age 56
Director, Cynthia A. Archer, age 58
Director, Stephen L. Cropper, age 62
Director, L. Wilson Berry Jr., age 68
President COO and Director, Michael J. (Mike) Hennigan, age 52
VP CFO and Director, Brian P. MacDonald, age 46
Director, William R. Silver
Auditors: Ernst&YoungLLP

LOCATIONS

HQ: Sunoco Logistics Partners L.P.
Mellon Bank Ctr. 1735 Market St. Ste. LL, Philadelphia PA 19103-1699
Phone: 215-977-3000 **Fax:** 215-977-3409
Web: www.sunocologistics.com

PRODUCTS/OPERATIONS

2011 Sales

	% of total
Crude oil acquisition &	92
Terminal	4
Crude oil	3
Refined product	1
Total	**100**

COMPETITORS

Buckeye Partners
CITGO
Enbridge Energy
Enterprise Products
Kinder Morgan Energy Partners
Kinder Morgan Management
Magellan Midstream
Marathon Petroleum
Plains All American Pipeline
RKA Petroleum
TransMontaigne
TransMontaigne Partners

HISTORICAL FINANCIALS

Company Type: Public

Income Statement FYE: December 31

	REVENUE ($ mil.)	NET INCOME ($ mil.)	NET PROFIT MARGIN	EMPLOYEES
12/11	10,918	313	2.9%	1,500
12/10	7,838	346	4.4%	1,400
12/09	5,429	250	4.6%	1,340
12/08	10,136	214	2.1%	1,270
12/07	7,405	120	1.6%	1,150
Annual Growth	10.2%	26.9%	—	6.9%

2011 Year-End Financials

Debt ratio: 31.00%
Return on equity: 28.56%
Cash ($ mil.): 5
Current ratio: 98.86
Long-term debt ($ mil.): 1,448
No. of shares (mil.): 103
Dividends
Yield: —
Payout: 63.39%
Market value ($ mil.): 4,071

STOCK PRICE ($) FY Close		P/E High/Low		PER SHARE ($) Earnings	Dividends	Book Value
12/11	39.40	41	14	2.54	0.00	10.61
12/10	83.59	27	20	3.11	1.51	9.72
12/09	66.89	32	21	2.16	1.37	9.27
12/08	45.14	32	17	1.66	1.22	7.79
12/07	50.18	56	43	1.12	1.11	6.89
Annual Growth	(5.9%)	—	—	22.7%	—	11.4%

SunTrust Banks, Inc.

Coca-Cola fast cars and SunTrust Banks –this Sun Belt company is southern to its core. Its flagship SunTrust Bank subsidiary operates more than 1650 branches in about a dozen southeastern and mid-Atlantic states. The bank offers standard retail and commercial services such as credit deposit and investment services. SunTrust also operates subsidiaries that offer mortgage wealth and investment management insurance investment banking equipment leasing and brokerage services. The company participated in the underwriting of the IPO of fellow Atlanta icon Coca-Cola and was one of its largest shareholders for many years; SunTrust is also the official bank of Grand American Road Racing.

The nationwide economic crisis impacted many of SunTrust's core markets in the Southeast particularly hard as credit markets froze and unemployment levels increased. The bank suffered some $1.6 billion in losses in 2009 alone mainly related to bad loans both on the consumer and commercial levels. By 2010 the company began to see improvements in charge-offs delinquencies and nonperforming loans but loan demand remained soft. In 2011 Sun Trust's financial performance improved and its loan portfolio grew by 6%. However the economic recovery was slow and spotty interest rates remained low and new federal regulations hit SunTrust's fee revenue streams.

Like many of its peers SunTrust took part in the Federal Reserve's bailout in 2008 selling the government about $4.9 billion in preferred shares. The company repaid the government in 2011. That helped contribute to better earnings that year. SunTrust also reported higher net interest income and lower provision for credit losses.

Sun Trust is focused on rebuilding and diversifying its loan portfolio with a particular interest on increasing commercial industrial government and consumer lending. Meanwhile SunTrust its reducing its exposure to risky real estate loans. The company still faces some lingering problems in its mortgage business. However it is working to reduce expenses and improve efficiency in order to offset some of those problems. SunTrust plans to eliminate around $300 million in expenses by 2013.

Another strategic priority for SunTrust is to diversify its lines of income. It is looking specifically to grow its wholesale business by improving client relationships and increasing its commercial lending activity. The company's corporate and investment banking division is growing. In 2011 the segment reported an 8% jump in revenue.Diversified commercial banking also saw a nearly double digit increase in sales that year.

The company is making other selective acquisitions to grow its core business. In 2012 SunTrust announced plans to acquire online lender FirstAgain. The deal will enhance Sun Trust's ability to lend directly to customers via the Internet.

SunTrust also has invested in its private banking unit that caters to people in the sports and entertainment industries particularly motor sports and country music. SunTrust Sports and Entertainment Specialty Group has about a half-dozen offices (including a San Diego office opened in 2010) and serves clients throughout the US. It built upon the unit again in 2011 with the purchase of CSI Capital Management which added five offices across the US and some $1.5 billion of assets under management.

A long time fan of sports and racecars it is no surprise that Sun Trust is devoting more attention to that unit. The company helped fund the construction of the home of the Daytona 500 Daytona International Speedway in Florida.

In addition to car racing SunTrust is linked to another southern tradition: Coca-Cola. Legend has it that the only written copy of the Coke formula was stored away for safe keeping in a SunTrust vault for decades (before it was moved to be put on display in 2011). SunTrust once owned a significant stake in the company but began gradually selling off its shares in 2007 in order to raise capital. It contributed some 3.6 billion of the company's common shares to its SunTrust Foundation and sold another 8.1 million. SunTrust still owns about 30 million Coke shares.

HISTORY

SunTrust was born from the union of old-money Georgia and new-money Florida. Founded in 1891 the Trust Company of Georgia (originally Commercial Traveler's Savings Bank) served Atlanta's oldest and richest institutions. It helped underwrite Coca-Cola's IPO in 1919; the bank's ownership stake in Coke stemmed from its early involvement with the beverage maker.

Beginning in 1933 Trust acquired controlling interests in five other Georgia banks. As regulation of multibank ownership relaxed in the 1970s Trust acquired the remaining interests in its original banks and bought 25 more. At the height of the Sun Belt boom in 1984 Trust was the most profitable bank in the nation. The next year it united with Sun Banks.

Sun Banks was formed in 1934 as the First National Bank at Orlando. It grew into a holding company in 1967 and in the early 1970s helped assemble the land for Walt Disney World. The Sun name was adopted in 1973.

Under president and CEO Joel Wells Sun Banks began an acquisition-fueled expansion within Florida. Between 1976 and 1984 Sun Banks' approximate asset growth was an astronomical 500% and branch count grew fivefold (51 to 274).

After a lingering courtship Sun and Trust formed a super holding company over the two organizations. When the marriage was consummated in 1985 Sun brought a dowry of $9.4 billion in assets and Trust contributed $6.2 billion. Trust's chairman Bob Strickland became chairman and CEO for the new Atlanta-based SunTrust and Wells became president.

In 1986 SunTrust bought Nashville Tennessee-based Third National Bank the #2 banking company in the Volunteer State. But problems with Tennessee real estate loans plagued SunTrust. In 1990 it increased the amount of loans it wrote off; the bank's ratings suffered because of nonperforming loans on properties in overbuilt Florida. While nonperforming assets decreased in Tennessee in 1991 they climbed in Florida and Georgia.

Strickland stepped down as chairman and CEO in 1990. Wells died in 1991 and James Williams a conservative banker who instilled strict fiscal management in the Trust banks became chairman and CEO. Under his direction the company reduced its nonperforming assets and began diversifying its business lines.

In 1993 the bank adopted accounting rules that caused it to revalue its Coca-Cola stock from its historic value of $110000 to almost $1.1 billion. The dividends from these holdings contributed substantially to revenues.

SunTrust continued developing its nonbanking financial services: It expanded its investment services outside its traditional southern US market and bought Equitable Securities (now SunTrust Equitable Securities) in 1998. That year president Phillip Humann succeeded Williams as chairman and CEO. SunTrust also nearly doubled its branch count when it bought Crestar Financial a banking powerhouse in the mid-Atlantic and Southeast.

In 1999 the company created a new trust business to serve high-net-worth clients and it consolidated its 27 banking charters in six states into one based in Georgia the following year. In 2001 SunTrust made an unsolicited offer for Wachovia which was on track to be acquired by First Union. After a heated proxy campaign Wachovia's board of directors and shareholders voted down SunTrust's bid. Also that year the company bought the institutional business of investment bank Robinson-Humphrey a unit of Citigroup's Salomon Smith Barney.

SunTrust bought National Commerce Financial in 2004 for some $7 billion. The deal helped the bank expand in existing territories as well as provide entry into the growing North Carolina market where SunTrust had been conspicuously absent. The company divested its 49% stake in First Market Bank (Ukrop's Super Markets owns the rest) which it acquired in the National Commerce deal. SunTrust unloaded the unit in part because it has branches in Kroger Publix Safeway and Wal-Mart stores.

The company placed on administrative leave or dismissed several financial officers after it had to restate its earnings for the first two quarters of 2004 due to miscalculations of its loan loss reserves. (The SEC concluded an investigation into the matter in 2006 without recommending penalties.)

Former president and COO Jim Wells became CEO in 2007; Humann remained as chairman but stepped down the following year.

SunTrust bought GB&T Bancshares in 2008 adding about 20 branches in north and central Georgia.

To raise money and streamline operations SunTrust spun off several noncore operations in 2008.

That year the company sold off several noncore assests including its interests in investment brokerage Lighthouse Investment Partners First Mercantile Trust Company a retirement-plan services firm; and TransPlatinum which provided fuel card services. In late 2010 the company sold more than $14 billion worth of money market funds managed by subsidiary RidgeWorth Capital Management to Federated Investors.

EXECUTIVES

EVP and Chief Human Resources, Kenneth J. (Ken) Carrig, age 55
Corporate EVP General Counsel and Corporate Secretary, Raymond D. Fortin, age 59
President and CEO SunTrust Mortgage, Jerome T. Lienhard II
Chairman and CEO, William H. (Bill) Rogers Jr., age 54, $500,000 total compensation
EVP National Sales and Production Manager, Sterling Edmunds Jr.
Corporate EVP and Wholesale Banking Executive, Mark A. Chancy, age 48, $560,000 total compensation
CFO and Treasurer, Aleem Gillani
Key Executive SunTrust Bank South Florida Region, James W. Rasmussen
Key Executive Sun Trust Bank Chattanooga Region, Michael R. Butler
Corporate EVP and Chief Risk Officer, Thomas E. (Tom) Freeman, age 61, $475,000 total compensation
Head Private Wealth Management and Institutional Investment Solutions, Willem Hattink
Chairman President and CEO SunTrust Bank Georgia Region, Kevin S. Blair
EVP and Head Treasury and Payment Solutions, Eric Brewer
Chief Investment Officer Private Wealth Management and Institutional Investment Solutions, Ernie Dawal
EVP of Consumer Banking & Private Wealth Management, Brad R. Dinsmore
CIO, Anil Cheriyan, age 54
Director, Alston D. (Pete) Correll Jr., age 70
Director, David H. Hughes, age 68
Director, G. Gilmer Minor III, age 71
Director, J. Hicks Lanier, age 71
Director, Thomas R. (Tom) Watjen, age 57
Director, Jeffrey C. (Jeff) Crowe, age 65
Director, Frank S. Royal, age 72
Director, M. Douglas Ivester, age 65
Chairman and CEO, William H. (Bill) Rogers Jr., age 54
Director, Blake P. Garrett Jr., age 71
Director, Phail Wynn Jr., age 64
Director, Robert M. Beall II, age 68
Director, William A. (Bill) Linnenbringer, age 63
Director, Kyle P. Legg, age 60
Auditors: Ernst&YoungLLP

LOCATIONS

HQ: SunTrust Banks Inc.
303 Peachtree St. NE, Atlanta GA 30308
Phone: 404-588-7711 **Fax:** 404-332-3875
Web: www.suntrust.com

PRODUCTS/OPERATIONS

2011 Sales

	$ mil.	% of total
Interest		
Loans including fees	5,219	55
Securities available for sale including dividends	791	8
Loans held for sale	93	1
Trading accounts	78	-
Noninterest		
Service charges on deposit accounts	685	7
Trust & investment management	531	6
Card fees	371	4
Investment banking	317	4
Trading income	248	3
Retail investment services	230	2
Mortgage servicing related income	224	2
Net securities gains	117	1
Other charges & fees	507	5
Other	191	2
Total	**9,602**	**100**

Selected Subsidiaries and Affiliates

GenSprings Holdings Inc.
GenSpring Family Offices L.L.C.
GenSpring International LLC
Southern Heritage Statutory Trust I
SunTrust 1031 Exchange Co.
SunTrust Bank Holding Company
Crestar Capital Trust I
STI Investment Management (Collateral) Inc.
SunTrust Bank
Double Haul Trading LLC
Premium Assignment Corporation
STB Capital LLC
STB Real Estate LLC
SunTrust Comunity Capital LLC
SunTrust Education Financial Services Corporation
SunTrust Robinson Humphrey Funding LLC
Twin Rivers II Inc.
SunTrust Capital I
SunTrust Plaza Associates LLC
SunTrust Preferred Capital I

COMPETITORS

BancorpSouth
Bank of America
BB&T
BBX Capital
Citigroup
Compass Bancshares
First Citizens BancShares
First Horizon
JPMorgan Chase
Regions Financial
Synovus
Wells Fargo

HISTORICAL FINANCIALS

Company Type: Public

Income Statement FYE: December 31

	ASSETS ($ mil.)	NET INCOME ($ mil.)	INCOME AS % OF ASSETS	EMPLOYEES
12/11	176,859	647	0.4%	29,182
12/10	172,874	189	0.1%	29,056
12/09	174,164	(1,563)	—	28,001
12/08	189,137	795	0.4%	29,333
12/07	179,573	1,634	0.9%	32,323
Annual Growth	(0.4%)	(20.7%)	—	(2.5%)

2011 Year-End Financials

Debt ratio: 7.13%
Return on equity: 3.22%
Cash ($ mil.): 3,717
Current ratio: —
Long-term debt ($ mil.): 12,618
No. of shares (mil.): 536
Dividends
Yield: —
Payout: 12.77%
Market value ($ mil.): 9,504

	STOCK PRICE ($) FY Close	P/E High	P/E Low	PER SHARE ($) Earnings	Dividends	Book Value
12/11	17.70	35	17	0.94	0.00	37.37
12/10	29.51	—	—	(0.18)	0.04	46.22
12/09	20.29	—	—	(3.98)	0.22	45.14
12/08	29.54	32	10	2.13	2.85	63.15
12/07	62.49	20	13	4.55	2.92	51.81
Annual Growth	(27.0%)	—	—	(32.6%)	—	(7.8%)

SUPERVALU INC

SUPERVALU is feeling pretty super following the acquisition of more than 1100 supermarkets from fallen grocery giant Albertsons. Its purchase of the Albertsons' stores catapulted the chain to second place in the traditional grocery retail market (behind Kroger) with about 4400 stores in some 40 US states. (It has since relinquished the #2 spot to Safeway.) The deal added half a dozen banners including Albertsons Acme Markets and Shaw's to SUPERVALU's roster of stores (which includes Jewel-Osco Cub Foods Save-A-Lot and Shop 'n Save). The company is also one of the nation's largest food wholesalers supplying some 1950 independently operated stores nationwide with brand-name and private-label goods.

HISTORY

SUPERVALU's predecessor was formed in Minneapolis in the 1870s –and again in 1926. In 1871 wholesalers Hugh Harrison George Newell and W. D. Washburn joined forces to create Newell and Harrison. Newell bought out his partners in 1874 and renamed the firm George R. Newell Co. Five years later Harrison formed his own operation H. G. Harrison Co. In 1926 the companies merged creating Winston & Newell Co. the largest grocery distributor to independent grocers in the Midwest.

The company was part of the Independent Grocers Alliance from 1928-1942 before adopting the name Super Valu Stores in 1954. It expanded by acquiring chains such as Piggly-Wiggly Midland (1958 Wisconsin) and a number of wholesale operations across the US.

Super Valu entered nonfood retailing in 1971 by acquiring ShopKo a discount department store chain. Two years later it founded clothing chain County Seat (sold 1983). Super Valu added a new format to its food operations by purchasing Cub Stores (warehouse-style groceries) in 1980; it later combined its Cub Stores and ShopKo formats. More acquisitions followed including Atlanta's Food Giant chain. Super Valu named Michael Wright CEO in 1981 and chairman in 1982.

Super Valu acquired Scott's an Indiana food store chain in 1991 and sold a 54% interest in ShopKo to the public. The company changed its name to SUPERVALU in 1992 and bought food wholesaler Wetterau making it the #1 independent food distributor in the US and giving it the Save-A-Lot franchise (launched in 1978).

Experiencing sluggish distribution growth SUPERVALU continued to expand its retail holdings. Acquisitions in 1994 included Sweet Life Foods (280 stores) and 30 Texas T Stores. In 1996 it acquired six St. Louis Price Chopper warehouse stores and Fleming's Sav-U-Foods converting the 21 stores to Save-A-Lots and establishing a presence in California. SUPERVALU sold its remaining 46% stake in ShopKo the next year. In 1999 the company signed a deal to supply 1350 Kmart stores. SUPERVALU also acquired distributor and food retailer Richfood Holdings.

Rival distributor Fleming Companies beat out SUPERVALU in 2001 to become Kmart's sole supplier of foods and consumable products. SUPERVALU later announced plans to cut 7% of its workforce and close some of its distribution centers and stores including its Laneco stores in Pennsylvania and New Jersey and its central Indiana Cub stores. Wright retired as CEO in mid-2001 and remained as chairman; president and CFO Jeff Noddle became CEO. In 2001 the company also bought nine Save-A-Lots in the Southeast and announced it was closing 19 Atlanta-area Cub Foods stores.

In May 2002 SUPERVALU acquired St. Louis-based Deal$ –Nothing Over a Dollar an extreme-value general merchandise retailer with 53 stores in the Midwest (sold in 2006 to Dollar Tree Stores for about $30.5 million). Later in the month Wright retired as chairman and was succeeded by Noddle. In June the company announced it would take a charge of up to $21 million because of accounting irregularities in its pharmacy division.

SUPERVALU expanded its agreement in 2003 with Target Corporation to supply all Super Target stores. In 2004 it sold off its minority interest in the regional grocery chain WinCo Foods.

In February 2005 SUPERVALU acquired Total Logistics a provider of third-party logistics services and maker of refrigeration systems for about $234 million. In March the grocery distributor launched a specialty produce distribution company called W. Newell & Co.

The company completed its acquisition of 1124 stores from Albertsons in June 2006. The new stores include Acme Markets Bristol Farms Jewel Shaw's Supermarkets Star Markets and Albertsons stores. Looking to take back sales lost to natural and organic grocery chains SUPERVALU launched its own natural foods division called Sunflower Market in 2006. (SUPERVALU originally had planned to open as many as 50 Sunflower Markets but in early 2008 announced it would close its five Sunflower Markets as they did not deliver expected results.)

In mid-2007 SUPERVALU sold its 18 Scott's Food & Pharmacy stores in Indiana to rival Kroger.

SUPERVALU added a private-label organic food line called Wild Harvest in 2008.

In 2009 the company named Craig Herkert a former Wal-Mart executive as its new president and CEO succeeding Jeff Noddle. As part of the executive shift president and COO Mike Jackson retired in August 2009 after more than 30 years with the company. Throughout the course of the year SUPERVALU closed or sold more than 100 stores nationwide including about about 40 Albertsons stores in Utah to grocery wholesaler Associated Food Stores. The closings were part of an effort by the company to scale back spending.

In 2010 SUPERVALU made several divestments. Early in the year it sold off its Payson Store Fixtures division which makes fixtures millwork and decor items to DGS Retail. It sold its Bristol Farms chain of more than a dozen upscale supermarkets in California to local management and the West Coast investment firm Endeavour Capital for an undisclosed amount in October. Late in 2010 SUPERVALU sold its Total Logistic Control subsidiary (TLC) to Ryder System.

In September 2011 the company sold more than 100 fuel centers associated with its Albertsons Cub

Foods Hornbacher's and Jewel-Osco banners to four different buyers. The sale was part of SUPERVALU's effort to raise cash by selling non-core assets.

Herkert was replaced as CEO by chairman Wayne Sales in July 2012 soon after he announced a turnaround plan for the ailing business.

EXECUTIVES

EVP and CFO, Sherry M. Smith, age 50
EVP Real Estate Market Development and Legal, J. Andrew (Andy) Herring, age 53
VP CFO Supply Chain Services and Interim Controller, David M. Oliver, age 54
Chairman President and CEO, Wayne C. Sales, age 62
President CEO and Director, Craig R. Herkert, age 52, $653,846 total compensation
EVP; President Retail Operations, Peter J. (Pete) Van Helden, age 51
EVP Human Resources and Corporate Communications, David E. (Dave) Pylipow, age 54, $412,120 total compensation
EVP Merchandising and Logistics, Janel S. Haugarth, age 56, $521,540 total compensation
EVP and CIO, Wayne R. Shurts, age 52
Group VP Finance Merchandising Marketing and Corporate Planning, Daniel J. Zvonek, age 47
SVP Merchandising, Tim Lowe
President Independent Business, Leon Bergmann
Investors and Financial Media, Kenneth B. Levy
Investors and Financial Media, Steve J. Bloomquist
President and CEO Save-A-Lot, Santiago Roces
SVP General Counsel and Corporate Secretary, Todd N. Sheldon
EVP and Chief Marketing Officer, Michael Moore, age 47
SVP and CIO, Kathy Persian, age 45
Director, Kathi P. Seifert
Director, Susan E. Engel, age 65
Director, Philip L. (Phil) Francis, age 65
Director, Edwin C. (Skip) Gage, age 71
Director, Prof Steven S. Rogers, age 54
Director, Ronald E. Daly, age 65
Director, Matthew E. (Matt) Rubel, age 54
President CEO and Director, Craig R. Herkert, age 52
Director, Donald R. Chappel, age 60
Director, Irwin Cohen, age 71
Auditors: KPMGLLP

LOCATIONS

HQ: SUPERVALU INC.
7075 Flying Cloud Dr., Eden Prairie MN 55344
Phone: 952-828-4000 **Fax:** 281-584-2721
Web: www.sysco.com

2012 Stores

	Traditional	Save-A-Lot
Alabama	29	
Arizona	1	
Arkansas	19	
California	214	15
Colorado	11	
Connecticut	10	
Delaware	12	7
Florida	131	
Georgia	35	
Idaho	33	-
Illinois	191	59
Indiana	5	55
Iowa	1	5
Kansas -	8	
Kentucky	1	123
Louisiana -	21	
Maine	22	8
Maryland	46	23
Massachusetts	84	11
Michigan -	96	
Minnesota	44	1
Mississippi -	22	
Missouri	27	65
Montana	30	-
New Hampshire	34	1
New Jersey	50	11
New Mexico - -		
New York -	52	
Nevada	35	-
North Carolina	1	28
North Dakota	6	-
Ohio -	130	
Oklahoma -	17	
Oregon	46	7
Pennsylvania	48	73
Rhode Island	10	5
South Carolina -	31	
Tennessee -	106	
Texas -	31	
Utah	4	-
Vermont	19	-
Virginia	58	22
Washington	72	3
West Virginia -	38	
Wisconsin -	16	
Wyoming	10	-
International -	6	
Total	**1,102**	**1,332**

PRODUCTS/OPERATIONS

2012 Stores

	No.
Company-owned	1,499
Licensed	935
Total	**2,434**

2012 Sales

	$ mil.	% of total
Retail food	27,906	77
Supply chain services	8,194	23
Total	**36,100**	**100**

2012 Sales

	% of total
Retail food	
Nonperishable	42
Perishable	22
Pharmacy	6
General merchandise & health & beauty	5
Fuel	1
Other	1
Independent business	
Product sales to independent	23
Services to independent	-
Total	**100**

Selected Retail Food Stores and Formats

Extreme Value Stores
- Save-A-Lot (licensed)

Price Superstore
- Cub Foods
- Shop ' n Save
- Shoppers Food & Pharmacy

Supermarkets
- Acme Markets
- Albertsons
- Farm Fresh
- Hornbacher' s
- Jewel-Osco
- Lucky
- Shaw' s Supermarkets
- Star Markets

Selected Services

Accounting
Category management
Consumer and market research
Financial assistance
Insurance
Merchandising assistance
Personnel training
Private-label program
Retail operations counseling
Site selection and purchasing or leasing assistance
Store design and construction
Store equipment
Store management assistance
Store planning
Strategic and business planning

Selected Private-Label Brands

Culinary Circle
essensia
equaline
Flavorite
HomeLife
Richfood
Shopper' s Value
Wild Harvest

COMPETITORS

A&P
Ahold U.S.A.
ALDI
Alex Lee
Arden Group
Associated Wholesale Grocers
Associated Wholesalers
Big Y Foods
BJ' s Wholesale Club
Bozzuto' s
C&S Wholesale
Costco Wholesale
CVS Caremark
Delhaize America
Dierbergs Markets
Dollar General
Dollar Tree
Family Dollar Stores
Giant Eagle
Hannaford Bros.
Harris Teeter
Jetro Cash & Carry
Krasdale Foods
Kroger
Marsh Supermarkets
McLane
Meijer
Nash-Finch
Piggly Wiggly Midwest
Rite Aid
Roundy' s
Safeway
Schnuck Markets
Sherwood Food
Spartan Stores
Stater Bros.
Stop & Shop
Target Corporation
Wakefern Food
Wal-Mart
Walgreen
White Rose
Whole Foods
Winn-Dixie

HISTORICAL FINANCIALS

Company Type: Public

Income Statement

FYE: February 25

	REVENUE ($ mil.)	NET INCOME ($ mil.)	NET PROFIT MARGIN	EMPLOYEES
02/12	36,100	(1,040)	—	130,000
02/11	37,534	(1,510)	—	142,000
02/10	40,597	393	1.0%	160,000
02/09	44,564	(2,855)	—	178,000
02/08	44,048	593	1.3%	192,000
Annual Growth	(4.9%)	—	—	(9.3%)

2012 Year-End Financials

Debt ratio: 51.90%
Return on equity: (-4952.38)%
Cash ($ mil.): 157
Current ratio: 89.83
Long-term debt ($ mil.): 5,868
No. of shares (mil.): 212
Dividends
Yield: —
Payout: —
Market value ($ mil.): 1,410

	STOCK PRICE ($) FY Close	P/E High	P/E Low	PER SHARE ($) Earnings	Dividends	Book Value
02/12	6.65	—	—	(4.91)	0.00	0.10
02/11	8.55	—	—	(7.13)	0.00	6.32
02/10	15.27	10	7	1.85	0.00	13.62
02/09	15.61	—	—	(13.51)	0.00	12.17
02/08	27.94	18	10	2.76	0.00	28.08
Annual Growth	(30.2%)	—	—	—	—	(75.6%)

Susquehanna Bancshares, Inc

Susquehanna Bancshares which bears the name of the river that flows through the heart of its market area is the holding company for Susquehanna Bank. The bank serves individuals and regional businesses through more than 250 branches in south-central and southeastern Pennsylvania Maryland New Jersey and West Virginia. It offers standard services such as deposits loans and credit cards. Non-banking subsidiaries provide wealth management insurance brokerage and employee benefits and vehicle leasing. Loans secured by commercial and residential real estate account for more nearly 60% of the bank's portfolio. Susquehanna Bancshares boasts assets of some $17.5 billion.

Operations

A regional financial services holding company Susquehanna's operations include a commercial bank that provides financial services at more than 250 office locations in the Mid-Atlantic region. Its business is divided into bank and non-bank subsidiaries. The commercial bank business comprises three regions: PA Division (with about 110 banking offices) MD Division (60 banking offices) and DV Division (more than 70 banking offices). Susquehanna's non-banking units include Susquehanna Trust & Investment Company Valley Forge Asset Management Corp. Stratton Management Company The Addis Group and Boston Service Company. The company's mortgage division also opened an operations center located in New York where bank employees set up process and underwrite residential mortgage loans for customers in Pennsylvania New Jersey Maryland West Virginia Delaware and Virginia.

Strategy

Susquehanna Bancshares has grown by acquiring new customers in existing and new markets. It also looks for acquisitions in strategic markets. The company makes a point to regularly cross-sell its financial services and products to its customers. Its long-term strategy involves enhancing customer relationships through sales and service while focusing on managing risk. The company leverages the use of rewards teamwork training communications technology and its organizational structure to achieve its strategic objectives. With plans to bring together more than 100 employees from four states Susquehanna Bank is developing a centralized training facility located in Mountville. The office boasts high-tech classrooms where employees from different locations can interact.

Financial Analysis

Total revenue in 2011 inched upward slightly from 2010 levels by nearly 2%. Its primary source of operating income —net interest income —increased to $433.2 million in 2011 from $426.5 million in 2010. The company's $7.8 million increase in its taxable equivalent net interest income in 2011 over 2010 numbers can be attributed to a more than $441 million rise in its average earning asset volumes. Susquehanna's non-interest income (excluding the net realized gain through acquisitions) dropped $8.6 million (roughly 6%) in 2011 vs. 2010. The company points to a variety of factors for the decrease such as a $9 million dip in net realized gain on securities and a decrease of $2.7 million in service charges on deposit accounts. In general cash flow in 2011 resulted in a greater cash inflow of $72 million against a cash outflow of $38 million in 2010. Overall the company has not been immune to the economic recession. To ride it out Susquehanna has shuttered more than a dozen branches in Pennsylvania as it worked to consolidate operations and cut costs. Susquehanna Bancshares returned to profitability in 2010 as the economy exhibited signs of a rebound and the company's provisions for loan and lease losses decreased.

Mergers & Acquisitions

The bank has expanded its operations by strengthening its foothold in existing markets though acquisitions. Its most recent purchase of Tower Bancorp completed in 2012 for a total value of $389 million added about 50 branches in central Pennsylvania. In 2011 the company bought Abington Bancorp in a deal valued at more than $150 million that gave Susquehanna 20 branches in suburban Philadelphia. To date the holding company's purchase of Community Banks in 2007 represented its largest acquisition resulting in an additional 75 branches in southeastern Pennsylvania. Susquehanna Bancshares has also built its retirement planning and investment management operations through acquisitions. Looking to the future the company considers buying other banks that serve four major growth corridors: the Lancaster/York/Baltimore area the Greater Delaware Valley area the Interstate 81 corridor and existing market areas that fill the gaps it currently serves.

EXECUTIVES

SVP; President Susquehanna Bank Pennsylvania Division, Jeffrey M. Seibert, age 52
Vice Chairman; Vice Chairman and President Susquehanna Bank, Eddie L. Dunklebarger, age 57, $500,000 total compensation
EVP and COO, Gregory A. Duncan, age 56, $347,392 total compensation
Chairman and CEO; Chairman Susquehanna Bank, William J. Reuter, age 62, $750,000 total compensation
EVP CFO and Treasurer, Drew K. Hostetter, age 57, $384,641 total compensation
EVP and Chief Administrative Officer, Edward Balderston Jr., age 64, $200,625 total compensation
EVP and Chief Corporate Credit Officer, Michael M. Quick, age 63, $340,000 total compensation
SVP and CTO, Rodney A. Lefever, age 45
SVP Secretary and Counsel, Lisa M. Cavage, age 47
EVP and Group Executive; President CEO and Director Susquehanna Bank, James G. Pierne, age 60
SVP and Group Executive, Peter J. Sahd, age 52
SVP and Group Executive; President and CEO Valley Forge Asset Management; Chief Investment Officer Susquehanna Trust & Investment; Chairman Stratton Management and Semper Trust; and Director Stratton Funds, Bernard A. Francis Jr., age 61, $325,000 total compensation
SVP; President Susquehanna Bank Delaware Valley Division, Joseph R. Lizza, age 53
President Hann Financial Service, Charles R. Dovico
President The Addis Group, F. Scott Addis
VP Investor Relations, Abram G. (Abe) Koser
SVP; President Susquehanna Bank Maryland Division, Michael E. Hough, age 47
SEVP; Managing Director Commercial Sales Susquehanna Bank Maryland Division, Christopher D. Holt
SVP; Managing Director Susquehanna Bank Commercial Division, John H. Montgomery, age 49
SVP and Chief Risk Officer, Edward J. Wydock, age 55
Manager Corporate Communications, Stephen (Steve) Trapnell
Vice Chairman; Vice Chairman and President Susquehanna Bank, Eddie L. Dunklebarger, age 57
Director, James A. Ulsh, age 65
Director, Peter DeSoto, age 72
Director, Wayne E. Alter Jr., age 59
Director, Guy W. Miller Jr., age 66
Director, Roger V. Wiest Sr., age 71
Director, Bruce A. Hepburn, age 69
Director, Scott J. Newkam, age 61
Director, Christine A. Sears, age 56
Director, E. Susan Piersol, age 57
Director, Robert W. White, age 67
Director, Michael A. Morello, age 58
Director, Donald L. Hoffman, age 69
Director, Anthony J. Agnone Sr., age 58
Auditors: PricewaterhouseCoopersLLP

LOCATIONS

HQ: Susquehanna Bancshares Inc.
26 N. Cedar St., Lititz PA 17543
Phone: 717-626-4721 **Fax:** 717-626-1874
Web: www.susquehanna.net

PRODUCTS/OPERATIONS

Selected Services

Brokerage services
Insurance services
Investment management services
Private banking
Retirement plan services
Trust & Estate services
Wealth management services

COMPETITORS

Capital One
First Niagara Financial
Fulton Financial
M&T Bank
National Penn Bancshares
PNC Financial
RBS Citizens Financial Group
Sovereign Bank
Sun Bancorp (NJ)
TD Bank USA

HISTORICAL FINANCIALS

Company Type: Public

Income Statement

FYE: December 31

	ASSETS ($ mil.)	NET INCOME ($ mil.)	INCOME AS % OF ASSETS	EMPLOYEES
12/11	14,974	54	0.4%	3,122
12/10	13,954	31	0.2%	3,039
12/09	13,689	12	0.1%	3,055
12/08	13,682	82	0.6%	3,271
12/07	13,077	69	0.5%	3,334
Annual Growth	3.4%	(5.6%)	—	(1.6%)

2011 Year-End Financials

Debt ratio: 4.86%
Return on equity: 2.51%
Cash ($ mil.): 332
Current ratio: —
Long-term debt ($ mil.): 727
No. of shares (mil.): 156
Dividends
Yield: —
Payout: 20.00%
Market value ($ mil.): 1,315

	STOCK PRICE ($) FY Close	P/E High/Low		PER SHARE ($) Earnings	Dividends	Book Value
12/11	8.38	26	14	0.40	0.00	13.96
12/10	9.68	91	45	0.13	0.04	15.27
12/09	5.89	—	—	(0.05)	0.37	22.91
12/08	15.91	24	12	0.95	1.04	22.58
12/07	18.44	22	13	1.23	1.01	20.12
Annual Growth	(17.9%)	—	—	(24.5%)	—	(8.7%)

Susser Holdings Corp

Stripes are in Circles are out at Susser Holdings. The company operates about 550 Stripes convenience stores in Texas New Mexico and Oklahoma. (The company's Circle K stores were converted to the Stripes name several years ago.) The chain offers restaurant service in about 340 of its stores primarily under its proprietary Laredo Taco Company (LTC) brand. LTC serves up breakfast and lunch tacos rotisserie chicken and other hot foods. Susser Holdings is the largest independent c-store operator and non-refining motor fuel distributor through Susser Petroleum in Texas. (Fuel accounts for more than 80% of total sales.) Founded by Sam J. Susser in 1938 the company is now run by his son.

Susser Holdings in September 2012 took its subsidiary Susser Petroleum public through the formation of a master limited partnership that operates the wholesale fuel business (~30% of sales). Susser raised nearly $210 million through the IPO which it plans to use to build or acquire more convenience stores and to repay debt. Susser Petroleum distributes branded motor fuel to some 565 independent dealers in Texas New Mexico Oklahoma and Louisiana. In 2011 Susser Petroleum acquired the assets of Dallas/Fort Worth-based Community Fuels of Texas LP increasing its presence in the D/FW and East Texas markets.

Operations

Susser Holdings' operations include retail convenience stores retail fuel sales and wholesale motor fuel distribution. The company's 540-plus Stripes stores sell about 10 different brands (including Chevron Exxon Shell and Valero) of fuel almost all of its purchased from its wholesale arm Susser Petroleum.

Financial Analysis

Texans' thirst for fuel and food propelled Susser's sales to more than $5 billion in 2011. Sales increased 32% in 2011 vs. 2010 driven by a 36% gain in retail fuel sales a 41% increase in wholesale fuel revenue and an increase in merchandise sales of more than 9%. The company's total gross profit for the year increased nearly 18% vs. 2010. Retail fuel sales benefitted from an 28% increase in the average retail price of fuel and about a 7% increase in gallons sold. Susser's sales has grown by about 130% since the company went public in 2006. Over that time the convenience store chain has built or acquired more than 200 stores all of which –since the conversion of the last of its Town & Country stores to the Stripes banner in 2011 –trade under the Stripes name.

Strategy

Susser's business has benefitted from the relative strength of the Texas economy particularly during the recession and its integrated retail/wholesale business model. While food service and merchandise (including beer candy and cigarettes) sales account for about a quarter of the chain's sales they return nearly 60% of its gross profit. To capitalize on the higher margins returned by prepared foods and its private-label fountain drinks the company is expanding its menu promoting its food service offering and fine tuning its store hours to more capture hungry customers. (Food service accounted for more than 21% of sales in 2011 vs. 20% two years ago.) Susser is also growing its retail presence focusing its expansion on the area along the Texas border between Brownsville and Laredo and the Houston area. It is also evaluating other growth markets.

Ownership

Wellspring Capital owns nearly a third of the company's shares while CEO Sam L. Susser owns about 11%.

EXECUTIVES

VP Marketing, Rodney J. (Rod) Martin
Director Environmental and Compliance, Jeff Turner
Director Internal Audit, Stephen G. Blume
Senior Director Petroleum Services, Craig Scotton
VP and Corporate Controller, Cathy Hauslein
VP Human Resources, Otis Peaks
SVP Retail Operations, Richard Sebastian
Senior Director Food Service Operations, Conrado Saldivar
EVP CFO and Treasurer, Mary E. Sullivan, age 55, $233,172 total compensation
EVP Secretary and General Counsel, E. V. (Chip) Bonner Jr., age 56, $305,567 total compensation
EVP; President and COO Wholesale, Rocky B. Dewbre, age 46, $245,952 total compensation
Director Information Technology, Sandra Brimhall
VP Facilities Management, Robert E. (Rob) Darville
VP Business Development Retail, David Wishard
VP Merchandising, Kevin J. Mahany
VP Business Development Wholesale, Cal McIntosh
Director Human Resources, Dee Suarez
VP Dealer Operations, Patrick Albro
Director Retail Accounting, Ella Cunningham
EVP; President and CEO Retail Operations, Steven C. (Steve) DeSutter, age 58, $467,308 total compensation
President CEO and Director, Sam L. Susser, age 48, $519,231 total compensation
Chairman, Bruce W. Krysiak, age 61
VP Real Estate, Jerry L. Susser
VP Wholesale Unbranded Fuels, Lee Rahmberg
Director Construction, Michael R. Choate
Director Financial Reporting, Chrissy Garcia
Director Maintenance, Ronnie Davis Jr.
Director T & C Wholesale Inc., Dave West
Director Operations Excellence, Clint Galloway
Director Wholesale Accounting, Richard Corbitt
VP Supply and Transportation, Les Phelps
VP Information Technology, George Mrvos
SVP Human Resources, Bob Swan
SVP Sales and Operations, Gail Workman
VP Marketing, Eduardo Pereda
Director, Ronald G. (Ron) Steinhart, age 71
Director, Armand S. Shapiro, age 70
Director, David P. Engel, age 61
Director, Sam J. Susser, age 72
Director, William F. Dawson Jr., age 47
President CEO and Director, Sam L. Susser, age 48
Auditors: Ernst&YoungLLP

LOCATIONS

HQ: Susser Holdings Corporation
4525 Ayers St., Corpus Christi TX 78415
Phone: 361-884-2463 **Fax:** 361-884-2494
Web: www.susser.com

2011 Stores

	No.
Rio Grande	171
Corpus	103
San Angelo/Central	65
Laredo	42
Lubbock	41
Midland/Odessa	39
Eastern New	29
Texoma (includes Wichita Falls & Lawton Duncan & Altus	26
Victoria	16
Houston	9
Total	541

PRODUCTS/OPERATIONS

2011 Sales

	$ mil.	% of total
Motor fuel - retail	2,715	52
Motor fuel - wholesale	1,549	30
Merchandise (includes food service)	881	17
Other	47	1
Total	5,194	100

2011 Merchandise Sales

	% of total
Food	21
Cigarettes	20
Beer	18
Packaged	17
Snacks	6
Candy	3
Nonfoods	3
Other	12
Total	100

COMPETITORS

7-Eleven
Allsup' s
Chevron
Exxon Mobil
H-E-B
Kroger
Love' s Country Stores
Royal Dutch Shell
Valero Energy
Wal-Mart

HISTORICAL FINANCIALS

Company Type: Public

Income Statement

FYE: January 1

	REVENUE ($ mil.)	NET INCOME ($ mil.)	NET PROFIT MARGIN	EMPLOYEES
01/12	5,194	47	0.9%	7,584
01/11	3,930	0	0.0%	7,165
01/10*	3,307	2	0.1%	7,211
12/08	4,239	16	0.4%	6,567
12/07	2,717	16	0.6%	6,156
Annual Growth	17.6%	30.7%	—	5.4%

*Fiscal year change

2012 Year-End Financials

Debt ratio: 41.18%
Return on equity: 14.20%
Cash ($ mil.): 120
Current ratio: 161.83
Long-term debt ($ mil.): 449
No. of shares (mil.): 20
Dividends
Yield: —
Payout: —
Market value ($ mil.): 471

	STOCK PRICE ($) FY Close	P/E High/Low		PER SHARE ($) Earnings	Dividends	Book Value
01/12	22.62	9	5	2.68	0.00	16.05
01/11	13.85	301	166	0.05	0.00	12.31
01/10*	8.59	122	69	0.12	0.00	12.23
12/08	13.24	29	8	0.97	0.00	11.99
12/07	20.50	27	15	0.97	0.00	10.81
Annual Growth	2.5%	—	—	28.9%	—	10.4%

*Fiscal year change

SUTTER HEALTH

EXECUTIVES

President and CEO, Patrick E. (Pat) Fry
Director and Secretary, Richard M. Levy, age 74
SVP and Chief Medical Officer, Gordon C. Hunt Jr.
SVP and CFO, Robert D. (Bob) Reed, age 59
President Sutter Health West Bay Region, Martin Brotman
Chair, Geraldine R. Brinton
President Sutter Health Central Valley Region, David P. Benn
VP Communications, Bill Gleeson
Director Communications, Karen Garner
President Sutter Health East Bay Region, Edward (Ed) Berdick
President Sutter Health East Bay Region, David Bradley
Chairman, Jim Gray, age 66
SVP and CIO, Jonathan (Jon) Manis
SVP; Executive Officer Sutter Medical Network, Jeffrey Burnich
President Sutter Health West Bay Region, Mike Cohill
President Sutter Health Sacramento Sierra Region, James E. Conforti
Communications Coordinator, Kami Lloyd
President Sutter Health Peninsula Coastal Region, Jeff Gerard
President CEO and Director, Patrick E. (Pat) Fry
Director and Secretary, Richard M. Levy, age 74
Director, Michael R. Gaulke, age 66
Director, Geraldine R. Brinton
Director, Gary L. Depolo, age 76
Director, Mary Brown
Director, Elizabeth Vilardo
Director, Todd Smith
Director, Jim Gray, age 67
Director, Alexander (Alex) Gonzalez
Director, David H. Jeppson
Director, Todd Murray
Director, Andrew Pansini
Director, Michael A. Roosevelt
Auditors: Ernst&YoungLLP

LOCATIONS

HQ: Sutter Health
2200 River Plaza Dr., Sacramento CA 95833
Phone: 916-733-8800 **Fax:** 847-483-7039
Web: www.alexianhealthsystem.org

Selected Hospitals

Alta Bates Summit Medical Center (Berkeley Oakland)
California Pacific Medical Center (San Francisco)
Eden Medical Center (Castro Valley)
Kahi Mohala (Ewa HI)
Marin General Hospital (Greenbrae)
Memorial Hospital Los Banos (Los Banos)
Memorial Medical Center (Modesto)
Menlo Park Surgical Hospital
Mills-Peninsula Health Services (Burlingame)
Novato Community Hospital (Novato)
Sutter Amador Hospital (Jackson)
Sutter Auburn Faith Hospital (Auburn)
Sutter Coast Hospital (Crescent City)
Sutter Davis Hospital (Davis)
Sutter Delta Medical Center (Antioch)
Sutter Lakeside Hospital (Lakeport)
Sutter Maternity & Surgery Center of Santa Cruz
Sutter Medical Center (Sacramento)
Sutter Medical Center of Santa Rosa
Sutter Roseville Medical Center
Sutter Solano Medical Center (Vallejo)
Sutter Tracy Community Hospital (Tracy)

PRODUCTS/OPERATIONS

Selected Operations (Northern California Southern Oregon and Hawaii)

Acute Care Hospitals
Neonatal Intensive Care Units
Cancer Centers
Cardiac Centers
Acute Rehabilitation Centers
Medical Foundations
Trauma Centers
Behavioral Health Services
Education Centers and Physician Training Programs
Express Medical Clinics
Home Health and Hospice Services
Long-term Care Centers
Medical Research Centers
Occupational Health Services
Long-Term Care Centers
Irene Swindells Alzheimer' s Residential Care Center San Francisco
Sutter Oaks Nursing Center Sacramento
Sutter Senior Care PACE Program Sacramento
Cancer Centers
Alta Bates Summit Comprehensive Cancer Center Berkeley and Oakland
California Pacific Medical Center San Francisco
Dorothy E. Schneider Cancer Center at Mills-Peninsula Health Services Burlingame
Eden Medical Center Castro Valley
Memorial Regional Cancer Center Modesto
Sutter Auburn Faith Hospital Auburn
Sutter Cancer Center Sutter Medical Center Sacramento
Sutter Cancer Center Sutter Roseville Medical Center Roseville
Sutter Solano Cancer Center Vallejo
Programs listed above are approved by the American College of Surgeons' Commission on Cancer.
Research Institutes
California Pacific Medical Center San Francisco
Palo Alto Medical Foundation Research Institute Palo Alto
Sutter Health Institute for Research and Education San Francisco
Sutter Institute for Medical Research Sacramento
Home Health and Hospice Services
Coming Home Hospice
Cohen Cormier Home Attendant & Care Management
Sutter Auburn Faith VNA & Hospice
Sutter Care at Home
Sutter Coast Home Care
Sutter Infusion & Pharmacy Services / Emeryville and Sacramento
Sutter Lakeside Home Medical Services
Sutter Lifeline / Sacramento
Sutter North Home Health Agency
VNA of the Central Valley
VNA of Santa Cruz County
Express Medical Clinics
Sutter Express Care (Three locations in Sacramento & Placer counties)

COMPETITORS

Adventist Health
Alta Bates Summit Medical Center
Ascension Health
California Pacific Medical Center
Children' s Hospital & Research Center at Oakland
Dignity Health
Hawai' i Pacific Health
HCA
Kaiser Permanente
Kuakini Health System
Memorial Health Services
Odyssey HealthCare
Providence Health & Services
Rehabilitation Hospital of the Pacific
Stanford Hospital and Clinics
Tenet Healthcare
UCSF Medical

HISTORICAL FINANCIALS

Company Type: Private - Not-for-Profit

Income Statement FYE: September 30

	REVENUE ($ mil.)	NET INCOME ($ mil.)	NET PROFIT MARGIN	EMPLOYEES
09/12*	7,179	761	10.6%	44,000
12/11	9,079	195	2.1%	0
12/10	9,116	978	10.7%	0
Annual Growth	(11.3%)	(11.8%)	—	—

*Fiscal year change

2012 Year-End Financials

Debt ratio: —
Return on equity: 10.60%
Cash ($ mil.): 307
Current ratio: 1.00
Long-term debt ($ mil.): —
Dividends
Yield: —
Payout: —
Market value ($ mil.): —

SVB Financial Group

SVB Financial Group is the holding company for Silicon Valley Bank which serves emerging and established companies involved in technology life sciences private equity and premium wine and provides customized financing to entrepreneurs executives and investors in such industries. It also offers deposit accounts loans and international banking and plays matchmaker for young firms and private investors. Subsidiaries SVB Asset Management and SVB Securities provide investment advisory brokerage and asset management services; SVB Private Client provides credit and banking services to wealthy individuals. The group has about 25 offices in the US as well as branches in the China India Israel and the UK.

SVB Financial makes venture capital and private equity investments through SVB Capital which has more than $1 billion of assets under management. The company's SVB Analytics unit provides valuation and corporate equity management services to venture capital firms and venture capital-backed enterprises. The division acquired Equity Enterprises from Boardroom Software in 2010 expanding its market to public companies and complex limited liability companies in addition to the private companies it already served.

Greg Becker who joined SVB Financial in 1993 was named the company's CEO in 2011. He succeeded Ken Wilcox who became chairman and is focused on the company's efforts to expand in China including a joint venture with Shanghai Pudong Development Bank.

As part of its lending activities Silicon Valley Bank sometimes pursues warrants to purchase equity stakes in its clients. About 80% of the bank's loan portfolio is dedicated to business loans. Traditionally focused on up-and-coming firms the bank has implemented a strategy of courting larger later-stage clients.

SVB Financial reported record earnings of nearly $172 million in 2011. Its results were driven in part by an increase in not only loans but also deposits which the company invests in low-risk securities. Improved credit quality helped as well.

HISTORY

Silicon Valley Bank was founded in 1983 by Roger Smith to provide banking services to tech startups in San Jose. The bank boomed along with tech companies during the 1980s lending to the likes of Cisco Systems.

In 1990 the bank spread east to Boston's burgeoning technology alley. It also expanded into residential and commercial real estate lending. The recession of 1989 to 1991 found Silicon Valley Bancshares with an overextended loan portfolio and in 1992 the bank booked a loss due to nonperforming loans; the next year it was put under federal supervision.

To rally stockholder confidence the company brought in new management and demoted Smith from chairman to vice chairman; he left the in 1995. The bank reduced its real estate lending and diversified into factoring foreign exchange and executive banking for venture capitalists and clients' upper management.

The 1995 IPO frenzy aided the company's turnaround. Silicon Valley cashed in on warrants it had taken as collateral from young companies. Regulatory supervision was lifted in 1996 and the bank soon opened offices in the Atlanta; Austin Texas; Boulder Colorado; Phoenix; and Seattle areas.

In 1999 Silicon Valley Bancshares created a website targeted at technology firms in need of financing employees office space and equipment. However nonperforming loans began to dog the bank once again affecting profits and bringing a regulatory request to boost capital reserves.

In 2000 despite being hammered by the high-tech stock selloff the company continued to expand opening offices in West Palm Beach Florida and North Carolina's Research Triangle and successfully capitalizing its first venture fund. The following year it bought tech-focused investment bank Alliant Partners (later renamed SVB Alliant) to broaden its service offerings.

Still licking its wounds from the tech bust the company ceased lending to the entertainment industry and to churches in 2002. Silicon Valley Bancshares changed its name to SVB Financial Services in 2005.

SVB Alliant struggled with losses for years and SVB Financial explored its options including spinning the unit off to management. It ultimately decided to shut down the division which ceased operations in 2008.

EXECUTIVES

Chief Strategy Officer and Risk Officer, Marc J. Verissimo, age 57, $310,679 total compensation
Chairman Silicon Valley Bank, Kenneth P. (Ken) Wilcox, age 64, $790,223 total compensation
Head Relationship Management; Vice Chairman Silicon Valley Bank, Harry W. Kellogg Jr., age 69, $311,262 total compensation
General Counsel, Mary Dent, age 51
Chairman, Alex W. (Pete) Hart, age 71
CEO, Greg Becker, age 44
Chairman, Roger F. Dunbar, age 47
Managing Director SVB India Advisors, Suresh Shanmugham
Managing Director Entrepreneur Services Group, Gerald Brady
Director Investor Relations, Meghan O'Leary
COO, Bruce Wallace
President Silicon Valley Bank, Gregory W. (Greg) Becker, age 45, $499,154 total compensation
Head Corporate Finance, Mark A. MacLennan, age 59, $338,013 total compensation
President India and China SVB Financial Group, Ash Lilani
Chief Marketing Officer, Brian K. Dennehy
Chief Administration Officer SVB Analytics, Cecilia Shea
SVP and Senior Relationship Manager Mid-Atlantic Office Silicon Valley Bank, Sean Stone
VP UK, Simon Andrews
Managing Director SVB Capital, Jonathan (Jon) Norris
CFO, Michael (Mike) Descheneaux, age 45, $408,548 total compensation
Director Public Relations, Carrie Merritt
Head Human Resources, Christopher (Chris) Edmonds-Waters, age 50
Head Relationship Management Dallas, Brian Brown
Managing Director SVB Capital, Doug Hamilton
Regional Manager Boston and New York SVB Silicon Valley Bank, James (Jim) Maynard
CFO and Chief Administrative Officer SVB Capital, Anne Rockhold
Head Relationship Management Venture Capital and Private Equity Division, John D. China
Managing Director Private Equity Group SVB Capital, Bill Howell
Managing Director SVB India Finance, Ajay Hattangdi
SVP SVB Global Asia, Daniel R. Quon
SVP SVB Financial Group UK, Andy Tsao
Managing Partner SVB Capital Funds, Aaron Gershenberg
General Counsel SVB Capital, Jason Doren
Director Sales SVB Analytics, Christian Groh
Managing Director SVB Analytics, Mitzi Lazich
SVP SVB Global China, Mike Yahng
COO SVB Analytics, James Walling
Marketing Director SVB Analytics, Christina Chiaramonte
Head UK Europe and Israel, Phil Cox
Chief Credit Officer, Dave A. Jones, age 55, $302,319 total compensation
Managing Director SVB Private Client Services, Kent Hakanson
President SVB Analytics, Iris Hit-Shagir
Head Cleantech Practice, Matt Maloney
Head Life Sciences Eastern Division, Michael Hanewich
Director SVB Accelerator, Lafe Vittitoe
Senior Relationship Manager, Albert Martinez
Senior Relationship Manager, Oscar Jazdowski
Senior Relationship Manager, Andy Pelletier
Senior Relationship Manager, Dale Kirkland
Senior Relationship Manager, Jim Parsons
Manager Northwest Market, Bruce Helberg
Market Manager Rocky Mountain Region, Mike Devery
Head SVB Capital, Sven Weber
Board Member, Eric A. Benhamou, age 57
Board Member, Lata Krishnan, age 52
Board Member, G. Felda Hardymon, age 65
Board Member, C. Richard (Dick) Kramlich, age 76
Board Member, Michaela K. Rodeno, age 66
Board Member, Joel P. Friedman, age 64
Board Member, Roger F. Dunbar, age 47
Board Member, Kyung H. Yoon, age 58
Board Member, Kate Mitchell, age 54
Board Member, David M. Clapper, age 61
Auditors: KPMGLLP

LOCATIONS

HQ: SVB Financial Group
3003 Tasman Dr., Santa Clara CA 95054-1191
Phone: 408-654-7400 **Fax:** 408-496-2405
Web: www.svb.com

Selected Offices

US
Atlanta
Austin TX
Broomfield CO
Chicago
Dallas
Irvine CA
Menlo Park CA
Minnetonka MN
New York
Newton MA
Palo Alto CA
Philadelphia
Phoenix
Pleasanton CA
Portland OR
Raleigh NC
Salt Lake City
San Diego
San Francisco
Santa Rosa CA
Seattle
St. Helena CA
Tysons Corner VA
International
Bangalore India
Beijing
Herzliya Pituach Israel
London
Mumbai India
Shanghai

PRODUCTS/OPERATIONS

2011 Sales

	$ mil.	% of total
Interest		
Loans	389	41
Taxable securities	165	18
Other	10	1
Noninterest		
Net gains on investment securities	195	21
Foreign exchange fees	43	5
Net gains on derivative instruments	38	4
Deposit service charges	31	3
Credit card fees	18	2
Client investment fees	12	1
Letters of credit	12	1
Other	30	3
Total	**947**	**100**

Selected Subsidiaries and Affiliates

Silicon Valley Bank
SVB Analytics Inc.
SVB Asset Management
SVB Business Partners (Beijing) Co. Ltd.
SVB Business Partners (Shanghai) Co. Ltd.
SVB Global Financial Inc.
SVB Global Investors LLC
SVB Growth Investors LLC
SVB India Advisors Pvt. Ltd.
SVB Israel Advisors Ltd.
SVB Qualified Investors Fund LLC
SVB Real Estate Investment Trust
SVB Securities
SVB Strategic Investors LLC
SVB Strategic Investors Fund L.P.
Venture Investment Managers L.P.

COMPETITORS

BancWest
Bank of America
City National
Comerica

Bridge Capital Holdings	Heritage Commerce
Citigroup	U.S. Bancorp
	UnionBanCal

HISTORICAL FINANCIALS

Company Type: Public

Income Statement FYE: December 31

	ASSETS ($ mil.)	NET INCOME ($ mil.)	INCOME AS % OF ASSETS	EMPLOYEES
12/11	19,968	171	0.9%	1,526
12/10	17,527	94	0.5%	1,357
12/09	12,841	48	0.4%	1,258
12/08	10,020	78	0.8%	1,244
12/07	6,692	123	1.8%	1,128
Annual Growth	31.4%	8.6%	—	7.8%

2011 Year-End Financials

Debt ratio: 3.02%
Return on equity: 10.95%
Cash ($ mil.): 939
Current ratio: —
Long-term debt ($ mil.): 603
No. of shares (mil.): 43
Dividends
Yield: —
Payout: —
Market value ($ mil.): 2,075

	STOCK PRICE ($) FY Close	P/E High/Low		PER SHARE ($) Earnings	Dividends	Book Value
12/11	47.69	16	9	3.94	0.00	36.07
12/10	53.05	24	16	2.24	0.00	30.15
12/09	41.66	68	18	0.66	0.00	27.30
12/08	26.23	28	10	2.29	0.00	30.04
12/07	50.40	15	13	3.37	0.00	20.71
Annual Growth	(1.4%)	—	—	4.0%	—	14.9%

SWS Group, Inc.

Southwest Securities hopes stock prices go northeast. The primary subsidiary of SWS Group provides securities clearing and brokerage services to retail and institutional clients in the US and Canada. Accounting for some three-fourths of revenues Southwest Securities counts some 150 financial services organizations among its clients. It also serves individual investors through its private client brokerages located in California Texas Nevada and Oklahoma. Southwest Securities performs securities underwriting securities lending and public finance activities for institutional customers. Thrift subsidiary Southwest Securities FSB specializes in commercial lending and mortgage banking in Texas and New Mexico.

Operations

The group has been working to strengthen Southwest Securities FSB which has been struggling with poor asset quality. In 2011 it received a $100 million capital injection –the bulk of which has been earmarked for the thrift –from investors Hilltop Holdings and Oak Hill Capital Partners. Together the firms now own more than 40% of the company. The investors also gained seats on SWS Group's board of directors. The deal came on the heels of SWS rejecting a $200 million takeover bid by Alabama-based investment bank and brokerage Sterne Agee. It cited numerous reasons to turn down the proposal including uncertainty about Sterne Agee's abilities to operate as a thrift holding company and the proposed price.

Strategy

The firm's strategies for growth center around its primary markets: Dallas Houston Los Angeles and San Francisco. The company believes that its regional expertise enables it to better recruit brokers and provide personalized customer service to its private clients.

Ownership

Hilltop Holdings and its chairman Gerald Ford own approximately 25% of the SWS Group. Oak Hill Capital Management holds another 21% stake.

HISTORY

Don Buchholz and the late Allen Cobb formed MidSouthwest Securities in 1972 ("Mid" was dropped in 1979) after the NYSE began letting members offer discounted commissions to nonmember firms. MidSouthwest Securities specialized in executing orders for nonmember brokerages expanding after the 1975 deregulation of brokerage commissions. It added clearing services (which soon became its core business) at the request of independent brokers. The firm expanded through such buys as Pine Securities (1974) and Quinn and Company (1987). It began offering corporate financing in 1978 and in 1987 started underwriting municipal and corporate securities.

The firm formed SWS Technologies in 1996. The next year it launched discount brokerage services through Sovereign Securities. Sovereign's online trading unit Mydiscountbroker.com was launched in 1997. By 1999 the online business had eclipsed Sovereign and the whole unit was renamed Mydiscountbroker.com. In 2000 SWS took advantage of deregulation in the US financial industry by acquiring ASBI Holdings owner of First Savings Bank in Arlington Texas.

After suffering a loss in 2002 SWS Group regrouped and returned its focus to banking brokerage and clearing. The company sold the accounts of its Mydiscountbroker.com subsidiary to Ameritrade in 2003. It also shuttered the information-technology-related services once offered by its SWS Technologies division.

In early 2005 SWS Group agreed to pay $10 million to settle allegations of mutual fund trading abuses. Former Southwest Securities president and CEO Daniel Leland who stepped down amid the investigations also was fined. Leland remained an EVP for the company.

SWS Group bought Beverly Hills California-based asset manager and brokerage M.L. Stern & Co. from Pacific Life in 2008. The firm's operations were transferred to Southwest Securities. The acquisition helped double the size of SWS Group's financial adviser network for private clients to around 300.

EXECUTIVES

Controller, Laura Leventhal
EVP, Paul D. Vinton, age 63
Interim CFO, Stacy M. Hodges, age 49
VP General Counsel and Secretary, Allen R. Tubb, age 58
EVP, Richard H. Litton, age 65, $225,000 total compensation
EVP and CIO, W. Norman Thompson, age 56
Chairman, Don A. Buchholz, age 83
EVP, Daniel R. (Dan) Leland, age 51, $225,000 total compensation
President CEO and Director, James H. (Jim) Ross, age 63, $350,000 total compensation
EVP; Chairman President and CEO Southwest Securities FSB, John L. Holt Jr., age 49
COO Southwest Securities FSB, Jerry Pavlas
EVP, Jeffrey J. Singer, age 42
President Banking Center Albuquerque Southwest Securities FSB, V. William (Bill) Dolan Jr.
Corporate Communications, Ben Brooks
Director, Brodie L. Cobb, age 51
Director, Frederick R. Meyer, age 84
President CEO and Director, James H. (Jim) Ross, age 63
Director, Larry A. Jobe, age 72
Director, Mike Moses, age 60
Director, I. D. Flores III, age 69
Director, Robert A. Buchholz, age 52
Director, Joel T. Williams III, age 63
Auditors: GrantThorntonLLP

LOCATIONS

HQ: SWS Group Inc.
1201 Elm St. Ste. 3500, Dallas TX 75270-2180
Phone: 214-859-1800 **Fax:** 214-859-6077
Web: www.swsgroupinc.com

PRODUCTS/OPERATIONS

Selected Subsidiaries

SWS Banc Holdings Inc.
FSB Development LLC
Southwest Securities FSB
SWS Financial Services Inc.
Southwest Insurance Agency Inc.
Southwest Insurance Agency of Alabama Inc.
Southwest Investment Advisors Inc.
Southwest Securities Inc.

COMPETITORS

Charles Schwab	Morgan Keegan
E*TRADE Financial	Piper Jaffray
Edward Jones	Raymond James Financial
Jefferies Group	TD Ameritrade
Legg Mason	Wells Fargo Advisors
Merrill Lynch	

HISTORICAL FINANCIALS

Company Type: Public

Income Statement FYE: June 29

	ASSETS ($ mil.)	NET INCOME ($ mil.)	INCOME AS % OF ASSETS	EMPLOYEES
06/12	3,546	(4)	—	1,065
06/11	3,802	(23)	—	1,073
06/10	4,530	(2)	—	1,142
06/09	4,199	23	0.6%	1,170
06/08	5,118	31	0.6%	1,193
Annual Growth	(8.8%)	—	—	(2.8%)

2012 Year-End Financials

Debt ratio: 4.17%
Return on equity: (-1.33)%
Cash ($ mil.): 111
Current ratio: —
Long-term debt ($ mil.): 147
No. of shares (mil.): 32
Dividends
Yield: 0.19%
Payout: —
Market value ($ mil.): 174

	STOCK PRICE ($) FY Close	P/E High/Low		PER SHARE ($) Earnings	Dividends	Book Value
06/12	5.33	—	—	(0.14)	0.01	10.92
06/11	5.64	—	—	(0.71)	0.12	11.07
06/10	10.17	—	—	(0.10)	0.36	11.85
06/09	13.53	26	12	0.87	0.36	12.48
06/08	16.99	19	9	1.17	0.34	11.88
Annual Growth	(25.2%)	—	—	—	(58.6%)	(2.1%)

Symantec Corp.

Symantec's future seems to be secure. The company provides security storage and systems management software for businesses and consumers. Its applications handle such functions as virus protection PC maintenance data backup and recovery intrusion detection data loss prevention spam control content filtering and remote server management. Symantec sells its products through a direct sales force as well as through distributors resellers computer manufacturers and systems integrators. The company also provides managed services and training. More than half of sales come from outside the US.

Symantec may be best known for its popular Norton family of consumer security software but the company generates more of its revenues from enterprise infrastructure management security and compliance applications and services. Delving into the market for cloud computing where users access applications over the Internet rather than installing software on their own computers the company offers a variety of applications through Symantec Hosted Services. Also known as software-as-a-service (SaaS) the field is seen as a growth area by Symantec.

Sales for fiscal 2012 were $6.7 billion a 9% increase over 2010. The company points to strong growth in backup SaaS data loss prevention and managed security products. Sales of the security and compliance segment rose 20% on increased sales of information security products user authentication and trust products and services. Sales of consumer products were up 8% on growth in its premium internet and security products and sales through its online store. In its storage and server management segment (its largest with 36% of sales) revenues were up 4% primarily due to sales from acquisitions which also negatively impacted profitability in the segment. (Overall sales from acquisitions made during fiscal 2011 added $54 million to fiscal 2012 results.)

Services revenues fell 14% as the company transitioned certain consulting operations to specialized partners in order to focus on its core software operations. Symantec continued to be profitable in fiscal 2012 with net income that increased by more than 95% to $1.2 billion from $597 million in the prior period.

Symantec has pursued an aggressive acquisition strategy to grow its enterprise business. In 2012 the company acquired mobile application management software developer Nukona to complement its previous purchase that year of Odyssey Software a maker of similar applications. The deals are part of Symantec's push to build its line of products for protecting and managing mobile apps and data as global demand for wireless devices continues to grow.

The company also fluffed up its cloud capabilities during the year with the $115 million purchase of archiving provider LiveOffice which offers its information storage and management on demand. In 2011 the company paid about $390 million for legal software developer Clearwell Systems. The deal added electronic discovery tools used by businesses to automate and manage functions related to government regulatory compliance and legal proceedings among other uses.

Symantec also held a 49% stake in a joint venture with Huawei Technologies that develops security and storage products for telecom service providers. The company had reported losses on the venture every year since its formation and in 2012 sold its stake to Huawei for $530 million. Symantec asserted that it was exiting the venture because it had achieved its goals which included an expanded presence in China and a burgeoning appliance business.

Founded in 1982 Symantec serves enterprise and individual customers in more than 50 countries worldwide.

HISTORY

Artificial intelligence expert Gary Hendrix founded Symantec in 1982. Gordon Eubanks a former student of the late industry pioneer Gary Kildall and founder of C&E Software was appointed CEO in 1983 and bought the company in 1984. Realizing that Symantec could not compete against Microsoft and Lotus Eubanks began buying niche-market software firms. In 1990 a year after going public Symantec merged with DOS utilities market leader Peter Norton Computing. It bought 13 companies between 1990 and 1994.

Symantec bought Delrina (maker of WinFax) in 1995 and then slowed its acquisition pace and concentrated on the growing Internet market. In 1996 it sold Delrina's electronic forms business to JetForm.

Symantec filed copyright-infringement charges against Network Associates (now McAfee) in 1997. The next year a suit was filed against Symantec on behalf of antivirus product users alleging that it ignored its warranty by charging to fix a year-2000 software glitch.

The company went on another acquisition binge buying the antivirus operations of both IBM and Intel in 1998 and acquiring rival Quarterdeck in 1999. When Eubanks left that year to head an enterprise software startup IBM exec John Thompson stepped in and became the first African-American CEO of a major software company.

In 2000 Symantec sold its Internet tools division to BEA Systems in a deal valued at about $75 million. It also acquired L-3 Communications' network security operations. Late that year it bought rival network security software maker AXENT Technologies in a $975 million deal.

The company divested its Web access management product line in 2001. Later that year it acquired Foster-Melliar's enterprise security management division. In 2002 it continued its acquisitive ways purchasing Recourse Technologies Riptech and SecurityFocus. The following year Symantec acquired Nexland PowerQuest and SafeWeb then purchased infrastructure management software provider ON Technology for about $100 million in 2004. Later that year Symantec also bought antispam software provider Brightmail for $370 million.

Symantec announced plans to purchase VERITAS Software for about $11 billion in 2004. The deal was completed in the following year.

It purchased WholeSecurity Inc. (a maker of security software used to thwart viruses worms and other malicious code) and Sygate Technologies (network access control solutions) in 2005. The following year it bought BindView Development Corporation (computer network management and security) IMlogic (enterprise instant messaging) and Relicore (data center change and configuration management). It also acquired UK-based Company-i a data center services firm focused on the finance sector as well as data protection software developer Revivio.

In 2007 Symantec acquired IT asset management software maker Altiris for approximately $830 million and data loss prevention specialist Vontu for $350 million. The company also formed a joint venture with China-based Huawei Technologies in 2007. In 2008 Symantec sold its Application Performance Management (APM) division to Vector Capital.

The company expanded its enterprise security and compliance line when it purchased longtime partner AppStream in 2008. AppStream developed application streaming technology that allows for remote program deployment and management. The purchase bolstered the company's SaaS offerings. The company also grew its professional services portfolio with the acquisition of MessageLabs for $695 million in cash in 2008. MessageLabs provided Symantec with a managed service for protecting email and other electronic communications.

Other purchases in 2008 bolstered the company's consumer software business including PC Tools (privacy and security software for Windows-based PCs) and SwapDrive (online storage and data backup services).

Thompson stepped down as CEO in 2009; he remained chairman. COO Enrique Salem was promoted to chief executive.

In 2010 Symantec purchased Gideon Technologies a provider of security software and services for public sector clients. Also that year it bought PGP Corporation for about $300 million in cash and GuardianEdge Technologies for around $70 million in cash extending its data protection capabilities.

In a transaction that contributed substantially to the company's online security portfolio Symantec bought the Authentication Services business of VeriSign in 2010. It paid about $1.28 billion in cash to acquire VeriSign's secure sockets layer (SSL) and code signing certificate services the Public Key Infrastructure (PKI) services the VeriSign Trust Seal and the VeriSign Identity Protection (VIP) authentication and VIP fraud detection services. The purchase strengthened Symantec's product line in a number of areas including identity security mobile device security and security for private and public computing clouds. The deal made Symantec a leading provider of SSL certificates.

EXECUTIVES

EVP and Chief Human Resources Officer, Rebecca A. Ranninger, age 53, $245,000 total compensation

Chairman President and CEO, Stephen M. (Steve) Bennett, age 58

EVP and CFO, James A. Beer, age 51, $660,000 total compensation

President CEO and Director, Enrique T. Salem, age 45, $625,000 total compensation

Group President Consumer Business Unit, Janice D. Chaffin, age 57, $450,000 total compensation

SVP and Chief Marketing Officer, Carine Clark

EVP General Counsel and Secretary, Scott C. Taylor, age 47

SVP Information Security Group, Art Gilliland

SVP Europe Middle East and Africa Geography, John F. Brigden, age 44

EVP Worldwide Sales & Services, William T. (Bill) Robbins, age 44, $453,375 total compensation

Group President SMB and the Symantec.cloud Business Unit, Rowan M. Trollope

SVP Asia Pacific and Japan Geography, Bernard Kwok

SVP and CTO, Stephen Trilling

Corporate Communications, Genevieve Haldeman

Group President Enterprise Products & Services, Francis deSouza, age 41

SVP Storage and Availability Management Group Symantec Corporation, Deepak Mohan
SVP Global Strategic Sales & Marketing, Rich Spring
SVP Enterprise Security Group, Anil S. Chakravarthy
Media Contact Executive Communications Office of the CEO, Melissa Martin
SVP Information Management Group, Chirantan (CJ) Desai
SVP and Chief Strategy Officer, Angela Tucci
Chairman, Steve Bennett
SVP and CIO, Marty Hodgett
Group President Information Technology and Services Group, David Thompson, age 44
SVP and Chief Accounting Officer, Phillip A. Bullock, age 45
Director, Daniel H. (Dan) Schulman, age 54
Director, Robert S. (Steve) Miller Jr., age 70
Director, Geraldine B. (Gerry) Laybourne, age 65
Director, Frank E. Dangeard, age 54
President CEO and Director, Enrique T. Salem, age 45
Director, David L. Mahoney, age 58
Director, V. Paul Unruh, age 63
Director, Stephen Gillett
Auditors: KPMGLLP

LOCATIONS

HQ: Symantec Corporation
350 Ellis St., Mountain View CA 94043
Phone: 650-527-8000 **Fax:** 212-365-2360
Web: www.transre.com

2012 Sales

	$ mil.	% of total
US	3,240	48
UK	580	9
Other countries	2,910	43
Total	**6,730**	**100**

PRODUCTS/OPERATIONS

2012 Sales

	$ mil.	% of total
Storage & server management	2,410	36
Consumer	2,104	31
Security & compliance	1,965	29
Services	251	4
Total	**6,730**	**100**

2012 Sales by Product

	% of total
Core consumer	28
Backup	20
Storage & availability	9
Endpoint security &	9
Others	34
Total	**100**

Selected Products

Consumer products
- Backup
- Fraud detection service
- Identity protection authentication
- Internet security
- PC tune-up

Security and compliance
- Compliance and security management
- Messaging management

Services
- Maintenance and support
- Training

Storage and server management
- Data protection
- Endpoint security
- Storage and server management

Selected Acquisitions

Nukona (2012 mobile application management software)
Odyssey Software (2012 mobile device management software)
LiveOffice (2012 hosted archiving provider)
Clearwell Systems (2011 legal software)
Gideon Technologies (2010 public-sector security software and services)
PGP Corporation (2010 data protection services)
GuardianEdge Technologies (2010 data protection services)
MessageLabs (2008 email protection service)
PC Tools (2008 privacy and security software)
SwapDrive (2008 online storage and data backup services)
AppStream (2008 remote program deployment and management services)
Vontu (2007 data loss prevention services)
Altiris (2007 IT asset management software)
Company-i (2006 financial data-center services)
Revivio (2006 data protection software)
Relicore (2006 data center change and configuration management)
IMlogic (2006 enterprise instant messaging)
BindView Development (2006 IT security compliance software)
Sygate Technologies (2005 network-access control services)
WholeSecurity (2005 antivirus software)

COMPETITORS

Avocent	Hewlett-Packard
CA Inc.	IBM
Carbonite	Kaspersky Lab
Check Point Software	LANDesk
Cisco Systems	McAfee
CommVault	Microsoft
Comodo	Novell
Courion	Oracle
DataCore	Quest Software
EMC	RSA Security
Entrust	SecureWorks
F-Secure	Smith Micro
F5 Networks	Sophos
FalconStor	Trend Micro
Go Daddy	Verizon
Google	Zone Labs

HISTORICAL FINANCIALS

Company Type: Public

Income Statement FYE: March 30

	REVENUE ($ mil.)	NET INCOME ($ mil.)	NET PROFIT MARGIN	EMPLOYEES
03/12*	6,730	1,172	17.4%	20,500
04/11	6,190	597	9.6%	18,600
04/10	5,985	714	11.9%	17,400
04/09	6,149	(6,728)	—	17,400
03/08	5,874	463	7.9%	17,600
Annual Growth	3.5%	26.1%	—	3.9%

*Fiscal year change

2012 Year-End Financials

Debt ratio: 15.66%	No. of shares (mil.): 724
Return on equity: 23.01%	Dividends
Cash ($ mil.): 3,162	Yield: —
Current ratio: 102.84	Payout: —
Long-term debt ($ mil.): 2,039	Market value ($ mil.): 13,539

	STOCK PRICE ($) FY Close	P/E High/Low		PER SHARE ($) Earnings	Dividends	Book Value
03/12*	18.70	13	10	1.57	0.00	7.04
04/11	18.46	24	16	0.76	0.00	5.97
04/10	16.77	22	16	0.87	0.00	5.70
04/09	16.23	—	—	(8.10)	0.00	4.83
03/08	16.82	40	28	0.52	0.00	13.07
Annual Growth	2.7%	—	—	31.8%	—	(14.3%)

*Fiscal year change

Synnex Corp

SYNNEX creates synergy between buyers and sellers. The company distributes PCs peripherals software and consumer electronics from manufacturers including Hewlett-Packard Acer Panasonic Lenovo Seagate and Microsoft. SYNNEX also provides design and support services; its online services include parts catalogs configuration and ordering. In addition the company offers contract design and assembly build-to-order and configure-to-order services for manufacturers and systems integrators. Its Global Business Services (GBS) segment offers customer support services using phone chat Web e-mail and digital print. SYNNEX founded in 1980 gets more than 85% of sales from customers in the US.

Sales for SYNNEX were up around 20% in fiscal 2011 over the prior period and the company remained solidly profitable. Its distribution business benefited from improvements in market conditions in the US and Canada as businesses began to reinvest in technology products. The company reported strong growth in sales of both networking products (up 30%) and system components. Its GBS unit attracted new customers and a higher volume of calls to its contact centers. SYNNEX has added more value-added and supply chain services to both of its businesses as part of its strategic growth plan.

SYNNEX created its GBS division to focus on developing services that help its customers find and keep their customers. Offerings include technical support customer service and renewals management and support. Because GBS provides services from many locations in multiple languages the division is also responsible for selling certain products in China. The 2011 purchase of outsourcing provider e4e added a presence in India.

GBS got its start in earlier acquisitions that included Link2Support (voice e-mail and technical chat support from the Philippines) and Concentrix (call center database analysis and print-on-demand services).

In 2010 SYNNEX boosted its Concentrix business when it acquired Encover (software that automates service renewals primarily for enterprises in the US) and UK-based Aspire Technology (offers renewals services through distributors and resellers primarily in Europe through its proprietary RenewalsManager hosted platform). Encover and Aspire are part of the renewals platform for GBS.

SYNNEX also bolstered its distribution business with acquisitions in 2010. Early in the year SYNNEX bought video game hardware and software distributor Jack of All Games from video game publisher Take-Two Interactive Software giving it a presence in the lucrative video game distribution market. The company ended the year with the purchase of Marubeni Infotec one of the largest IT distributors in Japan with sales of more than $1 billion. Renamed SYNNEX Infotec the unit provides a significant growth opportunity outside of North America.

On the flip side SYNNEX is exiting businesses it doesn't consider core to operations. In 2010 it sold its Brand Development Group (BDG) division; it also sold certain assets related to its contract assembly business (primarily inventory and customer contracts) to MiTAC International.

SYNNEX has operations in Canada China Costa Rico Hungary India Japan Mexico Nicaragua the Philippines the UK and the US. The company's more than 20000 reseller system integrator and retail customers include CDW Insight Enterprises Iron Bow Technologies Systemax and The Business Depot (the Canadian arm of Staples).

EXECUTIVES

President CEO and Director, Kevin M. Murai, age 48, $498,076 total compensation
SVP and General Manager Systems, Stephen Ichinaga, age 51
SVP Sales, Steve Jow, age 49
President US Distribution, Peter Larocque, age 50, $322,938 total compensation
SVP Operations, Timothy (Tim) Rush, age 51
SVP Partner Advocacy, Michael R. Thomson, age 66
SVP Product Management, Michael P. Van Gieson, age 55
President SYNNEX Canada, Mitchell P. Martin, age 49
SVP and CIO, Gary Gulmon, age 51
SVP HP Product Management, David Dennis, age 51
SVP HP Enterprise Technology Solutions, Peter J. (Pete) Coleman, age 56
SVP Marketing North America, Robert L. (Bob) Stegner
CFO, Thomas C. Alsborg, age 49, $259,615 total compensation
COO, Dennis Polk, age 45, $307,560 total compensation
SVP Product Management, T.J. Trojan
SVP Human Resources North America, Debra Latourette
SVP General Counsel and Corporate Secretary, Simon Y. Leung, age 46, $215,000 total compensation
Chairman, Dwight Steffensen, age 68
President New Age Electronics, Fred Towns
Director Investor and Public Relations, Laura Crowley
SVP Product Management, Gary Palenbaum
SVP and General Manager Global Business Services, Christopher Caldwell
SVP Strategy and General Manager VisionMAX IT Software Solutions, Pradip Madan
SVP and Corporate Controller, Mike Vaishnav
SVP Sales, Scott Barker
President and CEO SYNNEX Infotec Corporation, Yoshitake Matsumoto
Director, Gregory L. (Greg) Quesnel, age 63
President CEO and Director, Kevin M. Murai, age 48
Director, Duane E. Zitzner, age 64
Director, James C. Van Horne, age 76
Chairman Emeritus, Matthew F. C. Miau, age 65
Director, Fred A. Breidenbach, age 65
Director, Andrea M. Zulberti, age 60
Auditors: PricewaterhouseCoopersLLP

LOCATIONS

HQ: Synnex Corp
44201 Nobel Drive, Fremont, CA 94538
Phone: 510 656-3333
Web: www.synnex.com

2011 Sales

	$ mil.	% of total
North America	9,029	87
Asia/Pacific	1,283	12
Other countries	96	1
Total	**10,409**	**100**

PRODUCTS/OPERATIONS

2011 Sales

	$ mil.	% of total
Distribution	10,275	98
Global Business Services	163	2
Adjustments	(29)	—
Total	**10,409**	**100**

Selected Services

Distribution
- Contract assembly
- Distribution services
- Logistics services

Global Business Services
- Automated service renewals software
- Customer services
- Hosted renewals services software in Europe (RenewalsManager)
- Financing services
- Marketing services
- Outsourced back-office services
- Technical support services

COMPETITORS

Arrow Electronics
Avnet
Benchmark Electronics
Celestica
Convergys
D & H Distributing
Flextronics
Hon Hai
Ingram Micro
Jabil
Plexus
Premier Farnell
Sanmina
ScanSource
ServiceSource
Stream Global Services
Tech Data
Teleperformance
TeleTech
Viasystems
Westcon
Wistron
Yosun

HISTORICAL FINANCIALS

Company Type: Public

Income Statement

FYE: November 30

	REVENUE ($ mil.)	NET INCOME ($ mil.)	NET PROFIT MARGIN	EMPLOYEES
11/11	10,409	150	1.4%	10,948
11/10	8,614	127	1.5%	8,108
11/09	7,719	92	1.2%	7,320
11/08	7,768	83	1.1%	7,672
11/07	7,004	63	0.9%	6,616
Annual Growth	10.4%	24.2%	—	13.4%

2011 Year-End Financials

Debt ratio: 13.52%
Return on equity: 12.98%
Cash ($ mil.): 67
Current ratio: 177.69
Long-term debt ($ mil.): 223
No. of shares (mil.): 36
Dividends
Yield: —
Payout: —
Market value ($ mil.): 1,061

	STOCK PRICE ($) FY Close	P/E High/Low		PER SHARE ($) Earnings	Dividends	Book Value
11/11	29.35	9	6	4.08	0.00	32.03
11/10	28.66	9	6	3.58	0.00	27.91
11/09	28.31	11	3	2.70	0.00	24.35
11/08	10.46	10	3	2.52	0.00	21.28
11/07	20.66	11	9	1.93	0.00	19.30
Annual Growth	9.2%	—	—	20.6%	—	13.5%

Synovus Financial Corp.

Synovus has a nose for community banking. The holding company owns flagship subsidiary Synovus Bank and about 30 community banking divisions that offer deposit accounts and consumer and business loans in Alabama Florida Georgia South Carolina and Tennessee. Through more than 290 locations the bank provides checking and savings accounts loans and mortgages and credit cards. Other divisions offer insurance private banking wealth and asset management and other financial services. Nonbank subsidiaries include Synovus Mortgage Synovus Trust investment bank and brokerage Synovus Securities and GLOBALT which provides asset management and financial planning services.

Synovus has been looking for ways to cut costs raise capital and improve efficiency as it has been plagued by the residential and commercial real estate bust that hit the southeastern US particularly hard. Previously between 2008 and 2009 the company slashed about 10% of its workforce and it cut approximately 10% more in 2010 and 2011. The company also announced plans to close nearly 40 branches and is looking into consolidating others.

Meanwhile Synovus which has reported hundreds of millions of losses each of the last four fiscal years has been cleaning up its balance sheet. To that end Synovus completed the bulk sale of its distressed assets with a carrying value of about $530 million in December 2012. It divested more than $1 billion worth of distressed assets in 2010 and a further $702 million of bad assets the following year. Synovus also has been able to reduce its number of past-due loans and provisions for loan losses. It also managed to reduce the amount of charged-off loans.

However Synovus continued to struggle to dig itself out of a hole. In 2011 it reported a net loss of about $60 million (which was an improvement from the year before). Revenues fell in 2011 by 9%.

The company is focused on returning to profitability (something it managed to acheive in the last two quarters of 2011 and into 2012). It is deemphasizing commercial real estate lending and intends to increase its focus on commercial and industrial banking including specialized services such as asset-based lending international banking and treasury management in an effort to increase revenue. The company is courting large corporate clients in the health care manufacturing distribution financial services natural resources and transportation sectors. Among smaller enterprises it targets professional practices such as physicians attorneys and accountants particularly for its private banking business.

Synovus which has traditionally maintained separate charters and local boards of directors for its subsidiary banks consolidated all of its charters into one in 2010 in order to reduce complexity and improve efficiency. The company has been making such changes in order to better position itself and emerge stronger from the economic downturn.

Synovus has also consolidated by merging some of its banks in Georgia and Florida; two of its Florida banking subsidiaries (one "de novo" and the other formed in the merger of three subsidiaries' banking charters) have taken the Synovus Bank brand a new strategy for the company.

HISTORY

In 1885 W. C. Bradley founded his eponymous company (today a manufacturing and development concern). Three years later he invested in a new bank that would eventually bear the name of its Georgia hometown: Columbus Bank and Trust. (Bradley's investment in Atlanta-based Coca-Cola today accounts for the lion's share of his family's wealth.) When Bradley died his son-in-law Abbott

Turner joined the bank's board of directors followed by Turner's son William.

In 1958 the bank hired James Blanchard as president. The next year Columbus Bank and Trust became one of the first banks to issue credit cards. The company's credit processing business grew leading it to computerize the process in 1966 and train its own employees to operate the equipment. (It decided to go it alone after a failed joint-venture attempt with corporate cousin W.C. Bradley Co.)

In a little more than a decade Blanchard led the bank to triple its assets. When he died in 1969 the search for a new leader took the bank's directors in a surprising direction: They offered the position to Blanchard's son Jimmy a young attorney with no banking experience. The board pressed him to take the job which he did in 1971 after a brief apprenticeship.

From the start the younger Blanchard emphasized the company's financial services operations such as credit card processing. Taking advantage of new laws opening up the banking and financial services industry in the early 1970s the bank reorganized in 1972 incorporating CB&T Bancshares to serve as a holding company for Columbus Bank and Trust. In 1973 CB&T's financial services division finished a new software product called the Total System which allowed electronic access to account information. CB&T used the groundbreaking software to start processing other banks' paperwork including an ever-growing number of credit card accounts. In 1983 CB&T spun off financial services division Total System Services (TSYS) but retained a majority stake in the company.

Blanchard helped win passage of Georgia's multibank holding law and further deregulation in the early 1980s allowed the company to operate across state lines. It bought four banks in Florida and Georgia in 1983 and 1984 and snapped up six more (including an Alabama bank) in 1985. Meanwhile TSYS benefited from the trend to outsource credit card processing.

In 1989 CB&T changed its name to Synovus a combination of the words "synergy" and "novus" the latter word meaning (according to the company) "of superior quality and different from the others listed in the same category."

During the early 1990s Synovus swept up 20 banks in its market area after the bank bust. After 1993 acquisitions dropped off until 1998 when Synovus announced three acquisitions in two weeks. That year it also said it was planning to move further into Internet and investment banking as well as auto and life insurance. In 1999 the company bought banks in Georgia and Florida; it also moved into debt collection with its purchase of Wallace & de Mayo which was renamed Total System Services (TSYS). In 2007 Synovus spun off TSYS.

The company grew its retail investment operations with the acquisitions of Atlanta-area asset managers Creative Financial Group in 2001 and GLOBALT in 2002. Jimmy Blanchard who had ultimately become Synovus Financial's chairman retired as an executive in 2005 but remained on the board. The long-time executive stepped down from the board in 2012.

Fred Green abruptly stepped down as president of Synovus in 2009. CEO Richard Anthony assumed his responsibilities until early 2010 when Kessel Stelling was named president and COO of the company. Stelling was named CEO later that year after Anthony who remained chairman took a medical leave of absence. Anthony retired from the board in 2012. Stelling then took on the additional roll of chairman.

EXECUTIVES

EVP General Counsel and Corporate Secretary, Samuel F. Hatcher, age 66, $325,000 total compensation
Director; Chairman and CEO Total System Services, Philip W. (Phil) Tomlinson, age 65
EVP and CFO, Thomas J. Prescott, age 57, $387,000 total compensation
EVP and COO, Allen J. Gula Jr., age 57
EVP and Chief Risk Officer, Mark G. Holladay, age 56, $315,000 total compensation
Regional President and CEO Athens First Bank and Trust Athens, J. William Douglas
Chairman and CEO First National Bank of Jasper, L. Gwaltney McCollum Jr.
President and CEO First State Bank and Trust Valdosta, David A. Durland
Chairman and CEO Georgia Bank and Trust Calhoun, Larry Roye
Chairman Coastal Bank and Trust Pensacola, W. Luther Taylor
Chairman and CEO Bank of Tuscaloosa, James B. Flemming
President and CEO Security Bank and Trust Albany, Mark J. Lane
Chief Community Banking Officer, D. Wayne Akins Jr.
Chairman President and CEO Sterling Bank, W. Alan Worrell
President and CEO Synovus Mortgage, Michael L. Padalino
President Synovus Trust Company, George G. Flowers
Regional CEO; President and CEO Commerial Bank Thomasville, Frederick D. (Fred) Jefferson
President and CEO Community Bank and Trust Enterprise, H. Lamar Loftin
President and CEO First Coast Community Bank Fernandina Beach, James M. Townsend
Chairman and CEO First Commercial Bank of Huntsville, Charles E. Kettle
President and CEO First Community Bank Tifton, John M. Davis
Regional President and CEO First Commercial Bank Birmingham, Nelson S. Bean
Regional CEO; President and CEO The National Bank of South Carolina, Charles W. (Chuck) Garnett
Regional CEO Synovus Bank Tampa Bay, David W. Dunbar
Regional CEO; President and CEO Bank of North Georgia Alpharetta, Donald D. Howard
President and CEO Creative Financial Group, Robert W. Law
CEO Cohutta Banking Company Chattanooga, Michael M. Sarvis
President GLOBALT Investments, William H. Roach
Chairman President and CEO, Kessel D. Stelling Jr., age 56
CEO Bank of Coweta Newmnan, J. Randall (Randy) Carroll
External Communications Manager, Greg Hudgison
President and CEO Tallahassee State Bank, Sharon E. Weeden
President Synovus Bank of Jacksonville, Damon B. Olinto
Chief Accounting Officer, Liliana C. McDaniel, age 47
EVP Financial Management Services, J. Barton Singleton, age 48
CEO The Coastal Bank of Georgia Brunswick, R. Wayne Johnson
EVP and Chief Credit Officer, Kevin J. Howard, age 47
EVP and Chief Banking Officer, R. Dallis (Roy) Copeland Jr., age 43
Regional CEO; President and CEO Columbus Bank and Trust, William R. (Billy) Blanchard
President and CEO Commercial Bank and Trust LaGrange, William F. (Frank) McRae
Chief Commercial Officer, Curtis J. Perry
Regional CEO; President and CEO The Bank of Nashville Trust One Bank Nashville and Memphis, William R. (Bill) Nigh
President and CEO CB&T Bank of Middle Georgia Warner Robins, James E. Norris III
President and CEO CB&T East Alabama Phenix City, Wade Burford
President and CEO Citizens First Bank Rome, Angela W. Lewis
CEO Coastal Bank and Trust of FL Pensacola, Joseph R. Youd Jr.
Chief Information Security Officer, Susan Koski
CIO, Renee S. Roth
Director, James H. (Jim) Blanchard, age 70
Director; Chairman and CEO Total System Services, Philip W. (Phil) Tomlinson, age 65
Director, James D. (Jimmy) Yancey, age 70
Director, Daniel P. (Dan) Amos, age 60
Director, T. Michael (Mike) Goodrich, age 66
Director, Melvin T. Stith, age 66
Director, Richard Y. Bradley, age 73
Director, Gardiner W. Garrard Jr., age 71
Director, Mason H. Lampton, age 64
Director, H. Lynn Page, age 71
Director, V. Nathaniel Hansford, age 68
Director, Elizabeth C. Ogie, age 61
Director, Elizabeth W. (Betsy) Camp, age 60
Director, William B. (Brad) Turner Jr., age 60
Director, Frank W. Brumley, age 71
Chairman President and CEO, Kessel D. Stelling Jr., age 56
Auditors: KPMGLLP

LOCATIONS

HQ: Synovus Financial Corp.
1111 Bay Ave. Ste. 500, Columbus GA 31901
Phone: 706-649-2311 **Fax:** 706-641-6555
Web: www.synovus.com

2011 Bank Branches

	No.
Georgia	129
Florida	55
Alabama	47
South	42
Tennessee	20
Total	**293**

PRODUCTS/OPERATIONS

2011 Sales

	$ mil.	% of total
Interest		
Loans including fees	1,019	69
Investment securities available for sale	108	8
Other	14	1
Noninterest		
Service charges on deposit accounts	78	5
Investment securities gains net	75	5
Fiduciary & asset management fees	45	3
Bankcard fees	41	3
Mortgage banking income	20	1
Brokerage & investment banking	26	2
Other fee income	19	1
Other	31	2
Total	**1,480**	**100**

Selected Subsidiaries and Divisions

AFB&T
Bank of Coweta

The Bank of Nashville
Bank of North Georgia
The Bank of Tuscaloosa
CB&T Bank of East Alabama
CB&T Bank of Middle Georgia
Citizens First Bank
The Coastal Bank of Georgia
Coastal Bank and Trust
Coastal Bank and Trust of Alabama
Cohutta Banking Company
Columbus Bank & Trust
Commercial Bank
Commercial Bank and Trust Company
Community Bank & Trust of Southeast Alabama
The First Bank of Jasper
First Coast Community Bank
First Commercial Bank
First Commercial Bank of Huntsville
First State Bank & Trust
Georgia Bank & Trust
GLOBALT Inc.
NBSC
SB&T
Sea Island Bank
Sterling Bank
Synovus Bank
Synovus Bank of Jacksonville
Synovus Bank of Florida
Synovus Mortgage Corp.
Synovus Securities Inc.
Synovus Trust Company N.A.
The Tallahassee State Bank
Trust One Bank

COMPETITORS

BancorpSouth
Bank of America
BB&T
BBX Capital
Citigroup
Compass Bancshares
Fidelity Southern
First Citizens BancShares
First Horizon
Regions Financial
SunTrust
Trustmark
Wells Fargo

HISTORICAL FINANCIALS

Company Type: Public

Income Statement

FYE: December 31

	ASSETS ($ mil.)	NET INCOME ($ mil.)	INCOME AS % OF ASSETS	EMPLOYEES
12/11	27,162	(60)	—	5,224
12/10	30,093	(790)	—	6,109
12/09	32,831	(1,431)	—	6,385
12/08	35,786	(582)	—	6,876
12/07	33,018	526	1.6%	6,807
Annual Growth	(4.8%)	—	—	(6.4%)

2011 Year-End Financials

Debt ratio: 5.02%
Return on equity: (-2.14)%
Cash ($ mil.): 540
Current ratio: —
Long-term debt ($ mil.): 1,364
No. of shares (mil.): 785
Dividends
Yield: —
Payout: —
Market value ($ mil.): 1,107

	STOCK PRICE ($) FY Close	P/E High	P/E Low	PER SHARE ($) Earnings	Dividends	Book Value
12/11	1.41	—	—	(0.15)	0.00	3.60
12/10	2.64	—	—	(1.24)	0.04	3.82
12/09	2.05	—	—	(3.99)	0.04	5.82
12/08	8.30	—	—	(1.77)	0.46	11.46
12/07	24.08	21	14	1.60	0.82	10.43
Annual Growth	(50.8%)	—	—	—	—	(23.4%)

Sysco Corp.

This company has the menu that people depend on. Sysco is the #1 foodservice supplier in North America serving some 400000 customers with a fleet of 8700 delivery vehicles and about 180 distribution centers in the US Canada and Ireland. Its core broadline distribution business supplies food and non-food products to restaurants schools hotels health care institutions and other foodservice customers while its SYGMA Network focuses on supplying chain restaurants. Sysco distributes both nationally branded products and its own private-label goods. In addition Sysco supplies customers with specialty produce and meat products and it distributes kitchen equipment and supplies for the hospitality industry.

HISTORY

Sysco was founded in 1969 when John Baugh a Houston wholesale food distributor formed a national distribution company with the owners of eight other US wholesalers. Joining Baugh's Zero Foods of Houston to form Sysco were Frost-Pack Distributing (Grand Rapids Michigan) Louisville Grocery (Louisville Kentucky) Plantation Foods (Miami) Thomas Foods and its Justrite subsidiary (Cincinnati) Wicker (Dallas) Food Service Company (Houston) Global Frozen Foods (New York) and Texas Wholesale Grocery (Dallas). The company went public in 1970. Sysco which derives its name from Systems and Services Company benefited from Baugh's recognition of the trend toward dining out. Until Sysco was formed small independent operators almost exclusively provided food distribution to restaurants hotels and other non-grocers.

The company expanded through internal growth and the acquisition of strong local distributors benefiting through buyout agreements requiring the seller to continue managing its own operation while earning a portion of the sale price with future profits.

In 1988 when Sysco was already the largest North American foodservice distributor it acquired CFS Continental the third-largest North American food distributor. The CFS acquisition added a large truck fleet and increased the company's penetration along the West Coast of the US and into Canada. Also that year Sysco purchased Olewine's a Pennsylvania-based distributor. In 1990 the company bought Oklahoma City-based Scrivner later renamed Sysco Food Services of Oklahoma.

Sysco acquired Collins Foodservice (serving the Northwest) and Benjamin Polakoff & Son and Perloff Brothers (both serving the Northeast) in 1992. Later that year the company sold its only remaining retail business consumer-size frozen food distributor Global Sysco. St. Louis-based Clark Foodservice and New Jersey's Ritter Food were purchased in 1993. The next year Sysco acquired Woodhaven Foods a distributor owned by ARA (now ARAMARK) one of the nation's largest cafeteria and concession operators.

The company expanded into central Canada in 1996 when it acquired Strano Foodservice. Sysco formed an alliance with National Healthcare Logistics in 1997 to improve distribution to hospitals and integrated health care systems. Baugh at age 81 retired from his senior chairman post later that year.

Eager to expand its operations in Florida Sysco bought the foodservice distribution division of Beaver Street Fisheries in 1998. The company also purchased Maine-based Jordan's Meats. A number of large acquisitions followed in 1999 including Atlanta-based Buckhead Beef Company Newport Meat Company of Southern California and Virginia-based Doughtie's Foods (renamed SYSCO Food Services of Hampton Roads). Sysco also bought Watson Foodservice a distributor serving customers in Texas New Mexico and Oklahoma.

Company president Charles Cotros succeeded Bill Lindig as CEO in 2000. That year Sysco bought produce distributor FreshPoint and Canadian foodservice distributor North Douglas Distributors. Sysco acquired specialty meat supplier Freedman Meats in 2001. The company later expanded its operations serving the lodging industry when it purchased Guest Supply for nearly $240 million in stock.

Further expanding its Canadian operations Sysco acquired SERCA Foodservice from grocery store operator Sobeys in 2002. (SERCA's British Columbia operations were later sold to Gordon Food Service.) Other acquisitions that year included Ohio-based broadline distributor Abbott Foods fast-food products provider Pronamics and some assets of the Denver operations of Marriott Distribution Services. Richard Schnieders succeeded Cotros who retired at the end of that year.

Sysco acquired the specialty meat-cutting division of the Colorado Boxed Beef Company and its Florida broadline foodservice operation J&B Foodservice in 2003. Later that year the company purchased assets related to Smart & Final's foodservice operation located in Stockton California to expand SYSCO's coverage in the state.

Subsidiary Sysco Food Services of Central Alabama announced in 2004 that it planned to expand its foodservice agreement with Cuba and had signed a letter of intent with the Cuban food import agency Alimport. Within the same month though the unit retracted its offer reporting that the agreement asked for Sysco to assist "in normalizing trade relations" between the US and Cuba.

Sysco continued its string of acquisitions that year purchasing chain restaurant supplier International Food Group and Illinois-based Robert's Foods. The company added to its specialty meat offerings the following year with the acquisition of California-based Facciola Meat Company and Florida-based Royalty Foods. Also in 2005 it purchased specialty-food importer Walker Foods fresh fruit and vegetable distributor Piranha Produce and Western Foods an Arkansas-based broadline foodservice distributor.

In 2006 Sysco acquired the foodservice assets of Bunn Capitol a supplier to restaurants and other customers in Illinois. Founder Baugh died in 2007. Two years later CEO Schnieders retired and was replaced by Bill DeLaney a company veteran who had previously served as CFO.

In July 2010 Sysco acquired Nebraska-based Lincoln Poultry & Egg Co. a broadline foodservice provider with more than 800 customers primarily in the central US.

Adding to its international holdings in October 2012 Sysco acquired the foodservice distribution arm of Ireland-based produce company Keelings Foods.

EXECUTIVES

SVP Sysco Business Services, Kirk G. Drummond, age 57

EVP Merchandising and Supply Chain, William B. Day, age 55

VP Industry Relations and Diversity, Albert L. Gaylor

VP Agricultural Sustainability, Craig G. Watson, age 60
Chairman, Manuel A. (Manny) Fernandez, age 66
Member Directors' Council; President Sysco San Antonio, William D. Fisher, age 62
VP Learning and Organizational Capability, Mary Beth Moehring
VP and Member Directors' Council; President and CEO FreshPoint, Brian M. Sturgeon
VP Produce, Richard J. Dachman, age 56
VP Human Resources, Mark Wisnoski
EVP and Group President, Larry G. Pulliam, age 56, $532,000 total compensation
VP Sourcing, Cameron L. (Cam) Blakely, age 53
SVP and CIO, Twila M. Day, age 46
SVP Controller and Chief Accounting Officer, G. Mitchell Elmer, age 53
VP; Chairman and CEO SYGMA Network, Alan W. Kelso, age 61
VP Merchandising Sales and Sysco Brand Development, John T. McIntyre
VP and Assistant Treasurer, Kathy O. Gish
VP Deputy General Counsel and Assistant Corporate Secretary, Thomas P. Kurz
VP Organizational Effectiveness and Corporate Communications, Mark A. Palmer, age 48
SVP Distribution Services, C. Frederick (Fred) Lankford
SVP Multi Unit Sales; CEO Sysco Canada, G. Kent Humphries
VP Supply Chain Operations Enterprise Planning and Design, Theodore R. (Ted) Murray II, age 45
EVP Business Transformation, James D. Hope, age 52
SVP Foodservice Operations, Scott A. Sonnemaker
VP Finance and Accounting, Jesse E. Morris
EVP and Group President, Michael W. (Mike) Green, age 53, $494,000 total compensation
VP Foodservice Operations (Mideast), Thomas C. (Tom) Barnes
VP Foodservice Operations (Southeast), Robert J. Davis, age 54
SVP Foodservice Operations, Charles W. Staes, age 56
SVP Merchandising, Alan E. Hasty, age 54
VP Foodservice Operations (California), Thomas M. Kesteloot
VP; Chairman SYSCO Specialty Meat Companies, Andrew L. (Andy) Malcolm
VP and Assistant Controller, David L. Valentine, age 54
President Sysco Canada, Randy J. White
VP Employee Relations, Thomas P. Randt, age 59
VP and Assistant Controller, Gregory W. Neely
President CEO and Director, William J. (Bill) DeLaney III, age 56, $800,000 total compensation
VP Foodservice Operations (Southwest), W. Keith Miller
SVP Foodservice Operations (South), Michael S. Headrick, age 63
VP Supply Chain Management, Masao Nishi
SVP Human Resources, Paul T. Moskowitz, age 48
VP Sourcing and Supply Chain Services, Robert E. Howell
VP Quality Assurance, Mark Mignogna
VP Finance Specialty Businesses, Julie O. Swan
Member Directors' Council; VP Foodservice Operations (Midwest), Greg D. Bertrand, age 48
VP Distribution Services, Gary W. Cullen
VP Contract Sales, Richard E. Abbey, age 62
VP Contract Sales, James M. Worrall
VP Labor Relations, Charles A. Munn, age 61
VP Foodservice Operations (Northeast), James M. Danahy
VP Information Technology, John D. Holzem, age 52
Member Directors' Council; President and CEO Sysco Central Ontario Sysco Toront and Sysco Kingston, Rodney S. Stroud, age 50
VP Real Estate and Construction, D. Michael Downs
VP Merchandising and Supply Chain Management, Neil G. Theiss
Member Directors' Council; President Sysco Charlotte, Bruce H. Matthews
VP Safety and Crisis Management, Sandra G. Carson, age 49
VP Warehouse and Delivery, Gary M. Mills, age 62
VP Investor Relations, Neil A. Russell II, age 41
EVP and CFO, Robert C. (Chris) Kreidler, age 48, $378,766 total compensation
VP Information Technology, Lucas Wagenaar
SVP General Counsel and Secretary, Russell T. Libby, age 46
SVP; Prwesident Sysco Ventures, Brian C. Beach
VP Employment Compensation and Benefits, Evelyn J. Pulliam, age 49
VP Strategy, Jeanne-Mey Sun
VP Contract Sales, Nick Kruthaupt
VP Organizational Effectiveness, Lesley J. Huff
Member Directors' Council; VP Foodservice Operations (Rocky Mountains), Patrick H. Burton
Member Directors' Council; President Sysco Chicago, Louis P. Nasir
Member Directors' Council; President Sysco Atlanta, Marlin E. Turner
VP Foodservice Operations (Florida), Tim K. Brown
VP Foodservice Operations (Mid Atlantic), Christopher S. DeWitt
VP Corporate Business Development, Gregory S. Keller
VP Foodservice Operations (Canada), Joel T. Grade
VP Corporate Communications, Charley Wilson
EVP and CTO, Wayne Shurtz
Director, Richard G. Tilghman, age 72
Director, Joseph A. Hafner Jr., age 67
Director, Larry C. Glasscock, age 63
Director, John M. Cassaday, age 59
Director, Jacquelyn M. (Jackie) Ward, age 74
Director, Jonathan Golden, age 75
Director, Judith B. Craven, age 66
Director, Phyllis S. Sewell, age 82
Director, Nancy S. Newcomb, age 68
President CEO and Director, William J. (Bill) DeLaney III, age 56
Director, Hans-Joachim Koerber, age 66
Auditors: Ernst&YoungLLP

LOCATIONS

HQ: Sysco Corp.
1390 Enclave Parkway, Houston, TX 77077-2099
Phone: 281 584-1390 **Fax:** 281 584-2880
Web: www.sysco.com

2012 Sales

	$ mil.	% of total
US	37,596	89
Canada	4,246	10
Other countries	537	1
Total	**42,380**	**100**

PRODUCTS/OPERATIONS

2012 Sales

	$ mil.	% of total
Broadline	34,420	81
SYGMA	5,735	14
Other	2,396	6
Adjustment (171.7) (1)		
Total	**42,380**	**100**

2012 Sales

	$ mil.	% of total
Canned & dry products	7,948	19
Fresh & frozen meats	7,929	19
Frozen fruits vegetables bakery & other	5,757	14
Dairy products	4,456	11
Poultry	4,188	10
Fresh produce	3,332	8
Paper & disposables	3,295	7
Seafood	2,076	5
Beverage products	1,591	4
Janitorial products	952	2
Equipment & smallwares	613	1
Medical supplies	237	—
Total	**42,380**	**100**

2012 Sales

	% of total
Restaurants	63
Hospitals & nursing	10
Schools &	6
Hotels &	5
Other	16
Total	**100**

COMPETITORS

Ben E. Keith
Bunzl
Edward Don
Foodbuy
Golden State Foods
Gordon Food Service
MAINES
McLane Foodservice
Meadowbrook Meat Company
Performance Food
PrimeSource FoodService
Reinhart FoodService
Shamrock Foods
UniPro Foodservice
US Foods

HISTORICAL FINANCIALS

Company Type: Public

Income Statement FYE: June 30

	REVENUE ($ mil.)	NET INCOME ($ mil.)	NET PROFIT MARGIN	EMPLOYEES
06/12*	42,380	1,121	2.6%	47,800
07/11	39,323	1,152	2.9%	46,000
07/10	37,243	1,179	3.2%	46,000
06/09	36,853	1,055	2.9%	47,000
06/08	37,522	1,106	2.9%	50,000
Annual Growth	3.1%	0.3%	—	(1.1%)

*Fiscal year change

2012 Year-End Financials

Debt ratio: 24.96%
Return on equity: 23.94%
Cash ($ mil.): 688
Current ratio: 177.73
Long-term debt ($ mil.): 2,763
No. of shares (mil.): 585
Dividends
Yield: —
Payout: 42.11%
Market value ($ mil.): 17,467

	STOCK PRICE ($) FY Close	P/E High/Low		PER SHARE ($) Earnings	Dividends	Book Value
06/12*	29.81	17	13	1.90	0.00	8.00
07/11	31.39	17	14	1.96	0.00	7.95
07/10	28.27	16	11	1.99	0.00	6.51
06/09	22.98	20	11	1.77	0.00	5.85
06/08	28.22	20	15	1.81	0.00	5.67
Annual Growth	1.4%	—	—	1.2%	—	9.0%

*Fiscal year change

Targa Resources Corp

LOCATIONS

HQ: Targa Resources Corp
1000 Louisiana St, Suite 4300, Houston, TX 77002
Phone: 713 584-1000
Web: www.targaresources.com

HISTORICAL FINANCIALS

Company Type:

Income Statement FYE: December 31

	REVENUE ($ mil.)	NET INCOME ($ mil.)	NET PROFIT MARGIN	EMPLOYEES
12/11	6,994	30	0.4%	1,096
12/10	5,469	(15)	—	1,020
12/09	4,536	29	0.6%	1,000
12/08	7,998	37	0.5%	0
12/07	7,297	56	0.8%	0
Annual Growth	(1.1%)	(14.0%)	—	—

2011 Year-End Financials

Debt ratio: 40.90%
Return on equity: 19.42%
Cash ($ mil.): 145
Current ratio: 116.92
Long-term debt ($ mil.): 1,567
No. of shares (mil.): 42
Dividends
Yield: —
Payout: 125.89%
Market value ($ mil.): 1,725

	STOCK PRICE ($) FY Close	P/E High/Low		PER SHARE ($) Earnings	Dividends	Book Value
12/11	40.69	55	36	0.74	0.00	3.73
12/10	26.81	—	—	(30.94)	0.00	3.41
Annual Growth	51.8%	—	—	—	—	9.4%

Targa Resources Partners LP

Targa Resources Partners fuels its business by producing and processing natural gas. The midstream energy company owns or operates 10100 miles of natural gas gathering pipeline (and nine processing plants) with access to gas reserves in the New Mexico West and North Texas and the Gulf Coast. Targa Resources Partners also operates natural gas liquids (NGLs) storage and transportation facilities located primarily in the southern and southwestern US. Customers include oil and gas companies and utilities. The company's parent Targa Resources is controlled by investment firm Warburg Pincus. Its subsidiary Targa Resources Corp. holds a 14% limited partner and a 2% general partner stake.

Targa Resources formed Targa Resources Partners as a limited partnership to own operate acquire and develop a diversified portfolio of complementary midstream energy assets including a number from its parent. Between early in 2007 and the end of 2010 Targa Resources Partners acquired six natural gas gathering and processing and natural gas liquids businesses from Targa Resources for a total of $3.1 billion.

In 2010 Targa Resources Partners acquired 63% of Targa Resources Corp.'s stake in the Versado System (natural gas gathering and processing assets in Southeast New Mexico and West Texas) for $247 million.

That year in conjunction with the closing of the IPO of Targa Resources Corp. that company sold a 77% stake in Venice Energy Services (a natural gas processing and NGL fractionation complex in Louisiana) to Targa Resources Partners for $175.6 million. The deal boosted Targa Resources Partners' gas processing assets.

In 2012 the company announced that it has agreed to acquire 100% of Saddle Butte Pipeline LLC's ownership of its Williston Basin crude oil pipeline and terminal system and its natural gas gathering and processing operations for $950 million.

Targa Resources Partners saw its revenues double in 2009 largely because of acquisitions. It reported improved operating margins in its Logistics NGLs and wholesale marketing segments in 2009 helped offset a downturn in its natural gas segment which was negatively affected by lower commodity prices.

In 2010 higher commodity prices and increased natural gas sale volumes lifted revenues which coupled with gains from derivatives and lower interest charges also resulted in a jump in net income that year.

Further growing its assets in 2011 the company acquired a refined petroleum products and crude oil storage facility (544000 barrels of capacity) in Channelview Texas along the Houston Ship Channel.

EXECUTIVES

Natural Gas Marketing Louisiana, Mike Phillips
President Finance and Administration Targa Resources GP LLC, Jeffrey J. (Jeff) McParland, age 57, $253,000 total compensation
North Texas and Permian Operations, Bob Faircloth
Chairman, Rene R. Joyce, age 64, $322,500 total compensation
CEO and Director, Joe Bob Perkins, age 51, $290,250 total compensation
Chairman Targa Resources GP LLC, James W. Whalan, age 70, $290,250 total compensation
EVP Targa Resources GP LLC, Roy E. Johnson, age 67
President and COO, Michael A. Heim, age 63, $268,750 total compensation
EVP General Counsel and Secretary Targa Resources GP LLC, Paul W. Chung, age 51
Natural Gas Marketing, Stacey Duke
Natural Gas Marketing Texas and New Mexico, Rene Ruiz
Natural Gas Marketing. Louisiana, Steve Bingham
Natural Gas Marketing Texas and New Mexico, Steven Fieldler
NGL Marketing Houston Area Imports/Exports, Scott Pryor
NGL Marketing Distribution, Leigh Murphy
Engineering, Steve Hopaon
Business Development, Brad Reese
Assistant General Counsel, Jim Patin
Accounting, Bob Sparger
SVP CFO and Treasurer, Matthew J. (Matt) Meloy, age 34
VP and CIO, Mike Penny
Controller, John Klein
Tax, John Thompson
Human Resources, Tim Janisse
SVP and Chief Accounting Officer Targa Resources GP LLC, John R. Sparger, age 58
Director Targa Resources GP LLC, William D. (Bill) Sullivan, age 55
Director Targa Resources GP LLC, Barry R. Pearl, age 62
Director Targa Resources GP LLC, Robert B. (Bobby) Evans, age 63
Director Targa Resources GP LLC, Peter R. Kagan, age 44
CEO and Director Targa Resources GP LLC, Rene R. Joyce, age 64
CEO and Director, Joe Bob Perkins, age 51
Director Targa Resources GP LLC, In Seon Hwang, age 35
Auditors: PricewaterhouseCoopersLLP

LOCATIONS

HQ: Targa Resources Partners LP
1000 Louisiana St. Ste. 4300, Houston TX 77002
Phone: 713-584-1000 **Fax:** 713-584-1100
Web: www.targaresources.com

PRODUCTS/OPERATIONS

2010 Sales

	$ mil.	% of total
NGLs	4,115	74
Natural gas	1,076	20
Condensate	95	2
Fractionation & treating fees	55	1
Storage & teminalling fees	40	1
Transportation fees	33	1
Gas processsing fees	32	1
Hedge settlements	6	-
Other	5	-
Total	**5,460**	**100**

COMPETITORS

BP
Chevron
Copano Energy
DCP Midstream Partners
Devon Energy
El Paso Corporation
Enbridge
Enterprise Products
Exxon Mobil
Marathon Oil
ONEOK Partners
Royal Dutch Shell
Williams Companies
XTO Energy

HISTORICAL FINANCIALS

Company Type: Public

Income Statement FYE: December 31

	REVENUE ($ mil.)	NET INCOME ($ mil.)	NET PROFIT MARGIN	EMPLOYEES
12/11	6,987	204	2.9%	0
12/10	5,460	109	2.0%	0
12/09	4,095	52	1.3%	0
12/08	2,074	91	4.4%	0
12/07	1,661	40	2.4%	0
Annual Growth	43.2%	50.1%	—	—

2011 Year-End Financials

Debt ratio: 40.40%
Return on equity: 16.72%
Cash ($ mil.): 55
Current ratio: 102.46
Long-term debt ($ mil.): 1,477
No. of shares (mil.): 84
Dividends
Yield: —
Payout: 114.02%
Market value ($ mil.): 3,160

	STOCK PRICE ($) FY Close	P/E High/Low		PER SHARE ($) Earnings	Dividends	Book Value
12/11	37.28	20	16	1.98	0.00	14.43
12/10	33.96	37	23	0.92	2.10	12.18
12/09	24.31	29	8	0.86	2.07	13.35
12/08	7.75	16	3	1.83	1.85	16.51
12/07	29.62	43	29	0.81	0.84	13.30
Annual Growth	5.9%	—	—	25.0%	—	2.1%

Target Corp

Purveyor of all that is cheap yet chic Target Corp. is the nation's #2 discount chain (behind Wal-Mart). The fashion-forward discounter operates about 1765 Target and SuperTarget stores in 49 states as well as an online business at Target.com. Target and its larger grocery-carrying incarnation SuperTarget have carved out a niche by offering more upscale trend-driven merchandise than rivals Wal-Mart and Kmart. Target also issues its proprietary Target credit card good only at Target. After a reversal in fortune that coincided with the onset of the deep recession Target is growing its grocery business aggressively remodeling and expanding stores and –in 2013 –venturing into the Canadian market.

HISTORY

The panic of 1873 left Joseph Hudson bankrupt. After he paid his debts at 60 cents on the dollar he saved enough to open a men's clothing store in Detroit in 1881. Among his innovations were merchandise-return privileges and price marking in place of bargaining. By 1891 Hudson's was the largest retailer of men's clothing in the US. Hudson repaid his creditors from 1873 in full with interest. When Hudson died in 1912 four nephews expanded the business.

Former banker George Dayton established a dry-goods store in 1902 in Minneapolis. Like Hudson he offered return privileges and liberal credit. His store grew to a 12-story full-line department store.

After WWII both companies saw that the future lay in the suburbs. In 1954 Hudson's built Northland in Detroit then the largest US shopping center. Dayton's built the world's first fully enclosed shopping mall in Edina a Minneapolis suburb in 1956. In 1962 Dayton's opened its first discount store in Roseville (naming the store Target to distinguish the discounter from its higher-end department stores).

Dayton's went public in 1966 the same year it began the B. Dalton bookstore chain. Three years later it merged with the family-owned Hudson's forming Dayton Hudson. Dayton Hudson purchased more malls and invested in such specialty areas as consumer electronics and hard goods. Target had 24 stores by 1970.

The Target chain became the company's top moneymaker in 1977. The next year Dayton Hudson bought California-based Mervyn's (later Mervyns). In the late 1970s and 1980s it sold nine regional malls and several other businesses including the 800-store B. Dalton chain to Barnes & Noble. The Target stores division purchased Indianapolis-based Ayr-Way (1980) and Southern California-based Fedmart stores (1983). In the late 1980s Dayton Hudson took Target to Los Angeles and the Northwest. Robert Ulrich who began with the company as a merchandise trainee in 1967 became president and CEO of the Target stores division in 1987 and chairman and CEO of Dayton Hudson in 1994.

Dayton Hudson opened the first Target Greatland store in 1990. By this time it had 420 Target stores. Also that year Dayton Hudson bought the Marshall Field's chain of 24 department stores from B.A.T Industries. Marshall Field's began as a dry-goods business that Marshall Field bought in 1865 and subsequently built into Chicago's premier upscale retailer.

SuperTarget stores were introduced in 1995. The Target stores division opened stores in the Mid-Atlantic and Northeast the next year while the department store division began selling off its Marshall Field's locations in Texas.

In 1998 Dayton Hudson boosted its Internet presence by purchasing direct-marketing company Rivertown Trading; it also bought apparel supplier Associated Merchandising that year. In 2000 Dayton Hudson renamed itself Target Corporation. In early 2001 the company renamed its Dayton's and Hudson's chains Marshall Field's. Also that year Target acquired the rights to 35 former Montgomery Wards stores from the bankrupt retailer.

The nation's #2 discounter was #1 when it came to corporate giving in 2001. Target topped the "Forbes" list of America's Most Philanthropic Companies that year donating 2.5% of its 2000 income (nearly $86 million). By comparison Wal-Mart gave away $116.5 million in 2001 less than 1% of its income in 2000.

In 2002 the company reopened 30 of the former Montgomery Ward stores as Target outlets. Net of closings 94 Target stores opened in 2002 while neither Mervyns nor Marshall Field's added to their store counts. In March 2003 three new SuperTarget stores opened in the Dallas/Fort Worth area.

2004 was a year of divestments for Target. In January the discounter announced it was exiting the catalog business. To that end in April Target sold its Signals and Wireless gifts catalogs to Universal Screen Arts for an undisclosed sum. In July Target sold its Marshall Field's business to The May Department Stores Co. for about $3.2 billion in cash. In September Target completed the sale of 257 Mervyns stores in 13 states to an investment group that includes Cerberus Capital Management Lubert-Adler/Klaff and Partners and Sun Capital Partners as well as its Mervyns credit card receivables to GE Consumer Finance for a combined sum of approximately $1.65 billion in cash. (Later Mervyns filed for bankruptcy and closed the last of its stores by the end of 2008.)

In October 2005 vice chairman Gerald Storch resigned unexpectedly after more than a dozen years with the company. No reason was given for his departure. In the largest mass opening in Target's history the retailer opened 60 new stores on October 9.

In July 2006 Target.com extended its partnership with Amazon Enterprise Solutions a unit of online retailer Amazon.com through August 2010. Amazon provides e-commerce technology to the discount chain.

In May 2008 Ulrich who served as chairman and CEO since 1994 handed his CEO title to president Gregg Steinhafel. (Steinhafel joined the retailer in 1979 and worked his way up the executive ranks.) Also in May Target closed on the sale of a 47% stake in its credit-card receivable to JPMorgan Chase for $3.6 billion. The five-year deal allows Target to buy back the stake at the end of the term. In October the company opened a pair of stores in Alaska thereby expanding its retail presence to 48 states. In November Target said no thanks to a plan Ackman had proposed for Target to spin off its real estate holdings in a bid to increase shareholder value citing uncertainty about valuation assumptions and the potential reduction in financial flexibility as a result of spin off.

Ulrich retired from the board in January 2009 and Steinhafel added the chairman's title to his job description.

In April 2010 Target stopped offering new credit card applicants its co-branded Visa credit card.

EXECUTIVES

Chairman President and CEO, Gregg W. Steinhafel, age 57, $1,350,000 total compensation
EVP Property Development, John D. Griffith, age 50, $598,077 total compensation
SVP Communications, Susan D. Kahn
EVP and Chief Marketing Officer, Jeffrey L. Jones, age 44
EVP General Counsel and Corporate Secretary, Timothy R. (Tim) Baer, age 51
SVP Global Finance Systems; CFO Target Canada, Jane P. Windmeier
President Community Relations and Target Foundation, Laysha Ward, age 44
President Financial and Retail Services, Terrence J. (Terry) Scully, age 59
SVP Stores, Bryan Everett, age 42
SVP Distribution, Mitchell L. (Mitch) Stover
SVP Merchandise Planning, Keri Jones
EVP Merchandising and Supply Chain, Kathryn A. (Kathee) Tesija, age 49, $650,000 total compensation
EVP Stores, Tina M. Schiel, age 46
SVP Supply Chain Target Canada, Richard N. Maguire
SVP Merchandising Apparel and Accessories, Patricia Adams
EVP Human Resources, Jodeen A. Kozlak, age 48
SVP Merchandising Home, Stacia J. Andersen
SVP Financial Planning Analysis and Tax, Corey L. Haaland
SVP Stores, Derek L. Jenkins
VP Public Relations, Dustee Tucker Jenkins
Chairman and President Target India, Lalit Ahuja
SVP Target Sourcing Services, Carmela Batacchi
SVP Stores, Sid Keswani
SVP Merchandising Grocery, Annette Miller
SVP Real Estate, Scott Nelson
SVP Store Design, Rich Varda
EVP Target Technology Services and CIO, Beth M. Jacob, age 50
President Target.com, Stephen (Steve) Eastman
SVP Merchandising Operations, Mark Schindele
EVP and CFO, John Mulligan
SVP Target Sourcing Services, Barbara Dugan
SVP Store Operations, Janna Adair-Potts
SVP Target Sourcing Services, Cynthia Ho
President Target Sourcing Services, Timothy A. Mantel
President Target Canada, Anthony S. (Tony) Fisher, age 37
SVP Distribution Operations, Mike Robbins
SVP Merchandising Target Canada, John Morioka
SVP Supply Chain Target Canada, Todd Marshall
SVP Merchandising Hardlines, Casey Carl
SVP Merchandising Health and Beauty, Jose Barra
Director, John G. Stumpf, age 58
Director, Anne M. Mulcahy, age 60
Director, Roxanne S. Austin, age 51
Director, Stephen W. (Steve) Sanger, age 66
Director, Solomon D. (Sol) Trujillo, age 60
Director, Calvin (Cal) Darden, age 62
Director, James A. Johnson, age 68
Director, Mary E. Minnick, age 53
Director, Mary N. Dillon, age 50
Director, Derica W. Rice, age 47
Auditors: Ernst&YoungLLP

LOCATIONS

HQ: Target Corporation
1000 Nicollet Mall, Minneapolis MN 55403
Phone: 612-304-6073 **Fax:** 212-350-9911

2012 Locations

	No.
California	252
Texas	148
Florida	124

Illinois	87
Minnesota	74
New	66
Ohio	64
Pennsylvania	63
Michigan	59
Virginia	56
Georgia	55
Arizona	48
North	47
New	43
Colorado	41
Wisconsin	38
Maryland	36
Massachusetts	36
Missouri	36
Washington	35
Indiana	33
Tennessee	32
Iowa	22
Alabama	20
Connecticut	20
Kansas	19
Nevada	19
Oregon	18
South	18
Louisiana	16
Oklahoma	15
Kentucky	14
Nebraska	14
Utah	12
Arkansas	9
New	9
New	9
Montana	7
Idaho	6
Mississippi	6
West	6
Maine	5
South	5
Hawaii	4
North	4
Rhode	4
Alaska	3
Delaware	3
Wyoming	2
District of	1
Total	**1,763**

PRODUCTS/OPERATIONS

2012 Sales

	% of total
Household	25
Apparel &	19
Hardlines	19
Food & pet	19
Home furnishings &	18
Total	**100**

2012 Stores

	No.
General	637
Expanded food	875
SuperTarget	251
Total	**1,763**

Selected Designer Private Labels

Amy Coe (children' s bedding and accessories)
Liz Lange (maternity)
Michael Graves Design (housewares)
Mossimo (junior fashions)
Sonia Kashuk (cosmetics and fragrances)
Todd Oldham (bedding and furniture)

Selected Private Labels

Archer Farms (food)
Cherokee (apparel)
Choxie (candy)
Furio (housewares)
Honors (apparel)
In Due Time (maternity wear)
Market Pantry
Merona (apparel)
Nick & Nora (apparel)
Playwonder (toys)
Utility (apparel)
Xhilaration (apparel)

Store Formats
SuperTarget (groceries and general merchandise)
Target (upscale discount stores)

Other Operations
Rivertown Trading (catalogs and e-commerce)
- Britannia (British video and gifts)
- I Love A Deal (apparel housewares and jewelry)
- Seasons (traditional)

Target Capital Corp.
Target Commercial Interiors
Target Receivables Corp.

COMPETITORS

Bed Bath & Beyond	Kohl' s
Best Buy	Kroger
BJ' s Wholesale Club	Limited Brands
Burnes Home Accents	Macy' s
Container Store	PETCO
Costco Wholesale	Ross Stores
CVS Caremark	Sears
Dillard' s	SUPERVALU
Dollar General	The Gap
eBay	TJX Companies
Euromarket Designs	Toys ' ' R' ' Us
Foot Locker	Wal-Mart
Home Depot	Walgreen
J. C. Penney Company	Williams-Sonoma
Kmart	

HISTORICAL FINANCIALS

Company Type: Public

Income Statement

FYE: January 28

	REVENUE ($ mil.)	NET INCOME ($ mil.)	NET PROFIT MARGIN	EMPLOYEES
01/12	69,865	2,929	4.2%	365,000
01/11	67,390	2,920	4.3%	355,000
01/10	65,357	2,488	3.8%	351,000
01/09*	64,948	2,214	3.4%	351,000
02/08	63,367	2,849	4.5%	366,000
Annual Growth	2.5%	0.7%	—	(0.1%)

*Fiscal year change

2012 Year-End Financials

Debt ratio: 37.49%	No. of shares (mil.): 669
Return on equity: 18.51%	Dividends
Cash ($ mil.): 794	Yield: —
Current ratio: 115.13	Payout: 25.70%
Long-term debt ($ mil.): 13,697	Market value ($ mil.): 33,498

	STOCK PRICE ($) FY Close	P/E High	P/E Low	PER SHARE ($) Earnings	Dividends	Book Value
01/12	50.05	13	11	4.28	0.00	23.64
01/11	54.35	15	12	4.00	0.00	22.00
01/10	51.27	16	8	3.30	0.00	20.61
01/09*	31.20	20	9	2.86	0.00	18.22
02/08	57.05	21	14	3.33	0.00	18.70
Annual Growth	(3.2%)	—	—	6.5%	—	6.0%

*Fiscal year change

Taylor Capital Group, Inc

This company is tailor-made for small and mid-sized business owners. Taylor Capital Group is the holding company for Cole Taylor Bank which specializes in commercial banking real estate lending and wealth management services aimed primarily at closely-held and family-run businesses in the construction manufacturing distribution transportation and professional services industries. Business loans including working capital owner-occupied real estate financing and letters and lines of credit account for approximately 90% of the bank's loan portfolio. With about 10 branches in the Chicago metropolitan area the bank also offers traditional banking services to consumers.

Geographic Reach

Outside the Chicago area Taylor Capital Group has opened lending offices in about 10 other states including California Texas Washington and Wisconsin.

Financial Analysis

The bank's revenue fell more than 15% in 2011 vs. 2010 on declines in both interest and non-interest income down 10% and 32% respectively. A drop in interest and fees on loans and interest and dividends on securities depressed interest income. Despite falling revenue the bank returned to profitability in 2011 for the first year since 2006.

Chicago was one of the hardest hit areas during the recession and not coincidentally Taylor Capital Group reported losses each year between 2007 and 2010 as real estate prices plummeted. The company which increased its provisions for loan losses in 2010 is focusing on improving its asset quality. It has reduced its exposure to residential construction and land loans and ramped up its asset-based lending and residential mortgage operations.

Cole Taylor Bank sold its corporate trust business to Amalgamated Bank of Chicago in 2010 a move that allows it to focus on its core commercial banking business. The company supports organic growth by cross-selling financial products and services to middle-market businesses and their owners and executives.

Strategy

Taylor Capital Group is sticking to its "fix and grow" strategy in place since early 2008. The strategy focuses on remediating the asset quality issues caused by the downturn in the Chicago area real estate market in recent years while at the same time growing the diversifying its earnings. The bank has worked to reposition itself as a commercial and industrial lender to closely-held businesses in the Chicago area while reducing its exposure to risky residential real estate construction and land loans.

Ownership

Members of the Taylor family including brothers Bruce and Jeffrey Taylor (chairman and vice chairman of the company respectively) control nearly 19% of Taylor Capital's voting power. The bank was founded in 1929 by forefathers of the Taylor family.

EXECUTIVES

Vice Chairman, Jeffrey W. (Jeff) Taylor, age 59, $483,077 total compensation

Chairman, Bruce W. Taylor, age 56, $525,200 total compensation

EVP Cole Taylor Business Capital, Michael D. (Mike) Sharkey

President CEO and Director Taylor Capital Group and Cole Taylor Bank, Mark A. Hoppe, age 58, $475,962 total compensation

CFO and COO; EVP and COO Cole Taylor Bank, Randall T. (Randy) Conte, age 52

Head Cole Taylor Mortgage, William A. (Willie) Newman

Group SVP General Counsel and Secretary, Steven H. Shapiro, age 54
EVP and Chief Lending Officer, Lawrence G. (Larry) Ryan, age 53, $245,423 total compensation
Group SVP and Chief Credit Officer Cole Taylor Bank, Michael J. Morton, age 49
Vice Chairman Cole Taylor Bank, John Lynch Jr.
Group SVP and Treasurer Cole Taylor Bank, David Ide
IR Contact Officer, Ilene Stevens
Director, M. Hill Hammock, age 66
Vice Chairman, Jeffrey W. (Jeff) Taylor, age 59
Director, Ronald D. Emanuel, age 65
Director, Melvin E. Pearl, age 76
Director, Richard W. Tinberg, age 61
President CEO and Director Taylor Capital Group and Cole Taylor Bank, Mark A. Hoppe, age 58
Director, Shepherd G. (Shep) Pryor IV, age 65
Director, Michael H. Moskow, age 75
Director, Louise O'Sullivan, age 66
Director, Ronald L. (Ron) Bliwas, age 69
Director, Harrison I. Steans, age 76
Director, Jennifer W. Steans, age 48
Director, C. Bryan Daniels, age 53
Director, Elzie L. Higginbottom, age 70
Independent Director, Bryan Daniels
Independent Director, Hill Hammock
Independent Director, Louise OSullivan
Auditors: KPMGLLP

LOCATIONS

HQ: Taylor Capital Group, Inc
9550 West Higgins Road, Rosemont, IL 60018
Phone: 847 653-7978
Web: www.coletaylor.com

PRODUCTS/OPERATIONS

2011 Sales

	$ mil.	% of total
Interest		
Loans including fees	140	59
Taxable & tax-exempt investment securities	47	20
Other	0	-
Noninterest		
Mortgage origination revenue	20	9
Service charges	11	5
Gains on investment securities	5	2
Derivative & other	12	5
Total	**237**	**100**

COMPETITORS

Bank of America
Citigroup
Fifth Third
Harris
JPMorgan Chase
MB Financial
Old Second Bancorp
Park Bancorp
U.S. Bancorp

HISTORICAL FINANCIALS

Company Type: Public

Income Statement FYE: December 31

	ASSETS ($ mil.)	NET INCOME ($ mil.)	INCOME AS % OF ASSETS	EMPLOYEES
12/11	4,685	91	1.9%	638
12/10	4,483	(53)	—	591
12/09	4,403	(31)	—	434
12/08	4,388	(124)	—	451
12/07	3,556	(9)	—	418
Annual Growth	7.1%	—	—	11.2%

2011 Year-End Financials

Debt ratio: 19.71%
Return on equity: 22.25%
Cash ($ mil.): 121
Current ratio: —
Long-term debt ($ mil.): 923
No. of shares (mil.): 28
Dividends
Yield: —
Payout: 57.97%
Market value ($ mil.): 276

	STOCK PRICE ($) FY Close	P/E High	P/E Low	PER SHARE ($) Earnings	Dividends	Book Value
12/11	9.72	4	2	3.45	0.00	14.44
12/10	13.15	—	—	(5.27)	0.00	11.68
12/09	11.39	—	—	(4.10)	0.00	23.36
12/08	5.85	—	—	(13.72)	0.00	27.63
12/07	20.40	—	—	(0.89)	0.00	24.10
Annual Growth	(16.9%)	—	—	—	—	(12.0%)

TCF Financial Corp.

TCF Financial is the holding company for TCF National Bank which offers retail and small-business services through more than 430 locations. The bank is active mainly in Illinois Michigan Minnesota and Wisconsin but has been pushing into faster-growing states like Arizona and Colorado. TCF provides standard services such as checking and savings accounts CDs consumer and business loans mortgages and insurance and is a leading issuer of Visa debit cards. Residential mortgages account for nearly half of the company's loan and lease portfolio. TCF also offers specialized lending services such as commercial leasing equipment finance inventory finance and indirect auto loans across the US.

TCF aims to attract customers through convenience. To that end more than half its branches are inside supermarkets and many of its locations are open seven days a week. While many of the company's peers attempt to grow their branch networks through acquisitions TCF has expanded by opening up new branches —more than 100 since 2003.

Campus banking is also an important part the company's strategy. TCF has exclusive marketing alliances with several colleges including the University of Illinois and University of Michigan and is a leading provider of campus cards that serve as ID library security and stored-value cards in addition to ATM cards. Also as a part of its effort to build brand recognition on college campuses the company paid $35 million for the naming rights to the University of Minnesota's football stadium which opened in 2009 for 25 years.

In order to reduce its reliance on interest-based income such as loans and leases which are subject to interest rate fluctuations and other outside factors TCF Financial is focusing on growing its income from fees and service charges from products like checking accounts and credit cards. The company eliminated its Totally Free Checking product but the move contributed to increased attrition from checking customers and coupled with new overdraft fee regulations a decrease in retail banking-based fee revenue in 2011. Not coincidentally TCF's overall revenue and net income dipped during the year as well.

Meanwhile the company has experienced growth in its specialty finance operations including TCF Equipment Finance TCF Inventory Finance and Winthrop Resources which leases computers servers and other technology equipment. TCF continued to grow the business in 2011 when it bought California-based Gateway One a provider of consumer loans mainly for used cars. The company began providing inventory financing services in Canada in 2008.

EXECUTIVES

Managing Director Branch Banking, Mark L. Jeter, age 55
Chief Risk Officer, Neil W. Brown, age 54, $477,711 total compensation
Vice Chairman ad Executive Manager Corporate Development, Barry N. Winslow, age 64, $350,000 total compensation
EVP and COO; VP and CIO TCF Bank, Earl D. Stratton, age 64
SVP and Director Corporate Human Resources; EVP Corporate Human Resources TCF Bank; Head TCF Foundation, Barbara E. Shaw, age 56
Chairman and CEO, William A. Cooper, age 69, $401,923 total compensation
SVP TCF Operations, Richard J. Nelson, age 68
Vice Chairman and EVP Lending, Craig R. Dahl, age 57, $359,628 total compensation
SVP and Controller; Managing Director Corporate Development TCF Financial and TCF Bank; EVP and Controller TCF Bank, David M. Stautz, age 55
EVP Retail Lending, Joseph W. Doyle, age 64
President Gateway One Lending and Finance, David G. (Dave) MacInnis
Chief Credit Officer; Vice Chairman TCF Bank, Timothy P. Bailey, age 56, $325,026 total compensation
SVP; Treasurer TCF Financial and TCF Bank; EVP and Chief Investment Officer TCF Bank; SVP and Controller TCF Bank Michigan, James S. Broucek, age 48
SVP, James E. (Jason) Korstange, age 63
Managing Director Enterprise Risk Management and EVP TCF Bank, Paul B. Brawner, age 63
EVP TCF Branch Banking, Timothy G. Doyle
EVP; CTO TCF Bank, Gregg R. Goudy
SVP Retail Lending, Carol B. Schirmers
EVP Corporate Operations TCF Bank, James C. LaPlante, age 54
EVP TCF Branch Banking, Timothy B. Meyer, age 53
EVP TCF Branch Banking, James L. Koon, age 52
Vice Chairman and EVP Funding Operations and Finance, Thomas F. (Tom) Jasper, age 43, $259,615 total compensation
Managing Director Retail Lending, Mark W. Rohde, age 50
SVP; EVP General Counsel and Secretary TCF National Bank, Joseph T. Green, age 57
SVP and Chief Audit Executive, Steven D. Christensen
EVP TCF Branch Banking, Robert C. Borgstrom
EVP TCF Branch Banking, Louis J. Campos
SVP TCF Branch Banking, Delia M. Conrad
SVP TCF Branch Banking, Peter R. Daugherty
SVP TCF Branch Banking, James T. Dowiak
SVP TCF Branch Banking, Mark W. Gault
EVP TCF Branch Banking, Michael J. Olson
EVP TCF Retail Lending, Timothy J. Bosiacki
EVP Retail Lending, Claire M. Graupmann
EVP TCF Retail Lending, Paul R. Tokarczyk
EVP Retail Lending, Matthew R. Wiley
EVP Retail Lending, Robert J. Brueggeman
SVP Retail Lending, Rose M. Dickey
SVP Retail Lending, Michael A. Dill
SVP Retail Lending, Donald J. Hawkins
SVP Retail Lending, Daniel B. Hoffman
SVP Retail Lending, Vicki L. Makowka
SVP TCF Retail Lending, Raymond J. Swidron

SVP Retail Lending, Thomas K. Torassian
Managing Director Commercial Banking, James J. Urbanek
EVP Commercial Lending, Douglas W. Benner
EVP TCF Credit Quality, Robert A. Henry
EVP Commercial Lending, Michael R. Klemz
EVP TCF Credit Quality, David J. Veurink
SVP TCF Commercial Banking, Wesley M. Anderson
SVP Commercial Lending, John E. Boyle
SVP Commercial Lending, Michael Y. Chin
SVP Commercial Lending, Jeffrey T. Doering
SVP TCF Commercial Banking, Scott A. Fedie
SVP Commercial Lending, Russell P. McMinn
SVP TCF Commercial Banking, Luke K. Oosterhouse
SVP Commercial Lending, Douglas A. Ortyn
SVP Commercial Lending, William R. Patterson
SVP Commercial Lending, Guy J. Rau
SVP Commercial Lending, Janelle J. Rietz-Kamenar
SVP Commercial Lending, Michael Roidt
SVP Commercial Lending, Elizabeth A. Rojas
SVP TCF Commercial Banking, Steven E. Rykkeli
SVP Commercial Lending, Patrick P. Skiles
EVP and CFO TCF Financial and TCF Equipment Finance; EVP and Treasurer Winthrop Resources, Michael S. Jones, age 42
EVP and Chief Credit Officer TCF Bank and TCF Equipment Finance; SVP Winthrop Resources, Mark D. Nyquist, age 55
EVP TCF Equipment Finance, Bradley C. Gunstad
President and COO TCF Equipment Finance, William S. Henak
SVP TCF Equipment Finance, Gloria J. Charley
SVP TCF Equipment Finance, Richard J. Chenitz
SVP TCF Equipment Finance, Peter C. Darin
SVP TCF Equipment Finance, Walter E. Dzielsky
SVP TCF Equipment Finance, Michael A. Kloos
SVP TCF Equipment Finance, Jodie L. Palmer
SVP TCF Equipment Finance, Gary A. Peterson
SVP TCF Equipment Finance, Charles A. Sell Jr.
SVP TCF Equipment Finance, Robert J. Stark
SVP TCF Equipment Finance, Mark H. Valentine
SVP TCF Equipment Finance, Frederick M. Van Etten
Co-President Winthrop Resources, Paul L. Gendler
Co-President Winthrop Resources, Richard L. Pieper
SVP TCF Equipment Finance and Winthrop Resources, Gary W. Anderson
SVP Winthrop Resources, Dean J. Stinchfield
President and CEO TCF Inventory Finance, Rosario A. Perrelli
EVP TCF Inventory Finance, Howard J. Hentz
EVP TCF Inventory Finance, Vincent E. Hillery
EVP TCF Inventory Finance, Christopher Meals
SVP TCF Inventory Finance, Peter J. Baranowski
SVP TCF Inventory Finance, Larry M. Tagli
SVP TCF Inventory Finance, Mark J. Wrend
SVP TCF Inventory Finance, Dornett Wright
President TCF Commercial Finance Canada, Peter D. Kelley
SVP TCF Finance/Treasury, James M. Dunne
SVP TCF Finance/Treasury, Brian P. Engels
SVP Retail Lending, Jason R. Voronyak
SVP TCF Finance, Michelle O. Wright
SVP TCF Operations, Michael J. Beier
SVP TCF Operations, Ronald L. Britz
SVP TCF Operations, Beverly L. Burman
SVP TCF Support Services, Beverly M. Craig
SVP TCF Operations, Carol Jean F. Feith
SVP TCF Operations, Christopher N. Germann
SVP TCF Operations, James M. Matheis
SVP TCF Support Services, David B. McCullough
SVP TCF Operations, Anton J. Negrini
SVP TCF Operations, Leonard D. Steele
SVP TCF Operations, Cathleen L. Wilkins
SVP Human Resources, Edward J. Gallagher
SVP Human Resources, Viane R. Hoefs
SVP Human Resources, Roger T. Sorensen
SVP TCF Legal, Linda J. Firth-Hawkins
SVP TCF Legal, Shelley A. Fitzmaurice
SVP TCF Legal, Douglas B. Hiatt
SVP TCF Legal, Charles P. Hoffman Jr.
SVP TCF Legal, Gloria J. Karsky
SVP TCF Legal, Beth A. Paulson
SVP TCF Legal, R. Elizabeth Topoluk
SVP TCF Operations, Barbara L. Buss
SVP TCF Credit Quality, Scott D. Campbell
SVP TCF Credit Quality, Andrew D. Clark
SVP TCF Credit Quality, Larry M. Czekaj
SVP TCF Credit Quality, Gregory W. Drehmel
SVP TCF Credit Quality, Martin J. Krogman
SVP TCF Credit Quality, Dennis McClelland
SVP TCF Credit Quality, Kathleen M. Wacker
SVP Retail Lending, Bradley C. Barthels
SVP Retail Lending, Calvin E. Fuoss
SVP Retail Lending, Katrina Williams
EVP Commercial Lending, Thomas R. Bobak
EVP Commercial Lending, J. Thomas Finnegan
SVP Commercial Lending, Mark W. Lucke
SVP Commercial Lending, Lisa M. Salazar
SVP TCF Equipment Finance, Brick W. Moore
SVP Winthrop Resources, Abigail R. Nesbitt
SVP Winthrop Resources, Bradley R. Swenson
SVP TCF Inventory Finance, Thomas E. Evans
SVP TCF Inventory Finance, Kevin L. Harrington
SVP TCF Inventory Finance, James S. Raymond
CEO Gateway One Lending and Finance, G. Brian MacInnis
SVP TCF Branch Banking, Jennifer K. Rohling
SVP TCF Finance/Treasury, Susan D. Bode
SVP TCF Finance/Treasury, Christy A. Powers
Vice Chairman ad Executive Manager Corporate Development, Barry N. Winslow, age 64
Director, Ralph Strangis, age 75
Vice Chairman and EVP Lending, Craig R. Dahl, age 57
Director, Richard A. Zona, age 67
Director, Gerald A. Schwalbach, age 67
Director, Luella G. Goldberg, age 75
Director, George G. Johnson, age 69
Director, William F. Bieber, age 69
Director, Thomas A. Cusick, age 67
Director, Raymond L. Barton
Director, Karen L. Grandstrand
Vice Chairman and EVP Funding Operations and Finance, Thomas F. (Tom) Jasper, age 43
Director, Theodore J. (Ted) Bigos, age 59
Director, Peter Bell, age 60
Director, Vance K. Opperman, age 69
Auditors: KPMGLLP

LOCATIONS

HQ: TCF Financial Corporation
200 Lake St. East, Wayzata MN 55391-1693
Phone: 952-745-2760 **Fax:** 508-390-2828
Web: www.tjx.com

2011 Branches

	No.
Illinois	196
Minnesota	110
Michigan	53
Colorado	36
Wisconsin	26
Arizona	7
Indiana	5
South	1
Total	**434**

PRODUCTS/OPERATIONS

2011 Sales

	$ mil.	% of total
Interest		
Loans & leases	844	61
Securities available for sale	85	6
Investments & other	8	1
Noninterest		
Fees & service charges	219	16
Card revenue	96	7
Leasing & equipment finance	89	6
ATM revenue	27	2
Other	11	1
Total	**1,382**	**100**

2011 Branches by Type

	No.
Supermarket	231
Traditional	195
Campus	8
Total	**434**

Selected Subsidiaries

Fidelity National Capital Inc. (also dba Winthrop Capital)
TCF Agency Inc.
TCF Agency Insurance Services Inc.
TCF Bank International Inc.
TCF Commercial Finance Canada Inc. (also dba Financement Commercial TCF Canada Inc.)
TCF Equipment Finance Inc. (also dba TCF Leasing Inc.)
TCF Insurance Agency Inc.
TCF Inventory Finance Inc.
TCF Investments Management Inc.
TCF National Bank
TCF Portfolio Services Inc.
Winthrop Resources Corporation (also dba TCF Small Business Lending)

COMPETITORS

Anchor BanCorp
Associated Banc-Corp
Bank Mutual
Bank of America
Bremer Financial
Citizens Republic Bancorp
Northern Trust
U.S. Bancorp
Wells Fargo

HISTORICAL FINANCIALS

Company Type: Public

Income Statement

FYE: December 31

	ASSETS ($ mil.)	NET INCOME ($ mil.)	INCOME AS % OF ASSETS	EMPLOYEES
12/11	18,979	109	0.6%	7,143
12/10	18,465	146	0.8%	7,363
12/09	17,885	87	0.5%	7,573
12/08	16,740	128	0.8%	7,802
12/07	15,977	266	1.7%	8,183
Annual Growth	4.4%	(20.0%)	—	(3.3%)

2011 Year-End Financials

Debt ratio: 23.09%
Return on equity: 5.86%
Cash ($ mil.): 1,389
Current ratio: —
Long-term debt ($ mil.): 4,381
No. of shares (mil.): 160
Dividends
Yield: —
Payout: 28.17%
Market value ($ mil.): 1,655

	STOCK PRICE ($) FY Close	P/E High	P/E Low	PER SHARE ($) Earnings	Dividends	Book Value
12/11	10.32	24	12	0.71	0.00	11.65
12/10	14.81	18	12	1.05	0.20	10.30
12/09	13.62	31	17	0.54	0.40	9.10
12/08	13.66	23	10	1.01	1.00	11.72
12/07	17.93	14	8	2.12	0.97	8.68
Annual Growth	(12.9%)	—	—	(23.9%)	—	7.6%

Teachers Insurance & Annuity Assn. of America (N.Y.)

LOCATIONS

HQ: Teachers Insurance & Annuity Assn. of America (N.Y.)
730 Third Avenue, New York, NY 10017
Phone: 212 490-9000
Web: www.tiaa-cref.org

HISTORICAL FINANCIALS

Company Type:

Income Statement FYE: December 31

	ASSETS ($ mil.)	NET INCOME ($ mil.)	INCOME AS % OF ASSETS	EMPLOYEES
12/11	225,932	2,359	1.0%	0
12/10	214,544	1,381	0.6%	0
12/09	0	(452)	—	0
12/98	102,216	840	0.8%	0
12/97	93,795	1,226	1.3%	0
Annual Growth	24.6%	17.8%	—	—

2011 Year-End Financials

Debt ratio: 0.36%
Return on equity: 8.70%
Cash ($ mil.): 597
Current ratio: —
Long-term debt ($ mil.): 809
No. of shares (mil.): 0
Dividends
Yield: —
Payout: —
Market value ($ mil.): —

Tech Data Corp.

Tech Data is 100% committed to IT products distribution. One of the world's largest distributors of computer products Tech Data provides thousands of different items to about 125000 resellers in 100 countries. Its catalog of products includes computer components (disk drives keyboards and video cards) networking equipment (routers and bridges) peripherals (printers modems and monitors) systems (PCs and servers) and software. Tech Data also provides technical support configuration integration financing electronic data interchange (EDI) and other logistics and product fulfillment services. More than half of Tech Data's revenues are generated in Europe.

To further build its business in Europe Tech Data in late 2012 acquired several distribution companies owned by UK-based Specialist Distribution Group (SDG) in the UK France and the Netherlands. Combined the acquired businesses generate sales of about E1.4 billion ($1.75 billion). Previously Tech Data bought Triade Holding a Netherlands-based distributor of consumer electronics and IT products in 2010. The purchase strengthened Tech Data's IT business and accelerated its diversification into consumer electronics in the Netherlands Denmark and the Benelux region; it also supported operations across Europe by adding new specialty products vendors and customers. As part of the transaction Tech Data's joint venture with Brightstar Brightstar Europe (formed in 2007) acquired Triade subsidiary Mobile Communication Company (MCC) a mobility products distributor in Benelux. Total value of both deals was E83 million (about $123 million). (Later Tech Data in 2012 bought its joint venture partner Brightstar's 50% ownership in Brightstar Europe for more than $165 million as well as several distribution companies in the UK from the distribution arm of IT services company Specialist Computer Holdings.)

As Tech Data rebounded from the global recession it saw its fiscal 2011 sales increase by around 10% from the prior year. Some foreign currencies had negative impacts against the US dollar which dragged down the company's sales. Tech Data gained ground in the Americas with 2011 sales increasing by 10% and Europe increasing by some 11% (an increase of around 18% in euros). The increase was credited to acquisitions in Europe and the improving global economy.

As manufacturers have promoted more direct relationships with their customers the need for middlemen in the industry has dwindled and many tech product distributors have gone under. Tech Data was spared this fate due to its size and scope but it continually looks to cut costs in order to survive in a business characterized by thin margins. The company has also expanded its service offerings which range from pre- and post-sale technical support to customized shipping documents and electronic commerce integration.

Tech Data distributes products from such vendors as Apple Cisco Systems IBM Microsoft Sony and Hewlett-Packard (which accounts for some 27% of sales).

Janus Capital Management a part of Janus Capital Group owns around 14% of the company.

HISTORY

Tech Data grew out of an electronics distribution business founded by Edward Raymund a University of Southern California graduate who started out as a representative for electronics manufacturers. By the early 1960s he had established an industrial electronics distribution business in Florida. In 1974 he incorporated that business as Tech Data.

In 1981 Raymund's 25-year-old son Steven who had earned master's degrees in economics and international politics from Georgetown University's School of Foreign Service joined Tech Data on a temporary basis to work on the company's catalog. At that time Tech Data sold diskettes and other computer supplies to local companies and had about $2 million in sales.

Steven Raymund's favored status at the company angered a group of managers. Shortly after he arrived at Tech Data they copied the company's client list and walked out. The defection nearly sank Tech Data but Steven Raymund stayed on when his father handed him two-thirds of the company.

With the PC industry beginning to take off Steven Raymund positioned Tech Data as a middleman between computer and peripheral manufacturers and resellers. Steven was named COO in 1984. He became CEO in 1986 the year the company went public.

In 1990 fast growth strained Tech Data's resources and earnings slumped. The company cut inventory and management costs. The following year Steven Raymund became chairman when his father retired.

Tech Data began to distribute software in 1992 and a year later the company signed up Microsoft and inked a distribution deal for IBM computer systems. In 1994 Tech Data purchased U.S. Software Resource a California-based distributor of more than 500 business and entertainment software titles thereby increasing its software list and gaining high-profile publishers such as Borland International (now Borland Software) and Corel as suppliers.

Also in 1994 Tech Data began a global expansion when it bought France's largest distributor of wholesale computer products Softmart International.

Tech Data won US distribution rights for Apple subsidiary Claris (now named FileMaker) and its software line in 1995. The company one-upped its rivals that year when through a deal with MCI (later part of WorldCom) it became the first distributor to resell telephone line service employing advanced data transmission technologies. Tech Data resellers packaged line services with their computer networks; the resellers and Tech Data earned monthly usage fees on the services.

Tech Data in 1998 bought VIAG AG's majority stake in European distributor Computer 2000 for about $390 million. (To avoid geographic overlap the company sold its controlling stake in Germany-based Macrotron acquired in 1997 to rival Ingram Micro for $100 million.) Also in 1998 Tech Data began direct assembly and shipping at its distribution centers. In 1999 the company inked an estimated $2 billion outsourcing deal with GE Capital and expanded its Canadian presence with the purchase of Globelle Corporation.

In 2000 the company purchased the remainder of Computer 2000 and expanded its outsourcing offerings with a new business division. The next year Tech Data introduced an online software license purchasing and upgrade program; it also cut about 20% of its staff to keep costs down.

Tech Data broadened its menu of outsourcing services and added to its international operations with the acquisition of the UK's Azlan Group in 2003.

In 2006 the company named Robert Dutkowsky a veteran of data center infrastructure specialist Egenera as its CEO; Steven Raymund retained his chairmanship.

In September 2012 Tech Data acquired Brightstar Corp's. 50% interest in Brightstar Europe Ltd. for about $165.5 million. In Novemeber the firm completed the purchase of several companies owned by UK-based Specialist Distribution Group (SDG) in the UK France and the Netherlands.

EXECUTIVES

President Europe, Nestor Cano, age 48, $650,000 total compensation
President Canada, Rick Reid
SVP and Treasurer, Charles V. Dannewitz, age 57
SVP General Counsel and Secretary, David R. (Dave) Vetter, age 52
SVP and Controller, Joseph B. (Joe) Trepani, age 51, $365,000 total compensation
EVP CFO and Director, Jeffery P. (Jeff) Howells, age 55, $709,500 total compensation
Chairman, Steven A. (Steve) Raymund, age 57, $1,000,000 total compensation
CEO and Director, Robert M. (Bob) Dutkowsky, age 57, $957,000 total compensation
EVP and CIO, John Tonnison
President The Americas, Murray Wright
VP HP Solutions, John O'Shea
EVP CFO and Director, Jeffery P. (Jeff) Howells, age 55

Director, Harry J. Harczak Jr., age 55
Director, Maximilian Ardelt, age 72
CEO and Director, Robert M. (Bob) Dutkowsky, age 57
Director, Charles E. (Eddie) Adair, age 64
Director, Thomas I. (Tom) Morgan, age 58
Director, Savio W. Tung, age 62
Director, Kathleen Misunas, age 61
Director, David M. Upton, age 52
Auditors: Ernst&YoungLLP

LOCATIONS

HQ: Tech Data Corporation
5350 Tech Data Dr., Clearwater FL 33760-3122
Phone: 727-539-7429 **Fax:** 727-538-7803
Web: www.techdata.com

2011 Sales

	$ mil.	% of total
Europe	13,841	57
Americas	10,534	43
Total	**24,376**	**100**

PRODUCTS/OPERATIONS

2011 Sales

	% of total
Systems	33
Peripherals	32
Networking	17
Software	17
Total	**100**

2011 Sales by Channel

VARs (value added resellers)	53
Corporate resellers	21

COMPETITORS

Agilysys
Arrow Electronics
ASI Computer Technologies
Avnet
Black Box
Communications Supply
CompuCom
D & H Distributing
Dell
Gigaset
GTSI
IBM
Ingram Micro
Integralis
MA Laboratories
MicroAge
New Age Electronics
Ricoh USA
ScanSource
SED International
SHI International
Softmart
SYNNEX
Westcon
ZT Group

HISTORICAL FINANCIALS

Company Type: Public

Income Statement FYE: January 31

	REVENUE ($ mil.)	NET INCOME ($ mil.)	NET PROFIT MARGIN	EMPLOYEES
01/12	26,488	206	0.8%	8,300
01/11	24,375	214	0.9%	8,700
01/10	22,099	180	0.8%	7,600
01/09	24,080	123	0.5%	8,000
01/08	23,423	108	0.5%	8,300
Annual Growth	3.1%	17.5%	—	0.0%

2012 Year-End Financials

Debt ratio: 1.83%
Return on equity: 10.46%
Cash ($ mil.): 505
Current ratio: 147.75
Long-term debt ($ mil.): 57
No. of shares (mil.): 41
Dividends
Yield: —
Payout: —
Market value ($ mil.): 2,132

	STOCK PRICE ($) FY Close	P/E High	P/E Low	PER SHARE ($) Earnings	Dividends	Book Value
01/12	51.92	11	8	4.66	0.00	48.06
01/11	46.91	11	8	4.36	0.00	45.26
01/10	40.75	14	5	3.54	0.00	40.59
01/09	18.11	16	6	2.40	0.00	34.37
01/08	34.38	21	17	1.96	0.00	36.38
Annual Growth	10.9%	—	—	24.2%	—	7.2%

Telephone & Data Systems, Inc.

One of the top US phone companies without a regional Bell lineage Telephone and Data Systems (TDS) has more than 7 million local phone and wireless customers in 36 states. The company's core business unit U.S. Cellular serves about 6 million customers in 26 states; key markets are located in the central and mid-Atlantic regions. The company also offers fixed-line and broadband Internet services in rural and suburban markets in 31 states through its TDS Telecom subsidiary which provides local service to more than 1 million access lines through more than 100 incumbent local-exchange carriers (ILEC). Data networking and hosted telecom services are provided to business clients through the TDS Business unit.

Telephone and Data Systems is more telephone than data systems with more than 80% total revenue coming from wireless services sold by US Cellular. TDS owns 82% of US Cellular's stock. The company also owns 63% of Airadigm Communications a Wisconsin-based wireless provider. Airadigm operates independently from U.S. Cellular.

Aside from its core telecom operations TDS has an 80% interest in commercial printing business Suttle-Straus which provides corporate communications direct mail advertising materials and distribution services to customers primarily in the midwest.

Landline providers face significant challenges as more homes rely on cell phones as their primary phone. TDS Telecom is the seventh-largest carrier and the majority of its customers are businesses. With wireline service on the decline TDS Telecom expanded into VoIP telephony to compete with cable providers. It is also pushing customers to adopt broadband Internet access as part of their service bundles to fuel growth; in 2011 the company raised the percentage of residential subscribers with phone and broadband connections from 62% to 67%.

Meanwhile the company's partnership with satellite TV operator DISH Network enables it to offer bundled communications and entertainment service packages that include digital television to residential customers.

Telephone and Data Systems' $5.1 billion in sales for 2011 represented a 3% increase over the previous year. Meanwhile its profit rose nearly 40% despite higher operating expenses across most areas of the business.

In 2012 TDS Telecom plans to expand its terrestrial interactive video service from the trial markets in Tennessee to 19 additional markets counter mounting competition for video service. The company continues to expand its presence in the business broadband market with high-speed dedicated broadband hosted and managed IP telephony point-to-point Ethernet and other hosted and managed services such as colocation dedicated hosting hosted application management and cloud computing services.

Telephone and Data Systems uses acquisitions to expand its service area and diversify its selection of services. In 2012 it bought Des Moines Iowa-based IT services provider Vital Support Systems for $45 million to boost its hosted and managed services unit.

The previous year Telephone and Data Systems paid $95 million to acquire OneNeck IT Services a provider of hosted IT network and software services. The deal extended the company's hosted application management and managed hosting expertise. The purchase also expanded its presence in Arizona where OneNeck is based and it New Jersey Texas and Missouri where OneNeck's key clients are located.

In 2010 Telephone and Data Systems bought Minneapolis-based data center and managed hosting services provider VISI Incorporated in a move to broaden its network and data service portfolio for business customers and increase its presence in the state. Also that year the company acquired TEAM Technologies a data center operator in the Midwest for $47 million. Both acquired businesses were made part of TDS Telecom.

President and CEO LeRoy Carlson Jr. (son of founder LeRoy Carlson Sr.) and his family who also sit on the board of directors control more than half of the company's voting power.

HISTORY

LeRoy Carlson Sr. learned the ins and outs of rural phone operators when he owned a small firm that supplied equipment and forms to independent phone companies. In the mid-1950s he began buying some of these small phone companies which he consolidated with a phone book publisher and his equipment company to form Telephones Inc. Carlson sold the company to Contel in 1966.

Carlson continued to buy and sell rural carriers allowing them to retain local management while he provided centralized purchasing and system upgrades. In 1969 he bought 10 rural providers in Wisconsin and consolidated all of his companies into Telephone and Data Systems (TDS).

Between 1970 and 1975 TDS acquired 32 rural phone companies. When smaller companies in its established regions became scarce TDS bought rural phone providers from large independents. As TDS diversified the wireline subsidiary became TDS Telecommunications.

The company began offering paging services in Wisconsin in 1972 and later created subsidiary American Paging (1981). In 1975 TDS moved into cable TV service eventually creating TDS Cable Communications (1984) but it sold the holdings in 1986.

Getting a head start on the big Bells in the cellular race TDS began seeking licenses in the early 1980s eventually winning a 5% stake in the Los Angeles market. Although buffeted by larger independents it placed a high priority on cellular operations and formed subsidiary United States Cellular Corporation in 1983. Two years later US Cellular launched services in Tennessee and Oklahoma.

Carlson named his son LeRoy Jr. to replace him as CEO in 1986 but remained chairman. TDS reduced its ownership in U.S. Cellular to about 80% in 1988 when it took the subsidiary public. Coditel a Belgian cable TV company secured a minority stake in U.S. Cellular that year.

In 1993 TDS created subsidiary American Portable Telecom to bid for the new PCS wireless licenses. Three years later the subsidiary renamed Aerial Communications went public; TDS kept an 82% stake. Aerial began providing PCS service in 1997.

Expansion financed mainly through stock caused Michael Price's Franklin Mutual Advisers to complain that its shares were undervalued. To gain more leverage with management in 1997 Franklin organized a proxy contest to gain a seat on the board and veteran private investor Martin Solomon was elected.

That year in response to investor demand for more liquidity TDS planned to buy the shares in U.S. Cellular and Aerial that it didn't already own and to create three tracking stocks for its cellular PCS and wireline phone units. However TDS withdrew the proposal in 1998 because of poor market conditions. That year it acquired the 18% of American Paging that it didn't own and joined the company with TSR Paging. The deal left TDS with a 30% stake in the new TSR Wireless (but the company ceased operations in 2000 and declared bankruptcy).

Sonera Group (formerly Telecom Finland) acquired a significant minority stake in Aerial when it invested $200 million in the company in 1998. That year TDS made plans to spin off Aerial in an effort to raise cash. However TDS dropped the idea and sold its Aerial stake to VoiceStream Wireless for $1.8 billion in 2000. TDS took a 14% stake in VoiceStream which it swapped to Deutsche Telekom for cash and stock in 2001.

To add to its holdings in 2001 Telephone and Data Systems bought Wisconsin local telephone service provider Chorus Communications for $195 million and $30 million in assumed debt. The next year the company acquired two local phone service providers in New Hampshire.

TDS Telecom expanded its service area in rural New Hampshire when it bought Farmington-based Union Telephone Company in 2009. The deal added more than 8200 phone lines in five states.

EXECUTIVES

SVP Acquisitions and Corporate Development, Scott H. Williamson, age 61, $583,000 total compensation
VP Corporate Development, Bryon A. Wertz, age 62
SVP Finance and Treasurer, Peter L. Sereda, age 50
VP Corporate Relations, Jane W. McCahon
VP Human Resources, C. Theodore Herbert, age 76
EVP CFO and Director, Kenneth R. (Ken) Meyers, age 58, $614,000 total compensation
President CEO and Director, LeRoy T. (Ted) Carlson Jr., age 65, $1,275,000 total compensation
VP and Corporate Secretary, Kevin C. Gallagher
Chairman, Walter C. D. Carlson, age 58
SVP and CIO, Kurt B. Thaus, age 53
VP Acquisitions and Corporate Development, Kenneth M. Kotylo, age 47
VP Internal Audit, Frieda E. Ireland, age 56
President and CEO United States Cellular Corporation, Mary N. Dillon, age 50
SVP Technology Services and Strategy, Joseph R. Hanley, age 45
President and CEO TDS Telecommunications Corporation, David A. (Dave) Wittwer, age 51, $496,000 total compensation
SVP and Corporate Controller, Douglas D. Shuma, age 50
Assistant Treasurer, John M. Toomey
Assistant Controller - Tax, David D. Gillman
Assistant Corporate Controller, Douglas W. Chambers
VP IT Strategy Architecture and Quality, Laurie A. Ruchti
VP and Chief Information Security Officer, Theodore E. Wiessing
President Suttle-Straus, John Berthelsen
EVP CFO and Director, Kenneth R. (Ken) Meyers, age 58
President CEO and Director, LeRoy T. (Ted) Carlson Jr., age 65
Board Member, George W. Off, age 65
Board Memeber, Herbert S. Wander, age 77
Board Member, Christopher D. (Chris) O'Leary, age 53
Board Member, Clarence A. Davis, age 70
Board Member, Mitchell H. Saranow, age 66
Board Member, Donald C. Nebergall, age 83
Board Member, Letitia G. Carlson, age 51
Board Member, Gary L. Sugarman, age 59
Board Member, Prudence E. Carlson, age 60
Auditors: PricewaterhouseCoopersLLP

LOCATIONS

HQ: Telephone and Data Systems Inc.
30 N. LaSalle St. Ste. 4000, Chicago IL 60602
Phone: 312-630-1900 **Fax:** 312-630-1908
Web: www.teldta.com

PRODUCTS/OPERATIONS

2011 Sales

	$ mil.	% of total
US Cellular	4,343	84
TDS Telecom	815	15
Other	21	1
Total	**5,180**	**100**

COMPETITORS

AT&T
Atlantic Tele-Network
Cavalier Telephone
Cellco
CenturyLink
Cincinnati Bell
FairPoint Communications Inc.
Farmers Telecommunications
Horry Telephone
NTELOS
Sprint Nextel
Suddenlink Communications
T-Mobile USA
Verizon
XO Holdings

HISTORICAL FINANCIALS

Company Type: Public

Income Statement FYE: December 31

	REVENUE ($ mil.)	NET INCOME ($ mil.)	NET PROFIT MARGIN	EMPLOYEES
12/11	5,180	200	3.9%	12,300
12/10	4,986	143	2.9%	12,400
12/09	5,020	193	3.9%	12,400
12/08	5,092	93	1.8%	12,500
12/07	4,828	386	8.0%	11,800
Annual Growth	1.8%	(15.1%)	—	1.0%

2011 Year-End Financials

Debt ratio: 18.67%
Return on equity: 5.06%
Cash ($ mil.): 563
Current ratio: 195.13
Long-term debt ($ mil.): 1,529
No. of shares (mil.): 108
Dividends
Yield: —
Payout: 25.68%
Market value ($ mil.): 2,582

	STOCK PRICE ($) FY Close	P/E High/Low		PER SHARE ($) Earnings	Dividends	Book Value
12/11	23.81	17	10	1.83	0.00	36.54
12/10	31.52	23	18	1.36	0.00	36.70
12/09	30.20	17	13	1.77	0.00	35.64
12/08	28.10	72	28	0.80	0.00	33.59
12/07	57.60	21	15	3.22	0.00	33.33
Annual Growth	(19.8%)	—	—	(13.2%)	—	2.3%

Tenet Healthcare Corp.

Tenet Healthcare is here to spread the doctrine of good health. The for-profit company owns or leases 50 acute care hospitals with some 13000 beds in 10 US states. Almost two-thirds of Tenet's hospital beds are in California Florida and Texas. They range from small community facilities offering basic care to major hospitals such as the 600-bed Brookwood Medical Center in Birmingham Alabama. In addition to its acute care holdings Tenet also operates specialty hospitals skilled nursing facilities physician practices outpatient centers imaging centers and other health care facilities that form regional networks around its main hospitals.

HISTORY

Hospital attorney Richard Eamer along with attorneys Leonard Cohen and John Bedrosian founded National Medical Enterprises (NME) in 1969. After its IPO NME bought 10 hospitals nursing homes an office building and land in California. Within six years the company owned operated and managed 23 hospitals and a home health care business. It sold medical equipment and bottled oxygen and provided vocational training for nurses.

In the 1970s NME expanded into hospital construction and bought five Florida hospitals. By 1981 NME was the #3 health care concern in the US owning or managing 193 hospitals and nursing homes. In the 1980s NME diversified further buying nursing homes and mental health centers. By the end of the decade the company's Specialty Hospital Group brought in more than 50% of revenues. NME was the second-largest publicly owned health care company in the US (after HCA) by 1985.

In 1990 NME reversed course spinning off most of its long-term-care businesses but kept 19 UK nursing facilities operated by its Westminster Health Care subsidiary (sold 1996). In 1992 the company acquired an Australian hospital management firm.

That year several insurance companies sued NME alleging fraudulent psychiatric claims; NME settled the suits in 1993. Federal agents later raided company headquarters seizing papers related to the suspected fraud. That year investment banker Jeff Barbakow took over as CEO forcing out Eamer and Cohen.

In 1993 and 1994 NME dumped most of its psychiatric and rehabilitation facilities using the proceeds to help pay penalties stemming from the federal investigation into alleged insurance fraud kickbacks and patient abuse at its psychiatric units.

NME paid another $16 million in related state fines. (Related civil lawsuits were settled in 1997.)

The company's name change to Tenet Healthcare coincided with new purchases throughout the South in 1995 and 1996.

The next few years were mixed for Tenet. On the upside it bought OrNda HealthCorp which complemented Tenet's existing networks. Tenet and MedPartners (now Caremark Rx) then the #1 practice management firm formed a Southern California hospital-doctor network in 1997 that gave both companies heft in dealing with HMOs (the partnership crumbled in 1999 when MedPartners exited practice management to focus on pharmacy benefits management and ceased operations in California). Merger discussions began with embattled market leader Columbia/HCA (now HCA) but fizzled.

In 1998 Tenet bought eight Philadelphia hospitals owned by the bankrupt Allegheny Health Education & Research Foundation. The company was dogged by another investigation this time by the Health and Human Services Inspector General's office over allegations the company paid more than fair market value for a physician practice in return for kickbacks. Tenet in 2004 agreed to pay about $31 million to settle two lawsuits stemming from these allegations.

Like many companies in the industry in 1999 Tenet began feeling the effects of the Balanced Budget Act of 1997 which mandated more scrutiny of Medicare expenditures to health care providers. In response the company began divesting some of its hospitals; it also shed its practice management business and reorganized its corporate structure.

Tenet rebounded and acquired hospitals in 2001 and 2002 but the next year proved not so kind. Federal investigations into the company's billing practices particularly those related to Medicare began late in 2002. In 2003 the company settled claims brought by the Department of Justice that doctors performed unnecessary cardiac surgeries at its Redding Medical Center (now Shasta Regional Medical Center) in California; the settlement cost Tenet $54 million (plus millions more to settle patients' claims). Tenet sold the facility in 2004 and also disposed of more than a dozen other facilities cutting its holdings from 115 to 100.

An even larger sell-off began in 2004 and included nearly 20 hospitals in California and others in Louisiana Massachusetts (all three were sold to Vanguard Health Systems in early 2005) Missouri and Texas. The company also exited the Nevada market when it sold Lake Mead Hospital Medical Center in Las Vegas in early 2004. Additionally the company ended some operating leases and joint ventures primarily in California; sold its Barcelona Spain hospital; and sold about a dozen home health agencies and hospice providers to Amedisys.

Tenet Healthcare moved its headquarters from Santa Barbara California to Dallas in 2005. The move was intended to streamline operations and save money.

Tenet saw some hard times in 2005 and spent years struggling to emerge from several subsequent years of investigations lawsuits and bad publicity. Its New Orleans and Mississippi facilities were hit hard by Hurricane Katrina in 2005 and its Memorial Medical Hospital in New Orleans became a symbol of the city's devastation after several dozen bodies were found there in the aftermath of the storm. The company has since sold both locations.

In 2006 it resolved multiple federal investigations regarding its billing practices by agreeing to a $900 million deal with the Justice Department. Its sale of hospitals post-Katrina was part of a larger plan announced in 2006 to sell off about a dozen facilities ridding itself of some low-performing operations partly to pay its $900 million bill to government investigators and partly so it could invest in equipment upgrades at its remaining hospitals. (The sales followed a larger-scale divestiture of about 25 facilities begun earlier.) In 2009 Tenet sold the USC University Hospital and Kenneth Norris Jr. Cancer Hospital to the University of Southern California for $275 million.

In late 2010 fellow hospital operator and rival Community Health Systems(CHS) made an unsolicited bid to acquire Tenet in a deal worth some $7.3 billion ($3.3 billion in cash and stock plus the assumption of $4 billion in debt). Tenet responded with a resounding "thanks but no thanks" saying the bid undervalued the company. CHS remained persistent despite a "poison pill" plan Tenet adopted and a volley of lawsuits. After Tenet's board rejected a plumped up offer of $4.1 billion in cash CHS formally withdrew all offers in 2011.

EXECUTIVES

SVP Investor Relations, Thomas R. (Tom) Rice
EVP and CIO, Stephen F. Brown, age 57
President CEO and Director, Trevor Fetter, age 52, $1,081,000 total compensation
Chairman, Edward A. (Ed) Kangas, age 68
Vice Chairman, Stephen L. Newman, age 61, $720,800 total compensation
SVP Operations California, Jeffery (Jeff) Flocken, age 57
CEO Frye Regional Medical Center, Michael R. Blackburn, age 60
CEO Fountain Valley Regional Hospital and Medical Center, Debbie L. Walsh, age 56
CEO Doctors Medical Center of Modesto, Dennis (Denny) Litos, age 63
CEO Centennial Medical Center, Joe Thomason, age 52
CEO Nacogdoches Medical Center, Gary L. Stokes, age 62
President and CEO Creighton University Medical Center, Gary Honts, age 53
Senior Vice President - Public Affairs, Daniel R. Waldmann, age 43
CEO North Fulton Hospital, Deborah C. (Debbie) Keel, age 56
CEO Saint Francis Hospital, David L. Archer, age 54
CEO Saint Francis Hospital-Bartlett, Kem M. Mullins, age 39
CEO Hialeah Hospital, Ralph A. Aleman, age 65
CEO West Boca Medical Center, Mitch Feldman
VP Operations Southern States, Drew P. Kahn Sr., age 44
CEO Atlanta Medical Center, William T. (Bill) Moore, age 56
President and CEO Piedmont Medical Center, Charles F. Miller, age 61
CEO North Shore Medical Center, Manny Linares, age 47
SVP and Chief Managed Care Officer, Clint Hailey, age 47
CEO Palmetto General Hospital, Ana Mederos
CEO Central Carolina Hospital, Doug Doris, age 60
CFO, Daniel J. (Dan) Cancelmi, age 49
SVP Human Resources, Cathy Fraser, age 47, $342,300 total compensation
SVP and Chief Compliance Officer, Audrey T. Andrews, age 44
President and CEO Desert Regional Medical Center, Karolee M. Sowle
CEO Doctors Hospital of Manteca, Mark Lisa
CEO Los Alamitos Medical Center, Michele Finney
CEO Placentia-Linda Hospital, Kent Clayton
CEO John F. Kennedy Memorial Hospital, Dan Bowers
CEO San Ramon Regional Medical Center, Gary Sloan
CEO Sierra Vista Regional Medical Center, Candace Markwith
CEO Twin Cities Community Hospital, Rick Lyons
CEO Cypress Fairbanks Medical Center, Terry Wheeler
CEO Saint Louis University Hospital, Crystal L. Haynes
President and CEO Brookwood Medical Center, Garry Gause
CEO South Fulton Medical Center, James Clements
CEO Spalding Regional Medical Center, John Quinn
CEO Coral Gables Hospital, Jay Miranda
CEO St. Mary's Medical Center, Davide M. Carbon
CEO Hahnemann University Hospital, Michael P. Halter
Administrator Sylvan Grove Hospital, Edward Whitehouse
CEO St. Christopher's Hospital for Children, Carolyn Jackson
SVP General Counsel and Secretary, Gary K. Ruff, age 52, $340,000 total compensation
CEO Good Samaritan Medical Center, Mark Nosacka, age 52
CEO East Cooper Medical Center, Janie Sinacore-Jaberg
President Hospital Operations, Britt T. Reynolds
VP Outpatient Services, Kyle Burtnett
CEO Doctors Hospital at White Rock Lake, G. Scott Manis
VP and Treasurer, Tyler Murphy, age 42
SVP and Chief Medical Officer, Kelvin A. Baggett, age 41
CEO Palm Beach Gardens Medical Center, J. Michael Cowling
Chief Administrative Officer North Shore Medical Center Florida Medical Center Campus, Ben A. Rodriguez
CEO Coastal Carolina Hospital, Bill Masterton
President and CEO Hilton Head Regional Health Care, Mark T. O'Neil Jr.
SVP Operations Central, Robert L. Smith
VP Corporate Communications, Jeff Eller
SVP Operations Florida, Marsha Power
SVP Operations Southern States, John Holland
President and CEO Lakewood Regional Medical Center, Joseph Badalian
CEO Delray Medical Center, Mark Bryan
CEO Houston Northwest Medical Center, Linda Mercier
CEO Lake Pointe Medical Center, Eric Evans
Interim CEO Park Plaza Hospital, John Tressa
Director Media Relations, Rick Black
SVP and CIO, Paul T Browne, age 48
Director, Ronald A. (Ron) Rittenmeyer, age 65
President CEO and Director, Trevor Fetter, age 52
Director, Karen M. Garrison, age 63
Director, James A. Unruh, age 70
Director, J. Robert (Bob) Kerrey, age 68
Director, Floyd D. Loop, age 75
Director, Brenda J. Gaines, age 62
Director, Richard R. (Dick) Pettingill, age 63
Vice Chairman, Stephen L. Newman, age 61
Director, John E. (Jeb) Bush, age 59
Auditors: Deloitte&ToucheLLP

LOCATIONS

HQ: Tenet Healthcare Corporation
1445 Ross Ave. Ste. 1400, Dallas TX 75202
Phone: 469-893-2200 **Fax:** 469-893-8600
Web: www.tenethealth.com

Selected Hospitals

Alabama
- Brookwood Medical Center (Birmingham)

California
- Desert Regional Medical Center (Palm Springs)
- Doctors Hospital of Manteca
- Doctors Medical Center (Modesto)
- Fountain Valley Regional Hospital and Medical Center
- John F. Kennedy Memorial Hospital (Indio)
- Lakewood Regional Medical Center
- Los Alamitos Medical Center
- Placentia Linda Hospital
- San Ramon Regional Medical Center
- Sierra Vista Regional Medical Center (San Luis Obispo)
- Twin Cities Community Hospital (Templeton)

Florida
- Coral Gables Hospital
- Delray Medical Center (Delray Beach)
- Good Samaritan Hospital (West Palm Beach)
- Hialeah Hospital
- North Shore Medical Center (Miami)
- Palm Beach Gardens Medical Center
- Palmetto General Hospital (Hialeah)
- Saint Mary' s Medical Center (West Palm Beach)
- West Boca Medical Center (Boca Raton)

Georgia
- Atlanta Medical Center
- North Fulton Hospital (Roswell)
- South Fulton Medical Center (East Point)
- Spalding Regional Medical Center (Griffin)
- Sylvan Grove Hospital (Jackson)

Missouri
- Des Peres Hospital (St. Louis)
- Saint Louis University Hospital

North Carolina
- Central Carolina Hospital (Sanford)
- Frye Regional Medical Center (Hickory)

Pennsylvania
- Hahnemann University Hospital (Philadelphia)
- St. Christopher' s Hospital for Children (Philadelphia)

South Carolina
- Coastal Carolina Hospital (Hardeeville)
- East Cooper Regional Medical Center (Mt. Pleasant)
- Hilton Head Hospital
- Piedmont Medical Center (Rock Hill)

Tennessee
- Saint Francis Hospital (Memphis)
- Saint Francis Hospital-Bartlett

Texas
- Centennial Medical Center (Frisco)
- Cypress Fairbanks Medical Center (Houston)
- Doctors Hospital at White Rock Lake (Dallas)
- Houston Northwest Medical Center
- Lake Pointe Medical Center (Rowlett)
- Nacogdoches Medical Center
- Park Plaza Hospital (Houston)
- Providence Memorial Hospital (El Paso)
- Sierra Medical Center (El Paso)
- Sierra Providence East Medical Center (El Paso)

PRODUCTS/OPERATIONS

2011 Revenues

	$ mil.	% of total
General hospitals	9,273	97
Other operations	311	3
Doubtful accounts	(730)	-
Total	**8,854**	**100**

2011 Revenues

Managed care	57
Medicaid	9
Total	**0**	**100**

COMPETITORS

Adventist Health System Sunbelt Healthcare
Ascension Health
Banner Health
Baylor Health
Carolinas HealthCare System
Catholic Health Initiatives
CHRISTUS Health
Community Health Systems
Dignity Health
HCA
Health Management Associates
HealthSouth
Kaiser Permanente
Kindred Healthcare
LifePoint Hospitals
Memorial Health Services
Mercy Health
SSM Health Care
Sun Healthcare
Sutter Health
Texas Health Resources
United Surgical Partners
Universal Health Services
University Health Services
WellStar Health System

HISTORICAL FINANCIALS

Company Type: Public

Income Statement FYE: December 31

	REVENUE ($ mil.)	NET INCOME ($ mil.)	NET PROFIT MARGIN	EMPLOYEES
12/11	8,854	94	1.1%	57,705
12/10	9,205	1,152	12.5%	56,605
12/09	9,014	197	2.2%	57,613
12/08	8,663	25	0.3%	60,297
12/07	8,852	(89)	—	63,264
Annual Growth	0.0%	—	—	(2.3%)

2011 Year-End Financials

Debt ratio: 51.52%
Return on equity: 6.61%
Cash ($ mil.): 113
Current ratio: 129.86
Long-term debt ($ mil.): 4,294
No. of shares (mil.): 103
Dividends
Yield: —
Payout: —
Market value ($ mil.): 532

	STOCK PRICE ($) FY Close	P/E High/Low		PER SHARE ($) Earnings	Dividends	Book Value
12/11	5.13	16	7	0.48	0.00	13.71
12/10	6.69	1	0	8.16	0.00	14.54
12/09	5.39	4	1	1.48	0.00	5.37
12/08	1.15	34	5	0.20	0.00	0.86
12/07	5.08	—	—	(0.76)	0.00	0.46
Annual Growth	0.2%	—		—	—	133.7%

Tenneco Inc

Tenneco ensures vehicles are riding steady without exhausting a lot of smoke. The auto parts maker designs and distributes ride-control equipment (including shock absorbers struts and suspensions) under the Monroe brand and emissions-control systems (catalytic converters exhaust pipes and mufflers) under the Walker brand. It also makes Clevite elastomer products (bushings mounts and springs) for vibration control in cars and heavy trucks. It supplies both OEMs and aftermarket wholesalers and retailers. Major customers include GM Ford Advance Auto Parts and Uni-Select. Tenneco operates in Europe and the Americas and is growing its presence in key Asia/Pacific markets such as Australia.

HISTORY

Tennessee Gas and Transmission began in 1943 as a division of the Chicago Corporation headed by Gardiner Symonds and authorized to build a pipeline from West Virginia to the Gulf of Mexico. With the US facing WWII fuel shortages the group finished the project in 11 months.

After WWII Tennessee Gas went public with Symonds as president. It merged its oil and gas exploration interests into Tennessee Production Company (1954) which with Bay Petroleum (bought 1955) became Tenneco Oil in 1961. Symonds acquired complementary firms and entered the chemical industry by buying 50% of Petro-Tex Chemical in 1955.

Tenneco Oil moved its headquarters to Houston in 1963 to better ship natural gas from the Texas Gulf Coast. Symonds bought Packaging Corporation of America a maker of shipping containers pulp and paperboard products in 1965. A year later the company which had become a conglomerate adopted the Tenneco name. In 1967 it bought Kern County Land Company which owned 2.5 million acres of California farmland and two Racine Wisconsin manufacturers: J. I. Case (tractors and construction equipment) and automotive firm Walker Manufacturing. In 1968 Symonds bought Newport News Shipbuilding. The shipbuilder began making submarines and nuclear-powered aircraft carriers in the 1960s.

The 1970s brought the death of Symonds in 1971. Tenneco bought shock-absorber maker Monroe of Monroe Michigan and Philadelphia Life Insurance Company (sold to ICH Corporation in 1986) in 1977. In 1985 it bought UK chemical company Albright & Wilson while its Case subsidiary bought International Harvester's farm-equipment business. A farming recession prompted Tenneco to sell its agricultural operations in 1987. It sold its oil exploration and production business in 1988.

Tenneco restructured its operations in the early 1990s. It sold its natural gas liquids business to Enron its pulp chemicals business to Sterling Chemicals and a US soda ash plant to Belgium's Solvay. In turn it bought gas marketer EnTrade.

Under Dana Mead a former International Paper executive appointed COO in 1992 Tenneco sold some businesses to focus on automotive parts and packaging. It divested some of Case's assets through a 1994 IPO and sold the rest in 1996. In 1995 Tenneco bought Mobil's plastics division (Hefty Baggies) for nearly $1.3 billion. In 1996 the firm spun off Newport News Shipbuilding and sold its natural gas unit to El Paso Energy for $3.7 billion.

That same year Tenneco bought auto parts maker Pullman Company; relocated to Greenwich Connecticut; formed joint ventures in China and India; and opened a plant in Mexico. In 1997 Tenneco acquired the plastic-packaging division of NV Koninklijke KNP (now Buhrmann NV) and Richter Manufacturing (protective packaging) in 1998. Tenneco formed joint ventures with Shanghai Automotive Industry Group to make exhaust systems in China and with Sentinel Products to make foam automotive and sports products in the US.

Tenneco sold 55% of its container board business in 1999 to investment firm Madison Dearborn Partners for $2.2 billion forming joint venture Packaging Corporation of America. Tenneco split into two companies that year both based in Lake Forest Illinois. Tenneco's packaging unit was spun off as Pactiv Corporation and Tenneco was renamed Tenneco Automotive. Former president of automotive operations Mark Frissora became CEO that year.

Tenneco Automotive started experiencing a slump in 2000. In order to cut costs and pay down debt incurred by the spinoff of Pactiv the company made several reductions in its workforce over a two-year period between 2000 and 2002. It slashed about 2000 jobs closed eight plants in North America and Europe and sought lower-labor-cost regions to start up production.

Keeping to its strategy of transferring manufacturing operations to lower-labor-cost regions Tenneco Automotive opened a new plant in Togliatti Russia in 2003. The plant was intended to provide exhaust components for the Chevrolet Niva a car built by a joint venture between GM and Russian carmaker AvtoVAZ. In 2005 opened an engineering center in China to provide support for the company's five joint ventures in China.

The global economic recession of 2008/2009 coupled with tightening access to credit hammered the automotive industry and consequently Tenneco's performance. In 2009 Tenneco's sales slid 21% from 2008 largely driven by reduced OE activity in North America Europe and Australia plus smaller aftermarket sales in Europe. Tenneco chose to restructure and adopt an ongoing program to reduce costs and streamline manufacturing operations.

The company called for furloughs and temporary pay cuts for salaried employees and eliminated temporary workers; it also closed three North American manufacturing plants and an Australian engineering facility. Simultaneously the company relocated several of its operations to countries such as Brazil China India and Russia with lower manufacturing costs.

With the recession in full swing Tenneco took the opportunity to make some strategic acquisitions during the slump. In 2008 it acquired Gruppo Marzocchi an Italy-based supplier of suspension products for two-wheeled vehicles. That deal expanded Tenneco's current suspension products and gave the company better coverage of the two-wheeled vehicle market.

EXECUTIVES

EVP and CFO, Kenneth R. (Ken) Trammell, age 51, $462,500 total compensation
COO and Director, Hari N. Nair, age 52, $394,917 total compensation
EVP Technology Strategy and Business Development, Timothy E. (Tim) Jackson, age 54, $363,802 total compensation
SVP Global Human Resources, Barbara A. Kluth
SVP and General Manager North American Original Equipment Emission Control, Brent J. Bauer, age 56, $290,009 total compensation
VP and CIO, H. William Haser, age 55
VP and Controller, Paul D. Novas, age 53
EVP North America, Neal A. Yanos, age 50, $404,297 total compensation
VP Tax and Treasurer, John E. Kunz
Chairman and CEO, Gregg M. Sherrill, age 59, $885,000 total compensation
EVP Europe South America and India, Josep Fornos, age 59
VP Human Resources International, Wolfgang Fries
VP Global Communications, Jane Ostrander
Executive Director Communications International Group, Margie Pazikas
SVP Global Supply Chain Management and Manufacturing, Michael J. (Mike) Charlton, age 53
VP and Managing Director China, Patrick Guo
VP and Managing Director Japan, Jeff Jarrell
VP and General Manager North America Original Equipment Ride Control, Kevin Swint
VP and General Manager North America Aftermarket, Joseph A. (Joe) Pomaranski
SVP General Counsel and Secretary, James D. Harrington, age 51
Controller North America, James Kujawski
VP and General Manager Europe Aftermarket, Alex Gelbcke
Managing Director South America, Guillermo Minuzzi
VP Strategic Planning and Business Development, Maritza Gibbons
Executive Director Investor Relations, Linae Golla
VP and General Manager Global Elastomers, Marie Ffolkes
VP and General Manager Europe Original Equipment Emission Control, Enrique Orta
VP and General Manager Europe Original Equipment Ride Control, Sandro Paparelli
VP Finance International, Theo Bonneu
Manager Global Communications, Mike Alzamora
Director, David B. Price Jr., age 66
Director, Charles W. (Chuck) Cramb, age 65
Director, Dennis J. Letham, age 60
Director, Paul T. Stecko, age 67
COO and Director, Hari N. Nair, age 52
Director, Jane L. Warner, age 65
Director, Mitsunobu Takeuchi, age 70
Auditors: PricewaterhouseCoopersLLP

LOCATIONS

HQ: Tenneco Inc.
500 North Field Dr., Lake Forest IL 60045
Phone: 847-482-5000 **Fax:** 847-482-5940
Web: www.tenneco.com

2010 Sales

	$ mil.	% of total
North America	2,832	46
Europe South America India	2,594	42
Asia/Pacific	698	12
Adjustments	(187)	-
Total	**5,937**	**100**

2010 Sales by Area

	% of total
US	35
Other	65
Total	**100**

PRODUCTS/OPERATIONS

2010 Sales

	$ mil.	% of total
Emission-control systems & products		
OEM	3,507	59
Aftermarket	318	6
Ride-control systems & products		
OEM	1,261	21
Aftermarket	851	14
Total	**5,937**	**100**

Selected Brands and Products

Emission control systems (DNX DynoMax Fonos Gillet Thrush and Walker)
- Aftertreatment control units
- Burner systems
- Catalytic converters and diesel oxidation catalysts
- Diesel particulate filters (DPFs)
- Exhaust manifolds
- Hangers and isolators
- High-frequency turbo decoupler
- Hydrocarbon vaporizers and injectors
- Lean NOx traps
- Mufflers
- Pipes
- Resonators

Selective catalytic reduction (SCR)

Ride control systems (DNX Fric-Rot Kinetic Monroe and Rancho)
- Coil and leaf springs
- Computerized electronic suspension (CES)
- Corner and full axle modules
- Heavy duty truck and train shocks
- Kinetic suspension technology
- Shock absorbers and struts
- Suspension systems
- Top mounts
- Vibration control components (Clevite Elastomers)
  - Engine and body mounts
  - Exhaust isolators
  - Leaf and coil springs
  - Spring seats
  - Suspension control arm link and stabilizer bar bushings

COMPETITORS

Benteler Automotive
Cooper-Standard Automotive
Edelbrock
Faurecia Exhaust Systems
Kolbenschmidt Pierburg
Letts Industries
Meritor
Metaldyne
Wescast Industries
ZF Group NAO

HISTORICAL FINANCIALS

Company Type: Public

Income Statement FYE: December 31

	REVENUE ($ mil.)	NET INCOME ($ mil.)	NET PROFIT MARGIN	EMPLOYEES
12/11	7,205	157	2.2%	24,000
12/10	5,937	39	0.7%	22,000
12/09	4,649	(73)	—	21,000
12/08	5,916	(415)	—	21,000
12/07	6,184	(5)	—	21,000
Annual Growth	3.9%	—	—	3.4%

2011 Year-End Financials

Debt ratio: 36.68%
Return on equity: —
Cash ($ mil.): 214
Current ratio: 126.05
Long-term debt ($ mil.): 1,158
No. of shares (mil.): 60
Dividends
Yield: —
Payout: —
Market value ($ mil.): 1,800

	STOCK PRICE ($) FY Close	P/E High	P/E Low	PER SHARE ($) Earnings	Dividends	Book Value
12/11	29.78	18	9	2.55	0.00	(0.00)
12/10	41.16	66	27	0.63	0.00	(0.07)
12/09	17.73	—	—	(1.50)	0.00	(0.35)
12/08	2.95	—	—	(8.95)	0.00	(5.34)
12/07	26.07	—	—	(0.11)	0.00	8.58
Annual Growth	3.4%	—	—	—	—	—

Tennessee Valley Authority

Tennessee Valley Authority (TVA) may not be an expert on state attractions like Dollywood and the Grand Ole Opry but it is an authority on power generation. A US government-owned corporation TVA is the largest public power producer in the country. It sells wholesale electricity to more than 150 municipal and cooperative power distributors which serve some 9 million people in Tennessee and parts of Alabama Georgia Kentucky Mississippi North Carolina and Virginia. It also sells power directly to large industries and federal agencies. In addition TVA provides flood control and land management for the Tennessee River system and it assists utilities and state and local governments with economic development.

TVA was established by Congress in 1993 primarily to reduce flood damage improve navigation on the Tennessee River and promote agricultural and industrial development in the region. In 1999 government appropriations for the authority ceased. TVA has since funded its activities from the sale of electricity and the sale of bonds in financial markets. It receives no taxpayer money and makes no profits. In 2010 energy demand was up due to a record hot summer and cold winter. TVA earned about $10.9 billion in revenue for the year and net income from energy sales were reinvested into system improvements and economic development initiatives.

TVA provide electric power through a network of about 16000 miles of transmission line. Most of its power comes from traditional generation sources. Its facilities include fossil fuel-powered hydroelectric nuclear combustion turbine and combined-cycle plants. TVA has an agreement to produce tritium a radioactive gas that boosts the power of nuclear weapons for the US Department of Energy at its Watts Bar nuclear plant. The company plans to add three more nuclear plants by 2020 and is working with the DOE to reprocess waste from its existing plants. In 2009 more than half of its generating capacity came from coal-fired generators with roughly a third coming from nuclear plants.

More recently it has been expanding its renewable energy portfolio with more than a dozen solar energy sites and and one wind energy site. TVA is working toward obtaining 50% of its power supply from low- or zero-carbon-emitting or renewable sources by 2020. It also announced plans to replace its older and less efficient coal units with cleaner sources of power.

Still TVA faces various environmental issues. In 2008 a holding pond at TVA's coal-burning Kingston Fossil Plant failed and dumped some 5.4 million cu. yd. of fly ash over 400 acres in eastern Tennessee's Roane County. The slide knocked down utility poles and trees and damaged at least a dozen homes (some beyond repair). Although no one was hurt some residents were cut off by the spill prompting officials to build a new road. The flooding was the pond's third reported incident in six years. The cleanup will likely cost more than $1 billion and be completed by 2013. Some 14 lawsuits are pending against the TVA as a result of the incident.

HISTORY

In 1924 the Army Corps of Engineers finished building the Wilson Dam on the Tennessee River in Alabama to provide power for two WWI-era nitrate plants. With the war over the question of what to do with the plants became a political football.

An act of Congress created the Tennessee Valley Authority (TVA) in 1933 to manage the plants and Tennessee Valley waterways. New Dealers saw TVA as a way to revitalize the local economy through improved navigation and power generation. Power companies claimed the agency was unconstitutional but by 1939 when a federal court ruled against them TVA had five operating hydroelectric plants and five under construction.

During the 1940s TVA supplied power for the war effort including the Manhattan Project in Tennessee. During the postwar boom between 1945 and 1950 power usage in the Tennessee Valley nearly doubled. Despite adding dams TVA couldn't keep up with demand so in 1949 it began building a coal-fired unit. Because coal-fired plants weren't part of TVA's original mission in 1955 a Congressional panel recommended the authority be dissolved.

Though TVA survived its funding was cut. In 1959 it was allowed to sell bonds but it no longer received direct government appropriations for power operations. In addition it had to pay back the government for past appropriations.

TVA began to build the first unit of an ambitious 17-plant nuclear power program in Alabama in 1967. However skyrocketing costs forced it to raise rates and cut maintenance on its coal-fired plants which led to breakdowns. In 1985 five reactors had to be shut down because of safety concerns.

In 1988 former auto industry executive Marvin Runyon was appointed chairman of the agency. "Carvin' Marvin" cut management sold three airplanes and got rid of peripheral businesses saving $400 million a year. In 1992 Runyon left to go to the postal service and was replaced by Craven Crowell who began preparing TVA for competition in the retail power market.

TVA ended its nuclear construction program in 1996 after bringing two nuclear units on line within three months a first for a US utility. The next year it raised rates for the first time in 10 years planning to reduce its debt. In response to a lawsuit filed by neighboring utilities it agreed to stop "laundering" power by using third parties to sell outside the agency's legally authorized area.

In 1999 the authority finished installing almost $2 billion in scrubbers and other equipment at its coal-fired plants so that it could buy Kentucky coal along with cleaner Wyoming coal. That year however the EPA charged TVA with violating the Clean Air Act by making major overhauls on some of its older coal-fired plants without getting permits or installing updated pollution-control equipment. It ordered TVA to bring most of its coal-fired plants into compliance with more current pollution standards. The next year TVA contested the order in court stating compliance would jack up electricity rates.

TVA was fined by the US Nuclear Regulatory Commission in 2000 for laying off a nuclear plant whistleblower. The next year saw the beginning of a revolving door to the chairman's office —Crowell resigned in 2001 and Glenn McCullough Jr. was named chairman; he served in that role until May 2005. McCullough was replaced by Bill Baxter (who served until March 2006) and then by William Sansom (who served until February 2009). Mike Duncan served until May 2010 when Dennis Bottorff became chairman.

EXECUTIVES

President and CEO, Tom D. Kilgore, age 64, $853,270 total compensation
Chairman, William B. (Bill) Sansom, age 70
Environmental Program Administrator, Amy Brown
EVP and CFO, John M. Thomas III, age 49
EVP and Chief Nuclear Officer, Preston D. Swafford, age 52, $499,877 total compensation
SVP Environment and Technology and Sustainability Officer, Anda A. Ray, age 56
EVP and Chief Generation Officer, Kimberly S. (Kim) Greene, age 46, $527,020 total compensation
SVP and Treasurer, John M. Hoskins, age 57
SVP Clean Strategies and Project Development, Robert M. (Bob) Deacy Sr., age 60
EVP Performance Transition Office, Kenneth R. Breeden, age 64
VP Industrial Marketing, Gary Harris
VP and Controller, Steve Byone, age 53
COO, William R. (Bill) McCollum Jr., age 61, $748,381 total compensation
SVP Diversity and Labor Relations Chief Ethics Officer and Designated Agency Ethics Official, Peyton T. Hairston Jr., age 57
SVP Fleet Engineering, William R. (Bill) Campbell, age 61
SVP Government Relations, Emily J. Reynolds, age 56
Manager Regional Development and Field Operations, Tim Weston
VP Valley Relations, Robert (Bob) Morris
EVP and Chief Energy Delivery Officer, Robin E. (Rob) Manning, age 56
EVP Customer Relations, Van M. Wardlaw, age 52
SVP Nuclear Generation Development and Construction, Ashok S. Bhatnagar, age 56, $458,001 total compensation
EVP and Chief Administrative Officer, Janet C. Herrin, age 58
SVP River Operations, John J. McCormick Jr., age 50
Manager Southeast Valley District Valley Relations, Penny Judd
Manager West Tennessee District Valley Relations, Paul Phelan
Manager Kentucky District Valley Relations, Nancy Mitchell
Manager Northeast Valley District Valley Relations, Bert Robinson
Manager Mississippi District Valley Relations, Amy Tate
SVP Nuclear Operations, Donald E. Jernigan, age 56
VP and CIO, Daniel A. (Dan) Traynor, age 55
SVP Fossil Power Generation Group, Robert Fisher
VP Supply Chain, Russ Steward
VP Energy Efficiency and Demand Response, Robert M. (Bob) Balzar
SVP Commercial Operations and Pricing, John Trawick
SVP Strategy and Planning, Robert (Bob) Irvin
SVP Policy and Oversight, Joe Hoagland
Inspector General, Richard W. Moore
Member News Bureau Staff, Barbara Martocci
EVP and General Counsel, Ralph E. Rodgers, age 57
Manager Alabama District Valley Relations, Jason Harper
VP Transmission and Reliability, Bob Dalrymple
Manager Middle Tennessee District Valley Relations, Amy Arnold
Senior Manager Diversity and Labor Relations, Vyrone Cravanas
Program Manager Fossil Power Group, Ron Nash
General Manager River Scheduling, Chuck Bach
Senior Manager Generation Partners, Susan Curtis
CADNet Manager, Jim Kurtz
General Manager Customer Service West Tennessee District, Laura Campbell
Manager Customer Service Kentucky, Bryant Beames
Aquatic Biologist, Donny Lowery
Commander Police Field Operations, Raymond Jordan
Plant Manager Kingston Fossil Plant, Leslie Nale
VP and Director Police and Physical Security, David Jolley
VP Talent Management Group, Steve McMillen
Senior Manager Talent Sourcing and Support Services Group People and Performance Organization, Susan Stout
VP Technology Innovation, Ramesh Shankar
Fisheries Biologist, John Justice

Project Manager Energy Efficient Homes, David Dinse
Plant Manager Shawnee Fossil Plant, Mike Kaler
Senior Project Manager Electric System Projects Group Power System Operations, Randal Petty
VP Watts Bar Unit 2, David (Dave) Stinson
SVP Nuclear Construction, Michael D. (Mike) Skaggs
Director, Rev William H. Graves, age 75
Director, Marilyn A. Brown, age 63
Director, Barbara S. Haskew, age 72
Director, Neil McBride, age 66
Director, Richard Howorth
Auditors: Ernst&YoungLLP

LOCATIONS

HQ: Tennessee Valley Authority
400 W. Summit Hill Dr., Knoxville TN 37902
Phone: 865-632-2101 **Fax:** 888-633-0372
Web: www.tva.gov

2010 Sales

	$ mil.	% of total
Electricity sales		
Tennessee	6,693	62
Alabama	1,495	14
Kentucky	1,195	11
Mississippi	974	9
Georgia	253	2
North Carolina	53	1
Virginia	48	-
Other revenues	163	1
Total	**10,874**	**100**

PRODUCTS/OPERATIONS

2010 Sales

	$ mil.	% of total
Electricity sales		
Municipalities & cooperatives	9,275	85
Industries directly served	1,321	12
Federal agencies & other	117	1
Other revenues	161	2
Total	**10,874**	**100**

HISTORICAL FINANCIALS

Company Type: Government-owned

Income Statement

FYE: September 30

	REVENUE ($ mil.)	NET INCOME ($ mil.)	NET PROFIT MARGIN	EMPLOYEES
09/12	11,220	60	0.5%	12,762
09/11	11,841	162	1.4%	12,893
09/10	10,874	972	8.9%	12,457
09/09	11,255	726	6.5%	12,219
09/08	10,382	817	7.9%	11,584
Annual Growth	2.0%	(47.9%)	—	2.5%

2012 Year-End Financials

Debt ratio: 52.98%—
Return on equity: 1.13%
Cash ($ mil.): 868
Current ratio: 64.48
Long-term debt ($ mil.): 21,250
Dividends
Yield: —
Payout: —
Market value ($ mil.): —

	STOCK PRICE ($) FY Close	P/E High/Low	PER SHARE ($) Earnings	Dividends	Book Value
09/12	26.50	— —	(0.00)	0.00	(0.00)
09/11	26.06	— —	(0.00)	1.18	(0.00)
09/10	26.19	— —	(0.00)	1.18	(0.00)
09/09	27.08	— —	(0.00)	1.32	(0.00)
09/08	25.40	— —	(0.00)	1.37	(0.00)
Annual Growth	1.1%	— —	—	—	—

Terex Corp.

Terex is a "T-Rex" when it comes to making a variety of cranes aerial platforms and construction and materials processing equipment. Its construction business makes compaction equipment such as compact track loaders and excavators as well as off-highway trucks and road building products. Another arm makes aerial lifts from articulating to telescopic booms used in industrial and construction overhead jobs. Terex products are sold in more than 100 countries around the globe to the construction forestry and recycling shipping and utility industries under brands Terex Genie and Powerscreen. In North America it sells and rents equipment via its own distribution chain.

HISTORY

Real estate entrepreneur Randolph Lenz moved into heavy equipment manufacturing with the purchase of bankrupt snowplow maker FWD Corporation in 1981. That was followed the same year with the acquisition of Northwest Engineering a maker of construction equipment started in the 1920s.

In 1986 the company acquired Terex USA the North American distributor of parts for off-highway Terex trucks from General Motors and later Terex Equipment the UK-based truck maker. The company changed its corporate name to Terex Corporation in 1987. That year Terex entered the mobile-crane market with the purchase of Koehring Cranes. Terex acquired mining-truck maker Unit Rig in 1988 and trailer maker Fruehauf in 1989. It moved into aerial work platforms in 1991 with the acquisition of Mark Industries and picked up the forklift business of Clark Equipment the following year. (Clark invented the forklift truck in 1928.)

Overexpansion and heavy debt led to losses as the US slipped into recession in the early 1990s and Terex teetered on the brink of bankruptcy. The losses prompted the 1993 installation of new management led by former Case executive Ron DeFeo who refocused Terex on its core earthmoving and lifting businesses. In 1995 the company sold its stake in Fruehauf. It sold Clark Material Handling in 1996.

Terex added to its lifting-product business with the acquisition of PPM Cranes in 1995 and Simon Access and Baraga Products in 1997. It strengthened its earthmoving product line with the 1998 purchases of O&K Mining a maker of hydraulic mining excavators and Gru Comedil a maker of tower cranes. That year Lenz stepped down as chairman and DeFeo replaced him.

The company settled long-lived SEC and IRS investigations in 1999 which had negatively affected the company's stock price. (The IRS had audited the company; the SEC was probing its accounting methods.)

Terex began piling on new earthmoving businesses in 1999 including Amida Industries a maker of front-end dumpers and mobile floodlight towers. Also in 1999 Terex paid $294 million for UK-based Powerscreen International a maker of screening and crushing equipment for quarries and $170 million for Cedarapids Raytheon's road construction-equipment business. Terex then boosted its lifting business by acquiring Allegheny Teledyne's lift truck unit and Australian crane maker Franna Cranes.

Believing its stock undervalued the company announced it would buy back 7% of its shares in 2000. The same year Terex sold its truck-mounted forklift business to Finland-based Partek for about $144 million.

Early in 2001 Terex acquired Fermec Holdings Limited a UK-based maker of loader backhoes from CNH Global. Later the same year (in a deal worth about $150 million) it added CMI Corporation a maker of large-scale construction equipment and cut operating costs (about 30% of its workforce). The company also entered the power generation business selling diesel generators under the name Terex Power. In addition Terex expanded its reach into Europe by acquiring Atlas Weyhausen (cranes and excavators Germany) in 2001 and The Schaeff Group (construction equipment; Germany) in early 2002.

Also in 2002 Terex initiated investments in Tatra a.s. (heavy-duty trucks with commercial and military applications Czech Republic) increasing its share to 71% in 2003. Other 2002 acquisitions included distributors Utility Equipment (Oregon) and EPAC Holdings (which operated as Telelect East and Eusco or Telelect Southeast) Advance Mixer (cement mixer trucks) Demag Mobile Cranes (Germany) from Siemens AG and Genie Holdings (aerial work platforms) for $75 million.

The company continued to buy in 2003 adding utility equipment distributors Commercial Body and Combatel. The distributors perform final assembly and provide equipment rental and aftermarket services for the utility and telecom industries in the southern US. A deal that would have sent Terex's mining truck to Caterpillar and Caterpillar's mining shovel business to Terex was terminated in late 2003.

In late 2006 Terex sold its interest in Czech truck maker Tatra a.s. to Blue River s.r.o. a Czech-based private investment concern. However in 2008 the equipment giant expanded its construction arm by acquiring rubber track loader manufacturer ASV Inc.

Terex's interest in the port equipment business grew in 2009 when it took over Fantuzzi Industries and Noell Crane for EUR 155 million ($210 million). The addition diversified Terex's crane portfolio expanding it to a new industry segment and garnered facilities in Italy Germany and China as well as a global sales force. Expectations however for port equipment sales failed to materialize in 2010. Terex restructured the business and reduced headcount in order to realize a profit.

During the midst of the recession the US equipment giant's financial performance was hammered by a deteriorating worldwide economy coupled with a tightened credit market detering capital purchases. In 2009 net sales dropped more than 50% from 2008 and its bottom line crumbled to a $459.9 million loss. Year-over-year sales in 2010 rebounded 15% attributable to a more than 30% uptick in orders for aerial work platforms and less so materials processing and construction equipment. Despite restructuring expenses which climbed more than six-fold in 2010 over 2009 earnings pulled out of the red. The improvement was largely due to a gain realized on the sale of its discontinued operations.

EXECUTIVES

SVP Finance and Business Development, Brian J. Henry, age 53, $350,000 total compensation
SVP Secretary and General Counsel, Eric I. Cohen, age 53, $377,000 total compensation
Chairman and CEO, Ronald M. (Ron) DeFeo, age 60, $1,058,958 total compensation
President Terex Financial Services, Ramon Oliu
SVP Human Resources, Kevin A. Barr, age 52

President Terex Aerial Work Platforms, Timothy A. Ford, age 50, $454,250 total compensation
Investor Relations Associate, Elizabeth Gaal
SVP and CFO, Phillip C. Widman, age 57, $492,646 total compensation
VP Investor Relations, Tom Gelston
President Developing Markets and Strategic Accounts, Stoyan (Steve) Filipov, age 43, $414,375 total compensation
President Terex Materials Processing, Kieran Hegarty
VP and CIO, Greg Fell
VP Controller and Chief Accounting Officer, Mark I. Clair, age 51
President Terex Construction, George Ellis, age 52
Director Global Corporate Communications, Michael G. (Mike) Bazinet
President Terex Cranes, Kevin Bradley
VP and Chief Ethics and Compliance Officer, Stacey Babson-Smith
SVP Terex Business System, Doug Friesen
President Terex China, Kenneth D. Lousberg
Manager Engine Technology, Bob Keefer
Director, Thomas J. (Tom) Hansen, age 63
Director, Donald (Don) DeFosset, age 63
Director, Paula H. J. Cholmondeley, age 64
Director, David A. Sachs, age 52
Director, G. Chris Andersen, age 73
Director, Oren G. Shaffer, age 69
Director, David C. Wang, age 68
Auditors: PricewaterhouseCoopersLLP

LOCATIONS

HQ: Terex Corporation
200 Nyala Farm Rd., Westport CT 06880
Phone: 203-222-7170 **Fax:** 203-222-7976
Web: www.terex.com

2011 Sales

	$ mil.	% of total
US	1,858	29
Germany	582	9
Other European countries	1,320	20
Total	**6,504**	**100**

PRODUCTS/OPERATIONS

2011 Sales

Cranes	1,999	31
Aerial Work Platforms (AWP)	1,750	27
Materials Processing (MP)	682	10
Material Handling & Port Solutions (MHPS)	617	9
Adjustments	(50.5)	-

Selected Products

Cranes
- Lattice boom crawler cranes
- Lattice boom truck cranes
- Mobile telescopic cranes
- Specialized port and rail equipment
  - Gantry cranes
  - Lift trucks and forklifts
  - Mobile harbor cranes
  - Reach stackers
  - Replacement parts and components
  - Ship-to-shore cranes
  - Straddle and sprinter carriers
- Tower cranes
- Truck-mounted cranes (boom trucks)

Aerial Work Platforms
- Aerial work platform equipment
- Light towers
- Material lifts
- Portable aerial work platforms
- Replacement parts
- Scissor lifts
- Self-propelled articulating and telescopic booms
- Telehandlers
- Trailer-mounted articulated booms
- Trailer-mounted light towers
- Utility equipment

Construction
- Compact construction equipment
  - Compact track loaders
  - Crawler conversion parts for skid steer loaders and aerial work platforms
  - Loader backhoes
  - Mini and midi excavators
  - Site dumpers
  - Skid steer loaders
  - Tunneling equipment
  - Wheel loaders
- Heavy construction equipment
  - Articulated haul trucks
  - Material handlers
  - Off-highway rigid-haul trucks
  - Scrapers
- Roadbuilding equipment
  - Asphalt and concrete equipment (pavers transfer devices plants mixers reclaimers/stabilizers placers and cold planers)
  - Bridge inspection equipment
  - Landfill compactors

Materials processing
- Apron feeders
- Components and replacement parts
- Crushers (mobile base)
- Screens (mobile base)
- Washing systems

Material Handling and Port Solutions
- Crane components and equipment
- Process cranes
- Rope and chain hoists
- Standard cranes

COMPETITORS

Altec Industries
Astec Industries
Atlas Copco
Blount International
Caterpillar
Charles Machine Works
CNH Global
Deere
Doosan Heavy Industries
Dynapac
Fontaine Trailer
Furukawa
Gehl
Haulotte
Hitachi Construction Machinery
Hyundai Heavy Industries
Instant UpRight
J C Bamford Excavators
JLG Industries
Kobelco Construction Machinery America
Komatsu
Legris Industries Group
MANITOU BF
Manitowoc
Marmon Group
Metso
Multiquip
Oshkosh Truck
Sandvik
Skyjack
Sumitomo
Textron
Trail King Industries
Volvo
Wacker Neuson

HISTORICAL FINANCIALS

Company Type: Public

Income Statement FYE: December 31

	REVENUE ($ mil.)	NET INCOME ($ mil.)	NET PROFIT MARGIN	EMPLOYEES
12/11	6,504	45	0.7%	22,600
12/10	4,418	358	8.1%	16,300
12/09	4,043	(398)	—	15,900
12/08	9,889	71	0.7%	20,000
12/07	9,137	613	6.7%	21,000
Annual Growth	(8.1%)	(47.9%)	—	1.9%

2011 Year-End Financials

Debt ratio: 32.63%
Return on equity: 2.37%
Cash ($ mil.): 774
Current ratio: 212.16
Long-term debt ($ mil.): 2,223
No. of shares (mil.): 108
Dividends
Yield: —
Payout: —
Market value ($ mil.): 1,470

	STOCK PRICE ($) FY Close	P/E High/Low		PER SHARE ($) Earnings	Dividends	Book Value
12/11	13.51	93	23	0.41	0.00	17.52
12/10	31.04	9	5	3.30	0.00	19.27
12/09	19.81	—	—	(3.88)	0.00	15.38
12/08	17.32	102	13	0.72	0.00	18.32
12/07	65.57	16	9	5.85	0.00	23.36
Annual Growth	(32.6%)	—	—	(48.5%)	—	(6.9%)

Tesoro Corporation

Once a player in the exploration and production field Tesoro Corporation (formerly Tesoro Petroleum) has been enjoying a more refined existence in recent years as a downstream operator. The independent oil refiner and marketer operates seven US refineries –in Alaska California (two) Hawaii North Dakota Utah and Washington –with a combined capacity of 665000 barrels per day. It produces gasoline jet fuel diesel fuel fuel oil liquid asphalt and other fuel products. Tesoro markets fuel to 1200 branded retail gas stations (including 375 company-operated stations under the Tesoro Shell and USA Gasoline brands) in Alaska Hawaii and 15 western states.

Financial Analysis

Higher crude oil and petroluem product prices expanded production and the growth in gas stations drove up the company's revenues in 2011. That year Tesoro reported a strong jump in net income primarily due to increased gross refining margins in the Pacific Northwest and Mid-Continent regions.

Strategy

In 2012 the company announced plans to sell its Hawaii-based operations (94000000 barrel refinery and 32 gas stations) in order to raise cash and focus on its core Mid-Continent and West Coast businesses. Boosting its West Coast assets that year it agreed to buy BP's Southern California refining and marketing assets including the 266000 barrels-per-day Carson refinery for $2.5 billion.

As part of a strategy to step up its marketing efforts in the Western US in 2010 Tesoro bought Shell-branded wholesale supply contracts in North Dakota South Dakota Minnesota Utah and most of Idaho boosting its Shell-branded retail outlets to 650. Further agreements in 2011 with SUPERVALU and Thrifty Oil added another 290 gas stations.

To better support its refining and marketing businesses in 2011 the company spun off its logistics business as Tesoro Logistics. The IPO raised about $230 million which in part was used to help the parent company pay down debt.

On the oil supply side Tesoro has a major throughput deal that allows it to transport crude oil in a pipeline owned by Petroterminal de Panama (PTP). In 2009 PTP reversed the flow of its 81-mile trans-Panamanian pipeline to allow Tesoro to more economically transport crude oils produced in Africa the Atlantic coast of South America and the North Sea to Tesoro's five refineries on the Pacific Rim.

HISTORY

Founded by Robert West in 1964 as a spinoff of petroleum producer Texstar Tesoro Petroleum was hamstrung by debt from the get-go. In 1968 West merged Tesoro with Intex Oil and Sioux Oil to invigorate its financial standing.

Reborn the company constructed an Alaska refinery and began a 10-year stretch of petroleum-related acquisitions usually at bargain prices including almost half of the oil operations of British Petroleum (BP) in Trinidad which became Trinidad-Tesoro Petroleum. By 1973 earnings had quintupled.

In 1975 Tesoro paid $83 million for about a third of Commonwealth Oil Refining Company (Corco) a troubled Puerto Rican oil refiner one-and-a-half times its size. Debt soon was troubling Tesoro again and the company divested many of its holdings including refineries in Montana and Wyoming. Corco declared bankruptcy in 1978. That year Tesoro was hit with tax penalties and revealed it had bribed officials in foreign countries.

The company fought takeover attempts and bankruptcy in the 1980s and sold its half of Trinidad-Tesoro in 1985. In the 1990s it expanded its natural gas operations and returned to profitability.

In 1998 Tesoro bought a refinery and 32 retail outlets in Hawaii from an affiliate of BHP and a refinery in Washington from an affiliate of Shell. To concentrate on its downstream businesses the company in 1999 sold its exploration and production operations in the US (to EEX for $215 million) and in Bolivia (to BG for about $100 million).

Tesoro West Coast Co. a Tesoro subsidiary entered into a lease agreement with Wal-Mart in 2000 to build and operate retail fueling facilities at Wal-Mart locations in 11 western states (subsequently expanded to 13 states). That year the company reviewed the possibility of closing part or all of its Alaska properties including its underperforming refinery. But boosted by higher crude prices and its new deal with Wal-Mart Tesoro decided to leave its Alaska operations untouched.

In 2001 Tesoro bought refineries in North Dakota and Utah plus 45 gas stations and contracts to supply 300 others from BP for about $675 million. Tesoro bought the Golden Eagle (San Francisco-area) refinery and 70 retail service stations in Northern California from Valero Energy for $945 million in 2002. At the end of the year Tesoro sold 47 of those gas stations to help pay down debt. It also sold its Northern Great Plains Products System to Kaneb Pipe Line Partners L.P. for $100 million.

The 2003 sale of its marine services unit for $32 million was also part of the company's plan to focus on its refining and marketing operations and pay down debt. The group achieved its goal of shedding some $500 million of debt by the end of 2003 through asset sales and cost reductions.

Tesoro acquired a Los Angeles refinery and some 276 gas stations from Shell Oil Products US for about $1.6 billion in 2007. It then acquired more than 130 USA Petroleum gas stations primarily in California; these acquisitions nearly doubled Tesoro's retail presence.

In 2008 weak margins prompted the company to close most of its Mirastar gas stations.

EXECUTIVES

VP Kenai Refinery, Stephen W. Hansen, age 66
SVP and CFO, G. Scott Spendlove, age 48
SVP External Affairs and Chief Economist, Lynn D. Westfall, age 59
Chairman, Steven H. Grapstein, age 54
SVP Administration, Susan A. Lerette, age 53
SVP Logistics and Marine, Joseph M. (Joe) Monroe, age 57
SVP Commercial, David K. Kirshner
Manager Marketing Hawaii, Gordon Wong
SVP Strategy and Business Development, Claude A. (Chuck) Flagg, age 58
EVP General Counsel and Secretary, Charles S. (Chuck) Parrish, age 54, $477,945 total compensation
VP and Controller, Arlen O. Glenewinkel Jr., age 55
SVP Marketing, Claude P. Moreau, age 57
SVP Supply and Trading, Joe G. McCoy, age 63
Managing Director Finance and Investor Relations, Scott Phipps
VP Anacortes Refinery, Don J. Sorensen
Manager Human Resources Anacortes Refinery, John McDarment
Manager External Affairs Kenai Refinery, Kip Knudson
Manager Human Resources Mandan Refinery, Leif W. Peterson
VP Salt Lake City Refinery, Dan Cameron
Manager Human Resources Salt Lake City Refinery, Russ Jansen
VP Marketing California, Bob Mills
General Manager Marketing California, Doug Gray
General Manager Marketing Pacific Northwest and Alaska Region, Dennis Coyne
President CEO and Director, Gregory J. (Greg) Goff, age 55
Manager Government and Public Affairs Hawaii Refinery, Lance Tanaka
VP Northern Great Plains Region Mandan Refinery, John S. Berger
VP Wholesale Marketing, John Moore
Area Marketing Manager Southern California, Matt Thomas
Area Marketing Manager Northern California, Armin Ray
Area Marketing Manager Oregon, Jerry Guiliano
Area Marketing Manager Washington, Margaret Quigley
General Manager Marketing Northern Great Plains Mountain Region, Nancy K. Meisner
Area Marketing Manager Alaska, Jeff Dallmann
Area Marketing Manager Hawaii, Kurt Shimada
VP Aviation Fuels Marketing, Jeff Fabian
VP Heavy Fuels Marketing, Phil Wing
VP North American Crude Supply and Trading, Scott McCrary
Director Mid-Continent Crude Supply, Kevan Taylor
Director North American Crude Supply and Trading, Damon Van Zandt
VP International Crude, Lewis Schwartz
VP Arbitrage Trading, Doug Koskie
Manager International Crude Supply and Trading, Steve Kelly
Manager International Crude Trading, Dana Holden
VP Product Supply and Trading, Ed Peters
General Manager International Product Trading, Siomara Marquez de Cantafio
Director Product Supply and Trading, Morgan Norris
Manager Light Product Supply, Terry Houtchens
Manager Natural Gas Power and LPGs, Bonnie Hitschel
Manager Heavy Oils and Specialty Products, Mickey Richnow
VP Trading and Risk Management, Mark Smith
Manager Crude Supply Logistics, Cindi Walker
VP Marine, Charles Parks
Manager Commercial Shipping Marine, Alan Bartulis
Manager Commercial Marine Operations, Richard Caron
Director Contingency Planning and Response Marine, Eric Haugstad
Director West Coast Light Products Supply, Mike Reed
Manager West Coast Light Products Supply, Eric Pestano
Manager Product Supply Logistics, Ray Barner
VP Heavy Oils and Specialty Products, William Weimer
Director Pacific Rim Crude Supply, Simon Yim
Manager Pacific Rim Product Supply and Trading, Madelene Chung
Director Commercial Shipping and Operations Marine, Ranesh Sandhu
Manager Investor Relations, Brad McMurray
Director Investor Relations, Louie Rubiola
Manager Government and Pulbic Affairs, Mike Marcy
VP Information Technology and CIO, Michiel Espach
EVP Operations, Daniel R. (Dan) Romasko, age 48
VP and Treasurer, Tracy D. Jackson
VP Human Resources and Communications, Craig M. LaTorre
VP Environmental Health and Safety, Karma Thomson
SVP Refining, Frank Wheeler
Director, James W. (Jim) Nokes, age 65
Director, Robert W. (Bob) Goldman, age 69
Director, Rodney F. Chase, age 68
Director, Susan Tomasky, age 58
Director, Michael E. (Mike) Wiley, age 61
Director, William J. Johnson, age 77
Director, Donald H. Schmude, age 76
Director, Patrick Y. (Pat) Yang, age 64
President CEO and Director, Gregory J. (Greg) Goff, age 55
Auditors: Ernst&YoungLLP

LOCATIONS

HQ: Tesoro Corporation
19100 Ridgewood Pkwy., San Antonio TX 78259-1828
Phone: 210-626-6000 **Fax:** 210-579-4574
Web: www.tsocorp.com

PRODUCTS/OPERATIONS

2011 Sales

	$ mil.	% of total
Refining		
Refined products	29,058	83
Crude oil resales & other	747	2
Retail		
Fuel	5,095	14
Merchandise & other	224	1
Adjustments	(4821)	-
Total	**30,303**	**100**

Major Subsidiari
Tesoro Alaska Company
Tesoro Logistics GP LLC
Tesoro Refining and Marketing Company

COMPETITORS

Arctic Slope Regional Corporation
Big West Oil
Chemoil
Chevron U.S.A
Gas Depot
Gibson Energy
HollyFrontier
National Cooperative Refinery Association
Northern Tier Energy
Petro Star
Phillips 66
Shell Oil Products
Tauber Oil
Valero Energy
Western Refining Inc.

HISTORICAL FINANCIALS

Company Type: Public

Income Statement FYE: December 31

	REVENUE ($ mil.)	NET INCOME ($ mil.)	NET PROFIT MARGIN	EMPLOYEES
12/11	30,303	546	1.8%	5,400
12/10	20,583	(29)	—	5,300
12/09	16,872	(140)	—	5,500
12/08	28,309	278	1.0%	5,620
12/07	21,915	566	2.6%	5,500
Annual Growth	8.4%	(0.9%)	—	(0.5%)

2011 Year-End Financials

Debt ratio: 17.20%
Return on equity: 14.89%
Cash ($ mil.): 900
Current ratio: 127.76
Long-term debt ($ mil.): 1,283
No. of shares (mil.): 139
Dividends
Yield: —
Payout: —
Market value ($ mil.): 3,270

	STOCK PRICE ($) FY Close	P/E High	P/E Low	PER SHARE ($) Earnings	Dividends	Book Value
12/11	23.36	8	5	3.81	0.00	26.21
12/10	18.54	—	—	(0.21)	0.25	22.45
12/09	13.55	—	—	(1.01)	0.35	21.98
12/08	13.17	24	3	2.00	0.40	23.26
12/07	47.70	30	11	4.06	0.35	22.27
Annual Growth	(16.3%)	—	—	(1.6%)	—	4.2%

Texas Capital Bancshares Inc

Texas Capital Bancshares is the holding company for Texas Capital Bank which has about 10 branches in Austin Dallas Fort Worth Houston Plano and San Antonio. The bank targets high-net-worth individuals and businesses with more than $5 million in annual revenue with a focus on the real estate financial services transportation communications petrochemicals and mining sectors. Striving for personalized services for its clients the bank offers deposit accounts Visa credit cards commercial loans and mortgages equipment leasing wealth management and trust services. Its BankDirect division provides online banking services.

Texas Capital Bancshares was formed in 1998 with a Texas-sized bankroll of $80 million one of the largest ever for a community bank at that time. It believes that its Texas roots give it a competitive advantage over larger competitors that are headquartered out of state.

Doing business in Texas has also helped the bank's bottom line as the state has proven to be relatively recession-proof. While its percentage of nonperforming loans has remained below the national average Texas Capital Bancshares has grown its assets deposits and loan portfolio each of the past five years. The company has also reported three consecutive years of earnings growth following the global credit crisis of 2007-2008.

Lending accounts for around 90% of Texas Capital Bancshares' revenue. Commercial loans usually used by borrowers for working capital business growth acquisitions business insurance premium financing and to purchase real estate represent most of the company's lending activities. The bank has cut back on construction lending amid an industry-wide slowdown. It does not originate residential mortgages and consumer loans typically account for less than 1% of its loan book.

Texas Capital Bancshares has said that it is looking to grow within its main metropolitan markets but has also branched out beyond the borders of its home state. The bank has an Cayman Islands branch to offer offshore cash management and deposit products to it core clientele.

Insiders and institutional investors own approximately 40% of Texas Capital Bancshares' stock.

EXECUTIVES

President CEO and Director; CEO Texas Capital Bank, George F. Jones Jr., age 68, $484,167 total compensation
Chairman Emeritus, Joseph M. (Jody) Grant, age 73, $377,500 total compensation
President COO Chief Lending Officer Texas Capital Bank, C. Keith Cargill, age 59, $300,000 total compensation
EVP Texas Capital Bank, David L. Cargill
Regional President Texas Capital Bank Dallas, Vince A. Ackerson, $265,000 total compensation
Chairman Texas Capital Bank San Antonio, Mark M. Johnson
Chairman, James R. (Jim) Holland Jr., age 68
Regional President Texas Capital Bank Austin, Kerry L. Hall
Regional President Texas Capital Bank Plano, Michael (Mike) Robnett
Investor Relations Contact, Myrna Vance
EVP Texas Capital Bank, Russell Hartsfield
CFO and Director; CFO Texas Capital Bank, Peter B. Bartholow, age 63, $325,000 total compensation
Chief Credit Officer Texas Capital Bank, John D. Hudgens, $260,000 total compensation
Regional President Texas Capital Bank Houston, Bill Wilson
EVP and Controller, Julie Anderson
EVP and COO Texas Capital Bank, James C. (Jim) White
Regional President Texas Capital Bank Fort Worth, Jeff Moten
Regional President Texas Capital Bank San Antonio, Clay Jett
Director, Robert W. Stallings, age 62
Director, Frederick B. (Fred) Hegi Jr., age 68
Director, Elysia Holt Ragusa, age 61
President CEO and Director; CEO Texas Capital Bank, George F. Jones Jr., age 68
Chairman Emeritus, Joseph M. (Jody) Grant, age 73
Director, Steven P. (Steve) Rosenberg, age 53
Chairman, James R. (Jim) Holland Jr., age 68
Director, Walter W. (Bo) McAllister III, age 70
Director, Larry L. Helm, age 64
Director, Ian J. Turpin, age 67
CFO and Director; CFO Texas Capital Bank, Peter B. Bartholow, age 63
Director, Lee Roy Mitchell, age 75
Director, James H. Browning, age 62
Auditors: Ernst&YoungLLP

LOCATIONS

HQ: Texas Capital Bancshares Inc.
2100 McKinney Ave. Ste. 700, Dallas TX 75201
Phone: 214-932-6600 **Fax:** 214-932-6604
Web: www.texascapitalbank.com

PRODUCTS/OPERATIONS

2011 Sales

	$ mil.	% of total
Interest		
Loans including fees	314	89
Securities	6	2
Other	0	-
Noninterest		
Brokered loan fees	11	3
Service charges on deposit accounts	6	2
Trust fees	4	1
Other	10	3
Total	**353**	**100**

COMPETITORS

Amegy
Bank of America
BOK Financial
Comerica
Compass Bancshares
Cullen/Frost Bankers
JPMorgan Chase
Prosperity Bancshares
Wells Fargo

HISTORICAL FINANCIALS

Company Type: Public

Income Statement FYE: December 31

	ASSETS ($ mil.)	NET INCOME ($ mil.)	INCOME AS % OF ASSETS	EMPLOYEES
12/11	8,137	75	0.9%	786
12/10	6,446	37	0.6%	699
12/09	5,698	24	0.4%	631
12/08	5,140	24	0.5%	547
12/07	4,287	29	0.7%	510
Annual Growth	17.4%	26.8%	—	11.4%

2011 Year-End Financials

Debt ratio: 1.39%
Return on equity: 12.33%
Cash ($ mil.): 101
Current ratio: —
Long-term debt ($ mil.): 113
No. of shares (mil.): 37
Dividends
Yield: —
Payout: —
Market value ($ mil.): 1,153

	STOCK PRICE ($) FY Close	P/E High	P/E Low	PER SHARE ($) Earnings	Dividends	Book Value
12/11	30.61	15	10	1.98	0.00	16.36
12/10	21.34	22	13	1.00	0.00	14.30
12/09	13.96	33	12	0.55	0.00	13.40
12/08	13.36	25	15	0.87	0.00	12.53
12/07	18.25	21	16	1.10	0.00	11.22
Annual Growth	13.8%	—	—	15.8%	—	9.9%

Texas Instruments Inc.

Say hello to the big Texan. One of the world's oldest and largest semiconductor makers Texas Instruments (TI) is the market leader in digital signal processors (DSPs) and a leading maker of analog semiconductors which change real-world signals (such as sound and images) into the digital data streams processed by DSPs. Many wireless phones sold worldwide contain TI's DSPs which are also found in DVD players automotive systems and computer modems. The company's other semiconductor products include logic chips microprocessors microcontrollers and display components. TI also makes calculators. Nearly three-quarters of sales come from customers in the Asia/Pacific region.

Financial Analysis After a dip in sales and profits in 2008 and 2009 when the global recession dampened demand for consumer electronics TI's sales recovered in 2010 though not quite reaching the peak set in 2006. For 2011 the company reported that overall sales were essentially flat down by 2% compared to 2010 and net income fell 31% due in part to higher acquisition and restructuring costs and lower factory utilization. Revenue growth was held in check by revenue that was 15% lower in the wireless segment (related to its continued exit from the wireless baseband product line) partially offset by single-digit growth in its analog and embedded processing segments. Restructuring charges were primarily related to the closure of older plants in Texas and Japan.

Strategy TI touts its combination of expertise in analog and DSP technologies as a key advantage in allowing it to deliver more highly integrated components for customers in areas such as wireless and broadband communications. The breadth of its offerings means that in some cases it can supply several different kinds of chips for a single electronic device such as separate chips that enable the telephone and camera features in new wireless phones. The company is also banking on even larger markets for its DSPs in the future as their use becomes more widespread in areas such as wireline communications and medical equipment.

Mergers & Acquisitions As the electronics industry started to recover from the prolonged downturn in 2010 TI began to boost its capacity for the analog chips used in electronic gadgets. In 2010 the company bought two wafer fabs in Japan from the Japanese unit of Spansion. TI plans to run the first fab which could add capacity for around $1 billion in analog revenue per year; it plans to keep all of the plant's employees. The second facility will be used to expand future capacity. The company will also provide FLASH products foundry and sorting services to Spansion through June 2012. Also in 2010 TI sold its cable modem product line to Intel. The unit supplies customers such as ARRIS and Cisco's Scientific Atlanta brand with chips for cable modems. TI considered the operation non-core to ongoing operations. TI jockeys back and forth with European chip giant STMicroelectronics to be the world's top maker of analog chips; both companies far outpace other analog rivals. In 2011 TI looked to take the lead in the analog race when it bought smaller rival National Semiconductor for about $6.5 billion in cash. The deal did more than add to the breadth of TI's analog product lines; combined with those of National Semiconductor the company has a portfolio of nearly 45000 analog chips. The two companies share many of the same customers and chips from each are often included in the same end products. Where products do not overlap chips from the combined company expand TI's reach to additional customers in new markets particularly for power management applications. TI is consolidating the acquired operations into its analog segment under the name Silicon Valley Analog (SVA).

HISTORY

Clarence "Doc" Karcher and Eugene McDermott founded Geophysical Service Inc. (GSI) in Newark New Jersey in 1930 to develop reflective seismology a new technology for oil and gas exploration. In 1934 GSI moved to Dallas. The company produced military electronics during WWII including submarine detectors for the US Navy. GSI changed its name to Texas Instruments (TI) in 1951.

TI began making transistors in 1952 after buying a license from Western Electric. The company went public on the New York Stock Exchange in 1953. In 1954 it introduced the Regency Radio the first pocket-sized transistor radio. (That year TI also produced the first commercial silicon transistor.) Impressed by the radio IBM president Thomas Watson made TI a major supplier to IBM in 1957. That year the company opened a plant in the UK —its first foreign operation.

TI engineer Jack Kilby invented the integrated circuit (IC) in 1958. (Working independently Intel co-founder Robert Noyce developed an IC at the same time while working at Fairchild Semiconductor; the two men are credited as co-inventors. In 2000 Kilby was awarded the Nobel Prize in Physics for his work; Noyce could not be awarded the prize since he had died 10 years earlier.)

Other breakthroughs included terrain-following airborne radar (1958) handheld calculators (1967) and single-chip microcomputers (1971). During the 1970s TI introduced innovative calculators digital watches home computers and educational toys such as the popular Speak & Spell —the first TI product to use digital signal processors (DSPs) which decades later would become a major driver of TI's growth.

Low-cost foreign competition led TI to abandon its digital watch and PC businesses. Price competition in the chip market contributed to the company's first loss in 1983. In 1988 the company sold most of its remaining oil and gas operations to Halliburton.

As the chip market toughened TI leveraged its DRAM device know-how through strategic alliances including a 1993 agreement with Hitachi (the venture ended in 1998). TI sold its line of educational toys to Tiger Electronics in 1995.

When company head Jerry Junkins who built TI into a semiconductor force died unexpectedly in 1996 he was replaced by company veteran Thomas Engibous as president and CEO. (Engibous became chairman in 1998.)

Engibous refocused TI which in 1996 sold its custom manufacturing business to Solectron (now part of Flextronics) and acquired Silicon Systems (chips for mass storage devices). In 1997 TI sold its notebook computer business to Acer its defense electronics operation to Raytheon and its enterprise applications software unit to Sterling Software (now part of CA).

In 1998 TI sold its slumping memory chip operations to Micron Technology. The complex deal gave TI about a 15% stake in Micron —a stake it pared in 2000 and eliminated in 2003. A global chip slump and the loss of the memory chip business lowered TI's results in 1998 and led to the layoff of 3500 employees.

TI paid $7.6 billion in 2000 to acquire Burr-Brown an Arizona-based maker of analog and mixed-signal chips. That year it changed the name of its Materials and Controls business unit to Sensors and Controls after it sold its specialty materials unit to Blue Point Capital Partners. In 2001 TI began to lay off about 2500 workers in reaction to a softening market for its chips. In 2002 the company acquired a majority interest in Condat a German developer of software for wireless devices.

In 2004 COO Richard Templeton succeeded Engibous as president and CEO; Engibous remained chairman.

TI completed its acquisition of Norway-based Chipcon Group a developer of radio-frequency (RF) transceiver devices for about $200 million in 2006. Also that year TI sold its Sensors and Controls business to Bain Capital for $3 billion in cash. The business was rechristened Sensata Technologies. In selling the sensors and controls business TI held on to its radio-frequency identification (RFID) tags business making chips used in contactless payment systems health care manufacturing retail supply chain management and other applications.

In 2008 Engibous retired as chairman and was succeeded by Templeton.

EXECUTIVES

Chairman President and CEO, Richard K. (Rich) Templeton, age 53, $963,120 total compensation
SVP and Manager Communications and Investor Relations, Teresa L. (Terri) West, age 51
SVP Secretary and General Counsel, Joseph F. (Joe) Hubach, age 54
SVP Analog, Gregg A. Lowe, age 49, $535,020 total compensation
SVP and Worldwide Manager High-Performance Analog, Stephen (Steve) Anderson, age 50
SVP and Manager High Volume and Logic, Niels Anderskouv
SVP Technology and Manufacturing, Kevin J. Ritchie, age 55, $448,080 total compensation
SVP and Manager Silicon Valley Analog, David K. (Dave) Heacock, age 51
SVP and CFO, Kevin P. March, age 54, $465,000 total compensation
SVP; President Education Technology, Melendy E. Lovett, age 54
SVP Worldwide Human Resources, Darla H. Whitaker, age 46
VP Information Technology Services and CIO, Brian Bonner
SVP and General Manager DLP (Display Technologies and Platforms) Products, Kent Novak, age 46
SVP and General Manager Embedded Processing, R. Gregory (Greg) Delagi, age 49, $430,020 total compensation
SVP and Manager Worldwide Sales and Marketing, John Szczsponik, age 51
SVP and General Manager Analog, Brian Crutcher, age 39
SVP and Worldwide Manager Power Management, Sami Kiriaki, age 51
VP and General Manager DC Solutions, Jack Olson
Corporate Communications, Kimberly (Kim) Morgan
Financial Communications, Chris Rongone
Public Affairs, Gail Chandler
Media Relations Asia, Bill Yue
Media Relations Europe the Middle East and Asia, Sabine Meinitz
Director, Daniel A. (Dan) Carp, age 63
Director, Wayne R. Sanders, age 64
Director, David R. Goode, age 70
Director, Ralph W. Babb Jr., age 63
Director, Ruth J. Simmons, age 66
Director, Pamela H. (Pam) Patsley, age 55
Director, Carrie S. Cox, age 54
Director, Stephen P. (Steve) MacMillan, age 48
Director, David L. Boren, age 70
Director, Robert E. Sanchez, age 46
Director, Christine Todd Whitman, age 65
Auditors: Ernst&YoungLLP

LOCATIONS

HQ: Texas Instruments Incorporated
12500 TI Blvd., Dallas TX 75266-0199
Phone: 972-995-3773 **Fax:** 972-927-6377
Web: www.ti.com

2012 Sales

	$ mil.	% of total
Asia/Pacific		
Japan	1,357	11

Other countries	7,808	61
Europe	1,861	14
US	1,596	12
Other regions	203	2
Total	**12,825**	**100**

PRODUCTS/OPERATIONS

2012 Sales

	$ mil.	% of total
Analog	6,998	55
Embedded processing	1,971	15
Wireless	1,357	11
Other	2,499	19
Total	**12,825**	**100**

2012 Sales by Market

	% of total
Communications	31
Computing	25
Industrial	17
Consumer	13
Automotive	11
Education	3
Total	**100**

Selected Products

Semiconductors
- Analog and mixed-signal
  - Amplifiers and comparators
  - Clocks and timers
  - Data converters
  - Power management chips
  - Radio-frequency (RF) chips
- Application-specific integrated circuits (ASICs)
- Catalog and custom wireless products
- Digital light processors (DLPs micro-mirror-based devices for video displays)
- Digital signal processors (DSPs)
- Microcontrollers
- Microprocessors
- Standard logic

Educational Technology
- Calculators (including graphing handheld and printing models)

COMPETITORS

Analog Devices
Atmel
Broadcom
Canon
CASIO COMPUTER
CSR plc
Fairchild Semiconductor
Freescale Semiconductor
Hewlett-Packard
Infineon Technologies
Intel
Intersil
Linear Technology
Marvell Technology
Maxim Integrated Products
Microchip Technology
NVIDIA
NXP Semiconductors
ON Semiconductor
QUALCOMM
Renesas Electronics
Richtek Technology Corp.
Samsung Electronics
ST-Ericsson
STMicroelectronics

HISTORICAL FINANCIALS

Company Type: Public

Income Statement

FYE: December 31

	REVENUE ($ mil.)	NET INCOME ($ mil.)	NET PROFIT MARGIN	EMPLOYEES
12/11	13,735	2,236	16.3%	34,759
12/10	13,966	3,228	23.1%	28,412
12/09	10,427	1,470	14.1%	26,584
12/08	12,501	1,920	15.4%	29,537
12/07	13,835	2,657	19.2%	30,175
Annual Growth	(0.2%)	(4.2%)	—	3.6%

2011 Year-End Financials

Debt ratio: 27.28%	No. of shares (mil.): 1,139
Return on equity: 20.42%	Dividends
Cash ($ mil.): 992	Yield: —
Current ratio: 223.72	Payout: 29.79%
Long-term debt ($ mil.): 4,211	Market value ($ mil.): 33,171

	STOCK PRICE ($) FY Close	P/E High	P/E Low	PER SHARE ($) Earnings	Dividends	Book Value
12/11	29.11	19	13	1.88	0.00	9.61
12/10	32.50	13	8	2.62	0.49	8.94
12/09	26.06	23	12	1.15	0.45	7.84
12/08	15.52	23	10	1.45	0.41	7.30
12/07	33.40	21	15	1.84	0.30	7.43
Annual Growth	(3.4%)	—	—	0.5%	—	6.6%

Textron Inc.

Officers corporate and military really take to Textron: The company's E-Z-GO golf carts enrich their golfing jaunts while its Cessna airplanes and Bell helicopters whisk them around the world its auto parts keep their cars running and its Financial subsidiary provides loans. Besides golf carts and car parts Textron's industrial segment makes power tools electrical and fiber optic assemblies and turf maintenance equipment. The Textron systems segment sells land and marine systems sensors and unmanned aerial vehicles to the Defense Department. Various US government entities account for about one-third of Textron's sales; geographically customers in the US represent around two-thirds of sales.

HISTORY

Pioneer conglomerate builder Royal Little founded Special Yarns Corporation a Boston textile business in 1923 and merged it with the Franklin Rayon Dyeing Company in 1928. The result Franklin Rayon Corporation moved its headquarters to Providence Rhode Island in 1930 and changed its name to Atlantic Rayon in 1938.

The company expanded during WWII to make parachutes and in 1944 adopted the name Textron to reflect the use of synthetics in its textiles. Between 1953 and 1960 Textron bought more than 40 businesses including Bell Helicopter before banker Rupe Thompson took over in 1960.

Thompson sold weak businesses such as Amerotron Textron's last textile business (1963) but also bought 20 companies between 1960 and 1965. By 1968 when former Wall Street attorney William Miller replaced Thompson as CEO Textron made products ranging from chain saws to watchbands. Miller sold several companies and bought Jacobsen Manufacturers (lawn care equipment 1978) before leaving Textron in 1978 to head the Federal Reserve and become treasury secretary under President Jimmy Carter.

B. F. Dolan who became president in 1980 sold Textron's least profitable businesses. The company bought Avco Corporation (aerospace and financial services 1985) and UK-based Avdel (metal fastening systems 1989).

In 1992 Textron bought Cessna Aircraft. The company sold its Lycoming Turbine Engine division in 1994 and acquired Orag Inter AG of Switzerland Europe's #1 distributor of golf and turf care equipment. In 1995-96 Textron bought Household Finance of Australia and three fastening systems companies. Also in 1996 Textron acquired Kautex Werke Reinold Hagen AG (plastic fuel tanks) and sold most of its aircraft wing division to The Carlyle Group.

In 1997 Provident (now part of Unum Group) bought Textron's 83% stake in Paul Revere Corp. (insurance). The following year Textron bought UK-based Ransomes plc (turf care machinery and Cushman brand transports) and David Brown Group plc (industrial gears and hydraulic systems). Lewis Campbell Textron's president and COO became CEO in 1998 and added chairman to his duties in 1999.

Textron sold Avco Financial Services to Associates First Capital in 1999. That year the company bought 18 companies for about $2.5 billion; the largest of these purchases included Flexalloy (vendor-managed inventory services) Omniquip International (telescopic material handling equipment) InteSys Technologies (plastic and metal assemblies) Litchfield Financial (vacation timeshares) and the industry and aircraft finance divisions of Green Tree Financial Servicing.

In 2000 Textron acquired Karl Oelschlager GmbH & Co. a German maker of stamped metal parts and in early 2001 the company acquired telecommunications test equipment maker Tempo Research. Around the same time Textron announced plans to close or consolidate operations at about 20 manufacturing sites and cut more than 3600 jobs.

Late in 2001 Textron closed more plants and cut more jobs running the total announced layoffs for the year to around 7500 (the cutbacks were spread through the end of 2002). In December 2001 the company sold its TAC-Trim automotive trim unit to Collins & Aikman in a deal worth about $1.34 billion (including about $1 billion in cash and the assumption of $100 million in debt).

Restructuring continued in 2003 and 2004 and the cost savings goal grew to a reduction of 10000 jobs and 99 facilities. In 2005 Textron announced plans to sell its Fastening Systems business; it sold Fastening Systems for $630 million in cash to Platinum Equity in 2006.

Later in 2006 Textron sold its Jacobsen commercial grounds care products unit in order to focus more on its golf and professional turf operations. Near the end of 2006 Textron purchased Overwatch Systems for about $325 million. Overwatch was a maker of communications products and intelligence analysis tools for the US Department of Defense the US Department of Homeland Security and certain friendly foreign militaries.

Late in 2007 Cessna acquired bankrupt plane maker Columbia Aircraft for about $25.4 million. Columbia makes two models of single- piston-engine aircraft –the Columbia 350 and the 400. The purchase of Columbia increased Cessna's product line at the same time that it gave Columbia access to Cessna's broad sales and service network.

Just days after the Columbia deal was completed Textron's Greenlee unit part of the industrial segment acquired Paladin Tools a maker of tools and accessories used in the telecom datacom and wiring industries. The deal complemented Greenlee's existing line of products by expanding its number of distribution channels and its customer base.

One day after the Greenlee deal Textron completed the acquisition of United Industrial Corporation for $1.1 billion. United Industrial was a maker of avionics testing equipment combat systems training simulators and perhaps most importantly –unmanned aerial vehicles (UAVs). United

Industrial's wholly owned subsidiary AAI Corporation became part of Textron Systems.

Early in 2008 Bell Helicopter acquired SkyBOOKS a company that provided information resources for regulatory compliance with the FAA. SkyBOOKS' online service tracks maintenance flight operations expenses and document archiving. The move broadened Bell's offering of integrated services for its customers.

The company's Greenlee unit was also busy with acquisitions in 2008 too with the additions of the UK-based Utilux (cable connectors and assemblies) and Telefonix a cable testing equipment maker headquartered in California. The same year Textron sold its fluid & power business unit to the UK-based Clyde Blowers Ltd. for up to $645 million in cash notes and assumed liabilities.

In 2009 Textron sold its HR Textron unit to Woodward for $365 million in cash. HR Textron previously a unit of Textron Systems made actuators and other products for aircraft armored vehicles guided weapons and turbine engines. Textron realized a gain of about $265 million on the transaction. The company also maintained liquidity in 2009 by issuing convertible and senior notes and selling shares of stock.

EXECUTIVES

EVP Administration and Chief Human Resources Officer, John D. Butler, age 64, $560,000 total compensation
President and CEO Bell Helicopter, John L. Garrison Jr.
Chairman President and CEO, Scott C. Donnelly, age 50, $860,962 total compensation
President and CEO Cessna Aircraft, Scott A. Ernest
President and CEO Textron Systems, Frederick M. (Fred) Strader
VP and Treasurer, Mary F. Lovejoy
President Industrial Segment and Greenlee, J. Scott Hall
President E-Z-GO, Kevin P. Holleran
VP Mergers Acquisitions and Tax and General Tax Counsel, John R. (Jack) Curran
VP and Deputy General Counsel, Arnold M. Friedman
SVP Washington Operations, Robert O. Rowland
VP Investor Relations, Douglas R. Wilburne
SVP and Corporate Controller, Richard L. (Dick) Yates, age 61, $458,160 total compensation
President Jacobsen, Daniel F. (Dan) Wilkinson
VP and CIO, Gary Cantrell
VP Communications, Adele Suddes
VP Human Resources and Benefits, Cathy A. Streker
President and CEO Textron Systems, Ellen Lord
CEO Textron Financial Corporation, Warren R. Lyons
VP Audit Services, Robert J. (Bob) Ayotte
EVP and CFO, Frank T. Connor, age 52, $302,885 total compensation
VP Strategy and Business Development, Paul McGartoll
President and CEO Kautex, Vicente Perez, age 44
Manager Textron Systems Canada, Neil Rutter
Director, Lloyd G. Trotter, age 66
Director, Joe T. Ford, age 74
Director, James L. Ziemer, age 62
Director, Dain M. Hancock, age 70
Director, R. Kerry Clark, age 58
Director, Ivor J. (Ike) Evans, age 69
Director, Kathleen M. Bader, age 61
Director, Paul E. Gagne, age 65
Director, Lord Charles D. Powell, age 70
Director, Lawrence K. (Larry) Fish, age 67
Director, James T. Conway, age 64
Auditors: Ernst&YoungLLP

LOCATIONS

HQ: Textron Inc.
40 Westminster Street, Providence, RI 02903
Phone: 401 421-2800 **Fax:** 401 421-2878
Web: www.textron.com

2011 Sales

	$ mil.	% of total
US	7,138	63
Europe	1,577	14
Asia & Australia	1,032	9
Latin America & Mexico	820	7
Middle East & Africa	419	4
Canada	289	3
Total	**11,275**	**100**

PRODUCTS/OPERATIONS

2011 Sales

	$ mil.	% of total
Bell	3,525	31
Cessna	2,990	26
Industrial	2,785	25
Textron Systems	1,872	17
Finance	103	1
Total	**11,275**	**100**

Selected Products

Cessna
- Business jets
- Overnight express package carrier aircraft
- Single engine piston aircraft
- Single engine turboprops

Bell
- Commercial helicopters
- Military helicopters
- Tiltrotor aircraft

Industrial
- Kautex
  - Blow-molded fuel tank systems
  - Headlamp washer systems
  - Engine camshafts
  - Plastic bottles and containers

Selective satalytic reduction systems
  - Windshield washer systems
- E-Z-GO
  - Golf carts
  - Multipurpose utility vehicles
  - Off-road utility vehicles
- Greenlee
  - Electrical connectors
  - Electrical test instruments
  - Fiber optic assemblies
  - Hand tools
  - Hydraulic power tools
  - Measurement instruments
  - Powered equipment
- Jacobsen
  - Turf-maintenance equipment
  - Specialized turf-care vehicles

Textron Systems
- Advanced marine craft
- Airborne surveillance
- Armored security vehicles
- Countersniper devices
- Ground-based surveillance
- Intelligence software
- Precision weapons
- Situational awareness software
- Simulation systems
- Training systems
- Unmanned aircraft systems

Finance (captive commercial finance for new aircraft helicopter golf and turf-care equipment)

COMPETITORS

AgustaWestland
Boeing
Bombardier
Claverham
Deere
EADS
Eaton
Embraer
GE
General Dynamics
Honda
Honeywell International
Illinois Tool Works
Ingersoll-Rand
Johnson Controls
Kaman
Lockheed Martin
Magna International
Moog
Northrop Grumman
Northstar Aerospace
Piper Aircraft
Raytheon
Rolls-Royce
Spirit AeroSystems
Sun Hydraulics
Terex
Toro Company
TRW Automotive
United Technologies

HISTORICAL FINANCIALS

Company Type: Public

Income Statement FYE: December 31

	REVENUE ($ mil.)	NET INCOME ($ mil.)	NET PROFIT MARGIN	EMPLOYEES
12/11*	11,275	242	2.1%	32,000
01/11	10,525	86	0.8%	32,000
01/10	10,500	(31)	—	32,000
01/09	14,246	486	3.4%	43,000
12/07	13,225	917	6.9%	44,000
Annual Growth	(3.9%)	(28.3%)	—	(7.7%)

*Fiscal year change

2011 Year-End Financials

Debt ratio: 36.18%
Return on equity: 8.82%
Cash ($ mil.): 871
Current ratio: 179.56
Long-term debt ($ mil.): 4,780
No. of shares (mil.): 278
Dividends
Yield: —
Payout: 10.13%
Market value ($ mil.): 5,156

	STOCK PRICE ($) FY Close	P/E High	P/E Low	PER SHARE ($) Earnings	Dividends	Book Value
12/11*	18.49	33	17	0.79	0.00	9.84
01/11	23.64	79	52	0.28	0.00	10.78
01/10	18.81	—	—	(0.12)	0.00	10.38
01/09	15.37	34	6	1.95	0.00	9.78
12/07	71.62	34	15	3.60	0.00	14.02
Annual Growth	(28.7%)	—	—	(31.6%)	—	(8.5%)

*Fiscal year change

TFS Financial Corp

TFS Financial is the holding company for Third Federal Savings and Loan a thrift with some 45 branches and loan production offices in Ohio and southern Florida. The bank offers such deposit products as checking savings and retirement accounts and CDs. It uses funds from deposits to originate a variety of consumer loans primarily residential mortgages. Third Federal also offers IRAs annuities and mutual funds as well as retirement and college savings plans. TFS subsidiary Third Capital owns stakes in commercial real estate private equity funds and other investments. Mutual holding company Third Federal Savings and Loan Association of Cleveland owns nearly three-quarters of TFS Financial.

Residential mortgages and home equity loans account for nearly all of TFS Financial's loan portfolio. The bank operates in battered housing-market areas in Florida and Ohio where it is one of the largest home mortgage lenders in the Cleveland metropolitan area. It has traditionally targeted low-income buyers seeking to buy affordable housing particularly through its erstwhile Home Today loan program.

The bank didn't categorize the Home Today loans as subprime mortgages but nevertheless tightened its underwriting standards in 2009 in the wake of the subprime mortgage crisis. It also stopped issuing high loan-to-value ratio loans in 2008 and interest-only loans in 2009. It curtailed its home equity lending activity in 2010 after entering into a memorandum of understanding with regulators regarding that portion of its portfolio.

Like the banking industry overall TFS Financial has seen elevated levels of loan defaults and foreclosures as the economy reeled. Nonetheless the company has still been able to turn a profit.

EXECUTIVES

Chairman President and CEO, Marc A. Stefanski, age 58, $1,080,000 total compensation
Director; Director Human Resources Public Relations Training Security and Administrative Services, Marianne V. Piterans, age 57, $392,568 total compensation
CFO, David S. (Dave) Huffman, age 60, $358,507 total compensation
Director Public Relations, Monica M. Martines
CIO, Ralph M. Betters, age 60, $372,265 total compensation
COO Third Federal Savings and Loan, John P. Ringenbach, age 62, $463,191 total compensation
Secretary and Director, Bernard S. Kobak, age 83
COO and Chief Accounting Officer, Paul J. Huml, age 52
Public Relations Manager, Jennifer Rosa
Director; Director Human Resources Public Relations Training Security and Administrative Services, Marianne V. Piterans, age 57
Director, Robert B. (Yank) Heisler Jr., age 63
Director, Terrence R. (Terry) Ozan
Director, William C. Mulligan, age 58
Director, Thomas J. Baird, age 56
Director, John J. Fitzpatrick, age 71
Director, Paul W. Stefanik, age 87
Secretary and Director, Bernard S. Kobak, age 83
Director, Robert A. Fiala, age 58
Director, Martin J. Cohen, age 58
Director, Anthony J. Asher, age 73
Auditors: Deloitte&ToucheLLP

LOCATIONS

HQ: TFS Financial Corporation
7007 Broadway Ave., Cleveland OH 44105
Phone: 216-441-6000 **Fax:** 216-441-7030
Web: www.thirdfederal.com

PRODUCTS/OPERATIONS

2010 Sales

	$ mil.	% of total
$ mil % of total		
Interest		
Loans including fees	415	84
Investment securities	19	4
Other	2	1
Noninterest		
Net gain on sale of loans	25	5
Net fees & service charges	20	4
Bank-owned life insurance contracts	6	1
Other	6	1
Total	**496**	**100**

COMPETITORS

Bank of America
JPMorgan Chase
Citigroup
Fifth Third
FirstMerit
Huntington Bancshares
KeyCorp
PNC Financial
U.S. Bancorp
Wells Fargo

HISTORICAL FINANCIALS

Company Type: Public

Income Statement FYE: September 30

	ASSETS ($ mil.)	NET INCOME ($ mil.)	INCOME AS % OF ASSETS	EMPLOYEES
09/12	11,518	11	0.1%	0
09/11	10,892	9	0.1%	0
09/10	11,076	11	0.1%	0
09/09	10,598	14	0.1%	0
09/08	10,786	54	0.5%	0
Annual Growth	1.7%	(32.3%)	—	—

2012 Year-End Financials

Debt ratio: 4.24%
Return on equity: 0.64%
Cash ($ mil.): 308
Current ratio: —
Long-term debt ($ mil.): 488
No. of shares (mil.): 309
Dividends
Yield: —
Payout: —
Market value ($ mil.): 2,803

	STOCK PRICE ($) FY Close	P/E High/Low	PER SHARE ($) Earnings	Dividends	Book Value
09/12	9.07	249201	0.04	0.00	5.85
09/11	8.13	363260	0.03	0.00	5.74
09/10	9.19	359225	0.04	0.21	5.68
09/09	11.90	272206	0.05	0.26	5.66
09/08	12.52	79 56	0.17	0.15	5.83
Annual Growth	(7.7%)	— —	(30.4%)	—	0.1%

The Bancorp, Inc.

The Bancorp is –what else? –the holding company for The Bancorp Bank which provides financial services in the virtual world. On its home turf of the Philadelphia and Wilmington Delaware metropolitan areas The Bancorp Bank offers deposit lending and related services targeting wealthy individuals and small to midsized businesses it believes are underserved by larger banks in the market. Nationally The Bancorp provides private-label online banking services for some 300 affinity groups issues prepaid debit cards processes merchant credit card transactions and acts as a custodian for health savings accounts (HSAs).

As an online bank the company has no branches; however it does operate three loan production offices in the Philadelphia area. The company also operates vehicle fleet leasing businesses Jefferson Leasing and Mears Motor Leasing which are active in about 40 states. Commercial and constructin loans and commercial mortgages dominate The Bancorp's loan portfolio.

The company's strategies for growth include generating deposits through its prepaid card community banking merchant processing and wealth management operations the funds of which it will expand its lending operations. It also hopes to market its offerings to customers of its affinity groups and generally drive up business in its home region. The Bancorp has also explored the possibility of establishing a new savings bank in southern New Jersey adjacent to its primary market area; the move would add a thrift charter to help accelerate the bank's nationwide expansion.

The Bancorp's earnings have been growing since the company lost money in 2008. Revenues in 2011 grew 15% to $119 million while profits grew 70% to $8.9 million. The increases were buoyed by higher prepaid card fees resulting from higher transaction volumes. Additionally prepaid card wealth management health care and merchant processing deposits all grew that year. However the company increased its provision for loan losses in both 2010 and 2011 allowing for challenges in the economic climate.

EXECUTIVES

CEO and Director; Chairman and CEO The Bancorp Bank, Betsy Zubrow Cohen, age 71, $425,000 total compensation
EVP Strategy CFO and Secretary, Paul Frenkiel, age 60
President COO and Director The Bancorp Inc. and The Bancorp Bank, Frank M. Mastrangelo, age 44, $270,096 total compensation
EVP and Chief Credit Officer The Bancorp Inc. and The Bancorp Bank, Donald F. (Don) McGraw Jr., age 55
SVP and Chief Accounting Officer, Martin F. (Marty) Egan, age 44, $168,723 total compensation
EVP and Chief Lending Officer The Bancorp Inc. and The Bancorp Bank, Scott R. Megargee, age 60, $202,541 total compensation
EVP Commercial Loans The Bancorp Inc. and The Bancorp Bank, Arthur M. Birenbaum, age 55, $152,884 total compensation
EVP and CIO The Bancorp Bank, Peter (Pete) Chiccino
SVP Affinity Banking, Jill E. Kelly
Chairman; Vice Chairman The Bancorp Bank, Daniel Gideon Cohen, age 42, $196,154 total compensation
SVP Loan Administration, Sandra C. Reel
SVP Construction Lending, Maxine Prior
SVP Merchant Acquiring, Terrence Crowley
SVP Construction Lending, Mark A. Conners
SVP and Chief Risk Officer The Bancorp Bank, James D. Hilty
Director, William H. Lamb, age 72
Director, Michael J. Bradley, age 67
CEO and Director; Chairman and CEO The Bancorp Bank, Betsy Zubrow Cohen, age 71
Director, James Joseph McEntee III, age 54
Director, Matthew Cohn, age 42
President COO and Director The Bancorp Inc. and The Bancorp Bank, Frank M. Mastrangelo, age 44
Director, Walter T. Beach, age 45
Director, Leon A. Huff, age 70
Director, Joan Specter, age 78
Director, Linda Schaeffer, age 48
Auditors: GrantThorntonLLP

LOCATIONS

HQ: The Bancorp, Inc.
409 Silverside Road, Wilmington, DE 19809
Phone: 302 385-5000
Web: www.thebancorp.com

PRODUCTS/OPERATIONS

2011 Sales

	$ mil.	% of total
Interest		
Loans including fees	74	63
Securities	12	10
Other	1	1
Noninterest		

Prepaid fees	18	16
Service fees on deposit accounts	2	2
Other	9	8
Adjustments	(0.1)	-
Total	**119**	**100**

COMPETITORS

E*TRADE Bank
ING DIRECT USA
M&T Bank
PNC Financial
RBS Citizens Financial Group
Republic First Bank
Royal Bancshares
Sovereign Bank
Sun Bancorp (NJ)
TD Bank USA
WSFS Financial

HISTORICAL FINANCIALS

Company Type: Public

Income Statement FYE: December 31

	ASSETS ($ mil.)	NET INCOME ($ mil.)	INCOME AS % OF ASSETS	EMPLOYEES
12/11	3,010	8	0.3%	428
12/10	2,395	5	0.2%	373
12/09	2,043	4	0.2%	367
12/08	1,792	(42)	—	306
12/07	1,568	14	0.9%	306
Annual Growth	17.7%	(11.2%)	—	8.8%

2011 Year-End Financials

Debt ratio: 0.45%
Return on equity: 3.29%
Cash ($ mil.): 749
Current ratio: —
Long-term debt ($ mil.): 13
No. of shares (mil.): 33
Dividends
Yield: —
Payout: —
Market value ($ mil.): 239

	STOCK PRICE ($) FY Close	P/E High	P/E Low	PER SHARE ($) Earnings	Dividends	Book Value
12/11	7.23	38	23	0.28	0.00	8.20
12/10	10.17	—	—	(0.04)	0.00	7.60
12/09	6.86	397	129	0.02	0.00	9.37
12/08	3.75	—	—	(2.93)	0.00	12.39
12/07	13.46	29	12	0.98	0.00	12.11
Annual Growth	(14.4%)	—	—	(26.9%)	—	(9.3%)

The Gap, Inc.

LOCATIONS

HQ: The Gap, Inc.
Two Folsom Street, San Francisco, CA 94105
Phone: 415 427-0100
Web: www.gapinc.com

HISTORICAL FINANCIALS

Company Type:

Income Statement FYE: January 28

	REVENUE ($ mil.)	NET INCOME ($ mil.)	NET PROFIT MARGIN	EMPLOYEES
01/12	14,549	833	5.7%	132,000
01/11	14,664	1,204	8.2%	134,000
01/10	14,197	1,102	7.8%	135,000
01/09*	14,526	967	6.7%	134,000
02/08	15,763	833	5.3%	150,000
Annual Growth	(2.0%)	(0.0%)	—	(3.1%)

*Fiscal year change

2012 Year-End Financials

Debt ratio: 22.43%
Return on equity: 30.24%
Cash ($ mil.): 1,885
Current ratio: 202.49
Long-term debt ($ mil.): 1,606
No. of shares (mil.): 485
Dividends
Yield: —
Payout: 28.85%
Market value ($ mil.): 9,181

	STOCK PRICE ($) FY Close	P/E High	P/E Low	PER SHARE ($) Earnings	Dividends	Book Value
01/12	18.93	15	10	1.56	0.00	5.68
01/11	19.20	14	9	1.88	0.00	6.94
01/10	19.08	15	6	1.58	0.00	7.24
01/09*	11.28	16	7	1.34	0.00	6.32
02/08	19.34	21	15	1.05	0.00	5.82
Annual Growth	(0.5%)	—	—	10.4%	—	(0.6%)

*Fiscal year change

Thermo Fisher Scientific Inc

Whether for research analysis discovery or diagnostics Thermo Fisher Scientific gets the laboratory ready to assist mankind. Created through the merger between Thermo Electron and Fisher Scientific in 2006 Thermo Fisher makes and distributes analytical instruments equipment and laboratory supplies –from chromatographs to Erlenmeyer flasks. Thermo Fisher serves hundreds of thousands of customers worldwide in its key markets of health care and diagnostics biotech and pharmaceutical academic and government and industrial and applied settings including environmental quality and process control. Thermo Fisher gets about half of its sales in the US; no other country accounts for more than 6% of sales.

HISTORY

Predating the acquiring company Thermo Electron in 1902 20-year-old Chester Fisher bought the stockroom of Pittsburgh Testing Laboratories (established 1884) and formed Scientific Materials Co. The company's earliest products supplied from Europe included simple tools such as microscopes balances and calorimeters. It published its first catalog in 1904.

When the outbreak of WWI disrupted supplies from Europe Scientific Materials established its own R&D and manufacturing facilities. It acquired Montreal-based Scientific Supplies in 1925 and the following year changed its name to Fisher Scientific Company. By 1935 Fisher had doubled its size adding glass-blowing operations and an instrument shop.

During the German occupation of Greece in WWII George Hatsopoulos part of a well-to-do family packed with politicians and engineering professors made radios for the Greek resistance. After the war he came to the US and became a professor of mechanical engineering at MIT. With a $50000 loan Hatsopoulos founded Thermo Electron in 1956 to identify emerging technology needs and create solutions for them.

That year he built a machine that would turn heat directly into electrons. This thermionic converter though itself never commercialized formed the basis of many of the company's successful products including a battery-operated heart pump and a process for incinerating toxic material in polluted soils.

In its early years the company was funded by research grants and metal-fabrication contracts with other companies. In 1961 defense giant Martin Marietta (now part of Lockheed Martin) attracted by thermionics attempted to acquire the company but Hatsopoulos rejected the offer. Thermo Electron went public in 1967 and in the early 1970s introduced efficient industrial furnaces for the paper and metals markets.

Chester Fisher died in 1965 –the same year Fisher Scientific went public –leaving Fisher to sons Aiken Benjamin and James. Fisher acquired pipette maker Pfeiffer Glass (1966) scientific teaching equipment maker Stansi Scientific (1967) optical instruments maker Jerrell-Ash Company (1968) and Hi-Pure Chemicals (1974).

Aiken retired as chairman in 1975 and was replaced by Benjamin. That year former Pfeiffer Glass president Edward Perkins was appointed president and CEO –the first non-family member to hold this position. In 1977 Fisher bought the diagnostics division of American Cyanamid's Lederle Laboratories.

Thermo Electron began a string of spinoffs with the 1983 IPO of medical subsidiary Thermedics. Next to go were environmental services firm Thermo Process Systems and Thermo Instrument Systems in 1986 followed by Thermo Power in 1987 Thermo Cardiosystems in 1989 Thermo Voltek in 1990 ThermoTrex in 1991 paper-recycling equipment maker Thermo Fibertek in 1992 soil recycler Thermo Remediation (later ThermoRetec) in 1993 and ThermoLase a maker of lasers for hair removal in 1994.

Besides developing its own business lines Thermo Electron expanded through several acquisitions in the 1990s. The company bought the analytical instrument and process-control businesses of Baker Hughes (1994) the scientific-instruments division of Fisons (now part of Sanofi 1995) and respiratory-care equipment maker Sensormedics (1996).

In 1992 Fisher bought Hamilton Scientific the top US maker of laboratory workstations as well as a majority interest in Kuhn + Bayer a German supplier of scientific equipment. In 1995 Fisher acquired Curtin Matheson Scientific a leading US provider of diagnostic instruments. That year the company also boosted its global presence by acquiring Fisons plc a UK-based laboratory products supplier.

Thermo Electron spun off its Thermo Optek (optical instruments) Thermo Sentron (precision weighing and inspection equipment) ThermoQuest (mass spectrometers) and Thermo BioAnalysis (biochemistry and information management systems) units in 1996. Poor market conditions – stemming in part from the Asian financial crisis – led the company in 1998 to announce plans to cut the number of its majority-owned public companies from 23 to 12.

Former American Stock Exchange (now NYSE Amex) CEO Richard Syron replaced Hatsopoulos as CEO in 1999. The next year Syron announced a reorganization in which the Thermo Electron family would be reduced to three companies: Thermo Electron would concentrate on measurement and detection instruments while Thermo Fibertek (renamed Kadant in 2001) and a medical products company (later dubbed Viasys Healthcare) would be spun off to shareholders. As part of the plan in 2000 Thermo Electron began buying out minority shareholders in its publicly traded subsidiaries and arranging the sale of non-core businesses.

In 2001 Thermo Electron sold its power generation assets to independent power producer AES. Later that year the company completed its spinoff of both Kadant and Viasys Healthcare. The following year the company completed its reacquisition of laser maker Spectra-Physics (sold in 2004 to Newport). Also in 2002 Syron was named executive chairman and replaced as CEO by president and COO Marijn Dekkers. The next year Syron resigned as chairman and was replaced by board member Jim Manzi.

In 2003 Thermo Electron boosted its laboratory product line through the purchase of France-based laboratory equipment supplier Jouan SA for $137 million. Later the same year Thermo Electron acquired laboratory certification and consulting services firm Laboratory Management Systems for an undisclosed amount.

In 2003 Fisher acquired Sweden-based Perbio Science (consumable tools for protein-related research) for about $700 million. The following year Fisher continued its push into the life sciences market with two acquisitions: UK-based Oxoid (tools used to test for bacterial contamination) for $330 million and privately held Dharmacon (synthesized RNA used in genetic research) for $80 million.

In 2004 Thermo Electron added to its health care services business with the acquisition of asset management service firm US Counseling Services (USCS) for about $75 million. The same year Thermo Electron sold its Optical Technologies segment (including laser division Spectra-Physics) to Newport for about $300 million.

Also in 2004 Fisher acquired Apogent Technologies a maker of laboratory and life sciences equipment for health care and scientific research applications for nearly $4 billion.

Continuing its buying spree Thermo Electron acquired InnaPhase Corp. a supplier of laboratory information management systems (LIMS) to the pharmaceutical and biotechnology markets for about $65 million. In 2005 the company acquired SPX's Kendro Laboratory Products business for approximately $834 million and NITON a maker of portable X-ray analyzers for about $40 million. It sold its Thermo Biostar business (point-of-care and rapid diagnostics) to Inverness Medical Innovations (now Alere Inc.) for about $53 million in cash.

In 2006 Thermo Electron merged with Fisher Scientific International in a stock-swap transaction valued at nearly $11 billion. (Only a month after the companies completed their merger Thermo Fisher made its first acquisition: Cohesive Technologies a manufacturer of advanced sample extraction and liquid chromatography products.) As separate entities Thermo and Fisher were among the biggest companies in the scientific and technical instruments field. Fisher was twice the size of Thermo in terms of sales but combining the two created more muscle to compete against big names such as Agilent Technologies and Becton Dickinson. The merger worked because Thermo Electron was for the most part a manufacturer of scientific instruments while Fisher Scientific was largely a distributor of laboratory equipment and supplies. There was little overlap between their respective product lines and their sales forces were familiar with each other and with many of the same customers.

In 2007 Thermo Fisher formed a joint venture with Quintiles Transnational called Cenduit to provide interactive response technology (IRT) services during the clinical trial phase of drug development. Cenduit combined the Fisher Clinical Services IRT with the IRT operations of Quintiles. That same year the company acquired the test and measurement instrument sales business of Davis Inotek Instruments. The business rebranded as Davis Instruments and joined Thermo Fisher's Cole-Parmer customer channel to sell technical instruments equipment and supplies to industrial pharmaceutical academic and government agencies worldwide. (Davis Inotek kept its instrument calibration services business renamed as Davis Calibration.)

In 2008 Thermo Fisher strengthened its position in the ribonucleic acid (RNA) product market through the acquisition of Alabama-based Open Biosystems a provider of RNA interference and protein detection products. In addition the company bought FIBERLite Centrifuge a maker of carbon fiber centrifuge rotors and Raymond A. Lamb a maker of histology and anatomical pathology products.

The following year Thermo Fisher bought B.R.A.H.M.S. AG for about E330 million (approximately $470 million). B.R.A.H.M.S. makes diagnostic tests and instruments and ranks as Germany's third largest biotech business. In another 2009 acquisition Thermo Fisher bought the scientific and medical division (Biolab) of Australian distributor Alesco Corporation.

In 2009 CEO and president Marijn Dekkers resigned from the company to take the top job at Bayer AG. He was replaced by COO Marc Casper.

EXECUTIVES

VP Investor Relations, Kenneth J. Apicerno
SVP General Counsel and Secretary, Seth H. Hoogasian, age 57, $455,000 total compensation
VP and Chief Accounting Officer, Peter E. Hornstra, age 52
SVP and CFO, Peter M. Wilver, age 52, $595,758 total compensation
Chairman, Jim P. Manzi, age 60
President CEO and Director, Marc N. Casper, age 44, $790,220 total compensation
SVP; President Analytical Instruments, Gregory J. (Greg) Herrema, age 46, $456,992 total compensation
VP and CIO, Ina B. Kamenz
EVP and President Analytical Technologies, Alan J. Malus, age 52, $544,078 total compensation
VP Corporate Communications, Karen A. Kirkwood
SVP Global Business Services, Alexander G. Stachtiaris, age 48
VP Tax and Treasurer, Anthony H. Smith
SVP; President Customer Channels, Edward A. Pesicka, age 44, $451,754 total compensation
VP Financial Operations, Stephen Williamson
SVP Human Resources, Elizabeth S. Bolgiano
SVP; President Specialty Diagnostics, Kenneth Berger
SVP; President Laboratory Products, Tom Loewald, age 48
SVP; President Specialty Diagnostics, Andrew J. (Andy) Thomson, age 47
Director, Scott M. Sperling, age 54
Director, Judy C. Lewent, age 63
Director, Peter J. Manning, age 73
Director, Nelson J. Chai, age 47
Director, Thomas J. (Tom) Lynch, age 57
Director, Michael E. (Mike) Porter, age 64
President CEO and Director, Marc N. Casper, age 44
Director, Elaine S. Ullian, age 64
Director, William G. (Bill) Parrett, age 66
Director, C. Martin Harris, age 55
Director, Tyler Jacks, age 51
Director, Lars R. Sorensen
Auditors: PricewaterhouseCoopersLLP

LOCATIONS

HQ: Thermo Fisher Scientific Inc.
81 Wyman St., Waltham MA 02454-9046
Phone: 781-622-1000 **Fax:** 781-622-1207
Web: www.thermofisher.com

2011 Sales

	$ mil.	% of total
US	6,175	52
Germany	698	6
China	560	5
UK	472	4
Other countries	3,819	33
Total	**11,725**	**100**

PRODUCTS/OPERATIONS

2011 Sales

	$ mil.	% of total
Laboratory Products & Services	5,935	49
Analytical Technologies	3,845	31
Specialty Diagnostics	2,465	20
Adjustments	(520.7)	
Total	**11,725**	**100**

2011 Sales

	$ mil.	% of total
Products	10,052	86
Services	1,673	14
Total	**11,725**	**100**

Selected Acquisitions

2012
Doe & Ingalls Management ($175 million; specialty production chemicals and related supply chain services to the life sciences and advanced technology industries)

2011
Phadia ($3.5 billion; Sweden; diagnostic tests for allergies and autoimmune disorders)
Dionex ($2.1 billion; ion and liquid chromatography instruments)
TREK Diagnostic Systems (microbiological testing products)

2010
Ahura Scientific ($145 million; Massachusetts; analytical instruments for human pharmaceutical safety and security applications)
Fermentas International ($260 million; Canada; enzymes reagents and kits for molecular and cellular biology research)
Lomb Scientific (Australia; distributor of laboratory chemicals instruments and consumables to research and analytical laboratories hospitals and universities)
Finnzymes (Finland; reagents instruments consumables and kits)
NovaWave Technologies (chemical sensors for environmental monitoring industrial and safety applications)

COMPETITORS

Abbott Labs
Agilent Technologies
Beckman Coulter
Becton Dickinson
Bio-Rad Labs
Bruker
Corning
Danaher
Emerson Electric
Halma
Harvard Bioscience
Hitachi
Honeywell International
IDEXX Labs
Johnson & Johnson
Life Technologies Corporation
Mettler-Toledo
Newport Corp.
Nordion
PerkinElmer
QIAGEN
Roche Diagnostics
Roper Industries
Shimadzu
Sigma-Aldrich
Tektronix
VWR International
Waters Corp.
Yokogawa Electric

HISTORICAL FINANCIALS

Company Type: Public

Income Statement FYE: December 31

	REVENUE ($ mil.)	NET INCOME ($ mil.)	NET PROFIT MARGIN	EMPLOYEES
12/11	11,725	1,329	11.3%	39,300
12/10	10,788	1,035	9.6%	37,200
12/09	10,109	850	8.4%	35,400
12/08	10,498	994	9.5%	34,500
12/07	9,746	761	7.8%	33,000
Annual Growth	4.7%	15.0%	—	4.5%

2011 Year-End Financials

Debt ratio: 26.19%
Return on equity: 8.84%
Cash ($ mil.): 1,016
Current ratio: 154.89
Long-term debt ($ mil.): 5,755
No. of shares (mil.): 371
Dividends
Yield: —
Payout: —
Market value ($ mil.): 16,701

	STOCK PRICE ($) FY Close	P/E High/Low		PER SHARE ($) Earnings	Dividends	Book Value
12/11	44.97	19	12	3.46	0.00	40.49
12/10	55.36	22	16	2.53	0.00	39.25
12/09	47.69	24	16	2.01	0.00	37.70
12/08	34.07	26	12	2.29	0.00	35.71
12/07	57.68	33	24	1.72	0.00	34.89
Annual Growth	(6.0%)	—	—	19.1%	—	3.8%

Time Warner Cable Inc

Time Warner Cable (TWC) makes coaxial quiver. The company is the #2 US cable company after Comcast with operations in 28 states. Its core service areas are located in New York Ohio Texas the Carolinas and southern California. TWC serves mostly residential customers more than 12.5 million of which are video subscribers about 10.5 million high-speed data customers primarily through ISP brand Road Runner and about 4.8 million use its VoIP digital phone service in conjunction with Sprint Nextel. TWC also provides mobile broadband service through a wholesale deal with Clearwire and it operates local news broadcasting stations in New York Texas and North Carolina as well as regional sports networks.

Financial Analysis

TWC's core residential video subscriber base continued to shrink in 2011 dropping 3%. Also eating into its residential revenue was a nearly 5% drop in premium channel subscriptions and a 7% fall in pay-per-view purchases. TWC's video revenue eked out a nominal increase lifted by cable package price increases and customer upgrades to higher service tiers moved the average monthly revenues per subscriber up by 4%. Also growing DVR service sales (up about 10%) and equipment rental and installation (up nearly 6%) kicked in to keep residential video revenue from dipping. High-speed data services helped pick up the slack with that customer base growing more than 5% for the year with revenues up about 10% helping spur TWC's more than 4% overall revenue growth.

Mergers and Acquisitions

Acquisitions have played their part in keeping TWC in the mix. In 2011 it paid about $260 million in cash for some of Missouri-based NewWave Communications' cable business comprising service areas in Kentucky and western Tennessee. The deal expanded TWC's residential subscriber base by 70000 basic video accounts 42000 broadband customers and 26000 phone accounts. The following year TWC grabbed a hefty three-quarters of a million subscribers with the $3 billion purchase of Insight Communications which provides high-speed data video and voice services to more than 760000 subscribers in Indiana Kentucky and Ohio. That customer base included a welcome 670000 video subscribers helping it back to the 12 million-plus mark for that metric and generating a more than 2% increase over its video subscriber total from 2010.

With the Insight acquisition TWC's total subscriber base climbed to about 15.3 million with about 60% using at least two of its services and more than a quarter subscribed to all three. As its video subscriber base comes under increasingly intense pressure from services such as Netflix and Hulu TWC continues to rely on its high-speed data services to keep its top line growing.

That reality has led TWC to take steps to be more appealing to commercial clients which currently only number in the high triple digits for all services combined. The company increasingly markets digital phone service to small- and medium-sized businesses in many of its service areas and TWC is also looking to boost sales of its broadband Internet and advertising services for businesses. Bundling its services into packages that encourage customers to upgrade or add services is a key component of its strategy for growth.

To bolster its growing enterprise services business TWC paid more than $260 million in 2011 for NaviSite a business network application and data hosting services provider. NaviSite operates 10 data centers in the US and the UK. The company's other enterprise services include commercial networking and transport for clients with a need for high-capacity links between offices within a city or between cities.

TWC is also working toward an expanded wireless service through an ownership stake (3.4%) in and partnership with wireless broadband provider Clearwire. The company is counting on its more than half billion-dollar investment to yield improved mobile access for customers in some areas over the Clearwire network which was developed with Sprint Nextel. Conversely SpectrumCo - a joint venture between TWC Comcast and Bright House Networks - agreed in 2011 to sell its advanced wireless spectrum licenses to Verizon Wireless. TWC's portion of the proceeds will be about $1.1 billion. The agreement gives TWC more avenues into the wireless business as it includes the option to sell Verizon wireless services and then after four years obtain the services wholesale and offer them under a TWC brand.

Ownership

Former parent Time Warner which owned about 84% of TWC spun off the cable division to its shareholders in 2009 as part of a restructuring effort intended to boost Time Warner's overall performance.

EXECUTIVES

EVP and Chief Communications Officer, Ellen M. East, age 49
SVP and General Manager TWC Sports Regional Networks, Mark Shuken
SVP Investor Relations, Thomas B. (Tom) Robey
President and COO, Robert D. (Rob) Marcus, age 46, $800,000 total compensation
Chairman and CEO, Glenn A. Britt, age 63, $1,000,000 total compensation
EVP General Counsel and Secretary, Marc Lawrence-Apfelbaum, age 56, $550,000 total compensation
EVP; President Time Warner Cable Ventures, Carl U. J. Rossetti, age 63, $500,000 total compensation
EVP Operations West Region, William R. Goetz Jr.
EVP Human Resources, Tomas G. (Tom) Mathews, age 51
EVP and CTO, Michael L. (Mike) LaJoie, age 57, $525,000 total compensation
EVP and CFO, Irene M. Esteves, age 53
EVP Operations Midwest Region, Terry O'Connell
EVP Architecture Development and Engineering, Michael (Mike) Hayashi
EVP and Chief Programming Officer, Melinda C. Witmer, age 50
EVP Operations East Region, Carol A. Hevey
EVP and Chief Strategy Officer, Peter C. Stern, age 40
President TWC Sports, David Rone
VP Public Relations, Alexander (Alex) Dudley
EVP; President Time Warner Cable Media, Joan H. Gillman
EVP Business Services, Gerald D. (Gerry) Campbell
EVP National Network Operations, James Ludington
EVP Technology Policy and Product Management, Kevin Leddy
EVP and Chief Government Affairs Officer, Gail G. MacKinnon, age 49
VP External Affairs and Policy, Fernando LaGuarda
SVP Web Services and Technology, Matthew (Matt) Zelesko
VP Government Relations, Howard (Howie) Hodges
Senior Director Investor Relations, Laraine Mancini
Manager Investor Relations, Tara Atwood
SVP TWC Sports, Dan Finnerty
SVP Mobile Services, Michael Roudi
EVP and Chief Marketing Officer Residential Services, Jeffrey A. (Jeff) Hirsch, age 40
Director, James E. (Jim) Copeland Jr., age 67
Director, Donna A. James, age 54
Director, Don Logan, age 67
Director, Wayne H. Pace, age 65
Director, David C. Chang, age 70
Director, Thomas H. (Tom) Castro, age 57
Director, Peter R. Haje, age 77
Director, Edward D. (Ed) Shirley, age 55
Director, John E. Sununu, age 47
Auditors: Ernst&YoungLLP

LOCATIONS

HQ: Time Warner Cable Inc.
60 Columbus Circle, New York NY 10023
Phone: 212-364-8200 **Fax:** 203-328-0604
Web: www.timewarnercable.com

PRODUCTS/OPERATIONS

2011 Sales

	$ mil.	% of total
Residential		
Video	10,589	54
High-speed data	4,476	23
Voice	1,979	10
Other	49	-
Business services		
High-speed data	727	4
Video	286	1
Voice	197	1
Wholesale transport	154	1
Other	105	1
Advertising	880	4
Other	233	1
Total	**19,675**	**100**

COMPETITORS

Apple Inc.
AT&T
Cablevision Systems
Charter Communications
Cincinnati Bell
Clearwire
Comcast
Cox Communications
DIRECTV
DISH Network
Frontier Communications
Grande Communications
Hulu
Insight Communications
Level 3 Communications
Netflix
RCN Corporation
ReaLLinx
Skype
Sprint Nextel
Suddenlink Communications
T-Mobile USA
Verizon
Vonage
YouTube

HISTORICAL FINANCIALS

Company Type: Public

Income Statement

FYE: December 31

	REVENUE ($ mil.)	NET INCOME ($ mil.)	NET PROFIT MARGIN	EMPLOYEES
12/11	19,675	1,665	8.5%	48,500
12/10	18,868	1,308	6.9%	47,500
12/09	17,868	1,070	6.0%	47,000
12/08	17,200	(7,344)	—	46,600
12/07	15,955	1,123	7.0%	45,600
Annual Growth	5.4%	10.3%	—	1.6%

2011 Year-End Financials

Debt ratio: 54.77%
Return on equity: 22.11%
Cash ($ mil.): 5,177
Current ratio: 119.14
Long-term debt ($ mil.): 24,320
No. of shares (mil.): 315
Dividends
Yield: —
Payout: 38.63%
Market value ($ mil.): 20,025

	STOCK PRICE ($) FY Close	P/E High/Low		PER SHARE ($) Earnings	Dividends	Book Value
12/11	63.57	16	11	4.97	0.00	23.90
12/10	66.03	18	11	3.64	1.60	26.44
12/09	41.39	14	2	3.05	0.00	24.64
12/08	21.45	—	—	(22.56)	0.00	52.70
12/07	27.60	12	7	3.45	0.00	75.86
Annual Growth	23.2%	—	—	9.6%	—	(25.1%)

Time Warner Inc

Even among media titans this company is a giant. Time Warner is the world's third-largest media conglomerate behind Walt Disney and News Corporation with operations spanning television film and publishing. Through subsidiary Turner Broadcasting the company runs a portfolio of popular cable TV networks including CNN TBS and TNT. Time Warner also operates pay-TV channels HBO and Cinemax. Its Warner Bros. Entertainment meanwhile includes films studios (Warner Bros. Pictures New Line Cinema) TV production units (Warner Bros. Television Group) and comic book publisher DC Entertainment. In the magazine world venerable Time Inc. is the top publisher of consumer titles including People Time and Fortune.

HISTORY

Though formed in 2001 AOL Time Warner was the result of decades of advancement in the media industry. An elder statesman compared to relative newcomer America Online Time Warner's roots extend back to 1922 –the year that Henry Luce and Briton Hadden founded publisher Time Inc. and brothers Harry Abe Jack and Sam Warner established the origins of Warner Bros. which later became Warner Communications.

America Online's ancestry stretches back to the early 1980s when Stephen Case joined the management of a company called Control Video. Later renamed Quantum Computer Services the company created the online service that would become America Online in 1985. Quantum Computer Services changed its name to America Online in 1991. It went public the next year.

As America Online was germinating Time Inc. and Warner Communications were eyeing each other. The two companies merged in 1990 to form Time Warner. Gerald Levin was appointed CEO in 1992. To shave off debt Time Warner grouped several of its properties into Time Warner Entertainment in 1992 in which U S West (which later became MediaOne Group) bought a 25% interest.

Time Warner's 1996 acquisition of Ted Turner's Turner Broadcasting System further elevated Time Warner's profile on the media stage. For America Online 1996 marked the first year the company began charging its subscribers a flat rate vastly increasing the amount of time they spent online.

America Online grew through acquisitions of CompuServe in 1998 and Netscape Communications in 1999. Meanwhile Time Warner had created Time Warner Telecom and taken it public. After AT&T's announcement that it would acquire MediaOne MediaOne gave up its 50% management control of Time Warner Entertainment but retained its 25% ownership interest. AT&T's acquisition of MediaOne was completed in 2000 thus giving AT&T 25% of Time Warner Entertainment. (AT&T later boosted its stake to 27%.)

America Online announced that it would acquire Time Warner in early 2000. To please European regulators Time Warner subsequently abandoned its plans to combine the Warner Music Group with EMI Group's music operations. After a lengthy review by regulatory bodies America Online acquired Time Warner for $106 billion and formed AOL Time Warner in 2001. Case became chairman and Levin was appointed CEO. The newly formed company soon began streamlining cutting more than 2400 jobs in the process. (It cut another 1700 jobs at America Online later that year.) Also that year America Online invested about $100 million in Amazon.com.

Levin retired from the company in 2002 and was replaced by co-COO Richard Parsons. The following year AOL Time Warner finally succeeded in buying Comcast's stake in Time Warner Entertainment (Comcast gained its share of TWE when it bought the cable assets of AT&T in 2002). The following year Case and Turner both resigned their executive positions with the company but remained on the board of directors. (Case left the board in 2005.) And in a move to distance itself from the struggling online unit the company dropped AOL from its moniker and returned to being known as Time Warner Inc.

Time Warner started off 2004 by ridding itself of Warner Music Group which it sold for $2.6 billion to a group led by former Seagram executive Edgar Bronfman Jr. and investment firm Thomas H. Lee Partners. It also sold the NBA's Atlanta Hawks and the NHL's Atlanta Thrashers for $250 million to a private investment group called Atlanta Spirit.

The company's flagship Internet service officially shortened its name to simply AOL in early 2006. Also that year Time Warner sold its book publishing unit Time Warner Book Group to French media firm Lagardere. Time Warner Cable joined with Comcast to acquire Adelphia Communications for $17.6 billion in cash and stock; as part of the deal Adelphia shareholders sold part of their newly acquired stake in TWC through an IPO in 2007. Later that year Time Warner sold its Atlanta Braves baseball team (once owned by former vice chairman Ted Turner) to Liberty Media in a deal that valued the team at $460 million.

Parsons retired as CEO at the beginning of 2008 and was replaced by Jeffrey Bewkes who previously oversaw the company's entertainment divisions. Bewkes replaced Parsons as Time Warner chairman as well at the end of that year.

Never able to achieve significant synergies between the online media and traditional film and TV content arms despite several restructuring attempts Time Warner was burdened with debt and suffering losses. This ultimately led the company to spin off AOL as a separate publicly traded company in 2009. The separation valued AOL at less than $3 billion far less than the $124 billion valuation of the original AOL-Time Warner merger. In another high-profile disposal during 2009 Time Warner spun off its remaining stake in Time Warner Cable.

In 2011 the company's Filmed Entertainment unit released the final film in the immensely popular Harry Potter series. Harry Potter and the Deathly Hallows: Part 2 was the year's top film in terms of ticket sales pulling in a colossal $1.3 billion in 2011.

EXECUTIVES

EVP Global Public Policy, Carol A. Melton, age 57
EVP Corporate Marketing and Communications, Gary L. Ginsberg, age 50
President Warner Bros. Consumer Products, Brad Globe
CEO Time Inc., Laura W. Lang, age 56
SVP and CIO, William P. (Bill) Krivoshik
Chairman and CEO, Jeffrey L. (Jeff) Bewkes, age 59, $1,750,000 total compensation
EVP and General Counsel, Paul T. Cappuccio, age 50, $1,000,000 total compensation
Chairman and CEO Warner Bros. Entertainment, Barry M. Meyer
President and COO Warner Bros. Entertainment, Alan F. Horn
EVP and CFO Warner Bros. Entertainment, Edward A. Romano
EVP International Warner Bros. Entertainment, Richard J. Fox
President Warner Bros. Television Group, Bruce Rosenblum, age 53
President Warner Bros. Home Entertainment Group, Kevin Tsujihara
Vice Chairman Turner Broadcasting System, Andrew T. (Andy) Heller, age 57
EVP Turner Broadcasting System, Kelly Regal, age 43
EVP International and Corporate Strategy, Olaf Olafsson, age 49, $750,000 total compensation
EVP Worldwide Corporate Communications and Public Affairs Warner Bros. Entertainment, Susan N. Fleishman
Editor?in?Chief Time, John Huey
Chairman and CEO Home Box Office, Bill Nelson, age 63
Co-President Home Box Office, Richard L. Plepler
EVP CTO and Chief Digital Technology Strategist Turner Broadcasting System, Scott Teissler

President Warner Bros. Television, Peter Roth
EVP and CFO Turner Broadcasting System, John E. Kampfe
Chief Research Officer Turner Broadcasting System, Jack Wakshlag, age 62
CFO and Chief Administrative Officer, John K. Martin Jr., age 44, $1,000,000 total compensation
President DC Entertainment, Diane Nelson
President Domestic Distribution Warner Bros. Pictures, Dan Fellman
President Warner Bros. Studio Facilities, Jon Gilbert
President Worldwide Marketing Warner Bros. Pictures, Sue Kroll
President Distribution Warner Bros. Pictures International, Veronika Kwan-Rubinek
President Warner Bros. International Cinemas, Millard Ochs
President Warner Bros. International Television Distribution, Jeffrey R. Schlesinger
SVP Corporate Responsibility and Chief Diversity Officer, Lisa M. Quiroz
EVP Technology and CTO Home Box Office, Robert (Bob) Zitter
President HBO Home Entertainment, Henry W. McGee, age 58
EVP Corporate Communications Home Box Office, Quentin Schaffer
Co-President Home Box Office, Eric Kessler, age 56
EVP Business Affairs and President Film Programming Home Box Office, Bruce Grivetti
President Programming Home Box Office, Michael Lombardo
EVP and General Counsel Network Business Affairs Home Box Office, Thomas M. (Tom) Woodbury
EVP Information Technology and CIO Home Box Office, Michael Gabriel
President HBO Documentary Films, Sheila Nevins, age 73
COO The CW Television Network, John D. Maatta
President Warner Bros. Pictures Group, Jeff Robinov
President Worldwide Physical Production Warner Bros. Pictures, Steve Papazian
President CNN Worldwide, Jim Walton, age 53
President Warner Home Video, Ronald J. Sanders
SVP and Treasurer, Edward B. (Ed) Ruggiero, age 59
President and COO Turner Animation Young Adults and Kids Media, Stuart C. Snyder, age 53
Chairman and CEO Turner Broadcasting System, Philip I. (Phil) Kent, age 57
EVP Worldwide Human Resources Warner Bros. Entertainment, Akihiko F. (Kiko) Washington
EVP and CFO Home Box Office, Robert (Rob) Roth
President Turner Entertainment Networks Turner Broadcasting System, Steven R. (Steve) Koonin, age 54
EVP and General Counsel TBS Inc; President TBS International, Louise S. Sams, age 54
EVP Consumer Marketing Time, Brian Wolfe
President HBO Entertainment, Sue Naegle, age 42
EVP and COO CNN Sales and Marketing Turner Broadcasting System, Greg D'Alba
SVP Global Public Policy, Steve Vest, age 47
President Programming Distribution and International Home Box Office, Simon Sutton
EVP and CFO Time, Howard Averill
EVP Consumer Marketing Home Box Office, Courteney Monroe
President HBO Miniseries, Kary Antholis
Secretary, Paul F. Washington
President Time Corporate Sales and Marketing, Leslie Picard
EVP and General Counsel Warner Bros. Entertainment, John A. Rogovin
Chief Marketing Officer Global Media Group, Kristen O'Hara
VP Corporate Communications, Keith Cocozza
EVP Warner Bros. Theatre Ventures, Gregg Maday
President and CEO Retail Sales and Marketing, Richard A. (Rich) Jacobsen
President Warner Bros. Domestic Television Distribution, Kenneth (Ken) Werner, age 58
President Worldwide Business Affairs Warner Bros. Pictures, Steven S. Spira
EVP and General Counsel Time, Maurice F. Edelson
President Programming Sales Home Box Office, Charles Schreger
SVP and Controller, Pascal Desroches, age 47
SVP Worldwide Recruitment and Executive Search, Maggie Rubey Lynch
SVP, James (Jim) Burtson
VP Investor Relations, Douglas (Doug) Shapiro
President HBO Films, Len Amato
VP Global Public Policy, Vincent Jamois
President Music Warner Bros. Pictures, Paul Broucek
EVP Human Resources and Administration Home Box Office, Scott McElhone
VP International Relations and Public Policy Asia Pacific, Belinda Lui
VP Corporate Affairs, Richard Siklos
Chief Creative Officer Global Media Group, Michael Benson
VP Creative Global Media Group, David Statman
VP Marketing Strategy Global Media Group, Amy Swanson Sillan
VP Public Policy UK, Nick Toon
President Sales Distribution and Sports Turner Broadcasting System, David Levy
SVP and Group Managing Director Time Warner Investments, Rachel Lam
VP and Managing Director Time Warner Investments, Allison Goldberg
VP and Managing Director Time Warner Investments, Scott Levine
Director, Stephen F. Bollenbach, age 69
Director, Michael A. Miles, age 72
Director, Frank J. Caufield, age 72
Director, Deborah C. (Debbie) Wright, age 54
Director, Fred Hassan, age 66
Director, William P. Barr, age 61
Director, Kenneth J. (Ken) Novack, age 70
Director, Jessica P. Einhorn, age 64
Director, James L. Barksdale, age 69
Director, Paul Wachter, age 56
Director, Robert C. Clark, age 68
Director, Mathias Dopfner, age 49
Auditors: Ernst&YoungLLP

LOCATIONS

HQ: Time Warner Inc.
1 Time Warner Center, New York NY 10019-8016
Phone: 212-484-8000 **Fax:** -232
Web: www.icbt.com

2011 Sales

	$ mil.	% of total
US	19,894	69
UK	1,720	6
Germany	721	2
Canada	672	2
France	571	2
Japan	548	2
Other countries	4,848	17
Total	**28,974**	**100**

PRODUCTS/OPERATIONS

2011 Sales

	$ mil.	% of total
Content	12,635	44
Subscriptions	9,523	33
Advertising	6,116	21
Other	700	2
Total	**28,974**	**100**

2011 Sales

	$ mil.	% of total
Networks	13,654	47
Filmed entertainment	12,638	41
Publishing	3,677	12
Adjustments	(995)	-
Total	**28,974**	**100**

Selected Operations

Networks
- Cinemax (pay-television service)
- Home Box Office (HBO pay-television service)
- Turner Broadcasting System
  - Boomerang (classic cartoons)
  - Cartoon Network
  - Cable News Network (CNN)
  - TBS
  - truTV
  - Turner Classic Movies (TCM)
  - Turner Network Television (TNT)

Filmed entertainment
- Warner Bros. Entertainment
  - DC Entertainment
  - New Line Cinema
  - Warner Bros.Castle Rock EntertainmentWarner Bros. Pictures
  - Warner Bros. Consumer Products (product licensing)
  - Warner Bros. Home EntertainmentWarner Bros. Digital DistributionWarner Bros. Interactive EntertainmentWarner Home Video
  - Warner Bros. Television GroupTelepictures ProductionsWarner Bros. AnimationWarner Bros. TelevisionWarner Horizon Television

Publishing
- Time Inc.
  - Entertainment Weekly
  - Fortune
  - InStyle
  - People
  - Real Simple
  - Southern Living
  - Sports Illustrated
  - Time

COMPETITORS

Bertelsmann
CBS Corp
Discovery Communications
Disney
Hearst Corporation
Lagardere Active
Liberty Interactive
Meredith Corporation
NBCUniversal
News Corp.
Sony Pictures Entertainment
Viacom

HISTORICAL FINANCIALS

Company Type: Public

Income Statement

FYE: December 31

	REVENUE ($ mil.)	NET INCOME ($ mil.)	NET PROFIT MARGIN	EMPLOYEES
12/11	28,974	2,886	10.0%	34,000
12/10	26,888	2,578	9.6%	31,000
12/09	25,785	2,468	9.6%	31,000
12/08	46,984	(13,402)	—	87,000
12/07	46,482	4,387	9.4%	86,400
Annual Growth	(11.1%)	(9.9%)	—	(20.8%)

2011 Year-End Financials

Debt ratio: 28.80%
Return on equity: 9.63%
Cash ($ mil.): 3,476
Current ratio: 150.55
Long-term debt ($ mil.): 19,501
No. of shares (mil.): 974
Dividends
Yield: —
Payout: 34.69%
Market value ($ mil.): 35,200

	STOCK PRICE ($) FY Close	P/E High/Low		PER SHARE ($) Earnings	Dividends	Book Value
12/11	36.14	14	10	2.71	0.00	30.76
12/10	32.17	15	12	2.25	0.85	29.97
12/09	29.14	16	3	2.07	0.56	28.85
12/08	10.06	—	—	(11.22)	0.00	35.36
12/07	16.51	6	5	3.51	0.00	48.88
Annual Growth	21.6%	—	—	(6.3%)	—	(10.9%)

Timken Co. (The)

The Timken Company keeps its bearings straight. The company makes bearings that find their way into products from consumer appliances to railroad cars. Timken also makes power transmission components including automotive gear shafts and connecting rods to aircraft engine components. The company manufactures more than 450 grades of alloy and carbon steels producing bars billets tubing and custom components for automotive and industrial applications. It also offers lubricants seals and motion control systems. Timken serves 30 countries through some 60 manufacturing facilities 10 technology/engineering centers and 14 distribution centers and warehouses.

HISTORY

Veteran St. Louis carriage maker Henry Timken patented a design in 1898 for tapered roller bearings (enclosed bearings between a pair of concentric rings). The following year Timken and his sons William and Henry (H. H.) Timken founded the Timken Roller Bearing Axle Company to make bearings for carriage axles.

In 1902 the company moved to Canton Ohio to be near the growing steelworks of Pittsburgh and the new auto industries of Buffalo New York; Cleveland; and Detroit. With the debut of the Ford Motor Model T in 1908 the Timkens' business soared. In 1909 Henry Timken died. That year a separate company the Timken-Detroit Axle Company was formed in Michigan to serve the auto industry. The original company changed its name to the Timken Roller Bearing Company and continued to produce bearings. Also in 1909 Vickers began making bearings and axles under license from Timken (Timken acquired that operation in 1959).

Suffering steel shortages during WWI the company began making its own steel in 1916. By the 1920s the rail industry had adopted Timken bearings to increase the speed of trains. Timken stock was sold to the public for the first time in 1922.

WWII created increased demand for Timken's products and the company opened several new plants. The AP bearing –a revolutionary prelubricated self-contained railroad bearing unveiled by Timken in 1954 –boosted the company's railroad segment and a new plant the Columbus Railroad Bearing Plant opened in 1958.

H. H. Timken's son W. Robert Timken became president in 1960 and chairman in 1968. The company continued to grow during the 1960s by opening plants in Brazil and France. It adopted its current name in 1970. W. R. Timken Jr. grandson of the founder became chairman in 1975. That year the company bought specialty alloy maker Latrobe Steel.

In 1982 with increasing competition from Europe and Japan the company suffered its first loss since the Depression. Five years later it established Indian joint venture Tata Timken to make bearings for agricultural equipment heavy machinery and railcars.

Timken bought precision-bearing maker MPB Corporation in 1990. The company opened its first European steel operations in 1993; the following year it introduced its environmentally progressive Dynametal steel products. It bought the Rail Bearing Service Corporation in 1995.

Timken formed joint venture Yantai Timken in 1996 to make bearings in China. It also acquired US steel firms Ohio Alloy Steels and Houghton & Richards Sanderson Kayser in the UK (later called Sanderson Special Steels) and Prema Milmet (bearings) in Poland. In 1997 Timken purchased Gnutti Carlo SpA (bearings Italy) and the aerospace bearing operations of UK-based Torrington.

The company opened a bearings plant in the UK in 1998 and in December of that year it bought UK-based Desford Steel Tubes. The General Motors strike transformer outages and new equipment costs hurt the company's earnings however. As a result Timken closed its Australian bearing manufacturing operations.

In 1999 Timken cut production capacity to 80% and continued to consolidate operations and restructure into global business units. The company restructured operations in South Africa (cutting about 1700 jobs) and transferred its European distribution to an outside company in France.

To meet European demand Timken expanded production at its plants in Poland and Romania in 2000. In early 2001 the company announced that it would lay off more than 7% of its workforce. Timken entered into a joint venture with rival SKF in 2001 to make bearing components in Brazil. Later Timken acquired French steel component maker Lecheres Industries SAS. The next year Timken divided its aerospace and super precision (miniature bearings and precision assemblies) division into four integrated global businesses.

Timken acquired an Ingersoll-Rand unit The Torrington Co. for $840 million in 2003. That next year the company enhanced its Timken Aerospace subsidiary through the acquisition of Alcor Engine Company and Advance Repair Technologies. In 2004 it also acquired SES LLC's Technical Group a provider of infrared thermography and vibration analysis.

In 2005 Timken sold its Linear Motion Systems division with operations in Germany and Italy to an Italian firm Overseas Industries SpA. The division produced linear guides for industrial equipment manufacturers. Also that year the company purchased Bearing Inspection Inc. (Bii) which provided inspection and reconditioning services for aerospace bearings. Combined with similar Timken operations the company became Timken Aerospace Services and retained its existing management.

In mid-2006 the company sold its precision components business in Europe which served the automotive industry to investors including the management of the business. Blaming the woes of the North American automotive industry Timken laid off approximately 700 employees or about 5% of its Automotive Group in 2006.

The company in 2007 closed down its unprofitable plant in Desford UK which made seamless steel tubes. Four hundred employees lost their jobs as a result. The Desford facility primarily served the bearing industry in Europe with annual sales ranging from $85 million to $95 million.

In late 2006 Timken sold its Latrobe Steel subsidiary for about $215 million in cash to an investors group led by the Watermill Group Hicks Holdings and Sankaty Advisors (part of Bain Capital). Latrobe Steel made specialty steels and alloys for use in aerospace applications high-performance cutting tools aluminum casting dies extrusion and thread roll dies and other applications. Timken used the money from the sale for general corporate purposes including strategic growth initiatives and pension funding. Continuing the strategic divestitures the company sold its automotive steering business along with its related plants in Connecticut and Brazil to DriveSol Worldwide an affiliate of Sun Capital Partners.

Timken supplemented its aerospace business in 2007 by acquiring the assets of The Purdy Corp. for $200 million. Purdy made and maintained transmissions gears rotor-head systems and other components for helicopters and fixed-wing aircraft. Purdy's operations in Manchester Connecticut were renamed as Timken Aerospace Transmissions following the acquisition. In late 2007 Timken formed a joint venture with Xiangtan Electric Manufacturing Co. (XEMC) to manufacture ultra-large-bore bearings for the main rotor shafts of multi-megawatt wind turbines for the Chinese wind energy market. The JV partners built a plant in Xiangtan Hunan province.

That same year Timken committed about $60 million to expand its Harrison Steel Plant in Canton Ohio. The expansion completed in 2008 gave the company greater capabilities to produce steel bars down to one inch in diameter for applications in power transmission and friction management.

Timken reorganized in 2008 from three groups (Automotive Industrial and Steel) into two –a Bearings & Power Transmission group and a Steel group. The purchase of replacement engine parts maker EXTEX in 2008 supported Timken's strategy to expand the products offered by its Aerospace & Defense unit. EXTEX makes compressor and turbine blades and vanes shrouds gears and nozzles. Also that year Timkin purchased Boring Specialties a manufacturer of deep-hole oil and gas drilling and extraction products and services for about $60 million.

The company's sales and operations were rocked by the global economy and capital market crisis in 2009. As the worldwide recession took hold Timken trimmed its headcount by more than 10% and cut production by shortening work weeks and operating hours. Scheduled to close in 2007 the company's manufacturing facility in S?o Paulo Brazil was kept open to serve demand from industrial customers; it was finally shuttered in 2009.

EXECUTIVES

EVP Finance and Administration and CFO, Glenn A. Eisenberg, age 50, $578,658 total compensation

President Steel Group, Salvatore J. Miraglia Jr., age 61, $421,739 total compensation

President CEO and Director, James W. Griffith, age 58, $985,581 total compensation

Chairman, Ward J. (Tim) Timken Jr., age 44, $778,846 total compensation

SVP and General Counsel, William R. Burkhart, age 46

VP Ethics and Compliance and Corporate Secretary, Scott A. Scherff, age 54

VP Communications and Public Relations, Kari Groh

President Rail and Latin America Bearings and Power Transmission Group, Roger W. Lindsay

SVP Asia-Pacific Bearings and Power Transmission Group, J. Ron (Ron) Menning
SVP Human Resources and Organizational Advancement, Donald L. Walker
President Process Industries and Supply Chain Bearings and Power Transmission Group; Director Global Purchasing Organization and European Organization, Christopher A. Coughlin, age 51
SVP Strategy and CIO, Daniel E. Muller
VP Government Affairs, Robert J. Lapp
VP Distribution Bearings and Power Transmission Group, Michael J. Connors
VP Industrial Engineered Steel Solutions Steel Group, Cengiz S. Kurkcu
SVP and Group Controller Bearings and Power Transmission Group, Philip D. (Phil) Fracassa, age 42
SVP and Controller, J. Ted Mihaila, age 57
VP Mobile Industries Bearings and Power Transmission Group, Peter M. Sproson
VP Treasury, John C. Skurek
Director Capital Markets and Investor Relations, Steve D. Tschiegg
VP Steel Manufacturing Steel Group, Thomas D. Moline
VP Mobile On-Highway Engineered Steel Solutions Steel Group, Robert N. Keeler
VP Strategic Planning, Jeffrey A. Clark
President Mobile Industries Bearings and Power Transmission Group; Director Aerospace Segment, Richard G. Kyle, age 46
SVP Technology and Quality, Douglas H. Smith
VP Environmental Health and Safety, Alan C. Oberster
VP Auditing, Thomas A. Kirkpatrick
VP Operational Organizational Advancement, Ronald J. Myers
VP Corporate Development, Michael T. Schilling
Managing Director Europe Bearings and Power Transmission Group, Andreas Roellgen
VP Oil and Gas Engineered Steel Solutions Steel Group, Shawn J. Seanor
Manager Global Media and Strategic Communications, Lorrie Paul Crum
SVP Tax and Treasury, Christopher J. Holding
VP Quality Advancement, Russell F. Folger
Director Engineering Bearings and Power Transmission, Brent J. Dorman
VP Light Vehicle Systems Bearings and Power Transmission Group, Brian J. Ruel
Manager Community Relations, Elizabeth L. Engels
Director Sales Americas, James W. Skelly
Managing Director Latin America, Tom Diez
Director, John M. Ballbach, age 51
President CEO and Director, James W. Griffith, age 58
Director, John A. Luke Jr., age 63
Director, Frank C. Sullivan, age 51
Director, John P. Reilly, age 68
Director, Ward J. Timken, age 69
Director, John M. Timken Jr., age 60
Director, Jacqueline F. Woods, age 64
Director, Phillip R. Cox, age 65
Director, Joseph W. Ralston, age 68
Auditors: Ernst&YoungLLP

LOCATIONS

HQ: Timken Co. (The)
1835 Dueber Ave., SW, Canton, OH 44706-2798
Phone: 330 438-3000 **Fax:** 330 471-3452
Web: www.timken.com

2011 Sales

	$ mil.	% of total
US	3,494	68
Europe Middle East & Africa	652	12
Asia/Pacific	568	11
Canada & Mexico	268	5

PRODUCTS/OPERATIONS

2011 Sales

	$ mil.	% of total
Bearings & Power Transmissions group		
Process Industries	1,240	24
Aerospace & Defense	324	6

Selected Products and Services

Bearings & Power Transmission
- Aerospace bearing repair and component reconditioning
- Aftermarket distribution
- Bearing maintenance tools
- Condition monitoring equipment
- Cylindrical bearings
- Gears
- Helicopter transmission systems
- Lubricants
- Power transmission components
- Repair and overhaul of engine fuel controls and transmissions
- Rotor head assemblies
- Seals
- Spherical bearings
- Straight ball bearings
- Super-precision ball and roller bearings
- Turbine engine components
- Tapered bearings

Maintenance
Remanufacture and repair
Steel
- Custom precision steel components
- Mechanical seamless steel tubing
- Specialty steels and alloys
- Tool steel

COMPETITORS

Allegheny Technologies
Amatsuji Steel Ball
ArcelorMittal
BOHLER-UDDEHOLM
General Bearing
JTEKT
Kaydon
Linamar Corp.
Macsteel Service Centres
Minebea
Nippon Bearing
NSK
NTN
Nucor
Plymouth Tube
RBC Bearings
RBS Global
Republic Steel
Schaeffler Technologies
SKF
SKF USA
Steel Dynamics
Tata Europe
Tenaris
United States Steel
Universal Stainless
V & M Tubes (USA)

HISTORICAL FINANCIALS

Company Type: Public

Income Statement

FYE: December 31

	REVENUE ($ mil.)	NET INCOME ($ mil.)	NET PROFIT MARGIN	EMPLOYEES
12/11	5,170	454	8.8%	20,954
12/10	4,055	274	6.8%	19,839
12/09	3,141	(133)		16,667
12/08	5,663	267	4.7%	25,662
12/07	5,236	220	4.2%	25,175
Annual Growth	(0.3%)	19.9%	—	(4.5%)

2011 Year-End Financials

Debt ratio: 11.84%
Return on equity: 22.40%
Cash ($ mil.): 464
Current ratio: 271.41
Long-term debt ($ mil.): 478
No. of shares (mil.): 97
Dividends
Yield: —
Payout: 16.99%
Market value ($ mil.): 3,781

	STOCK PRICE ($) FY Close	P/E High	P/E Low	PER SHARE ($) Earnings	Dividends	Book Value
12/11	38.71	12	7	4.59	0.00	20.77
12/10	47.73	17	8	2.81	0.53	19.68
12/09	23.71	—	—	(1.39)	0.45	16.29
12/08	19.63	13	4	2.78	0.70	16.99
12/07	32.85	16	12	2.30	0.66	20.46
Annual Growth	4.2%	—	—	18.9%	—	0.4%

TJX Companies, Inc.

Rifling through the racks is an art at TJX stores. The TJX Companies operates about a half a dozen retail chains including the two largest off-price clothing retailers in the US: T.J. Maxx and Marshalls. T.J. Maxx sells brand-name family apparel accessories women's shoes domestics giftware and jewelry at discount prices at some 980 stores nationwide. Marshalls offers a full line of shoes and a broader selection of menswear through about 890 stores. Its HomeGoods chain of some 375 stores nationwide focuses exclusively on home furnishings. T.K. Maxx is the company's European retail arm with 350-plus stores in the UK Ireland Germany and now Poland. The retailer also operates about 310 stores in Canada.

HISTORY

Cousins Stanley and Sumner Feldberg opened the first Zayre (Yiddish for "very good") store in Hyannis Massachusetts in 1956. During the next 15 years the number of stores grew to nearly 200.

Zayre purchased the Hit or Miss chain which sold upscale women's clothing at discounted prices in 1969. When the recession of the early 1970s hit superb results at Hit or Miss prompted Zayre to look for further opportunities in the off-price apparel marketplace. Zayre hired Ben Cammarata to create a new store concept and in March 1977 he opened the first T.J. Maxx in Auburn Massachusetts to market discounted upscale family clothing. Six years later Zayre formed the catalog retailer Chadwick's of Boston to sell Hit or Miss apparel by mail.

The company came to rely increasingly on its specialty operations to provide consistent sales and income as its flagship general merchandise stores often struggled. By 1983 the specialty chains were producing almost half of Zayre's sales.

In the second half of the 1980s Zayre's upscale (yet still off-priced) retailers' sales rose while its general merchandise stores (targeting lower-income customers) dropped. To keep its specialty stores unhindered by its flagging Zayre stores it established The TJX Companies as a public company in 1987. Zayre sold about 17% of its new subsidiary to the public with Cammarata as CEO.

Zayre sold its 400 general merchandise stores in 1988 to Ames for about $430 million in cash $140 million in Ames stock and a receivable note. The next year the company spun off its warehouse club operations as Waban (the warehouse component eventually became BJ's Wholesale) and merged with its subsidiary The TJX Companies taking that name.

TJX acquired Winners Apparel a Toronto-based five-store apparel chain in 1990. That year in the same month that Ames declared bankruptcy TJX established a $185 million reserve against losses it might suffer through its ownership of Ames' stock. Ames emerged from bankruptcy two years later and TJX was left with 4% of Ames' voting shares and over 100 empty Ames stores. TJX sold or leased most of them.

Also in 1992 TJX opened HomeGoods gift and houseware outlets in three of its remaining Ames stores and closed about 70 Hit or Miss stores. That year the company paid off about $128 million of its long-term debt. Encouraged by the success of its off-price operations in Canada in 1994 TJX opened five T.K. Maxx stores (similar to T.J. Maxx and Winners Apparel) in the UK.

A year later TJX paid $550 million for Melville's ailing chain of 450 Marshalls clothing stores. In addition the company sold its Hit or Miss apparel chain.

To help pay for Marshalls TJX sold the Chadwick's of Boston catalog in 1996 to retailer Brylane for about $325 million. Two years later the company opened two T.K. Maxx stores in the Netherlands and said it planned to have 75 stores in Europe in three years. It also debuted the A.J. Wright discount chain in New England in 1998.

In 1999 TJX elected Cammarata to the additional post of chairman and elevated Ted English to president and COO. In 2000 Cammarata relinquished his CEO post to English but remained chairman. Citing the successes of its new stores the company announced in early 2001 it expected to increase its total number of stores 12% annually for the next several years. Also that year the company shuttered its T.K. Maxx stores in the Netherlands. Seven TJX employees perished on September 11 2001 when their flight bound for Los Angeles crashed into the World Trade Center during the worst terrorist attack in US history.

In 2002 the company opened HomeSense a new Canadian home furnishings chain fashioned after its US counterpart HomeGoods. In December 2003 TJX finalized its acquisition of Bob's Stores a Connecticut-based discount retail chain with 31 stores in the Northeast.

In September 2005 English resigned abruptly after five years as the company's CEO. In October the company closed down its tjmaxx.com and homegoods.com Web sites citing poor sales.

In March 2006 TJX cut about 250 jobs in its corporate and divisional offices and reduced the salaries of a dozen senior executives including its chairman and acting CEO and its president by 10% in an effort to increase profits.

A year after the abrupt resignation of CEO Edmond English in September 2005 TJX named company president Carol Meyrowitz to the post effective January 2007. (Cammarata had been acting CEO of the company in the interim.) Also in January 34 A.J. Wright stores were closed.

In November 2007 TJX reached a settlement with Visa and Fifth Third Bancorp stemming from a breach of its computer systems in which customer data was stolen. Under the terms of the agreement TJX will fund up to $40.9 million for recovery payments for US Visa issuers. Also in the fall of 2007 the retailer's European arm T.K. Maxx entered the German market with five stores there.

In August 2008 TJX sold money-losing Bob's Stores which has about 35 locations in the Northeast to the private equity firms Versa Capital Management and Crystal Capital for an undisclosed amount.

In 2009 T.K. Maxx opened its first stores in Poland.

In 2011 Marshalls entered Canada.

EXECUTIVES

Chairman, Bernard (Ben) Cammarata, age 72, $911,539 total compensation
CEO and Director, Carol M. Meyrowitz, age 58, $1,475,000 total compensation
VP, George L. Drummey
President, Ernie Herrman, age 51, $897,019 total compensation
SEVP; Group President Europe, Paul Sweetenham, age 47, $734,349 total compensation
SVP Global Communications, Sherry Lang
SEVP and Chief Administrative Officer, Jeffrey G. (Jeff) Naylor, age 53, $740,000 total compensation
President A.J. Wright, Celia Clancy, age 55
SEVP and Chief Human Resources Officer, Gregorio R. (Greg) Flores III
SEVP and Group President, Jerome Rossi, age 68, $700,000 total compensation
SEVP; President HomeGoods and TJX Canada, Nan Stutz, age 54
President Winners/HomeSense, Robert Cataldo, age 53
EVP Real Estate and New Business Development, Michael Skirvin
SVP Corporate Tax and Insurance, Alfred Appel
SVP Enterprise Risk Management and Chief Compliance Officer, Paul Kangas
SVP Real Estate and Property Development, Christina Lofgren
SVP Global Talent Development, Nancy Maher
VP, Nancy Bakacs
VP, Susan Beaumont
VP, Michael Brogan
VP, Elaine Espinola
VP, Mark Factor
VP, Thomas Flanagan Jr.
Controller, Prentice Gove
VP, David Hoffman
VP, Stephen Mack
EVP General Counsel and Secretary, Ann McCauley, age 61
VP, Jeanne Pratt
VP, Lisa Schwartz
VP, David Spooner
VP, Mark Walker
VP, Martin Whitmore Sr.
SVP and Treasurer, Mary B. Reynolds
SEVP and Group President The Marmaxx Group, Richard Sherr, age 54
SVP Marketing The Marmaxx Group, Karen Coppola
SVP Human Resources The Marmaxx Group, Amy Fardella
SVP Store Operations T.J. Maxx, Robert Garofalo
EVP Finance and CFO, Scott Goldenberg
SVP Merchandising The Marmaxx Group, Herbert S. Landsman
EVP and Chief Logistics Officer, Peter Lindenmeyer
SVP Planning and Allocation The Marmaxx Group, Peter Benjamin
President HomeGoods, Ken Canestrari, age 50
VP, Carlton Aird
VP, Stacey Lane
SVP Global Talent Development, Lynn Jack
SVP Store Operations HomeGoods, Colin Wren
SEVP TJX Europe, Michael MacMillan, age 56
SVP Brand Development, Barry Zelman
Managing Director HomeSense, David Alves
President TJX Canada, Douglas Mizzi, age 52
Managing Director T.K. Maxx, Gino Barrea
SVP Global Procurement, Marc Boesch
EVP and CIO, Kathy S. Lane
Chief Operating Officer, Gordon Bullock
Senior Vice President Administration, Robert Arnold
Lead Independent Director, John OBrien
Director, David T. Ching, age 59
CEO and Director, Carol M. Meyrowitz, age 58
Director, David A. Brandon, age 60
Director, John F. O'Brien, age 68
Director, Michael F. Hines, age 56
Director, Alan M. Bennett, age 62
Director, Willow B. Shire, age 64
Director, Fletcher H. Wiley, age 69
Director, Amy B. Lane, age 59
Director, Jose B. Alvarez, age 49
Independent Director, Zein Abdalla
Auditors: PricewaterhouseCoopersLLP

LOCATIONS

HQ: TJX Companies, Inc.
770 Cochituate Road, Framingham, MA 01701
Phone: 508 390-1000 **Fax:** 508 390-2091
Web: www.tjx.com

2012 Sales

	$ mil.	% of total
US		
Marmaxx	15,367	66
HomeGoods	2,244	10
A.J. Wright	9	-
Europe		
T.K. Maxx/HomeSense	2,890	12
Canada		
Winners/HomeSense	2,680	12
Total	**23,191**	**100**

2012 Stores

	No.
US	2,241
Europe	356
Canada	308
Total	**2,717**

PRODUCTS/OPERATIONS

2012 Stores

	No.
T.J.	983
Marshalls	890
HomeGoods	374
T.K.	332
Winners	216
HomeSense (Canada &	110
Total	**2,905**

2012 Sales

	% of total
Clothing &	60
Home	27
Jewelry &	13
Total	**100**

Selected Stores

HomeGoods (off-price home fashion chain)
HomeSense (off-price home fashion chain Canada and UK)
Marshalls (off-price retailer of apparel shoes home fashions)
Marshalls Mega-Stores (combination Marshalls and HomeGoods stores)
Sierra Trading Post (off-price online retailer of outdoor gear and apparel)
T.J. Maxx (off-price retailer of apparel shoes home fashions)
T.J. Maxx ' N More (combination T.J. Maxx and HomeGoods stores)
T.K. Maxx (off-price retailer of apparel shoes home fashions Europe)
Winners Apparel (off-price family apparel chain Canada)

COMPETITORS

Amazon.com
ASDA
Bed Bath & Beyond
Belk
Big Lots
Liberty Interactive
Loehmann' s
Macy' s
Men' s Wearhouse
Primark

Brown Shoe	Ross Stores
Burlington Coat Factory	Sears
Cato	Shopko Stores
Charming Shoppes	Sports Authority
Claire' s Stores	Stage Stores
Collective Brands	Stein Mart
Dillard' s	Target Corporation
Dollar General	Tesco
Eddie Bauer LLC	The Children' s Place
Foot Locker	The Gap
Inditex	Tuesday Morning Corporation
J. C. Penney	Wal-Mart
Kmart	Zellers
Kohl' s	

HISTORICAL FINANCIALS

Company Type: Public

Income Statement FYE: January 28

	REVENUE ($ mil.)	NET INCOME ($ mil.)	NET PROFIT MARGIN	EMPLOYEES
01/12	23,191	1,496	6.5%	168,000
01/11	21,942	1,343	6.1%	166,000
01/10	20,288	1,213	6.0%	154,000
01/09	18,999	880	4.6%	133,000
01/08	18,647	771	4.1%	129,000
Annual Growth	5.6%	18.0%	—	6.8%

2012 Year-End Financials

Debt ratio: 9.51%
Return on equity: 46.62%
Cash ($ mil.): 1,507
Current ratio: 167.55
Long-term debt ($ mil.): 784
No. of shares (mil.): 746
Dividends
Yield: —
Payout: 18.65%
Market value ($ mil.): 50,305

	STOCK PRICE ($) FY Close	P/E High/Low		PER SHARE ($) Earnings	Dividends	Book Value
01/12	67.37	35	24	1.93	0.00	4.30
01/11	47.71	29	22	1.65	0.00	3.98
01/10	38.01	28	13	1.42	0.00	3.53
01/09	19.42	35	18	1.00	0.00	2.59
01/08	30.22	37	30	0.83	0.00	2.49
Annual Growth	22.2%	—	—	23.5%	—	14.6%

Tompkins Financial Corp

Tompkins Financial is the holding company for Tompkins Trust Company The Bank of Castile and The Mahopac National Bank which offer traditional banking services through some 45 offices in upstate New York. It also owns Pennsylvania's VIST Bank. Funds from deposit products such as checking savings and money market accounts are mainly used to originate real estate loans and mortgages as well as commercial and consumer loans. Tompkins offers investment management services through Tompkins Investment Services and financial planning through subsidiary AM&M Financial Services (dba Tompkins Financial Advisors). Tompkins Insurance Agencies sells property/casualty coverage in central and western New York.

Tompkins Financial operates in two segments – banking and financial services. Its financial services operations led by its insurance and investment services units account for about 15% of the group's revenues. It expanded the business with the 2011 acquisition of Oliver & Associates Insurance in upstate New York. Other activities include broker-dealer services and risk management.

The company's strategy for growth includes making inroads into new markets and new business areas through acquisitions. It entered the southeastern Pennsylvania market with its 2012 acquisition of VIST Financial parent of VIST Bank (which continues to operate under a separate charter under existing management) VIST Insurance and VIST Capital Management. The deal added 21 branches to Tompkins' network.

Tompkins Financial's net income has been rising relatively steadily over the years although revenues did fall 3% in 2011 to $185.1 million. That year the company increased its provision for loan and lease losses as a result of a higher number of charge-offs (including a $5 million commercial real estate charge-off). Profits grew 5% in 2011 primarily due to higher noninterest earnings such as card services income as well as lower noninterest expenses. However service charges on deposit accounts have declined due to regulatory changes limiting overdraft fees that banks may charge customers. In financial services the company reported higher revenues from insurance commissions and fees in 2011.

EXECUTIVES

EVP Tompkins Services, Robert B. Bantle, age 60
EVP Operations and Systems, Lawrence A. Updike, age 66, $144,000 total compensation
EVP; EVP Tompkins Investment Services Division Tompkins Trust, Donald S. Stewart, age 67, $150,000 total compensation
Chairman Tompkins Financial Corporation and Tompkins Trust Company, James J. Byrnes, age 69, $455,000 total compensation
Vice Chairman; Chairman President and CEO Bank of Castile, James W. (Jim) Fulmer, age 60, $260,500 total compensation
Vice Chairman Tompkins Financial Corporation and Tompkins Trust Company, Thomas R. Salm, age 70
EVP CFO and COO, Francis M. Fetsko, age 47, $210,000 total compensation
President CEO and Director, Stephen S. Romaine, age 47, $340,000 total compensation
EVP; President and CEO Tompkins Insurance Agencies, David S. Boyce, age 45, $185,000 total compensation
VP and Corporate Risk Manager, Randy C. Lovell
Assistant VP and Corporate Secretary, Linda M. Carlton
EVP; President and CEO Tompkins Trust, Gregory J. Hartz, age 51, $195,000 total compensation
EVP; President and CEO Mahopac National Bank, Gerald J. Klein Jr., age 53, $201,000 total compensation
EVP and Corporate Marketing Officer, Kathleen M. Rooney, age 59
EVP; President and CEO AM & M Financial Services, Thomas J. Rogers, age 41
SVP and CTO, Richard W. Page Jr.
Vice Chairman; Chairman President and CEO Bank of Castile, James W. (Jim) Fulmer, age 60
Director, Reeder D. Gates, age 65
Director, Michael H. Spain, age 53
Director, William D. Spain Jr., age 59
Director; Vice Chairman Tompkins Insurance Agencies, James R. Hardie, age 68
Vice Chairman Tompkins Financial Corporation and Tompkins Trust Company, Thomas R. Salm, age 70
Director, John E. Alexander, age 59
Director, Craig Yunker, age 61
Director, Susan A. Henry, age 66
President CEO and Director, Stephen S. Romaine, age 47
Director, Carl E. Haynes, age 65
Director, Thomas R. Rochon
Director, Michael D. Shay, age 69
Director, Patricia A. Johnson, age 55
Director, Daniel Fessenden
Director, Sandra A. Parker
Director, Paul Battaglia
Auditors: KPMGLLP

LOCATIONS

HQ: Tompkins Financial Corp
The Commons, P.O. Box 460, Ithaca, NY 14851
Phone: 607 273-3210
Web: www.tompkinstrustco.com

PRODUCTS/OPERATIONS

2011 Sales

	$ mil.	% of total
Interest		
Loans	104	56
Available-for-sale securities	30	16
Other	3	2
Noninterest		
Investment services	14	8
Insurance commissions & fees	13	7
Service charges on deposit accounts	8	4
Card services income	5	3
Other	7	4
Adjustments	(0.5)	-
Total	185	100

COMPETITORS

Bank of America	HSBC USA
Chemung Financial	JPMorgan Chase
Citigroup	M&T Bank
Community Bank System	RBS Citizens Financial Group
Elmira Savings Bank	
First Niagara Financial	

HISTORICAL FINANCIALS

Company Type: Public

Income Statement FYE: December 31

	ASSETS ($ mil.)	NET INCOME ($ mil.)	INCOME AS % OF ASSETS	EMPLOYEES
12/11	3,400	35	1.0%	743
12/10	3,260	33	1.0%	766
12/09	3,153	31	1.0%	744
12/08	2,867	29	1.0%	734
12/07	2,359	26	1.1%	688
Annual Growth	9.6%	7.7%	—	1.9%

2011 Year-End Financials

Debt ratio: 6.21%
Return on equity: 11.90%
Cash ($ mil.): 49
Current ratio: —
Long-term debt ($ mil.): 211
No. of shares (mil.): 11
Dividends
Yield: —
Payout: 43.75%
Market value ($ mil.): 426

	STOCK PRICE ($) FY Close	P/E High/Low		PER SHARE ($) Earnings	Dividends	Book Value
12/11	38.51	13	11	3.20	0.00	26.91
12/10	39.16	14	11	3.11	1.33	25.08
12/09	40.50	19	11	2.96	1.24	25.10
12/08	57.95	21	13	2.78	1.20	20.53
12/07	38.80	19	12	2.45	1.13	18.78
Annual Growth	(0.2%)	—	—	6.9%	—	9.4%

Torchmark Corp.

Torchmark aims to be a beacon in the world of insurance. It is the holding company for a family of firms; its member companies specialize in lower-end individual life insurance and supplemental health insurance. Torchmark subsidiaries which include flagship Liberty National Life offer whole and term life insurance supplemental health insurance accidental death insurance Medicare supplements and long-term care health policies for the elderly. Its American Income Life sells life insurance policies to labor union and credit union members in the US Canada and New Zealand. Torchmark sells its products through direct marketing as well as a network of exclusive and independent agents.

Operations

Targeting middle-income citizens Liberty National Life operates primarily in the southeastern US. Torchmark's United American Insurance subsidiary writes supplemental health coverage and Medicare supplemental insurance. A smaller subsidiary Globe Life and Accident offers sells life insurance and supplemental health products direct to consumers through print online and television ads.

Geographic Reach

Torchmark's operations are based in Oklahoma and Texas although its services extend to customers across the US and in New Zealand and Canada.

Financial Analysis

The company reported a revenue increase of 0.29% in 2011 over 2010 due to a marginal increase in total premiums thanks to higher revenues from life health and other premiums. The increase was also due to better returns from net investment income realized investment gains and a decrease in other-than-temporary impairments.

Torchmark also had a marginal increase in net income in 2011 due to a slight increase in revenues which just outpaced a rise in total benefits costs and other expenses.

Many of Torchmark's subsidiaries are registered in Nebraska to take advantage of lower tax rates.

Strategy

Unlike many other life insurers Torchmark makes the bulk of its revenues from its premiums and relatively little (21% in 2011) from its investments. This allows it to ride out the economic downturns more smoothly while other life insurers take significant revenue hits when their investments fizzle.

To build up its supplemental health and life business the company acquired Family Heritage Life Insurance Company of America for $232 million.

At the close of 2010 Torchmark sold its United Investors Life Insurance Company to Protective Life. The sale brought in some $343 million and allowed Torchmark to exit the more volatile business of variable annuities.

HISTORY

It began as a scam plain and simple. In 1900 the Heralds of Liberty was founded as a fraternal organization —but its real reason for existence was to funnel money to its founders according to Frank Samford Torchmark's CEO from 1967 to 1985; Samford was also the great-grandson of the governor who signed the group's charter and the son of the state insurance commissioner who oversaw the Heralds of Liberty's rehabilitation into a real insurance company.

The Heralds offered a joint life distribution plan under which policyholders were divided by age; when a person died his or her beneficiary was paid along with the holder of the lowest-numbered insurance certificate in the class (if they were paid at all; the Heralds were not scrupulous about that). Postal authorities called this plan a lottery and it was illegal in many states. But the Heralds' fraternal order status allowed it to circumvent Alabama insurance laws until 1921 when its infractions could no longer be ignored.

The organization operated under state supervision until 1929 when it was recapitalized as stock company Liberty National. By 1934 despite the Depression the company was financially sound.

In 1944 Liberty National merged with funeral insurance company Brown-Service whose large sales force began selling Liberty National's policies. The added sales helped the company grow and make acquisitions from the 1950s through the 1970s. Even after it discontinued funeral insurance the company still paid out benefits. (As late as 1985 half of all Alabamans who died had the policies.)

Liberty National reorganized itself as a holding company in 1980 to accommodate the purchase of Globe Life And Accident. In 1981 it acquired Continental Investment Corp. which owned United Investors Life Insurance Waddell & Reed (financial services) and United American Insurance. In 1982 the holding company became Torchmark. Throughout its growth spurt it refrained from offering high-yield financial products and thus escaped the worst effects of the economic disruptions of the late 1980s. Its 1990 acquisition of Family Service Life Insurance put it back in the funeral insurance business (it exited again in 1995 and sold the unit in 1998).

Sales in the 1990s were affected by a decline in cash-value life insurance and Medicare supplements. Slack sales forced the company to stop having agents collect premiums personally and by 1996 all accounts were handled by mail.

In 1998 the company sought to sell its 28% stake in property insurer Vesta Insurance Group after that company became the target of numerous lawsuits. Torchmark was only able to reduce its stake to 24% on the open market but in 2000 Vesta bought out Torchmark's holdings.

Torchmark was haunted in 2000 by its own version of the undead —burial policies. An investigation by Alabama regulators was sparked by a Florida court order forcing the company to stop collecting premiums on old burial policies for which African-Americans had been charged higher premiums. In 2001 and 2002 Torchmark was hit by another dozen lawsuits including allegations of overcharging.

EXECUTIVES

Chairman, Mark S. McAndrew, age 58, $968,615 total compensation
VP Associate Counsel and Secretary, Carol A. McCoy
Controller, Spencer H. Stone
Co-CEO, Larry M. Hutchison, age 58, $529,712 total compensation
Co-CEO, Gary L. Coleman, age 59, $549,891 total compensation
President and CEO Liberty National; CEO American Income, Roger C. Smith
EVP and Chief Marketing Officer, Glenn D. Williams, age 52
EVP and Chief Administrative Officer; CEO United American, Vern D. Herbel, age 54, $454,038 total compensation
EVP and CFO, Frank M. Svoboda, age 51
VP and Chief Accounting Officer, Danny H. Almond, age 60
VP and Chief Investment Officer, W. Michael Pressley, age 60
VP and Director Human Resources, Arvelia Bowie
President and CEO Globe Life, Charles F. Hudson, age 55
VP and Actuary, Ben W. Lutek
VP Investor Relations, Mike Majors
EVP and Chief Agency Officer Liberty National Life Insurance Company, Steve DiChiaro
President American Income, Scott Smith
EVP and General Counsel, Robert Brian Mitchell, age 48
Director, David L. Boren, age 70
Director, Charles E. (Eddie) Adair, age 64
Director, Lamar C. Smith, age 64
Director, Paul J. Zucconi, age 71
Director, Gen. Lloyd W. Newton, age 69
Director, Sam R. Perry, age 77
Director, M. Jane Buchan, age 48
Director, Robert W. Ingram, age 63
Director, Darren M. Rebelez, age 46
Auditors: Deloitte&ToucheLLP

LOCATIONS

HQ: Torchmark Corp.
3700 South Stonebridge Drive, McKinney, TX 75070
Phone: 972 569-4000
Web: www.torchmarkcorp.com

PRODUCTS/OPERATIONS

2011 Premiums

	% of total
Life	65
Health	35
Total	**100**

Selected Subsidiaries

American Income Life Insurance Company
Family Heritage Life Insurance Company of America
Globe Life And Accident Insurance Company
Liberty National Life Insurance Company
United American Insurance Company

COMPETITORS

Aflac
Allstate
Amalgamated Life
Gerber Life
Guardian Life
Lincoln Financial Group
MassMutual
MetLife
Monumental Life
Northwestern Mutual
Penn Treaty
Prudential
State Farm
Texas Life
Unum Group
USAA

HISTORICAL FINANCIALS

Company Type: Public

Income Statement FYE: December 31

	ASSETS ($ mil.)	NET INCOME ($ mil.)	INCOME AS % OF ASSETS	EMPLOYEES
12/11	17,156	517	3.0%	3,187
12/10	16,159	517	3.2%	3,291
12/09	16,023	404	2.5%	3,505
12/08	13,529	452	3.3%	3,605
12/07	15,241	527	3.5%	3,596
Annual Growth	3.0%	(0.5%)	—	(3.0%)

2011 Year-End Financials

Debt ratio: 5.33%	No. of shares (mil.): 100
Return on equity: 12.25%	Dividends
Cash ($ mil.): 84	Yield: —
Current ratio: —	Payout: 9.39%
Long-term debt ($ mil.): 914	Market value ($ mil.): 4,364

	STOCK PRICE ($) FY Close	P/E High/Low		PER SHARE ($) Earnings	Dividends	Book Value
12/11	43.39	14	7	4.72	0.00	42.05
12/10	59.74	15	10	4.20	0.41	33.79
12/09	43.95	14	5	3.25	0.37	27.35
12/08	44.70	19	8	3.41	0.37	17.49
12/07	60.53	19	16	3.67	0.35	24.05
Annual Growth	(8.0%)	—	—	6.5%	—	15.0%

Tower Group Inc

Tower Group is hoping to stand tall in the insurance business. Through more than 15 subsidiaries the firm provides specialty commercial and personal property/casualty insurance to individuals and to small and midsized businesses throughout the US. Its commercial products include auto general liability and workers' compensation coverage largely for retail wholesale service real estate construction and niche industries while its personal insurance lines focus on home and automobile policies. Tower Group distributes its products through retail and wholesale agents; it also has an insurance services division that offers underwriting claims and reinsurance to other insurers.

Tower Group's commercial business accounts for about two-thirds of the firm's earned annual insurance premiums with more than half of its policy sales taking place in the northeastern US. The commercial division has 20 underwriting offices across the US and its policies are distributed through some 1300 independent retail and wholesale agencies. The remaining premiums come from the personal lines unit which distributes policies through 500 agents across the US; about 85% of personal line sales take place in the Northeast.

The company's smaller insurance services segment is made up of general agency subsidiaries including Tower Risk Management. Through the unit Tower Group earns commissions on policies it sells for other providers; it also provides underwriting and claims administration services. Reinsurance intermediary services are provided through the division's Bermuda-based CastlePoint Reinsurance subsidiary.

Through acquisitions Tower Group is working to transform itself into a global specialty insurance provider with a diverse offering of products and services. For instance in 2012 Tower moved to increase its international presence by investing $75 million for a 11% stake in private Channel Islands firm Canopius Group which will help Tower establish a presence on the Lloyd's of London exchange (an international policy marketplace based in the UK). Tower also plans to exercise its option to acquire the Canopius Bermuda unit to expand its reinsurance operations.

Tower Group has also made purchases to expand into new product segments especially in personal coverage and specialty (niche market) product lines. For instance it greatly widened its personal coverage of homes and autos through the purchase of OneBeacon's personal policy business in 2010. It has also moved to grow its operations outside of its core operating territories. The firm has acquired several small regional insurance companies in recent years to create a national presence across the US making targeted purchases to grow in the southeastern midwestern and northeastern regions.

An aggressive acquisition strategy has led to rapid revenue growth for Tower Group over the last few years including a 22% jump in sales to nearly $1.8 billion in 2011. However as with many property/casualty insurance firms Tower Group's profits were cut in half (dropping to some $60 million) due to larger than usual claims levels from catastrophic and severe weather events during the year.

CEO Michael Lee owns about 10% of Tower Group.

EXECUTIVES

Managing VP Midwest Zone and Specialty Underwriting, Fred Fontein
Managing VP Specialty Underwriting and Customized Solutions, David Brodsky, age 68
SVP and CFO, William E. Hitselberger, age 54
Managing VP Commercial Lines Executive, Mark Smith
Managing VP Corporate Planning and Development and Reinsurance, James Roberts
Chairman President and CEO, Michael H. Lee, age 54, $812,500 total compensation
SVP Marketing and Distribution, Christian K. Pechmann, age 62, $250,000 total compensation
SVP Actuarial Services, Joel S. Weiner, age 62, $255,150 total compensation
SVP Human Resources and Administration, Catherine M. Wragg
SVP Operations, Laurie Ranegar, age 50
SVP Claims, Scott T. Melnik
VP Reinsurance, Marina Contiero
Managing VP Planning, Angelica Facchini
SVP Specialty Business, Courtney C. Smith, age 64
SVP and Chief Actuary, William F. Dove
VP IT Governance, Michael J. Mihalik
VP Personal Lines, Edward A. Blomquist
Managing VP Specialty Underwriting, Robert Hedges
SVP and Chief Underwriting Officer, Gary S. Maier, age 47, $335,833 total compensation
Managing VP Corporate Development, Thomas (Tom) Song
Managing VP Commercial Lines, Brian Hosey
SVP National Marketing and Distribution, Bruce W. Sanderson, $268,500 total compensation
VP Operations, Joe Chamberlain
SVP General Counsel and Secretary, Elliot S. Orol, age 56, $325,000 total compensation
SVP and CIO, Salvatore V. Abano, age 48
VP Commercial Lines Small Business, Josephine Saenz-DeViteri
VP Information Technology, Matt Bates
VP and Corporate Counsel, Susan Eylward
VP Insurance Regulatory Counsel, Adam Perri
Managing VP West Zone, Larry Rogers
Managing VP Personal Lines, Dan Liparini
VP Home Office Operations, Rick Lustri
VP Information Technology, Saeed Fotovat
SVP and Chief Marketing Officer, Janice Co
Director, Jan R. Van Gorder, age 64
Director, Steven W. Schuster, age 57
Director, William A. Robbie, age 60
Director, Austin P. Young III, age 71
Director, Charles A. Bryan, age 65
Director, William W. Fox Jr., age 70

LOCATIONS

HQ: Tower Group Inc.
120 Broadway 31st. Fl., New York NY 10271
Phone: 212-655-2000 **Fax:** 212-655-2070
Web: www.twrgrp.com

PRODUCTS/OPERATIONS

2011 Sales

	$ mil.	% of total
Insurance premiums		
Commercial insurance	1,087	61
Personal lines	505	28
Net investment income	127	7
Commissions & fees	44	3
Net gains on investments	9	1
Insurance services	1	-
Total	**1,777**	**100**

Selected Acquisitions

2009
CastlePoint Holdings ($490 million Bermuda reinsurance)
HIG Inc. (aka Hermitage Insurance $130 million Southeast specialty property/casualty)
Specialty Underwriters' Alliance ($107 million Midwest niche commercial policies)
2010
Personal lines business of OneBeacon ($167 million Northeast private auto and homeowners' policies)
Renewal rights of AequiCap Commercial Automobile ($12 million Florida commercial auto and property)
2011
Renewal rights of NAV PAC Division of Navigators Group (midmarket commercial niche and auto policies)

Selected Operating Subsidiaries

Adirondack AIF LLC
CastlePoint Florida Insurance Company
CastlePoint Insurance Company
CastlePoint Management Corp.
CastlePoint National Insurance Company
CastlePoint Reinsurance Company
Hermitage Insurance Company
Kodiak Insurance Company
Massachusetts Homeland Insurance Company
Mountain Valley Indemnity Company
New Jersey Skylands Management LLC
North East Insurance Company
Preserver Insurance Company
Tower Insurance Company of New York (also operating as Tower Select Insurance Company in California)
Tower National Insurance Company
Tower Risk Management Corp.
York Insurance Company of Maine

COMPETITORS

ACE Limited
AIG
Allied World Assurance
Allstate
American Financial Group
AmTrust Financial
Chubb Corp
CNA Financial
Erie Insurance Exchange
GEICO
GNY Mutual Insurance
Hanover Insurance
Harleysville Group
Magna Carta Companies
Markel
Middlesex Mutual
Nationwide
Navigators
NYCM
Peerless Insurance
Philadelphia Insurance Companies
Preferred Mutual
Progressive Corporation
QBE Regional
Quincy Mutual

RLI
Safeco
Selective Insurance
State Farm
The Hartford
Travelers Companies
United States Liability Insurance Group
Utica Mutual Insurance
W. R. Berkley

HISTORICAL FINANCIALS

Company Type: Public

Income Statement FYE: December 31

	ASSETS ($ mil.)	NET INCOME ($ mil.)	INCOME AS % OF ASSETS	EMPLOYEES
12/11	4,442	60	1.4%	1,417
12/10	4,214	117	2.8%	1,360
12/09	3,312	109	3.3%	987
12/08	1,533	57	3.7%	588
12/07	1,354	45	3.3%	549
Annual Growth	34.6%	7.5%	—	26.8%

2011 Year-End Financials

Debt ratio: 9.61%
Return on equity: 5.82%
Cash ($ mil.): 114
Current ratio: —
Long-term debt ($ mil.): 426
No. of shares (mil.): 39
Dividends
Yield: —
Payout: 46.77%
Market value ($ mil.): 791

	STOCK PRICE ($) FY Close	P/E High/Low		PER SHARE ($) Earnings	Dividends	Book Value
12/11	20.17	19	13	1.47	0.00	26.37
12/10	25.60	10	7	2.70	0.39	26.22
12/09	23.41	11	7	2.76	0.26	23.35
12/08	28.21	13	7	2.47	0.20	14.36
12/07	33.40	18	12	1.93	0.15	13.34
Annual Growth	(11.8%)	—	—	(6.6%)	—	18.6%

TowneBank

LOCATIONS

HQ: TowneBank
5716 High Street, Portsmouth, VA 23703
Phone: 757 638-7500
Web: www.townebank.com

PRODUCTS/OPERATIONS

2009 Sales

	$ mil.	% of total
Interest		
Loans including fees	139	63
Investment securities	18	8
Other	3	1
Noninterest		
Net insurance commissions & other title fees & income	13	6
Net residential mortgage brokerage	11	5
Net real estate brokerage & property management	11	5
Gain on securities available for sale	11	5
Service charges on deposit accounts	6	3
Other	8	4
Total	**223**	**100**

Selected Subsidiaries and Affiliates

NewTowne Mortgage LLC
Prudential Towne Realty
TFA Benefits
Towne Insurance
Towne Investment Group
Towne Investments LLC
Towne Mortgage LLC
TowneBank Commercial Mortgage LLC
TowneBank Investment Corporation
TowneBank Mortgage
TowneBank of Currituck

HISTORICAL FINANCIALS

Company Type:

Income Statement FYE: December 31

	ASSETS ($ mil.)	NET INCOME ($ mil.)	INCOME AS % OF ASSETS	EMPLOYEES
12/11	4,081	33	0.8%	1,540
12/10	3,871	30	0.8%	1,512
12/09	3,606	26	0.7%	1,215
12/08	3,133	23	0.8%	1,131
12/07	2,501	23	0.9%	1,020
Annual Growth	13.0%	9.4%	—	10.8%

2011 Year-End Financials

Debt ratio: 7.49%
Return on equity: 6.48%
Cash ($ mil.): 314
Current ratio: —
Long-term debt ($ mil.): 305
No. of shares (mil.): 30
Dividends
Yield: —
Payout: 40.51%
Market value ($ mil.): 367

	STOCK PRICE ($) FY Close	P/E High/Low		PER SHARE ($) Earnings	Dividends	Book Value
12/11	12.24	22	14	0.77	0.00	17.13
12/10	15.89	24	15	0.71	0.31	16.54
12/09	11.68	38	17	0.64	0.31	16.18
12/08	24.79	30	14	0.86	0.31	16.60
12/07	16.10	22	16	0.89	0.31	10.35
Annual Growth	(6.6%)	—	—	(3.6%)	—	13.4%

Toyota Motor Credit Corp.

Toyota Motor Credit (TMCC) is the US financing arm of Toyota Financial Services which is a subsidiary of Toyota Motor Corporation the world's largest carmaker. TMCC provides retail leasing retail and wholesale sales financing and other financial services to Toyota and Lexus dealers and their customers for the purchase of new and used cars and trucks. It offers similar services to Toyota industrial equipment dealers. TMCC which underwrites and services the finance contracts operates three regional customer service centers and some 30 dealer sales and service branches across the US and Puerto Rico.

Through subsidiary Toyota Motor Insurance Services the company also underwrites and sells insurance products such as extended service coverage total loss protection and prepaid maintenance protection.

TMCC a retail loan portfolio worth approximately $45 billion. Around half of its lease assets are in its top five markets. California is the largest accounting for about a fifth of its lease assets followed by Texas New York and New Jersey. The company's credit losses which spiked during the depths of the economic crisis in 2008 have since come back down to Earth and TMCC returned to profitability in fiscal 2010 in spite of lower loan volumes and revenues.

Natural disasters in Japan and Thailand led to a disruption in Toyota vehicle manufacturing in 2012. As a result Toyota sales experienced a slight slump which contributed to an 8% decline in TMCC's revenues for the year. Investment and other income also declined and the company's profits for the year slipped 20% to $1.5 billion. The declines were slightly offset by cuts in operating and administrative expenses which had risen in fiscal 2011.

EXECUTIVES

President CEO and Director, George E. Borst, age 63, $432,938 total compensation
SVP Chief Administrative Officer Secretary and Director, David Pelliccioni, age 64, $305,401 total compensation
Director; Chairman Toyota Motor Sales, Yoshimi Inaba, age 66
Group VP and CFO TMCC and TFSA, Christopher (Chris) Ballinger, age 55
EVP Treasurer and Director, Ichiro Yajima, age 53
Chief Accounting Officer, Carman C. Turner Jr., age 49
EVP Treasurer and Director, Kiyohisa Funasaki, age 49
VP Accounting and Tax TMCC and TFSA, Ron Chu
President CEO and Director, George E. Borst, age 62
SVP Chief Administrative Officer Secretary and Director, David Pelliccioni, age 64
Director; Chairman Toyota Motor Sales, Yoshimi Inaba, age 66
Director, Yukitoshi (Yuki) Funo, age 65
Director, Takeshi Suzuki, age 63
Director, James E. (Jim) Lentz III, age 56
Director, Takahiko Ijichi, age 59
Director, Eiji Hirano, age 61
EVP Treasurer and Director, Ichiro Yajima, age 53
Director; Chairman and CEO TFSA, Takuo Sasaki
EVP Treasurer and Director, Kiyohisa Funasaki, age 49
Auditors: PricewaterhouseCoopersLLP

LOCATIONS

HQ: Toyota Motor Credit Corporation
19001 S. Western Ave., Torrance CA 90509
Phone: 310-468-1310 **Fax:** 310-468-7800
Web: www.toyotafinancial.com

PRODUCTS/OPERATIONS

2012 Sales

	$ mil.	% of total
Financing		
Operating leases	4,693	58
Retail	2,371	29
Dealer	365	5
Insurance premiums earned & contract revenues	604	7
Investment & other	113	1
Total	**8,146**	**100**

COMPETITORS

Ally Financial
American Honda Finance
AutoNation
Capital One Auto Finance
Daimler Financial Services
Ford Motor Credit
GM Financial
Mercedes-Benz Credit
Volkswagen Financial Services
Volvo Car Finance
Wells Fargo Auto Finance

HISTORICAL FINANCIALS

Company Type: Subsidiary

Income Statement FYE: March 31

	REVENUE ($ mil.)	NET INCOME ($ mil.)	NET PROFIT MARGIN	EMPLOYEES
03/12	8,146	1,486	18.2%	3,220
03/11	8,843	1,853	21.0%	3,170
03/10	8,843	1,063	12.0%	3,250
03/09	9,232	(623)	—	3,300
03/08	8,878	(107)	—	3,200
Annual Growth	(2.1%)	—	—	0.2%

2012 Year-End Financials

Debt ratio: 82.37%
Return on equity: 19.39%
Cash ($ mil.): 5,060
Current ratio: 23.64
Long-term debt ($ mil.): 51,987
No. of shares (mil.): 0
Dividends
Yield: —
Payout: —
Market value ($ mil.): —

Tractor Supply Co.

Farmers and ranchers can gear up for more than just a tractor pull at Tractor Supply Company (TSC). Besides providing agricultural machine parts the farm and ranch supply retailer offers animal feeds fencing power tools riding mowers and work clothing as well as tools for gardening irrigation welding and towing. TSC offers both name-brand merchandise and its own stable of private-label goods. It operates about 1085 stores in some 45 states under the Tractor Supply Company and Del's Farm Supply banners. Stores are concentrated in rural areas and near large cities to cater to full- and part-time farmers ranchers and contractors. TSC which also operates a growing online business was founded in 1938.

Already the largest farm and ranch supply chain in the nation TSC has rapidly expanded its retail footprint in recent years and will continue to do so in the future. In 2011 the chain added about 85 stores and posted strong financial results. Indeed sales topped $4.2 billion an increase of about 16% vs. 2010. Same-store sales (generally considered the best indicator of a retail chain's health) rose more than 8% and net income jumped nearly 33% during the same period.

Ultimately the company aims to operate some 1300 Tractor Supply stores nationwide. It has already identified more than 800 new markets for potential stores and is open to acquisition opportunities. Meanwhile TSC has stemmed the growth of Del's Farm Supply while working to refine its retail concept. With only about 25 Del's stores in the Pacific Northwest and Hawaii TSC opted not to add any new locations in 2010 or 2011. To capitalize on the rebound in the farm and general retail economy TSC is working to add up to 95 new stores in 2012.

EXECUTIVES

SVP General Counsel and Corporate Secretary, Benjamin F. Parrish Jr.
Chairman and CEO, James F. (Jim) Wright, age 62, $952,621 total compensation
SVP and Chief People Officer, Kimberly D. (Kim) Vella, age 45, $273,118 total compensation
SVP and CIO, James Callison
EVP CFO and Treasurer, Anthony F. (Tony) Crudele, age 55, $399,900 total compensation
President COO and Chief Merchandising Officer, Gregory A. (Greg) Sandfort, age 57, $424,882 total compensation
Director Investor Relations, Randy Guiler
SVP Store Operations, Lee Downing
SVP Finance and Strategy, Alex Stanton
Vice President of marketing for Special Products Co, Steve Rolin
Director, Edna K. Morris, age 60
Director, Peter D. Bewley, age 66
Director, George MacKenzie Jr., age 63
Director, William (Bill) Bass, age 49
Director, John C. (John) Adams Jr., age 64
Director, Cynthia T. Jamison, age 52
Director, Jack C. Bingleman, age 69
Auditors: Ernst&YoungLLP

LOCATIONS

HQ: Tractor Supply Co.
200 Powell Place, Brentwood, TN 37027
Phone: 615 440-4000
Web: www.tractorsupply.com

2011 Locations

	No.
Texas	129
Ohio	71
Michigan	65
New	65
Pennsylvania	62
Tennessee	62
North	47
Kentucky	44
Georgia	43
Indiana	40
Florida	38
Virginia	36
Alabama	31
Oklahoma	28
South	26
Louisiana	24
California	20
Washington	19
West	19
Arkansas	16
Illinois	16
Missouri	16
Wisconsin	15
Kansas	13
Mississippi	13
Maine	12
Nebraska	12
New	12
New	11
Massachusetts	10
Maryland	9
Minnesota	9
Connecticut	8
Iowa	8
North	7
South	6
Vermont	6
New	5
Delaware	3
Oregon	3
Hawaii	2
Montana	2
Idaho	1
Rhode	1
Total	**1,085**

PRODUCTS/OPERATIONS

2011 Sales

	% of total
Livestock &	40
Hardware tools &	23
Seasonal gift &	21
Clothing &	10
Agriculture	6
Total	**100**

Selected Private Label Brands

4health (pet food)
Bit & Bridle (apparel)
C.E. Schmidt (apparel and footwear)
Countyline (livestock farm and ranch equipment)
Groundwork (lawn and garden supplies)
Huskee (outdoor power equipment)
JobSmart (hardware and tools)
Masterhand (tools and tool chests)
Milepost (equine products)
Paws ' n Claws (pet food)
Red Shed (gifts and collectibles)
Retriever (pet food)
Royal Wing (bird feeding supplies)
Traveller (truck and automotive products)

COMPETITORS

Ace Hardware
Agrium
Farm King
Home Depot
Lowe' s
Miles Enterprises
Northern Tool
Sears
Southern States
Tennessee Farmers Co-op
True Value
Wal-Mart
Wilbur-Ellis

HISTORICAL FINANCIALS

Company Type: Public

Income Statement FYE: December 31

	REVENUE ($ mil.)	NET INCOME ($ mil.)	NET PROFIT MARGIN	EMPLOYEES
12/11	4,232	222	5.3%	16,400
12/10	3,638	167	4.6%	14,700
12/09	3,206	115	3.6%	13,300
12/08	3,007	81	2.7%	12,800
12/07	2,703	96	3.6%	11,600
Annual Growth	11.9%	23.3%	—	9.0%

2011 Year-End Financials

Debt ratio: 0.08%
Return on equity: 22.09%
Cash ($ mil.): 176
Current ratio: 236.69
Long-term debt ($ mil.): 1
No. of shares (mil.): 71
Dividends
Yield: —
Payout: 14.29%
Market value ($ mil.): 4,999

	STOCK PRICE ($) FY Close	P/E High	P/E Low	PER SHARE ($) Earnings	Dividends	Book Value
12/11	70.15	24	15	3.01	0.00	14.15
12/10	48.40	31	16	2.25	0.00	12.82
12/09	54.03	34	18	1.58	0.00	10.16
12/08	34.52	41	25	1.10	0.00	8.46
12/07	35.36	46	29	1.20	0.00	7.54
Annual Growth	18.7%	—	—	25.8%	—	17.0%

TRANSAMMONIA INC.

EXECUTIVES

Director Human Resources, Marguerite Harrington
SVP and CFO, Edward G. Weiner
Chairman and CEO, Ronald P. Stanton
CIO, Benjamin Tan

LOCATIONS

HQ: Transammonia Inc.
320 Park Ave., New York NY 10022-6987
Phone: 212-223-3200 **Fax:** 212-759-1410
Web: www.transammonia.com

PRODUCTS/OPERATIONS

Major Subsidiari
Sea-3 (liquefied propane)
Trammo Gas (LPG)
Trammo Petroleum (crude oil and oil products)
Trammochem (petrochem
Transammonia (fertilize

COMPETITORS

Cargill
CF Industries
ConAgra
Dynegy
HELM
Magellan Midstream
Yara

HISTORICAL FINANCIALS

Company Type: Private

Income Statement FYE: December 31

	REVENUE ($ mil.)	NET INCOME ($ mil.)	NET PROFIT MARGIN	EMPLOYEES
12/11	11,303	31	0.3%	320
12/10	8,414	35	0.4%	0
12/09	5,485	21	0.4%	0
12/08	11,214	68	0.6%	0
Annual Growth	0.3%	(22.9%)	—	—

2011 Year-End Financials

Debt ratio: —
Return on equity: 0.30%
Cash ($ mil.): 207
Current ratio: 0.90
Long-term debt ($ mil.): —
Dividends
Yield: —
Payout: —
Market value ($ mil.): —

TravelCenters of America LLC

TravelCenters of America (TCA) is in the fuel food and relaxation business for the long haul. The company's network of more than 235 interstate highway travel centers in some 40 US states and Ontario Canada is one of the largest in North America. Its TCA and Petro locations provide fuel fast-food and sit-down restaurants (Country Pride Buckhorn Family) convenience stores and lodging. With professional truck drivers as its main customers some outlets also offer "trucker-only" services such as laundry and shower facilities TV rooms and truck repair. TCA leases 185 of its 235 locations from Hospitality Properties Trust (HPT) its largest shareholder.

Operations

The company operates and franchises travel centers under two brands: TravelCenters of America with more than 165 locations; and Petro Stopping Centers (acquired in 2007) with about 70 locations about 50 of which company operated. TCA also operates "RoadSquad" the largest nationwide emergency roadside service network with more than 400 heavy-duty emergency vehicles.

Financial Analysis

After losing money every year since it was acquired by HPT in 2007 TravelCenters of America (TCA) finally turned a profit in 2011. Net income exceeded $23 million in 2011 compared with a loss of more than $65 million the prior year. Sales increased by about 32% in 2011 vs. 2010 driven by a 38% jump in fuel sales vs. a nearly 10% gain in nonfuel sales. The strong performance in 2011 followed a healthy 2010 when TCA's sales rose nearly 27% again buoyed by a hefty rise in fuel sales.

Strategy

The company is building its cross-country network of travel centers through acquisitions by opportunistically buying up smaller competitors struggling as a result of the recent recession. To that end it acquired eight travel centers for an aggregate price of $37 million in 2011 and in 2012 agreed to purchase eight more for about $32 million. With fuel accounting for such a large portion of its total sales (84% in 2011 vs. 80% in 2010) TCA is vulnerable to wild swings in prices. (About 90% of TCA's historical fuel sales are diesel while 10% are gasoline. The company is looking into expanding into natural gas as a motor fuel.) Another wildcard for the company is the 2010 merger of its two largest rivals: Pilot Travel Centers and Flying J to form Pilot Flying J an operator of more than 550 travel centers across North America. The merger created a more formidable competitor and could hinder TCA's sales and new-found profitability.

Ownership

The real estate investment firm Hospitality Properties Trust owns nearly 10% of TCA's shares.

EXECUTIVES

Secretary, Jennifer B. Clark, age 50
President CEO and Director, Thomas M. O'Brien, age 45, $300,000 total compensation
Managing Director, Barry M. Portnoy, age 66
Director Internal Audit and Compliance, William J. Sheehan
Director Advertising and Public Relations, Tom Liutkus
SVP Retail Marketing and Operations, Skip McGary
VP Investor Relations, Timothy A. (Tim) Bonang
Director Fleet Sales, Stan Culpepper
SVP Food Operations and Marketing, John Ponczoch
EVP Sales, Michael J. Lombardi, age 60, $339,000 total compensation
EVP, Ara A. Bagdasarian, age 55
EVP CFO and Treasurer, Andrew J. Rebholz, age 47, $275,000 total compensation
Manager Investor Relations, Carlynn Finn
EVP and General Counsel, Mark R. Young, age 49, $275,000 total compensation
EVP, Barry A. Richards, age 59
VP Fuel Supply, Tom Komos
Shop Coordinator, Jennifer Ina
Regional Sales Representative Canada, Ann Seidel
Regional Sales Representative West, Tom Smith
Regional Sales Representative Central, Mikle Gray
Regional Sales Representative South, Dan Backus
Regional Sales Representative Midwest, Elise Repp
Regional Sales Representative Southeast, Mike Nichols
Director Inside Sales, Sandra Sanford
Regional Sales Manager Northeast, Bob Boehnel
Regional Sales Manager Central, Kathy Perry
Regional Sales Manager Southeast, George Jacobson
Regional Sales Manager, Steve Miller
Regional Sales Manager, Coni Vander Aarde
National Accounts Fleet Sales, Jack Hassett
SVP Construction Maintenance and Environmental, Peter P. Ward
President CEO and Director, Thomas M. O'Brien, age 45
Managing Director, Barry M. Portnoy, age 66
Director, Patrick F. Donelan, age 69
Director, Arthur G. Koumantzelis, age 82
Director, Barbara D. Gilmore, age 61
Auditors: Ernst&YoungLLP

LOCATIONS

HQ: TravelCenters of America LLC
24601 Center Ridge Rd. Ste. 200, Westlake OH 44145-5639
Phone: 440-808-9100 **Fax:** 440-808-3306
Web: www.tatravelcenters.com

PRODUCTS/OPERATIONS

2011 Locations

	No.
TravelCenters of	168
Petro Stopping	69
Total	237

2011 Sales

	$ mil.	% of total
Fuel	6,603	84
Non-fuel	1,271	16
Rent & royalties	14	-
Total	7,888	100

COMPETITORS

Bowlin Travel Centers
Chevron
Exxon Mobil
Love' s Country Stores
Marathon Petroleum
Pilot Flying J
Royal Dutch Shell
Sapp Bros Travel Centers
Stuckey' s

HISTORICAL FINANCIALS

Company Type: Public

Income Statement FYE: December 31

	REVENUE ($ mil.)	NET INCOME ($ mil.)	NET PROFIT MARGIN	EMPLOYEES
12/11	7,888	23	0.3%	16,000
12/10	5,962	(65)	—	15,170
12/09	4,699	(89)	—	14,680
12/08	7,658	(40)	—	15,430
12/07	5,813	(101)	—	16,000
Annual Growth	7.9%	—	—	0.0%

2011 Year-End Financials

Debt ratio: 35.84%
Return on equity: 7.40%
Cash ($ mil.): 118
Current ratio: 168.29
Long-term debt ($ mil.): 364
No. of shares (mil.): 28
Dividends
Yield: —
Payout: —
Market value ($ mil.): 122

	STOCK PRICE ($) FY Close	P/E High/Low		PER SHARE ($) Earnings	Dividends	Book Value
12/11	4.25	13	3	0.98	0.00	11.07
12/10	3.77	—	—	(3.78)	0.00	13.95
12/09	4.42	—	—	(5.38)	0.00	18.23
12/08	2.40	—	—	(2.71)	0.00	24.19
12/07	12.50	—	—	(8.68)	0.00	30.33
Annual Growth	(23.6%)	—	—	—	—	(22.3%)

Travelers Companies Inc (The)

Running a business is a risk The Travelers Companies will insure. While it does offer personal auto and homeowners insurance the company's largest segment is commercial property/casualty insurance to businesses big and small. It is one of the largest business insurers in the US providing commercial auto property workers' compensation marine and general and financial liability coverage to companies in North America and the UK. The company also offers surety and fidelity bonds as well as professional and management liability coverage for commercial operations. The Travelers distributes its products through independent agencies and brokers.

In addition to serving general commercial accounts The Travelers maintains a group of industry-specific underwriting units serving the agribusiness construction oil and gas and technology industries as well as the public sector.

Personal insurance now accounts for a third of the company's premiums and it is slowly building up the business with geographic expansion. The personal products are distributed through some 12500 independent agents employee and affinity groups and direct marketing.

While the vast majority (over 90%) of the company's business is in the US it does have a presence in the UK where it operates through two arms: Travelers Insurance Company and Travelers Syndicate 5000 within Lloyd's of London. The two businesses offer commercial property/casualty and risk management services. Travelers also has modest operations in the neighboring countries of Canada and Ireland.

After reducing its international holdings in 2010 the company made a move to expand outside of its comfort zone by acquiring a 43% stake in J. Malucelli a leading provider of surety policies in the fast-growing Brazilian market. The move is part of Travelers' strategy to pursue opportunities in emerging markets; the firm is also considering expansion in high-growth countries such as India and China.

Despite general market turmoil The Traveler's revenues have remained placid in recent years —a sign that the company has spread itself smoothly across industries and took no significant hits to its premiums. Its investment income sagged briefly when its (and everyone else's) investments slipped in value during 2008. However the company's investment income revived just in time for an uptick of catastrophe claims in 2010 and 2011due to harsh weather events. Its net income dropped both years following common share repurchases.

HISTORY

St. Paul Minnesota was a boomtown in 1852 thanks to traffic on the Mississippi. Settlers knew fire insurance was a must in their wooden town but there were no local insurers. Buying policies from eastern companies and getting claims processed was difficult —especially in the winter when river traffic stopped.

In 1853 a group of local investors led by George and John Farrington and Alexander Wilkin formed St. Paul Mutual Insurance a mixed stock and mutual company (mutual members shared in the firm's profits and losses while stockholders could benefit by selling if the company's value rose). St. Paul Mutual sold its first policy the following year.

The company changed its name in 1865 to St. Paul Fire and Marine Insurance stopped offering mutual policies and expanded throughout the Midwest. Claims from the Chicago Fire in 1871 nearly sank the company which assessed its shareholders $15 for each share of stock but prompt and full payment of claims resulted in more business. By the turn of the century St. Paul Fire and Marine was operating nationwide.

Although the company was hard hit by shipping losses in WWI it continued expanding joining other US insurers in the American Foreign Insurance Association to market insurance in Europe.

In 1926 St. Paul Fire and Marine organized its first subsidiary St. Paul Mercury Indemnity to write liability insurance policies. Other additions included coverage for automobiles aircraft burglary and robbery and in 1940 turkey farming.

During WWII St. Paul Fire and Marine joined the War Damage Corp. a government-financed consortium that paid claims for war damage. The St. Paul Companies was formed in 1968 as the umbrella organization for the various subsidiaries and the firm grew through purchases.

Lines of business blossomed during the 1970s including life and title insurance leasing a mail-order consumer finance company oil and gas and real estate. Many of these were sold during the 1980s but one The John Nuveen Co. (1974) became the nucleus of St. Paul's financial services operations.

St. Paul posted a loss in 1992 after paying out huge claims related to Hurricane Andrew. In 1995 the company expanded its malpractice line when it bought NML Insurance. The Minet unit (a brokerage business) started Global Media Services that year to focus on insurance for the telecommunications industry. The division also bought London-based Special Risk Service a top insurance broker and Boston-based William Gallagher Associates a high-tech and biotechnology insurer.

In 1997 St. Paul sold its unprofitable Minet division. That year and the next the company was struck by catastrophic losses more than $150 million total.

St. Paul acquired USF&G in 1998. The purchase triggered a round of job cuts as the company assimilated its new operations; the deal also slammed the insurer's earnings. To focus on its more profitable commercial business the firm sold its personal insurance business (1999) and jettisoned its nonstandard auto insurance business (2000). In 2000 it bought MMI Companies to build its health care risk operations and decided later that year to close Unionamerica Holdings an unprofitable subsidiary of MMI. In 2001 St. Paul sold F&G Life a subsidiary of USF&G to UK-based insurer Old Mutual.

The World Trade Center attacks (in which the company paid out almost $1 billion in claims) and other disasters combined to make reinsurance a costlier game of dice. The company spun off its reinsurance business St. Paul Re into Bermuda-based Platinum Underwriters in 2002.

In a $16 billion blockbuster deal The St. Paul Companies acquired Travelers Property Casualty in 2004. (Travelers had been a subsidiary of Citigroup until its IPO in early 2002.) Reflecting the acquisition the company then changed its name to The St. Paul Travelers Companies.

The company got back to insurance basics long before getting back to basics was cool (or in some cases desperately necessary). It sold off its nearly 80% stake in asset management business Nuveen Investments in a series of transactions during 2005.

In early 2007 the company changed its name to The Travelers Companies Inc. and reclaimed the trademarked red umbrella logo used in previous Travelers incarnations.

EXECUTIVES

Vice Chairman, Charles J. (Chuck) Clarke, age 76
Vice Chairman, Irwin R. Ettinger, age 73
EVP and Chief Administrative Officer, Andy F. Bessette, age 58
Chairman and CEO, Jay S. Fishman, age 59, $1,000,000 total compensation
Media Contact Corporate and Financial, Shane Boyd
President Travelers First Party Group, James Chapman
Vice Chairman and Chief Investment Officer, William H. Heyman, age 63, $650,000 total compensation
President and CCOO, Brian W. MacLean, age 58, $700,000 total compensation
Vice Chairman and CFO, Jay S. Benet, age 59, $650,000 total compensation
EVP Human Resources, John P. Clifford Jr., age 56
EVP Strategic Development and Treasurer, Maria Olivo, age 47
EVP; CEO Claim Services and Personal Insurance, Doreen Spadorcia, age 54
SVP Human Resources, Diane D. Bengston
EVP and General Counsel, Kenneth F. (Ken) Spence III, age 56
EVP Marketing and Communications, Lisa M. Caputo, age 48
EVP Field Management, John J. Albano, age 62
VP Travelers Wedding Insurance, Chantal Cyr
Vice Chairman, Alan D. Schnitzer, age 46, $650,000 total compensation
Media Contact Auto and Homeowners Insurance, Matt Bordonaro
EVP Business Insurance, William E. (Bill) Cunningham Jr., age 46
President Field Management, Patrick Kinney
SVP Business Insurance, Michael F. Klein
Media Contact Corporate and Financial and Non-U.S. Operations, Jennifer Wislocki
EVP Public Policy, Joan Kois Woodward
SVP Investor Relations, Gabriella Nawi
President Inland Marine Business, Joseph Tracy
EVP Enterprise Risk Management Chief Risk Officer and Business Conduct Officer, Bill Hannon
SVP and Corporate Secretary, Matthew S. Furman
President Bond and Financial Products, Thomas M. Kunkel
President Personal Insurance, Greg Toczydlowski
President and CEO Select Accounts and Agribusiness, Marc Schmittlein
President International, Kevin C. Smith
Media Contact Business Insurance, Gail Liebl
Media Contact Business Insurance, Jennifer Bagdade
Media Contact Non-U.S. Operations, Karen Bigwood
Investor Relations Institutional Investors, Andrew Hersom
Shareholder Services Individual Investors, Marc Parr
VP Product and Underwriting Travelers Select Accounts, John P. O'Connor
President Travelers Construction, Bill Teed
SVP Claim, Patrick Gee
VP Enterprise Diversity and Inclusion, Joelle Hayes
EVP and CIO, Madelyn Lankton

Media Contact Corporate and Financial, Delker Herbert
Media Contact Public Policy and Community Relations, Ashley M. Maagero
President Travelers Commercial Accounts, Scott Higgins
VP RMIS, Michael Strietelmeier
VP Community Relations, Marlene Ibsen
EVP - Claim Services, Robert C. Brody
Vice Chairman, Charles J. (Chuck) Clarke, age 76
Director, Janet M. Dolan, age 62
Vice Chairman, Irwin R. Ettinger, age 73
Director, John H. Dasburg, age 69
Director, Donald J. Shepard, age 65
Director, Kenneth M. (Ken) Duberstein, age 67
Director, Thomas R. Hodgson, age 70
Vice Chairman and Chief Investment Officer, William H. Heyman, age 63
Director, Lawrence G. Graev, age 67
Director, Cleve L. Killingsworth Jr., age 60
Director, Laurie J. Thomsen, age 54
Director, Patricia L. Higgins, age 62
Director, Alan L. Beller, age 63
Vice Chairman and CFO, Jay S. Benet, age 59
Vice Chairman, Alan D. Schnitzer, age 46
Director, William J. Kane
Auditors: KPMGLLP

LOCATIONS

HQ: The Travelers Companies Inc.
485 Lexington Ave., New York NY 10017-2630
Phone: 917-778-6000 **Fax:** 516-750-1683
Web: www.atchealthcare.com

PRODUCTS/OPERATIONS

2011 Earned Premiums

Business insurance	52
Financial professional & international insurance	14

Selected Subsidiaries

St. Paul Fire and Marine Insurance Company
Travelers Property Casualty Corp.
The Standard Fire Insurance Company
Travelers Casualty and Surety Company
Travelers Casualty and Surety Company of America
The Travelers Indemnity Company
First Floridian Auto and Home Insurance Company
First Trenton Indemnity Company (Travelers of New Jersey)
The Premier Insurance Co. of Massachusetts
Travelers Insurance Company Limited (UK)

COMPETITORS

ACE Limited
AIG
Allianz
Allstate
American Financial Group
AXA
Chubb Corp
CNA Financial
Liberty Mutual Agency
Markel
Nationwide
The Hartford
W. R. Berkley
Zurich Financial Services

HISTORICAL FINANCIALS

Company Type: Public

Income Statement FYE: December 31

	ASSETS ($ mil.)	NET INCOME ($ mil.)	INCOME AS % OF ASSETS	EMPLOYEES
12/11	104,602	1,426	1.4%	30,600
12/10	105,181	3,216	3.1%	32,000
12/09	109,560	3,622	3.3%	32,000
12/08	109,751	2,924	2.7%	33,000
12/07	115,224	4,601	4.0%	33,300
Annual Growth	(2.4%)	(25.4%)	—	(2.1%)

2011 Year-End Financials

Debt ratio: 6.22%
Return on equity: 5.83%
Cash ($ mil.): 214
Current ratio: —
Long-term debt ($ mil.): 6,505
No. of shares (mil.): 392
Dividends
Yield: —
Payout: 47.32%
Market value ($ mil.): 23,242

	STOCK PRICE ($) FY Close	P/E High	P/E Low	PER SHARE ($) Earnings	Dividends	Book Value
12/11	59.17	19	14	3.36	0.00	62.31
12/10	55.71	9	7	6.62	1.41	58.62
12/09	49.86	9	5	6.33	1.23	52.69
12/08	45.20	11	6	4.82	1.19	43.27
12/07	53.80	8	7	6.86	1.13	42.40
Annual Growth	2.4%	—	—	(16.3%)	—	10.1%

Trico Bancshares (Chico, CA)

People looking for a community bank in California's Sacramento Valley can try TriCo. TriCo Bancshares is the holding company for Tri Counties Bank which serves customers through approximately 70 traditional and in-store branches in northern California. Founded in 1974 Tri Counties Bank provides a variety of deposit services including checking and savings accounts money market accounts and CDs. Most patrons are retail customers and small to midsized businesses. The bank primarily originates real estate mortgages which account for more than 60% of its loan portfolio; consumer loans contribute about 30%.

In addition to its retail banking products and services the company provides wholesale banking and investment services; TriCo offers brokerage services through an arrangement with Raymond James Financial. The company does not provide trust or international banking services.

The bank has been growing primarily through the opening of new branches; it frequently opens branches within grocery stores or other retailers including Wal-Mart. TriCo took a different tack with the 2010 acquisition of the three branches of Granite Community Bank which had been seized by regulators. The transaction which also included most of the failed bank's assets and deposits was facilitated by the FDIC and includes a loss-sharing agreement with the agency. The following year TriCo acquired Citizens Bank of Northern California. The FDIC-assisted deal included seven branches.

The acquisitions are part of TriCo's strategy of adding new customers. The company has remained profitable however it reported drops in net income in 2009 and 2010 as demand for loans remained weak during the recession and provisions for loan losses grew. Fewer loans resulted in reduced interest income. Revenues and net income both grew in 2011 as both net interest and noninterest income rose and loan loss provisions decreased. The growth was primarily related to the acquisition of Citizens Bank and its associated net interest income. Despite new regulations limiting the amount of overdraft fees a bank may charge its customers TriCo's noninterest income also grew due to heavier ATM usage mortgage banking servicing fees and commissions on sale of nondeposit investment products.

EXECUTIVES

EVP and CFO TriCo Bancshares and Tri Counties Bank, Thomas J. (Tom) Reddish, age 52, $278,920 total compensation
EVP and Chief Credit Officer Tri Counties Bank, Craig Carney, age 53, $218,158 total compensation
EVP Wholesale Banking Tri Counties Bank, Richard O'Sullivan, age 55, $242,812 total compensation
Chairman TriCo Bancshares and Tri Counties Bank, William J. Casey, age 67
Secretary and Director, Alex A. Vereschagin Jr., age 76
President CEO and Director TriCo Bancshares and Tri Counties Bank, Richard P. Smith, age 54, $483,691 total compensation
Vice Chairman, Donald E. Murphy, age 76
SVP and Director Human Resources Tri Counties Bank, Richard A. (Rick) Miller, age 68
SVP and CIO Tri Counties Bank, Raymond (Ray) Rios, age 55
Public Relations, Nicole Johansson
EVP Retail Banking and Bank Operations Tri Counties Bank, Daniel K. (Dan) Bailey, age 43, $229,881 total compensation
Media Relations, Jessica Freitas
Shareholder Relations, Suzanne Youngs
Executive Vice President; Chief Risk Officer, Carol Ward
Executive Vice President - Wholesale Banking of Tri Counties Bank, Richard Sullivan
Secretary and Director, Alex A. Vereschagin Jr., age 76
President CEO and Director TriCo Bancshares and Tri Counties Bank, Richard P. Smith, age 54
Director, Donald J. Amaral, age 59
Vice Chairman, Donald E. Murphy, age 76
Director, Craig S. Compton, age 56
Director, Carroll R. Taresh, age 74
Director, Steve G. Nettleton, age 73
Director, Michael W. Koehnen, age 51
Director, L. Gage Chrysler III, age 58
Director, W. Virginia Walker, age 67
Auditors: MossAdamsLLP

LOCATIONS

HQ: TriCo Bancshares
63 Constitution Dr., Chico CA 95973
Phone: 530-898-0300 **Fax:** 530-898-0310
Web: www.tricountiesbank.com

PRODUCTS/OPERATIONS

2011 Sales

	$ mil.	% of total
Interest		
Loans including fees	92	64
Debt securities	9	6
Other	1	1
Noninterest		
Service charges & fees	23	16
Bargain purchase gain	7	5
Gain on sale of loans	3	2
Other	8	6
Total	145	100

COMPETITORS

Bank of America
Bank of the West
Central Valley Community Bancorp
North Valley Bancorp
PremierWest
UnionBanCal
Wells Fargo
Westamerica

HISTORICAL FINANCIALS

Company Type: Public

Income Statement FYE: December 31

	ASSETS ($ mil.)	NET INCOME ($ mil.)	INCOME AS % OF ASSETS	EMPLOYEES
12/11	2,555	18	0.7%	799
12/10	2,189	6	0.3%	749
12/09	2,170	9	0.5%	739
12/08	2,043	16	0.8%	697
12/07	1,980	25	1.3%	716
Annual Growth	6.6%	(7.8%)	—	2.8%

2011 Year-End Financials

Debt ratio: 4.45%
Return on equity: 8.59%
Cash ($ mil.): 637
Current ratio: —
Long-term debt ($ mil.): 113
No. of shares (mil.): 15
Dividends
Yield: —
Payout: 31.03%
Market value ($ mil.): 227

	STOCK PRICE ($) FY Close	P/E High	P/E Low	PER SHARE ($) Earnings	Dividends	Book Value
12/11	14.22	14	10	1.16	0.00	13.55
12/10	16.15	61	35	0.37	0.40	12.64
12/09	16.65	40	17	0.62	0.52	12.71
12/08	24.97	31	9	1.05	0.52	12.56
12/07	19.30	17	12	1.57	0.52	11.87
Annual Growth	(7.4%)	—	—	(7.3%)	—	3.4%

Trustco Bank Corp. (N.Y.)

In Banking They Trust. TrustCo Bank Corp is the holding company for Trustco Bank which operates in eastern New York central and western Florida and parts of Vermont Massachusetts and New Jersey. It has more than 130 locations offering personal and business customers a variety of deposit products loans and mortgages and trust and investment services. It primarily originates residential and commercial mortgages which account for more than three-quarters of its loan portfolio; it also writes business construction and installment loans and home equity lines of credit.

From 2002 through 2009 TrustCo Bank more than doubled its branch network in New York and Florida by opening new locations (more than 75 of them). It has completed its major expansion plan but continues to open new branches albeit not as rapidly.

Despite a continued a weak economy (particularly in Florida) and increased regulation TrustCo Bank Corp reported a nearly 13% increase in net income in 2011. Its results were driven by growth in the bank's loan portfolio coupled with a decrease in provisions for loan loans. The company has also grown its low-cost deposit base which has helped its bottom line as well.

EXECUTIVES

EVP and CFO TrustCo Bank Corp and Trustco Bank, Robert T. (Bob) Cushing, age 56, $380,000 total compensation
Assistant Secretary; VP Personnel and Quality Control Trustco Bank, Sharon J. Parvis, age 61, $121,000 total compensation
President and CEO TrustCo Bank Corp and Trustco Bank, Robert J. McCormick, age 48, $360,000 total compensation
Chairman, William J. Purdy, age 77
VP Accounting and Finance Trustco Bank, Daniel R. Saullo
EVP and Chief Banking Officer Trustco Bank Corp and Trustco Bank, Scot R. Salvador, age 45, $225,000 total compensation
Administrative VP and Assistant Secretary Trustco Corp and Trustco Bank, Robert M. Leonard, age 49, $120,000 total compensation
Secretary; VP and Secretary Trustco Bank, Thomas M. Poitras, age 49
Florida Regional President Trustco Bank, Eric W. Schreck
VP Facilities Trustco Bank, George W. Wickswat
VP Branch Administration and Mortgage Originators Trustco Bank, Deborah K. Appel
Administrative VP Operations Trust Department Trustco Bank, Kevin M. Curley
Administrative VP Trust Department Trustco Bank, Patrick J. LaPorta
Auditor Trustco Bank, Kenneth E. Hughes Jr.
Administrative VP Branch Administration Trustco Bank, Patrick M. Canavan
VP Mortgage Loans Trustco Bank, Michael J. Lofrumento
VP Sales and Marketing Trustco Bank, Paul D. Matthews
Director, Joseph A. Lucarelli, age 71
Director, Anthony J. Marinello, age 56
Director, William D. Powers, age 70
Director, Thomas O. Maggs, age 68
Director, Dennis De Gennaro
Auditors: CroweHorwathLLP

LOCATIONS

HQ: Trustco Bank Corp. (N.Y.)
5 Sarnowski Drive, Glenville, NY 12302
Phone: 518 377-3311 **Fax:** 518 381-3668
Web: www.trustcobank.com

PRODUCTS/OPERATIONS

2011 Sales

	$ mil.	% of total
Interest		
Loans including fees	129	73
Securities	30	17
Other	1	1
Noninterest		
Fees for services to customers	8	5
Trustco Financial Services	5	3
Other	2	1
Total	**177**	**100**

COMPETITORS

Arrow Financial
Ballston Spa Bancorp
Bank of America
First Niagara Financial
HSBC USA
Hudson Valley FCU
KeyCorp
M&T Bank
NBT Bancorp
RBS Citizens Financial Group

HISTORICAL FINANCIALS

Company Type: Public

Income Statement FYE: December 31

	ASSETS ($ mil.)	NET INCOME ($ mil.)	INCOME AS % OF ASSETS	EMPLOYEES
12/11	4,243	33	0.8%	726
12/10	3,954	29	0.7%	738
12/09	3,679	28	0.8%	732
12/08	3,506	34	1.0%	756
12/07	3,377	39	1.2%	670
Annual Growth	5.9%	(4.3%)	—	2.0%

2011 Year-End Financials

Debt ratio: —
Return on equity: 9.77%
Cash ($ mil.): 532
Current ratio: —
Long-term debt ($ mil.): —
No. of shares (mil.): 93
Dividends
Yield: —
Payout: 67.48%
Market value ($ mil.): 524

	STOCK PRICE ($) FY Close	P/E High	P/E Low	PER SHARE ($) Earnings	Dividends	Book Value
12/11	5.61	17	10	0.39	0.00	3.62
12/10	6.34	19	14	0.38	0.26	3.31
12/09	6.30	26	13	0.37	0.30	3.21
12/08	9.51	29	16	0.45	0.44	3.10
12/07	9.92	22	17	0.53	0.64	3.15
Annual Growth	(13.3%)	—	—	(7.4%)	—	3.5%

TRUSTEES OF THE UNIVERSITY OF PENNSYLVANIA

LOCATIONS

HQ: TRUSTEES OF THE UNIVERSITY OF PENNSYLVANIA
3451 WALNUT ST, PHILADELPHIA, PA 191046205
Phone: 2158985000
Web: WWW.PENNLAW.NET

HISTORICAL FINANCIALS

Company Type:

Income Statement FYE: June 30

	REVENUE ($ mil.)	NET INCOME ($ mil.)	NET PROFIT MARGIN	EMPLOYEES
06/11	5,330	643	12.1%	20,433
06/10	4	0	5.1%	0
06/09	5,221	(1,285)	—	0
06/08	5,092	133	2.6%	0
Annual Growth	1.5%	68.9%	—	—

2011 Year-End Financials

Debt ratio: —
Return on equity: 12.10%
Cash ($ mil.): 947
Current ratio: —
Long-term debt ($ mil.): —
Dividends
Yield: —
Payout: —
Market value ($ mil.): —

Trustmark Corp.

Trustmark Corporation is the holding company for Trustmark National Bank which has more than 150 locations mainly in Mississippi but also in East Texas the Florida panhandle and Tennessee where it also operates its Somerville Bank & Trust subsidiary in the Memphis area. Focusing on individuals and small businesses Trustmark offers a range of financial products and services such as checking and savings accounts certificates of deposit credit cards insurance investments and trust services. Trustmark National Bank traces its roots to 1889 when it was first chartered in Mississippi. Today Trustmark Corp. is a diversified financial services firm with $9.9 billion in assets.

Geographic Reach

Mississippi by far is Trustmark's largest market accounting for 80% of 2011 revenue. Tennessee Texas and Florida contribute about 8% 7% and 5% respectively.

Operations

Subsidiary Fisher Brown Bottrell sells insurance while Trustmark Investment Advisors provides wealth management products and services including the proprietary Performance Fund family of mutual funds. The latter unit has approximately $9 billion of assets under management. In 2012 Trustmark agreed to sell approximately $900 million of its Performance Funds Trust assets to Federated Investors.

Financial Analysis

Trustmark's revenue declined 4% in 2011 vs. 2010 while net income increased 6% over the same period. The drop-off in revenue was due to both lower interest and non-interest income. Service charges on deposit accounts declined while bank card and other fees rose for the second consecutive year. Wealth management revenue rose as well.

Strategy

Trustmark grew in 2011 with the FDIC-assisted acquisition of Heritage Banking Group. It took over the failed bank's assets and deposits after the institution was closed by regulators. The transaction added four bank branches in Mississippi (four other locations were consolidated due to their proximity to existing Trustmark branches). In a more conventional deal the company in 2012 bought Bay Bank & Trust adding seven branches on the Florida panhandle. It now plans to buy BancTrust Financial Group for some $55 million. Trustmark has also been growing its branch network by opening new offices with a focus on the Houston and Memphis markets.

Ownership

BlackRock Inc. owns more than 11% of Trustmark Corp's. shares.

EXECUTIVES

Director; President and CEO Trustmark Corporation and Trustmark National Bank, Gerard R. (Jerry) Host, age 57, $244,167 total compensation

EVP and Corporate Banking Manager Trustmark National Bank, Duane A. Dewey, age 53, $300,000 total compensation

Chairman, Daniel A. (Dan) Grafton, age 65

Treasurer and Principal Financial Officer; EVP and CFO Trustmark National Bank, Louis E. Greer, age 57, $244,167 total compensation

Secretary; Secretary and General Counsel Trustmark National Bank, T. Harris Collier III, age 63

EVP and Mortgage Services Manager Trustmark National Bank, Breck W. Tyler, age 53, $300,000 total compensation

Assistant Secretary; SVP and Assistant Secretary and Director Corporate Communications and Board Relations Trustmark National Bank, Melanie A. Morgan

Director, David H. Hoster II, age 66

Director; President and CEO Trustmark Corporation and Trustmark National Bank, Gerard R. (Jerry) Host, age 57

Director, Adolphus B. (Dolph) Baker, age 55

Director, R. Michael Summerford, age 63

Director, John M. McCullouch, age 64

Director, William C. Deviney Jr., age 66

Director, Richard H. Puckett, age 57

Director, LeRoy G. Walker Jr., age 62

Director, William G. Yates III, age 39

Auditors: KPMGLLP

LOCATIONS

HQ: Trustmark Corp.
248 East Capitol Street, Jackson, MS 39201
Phone: 601 208-5111 **Fax:** 601 354-5053
Web: www.trustmark.com

2011 Revenue

	$ mil.	% of total
Mississippi	406	80
Tennessee	39	8
Florida	25	5
Texas	37	7
Total	**551**	**100**

PRODUCTS/OPERATIONS

2011 Sales

	$ mil.	% of total
Interest		
Loans including fees	309	56
Taxable securities	75	14
Other	6	1
Noninterest		
Service charges on deposit accounts	51	9
Bank card & other fees	27	5
Insurance commissions	27	5
Mortgage banking net	26	5
Wealth management	23	4
Other	3	1
Total	**551**	**100**

Selected Subsidiaries

F. S. Corporation
First Building Corporation
Somerville Bank & Trust Company
Trustmark National Bank
Fisher Brown Bottrell Insurance Inc.
Trustmark Investment Advisors Inc.
Trustmark Securities Inc.

COMPETITORS

BancorpSouth
Capital One
Citizens Holding
First Horizon
Great Southern Bancorp
Hancock Holding
Regions Financial
Renasant
Wells Fargo

HISTORICAL FINANCIALS

Company Type: Public

Income Statement

FYE: December 31

	ASSETS ($ mil.)	NET INCOME ($ mil.)	INCOME AS % OF ASSETS	EMPLOYEES
12/11	9,727	106	1.1%	2,537
12/10	9,553	100	1.1%	2,490
12/09	9,526	93	1.0%	2,524
12/08	9,790	92	0.9%	2,607
12/07	8,966	108	1.2%	2,612
Annual Growth	2.1%	(0.4%)	—	(0.7%)

2011 Year-End Financials

Debt ratio: 1.15%
Return on equity: 8.79%
Cash ($ mil.): 202
Current ratio: —
Long-term debt ($ mil.): 111
No. of shares (mil.): 64
Dividends
Yield: —
Payout: 55.42%
Market value ($ mil.): 1,558

	STOCK PRICE ($) FY Close	P/E High/Low		PER SHARE ($) Earnings	Dividends	Book Value
12/11	24.29	16	10	1.66	0.00	18.94
12/10	24.84	17	12	1.57	0.92	17.98
12/09	22.54	18	12	1.26	0.92	17.43
12/08	21.59	19	9	1.59	0.92	20.56
12/07	25.36	18	12	1.88	0.89	16.06
Annual Growth	(1.1%)	—	—	(3.1%)	—	4.2%

TRW Automotive Holdings Corp

TRW Automotive makes cars stop and go around the globe in addition to keeping passengers and pedestrians safe. The company designs and makes systems components and modules primarily for major automakers. Three OEM groups generate more than 45% of sales: Volkswagen (21%) Ford (16%) and General Motors (11%). Product lines range from chassis systems (brake steering and suspension systems) to safety systems such as airbags seat belts and security and safety electronics (crash and occupant weight sensors). Other products include body controls and engine valves. TRW Automotive has about 190 facilities in more than two dozen countries worldwide netting nearly 70% of its sales outside North America.

Geographic Reach

TRW operates globally with a focused presence within Brazil China the Czech Republic Germany Poland Spain the UK and the US. Europe accounts for almost 50% of its total sales each year.

Operations

TRW divides its operations across four chief segments. Chassis Systems generates the most revenue (around 60% of total sales) and makes brake control steering and linkage and suspension products. Occupant Safety Systems (around 20% of sales) makes airbags seat belts steering wheels and other related products while Automotive Components (10%) makes engine valves body controls and fasteners. Electronics (5% to 10%) manufactures radio frequency and electrical components used to make electric power steering vehicle control and safety systems.

Financial Analysis

From 2010 to 2011 TRW increased its revenue by 13% due in part to higher production volumes in all its major geographic regions and an uptick in demand for its active and passive safety products. TRW's cost savings initiatives and restructuring activities in 2010 helped it to achieve a net income in 2011 of $1.16 billion which constituted a 39% jump over 2010's net income of $834 million. The company had $163 million in net cash for 2011 and has used excess cash generated in 2010 to open new plants in China and Brazil. TRW invested more in 2011 and planned to spend between $650 million and $700 million on capital expenditures in 2012.

Strategy

TRW caters to a diverse client base by partnering with other companies with innovative technologies and opening new plants in key geographic locations that expand the company's presence in new and existing markets. In 2012 it launched in Brazil a new regional production base for making auto parts across South America. The newly launched facilities are focused on producing and selling electric power steering parts and components. The company also announced plans in 2011 to open a new braking plant in Mexico.

The company enters into joint ventures for strategic reasons as well. In 2010 TRW subsidiary TRW Asia Pacific Co. inked a deal with Xi'an Dong Fang Group Co. a division of China North Industries Group Corp. This venture with one of China's major machinery companies established an airbag inflator and seat belt pretensioner plant in Xi'an Shanxi Province –a mountainous frontier centered around coal and chemical production. To support its Chinese customers TRW announced in 2011 its plans to build a new technical center in Shanghai in 2013. Other significant partnerships have been established in Brazil India and Spain.

Ownership

The Blackstone Group owns a 16% stake in the company.

EXECUTIVES

Chairman President and CEO, John C. Plant, age 58, $1,680,000 total compensation
Lead Director, Neil P. Simpkins, age 45
EVP and COO, Steven (Steve) Lunn, age 63, $798,650 total compensation
VP Engineering Braking, Josef Pickenhahn
EVP Sales and Business Development, Peter J. Lake, age 56, $539,000 total compensation
EVP and CFO, Joseph S. Cantie, age 48, $500,000 total compensation
VP Quality and Business Excellence, Bryce A. Currie
VP Health Safety and Environmental, Thomas Koenig
VP and Corporate Controller, Tammy Mitchell
VP Treasury and Tax, Peter Rapin
EVP Human Resources, Neil E. Marchuk, age 54, $365,000 total compensation
VP Global Electronics, Edward L. (Ed) Carpenter
VP Strategic Planning, David Royce
VP Operations Asia/Pacific, Nancy Gougarty
Senior Manager Communications North America, John Wilkerson
Media Contact China, Nicole Lei
VP and General Manager Engineered Fasteners and Components, Kai-Uwe Wollenhaupt
VP Operations Chassis Systems and Occupant Safety Systems; President South America, Moises Bucci
VP Internal Audit, Ann Lipanski
VP and General Manager Steering North America, Mark Stewart
Director Communications Europe and Asia, Lynette Jackson
VP and General Manager Body Controls Systems North America, Ken Kaiser
VP Engineering Steering Engineering, Frank Lubischer
VP Finance and Global Strategic Initiatives, Gerald Dekker
VP Product Planning and Business Development, Matt Roney
Director Investor Relations, Mark Oswald
European Engineering Director Automotive Occupant Safety Systems Business, Alexander Heilig
EVP General Counsel and Secretary, Robin A. Walker-Lee, age 57
VP and General Manager Global Braking and Suspension, Douglas Del Grosso
VP and General Manager Global Occupant Safety Systems, Frank Mueller
VP Engineering Occupant Safety Systems Engine/Product and Process, Norbert Kagerer
VP European Steering, Michael Degen
VP and General Manager Engine Components, Robert Smith
VP and General Manager Body Controls Systems Europe and Emerging Markets, Ralf Jeskulke
VP Information Systems, Matt Peterson
VP and General Manager Aftermarket Europe and Asia/Pacific, Phil Cunningham
VP Global Inflatable Restraints North America Occupant Safety Systems, Joe Gaus
VP Purchasing, Martin Horneck
VP and General Manager Parts and Service North America, John Nielson
Executive Vice President; General Counsel; Secretary, Robin Lee
Director, J. Michael (Mike) Losh, age 65
Director, James F. (Jim) Albaugh, age 61
Director, Robert L. (Bob) Friedman, age 69
Director, Francois J. Castaing, age 66
Director, Jody G. Miller, age 54
Director, Michael R. (Mike) Gambrell, age 58
Director, Paul H. O'Neill, age 76
Director, David S. Taylor, age 54
Independent Director, Paul Neill
Independent Director, Paul ONeill
Auditors: Ernst&YoungLLP

LOCATIONS

HQ: TRW Automotive Holdings Corp.
12001 Tech Center Dr., Livonia MI 48150
Phone: 734-855-2600 **Fax:** 734-855-2999
Web: www.trwauto.com

2011 Sales

US	3,673	23
Other countries	9,948	61

PRODUCTS/OPERATIONS

2011 Sales

Chassis Systems	9,960	61
Automotive Components	1,862	11
Total	**16,244**	**100**

2011 Sales by Customer

	% of total
Volkswagen	21
Ford	16
GM	11
Other	52
Total	**100**

Selected Products

Automotive Components
- Body controls
- Engine valves
- Engineered fasteners and components

Chassis Systems
- Brake controls
- Foundation brakes
- Steering gears and systems
- Linkage and suspension
- Modules

Electronics
- Chassis electronics
- Driver assist systems
- Powertrain electronics
- Radio frequency electronics
- Safety electronics

Occupant Safety Systems
- Air bags
- Seat belts
- Steering wheels

COMPETITORS

Autoliv
Dana Holding
Delphi Automotive Systems
DENSO
Eaton
Illinois Tool Works
JTEKT
Key Safety Systems
Lear Corp
Meritor
Robert Bosch
Sumitomo Electric
Takata
Textron
Tokai Rika
Valeo
Visteon
ZF Friedrichshafen

HISTORICAL FINANCIALS

Company Type: Public

Income Statement FYE: December 31

	REVENUE ($ mil.)	NET INCOME ($ mil.)	NET PROFIT MARGIN	EMPLOYEES
12/11	16,244	1,157	7.1%	72,700
12/10	14,383	834	5.8%	69,800
12/09	11,614	55	0.5%	63,600
12/08	14,995	(779)	—	65,200
12/07	14,702	90	0.6%	66,300
Annual Growth	2.5%	89.4%	—	2.3%

2011 Year-End Financials

Debt ratio: 14.93%
Return on equity: 39.35%
Cash ($ mil.): 1,241
Current ratio: 120.49
Long-term debt ($ mil.): 1,428
No. of shares (mil.): 123
Dividends
Yield: —
Payout: —
Market value ($ mil.): 4,034

	STOCK PRICE ($) FY Close	P/E High	P/E Low	PER SHARE ($) Earnings	Dividends	Book Value
12/11	32.60	7	3	8.82	0.00	23.76
12/10	52.70	8	3	6.49	0.00	16.85
12/09	23.88	50	3	0.51	0.00	9.84
12/08	3.60	—	—	(7.71)	0.00	11.18
12/07	20.90	47	23	0.88	0.00	31.72
Annual Growth	11.8%	—	—	77.9%	—	(7.0%)

Tyson Foods, Inc.

With its bullish attitude Tyson is more than chicken. One of the largest US chicken producers Tyson's Fresh Meats division makes it a giant in the beef and pork sectors as well. The company also offers value-added processed and pre-cooked meats and refrigerated and frozen prepared foods.

Its chicken operations are vertically integrated –the company hatches the eggs supplies contract growers with the chicks and feed and brings them back for processing when ready. Tyson processes 42 million chickens 390000 pigs and 144000 head of cattle every week. Its customers include retail wholesale and foodservice customers in the US and more than 100 other countries.

HISTORY

During the Great Depression Arkansas poultry farmer John Tyson supported his family by selling vegetables and poultry. In 1935 after developing a method for transporting live poultry (he installed a food-and-water trough and nailed small feed cups on a trailer) he bought 500 chickens in Arkansas and sold them in Chicago.

For the next decade Tyson bought sold and transported chickens. By 1947 the year he incorporated the company as Tyson Feed & Hatchery he was raising the chickens himself. He emphasized chicken production opening his first processing plant in 1958 in Springdale where he implemented an ice-packing system that allowed the company to send its products greater distances.

John's son Don took over as manager in 1960 and in 1963 it went public as Tyson Foods. Tyson Country Fresh Chicken (packaged chicken that would become the company's mainstay) was introduced in 1967.

Rapid expansion included a new egg-processing building (1970) a new plant and computerized feed mill (1971) and the acquisitions of Prospect Farms (1969 precooked chicken) and the Ocoma Foods Division (1972 poultry) as well as hog operations.

Health-conscious consumers increasingly turned from red meats to poultry during the 1980s. Tyson became the industry leader with several key acquisitions of poultry operations including the Tastybird division of Valmac (1985) Lane Processing (1986) and Heritage Valley (1986). Its 1989 purchase of Holly Farms added beef and pork processing.

Don Tyson relinquished the CEO position to Leland Tollett in 1991. The company increased its presence in Mexico the next year through a joint venture with poultry producer Trasgo. Also in 1992 the firm plunged into seafood with the purchase of Arctic Alaska Fisheries and Louis Kemp Seafood.

Tyson bought Culinary Foods (frozen foods) and Trasgo in 1994 and the seafood division of International Multifoods in 1995. High feed costs and an oversupply of chickens brought down company earnings the next year. In 1997 the company pleaded guilty to charges that it illegally gave former Agriculture Secretary Mike Espy thousands of dollars' worth of gifts; the settlement included $6 million in fines and fees.

Tyson bought embattled Hudson Foods' poultry operations in 1998. The company said it would take a charge that year of $196 million to restructure. It also sold turkey processor Willow Brook Foods (now part of Cargill Meat Solutions) to Willow Brook management in 1998. That year John H. Tyson grandson of the founder was elected chairman.

In 1999 Tyson sold its seafood business for about $180 million in a two-part transaction to International Home Foods and Trident Seafoods. John Tyson became CEO in 2000.

As the winner in a bidding war with Smithfield Foods in 2001 Tyson agreed to buy IBP Inc. the #1 beef processor and #2 pork processor in the US for nearly $3.2 billion. Tyson tried to back away from the table after accounting irregularities were discovered at an IBP subsidiary but a Delaware judge ordered Tyson to sit down and finish dinner. The deal was made final in September and Tyson changed the beef processor's name to IBP Fresh Meats.

In late 2001 Tyson Foods and six managers were indicted for conspiring to smuggle illegal immigrants from Mexico and Central America to work for lower than legal wages in 15 of its US poultry processing plants. Two managers made plea bargains and testified for the government; another manager committed suicide. Tyson and the remaining three managers were acquitted of the conspiracy charges in 2003.

Suffering from mild indigestion after the merger in 2002 Tyson announced a restructuring to trim some fat from its fresh pork operations and agreed to sell its Specialty Brands (frozen foods) subsidiary. In early 2003 sold off its frozen appetizer business DFG Foods.

Following the discovery of bird flu on a Texas chicken farm in 2004 and the subsequent banning of the importation of US chicken products by other countries Tyson consolidated and automated its poultry operations resulting in hundreds of layoffs at the company.

Tyson announced in 2004 it was being formally investigated by the SEC regarding perquisites given to executives including retired senior chairman Don Tyson and then-current chairman and CEO John Tyson. By August the SEC recommended civil action against the company for its failure to disclose $1.7 million in corporate perks given to Don Tyson without authorization from Tyson's compensation committee. Although Don Tyson had already reimbursed the company $1.53 million for then-unspecified benefits the SEC also announced plans to recommend civil action be taken against him. With neither the company nor Tyson admitting any guilt the case was settled in 2005 with Tyson paying the SEC $700000 in fines and the company $1.5 million. Many of the perks were not disclosed because Don Tyson did not fill out SEC-required questionnaires; however disclosed perks included having the company pay for his housekeeping and lawn maintenance and routine non-business use of the corporate jet by his family and friends.

In 2005 the company opened its largest case-ready meat plant in Sherman Texas. However that January and February it suspended operations at four of its other beef plants and cut back at a fifth due to a shortage of cattle and the loss of beef exports due to the US's 2003 case of BSE (Bovine spongiform encephalopathy or "mad cow" disease).

Growing concern over the role of trans-fatty acids (from hydrogenated vegetable oils) in diet and health led Tyson to begin removing them from its processed foods such as breaded chicken nuggets and chicken tenders. The company announced the removal of trans-fats from all its retail poultry and school foodservice products in 2005.

In 2006 Don's son John Tyson stepped down as CEO; president and COO Richard Bond was named president and CEO. Tyson remained as chairman. Soon thereafter Bond announced $200 million in cost reductions to include reductions in staff recruiting relocation consulting sales-related expenses and supplies and travel. The plan included the elimination of 850 positions of which 420 were currently held and 430 were positions to be filled. Most of the jobs were managerial and involved no hourly workers at Tyson's plants. Later that year the company announced it would cut another 770 jobs as it closed and consolidated several meat slaughtering and processing plants in the northwestern US.

Recognizing the growing market for alternative and renewable fuels and recognizing its unending supply of meat by-products (in this case such lovelies as fat tallow lard and grease) Tyson decided to get into the alternative fuel market in 2007 with the formation of a 50-50 joint venture with fuel refiner Syntroleum called Dynamic Fuels. The joint venture was set up to explore the possibility of producing synthetic fuel from Tyson's waste products for the diesel- jet- and military-fuel markets. In conjunction with this joint venture Tyson created a new business unit Tyson Renewable Products.

Former chairman Don Tyson died at the age of 80 in January 2011.

EXECUTIVES

SVP Controller and Chief Accounting Officer, Craig J. Hart, age 56
EVP and General Counsel, David L. Van Bebber, age 56
EVP and CFO, Dennis Leatherby, age 52, $467,308 total compensation
VP Associate General Counsel and Secretary, R. Read Hudson
Chairman, John H. Tyson, age 58, $1,170,000 total compensation
President and CEO, Donnie Smith, age 53, $542,308 total compensation
Group VP Consumer Products, Wes Morris
SVP and Chief Human Resources Officer, Kenneth J. Kimbro, age 58
SVP and Chief Environmental Health and Safety Officer, Kevin J. Igli
Group VP Research and Development Logistics and Technical Services, Howell P. (Hal) Carper
EVP Corporate Affairs, Archie Schaffer III
Director Media Relations, Gary Mickelson
SVP Fresh Meats, Noel White, age 54
COO, James V. (Jim) Lochner, age 60, $612,692 total compensation
VP Investor Relations and Assistant Secretary, Ruth Ann Wisener
Group VP Food Service, Bernard F. Leonard, age 60, $439,615 total compensation
SVP Poultry and Prepared Foods, Donnie D. King, age 50
SVP Corporate Research and Development, Craig Bacon
SVP and CIO, Gary Cooper
EVP Corporate Affairs, Sara Lilygren
Group VP Food Service, Devin Cole
Manager Environmental Health and Safety Training Communication and Sustainability, Leigh Ann Johnston
SVP International, William D. Teeter
SVP International, James Young
VP Renewable Energy, Bob Ames
Director, Robert C. Thurber, age 65
Director, Kevin M. McNamara, age 56
Director, Gaurdie E. Banister Jr.
Director, Barbara A. Tyson, age 62
Director, Jim D. Kever, age 59
Director, Kathleen M. Bader, age 61
Director, Brad T. Sauer, age 53
Director, Albert C. Zapanta, age 71
Auditors: Ernst&YoungLLP

LOCATIONS

HQ: Tyson Foods Inc.
2200 Don Tyson Pkwy., Springdale AR 72762-6999
Phone: 479-290-4000 **Fax:** 479-290-4061
Web: www.tysonfoodsinc.com

PRODUCTS/OPERATIONS

2011 Sales

	% of total
Beef	41
Chicken	34
Pork	16
Prepared	9
Other —	
Intersegment —	
Total	**100**

Selected Products and Brands

Meats fresh
- Certified Angus Beef
- Chairman' s Reserve (beef)
- Golden Trophy Steaks (beef)
- Open Prairie Angus Beef
- Star Ranch Angus Beef
- Supreme Tender (pork)
- Tyson (beef chicken Cornish game hens pork)
- Tyson Holly Farms (chicken)

Meats processed
- Bonici (foodservice; chicken wings pizza toppings)
- Chicken Twists (foodservice)
- Premium Chunk (canned chicken)
- Right Size (foodservice; beef patties chicken patties)
- Tyson (bacon beef chicken pork)
- Wright (bacon)

Prepared foods
- Any' Tizers (chicken snacks)
- Doskocil (value-added meats for pizza industry)
- Heat ' N Eat Entrees (beef chicken pork)
- Lady Aster (entrees)
- Mexican Original (flour and corn tortilla products)
- Skillet Creations (beef and chicken meal kits)

COMPETITORS

Buckhead Beef
Cargill
Casa de Oro Foods
CGC
Clougherty Packing
Coleman Natural Foods
ConAgra
Cooper Farms
Del Monte Foods
Eberly Poultry
Empire Kosher Poultry
Foster Farms
Freedman Meats
Gruma
Gusto Packing
H. J. Heinz Limited
Hormel
JBS
Koch Foods
Kraft Foods Group Inc.
Laura' s Lean Beef Co.
Mars Incorporated
Mondelez International
National Beef Packing
New Market Poultry
Perdue Incorporated
Petaluma Poultry
Pilgrim' s Pride
Plainville Farms
Raeford Farms
Rosen' s Diversified
Sanderson Farms
Sara Lee North American Retail
Shelton' s
Smithfield Foods
Tecumseh Poultry
U.S. Premium Beef

HISTORICAL FINANCIALS

Company Type: Public

Income Statement FYE: September 29

	REVENUE ($ mil.)	NET INCOME ($ mil.)	NET PROFIT MARGIN	EMPLOYEES
09/12*	33,278	583	1.8%	115,000
10/11	32,266	750	2.3%	115,000
10/10	28,430	780	2.7%	115,000
10/09	26,704	(537)	—	117,000
09/08	26,862	86	0.3%	107,000
Annual Growth	5.5%	61.4%	—	1.8%

*Fiscal year change

2012 Year-End Financials

Debt ratio: 20.44%
Return on equity: 9.70%
Cash ($ mil.): 1,071
Current ratio: 190.92
Long-term debt ($ mil.): 1,917
No. of shares (mil.): 359
Dividends
Yield: —
Payout: 10.13%
Market value ($ mil.): 5,751

	STOCK PRICE ($) FY Close	P/E High	P/E Low	PER SHARE ($) Earnings	Dividends	Book Value
09/12*	16.02	13	9	1.58	0.00	16.75
10/11	17.36	10	7	1.97	0.00	15.29
10/10	16.26	10	6	2.06	0.00	13.70
10/09	12.32	—	—	(1.44)	0.00	11.57
09/08	12.69	78	49	0.24	0.00	13.30
Annual Growth	6.0%	—	—	60.2%	—	5.9%

*Fiscal year change

U.S. Bancorp (DE)

Not quite a bank for the entire US U.S. Bancorp is nonetheless one of the ten largest bank holding companies in the country. It owns U.S. Bank and other subsidiaries that provide consumer and commercial loans deposits and credit cards as well as merchant processing mortgage banking trust and investment management brokerage services insurance and corporate payments. The bank has more than 3000 branches and 5000 ATMs in some two dozen states in the Midwest and West including one of the most extensive networks of branches inside grocery stores. California is its largest market.

U.S. Bancorp has grown in recent years by scooping up failed banks that were brought down by the economy and seized by regulators. The strategy has allowed the company to add branches deposits loans and customers relatively cheaply and have helped boost its bottom line. U.S. Bancorp reported record net income in 2010 and 2011 in addition to deposit and loan growth. The company was also able to reduce its amount of non-performing assets as the US economy showed signs of improvement following the credit crisis.

U.S. Bancorp expanded in Tennessee through the 2012 acquisition of the banking operations of BankEast in an FDIC-assisted deal. In 2011 U.S. Bank established a presence in New Mexico through the acquisition of the banking operations of the failed First Community Bank. That FDIC-facilitated transaction which added nearly 40 branches did not include any assets of that company's parent First State Bancorporation. In 2010 U.S. Bancorp bought deposits and some branches in Nevada from BB&T which had acquired the operations from the failed Colonial BancGroup.

In 2009 U.S. Bancorp acquired the nine banking subsidiaries of the failed FBOP Corporation; the deal also facilitated by the FDIC added some 150 locations in Arizona California and Illinois to U.S. Bank's network. The company acquired the banking operations of the failed California-based banks Downey Savings & Loan and PFF Bank & Trust in FDIC-assisted transactions in late 2008.

U.S. Bancorp has also been expanding its fee-based services such as treasury management corporate trust institutional custody merchant processing and freight payment services. The company is also one of the largest providers of corporate credit cards and payment services to the US government. Its largest fee-gathering subsidiary is Elavon a leading processor of merchant credit card transactions in the US Canada Latin America and Europe. U.S. Bancorp has also been growing this business through acquisitions and is looking to expand internationally.

In 2009 U.S. Bank acquired the corporate trust bond administration business of AmeriServ Financial and the bond trustee business of First Citizens Bancshares. It bought the corporate trust administration business of F.N.B. Corporation and the securitization trust administration business of Bank of America the following year. The acquisitions raised the bank's corporate trust assets under administration to around $3 trillion.

In 2012 U.S. Bank made a similar deal when it agreed to buy Union Bank's institutional trust business adding some 4300 client relationships representing $42 billion in assets under administration. It also bought the Indiana-based corporate trust business of UMB Bank that year.

In 2011 U.S. Bancorp finalized the sale of its FAF Advisors asset management subsidiary to Nuveen Investments in exchange for a nearly 10% stake in Nuveen.

Warren Buffett's Berkshire Hathaway owns about 4% of U.S. Bancorp.

HISTORY

When Farmers and Millers Bank was founded in 1853 it operated out of a strongbox in a rented storefront. After surviving a panic in the 1850s the bank became part of the national banking system in 1863 as First National Bank of Milwaukee. The bank grew and in 1894 it merged with Merchants Exchange Bank (founded 1870).

In 1919 the bank merged again with Wisconsin National Bank (founded 1892) to form First Wisconsin National Bank of Milwaukee a leading financial institution in the area from the 1920s on.

First Wisconsin grew through purchases over the next decade though the number of banks fell after the 1929 stock market crash; by the end of WWII it had 11 banks. State and federal legislation particularly the 1956 Bank Holding Company Act (which proscribed acquisitions and branching) constrained postwar growth. In the 1970s Wisconsin eased restrictions on intrastate branching and the bank began to grow again.

Growth accelerated in the late 1980s after Wisconsin and surrounding states legalized interstate banking in adjoining states in 1987. That year First Wisconsin bought seven Minnesota banks and then moved into Illinois. The company focused on strong well-run institutions. Also that year it sold its headquarters and used the proceeds to fund more buys. In 1988 in its first foray outside the Midwest the company bought Metro Bancorp in Phoenix targeting midwestern retirees moving to Arizona.

In 1989 First Wisconsin changed its name to Firstar. The early 1990s saw the company move into Iowa (Banks of Iowa 1990) buy in-state rivals (Federated Bank Geneva Capital Corporation 1992) and roll into Illinois (DSB Corporation 1993). The next year it bought First Southeast Banking Corp. (of Wisconsin) and merged it along with Firstar Bank Racine and Firstar Bank Milwaukee into one bank.

The company was hit in 1994 with a $13 million charge to cover losses from a check-kiting fraud.

To strengthen its position against larger competitors Firstar continued its buying spree in 1995 (Chicago bank First Colonial Bankshares and Investors Bank Corp. of Minneapolis/St. Paul) and 1996 (Jacob Schmidt Company). The acquisitions left the company bloated: In 1996 Firstar began a restructuring designed to cut costs and increase margins. The restructuring project ended in 1997 but by then its performance lagged behind other midwestern banks considerably. In an effort to diversify it allied with EVEREN Securities to offer debt underwriting and sales fixed income products and public finance advisory services. But it was too little too late; under pressure from major stockholders to seek a partner Firstar began looking for a buyer.

It found Star Banc. Established in 1863 as The First National Bank of Cincinnati under a bank charter signed by Abraham Lincoln Star Banc over the years added branches and bought other banks. The company renamed all of its subsidiary banks Star Bank in 1988 and took the name Star Banc in 1989.

In 1998 Star Banc chairman Jerry Grundhofer approached Firstar about a combination. Negotiations proceeded quickly and a new Firstar was born.

The next year Firstar bought Mercantile Bancorporation. The purchase enabled the bank to expand its international banking services into such markets as Kansas Nebraska and Missouri. In 2000 the company made arrangements to buy U.S. Bancorp a Minneapolis-based bank with roots dating back to 1929. Under the terms of the acquisition Firstar would shed its own name in favor of the more appropriate U.S. Bancorp moniker. U.S. Bancorp completed the conversion of Firstar Bank branches to the U.S. Bank moniker during 2002.

In 2001 U.S. Bancorp bolstered its credit and debit card processing operations with the purchase of NOVA Corporation (now NOVA Information Systems). In late 2003 the company unloaded its investment bank subsidiary Piper Jaffray which for all intents and purposes already had autonomy in a spinoff to U.S. Bancorp shareholders (in exchange for a percentage of profits).

U.S. Bancorp built its banking networks through several acquisitions later in the decade. It bought Colorado's Vail Banks owner of WestStar Bank in 2006; Montana-based bank holding company United Financial in 2007; and Los Angeles-based Mellon 1st Business Bank from The Bank of New York Mellon in 2008.

EXECUTIVES

Vice Chairman Wealth Management and Securities Services, Terrance R. (Terry) Dolan, age 50
EVP General Counsel and Secretary, Lee R. Mitau, age 63, $413,891 total compensation
Vice Chairman Consumer and Small Business Banking, Richard C. (Rick) Hartnack, age 66, $581,819 total compensation
EVP Corporate Investor and Public Relations, Judy Murphy
Vice Chairman Payment Services; Chairman and CEO Elavon, Pamela A. (Pam) Joseph, age 53, $581,819 total compensation
EVP Human Resources, Jennie P. Carlson, age 51
Chairman President and CEO, Richard K. Davis, age 54, $915,491 total compensation
Vice Chairman and CFO, Andrew Cecere, age 51, $581,819 total compensation
Assistant VP Media Relations, Lisa Clark
President and CEO Elavon, Mike Passilla
Vice Chairman Wholesale Banking, Richard B. (Dick) Payne Jr., age 64
EVP and Chief Strategy Officer; Head Enterprise Revenue Office, Howell D. (Mac) McCullough III, age 55
EVP and Chief Risk Officer, Richard J. Hidy, age 49
Vice Chairman Commercial Real Estate, Joseph C. Hoesley, age 57
EVP and Chief Credit Officer, P. William (Bill) Parker, age 55
VP Media Relations, Teri Charest
Assistant VP Media Relations, Amy Frantti
Vice Chairman Technology and Operations Services, Jeffry H. (Jeff) von Gillern, age 46
Managing Director Loan Sales and Trading, Cheryl Neff
SVP Media Relations, Thomas (Tom) Joyce
Head Corporate Payment Systems U.S. Bank, Kurt Adams
Managing Director and Business Development Officer Corporate and Municipal Trust Sales Group U.S. Bank Corporate Trust Services, Eric Fischer
EVP U.S. Bank Corporate Trust Services, Terry McRoberts
Director, Y. Marc Belton, age 53
Director, Patrick T. (Pat) Stokes, age 69
Director, Arthur D. (Art) Collins Jr., age 64
Director, Joel W. Johnson, age 68
Director, Richard G. (Dick) Reiten, age 72
Director, Jerry W. Levin, age 67
Director, Craig D. Schnuck, age 63
Director, David B. O'Maley, age 65
Director, Douglas M. (Doug) Baker Jr., age 53
Director, Olivia F. Kirtley, age 61
Vice Chairman and CFO, Andrew Cecere, age 51
Director, Victoria Buyniski Gluckman, age 60
Director, O'dell M. Owens, age 64
Auditors: Ernst&YoungLLP

LOCATIONS

HQ: U.S. Bancorp
800 Nicollet Mall, Minneapolis MN 55402-7014
Phone: 651-466-3000 **Fax:** 787-766-1437
Web: www.santanderbancorp.com

Selected Locations

Arizona
Arkansas
California
Colorado
Idaho
Illinois
Indiana
Iowa
Kansas
Kentucky
Minnesota
Missouri
Montana
Nebraska
Nevada
New Mexico
North Dakota
Ohio
Oregon
South Dakota
Tennessee
Utah
Washington
Wisconsin
Wyoming

PRODUCTS/OPERATIONS

2011 Sales

	$ mil.	% of total
Interest		
Loans	10,570	49
Investment securities	1,820	9
Other	249	1
Noninterest		
Merchant processing services	1,355	6
Credit & debit card revenue	1,073	5
Trust & investment management fees	1,000	5
Mortgage banking	986	5
Commercial products	841	4
Corporate payment products	734	3
Deposit service charges	659	3
Treasury management fees	551	3
ATM processing services	452	2
Other	1,109	5
Total	**21,399**	**100**

Selected Subsidiaries

Elan Life Insurance Company
Elavon
Elavon Financial Services Limited (Ireland)
Miami Valley Insurance Company
Midwest Indemnity Inc.
Mississippi Valley Life Insurance Company
Quasar Distributors LLC
U.S. Bancorp Asset Management Inc.
U.S. Bancorp Equipment Finance Inc.
U.S. Bancorp Insurance and Investments Inc.
U.S. Bancorp Insurance Company Inc.
U.S. Bancorp Insurance Services LLC
U.S. Bancorp Insurance Services of Montana Inc.
U.S. Bancorp Investments Inc.
U.S. Bank National Association
U.S. Bank National Association ND
U.S. Bank Trust Company National Association
U.S. Bank Trust National Association
U.S. Bank Trust National Association SD

COMPETITORS

BancWest
Bank of America
Capital One
Citigroup
Fifth Third
First National of Nebraska
Great Western Bancorporation
Huntington Bancshares
JPMorgan Chase
KeyCorp
TCF Financial
UnionBanCal
Wells Fargo
Zions Bancorporation

HISTORICAL FINANCIALS

Company Type: Public

Income Statement

FYE: December 31

	ASSETS ($ mil.)	NET INCOME ($ mil.)	INCOME AS % OF ASSETS	EMPLOYEES
12/11	340,122	4,872	1.4%	62,529
12/10	307,786	3,317	1.1%	60,584
12/09	281,176	2,205	0.8%	58,229
12/08	265,912	2,946	1.1%	57,904
12/07	237,615	4,324	1.8%	52,277
Annual Growth	9.4%	3.0%	—	4.6%

2011 Year-End Financials

Debt ratio: 9.40%
Return on equity: 14.34%
Cash ($ mil.): 13,962
Current ratio: —
Long-term debt ($ mil.): 31,953
No. of shares (mil.): 1,909
Dividends
Yield: —
Payout: 20.33%
Market value ($ mil.): 51,661

	STOCK PRICE ($) FY Close	P/E High	P/E Low	PER SHARE ($) Earnings	Dividends	Book Value
12/11	27.05	12	8	2.46	0.00	17.79
12/10	26.97	16	12	1.73	0.20	15.37
12/09	22.51	26	9	0.97	0.20	13.57
12/08	25.01	23	14	1.61	1.70	14.99
12/07	31.74	15	12	2.43	1.63	12.18
Annual Growth	(3.9%)	—	—	0.3%	—	9.9%

U.S. VENTURE INC.

EXECUTIVES

Chairman, Thomas A. (Tom) Schmidt
CFO, Paul Bachman
General Counsel, Marjorie Young

President and CEO, John Schmidt
Director Safety and Risk Management, Tom Titzkowski
Director Human Resources, Lori Hoersch
CIO, Mark Duening

LOCATIONS

HQ: U.S. Venture Inc.
425 Better Way, Appleton WI 54915
Phone: 920-739-6101 **Fax:** 920-788-0531
Web: www.usventure.com

PRODUCTS/OPERATIONS

Selected Operations

Custom Manufacturing (tube bending and fabrication)
Design Air (heating and air conditioning equipment)
Express Convenience Centers (gas stations and car washes)
Petroleum Equipment (petroleum-related equipment installation)
U.S. AutoForce (exhaust pipe manufacturing and autoparts distribution)
U.S. Lubricants (motor oil and related products)
U.S. Oil (gasoline fuel oil and natural gas)

COMPETITORS

7-Eleven
Apex Oil
Marathon Oil
Motiva Enterprises
Quality State Oil Company
QuikTrip
Sunoco

HISTORICAL FINANCIALS

Company Type: Private

Income Statement FYE: July 31

	REVENUE ($ mil.)	NET INCOME ($ mil.)	NET PROFIT MARGIN	EMPLOYEES
07/12	5,906	60	1.0%	1,000
07/11	4,847	27	0.6%	0
07/10	1,940	38	2.0%	0
07/09	1,707	39	2.3%	0
Annual Growth	51.2%	15.1%	—	—

2012 Year-End Financials

Debt ratio: ——
Return on equity: 1.00%
Cash ($ mil.): 31
Current ratio: 0.50
Long-term debt ($ mil.): —
Dividends
Yield: —
Payout: —
Market value ($ mil.): —

UGI Corp.

UGI (derived from its original name United Gas Improvement) is a leading energy services marketing and distribution company and distributes propane across the US and internationally. The company is led by its 44%-owned propane distributor AmeriGas Partners the largest source of the holding company's sales and one of the top two US propane marketers (along with Ferrellgas). It also has utility operations: Its UGI Utilities subsidiary distributes electricity to 62000 customers and gas to about 563000 customers in Pennsylvania. The company's other operations include energy marketing in the mid-Atlantic region propane distribution in Asia and Europe and electricity generation and energy services.

Operations

Subsidiary AmeriGas sells propane to 1.3 million retail and wholesale customers a year from about 1200 locations in 50 states. AmeriGas also offers propane-related products and services and provides propane storage services. UGI subsidiary UGI Enterprises which operates the company's midstream and marketing division markets natural gas and electricity and offers HVAC (heating ventilation and air-conditioning) and energy management services to more than 150000 customers in the mid-Atlantic region of the US. Another subsidiary UGI Development is involved in power generation ventures in Pennsylvania.

Geographic Reach

Internationally UGI has interests in propane distributors in Austria China the Czech Republic Denmark France Hungary Poland Romania Slovakia and Switzerland primarily through its Antargaz and Flaga subsidiaries. In 2010 France-based Antargaz sold 280 million gallons of propane; Flaga 70 million gallons. Antargaz UGI's leading international business is pursuing expansion in Europe and is looking to grow its foothold in China.

Financial Analysis

Lingering effects of the global recession on gas prices (coupled with warmer than usual weather in its utility market which weakened demand) brought down the company's revenues and operating income in 2010. However UGI's net income increased thanks to the performance of its midstream business (which produced higher margins thanks to base rate increases) and the sale of its Energy Services Atlantic unit. These gains helped to offset declines in the International Propane and Amerigas segments.

Strategy

UGI is focused on expanding its core natural gas electric and propane operations. It is also seeking complementary opportunities to continue its growth in the US and abroad. In 2010 it took advantage of BP's need to raise cash due to its oil spill problems and acquired the liquefied petroleum gas distribution business of BP in Denmark. It also picked up Shell's LPG operations in Poland. Both deals expanded UGI's footprint in the European LPG market. In 2011 the company acquired more of Shell's LPG distribution operations in Europe. The terms of the deal were not disclosed but included the businesses in Belgium Denmark Finland Luxembourg the Netherlands Norway Sweden and the United Kingdom adding to the UGI's European market growth with an estimated 300 million gallons of LPG.

In 2012 it agreed to buy BP's LPG distribution business in Poland.

HISTORY

United Gas Improvement was set up in 1882 by Philadelphia industrialist Thomas Dolan and other investors to acquire a gasworks and a new coal-gas manufacturing process. The firm also bought electric utilities and street railways across the US and moved into construction. The 1935 Public Utility Holding Company Act led to United Gas Improvement's restructuring when the SEC ordered the divestiture of many of its operations in 1941. The company converted to natural gas in the 1950s and entered the liquefied petroleum gas (LPG) business in 1959. It became UGI Corporation in 1968.

UGI shifted its emphasis to propane in the late 1980s buying Petrolane in 1995 and combining it with AmeriGas Propane to create AmeriGas Partners which then went public. Overseas UGI launched a joint venture in 1996 to build an LPG import project in Romania. The next year it signed a deal to distribute propane in China.

In 1999 UGI moved into consumer products by opening its first Hearth USA retail store in Rockville Maryland which offered hearth items spas grills and patio accessories. It ventured into a growing European market by purchasing FLAGA GmbH a leading gas distributor in Austria and the Czech Republic.

That year a 1997 Pennsylvania law kicked in restructuring the state's electricity industry and enabling customers to choose their electricity provider. In response UGI separated its distribution and power generation operations and in 2000 contributed the bulk of its generation assets to a partnership with Allegheny Energy that sells power to UGI Utilities and other distributors.

In 2001 UGI Enterprises purchased a 20% interest in French propane distributor Antargaz. Also that year the company closed its Hearth USA retail stores. Through its UGI Energy Services subsidiary UGI completed the acquisition of TXU Energy in 2003.

UGI acquired the remaining 80% interest in Antargaz in 2004 expanding its operations in France. Later that year the company continued its European expansion through the acquisition of BP's retail propane distribution business in the Czech Republic.

In 2006 the company acquired the natural gas utility assets of PG Energy for about $580 million. During the next year its Gas Utility unit purchased approximately 79 billion cu. ft. of natural gas for sale to retail core market and off-system sales customers.

To expand its base of gas customers in Pennsylvania in 2008 UGI Utilities acquired PPL Gas Utilities for $32 million. It soon changed that company's name to UGI Central Penn Gas.

EXECUTIVES

Director Corporate Accounting and Reporting, Richard R. Eynon
President and CEO AmeriGas Propane, Eugene V. N. Bissell, age 58, $487,820 total compensation
VP New Business Development; President UGI Enterprises and UGI Energy Services, Bradley C. Hall, age 58
Associate General Counsel and Corporate Secretary, Margaret M. Calabrese
VP General Counsel and Assistant Secretary, Robert H. Knauss, age 58, $340,146 total compensation
Investor Relations, Robert W. (Bob) Krick
Chairman and CEO, Lon R. Greenberg, age 61, $1,067,975 total compensation
President COO and Director, John L. Walsh, age 56, $648,202 total compensation
Investor Relations, Brenda Blake
CFO, Kirk R. Oliver, age 54
Chairman and CEO Antargaz, Francois Varagne, age 56, $490,750 total compensation
VP Accounting and Financial Control and Chief Risk Officer, Davinder Athwal, age 44
General Auditor, Thomas A. Barry
VP UGI HVAC Enterprises, Robert L. Pistor
Managing Director Flaga GmbH, Josef Weinzierl
VP Information Services UGI Utilities, Scott A. Culbertson
Treasurer, Hugh J. Gallagher, age 49
President and CEO UGI Utilities, Robert F. Beard, age 46
Director General Antargaz, Eric Naddeo
Director, Anne Pol, age 65
Director, Marvin O. Schlanger, age 64
Director, Richard W. Gochnauer, age 62

President COO and Director, John L. Walsh, age 56
Director, Roger B. Vincent Sr., age 67
Director, Ernest E. Jones, age 68
Director, Stephen D. Ban, age 72
Director, M. Shawn Puccio, age 49
Auditors: PricewaterhouseCoopersLLP

LOCATIONS

HQ: UGI Corp.
460 North Gulph Road, King of Prussia, PA 19406
Phone: 610 337-1000
Web: www.ugicorp.com

PRODUCTS/OPERATIONS

2012 Sales

AmeriGas propane	2,921	45
Midstream & marketing		
Electric generation	43	1
Adjustments	6	-

Selected Subsidiaries and Affiliates

AmeriGas Inc.
AmeriGas Propane Inc.
- AmeriGas Partners L.P. (26%)
- AmeriGas Propane L.P.
- AmeriGas Technology Group Inc.
- Petrolane Incorporated

Four Flags Drilling Company Inc.
Ashtola Production Company
- UGI Ethanol Development Corporation

Newbury Holding Company
UGI Enterprises Inc. (energy marketing and services)
- CFN Enterprises Inc.
- Eastfield International Holdings Inc.
  - FLAGA GmbH (propane distribution; Austria the Czech Republic and Slovakia)
- Eurogas Holdings Inc.
- McHugh Service Company
- UGI Energy Services Inc.
  - GASMARK (gas marketing)
  - POWERMARK (electricity marketing)
- UGI International Enterprises Inc.
  - UGI Europe Inc.Antargaz (propane distribution France)FLAGA GmbH (propane distribution Austria)

UGI Properties Inc.
UGI Utilities Inc. (natural gas and electric utility)
United Valley Insurance Company

COMPETITORS

Chesapeake Utilities	Ferrellgas Partners
Dominion Resources	National Fuel Gas
Duquesne Light Holdings	NorthWestern
Energy Transfer	PPL Corporation
Exelon	Suburban Propane

HISTORICAL FINANCIALS

Company Type: Public

Income Statement

FYE: September 30

	REVENUE ($ mil.)	NET INCOME ($ mil.)	NET PROFIT MARGIN	EMPLOYEES
09/12	6,519	199	3.1%	9,200
09/11	6,091	232	3.8%	9,750
09/10	5,591	261	4.7%	9,800
09/09	5,737	258	4.5%	9,700
09/08	6,648	215	3.2%	9,500
Annual Growth	(0.5%)	(1.9%)	—	(0.8%)

2012 Year-End Financials

Debt ratio: 37.89%
Return on equity: 8.93%
Cash ($ mil.): 319
Current ratio: 101.18
Long-term debt ($ mil.): 3,347
No. of shares (mil.): 112
Dividends
Yield: —
Payout: 60.23%
Market value ($ mil.): 3,576

	STOCK PRICE ($) FY Close	P/E High/Low		PER SHARE ($) Earnings	Dividends	Book Value
09/12	31.75	18	14	1.76	0.00	19.83
09/11	26.27	16	12	2.06	1.02	17.68
09/10	28.61	12	10	2.36	0.90	16.53
09/09	25.06	11	8	2.36	0.79	14.63
09/08	25.78	14	12	1.99	0.76	13.14
Annual Growth	5.3%	—	—	(3.0%)	—	10.8%

UMB Financial Corp

UMB Financial is the holding company for four UMB-branded banks serving Arizona Colorado Illinois Kansas Nebraska Oklahoma and Missouri. Through some 130 branches the banks offer standard services such as checking and savings accounts credit and debit cards and trust and investment services. Commercial loans account for more than 40% of UMB's loan portfolio. Commercial real estate loans account for more than 25%. UMB Financial goes beyond the banking business. Its diversified portfolio includes subsidiaries that offer insurance brokerage services leasing treasury management health savings accounts and proprietary mutual funds.

UMB Financial operates in three business segments: commercial financial services; institutional financial services; and personal financial services. Its institutional financial services segment (corporate trust and escrow services and correspondent and investment banking) is the company's largest money maker (contributing more than 40% of revenues). Personal financial services (consumer banking wealth management private banking and trust services) makes up about 30% of UMB Financial revenues. And commercial financial services (contributing another 30% of revenues) includes commercial banking merchant services commercial lending and other services.

While growing deposits and increasing its loan portfolio remains a key strategy the company has also been keenly focused on growing its fee-based businesses. More than 50% of UMB's revenue is derived from fee income. Fees are not as dependent on fluctuating interest rates as traditional banking services.

In order to keep growing its fee-based business and diversify its business model UMB has made several recent acquisitions. The company built up its investment advisory and corporate trust business through several 2009 acquisitions. The following year UMB made 10 acquisitions including Prairie Capital Management and Indiana-based Reams Asset Management. The deals more than doubled UMB's Scout Investment Advisors' assets under management to more than $27 billion.

Subsidiary UMB Fund Services (UMBFS) performs accounting and administration functions for mutual fund and alternative investment managers. In 2009 UMBFS bought J.D. Clark & Company a third-party fund service provider to alternative investments firms. A year later the unit expanded its client base when it acquired the managed account business of J.P. Morgan Worldwide Securities Services. A new line of business Managed Account Services at UMBFS was created to service J.P. Morgan's clients.

UMB Financial also has built up its credit card portfolio through acquisitions. In 2010 UMB Bank the company's lead bank bought the credit card portfolio of 5Star Bank which provides banking services to members of the armed forces. The deal included $66 million in assets. That same year UMB Bank acquired CardPartner a firm that first teamed with UMB to offer credit cards for organizations and non-profits.

The family of chairman and CEO Mariner Kemper controls about 14% of UMB Financial's stock.

EXECUTIVES

CEO Healthcare Services, Dennis L. Triplett, age 59
EVP and General Counsel, Dennis R. Rilinger, age 64, $289,250 total compensation
EVP; EVP Loan Administration UMB Bank, Douglas F. (Doug) Page, age 68
President of UMB Bank, James A. (Jim) Sangster, age 57
Vice Chairman UMB National Bank of America, Richard A. Renfro, age 70
Chairman and CEO Oklahoma Region UMB Bank, Royce M. Hammons, age 66
Vice Chairman, Peter J. (Pete) Genovese, age 65, $290,809 total compensation
Director; Chairman and CEO Perfect Commerce, Alexander C. (Sandy) Kemper, age 46, $377,234 total compensation
EVP and Chief Risk Officer, David D. Kling, age 65, $245,028 total compensation
EVP Consumer Services UMB Bank, Bradley J. (Brad) Smith, age 56
Chairman and CEO; Chairman and CEO UMB Financial and UMB Bank Colorado, J. Mariner Kemper, age 39, $550,000 total compensation
EVP and Organizational Effectiveness Eastern Region Administration, Jacqueline A. (Jackie) Witte
EVP Sales Marketing and Communication, Heather K. Miller
President COO and Director; Chairman and CEO UMB Bank; Chairman UMB Fund Services, Peter J. deSilva, age 50, $540,000 total compensation
President and Chief Investment Officer Scout Investment Advisors, William B. (Bill) Greiner
Vice Chairman CFO and Chief Administrative Officer, Michael D. Hagedorn, age 45, $301,538 total compensation
EVP and Director Fund Services Client Relations UMB Fund Services, Peter J. Hammond
Chairman and CEO Greater Missouri Region, Gil Trout
President and Chief Lending Officer UMB Bank-Colorado, Jon M. Robinson
President and CEO Omaha Region UMB Bank, Dan Gomez
President Commercial Banking UMB Financial Corporation, Craig L. Anderson, age 52
Community Bank President Abilene (KS) Banking Center UMB National Bank of America, Daryl D. Roney
Regional President UMB Bank, James D. Rine
President North Central Missouri Region UMB Bank, Marty L. James
EVP Commercial Banking UMB Bank, Ronald G. Skaggs
EVP UMB Bank, David E. Skiles
SVP Consumer Credit UMB Bank, Rick S. Bennett
Community Bank President UMB Bank, Bradley R. Johnson
Community Bank President UMB Bank, Jon J. Henderson
Community Bank President UMB Bank, Thomas E. Brusnahan
Community Bank President UMB Bank, Randall P. Kancel

Community Bank President UMB Bank, James M. Brosnahan
Community Bank President Hudson Russell and Luray Banking Centers UMB National Bank of America, Gregg K. Fischer
SVP UMB Bank, William R. Summers
Community Bank President Atchison Banking Center UMB Bank, Kent R. Wohlgemuth
President and Chief Lending Officer UMB Bank Arizona, Mark E. Peterson
President Investment and Wealth Management, Dana Abraham
President and CEO Personal Financial Services UMB Bank, Clyde F. Wendel, age 64, $350,000 total compensation
Chairman and CEO UMB National Bank of America, William G. Watson
CEO UMB Fund Services, John Zader
CEO Scout Investment Advisors, Andrew J. Iseman, age 47
SVP and Corporate Controller, Bryan J. Walker, age 40
President and Chief Lending Officer UMB Bank St. Louis, David H. (Dave) Naunheim
Chairman and CEO UMB Bank St. Louis, W. Thomas (Tom) Chulick
VP and Senior Portfolio Manager Colorado, John Trujillo II
VP and Trust Advisor Colorado, Norm Close
SVP UMB Corporate Trust, Kenneth Buckius
EVP Operations and Technology Group, Daryl S. Hunt, age 55
EVP and Chief Organizational Effectiveness Officer, Lawrence G. Smith, age 64
EVP and Director Payment and Technology Solutions Division UMB Bank, Terry W. D'Amore, age 55
SVP and Director Purchasing, Nancy Grasse
EVP and Director Fund Services Transfer Agency UMB Financial Services, Maureen Quill
President UMB Bank Colorado, Bert Williams
EVP and Chief Investment Officer UMB Bank, K. C. Mathews
Investor Relations, Abigail Wendel
EVP Banking Services, Stephen m. Kitts
EVP Consumer Banking, Christine Pierson, age 49
Executive Vice President; Director - Payment & Technology Solutions Division of UMB Bank, Terry DAmore
Director, Theodore M. (Ted) Armstrong, age 72
Vice Chairman, Peter J. (Pete) Genovese, age 65
Director; Chairman and CEO Perfect Commerce, Alexander C. (Sandy) Kemper, age 46
Director, Terrence P. (Terry) Dunn
Director, Thomas D. Sanders, age 67
Director, David R. Bradley Jr., age 62
Director, John H. Mize Jr., age 72
Director, Kris A. Robbins, age 53
Director, L. Joshua Sosland, age 51
Director, Paul Uhlmann III, age 61
Director, Thomas J. Wood III, age 65
Director, Greg M. Graves, age 54
President COO and Director; Chairman and CEO UMB Bank; Chairman UMB Fund Services, Peter J. deSilva, age 50
Vice Chairman CFO and Chief Administrative Officer, Michael D. Hagedorn, age 45
Director, Nancy K. Buese, age 42
Director, Kevin C. Gallagher, age 43
Auditors: Deloitte&ToucheLLP

LOCATIONS

HQ: UMB Financial Corporation
1010 Grand Blvd., Kansas City MO 64106
Phone: 816-860-7000 **Fax:** 816-860-7610
Web: www.umb.com

PRODUCTS/OPERATIONS

2011 Segment Revenue

	$ mil.	% of total
Institutional financial services	309	43
Commercial financial services	203	29
Personal financial services	203	28
Total	**716**	**100**

Selected Subsidiaries & Affiliates

Grand Distribution Services LLC
J.D. Clark & Company
Kansas City Financial Corporation
Kansas City Realty Company
Prairie Capital Management LLC
Scout Distributors LLC
Scout Investment Advisors Inc.
UMB Banc Leasing Corp.
UMB Bank and Trust n.a.
UMB Bank Arizona n.a.
UMB Bank Colorado n.a.
UMB Capital Corporation
UMB Community Development Corporation
UMB Distribution Services LLC
UMB Financial Services Inc.
UMB Fund Services Inc.
UMB Insurance Inc.
UMB National Bank of America
UMB Realty Company LLC
UMB Redevelopment Corporation
UMB Trust Company of South Dakota
United Missouri Insurance Company

COMPETITORS

Bank of America
BOK Financial
Capitol Federal Financial
Commerce Bancshares
Dickinson Financial
First National of Nebraska
Great Southern Bancorp
Guaranty Bancorp
TCF Financial
U.S. Bancorp
Zions Bancorporation

HISTORICAL FINANCIALS

Company Type: Public

Income Statement FYE: December 31

	ASSETS ($ mil.)	NET INCOME ($ mil.)	INCOME AS % OF ASSETS	EMPLOYEES
12/11	13,541	106	0.8%	3,448
12/10	12,404	91	0.7%	3,355
12/09	11,663	89	0.8%	3,245
12/08	10,976	98	0.9%	3,274
12/07	9,342	74	0.8%	3,357
Annual Growth	9.7%	9.4%	—	0.7%

2011 Year-End Financials

Debt ratio: 0.05%
Return on equity: 8.94%
Cash ($ mil.): 1,668
Current ratio: —
Long-term debt ($ mil.): 6
No. of shares (mil.): 40
Dividends
Yield: —
Payout: 29.92%
Market value ($ mil.): 1,506

	STOCK PRICE ($) FY Close	P/E High	P/E Low	PER SHARE ($) Earnings	Dividends	Book Value
12/11	37.25	17	12	2.64	0.00	29.46
12/10	41.44	20	14	2.26	0.75	26.24
12/09	39.35	22	15	2.20	0.71	25.11
12/08	49.14	29	15	2.38	0.66	23.81
12/07	38.36	26	20	1.77	0.57	21.55
Annual Growth	(0.7%)	—	—	10.5%	—	8.1%

Umpqua Holdings Corp

Umpqua Holdings thinks of itself not so much as a bank but as a retailer that sells financial products. Consequently many of the company's 195-plus Umpqua Bank "stores" in northern California northern Nevada Oregon and Washington feature coffee bars and computer cafes. While customers sip Umpqua-branded coffee pay bills online attend a financial seminar catch a poetry reading or check out wares from local merchants staff members pitch deposit accounts mortgages loans life insurance investments and more. Subsidiary Umpqua Investments (formerly Strand Atkinson Williams & York) provides retail brokerage services through more than a dozen locations; most are inside Umpqua Bank branches.

Umpqua Bank differentiates itself by encouraging clients to come into its stores instead of using impersonal interfaces like ATMs and electronic banking more cost-effective methods preferred by many of its competitors. In 2010 it introduced its "Next Generation" stores which feature interactive touch-screen walls fresh fruit and cold drinks. It hopes the touchy-feely environment will inspire customers to make impulse purchases like home equity loans or investments.

Umpqua Bank has been expanding beyond its traditional market along the Interstate 5 corridor from Seattle to Sacramento. In 2010 the company entered northern Nevada when it acquired the failed Nevada Security Bank in an FDIC-facilitated transaction. In similar deals it previously acquired three failed banks in Washington State in 2009 and 2010. Umpqua Bank assumed two branches and other assets of the failed Bank of Clark County in Vancouver Washington and acquired the failed Seattle-based EvergreenBank and Rainier Pacific Bank in Tacoma. All of the transactions included loss-sharing agreements with the FDIC.

In a more traditional acquisition Umpqua in 2012 announced it would purchase Circle Bancorp for nearly $25 million to expand its presence in the San Francisco Bay area. The agreement came after Umpqua was outbid by PacWest Bancorp in an attempt to acquire American Perspective Bank. That deal would have expanded Umpqua's footprint in the central coast region of California.

Mainly consumer focused Umpqua Bank established a business banking division in 2011 to court small and mid-sized business clients. It is pursuing deposit growth assembling new lending teams and adding new stores in key metropolitan areas like Portland Oregon; Seattle; San Francisco; and California's Silicon Valley. It continues to look for other acquisition opportunities as well including those beyond its usual stomping grounds.

Umpqua Holdings has also focused on expanding its private banking operations targeting customers with more than $1 million to invest. The company established a wealth management division in 2009 and launched a trust services group the following year. It provides asset management services through an agreement with independent firm Ferguson Wellman Capital Management.

Despite all its efforts to be unique Umpqua Holdings was like many other banks during the recession when it reported a loss in 2009 mainly due to increased provisions for loan losses related to the downturn in the housing market. The company returned to profitability the following year buoyed by higher interest margins loan growth and lower loan losses. It maintained the momentum in 2011 as the economy continued to exhibit signs of life.

EXECUTIVES

SEVP and COO Umpqua Holdings and Umpqua Bank, Brad F. Copeland, age 64, $400,000 total compensation
Chairman, Allyn C. Ford, age 71
EVP Strategic Initiatives Umpqua Holdings and Umpqua Bank, Daniel A. (Dan) Sullivan, age 61, $200,000 total compensation
President CEO and Director Umpqua Holdings and Umpqua Bank, Raymond P. (Ray) Davis, age 63, $714,000 total compensation
Vice Chairman, Dan Giustina, age 63
EVP Creative Strategies Group Umpqua Bank, Lani Hayward, age 45
EVP Cultural Enhancement Umpqua Holdings and Umpqua Bank, Barbara J. Baker, age 63, $147,477 total compensation
EVP and Chief Auditor Umpqua Bank, Gary Neal, age 57
EVP Community Banking Umpqua Holddings and Umpqua Bank, Richard (Ric) Carey, age 64
EVP Corporate Secretary and General Counsel Umpqua Holdings and Umpqua Bank, Steven L. Philpott, age 61
EVP CFO and Principal Financial Officer Umpqua Holdings and Umpqua Bank, Ronald L. (Ron) Farnsworth Jr., age 42, $230,000 total compensation
EVP Treasurer and Principal Accounting Officer Umpqua Holdings and Umpqua Bank, Neal T. McLaughlin, age 44
SVP Corporate Communications, Eve Callahan
EVP Wealth Management Umpqua Holdings and Umpqua Bank, Kelly J. Johnson, age 51, $300,000 total compensation
EVP and Commercial Region Manager Washington State Umpqua Bank, Danielle Burd
VP Relationship Managers Private Bank Division, Jennifer Flickinger
VP Relationship Managers Private Bank Division, Rex Ritter
SVP and Manager Private Banking Division, Donna Huntsman
EVP and CIO Umpqua Holdings and Umpqua Bank, Colin D. Eccles, age 54, $280,000 total compensation
EVP Commercial Banking Umpqua Bank, Cort O?Haver
Director, Frank R. J. Whittaker, age 62
Director, Peggy Y. Fowler, age 60
President CEO and Director Umpqua Holdings and Umpqua Bank, Raymond P. (Ray) Davis, age 63
Director, David B. (Dave) Frohnmayer, age 72
Director, Ronald F. Angell, age 70
Director, William A. Lansing, age 67
Vice Chairman, Dan Giustina, age 63
Director, Bryan L. Timm, age 48
Director, Luis F. Machuca, age 55
Director, Hilliard C. Terry III, age 43
Director, Diane D. Miller, age 59
Director, Jose Hermocillo, age 58
Director, Stephen M. Gambee, age 49
Auditors: MossAdamsLLP

LOCATIONS

HQ: Umpqua Holdings Corporation
1 SW Columbia St. Ste. 1200, Portland OR 97258
Phone: 866-486-7782 **Fax:** 530-226-0514
Web: www.northvalleybank.com

PRODUCTS/OPERATIONS

2010 Sales

	$ mil.	% of total
Interest		
Loans including fees	410	73
Taxable investment securities	67	12
Other	11	2
Noninterest		
Service charges on deposit accounts	34	6
Mortgage banking	21	4
Brokerage commissions & fees	11	2
Other	8	1
Total	**564**	**100**

COMPETITORS

Bank of America
Bank of the West
Banner Corp
Columbia Banking
KeyCorp
U.S. Bancorp
Washington Federal
Wells Fargo
West Coast Bancorp

HISTORICAL FINANCIALS

Company Type: Public

Income Statement FYE: December 31

	ASSETS ($ mil.)	NET INCOME ($ mil.)	INCOME AS % OF ASSETS	EMPLOYEES
12/11	11,563	74	0.6%	2,255
12/10	11,668	28	0.2%	2,185
12/09	9,381	(153)	—	1,857
12/08	8,597	51	0.6%	1,700
12/07	8,340	63	0.8%	1,744
Annual Growth	8.5%	4.2%	—	6.6%

2011 Year-End Financials

Debt ratio: 3.82%
Return on equity: 4.45%
Cash ($ mil.): 598
Current ratio: —
Long-term debt ($ mil.): 441
No. of shares (mil.): 112
Dividends
Yield: —
Payout: 36.92%
Market value ($ mil.): 1,390

	STOCK PRICE ($) FY Close	P/E High/Low		PER SHARE ($) Earnings	Dividends	Book Value
12/11	12.39	20	12	0.65	0.00	14.91
12/10	12.18	105	69	0.15	0.20	14.34
12/09	13.41	—	—	(2.36)	0.20	18.05
12/08	14.47	23	11	0.82	0.62	24.72
12/07	15.34	28	13	1.05	0.74	20.67
Annual Growth	(5.2%)	—	—	(11.3%)	—	(7.8%)

Union First Market Bankshares Corp.

Union First Market Bankshares is the holding company for Union Bank & Trust which operates approximately 100 branches in central northern and coastal portions of Virginia. The bank offers standard services such as checking and savings accounts credit cards and certificates of deposit. Union Bank & Trust maintains a loan portfolio heavily weighted towards real estate: Commercial real estate loans make up more than 30% while one- to four-family residential mortgages and construction loans account for approximately 15% and 20% respectively. The bank also originates personal and business loans.

Other financial services are provided through subsidiaries Union Investment Services (brokerage and investment advisory services through an arrangement with Raymond James Financial) Union Insurance Group (long-term care and business owner coverage) and Union Mortgage Group which provides mortgage brokerage services from about 15 offices.

Union First Market Bankshares primarily operates in Virginia. Its Union Mortgage Group provides mortgage brokerage services from offices in Virginia Maryland and the Carolinas. Union Mortgage is additionally licensed to operate in states in the Mid-Atlantic the Southeast and in Washington DC.

The company's profits have risen dramatically due to the 2010 acquisition of First Market Bank. In 2010 profits nearly tripled (to $22.9 million from the 2009 earnings of $8.4 million) while in 2011 they rose a further 33% to $30.5 million. The acquisition led to an increase in net interest income a primary contributor to the company's growth. Also in 2011 Union First lowered it provision for loan losses as its loan portfolio continued to improve post-recession. Expenses that year were lower than in 2010 when the acquisition closed. Slightly offsetting the improvements mortgage earnings fell by nearly half in 2011 due to the stagnant residential mortgage market.Although profits have risen revenues have remained relatively flat falling 2% in 2011 to $232.9 million.

Union First Market Bankshares' strategy for growth includes buying other banks as well as opening new branches of its own. Then named Union Bank and Trust the company acquired First Market Bank in 2010 to nearly double its branch total. (The holding company then also added "First Market" to its name and moved its headquarters to Richmond.) The company has also grown through "de novo" branching and through purchases of branches and related companies. It acquired an existing branch in Harrisonburg plus some $74 million in loan assets from NewBridge Bank in 2011.

Also that year the bank opened up seven new locations inside Martin's grocery stores where it already had more than 20 in-store branches. In the past couple of years the company has consolidated its bank subsidiaries creating operating efficiencies as well as a stronger unified brand.

Virginia-based specialty insurer Markel Corporation owns 14% of Union First Market Bankshares.

EXECUTIVES

Chairman, Ronald L. Hicks, age 65
EVP and CFO, D. Anthony Peay, age 52, $198,900 total compensation
CEO and Director; CEO Union First Market Bank, G. William Beale, age 62, $354,200 total compensation
EVP and Chief Banking Officer; President Union First Market Bank, John C. Neal, age 62, $246,400 total compensation
President and CEO Northern Neck State Bank, N. Byrd Newton, $120,000 total compensation
Vice Chairman, W. Tayloe Murphy Jr., age 79
President Rappahannock National Bank, Michael T. Leake
EVP Consumer Financial Services, Myles W. H. Gaythwaite
VP Investments and Fund Management, John A. Lane
President Bay Community Bank, Robert L. Bailey
President Union Investments, Bernard (Bern) Mahon Jr.
EVP and Director Retail Banking, Elizabeth M. Bentley, age 51, $139,575 total compensation
VP, George Washington Jr.

EVP and Director Information Technology and Operations, Rex A. Hockemeyer, age 58, $102,708 total compensation
President and Director; EVP and Chief Banking Officer Union First Market Bank, David J. Fairchild
SVP and Chief Marketing Officer, Olen Thomas
EVP and Chief Credit Officer, Douglas F. Wooley III
Chairman President and CEO Prosperity Bank & Trust, Robert J. McDonough
EVP General Counsel and Secretary, Janis Orfe
VP and Director Human Resources, Rita Bartol
VP and Controller, William E. (Bill) Davis
President Northern Virginia Union Bank &Trust, Mark E. Wright
President and CEO Union Mortgage, Herbert W. Engler
EVP and Director Information Technology and Data Management, David S. (Smokey) Wilson, age 70, $118,000 total compensation
Director Internal Audit, Rawley H. Watson III
Director, Patrick J. McCann, age 55
Director, Steven A. Markel, age 63
CEO and Director; CEO Union First Market Bank, G. William Beale, age 62
Director, James E. (Jim) Ukrop, age 74
Director, Douglas E. Caton, age 69
Vice Chairman, W. Tayloe Murphy Jr., age 79
Director, Ronald L. (Ron) Tillett, age 56
President and Director; EVP and Chief Banking Officer Union First Market Bank, David J. Fairchild
Director, R. Hunter Morin, age 68
Director, Hullihen W. Moore, age 69
Director, L. Bradford (Brad) Armstrong
Director, Daniel I. Hansen, age 55
Auditors: YountHyde&BarbourP.C.

LOCATIONS

HQ: Union First Market Bankshares Corporation
111 Virginia St. Ste. 200, Richmond VA 23219
Phone: 804-633-5031 **Fax:** 408-546-4300
Web: www.jdsu.com

PRODUCTS/OPERATIONS

2011 Sales

	$ mil.	% of total
Interest		
Loans including fees	168	72
Securities including dividends	20	9
Other	0	-
Noninterest		
Gains on sales of loans	19	8
Service charges on deposit accounts	8	4
Other service charges commissions & fees	12	5
Other	4	2
Adjustments	(2.5)	-
Total	**232**	**100**

Selected Mergers and Acquisitions

2011
NewBridge Bank branch (Harrisonburg VA)
2010
First Market Bank ($105 million; Richmond VA; federal savings bank)

Selected Subsidiaries

Union First Market Bank
Union Insurance Group LLC
Union Investment Services Inc.
Union Mortgage Group Inc.

COMPETITORS

Bank of America
BB&T
C&F Financial
Eastern Virginia
PNC Financial
Regions Financial
SunTrust
TowneBank
Bankshares
JPMorgan Chase
Wells Fargo

HISTORICAL FINANCIALS

Company Type: Public

Income Statement

FYE: December 31

	ASSETS ($ mil.)	NET INCOME ($ mil.)	INCOME AS % OF ASSETS	EMPLOYEES
12/11	3,907	30	0.8%	1,045
12/10	3,837	22	0.6%	1,005
12/09	2,587	8	0.3%	662
12/08	2,551	14	0.6%	670
12/07	2,301	19	0.9%	690
Annual Growth	14.1%	11.4%	—	10.9%

2011 Year-End Financials

Debt ratio: 5.52%
Return on equity: 7.22%
Cash ($ mil.): 96
Current ratio: —
Long-term debt ($ mil.): 215
No. of shares (mil.): 26
Dividends
Yield: —
Payout: 26.17%
Market value ($ mil.): 347

	STOCK PRICE ($) FY Close	P/E High/Low		PER SHARE ($) Earnings	Dividends	Book Value
12/11	13.29	14	9	1.07	0.00	16.13
12/10	14.78	22	14	0.83	0.25	16.46
12/09	12.39	131	47	0.19	0.30	15.31
12/08	24.80	27	13	1.07	0.74	20.18
12/07	21.14	20	12	1.47	0.73	15.78
Annual Growth	(11.0%)	—	—	(7.6%)	—	0.5%

Union Pacific Corp

Venerable Union Pacific Railroad (UP) has been chugging down the track since the 19th century. Owned by Union Pacific Corporation (UPC) UP is one of the nation's leading rail carriers operating more than 74500 freight cars and about 8200 locomotives. UP transports automobiles; chemicals; energy (fuel); and industrial agricultural and other bulk freight over a system of some 32000 rail miles in 23 states in the western two-thirds of the US. UPC owns more than 26000 route miles of its rail network; leases and trackage rights which allow it to use other railroads' tracks account for the rest. UP's customers have included automakers General Motors and Toyota as well as retail outlet Lowe's.

HISTORY

In 1862 the US Congress chartered the Union Pacific Railroad (UP) to build part of the first transcontinental railway. The driving of the Golden Spike at Promontory Utah in 1869 marked the linking of the East and West coasts as UP's rails met those of Central Pacific Railroad (predecessor of Southern Pacific or SP) which had been built east from Sacramento California.

In 1872 the "New York Sun" revealed the Credit Mobilier scandal: UP officials had pocketed excess profits during the railroad's construction. Debt and lingering effects of the scandal forced UP into bankruptcy in 1893.

A syndicate headed by E. H. Harriman bought UP in 1897. After reacquiring the Oregon branches it lost in the bankruptcy UP gained control of SP (1901) and Chicago & Alton (1904). The Supreme Court ordered UP to sell its SP holdings in 1913 on antitrust grounds. In the 1930s UP diversified into trucking and in the 1970s and 1980s it moved into oil and gas production.

UP bought trucking firm Overnite Transportation in 1986. During the 1980s UP also built up its rail operations acquiring the Missouri Pacific and Western Pacific railroads in 1982 and the Missouri-Kansas-Texas Railroad in 1988. It joined Chicago and North Western (CNW) Railway managers in an investment group led by Blackstone Capital Partners that bought CNW in 1989.

CNW traced its roots to the Galena & Chicago Union Railroad which was founded by Chicago's first mayor W. B. Ogden in 1836 and merged with CNW in 1864. By 1925 the North Western (as it was then known) had tracks throughout the Midwest. In 1995 UP completed its purchase of CNW and made a bid for SP.

SP was founded in 1865 but its history dates to 1861 when four Sacramento merchants founded Central Pacific. By building new track and buying other railroads (including SP in 1868) Central Pacific had expanded throughout California Texas and Oregon by 1887. The two railroads merged in 1885 under the SP name. In 1983 SP was sold to a holding company controlled by Philip Anschutz which in 1995 agreed to sell the company to UP.

UP completed its SP acquisition in 1996 but assimilation of the purchase led to widespread rail traffic jams. UP also sold its remaining interest in Union Pacific Resources an oil company it had spun off the year before. In 1997 UP moved from Bethlehem Pennsylvania to Dallas and joined a consortium led by mining company Grupo Mexico that won a bid to run two major Mexican rail lines. In the US however fatal collisions led to a federal review of UP which found a breakdown in rail safety such as overworked employees and widespread train defects. Meanwhile regulators seeking to resolve UP's massive freight backlog ordered the railroad to open its Houston lines to competitors.

The company decentralized its management into three regions (north south and west) in 1998 to improve traffic flow. It also hired more workers added new trains and realigned routes while selling Skyway Freight Systems its logistics services unit.

In 1999 UP moved its headquarters from Dallas to Omaha Nebraska where Union Pacific Railroad offices already were located. In 2000 it formed Fenix a holding company charged with developing and expanding the company's telecommunications and technology assets. (By 2003 however UP had reabsorbed Fenix and scaled back its support for its remaining technology subsidiaries.)

The company expanded its less-than-truckload operations into the western US in 2001 by buying Motor Cargo Industries. Also that year it completed the integration of Southern Pacific's operations.

UP sold its trucking unit Overnite Corporation (a holding company for Overnite Transportation and Motor Cargo Industries) in an IPO in 2003. (Overnite Corporation was acquired by United Parcel Service in 2005 and renamed UPS Freight the next year.) UP sold its Timera subsidiary (workforce management software) in 2004.

Traffic congestion in the UP system brought on by a shortage of train crews caused some freight from UPS and other customers to be rerouted onto trucks in 2004. The crew shortage was attributed in part to a greater-than-expected number of retirements in 2003. UP accelerated its hiring and training efforts but the company still had to restrict freight volume in an effort to minimize bottlenecks.

In 2006 Union Pacific Railroad reorganized its operating structure going from four regions to three: northern southern and western. Service units of the company's central region were reassigned to the northern and southern regions. The company added 45 miles of double track to its Sunset Corridor in 2008.

In the midst of the Great Recession UPC's 2009 freight volumes decreased 16% from 2008's numbers. The company was forced to raise its rates by about 6%; it also parked approximately 26% of its locomotives 18% of its freight car stock and furloughed about 3000 employees.

As the nation slowly recovered economically UPC realized a 13% increase in volume in 2010 over 2009 with automotive intermodal and industrial product shipments showing the strongest growth. Even with 2010 fuel prices more than 30% higher than 2009 the company's freight revenues increased 20% in 2010. UPC cited economic improvement across the majority of its market sectors as the reason for the recovery.

EXECUTIVES

VP and Treasurer Union Pacific Corporation and Union Pacific Railroad, Mary S. Jones
President and CEO Union Pacific Corporation and Union Pacific Railroad, John J. (Jack) Koraleski, age 61
SVP Strategic Planning and Administration Union Pacific Corporation and Union Pacific Railroad, Charles R. Eisele
Chairman President and CEO Union Pacific Corporation and Union Pacific Railroad, James R. (Jim) Young, age 59, $1,150,000 total compensation
SVP Human Resources; Corporate Secretary Union Pacific Corporation and Union Pacific Railroad, Barbara W. Schaefer, age 58
SVP Corporate Relations Union Pacific Corporation and Union Pacific Railroad, Robert W. Turner
EVP Finance; CFO Union Pacific Corporation and Union Pacific Railroad, Robert M. Knight Jr., age 54, $455,000 total compensation
SVP Special Projects, J. Michael (Mike) Hemmer, age 62, $428,988 total compensation
Assistant VP Corporate Communications, Donna Kush
Director Corporate Relations and Media Northern Region, Mark Davis
SVP and CIO Union Pacific Corporation and Union Pacific Railroad, Lynden L. Tennison
EVP Operations Union Pacific Railroad, Lance M. Fritz, age 49
EVP Marketing and Sales, Eric L. Butler
VP Purchasing Union Pacific Corporation and Union Pacific Railroad, Joseph E. O'Connor Jr.
VP Continuous Improvement Union Pacific Corporation and Union Pacific Railroad, D. Lynn Kelley, age 56
VP External Relations Union Pacific Corporation and Union Pacific Railroad, Michael (Mike) Rock
VP and Controller; Chief Accounting Officer and Controller Union Pacific Railroad, Jeffrey P. Totusek, age 53
Director Public Affairs Western Region (Arizona and New Mexico), Zoe Richmond
Director Corporate Relations and Media Southern Region, Raquel Espinoza
Director Corporate Communications, Tom Lange
VP Labor Relations Union Pacific Corporation and Union Pacific Railroad, William R. (Rick) Turner
Director Corporate Relations and Media Western Region, Aaron Hunt
Director Public Affairs Northern Region (Colorado and Wyoming), Dick Hartman
Director Public Affairs Northern Region (Iowa and Nebraska), Brenda Mainwaring
Assistant VP Government Affairs Northern Region (Illinois Minnesota and Wisconsin), Mike Payette
Director Public Affairs Northern Region (Kansas and Missouri), Ben Jones
VP Public Affairs Northern Region, Joe Bateman
Director Public Affairs Southern Region (Arkansas Louisiana and Tennessee), Drew Tessier
Director Public Affairs Southern Region (Texas (Buda Texas North East and West Texas) and Oklahoma), Clint Schelbitzki
Director Border and Community Affairs Southern Region (Texas — San Antonio and Border Regions), Ivan Jaime
VP Public Affairs Southern Region, Joe Adams
Director Public Affairs Western Region (Idaho Montana and Utah), Dan Harbeke
Director Public Affairs Western Region (Oregon and Washington), Brock Nelson
Director Port Affairs Western Region (Los Angeles Long Beach and Oakland), Andy Perez
Director Public Affairs Western Region (Southern California), Lupe Valdez
VP Public Affairs Western Region, Scott Moore
VP Taxes and General Tax Counsel, Patrick (Pat) O'Malley
VP and General Manager Industrial Products, Bradley A. Thrasher
SVP Law and General Counsel, Gayla L. Thal
VP Law and Chief Compliance Officer, Michael L. Whitcomb
Director, Jose H. Villarreal, age 59
Director, Steven R. (Steve) Rogel, age 69
Director, Erroll B. Davis Jr., age 67
Director, Archie W. Dunham, age 73
Director, Charles C. Krulak, age 70
Director, Andrew H. (Andy) Card Jr., age 64
Director, Thomas F. (Mack) McLarty III, age 66
Director, Thomas J. Donohue, age 73
Director, Judith Richards Hope, age 69
Director, Michael R. (Mike) McCarthy, age 61
Director, Michael W. (Mike) McConnell, age 69
Auditors: Deloitte&ToucheLLP

LOCATIONS

HQ: Union Pacific Corporation
1400 Douglas St., Omaha NE 68179
Phone: 402-544-5000 **Fax:** 402-501-2133
Web: www.up.com

PRODUCTS/OPERATIONS

2011 Sales

	$ mil.	% of total
Freight		
Intermodal	3,609	19
Industrial products	3,166	16
Automotive	1,510	8
Total	**19,557**	**100**

COMPETITORS

American Commercial Lines
Burlington Northern Santa Fe
Canadian National Railway
Canadian Pacific Railway
CSX
Ingram Industries
J.B. Hunt
Kansas City Southern
Kirby Corporation
Landstar System
Norfolk Southern
Pacer International
Schneider National
Werner Enterprises

HISTORICAL FINANCIALS

Company Type: Public

Income Statement

FYE: December 31

	REVENUE ($ mil.)	NET INCOME ($ mil.)	NET PROFIT MARGIN	EMPLOYEES
12/11	19,557	3,292	16.8%	44,861
12/10	16,965	2,780	16.4%	42,884
12/09	14,143	1,898	13.4%	43,531
12/08	17,970	2,338	13.0%	48,242
12/07	16,283	1,855	11.4%	50,089
Annual Growth	4.7%	15.4%	—	(2.7%)

2011 Year-End Financials

Debt ratio: 19.75%
Return on equity: 17.72%
Cash ($ mil.): 1,217
Current ratio: 112.36
Long-term debt ($ mil.): 8,697
No. of shares (mil.): 479
Dividends
Yield: —
Payout: 28.72%
Market value ($ mil.): 50,844

	STOCK PRICE ($) FY Close	P/E High	P/E Low	PER SHARE ($) Earnings	Dividends	Book Value
12/11	105.94	16	12	6.72	0.00	38.71
12/10	92.66	17	11	5.53	1.31	36.14
12/09	63.90	18	9	3.75	1.08	33.54
12/08	47.80	34	9	4.54	0.98	30.70
12/07	125.62	39	26	3.46	0.75	29.87
Annual Growth	(4.2%)	—	—	18.1%	—	6.7%

United Bankshares, Inc.

United Bankshares (no relation to Ohio's United Bancshares) keeps it together as the holding company for two subsidiaries doing business as United Bank (WV) and United Bank (VA). Combined the banks operate more than 120 offices that serve West Virginia Virginia and Washington DC as well as nearby portions of Maryland Pennsylvania and Ohio. The branches offer traditional deposit trust and lending services with a focus on residential mortgages and commercial loans. United Bankshares also owns United Brokerage Services which provides investments asset management and financial planning in addition to brokerage services.

Operations

United Bankshares

Financial Analysis

United Bankshares' 2011 revenue declined nearly 5% vs. 2010 due to an decrease in interest and other income. (2011 marked the third consecutive year of falling revenue for the bank.) The decline in interest revenue was attributed to a decrease in taxable interest and dividends on securities. An increase in nonperforming loans ($79.7 million in 2011 vs. $67.2 million in 2010) and fees from trust and brokerage services among other factors conspired to drive interest income down vs. the prior year. Net income grew 5% over the same period on decreased interest expenses. United Bankshares has consolidated assets of approximately $8.4 billion.

Strategy

United Bankshares has expanded through acquisitions closing more than 25 purchases in the past quarter-century. Its growth strategy has mainly been focused in on the Washington/suburban Maryland/northern Virginia market but its latest deal the 2011 acquisition of West Virginia-based Centra Financial Holdings gave United Bankshares its first branches in Pennsylvania and entry into the Pittsburgh market.

Like many banks United Bankshares has seen a rise in nonperforming loans during the economic downturn but its ratio remains below that of its peers. (As of December 31 2011 nonperforming loans held by the bank were $79.66 million or 1.28% of loans.)

EXECUTIVES

EVP United Bankshares and United Bank (WV), James B. Hayhurst Jr., age 66, $225,000 total compensation
EVP CFO Secretary and Treasurer United Bankshares and United Bank (WV), Steven E. Wilson, age 64, $257,348 total compensation
Chairman and CEO United Bankshares and United Bank (WV), Richard M. Adams, age 66, $650,000 total compensation
EVP United Bankshares and United Bank (WV), Joe L. Wilson, age 65, $204,510 total compensation
EVP; President United Bank (WV), Richard M. Adams Jr., age 44, $225,000 total compensation
EVP; President and CEO United Bank (VA), James J. Consagra Jr., age 52, $265,000 total compensation
EVP, Craige Smith, age 60
Director, Donald L. Unger, age 71
Director, W. Gaston Caperton III, age 72
Director, J. Paul McNamara, age 64
Director, Robert G. Astorg, age 69
Director, Theodore J. Georgelas, age 66
Director, F. T. Graff Jr., age 74
Director, John M. McMahon, age 72
Director, William C. Pitt III, age 68
Director, P. Clinton Winter Jr., age 65
Director, Mary K. Weddle, age 63
Director, Gary G. White, age 63
Director, Lawrence K. Doll, age 63
Auditors: Ernst&YoungLLP

LOCATIONS

HQ: United Bankshares Inc.
300 United Center 500 Virginia St. East, Charleston WV 25301
Phone: 304-424-8800 **Fax:** 304-424-8805
Web: www.ubsi-inc.com

PRODUCTS/OPERATIONS

2011 Sales

	$ mil.	% of total
Interest		
Loans including fees	288	78
Taxable investment securities	23	6
Tax-exempt investment securities	4	1
Other	1	-
Noninterest		
Fees from deposit services	41	11
Fees from trust & brokerage services	13	4
Other	15	4
Adjustment (losses) (18.8) (4)		
Total	**367**	**100**

COMPETITORS

Bank of America
BB&T
Burke & Herbert Bank
Cardinal Financial
City Holding
Fifth Third
Fulton Financial
Huntington Bancshares
JPMorgan Chase
M&T Bank
PNC Financial
SunTrust
Susquehanna Bancshares
United Bancorp
Virginia Commerce Bancorp
WesBanco

HISTORICAL FINANCIALS

Company Type: Public

Income Statement FYE: December 31

	ASSETS ($ mil.)	NET INCOME ($ mil.)	INCOME AS % OF ASSETS	EMPLOYEES
12/11	8,451	75	0.9%	1,619
12/10	7,155	71	1.0%	1,451
12/09	7,805	67	0.9%	1,477
12/08	8,102	86	1.1%	1,531
12/07	7,994	90	1.1%	1,537
Annual Growth	1.4%	(4.4%)	—	1.3%

2011 Year-End Financials

Debt ratio: 4.09%
Return on equity: 7.80%
Cash ($ mil.): 634
Current ratio: —
Long-term debt ($ mil.): 345
No. of shares (mil.): 50
Dividends
Yield: —
Payout: 75.16%
Market value ($ mil.): 1,420

	STOCK PRICE ($) FY Close	P/E High/Low	PER SHARE ($) Earnings	Dividends	Book Value
12/11	28.27	19 12	1.61	0.00	19.29
12/10	29.20	19 12	1.65	1.20	18.18
12/09	19.97	21 9	1.55	1.17	17.53
12/08	33.22	18 10	2.00	1.16	16.97
12/07	28.02	18 12	2.15	1.13	17.61
Annual Growth	0.2%	— —	(7.0%)	—	2.3%

United Community Banks, Inc. (Blairsville, GA)

United Community Banks is the holding company for 27 community banks united in their quest to provide consumer and business banking services in Georgia western North Carolina and eastern Tennessee. Operating mainly under the United Community Bank or UCB banners the banks collectively have more than 100 branches offering deposit products mortgages and other services. Commercial loans including construction loans and mortgages account for the largest segment of United Community Banks' loan portfolio (more than 50%); residential mortgages make up another 25%. The company provides insurance through its United Community Insurance Services subsidiary which does business as United Community Advisory Services.

United Community Banks has been growing through acquisitions. In 2009 it purchased the assets of two failed banks Southern Community Bank of Georgia and Community Bank of West Georgia which were closed by the FDIC; both were merged into United Community Bank. United Community Banks purchased two other Georgia banks –Gwinnett Commercial Group and Southern Bancorp –in 2007 and 2006. Those deals followed the acquisitions of five other community banks in 2004 and 2003.

Despite the growth the bank's revenues have been slipping every year since 2007 largely due to real estate loan losses. It unloaded some $100 million in bad loan assets to asset management firm Fletcher International in 2010. The sale comprised about one-fourth of the company's non-performing loans including commercial and residential mortgages. Fletcher also entered a securities purchase agreement with United in which it has the right to purchase up to $65 million of the bank's preferred stock over a period of two years. (It currently holds a 10% stake in the bank.)

In another asset sale United Community Banks sold consulting subsidiary Brintech for an undisclosed price in 2010. Sheshunoff Consulting and Solutions acquired the firm which provides consulting services to community banks and other financial services companies throughout the US.

In 2011 the company sold some $266 million in substandard and non-performing loans to further reduce its risky holdings. United Community Banks also raised some $380 million of capital in a private stock placement through which investment group Corsair Capital gained a 23% stake in the company. Corsair was also granted a seat on the bank's board of directors

With the added capital and the toxic assets off its balance sheets United Community Banks can pursue other growth opportunities (both organic and through acquisitions) that should help it return to profitability which it hasn't seen since 2007.

EXECUTIVES

President CEO and Director; Chairman United Community Bank Union and Travis Counties, Jimmy C. Tallent, age 59, $480,000 total compensation
EVP and COO, Guy W. Freeman, age 75, $295,000 total compensation
EVP and CFO; Chairman Brintech, Rex S. Schuette, age 59, $283,000 total compensation
President United Community Bank Habersham/Jackson County, James H. Burrell
SVP and Chief Credit Officer North Region, Patrick S. (Shep) Calhoun
SVP Chief Compliance Officer, Carol A. Chastain
President United Community Bank Blue Ridge, John W. Chastain Jr.
SVP SBA Lending, Carol J. Clark
SVP Banking, Robert L. Cochran
President United Community Bank Adairsville, Gary W. Floyd
SVP Human Resources, Susan L. (Susie) Hooper
Chairman United Community Bank Rome, Steven E. Kemp
President United Community Bank Towns County, Richard E. Martin Jr.
SVP and CTO, Jim Stewart
President United Community Bank White County, Eugene B. White
President United Community Bank Union County, Andrew M. Williams III
Chairman, Robert L. Head Jr., age 72
Vice Chairman, W. C. Nelson Jr., age 68
EVP Marketing, Craig Metz, age 52
President and CEO Brintech, Hal Oswalt
Chairman United Community Bank Henry, William N. Strawn Jr.
SVP Retail Banking; Chairman United Community Bank Adairsville and Summerville, William M. (Bill) Gilbert, age 55
Chairman United County Bank Brunswick, H. Mel Baxter
President United Community Bank West Georgia, Timothy I. Warren
President United Community Bank Summerville, J. Scott Tucker
President United Community Bank Gilmer County, Jamie C. Tallent

President United Community Bank Lumpkin County, Larry L. Odom
President and Chairman United Community Bank Cobb, Robert K. Walsh Jr.
President United Community Bank Forsyth County, Tim Heard
President United Community Bank Dawson County, James N. Askew
President United Community Bank Tennessee, Steve Hurst
President United Community Bank McCaysville, Billy Hyde
Chairman United Community Bank North Carolina, Greg Hining
President United Community Bank Brunswick, Gene Haskins
Regional Manager United Community Bank North Carolina, Dale Cable
President United Community Bank Rabun County, Jeffrey E. Fulp
SVP Technology, Lawrence F. DesPres
SVP Controller, Alan H. Kumler
SVP Chief Credit Officer South Region, Chris Jones
Chairman United Community Bank West Georgia, Phillip Kauffman
Director; Chairman Gwinnett Commercial Group, John D. Stephens, age 71
EVP and Chief Risk Officer, David P. Shearrow, age 52, $275,000 total compensation
President Atlanta Region, Glenn S. White, $320,000 total compensation
SVP and CIO, Stephen W. McCoy
SVP and Legal Counsel, Brad Miller
SVP and General Auditor, David T. Sutton
Chairman and President United Community Bank Cherokee County, Steven L. Holcomb
Chairman United Community Bank Blue Ridge, Hoyt O. Holloway
Chairman United Community Bank Dawson County, Herb Burnsed
Chairman United Community Bank Fairburn, Edward C. Wyatt
Chairman United Community Bank Gilmer County, Mitchell Morgan
President United Community Bank Gwinnett, Steven W. Williams
Chairman United Community Bank Habersham/Jackson County, James L. Bruce Jr.
CEO United Community Bank Hall County, Richard L. Valentine
President United Community Bank Hall County, Burton R. Stephens
Chairman United Community Bank Hall County, Joe T. Wood Jr.
President United Community Bank Henry, Kenneth M. Palmer Jr.
Chairman United Community Bank Lumpkin County, John H. Owen
Chairman United Community Bank McCaysville, Don Clement
President United Community Bank Rome, David W. Johnson
Chairman United Community Bank Savannah, Michael Wakely
Chairman United Community Bank White County, Donald E. Stanley
President United Community Bank North Carolina, John D. Goins
Chairman United Community Bank Tennessee, Barry Gordon
Chairman and President United Community Bank Cleveland, Mickey Torbett
President CEO and Director; Chairman United Community Bank Union and Travis Counties, Jimmy C. Tallent, age 59
EVP and COO, Guy W. Freeman, age 75
Vice Chairman, W. C. Nelson Jr., age 68
Director, Robert H. Blalock, age 64
Director, Hoyt O. Holloway, age 72
Director, Tim Wallis, age 60
Director, A. William Bennett, age 70
Director Emeritus, Zell B. Miller, age 80
Director, Cathy Cox, age 50
Director; Chairman Gwinnett Commercial Group, John D. Stephens, age 71
Auditors: PorterKeadleMooreLLP

LOCATIONS

HQ: United Community Banks Inc.
63 Hwy. 515, Blairsville GA 30512
Phone: 706-781-2265 **Fax:** 706-745-8960
Web: www.ucbi.com

PRODUCTS/OPERATIONS

2011 Sales

	$ mil.	% of total
Interest		
Loans including fees	239	69
Taxable investment securities	55	16
Other	3	1
Noninterest		
Service charges & fees	29	8
Mortgage loans & related fees	5	2
Brokerage fees	3	1
Net securities gains	0	-
Other	12	3
Adjustment	(0.7)	-
Total	**347**	**100**

COMPETITORS

Atlantic Coast Financial
Bank of America
Bank of Oak Ridge
BB&T
Fidelity Southern
First Citizens BancShares
Georgia Bancshares
Georgia-Carolina Bancshares
Peoples Bancorp (NC)
Regions Financial
Southeastern Bank Financial
Southeastern Banking
SunTrust
Synovus
WGNB

HISTORICAL FINANCIALS

Company Type: Public

Income Statement FYE: December 31

	ASSETS ($ mil.)	NET INCOME ($ mil.)	INCOME AS % OF ASSETS	EMPLOYEES
12/11	6,983	(226)	—	1,706
12/10	7,443	(345)	—	1,763
12/09	7,999	(228)	—	1,801
12/08	8,520	(63)	—	1,919
12/07	8,207	57	0.7%	1,944
Annual Growth	(4.0%)	—	—	(3.2%)

2011 Year-End Financials

Debt ratio: 2.30%
Return on equity: (-39.40)%
Cash ($ mil.): 378
Current ratio: —
Long-term debt ($ mil.): 160
No. of shares (mil.): 57
Dividends
Yield: —
Payout: —
Market value ($ mil.): 402

	STOCK PRICE ($) FY Close	P/E High/Low		PER SHARE ($) Earnings	Dividends	Book Value
12/11	6.99	—	—	(5.97)	0.00	10.00
12/10	1.95	—	—	(18.80)	0.00	33.56
12/09	3.39	—	—	(19.75)	0.00	51.16
12/08	13.58	—	—	(6.75)	0.00	103.04
12/07	15.80	5	2	6.20	0.00	88.68
Annual Growth	(18.4%)	—	—	—	—	(42.1%)

United Continental Holdings Inc

United Continental Holdings (formerly UAL Corporation) unites cities around the globe through subsidiaries United Air Lines and Continental titans among passenger and cargo air carriers. While United Air Lines and Continental are its main lines the company also has regional operations which are operated under contract by United Express Continental Express and Continental Connection. Combined the company handles more than 5600 flights a day to more than 370 domestic and international destinations from hubs that include Chicago Houston Los Angeles New York San Francisco and Washington DC. UAL Corporation changed its name to United Continental Holdings following a merger deal in 2010.

HISTORY

In 1929 aircraft designer Bill Boeing and engine designer Fred Rentschler of Pratt & Whitney joined forces to form United Aircraft and Transport. Renamed United Air Lines in 1931 the New York-based company offered one of the first coast-to-coast airline services. In 1934 United's manufacturing and transportation divisions split. Former banker Bill Patterson became president of the latter United Air Lines and moved it to the Chicago area.

Led by Patterson until 1963 United was slow to move and began offering jet service in 1959 after rival American. But in 1961 United bought Capital Airlines and became the US's #1 airline.

In 1969 UAL Corp. was formed as a holding company. In 1979 a year after airline deregulation hotelier Richard Ferris became CEO. Dreaming of a travel conglomerate he bought Hertz (1985) and Hilton International (1987). Angered by the diversification the pilots staged a strike in 1985 and then tried to buy the airline in 1987. That year after dropping $7.3 million to change United's name to Allegis Ferris left when leading shareholder Coniston Partners threatened to oust the board and liquidate the firm. Assuming its old name and a new CEO Stephen Wolf (former chief of cargo carrier Flying Tigers) UAL shed its hotels and car rental business and 50% of its computer reservation partnership Covia.

A 1989 takeover bid by Los Angeles billionaire Marvin Davis and Coniston triggered an unsuccessful buyout effort by United pilots management and British Airways. Gerald Greenwald a turnaround expert from Chrysler headed the attempt. Coniston later sold most of its stake in exchange for two seats on the board.

Fare wars and the rise of short-haul rivals caused profits to flag from 1991 to 1993. United began expanding globally and added routes in the Asia/Pacific region (bought from Pan Am in 1986 and 1991). It also laid off thousands of employees and cut executive pay. Finally the 1993 sale of United's kitchen operations (slashing 5800 union jobs) brought the unions to the table with an employee stock ownership plan (ESOP). The ESOP which ceded 55% of UAL to employees in exchange for $4.8 billion in wage concessions was approved in 1994. The deal effectively ended Wolf's reign at UAL since he had fallen out of favor with employees; Greenwald became CEO. United also launched its low-fare carrier that year.

In 1995 workers vetoed a proposed merger with US Airways largely because of pilots' concerns about combining seniority lists. Two years later United formed the Star Alliance with Lufthansa Scandinavian Airlines System Air Canada and Thai Airways.

President James Goodwin a 32-year United veteran took over as CEO after Greenwald's 1999 retirement. Also that year Russian airspace –off-limits to foreign airlines for more than 50 years –was opened to United. In 2000 UAL again made plans to buy US Airways this time for $4.3 billion in cash and $7.3 billion in assumed debt.

The next year the company formed a subsidiary to offer fractional ownership of business jets. Through its United NewVentures unit UAL also bought Internet-based direct marketing firm MyPoints.com. (UAL sold MyPoints.com to Internet service provider United Online –no relation to United Airlines –in 2006.)

Later in 2001 however US antitrust regulators moved to block the UAL-US Airways deal citing concerns that the combination would reduce competition and lead to higher fares. The companies called off the transaction and UAL was to pay US Airways a $50 million termination fee.

Also that year United Airlines lost two planes in the September 11 terrorist attacks on New York and Washington DC. As demand for air travel slumped after the attacks UAL eliminated flights and laid off more than 20% of its workforce. A month after the attacks chairman and CEO James Goodwin resigned under pressure from employee unions; UAL director and former Weyerhaeuser chief John Creighton replaced him on an interim basis. The cutbacks however were not enough to prevent the airline from posting a $2.1 billion loss for 2001.

The following year UAL avoided a potentially disastrous strike by its mechanics when they approved a new contract giving them their first raise since 1994. The airline managed to convince its pilots and salaried managers to take a pay cut in 2002 to alleviate some of its debt. Also that year UAL applied for a $1.8 billion loan under the federal loan guarantee program created to help airlines in the aftermath of the September 11 attacks. Creighton retired and was replaced by Glenn Tilton an oil industry executive who had served as vice chairman of ChevronTexaco and interim chairman of Dynegy. UAL's financial troubles continued to mount however and the company filed for Chapter 11 bankruptcy protection in December 2002.

To assist with its emergence from bankruptcy UAL petitioned for an additional loan from the US government in 2004 but it was denied. Instead the government extended the repayment deadline. In the course of its reorganization UAL launched low-fare carrier Ted renegotiated labor agreements and won court permission to terminate its four employee pension plans. Employees also lost their controlling stake in the company. The federal Pension Benefit Guaranty Corporation wound up with responsibility for the pension plans and a stake in UAL.

United Continental later shut down its one-class low-fare carrier Ted and reconfigured the unit's 55-plus aircraft to include first-class sections for main line use. It also followed archrival American Airlines in imposing a first-checked-bag fee for most customers.

UAL emerged from bankruptcy protection in February 2006. Four years later in October 2010 United acquired Continental Airlines. The holding company changed its name from UAL Corporation to United Continental Holdings.

In 2010 United Continental linked up with All Nippon Airways to create a joint venture which combined their trans-Pacific networks beginning in spring 2011.

EXECUTIVES

Chairman, Glenn F. Tilton, age 64, $850,000 total compensation
EVP and COO, Peter D. (Pete) McDonald, age 61, $754,292 total compensation
SVP and COO Mileage Plus Holdings United Airlines, Thomas F. (Tom) O'Toole, age 54
President CEO and Director, Jeffery A. (Jeff) Smisek, age 57
EVP and Chief Revenue Officer, James E. (Jim) Compton, age 56
SVP Technical Operations, James E. (Jim) Keenan
SVP Labor Relations, P. Douglas (Doug) McKeen
SVP Sales, Dave Hilfman
SVP System Operations Control and United Express, Alexandria P. (Alex) Marren
EVP; President Mileage Plus, Jeffrey T. (Jeff) Foland, age 41
EVP General Counsel and Secretary, Brett J. Hart, age 43
SVP Marketing, Mark Bergsrud
SVP Flight Operations, Frederick C. (Fred) Abbott
EVP Communications and Government Affairs, Irene E. (Nene) Foxhall, age 60
SVP Network, Greg Hart
VP and Controller, Chris T. Kenny, age 48
SVP Pricing and Revenue Management, Leon Kinloch
EVP and CFO, John Rainey
SVP Corporate Strategy and Business Development, Rohit Philip
Managing Director Investor Relations, Tyler Reddien
EVP Human Resources and Labor Relations, Michael P. (Mike) Bonds, age 49
SVP Finance and Treasurer, Gerry Laderman
Senior Manager Investor Relations, Sarah Rae Murphy
SVP and CIO, Robert (Bob) Edwards
SVP Alliances Regulatory and Policy, Hershel I. Kamen
SVP Airport Operations and Cargo United, Jonathan (Jon) Roitman
Director, David J. Vitale, age 65
Director, Henry L. Meyer III, age 62
Director, John H. Walker, age 54
President CEO and Director, Jeffery A. (Jeff) Smisek, age 57
Director, Walter Isaacson, age 59
Director, James J. O'Connor, age 75
Director, Charles A. Yamarone, age 53
Director, Stephen R. Canale, age 67
Director, Kirbyjon H. Caldwell, age 58
Director, Jane C. Garvey, age 68
Director, Oscar Munoz, age 54
Director, Carolyn Corvi, age 61
Director, Capt. Wendy J. Morse, age 51
Auditors: Ernst&YoungLLP

LOCATIONS

HQ: United Continental Holdings Inc.
77 W. Wacker Dr., Chicago IL 60601
Phone: 312-997-8000 **Fax:** 610-992-3254
Web: www.ugicorp.com

2011 Sales

	$ mil.	% of total
Domestic (US & Canada)	21,922	59
Atlantic	6,675	18
Pacific	5,404	15
Latin America	3,109	8
Total	**37,110**	**100**

PRODUCTS/OPERATIONS

2011 Sales

	$ mil.	% of total
Passenger		
Main line	25,975	70
Regional	6,536	18
Cargo	1,167	3
Other	3,432	9
Total	**37,110**	**100**

COMPETITORS

Air France-KLM
AirTran Airways
Alaska Air
Alitalia
AMR Corp.
British Airways
Delta Air Lines
FedEx
Frontier Airlines
Japan Airlines
JetBlue
Mesa Air
Pinnacle Airlines
Qantas
SkyWest
Southwest Airlines
UPS
US Airways
Virgin Atlantic Airways

HISTORICAL FINANCIALS

Company Type: Public

Income Statement FYE: December 31

	REVENUE ($ mil.)	NET INCOME ($ mil.)	NET PROFIT MARGIN	EMPLOYEES
12/11	37,110	840	2.3%	8,700
12/10	23,229	253	1.1%	86,000
12/09	16,335	(651)	—	47,000
12/08	20,194	(5,348)	—	50,000
12/07	20,143	403	2.0%	55,000
Annual Growth	16.5%	20.2%	—	(36.9%)

2011 Year-End Financials

Debt ratio: 33.52%
Return on equity: 46.51%
Cash ($ mil.): 7,762
Current ratio: 96.52
Long-term debt ($ mil.): 11,424
No. of shares (mil.): 330
Dividends
Yield: —
Payout: —
Market value ($ mil.): 6,244

	STOCK PRICE ($) FY Close	P/E High/Low		PER SHARE ($) Earnings	Dividends	Book Value
12/11	18.87	11	6	2.26	0.00	5.46
12/10	23.82	24	10	1.08	0.00	5.27
12/09	12.91	—	—	(4.32)	0.00	(16.77)
12/08	11.02	—	—	(42.21)	0.00	(17.60)
12/07	35.66	15	10	2.79	0.00	20.68
Annual Growth	(14.7%)	—	—	(5.1%)	—	(28.3%)

United Fire Group, Inc.

The United Fire Group companies join together to offer a unified range of property/casualty and life insurance products. The group operates through its United Fire & Casualty subsidiary which in turn holds entities that carry a variety of property/casualty offerings including fidelity and surety bonds and fire auto employee liability homeowners and workers' compensation lines. More than 1300 independent agencies in some 45 states sell its property/casualty products to businesses and individuals. The United Life division of United Fire & Casualty sells life annuity and credit life products to individuals and groups through some 950 independent agents in more than 30 states.

The company completed a corporate reorganization in 2012 through which United Fire Group became the ultimate parent of the United Fire & Casualty group of companies. The conversion to a holding company structure gave the group a more flexible operating platform to conduct future growth measures. Through the restructuring United Fire Group took on the publicly traded status of United Fire & Casualty while United Fire & Casualty became an intermediate holding entity for the group's operating subsidiaries including property/casualty providers Addison Insurance Lafayette Insurance United Fire Lloyd's Mercer Insurance Franklin Insurance and Financial Pacific Insurance as well as United Life.

United Fire's property/casualty insurance offerings account for more than 90% of its annual insurance premiums with a majority of those policies being written to commercial group customers. The company also offers certain personal policies to individual customers. It markets its products from its headquarters in Iowa and from four regional offices in California Colorado New Jersey and Texas and it operates primarily in adjacent areas of the midwestern southern and western US. About two-thirds of United Fire's 2011 property/casualty business was written in Texas Iowa California Missouri Louisiana New Jersey Illinois and Colorado. In the life insurance realm Iowa is the largest operating territory acounting for about 30% of premiums; other key states include Minnesota Illinois Nebraska and Wisconsin.

In order to increase policy placement in its existing markets United Fire offers profit-sharing and commission programs to its independent agents. It also seeks to provide modern technological tools to best serve both its agents and its policyholders. At the same time United Fire looks to expand into new markets to reduce the risk potential in its concentrated areas of operation.

Towards that end United Fire entered the Mid-Atlantic and West Coast markets in 2011 when it acquired Mercer Insurance (and its Franklin Insurance and Financial Pacific Insurance subsidiaries) in a cash-and-debt deal worth some $192 million. The purchase strengthened United Fire's property/casualty offerings adding some 200 agents in states where United Fire lacked an existing presence; it also diversified United Fire's commercial customer base as Mercer largely serves small to midsized businesses (along with some large businesses and individual customers).

However the company has occasionally had to reduce operations in some less-profitable territories. Its Lafayette Insurance Company subsidiary ceased writing new property/casualty policies in Louisiana in 2010 due to instability in that regional market. United Fire experienced a high volume of claims in the state following the disastrous 2005 Hurricane Katrina and had trouble recovering from the catastrophe losses.

Natural catastrophes took a heavy toll on United Fire's profits in 2011 a year of record losses for the property/casualty industry. The company's net income levels declined from $47 million to a meager $11000 that year. Conversely revenues increased some 19% to $705 million due to increased premium rates across all of its product lines; the company had experienced reduced revenues in 2009 and 2010 due to a decline in commercial premium levels from the economic recession and competitive conditions in the insurance marketplace. Such ups and downs are typical for property/casualty insurers' financial results which are highly cyclical in nature.

United Fire was founded by Scott McIntyre in 1946; descendants of the founder own a 14% stake in the company.

EXECUTIVES

VP General Counsel and Secretary, Neal R. Scharmer, age 55
Vice Chairman, John A. Rife, age 69, $250,000 total compensation
VP and CFO, Dianne M. Lyons, age 48, $225,000 total compensation
EVP Corporate Administration, Michael T. Wilkins, age 48, $240,000 total compensation
Chairman, Jack B. Evans, age 63
VP and Chief Investment Officer, Barrie W. Ernst, age 57, $230,000 total compensation
Resident VP Denver Regional Office, David L. Hellen, age 59
Corporate Secretary and Fidelity and Surety Claims Manager, David A. Lange, age 54
President and CEO, Randy A. Ramlo, age 50, $350,000 total compensation
Treasurer, Galen E. Underwood, age 71
VP and Chief Claims Officer, David E. Conner, age 53
VP Human Resources, Timothy G. Spain, age 60
VP Fidelity and Surety, Dennis J. Richmann, age 47
Branch Manager Gulf Coast Regional Office, Joseph B. Johnson, age 59
VP and General Manager United Life Insurance Company, Kent J. Hutchins, age 53
VP Great Lakes Regional Office, Brian S. Berta, age 47
Controller, Kevin Helbing
VP Information Services, Scott A. Minkel, age 50
VP Midwest Regional Office, Douglas A. Penn, age 63
VP Corporate Underwriting, Allen R. Sorensen, age 54
VP E-Solutions, Colleen R. Sova, age 58
Vice Chairman, John A. Rife, age 69
Director, Douglas M. (Doug) Hultquist, age 56
Director, Mary K. Quass, age 61
Director, James W. (Jim) Noyce, age 56
Director, Christopher R. Drahozal, age 50
Director, Kyle D. Skogman, age 61
Director, Casey D. Mahon, age 60
Director, George D. Milligan, age 55
Director, Frank S. Wilkinson Jr., age 72
Director, Thomas W. Hanley, age 59
Auditors: Ernst&YoungLLP

LOCATIONS

HQ: United Fire Group Inc.
118 2nd Ave. SE, Cedar Rapids IA 52401
Phone: 319-399-5700 **Fax:** 319-399-5499
Web: www.unitedfiregroup.com

PRODUCTS/OPERATIONS

2011 Premiums

	% of total
Property/casualty	
General liability (including	27
Fire & allied	26
Automobile	23
Workers'	9
Fidelity &	3
Reinsurance & other	3
Life	9
Total	**100**

Selected Subsidiaries

United Fire & Casualty Company
- Addison Insurance Company
- American Indemnity Financial Corporation
  - Texas General Indemnity Company
- Lafayette Insurance Company
- Mercer Insurance Group Inc.
  - Financial Pacific Insurance Company
  - Mercer Insurance CompanyFranklin Insurance CompanyMercer Insurance Company of New Jersey Inc.
- United Fire & Indemnity Company
  - United Fire Lloyds
- United Life Insurance Company

COMPETITORS

ACE Limited
AIG
Allstate
American Family Insurance
American Financial Group
Arrowpoint Capital Corp.
Chubb Corp
CNA Surety
Erie Indemnity
Farmers Group
Fireman' s Fund Insurance
GEICO
Hanover Insurance
John Hancock Financial Services
Liberty Mutual
MassMutual
Progressive Corporation
Prudential
State Farm
The Hartford
Travelers Companies
White Mountains Insurance Group

HISTORICAL FINANCIALS

Company Type: Public

Income Statement FYE: December 31

	ASSETS ($ mil.)	NET INCOME ($ mil.)	INCOME AS % OF ASSETS	EMPLOYEES
12/11	3,618	0	0.0%	894
12/10	3,007	47	1.6%	654
12/09	2,902	(10)	—	673
12/08	2,687	(13)	—	674
12/07	2,760	111	4.0%	667
Annual Growth	7.0%	(90.0%)	—	7.6%

2011 Year-End Financials

Debt ratio: 1.24%
Return on equity: —
Cash ($ mil.): 144
Current ratio: —
Long-term debt ($ mil.): 45
No. of shares (mil.): 25
Dividends
Yield: —
Payout: 140972.73%
Market value ($ mil.): 515

	STOCK PRICE ($) FY Close	P/E High	P/E Low	PER SHARE ($) Earnings	Dividends	Book Value
12/11	20.18	—	—	(0.00)	0.00	27.29
12/10	22.32	13	9	1.80	0.60	27.35
12/09	18.23	—	—	(0.39)	0.60	25.35
12/08	31.07	—	—	(0.48)	0.60	24.10
12/07	29.09	11	7	4.03	0.56	27.63
Annual Growth	(8.7%)	—	—	—	—	(0.3%)

United Natural Foods Inc.

Distribution is second nature for United Natural Foods Inc. (UNFI). The company is one of the top wholesale distributors of natural organic and specialty foods in the US and Canada. It owns more than 25 distribution centers that supply 60000-plus items to 23000 customers including independently owned retailers supernatural chain Whole Foods (its #1 customer) and traditional supermarkets. The company offers groceries supplements produce frozen foods and ethnic and kosher food products. UNFI also operates about a dozen natural-products retail stores under the name NRG (mostly in Florida) and it produces roasted nuts dried fruits and other snack items through subsidiary Woodstock Farms.

Operations

UNFI's wholesale division (97% of sales) is augmented by specialty products units such as subsidiary Albert's Organics which supplies more than 5000 customers with fruits vegetables and other perishable items. The division includes distribution of vitamins through Select Nutrition and ethnic food items and related products through its UNFI Specialty business. The company has built up its own food brands through subsidiary Blue Marble Brands. The unit offers more than 900 products marketed under 25-brand names directly to retailers as well as third party distributors.

UNFI's retail arm Earth Origins operates 13 natural products stores in Florida Maryland and Massachusetts. The company also has a retail store in Vancouver British Columbia.

Geographic Reach

Through its acquisition of SunOpta Distribution Group the company's wholly-owned subsidiary UNFI Canada became the largest distributor of natural organic and specialty foods including kosher fare in Canada. UNFI has five distribution centers in Canada. UNFI Canada contributes about 5% of UNFI's sales.

Financial Analysis

UNFI's fiscal 2012 (ends July) sales increased more than 15% vs. the prior year while net income grew by about 19% over the same period. The double-digit sales increase resulted from growth of the company's core wholesale business which added grocery-giant Safeway and Giant Eagle as customers over the course of the year. Riding a wave of increased demand for healthier (presumably natural and organic) food and acquisitions UNFI has seen its sales nearly double over the past five years.

Strategy

In a move to focus on the edible side of the natural and organic products aisle UNFI in 2011 sold the non-foods and general merchandise lines of its UNFI Specialty business to L&R Distributors. The deal included UNFI's portfolio of cosmetics seasonal goods health and beauty products and household goods picked up as part of its $85 million acquisition of Millbrook Distribution Services in 2007. In a follow-on deal UNFI's Canadian subsidiary in late 2011 bought the food distribution assets of B.K. Sethi Distribution which specializes in Asian Indian Hispanic and Caribbean food distribution.

The company has succeeded at taking market share away from its competition thanks to demand for its slate of premium services coupled with expanded distribution capacity and targeted acquisitions. In mid-2010 UNFI acquired the food distribution assets of Ontario-based rival SunOpta the largest supplier of organic kosher and specialty foods in Canada –a promisingly dynamic market. The deal worth some C$68 million (nearly $67 million) gave UNFI a prominent position north of the US-Canada border.

The bulk of the company's business comes from independently owned retail stores (35% of sales) and from supernatural chains that specialize in natural food products (36%). Its largest customer is Whole Foods Market which accounts for more than a third of sales. Other customers include conventional supermarkets Kroger Publix and Wegman's.

Nonetheless competition is fierce; UNFI goes head-to-head with Kehe Food which acquired another rival Tree of Life from Dutch food giant Wessanen in 2010. The company also contends with traditional grocery wholesalers such as C & S Wholesale and Nash-Finch that distribute a growing number of organic food items.

Ownership

FMR LLC owns nearly 12% of UNFI's shares.

HISTORY

Rhode Island retailer Norman Cloutier founded Cornucopia Natural Foods in 1978 and soon focused on distribution. During the 1980s Cornucopia grew by acquiring other natural foods distributors. It bought suppliers Natural Food Systems (seafood) and BGS Distributing (vitamins) in 1987 and 1990 respectively. Cornucopia expanded into the Southeast in 1991 when it opened a distribution center in Georgia.

Reviving its interest in retailing Cornucopia formed Natural Retail Group in 1993 to buy and run natural foods stores. During the next two years it acquired several retailers. The company expanded its distribution operations in the West in 1995 adding Denver-based Rainbow Distributors.

In 1996 Cornucopia merged with the leading natural foods distributor in the western US Sacramento-based Mountain People's which Michael Funk had founded 20 years earlier. The combined company became United Natural Foods with Cloutier as chairman and CEO and Funk as president and vice chairman; it went public later that year.

United Natural Foods became the largest natural foods distributor when it bought New Hampshire-based Stow Mills in 1997. The next year it added Hershey Imports an importer and processor of nuts seeds and snacks and Albert's a distributor of organic produce. With the purchase of Mother Earth Markets in 1998 the company's retailing operations had grown to 16 stores but by mid-1999 it had sold four stores. That year United Natural Foods' East Coast consolidation problems became so profound that top customer Whole Foods announced it was finding backup distribution sources.

Funk replaced Cloutier as CEO and the company handed the chairman's post to board member Thomas Simone in 1999. In 2000 after the resignation of Cloutier from the board of directors United Natural Foods adopted a poison-pill plan to block potential takeovers. The company leased a distribution center in the Los Angeles area in 2001 to increase market share in the Southwest. It also acquired Florida's Palm Harbor Natural Foods.

In mid-2002 United Natural Foods lost one of its two largest customers —Wild Oats Markets — when that company defected to rival specialty foods distributor Tree of Life. However United Natural Foods soon won that business back. In October the company completed the acquisition of privately held Blooming Prairie Cooperative for approximately $31 million. In late 2002 the company merged with Northeast Cooperatives a natural foods distributor in the Midwest and Northeast.

That year United Natural Foods discontinued the management sales and support operations at its Hershey Imports subsidiary but continued to manufacture and distribute products from the Edison New Jersey plant.

In 2004 the company renewed its distribution agreement with Wild Oats with a five-year pact. United Natural Foods later announced a new three-year distribution agreement with Whole Foods which it renewed in 2006. Whole Foods later acquired Wild Oats in 2007. That year United Natural Foods acquired ethnic and specialty food distributor Millbrook Distribution Services for about $85 million.

CEO Funk stepped down in 2008 and was replaced by former Performance Food Group chief Steven Spinner.

EXECUTIVES

Chairman, Michael S. Funk, age 58, $193,558 total compensation
President CEO and Director, Steven L. (Steve) Spinner, age 52
Vice Chairman, Gordon D. Barker, age 66
SVP National Distribution, Sean F. Griffin, age 52
SVP General Counsel Chief Compliance Officer and Corporate Secretary, Joseph J. (Joe) Traficanti, age 61
SVP and Chief Human Resource and Sustainability Officer, Thomas A. Dziki, age 51
SVP CFO and Treasurer, Mark E. Shamber, age 43, $297,000 total compensation
President Western Region, Kurt Luttecke, age 45
VP IT Operations and Applied Technologies, Joshua Sigel
SVP and CIO, John A. Stern, age 45, $280,000 total compensation
President UNFI International, David A. Matthews, age 46
President Woodstock Farms Manufacturing Select Nutrition and Natural Retail Group, Thomas Grillea, age 55
President Eastern Region, Craig H. Smith
SVP and CIO, Eric Dorne
President CEO and Director, Steven L. (Steve) Spinner, age 52
Vice Chairman, Gordon D. Barker, age 66
Director, Mary E. (Betsy) Burton, age 60
Director, Peter A. Roy, age 55
Director, Joseph M. Cianciolo, age 73
Director, James P. Heffernan, age 66
Director, Gail A. Graham, age 61
Auditors: KPMGLLP

LOCATIONS

HQ: United Natural Foods Inc.
313 Iron Horse Way, Providence RI 02908
Phone: 401-528-8634 **Fax:** -11151
Web: www.boc.cn

PRODUCTS/OPERATIONS

2012 Sales by Customer Typ

	$ mil.	% of total
Independently owned natural products retailers	1,847	35
Supernatural chains	1,883	36
Conventional supermarkets	1,246	24
Other	260	5
Total	**5,236**	**100**

2012 Sales

	$ mil.	% of total
Wholesale	5,175	97
Other	163	3
Adjustments	(102.7)	-
Total	**5,236**	**100**

Selected Acquisitions

Fiscal 2012
B.K. Sethi Distribution Ltd. ($3 million; Ontario Canada; specialty food distribution)
Fiscal 2011
SunOpta Distribution Group ($66 million; Ontario Canada; specialty food distribution)

Selected Operations

Manufacturing division
Woodstock Farms (import roasting packaging and distribution of nuts dried fruit seeds trail mixes granola natural and organic snack items and confections and Blue Marble Brands products)
Retail division
Natural Retail Group (NRG) (natural products retail stores within the US)
Wholesale division
Albert' s Organics (distributor of organically grown produce and perishable items)

Select Nutrition (distributor of vitamins minerals and supplements)

UNIFI Canada (natural organic and specialty business in Canada)
UNFI Specialty (specialty distributor in the Eastern and Midwestern portions of the US)

COMPETITORS

Associated Wholesale Grocers
Associated Wholesalers
C&S Wholesale
DPI Specialty Foods
KeHE Distributors
Nash-Finch
SUPERVALU
Wal-Mart

HISTORICAL FINANCIALS

Company Type: Public

Income Statement

FYE: July 28

	REVENUE ($ mil.)	NET INCOME ($ mil.)	NET PROFIT MARGIN	EMPLOYEES
07/12	5,236	91	1.7%	7,000
07/11	4,530	76	1.7%	6,900
07/10*	3,757	68	1.8%	6,500
08/09	3,454	59	1.7%	6,000
08/08	3,365	48	1.4%	6,300
Annual Growth	11.7%	17.2%	—	2.7%

*Fiscal year change

2012 Year-End Financials

Debt ratio: 7.76%
Return on equity: 9.33%
Cash ($ mil.): 16
Current ratio: 283.35
Long-term debt ($ mil.): 115
No. of shares (mil.): 49
Dividends
Yield: —
Payout: —
Market value ($ mil.): 2,677

	STOCK PRICE ($) FY Close	P/E High/Low		PER SHARE ($) Earnings	Dividends	Book Value
07/12	54.62	30	18	1.86	0.00	19.97
07/11	41.75	28	20	1.60	0.00	17.93
07/10*	33.73	22	15	1.57	0.00	14.48
08/09	27.03	20	9	1.38	0.00	12.66
08/08	18.77	28	14	1.13	0.00	11.20
Annual Growth	30.6%	—	—	13.3%	—	15.6%

*Fiscal year change

United Parcel Service Inc

The ubiquitous Brown is more than chocolate-colored trucks or a plain-vanilla delivery business. United Parcel Service (UPS) is the world's largest package delivery company transporting more than 15 million packages and documents per business day throughout the US and to 220-plus countries. Its delivery operations use a fleet of more than 100000 motor vehicles and 500-plus aircraft. In addition to package delivery the company offers services such as logistics and freight forwarding through UPS Supply Chain Solutions and less-than-truckload (LTL) and truckload (TL) freight transportation through UPS Freight. UPS is acquiring TNT Express for about $6.8 billion.

HISTORY

Seattle teens Jim Casey and Claude Ryan started American Messenger Company a delivery and errand service in 1907. They were soon making small-parcel deliveries for local department stores and in 1913 changed the company's name to Merchants Parcel Delivery. Casey who led the company for 50 years established a policy of manager ownership best service and lowest rates. In 1916 new employee Charlie Soderstrom chose the brown paint still used on the company's vehicles.

Service expanded outside Seattle in 1919 when Merchants Parcel bought Oakland California-based Motor Parcel Delivery later changing its name to United Parcel Service (UPS). By 1930 the company served residents in New York City (its headquarters from 1930 to 1975) and New Jersey as well as all major cities along the Pacific Coast.

Offering small-package delivery within a 125-mile radius of certain cities starting with Los Angeles in 1927 UPS grew in relative obscurity as it expanded westward from the East Coast and eastward from the West Coast. The company gained notice in 1952 when the U.S. Postal Service named UPS as a competitor. Noted for its employee-oriented culture the company through the 1960s required all executives to start as drivers.

In 1975 after becoming the first package delivery company to serve every address in the 48 contiguous US states UPS crossed the border to Canada and Germany followed the next year. (UPS had been offering two-day air parcel delivery service to major cities on both coasts via cargo holds on regularly scheduled airline flights since 1953.) By 1977 UPS Blue Label Air (now UPS Next Day Air) guaranteed 48-hour delivery anywhere on the mainland.

Overnight service began in 1981 and was nationwide by 1985 (also serving six European countries). It started air express delivery from its hub in Louisville Kentucky in 1982. After purchasing its own jet cargo fleet and getting authorization from the FAA to operate its own aircraft in 1988 UPS Airlines officially became an airline (and the fastest-growing one in FAA history). By 1990 UPS Airlines was delivering to more than 175 countries in North and South America Africa Europe and Asia.

Moving to its headquarters in Atlanta in 1991 the company began to work on its customer service. As part of a technology revamp UPS created the electronic clipboard still used by drivers to track packages and digitize signatures. In 1994 UPS went online allowing customers to track packages in transit.

In 1994 Teamsters staged a one-day strike to protest UPS's new per-package weight limit (raised from 70 to 150 pounds). The next year the firm allowed rank-and-file employees to buy UPS stock. Nevertheless in 1997 UPS was hit by a 15-day Teamsters strike that cost the company hundreds of millions of dollars. UPS settled the strike by combining part-time jobs into 10000 new full-time positions; in 1998 the company headed off another labor threat by giving its pilots a five-year contract with pay raises. Also in 1998 UPS ordered 30 Airbus A300-600 aircraft.

After losing a tax dispute in 1999 UPS paid $1.8 billion into a special account with the Internal Revenue Service pending appeal. (The company prevailed on appeal in 2001 and the case went back to the U.S. Tax Court. UPS and the IRS settled the case in 2002 and UPS was to receive about $1 billion worth of credits and refunds over several years.)

Chinese government-owned logistics giant Sinotrans proved friendlier than the IRS teaming up with UPS in 1999 to expand UPS-branded service across China. To fund global expansion UPS sold about 10% of its stock in 1999 in a public offering valued at more than $5 billion –then the largest IPO in US history. The company also agreed to buy Challenge Air Cargo (completed in 2001) a Miami cargo airline serving Latin America. The international push continued in 2000 as UPS expanded operations into Australia.

Not only expanding geographically UPS broadened its services to better compete with rivals FedEx and the United States Postal Service. In 2000 the company formed its e-Ventures unit to develop subsidiaries focused on supporting e-commerce businesses.

In 2001 UPS bought Mail Boxes Etc. a franchiser of stores that offer mail packing and shipping services. It also acquired global logistics management provider Fritz Companies which was renamed UPS Freight Services and expanded its financial services by buying First International Bancorp (now UPS Capital). That year UPS also placed its largest-ever aircraft order: 60 Airbus A300-600 cargo planes to be delivered by 2009. (UPS and Airbus subsequently renegotiated the order and in 2005 Airbus agreed to supply newer A380 freighters instead of some of the planes that UPS originally ordered. Two years later UPS said it would cancel its order for A380s because of delays in production of the aircraft.)

The company's contract with employees represented by the Teamsters came up for renewal in 2002 and a new six-year deal was approved. That year the company moved to combine UPS Freight Services and UPS Logistics Group to form UPS Supply Chain Solutions. In 2003 UPS sold its aviation technologies unit to Garmin International.

To reflect the evolution of its mix of services UPS in 2003 updated its company logo for the first time since 1961 losing the familiar package wrapped up in string. Brown remained the company's predominant color but complementary hues were introduced on UPS aircraft and packages. Drivers' uniforms received the new logo but didn't change otherwise.

UPS in 2004 expanded its freight forwarding business by buying Menlo Worldwide Forwarding from Con-Way for $150 million and $110 million in assumed debt. The next year UPS bought trucking company Overnite for about $1.2 billion. The acquisition brought UPS into the less-than-truckload (LTL) freight transportation business and –not coincidentally –countered a move by FedEx which formed nationwide LTL carrier FedEx Freight in 2001. Overnite's operating units Overnite Transportation and Motor Cargo Industries were consolidated under the UPS Freight brand in 2006.

UPS's efforts to deliver more services to more customers in more places are being overseen by a new driver. Vice chairman and CFO Scott Davis took over as chairman and CEO in 2008 succeeding Mike Eskew who stepped down after five years of running the company.

In 2009 UPS expanded its reach into Eastern Europe and Central Asia. That year the company acquired the small package operations of its shipping contractors in Turkey and Slovenia to add to similar operations in Romania that it purchased a year prior. UPS set up a joint venture based in Dubai that coordinates services across the Middle East Turkey and parts of Central Asia.

In 2010 UPS formed a joint venture in Vietnam with P&T Express a subsidiary of VN Post –the service agent UPS used to launch its service in Vietnam in 1994. UPS Vietnam took root in Hanoi a fertile site for growing the company's transportation and logistics businesses. The deal followed UPS's move to add flights between the US and Japan and a new air hub in Shanghai which links Chinese domestic and international routes.

EXECUTIVES

Chairman and CEO United Parcel Service and UPS Supply Chain Solutions, D. Scott Davis, age 60, $1,000,000 total compensation
SVP Worldwide Sales Marketing and Strategy, Alan Gershenhorn, age 53
VP Corporate Public Relations, Dale Hayes, age 55
SVP and COO, David P. Abney, age 57, $462,500 total compensation
SVP and CFO, Kurt P. Kuehn, age 57, $400,000 total compensation
SVP; President UPS International, Daniel J. (Dan) Brutto, age 55
SVP Human Resources and Labor Relations, John J. McDevitt, age 53, $420,000 total compensation
President Global Freight Forwarding, Stephen D. (Steven) Flowers
President Airlines, Mitch Nichols
President Central Region, George W. Brooks Jr.
SVP and CIO, David A. (Dave) Barnes, age 56
SVP Communications and Brand Management, Christine M. Owens, age 56
SVP Legal Compliance Audit and Public Affairs General Counsel and Corporate Secretary, Teri P. McClure, age 48
President UPS Americas Region, Romaine Seguin
President US Operations, Myron A. Gray, age 54, $381,250 total compensation
President West Region, Gerald R. (Jerry) Mattes
President The UPS Foundation, Ken Sternad
Public Relations Manager, Donna Longino
President Worldwide Sales, Kate Gutmann
Chief Sustainability Officer, Scott Wicker
VP Flight Operations UPS Airlines, Matt Capozzoli
Director, F. Duane Ackerman, age 69
Director, Michael J. Burns, age 60
Director, William R. (Bill) Johnson, age 63
Director, John W. Thompson, age 62
Director, Michael L. (Mike) Eskew, age 62
Director, Rudy H. P. Markham, age 66
Director, Carol B. Tome, age 55
Director, Stuart E. Eizenstat, age 69
Director, Ann M. Livermore, age 53
Director, Clark T. (Sandy) Randt Jr., age 66
Auditors: Deloitte&ToucheLLP

LOCATIONS

HQ: United Parcel Service Inc.
55 Glenlake Pkwy. NE, Atlanta GA 30328
Phone: 404-828-6000 **Fax:** 703-683-7840
Web: www.liveunited.org

2011 Sales

	$ mil.	% of total
US	39,347	74
Other countries	13,758	26
Total	**53,105**	**100**

PRODUCTS/OPERATIONS

2011 Sales

	$ mil.	% of total
US domestic package		
Ground	22,189	42
Next day air	6,229	12
Deferred	3,299	6
International package		
Export	9,056	17
Domestic	2,628	5
Cargo	565	1
Supply chain & freight		
Forwarding & logistics	6,103	11
Freight	2,563	5
Other	473	1
Total	**53,105**	**100**

COMPETITORS

AMR Corp.
Canada Post
Con-way Inc.
Deutsche Post
FedEx
Japan Post
La Poste
Lufthansa
Nippon Express
Panalpina
Royal Mail
Ryder System
United Continental
US Postal Service
YRC Worldwide

HISTORICAL FINANCIALS

Company Type: Public

Income Statement FYE: December 31

	REVENUE ($ mil.)	NET INCOME ($ mil.)	NET PROFIT MARGIN	EMPLOYEES
12/11	53,105	3,804	7.2%	398,000
12/10	49,545	3,488	7.0%	400,600
12/09	45,297	2,152	4.8%	408,000
12/08	51,486	3,003	5.8%	426,000
12/07	49,692	382	0.8%	425,300
Annual Growth	1.7%	77.6%	—	(1.6%)

2011 Year-End Financials

Debt ratio: 32.07%
Return on equity: 54.07%
Cash ($ mil.): 3,034
Current ratio: 188.58
Long-term debt ($ mil.): 11,095
No. of shares (mil.): 963
Dividends
Yield: —
Payout: 54.17%
Market value ($ mil.): 70,482

	STOCK PRICE ($) FY Close	P/E High/Low	PER SHARE ($) Earnings	Dividends	Book Value
12/11	73.19	20 16	3.84	0.00	7.31
12/10	72.58	21 16	3.48	1.88	8.05
12/09	57.37	27 18	2.14	1.80	7.68
12/08	55.16	25 15	2.94	1.80	6.79
12/07	70.72	218192	0.36	1.68	11.70
Annual Growth	0.9%	— —	80.7%	—	(11.1%)

United States Cellular Corp

United States Cellular takes calls from sea to shining sea. Doing business as U.S. Cellular the company provides wireless phone service to about 6 million customers in more than two dozen states in the US largely in the Midwest and the South where it more than 6 million customers. Its products and services –marketed directly through the Internet and from about 400 retail stores –include mobile messaging prepaid calling international long distance mobile Internet and directory assistance. U.S. Cellular service is also sold through contracts with resellers. The company offers phones from HTC LG Electronics Research In Motion and Samsung Electronics among other vendors.

Geographic Reach

U.S. Cellular provides its range of wireless products and services to more than 5.8 million customers in 26 states.

Strategy

U.S. Cellular announced it is exiting the Chicago and other midwestern markets in order to help its profitability. In late 2012 it agreed to sell Chicago and select other markets in the region to Sprint Nextel for $480 million. The divestiture expected to close by mid-2013 is prompted by the company's effort to get stronger by initially downsizing in markets where it is not seeing profitable customer growth. The move also will allow U.S. Cellular to continue to roll out the 4G LTE network to its remaining markets faster.

Ownership

Telephone and Data Systems owns 84% of U.S. Cellular.

HISTORY

LeRoy Carlson a Chicago-based investor formed Telephone and Data Systems (TDS) in 1969 by consolidating the rural phone companies he owned. In the early 1980s TDS began acquiring cellular licenses including the rights to operate 5% of the Los Angeles market. Getting a jumpstart on the Bells TDS created United States Cellular as a subsidiary in 1983.

United States Cellular began operations in Knoxville Tennessee and Tulsa Oklahoma in 1985. Three years later TDS took the company public and reduced its stake to 82%. Belgian cable television operator Coditel was an initial investor.

Hefty startup and acquisition costs kept the company from making a profit until 1993. After moving into the black it began selling its phones (purchased from suppliers) at kiosks in Wal-Mart stores in 1995. Meanwhile it continued to add networks: In 1995 and 1996 United States Cellular added markets in Arizona Florida Iowa Texas and Virginia.

In 1997 United States Cellular traded its controlling interests in 10 markets primarily in Indiana and Kentucky for BellSouth's controlling interests in 12 markets in Illinois and Wisconsin (including Milwaukee). That year the firm also began converting its network to digital technologies (both TDMA time division multiple access and the newer CDMA code division multiple access).

United States Cellular acquired majority interests in six more markets in 1998. That year the firm also sold several minority interests in markets in which it did not operate to Vodafone. In 1999 the company introduced a new logo and began doing business as U.S. Cellular. Also that year it began providing CDPD (cellular digital packet data) service which allows for data transmission over cellular networks to police departments and government agencies in Illinois.

The company agreed in 2001 to acquire PCS licenses in Illinois Iowa and Nebraska from McLeodUSA for $74 million to bolster its Midwest operations. It purchased PrimeCo Wireless Communications in a 2002 deal valued at $610 million gaining entrance into the Chicagoland market as well as Bloomington-Normal Champaign-Urbana Decatur and Springfield Illinois with expanded service to Peoria and Rockford Illinois. Additionally U.S. Cellular provided service to South Bend and Fort Wayne Indiana and Benton Harbor Michigan.

In a 2003 swap agreement with AT&T Wireless the company acquired wireless licenses and properties in 13 states in the US's Midwest and Northeast in exchange for assets in northern Florida and southern Georgia.

U.S. Cellular in 2008 exchanged surplus wireless spectrum licenses covering parts of Illinois for licenses held by Sprint Nextel for areas of Iowa Maryland Oklahoma and West Virginia.

EXECUTIVES

VP Corporate Relations Telephone and Data Systems, Jane W. McCahon
VP and Assistant Treasurer, Kenneth R. (Ken) Meyers, age 58, $432,915 total compensation
Chairman, LeRoy T. (Ted) Carlson Jr., age 65, $766,500 total compensation
EVP Finance CFO and Treasurer, Steven T. Campbell, age 61, $437,100 total compensation
EVP Engineering and CTO, Michael S. (Mike) Irizarry, age 50, $509,220 total compensation
EVP Operations, Alan D. Ferber, age 44
EVP Sales and Customer Service, Carter S. Elenz
VP Central Operations, Katherine (Kathy) Hust
VP Midwest Operations, Rochelle J. Boersma, age 52
EVP and Chief Human Resources Officer, Jeffrey J. (Jeff) Childs, age 55, $418,200 total compensation
VP East Operations, Thomas P. (Tom) Catani
President CEO and Director, Mary N. Dillon, age 50
VP West Operations, Nick B. Wright, age 48
VP National Network Operations, Kevin R. Lowell
VP Financial and Real Estate Services, Thomas (Tom) Weber
VP Public Affairs and Communications, Karen C. Ehlers
VP Organizational Learning and Chief Teaching Officer, Thomas J. Griffin, age 54
VP Legal and Regulatory Affairs, John C. Gockley, age 56
VP Information Technology Delivery, John M. Cregier
VP Customer Service, R. Lynn Costlow
VP Marketing and Sales Operations, Edward C. Perez
VP Financial Planning and Analysis, Jeffrey S. Hoersch, age 45
Area Sales Manager, Shaun Spann
SVP Marketing and Chief Marketing Officer, David Kimbell
Director, LeRoy T. Carlson Sr., age 95
Director, Harry J. Harczak Jr., age 55
Director, Gregory P. Josefowicz, age 58
Director, James E. (Jim) Barr III, age 72
Director, Walter C. D. Carlson, age 58
Director, Paul-Henri Denuit, age 77
Director, J. Samuel Crowley, age 61
Director, Ronald E. Daly, age 65
President CEO and Director, Mary N. Dillon, age 50
Auditors: PricewaterhouseCoopersLLP

LOCATIONS

HQ: United States Cellular Corporation
8410 W. Bryn Mawr Ste. 700, Chicago IL 60631
Phone: 773-399-8900 **Fax:** 773-399-8936
Web: www.uscellular.com

Selected Markets

Mid-Atlantic Region
- Eastern North Carolina/South Carolina
- Virginia/North Carolina
- West Virginia/Maryland/Pennsylvania

Midwest Region
- Central Illinois/Indiana
- Chicago MTA
- Iowa
- Kansas
- Missouri
- Nebraska/Missouri/Iowa
- Western Illinois
- Wisconsin/Minnesota

Northwest Region
- Oregon/California
- Washington/Oregon

Other Markets
- Eastern Tennessee/Western North Carolina
- Florida/Georgia
- Maine/New Hampshire/Vermont
- Missouri/Illinois/Kansas/Arkansas
- Southern Texas
- Texas/Oklahoma/Missouri/Kansas/Arkansas

PRODUCTS/OPERATIONS

COMPETITORS

AT&T Mobility
Boost Mobile
Cellco
CenturyLink
Leap Wireless
MetroPCS
Sprint Nextel
T-Mobile USA
Virgin Mobile USA

HISTORICAL FINANCIALS

Company Type: Public

Income Statement

FYE: December 31

	REVENUE ($ mil.)	NET INCOME ($ mil.)	NET PROFIT MARGIN	EMPLOYEES
12/11	4,343	175	4.0%	8,743
12/10	4,177	132	3.2%	9,000
12/09	4,214	216	5.1%	9,200
12/08	4,243	32	0.8%	8,470
12/07	3,946	314	8.0%	8,400
Annual Growth	2.4%	(13.6%)	—	1.0%

2011 Year-End Financials

Debt ratio: 13.91%
Return on equity: 4.84%
Cash ($ mil.): 424
Current ratio: 178.99
Long-term debt ($ mil.): 880
No. of shares (mil.): 84
Dividends
Yield: —
Payout: —
Market value ($ mil.): 3,689

	STOCK PRICE ($) FY Close	P/E High/Low		PER SHARE ($) Earnings	Dividends	Book Value
12/11	43.63	25	18	2.05	0.00	42.81
12/10	49.94	33	23	1.53	0.00	40.69
12/09	42.41	19	12	2.48	0.00	39.34
12/08	43.24	223	75	0.38	0.00	36.74
12/07	84.10	29	19	3.56	0.00	36.49
Annual Growth	(15.1%)	—	—	(12.9%)	—	4.1%

United States Steel Corp.

Steel crazy after all these years United States Steel is North America's largest integrated steelmaker and the world's eighth-largest steel producer. The company operates mills throughout the Midwest in the US; in Ontario Canada; and in Slovakia. U.S. Steel makes a wide range of flat-rolled and tubular steel products and its annual production capacity is about 30 million net tons of raw steel. Its customers are primarily in the automotive appliance construction oil and gas and petrochemical industries. In addition U.S. Steel mines iron ore and procures coke which provide the primary raw materials used in steelmaking. It is also engaged in railroad and barge operations and real estate.

HISTORY

United States Steel Corporation was conceived through a 1901 merger of 10 steel companies that combined their furnaces ore deposits railroad companies and shipping lines. The deal involved industrial pioneers Andrew Carnegie Charles Schwab Elbert Gary and J. P. Morgan.

Morgan had helped organize the Federal Steel Company in 1898 and he then wanted to create a centralized trust to dominate the soaring steel market. Carnegie owned the largest US steel company at the time Carnegie Steel but wanted to retire.

In 1900 Schwab Carnegie Steel's president outlined the idea of the steel trust based on a merger of the Carnegie and Federal steel companies. Morgan asked Schwab to persuade Carnegie to sell his steel mills and name his price. Morgan didn't haggle when Carnegie responded that he would sell for almost half a billion dollars.

The Carnegie-Morgan combination created the world's first billion-dollar company. It produced 67% of the country's steel in its first year (its steel complex and the Indiana town where it was located were named after Gary who was CEO until 1927).

The company boomed during WWI and WWII. But its market share fell to about 30% by the 1950s although it set new profit records in 1955. During the 1970s prospects for long-term growth in steel became dismal in light of rising costs foreign competition and competitive pricing.

In 1982 U.S. Steel doubled its size when it bought Marathon Oil a major integrated energy company with huge oil and gas reserves in the US and abroad. It continued to cut back its steelmaking capacity laying off 100000 employees closing steel mills and selling off assets.

The company bought Texas Oil & Gas in 1986 and renamed itself USX Corporation to reflect the decreasing role of steel in its business. Also that year corporate raider Carl Icahn USX's largest single shareholder unsuccessfully tried to get the company to sell its steel operations. In 1988 USX bought 49% of Transtar a group of rail and water transport providers. (It purchased the remaining stake in 2001 making Transtar a wholly owned subsidiary.)

Stockholders in 1991 approved splitting the company into two separate entities under the USX umbrella: U.S. Steel and Marathon. During the 1990s U.S. Steel continued to close steelmaking facilities. In 1992 USX joined five other leading US steel producers in a suit against subsidized foreign steelmakers. The next year the company formed two joint ventures with Japan's Kobe Steel.

In 1994 U.S. Steel teamed up with rival Nucor to explore a new technology that would reduce much of the cost and pollution of the steelmaking process. The company agreed to pay $106 million in fines and improvements in 1996 to settle charges of air pollution violations involving its Indiana plant. That year blast furnace outages at two U.S. Steel plants cost the company more than $100 million.

U.S. Steel began upgrading several of its facilities in 1997 and 1998 and entered into a number of domestic and foreign joint ventures including one in Slovakia and another in Mexico. Seeing prices drop in 1998 and 1999 the company cut production and joined other US steelmakers in charging rivals in Brazil Japan and Russia with unlawfully dumping low-priced steel in the US.

In 2000 U.S. Steel acquired the core activities of leading central European steelmaker VSZ. The $495 million (excluding investments) deal –U.S. Steel's first major foray into Europe –included an agreement to invest some $700 million in VSZ's facilities.

Early in 2001 USX spun off its steel operations as United States Steel Corporation; the remaining energy businesses began operating as Marathon Oil Corporation. Also that year USX-U.S. Steel and Bethlehem Steel announced they were in talks about possibly merging the two companies. Subsequently USX-U.S. Steel and National Steel (U.S. subsidiary of NKK) began talks of merging its businesses. In order for the deal to close National Steel would have to restructure its debt and the Bush administration would have to implement its plan to curtail steel imports. At the end of 2001 due to shareholder pressure USX-U.S. Steel split apart from its holding company USX Corporation and the steel operations unit went back to trading under its original name United States Steel Corporation. The breakup left the company with over $1.3 billion in debt (Marathon Oil assumed $900 million of the company's debt).

U.S. Steel signed an option agreement to purchase the remaining 53% of National Steel in 2002. That year U.S. Steel sold its stake in VSZ.

In its pursuit to consolidate U.S. Steel along with other US steelmakers received concessions (40% import tariffs and assistance with its huge retiree health-care costs) from the Bush administration. In March 2002 the Bush administration on recommendations of the International Trade Commission imposed tariffs of 8%-30% providing temporary relief to U.S. Steel and the US steel industry. The administration rejected any retiree bailout plan and in December 2003 ended the tariffs 16 months ahead of schedule.

In 2003 U.S. Steel made the monumental move to purchase National Steel for roughly $1.1 billion in cash including liabilities. AK Steel which had an offer of roughly $1.1 billion vehemently challenged U.S. Steel but the deal fell through after labor negotiations with United Steelworkers of America proved unsuccessful. With the combined manufacturing capabilities of National Steel and U.S. Steel the company's raw steel production came in at around 20 million tons of steel annually both domestically and internationally which made it the nation's largest steel producer until the formation of Mittal Steel USA in 2005. The year 2003 also saw the expansion of U.S. Steel's European businesses with the acquisition of Sartid.

U.S. Steel again jumped into the industrywide consolidation game in 2007 when it spent a combined $3.3 billion to buy tubular goods maker Lone Star Technologies and the former Stelco in separate deals. Lone Star Technologies was among the nation's largest makers of welded steel tubes for use in the oilfield. The acquired business complemented U.S. Steel's own product line for the energy industry which consisted largely of seamless tubes. The Stelco deal on the other hand added to the company's core business. Focusing on slab products used in the flat-rolled market Stelco raised U.S. Steel's production capacity to more than 30 million tons a year. Upon closing of the deal U.S. Steel changed Stelco's name to U.S. Steel Canada.

Although U.S. Steel agreed to maintain certain production and employment levels at the plants in Canada it stopped operations in 2009 when demand weakened in response to the global economic slump. The Canadian government responded by taking the company to court in 2009 and a later settlement of the dispute led U.S. Steel to agree to invest $50 million in its two Canadian plants by 2015.

U.S. Steel Canada sold its Bar Mill and Bloom and Billet Mill at its Ontario operations to Max Aicher (North America) in 2010. Also in 2010 U.S. Steel sold the assets of its Mobile River Terminal Company and of Warrior and Gulf Navigation.

EXECUTIVES

VP Human Resources, Susan M. (Sue) Suver, age 52
EVP and CFO, Gretchen R. Haggerty, age 56, $555,750 total compensation
VP Tubular Technology and Business Development, David L. Britten, age 52
SVP European Operations and Global Operations Services, George F. Babcoke, age 56
SVP Corporate Affairs and General Counsel, James D. Garraux, age 59, $451,260 total compensation
SVP Strategic Planning Business Services and Administration, David H. (Dave) Lohr, age 58, $441,750 total compensation
VP Procurement Raw Material and Real Estate, Michael J. Hatcher, age 54
VP and Controller, Gregory A. Zovko, age 51
Chairman and CEO, John P. Surma Jr., age 57, $1,130,004 total compensation
VP Sales, Joseph R. (Joe) Scherrbaum Jr., age 55
SVP North American Flat-Roll Operations, Michael S. Williams, age 51
VP and Treasurer, John J. Quaid
VP U.S. Flat-Rolled Operations, Anton Lukac, age 50
VP Engineering and Technology, Anthony R. Bridge, age 58
SVP and Chief Risk Officer, Larry T. Brockway, age 49
General Manager Delivery Performance and Processed Products, Peter J. Alvarado, age 55
President and General Manager U.S. Steel Canada, Anton Jura, age 46
SVP Tubular Operations, Douglas R. Matthews, age 46
Gerneral Manager Great Lakes Works, Scott H. Coleman, age 45
VP European Operations and President U.S. Steel Ko?ice, David J. Rintoul, age 55
President United Spiral Pipe, Patrick J. Mullarkey, age 54
VP Supply Chain and Customer Service, Sharon K. Owen, age 58
VP Commercial Europe, Robert J. Beltz, age 43
General Manager North American Flat-Rolled Marketing, Robert Y. Kopf III, age 45
General Manager Minnesota Ore Operations, Thomas Kelly, age 56
General Manager Sales, William L. Reder, age 47
General Manager Raw Materials, Marc F. Stoken, age 57
Plant Manager Clairton, James F. Dudek, age 38
General Manager Customer Service, Gerald W. Gagliano, age 57
General Manager Logistics Services, James V. Bard, age 55
VP Tubular Commercial, Geroge H. Thompson Jr.
Director, David S. (Dave) Sutherland, age 62
Director, Dan O. Dinges, age 58
Director, John G. (Jack) Drosdick, age 69
Director, Graham B. Spanier, age 63
Director, Charles R. Lee, age 72
Director, Frank J. Lucchino, age 72
Director, Seth E. Schofield, age 72
Director, Richard A. (Dick) Gephardt, age 70
Director, Glenda G. McNeal, age 51
Director, Patricia A. Tracey, age 61
Auditors: PricewaterhouseCoopersLLP

LOCATIONS

HQ: United States Steel Corporation
600 Grant St., Pittsburgh PA 15219-2800
Phone: 412-433-1121 **Fax:** 412-433-5733
Web: www.ussteel.com

2011 Sales

	$ mil.	% of total
North America	15,578	78
Europe	4,306	22

2010 Sales

North America	13,385	77

PRODUCTS/OPERATIONS

2011 Sales

	$ mil.	% of total
Flat-rolled	12,367	62
Tubular Products	3,034	15
Total	**19,884**	**100**

Selected Subsidiaries

Acero Prime S. R. L de CV (44% steel processing and warehousing)
Delray Connecting Railroad Company (transportation)
Double Eagle Steel Coating Company (50% with Severstal; steel processing)
PRO-TEC Coating Co. (50% with Kobe Steel; steel processing)
Transtar Inc. (transportation)
U. S. Steel Kosice sro (steelmaking Slovakia)
USS-POSCO Industries (50% with Pohang Iron & Steel; steel processing)
Worthington Specialty Processing (50% with Worthington Industries; steel processing)

COMPETITORS

AK Steel Holding Corporation
Allegheny Technologies
ArcelorMittal
Baosteel
BlueScope Steel
BOHLER-UDDEHOLM
Carpenter Technology
Gerdau Ameristeel
JFE Holdings
Kobe Steel
Nippon Steel & Sumitomo Metal Corporation
Nucor
POSCO
Salzgitter
Severstal North America
Simec
SSAB North America
SSAB Svenskt
Steel Dynamics
Tata Steel
Ternium

ThyssenKrupp Steel
Wuhan Iron & Steel

HISTORICAL FINANCIALS

Company Type: Public

Income Statement FYE: December 31

	REVENUE ($ mil.)	NET INCOME ($ mil.)	NET PROFIT MARGIN	EMPLOYEES
12/11	19,884	(53)	—	43,000
12/10	17,374	(482)	—	42,000
12/09	11,048	(1,401)	—	43,000
12/08	23,754	2,112	8.9%	49,000
12/07	16,873	879	5.2%	49,000
Annual Growth	4.2%	—	—	(3.2%)

2011 Year-End Financials

Debt ratio: 26.30%
Return on equity: (-1.51)%
Cash ($ mil.): 408
Current ratio: 158.24
Long-term debt ($ mil.): 3,828
No. of shares (mil.): 144
Dividends
Yield: —
Payout: —
Market value ($ mil.): 3,810

	STOCK PRICE ($) FY Close	P/E High/Low		PER SHARE ($) Earnings	Dividends	Book Value
12/11	26.46	—	—	(0.37)	0.00	24.30
12/10	58.42	—	—	(3.36)	0.20	26.80
12/09	55.12	—	—	(10.42)	0.45	32.62
12/08	37.20	11	1	17.96	1.10	42.13
12/07	120.91	17	9	7.40	0.80	46.87
Annual Growth	(31.6%)	—	—	—	—	(15.1%)

United Stationers Inc.

Don't think that United Stationers is just another paper pusher. The company is a leading wholesale distributor of office supplies and equipment in North America offering some 100000 of its own and national brand products to more than 25000 customers. Through subsidiaries United Stationers Supply (USS) Lagasse and ORS Nasco United Stationers supplies such items as business machines computer products and peripherals janitorial supplies and office products and furniture. It also offers office furniture for such markets as education and health care. United Stationers sells primarily to resellers through catalogs and over the Internet as well as through its direct sales force.

Geographic Reach

Of the $5 billion in sales United Stationers rang up in 2011 $100 million was generated by its international operations.

Strategy

As part of its key merchandising strategy United Stationers keeps its costs low through high-volume purchasing. It orders products from more than 1000 manufacturers. Some 20% of the company's purchases were made from Hewlett-Packard in 2011. The company's largest customer W.B. Mason Co. accounted for about 11% of 2011 sales.

To strengthen its foothold in product distribution United Stationers has been acquiring the assets of its rivals. Most recently the company bought privately-owned welding safety and industry products wholesaler O.K.I. Supply Co. for $90 million in late 2012. The Ohio-based firm joins the company's ORS Nasco business. Previously the company's USS subsidiary acquired Denver-based MBS Dev a software solutions provider to business products resellers for $15 million in early 2010. The purchase is expected to bolster the company's online merchandising and marketing capabilities.

United Stationers recently saw a shift in its executive suite. Richard Gochnauer retired as CEO of the company in May 2011 succeeded by P. Cody Phipps the president and COO of United Stationers. Before joining the firm in 2003 Phipps was a partner with McKinsey & Company.

Financial Analysis

United Stationers' net sales increased by more than 3% to $5 billion in 2011 compared with $4.8 billion in 2010. Net income fell by more than 3% over the same period. The sales growth was driven by double-digit increases in sales of industrial and janitorial and breakroom supplies. Traditional office products eked out a 1.5% sales gain while sales of technology products which account for a third of the company's total declined 2%. Office furniture sales fell nearly 7%. The sales growth was notable as the company lost its largest customer – office supply retailer Staples. (Staples accounted for about 11% of its 2010 sales.) Staples acquired office products wholesaler Corporate Express (a key competitor of United Stationers) in 2008.

Ownership

FMR is the company's largest shareholder with nearly 15% of the company's shares. Neuberger Berman Group owns about 12% of United Stationers.

HISTORY

Morris Wolf and Harry Hecktman former office supply salesmen and Israel Kriloff a grocer purchased Utility Supply Company (founded in 1906) and began selling office supplies in downtown Chicago in 1921. Weathering the Depression Utility Supply's business grew steadily during the 1930s. In 1935 the company published its first catalog and it opened its first retail store in downtown Chicago two years later. The partners bought out Kriloff in 1939.

WWII created a scarcity of raw materials and Utility Supply had difficulty in obtaining merchandise. The company tried selling non-office products unsuccessfully. Fortunately the war's end brought an end to the inventory drought. During the postwar era Utility Supply began mailing a series of catalogs to retailers nationwide. By 1948 mail-order business accounted for 40% of sales. A wholesale division to sell products to independent resellers was created in the 1950s.

In 1960 the company adopted the name United Stationers Supply and the retail stores became the Utility Stationery Stores. Business increased as independent retailers began to appreciate the advantages of ordering through a wholesaler instead of a manufacturer –purchasing goods on an as-needed basis. Howard Wolf the founder's son became CEO in 1967 and began emphasizing computers and automation to track inventory and costs.

Wholesale trade accounted for about two-thirds of sales by 1970. United Stationers introduced a series of abridged catalogs targeting specific groups and marketing segments such as furniture and electronics. The following year United Stationers developed regional redistribution centers that offered overnight delivery. The company sold its retail outlets in 1978.

Three years later United Stationers went public. During the 1980s the advent of warehouse clubs and office supply superstores threatened independent retailers. The company developed marketing concepts to help its independent resellers even as it aggressively targeted mail-order houses and superstores. The downsizing trend in the late 1980s caused the corporate market to shrink and United Stationers lowered prices; it instituted a decentralization plan in 1990.

The next year the company expanded into Canada opening its first non-US subsidiary and it acquired archrival Stationers Distributing and its distribution centers across the US in 1992. In 1994 it established its United Facility Supply unit to distribute maintenance supplies.

Investment firm Wingate Partners which controlled rival Associated Stationers bought United Stationers in 1995 and combined the operations of the two companies under the United Stationers name. United Stationers acquired janitorial supplies wholesaler Lagasse Bros. in 1996. In 1998 the company acquired the US and Mexican operations of Abitibi-Consolidated including Azerty. (It acquired Azerty Canada in 2000.)

United Stationers launched a venture with E-Commerce Industries in 1999 to help customers sell products over the Internet. The next year the company started The Order People a third-party call center fulfillment business aimed at online retailers; however the dot-com bust and higher losses than planned led United Stationers to curtail operations in 2001. Also that year it bought Peerless Paper Mills (merging the wholesale distributor of janitorial and paper products into Lagasse).

The company sold its Canadian operations in 2006 following an accounting scandal. United Stationers discovered that its Canadian operation was incorrectly accounting for supplier allowances and other receivables.

United Stationers acquired ORS Nasco a wholesale distributor of industrial supplies for about $180 million in 2007.

In 2008 it purchased Emco Distribution a New Jersey-based business product distributor for $15 million.

United Stationers promoted P. Cody Phipps its president and COO to the position of CEO in May 2011 when CEO Richard Gochnauer retired.

EXECUTIVES

Chairman, Charles K. (Chuck) Crovitz, age 58
SVP General Counsel and Secretary, Eric A. Blanchard, age 55, $300,203 total compensation
Chairman, Frederick B. (Fred) Hegi Jr., age 68
VP and Treasurer, Robert J. Kelderhouse, age 56
SVP Trade Development, Joseph R. Templet, age 64, $273,600 total compensation
SVP National Accounts and Channel Management, Jeffrey G. Howard, age 56
Investor Relations, Mary Disclafani
SVP Supply Chain, Ronald C. Berg, age 52
Group President Lagasse and ORS Nasco, Stephen A. (Steve) Schultz, age 45, $372,399 total compensation
President CEO and Director, P. Cody Phipps, age 50, $469,018 total compensation
SVP eBusiness Services and Corporate CIO, S. David Bent, age 51
President United Stationers Supply, Todd A. Shelton, age 45
SVP Sales, Patrick T. (Pat) Collins, age 51, $334,620 total compensation
VP Controller and Chief Accounting Officer, Kenneth M. Nickel, age 44
SVP and CFO, Fareed A. Khan, age 46
President Operations and Logistics Services, Timothy P. Connolly, age 48
SVP Human Resources, Barbara J. Kennedy, age 45

VP IDC Sales, Harry A. Dochelli, age 52
Manager Marketing Azerty de Mexico, Raquel Ornelas
President ORS Nasco, Larry D. Davis
VP Global and Strategic Sourcing United Stationers Supply Co., Peter Dehio
VP Cost to Serve ORS Nasco, Derek DalPiaz
President Lagasse Inc., Paul J. Barrett
IR Officer, Emma Gutheim
Director, Jean S. Blackwell, age 57
Director, Charles K. (Chuck) Crovitz, age 58
Director, William (Bill) Bass, age 48
Director, Roy W. Haley, age 65
Director, Alex D. Zoghlin, age 42
Director, Jonathan P. (Jon) Ward, age 58
Director, Benson P. Shapiro, age 70
Director, Daniel J. (Dan) Connors, age 53
President CEO and Director, P. Cody Phipps, age 50
Director, Robert B. (Bob) Aiken Jr., age 49
Independent Director, Alexander Schmelkin
Independent Director, Stuart Taylor
Independent Director, Susan Riley
Auditors: Ernst&YoungLLP

LOCATIONS

HQ: United Stationers Inc.
One Parkway North Boulevard, Suite 100, Deerfield, IL 60015-2559
Phone: 847 627-7000 **Fax:** 847 627-7001
Web: www.unitedstationers.com

PRODUCTS/OPERATIONS

2011 Sales

	$ mil.	% of total
Technology products	1,630	33
Traditional office products	1,357	27
Janitorial & breakroom supplies	1,223	24
Industrial supplies	349	7
Office furniture	323	6
Freight revenue	88	2
Other	33	1
Total	**5,005**	**100**

Selected Products

Technology products
- Computer monitors
- Copiers and fax machines
- Data storage
- Digital cameras
- Printers and printer cartridges

Traditional office products
- Calendars
- Organizers
- Paper products
- Writing instruments

Office furniture
- Computer furniture
- Leather chairs
- Vertical and lateral file cabinets
- Wooden and steel desks

Janitorial and sanitation products
- Food service disposables
- Janitorial and sanitation supplies
- Paper and packaging supplies
- Safety and security items

Industrial supplies
- Hand and power tools
- Safety and security supplies
- Janitorial equipment and supplies
- Maintenance repair and operations items
- Oil field and welding supplies

COMPETITORS

D & H Distributing
Gould Paper
Ingram Micro
Newell Rubbermaid
S.P. Richards
SED International
Staples
Supplies Network

HISTORICAL FINANCIALS

Company Type: Public

Income Statement FYE: December 31

	REVENUE ($ mil.)	NET INCOME ($ mil.)	NET PROFIT MARGIN	EMPLOYEES
12/11	5,005	109	2.2%	5,950
12/10	4,832	112	2.3%	5,950
12/09	4,710	100	2.1%	5,700
12/08	4,986	98	2.0%	5,800
12/07	4,646	107	2.3%	6,100
Annual Growth	1.9%	0.4%	—	(0.6%)

2011 Year-End Financials

Debt ratio: 24.90%
Return on equity: 15.47%
Cash ($ mil.): 11
Current ratio: 210.81
Long-term debt ($ mil.): 496
No. of shares (mil.): 42
Dividends
Yield: —
Payout: 21.49%
Market value ($ mil.): 1,373

	STOCK PRICE ($) FY Close	P/E High/Low		PER SHARE ($) Earnings	Dividends	Book Value
12/11	32.56	30	10	2.42	0.00	16.72
12/10	63.81	28	18	2.34	0.00	16.45
12/09	56.88	27	9	2.10	0.00	14.74
12/08	33.49	27	14	2.07	0.00	12.02
12/07	46.21	36	23	1.92	0.00	11.68
Annual Growth	(8.4%)	—	—	6.0%	—	9.4%

United Technologies Corp.

United Technologies (UTC) lifts you up and cools you down. Carrier Otis UTC Climate Controls & Security Pratt & Whitney Sikorsky and Power develop technologies systems and services for the aerospace construction and security industries. Under the Carrier brand and through Otis UTC is a world leader in HVAC units and elevators/escalators respectively. Pratt & Whitney is a leading supplier of commercial and military engines while Sikorsky makes helicopters. Hamilton Sundstrand produces engine controls auxiliary power units propellers and flight systems for military and commercial clients. UTC operates in more than 70 countries; more than half of its sales are outside the US.

HISTORY

In 1925 Frederick Rentschler and George Mead founded Pratt & Whitney Aircraft (P&W) to develop aircraft engines. P&W merged with Seattle-based Boeing Airplane Company and Chance Vought Corporation in 1929 to form United Aircraft & Transport. United Aircraft soon bought aviation companies Hamilton Aero Standard Steel Propeller and Sikorsky.

After congressional investigations led to new antitrust laws United Aircraft split in 1934 into three independent entities: United Airlines Boeing Airplane Company and United Aircraft. United Aircraft retained P&W and several other manufacturing interests.

During WWII United Aircraft produced half of all the engines used in US warplanes. Sikorsky developed helicopters and Vought made the Corsair and Cutlass planes. After a postwar decline in sales the company retooled for jet engine production. United Aircraft spun off Chance Vought in 1954 and bought Norden-Ketay (aeronautical electronics) in 1958.

A design flaw in engines produced for Boeing 747s sent P&W on an expensive trip back to the drawing board in the late 1960s. A concerned board of directors appointed Harry Gray a 17-year veteran of Litton Industries as president in 1971. Gray transformed the company into a conglomerate; it adopted its present name in 1975.

To decrease UTC's dependence on government contracts Gray diversified the company by acquiring Otis Elevator (1976) and Carrier (1979). Acquisitions expanded sales to $15.7 billion by 1986. Under pressure from his board Gray tapped Bob Daniell to head the company in 1986. Gray retired a year later.

Daniell a 25-year Sikorsky veteran stressed profitability over growth and sold businesses cut jobs and changed management. UTC enjoyed record earnings in 1990. However the next year reduced orders from the military and the auto and building industries resulted in UTC's first operating loss in 20 years.

UTC paid a $6 million fine in 1992 for hiring advisers to illegally inform it about competing bids for a Pentagon contract. The company sold its Norden radar unit and its stake in the Westland Helicopter Company in 1994. UTC president and COO George David became CEO that year (eventually replacing Daniell as chairman in 1997). In 1995 P&W introduced the most powerful jet engine in history and Sikorsky flew the prototype of the world's first radar-evading helicopter.

In 1996 Ford recalled 8.7 million vehicles –the most in its history –due to faulty auto ignition switches made by UT Automotive. Hamilton Standard boosted its European presence in 1998 buying aviation company Ratier-Figeac (France). That year P&W won a $435 million contract from the US Air Force to overhaul and repair F-15 and F-16 jet engines but it wasn't enough to forestall plans to cut 2000 jobs. The company established its R&D center known as the United Technologies Research Center (UTRC) in Shanghai in 1997.

UTC bought Sundstrand (aerospace components) for $4.3 billion in 1999. Sundstrand's operations were rolled into UTC's Hamilton Standard unit to form Hamilton Sundstrand Corporation. The company sold its auto parts unit (headliners door and instrument panels) to Lear for $2.3 billion. It paid more than $700 million for air-conditioning and heat-pump maker International Comfort Products and it bought Dallas Aerospace from The Fairchild Corporation for $57 million. The purchases were accompanied by consolidation primarily in the Otis and Carrier businesses. About 15000 jobs were cut; the company's overall employee count dropped 17%.

In 2000 UTC bought Cade Industries and merged it into Pratt & Whitney Engine Services' Sphere Corp. It also bought food-service refrigeration equipment maker Specialty Equipment Companies for $708 million. The same year UTC made a $40 billion bid for Honeywell International but Honeywell accepted General Electric's $45 billion counteroffer (that deal was later scuttled by European regulators).

As the economy cooled UTC cut jobs and restructured its operations to enhance its focus around its core businesses. The company eliminated about 4600 jobs in 2001. Restructuring continued in 2002 as UTC continued reducing costs and cutting another 7000 more jobs. On the 2002 acquisition front Sikorsky acquired Derco Holdings an aerospace parts distribution repair and overhaul and inventory management company.

The company's appetite for acquisitions resumed after the cutback in spending of 2001 and 2002. UTC spent $1.3 billion $525 million and $424 million on acquisitions in 2000 2001 and 2002 respectively. In 2003 UTC spent about $1.3 billion including charges associated with its acquisition of security service provider Chubb plc. The following year Hamilton Sundstrand subsidiary acquired pump and valve manufacturer Haskel International to bolster its oil and gas presence particularly in the Middle East.

Near the end of 2004 UTC targeted British firefighting equipment maker Kidde PLC for a takeover in hopes of merging the company with its Chubb subsidiary. UTC eventually bid $3 billion and a deal was struck in December 2004. After the transaction was completed in 2005 UTC formed a new segment UTC Fire & Security which combined the operations of Chubb and Kidde.

Pratt & Whitney bought up Boeing's Rocketdyne unit for around $700 million in 2005. Rocketdyne designed and manufactured rocket propulsion systems and made the rocket boosters for the Space Shuttle. Also that year UTC bought privately held security firm Lenel Systems (fingerprint scanners and security software among other products) for $400 million; the company was moved into the Fire & Security segment.

Louis Chenevert was named president and COO in 2006. That same year UTC agreed to pay $283 million to the US Department of Defense to settle a contract accounting dispute with the government over Pratt & Whitney's cost accounting for engine parts on commercial engine collaboration programs from 1984 through 2004. In 2007 UTC acquired the Initial Electronic Security Group of Rentokil Initial for #595 million.

Louis Chenevert was promoted to CEO in 2008 retaining the president's title. George David remained as chairman. The company push to market several green innovations led it to develop related systems starting in 2008. Carrier introduced a water-cooled chiller hailed as 40% more efficient. A Pratt & Whitney engine was developed to raise fuel burn cutting both nitrogen oxide emissions and noise by 50%. Not to be left off the green scorecard Otis' Gen2 elevator (rolled out in 2000) was touted to be 50% more energy efficient than current systems slashing energy use by close to 75% when tied with Otis drives which distribute the energy (created by descending elevators) back into a building's systems.

In 2009 UTC bought GST Holdings Limited a China-based fire alarm provider furthering its global reach in the fire safety industry and Washington State-based LifePort an aircraft accessories manufacturer specializing in air medical systems and lightweight armor for fixed and rotary wing aircraft.

UTC acquired Clipper Windpower in 2010 for approximately $385 million but it later decided that the company did not fit with its new focus on serving the aerospace and construction industries.

The 2010 acquisition of GE Security which was the electronic security and fire safety division of GE was valued at more than $1.8 billion plus debt assumption of $32 million. GE Security expanded UTC's North American presence and bolstered its security portfolio –especially for the construction and aerospace sectors.

EXECUTIVES

President North and East Europe and Africa Otis, Bruno Grob
President and CEO UTC Climate Controls & Security, Geraud Darnis, age 52, $804,872 total compensation
President 787 Space Systems and U.S. Classified Programs Hamilton Sundstrand, Robert F. Leduc, age 52
SVP Operations Carrier, Raymond J. (Ray) Moncini
VP Tax, Tobin J. Treichel
President Residential and Commercial Systems North America Carrier, Robert J. (Bob) McDonough
President Industrial Hamilton Sundstrand, John J. Doucette, age 51
VP and Controller, Peter F. Longo, age 53
SVP Science and Technology, J. Michael McQuade, age 56
Chairman and CEO, Louis R. Chenevert, age 54, $1,435,000 total compensation
President Pratt & Whitney, David P. Hess, age 56
VP and Treasurer, Thomas I. Rogan, age 59
SVP Global Government Relations, Gregg Ward
President North Asia Pacific Otis, Charles M. Vo
SVP Human Resources and Organization, J. Thomas Bowler Jr., age 59
President and COO UTC Propulsion & Aerospace Systems, Alain M. Bellemare, age 50
President Commercial Engines and Global Services Pratt & Whitney, Todd J. Kallman, age 56
SVP and CFO, Gregory J. Hayes, age 51, $575,000 total compensation
VP and General Manager Customer Service Hamilton Sundstrand, Matthew F. Bromberg
President Sikorsky Aerospace Services, David Adler
VP Environment Health and Safety, Richard H. (Rick) Bennett Jr.
President Sikorsky, Jeffrey P. (Jeff) Pino, age 57
President North and South America Otis, Randal E. Wilcox
President South Europe and Mediterranean Otis, Pedro Sainz de Baranda
VP Operations, Eileen P. Drake
President Otis Elevator Company, Didier Michaud-Daniel, age 54
SVP Corporate Strategy and Development, William M. (Bill) Brown, age 49, $543,750 total compensation
VP Business Practices, Michael A. Monts
SVP Sales and Marketing UTC Fire & Security, Kelly A. Romano
Chief Marketing Officer; President Sikorsky Global Helicopters, Carey E. Bond
SVP and General Counsel, Charles D. Gill Jr., age 48
SVP Engineering Pratt & Whitney, Paul Adams
President Hamilton Sundstrand, Michael R. (Mike) Dumais, age 45
VP Research; Director United Technologies Research Center, David E. Parekh, age 52
President South Asia Pacific and Gulf Otis, Pierre Dejoux
President EMEA Carrier, Philippe Delpech
President UK and Central Europe Otis, Lindsay Harvey
President Pratt & Whitney Canada, John Saabas, age 52
President Pratt & Whitney Power Systems, Peter C. Christman Jr.
VP Secretary and Associate General Counsel, Kathleen M. Hopko
President Pratt & Whitney Rocketdyne, James G. Maser
President Aerospace Customers and Business Development Hamilton Sundstrand, David L. Gitlin
President HVAC Asia Carrier, Ross B. Shuster
VP and CIO, Nancy M. Davis
President Carrier Transicold, David G. Appel
President Building Systems and Services North America Carrier, Ervin F. (Erv) Lauterbach
President Sikorsky Military Systems, Michael B. Maurer
President Global Security Products UTC Fire & Security, Mark J. Barry
President Military Engines Pratt & Whitney, Warren M. Boley Jr.
President UTC Fire & Security, Scott A. Buckhout
Director, Jamie S. Gorelick, age 61
Director, John V. Faraci, age 62
Director, Harold W. (Terry) McGraw III, age 63
Director, Jean-Pierre (JP) Garnier, age 64
Director, Ellen J. Kullman, age 56
Director, Andre-Francois H. Villeneuve, age 67
Director, Richard D. McCormick, age 71
Director, H. Patrick Swygert, age 69
Director, Edward A. (Ed) Kangas, age 68
Director, Christine Todd Whitman, age 65
Director, Richard B. (Dick) Myers, age 70
Auditors: PricewaterhouseCoopersLLP

LOCATIONS

HQ: United Technologies Corporation
1 Financial Plaza, Hartford CT 06103
Phone: 860-728-7000 **Fax:** 860-565-5400
Web: www.utc.com

2011 Sales

	$ mil.	% of total
US	30,438	53
Europe	12,601	22
Asia/Pacific	9,394	16
Other	5,380	9
Eliminations	377	-
Total	**58,190**	**100**

PRODUCTS/OPERATIONS

2011 Sales

	$ mil.	% of total
Pratt & Whitney	13,430	23
Otis	12,437	21
Carrier	11,969	20
Sikorsky	7,355	13
UTC Fire & Security	6,895	12
Hamilton Sundstrand	6,150	11
Eliminations	(46)	-
Total	**58,190**	**100**

2011 Sales

	$ mil.	% of total
Product sales	41,289	71
Service sales	16,901	29
Total	**58,190**	**100**

2011 Sales by Market

	% of total
Commercial &	58
Commercial	22
Military aerospace &	20
Total	**100**

2011 Sales by Segment

	% of total
Original	58
Aftermarket parts &	42
Total	**100**

Selected Mergers & Acquisitions

FY2012

Goodrich Corporation ($16.5 billion; Charlotte NC; maker of landing systems flight control systems and aircraft components)

Selected Operations Products and Services

Carrier

Commercial and residential heating ventilation and air-conditioning (HVAC) equipment

Commercial and transport refrigeration equipment
HVAC replacement parts and services
Micro-turbine-based HVAC and power systems

Fire & Security
- Access control
- Fire detection and suppression
- Intrusion detection
- Video surveillance

Hamilton Sundstrand
- Aerospace equipment (engine and flight controls environmental controls space life support propulsion systems)
- Industrial equipment (air compressors fluid-handling equipment metering devices)
- Space and defense fuel cell power plants

Otis
- Elevators
- Escalators
- Installation maintenance and repair services
- Moving sidewalks

Pratt & Whitney
- Commercial and military aircraft engines parts and services
- Geothermal power systems
- Industrial gas turbines
- Space propulsion systems

Sikorsky (commercial and military helicopters and maintenance)

COMPETITORS

AAR Corp.
AgustaWestland
BAE SYSTEMS
Boeing
DynCorp International
Eaton
Emerson Electric
GE
GenCorp
General Dynamics
Goodrich Corp.
Hitachi
Honeywell International
IDEX
Kaman
L-3 Communications
Lennox
Lockheed Martin
Mitsubishi Electric
Northrop Grumman
Parker-Hannifin
Precision Castparts
Raytheon
Rolls-Royce
SAFRAN
Siemens AG
SPX
Textron
ThyssenKrupp
Tomkins
Trane Inc.
Tyco

HISTORICAL FINANCIALS

Company Type: Public

Income Statement FYE: December 31

	REVENUE ($ mil.)	NET INCOME ($ mil.)	NET PROFIT MARGIN	EMPLOYEES
12/11	58,190	4,979	8.6%	199,900
12/10	54,326	4,373	8.0%	208,200
12/09	52,920	3,829	7.2%	206,700
12/08	58,681	4,689	8.0%	223,100
12/07	54,759	4,224	7.7%	225,600
Annual Growth	1.5%	4.2%	—	(3.0%)

2011 Year-End Financials

Debt ratio: 16.70%
Return on equity: 22.76%
Cash ($ mil.): 5,960
Current ratio: 138.36
Long-term debt ($ mil.): 9,501
No. of shares (mil.): 907
Dividends
Yield: —
Payout: 33.97%
Market value ($ mil.): 66,309

	STOCK PRICE ($) FY Close	P/E High/Low		PER SHARE ($) Earnings	Dividends	Book Value
12/11	73.09	16	12	5.49	0.00	24.12
12/10	78.72	17	13	4.74	1.70	23.21
12/09	69.41	17	9	4.12	1.54	21.42
12/08	53.60	15	9	4.90	1.35	16.86
12/07	76.54	19	14	4.27	1.17	21.71
Annual Growth	(1.1%)	—	—	6.5%	—	2.7%

UnitedHealth Group Inc

UnitedHealth Group unites its health plans with consumers across the US. A leading health insurer it offers a variety of plans and services to group and individual customers nationwide. Its UnitedHealthcare health benefits segment manages HMO PPO and POS (point-of-service) plans as well as Medicare Medicaid state-funded and supplemental vision and dental options. Together the UnitedHealthcare businesses serve about 38 million members. In addition UnitedHealth's Optum health services units —OptumHealth OptumInsight and OptumRx —provide wellness and care management programs financial services information technology solutions and pharmacy benefit management (PBM) services.

HISTORY

Dr. Paul Ellwood became known as the "Father of the HMO" for his role as an early champion of the health care concept. As a neurology student in the 1950s Ellwood recognized that applying business principles to medicine could minimize costs and make health care more affordable. Although the HMO was considered a radical approach to health care reform Ellwood got Congress and the Nixon administration to approve his HMO model in 1970; the next year he hired Richard Burke to put the model into action. Burke established United HealthCare (UHC) in 1974 to manage the not-for-profit Physicians Health Plan of Minnesota (PHP). UHC incorporated in 1977.

The company bought HMOs and began managing others operating 11 HMOs in 10 states by 1984 the year it went public. Its expansion continued with the purchases of HMOs Share Development (1985) and Peak Health Care (1986). Unfortunately acquisitions and startups began to eat away at UHC's financial health. Meanwhile Burke CEO of both UHC and PHP was accused by PHP doctors of having a conflict of interest after a change in the HMO's Medicare policy threatened to cut off patients from some member hospitals. Burke resigned in 1987 and was replaced by Kennett Simmons formerly president of Peak.

That year investment firm Warburg Pincus bought nearly 40% of UHC providing it with much-needed cash. UHC lost nearly $16 million in 1987 largely from a restructuring that axed the company's Phoenix HMO as well as startups in six other markets. The next year UHC sold its share of Peak Health Care.

In the late 1980s UHC adopted a new strategy of acquiring specialty companies that provided fee income. It also continued building its HMO network through acquisitions hoping to gain critical mass in such varied markets as the Midwest and New England.

Physician William (Bill) McGuire another former Peak president was named UHC's chairman and CEO in 1991. That year PHP and Share merged into Medica. Warburg Pincus distributed its UHC shares to several pension funds and financial institutions.

The company's expansion accelerated in the 1990s with a string of purchases in the Midwest but there were also divestitures. In 1994 UHC sold subsidiary Diversified Pharmaceutical Services providing cash for still more purchases including GenCare (St. Louis) Group Sales and Service of Puerto Rico and MetraHealth a former joint venture of Travelers Group and Metropolitan Life. UHC's interest in fee-based businesses continued with the 1997 purchase of Medicode a major provider of health care information products.

In 1998 the firm planned to buy rival Humana. However bloated UHC decided it should slim down to prepare to consummate the agreement; when UHC announced that it would charge $900 million in costs against earnings its plummeting stock price devalued the primary currency of the deal which quickly collapsed. That year it began offering MediGap and other supplements to AARP members.

The company changed its name to UnitedHealth Group in 2000. It also added UK-based contract research organization ClinPharm International to Ingenix that year and it announced it would let doctors —not administrators —choose what treatment patients would get partially because it was spending more on care scrutiny than the practice saved. Nevertheless many doctors claimed the process was still restrictive.

In 2000 the American Medical Association (AMA) and other parties sued the company claiming it used faulty Ingenix data to reduce payments to member doctors. (UnitedHealth settled the AMA lawsuit in 2009 for $350 million without admitting any wrongdoing as well as some state lawsuits related to the database.)

UnitedHealth's strategy for expansion in the early 21st century concentrated on acquisitions and joint ventures. To expand its Medicaid services business the firm bought AmeriChoice in 2002. The company also bought Mid Atlantic Medical Services because its HMOs and specialty health care operations complemented UnitedHealth's core operations. Golden Rule was acquired in late 2003 so UnitedHealth could enter the individual health insurance market by providing medical savings accounts. UnitedHealth also bought individual health care reimbursement account provider Definity Health in late 2004 for the same purpose. To increase its market share in the northeastern US the company bought Oxford Health Plans that year.

UnitedHealth spent $8.8 billion to acquire and integrate PacifiCare in 2005. Adding three million customers the acquisition gave UnitedHealth a leading position in the California and West Coast markets but it also prompted a landslide of complaints from customers alleging mishandled claims. The California Insurance Commissioner and other state agencies sought fines of more than $1 billion. While PacifiCare continued to exist as a health plan brand of UnitedHealth the PacifiCare administrative operations were integrated into other UnitedHealth units including UnitedHealthcare. The PacifiCare Prescription Benefits unit became separate operating division of UnitedHealth.

Chairman and CEO McGuire became the focus of inquiry in 2006 over a scandal involving the back-dating of stock options awarded to him and other company executives. Following a board inquiry McGuire was shown the door and was replaced by Stephen Hemsley formerly the company's president and COO. The back-dating brouhaha continued to be a distraction for UnitedHealth and in 2008 it opted to settle several related shareholder lawsuits by agreeing to pay more than $900 million.

Continuing the acquisitive strategy it laid out after the turn of the millennium the company in 2006 bought Deere & Company's employee health plan as well as Student Resources the student insurance division of HealthMarkets' MEGA Life subsidiary.

The company changed the name of its supplemental health division from Specialized Care Service to OptumHealth in 2007. As part of the restructuring a number of other UnitedHealth businesses were merged into OptumHealth including ACN Group United Resources Networks United Behavioral Health PacifiCare Behavioral Health Exante Bank and Exante Financial Services.

UnitedHealth completed several large acquisitions in 2008 spending $730 million to purchase Fiserv's health-related businesses including Fiserv Health (benefits administration for 2 million members) Avidyn Health (care facilitation) Fiserv Health Specialty Solutions (administration) and Innoviant Pharmacy Benefits Management. UnitedHealth also paid $980 million to acquire Unison Health Plans and used it to expand its AmeriChoice unit.

UnitedHealth completed its controversial purchase of Nevada insurance provider Sierra Health Services for approximately $2.6 billion in 2008 gaining some 600000 health plan members in the state and boosting its position in the growing Southwest market. The acquisition took nearly a year to receive approval from the Department of Justice due to competition concerns. Approval was finally gained on the contingency that UnitedHealth sell its Las Vegas Medicare Advantage program representing some 27000 customers to Humana for $185 million. Sierra Health's operating units including Health Plan of Nevada and Sierra Health and Life became part the UnitedHealthcare Nevada division following the acquisition.

UnitedHealth bought up the northeastern US operations of rival Health Net to solidify its position in the region in 2009. The deal which included health plans in Connecticut New Jersey and New York was valued at close to $630 million.

The company's OptumInsight (formerly Ingenix) unit also expanded its cost-control services through purchases of claims management and revenue cycle management firms AIM Healthcare and CareMedic in 2009. After the unit settled a portion of the lawsuits over its reimbursement rate advisory services that year the firm moved away from those operations.

Also in 2009 the OptumHealth division expanded its international employee assistance program (EAP) operations through the acquisition of UK-based PPC Worldwide. OptumHealth further expanded its EAP offerings in 2010 through the purchase of IPS Worldwide. also added an onsite health screening business through the 2010 purchase of Wellness Inc.

The OptumInsight unit bolstered growth in the EHR and ACO markets through acquisitions of software makers Picis and Axolotl in 2010.

EXECUTIVES

EVP, William A. Munsell, age 60, $700,000 total compensation
President CEO and Director, Stephen J. (Steve) Hemsley, age 59, $1,300,000 total compensation
EVP, Jeannine M. Rivet, $465,000 total compensation
SVP, John S. Penshorn
SVP and Chief Accounting Officer, Eric S. Rangen, age 55
EVP and Chief Medical Affairs, Reed V. Tuckson, age 60
Chairman, Richard T. Burke Sr., age 68
EVP, Anthony Welters, age 57, $700,000 total compensation
EVP; CEO Optum, Larry C. Renfro, age 58, $535,385 total compensation
Executive Vice President and Chief Legal Officer, Richard N. (Rich) Baer, age 55
EVP; CEO UnitedHealthcare, Gail K. Boudreaux, age 51
CEO OptumRx, Jacqueline B. (Jackie) Kosecoff, age 63
CEO OptumHealth, Dawn Owens
EVP and CFO; President UnitedHealth Group Operations, David S. Wichmann, age 49, $696,058 total compensation
EVP; President Global Health, Simon Stevens
Media Contact, Tyler Mason
CEO OptumInsight, Andrew M. (Andy) Slavitt, age 45
EVP and Chief Legal Officer, Marianne D. Short
SVP and Chief Communications Officer, Don Nathan
EVP Human Capital, Lori K. Sweere, age 54
EVP and General Counsel, Mitchell E. (Mitch) Zamoff, age 44
Investor Relations, Frances Jacobs
EVP and General Counsel, Christopher J. (Chris) Walsh, age 46
VP Social Responsibility; President United Health Foundation, Kate Rubin
Director, Rodger A. Lawson, age 65
Director, Robert J. Darretta Jr., age 65
Director, Douglas W. Leatherdale, age 75
President CEO and Director, Stephen J. (Steve) Hemsley, age 59
Director, Michele J. Hooper, age 60
Director, Gail R. Wilensky, age 68
Director, William C. Ballard Jr., age 71
Director, Glen M. Renwick, age 56
Director, Kenneth I. Shine, age 77
Auditors: Deloitte&ToucheLLP

LOCATIONS

HQ: UnitedHealth Group Incorporated
UnitedHealth Group Center 9900 Bren Rd. East, Minnetonka MN 55343
Phone: 952-936-1300 **Fax:** 952-936-1819
Web: www.unitedhealthgroup.com

PRODUCTS/OPERATIONS

2011 Sales

	$ mil.	% of total
UnitedHealthcare	95,336	77
OptumHealth	6,704	5
Adjustments	(22127)	-

2011 UnitedHealthcare Sales

	% of total
UnitedHealthcare Employer &	48
UnitedHealthcare Medicare &	38
UnitedHealthcare Community &	14
Total	**100**

Selected Operations

Optum (Health Services division)
- OptumHealth (specialty benefits)
- OptumInsight (formerly Ingenix information technology and consulting services)
- OptumRx (formerly Prescription Solutions pharmacy benefit management)

UnitedHealthcare (Health Plans division)
- UnitedHealthcare Community & State (former operations of AmeriChoice public-sector programs)
- UnitedHealthcare Employer & Individual (health plans for individuals businesses employers)
- UnitedHealthcare Medicare & Retirement (former operations of Ovations benefits for people age 50 and older)

COMPETITORS

ActiveHealth Management
Aetna
Affiliated Computer Services
AMERIGROUP
APS Healthcare
Centene
HCSC
Health Net
Healthways Inc.
Humana
IMS Health
Kaiser Foundation Health Plan
Magellan Health
CIGNA
Coventry Health Care
CVS Caremark
Delta Dental Plans
Dental Health Alliance
Express Scripts
MetLife
Molina Healthcare
Prudential
Qmedtrix Systems
WellCare Health Plans
WellPoint

HISTORICAL FINANCIALS

Company Type: Public

Income Statement FYE: December 31

	ASSETS ($ mil.)	NET INCOME ($ mil.)	INCOME AS % OF ASSETS	EMPLOYEES
12/11	67,889	5,142	7.6%	99,000
12/10	63,063	4,634	7.3%	87,000
12/09	59,045	3,822	6.5%	80,000
12/08	55,815	2,977	5.3%	75,000
12/07	50,899	4,654	9.1%	67,000
Annual Growth	7.5%	2.5%	—	10.3%

2011 Year-End Financials

Debt ratio: 15.70%
Return on equity: 18.17%
Cash ($ mil.): 9,429
Current ratio: —
Long-term debt ($ mil.): 10,656
No. of shares (mil.): 1,039
Dividends
Yield: —
Payout: 12.95%
Market value ($ mil.): 52,657

	STOCK PRICE ($) FY Close	P/E High/Low		PER SHARE ($) Earnings	Dividends	Book Value
12/11	50.68	11	8	4.73	0.00	27.23
12/10	36.11	9	7	4.10	0.41	23.78
12/09	30.48	10	5	3.24	0.03	20.58
12/08	26.60	24	7	2.40	0.03	17.30
12/07	58.20	17	13	3.42	0.03	16.01
Annual Growth	(3.4%)	—	—	8.4%	—	14.2%

Universal Health Services, Inc.

With dozens of health care facilities in nearly every state Universal Health Services (UHS) isn't quite ubiquitous but it's working on it. One of the largest for-profit hospital operators in the nation UHS owns or leases about 25 acute care hospitals with a total of 5500 beds primarily in midsized rural and suburban communities. The company also operates several outpatient surgery centers and radiation treatment facilities most of which are located near its acute care hospitals. In addition UHS' behavioral health division operates about 200 psychiatric and substance abuse hospitals with a combined capacity of about 20000 beds. The company is controlled by founder and CEO Alan Miller.

Geographic Reach

UHS' acute care facilities are located in more than half a dozen states and are situated mostly in smaller towns and cities with limited competition though the division does have facilities in a few larger markets (such as Las Vegas and Washington DC). UHS' behavioral health hospitals are scattered across about 40 US states as well as Puerto Rico and the US Virgin Islands. The company's biggest markets for both segments are California

Nevada and Texas which together account for nearly half of the company's revenue.

Operations

UHS receives about 55% of its annual revenues from its acute care segment which includes medical hospitals surgical outpatient facilities and radiation oncology centers. The remainder of the company's revenue comes from its portfolio of behavioral health hospitals which includes residential facilities for teens adult psychiatric hospitals substance abuse facilities and special education schools for students with emotional problems.

The company's behavioral health business accounted for a larger portion of sales in 2011 (45% up from 30% the previous year) due to UHS' acquisition of Psychiatric Solutions in late 2010.

Sales & Marketing

Both of UHS' operating segments (acute care hospitals and behavioral health hospitals) earn between 40% and 50% of revenues from managed care providers (HMOs PPOs Medicare Advantage and other commercial plans) with the remainder of sales coming from traditional Medicare and Medicaid plans self-pay customers and other sources.

Financial Analysis

UHS' growth strategies have helped it to steadily increase sales over the past decade. The firm saw its revenues jump by 35% to some $7.5 billion in 2011 largely due to the Psychiatric Services acquisition the previous year. Net income levels also rose by more than 70% to $398 million that year reaffirming the company's profitability after a slight dip in net income levels in 2010 (largely due to acquisition costs).

Strategy

While the company's growth strategy is to build or purchase new facilities in rapidly growing areas —it has grown both of its units through selective acquisitions and construction efforts over the years —UHS also has no qualms about ridding itself of operations that just don't quite fit anymore. The company sold some $118 million and $21 million in assets in 2011 and 2010 respectively; divestitures in 2011 included several behavioral health facilities that the FTC required UHS to sell following the Psychiatric Solutions acquisition. In 2012 the company exited the Washington State acute care market through the sale of its Auburn Regional Medical Center.

By focusing its operations on high-growth regions UHS also works towards its goal of increasing hospital utilization rates (which is often a key indicator of the financial health of a hospital). To further draw more patients and high-quality physicians to its existing facilities the company invests in new technology makes capital improvements and increases the breadth of services it offers. Initiatives include upgrades to surgical equipment and billing systems as well as the implementation of electronic health record (EHR) systems to improve patient care coordination. UHS is especially expanding its outpatient service capabilities as payers put pressure on hospitals to control inpatient care costs.

Mergers & Acquisitions

The $3.1 billion acquisition of Psychiatric Solutions in 2010 doubled the behavioral health division's operations by adding roughly 100 mental health care facilities in more than 30 states. UHS had already been growing the division through smaller purchases.

UHS further expanded the behavioral health business in 2012 by acquiring private psychiatric hospital provider Ascend Health for $500 million. The purchase added Ascend's nine freestanding psychiatric inpatient facilities in five states in the Southwest.

Ownership

Chairman and CEO Alan Miller who founded the company in 1978 controls about 80% of UHS' voting power.

EXECUTIVES

VP and Controller, Charles F. Boyle, age 52
SVP CFO and Secretary, Steve G. Filton, age 54, $425,016 total compensation
VP Development, Richard C. (Dick) Wright, age 64, $253,760 total compensation
Chairman and CEO, Alan B. Miller, age 74, $1,350,052 total compensation
SVP; President Behavioral Health Care, Debra K. Osteen, age 56, $425,016 total compensation
VP and Treasurer, Cheryl K. Ramagano, age 49
Regional VP Behavioral Health Services, Craig I. Nuckles
SVP; President Acute Care, Marvin G. Pember, age 58
President and Director, Marc D. Miller, age 41, $430,017 total compensation
VP Behavioral Health Services, Carothers H. Evans
VP Behavioral Health Services, Karen E. Johnson
VP Acute Finance, John Paul Christen
VP Acute Care, Douglas A. Matney
Regional VP Behavioral Health Services, Matthew W. Crouch
Regional VP Behavioral Health Services, Geoffrey Botak
VP Acute Care, Francisco Lopez IV
VP Behavioral Finance, Larry Harrod
VP and General Counsel, Matthew D. Klein
VP Information Services, Michael S. Nelson
VP Acute Care, Karla J. Perez
VP Behavioral Health Services, Darien Applegate
VP Behavioral Health Services, Philip J. Moraci
VP Acute Care, Kevin DiLallo
VP Human Resources, Gerry Johnson Geckle
Director, John H. Herrell, age 71
Director, Anthony Pantaleoni, age 72
Director, Leatrice Ducat, age 79
Director, Robert H. (Bob) Hotz, age 67
President and Director, Marc D. Miller, age 41
Director, Lawrence S. Gibbs, age 40
Auditors: PricewaterhouseCoopersLLP

LOCATIONS

HQ: Universal Health Services Inc.
Universal Corporate Center 367 S. Gulph Rd., King of Prussia PA 19406-0958
Phone: 610-768-3300 **Fax:** 610-768-3336
Web: www.uhsinc.com

Selected Acute Care Hospitals and Specialty Centers

California
- Corona Regional Medical Center (Corona)
- Palmdale Regional Medical Center (Palmdale)
- Southwest Healthcare System —Inland Valley Campus (Wildomar)
- Southwest Healthcare System —Rancho Springs Campus (Murrieta)
- Temecula Valley Day Surgery and Pain Therapy Center (Murrieta)

Florida
- Lakewood Ranch Medical Center (Bradenton)
- Manatee Memorial Hospital (Bradenton)
- Palms Westside Clinic ASC (50% Royal Palm Beach)
- Wellington Regional Medical Center (West Palm Beach)

Nevada
- Centennial Hills Hospital Medical Center (Las Vegas)
- Desert Springs Hospital (72% Las Vegas)
- Northern Nevada Medical Center (Sparks)
- Spring Valley Hospital Medical Center (72% Las Vegas)
- Summerlin Hospital Medical Center (72% Las Vegas)
- Valley Hospital Medical Center (72% Las Vegas)

South Carolina
- Aiken Regional Medical Centers (Aiken)
- Aurora Pavilion (Aiken)
- Cancer Care Institute of Carolina (Aiken)

Oklahoma
- St. Mary' s Regional Medical Center (Enid)

Puerto Rico
- OJOS/Eye Surgery Specialists of Puerto Rico (Santurce)

Texas
- Cornerstone Regional Hospital (50% Edinburg)
- Doctors' Hospital of Laredo (Laredo)
- Fort Duncan Regional Medical Center (Eagle Pass)
- Northwest Texas Healthcare System (Amarillo)
  - Northwest Texas Surgery Center (majority owned Amarillo)
  - The Pavilion at Northwest Texas Healthcare System (Amarillo)
- South Texas Health System (Edinburg)
  - Edinburg Regional Medical Center (Edinburg)
  - Edinburg Children's Hospital (Edinburg)
  - McAllen Medical Center (McAllen)
  - McAllen Heart Hospital (McAllen)
  - South Texas Behavioral Health System (Edinburg)
- Texoma Medical Center (Denison)
  - TMC Behavioral Health Center (Denison)

Washington D.C.
- The George Washington University Hospital (80%)

PRODUCTS/OPERATIONS

2011 Sales

	$ mil.	% of total
Acute care hospital services	4,071	54
Other	27	1

2011 Sales

	% of total
Managed care (HMOs PPOs & managed	43
Medicare	22
Medicaid	15
Other	120
Total	**100**

COMPETITORS

Adventist Health
Adventist Health System Sunbelt Healthcare
AmSurg
Ascension Health
Banner Health
Catholic Health Partners
CHRISTUS Health
Community Health Systems
CRC Health
Devereux Foundation
Hazelden
HCA
Health Management Associates
Kaiser Permanente
LifePoint Hospitals
Mercy Health
Northwestern Human Services
Sutter Health
Tenet Healthcare
Texas Health Resources
UBH
United Surgical Partners
Vanguard Health Systems

HISTORICAL FINANCIALS

Company Type: Public

Income Statement FYE: December 31

	REVENUE ($ mil.)	NET INCOME ($ mil.)	NET PROFIT MARGIN	EMPLOYEES
12/11	7,500	398	5.3%	65,400
12/10	5,568	230	4.1%	65,100
12/09	5,202	260	5.0%	39,900
12/08	5,022	199	4.0%	39,500
12/07	4,751	170	3.6%	39,900
Annual Growth	12.1%	23.6%	—	13.1%

2011 Year-End Financials

Debt ratio: 47.67%
Return on equity: 17.34%
Cash ($ mil.): 41
Current ratio: 163.08
Long-term debt ($ mil.): 3,651
No. of shares (mil.): 96
Dividends
Yield: —
Payout: 4.95%
Market value ($ mil.): 3,754

	STOCK PRICE ($) FY Close	P/E High/Low		PER SHARE ($) Earnings	Dividends	Book Value
12/11	38.86	14	8	4.04	0.00	23.77
12/10	43.42	18	12	2.34	0.20	20.31
12/09	30.50	25	11	2.64	0.17	18.07
12/08	37.57	33	16	1.97	0.16	15.61
12/07	51.20	40	30	1.59	0.16	14.43
Annual Growth	(6.7%)	—	—	26.3%	—	13.3%

UNIVERSITY OF PENNSYLVANIA

LOCATIONS

HQ: UNIVERSITY OF PENNSYLVANIA
3451 WALNUT ST RM 100, PHILADELPHIA, PA 191046243
Phone: 2158985000

HISTORICAL FINANCIALS

Company Type:

Income Statement FYE: June 30

	REVENUE ($ mil.)	NET INCOME ($ mil.)	NET PROFIT MARGIN	EMPLOYEES
06/11	6,036	1,600	26.5%	70
Annual Growth	—	—	—	—

2011 Year-End Financials

Debt ratio: —
Return on equity: 26.50%
Cash ($ mil.): 965
Current ratio: —
Long-term debt ($ mil.): —
Dividends
Yield: —
Payout: —
Market value ($ mil.): —

Unum Group

Through injury or illness Unum Group works to keep employees employed. A top disability insurer in the US and the UK the company offers short-term and long-term disability insurance as well as life and accidental death and dismemberment insurance to individuals and groups in a workplace benefits setting. Specialty coverage offerings include cancer dental and travel insurance. US subsidiaries include Unum Life Insurance Company of America Provident Life and Accident First Unum Life Colonial Life & Accident Insurance and The Paul Revere Life Insurance Company. The company operates as Unum Limited in the UK. Unum's products are sold through field sales agents and independent brokers.

Geographic Reach

Unum runs four primary operating centers and about 35 sales offices scattered across the US market. Its Unum Limited office is the headquarters for the smaller Unum UK operations.

Operations

More than half of Unum's annual premiums come from group disability life and accident policies with the majority of other premiums coming from individual supplemental and voluntary policies sold in the workplace setting. It also generates revenue from its closed block business which services policies in the segments (long-term care and non-workplace individual disability) where the company no longer issues new policies.

Sales & Marketing

The company strives to maintain close relationships with its sales force as well as with its independent agents and brokers as it relies on these representatives to market its products to employers.

Financial Analysis

Unum's revenues climbed less than 1% in both 2010 and 2011 (to $10.2 and $10.3 billion respectively). While its overall revenue growth has been slow as of late –which Unum primarily attributes to economic impacts on US employment levels – the company believes its strategic restructuring measures will provide for an increase in future sales levels. However Unum took an impairment charge on the discontinuation of its group long-term care policies that ultimately led its annual net income figure to drop by more than 70% in 2011 (from $886 million to $235 million).

Strategy

Unum seeks to achieve a competitive edge by providing group individual and voluntary workplace products that can be combined with other coverage to better integrate benefits for customers. The insurer has stayed ahead of the game in the disability market by sticking to conservative investment and growth strategies primarily seeking to expand its group product offerings and its geographic presence through organic measures.

The company has especially seen growth in its voluntary benefits products which allow employees to purchase individual coverage products on a supplemental basis. Such options are increasingly important as economic difficulties put pressure on low and middle-income workers.

Unum has also expanded its offering of services to help employers and government agencies manage costs such as its leave management program flexible corporate contribution programs and wellness initiatives as well as new reform information and enrollment websites launched in 2011. Also in 2011 Unum added a new offering for group dental coverage through a partnership with United Concordia.

While expanding in areas where the greatest market needs are seen the firm also exits certain businesses where demand has slowed. For instance in 2011 the company decided to exit the group long-term care insurance business (it had already stopped selling individual long-term care policies in 2009).

HISTORY

Coal was discovered in eastern Tennessee in the 1870s; in 1887 several Chattanooga professional men formed the Provident Life & Accident Insurance Co. to provide medical insurance to miners. But it was a case of the inexperienced serving the uninsurable and by 1892 the company was on the brink of ruin. The founders sold half the company for $1000 to Thomas Maclellan and John McMaster two Scotsmen who had failed at banking in Canada.

While Maclellan handled the business end McMaster scoured the coalfields for customers. He even went into the mines pitching to individual miners and bringing along someone to dig coal for them so they wouldn't lose money by stopping work to listen.

The partners bought the rest of the company in 1895. Provident grew thanks to the cooperation of mining companies which deducted premiums from miners' pay. Provident added sickness and industrial insurance (low-benefit life policies). In 1900 after a period of strained relations Maclellan bought out McMaster.

After 1905 northern insurers began moving into the industrializing South. To meet the competition Provident reorganized and added capital and its stepped-up sales efforts brought in such lucrative business as railroad accounts. Provident added life insurance in 1917. The first policy was bought by Robert Maclellan who became president when his father died in 1916.

Provident acquired the Southern Surety Co. in 1931. During and after WWII group sales exploded as employee benefit packages proliferated. Provident which by then operated nationally entered Canada in 1948. Four years later R. L. Maclellan succeeded his father as president (R. L. stepped down in 1971). Provident's growth in the 1970s stemmed from its life units but it also developed a large health insurance operation.

The health care operations were hammered by rising medical costs in the 1980s so the company moved into managed care. But the combination of increased health care costs and a real estate crash gave the company a one-two punch in the late 1980s and early 1990s. An accounting change in 1993 further hit profits. In 1994 new president Harold Chandler initiated a reevaluation of Provident's operations and future which resulted in Provident's exit from the health care business beginning in 1995.

Provident began a major move into disability insurance in 1997. It bought 83% of rival disability insurer The Paul Revere Corporation from Textron. About 10000 Paul Revere insurance brokers later filed suit alleging they were denied millions of dollars in commissions. In exchange for its $300 million aid in the purchase Switzerland's Zurich Insurance (now Zurich Financial Services) received about 15% of Provident. The company also acquired GENEX Services (vocational rehabilitation and related services) and sold its dental insurance business to Ameritas Life Insurance. In 1998 Provident sold its annuity business to American General (now a subsidiary of AIG).

In 1998 with both Provident and Unum Corporation looking for ways to enhance business the companies commenced merger negotiations and completed the transaction the next year. But the merger was more expensive than anticipated and problems in integrating the companies' sales forces slowed policy sales.

Company operations began melding more smoothly and UnumProvident began addressing the problems with its sales force as well as adding customer service staff in 2000. It pulled money out of reserves by reinsuring several blocks of acquisition-related businesses and sold an inactive shell subsidiary licensed to sell annuities in most states to Allstate. In 2001 the company sold its Provident National Assurance subsidiary to Allstate. UnumProvident faced accusations that the company denied valid disability claims in 2002. These accusations resulted in legal actions in a number of states.

UnumProvident acquired Sun Life Financial's UK life insurance group in 2003 in a move designed to expand the company's operations in the UK. UnumProvident sold its Unum Japan Accident Insurance subsidiary to Hitachi Capital Corporation (Hitachi) in 2004.

As part of a rebranding effort following years of corporate restructuring to focus on core operations the company changed its name from UnumProvident to Unum Group in 2007.

In 2007 the company divested its GENEX Services unit a provider of disability management and workers' compensation services. GENEX's specialty services no longer fit into Unum's strategy to focus on its primary disability insurance operations. In 2009 it stopped offering new individual long-term care policies as part of its strategy to focus on core offerings in the workplace setting.

EXECUTIVES

EVP; President and CEO Colonial Life & Accident Insurance Company, Randall C. (Randy) Horn, age 59, $478,654 total compensation
SVP Human Resources, Eileen C. Farrar
Chairman, William J. (Bill) Ryan, age 68
EVP Global Business Technology, Robert O. (Bob) Best, age 62, $518,961 total compensation
President CEO and Director, Thomas R. (Tom) Watjen, age 57, $1,094,902 total compensation
VP Transactions SEC and Corporate Secretary, Susan N. Roth
EVP and COO; President and CEO Unum US, Kevin P. McCarthy, age 56, $569,346 total compensation
SVP and Chief Marketing Officer, Joseph R. (Joe) Foley
EVP and CFO, Richard P. (Rick) McKenney, age 43, $300,000 total compensation
SVP Integrated Underwriting Unum US, Tim Arnold
SVP and Global CIO, Kathleen L. (Kathy) Owen
SVP Investor Relations, Thomas A. H. (Tom) White
SVP and Treasurer, Kevin McMahon
EVP and General Counsel, Liston (Bo) Bishop III, age 65
VP Corporate Communications, Jim Sabourin
Director Media Relations, Mary Clark (MC) Clark Guenther
Manager Media Relations, Mary Fortune
SVP Growth Operations, Mike Simonds
EVP; President and CEO Unum UK, John F. (Jack) McGarry, age 54
SVP Risk Operations, Chris Jerome
Manager Media Relations, Dawn McAbee
SVP and Chief Risk Officer, Mike Temple
SVP and Controller, Vicki Corbett
SVP and Chief Government Affairs Officer, Scott Maker
SVP National Client Group Unum US, Don Boutin
SVP Benefit Operations, Diane Garofalo
VP Enrollment, Bill Dalicandro
VP Simply Unum National Practice, Andrea Gordon
Assistant VP Hispanic Marketing, Bilda Acu?a
VP Large Case National Practice, Phil Bruen
Assistant VP Product and Market Development, Mary Ann Beliveau
National Sales Leader Executive Benefits, Branden Pierson
VP Long Term Care and Voluntary Benefits Underwriting, Guy Bertsch
Director Product and Market Development, Debbie Cecil
VP and Chief Information Security Officer, Lynda Fleury
SVP and Chief Actuary, Al Riggieri
SVP and Chief Investment Officer, Breege A. Farrell
Director Product and Market Development, Kathy Plummer
VP and Voluntary Practice Leader, Neiciee Durrence
VP Government Affairs, Martin McGuinness
VP Global IT Operations and Risk Management, Sydney Crisp
Director, Kevin T. Kabat, age 55
President CEO and Director, Thomas R. (Tom) Watjen, age 57
Director, Ronald E. Goldsberry, age 69
Director, A. S. (Pat) MacMillan Jr., age 68
Director, Edward J. Muhl, age 67
Director, Gloria C. Larson, age 61
Director, E. Michael Caulfield, age 65
Director, Thomas Kinser, age 68
Director, Pamela H. Godwin, age 63
Director, Michael J. Passarella, age 70
Auditors: Ernst&YoungLLP

LOCATIONS

HQ: Unum Group
1 Fountain Sq., Chattanooga TN 37402
Phone: 423-294-1011 **Fax:** 973-595-9120
Web: www.capeziodance.com

PRODUCTS/OPERATIONS

2011 Sales

	$ mil.	% of total
Unum US	5,369	52
Closed block (individual disability & long-term care)	2,691	26
Colonial Life	1,268	12
Unum UK	877	9
Corporate & other	71	1
Total	**10,278**	**100**

Selected Subsidiaries

Colonial Life & Accident Insurance Company
Duncanson & Holt Inc.
  Duncanson & Holt Services Inc.
  Duncanson & Holt Syndicate Management Ltd. (UK)
    Trafalgar Underwriting Agencies Ltd. (UK)
  Duncanson & Holt Underwriters Ltd. (UK)
First Unum Life Insurance Company
Provident Investment Management LLC
Provident Life and Accident Insurance Company
Provident Life and Casualty Insurance Company
The Paul Revere Life Insurance Company
  The Paul Revere Variable Annuity Insurance Company
Unum Life Insurance Company of America
Unum European Holding Company Limited (UK)
  Claims Services International Limited (UK)
  Group Risk Insurance Services Limited (UK)
  Unum Limited (UK)
UnumProvident International Ltd. (Bermuda)

COMPETITORS

AEGON
Aflac
Allianz
American General
Assurant
AXA Financial
CIGNA
CNA Financial
GatesMcDonald
Guardian Life
John Hancock Financial Services
Liberty Mutual
Lincoln Financial Group
MassMutual
MetLife
Mutual of Omaha
Northwestern Mutual
Principal Financial
Prudential
Torchmark

HISTORICAL FINANCIALS

Company Type: Public

Income Statement FYE: December 31

	ASSETS ($ mil.)	NET INCOME ($ mil.)	INCOME AS % OF ASSETS	EMPLOYEES
12/11	60,179	235	0.4%	9,400
12/10	57,307	886	1.5%	9,500
12/09	54,477	852	1.6%	9,700
12/08	49,417	553	1.1%	9,800
12/07	52,432	679	1.3%	9,700
Annual Growth	3.5%	(23.3%)	—	(0.8%)

2011 Year-End Financials

Debt ratio: 4.27%
Return on equity: 2.75%
Cash ($ mil.): 116
Current ratio: —
Long-term debt ($ mil.): 2,570
No. of shares (mil.): 292
Dividends
  Yield: —
  Payout: 50.64%
Market value ($ mil.): 6,168

	STOCK PRICE ($) FY Close	P/E High/Low		PER SHARE ($) Earnings	Dividends	Book Value
12/11	21.07	34	26	0.78	0.00	29.30
12/10	24.22	10	7	2.71	0.35	28.25
12/09	19.52	9	3	2.57	0.32	25.62
12/08	18.60	16	6	1.62	0.30	19.32
12/07	23.79	14	10	1.91	0.30	22.28
Annual Growth	(3.0%)	—	—	(20.1%)	—	7.1%

URS Corp

URS Corporation provides a range of engineering construction maintenance and technical services for customers around the world. Through its infrastructure and environment division URS builds manages operates and maintains projects for government agencies and private corporations. Its federal services segment provides management decommissioning and technical support services to agencies including the Department of Defense and the Department of Homeland Security. URS' energy and construction segment provides design management construction maintenance and closure services. Projects include work on power generating facilities transportation networks biotechnology labs and manufacturing plants.

URS operates in more than 40 countries. About half of its business is derived from government projects. A key federal defense contractor URS provides operations management and maintenance services to all branches of the military and entities such as NASA. The US Army is the company's largest customer accounting for about 18% of all sales. For the military URS refurbishes military vehicles modernizes weapons systems manages military facilities provides logistic support trains pilots and is trained to decommission nuclear chemical and biological weapons.

For the industrial and commercial sectors URS offers a range of services including construction modification and decommissioning for facilities including oil and gas refineries biotechnology and other research laboratories and manufacturing facilities. It is also a leading nuclear plant remediation and decommissioning services provider.

In the infrastructure sector URS assists with the building and modernizing of infrastructure such as highways airports light rail subways piers seawalls marinas and water treatment systems. It also builds schools correctional facilities hospitals industrial plants and sports and recreational structures.

Revenues dropped for the company from 2009 through 2010. However the company's diversity helped it stay afloat even when demand for some of its services fell. Increased spending in the public sector in particular helped URS as corporations and other private clients cut capital expenditures.

Sales inched up (by 4%) in 2011. Revenues climbed that year in URS' power federal and industrial and commercial sectors. Sales declined in the infrastructure segment as some major projects were completed. URS reported a $465 million net loss in 2011. The results included a more than $730 million goodwill charge tied to a decrease in the company's stock price. Weakness in the European and Middle East markets also impacted results as URS was forced to restructure some of its operations in those areas.

URS Corporation is positioning itself for growth as the economy rebounds from the recession. It anticipates each of its segments to benefit from increased spending and growing demand for oil and gas engineering projects. Acquisitions are always a part of the company's growth strategy. URS often adds to its services portfolio and geographic footprint by making acquisitions.

URS is strengthening its successful federal services and infrastructure segments. In 2011 URS Corporation acquired Apptis Holdings a provider of information technology and communications services to the federal government. The deal expanded URS' federal government services business which caters to the US Department of Defense and other federal entities. Also in 2011 URS acquired CATI Training Systems a designer and developer of flight simulators and other training systems for the Department of Defense and commercial customers. In early 2012 URS bought Flint Energy Services a Canada-based provider of services to the North American oil and gas industry (a priority strategic market for the company).

HISTORY

Founded as an engineering research partnership in 1951 and incorporated as Broadview Research Corp. in 1957 the company won its first big contract (which lasted until 1971) with the US Army to automate logistical and personnel systems. In 1962 it changed its name to United Research Services shortening it to URS two years later. Through the 1960s the firm tried to reduce its reliance on the Army contract by diversifying into leasing and training (even owning Evelyn Wood Reading Dynamics at one point). URS went public in 1976.

Diversification was not the answer however and in 1984 URS returned to its engineering and architecture roots. Laden with debt from the earlier acquisitions and overextended overseas it was ill-equipped to deal with lower construction spending in the late 1980s on public infrastructure and the environment. The firm was near bankruptcy in 1989 when CEO Martin Koffel took the helm. URS sold noncore assets and cut foreign operations settled shareholder lawsuits and pared down debt. By 1991 it was profitable again.

Focused on its core business in 1995 URS bought E.C. Driver & Associates specialists in highway and bridge design. The next year URS acquired Greiner Engineering forming URS Greiner which doubled its US offices and gave it a presence in Asia. On a roll in 1997 URS doubled its private-sector business by acquiring geotechnical and environmental engineering specialists Woodward-Clyde.

Continuing to grow through acquisitions the company bought Thorburn Colquhoun a UK civil and structural engineering consulting firm in 1999. Also that year URS won a major prize when it purchased Los Angeles-based engineering and construction services firm Dames & Moore in a $600 million deal. The acquisition more than doubled URS's size again and strengthened the company's presence in Asia Australia and Europe.

URS projects in 2000 included a contract to provide environmental services to US Air Force installations worldwide and a contract to design a water treatment plant in Lancaster Ohio. Among the projects URS began working on in 2001 was the design of downtown Atlanta's 17th Street Bridge. The firm also won contracts to provide environmental consulting to the US Postal Service and the US Coast Guard. After helping both public and private companies with their heightened security concerns following the September 11 attacks URS decided in 2002 to form a security services group to help protect buildings airports and infrastructure against natural disasters and terrorist attacks.

To gain even more earnings from federal defense contracts (particularly for national and homeland defense projects) URS in 2002 acquired outsourced operations and maintenance provider EG&G from Carlyle Group a DC-based investing firm with several ties to the defense industry. In 2007 URS acquired Washington Group International (renamed The Washington Division) for $2.6 billion in 2007. That deal made URS a powerhouse in the nuclear industry sector just in time for the growing resurgence in nuclear power. In 2010 the company integrated EG&G and the Washington Division under the URS brand.

In 2008 URS bought Tryck Nyman Hayes which helped URS build its presence in Alaska infrastructure and LopezGarcia a Texas-based group focused on infrastructure engineering.

The company has expanded through significant acquisitions including the Washington Division and EG&G (both rebranded under the URS name in 2010). URS also beat out rival CH2M Hill in a bidding war over UK-based Scott Wilson Group in 2010. The $336 million acquisition bolstered URS's presence in the UK infrastructure market and gave it entry into other geographic markets overseas such as Hong Kong India Poland and the United Arab Emirates. The deal also expanded URS's presence by adding 80 offices around the world.

EXECUTIVES

VP; Chairman Energy and Construction, Thomas H. (Tom) Zarges, age 63, $700,000 total compensation

VP General Counsel and Secretary, Joseph Masters, age 55, $255,050 total compensation

Chairman President and CEO, Martin M. Koffel, age 73, $1,000,002 total compensation

VP Communications, Susan B. Kilgannon, age 53

EVP Public Sector Business Development Infrastructure and Environment Management, Martin S. Tanzer

VP and Chief Accounting Officer, Reed N. Brimhall, age 58, $395,116 total compensation

President Energy and Construction, Robert W. (Bob) Zaist

VP; President Federal Services, Randall A. (Randy) Wotring, age 55, $525,013 total compensation

VP; President Infrastructure and Environment, Gary V. Jandegian, age 59, $600,018 total compensation

SVP Infrastructure & Environment Division, Thomas W. (Tom) Bishop, age 65, $317,328 total compensation

VP Corporate Planning, Olga Perkovic

EVP Private Sector Business Development Infrastructure and Environment Management, Dhamo S. Dhamotharan

VP and Treasurer, Judy L. Rodgers

VP Corporate Information Technology, Thomas J. Lynch

VP and CFO, H. Thomas (Tom) Hicks, age 61, $550,014 total compensation

VP Investor Relations, Sreeram (Sam) Ramraj

COO Energy and Construction, George L. Nash Jr.

VP; SVP International Operations, Hugh Blackwood, age 63

Director, Donald R. (Don) Knauss, age 61

Director, William P. (Bill) Sullivan, age 61

Director, Mickey P. Foret, age 66

Director, John D. Roach, age 68

Director, William D. Walsh, age 81

Director, Armen Der Marderosian, age 74

Director, Douglas W. Stotlar, age 51

Director, Joseph W. Ralston, age 68

Director, Lydia H. Kennard, age 57

Director, William H. (Bill) Frist, age 60

Auditors: PricewaterhouseCoopersLLP

LOCATIONS

HQ: URS Corporation
600 Montgomery St. 26th Fl., San Francisco CA 94111-2728

Phone: 415-774-2700 **Fax:** 415-398-1905

Web: www.urscorp.com

2011 Sales

	$ mil.	% of total
US	8,329	87
International	1,245	13
Adustments	(30.3)	-
Total	**9,545**	**100**

PRODUCTS/OPERATIONS

2011 Sales by Segment

	$ mil.	% of total
Infrastructure and Environment	3,760	39
Energy and Construction	3,251	33
Federal Services	2,695	28
Adjustments	(162.4)	-
Total	**9,545**	**100**

2011 Sales by Sector

	$ mil.	% of total
Federal	4,639	49
Industrial and commercial	1,917	20
Infrastructure	1,861	19
Power	1,126	12
Total	**9,545**	**100**

Selected Services

Design
- Architectural and interior design

Civil structural mechanical electrical sanitary environmental water resource geotechnical/underground dam mining and seismic engineering
Engineering and design studies for the upgrade and maintenance of military hardware

Operations and maintenance
Management of base logistics
Operation and maintenance of chemical agent disposal systems
Oversight of construction testing and operation of base systems and processes
Support of high-security systems

Planning
Archaeological and cultural resources studies
Coordination of community involvement programs
Development and analysis of alternative concepts
Environmental impact studies
Environmental site analyses
Facilities planning
Master planning
Permitting
Programming
Technical and economic feasibility studies
Traffic and revenue studies

Program and construction management
Cash flow analyses
Constructability reviews
Construction and bid management
Construction and life-cycle cost estimating
Construction or demolition of buildings

Selected Subsidiaries

URS Energy & Construction International Inc. (formerly Washington International Inc.)
URS Federal Technical Services Inc. (formerly known as EG&G Technical Services Inc.)
URS Global Holdings Inc.
URS Global Holdings UK Ltd.
URS Global Luxembourg Sarl
URS Holdings Inc.
URS/Scott Wilson
WGI Netherlands BV

COMPETITORS

AECOM
AMEC
Babcock & Wilcox
Baran Group
Bechtel
Black & Veatch
CACI International
Camp Dresser McKee
CH2M HILL
Computer Sciences Corp.
DynCorp International
Fluor
Foster Wheeler
Granite Construction
Jacobs Engineering
KBR
Lockheed Martin
ManTech
Morganti
NCI
Parsons Brinckerhoff
Peter Kiewit Sons'
Skidmore Owings
Tetra Tech

HISTORICAL FINANCIALS

Company Type: Public

Income Statement FYE: December 30

	REVENUE ($ mil.)	NET INCOME ($ mil.)	NET PROFIT MARGIN	EMPLOYEES
12/11	9,545	(465)	—	46,000
12/10*	9,177	287	3.1%	47,000
01/10	9,249	269	2.9%	45,000
01/09	10,086	219	2.2%	50,000
12/07	5,383	132	2.5%	56,000
Annual Growth	15.4%	—	—	(4.8%)

*Fiscal year change

2011 Year-End Financials

Debt ratio: 11.64%
Return on equity: (-13.79)%
Cash ($ mil.): 436
Current ratio: 178.04
Long-term debt ($ mil.): 737
No. of shares (mil.): 76
Dividends
Yield: —
Payout: —
Market value ($ mil.): 2,694

	STOCK PRICE ($) FY Close	P/E High/Low		PER SHARE ($) Earnings	Dividends	Book Value
12/11	35.12	—	—	(6.03)	0.00	44.03
12/10*	41.61	15	10	3.54	0.00	50.30
01/10	44.52	16	8	3.29	0.00	46.49
01/09	41.40	20	8	2.66	0.00	43.18
12/07	54.80	26	17	2.35	0.00	41.76
Annual Growth	(10.5%)	—	—	—	—	1.3%

*Fiscal year change

US Airways Group Inc

US Airways Group takes wing as one of the nation's leading passenger carriers. Along with its regional affiliates US Airways serves more than 200 cities mainly in the US and Canada but also in Latin America the Caribbean the Middle East and Europe. It uses about 340 jets on mainline routes; regional service is provided by subsidiaries Piedmont Airlines and PSA with more than 90 aircraft. US Airways extends its network via the Star Alliance a marketing and code-sharing partnership led by US Airways United Continental's United Airlines Lufthansa and Singapore Airlines. (Code-sharing allows airlines to sell tickets on one another's flights and thus offer more destinations.)

HISTORY

Richard du Pont (of the DuPont chemical dynasty) founded All American Aviation as an airmail service in 1939 to serve Pennsylvania and the Ohio Valley. Pilots used a system of hooks and ropes to pick up and drop off mail "on the fly." Ten years later the company expanded its service began carrying passengers and changed its name to All American Airways.

The carrier became Allegheny Airlines in 1953. It bought smaller airlines in 1968 and 1972 expanding into the Midwest and up the East Coast. In 1978 the US airline industry was deregulated; Allegheny became USAir in 1979 and began flying across the South and to California.

In 1987 USAir bought two major regional carriers —Pacific Southwest Airlines and Piedmont Airlines. The USAir/Piedmont merger was at the time the largest in US airline history. It also gave USAir its hub in Charlotte North Carolina; its first international route (Charlotte-London); and an East Coast commuter airline. In 1988 USAir bought a small stake in Covia operator of the Apollo computer reservations system (CRS). (Covia merged with Galileo a European CRS operator in 1992.)

High fuel prices and fare wars in the early 1990s put USAir in the red for six years (and forced it to lay off 9000 workers by 1996). Seth Schofield became CEO in 1991 and USAir acquired TWA's London routes in 1992. Taking a 40% stake in Trump Shuttle USAir began a joint marketing effort under the name USAir Shuttle. (It bought the shuttle outright in 1997.) The next year USAir and British Airways (BA) began code-sharing and BA took a stake in USAir which gave up its London routes.

The year 1994 was not one of USAir's best: It took a beating as it lowered fares to compete with Continental Airlines which by then challenged USAir in almost half its routes. The airline tried in vain to wring wage concessions from its unions. Then disaster struck: A jet carrying 132 passengers crashed at Pittsburgh —USAir's second fatal crash that year.

Though USAir returned to profitability in 1996 Schofield resigned. The new CEO Stephen Wolf demanded labor concessions. USAir which became US Airways in 1997 finally won a new contract with its pilots.

The company's relationship with BA soured after US Airways sued BA to gain access to London's Heathrow Airport. The two canceled code-sharing in 1997 and by 1998 BA had sold its US Airways stock.

US Airways launched low-fare carrier MetroJet in 1998. The next year Wolf disciple Rakesh Gangwal became CEO; Wolf remained chairman. US Airways suffered a pilot shortage after more than 300 pilots took early retirement and others were called up by the US military to support the Kosovo conflict.

To remain aloft after the terrorist attacks in New York and Washington DC in 2001 the carrier announced that it would cut back on its flights and lay off about 20% of its workforce. It also discontinued MetroJet.

Later that year Gangwal resigned and Wolf stepped back in as CEO until March 2002 when Avis Rent A Car CEO David Siegel a Continental Airlines veteran was named president and CEO.

The group filed for bankruptcy protection in 2002 and in conjunction with its filing the company received a bid from Texas Pacific Group; it also it won a $900 million loan guarantee from the federal government. The Texas Pacific deal was replaced by The Retirement Systems of Alabama which invested $240 million in exchange for a 36% ownership (and a 72% voting) stake in the company. It emerged from bankruptcy in 2003.

Restructured and with new ownership the carrier was poised to return to its place as a leading US airline. It strengthened its European presence in 2003 when it began a code-sharing agreement with top German airline Lufthansa which eventually led to its inclusion in the Star Alliance.

Its new structure however didn't prove viable and the carrier found itself overwhelmed by heavy costs primarily record-high fuel prices. It was forced once again to seek the protection of bankruptcy courts in 2004. US Airways merged with America West and emerged from Chapter 11 in 2005. US Airways Group unified its US Airways and America West businesses under the US Airways brand.

To accelerate its growth US Airways offered to buy rival Delta in 2006 before withdrawing the bid the next year. US Airways initially made an unsolicited offer in November 2006 to pay about $8 billion half in cash and half in stock for Delta which was reorganizing under bankruptcy protection. Hoping to put pressure on Delta's creditors to agree to a deal US Airways upped its bid to about $10 billion in January 2007. Delta failed to bite however spoiling US Airways' dreams of creating the world's largest airline.

In mid-2008 US Airways raised $179 million and $950 million in two rounds of financing. That same year the carrier joined peers in cutting domestic capacity by selling aircraft reducing its workforce and imposing new fees (including charges for checked bags premium seats and pillow-and-blanket sets). The economic recession which caused major turbulence for the airline industry in 2009 (overall airline passenger revenues declined by 18% in 2009 year-over-year) got its start the year prior when high fuel prices changed the trajectory for all air carriers. Even though fuel prices were 50% lower in 2009 compared to 2008 it was not enough to mitigate for decreased passenger demand. In 2009 the carrier added service between Philadelphia and Rio de Janeiro as well as service to Oslo Norway; Montego Bay Jamaica; and Tel Aviv Israel.

In January 2009 US Airways Flight 1549 had just taken off from New York on its way to Charlotte North Carolina when it struck a flock of Canada geese causing failure in both the plane's engines. Captain Chesley "Sully" Sullenberger made international news by skillfully "ditching" the plane in the Hudson River saving the lives of all 155 people aboard. The averted tragedy was a bright spot in airline industry news in the midst of the ongoing economic recession.

EXECUTIVES

VP and Controller, Michael R. (Mike) Carreon
EVP Corporate and Government Affairs, Stephen L. (Steve) Johnson, age 55, $318,750 total compensation
Chairman and CEO, W. Douglas (Doug) Parker, age 50, $550,000 total compensation
VP Legal Affairs, Paul A. Galleberg, age 52
VP InFlight Services, Hector E. Adler
President US Airways Group and US Airways, J. Scott Kirby, age 44, $510,000 total compensation
EVP People Communications and Public Affairs, Elise R. Eberwein, age 46, $299,600 total compensation
VP Operations Control Center and Air Traffic Control, Bob Maloney, age 59
SVP Airport Customer Service International and Cargo, Suzanne Boda
EVP and CFO, Derek J. Kerr, age 47, $370,234 total compensation
SVP Marketing and Planning, Andrew P. Nocella
EVP and COO, Robert D. Isom Jr., age 48, $450,000 total compensation
President and CEO PSA Airlines, Keith D. Houk
President and CEO Piedmont Airlines, Stephen R. (Steve) Farrow
VP; President Express Operations, Dion Flannery
SVP Technical Operations, David Seymour
SVP Flight Operations/Inflight, Capt. Edward W. (Ed) Bular
VP Airport Customer Service and Operations Support, Donna Paladini
Vice Chairman, Bruce R. Lakefield, age 68, $356,173 total compensation
VP Labor Relations, E. Allen (Al) Hemenway
Corporate Communications Manager, Michelle Mohr
VP and Treasurer, Tom Weir
VP Revenue Management, Thomas (Tom) Trenga
VP Safety and Regulatory Compliance, Capt. Paul Morell
Corporate Secretary, Caroline B. Ray
VP Government Affairs, Thomas B. (Tom) Chapman
VP Legal and Government Affairs, Michael J. (Mike) Minerva
SVP Operations Planning and Support, Kerry Hester, age 42
VP Philadelphia Operation, Robert (Bob) Ciminelli
VP IT Infrastructure, Alan Ferayorni
Director Investor Relations, Daniel E. Cravens
VP Flight Operations, Capt. Lyle Hogg
SVP and CIO, Brad Jensen
Corporate Communications, Elizabeth (Liz) Landau
SVP Finance, Keith A. Bush
VP Business Technology, Todd L. Christy
VP Airport Customer Service/Charlotte Hub, Terri Pope, age 54
VP Technical Services, Kevin Brickner, age 42
VP Legal Affairs, Paul Jones, age 61
VP Legal and Government Affairs, Howard Kass
VP Business Technology Delivery, Madeleine Gray
VP Reservations and Customer Planning, Tim Lindemann, age 46
VP Corporate Communications, John McDonald
VP Human Resources, Ryan Price
Director, Matthew J. Hart, age 60
Director, Herbert M. (Herb) Baum, age 75
Director, J. Steven Whisler, age 57
Director, Denise M. O'Leary, age 55
Director, Richard C. Kraemer, age 68
Director, George M. Philip, age 64
Director, Cheryl Gordon Krongard, age 56
Vice Chairman, Bruce R. Lakefield, age 68
Auditors: KPMGLLP

LOCATIONS

HQ: US Airways Group Inc.
111 W. Rio Salado Pkwy., Tempe AZ 85281
Phone: 480-693-0800 **Fax:** 312-436-4093
Web: www.usg.com

2011 Sales

	$ mil.	% of total
US	9,709	74
Other countries	3,346	26
Total	**13,055**	**100**

PRODUCTS/OPERATIONS

2011 Sales

	$ mil.	% of total
Mainline passenger	8,501	65
Express passenger	3,061	24
Cargo	170	1
Other	1,323	10
Total	**13,055**	**100**

Selected Subsidiaries

Airways Assurance Limited
Material Services Company Inc.
Piedmont Airlines Inc.
PSA Airlines Inc.
US Airways

COMPETITORS

Air France-KLM
AirTran Airways
Alaska Air
Allegiant Travel
AMR Corp.
British Airways
Delta Air Lines
Frontier Airlines
JetBlue
Southwest Airlines
United Continental
Virgin Atlantic Airways

HISTORICAL FINANCIALS

Company Type: Public

Income Statement FYE: December 31

	REVENUE ($ mil.)	NET INCOME ($ mil.)	NET PROFIT MARGIN	EMPLOYEES
12/11	13,055	71	0.5%	31,500
12/10	11,908	502	4.2%	35,800
12/09	10,458	(205)	—	36,000
12/08	12,118	(2,210)	—	37,500
12/07	11,700	427	3.6%	39,600
Annual Growth	2.8%	(36.1%)	—	(5.6%)

2011 Year-End Financials

Debt ratio: 54.78%
Return on equity: 47.33%
Cash ($ mil.): 1,947
Current ratio: 96.49
Long-term debt ($ mil.): 4,130
No. of shares (mil.): 162
Dividends
Yield: —
Payout: —
Market value ($ mil.): 822

	STOCK PRICE ($) FY Close	P/E High	P/E Low	PER SHARE ($) Earnings	Dividends	Book Value
12/11	5.07	26	9	0.44	0.00	0.93
12/10	10.01	4	2	2.61	0.00	0.52
12/09	4.84	—	—	(1.54)	0.00	(2.20)
12/08	7.73	—	—	(22.06)	0.00	(4.43)
12/07	14.71	13	3	4.52	0.00	15.66
Annual Growth	(23.4%)	—	—	(44.1%)	—	(50.6%)

Valero Energy Corp.

Valero Energy was not only named after a mission (the Mission San Antonio de Valero) it is on a mission to be the largest independent refiner in the US. Although Phillips 66 is larger by sales Valero bests that rival by capacity churning out about 3 million barrels per day. Valero refines low-cost residual oil and heavy crude into cleaner-burning higher-margin products including low-sulfur diesels. It operates 16 refineries in the US Canada and the UK. It also has 10 ethanol plants. Valero has a network of some 6800 retail and wholesale gas stations bearing the Corner Store Diamond Shamrock Shamrock Ultramar Valero Stop N Go and Beacon names in 44 US states and in Canada.

Valero is pursuing a long-term strategy of selling about a third of its high-cost North American refineries and other non-core US assets in order to explore more cost-efficient projects in faster-growing markets in Europe the Middle East and Asia. To cut costs in 2010 it sold its Delaware City refinery. It also sold its Paulsboro New Jersey refinery that year to PBF Holding for $340 million. It also sold its 50% stake in a pipeline that brings deepwater crude oil from the Gulf of Mexico to the US to Genesis Energy for $330 million.

Hedging its bets Valero has also moved into the alternative fuel business. Given that ethanol is a requirement in many of the gasoline fuel mixes it sells the company decided that it could cut costs by owning ethanol plants rather than buying ethanol wholesale. It made its first foray into ethanol production in 2009 buying seven ethanol production facilities from VeraSun Energy which was operating under Chapter 11 bankruptcy protection. Valero paid about $475 million for the facilities. After acquiring other ethanol companies in 2010 the company owned a total of 10 ethanol plants with a collective capacity of 1.1 billion gallons a year.

Valero also operates a 50-MW 33-turbine wind farm (completed in 2010) in the Texas Panhandle to provide green energy to its McKee Refinery.

Expanding its global footprint in 2011 Valero bought Chevron's Pembroke refinery and marketing and logistics assets across the UK for $1.7 billion. It also boosted its US assets that year buying Murphy Oil's refinery outside New Orleans for $585 million to complement its St. Charles facility.

High oil prices and high refining margins in addition to the expansion of its operations helped to lift 2011 revenues by more than 53% and its net income by more than 545%.

Due to the high costs of operating its Aruba refinery in 2010 Valero announced the suspension of activities at the refinery while it sought alternative uses of the facility.

HISTORY

Valero Energy was created as a result of the sins of its father Houston-based Coastal States Gas Corporation. Led by flamboyant entrepreneur Oscar Wyatt energy giant Coastal had established Lo-Vaca Gathering Company as a gas marketing subsidiary. Bound by long-term contracts to several Texas cities Coastal was not able to meet its contractual obligations when gas prices rose in the early 1970s and major litigation against the company resulted. The Texas Railroad Commission (the energy-regulating authority) ordered Coastal to refund customers $1.6 billion.

To meet the requirements 55% of Lo-Vaca was spun off to disgruntled former customers as Valero Energy at the end of 1979. The new company was born fully grown –as the largest intrastate pipeline in Texas –with accountant-cum-CEO Bill Greehey the court-appointed chief of Lo-Vaca at its head. Greehey relocated the company to San Antonio where it took its Valero name (from the Alamo or Mission San Antonio de Valero) and put some distance between itself and its discredited former parent. Under Greehey's direction Valero developed a squeaky-clean image by giving to charities stressing a dress code and keeping facilities clean.

Greehey diversified the company into refining unleaded gasoline. Valero bought residual fuel oil from Saudi Arabian refiners and in 1981 built a refinery in Corpus Christi Texas which went on line two years later. But in 1984 a glut of unleaded gasoline on the US market from European refiners undercut Valero's profits. To stay afloat Valero sold pipeline assets including 50% of its West Texas Pipeline in 1985 and 51% of its major pipeline operations in 1987. Refining margins finally began to improve in 1988. With one of the most modern refineries in the US Valero did not have to spend a bundle to upgrade its refining processes to meet the tougher EPA requirements of the 1990s.

In 1992 Valero expanded its refinery's production capacity and acquired two gas processing plants and several hundred miles of gas pipelines from struggling oil firm Oryx Energy (acquired by Kerr-McGee in 1999). That year Valero became the first non-Mexican business engaged in Mexican gasoline production when it signed a deal with state oil company Petroleos Mexicanos S.A. to build a gasoline additive plant there.

To expand its natural gas business substantially in 1994 Valero bought back the 51% of Valero Natural Gas Partners it didn't own. Valero also teamed up with regional oil company Swift Energy in a transportation marketing and processing agreement. As part of that arrangement Valero agreed to build a pipeline linking Swift's Texas gas field with a Valero plant.

In 1997 the company sold Valero Natural Gas to California electric utility PG&E gaining $1.5 billion for expansion. It then purchased Salomon's oil refining unit Basis Petroleum (two refineries in Texas and one in Louisiana) and the next year picked up Mobil's refinery in Paulsboro New Jersey.

With low crude oil prices hurting its bottom line in 1999 Valero explored partnerships with other refiners as a way to cut operating costs. In 2000 the company bought Exxon Mobil's 130000-barrel-per-day Benicia California refinery along with 340 retail outlets for about $1 billion.

In 2001 Valero gained two small refineries when it bought Huntway Refining a leading supplier of asphalt in California. Dwarfing that deal Valero also bought Ultramar Diamond Shamrock for $4 billion in cash and stock (it assumed about $2.1 billion of debt in the deal). As part of the deal and to comply with the demands of regulators in 2002 Valero sold the Golden Eagle (San Francisco-area) refinery and 70 retail service stations in Northern California to Tesoro for $945 million.

In 2003 the company acquired Orion Refining's Louisiana refinery for about $530 million and the next year it acquired an Aruba refinery from asset-shedding El Paso Corp. for $640 million. Suncor Energy bought a Colorado-based refinery from Valero for a reported $30 million in 2005.

The 2005 acquisition of Premcor made Valero the largest independent refiner on the Gulf Coast a major national player.

Greehey turned over the leadership reins to another company veteran Bill Klesse in early 2006. The following year the company sold its Lima Ohio refinery to Husky Energy.

In 2008 the company sold its Krotz Springs Louisiana refinery to Alon USA Energy for $333 million.

In 2009 Valero had an opportunity for international refinery expansion and a foothold in Europe when it agreed to acquire Dow Chemical's 45% interest in Dutch refinery Total Raffinaderij Nederland N.V. However the deal fell through and the stake was sold to LUKOIL.

EXECUTIVES

SVP Corporate Law and Secretary, Jay D. Browning
EVP and Chief Development Officer, S. Eugene (Gene) Edwards, age 55, $410,000 total compensation
Chairman President and CEO, William R. (Bill) Klesse, age 65, $1,500,000 total compensation
VP Supply Chain Management, John Emley
EVP Corporate Communications Supply Chain Management Information Services and Retail, Jean Bernier, age 55
VP Internal Audit, Lee Bailey
Corporate SVP and President Retail, Gary L. Arthur Jr.
Corporate VP Information Services and CIO, Cheryl Thomas
EVP and CFO, Michael S. (Mike) Ciskowski, age 54, $750,000 total compensation
VP and Treasurer, Donna M. Titzman
President Europe, Eric Fisher
SVP and Controller, Clayton E. (Clay) Killinger
EVP and General Counsel, Kimberly S. (Kim) Bowers, age 47, $494,000 total compensation
EVP Chief Commercial Officer and President Valero Europe, Joseph W. (Joe) Gorder, age 54, $460,000 total compensation
SVP Human Resources, R. Michael (Mike) Crownover
VP Regional Wholesale Marketing, Lee Rahmberg
Director Unbranded Sales, Bob Ryan
Director Branded Sales, Curtis Bissonnette
SVP Product Supply and Wholesale Marketing, David Parker
Executive Director Media Relations, Bill Day
VP Assistant Secretary and Disclosure and Compliance Officer, Steve Gilbert
VP and General Manager Valero Port Arthur Refinery, Greg Gentry
VP Government Affairs, John Greenwood
VP Energy and Gases, Travis Capps
VP Process Safety Management and Reliability, Eric Honeyman
SVP Project Execution, Tony Jones
SVP Strategic Development and Technology, John Roach
SVP Refining Operations, Lane Riggs
VP Refining Business Support and Analysis, Loren Bates
VP Crude Feedstock Suppy and Trading, Martin Parrish
SVP Alternative Energy and Project Development, Jim Gillingham
VP Optimization Planning and Economics, Gary Simmons
Director, Randall J. Weisenburger, age 53
Director, Ronald K. Calgaard, age 74
Director, Bob Marbut, age 76
Director, Robert A. Profusek, age 62
Director, Rayford (Ray) Wilkins Jr., age 60
Director, Ruben M. Escobedo, age 74
Director, Jerry D. Choate, age 73
Director, Susan Kaufman Purcell, age 69
Director, Stephen M. Waters, age 65
Director, Donald L. (Don) Nickles, age 63
Director, Philip J. Pfeiffer
Auditors: KPMGLLP

LOCATIONS

HQ: Valero Energy Corporation
One Valero Way, San Antonio TX 78249-1112
Phone: 210-345-2000 **Fax:** 210-345-2646
Web: www.valero.com

2011 Sales

	$ mil.	% of total
US	98,806	79
Canada	10,110	8
UK	4,297	3
Other countries	12,774	10
Total	**125,987**	**100**

PRODUCTS/OPERATIONS

2011 Sales

	$ mil.	% of total
Refining	109,138	87
Retail	11,699	9
Ethanol	5,150	4
Total	**125,987**	**100**

Selected Products

Asphalt
Bunker oils
CARB Phase II gasoline
Clean-burning oxygenates
Conventional gasoline
Crude mineral spirits
Customized clean-burning gasoline blends for export markets
Ethanol
Gasoline blendstocks
Home heating oil
Jet fuel
Kerosene
Low-sulfur diesel
Lube oils
Petrochemical feedstocks
Petroleum coke
Premium reformulated and conventional gasolines
Reformulated gasoline
Sulfur

COMPETITORS

ADM
Aventine
BioFuel Energy
BP
Chevron
CITGO
ConocoPhillips
Exxon Mobil
Hess Corporation
HollyFrontier
Marathon Petroleum
Motiva Enterprises
National Cooperative Refinery Association
Shell Oil Products
Sinclair Oil
Sunoco
Tesoro
TOTAL
TPC Group

HISTORICAL FINANCIALS

Company Type: Public

Income Statement FYE: December 31

	REVENUE ($ mil.)	NET INCOME ($ mil.)	NET PROFIT MARGIN	EMPLOYEES
12/11	125,987	2,090	1.7%	21,942
12/10	82,233	324	0.4%	20,313
12/09	68,144	(1,982)	—	20,920
12/08	119,114	(1,131)	—	21,765
12/07	95,327	5,234	5.5%	21,651
Annual Growth	7.2%	(20.5%)	—	0.3%

2011 Year-End Financials

Debt ratio: 18.09%
Return on equity: 12.73%
Cash ($ mil.): 1,024
Current ratio: 125.68
Long-term debt ($ mil.): 6,732
No. of shares (mil.): 556
Dividends
Yield: —
Payout: 8.15%
Market value ($ mil.): 11,721

	STOCK PRICE ($) FY Close	P/E High	P/E Low	PER SHARE ($) Earnings	Dividends	Book Value
12/11	21.05	8	5	3.68	0.00	29.49
12/10	23.12	41	27	0.57	0.20	26.43
12/09	16.75	—	—	(3.67)	0.60	26.08
12/08	21.64	—	—	(2.16)	0.57	30.26
12/07	70.03	8	5	8.88	0.48	34.49
Annual Growth	(26.0%)	—	—	(19.8%)	—	(3.8%)

Valley National Bancorp

Valley National is high on New Jersey and New York. The holding company owns Valley National Bank which serves commercial and retail clients through more than 200 branches in northern and central New Jersey and in the New York City boroughs of Manhattan Brooklyn and Queens as well as on Long Island. The bank provides standard services like checking and savings accounts loans and mortgages credit cards and trust services. Subsidiaries offer asset management mortgage and auto loan servicing title insurance asset-based lending and property/casualty life and health insurance.

Valley finalized its approximately $222 million acquisition of New York-based bank holding company State Bancorp at the beginning of 2012. The deal which brought in 17 branches is part of Valley's overall strategy to expand its presence throughout New York City metropolitan area. It marked the company's first foray in Long Island and added locations in Manhattan and Queens as well. It also provides an opportunity to build retail relationships in new markets as State Bancorp focused more on commercial clients. Valley typically targets consumers disillusioned with larger banks.

In 2010 the company acquired the branches and most of the assets and deposits of failed Manhattan-based financial institutions LibertyPointe Bank and Park Avenue Bank in FDIC-assisted transactions. It also opened a loan production office in Bethlehem Pennsylvania to offer residential mortgages and title insurance. Valley continues to look for additional expansion opportunities.

Despite a sluggish economic environment Valley's net income increased 35% in 2010 as markets improved and a more modest 2% in 2011. Higher interest rate spreads sales of mortgages and investment securities and gains related to its acquisitions contributed to its results. The bank's past-due loans also remained below the industry norm.

Commercial real estate and construction loans account for the largest portion of Valley's loan porfolio. However the bank has ramped up its residential lending and has been actively marketing its home loan refinancing products amid continued low interest rates. It also specializes in general aviation financing commercial equipment leasing and custom financing for health care professionals and law firms.

The company was founded as The Passaic Park Trust Company in 1927. It adopted its current name after a 1976 merger. Chairman president and CEO Gerald Lipkin has led Valley for more than 35 years.

EXECUTIVES

EVP Valley National Bancorp and Valley National Bank, James G. Lawrence, age 68, $408,890 total compensation
EVP and Chief Administrative Officer, Robert J. Mulligan, age 64
First SVP Valley National Bank, Richard P. Garber, age 68
EVP and Chief Credit Officer Valley National Bancorp and Valley National Bank, Robert E. Farrell, age 65
SEVP and COO Valley National Bancorp and Valley National Bank, Peter Crocitto, age 54, $370,000 total compensation
EVP and Chief Commercial Lending Officer, Robert M. (Rob) Meyer, age 65, $360,000 total compensation
First SVP and Human Resources Director Valley National Bank, Carol Diesner
SEVP CFO and Corporate Secretary Valley National Bancorp and Valley National Bank, Alan D. Eskow, age 63, $370,000 total compensation
Chairman President and CEO Valley National Bancorp and Valley National Bank, Gerald H. Lipkin, age 71, $700,000 total compensation
First SVP National Valley Bank, Russell C. Murawski, age 62
President Wealth Management and Insurance Services Valley National Bank, Anthony M. Bruno Jr., age 57
EVP and Chief Retail Lending Officer, Albert L. Engel, age 63, $340,000 total compensation
First SVP Valley National Bank, Eric W. Gould, age 43
First SVP Valley National Bank, Kermit R. Dyke, age 64
First SVP and Director Marketing and Public Relations, Dianne M. Grenz
SVP Valley National Bank, Stephen P. Davey, age 56
First SVP Valley National Bank, Elizabeth E. De Laney, age 47
AVP Secretary Valley National Bank, Wilma Falduto
SVP and General Counsel Valley National Bank, Lucinda Long
First VP and Senior Attorney Valley National Bank, Gary G. Michael
First VP and Senior Attorney Valley National Bank, Harold S. Steinberg
First SVP Valley National Bank, John H. Noonan, age 65
SVP Valley National Bank, Robert A. Ewing, age 57
EVP and Director Sales and Client Development, Bernadette M. Mueller, age 53
SVP and Director Trust Services Valley National Bank, John P. Genn III
First SVP Valley National Bank, Maureen J. Zegler
First SVP and Treasurer Valley National Bancorp and Valley National Bank, Ira Robbins, age 37
First SVP Valley National Bank, Marianne Potito
First VP Valley National Bank, Robert Peterson
VP Valley National Bank, Cristina Felix
VP Valley National Bank, Ana Mauriello
Branch Sales Manager Whippany Valley National Bank, Kenneth (Ken) Kimmel
First SVP, Barbara Mohrbutter
Branch Sales Manager Lyndhurst Branch Valley National Bank, Alfonso Ugarte
Branch Sales Manager West Orange Branch Valley National Bank, Ronna D'Arcangelo
SVP Valley National Bank, John Siberio
Branch Sales Manager Chatham Branch Valley National Bank, Mark Newton
Branch Sales Manager Richfield Valley National Bank, Carlos I. Vargas
SVP and Operations Coordinator Valley National Bank, Lynn Borelli
First SVP Valley National Bank, Andrea Onorato
SVP Special Assets Valley National Bank, Robert Sierchio
VP and Team Leader Healthcare Financial Services Valley National Bank, Ron Krauskopf
First VP Special Assets Valley National Bank, Robert (Bob) Kochenthal
VP and Branch Sales Manager Val-ley Na-tion-al Bank, John Gallagher
VP Special Assets, Tony Ze-leszko
First Senior Vice President of Valley National Bank, Elizabeth Laney
Director, Mary J. Steele Guilfoile, age 57
Director, Andrew B. Abramson, age 58
Director, Pamela R. Bronander, age 55
Director, Graham O. Jones, age 67
Director, Walter H. Jones III, age 69
Director, Gerald Korde, age 68
Director, Robinson Markel, age 77
Director, Richard S. Miller, age 77
Director, Barnett Rukin, age 71
Director, Robert C. Soldoveri, age 58
Director, Eric P. Edelstein, age 62
Director, Michael L. LaRusso, age 66
Director, Marc J. Lenner, age 46
Director, Suresh L. Sani, age 47
Independent Director, Jeffery Wilks
Auditors: KPMGLLP

LOCATIONS

HQ: Valley National Bancorp
1455 Valley Rd., Wayne NJ 07470
Phone: 973-305-8800 **Fax:** 973-696-2044
Web: www.valleynationalbank.com

PRODUCTS/OPERATIONS

2011 Sales

	$ mil.	% of total
Interest		
Loans including fees	547	70
Investment securities	126	16
Other	0	-
Noninterest		
Net gains on securities transactions	32	4
Service charges on deposit accounts	22	3
Insurance commissions	15	2
Gain on FDIC share-loss receivable	13	2
Net gains on sales of loans	10	1
Trust & investment services	7	1
Other	10	1
Total	**786**	**100**

COMPETITORS

Bank of America
Capital One
Citigroup
Dime Community Bancshares
Hudson City Bancorp
JPMorgan Chase
New York Community Bancorp
PNC Financial
TD Bank USA
Wells Fargo

HISTORICAL FINANCIALS

Company Type: Public

Income Statement FYE: December 31

	ASSETS ($ mil.)	NET INCOME ($ mil.)	INCOME AS % OF ASSETS	EMPLOYEES
12/11	14,244	133	0.9%	2,754
12/10	14,143	131	0.9%	2,720
12/09	14,284	116	0.8%	2,722
12/08	14,718	93	0.6%	2,783
12/07	12,748	153	1.2%	2,562
Annual Growth	2.8%	(3.4%)	—	1.8%

2011 Year-End Financials

Debt ratio: 20.44%
Return on equity: 10.56%
Cash ($ mil.): 379
Current ratio: —
Long-term debt ($ mil.): 2,911
No. of shares (mil.): 178
Dividends
Yield: —
Payout: 87.20%
Market value ($ mil.): 2,210

	STOCK PRICE ($) FY Close	P/E High/Low		PER SHARE ($) Earnings	Dividends	Book Value
12/11	12.37	20	13	0.75	0.00	7.09
12/10	14.30	23	17	0.73	0.65	7.28
12/09	14.13	35	15	0.58	0.66	7.07
12/08	20.25	42	25	0.58	0.66	8.31
12/07	19.06	27	18	1.00	0.65	6.20
Annual Growth	(10.2%)	—	—	(6.9%)	—	3.4%

Valspar Corp.

Valspar wants you to put on a coat. The firm makes a variety of coatings and paints for manufacturing automotive and food-packaging companies as well as for consumers. The company's industrial coatings – used by OEMs including building product appliance and furniture makers – include coatings for metal wood plastic and glass. Packaging products include coatings and inks for rigid containers such as food and beverage cans. Its consumer paints include interior and exterior paints primers stains and varnishes sold through mass merchandisers like Wal-Mart and Lowe's. Valspar also makes auto paints colorants and gel-coats. It is active in Asia the Americas and Europe.

Valspar manufactures and distributes a wide range of coatings paints and related products. It operates two divisions: Coating and Paints.

The company has operations in 25 countries in Asia the Americas and Europe.

Valspar grew in 2011 boosting its revenues by more than 22% attributable to improvements in global market conditions and its acquisition of new businesses higher prices and a strong performance from its Coatings segment. However its net income fell from $222 million in 2010 to a net loss of $139 million in 2011 largely due to increased sales costs higher operating expenses and restructuring costs and a $409.7 million charge for impairment of goodwill and intangible assets related to the fair value of its wood and gelcoat reporting assets.

To improve its financial performance in fiscal 2011 the company began to restructure its wood product line within the Coating segment announcing plans to reduce manufacturing plants and headcount globally in this segment. It also announced similar measures for its Paints segment in Australia.

Lowe's accounted for more than 10% of the company's sales in 2011 and the hardware and home repair giant has named Valspar paint supplier of the year over several years. Valspar uses its own brand at Lowe's (replacing generic-sounding store brands) in an effort to boost consumer recognition. Valspar has made a point to tailor its products to the needs of retail customers to the point of placing in-store employees to answer paint questions.

Valspar has boosted its core business through buying smaller coatings companies around the world; in the past decade it made more than 20 bolt-on acquisitions including joint venture interests. That strategy has made Valspar one of the top global industrial coatings makers.

In 2012 the company announced a deal with B&Q a unit of Kingfisher plc to supply a full range of premium Valspar paint to all 350 of its locations in the UK and Ireland.

In 2011 Valspar acquired Brazilian powder coatings maker Isocoat Tintas e Vernizes Ltda. in a deal valued at $34 million. Isocoat serves industrial customers in Brazil Argentina and Colombia.

In 2010 Valspar acquired Australian paint manufacturer Wattyl Limited in a $135 million deal.

It made a major move into the China market in 2006 acquiring an 80% stake in Chinese coatings manufacturer Huarun Paints a maker of wood and furniture coatings.

HISTORY

Samuel Tuck began the company as Paint and Color in Boston in 1806. It was known as Valentine & Co. by 1866. Then-owner Lawson Valentine hired chemist Charles Homer (brother of artist Winslow Homer) who perfected finishing varnishes. In 1903 Valentine's grandson L. Valentine Pulsifer invented the first clear varnish –dubbed Valspar –which became the company's name in 1932. Valspar grew by mergers including Rockcote Paint (1960) and Minnesota Paints (1970). CEO Angus Wurtele became chairman in 1973. Valspar's sales tripled by the time it acquired Mobil Oil's packaging coatings business in 1984.

Valspar formed a joint venture with China Merchants in 1994 (packaging coatings) and then bought US-based Sunbelt Coatings (auto refinishing 1995) Gordon Bartels (packaging coatings 1996) and Sureguard (industrial coatings 1997). Valspar swapped its maintenance coatings business in 1997 with Ameron International's product finishes unit and formed a joint venture in Brazil with Renner Herrmann SA.

President and CEO Richard Rompala replaced Wurtele as chairman in 1998. Acquisitions that year included Plasti-Kote (consumer aerosol and specialty paints) Australia-based Anzol (packaging and industrial coatings) and Dyflex Polymers (specialty water-based polymers).

The company began divesting noncore businesses selling its functional powder coatings unit in 1998 and its marine and packaging coatings product lines in 1999. Also in 1999 it bought the packaging coatings business of Dexter Corporation (now a part of Life Technologies) and its subsidiary in France and the Netherlands-based resins maker Dyflex. The next year Valspar bought rival coatings maker Lilly Industries in a $975 million deal which made Valspar a top global maker of coatings for wood mirrors and coils (used in doors and appliances).

From 1996 to 2001 in a four-phase deal the company acquired packaging coatings firm Coates Coatings which operated in North America Europe Australia Africa and Asia. This acquisition boosted Valspar into the top of the market for metal packaging coatings.

In 2004 the company acquired Dutch automotive coatings maker De Beer Lakfabrieken as well as the Forest Products division of wood coatings firm Associated Chemists.

William Mansfield became CEO in February 2005 but Rompala stayed on as chairman until his retirement in mid-year. Thomas McBurney assumed the chairmanship for two years before Mansfield was named chairman in 2007.

EXECUTIVES

EVP, Steven L. Erdahl, age 60, $483,000 total compensation
EVP General Counsel and Secretary, Rolf Engh, age 58, $442,000 total compensation
Chairman, William L. (Bill) Mansfield, age 63, $900,000 total compensation
VP, Thomas V. Kelliher
Group VP Architectural, Kenneth H. Arthur
SVP and CFO, Lori A. Walker, age 55, $375,000 total compensation
VP, Kathleen J. (Kate) Bass
SVP, Howard C. Heckes, age 47
VP Coil and Extrusion Coatings, Alfred N. (Al) Dunlop
Group VP, Brian Falline
SVP Global Operations, John Wardzel, age 53
Chairman President and CEO, Gary E. Hendrickson, age 55, $525,000 total compensation
SVP and CTO, Cynthia A. Arnold
SVP Global Industrial, Roeland H. Polet, age 49
SVP, Bernard J. (Bern) Ouimette
VP, Steve Person
SVP Human Resources, Anthony L. Blaine, age 45
VP and Controller, Tracy C. Jokinen
VP and Treasurer, Tyler N. Treat
Group VP, J.R. Benites
VP, Andrew Hecker
Color Trend and Forecast Specialist, Sue Kim
VP Coil Coatings, Jeff Alexander
VP Marketing, Scot Karstens
Group VP, James E. Randolph
VP, Robert Lavichant
Director, Ian R. Friendly, age 51
Director, Jeffrey H. (Jeff) Curler, age 61
Director, Gregory R. Palen, age 56
Director, Charles W. Gaillard, age 71
Director, Mae C. Jemison, age 55
CEO and Director, Gary E. Hendrickson, age 54
Director, Stephen D. Newlin, age 58
Director, Janel S. Haugarth, age 56
Director, John S. Bode, age 64
Auditors: Ernst&YoungLLP

LOCATIONS

HQ: The Valspar Corporation
901 3rd Ave. South, Minneapolis MN 55402
Phone: 612-851-7000 **Fax:** 612-851-3535
Web: www.valspar.com

2011 Sales

	$ mil.	% of total
US	2,055	52
China	488	12

Australia	481	12
Other countries	927	24
Total	**3,952**	**100**

PRODUCTS/OPERATIONS

2011 Sales

	$ mil.	% of total
Coatings	2,092	51
Paints	1,612	40
Other	360	9
Adjustments	(111.9)	-
Total	**3,952**	**100**

Selected Products

Industrial
- Fillers
- Mirror coatings
- Primers
- Stains
- Topcoats

Architectural automotive and specialty
- Aerosols
- Enamels
- Faux finishes
- Interior and exterior paints
- Primers
- Sealers
- Stains
- Varnishes

Packaging
- Coatings
- Inks

Other
- Colorants
- Composites
- Powder coatings for metal surfaces
- Specialty polymers

Selected Brands

Cabot
De Beer
Goof Off
House of Kolor
McCloskey
Mr. Spray
Plasti-Kote
Tempo
Valspar

COMPETITORS

Akzo Nobel
BASF Coatings AG
BEHR
Benjamin Moore
DuPont
Ferro
H.B. Fuller
Kelly-Moore
PPG Industries
Sherwin-Williams

HISTORICAL FINANCIALS

Company Type: Public

Income Statement FYE: October 26

	REVENUE ($ mil.)	NET INCOME ($ mil.)	NET PROFIT MARGIN	EMPLOYEES
10/12	4,020	292	7.3%	9,800
10/11	3,952	(138)	—	10,000
10/10	3,226	222	6.9%	10,180
10/09	2,879	160	5.6%	8,800
10/08	3,482	150	4.3%	9,400
Annual Growth	3.7%	18.0%	—	1.0%

2012 Year-End Financials

Debt ratio: 31.74%
Return on equity: 23.91%
Cash ($ mil.): 253
Current ratio: 141.14
Long-term debt ($ mil.): 1,012
No. of shares (mil.): 90
Dividends
Yield: 1.46%
Payout: 25.81%
Market value ($ mil.): 4,956

	STOCK PRICE ($) FY Close	P/E High/Low		PER SHARE ($) Earnings	Dividends	Book Value
10/12	54.96	19	10	3.10	0.80	13.57
10/11	35.83	—	—	(1.47)	0.72	12.96
10/10	32.10	15	11	2.20	0.64	16.63
10/09	25.37	19	10	1.49	0.60	15.12
10/08	20.45	19	12	1.38	0.56	14.87
Annual Growth	28.0%	—	—	22.4%	9.3%	(2.3%)

Vanguard Health Systems, Inc.

Vanguard Health Systems wants to lead the way to better health care. The company operates 25 acute care and three specialty hospitals located in urban and suburban markets in Arizona Illinois Massachusetts Michigan and Texas. Combined the hospitals have about 7100 licensed beds. Vanguard's medical facilities provide a continuum of care and generally include outpatient centers and medical office buildings that form regional health care networks. It also runs four managed health care plans that serve some 234500 members in Arizona Illinois and Texas. The Blackstone Group owns a significant stake in Vanguard which completed an IPO in 2011.

IPO

Vanguard raised some $400 million through the public offering. Proceeds are being used to pay down debt which the company primarily incurred through acquisitions.

Operations

Patient services at Vanguard's hospitals account for 85% of its revenue. Vanguard's remaining operations include Phoenix Health Plan a Medicaid managed care plan serving more than 130000 members in the Phoenix area and MacNeal Health Providers an organization affiliated with the company's Chicago-area facility MacNeal Hospital. Its third health plan Abrazo Advantage provides Medicare Advantage and prescription drug plans to Phoenix-area Medicare members who are also eligible for Medicaid. Valley Baptist Insurance provides government HMOs in Texas.

Sales & Marketing

Vanguard enjoys a fairly diverse payer mix. The biggest single source of income comes from managed care plans (about 35%) while Medicare and Medicaid account for 25% and 7% respectively. The remainder is made up of commercial payers and self-pay patients.

Strategy

Vanguard plans to continue to build up its presence in targeted regions both by expanding its integrated care networks in existing core markets and by establishing operations in new areas that present attractive growth opportunities. Vanguard Health typically acquires facilities that fit its preferred profile: struggling not-for-profits located in fast-growing urban and suburban areas. It has historically established operations in regions that present attractive demographics and payer mixes promising competitive conditions and opportunities for further expansion.

Like most hospital operators the company hopes to attract customers by providing high quality care recruiting good doctors and expanding its services. It particularly looks to add high-margin services in areas such as cardiology and orthopedics and to increase its hospitals' ability to offer private rooms. Vanguard Health has also been expanding its hospitalist programs which help coordinate care between specialist physicians and the nursing staff.

Mergers & Acquisitions

Vanguard's IPO came on the heels of a veritable hospital shopping spree in 2010. The company bumped up its acute care holdings in Chicago with the purchases of the 235-bed West Suburban Medical Center and the 225-bed Westlake Hospital in suburban Chicago from Resurrection Health Care for about $45 million. Vanguard also added to its Arizona-based Abrazo Health Care business by snapping up the Arizona Heart Institute an outpatient physicians group that had filed for bankruptcy protection. At the same time the company paid $31.5 million to acquire the Arizona Heart Hospital from MedCath.

Vanguard added a fifth market to its roster at the dawn of 2011 when it paid $365 million in cash (plus $420 million in debt) to acquire Detroit Medical Center (DMC) an eight-hospital system located in and around... where else? Detroit. As part of the deal Vanguard agreed to make about $850 million in capital improvements to DMC's hospitals which combined have more than 1700 beds.

In mid-2011 the company formed a joint venture with the Valley Baptist Health System (VBHS) in south Texas. By forming the venture Vanguard gained 51% ownership of VBHS's assets and took over day-to-day operations of the system which includes two hospitals. The purchase is a shift in strategies for Vanguard as it represents smaller urban markets than Vanguard's usual activities. As a follow-on to the deal Vanguard purchased full ownership of Valley Baptist Insurance Company (VBIC) neatly extending its health plan business into Texas.

Ownership

Following Vanguard's 2011 IPO Blackstone's stake in the company was reduced from about 66% to some 36%. Another investor Morgan Stanley reduced its stake from 17% to 10%.

EXECUTIVES

Chairman and CEO, Charles N. (Charlie) Martin Jr., age 69, $1,036,942 total compensation
SVP Market Strategy and Government Affairs, Reginald M. Ballantyne III, age 68
SVP Human Resources, Larry L. Fultz, age 57
EVP, Joseph D. (Joe) Moore, age 65, $574,998 total compensation
Vice Chairman, Keith B. Pitts, age 55, $632,497 total compensation
EVP General Counsel and Secretary, Ronald P. (Ron) Soltman, age 65, $517,498 total compensation
SVP Compliance and Ethics, Bruce F. Chafin, age 56
EVP CFO and Treasurer, Phillip W. (Phil) Roe, age 51
SVP and Assistant General Counsel and Assistant Secretary, James H. (Jim) Spalding, age 53
SVP Operations Finance, Alan G. Thomas, age 58
SVP Managed Care, Thomas M. Ways, age 62
SVP Controller and Chief Accounting Officer, Gary D. Willis, age 47
SVP Operations, Michael E. (Mike) Duggan, age 53
SVP Operations, Joseph J. Mullany, age 48
President and COO, Kent H. Wallace, age 57, $560,383 total compensation
SVP Operations, Dan F. Ausman, age 57
SVP and Chief Development Officer, Harold H. Pilgrim III, age 51

EVP Strategy and Innovation; Chief Transformation Officer, Bradley A. (Brad) Perkins, age 52
EVP and Chief Medical Officer, Mark R. Montoney, age 55
SVP Development, Paul T. Dorsa, age 55
SVP Operations, Graham Reeve, age 48
SVP and CIO, Scott Blanchette, age 40
Director, M. Fazle Husain, age 48
Director, Neil P. Simpkins, age 45
Vice Chairman, Keith B. Pitts, age 55
Director, James A. Quella, age 62
Director, Michael A. Dal Bello, age 41
Director, Stephen R. D?Arcy, age 57
Auditors: Ernst&YoungLLP

LOCATIONS

HQ: Vanguard Health Systems Inc.
20 Burton Hills Blvd. Ste. 100, Nashville TN 37215
Phone: 615-665-6000 **Fax:** 615-665-6099
Web: www.vanguardhealth.com

Selected Locations

Arizona
- Glendale
- Goodyear
- Phoenix

Illinois
- Berwyn
- Chicago
- Melrose Park
- Oak Park

Massachusetts
- Framingham
- Natick
- Worcester

Michigan
- Commerce
- Detroit
- Madison Heights

Texas
- Brownsville
- Harlingen
- San Antonio

PRODUCTS/OPERATIONS

2011 Payor Mix

	% of total
Managed	38
Medicare	27
Managed	16
Managed	10
Medicaid	7
Self-pay	1
Other	1
Total	**100**

Selected Facilities

Arizona Heart Hospital (Phoenix AZ)
Arrowhead Hospital (Glendale AZ)
Baptist Medical Center (San Antonio TX)
DMC Children' s Hospital of Michigan (Detroit)
DMC Detroit Receiving Hospital (Detroit)
DMC Harper University Hospital (Detroit)
DMC Huron Valley - Sinai Hospital (Commerce MI)
DMC Hutzel Women' s Hospital (Detroit)
DMC Rehabilitation Institute of Michigan (Detroit)
DMC Sinai - Grace Hospital (Detroit)
DMC Surgery Hospital (Madison Heights MI)
Louis A. Weiss Memorial Hospital (80.1% joint venture with the University of Chicago Hospitals; Chicago)
MacNeal Hospital (Berwyn IL)
Maryvale Hospital (Phoenix AZ)
MetroWest Medical Center - Framingham Union Hospital (MA)
MetroWest Medical Center - Leonard Morse Hospital (Natick MA)
Mission Trail Baptist Hospital (San Antonio TX)
North Central Baptist Hospital (San Antonio TX)
Northeast Baptist Hospital (San Antonio TX)
Paradise Valley Hospital (Phoenix AZ)
Phoenix Baptist Hospital (Phoenix AZ)
Saint Vincent Hospital at Worcester Medical Center (MA)
St. Luke' s Baptist Hospital (San Antonio TX)
Valley Baptist Medical Center - Brownsville (TX)
Valley Baptist Medical Center (Harlingen TX)
West Suburban Medical Center (Oak Park IL)
West Valley Hospital (Goodyear AZ)
Westlake Hospital (Melrose Park IL)

COMPETITORS

Advocate Health Care
Banner Health
Baylor Health
Blue Cross Blue Shield of Arizona
CHRISTUS Health
Community Health Systems
Covenant Ministries
Dignity Health
Essent Healthcare
HCA
Henry Ford Health System
John C. Lincoln Health Network
Massachusetts General Hospital
Methodist Healthcare System
Partners HealthCare
Rush System for Health
St. John Health
Tenet Healthcare
Universal Health Services
University Health System
WellGroup HealthPartners

HISTORICAL FINANCIALS

Company Type: Public

Income Statement

FYE: June 30

	REVENUE ($ mil.)	NET INCOME ($ mil.)	NET PROFIT MARGIN	EMPLOYEES
06/12	5,949	57	1.0%	40,900
06/11	4,895	(10)	—	38,600
06/10	3,376	(49)	—	38,500
06/09	3,185	28	0.9%	0
06/08	2,775	(0)	—	0
Annual Growth	21.0%	—	—	—

2012 Year-End Financials

Debt ratio: 56.53%
Return on equity: 16.46%
Cash ($ mil.): 455
Current ratio: 160.11
Long-term debt ($ mil.): 2,695
No. of shares (mil.): 75
Dividends
Yield: —
Payout: —
Market value ($ mil.): 671

	STOCK PRICE ($) FY Close	P/E High/Low		PER SHARE ($) Earnings	Dividends	Book Value
06/12	8.89	24	10	0.71	0.00	4.61
06/11	17.17	—	—	(0.24)	0.00	3.29
Annual Growth	(48.2%)	—	—	—	—	40.1%

Verizon Communications Inc

Verizon Communications is the #2 US telecom services provider overall after AT&T but it holds the top spot in wireless services ahead of rival AT&T Mobility. The company's core mobile business (more than 60% of sales) is primarily retail and is overseen by Verizon Wireless which operates as a joint venture with Vodafone; it serves nearly 110 million customers. Verizon's wireline unit with nearly 24 million landline accounts provides local telephone long-distance Internet access and digital TV services to residential and wholesale customers. In addition to those services Verizon offers a wide range of telecom managed network and IT services to commercial and government clients in more than 150 countries.

HISTORY

Verizon Communications (the name is a combination of "veritas" the Latin word for truth and horizon) was born in 2000 when Bell Atlantic bought GTE but the company's roots are as old as the telephone. What is now Verizon began as one of the 1870s-era phone companies that evolved into AT&T Corp. and its Bell System of regional telephone operations.

AT&T lived happily as a regulated monopoly until a US government antitrust suit led to its breakup in 1984. Seven regional Bell operating companies (RBOCs or Baby Bells) emerged in 1984 including Bell Atlantic. The new company based in Philadelphia received local phone service rights in six states and Washington DC; cellular company Bell Atlantic Mobile Systems; and one-seventh of Bellcore the R&D subsidiary (now Telcordia).

Bell Atlantic pursued unregulated businesses such as wireless Internet directory publishing and catalog sales of computer parts and office supplies. It invested heavily in data-transport markets to supplement existing voice services offering the first CO-LAN (central-office local area network) system in 1985. A year later it introduced a switched public data network and began testing integrating services digital network (ISDN) technology that combined voice and data transmissions over the same lines.

Bell Atlantic expanded internationally in the early 1990s. It was selected with Ameritech to buy Telecom New Zealand from the New Zealand government in 1990. Bell Atlantic and Ameritech reduced their ownership over time; Ameritech sold its last shareholding in 1997 and Bell Atlantic (as Verizon) sold its remaining stake in 2002. Bell Atlantic also partnered with U S WEST to offer cellular services in the former Czechoslovakia in 1991 and in 1993 it bought a stake in Mexico's Grupo Iusacell (sold 2003). Its 1992 acquisition of Metro Mobile gave it extensive East Coast cellular phone coverage.

In 1994 Bell Atlantic tried and failed to buy cable giant TCI (now part of AT&T) but succeeded in forming the PrimeCo partnership with NYNEX U S WEST and AirTouch which began offering PCS. Enjoying freedom from wires Bell Atlantic and NYNEX combined their cellular and paging operations in 1995. In 1996 Bell Atlantic and the six other RBOCs sold Bellcore to Science Applications International.

Bell Atlantic doubled in size with the $25.6 billion purchase of New York City-based NYNEX in 1997 moving from the Cradle of Liberty to the Big Apple. The deal created the second-largest US telecom services firm (after AT&T) but brought with it NYNEX's reputation for poor service.

In 1999 Bell Atlantic agreed to buy GTE the giant non-Bell local phone company in a $53 billion deal. To gain regulatory clearance to be acquired by Bell Atlantic GTE sold off 90% of its Genuity Internet backbone operation (formerly GTE Internetworking). Verizon retained an option to regain control of the business but abandoned the option when the troubled operator struggled with a lack of demand for services brought by a glut of capacity in the industry.

Later that year the FCC granted Bell Atlantic permission to sell long-distance phone service in

New York making the company the first of the Baby Bells to be allowed to offer long-distance in its home territory. Verizon later received the green light to offer long-distance in Massachusetts Connecticut and Pennsylvania (2001); in Delaware New Hampshire and Rhode Island (2002); and in Maryland West Virginia and Washington DC (2003).

Bell Atlantic and Vodafone AirTouch (which became Vodafone Group) combined their US wireless operations including PrimeCo to form Verizon Wireless in 2000. Regulators later that year approved Bell Atlantic's acquisition of GTE and Verizon Communications was formed. Tapped to run the new company were chairman and co-CEO Charles Lee formerly of GTE and president and co-CEO Ivan Seidenberg formerly of Bell Atlantic (Lee later gave up the co-CEO position and subsequently stepped down as chairman in 2003).

Based in New York City Verizon felt severe effects from the terrorist attack on lower Manhattan in 2001. The company reported damage to its central office facility adjacent to the World Trade Center and the loss of some cell sites in the vicinity of the destruction. Verizon also provided phone services to the Pentagon and suffered damage in that attack. Verizon teamed up with FLAG Telecom to develop a European backbone network.

Verizon began divesting certain holdings in 2002 as part of an effort to reduce debt by eliminating noncore assets including its 5% stake in Cable and Wireless in a deal valued at $280 million. It also sold its nearly 18% stake in the Greek wireless operator STET Hellas (now WIND Hellas to Telecom Italia Mobile (later a part of Telecom Italia); its stake in Telecom New Zealand to investment firms; and its nearly 25% stake in Czech mobile operator Eurotel Praha owned jointly with AT&T Wireless to Cesky Telecom for $1.05 billion.

Also in 2002 Verizon completed the sale of access lines in Alabama and Missouri to CenturyLink as well as additional lines in Kentucky to ALLTEL in deals valued at just over $4 billion. The next year Verizon sold its 39% stake in troubled Mexican wireless operator Grupo Iusacell to paging company Movil@ccess in a deal valued at $7.4 million. Also in 2003 the company sold its nearly 25% stake in Eurotel Praha the wireless services provider in the Czech Republic and its stake in Argentinean wireless operator CTI Holdings. Verizon also sold its European directory businesses in 2003 and the next year it sold its Canadian directories business called SuperPages Canada to Bain Capital in a deal valued at $1.54 billion. The company used the proceeds from the sale of the Canadian asset to pay off debt and make investments in new technology

The company sold its wireline business in Hawaii to The Carlyle Group in a 2005 deal valued at $1.7 billion. Also that year Verizon made an initial $6.5 billion offer to acquire independent long-distance carrier MCI. The company made a revised $7.6 billion offer to counter a bid from rival Qwest Communications. Verizon ultimately won the bidding war and paid nearly $8.5 billion for MCI in early 2006.

The acquisition created Verizon Business which combined the large business and government services of MCI with related services at Verizon that were formerly part of its Domestic Telecom unit. The deal enabled Verizon to expand its broadband data services but led to about 7000 job cuts at the combined company.

Verizon (once a leading publisher of both print and electronic directories in North America Europe and Latin America) spun off its remaining directories publishing business to its shareholders in an IPO in 2006 creating a company called Idearc (later renamed SuperMedia). Also that year Verizon sold its Caribbean region and Latin American operations to various companies controlled by Mexican entrepreneur Carlos Slim Helu in three separate deals valued at a combined $3.7 billion.

To cut costs related to its declining landline business the company laid off thousands of workers from that segment during 2009. The move saved the company money in the long run but ate away at profits for the year due to the related expenses despite a 10% increase in sales.

Verizon bought smaller rival Rural Cellular Corporation that year for about $2.6 billion increasing the company's wireless subscriber base by about 650000. Meanwhile the company divested some of its non-core subsidiaries that year including its Airfone business (which installed telephones in the back of US commercial airplane seats in the US) which was sold to JetBlue Airways and its South African enterprise services operations which were sold to MTN Group.

To build up its wireless business the company paid $28.1 billion to buy rival Alltel that year in a deal that added about 13 million subscribers to Verizon's books and created the largest cellular provider in the US in terms of sales and subscribers. It also boosted the company's retail presence with the addition of 750 Alltel-branded distribution points.

In order to meet regulatory approval for the acquisition Verizon was compelled by the Federal Trade Commission to sell assets in 22 states where its operations overlapped with Alltel's. Buyers included AT&T which paid $2.3 billion for assets that included 1.6 million lines in 18 states and Atlantic Tele-Network which picked up former Alltel operations in six mainly southern and midwestern states. The largest transaction however was with Frontier Communications which paid $8.6 billion in cash and stock in mid-2010 for wireline assets spun off by Verizon that included about 4 million phone and broadband Internet subscribers in 14 states. The stock portion of the deal amounted to about two-thirds of Frontier's shares.

EXECUTIVES

EVP Public Affairs Policy and Communications, Thomas J. (Tom) Tauke, age 61
Chairman and CEO, Lowell C. McAdam, age 58, $825,000 total compensation
EVP, Richard Lynch, age 64
EVP and CIO, Roger Gurnani, age 51
EVP and Chief Administrative Officer, Marc C. Reed, age 53
EVP; President and CEO Verizon Wireless Joint Venture, Daniel S. (Dan) Mead, age 59
EVP; President Verizon Enterprise, John G. Stratton, age 51
EVP Strategy Development and Planning, John W. Diercksen, age 62, $497,462 total compensation
Manager Investor Relations, John D. Adams
Manager Investor Relations, Bonnie S. Palmieri
Executive Director Investor Relations and Shareowner Services, Kevin R. Tarrant
President nPhase, Steve Pazol
EVP and CFO, Francis J. (Fran) Shammo, age 51
VP Talent Management and Diversity, Magda Yrizarry
EVP; President Verizon Services Operations, Virginia P. Ruesterholz, age 50
President Consumer and Mass Business Markets, W. Robert (Bob) Mudge, age 52
SVP and Controller, Robert J. (Bob) Barish, age 50
President Southeast Region, Michelle A. Robinson
EVP and General Counsel, Randal S. (Randy) Milch, age 53
President Global Enterprise and Verizon Business, Robert A. (Bob) Toohey
Staff Manager Shareowner Services, Bianca G. Nebab
Manager Shareowner Services, Donald A. (Don) Weber
Specialist Shareowner Services, Mark L. Gereb
Executive Director Media Relations, Robert (Bob) Varettoni
EVP and CTO, Anthony J. (Tony) Melone Sr., age 51
President Global Wholesale, Michael H. Millegan
Group President Worldwide Sales and Consulting Services Verizon Business, D. Blair Crump
CEO Terremark Worldwide, Kerry Bailey
SVP and Treasurer, Holyce Hess (Holly) Groos
President Verizon Foundation, Rose M. Kirk
SVP Investor Relations, John Doherty
SVP Deputy General Counsel and Corporate Secretary, William L. Horton Jr.
VP Network Operations Verizon Wireless, Nicola Palmer
SVP Internal Auditing, Shane A. Sanders
Executive Director Investor Relations, Nancy Gudino
Manager Investor Relations, James D. (Jim) Peshek
Manager Investor Relations, Danielle S. Kloeblen
Chief Communications Officer, Peter W. Thonis
Manager Media Relations Corporate Issues, Ray McConville
Manager Media Relations Labor Issues, Rich Young
Director External Communications Legislative and Regulatory Issues, Ed McFadden
Manager Media Relations Verizon Foundation and Literacy Programs, Brian C. Malina
Director Industry Analyst Relations, Les Kumagai
Director, Robert W. (Bob) Lane, age 62
Director, Joseph (Joe) Neubauer, age 70
Director, Clarence Otis Jr., age 56
Director, Richard L. Carrion, age 59
Director, Hugh B. Price, age 70
Director, Donald T. (Don) Nicolaisen, age 67
Director, M. Frances (Fran) Keeth, age 65
Director, John W. Snow, age 72
Director, Rodney E. Slater, age 57
Auditors: Ernst&YoungLLP

LOCATIONS

HQ: Verizon Communications Inc.
140 West St., New York NY 10007
Phone: 212-395-1000 **Fax:** 317-575-9401
Web: www.bellind.com

PRODUCTS/OPERATIONS

2011 Sales

	$ mil.	% of total
Domestic wireless		
Service	59,157	53
Equipment & other	10,997	10
Wireline		
Mass markets		
FiOS	8,332	8
Other	8,005	7
Global enterprise	15,622	14
Global wholesale	7,973	7
Other	750	1
Other	39	-
Total	**110,875**	**100**

Selected Acquisitions

CloudSwitch (2011 cloud computing software)
Terremark Worldwide (2011 IT infrastructure services)
Alltel (2009 wireless telecommunications services)
Rural Cellular (2009 wireless telecommunications)
Cybertrust (2007 data security services)

COMPETITORS

360networks
AT&T
CenturyLink
Charter Communications
Comcast
Cox Communications
Leap Wireless
Level 3 Communications
MetroPCS
Sprint Nextel
T-Mobile USA
Time Warner Cable
tw telecom
U.S. Cellular
XO Holdings
Yellowbook

HISTORICAL FINANCIALS

Company Type: Public

Income Statement FYE: December 31

	REVENUE ($ mil.)	NET INCOME ($ mil.)	NET PROFIT MARGIN	EMPLOYEES
12/11	110,875	2,404	2.2%	193,900
12/10	106,565	2,549	2.4%	194,400
12/09	107,808	3,651	3.4%	222,900
12/08	97,354	6,428	6.6%	223,900
12/07	93,469	5,521	5.9%	235,000
Annual Growth	4.4%	(18.8%)	—	(4.7%)

2011 Year-End Financials

Debt ratio: 23.93%—
Return on equity: 6.68%
Cash ($ mil.): 13,362
Current ratio: 100.58
Long-term debt ($ mil.): 50,303
Dividends
Yield: —
Payout: 230.88%
Market value ($ mil.): —

	STOCK PRICE ($) FY Close	P/E High/Low		PER SHARE ($) Earnings	Dividends	Book Value
12/11	40.12	47	39	0.85	0.00	12.69
12/10	35.78	40	29	0.90	1.91	13.64
12/09	33.13	27	20	1.29	1.86	14.67
12/08	33.90	19	11	2.26	1.75	14.68
12/07	43.69	24	19	1.90	1.65	17.58
Annual Growth	(2.1%)	—	—	(18.2%)	—	(7.8%)

VF Corp.

V.F. Corporation is the name behind the label. Among the world's top jeans makers it owns a bevy of denim brands: Lee Riders Rustler Wrangler and Rock & Republic. Other holdings include JanSport and Eastpak (backpacks) North Face and Eagle Creek (outdoor gear) Red Kap and Bulwark (work clothes) Nautica (sportswear) lucy (women's athletic apparel) 7 For All Mankind (premium denim casual wear) and Vans (footwear). V.F.'s Majestic label offers licensed MLB NFL and NBA apparel. Direct sales to consumers are rung up through Internet sites and more than 1050 VF-operated retail stores worldwide. Some 80% of V.F. products are sold through department and specialty stores mass merchants and discounters.

HISTORY

In 1899 six partners including banker John Barbey started the Reading Glove and Mitten Manufacturing Company. Barbey bought out his five partners in 1911 and changed the name of the Reading Pennsylvania company to Schuylkill Silk Mills in 1913. Barbey expanded the mills' production to include underwear and changed the mills' name to Vanity Fair Silk Mills (after a contest with a $25 prize in 1919).

Barbey (who banned the word "underwear") and his son J. E. led their lingerie company to national prominence. The mills made only silk garments until the 1920s when synthetics were developed. In response to the US embargo on silk in 1941 Vanity Fair changed to rayon finally converting to the new wonder fabric nylon tricot in 1948. Vanity Fair was then manufacturing all stages of its nylon products from filament to finished garment. It won awards for its innovative advertising with photographs of live models in Vanity Fair lingerie.

J. E. owned all of Vanity Fair's stock until 1951 when he sold one-third of his holdings to the public. In 1966 the stock previously traded over the counter was listed on the NYSE.

The company used acquisitions to expand its lingerie business and to begin producing sportswear and blue jeans. It bought Berkshire International (hosiery 1969) and H.D. Lee (jeans 1969). To better reflect its diverse offerings the company changed its name to V.F. Corporation that year.

V.F. doubled in size in 1986 by purchasing Blue Bell a North Carolina maker of branded apparel by Wrangler Rustler Jantzen Jansport and Red Kap. It then added the Vassarette brand name from Munsingwear (1990) and Healthtex (infants' and children's apparel 1991). In 1992 V.F. acquired European lingerie brands Lou Bolero Intimate Cherry and Variance.

The company bought sports apparel makers Nutmeg Industries and H.H. Cutler in 1994. The next year it cut costs by laying off 7800 workers closing 14 plants and moving production operations to Mexico and the Caribbean. Also in 1995 V.F. began licensing swimwear and sportswear from NIKE.

Mackey McDonald became CEO in 1996. He moved the company to consolidate its 17 operating divisions into five units in 1997 (a sixth was added later). Also that year V.F. bought Brittania Sportswear from Levi Strauss. In 1998 it moved from Pennsylvania to North Carolina closer to the company's production facilities. The firm also acquired Bestform Intimates (Lily of France) in 1998.

V.F. acquired Bulwark Protective Apparel (flame-resistant apparel 1996) Penn State textiles (kitchen and hospitality apparel 1998) Fibrotek (clean room apparel 1999) Horace Small (public safety and postal apparel 1999) and American Household's Eastpak (backpacks 2000). Later it purchased the Chic and H.I.S. jeans names from Chic by H.I.S. Gitano jeanswear brand from bankrupt Fruit of the Loom and troubled outdoor apparel retailer The North Face.

In 2000 V.F. combined its workwear and knitwear units and took action to exit certain underperforming businesses including Fibrotek and its private-label knitwear group. It cut its global workforce by 18% in November 2001 and in March 2002 the company completed its sale of swimwear unit Jantzen to Perry Ellis International. Adding to its rash of large-scale acquisitions in 2003 V.F. entered into an agreement to acquire sportswear maker Nautica Enterprises; the deal was intended to enable Nautica to focus on strengthening its menswear line. V.F. also acquired David Chu and Company's rights to 50% of royalty from licensing the Nautica trademark and placed Chu at the helm of Nautica. With the sizable acquisition came the restructuring of the company to include a Sportswear Coalition that includes the Nautica Earl Jean John Varvatos and E. Magrath brands.

In 2004 V.F. acquired Green Sport Monte Bianco S.p.A and footwear maker Vans (at a price of about $400 million).

The company sold its Earl Jean brand to Jordache Enterprises and an investor group in 2006. Continuing its divestment of noncore brands in April 2007 V.F. sold its intimates apparel business to Fruit of the Loom for about $350 million. The deal involved US brands (Vanity Fair Lily of France Vassarette Bestform Curvation) as well as those in Europe (Lou Gemma Belcor). Also that year V.F. sold its H.I.S. brand of women's casual apparel and denim marketed primarily in Germany for $11 million.

In August 2007 V.F. completed two acquisitions: Lucy Activewear (for $110 million) which operates some 50 stores in about a dozen states and lucy.com and premium denim firm Seven For All Mankind (for $775 million).

V.F. saw its leadership change in January 2008 when Mackey McDonald stepped down as CEO. (McDonald stayed on as the company's chairman.) He was replaced by Eric Wiseman who'd served as president and COO.

Also in 2008 VF bought out its former partner in a joint venture that marketed Lee products in Spain and Portugal. It paid $25 million for the 50% stake.

In July 2009 V.F. formed a Licensed Brands group which completed its first acquisition –the trademarks and intellectual property of Rock and Republic Enterprises –for about $57 million out of bankruptct in March 2011.

EXECUTIVES

VP Human Resources, Susan L. Williams
VP Administration General Counsel and Secretary, Candace S. Cummings, age 64, $527,169 total compensation
VP and Treasurer, Frank C. Pickard III, age 67
SVP and CFO, Robert K. (Bob) Shearer, age 60, $659,977 total compensation
VP; Group President Outdoor & Action Sports Americas, Steve Rendle, age 52
Chairman President and CEO, Eric C. Wiseman, age 56, $1,036,539 total compensation
VP; Group President International, Karl Heinz Salzburger, age 54, $794,808 total compensation
President Contemporary Brands Coalition, Susan Kellogg
VP; Group President Jeanswear Americas and Imagewear, Scott Baxter, age 47
VP VF Direct/Customer Teams, Michael T. (Mike) Gannaway, age 60, $457,808 total compensation
VP; President Supply Chain, Boyd Rogers, age 62, $412,000 total compensation
VP Controller and Chief Accounting Officer, Bradley W. (Brad) Batten, age 56
VP Mergers and Acquisitions, Franklin L. (Frank) Terkelsen
VP Strategy and Innovation, Stephen F. Dull
VP and CIO, Martin Schneider
President 7 For All Mankind, Barry Miguel
Director, Ursula O. Fairbairn, age 68
Director, W. Alan McCollough, age 62
Director, Raymond G. Viault, age 67
Director, Juan Ernesto de Bedout, age 67
Director, Robert J. (Bob) Hurst Jr., age 66
Director, Clarence Otis Jr., age 56
Director, George Fellows, age 69
Director, M. Rust Sharp, age 71
Director, Charles V. (Chip) Bergh, age 55
Director, Richard T. (Rick) Carucci, age 55
Director, Juliana L. Chugg, age 44
Auditors: PricewaterhouseCoopersLLP

LOCATIONS

HQ: V.F. Corporation
105 Corporate Center Blvd., Greensboro NC 27408
Phone: 336-424-6000 **Fax:** 336-424-7631
Web: www.vfc.com

2011 Sales

	$ mil.	% of total
US	6,220	66
Foreign primarily Europe	3,238	34
Total	**9,459**	**100**

PRODUCTS/OPERATIONS

2011 Sales

	$ mil.	% of total
Outdoor & action sports	4,562	48
Jeanswear	2,731	29
Imagewear	1,025	11
Sportswear	543	6
Contemporary brands	485	5
Other	111	1
Total	**9,459**	**100**

2011 Sales

	$ mil.	% of total
Net sales	9,365	99
Royalty income	93	1
Total	**9,459**	**100**

Selected Brands

Contemporary brands
- 7 For All Mankind
- Ella Moss
- Splendid

Imagewear
- Bulwark
- Chef Designs
- Horace Small
- Majestic
- Red Kap

Jeanswear
- Lee
- Riders
- Rock & Republic
- Rustler
- Timber Creek by Wrangler
- Wrangler

Sportswear
- Kipling
- Nautica

Outdoor and action sports
- Eagle Creek
- Eastpak
- JanSport
- Kipling
- lucy
- Napapijri
- Reef
- SmartWool
- The North Face
- Timberland
- Vans

Selected Licenses

Harley-Davidson Motor Company
Major League Baseball
MLB Players Association
National Basketball Association
National Football League
National Hockey League

Selected major colleges and universities

COMPETITORS

Abercrombie & Fitch
American Eagle Outfitters
Calvin Klein
Columbia Sportswear
Diesel SpA
Fifth & Pacific
Guess?
J. C. Penney
Joe' s Jeans
Johnson Outdoors
Kellwood
Koos Manufacturing
L.L. Bean
Levi Strauss
Limited Brands
OshKosh B' Gosh
Patagonia Inc.
Reebok
REI
Rocky Brands
Russell Brands
Sears Holdings
The Gap
Timberland
Tommy Hilfiger
True Religion Apparel
Wet Seal
Williamson-Dickie Manufacturing

HISTORICAL FINANCIALS

Company Type: Public

Income Statement FYE: December 31

	REVENUE ($ mil.)	NET INCOME ($ mil.)	NET PROFIT MARGIN	EMPLOYEES
12/11	9,459	888	9.4%	58,000
12/10*	7,702	571	7.4%	47,000
01/10	7,220	461	6.4%	45,700
01/09	7,642	602	7.9%	46,600
12/07	7,219	591	8.2%	54,200
Annual Growth	7.0%	10.7%	—	1.7%

*Fiscal year change

2011 Year-End Financials

Debt ratio: 22.72%
Return on equity: 19.62%
Cash ($ mil.): 341
Current ratio: 191.35
Long-term debt ($ mil.): 1,831
No. of shares (mil.): 110
Dividends
Yield: —
Payout: 32.71%
Market value ($ mil.): 14,040

	STOCK PRICE ($) FY Close	P/E High	P/E Low	PER SHARE ($) Earnings	Dividends	Book Value
12/11	126.99	17	10	7.98	0.00	40.94
12/10*	86.18	17	13	5.18	2.43	35.77
01/10	73.24	19	11	4.13	0.00	34.59
01/09	56.87	15	7	5.42	0.00	32.37
12/07	70.22	18	13	5.22	0.00	32.58
Annual Growth	16.0%	—	—	11.2%	—	5.9%

*Fiscal year change

Viacom Inc

Viacom might not be a household name but its famous entertainment brands are welcomed into most living rooms on a daily basis. The company is a leading media conglomerate with an extensive portfolio of cable TV and film production assets. Its MTV Networks unit runs such cable networks as Comedy Central Nickelodeon and the family of MTV channels (MTV MTV2 VH1). Viacom also owns Black Entertainment Television which airs programming on BET BET Gospel and BET Hip Hop. In the film business Viacom operates through Paramount Pictures which includes imprints Paramount Pictures and Paramount Vantage. Chairman Sumner Redstone controls a majority of Viacom through his National Amusements movie theater chain.

Operations

Flagship channel MTV focuses on younger viewers and popular culture and continues to draw one of the largest television audiences in the 18-34 age group. Nickelodeon meanwhile has become a popular destination for children's programming. Comedy Central appeals to young adults with programs such as as The Daily Show with Jon Stewart and its offshoot The Colbert Report while BET dominates the important urban demographic with entertainment music and special interest programming.

The company's filmed entertainment division meanwhile is responsbile for hits such as the big budget Transformers movie. Its sequel Transformers: Revenge of the Fallen (co-produced with DreamWorks) took in more than $300 million in its first 14 days of release in 2009. The blockbuster performance followed on the heels of Paramount's latest Star Trek adventure which opened with more than $75 million at the box office.

Viacom also expanded its holdings in cable programming with a new pay-TV channel called EPIX. The network a partnership with movie studios MGM and Lions Gate debuted in 2009 and offers an online subscription movie service along with its traditional cable and satellite channel. The partners hope the new channel will offer a larger slice of revenue for their movies than distributing them through such rivals as HBO (owned by Time Warner) and Showtime (CBS Corporation).

Strategy

Viacom does not have the broad complement of media assets that characterize integrated conglomerates such as Time Warner and Walt Disney but the company still realizes some potential by integrating its TV and film businesses such as through DVD sales and cross-promotion.

The company is primarily focused on its television operations which account for about 60% of sales. Generating most of their revenue from a combination of commercial advertising and carriage fees paid by cable system operators the TV networks provide a steady anchor for the the company balancing against the uneven feature film business and the sometimes fickle tastes of movie goers.

What particularly drives Viacom's business is its success in building entertainment brands. The company is notable for creating and promoting such names as MTV and Nickelodeon into easily recognizable banners that stand for a particular form of entertainment.

Viacom has been looking to expand its reach into digital media in an effort to reach its young and increasingly online target audience. However the company announced plans to sell video game developer Harmonix Music Systems in 2010 after lagging sales of the popular Rock Band video game began to hurt the company's bottom line.

EXECUTIVES

Chairman and CEO BET Networks, Debra L. Lee, age 57
EVP General Counsel and Secretary, Michael D. Fricklas, age 52, $1,050,000 total compensation
EVP Corporate Communications, Carl D. Folta, age 54
Senior EVP COO and Director, Thomas E. (Tom) Dooley, age 55, $2,000,000 total compensation
President CEO and Director, Philippe P. Dauman, age 58, $2,500,000 total compensation
Chairman, Sumner M. Redstone, age 88, $1,250,000 total compensation
Vice Chairman, Shari E. Redstone, age 58
Chairman and CEO Paramount Pictures Corporation, Brad Grey
EVP and CFO, James W. (Jimmy) Barge, age 57
SVP Investor Relations, James Bombassei
President and CEO International Media Networks, Robert M. (Bob) Bakish, age 48, $931,731 total compensation
EVP Government Affairs, Doretha F. (DeDe) Lea, age 47

CFO and EVP Strategy & Corporate Development, Wade Davis, age 40
EVP Human Resources and Administration, Denise White, age 58, $825,000 total compensation
Senior Vice President; Chief Accounting Officer; Controller, Katherine Charest
Senior EVP COO and Director, Thomas E. (Tom) Dooley, age 55
President CEO and Director, Philippe P. Dauman, age 58
Director, William Schwartz, age 78
Vice Chairman, Shari E. Redstone, age 58
Director, Robert K. Kraft, age 70
Director, Frederic V. (Fred) Salerno, age 68
Director, George S. Abrams, age 80
Director, Blythe J. McGarvie, age 56
Director, Alan C. (Ace) Greenberg, age 84
Director, Charles E. (Chuck) Phillips Jr., age 52
Auditors: PricewaterhouseCoopersLLP

LOCATIONS

HQ: Viacom Inc.
1515 Broadway, New York NY 10036
Phone: 212-258-6000 **Fax:** 212-258-6464
Web: www.viacom.com

PRODUCTS/OPERATIONS

COMPETITORS

Discovery Communications
Disney
Lionsgate
MGM
NBCUniversal
Sony Pictures Entertainment
Time Warner

HISTORICAL FINANCIALS

Company Type: Public

Income Statement FYE: September 30

	REVENUE ($ mil.)	NET INCOME ($ mil.)	NET PROFIT MARGIN	EMPLOYEES
09/12	13,887	1,981	14.3%	10,620
09/11	14,914	2,136	14.3%	10,580
09/10*	9,337	854	9.1%	10,900
12/09	13,619	1,611	11.8%	11,200
12/08	14,625	1,251	8.6%	11,500
Annual Growth	(1.3%)	12.2%	—	(2.0%)

*Fiscal year change

2012 Year-End Financials

Debt ratio: 36.62%
Return on equity: 26.60%
Cash ($ mil.): 848
Current ratio: 126.71
Long-term debt ($ mil.): 8,131
No. of shares (mil.): 507
Dividends
Yield: —
Payout: 28.46%
Market value ($ mil.): 27,170

	STOCK PRICE ($) FY Close	P/E High/Low		PER SHARE ($) Earnings	Dividends	Book Value
09/12	53.59	15	10	3.69	0.00	14.69
09/11	38.74	14	10	3.59	0.80	15.48
09/10*	36.19	26	20	1.40	0.30	15.26
12/09	29.73	12	5	2.65	0.00	14.33
12/08	19.06	22	6	2.00	0.00	11.59
Annual Growth	29.5%	—	—	16.5%	—	6.1%

*Fiscal year change

Virgin Media Inc

Virgin Media is no novice when it comes to keeping Britons connected. Through its subsidiaries in the UK the company is a "quadruple-play" communications services provider offering cable TV Internet fixed-line voice and mobile services to consumers and businesses. One of the largest telecom companies in the UK its Virgin Phone unit trails only BT in total landline subscribers. It serves more than 3 million wireless subscribers through its Virgin Mobile arm; 4 million customers use Virgin Broadband Internet service; digital cable telephony customers number about 4 million; and almost 5 million homes subscribe to its cable TV service which uses TiVo brand digital video recorders (DVRs).

In addition its Virgin Media Business offers voice data and Internet service (ranging from analog phone lines to managed data networks) to businesses public sector organizations and service providers in the UK. The segment counts about 60000 businesses and almost 250 local councils as customers. It also supplies communications services to around three-quarters of the UK's health and emergency services providers and nearly half of its police forces. Virgin Media Business accounts for about 15% of overall sales.

More than 60% of the company's residential customers are "triple-play"–receiving cable Internet and fixed- line telephone service. About 12% are "quadruple-play" customers that also use Virgin Phone. In the pay TV space the company has faced off against leading satellite broadcaster British Sky Broadcasting (BSkyB) which is the exclusive supplier of some programming including its Sky Sports channels and Sky Movies channels. Virgin Media has to buy premium programming and pay-per-view sporting events from BSkyB; however regulatory authorities recently ruled that BSkyB must lower its rates for its top two premium sports channels.

It costs a lot of money to build out communications networks and Virgin Media has an accumulated deficit of more than $3 billion. Looking for ways to pay down its debt the company sold its businesses that produce television content and own television stations. In October 2011 Virgin Media sold its 50% stake in UKTV a television programming joint venture with BBC Worldwide to US-based cable network operator Scripps Networks Interactive in a deal worth about #340 million ($550 million). UKTV operates 10 channels including G.O.L.D. Yesterday Eden Alibi Blighty Good Food and Dave. The year before it sold its Virgin Media TV unit (now Living TV Group) to BSkyB for about #105 million ($160 million). The channels sold included LIVING LIVINGit Challenge Challenge Jackpot Bravo Bravo 2 Virgin1 and related websites.

HISTORY

In 2006 Telewest Group (formerly Telewest Communications) acquired NTL in a deal worth about $6 billion; the combined business took the NTL name and reduced its workforce by 6000 employees. NTL added mobile phone service that year with the acquisition of Virgin Mobile Holdings making it the first "quadruple-play" carrier in the UK. The combined company was renamed Virgin Media in 2007.

Layoffs continued during 2008 and 2009 as Virgin Media attempted to simplify its organizational structure and bring down costs. In 2009 it continued to integrate the operations of its predecessor companies.

The company secured a listing on the London Stock Exchange in that year in addition to its NASDAQ listing. Virgin Media said that the secondary listing was intended to raise awareness of its business in the UK and Europe and encourage increased investment in the company.

EXECUTIVES

Chairman, James F. (Jim) Mooney, age 57, $1,250,000 total compensation
COO, Andrew Barron, age 46, $516,549 total compensation
Director Investor Relations, Richard Williams
Executive Director Brand and Marketing, Ashley Stockwell
CFO and Director, Eamonn O'Hare, age 48, $154,388 total compensation
CIO, Martin Wyke
VP and Controller, Robert C. Gale, age 52, $309,594 total compensation
Chief Marketing Officer, Nigel Gilbert
Executive Director Television, Cindy Rose
CEO and Director, Neil A. Berkett, age 56, $860,915 total compensation
Chief Commercial Officer, Mark Schweitzer, age 52, $650,480 total compensation
Chief People Officer, Elisa Nardi
Executive Director Corporate Affairs, Paul Richmond
Senior Public Relations Manager Regional Media, Rebecca Burke
Head Commercial and Strategy TV, Asanga Gunatillaka
Head Product TV, Nick Hopkins
Chief Customer Technology and Networks Officer, Paul Buttery, age 48
Manager Investor Relations, Vani Bassi
Head Media Relations National Consumer Media, Asam Ahmad
Head Media Relations National Business Media, Gareth Mead
Manager Corporate Affairs National Business Media, Emma Hutchinson
Head Music, Richard Wheeler
Executive Director Broadband, Jon James
Director Treasury, Rick Martin
Director On Demand Television Services and Strategy, Aleks Habdank
General Counsel and Company Secretary, Scott Dresser
Director Mobile, Jamie Heywood
Director, George R. Zoffinger, age 63
Director, William R. Huff, age 62
Director, Charles L. Allen, age 55
Director, James A. (Jim) Chiddix, age 67
CFO and Director, Eamonn O'Hare, age 48
CEO and Director, Neil A. Berkett, age 56
Director, Gordon D. McCallum, age 52
Director, Andrew J. Cole, age 45
Director, John N. Rigsby, age 65
Director, Steven J. Simmons, age 65
Auditors: Ernst&YoungLLP

LOCATIONS

HQ: Virgin Media Inc.
65 Bleecker St. 6th Fl., New York NY 10012
Phone: 212-906-8440 **Fax:** 212-752-1157
Web: www.virginmedia.com

PRODUCTS/OPERATIONS

2011 Sales

	% of total
Consumer	84
Business	16
Total	**100**

Selected Services

Cable Segment
- Business phone services
- Cable TV
- Enterprise data network services
- Internet access broadband and dial-up
- Managed Internet services
- Residential phone services
- Video-on-demand

Mobile
- Prepaid wireless services
- Contract wireless services

Content Segment
- Interactive auction-based TV channels
  - bid TV
  - price-drop TV
  - speed auction TV

COMPETITORS

BBC
BSkyB
BT
Cable & Wireless
Everything Everywhere
Freeview
Hutchison 3G UK Limited
ITV
Orange
T-Mobile (UK)
TalkTalk
Vodafone

HISTORICAL FINANCIALS

Company Type: Public

Income Statement FYE: December 31

	REVENUE ($ mil.)	NET INCOME ($ mil.)	NET PROFIT MARGIN	EMPLOYEES
12/11	6,166	117	1.9%	12,689
12/10	6,017	(219)	—	12,400
12/09	6,161	(579)	—	12,107
12/08	5,852	(1,331)	—	14,609
12/07	8,161	(928)	—	15,060
Annual Growth	(6.8%)	—	—	(4.2%)

2011 Year-End Financials

Debt ratio: 113.94%
Return on equity: 18.35%
Cash ($ mil.): 464
Current ratio: 66.07
Long-term debt ($ mil.): 8,926
No. of shares (mil.): 286
Dividends
Yield: —
Payout: 107.19%
Market value ($ mil.): 6,130

	STOCK PRICE ($) FY Close	P/E High/Low	PER SHARE ($) Earnings	Dividends	Book Value
12/11	21.38	347206	0.37	0.00	3.44
12/10	27.24	— —	(0.67)	0.16	6.10
12/09	16.83	— —	(1.77)	0.16	7.33
12/08	4.99	— —	(4.07)	0.16	8.34
12/07	17.14	— —	(2.85)	0.13	17.19
Annual Growth	5.7%	— —	—	—	(33.1%)

Virginia Commerce Bancorp, Inc.

Virginia Commerce Bancorp is the holding company for Virginia Commerce Bank which has about 30 offices serving metropolitan Washington DC's northern Virginia suburbs. The bank's customer base includes consumers not-for-profit groups and small to midsized businesses particularly those that have contracts with the US government. The bank also offers wealth management services such as retirement planning asset management and investments such as mutual funds. Virginia Commerce primarily originates real estate loans including mortgages and construction loans which account for nearly 90% of its portfolio.

Although real estate loans were big money makers for the bank before the recession the downturn caused Virginia Commerce Bancorp to struggle under the weight of nonperforming loans in 2009. That year the company recorded a net loss of $33 million. Despite the challenges the bank remained focused on boosting deposits and increasing prudent lending. It even opened a new branch in 2010. By that year the company had improved profits and made a dent in those problem loans.

Virginia Commerce Bancorp strengthened its capital base by more than $95 million in 2010 through a direct investment by the bank's board of directors and members of the executive management team. Moving forward the company is looking to diversifying its loan portfolio and expand banking services especially in its wealth management division.

Earnings slipped again in 2011 despite a lower provision for loan losses. The lower numbers were primarily due to decreased interest and fees on loans which fell 5%. That year the company reported $149.9 million in overall revenues a 2% decline from the year before. However net income rose 26% to $27.1 million. Helping Virginia Commerce's bottom line was an increase in noninterest income such as investment services commissions; the company also increasingly invested in short-term securities to boost its interest income.

EXECUTIVES

Treasurer and CFO; EVP and CFO Virginia Commerce Bank, William K. Beauchesne, age 55, $190,550 total compensation

EVP Human Resources Virginia Commerce Bank, Patricia M. Ostrander, age 45, $110,000 total compensation

President CEO and Director; President and CEO Virginia Commerce Bank, Peter A. Converse, age 61, $381,000 total compensation

Chairman, W. Douglas Fisher, age 74

Vice Chairman, David M. Guernsey, age 63

EVP and Chief Lending Officer Virginia Commerce Bank, Richard B. Anderson Jr., age 57, $231,750 total compensation

SVP Commercial Lending Virginia Commerce Bank, Gregory M. Motheral

Secretary and Director, Robert H. L'Hommedieu, age 85

Vice Chairman, Arthur L. Walters, age 92

SVP Commercial Lending Virginia Commerce Bank, Timothy M. Aldinger

SVP Commercial Lending Virginia Commerce Bank, George L. Greco

SVP Construction Lending Virginia Commerce Bank, James R. Nalls

SVP Residential Mortgage Lending Virginia Commerce Bank, Kenneth L. (Ken) O'Shea

SVP Construction Lending Virginia Commerce Bank, Thomas E. Williams

VP Human Resources Virginia Commerce Bank, Linda M. Fourney

SVP Commercial Lending Virginia Commerce Bank, David K. Stephens

SVP Government Contract Lending Virginia Commerce Bank, Jeffrey H. Satterly

VP Construction Lending Virginia Commerce Bank, Brian Murphy

SVP Loan Administration, Eleanor E. (Rusty) Golden

EVP Retail Banking Virginia Commerce Bank, Steven A. (Steve) Reeder, age 45, $160,000 total compensation

SVP Retail Banking Virginia Commerce Bank, Linda K. Martin

SVP Retail Banking Virginia Commerce Bank, Kelly J. Bell

SVP Community Banking Virginia Commerce Bank, Jo Ann Bell

SVP Marketing and Retail Administration Virginia Commerce Bank, Robin P. Coracci

VP Commercial Lending Virginia Commerce Bank, Kevin D. Albrigo

Construction Lending Operations Officer Virginia Commerce Bank, Lisa K. Bluntzer

VP Investment Services Virginia Commerce Bank, Michael F. (Mike) Bolen

SVP Residential Mortgage Lending Virginia Commerce Bank, Marsha A. Bradshaw

SVP Community Banking Virginia Commerce Bank, Christopher R. Broad

SVP Compliance and BSA Virginia Commerce Bank, Wendy M. Clark

SVP Retail Banking Virginia Commerce Bank, Lisa A. D'Ambrosio-Irons

SVP Security and Retail Operations Virginia Commerce Bank, Wendy M. Dunham

SVP Commercial Lending Virginia Commerce Bank, James C. Elliott

SVP Internal Audit Virginia Commerce Bank, Mark T. Friedman

VP Project Management Virginia Commerce Bank, Lynn B. Gonzalez

VP Information Technology Virginia Commerce Bank, James D. Holter

VP Clarendon Branch Virginia Commerce Bank, Nancy Hong

VP Accounting Virginia Commerce Bank, Marcia J. Hopkins

SVP Commercial Lending Virginia Commerce Bank, Edward M. (Ted) Johnson

SVP Facilities Virginia Commerce Bank, Susan T. Johnson

SVP Retail Banking Virginia Commerce Bank, Robert L. McCoy

SVP Community Banking Virginia Commerce Bank, Byron K. Schulze

VP Community Banking Virginia Commerce Bank, Stacey L. Sim

SVP Deposit Operations Virginia Commerce Bank, Suzie G. Spannuth

VP Credit Aministration Virginia Commerce Bank, Dana A. Bomkamp

VP Consumer Lending Virginia Commerce Bank, Karen M. Clinton

VP Training Virginia Commerce Bank, Jacqueline A. Freeman

VP Commercial Lending Virginia Commerce Bank, Barry L. Huitema

VP Spring Hill Branch Virginia Commerce Bank, Stephanie D. Lykins

VP Residential Mortgage Lending Virginia Commerce Bank, Robert J. Naden

VP Battlefield Branch Virginia Commerce Bank, Amy M. Tanner
Assistant VP Loan Operations Virginia Commerce Bank, Linda L. Trout
VP Credit Administration Virginia Commerce Bank, Brandon M. Barg
Assistant VP King Street Branch Virginia Commerce Bank, Daniel E. Marks
VP Credit Administration Virginia Commerce Bank, Kathleen T. Ryan
VP Human Resources Virginia Commerce Bank, Patricia B. Smith
SVP Business Development and Sales Management Virginia Commerce Bank, Vicki J. Adams
SVP Credit Administration Virginia Commerce Bank, C. Evan Becker
SVP Commercial Lending Virginia Commerce Bank, Kevin A. Fastabend
SVP Commercial Lending Virginia Commerce Bank, Gregory L. Jay
SVP Commercial Lending Virginia Commerce Bank, Stephen R. Lomicka
SVP Construction Lending Virginia Commerce Bank, Thomas P. Loomis
SVP Information Technology and Project Management Virginia Commerce Bank, Sharon E. Moynihan
SVP Construction Lending Virginia Commerce Bank, Steven R. Ross
VP Leesburg Branch Virginia Commerce Bank, Leah M. Day
VP Cameron Station Branch Virginia Commerce Bank, Evelyn O. deLottinville
VP Mt. Vernon Branch Virginia Commerce Bank, Tamara L. Freeman
VP Commercial Lending Virginia Commerce Bank, Andrew C. Fuller
VP Finance Virginia Commerce Bank, Jennifer E. Manning
Vp Commercial Lending Virginia Commerce Bank, Mary Anne Martins
VP Community Banking Virginia Commerce Bank, John C. McManus Jr.
VP McLean Branch Virginia Commerce Bank, Tamara M. Mitchell
VP Commercial Lending Virginia Commerce Bank, Catherine A. Morris
VP Cash Management Virginia Commerce Bank, Deborah L. Moshides
VP Community Banking Virginia Commerce Bank, Kamara Napper-Ramsay
VP Loan Operations Virginia Commerce Bank, Teresa L. Peterson
VP Residential Mortgage Lending Virginia Commerce Bank, John J. Ragano
VP Newington Branch Virginia Commerce Bank, Sun Hee Waite
VP Merchant Bankcard Services Virginia Commerce Bank, Stephen A. Witt
VP Commercial Banking Virginia Commerce Bank, Paul T. Yeloushan
Assistant VP Del Ray Branch Virginia Commerce Bank, Keshaun R. Clark-Heflin
Assistant VP Internal Audit Virginia Commerce Bank, Lisa E. DeAngelis
Assistant VP Residential Mortgage Lending Virginia Commerce Bank, Teresa I. Fields
Assistant VP Project Management Virginia Commerce Bank, Elizabeth S. Fike
Assistant VP Courthouse Road Branch Virginia Commerce Bank, Kimberly Gideon
Assistant VP Deposit Operations Virginia Commerce Bank, Carol Hockensmith
Assistant VP Commercial Lending Virginia Commerce Bank, Deborah W. Hoover
Assistant VP Ryan Park Branch Virginia Commerce Bank, Charles A. Kapur
Assistant VP Fairfax Branch Virginia Commerce Bank, Amy W. Nocera
Assistant VP Centerville Branch Virginia Commerce Bank, Mansur A. Rahim
Assistant VP Internal Audit Virginia Commerce Bank, Mary E. Slayton
Assistant VP Vienna Branch Virginia Commerce Bank, Shahriar Tabib
Assistant VP Marketing Virginia Commerce Bank, J. Shannon Vega
Information Security Officer Virginia Commerce Bank, Jose M. Arvelo
Brand Officer Tysons Corner Branch Virginia Commerce Bank, Puneet Bhasin
Assistant BSA Officer Virginia Commerce Bank, Karen U. Bogan
Loan Administration Officer Virginia Commerce Bank, Kimberly M. Clay
Assistant to President. Virginia Commerce Bank, Lynda S. Cornell
Assistant Compliance Officer Virginia Commerce Bank, Caroline J. Foster
Loan Administration Officer Virginia Commerce Bank, Beverly C. Goins
Residential Mortgage Loan Officer Virginia Commerce Bank, Jeffrey W. Hall
Branch Officer Chantilly Branch Virginia Commerce Bank, Shamsul Islam
Residential Mortage Loan Officer Virginia Commerce Bank, Jeffery J. Jerge
Residential Mortgage Loan Officer Virginia Commerce Bank, Jean Keller
Cash Management Officer Virginia Commerce Bank, Selwyn M. Lovell
Credit Administration Officer Virginia Commerce Bank, Manisha Mahnot
Portfolio Administration Officer Virginia Commerce Bank, Monica C. Rodriquez
Branch Officer Williamsburg Boulevard Branch Virginia Commerce Bank, Sylvana F. Mascarenhas
Branch Officer Central Park Branch Virginia Commerce Bank, Matthew G. Mitchell
Branch Officer Reston Branch Virginia Commerce Bank, Nicholas D. Paradise
Residential Mortgage Loan Officer Virginia Commerce Bank, Lawrence E. Russ
Portfolio Administration Officer Virginia Commerce Bank, Wanda L. Satterfield
Portfolio Administration OfficerVirginia Commerce Bank, Cynthia B. Scialdo
Branch Officer Prince Street Branch Virginia Commerce Bank, Diane L. Webster
Branch Officer Walney Road Branch Virginia Commerce Bank, Jennifer L. Whitesides
Branch Officer Annandale Branch Virginia Commerce Bank, Soo J. Yeo
EVP and CFO, Mark S. Merrill
EVP and COO, Christopher Ewing
President CEO and Director; President and CEO Virginia Commerce Bank, Peter A. Converse, age 61
Vice Chairman, David M. Guernsey, age 63
Secretary and Director, Robert H. L'Hommedieu, age 85
Director, Leonard W. Alder, age 76
Director, Norris E. Mitchell, age 75
Vice Chairman, Arthur L. Walters, age 92
Director, Kenneth R. Lehman, age 53
Director, Todd A. Stottlemyer, age 48
Auditors: YountHyde&BarbourP.C.

LOCATIONS

HQ: Virginia Commerce Bancorp Inc.
5350 Lee Hwy., Arlington VA 22207
Phone: 703-534-0700 **Fax:** 703-534-1782
Web: www.vcbonline.com

PRODUCTS/OPERATIONS

2011 Sales

	$ mil.	% of total
Interest		
Loans including fees	126	83
Investment securities including dividends	14	10
Other	0	-
Noninterest		
Service charges & other fees	3	2
Fees & net gains on loans held for sale	2	2
Non-deposit investment services commissions	1	1
Other	3	2
Adjustments	(3.1)	-
Total	**150**	**100**

COMPETITORS

Bank of America
BB&T
Burke & Herbert Bank
Cardinal Financial
JPMorgan Chase
SunTrust
United Bankshares
Wells Fargo

HISTORICAL FINANCIALS

Company Type: Public

Income Statement FYE: December 31

	ASSETS ($ mil.)	NET INCOME ($ mil.)	INCOME AS % OF ASSETS	EMPLOYEES
12/11	2,938	27	0.9%	313
12/10	2,741	21	0.8%	299
12/09	2,725	(33)	—	288
12/08	2,715	13	0.5%	312
12/07	2,339	25	1.1%	299
Annual Growth	5.9%	1.2%	—	1.2%

2011 Year-End Financials

Debt ratio: 3.12%
Return on equity: 9.55%
Cash ($ mil.): 82
Current ratio: —
Long-term debt ($ mil.): 91
No. of shares (mil.): 30
Dividends
Yield: —
Payout: —
Market value ($ mil.): 234

	STOCK PRICE ($) FY Close	P/E High	P/E Low	PER SHARE ($) Earnings	Dividends	Book Value
12/11	7.73	11	7	0.71	0.00	9.38
12/10	6.18	13	6	0.57	0.00	8.48
12/09	3.75	—	—	(1.42)	0.00	8.18
12/08	5.17	26	7	0.47	0.00	9.53
12/07	11.73	22	11	0.95	0.00	6.40
Annual Growth	(9.9%)	—	—	(7.0%)	—	10.0%

Virginia Electric & Power Co.

Yes Virginia there is power in the Old Dominion thanks to Virginia Electric and Power. The company (which operates as Dominion Virginia Power and Dominion North Carolina Power) provides regulated electric delivery services to about 2.4 million homes and businesses. Power generation is derived by means of coal gas oil hydro and nuclear plants. The utility's power plants (with more than 27610 MW of generating capacity) are managed by the Dominion Generation unit of parent Dominion Resources. Control of Virginia Electric and Power's transmission facilities is maintained by PJM Interconnection. As well as serving its utility customers Virginia Electric and Power sells wholesale power to other users.

The company has been investing heavily in upgrading its infrastructure to meet growing demand. In 2007 Virginia Electric and Power announced plans to build new generating units and a high-voltage transmission line to serve the growing demand for electricity in the fast-growing Northern Virginia region. In 2009 it awarded Fluor with a contract to build a $619 million 580 MW gas-fired combined-cycle Bear Garden Station in Buckingham County Virginia. (The unit was completed in 2011.) In 2010 the company announced that it will add more than 400 MW of additional capacity by upgrading 13 power plants.

The company is also trying to beef up its green energy profile. In addition to exploring wind farm options to help produce alternative energy in 2010 Virginia Electric and Power was pushing energy conservation programs with the aim of cutting peak demand by electric consumers in Virginia by 650 MW.

In 2009 the company posted lower revenues and income not the result of the global recession and its impact on weakening demand for power but primarily due to $430 million in after-tax expenses related to the settlement of a 2009 rate case.

A growth in customers and favorable weather conditions (which spiked power demand in summer and winter) helped to lift the company's revenues and income in 2010.

EXECUTIVES

CEO Dominion Virginia Power, Paul D. Koonce, age 52, $100,047 total compensation
Chairman and CEO, Thomas F. Farrell II, age 58, $452,833 total compensation
EVP and CFO, Mark F. McGettrick, age 54, $327,253 total compensation
CEO Dominion Generation, David A. Christian, age 57, $263,498 total compensation
President and Chief Nuclear Officer Dominion Nuclear, David A. Heacock, age 54, $289,628 total compensation
CEO Dominion Energy, Gary L. Sypolt, age 58
Director Media Relations, David B. Botkins
Community Affairs and Broadcasting Liaison The Piedmont and Shenandoah Valley Dominion Virginia Power and Dominion North Carolina Power, Daisy Pridgen
Auditors: Deloitte&ToucheLLP

LOCATIONS

HQ: Virginia Electric and Power Company
120 Tredegar St., Richmond VA 23219
Phone: 804-819-2000 **Fax:** 804-819-2233
Web: www.dom.com/dominion-virginia-power/index.jsp

PRODUCTS/OPERATIONS

COMPETITORS

Appalachian Power
Columbia Gas of Virginia
Duke Energy Carolinas
Pepco Holdings
Progress Energy Carolinas
Rappahannock Electric Cooperative
SCANA
South Carolina Electric & Gas

HISTORICAL FINANCIALS

Company Type: Subsidiary

Income Statement FYE: December 31

	REVENUE ($ mil.)	NET INCOME ($ mil.)	NET PROFIT MARGIN	EMPLOYEES
12/11	7,246	822	11.3%	6,800
12/10	7,219	852	11.8%	6,800
12/09	6,584	356	5.4%	7,400
12/08	6,934	864	12.5%	7,500
12/07	6,181	448	7.2%	7,100
Annual Growth	4.1%	16.4%	—	(1.1%)

2011 Year-End Financials

Debt ratio: 30.33%
Return on equity: 9.13%
Cash ($ mil.): 29
Current ratio: 78.05
Long-term debt ($ mil.): 6,246
No. of shares (mil.): 0
Dividends
Yield: —
Payout: —
Market value ($ mil.): 29

	STOCK PRICE ($) FY Close	P/E High/Low	PER SHARE ($) Earnings	Dividends	Book Value
12/11	103.96	— —	(0.00)	0.00	32,785.75
12/10	103.00	— —	(0.00)	0.00	31,901.22
12/09	87.75	— —	(0.00)	7.05	30,739.32
12/08	95.00	— —	(0.00)	0.00	31,124.75
12/07	91.25	— —	(0.00)	0.00	29,275.88
Annual Growth	3.3%	— —	—	—	2.9%

Visa Inc

Paper or plastic? Visa hopes you choose the latter. Visa operates the world's largest consumer payment system (ahead of MasterCard and American Express) with some 1.7 billion credit and other payment cards in circulation. It licenses the Visa name to member institutions which issue and market their own Visa products and participate in the VisaNet payment system that provides authorization processing and settlement services. The company also offers debit cards Internet payment systems value-storing smart cards and traveler's checks. Visa's network connects thousands of financial institutions around the world.

HISTORY

Although the first charge card was issued by Western Union in 1914 it wasn't until 1958 that Bank of America (BofA) issued its BankAmericard which combined the convenience of a charge account with credit privileges. When BofA extended its customer base outside California the interchange system controlling payments began to falter because of design problems and fraud.

In 1968 Dee Hock manager of the BankAmericard operations of the National Bank of Commerce in Seattle convinced member banks that a more reliable system was needed. Two years later National BankAmericard Inc. (NBI) was created as an independent corporation (owned by 243 banks) to buy the BankAmericard system from BofA.

With its initial ad slogan "Think of it as Money" the Hock-led NBI developed BankAmericard into a widely used form of payment in the US. A multinational corporation IBANCO was formed in 1974 to carry the operations into other countries. People outside the US resisted BankAmericard's nominal association with BofA and in 1977 Hock changed the card's name to Visa. NBI became Visa USA and IBANCO became Visa International.

By 1980 Visa had debuted debit cards begun issuing traveler's checks and created an electromagnetic point-of-sale authorization system. Visa developed a global network of ATMs in 1983; it was expanded in 1987 by the purchase of a 33% stake in the Plus System of ATMs then the US's second-largest system. Hock retired in 1984 with the company well on its way to realizing his vision of a universal payment system.

The company built the Visa brand image with aggressive advertising such as sponsorship of the 1988 and 1992 Olympics and by co-branding (issuing cards through other organizations with strong brand names such as Blockbuster and Ford).

In 1994 Visa teamed up with Microsoft and others to develop home banking services and software. Visa Cash was introduced during the 1996 Olympics. Visa pushed its debit cards in 1996 and 1997 with humorous ads featuring presidential also-ran Bob Dole and showbiz success story Daffy Duck.

Visa expanded its smart card infrastructure in 1997. It published with MasterCard encryption and security software for online transactions. The gloves came off the next year as the companies vied to convince the world to rally around their respective e-purse technology standards.

During the 1990s Visa fought American Express' attempts to introduce a bank credit card of its own by forbidding Visa members in the US from issuing the product; the Justice Department responded with an antitrust suit against Visa and MasterCard. The case went to trial in 2000 with the government claiming that Visa and MasterCard stifle competition and enjoy an exclusive cross-ownership structure. Visa eventually agreed to pay American Express $2.25 billion to settle the case.

Also in 2000 the company made a deal with Gemplus the French smart card company to enable payments over wireless networks. Visa then inked e-commerce agreements with telecommunications companies Nokia and Ericsson. The company continued its technology push with a deal with Financial Services Technology Consortium to test biometrics —the use of fingerprints irises and voice recognition to identify cardholders. The company also launched a prepaid card Visa Buxx targeted at teenagers.

The European Union in 2000 launched an investigation into the firm's transaction fees alleging that the fees could restrict competition. The following year Visa International agreed to drop its fee to 0.7% of the transaction value over five years.

Led by retail giant Wal-Mart some 4 million merchants claimed Visa and MasterCard violated antitrust laws and attempted to monopolize a legally defined market for debit cards. The plaintiffs sought up to $200 billion in damages in their class-action suit. Just as the 1996 lawsuit was to go to trial in early 2003 Visa settled agreeing to pay $2 billion (twice that of co-defendant MasterCard) over the next decade. Both agreed to pay

$25 million immediately as well as reduce the fee merchants pay for signature-based debit cards.

Visa settled a similar case with Discover Financial in 2008. Visa's net share of the deal totaled some $1.8 billion; MasterCard which was also named agreed to pay $862.5 million.

The group restructured in 2007 in order to offer a more seamless international payments processing platform and to take itself public. Visa International Visa Canada Visa U.S.A. and several other regional organizations merged to create Visa Inc. which became the new parent of the group. It raised about $17 billion in a 2008 IPO.

Visa dedicated some of the funds raised to exploring new payment-related technologies and expanding into more regions. It established joint ventures with payment processors and banks to strengthen its global payment network. Other funds were set aside to cover costs resulting from legal settlements with American Express and Discover Financial totaling more than $4 billion.

EXECUTIVES

Global Head Human Resources, Scott P. Sullivan
Global Head Enterprise Risk, Ellen Richey, age 63
Global Head Technology, Michael L. Dreyer
Chairman and CEO, Joseph W. (Joe) Saunders, age 67, $950,037 total compensation
President, John M. Partridge, age 63, $750,029 total compensation
Global Head Investor Relations, Jack Carsky
Country Manager Canada, Jim Allhusen
CFO, Byron H. Pollitt Jr., age 61, $650,025 total compensation
Global Head Corporate Relations, Douglas (Doug) Michelman
Group President Asia Pacific Central Europe the Middle East and Africa, Elizabeth L. Buse, age 51
General Counsel, Joshua R. (Josh) Floum, age 54, $555,021 total compensation
President and CEO CyberSource Corporation, Michael A. Walsh, age 43
Group President Americas, William M. (Bill) Sheedy, age 45, $525,020 total compensation
Global Chief Marketing Strategy and Corporate Development Officer, Antonio J. Lucio, age 53
Head Global Corporate Legal, Thomas A. (Tom) M'Guinness
Group Executive North America, Oliver Jenkyn, age 39
Global Head Product, James F. (Jim) McCarthy
Secretary, Ariela St. Pierre
Global Head Processing, Darren Parslow
Group Country Manager North Asia Visa, Chris Clark
Global Head Client Support Services, Brian Kieley
Group Country Manager Southeast Asia and Australasia, Peter Maher
Director, William S. (Bill) Shanahan, age 72
Director, David J. Pang, age 69
Director, Mary B. Cranston, age 64
Director, John A. Swainson
Director, Gary P. Coughlan, age 68
Director, Robert W. Matschullat, age 64
Director, Cathy E. Minehan, age 63
Director, Suzanne Nora Johnson, age 54
Director, Francisco J. Fernandez-Carbajal, age 57
Auditors: KPMGLLP

LOCATIONS

HQ: Visa Inc
P.O. Box 8999, San Francisco, CA 94128-8999
Phone: 415 932-2100
Web: www.corporate.visa.com

2012 Sales

	$ mil.	% of total
US	5,720	55
Other countries	4,478	43
Visa Europe contractual agreement	223	2
Total	10,421	100

PRODUCTS/OPERATIONS

2012 Sales

	$ mil.	% of total
Service fees	4,872	39
Data processing fees	3,975	31
International transaction fees	3,025	24
Other	704	6
Adjustments	(2155)	-
Total	10,421	100

Selected Products and Services

Commercial and government
- Visa Business Credit Card (small business)
- Visa Business Debit Card (small business)
- Visa Business Electron (international)
- Visa Business Line of Credit
- Visa Commercial One Card
- Visa Corporate Card (travel and entertainment)
- Visa Gift Card
- Visa Incentive Card
- Visa Purchasing Card
- Visa Signature Business Card

Consumer credit
- Visa Classic
- Visa Gold
- Visa Infinite
- Visa Platinum

Consumer deposit
- Interlink Debit (POS debit network)
- Prepaid
- Visa Debit
  - Visa Classic
  - Visa Gold
  - Visa Infinite
  - Visa Platinum
- Visa Electron Debit

COMPETITORS

American Express
Citigroup
Discover
JCB International
MasterCard
Rewards Network

HISTORICAL FINANCIALS

Company Type: Public

Income Statement FYE: September 30

	REVENUE ($ mil.)	NET INCOME ($ mil.)	NET PROFIT MARGIN	EMPLOYEES
09/12	10,421	2,144	20.6%	8,500
09/11	9,188	3,650	39.7%	7,500
09/10	8,065	2,966	36.8%	6,800
09/09	6,911	2,353	34.0%	5,700
09/08	6,263	804	12.8%	5,765
Annual Growth	13.6%	27.8%	—	10.2%

2012 Year-End Financials

Debt ratio: —
Return on equity: 7.76%
Cash ($ mil.): 2,074
Current ratio: 148.18
Long-term debt ($ mil.): —
No. of shares (mil.): 811
Dividends
Yield: —
Payout: 27.85%
Market value ($ mil.): 108,901

	STOCK PRICE ($) FY Close	P/E High/Low		PER SHARE ($) Earnings	Dividends	Book Value
09/12	134.28	43	27	3.16	0.00	34.07
09/11	85.72	18	13	5.16	0.60	32.56
09/10	74.26	24	16	4.01	0.50	29.95
09/09	69.11	24	14	3.10	0.42	27.41
09/08	61.39	92	59	0.96	0.11	23.21
Annual Growth	21.6%	—	—	34.7%	—	10.1%

Visteon Corp.

Visteon is the visionary-sounding name Ford Motor bestowed on its automotive components unit when it was spun off in 2000. One of the largest auto parts makers in the US the company has evolved to operate three business groups: Climate Control (climate systems powertrain cooling systems); Electronic Products (audio systems driver control systems infotainment systems powertrain and feature control modules); and Interior Products (cockpits door modules consoles). Ford represents about 25% of sales; Visteon also provides products and services to aftermarket customers. More than 80% of its sales are made outside the US.

Bankruptcy

The company is attempting to bounce back after a bout of bankruptcy. It filed for Chapter 11 in spring 2009 and emerged in fall 2010. Like the rest of the auto parts industry the company suffered significantly from decreased orders and sales from OEMs and the bankruptcies of customers GM and Chrysler further decimated its balance sheet. Visteon completed its reorganization having reduced its debt by more than $2 billion. It was allowed to convert its existing debt –about $1.6 billion - to stock in a new company.

Geographic Reach

Visteon has corporate offices in Van Buren Township Michigan; Shanghai; and Chelmsford UK. It owns facilities worldwide in more than 25 countries.

Sales & Marketing

Despite its recent bankruptcy Visteon's customers remained true during its reorganization. While Ford represents a quarter of Visteon's business the Hyundai Kia Automotive Group tops that commanding around 30% of the company's revenues. Visteon provides components to a lion's share of the top global automotive OEMs –Daimler Honda Toyota and Volkswagen is the short list.

Financial Analysis

Although Visteon's net sales increased by almost 8% ($7.5 billion to almost $8.1 billion) from 2010 to 2011 its net income plunged significantly (92%) from $1 billion to a paltry $80 million. Restructuring expenses of $34 million along with the higher costs involved in maintaining its operations ate into its profits during 2011.

Strategy

Visteon has been getting rid of extraneous divisions and units in order to focus on its more profitable operations. In 2012 Visteon sold its automotive lighting operations to Varroc Group a fellow provider of automotive parts for $72 million in cash. The business included front and rear lighting systems and auxiliary lamps and key parts such as projectors and electronic modules. The divesture allowed Visteon to focus on its most lucrative business segment: Climate Control. Visteon also wishes to concentrate on the more profitable products within its Electronic Products operations.

EXECUTIVES

Chairman, Francis M. (Fran) Scricco, age 63
EVP and CFO, Martin E. (Marty) Welch III, age 63
President CEO and Director, Timothy D. (Tim) Leuliette, age 62
Chairman President and CEO, Donald J. (Don) Stebbins, age 54, $1,070,000 total compensation
Senior Marketing Manager Asia Pacific, Thomas Li
VP North American Customer Group Strategy and Global Communications, Julie A. Fream, age 48
SVP; President Global Customer Group, Robert C. Pallash, age 60
VP Interim CFO Corporate Controller and Chief Accounting Officer, Michael J. Widgren, age 43
Director Corporate Communications and the Americas, James (Jim) Fisher
VP and, Joy M. Greenway, age 51, $433,146 total compensation
VP and President ElectronicsProduct Group, Steve Meszaros, age 48
VP and CIO, James F. (Jim) Sistek, age 47
Corporate Communications Asia Pacific, Annouk Ruffo-Leduc
Corporate Communications Product and Customer News, Melissa Andrade
Corporate Communications Europe, Jonna Christensen
Government Affairs Mexico, Alonso Martinez
Account Manager Mexico, Mauricio Hernandez
Director Investor Relations, Steven (Steve) Ward, age 49
Director Human Resources South America, Leonardo Bissoli
Media Relations South America, Alessandra Silva
Director Global Innovation Design and Advanced Electronics, Tim Yerdon
General Manager Halla Climate Control (Shanghai), K. I. Kim
VP and General Counsel, Michael K. Sharnas, age 40
SVP Human Resources, Keith M. Shull
VP Investor Relations, Charles E. (Chuck) Mazur Jr.
Director, Herbert L. (Herb) Henkel, age 64
Director, Karl J. Krapek, age 63
Director, David L. Treadwell, age 57
President CEO and Director, Timothy D. (Tim) Leuliette, age 62
Director, Mark T. Hogan, age 61
Director, Duncan H. Cocroft, age 68
Director, Kevin I. Dowd, age 66
Director, Philippe Guillemot, age 52
Director, Jeffrey D. Jones, age 59
Director, Harry J. Wilson, age 40
Director, Robert Manzo
Auditors: PricewaterhouseCoopersLLP

LOCATIONS

HQ: Visteon Corporation
1 Village Center Dr., Van Buren Township MI 48111
Phone: 734-710-5000 **Fax:** 479-273-3188
Web: www.whistlergroup.com

2011 Sales

	$ mil.	% of total
North America		
Canada	105	1
Europe		
Czech Republic	597	7
Portugal	468	5
Germany	199	2
Other countries	517	6
Korea	2,488	27
India	355	4
Other countries	244	3
Adjustments	(976)	-

PRODUCTS/OPERATIONS

2011 Sales

	$ mil.	% of total
Products		
Interiors	2,285	28
Lighting	531	6
Total	**8,047**	**100**

Selected Operating Segments and Products

Climate control products and systems
- Battery cooling module
- Compressors
- Fluid transport systems
- Heat exchangers
- HVAC systems
- Powertrain cooling systems

Electronic products and systems
- Audio systems
- Control panels and displays
- Driver awareness systems
- Driver information systems
- Engine induction systems
- Integrated electronics and infotainment systems
- Powertrain and feature control (engine and transmission controls fuel delivery modules)

Interior products and systems
- Cockpit systems
- Consoles
- Door trim modules and seat systems

COMPETITORS

Autoliv
Behr Industries
Calsonic Kansei
Clarion Technologies
Continental AG
Delphi Automotive Systems
DENSO
Faurecia
Federal-Mogul
Garmin
Harman International
Hella
IAC Group
Inergy Automotive
Johnson Controls
JTEKT
KOITO MANUFACTURING
Lear Corp
Magna International
Magneti Marelli Powertrain USA
Metaldyne
Modine Manufacturing
Parker-Hannifin
Rheinmetall
Robert Bosch
Standard Motor Products
TI Automotive
TRW Automotive
Valeo

HISTORICAL FINANCIALS

Company Type: Public

Income Statement FYE: December 31

	REVENUE ($ mil.)	NET INCOME ($ mil.)	NET PROFIT MARGIN	EMPLOYEES
12/11	8,047	80	1.0%	26,000
12/10*	1,887	86	4.6%	26,500
10/10	5,579	940	16.8%	0
12/09	6,685	128	1.9%	29,500
12/08	9,544	(681)	—	33,500
Annual Growth	(4.2%)	—	—	(6.1%)

*Fiscal year change

2011 Year-End Financials

Debt ratio: 12.05%
Return on equity: 6.12%
Cash ($ mil.): 723
Current ratio: 160.44
Long-term debt ($ mil.): 512
No. of shares (mil.): 52
Dividends
Yield: —
Payout: —
Market value ($ mil.): 2,597

	STOCK PRICE ($) FY Close	P/E High/Low		PER SHARE ($) Earnings	Dividends	Book Value
12/11	49.94	49	26	1.54	0.00	25.13
12/10*	74.25	43	33	1.66	0.00	24.71
Annual Growth	(32.7%)	—	—	(7.2%)	—	1.7%

*Fiscal year change

Wachovia Preferred Funding Corp

LOCATIONS

HQ: Wachovia Preferred Funding Corp
90 South 7th Street, 13th Floor, Minneapolis, MN 55402
Phone: 855 825-1437
Web: www.wellsfargo.com

HISTORICAL FINANCIALS

Company Type:

Income Statement FYE: December 31

	ASSETS ($ mil.)	NET INCOME ($ mil.)	INCOME AS % OF ASSETS	EMPLOYEES
12/11	13,534	795	5.9%	10
12/10	18,178	769	4.2%	10
12/09	18,410	867	4.7%	11
12/08	18,836	767	4.1%	11
12/07	18,233	1,067	5.9%	17
Annual Growth	(7.2%)	(7.1%)	—	(12.4%)

2011 Year-End Financials

Debt ratio: —
Return on equity: 5.89%
Cash ($ mil.): 1,186
Current ratio: —
Long-term debt ($ mil.): —
No. of shares (mil.): 100
Dividends
Yield: —
Payout: 29.62%
Market value ($ mil.): 2,582

	STOCK PRICE ($) FY Close	P/E High/Low		PER SHARE ($) Earnings	Dividends	Book Value
12/11	25.82	4	4	6.12	0.00	135.02
12/10	25.59	4	4	5.84	1.81	181.22
12/09	22.23	3	1	7.07	1.81	183.35
12/08	20.16	5	1	4.74	1.81	185.86
12/07	22.69	4	3	6.80	1.81	178.44
Annual Growth	3.3%	—	—	(2.6%)	—	(6.7%)

WAKEFERN FOOD CORP.

EXECUTIVES

President and COO, Dean Janeway
President and COO, Joseph Sheridan
SVP, Natan Tabak
CFO, Douglas (Doug) Wille

SVP, Frank Rostan
VP Consumer and Corporate Communications, Karen Meleta
VP Strategic Development and Member Relations, William (Bill) Crombie
VP E-Commerce, Cheryl Williams
Chairman and CEO, Joseph S. (Joe) Colalillo, age 51
VP Logistics, Peter (Pete) Rolandelli
VP Information Services Division, Alan Aront
SVP Marketing, Jeff Reagan
SVP Perishables, Bill Mayo
VP Human Resources, Ann Marie Burke
SVP Non-Perishables, Chris Lane
Corporate Communications and Media Relations Specialist, Jeannette Castaneda
VP Quality Assurance, Mike Ambrosio
President PriceRite, Neil Duffy
President ShopRite Supermarkets Inc., David Figurelli

LOCATIONS

HQ: Wakefern Food Corp.
5000 Riverside Dr., Keasbey NJ 08832
Phone: 908-527-3300 **Fax:** 908-527-3397
Web: www.wakefern.com

PRODUCTS/OPERATIONS

COMPETITORS

A&P	Krasdale Foods
Acme Markets	Nash-Finch
Associated Wholesalers	Pathmark Stores
Bozzuto' s	Stop & Shop
C&S Wholesale	SUPERVALU
CVS Caremark	Wal-Mart
Hannaford Bros.	Wawa Inc.
IGA	White Rose

HISTORICAL FINANCIALS

Company Type: Private - Cooperative

Income Statement FYE: October 1

	REVENUE ($ mil.)	NET INCOME ($ mil.)	NET PROFIT MARGIN	EMPLOYEES
10/11*	10,325	5	0.0%	3,500
09/08	8,396	6	0.1%	0
09/07	7,846	5	0.1%	0
09/06	1,340,014	0	—	0
Annual Growth	—	146.2%	—	—

*Fiscal year change

2011 Year-End Financials

Debt ratio: —
Return on equity: —
Cash ($ mil.): 124
Current ratio: 0.40
Long-term debt ($ mil.): —
Dividends
Yield: —
Payout: —
Market value ($ mil.): —

Wal-Mart Stores, Inc.

Wal-Mart Stores is an irresistible (or at least unavoidable) retail force that has yet to meet any immovable objects. Bigger than Europe's Carrefour Metro AG and Tesco combined it's the world's #1 retailer with some 2.2 million employees. In the US Wal-Mart operates more than 4000 stores including 3000-plus Supercenters that sell groceries and general merchandise 610 Sam's Club warehouses and a growing number of smaller format stores. The company's faster growing international division (28% of sales) numbers more than 5600 locations; Wal-Mart is the #1 retailer in Canada and Mexico and has operations in Asia (where it owns a 95% stake in Japanese retailer SEIYU) Africa Europe and South America.

HISTORY

Sam Walton began his retail career as a J. C. Penney management trainee and later leased a Ben Franklin-franchised dime store in Newport Arkansas in 1945. In 1950 he relocated to Bentonville Arkansas and opened a Walton 5 & 10. By 1962 Walton owned 15 Ben Franklin stores under the Walton 5 & 10 name.

After Ben Franklin management rejected his suggestion to open discount stores in small towns Walton with his brother James "Bud" Walton opened the first Wal-Mart Discount City in Rogers Arkansas in 1962. Wal-Mart Stores went public in 1970 with 18 stores and sales of $44 million.

Avoiding regional retailers Walton opened stores in small and midsized towns in the 1970s. The company sold its Ben Franklin stores in 1976. By 1980 Wal-Mart's 276 stores had sales of $1.2 billion.

In 1983 Wal-Mart opened SAM'S Wholesale Club a concept based on the successful cash-and-carry membership-only warehouse format pioneered by the Price Company of California (now Costco Wholesale Corp.).

The company started Hypermart*USA in 1987 as a joint venture with Dallas-based supermarket chain Cullum Companies (now Randall's Food Markets). The 200000-sq.-ft. discount store/supermarket hybrid was later retooled as Wal-Mart Supercenters. Sam stepped down as CEO in 1988 and president David Glass was appointed CEO. Wal-Mart bought out Cullum the next year.

Wal-Mart acquired wholesale distributor McLane Company in 1990. In 1992 the year Sam died the company expanded into Mexico through a joint venture to open SAM'S CLUBS with Mexico's largest retailer Cifra (renamed Wal-Mart de Mexico in 2000). Wal-Mart acquired 122 former Woolco stores in Canada in 1994. Co-founder Bud died a year later.

More international expansion included entering China in 1996; the acquisition of German hypermarket chain Wertkauf in 1997; the purchase of Brazilian retailer Lojas Americanas' 40% interest in a joint venture (1998); and the addition of four stores and other sites in South Korea. Also in 1998 the company began testing the Neighborhood Market format a 40000-sq.-ft. grocery and drug combination store. In 1999 Wal-Mart bought 74 German-based Interspar hypermarkets and acquired ASDA Group the UK's third-largest supermarket chain.

COO Lee Scott succeeded Glass as CEO in 2000; Glass stayed on as chairman of the executive committee. Wal-Mart later began testing its customers' demand for appliances by selling household appliances in selected stores.

Following the bankruptcy and closure of the Montgomery Ward department store chain in 2001 Wal-Mart offered to replace Ward's customers' credit cards with Wal-Mart branded cards. Wal-Mart also formed an alliance with America Online to offer Internet access and later launched its No Boundaries private-label cosmetics for preteens and teenagers. In June 2001 a group of six current and former female Wal-Mart employees filed a sex-discrimination lawsuit (seeking to represent up to 500000 current and former Wal-Mart workers) against the company. The next month Wal-Mart said it would acquire all the minority interests in Walmart.com and integrate its online operations with its store operations. It also laid off 100 employees at its corporate headquarters and eliminated 300 unfilled positions. In August it said it was testing the sale of Sealy and private-label mattresses in some of its superstores and it began offering college textbooks discounted up to 30% at its online College Bookstore.

2002 was a huge year for Wal-Mart both at home and abroad. In April the company was crowned America's largest corporation by "FORTUNE" magazine. In March Wal-Mart gained a foothold in Japan taking a 6% stake in one of Japan's top retailers SEIYU . That December it increased its SEIYU stake to 36% and retains the option to up that to nearly 67% by 2007. In a rare defeat Wal-Mart in July closed its first store in Germany and 2000 workers there went on a two-day strike over wages. (In 2001 Wal-Mart scrapped plans to open 50 more Supercenters there by 2003.) Also in 2002 Wal-Mart Puerto Rico acquired Supermercados Amigo the #1 supermarket chain on the island. (Wal-Mart opened its first Supercenter there in April 2001.)

Overall in 2002 Wal-Mart opened 178 supercenters 33 discount stores and 25 SAM'S CLUB stores. It opened 107 international units with two in Brazil 22 in Canada eight in China two in Germany three in South Korea 59 in Mexico two in Puerto Rico and nine in the UK. The company's attempt to open a state industrial bank in California in 2002 failed however after legislators barred retailers.

In May 2003 Wal-Mart sold its McLane grocery distribution business to Berkshire Hathaway; a rare divestment for the world's largest retailer. In July it opened its first store in Beijing.

In February 2004 a federal judge ruled that Wal-Mart should pay workers for overtime hours. The complaint which was brought by plaintiffs who said they were forced to work unpaid overtime between 1994 and 1999 came at a time when working conditions at the company were being scrutinized. Also that month Wal-Mart acquired the 118-store Bompreco chain of Brazilian supermarkets and hypermarkets from troubled Dutch retailer Royal Ahold for $300 million advancing the world's largest retailer from fifth to third place in the Brazilian market. In March Wal-Mart opened its online music store which sells digital downloads for 11 cents less than major competitors (including Apple's iTunes and Napster). In April voters in Inglewood California overwhelmingly rejected Wal-Mart's proposal to build a supercenter there over the objections of local officials. Wal-Mart had sought to bypass local development and environmental regulations by spending more than $1 million to take its case directly to the voters. Also in April Wal-Mart's Japanese partner Seiyu opened its first Wal-Mart-style supercenter in Numazu.

In May 2004 Wal-Mart agreed to pay $3.1 million in fines for violating the Clean Water Act at 24 sites in nine states. (The retailer was fined $1 million in 2001 for similar violations involving its failure to manage storm-water runoff.)

Vice chairman Tom Coughlin retired in January 2005 after 25 years with Wal-Mart. Coughlin remained on the company's board until March 25 2005 when he resigned prematurely following an internal investigation related to "the alleged unauthorized use of corporate-owned gift cards and personal reimbursements." He was due to retire from the board on June 3 2005. In June the company rescinded Coughlin's retirement agreement including stock awards and incentive payments which may total as much as $12 million.

Also in January Wal-Mart agreed to pay $135540 to settle federal charges that it violated child labor laws. The 24 violations which the retailer denied involved teenage workers in three states using hazardous equipment such as chain saws paper balers and fork lifts. Soon after Wal-Mart was ordered to pay $7.5 million in damages to a disabled former employee who claimed the retailer unfairly reassigned him. In March the retailer settled a high-profile lawsuit by agreeing to pay $11 million to the US government to close an investigation into the use of illegal immigrants by Wal-Mart contractors to clean its stores. In May Wal-Mart increased its stake in SEIYU to 42% (up from 37%).

In August 2005 Wal-Mart signed Garth Brooks to a multiyear exclusive contract under which the country star's music will only be sold in Wal-Mart-owned stores. The deal marks the first time an artist has contracted himself and his entire catalog of music with a single chain. In October the company launched its Metro 7 line of urban women's apparel in 500 stores in and around urban areas. In December Wal-Mart opened its third superstore in the downtown Xuanwu District of Beijing. Also in December Wal-Mart acquired some 140 stores in Brazil from Portuguese retailer Sonae for about $757 million increasing the number of outlets it operates in Brazil to nearly 300.

In January 2006 Wal-Mart opened a supercenter in Santa Clarita California its second in Los Angeles County. In February the company acquired an additional 17.7% interest in CARHCO from Royal Ahold increasing its stake in the Central America supermarket operator to 51%. Wal-Mart's former vice chairman Thomas Coughlin who was accused of misusing more than $500000 in company funds pleaded guilty to fraud and tax charges in January 2006. In August he was sentenced to 27 months of house arrest and ordered to pay $400000 in restitution to his former employer. Wal-Mart itself was ordered by a Pennsylvania jury to pay more than $78 million in damages in a class-action suit brought by employees alleging that they were forced to work during breaks and off the clock. In October Wal-Mart disposed of its retail operations in Germany and South Korea. It sold the last of its 85 stores in Germany to rival METRO AG and sold 16 stores in South Korea to Shinsegae Co. for about $882 million.

In early 2007 Wal-Mart agreed to pay $33.5 million in back wages and interest to settle a federal lawsuit that accused the company of violating ovetime laws involving more than 86000 employees. In February the company announced an agreement with all six major Hollywood studios to sell digital movies and TV shows on walmart.com becoming the first traditional retail chain to do so. In April Helen Robson Walton wife of Wal-Mart founder Sam Walton died at the age of 87. Wal-Mart and Bharti Enterprises formed a 50:50 joint venture in August to jointly build wholesale outlets that will buy goods from farmers and small manufacturers and sell to retailers through a nationwide supply chain. True to form Wal-Mart again cut prices of toys and some 15000 more items such as apparel home and food products for the 2007 holiday selling season.

In May 2008 the retailer revised its $4 prescription program launched in 2006 to cover 90-day prescriptions for $10. In November Mike Duke was named to Wal-Mart's board of directors in preparation for his elevation to president and CEO of the company in February 2009. Also in November Eduardo Castro-Wright president and CEO of Walmart US was promoted to vice chairman of Wal-Mart Stores. He assumed responsibility for the firm's global procurement operation.

The management shuffle continued in 2009 with Lee Scott retiring as CEO in February. Scott was succeeded by Duke who had headed the international arm of the company. In January Wal-Mart acquired a majority stake in Chile's largest food retailer Distribucion y Servicio through a tender offer. In May of that year it opened its first location in India vis a joint venture with Bharti Enterprises.

In February 2010 the company opened its new Latin America regional headquarters in Miami Florida.

In June 2011 Walmart International acquired a 51% stake in South African retailer Massmart which operates 288 stores in 13 countries in sub-Saharan Africa in a deal valued at about $2.4 billion. Massmart operates stores under the Makro Game Dion Wired Builders Warehouse Builders Express Builders Trade Depot CBW Jumbo Cash and Carry and the Shield buying group. On the day of the Massmart closing the company scored a huge win when the US Supreme Court threw out a massive employment discrimination class-action lawsuit (Dukes vs. Wal-Mart) brought filed back in 2001. While the court did not rule on whether or not Wal-Mart discriminated against women it said they could not proceed as a class.

EXECUTIVES

Chairman, S. Robson (Rob) Walton, age 67
EVP Corporate Affairs, Leslie A. Dach, age 57
EVP; President and CEO Latin America; Chairman Mexico, Eduardo Solorzano Morales, age 55
President CEO and Director, Michael T. (Mike) Duke, age 62, $1,203,228 total compensation
EVP and Chief Administrative Officer Walmart U.S., Thomas A. (Tom) Mars, age 54
VP Investor Relations, Carol A. Schumacher
EVP; President and CEO Wal-Mart International, C. Douglas (Doug) McMillon, age 45, $852,312 total compensation
EVP and CFO, Charles M. Holley Jr., age 55
SVP Merchandise Execution, Michelle J. Gloeckler
Chief Administrative Officer, Rollin L. Ford, age 49
President and CEO Global eCommerce, Neil M. Ashe, age 44
President and CEO Walmart Canada, Shelley G. Broader
SVP Finance and Treasury, Jeff Davis
EVP and Chief Marketing Officer Walmart U.S., Stephen F. Quinn
EVP; Chief Merchandising Officer US, Duncan C. Mac Naughton, age 49
EVP People Division, M. Susan Chambers, age 54
EVP Global Sourcing, Edward J. Kolodzieski
EVP and Chief Merchandising Officer Sam's Club, Linda P. Hefner
President and CEO ASDA Stores, A. J. (Andy) Clarke
EVP; President and CEO Canada UK and Sub-Saharan Africa, David Cheesewright
President and CEO Walmart Asia and Interim CEO Walmart China, Scott Price, age 51
Chief Information Officer, Karenann K. Terrell, age 50
EVP; President and CEO Walmart U.S., William S. (Bill) Simon, age 52
SVP Global Food and Consumables Global Merchandise Center, Pamela K. (Pam) Kohn
EVP Global eCommerce Developed Markets, Raul Vazquez
EVP Softlines Walmart U.S., James A. (Andy) Barron
EVP General Merchandise and Replenishment Walmart U.S., John T. Westling
SVP Marketing Operations, Matt Kistler
President and CEO Sam's Club, Rosalind G. Brewer, age 49
EVP; President Wal-Mart Realty Walmart U.S., Eric S. Zorn
EVP Logistics and Supply Chain Walmart U.S., Johnnie C. Dobbs Jr.
SVP and Controller, Steven P (Steve) Whaley, age 52
COO China, Sean Clarke
SVP Walmart.com, Steve Nave
CIO Walmart.com, Eugene (Gene) Wojciechowski
EVP Food Walmart U.S., Jack L. Sinclair, age 51
Chief Marketing Officer China, Steve Smith
EVP Global Customer Insights, Cindy Davis
EVP General Counsel and Corporate Secretary, Jeffrey J. (Jeff) Gearhart, age 47
EVP; President Walmart Central Walmart U.S., Michael S. (Mike) Moore
SVP Sustainability, Andrea Thomas
EVP Operations Sam?s Club, P. Todd Harbaugh
EVP; COO Walmart U.S., Gisel Ruiz, age 41
Media Relations Contact, David (Dave) Tovar
SVP and Chief Leverage Officer, Lev Khasis, age 46
CEO Japan, Steve Dacus
EVP; President Walmart West Walmart U.S., Michael J. Bender
SVP Walmart International Business Development, J. P. Suarez
President Walmart Foundation, Sylvia Mathews Burwell
Director, Douglas N. Daft, age 69
Director, M. Michele Burns, age 53
Director, Steven S. (Steve) Reinemund, age 64
Director, H. Lee Scott Jr., age 63
Director, James W. (Jim) Breyer, age 51
Director, Roger C. Corbett, age 69
Director, Arne M. Sorenson, age 53
Director, James I. Cash Jr., age 63
President CEO and Director, Michael T. (Mike) Duke, age 62
Director, Gregory B. (Greg) Penner, age 42
Director, Jim C. Walton, age 63
Director, Aida M. Alvarez, age 62
Director, Christopher J. (Chris) Williams, age 54
Director, Marissa Mayer
Auditors: Ernst&YoungLLP

LOCATIONS

HQ: Wal-Mart Stores Inc.
702 SW 8th St., Bentonville AR 72716-8611
Phone: 479-273-4000 **Fax:** 479-277-1830
Web: www.walmartstores.com

2012 Stores

	No.
North America	
US	4,479
Canada	333
Latin America	
Mexico	2,088
Brazil	512
Chile	316
Costa	200
Guatemala	200
El	79
Argentina	88
Nicaragua	73
Honduras	70
Asia	
Japan	419
China	370
India	15
UK	541
South	305
Sub-Saharan	42
Total	**10,130**

PRODUCTS/OPERATIONS

2012 Stores

	No.
US	
Supercenters	3
Discount	629
SAM'S	611
Neighborhood Markets & other small	210
International	5,651
Total	**10,130**

2012 US Sales

	% of total
Grocery	55
Entertainment	12
Health &	11
Hardlines	10
Apparel	7
Home	5
Total	**100**

2012 Sales

	$ bil.	% of total
Wal-Mart US	264	60
International	125	28
SAM'S CLUB	53	12
Membership & other	3	-
Total	**446**	**100**

Selected Mergers and Acquisitions

2011
- Massmart Holdings Ltd. (51%; $2.5 billion; South Africa; Retail stores)
- Netto Food Stores ($1.2 billion; UK; Retail food stores)

Selected Retail Divisions

ASDA (large combination general merchandise and food stores)
Neighborhood Markets (traditional supermarkets)
SAM' S CLUB (members-only warehouse clubs)
Supercenters (large combination general merchandise and food stores)
Wal-Mart International Division (foreign operations)
Wal-Mart Stores (general merchandise)

Selected Private Labels and Licensed Brands

Athletic Works
Better Homes & Gardens (licensed)
Black & Decker (licensed)
Canopy
Danskin Now (licensed)
Disney (licensed)
Equate (health and beauty aids)
Everstart
Faded Glory (jeans licensed)
General Electric (licensed)
George
Great Value (dairy dry grocery meat and produce)
Home Trends
Just My Size (licensed)
Mainstays
Marketside
No Boundaries
Oak Leaf
Ol' Roy (dog food)
OP (licensed)
Ozark Trail
Parent' s Choice
Prima Della
Puritan
Rival (licensed)
Sam' s Choice (grocery items)
Secret Treasures
Spring Valley
Starter
White Stag

COMPETITORS

99 Cents Only
Ace Hardware
AEON
Ahold U.S.A.
Albertsons
J Sainsbury
J. C. Penney
Katz Group
King Kullen Grocery
Kmart
ALDI
Army and Air Force Exchange
Aurora Wholesalers
AutoZone
Bed Bath & Beyond
Best Buy
Big Lots
BJ' s Wholesale Club
Bridgestone Retail Operations
Brookshire Grocery
Carrefour
Chedraui
Comerci
Costco Wholesale
CVS Caremark
Delhaize
Dollar General
El Puerto de Liverpool
Family Dollar Stores
Farmacias Benavides
Gigante
Grupo Carso
Grupo Elektra
H-E-B
Home Depot
Hudson' s Bay
Kohl' s
Kroger
Lianhua Supermarket
Loblaw
Lowe' s
Maruetsu
Meijer
METRO AG
Office Depot
Pep Boys
PETCO
Publix
RadioShack
Rite Aid
Safeway
Sanborns
Sears
Sears Canada
Soriana
Staples
SUPERVALU
Target Corporation
Tesco
The Gap
TJX Companies
Toys ' ' R' ' Us
True Value
Walgreen

HISTORICAL FINANCIALS

Company Type: Public

Income Statement

FYE: January 31

	REVENUE ($ mil.)	NET INCOME ($ mil.)	NET PROFIT MARGIN	EMPLOYEES
01/12	446,950	15,699	3.5%	2,200,000
01/11	421,849	16,389	3.9%	2,100,000
01/10	408,214	14,335	3.5%	2,100,000
01/09	405,607	13,400	3.3%	2,100,000
01/08	378,799	12,731	3.4%	2,100,000
Annual Growth	4.2%	5.4%	—	1.2%

2012 Year-End Financials

Debt ratio: 27.62%—
Return on equity: 22.01%
Cash ($ mil.): 6,550
Current ratio: 88.24
Long-term debt ($ mil.): 47,079

Dividends
Yield: 2.38%
Payout: 32.30%
Market value ($ mil.): —

	STOCK PRICE ($) FY Close	P/E High/Low		PER SHARE ($) Earnings	Dividends	Book Value
01/12	61.36	14	11	4.52	1.46	20.86
01/11	56.07	13	11	4.47	1.21	19.49
01/10	53.43	15	13	3.70	0.00	18.69
01/09	47.12	19	14	3.39	0.00	16.63
01/08	50.74	16	14	3.13	0.88	16.26
Annual Growth	4.9%	—	—	9.6%	13.5%	6.4%

Walgreen Co.

LOCATIONS

HQ: Walgreen Co.
108 Wilmot Road, Deerfield, IL 60015
Phone: 847 315-2500 **Fax:** 847 914-2804
Web: www.walgreens.com

2011 Locations

	No.
Florida	864
Texas	700
California	627
Illinois	598
New	524
Ohio	271
Tennessee	261
Arizona	254
Wisconsin	231
Michigan	230
Indiana	211
Georgia	203
Missouri	201
North	201
New	199
Massachusetts	180
Colorado	167
Minnesota	156
Louisiana	147
Pennsylvania	138
Virginia	133
Washington	130
Connecticut	117
South	110
Oklahoma	105
Kentucky	102
Alabama	101
Nevada	87
Oregon	73
Iowa	72
Mississippi	71
Kansas	69
Delaware	67
Maryland	66
New	66
Nebraska	61
Arkansas	60
Utah	43
Idaho	42
New	35
Rhode	29
West	21
Maine	14
South	14
Montana	13
Hawaii	11
Wyoming	11
Alaska	5
Vermont	4
District of	3
North	1
Puerto	110
Guam	1
Total	**8,210**

PRODUCTS/OPERATIONS

2011 Locations

	No.
Drugstores	7,761
Worksite	355
Home care	83
Specialty	9
Mail service	2
Total	**8,210**

2011 Sales

	% of total
Prescription	65
General	25
Nonprescription	10
Total	**100**

Selected Operations & Subsidiaries

Beauty.com Inc.
drugstore.com inc.
Duane Reade Inc.
SeniorMed LLC (pharmacy provider for long-term care facilities)
Take Care Health Systems Inc.
Walgreens.com Inc. (e-commerce)
Walgreens Health and Wellness (in-store clinics)
Walgreens Health Services (managed care services)
Walgreens Home Care Inc.

Walgreens Mail Service Inc. (mail order pharmacy)
Walgreens Specialty Pharmacy LLC

HISTORICAL FINANCIALS

Company Type:

Income Statement FYE: August 31

	REVENUE ($ mil.)	NET INCOME ($ mil.)	NET PROFIT MARGIN	EMPLOYEES
08/12	71,633	2,127	3.0%	240,000
08/11	72,184	2,714	3.8%	247,000
08/10	67,420	2,091	3.1%	244,000
08/09	63,335	2,006	3.2%	238,000
08/08	59,034	2,157	3.7%	237,000
Annual Growth	5.0%	(0.3%)	—	0.3%

2012 Year-End Financials

Debt ratio: 16.11%
Return on equity: 11.66%
Cash ($ mil.): 1,297
Current ratio: 123.37
Long-term debt ($ mil.): 4,073
No. of shares (mil.): 944
Dividends
Yield: 2.66%
Payout: 39.26%
Market value ($ mil.): 33,759

	STOCK PRICE ($) FY Close	P/E High/Low		PER SHARE ($) Earnings	Dividends	Book Value
08/12	35.76	15	12	2.42	0.95	19.32
08/11	35.21	15	9	2.94	0.75	16.70
08/10	26.88	19	12	2.12	0.59	15.34
08/09	33.88	18	11	2.02	0.48	14.54
08/08	36.43	22	14	2.17	0.00	13.01
Annual Growth	(0.5%)	—	—	2.8%	—	10.4%

Walter Investment Management Corp

Walter Investment Management deals with the credit-challenged. The company owns and services residential mortgages particularly those of the subprime and nonconforming variety. Walter Investment Management services one million accounts with an unpaid principal balance of $86 billion. It operates through subsidiaries: Walter Mortgage Company; Hanover Capital; Marix Servicing; and Best Insurors. In 2011 Walter Investment Management increased its loan portfolio and transformed into a fee-based service provider when it paid $1 billion for GTCS Holdings the parent of Green Tree Servicing. Green Tree specializes in high-touch third-party credit servicing.

As a result of the deal Walter Investment Management no longer qualified as a real estate investment trust (REIT). The Green Tree acquisition represented a dramatic increase the size and scope of Walter Investment Management's business. The company's servicing portfolio grew by 50% and nearly 2000 employees were added. Green Tree also increased Walter Investment Management's geographic footprint by adding 27 offices in the US.

An increase in delinquencies and foreclosures during the recession has forced traditional loan servicers and owners such as banks to look for third party assistance. Walter Investment hopes to tap into growing demand from big lenders looking to shift its debt servicing functions to outside firms such as Green Tree.

The company diversified further in late 2012 with the purchase of Reverse Mortgage Solutions (RMS) for some $120 million. RMS provides servicing origination asset management and technology services to the fast-growing reverse mortgage industry.

The Green Tree acquisition helped boost Walter Investment Management's sales in 2011. However the company reported a $69 million net loss due to income tax costs (related to its conversion from a REIT) and expenses related to the Green Tree acquisition.

Walter Investment Management was created in 2009 when Hanover Capital Mortgage merged with the home financing business of Walter Industries (now Walter Energy). Walter Energy was spun off after the closure of troubled homebuilder Jim Walter Homes.

EXECUTIVES

Chairman and CEO, Mark J. O?Brien, age 69
President and COO, Charles E. Cauthen Jr., age 53
VP CFO and Treasurer, Kimberly A. Perez, age 44
Vice Chairman and EVP, Denmar J. Dixon
Director Investor Relations, Whitney Finch
VP General Counsel and Secretary, Stuart Boyd
Director, Michael T. Tokarz, age 62
Director, Steven R. (Steve) Berrard, age 57
Director, Shannon E. Smith, age 46
Director, William J. Meurer, age 68
Director, John N. Rees, age 79
Director, John A. Clymer, age 63
Director, James F. Stone, age 72
Director, Ellyn L. Brown, age 62
Vice Chairman and EVP, Denmar J. Dixon
Auditors: GrantThorntonLLP

LOCATIONS

HQ: Walter Investment Management Corp.
3000 Bayport Dr. Ste. 1100, Tampa FL 33607
Phone: 813-421-7600 **Fax:** 720-494-6600
Web: www.intrado.com

PRODUCTS/OPERATIONS

2011 Sales

	$ mil.	% of total
$ in mil. % of total		
Servicing revenue & fees	186	46
Interest income on loans	164	41
Insurance revenue	41	10
Other	9	3
Total	**402**	**100**

COMPETITORS

Annaly Capital Management
Aurora Loan Services
Capstead Mortgage
CIFC
DVL
FirstCity Financial
Nationstar Mortgage
Newcastle Investment
Ocwen Financial
Redwood Trust
Resource Capital

HISTORICAL FINANCIALS

Company Type: Public

Income Statement FYE: December 31

	ASSETS ($ mil.)	NET INCOME ($ mil.)	INCOME AS % OF ASSETS	EMPLOYEES
12/11	4,093	(69)	—	2,600
12/10	1,895	37	2.0%	349
12/09	1,887	113	6.0%	219
12/08	12	(15)	—	16
12/07	135	(79)	—	17
Annual Growth	134.6%	—	—	251.7%

2011 Year-End Financials

Debt ratio: 72.49%
Return on equity: (-13.06)%
Cash ($ mil.): 32
Current ratio: —
Long-term debt ($ mil.): 2,967
No. of shares (mil.): 27
Dividends
Yield: —
Payout: —
Market value ($ mil.): 572

	STOCK PRICE ($) FY Close	P/E High/Low		PER SHARE ($) Earnings	Dividends	Book Value
12/11	20.51	—	—	(2.51)	0.00	19.04
12/10	17.94	14	10	1.38	2.00	21.54
12/09	14.33	3	0	5.25	1.50	22.16
12/08	0.09	—	—	(87.00)	0.00	(234.78)
12/07	0.38	—	—	(484.00)	0.00	(148.11)
Annual Growth	171.0%	—	—	—	—	—

Washington Federal Inc.

Washington Federal is the holding company for Washington Federal Savings which operates about 190 branches in eight western states. The thrift which was founded in 1917 collects deposits from consumers and business by offering standard products such as CDs IRAs and checking savings and money market accounts. With these funds the bank mainly originates single-family residential mortgages which account for nearly three-quarters of its loan portfolio. The bank also writes business consumer construction land and multifamily residential loans. Washington Federal sells life home and auto coverage to individuals and businesses through its First Insurance Agency subsidiary.

Geographic Reach

As its name suggests Washington State is Washington Federal's largest market: home to 65 of its branches and the recipient of about 45% of its loan activity. Oregon and Arizona are other major markets for the bank.

Operations

In addition to its consumer and commercial banking operations Washington Federal has four wholly-owned subsidiaries: First Insurance Agency which offers a full line of individual and business insurance products to its customers and others; Statewide Mortgage Services Co. which holds about $18.6 million of real estate held for investment (REHI); Washington Services which also holds and markets REHI; and First Mutual Sales Finance a servicer of consumer loans.

Financial Analysis

Washington Federal's fiscal 2012 (ends September) revenue fell by about 9.5% vs. the previous year due to a decrease both interest and non-interest income. Total interest income which accounts for about 97% of WF's total revenue declined 8% on fewer loans mortgage-backed securities and investment securities and cash equivalents. Other income fell 36%. With the exception of fiscal 2010 which saw a slight gain in revenue WF's revenue has been declining for several years. Net income increased 24% in fiscal 2012 vs. the prior year due to overall lower credit costs.

Strategy

Small relative to its national bank competitors Washington Federal has been building its business through acquisitions adding new markets and growing in established ones. Acquisitions have included both healthy smaller rivals and failed banks seized by regulators. In a bid to unify its brand and increase its name recognition WF rebrands acquired banks under its own moniker.

The bank is also working through its portfolio of nonperforming loans which peaked during the height of the recession in 2009 but now are on the decline.

Mergers and Acquisitions

Most recently Washington Federal acquired South Valley Bancorp parent of the 24-branch South Valley Bank & Trust in Oregon for about $10.4 million. The purchase which closed in October 2012 boosted WF's branch count to 190 locations with total assets of about $13.3 billion and total deposits on approximately $9.3 billion. In 2011 WF acquired six branches of Charter Bank. The deal expanded its presence in New Mexico. Later in the year WF purchased most of the deposits and loans of Phoenix's three-branch Western National Bank which was closed by the Office of the Comptroller of the Currency.

EXECUTIVES

Chairman President and CEO, Roy M. Whitehead, age 60, $468,000 total compensation
SVP Corporate Real Estate, Keith D. Taylor
EVP Mortgage and Consumer Lending and Corporate Secretary, Edwin C. Hedlund, age 56, $231,000 total compensation
EVP Business Banking, Richard J. (Rick) Collette, age 64
SVP Information Systems and Chief Software Architect, Terry O. Permenter
EVP Commercial Real Estate, Jack B. Jacobson, age 62, $231,000 total compensation
EVP and CFO, Brent J. Beardall, age 41, $201,000 total compensation
SVP Internal Audit, Barbara A. Murphy
SVP Consumer Underwriting, Michael R. Bush
SVP and General Counsel, Paul I. Tyler
SVP Credit Administration, Dale R. Sullivan
SVP Marketing and Investor Relations, Cathy E. Cooper
EVP Human Resources and Deposit Operations, Linda S. Brower, age 59, $192,000 total compensation
SVP and Northern Washington Regional Executive, Thomas F. (Tom) Kenney, age 61
SVP Wholesale Underwriter, Colleen E. Wells
VP Mortgage Loan Operations, Leann H. Burke
VP and Controller, Chad J. Leonard
VP Internal Controls and Taxation, Robert C. Zirk
EVP and Chief Credit Officer, Mark A. Schoonover, age 54
VP Credit Administration, David J. Daniel
VP Permanent Loan Production, Patrick J. Carson
SVP and Division Manager South Sound Washington, Gregory J. Toso
SVP and Division Manager Northern Washington, Gregory A. Peck
SVP and Division Manager Western Idaho, Robert P. Link
VP and Division Manager Eastern Idaho, Jeffrey B. Harris
SVP and Division Manager Utah, Marlise G. Fisher
SVP and Division Manager Phoenix, John J. Pirtle
SVP and Division Manager Tucson, Georgia E. Velarde
VP and Division Manager Nevada, Pamela K. Callahan
SVP Mortgage Loan Operations, Ronda F. Tomlinson
EVP Business Banking, Thomas E. (Tom) Kasanders
VP Commercial Loan Servicing, Judy R. Grams
SVP and Division Manager Midsouth Washington, Lisa M. King
SVP and Division Manager Eastside Washington, Victor I. Mizumori
SVP and Division Manager Oregon, Peggy L. Hobin
SVP and Division Manager New Mexico, R. Hal Bailey
SVP Commercial Real Estate, Thomas R. Pozarycki
SVP Commercial Real Estate, Fred H. Reininger
VP Credit Administration, Marc A. Rasmussen
SVP Special Assets, Ronald McKenzie
VP Commercial Appraisal Review, James Corbin
SVP Deposit Operations, Teresa M. Rodin
President First Insurance Agency, Duane E. Henson
Director, Charles R. Richmond, age 73
Director, James J. (Jim) Doud Jr., age 74
Director, John F. Clearman, age 74
Director, Derek L. Chinn, age 64
Director, Thomas J. Kelley, age 64
Director, Barbara L. Smith, age 63
Auditors: Deloitte&ToucheLLP

LOCATIONS

HQ: Washington Federal Inc.
425 Pike Street, Seattle, WA 98101
Phone: 206 624-7930 **Fax:** 206 624-2334
Web: www.washingtonfederal.com

Selected Markets

Arizona
Idaho
Nevada
New Mexico
Oregon
Texas
Utah
Washington

PRODUCTS/OPERATIONS

2012 Sales

	$ mil.	% of total
Interest		
Loans	484	80
Mortgage-backed securities	96	16
Investment securities	9	1
Other income		
Gain on sale of investments	95	16
Other	16	3
Prepayment penalty on long-term debt	(95.5)	(16)
Total	**606**	**100**

COMPETITORS

BancWest
Bank of America
Banner Corp
KeyCorp
Sterling Financial (WA)
U.S. Bancorp
Washington Banking
Wells Fargo
Zions Bancorporation

HISTORICAL FINANCIALS

Company Type: Public

Income Statement FYE: September 30

	ASSETS ($ mil.)	NET INCOME ($ mil.)	INCOME AS % OF ASSETS	EMPLOYEES
09/12	12,472	138	1.1%	1,297
09/11	13,440	111	0.8%	1,250
09/10	13,486	118	0.9%	1,223
09/09	12,582	48	0.4%	1,152
09/08	11,796	62	0.5%	1,134
Annual Growth	1.4%	22.0%	—	3.4%

2012 Year-End Financials

Debt ratio: 15.07%
Return on equity: 7.27%
Cash ($ mil.): 751
Current ratio: —
Long-term debt ($ mil.): 1,880
No. of shares (mil.): 106
Dividends
Yield: —
Payout: 23.26%
Market value ($ mil.): 1,769

	STOCK PRICE ($) FY Close	P/E High	P/E Low	PER SHARE ($) Earnings	Dividends	Book Value
09/12	16.66	14	10	1.29	0.00	17.89
09/11	12.74	19	13	1.00	0.23	17.49
09/10	15.28	20	13	1.05	0.20	16.37
09/09	16.86	43	22	0.46	0.36	15.55
09/08	18.45	38	19	0.71	0.84	15.16
Annual Growth	(2.5%)	—	—	16.1%	—	4.2%

Washington Post Co.

It might be said this company can teach you something about newspapers. Best known as the publisher of The Washington Post newspaper The Washington Post Company actually gets the lion's share of its revenue from Kaplan a well-known source of test preparation materials. Washington Post's flagship newspaper meanwhile boasts a circulation of about 525000 in the Washington DC area. Other media operations include a portfolio of six TV stations and online publishing operations such as Slate. Washington Post also owns cable TV systems operator Cable One. The company is controlled by chairman Donald Graham and his family.

Like other newspaper and magazine publishers Washington Post struggles to manage the long slow decline of print publications. Its saving grace though is its Kaplan education and Cable One units which help keep the rest of the business afloat. Kaplan is best known for its test preparation materials but it also runs a popular online university that boasts about 50000 students. Cable One meanwhile is focused on rolling out additional voice and data services to its subscribers. Together the two operations account for about three-fourths of Washington Post's sales.

In other attempts to diversify its revenue streams and focus on a long-term investment in 2012 Washington Post switched gears away from media and education when it agreed to acquire a majority stake in Celtic Healthcare. A provider of home healthcare and hospice services Celtic has 9 locations in Maryland and Pennsylvania. The purchase is part of the company's ongoing strategy of investing in companies with demonstrated earnings potential.

The company sold Newsweek in 2010 for just $1 plus about $47 million in financial liabilities to Sidney Harmon founder of audio equipment maker Harman International Industries. The weekly news magazine had suffered from growing competition along with declining circulation and advertising revenues. Harmon in 2011 merged the magazine publisher with current events website the Daily Beast to form The Newsweek/Daily Beast Company.

The Washington Post meanwhile has taken aggressive steps to mitigate the steep declines in revenue through staff reductions and by closing its news bureaus outside Washington DC and shuttering a printing plant in Maryland. Also focused on boosting readership online the Post integrated its print and digital media operations early in 2010.

Chairman Donald Graham is the son of the late Katharine Graham who had taken over the business after her husband died in the early 1960s and became a legend in the publishing business. She led the Post in its decisions to publish the Pentagon papers and pursue the Watergate story.

Investment icon Warren Buffett owns almost 20% of the company through Berkshire Hathaway.

HISTORY

The Washington Post was first published in 1877 focusing on society columns color comics and sensational headlines. Hard news coverage took a back page to crime and scandal –by 1916 the "Post" was filled with yellow journalism. Any credibility the paper had was ruined by owner Ned McLean's lying to a Senate committee in 1924 about his involvement in the Teapot Dome oil scandal.

Eugene Meyer bought the bankrupt "Post" for $825000 in 1933 and built a first-class news staff. By 1946 when Meyer's son-in-law Philip Graham took over as publisher the "Post" was in the black again. In 1948 Meyer transferred his stock to his daughter Katharine and to Philip her husband.

Graham bought radio and TV stations and established overseas bureaus. In 1961 he bought "Newsweek" magazine and started a news service with the "Los Angeles Times." In 1963 Graham lost a struggle with manic depression and killed himself.

An editor since 1939 Katharine became publisher after her husband's death. The Washington Post Company began publishing the "International Herald Tribune" with The New York Times Company in 1967. In 1971 the company went public though the Graham family retained control. The next year reporters Bob Woodward and Carl Bernstein broke the Watergate story which led to President Richard Nixon's resignation and a Pulitzer Prize for the "Post." In the 1970s and 1980s under the tutelage of investor (and former "Post" paper boy) Warren Buffett Katharine Graham bought TV and radio stations cable TV firms newspapers newsprint mills and Stanley H. Kaplan Educational Centers.

The guard changed at The Washington Post Company in 1991 when the Grahams' son Donald became CEO. In 1992 it invested in ACTV (interactive television) and bought 84% of Gaithersburg Gazette Inc. (community newspapers upped to 100% in 1993) and a sports cable TV system. Donald Graham became chairman when his mother stepped down in 1993.

In the search for a place in new media The Washington Post Company made some mammoth errors. In 1995 the firm wrote off the $28 million it had invested in Mammoth Micro Products a CD-ROM maker it had purchased in 1994. Also that year blaming costs and delays the company sold its 80% stake (acquired 1990) in American Personal Communications (wireless telephone systems).

In 1996 "Newsweek" columnist Joe Klein resigned after it was revealed that he was the anonymous author of "Primary Colors" a thinly veiled satire of the 1992 Clinton campaign. Two years later the company completed the sale of its 28% interest in Cowles Media publisher of the Minneapolis "Star Tribune" and sought to bolster its coverage of information technology by buying two magazines and two Washington DC-based conferences from Reed Elsevier. The company put "Newsweek" online in fall 1998 as Newsweek.com (the magazine had been available on the Web only through America Online).

The company sold key assets of its Legi-Slate service to Congressional Quarterly in 1999. Later that year it formed a partnership with TV network NBC in which the two firms agreed to share news content technology and promotional resources. The Washington Post Company branched out into travel information near the end of 1999 with its purchase of "Arthur Frommer's Budget Travel" (sold in 2010). Its Kaplan subsidiary created Kaplan Ventures in 2000 to invest in education and career services companies and subsequently acquired postsecondary school operator Quest Education.

The Washington Post Company purchased 10 Maryland community papers from Chesapeake Publishing in 2001. The company's 2001 contract dispute with "Post" employees made headlines when reporters refused to allow their bylines to be used above their stories for several editions. Katharine Graham died later that year at age 84. In 2002 the company sold its stake in the "International Herald Tribune".

Looking to expand its online publishing operations Washington Post acquired Slate Magazine from Microsoft in 2005. The following year it sold its 49% stake in online recruitment firm BrassRing to Kenexa. Washington Post sold Newsweek in 2010.

EXECUTIVES

VP and Treasurer, Daniel J. Lynch
SVP Planning and Development, Gerald M. Rosberg, age 65, $515,000 total compensation
Chairman and CEO, Donald E. (Don) Graham, age 67, $400,000 total compensation
SVP; Publisher Express and WhoRunsGov.com, Christopher Ma
Vice Chairman; Chairman Washington Post Newspaper, Boisfeuillet (Bo) Jones Jr., age 65, $678,300 total compensation
VP Corporate Solutions and Assistant Treasurer, Pinkie Dent Mayfield
Chairman and CEO Kaplan, Andrew S. (Andy) Rosen
SVP Human Resources, Ann L. McDaniel, age 56, $470,000 total compensation
VP Central Division Cable One, T. Mitchell Bland
SVP and CTO Cable ONE, Stephen A. (Steve) Fox
SVP and Chief Sales and Marketing Officer Cable ONE, Gerald W. (Jerry) McKenna
President and CEO Cable One, Thomas O. (Tom) Might
VP and Treasurer. Cable ONE, Patrick A. (Pat) Dolohanty
VP Human Resources Cable ONE, Janiece St. Cyr
SVP Finance and CFO, Hal S. Jones, age 59, $600,000 total compensation
VP Finance and Chief Accounting Officer, Wallace R. Cooney, age 49
SVP Sales and Business Development Avenue100 Media Solutions, Rob Carbonaro
VP Communications Kaplan, Mark Harrad
SVP General Counsel and Secretary, Veronica Dillon, age 62, $500,000 total compensation
President and General Manager The Washington Post, Stephen P. (Steve) Hills
VP At Large The Washington Post, Leonard Downie Jr.
VP Production The Washington Post, James W. Coley Jr.
General Manager The Daily Herald, David C. Dadisman
President and CEO Post-Newsweek Stations, Alan Frank
Chairman and Editor-in-Chief The Slate Group, Jacob Weisberg, age 48
VP Engineering Cable ONE, James J. Hannan
VP West Division Cable ONE, John D. Gosch
SVP and COO Cable ONE, Julia M Laulis
VP Digital Sales and Advertising The Washington Post, Steve Stup
VP Information Technology Cable One, Thaddeus Crawford
VP Finance and Administration and CFO The Washington Post, Usha Chaudhary
VP Internet Services and Customer Experience Cable ONE, Aldo R. Casartelli
Managing Editor The Washington Post, Raju Narisetti, age 45
VP Business Sales Cable ONE, Michael E. Bowker
VP Corporate Audit Services, Jocelyn E. Henderson
Director; CEO Washington Post Media; Publisher The Washington Post, Katharine Weymouth, age 45
Editorial Page Editor The Washington Post, Fred Hiatt
CEO Post-Newsweek Media; Corporate Manager The Daily Herald, Charles A. Lyons
President and Publisher The Daily Herald, Allen B. Funk
Executive Editor The Washington Post, Marcus W. Brauchli, age 50
Editor Slate Magazine, David Plotz
Assistant Treasurer, Aloma L. Myers
General Manager The Slate Group; Publisher Slate, John Alderman
Assistant Secretary and Associate General Counsel, Nicole M. Maddrey
SVP and Chief Digital Officer, Vijay Ravindran
VP Communications and External Relations, Rima Calderon
VP Information Security and Privacy, Stacey Halota
VP Tax, Anthony Lyddane
Assistant Controller, Andrea Papa
Director Communications, Kris Coratti
Director Human Resources Post-Newsweek Stations, Jeanine Katona
SVP Marketing Kaplan, Melissa Mack
Editor in Chief Foreign Policy, Susan Glasser
General Manager Conferences and Events The Washington Post, Jenny Abramson
Chief Revenue Officer The Washington Post, Kenneth R. (Ken) Babby
Editor Capital Business, Dan Beyers
General Manager Capital Business El Tiempo Latino and Express, Arnie Applebaum
VP Technology and CTO, Yuvinder (Yuvi) Kochar
Managing Editor The Washington Post, Elizabeth Spayd
Deputy Managing Editor The Washington Post, Shirley Carswell
Deputy Editorial Page Editor The Washington Post, Jackson Diehl
VP Human Resources The Washington Post, L. Wayne Connell

VP Circulation The Washington Post, Gregg J. Fernandes
VP Labor The Washington Post, John B. Kennedy
VP Counsel The Washington Post, Eric N. Lieberman
Executive Editor The Herald, Neal Pattison
VP and General Manager WDIV?Detroit, Marla Drutz
VP and General Manager WPLG-TV Miami, David Boylan
VP and General Manager KSAT-TV San Antonio, James E. Joslyn
VP and General Manager WKMG-Orlando, Skip Valet
VP and General Manager WJXT-TV Jacksonville, Bob Ellis
VP Southeast Division Cable One, Michelle Cameron
VP and General Counsel Cable ONE, Alan H. Silverman
Publisher Foreign Policy, Amer Yaqub
CEO Avenue100 Media Solutions, Brian Eberman
Chairman and General Manager GetTheJob.com, Greg Titus
VP Engineering Avenue100 Media Solutions, Todd Rodgers
VP Human Resources, Denise Demeter
Director, Anne M. Mulcahy, age 60
Director, G. Richard (Rick) Wagoner Jr., age 59
Director, Lee C. Bollinger, age 65
Director, Barry Diller, age 70
Director, Ronald L. (Ron) Olson, age 70
Director, John L. Dotson Jr., age 75
Director, Christopher C. (Chris) Davis, age 47
Director, Larry D. Thompson, age 66
Director, Thomas S. Gayner, age 50
Director; CEO Washington Post Media; Publisher The Washington Post, Katharine Weymouth, age 45
Auditors: PricewaterhouseCoopersLLP

LOCATIONS

HQ: Washington Post Co.
1150 15th Street N.W., Washington, DC 20071
Phone: 202 334-6000 **Fax:** 202 334-1031
Web: www.washpostco.com

PRODUCTS/OPERATIONS

Selected operations

Education
- Kaplan Higher Education
- Kaplan International
- Kaplan Test Preparation

Cable television systems
- Cable ONE

Newspaper publishing
- The Herald (Everett WA)
- Express Publications
  - Express (free weekly)
- Greater Washington Publishing (free advertisers)
- Post-Newsweek Media (community newspapers)
  - Fairfax County Times
  - The Gazette Newspapers
  - Southern Maryland Newspapers
- The Slate Group (online publishing)
  - The Big Money
  - Foreign Policy
  - Slate
- El Tiempo Latino (Spanish-language newspaper; Washington DC)
- The Washington Post

Television broadcasting
- KPRC (NBC Houston)
- KSAT (ABC San Antonio)
- WDIV (NBC Detroit)
- WJXT (Ind.; Jacksonville FL)
- WKMG (CBS; Orlando FL)
- WPLG (ABC Miami)

Other
- Avenue100 Media Solutions (digital marketing services)
- Bowater Mersey Paper Company (newsprint manufacturing Canada)

COMPETITORS

A. H. Belo
Advance Publications
Apollo Group
DeVry
DIRECTV
DISH Network
Educate
Gannett
ITT Educational
Laureate Education
New York Times
News Corp.
News World Communications
Pearson plc
Seattle Times
The Princeton Review
Tribune Company

HISTORICAL FINANCIALS

Company Type: Public

Income Statement FYE: December 31

	REVENUE ($ mil.)	NET INCOME ($ mil.)	NET PROFIT MARGIN	EMPLOYEES
12/11*	4,214	117	2.8%	18,000
01/11	4,723	278	5.9%	20,000
01/10	4,569	92	2.0%	21,500
12/08	4,461	65	1.5%	20,000
12/07	4,180	288	6.9%	19,000
Annual Growth	0.2%	(20.2%)	—	(1.3%)

*Fiscal year change

2011 Year-End Financials

Debt ratio: 11.27%
Return on equity: 4.48%
Cash ($ mil.): 381
Current ratio: 125.12
Long-term debt ($ mil.): 452
No. of shares (mil.): 7
Dividends
Yield: —
Payout: 63.95%
Market value ($ mil.): 2,860

	STOCK PRICE ($) FY Close	P/E High/Low		PER SHARE ($) Earnings	Dividends	Book Value
12/11*	376.81	31	21	14.70	0.00	344.25
01/11	439.50	17	10	31.04	0.00	344.88
01/10	439.60	50	31	9.78	0.00	318.46
12/08	382.23	117	47	6.87	0.00	306.38
12/07	801.50	28	25	30.19	0.00	364.96
Annual Growth	(17.2%)	—	—	(16.5%)	—	(1.4%)

*Fiscal year change

Washington Trust Bancorp, Inc.

Without seeming naive Washington Trust Bancorp can utter "Washington" and "trust" in the same breath. The holding company owns The Washington Trust Company one of the oldest and largest banks in Rhode Island and one of the oldest banks in the entire US. Chartered in 1800 the bank operates more than 15 branches in the state as well as in southeastern Connecticut. The bank offers standard services such as deposit accounts CDs and credit cards. Business lending including commercial mortgages and commercial and industrial loans accounts for more than half of its loan portfolio. Residential mortgages make up about a third while consumer loans are around 15%. The bank also offers wealth management services.

Washington Trust's wealth management division includes Washington Trust Investors Weston Financial and 1800 Asset Management. The division offers financial planning investment management and trust services and has more than $4 billion of assets under administration.

Though Washington Trust's Bancorp's revenues were up a mere 1% in 2011 compared to the previous year its net income increased nearly 25% from $24.1 million to $29.7 million. An increase in earnings from the wealth management segment and mortgage banking activities along with declines in changed-off loans and loan loss provisions contributed to the company's improved results.

Washington Trust Bank is growing by opening new branches and loan production offices including a residential mortgage office in Massachusetts its first in the state. The company already had a wealth management office there to go with two others in Rhode Island. In addition the bank lends beyond its core market mainly commercial real estate loans throughout the Northeast. It also originates residential mortgages nationwide.

EXECUTIVES

EVP Sales Service and Delivery The Washington Trust Company, B. Michael Rauh Jr., age 52, $151,000 total compensation
EVP Retail Lending The Washington Trust Company, Stephen M. Bessette, age 64, $120,000 total compensation
SVP and Director Office for Non-Profit Resources, Harvey C. Perry II, $153,600 total compensation
SVP Human Resources The Washington Trust Company, Vernon F. Bliven, age 62
EVP CFO Treasurer and Secretary Washington Trust Bancorp and The Washington Trust Company, David V. Devault, age 57, $219,923 total compensation
SVP Risk Management The Washington Trust Company, William D. Gibson, age 65
SVP Operations and Technology The Washington Trust Company, Barbara J. Perino, age 50
EVP and Chief Credit Officer The Washington Trust Company, James E. Vesey, age 64, $167,954 total compensation
Chairman President and CEO Washington Trust Bancorp and The Washington Trust Company, Joseph J. (Joe) MarcAurele
SVP Marketing The Washington Trust Company, Elizabeth B. Eckel, age 51
SVP Chief Compliance Officer and Director Community Affairs The Washington Trust Company, Dennis L. Algiere, age 51
SVP and Chief Investment Officer The Washington Trust Company, Mary M. McGoldrick
SVP Commercial Real Estate The Washington Trust Company, Julia Anne M. Slom
SVP Branch Sales and Service The Washington Trust Company, Carl M. Amaral
SVP Commercial Lending The Washington Trust Company, Russell W. Hahn
VP and Mortgage Loan Officer The Washington Trust Company, Gina R. Mead
VP and Retail Lending Officer The Washington Trust Company, Linda S. Smith
VP and Market Manager The Washington Trust Company, Amy U. Arruda
VP and Trust Officer The Washington Trust Company, Paul D. Nunes
Corporate Communications Manager, Brenda D. Farrell

EVP Wealth Management Washington Trust Bancorp and The Washington Trust Company, Galan G. Daukas, age 48, $309,962 total compensation
SVP Retail Lending The Washington Trust Company, Philip L. (Phil) Friend
VP and Branch Manager The Washington Trust Company, Barbara A. MacMullan
VP and Branch Manager The Washington Trust Company, Ann Cook
VP and Branch Manager The Washington Trust Company, Paula R. Spirito
VP Branch Manager Retail Sales and Incentive Manager, Nancy J.S. Ferrara
VP Technology Security The Washington Trust Company, Donald J. McCarron
SVP Financial Planning and Asset Liability Management The Washington Trust Company, Mark K. W. Gim, age 46
SVP Wealth Management Client Services The Washington Trust Company, Rogean B. Makowski
Director, Gary P. Bennett, age 72
Director, Robert A. (Bob) DiMuccio, age 55
Director, Patrick J. Shanahan Jr., age 65
Director, Edward M. Mazze, age 71
Director, Katherine W. Hoxsie, age 64
Director, H. Douglas Randall III, age 62
Director, Steven J. Crandall, age 57
Director, Victor J. Orsinger II, age 66
Director, Barry G. Hittner, age 67
Director, Kathleen McKeough, age 62
Auditors: KPMGLLP

LOCATIONS

HQ: Washington Trust Bancorp Inc.
23 Broad St., Westerly RI 02891
Phone: 401-348-1200 **Fax:** 904-358-7013
Web: www.intl-baler.com

PRODUCTS/OPERATIONS

2011 Sales

	$ mil.	% of total
Interest		
Loans including fees	99	57
Securities	21	12
Other	0	-
Noninterest		
Wealth management services	28	16
Merchant processing fees	9	6
Loan sales & commissions	**5.1**	**3**
Service charges on deposit accounts	3	2
Other	6	4
Total	**174**	**100**

COMPETITORS

Bank of America
Liberty Bank
Newport Bancorp
People' s United Financial
RBS Citizens Financial Group
Sovereign Bank
Webster Financial

HISTORICAL FINANCIALS

Company Type: Public

Income Statement FYE: December 31

	ASSETS ($ mil.)	NET INCOME ($ mil.)	INCOME AS % OF ASSETS	EMPLOYEES
12/11	3,064	29	1.0%	558
12/10	2,909	24	0.8%	528
12/09	2,884	16	0.6%	512
12/08	2,965	22	0.7%	483
12/07	2,539	23	0.9%	474
Annual Growth	4.8%	5.7%	—	4.2%

2011 Year-End Financials

Debt ratio: 18.71%
Return on equity: 10.56%
Cash ($ mil.): 82
Current ratio: —
Long-term debt ($ mil.): 573
No. of shares (mil.): 16
Dividends
Yield: —
Payout: 48.35%
Market value ($ mil.): 389

	STOCK PRICE ($) FY Close	P/E High/Low		PER SHARE ($) Earnings	Dividends	Book Value
12/11	23.86	13	10	1.82	0.00	17.27
12/10	21.88	15	10	1.49	0.84	16.63
12/09	15.58	20	11	1.00	0.84	15.89
12/08	19.75	17	10	1.57	0.83	14.75
12/07	25.23	16	13	1.75	0.80	13.97
Annual Growth	(1.4%)	—	—	1.0%	—	5.4%

Waste Management, Inc. (DE)

Holding company Waste Management tops the heap in the US solid-waste industry. Through subsidiaries the company serves more than 20 million residential industrial municipal and commercial customers in the US and Canada. Waste Management along with subsidiary Wheelabrator Technologies provides waste collection transfer recycling and resource recovery and disposal services. Its sites include about 270 owned or operated landfills (the industry's largest network) 290 transfer stations around 110 material recovery facilities and nearly 20 waste-to-energy plants. Collection and landfill services account for about three-quarters of sales.

Operations

Waste Management operates one of the largest trucking fleets in the industry for its collection services. At its hazardous waste sites the group accepts hazardous waste primarily in a stable solid form. Some of its secure sites accept hazardous waste that has been treated before disposal. The group operates one facility that isolates treated hazardous waste in liquid form and injects it into deep wells.

Other company operations include the rental and servicing of portable restroom facilities to municipalities and commercial customers (Port-O-Let) fluorescent lamp recycling portable self-storage healthcare operations and oil and gas producing properties. Wheelabrator also owns or operates five independent power producers (IPPs) that convert waste and conventional fuels into electricity and produce steam. During 2011 the company's waste-to-energy facilities processed 8 million tons of solid waste or an average of 22000 tons per day.

Financial Analysis

That year the company's revenue growth reflected the payoff for implementing some of those strategy initiatives. Waste Management posted $13.4 billion in revenues a hike of nearly 7% from its 2010 revenues of $12.5 billion. The company attributed the increase to internal growth from its collection and disposal business increases from its recyclable commodity prices and increases from its acquired businesses (including $251 million from its latest purchase Oakleaf Waste Management.)

Strategy

Waste Management's strategy for growth includes making key acquisitions managing commodity pricing growing customer loyalty and increasing the amount of recyclable materials the company handles each year. The company also wants to enter new markets by investing in greener technologies and to make improvements to its operations and cost structure. Information technology is an important part of Waste Management's ongoing improvements. In 2011 it racked up $9 million in costs for IT systems improvements.

In 2011 Waste Management picked up Connecticut-based Oakleaf and its operations for $425 million. The unit manages a North American network of some 2500 operators who provide hauling disposal waste diversion and recycling services.

The company has been growing its healthcare operations and its WM Healthcare Solutions subsidiary provides medical waste services for hospitals and pharmacies. In 2009 the company acquired PharmEcology Associates a national pharmaceutical waste management consulting services firm and Mountain High Medical Disposal Services. In 2010 it added some medical waste assets from MedServe following that company's acquisition by Stericycle. It also acquired a medical waste processing facility and other assets from Milum Textile Services in Phoenix.

In 2010 it invested in Canadian waste-to-biofuels company Enerkem. Further expanding its "green" businesses the company acquired control of Garick LLC a leading maker and distributor of organic lawn and garden products. The deal helped grow Waste Management's organics recycling services business.

HISTORY

In 1956 Dean Buntrock joined his in-laws' business Ace Scavenger Service an Illinois company that Buntrock expanded into Wisconsin.

Waste Management Inc. was formed in 1971 when Buntrock joined forces with his cousin Wayne Huizenga who had purchased two waste routes in Florida in 1962. In the 1970s Waste Management bought companies in Michigan New York Ohio Pennsylvania and Canada. By 1975 it had an international subsidiary.

The company divided into specialty areas by forming Chemical Waste Management (1975) and offering site-cleanup services (ENRAC 1980) and low-level nuclear-waste disposal (Chem-Nuclear Systems 1982).

USA Waste was founded in 1987 to run disposal and collection operations in Oklahoma. It went public in 1988 and in 1990 Don Moorehead a founder and former CEO of Mid-American Waste Systems bought a controlling interest (most of which he later sold). Moorehead moved the business to Dallas and began buying companies in the fragmented industry. John Drury a former president of Browning-Ferris joined USA Waste in 1994 as CEO.

As USA Waste gathered steam Waste Management got off track. It diversified and Buntrock renamed the company WMX Technologies in 1993 to de-emphasize its waste operations. In 1997 however the company reverted to the Waste Management name and pressured by disappointed investor George Soros CEO Phillip Rooney resigned. After more management changes turnaround specialist Steve Miller became CEO the fourth one in eight months and Buntrock retired.

USA Waste picked up market share with large acquisitions including Envirofill (1994) Chambers Development Corporation (1995) and Western Waste Industries and Sanifill (1996). In 1996 the company moved to Houston. During the next two years it bought United Waste Systems Mid-American Waste the Canadian operations of Allied Waste and Waste Management and TransAmerican Waste Industries.

1998 saw the $20 billion merger between USA Waste and Waste Management. The new company bearing the Waste Management name and led by Drury and other former USA Waste executives controlled nearly a quarter of North America's waste business. The company finished the year by agreeing to pay shareholders $220 million in a suit over overstated earnings.

The new Waste Management bought Eastern Environmental Services for $1.3 billion in 1999. (A legal battle over negotiations between Eastern and Waste Management executives was settled out of court in 2000.) Drury took leave in 1999 because of an illness that would claim his life and director Ralph Whitworth known as a shareholder activist stepped in as acting chairman.

The company faced shareholder lawsuits after it was reported that executives had sold shares before a second-quarter earnings shortfall was announced. Waste Management said it would investigate the sales; later so did the SEC. (By 2001 the company had settled with both the SEC and shareholders.) In the fallout president and COO Rodney Proto who had sold shares before the earnings announcement was fired. Later that year the company tapped Maury Myers CEO of trucking company Yellow Corp. to take over as chairman and CEO.

In 2000 to concentrate on its core business in North America Waste Management sold operations in Europe Asia and South America in a series of transactions that raised about $2.5 billion. The next year the company established a pulp and paper trading group.

Waste Management announced plans in early 2002 to restructure the company by reorganizing its operating areas and cutting its workforce of 57000 by about 3.5%. Also that year the SEC sued six former Waste Management executives charging that they had enriched themselves through accounting fraud between 1992 and 1997.

The company formed a new recycling unit Recycle America Alliance in 2003 after acquiring Milwaukee-based The Peltz Group the largest privately held recycler in the US. The company also acquired 75 complementary collection businesses for about $337 million and divested some operations for about $18 million. That year two former executives of Waste Management Proto and CFO Earl DeFrates agreed to a settlement with the SEC on allegations that they had profited from insider trading in 1999.

In a bid to consolidate its leadership position in the US waste market in 2008 the company made a bid to acquire Republic Services but was rebuffed.

EXECUTIVES

VP Corporate Communications, Lynn C. Brown
VP Finance and Treasurer, Cherie C. Rice, age 49
EVP Growth and Innovation and Field Support, James E. (Jim) Trevathan Jr., age 59, $562,105 total compensation
EVP Finance Recycling and Energy Services, Steven C. (Steve) Preston
SVP Organic Growth, Carl V. Rush Jr., age 56
SVP Midwestern Group, Jeff M. Harris, age 57
Chairman, John C. (Jack) Pope, age 63
President CEO and Director, David P. Steiner, age 52, $1,066,049 total compensation
President Wheelabrator Technologies, Mark A. Weidman, age 55
Chairman, W. Robert (Bob) Reum, age 69
SVP Government Affairs and Corporate Communications, Barry H. Caldwell, age 51
SVP General Counsel and Chief Compliance Officer, Richard L. (Rick) Wittenbraker, age 64
Corporate Secretary, Linda J. Smith
VP and Chief Accounting Officer, Greg A. Robertson, age 58
SVP Western Group, Duane C. Woods, age 60, $561,521 total compensation
Chief Sales and Marketing Officer, David A. (Dave) Aardsma, age 55
President Waste Management Recycle America, Patrick J. (Pat) DeRueda, age 50
SVP People, Michael J. (Jay) Romans, age 61
SVP Southern Group, Brett Frazier
SVP Customer Experience, Grace E. M. Cowan, age 53
VP Tax, Don P. Carpenter
SVP and CIO, Puneet Bhasin, age 49
EVP and CFO, James C. Fish Jr.
Director Investor Relations, Ed Egl
Senior Business Director, Rick Cochrane
VP Product Recovery Group, Matt Coz
Managing Director Organic Growth, Tim Cesarek
VP Public Sector Solutions, Paul Pistono
VP Healthcare Solutions, Mike McInerney
Director, John C. (Jack) Pope, age 63
Director, Thomas H. (Tom) Weidemeyer, age 64
President CEO and Director, David P. Steiner, age 52
Director, Pastora S. J. Cafferty, age 71
Director, Steven G. (Steve) Rothmeier, age 64
Director, Patrick W. (Pat) Gross, age 67
Director, W. Robert (Bob) Reum, age 69
Auditors: Ernst&YoungLLP

LOCATIONS

HQ: Waste Management Inc.
1001 Fannin St. Ste. 4000, Houston TX 77002
Phone: 713-512-6200 **Fax:** 713-512-6299
Web: www.wm.com

2011 Sales

	$ mil.	% of total
US & Puerto Rico	12,578	94
Total	**13,378**	**100**

PRODUCTS/OPERATIONS

2011 Sales

	$ mil.	% of total
Southern	3,390	22
Midwest	3,213	21
Other	1,532	10
Adjustments	(2031)	-

2011 Sales

Collection	8,406	55
Recycling	1,580	10

Selected Services

Collection
Disposal
Hazardous waste management
Landfill management
Portable sanitation services
Recycling
Transfer stations
Treatment

COMPETITORS

Casella Waste Systems
Progressive Waste
Republic Services
Rumpke
Safety-Kleen
Veolia ES Solid Waste
Waste Connections
WCA Waste

HISTORICAL FINANCIALS

Company Type: Public

Income Statement FYE: December 31

	REVENUE ($ mil.)	NET INCOME ($ mil.)	NET PROFIT MARGIN	EMPLOYEES
12/11	13,378	961	7.2%	44,300
12/10	12,515	953	7.6%	42,800
12/09	11,791	994	8.4%	43,400
12/08	13,388	1,087	8.1%	45,900
12/07	13,310	1,163	8.7%	47,400
Annual Growth	0.1%	(4.7%)	—	(1.7%)

2011 Year-End Financials

Debt ratio: 43.23%
Return on equity: 15.83%
Cash ($ mil.): 258
Current ratio: 77.54
Long-term debt ($ mil.): 9,125
No. of shares (mil.): 460
Dividends
Yield: —
Payout: 66.67%
Market value ($ mil.): 15,064

	STOCK PRICE ($) FY Close	P/E High/Low		PER SHARE ($) Earnings	Dividends	Book Value
12/11	32.71	19	14	2.04	0.00	13.18
12/10	36.87	19	16	1.98	1.26	13.18
12/09	33.81	17	11	2.01	1.16	12.93
12/08	33.14	18	12	2.19	1.08	12.03
12/07	32.67	18	15	2.23	0.96	11.58
Annual Growth	0.0%	—	—	(2.2%)	—	3.3%

Watson Pharmaceuticals, Inc.

Watson Pharmaceuticals tries to have the best of both worlds with operations in both the generics market and the higher-profit-margin branded drug business. Its broad generics portfolio of more than 160 products includes treatments for hypertension and pain smoking cessation aids antidepressants and oral contraceptives. Its line of some 30 branded drugs is focused on urology and nephrology and marketed to specialist physicians in the US. Watson also distributes its own and third-party products to independent pharmacies and health care providers in the US through its Anda subsidiary. In 2012 Watson agreed to acquire Actavis Group which will make it the third-largest global generics company.

Operations Watson Pharmaceuticals' bread and butter is its generics line accounting for more than 70% of sales. An important part of the company's generics business is its generic oral contraceptive line. Watson has a leading position in the US in generic oral contraceptives with roughly two dozen different oral contraceptive products and about a 35% market share. Major products in the company's branded drug segment include prostate therapies Rapaflo and Trelstar. Watson is building its branded product line through several partnerships and joint ventures as well as through acquisitions of later-stage drug candidates. Once such arrangement is the exclusive licensing agreement struck in 2010 to commercialize and market the emergency contraceptive ella developed by HRA Pharma.

Geographic Reach The company generates some 90% of sales in the US. Internationally its areas of focus include Australia Canada France Greece and the UK.

Financial Analysis Watson has seen consistent revenue growth over the past decade including an increase of nearly 30% in 2011 to $4.6 billion. Growth of nearly 45% in its largest segment generics offset a nearly 55% drop in distribution revenue as sales from third-party product launches fell. The generics segment was boosted in part by new generic versions of Concerta (ADHD) and Lipitor (cholesterol). The company also saw strong growth in net income which rose more than 40% to $261 million. Strategy Even generic pharmaceutical makers face competition from other generic drugs and new drug introductions. Watson's strategy to stay ahead is to maintain a full development pipeline of products —both generic and branded. One method of securing fresh products is by striking exclusive agreements to make the authorized generic version of branded drugs nearing the end of their patent protection. Watson has held several such agreements including one struck in 2010 with Ortho-McNeil-Janssen to market the generic version of Concerta used to treat Attention Deficit Hyperactivity Disorder. However the exclusivity edge dulls after only a couple of years as other generic makers add their versions. To remain keen Watson steadily refreshes with new agreements. To reduce manufacturing and development costs Watson has been consolidating some of its operations. It established a plant in Goa India and has since announced closures of research and development facilities in Australia and the US. It owns or has invested in plants in China and other parts of India and plans to continue its overseas growth. After deciding that active pharmaceutical ingredients were not key to its strategy Watson divested its interest in an active pharmaceutical ingredients plant in Taiwan in 2010.

Mergers and Acquisitions While domestic sales account for most of the company's revenue Watson has been working to increase its international reach. It spent about $1.75 billion to acquire privately held Arrow Group in 2009. Arrow develops and manufactures generic pharmaceuticals in Canada Malta and Brazil and distributes its products in more than 20 countries. In 2011 it increased its presence in the Greek market with the $562 million buy of Specifar Pharmaceuticals. The purchase gave Watson esomeprazole –a drug that will compete with AstraZeneca's blockbuster heartburn treatment Nexium. In 2012 the company became Singapore's largest and Australia's fifth-largest generic pharmaceutical business after purchasing Ascent Pharmahealth from Strides Arcolab for AU$375 million (about $393 million) in cash. The buy not only added Ascent's portfolio of generics brands branded-generic and over-the-counter and dermatology and skin care products it also provided an established commercial base in Southeast Asia through Ascent's extended presence in Hong Kong Malaysia Thailand and Vietnam. And in a move that will essentially sew up Watson's global expansion plans it will make an upfront payment of about E4.25 billion (about $5.6 billion) in cash to acquire Swiss generic drug giant Actavis with the possibility of Actavis shareholders receiving a contingent payment valued at E250 million in 2013 for up to 5.5 million shares of Watson's common stock. The move will more than double its international access in established markets and in emerging markets such as Russia and Central and Eastern Europe.

HISTORY

As a youth Watson Pharmaceuticals founder Allen Chao worked at his parents' Taiwan drug factory. After earning a PhD in pharmacology in the US and working at G.D. Searle for 10 years Chao co-founded Watson in 1984 with $4 million raised from family and friends. Watson (an anglicized version of "Hwa's son" —based on his mother's name) introduced its first generic drug a furosemide tablet (a diuretic) in 1985. The company went public in 1993.

At first Watson focused on products that posed manufacturing challenges or had limited markets. In the mid-1990s it diversified into drug development in cooperation with other firms such as Rhone-Poulenc (now part of Sanofi-Aventis). It bought competitors (Circa Pharmaceuticals 1995) and invested in drug research companies. In 1996 the company launched its first proprietary drug Microzide an antihypertensive. Watson acquired Royce Laboratories (generic drugs) and Oclassen Pharmaceuticals (dermatology products) and boosted its sales force substantially in 1997. It also acquired rights to several products including Dilacor XR.

In 1998 Watson bought drug-delivery systems maker TheraTech (taking immediate steps to regain control of its transdermal hormone-replacement system) and Rugby Group the US generic drug unit of Hoechst (now part of Sanofi). The 1999 launch of the company's Nicotine Polacrilax (an off-patent version of the nicotine gum made by SmithKline Beecham now GlaxoSmithKline) was hampered by SmithKline's claim that accompanying instructional materials breached its copyrights (the courts ruled in favor of Watson in 2000). To boost its research activities in 2000 the firm bought Makoff R&D Laboratories and Schein Pharmaceutical. Three years later it bought Amarin Corp.'s Swedish R&D subsidiary.

Watson had marketed a Parkinson's disease treatment through a 50-50 joint venture with Mylan Laboratories but in 2008 Mylan bought out Watson's share of the venture known as Somerset Pharmaceuticals. Somerset had also developed depression treatment EmSam which is marketed by Bristol-Myers Squibb.

A big pinch to its bottom line came in 2007 when a distribution agreement with Purdue Pharma for a time-released oxycodone HCl (generic OxyContin) ended. Name-brand drug companies sometimes authorize an "official" generic form when a drug goes off-patent in order to recoup some losses that inevitably result from generic competition. Watson had distributed the authorized generic of OxyContin since the drug lost patent protection in 2005 and the drug was a big contributor to the company's revenue.

To restore its product pipeline in 2008 Watson picked up a portfolio of products from Teva. Teva needed to offload them as part of its acquisition of Barr Pharmaceuticals. Watson paid $36 million for the portfolio which included 15 approved products and two products in development.

EXECUTIVES

President CEO and Director, Paul M. Bisaro, age 51, $1,038,462 total compensation
EVP Global Brands, G. Frederick (Fred) Wilkinson, age 55, $173,077 total compensation
SVP and CIO, Thomas R. Giordano, age 61
SVP Research and Development, Charles D. Ebert, age 58, $402,556 total compensation
Chairman, Andrew L. Turner, age 65
EVP and CFO, R. Todd Joyce, age 54, $359,907 total compensation
SVP Sales and Marketing U.S. Generics Division, Andrew Boyer
VP Sales, Allan Slavsky
EVP General Counsel and Secretary, David A. Buchen, age 47, $534,410 total compensation
VP Investor Relations and Corporate Communications, Patricia L. (Patty) Eisenhaur, age 49
SVP Quality Assurance, Gordon Munro, age 65
SVP Global Generics Research and Development, Francois A. Menard, age 52
SVP Human Resources, Clare M. Carmichael, age 52
EVP Global Generics, Sigurdur O. Olafsson, age 43
EVP and COO Anda, Albert Paonessa III, age 51
EVP Global Operations, Robert A. (Bob) Stewart, age 44
SVP Corporate Affairs, Charles M. Mayr, age 55
President CEO and Director, Paul M. Bisaro, age 51
Director, Jack Michelson, age 77
Director, Ronald R. Taylor, age 64
Director, Michel J. Feldman, age 69
Director, Fred G. Weiss, age 70
Director, Michael J. Fedida, age 65
Director, Albert F. Hummel, age 67
Director, Catherine M. Klema, age 53
Director, Christopher W. (Chris) Bodine, age 57
Director, Anthony S. (Tony) Tabatznik, age 64
Auditors: PricewaterhouseCoopersLLP

LOCATIONS

HQ: Watson Pharmaceuticals Inc.
Morris Corporate Center III 400 Interpace Pkwy., Parsippany NJ 07054
Phone: 862-261-7000 **Fax:** 832-295-8301
Web: seitel.com

2011 Product Sales

	% of total
US	89
International	11
Total	**100**

PRODUCTS/OPERATIONS

2011 Sales

	$ mil.	% of total
Generic drugs	3,367	73
Branded drugs	441	10

2011 Product Sales

	% of total
Central nervous	34
Cardiovascular	22
Hormones & synthetic	16
Anti-infective	5
Urology	3
Other	20
Total	**100**

Selected Products

Branded
- Androderm (male testosterone replacement)
- Condylox (antiviral)
- Crinone (progesterone replacement)
- Ella (emergency contraceptive)
- Fioricet (analgesic)
- Gelnique (overactive bladder)
- INFeD (anemia)
- Oxytrol (overactive bladder)
- Rapaflo (prostate cancer)
- Trelstar (prostate cancer)

Generic
- Bupropion hydrochloride SR (Zyban smoking cessation)
- Bupropion hydrochloride SR (Wellbutrin SR antidepressant)
- Bupropion hydrochloride ER (Wellbutrin XL antidepressant)

Glipizide ER (Glucotrol XL anti-diabetic)
Hydrocodone bitartrate/acetaminophen (Lorcet Vicodin Lortab Norco; analgesic)
Levora (Nordette oral contraceptive)
Low-Ogestrel (Lo-Ovral oral contraceptive)
Lutera (Alesse oral contraceptive)
Microgestin/Microgestin Fe (Loestrin/Loestrin Fe oral contraceptive)
Necon (Ortho-Novum Modicon; oral contraceptive)
Nicotine polacrilex gum (Nicorette smoking cessation)
Oxycodone/acetaminophen (Percocet analgesic)
Quasense (Seasonale oral contraceptive)
TriNessa (Ortho Tri-Cyclen oral contraceptive)
Trivora (Triphasil oral contraceptive)

COMPETITORS

Abbott Labs
Allergan Limited
AmerisourceBergen
Auxilium Pharmaceuticals
Bayer HealthCare Pharmaceuticals
Boehringer Ingelheim Corporation
Bristol-Myers Squibb
Cardinal Health
Cephalon
Dr. Reddy' s
Endo
Forest Labs
Genzyme
GlaxoSmithKline
Hospira
Johnson & Johnson
McKesson
Medicis Pharmaceutical
Merck
Mylan
Novartis
Par Pharmaceutical Companies
Pfizer
Purdue Pharma
Sanofi
Shire
Teva
Valeant Pharmaceuticals
Warner Chilcott

Webster Financial Corp (Waterbury, Conn)

Webster Financial is the holding company for Webster Bank which operates about 170 branches in southern New England primarily in Connecticut but also in Massachusetts New York and Rhode Island. The bank provides commercial and retail services such as deposit accounts loans and mortgages and consumer finance as well as government and institutional banking services. It performs asset-based lending through its Webster Business Credit subsidiary and equipment financing through Webster Capital Finance. The company's HSA Bank division offers health savings accounts nationwide. Webster Bank provides brokerage and investment services through an agreement with UVEST a division of LPL Financial.

During 2010 investment firm Warburg Pincus invested some $115 million in Webster Financial netting a nearly 25% stake in the company. The move came after Webster Financial suffered two consecutive years in the red in part due to increased provisions for credit losses. After enhancing its risk management efforts the company returned to profitability in fiscal 2010 and its number of past-due and non-performing loans went down. With the infusion of cash from Warburg Pincus the bank contunued its momentum into 2011.

Webster Financial has reduced its number of locations in order to cut costs but is expanding geographically by opening branches in new markets particularly in Boston and the wealthy Westchester County suburbs of New York City. The bank is also emphasizing customer service by extending operating hours at many of its branches and by making technological upgrades. The focus on relationship banking contributed to deposit growth and higher loan volume in 2011.

To focus on being a pure regional commercial bank Webster Financial divested or curtailed several business lines. In 2007 it closed subsidiary People's Mortgage Company terminated its mezzanine lending operations through Webster Growth Capital and discontinued indirect residential construction lending outside of its primary New England market.

The following year the company sold subsidiary Webster Insurance to USI Holdings and Webster Risk Services a third-party workers' compensation claims administrator to PMA Capital. In 2009 Webster Financial scaled back Webster Business Credit by closing offices outside of its primary market in the Northeast and restructured (and renamed) Webster Capital Finance formerly Center Capital to focus on the construction transportation environmental and manufacturing markets.

HISTORICAL FINANCIALS

Company Type: Public

Income Statement FYE: December 31

	REVENUE ($ mil.)	NET INCOME ($ mil.)	NET PROFIT MARGIN	EMPLOYEES
12/11	4,584	260	5.7%	6,686
12/10	3,566	184	5.2%	6,030
12/09	2,793	222	7.9%	5,830
12/08	2,535	238	9.4%	5,070
12/07	2,496	141	5.6%	5,640
Annual Growth	16.4%	16.6%	—	4.3%

2011 Year-End Financials

Debt ratio: 14.60%
Return on equity: 7.32%
Cash ($ mil.): 209
Current ratio: 139.70
Long-term debt ($ mil.): 665
No. of shares (mil.): 127
Dividends
Yield: —
Payout: —
Market value ($ mil.): 7,675

	STOCK PRICE ($) FY Close	P/E High/Low		PER SHARE ($) Earnings	Dividends	Book Value
12/11	60.34	34	24	2.06	0.00	28.02
12/10	51.65	34	25	1.48	0.00	26.09
12/09	39.61	19	11	1.96	0.00	24.50
12/08	26.57	13	9	2.09	0.00	20.16
12/07	27.14	24	18	1.27	0.00	17.84
Annual Growth	22.1%	—	—	12.9%	—	11.9%

EXECUTIVES

Chairman and CEO, James C. Smith, age 62, $1,335,800 total compensation
EVP Commercial Banking Webster Financial and Webster Bank, Joseph J. Savage, age 59, $406,000 total compensation
EVP Secretary and General Counsel Webster and Webster Bank, Harriet M. Wolfe, age 58
SVP Investor Relations, Terrence K. (Terry) Mangan
EVP Human Resources Marketing and Communications, Jeffrey N. Brown, age 54, $401,000 total compensation
EVP Webster Financial Advisors Webster Bank, Bruce E. Wolfe
President Webster Investment Services, Thomas N. Howe
President Webster Business Credit Corporation, Warren K. Mino
SVP and Chief Accounting Officer Webster Financial and Webster Bank, Gregory S. Madar, age 50
President and COO, Gerald P. (Jerry) Plush, age 53, $651,000 total compensation
EVP and Chief Marketing Officer Webster Financial and Webster Bank, Michelle M. Crecca, age 42, $294,400 total compensation
SVP Business and Professional Banking Retail Banking Webster Bank, John L. Guy Jr.
VP Public Affairs, Ed Steadham
EVP Middle Market Webster Bank N.A, John R. Ciulla
President and COO Webster Capital Finance, Walter F. (Walt) Greenfield
EVP Consumer Finance Webster and Webster Bank, Nitin J. Mhatre
CFO, Glenn I. MacInnes
EVP Retail Banking Webster Financial and Webster bank, Anne M. Slattery
EVP and Chief Risk Officer, Daniel H. Bley
Director, Charles W. (Chuck) Shivery, age 66
Director, Karen R. Osar, age 62
Lead Director, John J. Crawford, age 67
Director, Mark Pettie, age 55
Director, David A. (Dave) Coulter, age 65
Director, C. Michael Jacobi, age 70
Director, Joel S. Becker, age 63
Director, Robert A. Finkenzeller, age 61
Director, Laurence C. Morse, age 60
Vice Chairman and COO Webster Financial and Webster Bank, Gerald P. (Jerry) Plush, age 53
Auditors: Ernst&YoungLLP

LOCATIONS

HQ: Webster Financial Corporation
Webster Plaza 145 Bank St., Waterbury CT 06702
Phone: 203-578-2202 **Fax:** 319-277-0144
Web: www.raboag.com

2011 Bank Branches

	No.
Connecticut	125
Massachusetts	22
Rhode	12
New	9
Total	**168**

PRODUCTS/OPERATIONS

2011 Sales

	$ mil.	% of total
Interest		
Loans & leases including fees	488	56
Securities & dividends	211	24
Noninterest		
Deposit service fees	102	12
Wealth & investment services	26	3
Loan-related fees	20	2
Other	27	3
Total	**876**	**100**

COMPETITORS

Bank of America
Citibank
Fairfield County Bank
JPMorgan Chase
KeyCorp
Patriot National Bancorp
People' s United Financial
RBS Citizens Financial Group
TD Bank USA
Washington Trust Bancorp

HISTORICAL FINANCIALS

Company Type: Public

Income Statement FYE: December 31

	ASSETS ($ mil.)	NET INCOME ($ mil.)	INCOME AS % OF ASSETS	EMPLOYEES
12/11	18,714	151	0.8%	2,961
12/10	18,038	74	0.4%	3,123
12/09	17,739	(75)	—	2,942
12/08	17,583	(321)	—	2,935
12/07	17,201	96	0.6%	3,609
Annual Growth	2.1%	11.8%	—	(4.8%)

2011 Year-End Financials

Debt ratio: 9.65%
Return on equity: 8.20%
Cash ($ mil.): 292
Current ratio: —
Long-term debt ($ mil.): 1,805

No. of shares (mil.): 87
Dividends
Yield: —
Payout: 9.94%
Market value ($ mil.): 1,778

	STOCK PRICE ($) FY Close	P/E High	P/E Low	PER SHARE ($) Earnings	Dividends	Book Value
12/11	20.39	14	9	1.61	0.00	21.16
12/10	19.70	34	19	0.60	0.04	20.42
12/09	11.87	—	—	(2.14)	0.04	25.01
12/08	13.78	—	—	(6.42)	1.20	35.62
12/07	31.97	29	17	1.76	1.17	33.28
Annual Growth	(10.6%)	—	—	(2.2%)	—	(10.7%)

WellCare Health Plans Inc

WellCare knows that to get well all you need is a little care. WellCare Health Plans provides managed-care administrative services to government-funded health care programs that provide health care benefits via Medicaid Medicare and various State Children's Health Insurance Programs (SCHIPS). Services include benefits management claims processing and other services. WellCare Health Plans administers its Medicaid plans under various brands such as Staywell and HealthEase in Florida; WellCare in Ohio (ending in 2013) Georgia Kentucky and New York; Harmony in Illinois; and 'Ohana in Hawaii. The company's Medicare prescription-drug and Medicare Advantage plans operate primarily under the WellCare brand.

Operations

WellCare serves some 2.6 million members nationwide. About 1.5 million customers are Medicaid members (including SCHIP members) and more than 1.1 million of those are recipients of Temporary Assistance to Needy Families (TANF) benefits. The Medicare customers include about 1 million prescription members throughout the US while its 135000 Medicare Advantage customers are largely enrolled in HMO coordinated care plans (CCPs) in about a dozen states.

Financial Analysis

After several years of reporting decreased earnings (due to troubles including legal and regulatory issues) in 2011 WellCare was able to increase both its revenues and net income levels. The firm reported a 12% increase in sales to $6.1 billion and a return to profitability with a $264 million net income figure that year largely attributed to growth in the core Medicare and Medicaid markets as well as decreased legal expenses and successfully implemented cost control efforts.

Strategy

The company seeks growth by expanding Medicaid coverage in the states where it already has a presence as well as the occasional entrance into new states where conditions are attractive. For instance in 2011 it gained Medicaid TANF contracts in Hawaii and entered the new Medicaid territory of Kentucky giving its annual Medicaid enrollment levels a 12% boost. However as a provider of services to federal and state Centers for Medicare & Medicaid Services (CMS) entities WellCare is also subject to the loss of contracts when they are awarded to different providers. For instance in 2012 the firm's Medicaid contracts in Missouri and Ohio expired and were not renewed for 2013; the state of Ohio however extended its contract for a transitional period (possibly through mid-2013) during which WellCare may provide services to its Medicaid members until they transfer to other plans.

WellCare successfully added more members to its Medicare plans in 2011 doubling the membership level of its Medicare Advantage programs (especially in special needs plans for members who qualify for both Medicare and Medicaid coverage) and increasing Part D enrollment by 27%. Like the Medicaid programs covered territories for Medicare Advantage plans can shift each year: WellCare added Hawaii to its territory roster in 2010 but exited the Indiana market the following year.

WellCare decided to exit the less-profitable Medicare Advantage private-fee-for-service (PFFS) market in 2010 after CMS changed how the plans were regulated. The move affected about 110000 customers in some 40 states and caused a dip in Medicare enrollment that year.

Mergers and Acquisitions

In 2012 WellCare agreed to acquire the South Carolina Medicaid business of UnitedHealth. The purchase adds some 65000 members throughout most of South Carolina and gives WellCare further opportunities for growth in the region.

Company Background

Though it successfully rejuvinated its finances in 2011 WellCare spent several years prior to 2011 cleaning up a rash of regulatory and legal difficulties. The company's troubles started with a raid on its headquarters in late 2007 and a subsequent federal investigation into possible Medicaid fraud in the Florida market (which also led to a management shakeup and the restatement of the company's finances for several previous years). WellCare settled the fraud allegations by paying some $80 million to the US Attorney's Office through an agreement reached in 2009. As part of the agreement WellCare agreed to operate under the supervision of an independent monitor to avoid facing formal criminal charges; the three-year supervision term was successfully completed in 2012.

In addition the company agreed to pay some $138 million to settle a handful of civil whistleblower suits in 2011; that settlement was finalized in 2012. Other related settlements include a $10 million payout in 2009 to resolve charges leveled by the SEC that it failed to refund money due a Florida health care administration agency and a 2011 shareholder class action settlement for misrepresentation that cost WellCare some $200 million in cash and bonds. Personal criminal charges for three former officers are still pending.

EXECUTIVES

Chairman, Charles G. (Chuck) Berg, age 54, $591,346 total compensation
SVP General Counsel and Secretary, Lisa G. Iglesias
SVP and CFO, Thomas L. (Tom) Tran, age 55, $475,000 total compensation
President National Health Plans, Daniel R. Paquin, age 45
Chief Medical Officer, Ann O. Wehr, age 54
VP Corporate Communications, Amy Knapp
President South Division, Jesse L. Thomas, age 60
SVP and Chief Human Resources Officer, Lawrence D. (Larry) Anderson, age 51
SVP and Chief Compliance Officer, Blair W. Todt, age 44
Chief Administrative Officer, Walter W. Cooper, age 48
VP Investor Relations, Gregg Haddad
CIO, Mark Lantzy
SVP Health Care Delivery, Scott D. Law, age 48, $58,462 total compensation
CEO and Director, Alec R. Cunningham, age 45, $341,538 total compensation
VP and Chief Litigation Counsel, John C. Richter
President Florida and Hawaii Division, Christina C. (Chrissie) Cooper, age 41
President North Division, Marc S. Russo, age 42
Director, William L. (Bill) Trubeck, age 65
Director, Paul E. Weaver, age 66
Director, Glenn D. Steele Jr., age 67
Director, Kevin F. Hickey, age 60
Director, David J. Gallitano, age 64
Director, Christian P. Michalik, age 43
Director, D. Robert (Bob) Graham, age 75
CEO and Director, Alec R. Cunningham, age 45
Director, Carol J. Burt, age 54
Auditors: Deloitte&ToucheLLP

LOCATIONS

HQ: WellCare Health Plans Inc.
8725 Henderson Rd. Renaissance 1, Tampa FL 33634
Phone: 813-290-6200 **Fax:** 813-262-2802
Web: www.wellcare.com

2011 Membership

	No. of members	% of total
Georgia	607,000	24
Florida	509,000	20
California	282,000	11
Illinois	165,000	6
Kentucky	144,000	6
New York	138,000	5
Other states	717,000	28
Total	2,562,000	100

PRODUCTS/OPERATIONS

2011 Sales

	$ mil.	% of total
Medicaid	3,581	59
Medicare		
Medicare Advantage	1,479	24
Prescription drug plan	1,036	17
Other	8	-

COMPETITORS

Aetna
AMERIGROUP
Blue Cross and Blue Shield of Florida
Blue Shield Of California
Centene
CIGNA
Coventry Health Care
Health First Health Plans
Health Net
HealthSpring
Humana
Kaiser Foundation Health Plan
Molina Healthcare
UnitedHealth Group
Universal American
WellPoint

HISTORICAL FINANCIALS

Company Type: Public

Income Statement FYE: December 31

	REVENUE ($ mil.)	NET INCOME ($ mil.)	NET PROFIT MARGIN	EMPLOYEES
12/11	6,106	264	4.3%	3,990
12/10	5,440	(53)	—	3,300
12/09	6,878	39	0.6%	3,419
12/08	6,521	(36)	—	4,100
12/07	5,390	216	4.0%	3,900
Annual Growth	3.2%	5.1%	—	0.6%

2011 Year-End Financials

Debt ratio: 5.88%
Return on equity: 23.66%
Cash ($ mil.): 1,325
Current ratio: 188.75
Long-term debt ($ mil.): 135
No. of shares (mil.): 42
Dividends
Yield: —
Payout: —
Market value ($ mil.): 2,250

	STOCK PRICE ($) FY Close	P/E High/Low		PER SHARE ($) Earnings	Dividends	Book Value
12/11	52.50	9	5	6.10	0.00	26.06
12/10	30.22	—	—	(1.26)	0.00	19.56
12/09	36.76	41	7	0.95	0.00	20.79
12/08	12.86	—	—	(0.89)	0.00	19.07
12/07	42.41	23	4	5.16	0.00	19.28
Annual Growth	5.5%	—	—	4.3%	—	7.8%

WellPoint Inc

Like B. B. King but without the guitar health benefits provider WellPoint is the king of the Blues. Through its subsidiaries the firm provides health coverage to some 34 million members. One of the largest health insurers in the US it is a Blue Cross and Blue Shield Association (BCBSA) licensee in more than a dozen states (where it operates under the Anthem Empire and BCBS monikers) and provides plans under the Unicare and CareMore names in other parts of the country. Plans include PPO HMO indemnity and hybrid plans offered to employers individuals and Medicare and Medicaid recipients. It also provides administrative services to self-insured groups as well as specialty insurance products.

HISTORY

Anthem's earliest predecessor prepaid hospital plan Blue Cross of Indiana was founded in 1944. Unlike other Blues Blue Cross of Indiana never received tax advantages or mandated discounts so it competed as a private insurer. Within two years it had 100000 members; by 1970 there were nearly 2 million.

Blue Shield of Indiana another Anthem precursor also grew rapidly after its 1946 formation as a mutual insurance company to cover doctors' services. The two organizations shared expenses and jointly managed the state's Medicare and Medicaid programs.

The 1970s and early 1980s were difficult as Indiana's economy stagnated and health insurance competition increased. In 1982 the joint operation restructured adding new management and service policies to improve its performance.

Following the 1982 merger of the national Blue Cross and Blue Shield organizations the Indiana Blues merged in 1985 as Associated Insurance Companies. The next year the company moved outside Indiana began diversifying to help insulate itself from such industry changes as the shift to managed care and renamed itself Associated Group to reflect a broader focus.

By 1990 Associated Group had more than 25 operating units with nationwide offerings including health insurance HMO services life insurance insurance brokerage financial services and software and services for the insurance industry.

The group grew throughout the mid-1990s buying health insurer Southeastern Mutual Insurance (including Kentucky Blue Cross and Blue Shield) in 1992 diversified insurer Federal Kemper (a Kemper Corporation subsidiary) in 1993 and Seattle-based property/casualty brokerage Pettit-Morry in 1994. That year it entered the health care delivery market with the creation of American Health Network.

In 1995 the company merged with Ohio Blues licensee Community Mutual and took the Anthem name. Merger-related charges caused a loss that year.

Anthem bounced back the next year thanks to cost-cutting and customers switching to its more profitable managed care plans. Anthem divested its individual life insurance and annuity business and its Anthem Financial subsidiaries. Its 1996 deal to buy Blue Cross and Blue Shield of New Jersey fell apart in 1997 because of New Jersey Blue's charitable status. Anthem did manage to buy Blue Cross and Blue Shield of Connecticut that year.

Anthem in 1997 sold four property/casualty insurance subsidiaries to Vesta Insurance Group. It bought the remainder of its Acordia property/casualty unit (workers' compensation) then sold Acordia's brokerage operations. That year Anthem was involved in court battles regarding the Blue mergers in Kentucky as well as in Connecticut where litigants feared a rise in their premiums. Expenses related to merging Blues organizations contributed to a loss that year.

Anthem shed the rest of its noncore operations in 1998 selling subsidiary Anthem Health and Life Insurance Company to Canadian insurer Great-West Life Assurance. Its proposed purchase of Blue Cross and Blue Shield of Maine (which it acquired in 2000) and merger with the Blues in Rhode Island were met with outcries similar to those that dogged earlier pairings.

Larry Glasscock was appointed president and CEO of the company in 1999. Under Glasscock's leadership Anthem aggressively expanded through mergers and acquisitions. It bought Blues plans in Colorado Nevada and New Hampshire in 1999 and finalized the acquisition of Maine's Blue plan in 2000.

In 2001 it became a publicly traded company and sold its military insurance business to Humana. In the next couple of years it snapped up Virginia-based Trigon Healthcare and a Wisconsin Blue plan.

And in 2004 Anthem made its biggest leap yet deciding to merge with WellPoint Health Networks in a deal that would make it the nation's largest health insurer. After the merger —which added Blue plans in California Georgia Missouri and Wisconsin —Anthem changed its name to WellPoint.

The company continued its growth-by-acquisition strategy with the 2005 purchases of WellChoice (parent of New York insurer Empire Blue Cross Blue Shield) and Lumenos (a provider of consumer-directed health plans).

WellPoint underwent a major management change in 2007. Larry Glasscock who as CEO had overseen the company's regional expansion through acquisitions its mega-merger with WellPoint Health Networks and its name change from Anthem to WellPoint Inc. stepped down. President of Missouri's Blues Angela Braly was named as his replacement as CEO. In early 2010 Glasscock then stepped down as chair and Braly assumed that role as well.

WellPoint provided pharmacy benefit management (PBM) services through its NextRx unit until 2009 when it was sold to Express Scripts for nearly $4.7 billion. Express Scripts will provide PBM services to WellPoint for 10 years through the deal which WellPoint hopes will improve the cost-effectiveness of PBM services for its customers.

Also in 2009 the company acquired DeCare a dental benefits administrator operating in the US and Ireland. The acquisition expanded WellPoint's dental operations significantly adding some 4 million new members. The same year it set up an office in Beijing (under the Anthem Insurance name) to explore opportunities for joint ventures in the Chinese market.

Following audits conducted by the company and the Centers for Medicare and Medicaid Services (CMS) in 2009 WellPoint was temporarily suspended by the CMS from adding new Medicare patients to its programs until certain compliance problems were remedied. The programs resumed enrollment later that year.

EXECUTIVES

Chair President and CEO, Angela F. Braly, age 50, $1,144,000 total compensation
EVP and Chief Human Resources Officer, Randal L. (Randy) Brown, age 53
Interim President and CEO and EVP General Counsel Corporate Secretary. and Chief Public Affairs Officer, John Cannon III, age 58
EVP Clinical Health Policy and Chief Medical Officer, Samuel R. (Sam) Nussbaum, age 63
Chairman, Jackie M. Ward, age 73
EVP; President and CEO Consumer Business Unit, Brian A. Sassi, age 51, $625,000 total compensation
EVP; President and CEO Commercial Business Unit, Ken R. Goulet, age 52, $700,000 total compensation
EVP and CFO, Wayne S. DeVeydt, age 42, $700,000 total compensation
VP Investor Relations, Michael Kleinman
VP Product Management Commercial, Krishnan Sastry
SVP Chief Accounting Officer Controller and Chief Risk Officer, John E. Gallina, age 52
EVP Enterprise Business Services, Lori A. Beer, age 44
SVP Provider Engagement and Contracting, Douglas J. (Doug) Wenners
President and CEO National Accounts, John Martie
VP Health Information Technology, Charles D. Kennedy
News Media Contact, Kristin Binns
Director Investor Relations, Sean Meenan
EVP Senior Business and Chief Transformation Officer, Venkata Raja Rajamannar Madabhushi, age 50
News Media Contact, Jon Mills
VP Diversity and Inclusion and Chief Diversity Officer, Linda Jimenez
VP Sales National Accounts, Jerry Kertesz
VP Account Management National Accounts, Perry Pogany

VP InterPlan and National Accounts Planning, Jai Bills
SVP Care Management, Anthony Nguyen
Specialty Market President National Accounts Consumer Business and UniCare California Local Group, Nicholas (Nick) Brecker
President and General Manager Life and Disability, Patrick (Pat) Murphy
SVP and Chief Marketing Officer, Kate Quinn
VP Underwriting National Accounts, Andrea Schell
VP Commercial Underwriting, Norm Sowatzke
VP Consumer Experience and e-Marketing, Meg Rush
SVP; CFO Strategic Business Units and Centers of Enterprise Excellence, Jeffrey P. Fusile
EVP Comprehensive Health Solutions, Harlan Levine
Director, Warren Y. Jobe, age 71
Director, Ramiro G. (Ramey) Peru, age 56
Director, George A. Schaefer Jr., age 66
Director, William J. (Bill) Ryan, age 68
Director, William G. Mays, age 66
Director, William H. T. Bush, age 73
Director, Susan B. Bayh, age 52
Director, Lenox D. Baker Jr., age 70
Director, Donald W. (Don) Riegle Jr., age 74
Director, Sheila P. Burke, age 61
Director, Julie A. Hill, age 65
Director, Jackie M. Ward, age 73
Director, Robert L. Dixon Jr.
Auditors: Ernst&YoungLLP

LOCATIONS

HQ: WellPoint Inc.
120 Monument Circle, Indianapolis IN 46204
Phone: 317-532-6000 **Fax:** 317-488-6028
Web: www.wellpoint.com

PRODUCTS/OPERATIONS

2011 Sales

	$ mil.	% of total
Premiums	55,969	92
Other	41	—
Net investment income	703	1
Adjustments (93.3) —		

2011 Premiums

	% of total
Commercial	56
Consumer	32
Other	12
Total	**100**

Selected Operations

Blue-licensed subsidiaries
- Anthem Blue Cross (California)
- Anthem Blue Cross and Blue Shield (Colorado Connecticut Kentucky Indiana Maine Missouri Nevada New Hampshire Ohio Virginia Wisconsin)
- Blue Cross Blue Shield of Georgia
- Empire Blue Cross Blue Shield (New York)

Non-Blue Cross Subsidiaries and Affiliates
- AIM Specialty Health (benefits management)
- American Imaging Management (Diagnostic imaging)
- Anthem Life Insurance (life and accident)
- Anthem Workers' Compensation
- CareMore (Medicare Advantage and special needs plans)
- DeCare Dental (Dental benefit management)
- HealthCore (Clinical research)
- HealthLink (Administrative services)
- Golden West Dental & Vision (Dental/vision California)
- Meridian Resource Company (Cost containment)
- National Government Services (Administration of government contracts)
- Resolution Health (Cost containment)
- TrustSolutions (Fraud prevention)
- UniCare (Health care plans)

COMPETITORS

Aetna
AMERIGROUP
Assurant
Catalyst Health Solutions
CIGNA
ConnectiCare
Coventry Health Care
Delta Dental Plans
Harvard Pilgrim
HCSC
Health Net
Humana
Kaiser Foundation Health Plan
Medical Mutual
MetLife
Molina Healthcare
Southern California Permanente Medical Group
UnitedHealth Group
WellCare Health Plans

HISTORICAL FINANCIALS

Company Type: Public

Income Statement FYE: December 31

	ASSETS ($ mil.)	NET INCOME ($ mil.)	INCOME AS % OF ASSETS	EMPLOYEES
12/11	52,018	2,646	5.1%	37,700
12/10	50,166	2,887	5.8%	37,500
12/09	52,125	4,745	9.1%	40,500
12/08	48,403	2,490	5.1%	42,900
12/07	52,060	3,345	6.4%	41,700
Annual Growth	(0.0%)	(5.7%)	—	(2.5%)

2011 Year-End Financials

Debt ratio: 18.64%
Return on equity: 11.36%
Cash ($ mil.): 2,201
Current ratio: —
Long-term debt ($ mil.): 9,695
No. of shares (mil.): 339
Dividends
Yield: —
Payout: 13.79%
Market value ($ mil.): 22,483

	STOCK PRICE ($) FY Close	P/E High/Low		PER SHARE ($) Earnings	Dividends	Book Value
12/11	66.25	11	8	7.25	0.00	68.62
12/10	56.86	10	7	6.94	0.00	63.04
12/09	58.29	6	3	9.88	0.00	55.28
12/08	42.13	19	6	4.76	0.00	42.59
12/07	87.73	16	13	5.56	0.00	41.33
Annual Growth	(6.8%)	—	—	6.9%	—	13.5%

Wells Fargo & Co.

This stagecoach likely makes a stop near you. Wells Fargo & Company owns Wells Fargo Bank which is one of the largest banks in the US with about 6200 bank branches in some 40 states. Community banking represents Well's Fargo's largest segment. Its wholesale banking arm handles corporate banking across the US and around the world; activities include investment banking and capital markets securities investment commercial real estate and capital finance. Its wealth brokerage and retirement segment provides financial advisory services. The company also runs Wells Fargo Home Mortgage and Wells Fargo Insurance Services.

HISTORY

Wells Fargo predecessor Norwest's history begins with the Depression which came early to the Great Plains. Farmers overexpanded in WWI and went bust as demand fell soon followed by the banks that held their mortgages. To protect themselves from eastern financial interests several Midwest banks in 1929 joined Northwestern National Bank of Minneapolis to form a holding company-type banking cooperative Northwest Bancorp (known as Banco). Each bank assigned its ownership to the company in return for an interest in the new public company. Banco in turn provided services to its members though it could not unify them operationally because of interstate banking bans.

Banco added 90 banks in its first year and by 1932 had 139 affiliates. The Depression thinned membership: By 1940 only 83 remained. Postwar prosperity didn't help and by 1952 the number had dwindled to 70 as members consolidated were sold or quit.

It experienced functional problems in the 1960s because each member had its own system. In the 1970s Banco developed centralized data processing but struggled against national competition.

In the 1980s Banco member Northwestern National of Minneapolis began buying financial services firms and formed several new business units. Banco which had become a conventional bank holding company reorganized along regional lines and in 1983 it and its affiliates became Norwest.

Forecasts of food shortages had many farmers expanding production through debt financing in the 1970s and many went bankrupt when the shortages failed to appear. Norwest needed most of the 1980s to reduce its bad loan portfolio. In response the bank diversified into mortgage banking and consumer finance and entered such markets as Nevada and Texas.

In 1997 Norwest bought banks in Nebraska Minnesota and Texas as well as an Alabama-based home improvement loan writer and BankBoston's used car finance unit Fidelity Acceptance. The next year Norwest Financial entered South America buying a Buenos Aires-based lender. The bank agreed to merge with Wells Fargo in 1998.

Wells Fargo (descended from the famous Old West stagecoach line) was primed for a merger after watching other pairings (NationsBank with BankAmerica to form Bank of America; BANC ONE with First Chicago). Norwest came a-courting with an attractive proposal: complementary regional coverage and expected cost savings of $650 million. Norwest was the surviving entity (touted as a merger of equals) but the new company adopted the Wells Fargo name.

Since the 1998 merger Wells Fargo has not put on the brakes –it has made some 50 purchases including Seattle brokerage Ragen MacKenzie; Dallas-area financial planner H.D. Vest; other companies' mortgage portfolios; and a host of community banks.

Three Wells Fargo mortgage subsidiaries formed a joint venture in 1999 with The First American Corporation to provide title insurance appraisal services and escrow closings. The bank agreed to sell almost all mortgages it originates to Freddie Mac in exchange for a streamlined approval process. That year Wells Fargo bought a stake in Navidec and its auto sales unit DriveOff.com and it bought First Place Financial (of New Mexico).

Wells Fargo bought banks in Alaska California Michigan Nebraska and Utah in 2000 as well as student loan writer Servus Financial; securities brokerage firm Ragen McKenzie and leasing firm

Charter Financial. It also acquired mortgage-servicing portfolios from First Union GE Capital and Bingham Financial boosting its portfolio over the $400 billion mark.

The company in 2002 moved its retail banking headquarters from San Francisco to Los Angeles targeting that market's growing Hispanic and Asian communities and hoping to take advantage of the dearth of superregional banks based there.

Wells Fargo bought most of the funds and assets under management of troubled mutual fund manager Strong Financial in 2005. A week prior to the announcement of the deal in May 2004 Strong Financial and its founder (Richard Strong who has been banned from the industry) paid $175 million in fines to settle securities fraud charges. Because of the troubles Wells Fargo was able to buy the company at a substantial discount (reportedly in the neighborhood of $500 million to $700 million for some $34 billion of assets) and in the process became one of the largest mutual fund managers in the banking industry.

Wells Fargo continued to augment its presence in fast-growing states like Arizona California Colorado and Texas with smaller purchases such as Houston's First Community Bank (2005) and California-based banks Placer Sierra Bancshares and Greater Bay Bancorp (2007). It bought the banking operations (five banks in Wyoming and Idaho) of United Bancorporation of Wyoming in 2008 and also bought Century Bancshares expanding Wells Fargo's presence in the Dallas-Fort Worth metroplex and into Arkansas. Later that year the company expanded in a big way by acquiring Wachovia for some $12.5 billion.

Wachovia had first agreed to sell its banking business to Citigroup for about $2 billion but Wells Fargo countered with a far-sweeter bid. Wells Fargo's $12.5 billion deal for Wachovia included all of Wachovia's operations and did not require government assistance. Citigroup challenged the deal in court but later backed off instead opting to sue the other two firms for breach-of-contract damages.

The company underwent some rebranding in 2008. It renamed HLA Global Network which is part of its insurance operations Wells Fargo Global Broker Network. It also renamed Wells Fargo Century its supply chain financing unit Wells Fargo Trade Capital.

Also in 2008 the US government bought some $25 billion worth of Wells Fargo preferred shares as part of a $250 billion stimulus plan to help grease the wheels of US credit markets. Wells Fargo repaid the government including interest in late 2009 following similar repayments from Citigroup and Bank of America and signaling an end to the era of big bailouts.

In 2009 Wells Fargo agreed to buy back about $1.4 billion in adjustable-rate bonds that had been frozen since the credit crisis struck in early 2008 forcing many of its customers to sell them at a considerable loss. Before the crisis small investors around the country bought billions of dollars of so-called auction-rate securities that Wells Fargo and others had marketed as being as safe as savings accounts and money market funds. The company agreed to buy the affected securities back at par value.

EXECUTIVES

Chairman President and CEO, John G. Stumpf, age 58, $5,600,000 total compensation
SEVP Home and Consumer Finance, Mark C. Oman, age 57, $3,866,667 total compensation
Wells Capital Management, Robert W. (Bob) Bissell
SEVP and Chief Loan Examiner, Eric D. Shand
EVP and Controller, Richard D. (Rich) Levy, age 54
SEVP Wealth Brokerage and Retirement Services, David M. Carroll, age 55, $700,000 total compensation
Family Wealth Brokerage and Retirement, Clyde W. Ostler, age 65
Regional President Alaska, Richard Strutz
Managing Partner Norwest Venture Partners, Promod Haque, age 63
Managing Partner Norwest Venture Partners, John E. Lindahl, age 67
EVP Investor Relations, James H. Rowe, age 53
SEVP Wholesale Banking Group, David A. (Dave) Hoyt, age 56, $386,666 total compensation
SEVP and Chief Administrative Officer, Patricia R. (Pat) Callahan, age 58
President and CEO Corporate Banking Group, J. Michael Johnson
Chairman and CEO Eastdil Secured, Benjamin V. Lambert
Regional President Carolinas, Stanhope A. (Stan) Kelly, age 55
SEVP and Corporate Secretary, Laurel A. Holschuh
President and CEO Wells Fargo Insurance, Neal R. Aton
CEO and President Diversified Products Group, Michael R. James
SEVP Community Banking, Carrie L. Tolstedt, age 52, $495,192 total compensation
Regional President Florida, Shelley Freeman
SEVP and Chief Auditor, Kevin McCabe
President and CEO Wells Fargo Advisors, Daniel J. (Danny) Ludeman, age 56
SEVP Social Responsibility, Jon R. Campbell
Regional President Texas Arkansas and Border Banking, Paul W. (Chip) Carlisle
Regional President Mountain West, Thomas W. Honig
Regional President Eastern Region, Laura A. Schulte
SEVP and General Counsel, James M. (Jim) Strother, age 60
President Multi-family Housing, Alan H. Wiener
Division Co-President Wells Fargo Home Mortgage, Cara K. Heiden
Regional President Greater Gulf Coast, Carl A. Miller Jr.
Regional President North Dakota and South Dakota, Daniel P. Murphy
Regional President Montana, Joy N. Ott
Regional President Great Lakes, James O. Prunty
Regional President San Francisco Bay Area, Michael F. Billeci
Business Banking Support Group Diversified Products Group, Robert D. (Bob) Worth
Regional President Nevada, Kirk V. Clausen
Regional President Arizona, Pamela M. Conboy
Regional President Colorado, Nathan E. Christian
Regional President California, Lisa J. Stevens
Regional President Southern California, Kim M. Young, age 56
Regional President Desert Mountain, Gerrit van Huisstede
SEVP Consumer Lending, Avid Modjtabai, age 50
President and CEO Wealth Management Group, Jay S. Welker
President and CEO Consumer Credit Card, Michael R. (Mike) McCoy
Regional President Penn-Del, Hugh C. Long II
President Research and Economics, Diane Schumaker-Krieg
President Global Banking Group, Sanjiv S. Sanghvi
President and CEO Wholesale Services, Stephen M. (Steve) Ellis
SEVP and Treasurer, Paul R. Ackerman, age 50
CEO and President Wholesale Credit and Risk Management, David J. (Dave) Weber
Regional President Nebraska and Kansas, Kirk L. Kellner
EVP and President Wells Fargo Home Mortgage, Michael J. Heid, age 54
Regional President Dallas-Fort Worth, John T. Gavin
Regional President Houston, Glenn V. Godkin
Regional President Central Texas, Don C. Kendrick Jr.
Regional President Greater Texas, Kenneth A. Telg
Regional President Northern California, Felix S. Fernandez
Regional President Utah, Gregory A. (Greg) Winegardner
SEVP and CFO, Timothy J. (Tim) Sloan, age 51
Commercial Real Estate, A. Larry Chapman
President and CEO Insurance Services Group, David J. Zuercher
CEO and President Asset Management, Michael J. Niedermeyer
President and CEO International Group, Richard J. L. Yorke, age 44
Co-Head Investment Banking and Capital Markets Group, Robert A. (Rob) Engel
SEVP and Chief Risk Officer, Michael J. (Mike) Loughlin, age 56
SEVP Corporate Development, Bruce E. Helsel
SEVP Customer Connection, Diana L. Starcher
Business Payroll Services Diversified Products Group, Todd A. Reimringer
Co-Head Investment Banking and Capital Markets Group, Jonathan Weiss
Head Commercial Banking East, Carlos Evans
Regional President Wyoming, Michael J. Matthews
Regional President Iowa and Illinois, J. Scott Johnson
Regional President Washington, Patrick G. Yalung
Regional President Los Angeles Metro, John K. Sotoodeh
SEVP Technology and Operations and CIO, Kevin A. Rhein, age 58
President and CEO Corporate Properties, Donald E. Dana
Co-President Fixed Income Sales and Trading, Tim Mullins
Mortgage Servicing/Post Closing Wells Fargo Home Mortgage, Mary C. Coffin
SEVP and Chief Operational Risk Officer, Caryl J. Athanasiu
Regional President Greater Minnesota, James D. (Jim) Hanson
Regional President Michigan and Wisconsin, Frederick A. Bertoldo
Regional President Southeast, Darryl G. Harmon
Regional President Border Banking, Suzanne M. Ramos
Small Business Segment and Business Direct Lending Diversified Products Group, Marc L. Bernstein
Home Equity Lending Diversified Products Group, Kevin Moss
Merchant Payment Solutions Diversified Products Group, Debra B. Rossi
SBA Lending Diversified Products Group, David J. Rader
Consumer and Small Business Deposits Diversified Products Group, Kenneth A. Zimmerman
President and CEO Specialized Lending Servicing and Trust, J. Edward Blakey
President Credit and Risk Management Corporate Banking Group, David B. Marks
President and CEO Wells Fargo Securities, John R. Shrewsberry

President Corporate Trust Services, Brian J. Bartlett
President Global Transaction Banking, Peter P. Connolly
President and CEO Wells Fargo Capital Finance, Henry K. Jordan
President Corporate Finance Wells Fargo Capital Finance, Scott R. Diehl
Regional President Commercial Banking West, Petros G. (Perry) Pelos
Regional President Southeast Florida, Kathryn G. Dinkin
President Treasury Management Group, Daniel C. Peltz
Regional President Idaho, Dana B. Reddington
EVP Corporate Communications, Oscar Suris
President Auto Finance, Robert Hurzeler
Regional President Indiana and Ohio, Mary E. Bell
Regional President Greater San Francisco Bay Area, James W. Foley
Regional President Central California, David A. Galasso
Regional President Oregon, Donald J. Pearson
Regional President New Mexico, Lisa J. Riley
Regional President North Florida, Scott M. Coble
Regional President Gold Coast, Frank M. Newman III
Regional President Atlanta, Jerome J. Byers
Regional President MidSouth/ Tennessee Alabama Mississippi, Michael S. (Mike) Donnelly
Regional President Washington D.C., Michael L. Golden
Regional President Mid-Atlantic, Ebbert E. (Pete) Jones Jr.
Regional President Baltimore, Andrew M. Bertamini
Regional President Greater Virginia, Timothy A. Butturini
Regional President Western Virginia, Deborah E. (Dee) O'Donnell
Regional President Charlotte, Kendall K. Alley
Regional President Triangle/Eastern North Carolina, Jack O. Clayton
Regional President Western/Triad North Carolina, Leslie L. Hayes
Regional President South Carolina, Forrest R. (Rick) Redden
Regional President Northeast, Michelle Y. Lee
Regional President Northern New Jersey, Lucia D. Gibbons
Regional President New York and Connecticut, Joe F. Kirk
Regional President Southern New Jersey, Brenda K. Ross-Dulan
Regional President Greater Philadelphia and Delaware, Vincent J. Liuzzi III
Auto Dealer Commercial Services Diversified Products Group, Jerry Bowen
Wells Fargo Dealer Services Diversified Products Group, Thomas A. Wolfe
CEO and President Internet Services Group, James P. Smith
Correspondent Lending Wells Fargo Home Mortgage, Eric P. Stoddard
Wholesale Lending Wells Fargo Home Mortgage, Kathleen L. Vaughan
President Workout Wholesale Credit, Michael P. Sadilek
President and CEO Global Remittance Services, Daniel L. Ayala
President and CEO Education Financial Services, R. Kirk Bare
President and CEO Consumer and Business Debit Card/Prepaid Products, Edward M. Kadletz
President and CEO Wells Fargo Rewards and Enhancement Services, Robert A. Ryan
President and CEO Personal Credit Management, R. Brent Vallat
President and CEO Business Services, Christine A. Deakin
President and CEO Retirement, John M. Papadopulos
President Global Financial Institutions, Charles H. Silverman
Managing Director Life Insurance Group, Linda Need
EVP and Head Foreign Exchange Services, Gregg Napoli
EVP Human Resources, Hope A. Hardison
EVP and Chief Credit Officer, Joseph J. Rice
EVP Investment Portfolio, Joseph R. York
Regional President Central Florida, Larisa F. Perry
Regional President Greater Pennsylvania, Gregory S. Redden
Regional President Orange County, Robert W. Myers
National Retail Sales/ Fulfillment Services Wells Fargo Home Mortgage, Franklin R. Codel
President and CEO Wells Fargo Ventures, Joe F. Jackson
President Affiliated Managers, thomas K. Hoops
President Wells Fargo Funds Management, Karla M. Rabusch
President Real Estate Banking Group, Charles H. (Chip) Fedalen
President Hospitality Finance Group, Christopher J. Jordan
President Middle Market Real Estate Group, Robin W. Michel
President Real Estate Capital Investments Group, Stephen F. St. Thomas
Wells Fargo Restaurant Finance Corporate Banking Group, J. Nicholas Cole
President U.S. Corporate Banking, James D. Heinz
President Energy Group Corporate Banking Group, Kyle G. Hranicky
President Equity Funds Group Corporate Banking Group, John R. Hukari
President Gaming Division Corporate Banking Group, Jay J. Kornmayer
President Financial Sponsors Group Corporate Banking Group, Brian J. Van Elslander
President Financial Institutions Gropu and Power Utilities Group Corporate Banking Group, Daniel P. Weiler
President Rural Community Insurance Services, Michael P. Day
President and CEO Special Situations Group, Mark L. Myers
President Commercial Mortgage Servicing, Joseph R. Becquer
President Asset Backed Finance, Julie Caperton
President Real Estate Capital Markets, Adam Davis
President Community Lending and Investment, Lesley A. Eckstein
President Commercial and Retail Finance, William J. Mayer
President Equity Sales and Trading, Christopher Bartlett
Co-President Fixed Income Sales and Trading, Walter Dolhare
President Government and Institutional Banking, Phil D. Smith
President Principal Investments, George Wick
President Wholesale Internet Services, Deborah M. Ball
President Payment Strategies, Michael J. Kennedy
CIO Internet Services, George Tumas
Head Enterprise Hosting Services, Jim Borendame
Director, Stephen W. (Steve) Sanger, age 66
Director, Philip J. (Phil) Quigley, age 69
Director, Mackey J. McDonald, age 65
Director, Donald M. (Don) James, age 63
Director, John D. Baker II, age 63
Director, John S. Chen, age 56
Director, Susan E. Engel, age 65
Director, Lloyd H. Dean, age 61
Director, Nicholas G. (Nick) Moore, age 69
Director, Susan G. (Sue) Swenson, age 62
Director, Enrique (Rick) Hernandez Jr., age 56
Director, Cynthia H. Milligan, age 65
Director, Elaine L. Chao, age 59
Director, Judith M. Runstad, age 67
Auditors: KPMGLLP

LOCATIONS

HQ: Wells Fargo & Company
420 Montgomery St., San Francisco CA 94163
Phone: 866-878-5865 **Fax:** 415-693-9501
Web: www.caitreit.com

PRODUCTS/OPERATIONS

2011 Sales

	$ mil.	% of total
Interest		
Loans	37,247	43
Securities available for sale	8,475	10
Loans & mortgages held for sale	1,702	2
Trading assets	1,440	2
Other	548	1
Noninterest		
Trust & investment fees	11,304	13
Mortgage banking	7,832	9
Service charges on deposit accounts	4,280	5
Card fees	3,653	4
Insurance	1,960	2
Net gains from equity investments	1,482	2
Net gains from trading activities	1,014	1
Operating fees	524	1
Other fees	4,193	5
Other	1,943	2
Total	**87,597**	**100**

Selected Subsidiaries

A.G. Edwards & Sons LLC
AGE International Inc.
Azalea Asset Management Inc.
Bitterroot Asset Management Inc. (Cayman Islands)
Cardinal International Leasing LLC
Carnation Asset Management Inc.
Century Bancshares Inc.
Eastdil Secured L.L.C.
Evergreen Alternative Capital Inc.
Falcon Asset Management Inc.
Metropolitan West Capital Management LLC
Mulberry Asset Management Inc.
Norwest Financial Funding Inc.
Peregrine Capital Management Inc.
Santa Fe Mortgage LLC
Union Commerce Title Company LLC
United Bancshares Inc.
Wachovia Capital Investments Inc.
Wachovia Risk Services Inc.
Wells Capital Management Incorporated
Wells Fargo Advisors LLC
Wells Fargo Auto Finance Inc.
Wells Fargo Bank Ltd.
Wells Fargo Business Credit Canada ULC
Wells Fargo Equipment Finance Company
Wells Fargo Financial Canada Corporation
Wells Fargo Financial Investment Inc.
Wells Fargo Funds Management LLC
Wells Fargo Home Mortgage of Hawaii LLC
Wells Fargo Insurance Inc.
Wells Fargo Retail Finance II LLC
Wells Fargo Securities LLC
Wells Fargo Trade Capital LLC
Yucca Asset Management Inc.

COMPETITORS

Bank of America	JPMorgan Chase
Bank of New York Mellon	PNC Financial
BB&T	State Street
Capital One	SunTrust
Citigroup	U.S. Bancorp
	UnionBanCal

HISTORICAL FINANCIALS

Company Type: Public

Income Statement FYE: December 31

	ASSETS ($ mil.)	NET INCOME ($ mil.)	INCOME AS % OF ASSETS	EMPLOYEES
12/11	1,313,867	15,869	1.2%	264,200
12/10	1,258,128	12,362	1.0%	272,200
12/09	1,243,646	12,275	1.0%	267,300
12/08	1,309,639	2,655	0.2%	158,900
12/07	575,442	8,057	1.4%	159,800
Annual Growth	22.9%	18.5%	—	13.4%

2011 Year-End Financials

Debt ratio: 9.54%—
Return on equity: 11.32%
Cash ($ mil.): 39,552
Current ratio: —
Long-term debt ($ mil.): 125,354
Dividends
Yield: —
Payout: 17.02%
Market value ($ mil.): —

	STOCK PRICE ($) FY Close	P/E High/Low		PER SHARE ($) Earnings	Dividends	Book Value
12/11	27.56	12	8	2.82	0.00	26.65
12/10	30.99	15	10	2.21	0.20	24.02
12/09	26.99	18	5	1.75	0.49	21.59
12/08	29.48	57	29	0.70	1.30	23.43
12/07	30.19	16	12	2.38	1.18	14.45
Annual Growth	(2.3%)	—	—	4.3%	—	16.5%

WesBanco, Inc.

WesBanco wants to be the "BesBanco" for its customers. The holding company owns WesBanco Bank which has more than 110 branches in West Virginia Ohio and western Pennsylvania. In addition to providing traditional services such as deposits and loans the bank operates a wealth management department with ten offices in West Virginia and Ohio and some $3 billion of assets under management and custody including the company's proprietary WesMark mutual funds. Other units include brokerage firm WesBanco Securities and multiline insurance provider WesBanco Insurance Services.

Commercial loans including real estate and operating loans account for more than half of of WesBanco's loan portfolio. Its retail portfolio mainly consists of home equity loans and deposit overdraft limits. The bank usually sells new residential mortgages that it originates into the secondary market. It plans to continue to grow its portfolio of commercial and industrial loans.

Fee-based services such as electronic banking trust and wealth management are also an area of growth for WesBanco. In 2011 the company formed a private banking department to provide personalized financial advice to retail clients. Though revenues were down that year the company's net income jumped nearly 25% (from $35.6 million to $43.8 million) thanks mainly to improved credit quality despite continued high unemployment and depressed housing prices in its market.

WesBanco has also grown by acquiring more than 50 banks and financial services firms in the past 25 years. In 2012 the company announced plans to expand in the Pittsburgh area through the acquisition of Fidelity Bancorp. Valued at more than $70 million the deal will bring in about a dozen branches in the city and its northern suburbs.

Other recent WesBanco acquisitions include Western Ohio Financial (2004) Winton Financial (2005) Oak Hill Financial (2007) and five branches from AmTrust Bank (2009) in Columbus Ohio a target area for growth for the bank. WesBanco continues to keep an eye out for potential acquisitions in and around its market area.

EXECUTIVES

Corporate Secretary; President Parkersburg Region WesBanco Bank, Larry G. Johnson, age 64
EVP Treasury, Brent E. Richmond, age 48
EVP Investments and Trusts, Jerome B. Schmitt, age 62, $220,885 total compensation
EVP and Chief Credit Officer, Peter W. Jaworski, age 56
Chairman, James C. (Jim) Gardill, age 65
EVP Human Resources, John W. Moore Jr., age 64, $142,827 total compensation
President CEO and Director; President and CEO WesBanco Bank, Paul M. Limbert, age 65, $365,192 total compensation
Vice Chairman, John D. Kidd, age 72
EVP and CFO, Robert H. Young, age 55, $230,845 total compensation
EVP Community Relations, Kristine N. Molnar, age 60, $621,040 total compensation
EVP and COO WesBanco and WesBanco Bank, Dennis G. Powell, age 62, $260,334 total compensation
SVP Risk Management, Michael L. Perkins
SVP and Auditor, Stephen J. Lawrence
EVP Commercial Banking, Bernard P. Twigg, age 57
President CEO and Director; President and CEO WesBanco Bank, Paul M. Limbert, age 65
Director, D. Bruce Knox, age 51
Vice Chairman, John D. Kidd, age 72
Director, Jay T. McCamic, age 56
Director, Christopher V. Criss, age 55
Director, Ernest S. Fragale, age 64
Director, Reed J. Tanner, age 58
Director, Henry L. Schulhoff, age 68
Director, Abigail M. Feinknopf, age 44
Director, R. Peterson Chalfant, age 71
Director, Joan C. Stamp, age 60
Director, Neil S. Strawser, age 69
Director, Donald P. (Don) Wood, age 67
Director, Vaughn L. Kiger, age 67
Director, Prof John W. Fisher II, age 69
Director, F. Eric Nelson Jr., age 51
Director, Robert M. D'Alessandri, age 66
Auditors: SchneiderDowns&Co.Inc.

LOCATIONS

HQ: WesBanco Inc.
1 Bank Plaza, Wheeling WV 26003
Phone: 304-234-9000 **Fax:** 304-234-9298
Web: www.wesbanco.com

PRODUCTS/OPERATIONS

2011 Sales

	$ mil.	% of total
Interest		
Loans including fees	175	62
Securities	48	17
Other	0	-
Noninterest		
Service charges on deposits	18	6
Trust fees	17	6
Electronic banking fees	10	4
Other	14	5
Total	**284**	**100**

COMPETITORS

1st West Virginia Bancorp
Bank of America
BB&T
Camco Financial
Central Federal
Cheviot Financial
Citizens Financial Corp.
City Holding
DCB Financial
First Century Bankshares
First Community Bancshares
Huntington Bancshares
Ohio Valley Banc
PNC Financial
United Bancorp
United Bankshares

HISTORICAL FINANCIALS

Company Type: Public

Income Statement FYE: December 31

	ASSETS ($ mil.)	NET INCOME ($ mil.)	INCOME AS % OF ASSETS	EMPLOYEES
12/11	5,536	43	0.8%	1,368
12/10	5,361	35	0.7%	1,377
12/09	5,397	23	0.4%	1,393
12/08	5,222	38	0.7%	1,501
12/07	5,384	44	0.8%	1,562
Annual Growth	0.7%	(0.5%)	—	(3.3%)

2011 Year-End Financials

Debt ratio: 4.95%
Return on equity: 6.91%
Cash ($ mil.): 140
Current ratio: —
Long-term debt ($ mil.): 274
No. of shares (mil.): 26
Dividends
Yield: —
Payout: 37.58%
Market value ($ mil.): 518

	STOCK PRICE ($) FY Close	P/E High/Low		PER SHARE ($) Earnings	Dividends	Book Value
12/11	19.47	13	10	1.65	0.00	23.80
12/10	18.96	15	9	1.34	0.56	22.83
12/09	12.34	39	17	0.70	0.84	22.16
12/08	27.21	21	10	1.42	1.12	24.82
12/07	20.60	16	10	2.09	1.10	21.86
Annual Growth	(1.4%)	—	—	(5.7%)	—	2.1%

Wesco International, Inc.

When contractors and manufacturers need parts it's WESCO to the rescue. The company distributes electrical products (fuses terminals connectors enclosures circuit breakers transformers switchboards) industrial supplies (tools abrasives filters safety equipment) lighting (lamps fixtures ballasts) wire and conduit materials automation equipment (motors drives logic controllers) and data communication gear (patch panels terminals connectors). WESCO offers more than a million products from some 18000 suppliers with about 65000 customers worldwide. It operates through a dozen subsidiaries. The company gets nearly all of its sales in North America predominantly the US.

Sales and Marketing

Sales to electrical contractors range from major industrial commercial and data communication projects to small residential contractors. Utilities and specialty utility contractors include large and rural electric cooperatives and municipal power authorities which maintain transmission distribution lines and power plants. Commercial institutional and governmental customers includes schools hospitals property management firms retailers and government agencies of all types. WESCO sells integrated lighting control and distribution equipment in a single package for multisite specialty retailers restaurant chains and department stores. Its largest supplier Eaton Corporation accounts for about 12% of the company's total purchases.

Financial Analysis

The recessionary year of 2009 was rough as it was on many companies. WESCI saw sales decline by one quarter profits fall by one half and the company reduced its workforce by about 15% as a result. As WESCO picks up in the aftermath of the recession the company must contend with around $874 million in debt. WESCO plans to repay nearly $147 million of that debt over three years.

Strategy

WESCO plans to build its business through acquisitions and organic growth. The company has said that it will focus on its global account and integrated supply programs to increase its customer base and to extend its use of supply services to customers. It targets customers in the fields of construction contracting; education; engineering procurement and construction firms; government; health care; and utilities. Among product growth areas WESCO looks toward data communications and security systems and to clean tech lighting systems.

WESCO purchased Canada-based EECOL Electric Corporation in late 2012 for around $1.4 billion. Serving more than 20000 customers EECOL is an electric products distributor operating from around 55 locations across Canada and 20 locations in South America.

In December 2011 WESCO obtained Michigan-based RS Electronics for an undisclosed amount. RS Electronics distributes electronic and electrical products to the industrial medical equipment automotive and contract manufacturing industries from eight branches in the Midwest and Southeast. Earlier that year WESCO bought RECO a top distributor of Siemens industrial automation and controls. The purchase expanded WESCO's automation controls and electrical distribution and services business and adds six branches located in the midwestern and southeastern regions of the US.

HISTORY

WESCO International got its start as a subsidiary of electrical power pioneer Westinghouse Electric Company. George Westinghouse founded the company bearing his name in Pittsburgh in 1886. The company installed the nation's first alternating current power system in Telluride Colorado in 1891. Two years later Westinghouse built the generating system that powered the Chicago World's Fair. The company also was chosen to provide generators for the hydroelectric power station at Niagara Falls.

George Westinghouse was ousted in 1910 after the company was unable to meet its debt obligations. He died four years later at the age of 67. During the next decade the company added the burgeoning radio and appliance markets to its portfolio of electrical distribution and production operations.

In 1922 the firm established Westinghouse Electric Supply Company (WESCO) to distribute power products and appliances. Westinghouse had its share of troubles over the years many of which were caused by ill-advised diversification attempts. These included forays into uranium supply financial services and real estate.

By the 1990s Westinghouse was buried under nearly $10 billion in debt and too busy putting out fires to tend to day-to-day operations properly. Not surprisingly WESCO was caught up in Westinghouse's problems: Sales declined four years in a row and employee turnover was around 25% a year.

Westinghouse embarked on a divestiture program and sold WESCO to investment firm Clayton Dubilier & Rice (CD&R) in 1994 for about $340 million. At the time WESCO had about 250 branch locations. The new owners brought in Roy Haley a veteran insurance and finance executive to turn the ailing business around. Haley tied pay and bonuses to performance and emphasized multisite customers such as contractors and companies with multiple retail industrial or administrative locations. WESCO grew through acquisitions and in 1995 sales reached $2 billion.

By 1996 the company had added 1000 employees; it operated about 300 distribution branches throughout the world. Sales reached $2.6 billion in 1997 as WESCO continued acquiring complementary companies and formed an alliance with Australian mining and steel company BHP (now BHP Billiton). Managers led a $1.1 billion buyout of the company in 1998 increasing their stake in WESCO from 15% to 33%. Costs related to acquisitions and the buyout caused WESCO to post a loss even though 1998 sales passed the $3 billion mark. The company opened sales offices in the UK Singapore and Mexico.

As it geared up for its IPO in 1999 WESCO bought distributors Industrial Electric Supply Company and Statewide Electrical Supply. The company continued to shop during 2000 adding electrical distributors Orton Utility Supply (Tennessee) Control Corporation of America (Virginia) and KVA Supply Company (Colorado and California).

In 2001 WESCO acquired two distributors (Herning Underground Supply and Alliance Utility Products) that supplied contractors who install gas lighting and communication utility infrastructure in Arizona California Utah and Washington.

The Cypress Group the private-equity firm that helped lead the $1.1 billion management buyout in 1998 sold most of its shares in WESCO in 2004 and 2005. Cypress owned nearly half of WESCO prior to those sales.

WESCO acquired fastener distributor Fastec Industrial and electronics distributor Carlton-Bates in 2005. The following year it bought Communications Supply Corporation (CSC) a distributor of low-voltage network infrastructure and industrial wire and cable products for about $525 million in cash.

In 2007 WESCO acquired J-Mark a supplier of building products which strengthened the company's position in the manufactured housing industry. It also acquired the assets of Monti Electric Supply which provides electricity and furnishes lighting. The purchase gave WESCO a broader market position in the reconstruction of the Gulf Coast region. The company sold a 60% stake in LADD which is a distributor of industrial electrical connectors and accessories to Deutsch Engineered Connecting Devices for approximately $75 million. Proceeds were earmarked to purchase shares of WESCO's common stock.

In 2008 WESCO offered to purchase Industrial Distribution Group (IDG) for about $130 million in cash topping a bid for IDG by Platinum Equity.

Roy Haley stepped aside as CEO in 2009 becoming WESCO's executive chairman. SVP/COO John Engel was promoted to president and CEO as a result.

WESCO acquired TVC Communications for about $246 million in late 2010. The deal expanded WESCO's broadband and telecom distribution network in the Americas and its ties to manufacturers.

EXECUTIVES

VP Investor Relations Corporate Affairs and Treasurer, Daniel A. Brailer, age 54
Chairman President and CEO, John J. Engel, age 50, $591,828 total compensation
VP Operations, Ronald P. Van Jr., age 51, $237,500 total compensation
VP Operations, Robert B. Rosenbaum, age 54
SVP COO and Director, Stephen A. Van Oss, age 57, $534,136 total compensation
Corporate Controller, Timothy A. (Tim) Hibbard, age 55
VP Operations, David Bemoras, age 54
VP Legal Affairs, Diane E. Lazzaris, age 45
VP Operations, Andrew J. Bergdoll, age 49, $250,000 total compensation
Director Internal Audit, Allen A. Duganier, age 56
VP Human Resources, Robert J. Powell, age 49
VP Operations, James R. Griffin, age 50
VP Human Resources, Kim Windrow
CIO, John Conte
VP and CFO, Kenneth S. Parks
Director, Steven A. (Steve) Raymund, age 57
Director, John K. Morgan, age 58
Director, Robert J. Tarr Jr., age 68
SVP COO and Director, Stephen A. Van Oss, age 57
Director, George L. Miles Jr., age 70
Director, James L. Singleton, age 56
Director, William J. (Bill) Vareschi Jr., age 70
Director, Sandra Beach (Sandy) Lin, age 54
Director, Lynn M. Utter, age 49
Auditors: PricewaterhouseCoopersLLP

LOCATIONS

HQ: WESCO International Inc.
225 W. Station Square Dr. Ste. 700, Pittsburgh PA 15219
Phone: 412-454-2200 **Fax:** 412-454-2505
Web: www.wesco.com

2009 Sales

	$ mil.	% of total
US	3,928	85
Canada	559	12
Other countries	136	3
Total	**4,624**	**100**

PRODUCTS/OPERATIONS

2009 Sales

	% of total
Industrial	40
Electrical	36
Utilities & special utility	17
Commercial institutional & governmental	7
Total	**100**

Selected Products

Automation equipment
Ballasts
Boxes
Busways
Cable
Circuit breakers
Connectors
Data communications products
Drives
Electrical products
Fittings
Fixtures

Fuses
Industrial supplies
Light bulbs
Lighting
Lugs
Metallic and nonmetallic conduits
Motor control devices
MRO supplies
Operator interfaces
Panelboards
Patch panels
Premise wiring
Programmable logic controllers
Pushbuttons
Switchboards
Tape
Terminals
Tools
Transformers
Wire
Wire and conduit products

COMPETITORS

Anixter International
Bearing Distributors
Border States Electric
Consolidated Electrical
Electro-Wire
Electrocomponents
Graybar Electric
HWC
McNaughton-McKay
Premier Farnell
Rexel Inc.
Richardson Electronics
Sonepar USA
SUMMIT Electric Supply
W.W. Grainger

HISTORICAL FINANCIALS

Company Type: Public

Income Statement FYE: December 31

	REVENUE ($ mil.)	NET INCOME ($ mil.)	NET PROFIT MARGIN	EMPLOYEES
12/11	6,125	196	3.2%	7,100
12/10	5,063	115	2.3%	6,800
12/09	4,623	105	2.3%	6,100
12/08	6,110	212	3.5%	7,200
12/07	6,003	240	4.0%	7,300
Annual Growth	0.5%	(5.0%)	—	(0.7%)

2011 Year-End Financials

Debt ratio: 21.09%
Return on equity: 14.58%
Cash ($ mil.): 63
Current ratio: 205.41
Long-term debt ($ mil.): 642
No. of shares (mil.): 43
Dividends
Yield: —
Payout: —
Market value ($ mil.): 2,302

	STOCK PRICE ($) FY Close	P/E High	P/E Low	PER SHARE ($) Earnings	Dividends	Book Value
12/11	53.01	14	7	3.96	0.00	31.00
12/10	52.80	20	10	2.50	0.00	26.71
12/09	27.01	12	5	2.46	0.00	23.49
12/08	19.23	9	2	4.91	0.00	17.33
12/07	39.64	13	7	4.99	0.00	14.10
Annual Growth	7.5%	—	—	(5.6%)	—	21.8%

West Coast Bancorp (OR)

West Coast Bancorp is the holding company for West Coast Bank which has nearly 60 branches serving western Oregon and western Washington. Targeting area consumers and businesses the bank offers standard services such as checking and savings accounts credit and debit cards and CDs. Funds from deposits are mainly used to originate loans primarily commercial mortgages as well as residential mortgages business loans and consumer loans. The bank also offers equipment leasing and merchant services. Another subsidiary West Coast Trust provides trust and fiduciary services asset management and life insurance. West Coast Bank is being acquired by fellow Pacific Northwest bank Columbia Banking System.

West Coast Bancorp suffered major losses in 2009 as a result of the recession and housing slump. Like many lenders it faced the double-edged sword of a rise in loan defaults and a general decline in property values of the assets held as collateral. In response West Coast Bank sold assets and raised funds through stock and warrant offerings.

In 2010 West Coast Bancorp entered into a memorandum of understanding with regulators that stipulated that the bank raise its capital levels and refrain from paying dividends. The company turned a slight profit that year as the economy showed signs of recovery charged-off loans declined interest rate spreads improved and loan demand picked up.

It kept the momentum going into 2011 as profits increased more than tenfold from $3.2 million to $33.8 million and the company continued to record fewer nonperforming assets charged-off loans and provisions for loan losses

EXECUTIVES

President CEO and Director; President and CEO West Coast Bank, Robert D. Sznewajs, age 65, $360,000 total compensation
EVP and Director Human Resources West Coast Bancorp and West Coast Bank, Cynthia J. (Cyndi) Sparacio
EVP and CIO West Coast Bancorp and West Coast Bank, James D. (Jim) Bygland, age 50, $150,000 total compensation
EVP and CFO West Coast Bancorp and West Coast Bank, Anders Giltvedt, age 52, $200,000 total compensation
EVP and Manager Commercial Banking West Coast Bancorp and West Coast Bank, Xandra T. McKeown, age 54, $200,000 total compensation
Chairman, Lloyd D. Ankeny, age 74
SVP and Controller West Coast Bancorp and West Coast Bank, Kevin M. McClung, age 42
President West Coast Trust, Sandra C. (Sandy) Mico
Chief Investment Officer West Coast Trust, William R. (Rick) Trout
SVP Retail Operations Manager West Coast Bank, Ann Higgins
SVP Finance Manager West Coast Bank, David B. Martz
SVP Sales Administration Manager West Coast Bank, Kristie L. Nockleby
SVP Corporate Risk Manager, Gregory B. (Greg) Schumacher
SVP Credit Review Manager West Coast Bank, Richard M. (Rich) Virkelyst
Regional President Puget Sound West Coast Bank, Timothy P. (Tim) Dowling
Regional President Coast-Willamette Valley West Coast Bank, Kenneth L. (Ken) Jundt
Regional President Portland/Vancouver West Coast Bank, David S. (Dave) Hansen
SVP Commercial Commercial Bank Team Leader West Coast Bank, Peter D. Perrine
SVP Regional Credit Administrator West Coast Bank, Lisa K. Dow
SVP Commercial Banking West Coast Bank, Dan R. Ebert
SVP Commercial Bank Team Leader West Coast Bank, Steven J. Ryan
SVP Commercial Banking West Coast Bank, Jeffery A. Bertalotto
SVP Commercial Banking West Coast Bank, Dahr Fry
SVP Commercial Banking West Coast Bank, Gary E. DesRochers
SVP Regional Credit Administrator West Coast Bank, Bob Dickie
SVP Regional Credit Administrator West Coast Bank, Michael Kiyokawa
VP and Government Guaranteed Lending Manager West Coast Bank, Jerry Burns
VP Relationship Manager West Coast Bank, Craig Starkey
Assistant Vice President Relationship Manager Eugene Branch West Coast Bank, Brent Murray
VP and Team Leader Coast Commercial Banking Team West Coast Bank, Tim Johnson
SVP and Manager Operating Services West Coast Trust, David P. Bell
VP and Relationship Manager Salem Commercial Banking West Coast Bank, Chris Bohl
VP and Manager Trust Market West Coast Trust, Tom McGirr
VP and Branch Manager MLK and Main Branch West Coast Bank, Lihua Lennox
VP and Relationship Manager Portland Commercial Banking West Coast Bank, Marcia Janner
SVP Employee Development West Coast Bank, Bill Malak
VP and Relationship Manager Salem Commercial Banking West Coast Bank, Andy Bennett
SVP and Manager Human Resources West Coast Bank, Jill Faughender
SVP Compensation and Benefits, Laurie Ferris
VP and Branch Manager Newport Main, Julie Hanrahan
VP and Manager Trust Client Services West Coast Trust, Tim Whalen
EVP and Chief Credit Officer, Hadley Robbins, age 55, $200,000 total compensation
SVP Retail and Manager Loan Production, Don Kasinger
VP and Manager Eugene North, Ginger Balazs
VP and Portland Trust Team Leader West Coast Trust, Ed Duvall
EVP and Secretary, David Bouc
SVP and Manager Retail Loans, Craig Hummel
President CEO and Director; President and CEO West Coast Bank, Robert D. Sznewajs, age 65
Director, Duane C. McDougall, age 60
Director, Steven N. Spence, age 64
Director, Nancy A. Wilgenbusch, age 63
Director, Steven J. Oliva, age 71
Director, John T. Pietrzak, age 39
Director, Shmuel D. (Sam) Levinson
Auditors: Deloitte&ToucheLLP

LOCATIONS

HQ: West Coast Bancorp
5335 Meadows Rd. Ste. 201, Lake Oswego OR 97035
Phone: 503-684-0884 **Fax:** 503-684-0781
Web: www.wcb.com

PRODUCTS/OPERATIONS

2011 Sales

	$ mil.	% of total
Interest		
Loans including fees	80	62
Investment securities	18	14
Other	0	-

Noninterest		
Service charges on deposit accounts	13	10
Payment systems-related revenue	12	10
Trust & investment services	4	3
Other	1	1
Total	**130**	**100**

COMPETITORS

Bank of America
Cascade Bancorp
Citigroup
JPMorgan Chase
U.S. Bancorp
Umpqua Holdings
Wells Fargo
Zions Bancorporation

HISTORICAL FINANCIALS

Company Type: Public

Income Statement FYE: December 31

	ASSETS ($ mil.)	NET INCOME ($ mil.)	INCOME AS % OF ASSETS	EMPLOYEES
12/11	2,429	33	1.4%	718
12/10	2,461	3	0.1%	735
12/09	2,733	(91)	—	750
12/08	2,516	(6)	—	800
12/07	2,646	16	0.6%	850
Annual Growth	(2.1%)	19.0%	—	(4.1%)

2011 Year-End Financials

Debt ratio: 7.04%
Return on equity: 10.74%
Cash ($ mil.): 87
Current ratio: —
Long-term debt ($ mil.): 171
No. of shares (mil.): 19
Dividends
Yield: —
Payout: —
Market value ($ mil.): 301

	STOCK PRICE ($) FY Close	P/E High/Low		PER SHARE ($) Earnings	Dividends	Book Value
12/11	15.60	11	2	1.58	0.00	16.30
12/10	2.82	23	14	0.15	0.00	14.13
12/09	2.10	—	—	(29.15)	0.00	79.62
12/08	6.59	—	—	(2.05)	0.00	63.13
12/07	18.50	6	3	5.25	0.00	66.77
Annual Growth	(4.2%)	—	—	(25.9%)	—	(29.7%)

West End Indiana Bancshares Inc.

LOCATIONS

HQ: West End Indiana Bancshares Inc.
34 South 7th Street, Richmond, IN 47374
Phone: 765 962-9587
Web: www.westendbank.com

HISTORICAL FINANCIALS

Company Type:

Income Statement FYE: December 31

	REVENUE ($ mil.)	NET INCOME ($ mil.)	NET PROFIT MARGIN	EMPLOYEES
12/11	12,887	692	5.4%	62
12/10	12,426	498	4.0%	0
Annual Growth	3.7%	38.9%	—	—

2011 Year-End Financials

Debt ratio: 11.21%
Return on equity: 3.84%
Cash ($ mil.): 22,734
Current ratio: 12.98
Long-term debt ($ mil.): 27,000
No. of shares (mil.): 1
Dividends
Yield: —
Payout: —
Market value ($ mil.): —

WestAmerica Bancorporation

Annie get your checkbook? Maybe not as wild as Buffalo Bill's West but Westamerica Bancorporation still shoots high with its subsidiary Westamerica Bank. The bank operates about 100 branches in Northern and Central California. It offers individuals and businesses such standard fare as checking and savings accounts as well as electronic banking trust services and credit cards. It focuses on the banking needs of small businesses; business loans and commercial mortgages together account for more than half of the company's loan portfolio. Westamerica Bank chartered in 1884 also originates construction residential mortgage and consumer loans.

Westamerica Bank subsidiary Community Banker Services Corporation provides the company and its other subsidiaries with data processing and various support services.

The company's conservative lending practices (it avoided the clamor towards subprime lending) and operating principals helped it weather the economic recession better than some of its banking peers. However the company's revenues and profits have fallen since 2009 when Westamerica netted a record $125 million. In 2011 net income fell 7% to $88 million (versus the $95 million it made in 2010) partly due to higher expenses as the company absorbed the operations of the recently acquired Sonoma Valley Bank. Revenues also fell 5% to $268 million. The declines were attributed to interest and fee earnings which fell as the company's lending activities slowed down and regulatory changes limited the amount of service charges banks can charge. (However both merchant processing fees and trust fees increased as those businesses grew.)

Over the years Westamerica has grown through acquisitions of other banks. In 2010 it added three branches in northern California when it acquired most of the assets and deposits of the failed Sonoma Valley Bank; the deal included loss-sharing agreements with the FDIC. That deal followed a similar transaction when the bank acquired County Bank after it was seized by regulators. That deal added nearly 40 branches to Westamerica Bank's network most of them in California's Central Valley.

Westamerica is currently not seeking to aggressively grow its loan portfolio especially in light of lower yields and soft demand.

EXECUTIVES

SVP Operations and Systems and Division Manager, Dennis R. Hansen, age 62, $130,008 total compensation
SVP and Treasurer, Jennifer J. Finger, age 58, $129,996 total compensation
Chairman President and CEO, David L. Payne, age 57, $371,000 total compensation
SVP and CFO, John A. (Robert) Thorson, age 52, $142,000 total compensation
VP and General Auditor, James J. Schneck
SVP and Manager Banking Division Westamerica Bank, David L. Robinson, age 53, $150,000 total compensation
SVP and Chief Credit Administrator Westamerica Bank, Russell Rizzardi, age 57
Director, E. Joseph Bowler, age 76
Director, Etta Allen, age 83
Director, Louis E. Bartolini, age 80
Director, Arthur C. Latno Jr., age 83
Director, Patrick D. Lynch, age 79
Director, Catherine C. MacMillan, age 65
Director, Ronald A. Nelson, age 70
Director, Edward B. Sylvester, age 76
Auditors: KPMGLLP

LOCATIONS

HQ: Westamerica Bancorporation
1108 Fifth Ave., San Rafael CA 94901
Phone: 415-257-8000 **Fax:** 817-878-3430
Web: www.ushealthgroup.com

PRODUCTS/OPERATIONS

2011 Sales

	$ mil.	% of total
Interest		
Loans	160	60
Investment securities held to maturity	25	10
Investment securities available for sale & other	21	8
Noninterest		
Service charges on deposit accounts	29	11
Merchant processing services	9	3
Debit card fees	5	2
ATM processing fees	3	1
Other	12	5
Total	**268**	**100**

COMPETITORS

Bank of America
Citigroup
Comerica
First Republic (CA)
JPMorgan Chase
Mechanics Bank
U.S. Bancorp
UnionBanCal
Wells Fargo
Western Alliance

HISTORICAL FINANCIALS

Company Type: Public

Income Statement FYE: December 31

	ASSETS ($ mil.)	NET INCOME ($ mil.)	INCOME AS % OF ASSETS	EMPLOYEES
12/11	5,042	87	1.7%	961
12/10	4,931	94	1.9%	999
12/09	4,975	125	2.5%	1,051
12/08	4,032	59	1.5%	881
12/07	4,558	89	2.0%	887
Annual Growth	2.6%	(0.5%)	—	2.0%

2011 Year-End Financials

Debt ratio: 0.81%
Return on equity: 15.73%
Cash ($ mil.): 530
Current ratio: —
Long-term debt ($ mil.): 41
No. of shares (mil.): 28
Dividends
Yield: —
Payout: 47.39%
Market value ($ mil.): 1,236

	STOCK PRICE ($) FY Close	P/E High/Low		PER SHARE ($) Earnings	Dividends	Book Value
12/11	43.90	18	12	3.06	0.00	19.85
12/10	55.47	19	15	3.21	1.44	18.74
12/09	55.37	14	8	4.14	1.41	17.31
12/08	51.15	31	19	2.04	1.39	14.19
12/07	44.55	18	13	2.98	1.36	13.60
Annual Growth	(0.4%)	—	—	0.7%	—	9.9%

Western Alliance Bancorporation

The allies behind holding company Western Alliance Bancorporation are Western Alliance Bank (which operates as Alliance Bank of Arizona and First Independent Bank of Nevada) Las Vegas-based Bank of Nevada and Torrey Pines Bank which is active throughout California. Together the banks operate about 40 branches. Serving local businesses real estate developers and investors not-for-profit organizations and consumers the banks provide standard deposit products such as checking savings and money market accounts and CDs. Loans to businesses including real estate mortgages commercial and industrial loans and construction and land development loans dominate the banks' lending activities.

Other subsidiaries of Western Alliance Bancorporation include Shine Investment Advisory Services (80% owned) and Western Alliance Equipment Leasing. To build up its operations in Las Vegas in 2012 the company agreed to buy Western Liberty Bancorp holding company of the three-branch Service1st Bank of Nevada.

After three consecutive years of losses Western Alliance Bancorporation recorded positive net income in 2011 as all three of its subsidiary banks were profitable for the first time since 2007. The company's results were bolstered by loan growth improved interest rate margins and spreads and a decrease in loan loss provisions. The economic turmoil that had gripped its key markets of California Phoenix and Las Vegas during the depths of the recession also abated.

The company exited or divested some non-core businesses during its years in the red. In 2009 it sold a majority of investment advisor Miller/Russell & Associates to that firm's management and sold wealth manager Premier Trust to Ladenburg Thalmann the following year. Also in 2010 Western Alliance ceased operations related to PartnersFirst its affinity credit card platform.

The company did not totally retrench however. Its Bank of Nevada subsidiary was approved by the FDIC in 2009 to acquire deposits and assets of the failed Security Savings Bank in a transaction that included loss-sharing agreements with the regulator. Western Alliance Bancorporation also opened three new bank branches in 2010.

Western Alliance's chairman president and CEO Robert Sarver is also majority owner of the Phoenix Suns NBA franchise.

EXECUTIVES

EVP and Chief Credit Officer, Robert R. (Bob) McAuslan, age 59
Chairman and CEO, Robert G. Sarver, age 50, $597,141 total compensation
EVP and CFO; EVP Bank of Nevada, Dale M. Gibbons, age 51, $311,539 total compensation
EVP and Chief Administrative Officer, Merrill S. Wall, age 64, $290,096 total compensation
President and CEO Alta Alliance Bank, Sedrick A. Tydus
President COO and Director, Kenneth A. (Ken) Vecchione, age 57
EVP Southern California Administration; CEO Torrey Pines Bank, Gerald (Gary) Cady, age 57, $283,942 total compensation
Chief Credit Officer Western Alliance Bank; Vice Chairman Alliance Bank of Arizona, Duane Froeschle, age 59, $222,307 total compensation
EVP Arizona Administration; President and CEO Alliance Bank of Arizona, James H. (Jim) Lundy, age 62, $231,246 total compensation
EVP Operations and Secretary, Linda N. Mahan, age 54, $160,365 total compensation
President and CEO Premier Trust, Mark Dreschler
SVP Controller and Principal Accounting Officer, Susan C. Thompson, age 49
EVP Southern Nevada Administration; CEO Bank of Nevada, Bruce Hendricks, age 61, $275,192 total compensation
EVP Northern Nevada Administration; President and CEO First Independent Bank of Nevada, James (Jim) DeVolld, age 53
President and CEO Western Alliance Leasing, Michael (Mike) Brown
SVP and Director Human Resources Bank of Nevada, Flossie Christensen
Chief Information Technology Officer Bank of Nevada, Ron Pochop
Director, Steven J. (Steve) Hilton, age 50
Director, Donald D. (Don) Snyder, age 64
Director, William S. (Bill) Boyd, age 80
Director, James E. Nave, age 67
Director, Cary P. Mack, age 52
President COO and Director, Kenneth A. (Ken) Vecchione, age 57
Director, Sung Won Sohn, age 67
Director, Marianne B. Johnson, age 53
Director, Todd Marshall, age 55
Director, M. Nafees Nagy, age 68
Director, Bruce Beach, age 62
Director, John P. Sande III, age 62
Auditors: McGladreyLLP

LOCATIONS

HQ: Western Alliance Bancorporation
1 E. Washington St. Ste. 1400, Phoenix AZ 85004
Phone: 602-389-3500 **Fax:** 604-684-8092
Web: www.northerndynastyminerals.com

PRODUCTS/OPERATIONS

2011 Sales

	$ mil.	% of total
Interest		
Loans including fees	261	79
Taxable securities	28	8
Other	6	2
Noninterest		
Service charges & fees	9	3
Mark to market gains net	5	2
Bank-owned life insurance	5	2
Net gain on sales of securities	4	1
Trust & investment advisory fees	2	1
Other fee revenue	3	1
Other	3	1
Total	**331**	**100**

COMPETITORS

BancWest
Bank of America
Bank of the West
Desert Schools FCU
First Banks
PacWest Bancorp
U.S. Bancorp
UnionBanCal
Wells Fargo
Westamerica
Zions Bancorporation

HISTORICAL FINANCIALS

Company Type: Public

Income Statement FYE: December 31

	ASSETS ($ mil.)	NET INCOME ($ mil.)	INCOME AS % OF ASSETS	EMPLOYEES
12/11	6,844	31	0.5%	942
12/10	6,193	(7)	—	908
12/09	5,753	(151)	—	930
12/08	5,242	(236)	—	1,020
12/07	5,016	32	0.7%	992
Annual Growth	8.1%	(1.1%)	—	(1.3%)

2011 Year-End Financials

Debt ratio: 5.70%
Return on equity: 4.95%
Cash ($ mil.): 155
Current ratio: —
Long-term debt ($ mil.): 390
No. of shares (mil.): 82
Dividends
Yield: —
Payout: —
Market value ($ mil.): 513

	STOCK PRICE ($) FY Close	P/E High/Low		PER SHARE ($) Earnings	Dividends	Book Value
12/11	6.23	44	25	0.19	0.00	7.73
12/10	7.36	—	—	(0.23)	0.00	7.37
12/09	3.78	—	—	(2.74)	0.00	7.94
12/08	10.09	—	—	(7.27)	0.00	12.84
12/07	18.77	31	16	1.06	0.00	16.63
Annual Growth	(24.1%)	—	—	(34.9%)	—	(17.4%)

Western Digital Corp.

When it comes to data storage Western Digital has drive. The company is one of the largest independent makers of hard-disk drives which record store and recall volumes of data. Drives for PCs account for most of Western Digital's sales although the company also makes devices used in servers cloud computing data centers and home entertainment products such as set-top boxes and video game consoles. The company sells to manufacturers and through retailers and distributors. More than 60% of its sales are to OEMs such as Hewlett-Packard which is Western Digital's largest customer. The company gets more than half of its sales from the Asia/Pacific region.

HISTORY

Western Digital was founded in 1970 as a manufacturer of specialized semiconductors and electronic calculators. The company filed for Chapter 11 bankruptcy in 1976. However it reorganized and emerged successfully in 1978. Roger Johnson after a succession of executive positions at Memorex Measurex and Burroughs came to Western Digital as EVP and COO in 1982. Sales were merely $34 million hurt by the acquisition of several ill-fitting computer and electronics businesses. By 1984 Johnson became president and CEO; he sold off several companies to concentrate on storage control devices. A contract with IBM contributed to Western Digital's sales topping $460 million in 1987.

Anticipating a change in technology that would have disk drive makers building storage control into the drives themselves Western Digital began to shift its efforts toward making disk drives in 1988. Ten-year company veteran Kathy Braun oversaw the purchase of Tandon's disk drive operations. Tandon was considered a second-rate manufacturer using aging technology but its drives continued to sell well for a period following the acquisition. This created a false sense of security for Western Digital and delayed the development of more competitive drives. In 1990 the market for storage controller boards essentially disappeared. Losses prompted a restructuring that in turn violated Western Digital's credit agreements.

In 1991 the US economy slowed and the disk drive industry began a price war. That year Western Digital appearing close to bankruptcy sold its profitable departmental network business to Standard Microsystems.

As the PC market improved in 1992 so did Western Digital's prospects. A big boost came when the cash-strapped company introduced a line of disk drives with a commonality of parts. In 1993 Western Digital's IPO and sale of its wafer factory to Motorola reduced its high debt. That year the Clinton administration appointed CEO Johnson head of the General Services Administration. IBM veteran Charles Haggerty who joined Western Digital in 1992 assumed the company's top post. Johnson a lifelong Republican served nearly three years in the GSA post and resigned in 1996 to work for President Bill Clinton's re-election; he died in 2005.

In 1994 Western Digital enjoyed its first profit in four years. The company sold off its Microcomputer Products Group which made proprietary semiconductors in 1996 and introduced its first hard drives aimed at the corporate network computing market.

In 1997 a number of Asian manufacturers jumped into the market at the same time that computer makers were taking on sales approaches to eliminate the need for large inventories of hard drives and other stock. Those factors combined with stalled PC demand and Western Digital's slow transition to newer recording head technologies caused a loss for fiscal 1998. To respond Western Digital cut more than 20% of its workforce and slashed production. Braun by then second in command at the company and one of the industry's highest-paid women retired in 1998.

In 1999 the company sold its disk media business producer of magnetically coated disks that store data in hard drives to longtime supplier Komag. Later that year Western Digital took a financial hit following its recall of 400000 defective disk drives; it announced it would lay off another 2500 employees primarily in Singapore.

In 2000 Haggerty retired from the CEO post; COO Matthew Massengill was tapped to replace him. Also that year the company branched into new markets through two subsidiaries: Connex (network storage) and SageTree (supply chain software).

In 2001 Western Digital sold Connex to former rival Quantum after that company exited the hard drive market. It also sold its SANavigator storage-area network management software unit to McDATA for about $30 million. Massengill was named chairman later that year. In 2003 it acquired most of the assets of bankrupt drive component maker Read-Rite for approximately $95 million in cash.

Massengill stepped down as CEO in 2005 while remaining executive chairman. Arif Shakeel Western Digital's president and COO since 2002 succeeded Massengill as CEO keeping the president's title.

Shakeel gave up the president's post in 2006 and stepped down as CEO in 2007. John Coyne a Western Digital employee since 1983 succeeded him in both posts. Also in 2007 Massengill stepped down as chairman while remaining on the board and was succeeded by Thomas Pardun a veteran telecommunications executive who served as Western Digital's chairman for two years earlier in the decade.

On the acquisition front Western Digital acquired disk component maker Komag for $1 billion in 2007. The purchase allowed Western Digital to manufacture the media and substrates used in its drives. Looking to cut costs in 2009 the company sold its media substrate manufacturing facility in Sarawak Malaysia which it acquired from Komag to competitor Hitachi Global Storage Technologies (HGST).

In 2009 Western Digital purchased SiliconSystems for $65 million in cash entering the market for solid-state drives. Used primarily in embedded systems Western Digital used the acquisition to develop solid-state products for the enterprise storage market.

EXECUTIVES

EVP Worldwide Sales and Sales Operations, James J. (Jim) Murphy, age 52
Chairman, Thomas E. Pardun, age 68
COO, Timothy M. (Tim) Leyden, age 60, $507,692 total compensation
VP Investor Relations, Bob Blair, age 61
President CEO and Director, John F. Coyne, age 62, $807,692 total compensation
VP and General Manager Enterprise Storage Solutions, Thomas (Tom) McDorman
EVP and General Manager Branded Products, James K. (Jim) Welsh
Public Relations, Steve Shattuck
VP Marketing Branded Products Group, Dale Pistilli
EVP Operations, Martin W. (Marty) Finkbeiner, $412,318 total compensation
SVP and CFO, Wolfgang U. Nickl, age 43
Public Relations, Heather Skinner
EVP and General Manager Storage Products, James D. Morris
Director, Len J. Lauer, age 55
Director, Arif Shakeel, age 57
Director, Matthew E. (Matt) Massengill, age 51
Director, Peter D. Behrendt, age 73
Director, Henry T. DeNero, age 66
Director, Kathleen A. (Kathy) Cote, age 63
Director, William L. (Bill) Kimsey, age 70
President CEO and Director, John F. Coyne, age 62
Auditors: KPMGLLP

LOCATIONS

HQ: Western Digital Corporation
3355 Michelson Dr. Ste. 100, Irvine CA 92612
Phone: 949-672-7000 **Fax:** 949-672-5408
Web: www.wdc.com

2012 Sales

	$ mil.	% of total
Asia	7,219	58
US	2,366	19
Europe Middle East & Africa	2,325	19
Other	568	4
Total	**12,478**	**100**

PRODUCTS/OPERATIONS

2012 Sales by Channel

	% of total
OEM	63
Distributors	25
Retailers	12
Total	**100**

Selected Products

Internal Hard Drives
- Audio/Video hard drives (Performer)
- Desktop PCs and entry-level servers (Caviar Protege)
- Servers and storage systems (Raptor)

External Hard Drives
- FireWire for PCs and Macs

Accessories
- Desktop (FireWire adapter)
- Mobile (FireWire CardBus PC card)

COMPETITORS

Apple Inc.
EMC
Fujitsu
Intel
Iomega
LaCie
Micron Technology
Roku
Samsung Electronics
Seagate Technology
SMART Modular Technologies
STEC
TEAC
Toshiba

HISTORICAL FINANCIALS

Company Type: Public

Income Statement FYE: June 29

	REVENUE ($ mil.)	NET INCOME ($ mil.)	NET PROFIT MARGIN	EMPLOYEES
06/12*	12,478	1,612	12.9%	103,111
07/11	9,526	726	7.6%	65,431
07/10	9,850	1,382	14.0%	62,500
07/09	7,453	470	6.3%	45,991
06/08	8,074	867	10.7%	50,072
Annual Growth	11.5%	16.8%	—	19.8%

*Fiscal year change

2012 Year-End Financials

Debt ratio: 15.38%
Return on equity: 21.02%
Cash ($ mil.): 3,208
Current ratio: 177.11
Long-term debt ($ mil.): 1,955
No. of shares (mil.): 246
Dividends
Yield: —
Payout: —
Market value ($ mil.): 7,498

	STOCK PRICE ($) FY Close	P/E High/Low		PER SHARE ($) Earnings	Dividends	Book Value
06/12*	30.48	5	4	6.58	0.00	31.17
07/11	7.63	—	—	3.09	0.00	23.55
07/10	7.63	—	—	5.93	0.00	20.39
07/09	7.63	—	—	2.08	0.00	14.19
06/08	7.63	—	—	3.84	0.00	12.04
Annual Growth	41.4%	—	—	14.4%	—	26.8%

*Fiscal year change

Western Refining Inc

It's the quality and volumes of its refined products that makes Western Refining a major player in the West. The independent oil refiner operates primarily in the Southwest region of the US although it does have some marketing operations on the East Coast. Western Refining's refineries (one in El Paso one in the Four Corners region of northern New Mexico) have a crude oil refining capacity of 151000 barrels per day. More than 90% of its refined products are made up of light transportation fuels including diesel and gasoline. It owns a wholesale division that complements the refining operations. Western Refining also owns 210 convenience stores and gas stations in four Southwestern states.

Geographic Reach

In addition to its refineries in New Mexico and Texas the company has refined product distribution terminals in Albuquerque and Bloomfield New Mexico; asphalt terminals in Albuquerque El Paso Phoenix and Tucson; retail service stations and convenience stores in Arizona Colorado New Mexico and Texas; and wholesale petroleum product distribution operations in Arizona California Colorado Nevada New Mexico Texas Maryland and Virginia.

Sales & Marketing

Western Refining's El Paso refinery the company's largest has operating agreements with Kinder Morgan Energy Partners and Chevron that give it access to crude oil and refined product pipelines.

Financial Analysis

In 2011 Western Refining reported a 14% jump in revenues thanks to a recovering economy and robust oil and petroleum product prices. The company also reported a jump from a net loss of $17 million in 2010 to a net income of $132.7 million in 2011 thanks to higher revenues and lower interest and amortization expenses.

Strategy

The company's refined products sell at a premium on the Gulf Coast due to increasing demand and limited local refining capacity. In Phoenix Western Refining also benefits from tighter EPA fuel specifications that require the use of cleaner burning gasoline. As a consequence Phoenix CBG fuel is the company's highest-margin product.

To cut costs and exit a difficult regional refining market in September 2010 it suspended refining operations at its 70000-barrels-per-day Yorktown Virginia facility. In 2011 Western Refining sold that plant and an underused segment of its crude oil pipeline in southeast New Mexico to units of Plains All American Pipeline for $220 million.

Company Background

The company achieved its standing as a national player through the 2007 acquisition of Giant Industries for $1.1 billion a move that dramatically boosted Western Refining's refining capacity and geographic coverage (expanding its Southwest presence and giving it access to MidAtlantic markets).

EXECUTIVES

CFO, Gary R. Dalke, age 59, $350,013 total compensation
VP Assistant Treasurer Assistant Secretary and Director, Scott D. Weaver, age 53, $337,500 total compensation
SVP Treasurer Director Investor Relations and Assistant Secretary, Jeffrey S. (Jeff) Beyersdorfer, age 49
Chairman, Paul L. Foster, age 54, $646,994 total compensation
President CEO and Director, Jeff A. Stevens, age 48, $503,474 total compensation
President Refining and Marketing, Mark J. Smith, age 52, $439,925 total compensation
SVP Legal General Counsel and Secretary, Lowry Barfield, age 54, $311,238 total compensation
Chief Accounting Officer, William R. Jewell, age 57
Director Information Technology, Blake Larsen
Senior Vice President Chief Financial Officer, Sigmund Cornelius
VP Assistant Treasurer Assistant Secretary and Director, Scott D. Weaver, age 53
Director, Carin M. Barth, age 49
President CEO and Director, Jeff A. Stevens, age 48
Director, Ralph A. Schmidt, age 65
Director, L. Frederick (Rick) Francis, age 55
Director, Brian J. Hogan
Director, William D. Sanders, age 70
Auditors: Deloitte&ToucheLLP

LOCATIONS

HQ: Western Refining Inc.
123 W. Mills Ave. Ste. 200, El Paso TX 79901
Phone: 915-534-1400 **Fax:** -8148
Web: www.asus.com

PRODUCTS/OPERATIONS

2011 Sales

	$ mil.	% of total
Refining	4,124	46
Wholesale	4,032	44
Retail	914	10
Total	**9,071**	**100**

2011 Product Sales

	% of total
Gasoline	44
Diesel	35
Jet	13
Asphalt	4
Other	4
Total	**100**

COMPETITORS

Alon USA Energy
Chevron
ConocoPhillips
Hess Corporation
HollyFrontier
Suncor
Tesoro
Valero Energy

HISTORICAL FINANCIALS

Company Type: Public

Income Statement FYE: December 31

	REVENUE ($ mil.)	NET INCOME ($ mil.)	NET PROFIT MARGIN	EMPLOYEES
12/11	9,071	132	1.5%	3,600
12/10	7,965	(17)	—	2,950
12/09	6,807	(350)	—	3,300
12/08	10,725	64	0.6%	3,300
12/07	7,305	238	3.3%	3,149
Annual Growth	5.6%	(13.6%)	—	3.4%

2011 Year-End Financials

Debt ratio: 31.28%
Return on equity: 16.18%
Cash ($ mil.): 170
Current ratio: 181.87
Long-term debt ($ mil.): 800
No. of shares (mil.): 89
Dividends
Yield: —
Payout: —
Market value ($ mil.): 1,187

	STOCK PRICE ($) FY Close	P/E High/Low		PER SHARE ($) Earnings	Dividends	Book Value
12/11	13.29	15	7	1.34	0.00	9.18
12/10	10.58	—	—	(0.19)	0.00	7.65
12/09	4.71	—	—	(4.43)	0.00	7.82
12/08	7.76	26	5	0.95	0.18	11.97
12/07	24.21	18	7	3.53	0.22	11.20
Annual Growth	(13.9%)	—	—	(21.5%)	—	(4.9%)

Western Union Co.

Western Union's wires don't carry telegrams anymore STOP But they keep on humming with international money transfers STOP The firm has an agent network of 485000 locations in 200 countries worldwide that allow individuals and business customers to transfer money or make payments electronically. The pioneering company has taken advantage of technological advances and rolled with the changes since it was founded in 1851. Starting out as a messaging medium it then added the US's first stock ticker helped standardize timekeeping nationally debuted an early charge card and the singing telegram and finally shifted to money transfer services.

Boasting an average of nearly 20 money transfers every second Western Union carries out some 600 million payment transactions each year. Some are consumer-to-business transfers but consumer-to-consumer transfers account for more than 80% of the company's revenues. Its consumer-to-consumer transfer business relies heavily on immigrants who often send money between countries.

With the exception of recession-plagued 2009 the money transfer market has been growing and Western Union's business has followed suit. Although its revenues dipped that year due to the overall global economic downturn they rebounded in 2010. Revenue increased by more than 5% in 2011. Consumer-to-consumer transaction growth continued to drive success for Western Union in 2011.

While consumer-to-consumer business is key to Western Union the company is trying to bolster consumer-to-business transfers. Two recent acquisitons in that segment have helped boost overall revenues for the company. The additions also helped drive international growth. In 2009 Western Union bought Canadian business-to-business payment provider Custom House (renamed Western Union Business Solutions) which operates globally. Two years later Western Union acquired the international business payments arm of Travelex for some $975 million. The deal expanded its business-to-business platform to 16 countries.

Western Union also is looking at expanding into new types of service offerings such as prepaid debit cards and mobile money transfer services. With most of the company's transactions made in person it is developing alternatives to its traditional wire transfers. In the US and UK the company offers goCASH which enables customers to purchase money transfers in pre-set amounts at retail points of sale then complete the transfer by phone or Internet. In 2012 Western Union also launched its WU online payment platform that allows customers to pay online merchants.

Another way that the company is growing its business is through loyalty cards which offer faster service at the point of sale and in some countries cash back or reduced fees; approximately a third of its consumer-to-consumer money transfers are made by customers with a loyalty card and that number is growing.

Western Union also is trying to persuade banks to become a partner instead of a rival. The company has an agreement with Fidelity National Information Services to offer its international transfer services to that firm's 8500 bank clients. Also big banks like US Bancorp and Fifth Third Bank have chosen Western Union to handle money transfers. In 2010 Western Union inked its first bank agreement in China.

Western Union has operations in more than 200 countries and territories; some 85% of its agent locations (including those of subsidiaries such as Orlandi Valuta and Vigo in Latin America) are outside the US. The company has made several acquisitions in places like Panama to boost its international presence in recent years. In addition to expanding in the Latin American market the company has been focusing on growth in such areas as India and China. Its international growth strategy has included alliances with postal services banks and retailers in many countries. Western Union has been expanding its reach in Europe with the acquisition of the money transfer businesses. In 2011 Western Union acquried Finint a leading money transfer agent in Europe.

EXECUTIVES

Chairman, Jack M. Greenberg, age 69
CIO, J. David Thompson, age 45
SVP Investor Relations, Michael A. (Mike) Salop, age 47
EVP and President Global Consumer Financial Services, Stewart A. Stockdale, age 50, $550,000 total compensation
EVP and Chief Integration Officer, Robin Heller, age 46
EVP and CFO, Scott T. Scheirman, age 49, $533,300 total compensation
EVP and Interim General Counsel, David Schlapbach, age 53
EVP Human Resources, Grover Wray, age 51
President CEO and Director, Hikmet Ersek, age 51, $802,100 total compensation
SVP and General Manager North America, Victoria Lopez-Negrete
VP Corporate Affairs, Tom Fitzgerald
SVP and Assistant Secretary, Sarah J. Kilgore
Director Online Services Westernunion.com, Karina Elrod
President The Western Union Foundation, Luella Chavez D'Angelo
Senior Counsel EMEASA, Christopher Fischer
Senior Manager Corporate Communications Phillipines, Connie Yip
EVP General Counsel and Secretary, John R. Dye
EVP and Chief Marketing Officer; President Western Union Ventures, Diane Scott
SVP Europe and Commonwealth of Independent States, Jan Hillered
Interim General Counsel Asia Pacific, Joseph Cachey
President Western Union Business Solutions, Raj Agrawal
SVP and Managing Director Latin America and Caribbean, Odilon Almeida
SVP Middle East and Africa, Jean Claude Farah
SVP Electronic Channels, Khalid Fellahi
Chief Human Resources Officer, Paula S. Larson
Director, Betsy D. Holden, age 56
Director, Lord Dennis Stevenson, age 66
Director, Michael A. (Mike) Miles Jr., age 50
Director, Roberto G. Mendoza, age 66
Director, Wulf von Schimmelmann, age 65
Director, Linda F. Levinson, age 71
Director, Linda Fayne Levinson, age 69
Director, Dinyar S. Devitre, age 65
Director, Richard A. Goodman, age 64
President CEO and Director, Hikmet Ersek, age 51
Auditors: Ernst&YoungLLP

LOCATIONS

HQ: The Western Union Company
12500 E. Belford Ave., Englewood CO 80112
Phone: 720-332-1000 **Fax:** 720-332-4753
Web: www.westernunion.com

2011 Sales

	$ mil.	% of total
US	1,568	29
International	3,922	71
Total	**5,083**	**100**

PRODUCTS/OPERATIONS

2011 Sales

	$ mil.	% of total
Transaction fees	4,220	77
Foreign exchange revenue	1,151	21
Commissions & other	120	2
Total	**5,491**	**100**

2011 Sales by Segment

	$ mil.	% of total
Consumer-to-Consumer		
Transaction fees	3,580	65
Foreign exchange revenue	983	18
Other	45	-
Global Business Payments		
Transaction fees	587	11
Foreign exchange revenue	168	3
Other	28	1
Other	98	2
Total	**5,491**	**100**

COMPETITORS

American Express
Citigroup
Financiero Santander
First Data
Global Payments
MasterCard
MoneyGram International
PayPal
Sigue
US Postal Service
Visa Inc

HISTORICAL FINANCIALS

Company Type: Public

Income Statement FYE: December 31

	REVENUE ($ mil.)	NET INCOME ($ mil.)	NET PROFIT MARGIN	EMPLOYEES
12/11	5,491	1,165	21.2%	8,000
12/10	5,192	909	17.5%	7,000
12/09	5,083	848	16.7%	6,800
12/08	5,282	919	17.4%	5,900
12/07	4,900	857	17.5%	6,100
Annual Growth	2.9%	8.0%	—	7.0%

2011 Year-End Financials

Debt ratio: 39.51%
Return on equity: 130.24%
Cash ($ mil.): 1,370
Current ratio: 92.69
Long-term debt ($ mil.): 3,286
No. of shares (mil.): 619
Dividends
Yield: —
Payout: 16.85%
Market value ($ mil.): 11,310

	STOCK PRICE ($) FY Close	P/E High	P/E Low	PER SHARE ($) Earnings	Dividends	Book Value
12/11	18.26	12	8	1.84	0.00	1.45
12/10	18.57	15	11	1.36	0.25	0.89
12/09	18.85	17	9	1.21	0.06	0.51
12/08	14.34	23	9	1.24	0.04	(0.01)
12/07	24.28	22	16	1.11	0.04	0.07
Annual Growth	(6.9%)	—	—	13.5%	—	113.3%

Weyerhaeuser Co.

If a tree falls in a Weyerhaeuser forest someone is there to hear it –and he has a chainsaw. The forest products company produces a variety of softwood lumber and other building materials in North America. It also offers cellulose fibers products used to make paper packaging and textiles. The company harvests trees for its products through its timberlands division which manages more than 20 million acres of forest in the US and Canada. Its Weyerhaeuser Real Estate unit develops housing and master-planned communities around the country. Weyerhaeuser was incorporated in 1900 and is a real estate investment trust (REIT). It operates offices in about a dozen countries and serves customers worldwide.

HISTORY

Frederick Weyerhaeuser a 24-year-old German immigrant bought his first lumberyard in 1858 in Illinois. He also participated in joint logging ventures in Illinois Minnesota and Wisconsin. In 1900 he and 15 partners bought 900000 timbered acres from the Northern Pacific Railway. The venture was named Weyerhaeuser Timber Company.

During the Depression the business recouped losses in the deflated lumber market by selling wood pulp. Frederick's grandson J. P. "Phil" Weyerhaeuser Jr. took over as CEO in 1933.

Diversification into the production of containerboard (1949) particleboard (1955) paper (1956) and other products led the company to drop "Timber" from its name in 1959. In 1963 Weyerhaeuser went public and opened its first overseas office in Tokyo.

In the 1970s George Weyerhaeuser (Phil's son) diversified further to insulate the company from the forest-product industry's cyclical nature and ended up with a mishmash of businesses and products from private-label disposable diapers to pet supplies.

The eruption of Mount St. Helens in 1980 destroyed 68000 acres of Weyerhaeuser timber. That disaster and the soft US lumber market depressed the company's earnings through 1982. Weyerhaeuser reduced its workforce by 25% during this period.

Under John Creighton (president since 1988 and CEO from 1991 until 1998) Weyerhaeuser refocused on forest products and organized along product lines rather than by geographic region. Less-successful ventures were put up for sale including milk carton hardwood and gypsum board plants. The company took a $497 million pretax charge in 1989 related to the decision to close unprofitable operations. Earnings improved in 1990 but dropped again in 1991 reflecting the recession in the US and plant closures.

In 1992 the company outbid Georgia-Pacific paying $600 million for two pulp mills three sawmills and more than 200000 acres of forest land to boost its market-pulp capacity by 40%. The following year the company sold its disposable-diaper business through a public offering in a new company Paragon Trade Brands. It also sold GNA Corporation to General Electric subsidiary GE Capital.

The federal government in 1995 allowed the company to harvest trees in an area inhabited by the endangered northern spotted owl. The move angered environmental groups. In 1997 Weyerhaeuser began to reorganize its recycling business by selling or closing noncore units. It also purchased a stake in 193000 acres on New Zealand's South Island the company's first overseas investment in more than a decade. In 1998 the company restructured its joint venture with Nippon Paper with Weyerhaeuser decreasing its stake in North Pacific Paper Company from 80% to 50% and closed a lumber mill in Canada. Also that year Steve Rogel a veteran from competitor Willamette succeeded Creighton as CEO and became the first outsider to head Weyerhaeuser.

In 1999 Weyerhaeuser paid $2.5 billion for Canada's MacMillan Bloedel and early in 2000 it acquired TJ International 51% owner of leading engineered lumber products company Trus Joist MacMillan (Weyerhaeuser already owned the other 49%). Also in 2000 Weyerhaeuser purchased two sawmills and a 70% stake in lumber distributor Pine Solutions from Australia-based CSR Limited. Weyerhaeuser sold its Marshfield Door architectural wood door business and closed some of its manufacturing operations to consolidate its business.

After a protracted courtship in March 2002 Weyerhaeuser acquired Oregon-based Willamette Industries in a $6.1 billion cash deal. The company closed three North American plants (in Colorado Louisiana and Oregon) later that year. In October the company closed a Canadian containerboard mill cutting 140 jobs in the process. At the close of the year Weyerhaeuser sold approximately 115000 acres of timberlands in western Washington to Boston-based Hancock Timber Resource Group (international timber investment and management) for about $211 million to aid in paying down its debt associated with the Willamette acquisition.

On the heels of the deals for MacMillan Bloedel Trus Joist MacMillan and Willamette Weyerhaeuser moved to pay down debt. It sold more than 320000 acres of the timberland (in the Carolinas and Tennessee) that it acquired with the Willamette purchase. Before the end of 2003 Fountain Investments had acquired about 168000 acres of the west-central Tennessee acreage and Forest Investment Associates purchased about 160000 acres of western North Carolina and South Carolina timberlands. Weyerhaeuser gained about $140 million in after-tax proceeds from the latter sale.

Also in 2003 Weyerhaeuser sold its Nipigon Multiply hardwood plywood underlayment operation in Ontario Canada to Columbia Forest Products. Late in the year the company closed its fine-paper operations in Longview Washington (eliminating 119 jobs there). Altogether Weyerhaeuser closed 12 facilities and sold about 444000 acres of non-strategic timberlands in 2003 in keeping with its plan to reduce company debt and increase productivity.

The company closed its Grande Cache Alberta sawmill in 2004 (affecting more than 150 jobs there) and sold its oriented strand board (OSB) mill in Slave Lake Alberta to Tolko Industries for about $43 million. Also in 2004 Weyerhaeuser sold roughly 270000 acres of timberlands in central Georgia for about $400 million to investment and property firms in Georgia and South Carolina.

Also in 2004 subsidiary Weyerhaeuser Brasil Participac?es acquired two-thirds ownership in Brazil-based Aracruz Produtos de Madeira (APM) a subsidiary of Aracruz Cellulose to produce lumber made from a eucalyptus hybrid for use in furniture flooring cabinetry and other applications. Aracruz Cellulose holds the remaining third ownership in the joint venture. Also that year Weyerhaeuser changed the name of its pulp business to Weyerhaeuser Cellulose Fibers to reinforce its focus on developing unique or specialized applications for cellulose fibers.

Weyerhaeuser agreed early in 2005 to sell five Canadian sawmills two finishing plants 635000 acres of timber and some government land-cutting rights to Brascan for $970 million. It had acquired the timber and sawmill assets when it bought MacMillan Bloedel in 1999.

The company's debt reduction strategy continued in 2004. Weyerhaeuser sold roughly 270000 acres of its timberlands in Georgia and several mills in the US and Canada. The sale of the assets helped the company more than quadruple net earnings for 2004: $1.3 billion its best result of the decade. It used the proceeds to reduce debt by some $730 million. In the meantime Weyerhaeuser reported that it wrung out the $300 million in expected Willamette-related synergies in half the time predicted.

Weyerhaeuser continued to streamline and focus on its softwood lumber business in 2005 selling $970 million in assets (five sawmills two finishing plants 635000 acres and timber rights) to Brascan. Weyerhaeuser also closed a Saskatchewan pulp and paper mill in 2006 cutting 690 jobs; not long afterward amid weak profits it announced multiple plant closures and sales including another pulp mill another sawmill several corrugated plants and a paper bag plant.

In 2007 Weyerhaeuser merged its fine paper business with Domtar. According to the terms of the $3.3 billion deal Weyerhaeuser shareholders got a 55% stake in the renamed company Domtar Corporation. Weyerhaeuser controls the board and several Weyerhaeuser executives manage the company.

The company sold its Trus Joist commercial business including four manufacturing plants to Atlas Holdings in 2009. Also that year Weyerhaeuser announced it was closing its noncore trucking division. Other divestitures in 2009 included non-strategic timberland in Oregon (representing about 10% of its holdings in the Pacific Northwest) in an effort to focus on Douglas fir production in that region.

Weyerhaeuser converted to a real estate investment trust (REIT) in 2010. The status allows the company to pay less in taxes and pay its shareholders larger dividends. Weyerhaeuser folded its timberland operations into the REIT while its real estate wood products and cellulose fibers units operate under a taxable REIT subsidiary.

EXECUTIVES

SVP Research and Development and CTO, Miles P. Drake, age 62
Chairman, Charles R. (Chuck) Williamson, age 63
SVP and General Counsel, Sandy D. McDade, age 60
VP and Treasurer, Jeffrey W. Nitta
VP Investor Relations, Kathryn F. McAuley
VP Secretary and Assistant General Counsel, Claire S. Grace
VP Policy Finance and Strategic Planning, Scott R. Marshall
Director Company Communications, Bruce Amundson
EVP Timberlands, Thomas F. (Tom) Gideon, age 60, $602,308 total compensation
EVP and CFO, Patricia M. (Patty) Bedient, age 58, $577,385 total compensation
President CEO and Director, Daniel S. (Dan) Fulton, age 63, $830,769 total compensation
VP Corporate Affairs Sustainability Environment Health and Safety (EHS), Sara S. Kendall
President Pardee Homes, Michael V. (Mike) McGee, age 57
VP Sustainable Forestry, Catherine L. Phillips
VP and Director Taxes, Thomas M. Smith
President Winchester Homes, Alan Shapiro
President and CEO Weyerhaeuser Real Estate Company, Peter M. Orser, age 55
President Quadrant Corporation, Ken Krivanec
SVP Wood Products, Lawrence B. (Larry) Burrows, age 59, $519,231 total compensation
VP Softwood Lumber Technologies, Robert W. Taylor
VP Hardwoods and Industrial Products, Nancy Arend
SVP Cellulose Fibers, Srinivasan (Shaker) Chandrasekaran, age 62, $404,154 total compensation
VP Western Timberlands, Richard C. (Rich) Wininger, age 59
VP Operations and Controller, Jeanne M. Hillman, age 52
VP Strand Technologies, Philip C. (Phil) Dennett
VP iLevel Sales, Carlos J. Guilherme
SVP Human Resources, John A. Hooper, age 57
VP Veneer Technologies, Catherine I. Slater
VP Cellulose Fibers Manufacturing, John Yerke
VP Information Technology and CIO, Kevin Shearer, age 56
VP Timberlands Technology, Christine Dean
President Trendmaker Homes, Floyd W. (Will) Holder
President Weyerhaeuser Company Limited, Anne Giardini
VP Strategic Planning, Elizabeth W. Seaton
President Maracay Homes, Andy Warren
VP Southern Timberlands, Rhonda Hunter
VP Minerals and Energy Products, David L. Godwin
Manager Shareholder Services, Vicki Merrick
Manager Investor Relations, April Meier
EVP and COO Quadrant, Mark Gray
Chief Accounting Officer, Jerry Richards, age 44
President Weyerhaeuser Solutions, Marvin R. (Ray) Risco
Media Relations Canada, Wayne Roznowsky
Director, Wayne W. Murdy, age 68
Director, Debra A. Cafaro, age 54
Director, Richard H. Sinkfield, age 69
Director, John I. Kieckhefer, age 67
Director, Nicole W. Piasecki, age 49
President CEO and Director, Daniel S. (Dan) Fulton, age 63
Director, D. Michael Steuert, age 63
Director, Mark A. Emmert, age 59
Director, Kim Williams, age 56
Auditors: KPMGLLP

LOCATIONS

HQ: Weyerhaeuser Company
33663 Weyerhaeuser Way South, Federal Way WA 98003-9777
Phone: 253-924-2345 **Fax:** 914-696-8684
Web: www.handyharman.com

2011 Sales

	$ mil.	% of total
US	4,008	65
Japan	640	10
China	446	7
Europe	331	5
Canada	271	5
South America	75	1
Other regions	445	7
Total	**6,216**	**100**

PRODUCTS/OPERATIONS

2011 Sales

	$ mil.	% of total
Wood products	2,276	37
Cellulose fibers	2,058	33
Timberlands	1,044	17
Real estate	838	13
Total	**6,216**	**100**

Selected Products and Services

Wood and Building Products
- Engineered lumber products
- Flooring
- Lumber (softwood)
- Oriented Strand Board
- Plywood
- Structural panels
- Veneer

Cellulose Fiber and White Paper
- Paper and liquid packaging
- Paper
- Pulp
- Textiles

Real Estate and Related Assets
- Master-planned communities
- Multifamily homes
- Residential lots
- Single-family homes

Timberlands
- Chips
- Logs
- Mineral resources
- Seedlings
- Weyerhaeuser Select Douglas Fir seed

Other
- Recycling
- Transportation

Selected Subsidiaries

Ouachita Timberlands LLC
Weyerhaeuser International Inc.
Weyerhaeuser NR Company
Westwood Shipping Lines Inc.
Weyerhaeuser Real Estate Company?

COMPETITORS

Buckeye Technologies
Canfor
Cascades Boxboard
ENCE
Georgia-Pacific
Indiana Veneers
Louisiana-Pacific
McFarland Cascade
MeadWestvaco
Mendocino Redwood Company
Norbord
Packaging Corp. of America
Plum Creek Timber
Potlatch
Pratt Industries USA
Rayonier
Resolute Forest Products
Sierra Pacific Industries
Smurfit Kappa
Stora Enso
Tembec
Temple-Inland
Tenon
UPM-Kymmene
West Fraser Timber

HISTORICAL FINANCIALS

Company Type: Public

Income Statement FYE: December 31

	REVENUE ($ mil.)	NET INCOME ($ mil.)	NET PROFIT MARGIN	EMPLOYEES
12/11	6,216	331	5.3%	128,000
12/10	6,552	1,281	19.6%	14,250
12/09	5,528	(545)	—	14,888
12/08	8,018	(1,176)	—	19,843
12/07	16,308	790	4.8%	37,857
Annual Growth	(21.4%)	(19.5%)	—	35.6%

2011 Year-End Financials

Debt ratio: 35.55%
Return on equity: 7.76%
Cash ($ mil.): 953
Current ratio: 219.77
Long-term debt ($ mil.): 4,466
No. of shares (mil.): 536
Dividends
Yield: —
Payout: 98.36%
Market value ($ mil.): 10,015

	STOCK PRICE ($) FY Close	P/E High/Low		PER SHARE ($) Earnings	Dividends	Book Value
12/11	18.67	41	25	0.61	0.00	7.95
12/10	18.93	13	4	3.99	26.66	8.61
12/09	43.14	—	—	(2.58)	0.60	19.13
12/08	30.61	—	—	(5.57)	2.40	22.78
12/07	73.58	24	17	3.59	0.00	37.80
Annual Growth	(29.0%)	—	—	(35.8%)	—	(32.3%)

Whirlpool Corp

With brand names recognized by just about anyone who has ever separated dark colors from light Whirlpool is one of the world's top home appliance makers. It specializes in laundry appliances refrigerators and freezers cooking appliances dishwashers and compressors which are sold under a bevy of brand names including Whirlpool Amana KitchenAid Maytag and Roper. The company markets and distributes these major home appliances in North America Latin America EMEA (Europe the Middle East and Africa) and Asia. It has manufacturing operations in about a dozen countries. Major customers include retailers Lowe's Home Depot Sears and Best Buy.

HISTORY

Brothers Fred and Lou Upton and their uncle Emory Upton founded the Upton Machine Company manufacturer of electric motor-driven washing machines in 1911 in St. Joseph Michigan. Sears Roebuck and Co. began buying their products five years later and by 1925 the company was supplying all of Sears' washers. The Uptons combined their company with the Nineteen Hundred Washer Company in 1929 to form the Nineteen Hundred Corporation the world's largest washing machine company.

Sears and Nineteen Hundred prospered during the Great Depression and during WWII Nineteen Hundred's factories produced war materials. In 1948 it began selling its first automatic washing machine (introduced a year earlier) under the Whirlpool brand. In 1950 the company changed its name to Whirlpool following the success of the product and introduced its first automatic dryer.

During the 1950s and 1960s Whirlpool became a full-line appliance manufacturer while continuing as Sears' principal Kenmore appliance supplier. In 1955 the company bought Seeger Refrigerator Company and the stove and air-conditioning interests of RCA. Three years later it made its first investment in Multibras Eletrodomesticos an appliance maker in Brazil. (It has increased that investment over the years.) Other purchases included the gas refrigeration and ice-maker manufacturing facilities of Servel (1958); a majority interest in Heil-Quaker makers of central heaters and space heaters (1964); Sears' major television set supplier Warwick Electronics (1966); and 33% of Canadian appliance maker John Inglis Company (1969). It made a deal with Sony in 1973 for the distribution of Whirlpool-brand products in Japan. Whirlpool sold its TV manufacturing business to SANYO of Japan three years later.

Between 1981 and 1991 despite a static US market Whirlpool's sales tripled to almost $6.6 billion. In 1986 the firm bought top-end appliance manufacturer KitchenAid (from Dart and Kraft) and 65% of Italian cooling compressor manufacturer Aspera. Also that year it sold its Heil-Quaker central heating business. David Whitwam was appointed CEO in 1987. Whirlpool took over total ownership of Inglis in 1990.

The company formed Whirlpool Europe a joint venture with Philips Electronics in 1989; in 1991 it bought out Philips. Two years later Whirlpool took control of appliance marketer SAGAD of Argentina and entered a joint venture with Slovakia's Tatramat (which it bought out in 1994).

Whirlpool acquired control of Kelvinator of India in 1994 and formed a joint venture in China with Shenzhen Petrochemical Holdings in 1995 to produce air conditioners. The following year Whirlpool merged its Whirlpool Washing Machines and Kelvinator of India companies to form Whirlpool of India. The company's European division plunged into the red when competition and a recession kept consumers away from its higher-priced appliances.

In 1997 Whirlpool initiated a restructuring (due to losses from its foreign operations) that included plant closures and substantial layoffs (as much as 10% of its workforce). The next year Whirlpool sold its appliance financing subsidiary to Transamerica. The company also began using a new more efficient product development model in 1998 similar to one used in the auto industry. In 2000 Whirlpool launched the Cielo Bath line of jetted tubs and in 2001 it introduced the Calypso dishwasher and the Duet washer and dryer.

Another global restructuring plan swept through the company in 2000 resulting in significant pretax charges ($373 million incurred in 2001 and 2002) and the elimination of about 6000 employees by October 2003.

In February 2002 Whirlpool bought the remaining 51% of Vitromatic it didn't already own. (Vitromatic —the second-largest appliance manufacturer in Mexico –is now called Whirlpool Mexico.) In March the company purchased 95% of Polar Poland's second-largest appliance maker.

Whirlpool introduced Gladiator GarageWorks (modular storage systems for the garage) and Polara (the first electric range with cooking and refrigeration capabilities) in 2002.

Whirlpool acquired Maytag in early 2006 for about $1.9 billion. The deal added several top brands to its already bulging portfolio including Admiral Amana Jenn-Air Magic Chef and of course the eponymous Maytag. Once the dust settled Whirlpool sold several businesses including Dixie-Narco the Amana commercial business its Hoover unit to Techtronic Industries and its Jade unit to Middleby Corporation. Buying Maytag also spurred Whirlpool to streamline operations and purge staff. In 2006 it laid off some 4500 employees consolidated duplicate functions related to administration and manufacturing and shuttered some offices including a Maytag research and development center based in Newton Illinois. Whirlpool shuttered Maytag's Iowa-based administrative offices and moved them to Michigan and other locations. The company cut 700 jobs at several Tennessee plants the following year.

In 2007 Whirlpool acquired a minority stake in Elica Group in its effort to extend its reach into the global air ventilation market.

The company formed a 50-50 joint venture in 2008 with China's Hisense-Kelon Electrical Holdings to make and sell home appliances there.

In June 2010 Whirlpool closed its refrigerator factory in Evansville Indiana; some 1100 US jobs were lost as a result of the move.

EXECUTIVES

SVP Global Human Resources, David A. (Dave) Binkley
Chairman and CEO, Jeff M. Fettig, age 54, $1,275,000 total compensation
President Whirlpool International; Director, Michael A. (Mike) Todman, age 55, $760,000 total compensation
EVP; President Whirlpool North America, Marc R. Bitzer, age 47, $648,013 total compensation
EVP Global Product Organization, David T. (Dave) Szczupak, age 57
SVP Corporate Affairs and General Counsel, Daniel F. Hopp, age 64
EVP and CFO, Larry M. Venturelli, age 51
EVP; President Latin America, Jo?o C. Brega
EVP; President Europe Middle East and Africa, Jose A. Drummond Jr., age 47
Senior Manager Public Relations Global Brands, Monica Teague
Corporate Secretary, Robert J. LaForest
VP and General Manager Canada, Joseph T. Liotine
CIO North America, Alan Douville
Corporate VP and Global CIO, Kevin Summers
VP Information Technology Office of the CIO, David Langendonk
Brand Director Whirlpool Europe, Tanneke Reinders
Director KitchenAid and Premium Brands Europe, Andrea Riggio
Brand Director Brastemp Consul and KitchenAid Brands Latin America, Daniela Cianciaruso
Corporate Communications Senior Manager Mexico, Luis Mercado
Corporate Communication Manager Latin America, Paula Santis
Director Communications and Corporate Affairs EMEA, Giuseppe Geneletti
Media Relations Manager EMEA, Pierre Ley
Manager Communications and Corporate Affairs Europe, Eileen Robinson
Associate Manager External Communications China, Sophie Lu
VP Corporate Affairs and Strategy India, Shantanu Das Gupta
General Manager Corporate Communications India, Sita Singhal
President Embraco, Roberto H. Campos
Director, Michael D. (Mike) White, age 61
Director, Samuel R. (Sam) Allen, age 58
Director, Miles L. Marsh, age 65
Director, William T. (Bill) Kerr, age 70
Director, Gary T. DiCamillo, age 62
Director, William D. (Bill) Perez, age 64
Director, Herman Cain, age 67
President Whirlpool International; Director, Michael A. (Mike) Todman, age 55
Director, Paul G. Stern, age 74
Director, Janice D. Stoney, age 71
Director, Kathleen J. Hempel, age 62
Director, Michael F. (Mike) Johnston, age 64
Director, John D. Liu, age 44
Auditors: Ernst&YoungLLP

LOCATIONS

HQ: Whirlpool Corporation
2000 N. M-63, Benton Harbor MI 49022-2692
Phone: 269-923-5000 **Fax:** 269-923-3722
Web: www.whirlpoolcorp.com

2011 Sales

	$ mil.	% of total
North America	9,582	51
Latin America	5,062	27
Europe the Middle East & Africa	3,305	17
Asia	881	5
Total	**18,666**	**100**

PRODUCTS/OPERATIONS

2011 Sales

	$ mil.	% of total
Refrigerators & freezers	5,620	30
Laundry appliances	5,612	30
Cooking appliances	3,120	17
Other	4,314	23
Total	**18,666**	**100**

Selected Brands

Air conditioning equipment
- Amana
- Brastemp
- Whirlpool

Cooking appliances
- Amana
- Brastemp
- Consul
- Jenn-Air
- KitchenAid
- Roper
- Whirlpool

Dishwashers
- Amana
- Brastemp
- Consul
- Jenn-Air
- KitchenAid
- Maytag
- Whirlpool

Freezers
- Amana

Laundry appliances
- Amana
- Brastemp
- Consul
- Maytag
- Roper
- Whirlpool

Mixers
- KitchenAid

Refrigerators
- Amana
- Consul
- Jenn-Air
- KitchenAid
- Maytag
- Whirlpool

Small household appliances
- Brastemp
- Consul
- Jenn-Air
- KitchenAid
- Maytag
- Whirlpool

COMPETITORS

BSH Bosch und Siemens Hausgerate
Candy Group
Daewoo Electronics
Electrolux
Electrolux Home Appliances China
Fisher & Paykel Appliances Holdings
GE Appliances & Lighting
Goodman Manufacturing
Gree Electrical Appliances
GuangDong Midea
Haier Group
Hitachi
Indesit
LG Electronics
Panasonic Corp
Samsung Electronics America
SANYO
Sears Holdings
Sharp Corp.
Sub-Zero
Viking Range

HISTORICAL FINANCIALS

Company Type: Public

Income Statement FYE: December 31

	REVENUE ($ mil.)	NET INCOME ($ mil.)	NET PROFIT MARGIN	EMPLOYEES
12/11	18,666	390	2.1%	68,231
12/10	18,366	619	3.4%	70,758
12/09	17,099	328	1.9%	66,884
12/08	18,907	418	2.2%	69,612
12/07	19,408	640	3.3%	73,000
Annual Growth	(1.0%)	(11.6%)	—	(1.7%)

2011 Year-End Financials

Debt ratio: 16.41%
Return on equity: 9.33%
Cash ($ mil.): 1,109
Current ratio: 101.99
Long-term debt ($ mil.): 2,129
No. of shares (mil.): 76
Dividends
Yield: —
Payout: 38.68%
Market value ($ mil.): 3,628

	STOCK PRICE ($) FY Close	P/E High/Low		PER SHARE ($) Earnings	Dividends	Book Value
12/11	47.45	18	9	4.99	0.00	54.69
12/10	88.83	14	9	7.97	1.72	55.61
12/09	80.66	19	4	4.34	1.72	48.85
12/08	41.35	17	6	5.50	1.72	41.18
12/07	81.63	14	9	8.01	1.72	51.46
Annual Growth	(12.7%)	—	—	(11.2%)	—	1.5%

Whole Foods Market, Inc.

With food and other items that are free of pesticides preservatives sweeteners and cruelty Whole Foods Market knows more about guiltless eating and shopping than most retailers. The world's #1 natural foods chain by far –now that it has digested its main rival Wild Oats Markets –the company operates about 340 stores throughout the US Canada and the UK. The stores emphasize perishable products which account for about two-thirds of sales. Whole Foods Market offers some 2200 items in four lines of private-label products (such as the premium Whole Foods line). Founded in Austin Texas in 1980 Whole Foods Market pioneered the supermarket concept in natural and organic foods retailing.

HISTORY

With a $10000 loan from his father John Mackey started SaferWay Natural Foods in Austin Texas in 1978. Despite struggling Mackey dreamed of opening a larger supermarket-sized natural foods store. Two years later SaferWay merged with Clarksville Natural Grocery and Whole Foods Market was born. Led by Mackey that year it opened an 11000-sq.-ft. supermarket in a counterculture hotbed of Austin. The store was an instant success and a second store was added 18 months later in suburban Austin.

The company slowly expanded in Texas opening or buying stores in Houston in 1984 and Dallas in 1986. Whole Foods expanded into Louisiana in 1988 with the purchase of like-named Whole

Food Co. a single New Orleans store owned by Peter Roy (who served as the company's president from 1993 to 1998). Sticking to university towns Whole Foods added another store in California the next year and acquired Wellspring Grocery (two stores North Carolina) in 1991. In 1992 it debuted its first private-label products under the Whole Foods name. Seeking capital to expand even more the company raised $23 million by going public in early 1992 with 12 stores.

Every competitor in the fragmented health foods industry became a potential acquisition and the chain began growing rapidly. In 1992 Whole Foods bought the six-store Bread & Circus chain in New England. The next year it added Mrs. Gooch's Natural Foods Markets (seven stores in the Los Angeles area). Its biggest acquisition came in 1996 when it bought Fresh Fields the second-largest US natural foods chain (22 stores on the East Coast and in Chicago). Although the purchase hurt profits in 1996 sales surpassed $1 billion for the first time in fiscal 1997 as Whole Foods neared 70 stores. In 1997 it introduced the less-expensive 365 private label and acquired the Granary Market (Monterey California) and Bread of Life (two stores South Florida) natural foods supermarkets.

Capitalizing on the growing popularity of nutraceuticals (natural supplements with benefits similar to pharmaceuticals) the company paid $146 million in 1997 for Amrion a maker of nutraceuticals and other nutritional supplements (merged with subsidiary WholePeople.com in 2000). It capped the year by buying coffee roaster Allegro Coffee. (Both companies are based in Boulder Colorado home of its former main rival the smaller Wild Oats.) Also in 1997 Whole Foods acquired the six-store Merchant of Vino natural foods and wine shop chain to foster the development of its wine departments.

In 1998 Whole Foods opened its first store in Boulder –a 39000-sq.-ft. superstore with amenities such as a juice bar and a prepared foods section. At year's end Roy resigned as president and was replaced by Chris Hitt. In 1999 Whole Foods bought four-store Boston-area chain Nature's Heartland.

In 2000 Whole Foods merged its online operations (wholefoods.com) with its direct marketing and nutritional supplement unit (Amrion) to form Wholepeople.com. Later that year the company merged Wholepeople.com with lifestyle marketing firm Gaiam; Whole Foods received a minority stake in Gaiam and started selling food online through Gaiam.com.

Hitt resigned in mid-2001 and Mackey took over his duties. Later that year Whole Foods acquired the three upscale Harry's Farmers Market stores in Atlanta; the sale did not include the Harry's In A Hurry stores which later shut down.

In 2002 Whole Foods crossed the border into Canada. Its first foreign store opened in downtown Toronto that May.

Mackey was named Entrepreneur of the Year in 2003 by consulting firm Ernst & Young. That year Whole Foods acquired Select Fish a Seattle-based seafood processor and distributor and opened a seafood distribution facility in Atlanta.

In 2004 Whole Foods opened a 59000-sq.-ft. store in the new Time Warner Center in Manhattan. The new store which includes a 248-seat cafe sushi bar wine shop and gourmet bakery is the largest supermarket in New York City. That year the company acquired the UK organic-food retailer Fresh & Wild for $38 million.

To support its rapid growth in 2004 Whole Foods Market expanded its number of operating regions from eight to 10 by separating the Southwest region into the Southwest and Rocky Mountain regions and the Northern Pacific region into the Northern California and Pacific Northwest region. The company announced the opening of its first Gluten-Free Bakehouse a dedicated gluten-free baking facility located outside Raleigh North Carolina. Overall the company opened 12 new stores in 2004.

In January 2005 Whole Foods launched the Animal Compassion Foundation an independent non-profit organization dedicated to the compassionate treatment of livestock. The company moved that month to its new corporate headquarters across the street from its old location in downtown Austin. Its new flagship store opened its doors in March at the same location. In October Whole Foods increased its number of operating regions from 10 to 11 by separating the North Atlantic region into the North Atlantic and Tri-State regions. Overall in fiscal 2005 the company opened a dozen new stores including its first in Nebraska and Ohio. In 2006 the company acquired a store in Portland Maine and converted it to the Whole Foods Market banner.

In August 2007 Whole Foods acquired its main competitor —Boulder Colorado-based Wild Oats Markets —in a deal valued at about $565 million (plus $106 million in debt). In early October the company sold 35 Henry's Farmers Market and Sun Harvest stores to a subsidiary of Los Angeles-based Smart & Final for about $166 million. The stores in California and Texas were acquired with Wild Oats.

The company launched a bi-monthly magazine called Whole Foods Market Magazine at its midwestern stores in 2008. On the heels of its disappointing third-quarter results in August 2008 shares of the company's stock fell to a six-year low and Whole Foods suspended its dividend. Blaming the poor economy the company announced the layoffs of some 50 employees at its Austin headquarters in August 2008. Overall in fiscal 2008 the company introduced about 300 new private-label items.

For the first time in its 29-year history Whole Foods reported negative same-store sales in the quarter ended December 2008 as traffic in its stores fell.

In March 2009 the company reached a settlement in its long-running dispute with the FTC over its acquisition of Wild Oats in 2007. Whole Foods agreed to sell 32 stores including 19 Wild Oats locations that had already been closed. In exchange the FTC dropped its crusade to undo the merger. In December 2009 John Elstrott was named chairman of Whole Foods Market after Mackey voluntarily relinquished the chairmanship which he had held since 1980. In May 2010 Walter Robb formerly co-president of the company was promoted to co-CEO of Whole Foods a title he now shares with Mackey.

EXECUTIVES

EVP Growth and Business Development, James P. (Jim) Sud, age 59, $386,769 total compensation
EVP and CFO, Glenda J. Flanagan, age 59, $234,598 total compensation
Co-CEO and Director, John P. Mackey, age 58, $1 total compensation
Senior Global VP Purchasing Distribution and Communications, Michael Besancon, age 65, $145,000 total compensation
President and COO, A. C. Gallo, age 58, $359,822 total compensation
President Florida Region, Juan Nunez, age 53
Co-CEO and Director, Walter E. Robb IV, age 59, $365,370 total compensation
President Northern California Region, David Lannon, age 45
President Mid-Atlantic Region, Kenneth (Ken) Meyer, age 43
Chairman, John B. Elstrott, age 63
President Rocky Mountain Region, William (Will) Paradise, age 51
Global VP Investor Relations, Cynthia M. (Cindy) McCann
Global VP Quality Standards and Public Affairs, Margaret Wittenberg
VP and CIO, Michael (Mike) Clifford
Global VP Growth and Business Development, Betsy Foster
VP Procurement - Perishables, Edmund LaMacchia
Global VP Legal Affairs and General Counsel, Roberta Lang
Global VP Construction and Store Development, Lee Matecko
President U.K. Region, Jeff Turnas, age 39
President Northeast Region, Christina Minardi, age 45
Team Leader Gluten-Free Bakehouse, Lee Tobin
President Southwest Region, Mark Dixon, age 49
President Southern Pacific Region, Patrick Bradley, age 51
President South Region, Scott Allshouse, age 49
Global Animal Production and Welfare Coordinator, Anne Malleau
President Pacific Northwest Region, Joe Rogoff
Global Meat Buyer, Theo Weening
Regional VP Pacific Northwest, Bruce Silverman
Food and Nutrition Quality Standards Coordinator, Jody Villecco
Global VP Procurement - Non Perishables, Jim Speirs
Global Cheese Buyer, Cathy Strange
Global VP Distribution, Bart Beilman
Global VP Accounting and Controller, Sam Ferguson
Global Seafood Buyer, David Pilat
Global Wine Buyer West Coast, Geof Ryan
Global Wine Buyer East Coast, Doug Bell
President Pacific Northwest Region, John Clougher
Food Organic and Environmental Quality Standards Contributor, Joe Dickson
Media Contact, Libba Letton
Media Contact, Liz Burkhart
Media Contact, Ashley Hawkins
Media Contact and Spokeswoman, Kate Lowery
Seafood Quality Standards Coordinator, Carrie Brownstein
Global Whole Body Buyer, Jeremiah McElwee
Global Produce Buyer, Karen Christensen
Global VP Team Member Services, Mark Ehrnstein
Immersion Program Coordinator and Research and Development Chef, Chad Sarno
Senior Healthy Eating and Wellness Educator, Kathy (Akua) Woolbright
Senior Healthy Eating Chef and Culinary Educator, Derek Sarno
Global Leader Sustainable Engineering and Energy Management, Kathy Loftus
President Midwest Region, Michael Bashaw
President North Atlantic Region, Laura Derba
Global VP Communications, Sirr Less
Global VP Operational Finance, Brian O'Connell
Media Contact, Elizabeth Leader-Smith
Media Contact, Lindsay Lehfeld
Director, Blake W. Nordstrom, age 51
Director, Stephanie Kugelman, age 64
Co-CEO and Director, John P. Mackey, age 58
Director, Morris J. (Mo) Siegel, age 62
Director, William A. (Kip) Tindell, age 58
Co-CEO and Director, Walter E. Robb IV, age 59

Director, Jonathan A. (Jon) Seiffer, age 40
Director, Ralph Z. Sorenson, age 78
Director, Jonathan D. (Jon) Sokoloff, age 54
Director, Gabrielle E. (Gaby) Greene, age 51
Director, S.M. (Hass) Hassan, age 64
Auditors: Ernst&YoungLLP

LOCATIONS

HQ: Whole Foods Market Inc.
550 Bowie St., Austin TX 78703
Phone: 512-477-4455 **Fax:** 512-482-7000
Web: www.wholefoodsmarket.com

2011 Sales

	% of total
US	96
Canada &	3
Total	**100**

2011 Stores

	No.
US	
California	65
Massachusetts	20
Colorado	17
Illinois	17
Texas	17
Florida	16
New	10
New	10
Virginia	9
Connecticut	8
Georgia	8
Maryland	8
Pennsylvania	8
Arizona	7
North	7
Oregon	7
Ohio	6
Washington	6
Michigan	5
Nevada	5
District of	4
New	4
Tennessee	4
Utah	4
Louisiana	3
Rhode	3
Hawaii	2
Indiana	2
Kansas	2
Kentucky	2
Minnesota	2
Missouri	2
South	2
Wisconsin	2
Alabama	1
Arkansas	1
Maine	1
Nebraska	1
Oklahoma	1
Canada	7
UK	5
Total	**311**

PRODUCTS/OPERATIONS

2011 Sales

	% of total
Non-perishables	33
Prepared foods &	19
Other	48
Total	**100**

Selected Product Categories

Bakery
Body care
Educational products
Floral
Grocery
Household products
Meat and poultry
Nutritional supplements
Pet products
Prepared foods
Produce
Seafood
Specialty (beer wine cheese)
Textiles

COMPETITORS

Ahold U.S.A.
Albertsons
AMCON Distributing
Arden Group
Bristol Farms
Citarella
Costco Wholesale
Delhaize America
Earth Fare
Fiesta Mart
Forever Living
GNC
H-E-B
J Sainsbury
Kroger
Loblaw
Marks & Spencer
Minyard Group
Natural Grocers by Vitamin Cottage
NBTY
Publix
Safeway
Shaw' s
Sobeys
Sprouts
SUPERVALU
Tesco
Trader Joe' s
United Supermarkets
Wal-Mart
Winn-Dixie
Wm Morrison Supermarkets

HISTORICAL FINANCIALS

Company Type: Public

Income Statement

FYE: September 30

	REVENUE ($ mil.)	NET INCOME ($ mil.)	NET PROFIT MARGIN	EMPLOYEES
09/12	11,698	465	4.0%	72,700
09/11	10,107	342	3.4%	64,200
09/10	9,005	245	2.7%	58,300
09/09	8,031	146	1.8%	52,500
09/08	7,953	114	1.4%	52,800
Annual Growth	10.1%	42.0%	—	8.3%

2012 Year-End Financials

Debt ratio: 0.46%
Return on equity: 12.24%
Cash ($ mil.): 89
Current ratio: 215.17
Long-term debt ($ mil.): 23
No. of shares (mil.): 185
Dividends
Yield: —
Payout: 22.22%
Market value ($ mil.): 18,062

	STOCK PRICE ($) FY Close	P/E High/Low		PER SHARE ($) Earnings	Dividends	Book Value
09/12	97.40	39	24	2.52	0.00	20.51
09/11	68.20	37	18	1.93	0.00	16.72
09/10	37.07	29	17	1.43	0.00	13.80
09/09	28.77	35	10	0.85	0.00	14.52
09/08	20.64	65	22	0.82	0.00	10.74
Annual Growth	47.4%	—	—	32.4%	—	17.6%

Williams Cos Inc (The)

LOCATIONS

HQ: Williams Cos Inc (The)
One Williams Center, Tulsa, OK 74172
Phone: 918 573-2000 **Fax:** 918 588-2334
Web: www.williams.com

HISTORICAL FINANCIALS

Company Type:

Income Statement

FYE: December 31

	REVENUE ($ mil.)	NET INCOME ($ mil.)	NET PROFIT MARGIN	EMPLOYEES
12/11	7,930	376	4.7%	4,293
12/10	9,616	(1,097)	—	5,022
12/09	8,255	285	3.5%	4,801
12/08	12,352	1,418	11.5%	4,704
12/07	10,558	990	9.4%	4,319
Annual Growth	(6.9%)	(21.5%)	—	(0.2%)

2011 Year-End Financials

Debt ratio: 52.85%
Return on equity: 20.97%
Cash ($ mil.): 889
Current ratio: 113.07
Long-term debt ($ mil.): 8,369
No. of shares (mil.): 591
Dividends
Yield: —
Payout: 123.02%
Market value ($ mil.): 19,515

	STOCK PRICE ($) FY Close	P/E High/Low		PER SHARE ($) Earnings	Dividends	Book Value
12/11	33.02	52	36	0.63	0.00	3.03
12/10	24.72	—	—	(1.88)	0.49	12.46
12/09	21.08	44	20	0.49	0.44	14.49
12/08	14.48	17	5	2.40	0.43	14.60
12/07	35.78	22	15	1.63	0.39	10.88
Annual Growth	(2.0%)	—	—	(21.2%)	—	(27.4%)

Williams Partners L.P.

Fractionating natural gas liquids (NGLs) is only a fraction of what Williams Partners does. The company is also engaged in the gathering and processing of natural gas and the storage of NGLs and the operation of three major interstate natural gas pipelines. (These pipelines deliver 14% of the natural gas consumed in the US.) Williams Partners assets include a 3800-mile natural gas gathering system in the San Juan Basin; 60% of Discovery Producer Services and Carbonate Trend (gas gathering systems); and the 9800-mile Transco intestate natural gas pipeline. The Williams Companies has merged its Williams Pipeline Partners (pipelines) unit into Williams Partners (which had focused on midstream operations).

The $12 billion restructuring (in 2010) established Williams Partners as a major integrated interstate pipeline and midstream player. The deal allowed The Williams Companies to pool its pipelines assets streamline its operations and cut costs. Williams Companies owns 75% of the expanded entity.

The company's NGL business operates NGL storage facilities and holds a 50% stake in an NGL fractionator near Conway Kansas. These assets are located at one of only two major NGL trading hubs in the lower 48. NGLs the result of natural gas processing and crude oil refining are used in a number of industry applications including gasoline additives heating fuels and petrochemical feedstocks.

Further growing its NGL business in 2010 the company acquired 49% of Kansas-based NGL pipeline (Overland Pass Pipeline Company) from ONEOK Partners for $424 million. Both Williams Partners and ONEOK Partners own 50% of the pipeline.

Growing its midstream assets it acquired Williams Companies' gathering and processing assets in Colorado's Piceance Basin for $782 million. In a move to expand its presence in the fast-growing Marcellus Shale region in 2011 it acquired Cabot Oil & Gas' midstream assets in Susquehanna County Pennsylvania for $150 million.

In 2011 the company also boosted its holdings in the GulfStream interstate gas pipeline system to 49% buying 25% from Williams Companies for $330 million.

Williams Partners' acquisitions pipeline expansions higher gas gathering fees and high NGL prices lifted the company's revenues in 2011 outpacing a growth in costs and operating expenses resulting in an improved net income for the year.

In 2012 it acquired the Laser Northeast Gathering System and other midstream businesses in the Marcellus Shale from Delphi Midstream Partners for about $750 million. The Laser System consists of 33 miles of natural gas pipeline in Pennsylvania and 10 miles of pipeline in New York. The deal extends Williams Partners' strategy of serving producers through midstream infrastructure in the Marcellus Shale and other basins.

That year the company also bought Caiman Eastern Midstream from Caiman Energy for $2.4 billion. The purchase anchors Williams Partners' Ohio Valley Midstream business (which includes gathering contracts in 236000 acres from 10 producers and processing commitments for 100 million cu. ft. per day) and gives Williams Partners a major presence in the liquid-rich area of the Marcellus Shale formation.

It also Williams' 83% stake in the Geismar olefins production facility as well as Williams' refinery-grade propylene splitter for $2.3 billion and pipelines in the Gulf region for $100 million.

Williams Companies spun off Williams Partners in 2005.

EXECUTIVES

SVP and General Counsel; General Counsel Williams Partners GP LLC, James J. (Jim) Bender, age 55
Chairman and CEO, Alan S. Armstrong, age 49
SVP and CFO; CFO and Director Williams Partners GP LLC, Donald R. Chappel, age 60
Director and SVP Midstream, Rory L. Miller, age 51
Director Williams Partners GP LLC, H. Michael Krimbill, age 58
Director Williams Partners GP LLC, Alice M. Peterson, age 59
Director, Randall L. (Randy) Barnard, age 53
SVP and CFO; CFO and Director Williams Partners GP LLC, Donald R. Chappel, age 60
Director, H. Brent Austin, age 57
Director and SVP Midstream, Rory L. Miller, age 51
Auditors: Ernst&YoungLLP

LOCATIONS

HQ: Williams Partners L.P.
1 Williams Ctr., Tulsa OK 74172-0172
Phone: 918-573-2000 **Fax:** 310-393-7799
Web: www.blssi.com

PRODUCTS/OPERATIONS

2011 Sales

	$ mil.	% of total
Midstream	5,051	75
Gas pipleine	1,678	25
Total	**6,729**	**100**

COMPETITORS

BP NGL
Dynegy
El Paso Corporation
Enterprise Products
Kinder Morgan
Martin Midstream Partners
Questar Pipeline
Spectra Energy
TransCanada
TransMontaigne

HISTORICAL FINANCIALS

Company Type: Public

Income Statement FYE: December 31

	REVENUE ($ mil.)	NET INCOME ($ mil.)	NET PROFIT MARGIN	EMPLOYEES
12/11	6,729	1,378	20.5%	0
12/10	5,715	1,085	19.0%	0
12/09	470	152	32.4%	0
12/08	637	191	30.0%	0
12/07	572	164	28.7%	0
Annual Growth	85.1%	70.1%	—	—

2011 Year-End Financials

Debt ratio: 50.33%
Return on equity: 20.23%
Cash ($ mil.): 163
Current ratio: 71.86
Long-term debt ($ mil.): 6,913
No. of shares (mil.): 290
Dividends
Yield: —
Payout: 78.59%
Market value ($ mil.): 17,426

	STOCK PRICE ($) FY Close	P/E High/Low		PER SHARE ($) Earnings	Dividends	Book Value
12/11	59.99	16	12	3.69	0.00	18.00
12/10	46.65	18	12	2.66	2.65	17.51
12/09	30.67	11	3	2.88	2.54	4.08
12/08	11.94	15	4	2.55	2.44	3.86
12/07	39.20	25	19	1.97	2.05	3.53
Annual Growth	11.2%	—	—	17.0%	—	50.3%

Wilshire Bancorp Inc

Wilshire Bancorp is the holding company for Wilshire State Bank where ethnic minorities are the banking majority. Based in the Koreatown section of Los Angeles the bank has more than 20 branches –mainly in California but also in New Jersey New York and Texas. It also has about 10 lending offices that specialize in making Small Business Administration (SBA) loans. Wilshire State Bank targets small to midsized minority-owned businesses and ethnic groups underserved by many national banking institutions. In addition to offering standard deposit services (including checking and savings accounts CDs and IRAs) the bank also offers a variety of loans such as mortgages and import/export financing.

Wilshire State Bank sees growth possibilities in its niche market of Korean Americans largely due to the recent passage of the Republic of Korea-US Free Trade Agreement and admission of South Korea into the US Visa Waiver Program. Its target demographic is also one of the faster-growing populations in the country. However expanding beyond its traditional Korean-American customer base Wilshire State Bank also serves the Hispanic and Vietnamese communities.

The bank has been dealing with its exposure to bad loans mainly commercial mortgages based in California; some 85% of its loan portfolio is real estate-related. Revenues have therefore suffered – they fell 20% in 2011 to $153.8 million (it earned $192.3 million in 2010 and $215.7 million in 2009) and the company has reported net losses for two years in a row. In response Wilshire has sold some loans and doubled down on its risk management efforts; it split its lending and underwriting functions in early 2011.

The company has opened several new bank branches and is continuing to expand its branch network both on the East and West Coast with New York and New Jersey as target markets for growth. In 2011 Wilshire opened two new loan production offices as well. The bank is keeping its focus on deposits and loans rather and has no plans to begin offering brokerage or investment services.

EXECUTIVES

Chairman, Steven S. Koh, age 66
EVP and Chief Lending Officer, Sung Soo Han, age 54, $190,000 total compensation
First VP and Western Office Manager, Diane Y. Park
SVP and Branch Manager Valley Office, Susan Magidow
President CEO and Director, Joanne Kim, age 57, $247,500 total compensation
First VP Deputy CFO Controller and Accounting Manager, Elaine S. Jeon, age 51
First VP Valley Office, Sun Han
Financial VP and Assistant Corporate Secretary, Cynthia Peters
SVP and Manager Trade Finance Department, Radu M. Spiridon
President CEO and Director, Jae Whan (J. W.) Yoo, age 62
SVP Deputy CFO Controller and Accounting Manager, Danny Jeon
VP Auto Center Manager, Tommy Hur
SVP and Manager Home Loan Center, Gene Sheen
SVP and Chief Compliance Officer, Jean Lim
SVP and Chief Information Officer, Jake Seo
First VP Note Manager, Young Kim
VP Seattle Office BDO, Jimmy Kim
VP San Jose Office BDO, Rick Pak
SVP and Branch Manager Dallas Branch, J. P. Park
VP Oklahoma City Office BDO, Clyde Caldwell
VP San Antonio Office BDO, Roger Guerra
First VP Houston Office BDO, Anees Khan
Assistant VP Las Vegas Office BDO, Jim Ho Huh
Financial VP and Treasurer and Investor Relations Manager, Edward S. Han
EVP and CFO Wilshire Bancorp and Wilshire State Bank, Gunho (Alex) Ko, age 45, $154,404 total compensation
SVP and Chief Credit Officer, Seung Hoon Kang
EVP and Chief Credit Officer, Jack Choi
President CEO and Director, Joanne Kim, age 57
Director, Kyu-Hyun Kim, age 77
Director, Richard Y. Lim, age 79
Director, Fred F. Mautner, age 82
Director, Young Hi Pak, age 63
Director, Harry Siafaris, age 79
Director, Donald D. Byun, age 59
President CEO and Director, Jae Whan (J. W.) Yoo, age 62
Director, Lawrence Jeon, age 45
Auditors: Deloitte&ToucheLLP

LOCATIONS

HQ: Wilshire Bancorp Inc.
3200 Wilshire Blvd., Los Angeles CA 90010
Phone: 213-387-3200 **Fax:** 213-427-6562
Web: www.wilshirebank.com

PRODUCTS/OPERATIONS

2011 Sales

	$ mil.	% of total
Interest		
Loans including fees	121	77
Investment securities	7	4
Federal funds sold	1	1
Noninterest		
Service charges on deposit accounts	12	8
Net gain on sale of loans	5	4
Loan-related servicing fees	4	3
Other	4	3
Adjustments	(3.1)	-
Total	**153**	**100**

COMPETITORS

Bank of America
Bank of the West
BBCN
Broadway Financial
Cathay General Bancorp
Citibank
City National
Comerica
East West Bancorp
Hanmi Financial
U.S. Bancorp
UnionBanCal

HISTORICAL FINANCIALS

Company Type: Public

Income Statement FYE: December 31

	ASSETS ($ mil.)	NET INCOME ($ mil.)	INCOME AS % OF ASSETS	EMPLOYEES
12/11	2,696	(30)	—	382
12/10	2,970	(34)	—	405
12/09	3,436	20	0.6%	405
12/08	2,450	26	1.1%	349
12/07	2,196	26	1.2%	369
Annual Growth	5.3%	—	—	0.9%

2011 Year-End Financials

Debt ratio: 5.46%
Return on equity: (-9.80)%
Cash ($ mil.): 325
Current ratio: —
Long-term debt ($ mil.): 147
No. of shares (mil.): 71
Dividends
Yield: —
Payout: —
Market value ($ mil.): 259

	STOCK PRICE ($) FY Close	P/E High	P/E Low	PER SHARE ($) Earnings	Dividends	Book Value
12/11	3.63	—	—	(0.61)	0.00	4.34
12/10	7.62	—	—	(1.30)	0.15	7.77
12/09	8.19	17	6	0.56	0.20	9.05
12/08	9.08	17	7	0.90	0.20	8.67
12/07	7.85	21	9	0.91	0.20	5.87
Annual Growth	(17.5%)	—	—	—	—	(7.3%)

Windstream Corp

Instead of relying on the prevailing breeze to deliver its services Windstream makes use of more tangible connections such as fiber optics and copper wire. The company provides communications and technology services to business and residential customers in the US through a network of 115000 miles of fiber and from more than 20 data centers. Business services include multi-site networking Internet access cloud computing colocation online backup and other managed services. Along with Internet and voice for its residential customers it also offers video services mainly through an agreement with DISH Network. Call connection and backhaul services are offered to phone companies and wireless carriers.

Technology advances have made its consumer business prospects increasingly difficult as wireless carriers have siphoned off wireline customers and cable companies have been able to effectively woo voice and Internet customers. The expanding need for data services from the enterprise customer side has become the company's new focus.

In 2011 Windstream planted a major stake in the ground towards that strategy with the acquisition of PAETEC Holding based near Rochester New York for about $2.3 billion (giving PAETEC shareholders about 13% of Windstream) to further expand its Internet protocol (IP)-based communications services cloud computing and managed hosting services business. The deal extended Windstream's reach significantly adding medium- and large-sized business customers in more than 20 states about 37000 miles of fiber to its network and seven data centers. The combined company serves nearly half a million businesses including most FORTUNE 500 companies.

The growth in its consumer segment was nominal and doesn't contradict Windstream's strategy shift as the underlying numbers show double-digit declines in the area of concern: voice and long distance. And the nominal half-percent increase in the segment over 2010 is a notable drop from the 5% growth over 2009. All of that is reinforced by the change in growth for the new focus its data and integrated services which increased by about $54 million in 2011 compared to $7.6 million in 2010 —and that's apart from acquisitions. Some of that was existing customers switching from fragmented services to integrated voice and data but the overall trend is what Windstream sees as its future. Indeed even now its business service revenues have climbed to nearly 50% of total sales.

As its PAETEC merger might suggest Windstream has fueled its growth through an aggressive acquisition strategy. In fact 90% of its growth for 2010 and nearly 100% of the growth for 2011 came from acquisitions. In 2010 the company grew in a number of regional markets. Its $650 million purchase of South Carolina-based NuVox boosted its footprint in the Southeast and Midwest regions and its $1.2 billion acquisition of Iowa Telecom added rural markets in Iowa and Minnesota. Additionally that year the company bought privately held local phone carrier and fiber transport services provider Q-Comm based near Kansas City for nearly $820 million. The purchase included Q-Comm's Kentucky Data Link (fiber services in 23 states) and Norlight (Midwest CLEC) subsidiaries and approximately doubled Windstream's fiber network infrastructure. That deal bolstered its wholesale prospects improving its capacity to provide signal transport services over landlines for wireless carriers.

Windstream also paid $310 million to buy hosted data network and application services provider Hosted Solutions from private equity firm ABRY Partners in late 2010. The deal significantly expanded the company's data center business adding Hosted Solutions' five data centers in North Carolina and Boston.

HISTORY

Windstream was formed in 2006 through the combination of ALLTEL's wireline business with VALOR Communications Group after Little Rock-based ALLTEL turned its full attention to wireless communications services. Its decision to spin off its wireline operations came after several acquisitions of smaller wireless carriers including Western Wireless and Midwest Wireless both in 2005; and its purchase of First Cellular the following year. With its acquisition of VALOR and subsequent spin-off of its wireline operations as Windstream ALLTEL became a purely wireless communications service provider.

In 2007 Windstream boosted its subscriber numbers by about 160000 phone lines through its acquisition of North Carolina-based CT Communications for $584 million. Later that year the company spun off its publishing business Windstream Yellow Pages to affiliates of Welsh Carson Anderson & Stowe for about $500 million. In 2008 it sold its wireless business in North Carolina to AT&T Mobility for about $57 million.

In 2009 Windstream paid about $333 million in stock for Pennsylvania-based D&E Communications in 2009. The deal added about 160000 rural access lines including about 40000 broadband subscriptions. Windstream also acquired North Carolina-based Lexcom that year for $141 million in cash.

While it bulked up in the area of core communications services during 2009 the company sold its Windstream Supply distribution business to Walker and Associates. Windstream Supply distributed telephony and communications equipment largely to affiliated carriers and institutions.

EXECUTIVES

President CEO and Director, Jeffery R. (Jeff) Gardner, age 52, $991,000 total compensation
Chairman, Dennis E. Foster, age 71
Media Contact, David Avery
EVP Business Sales, A. John Leach Jr., age 48
EVP Network Operations, W. Grant Raney, age 51
CIO, Cynthia B. (Cindy) Nash, age 47
EVP General Counsel and Secretary, John P. Fletcher, age 46, $412,500 total compensation
COO, Brent K. Whittington, age 41, $519,231 total compensation
SVP Government Affairs, Eric Einhorn
SVP and Treasurer, Robert G. (Rob) Clancy Jr., age 47, $284,231 total compensation
SVP Human Resources, Susan Bradley, age 60, $213,846 total compensation
SVP Governmental Affairs, Michael D. (Mike) Rhoda, age 51
EVP and Chief Marketing Officer, Richard J. (Ric) Crane, age 57, $310,000 total compensation
CFO, Anthony W. (Tony) Thomas, age 40, $308,077 total compensation
SVP Consumer Sales, Gregg Richey
SVP Data Center Operations, Christopher (Kip) Turco
SVP Customer Services, Joe Marano
Media Contact, Larry White
VP and Controller, John C. Eichler, age 40
VP Channel Sales, Dan Sterling
Director Capital Markets and Investor Relations, Mary Michaels
SVP Service Delivery and Operations, Jack Norris
SVP Fiber Transport Services, John Greenbank
SVP Network Services, William Bellando
Staff Manager Investor Relations and Capital Markets, Genesis White
Media Contact, Scott Morris
VP Business Marketing, Don Perkins
VP Direct Sales North Carolina South Carolina Georgia Alabama and Florida, Todd Klas
VP Direct Sales Florida Louisiana Coastal Alabama and Mississippi, Andy Drotleff
EVP and Chief Human Resources Officer, David Works
SVP Financial Planning and Treasury, Bob Gunderman

President CEO and Director, Jeffery R. (Jeff) Gardner, age 52
Director, Francis X. (Skip) Frantz, age 58
Director, Samuel E. (Sandy) Beall III, age 62
Director, Jeffrey T. Hinson, age 57
Director, Carol B. Armitage, age 54
Director, Alan L. Wells, age 52
Director, William A. Montgomery, age 63
Director, Judy K. Jones, age 68
Auditors: PricewaterhouseCoopersLLP

LOCATIONS

HQ: Windstream Corp
4001 Rodney Parham Road, Little Rock, AR 72212
Phone: 501 748-7000
Web: www.windstream.com

PRODUCTS/OPERATIONS

2011 Sales

	$ mil.	% of total
Service		
Business	2,098	49
Consumer	1,380	32
Wholesale	626	15
Other	51	1
Product	129	3
Total	**4,285**	**100**

COMPETITORS

8x8
AT&T
Cox Communications
Equinix
FullNet Communications
Hickory Tech
Momentum Telecom
Onvoy Voice Services
Sprint Nextel
Verizon

HISTORICAL FINANCIALS

Company Type: Public

Income Statement FYE: December 31

	REVENUE ($ mil.)	NET INCOME ($ mil.)	NET PROFIT MARGIN	EMPLOYEES
12/11	4,285	172	4.0%	14,638
12/10	3,712	310	8.4%	10,086
12/09	2,996	334	11.2%	7,385
12/08	3,171	412	13.0%	7,349
12/07	3,260	917	28.1%	7,570
Annual Growth	7.1%	(34.2%)	—	17.9%

2011 Year-End Financials

Debt ratio: 63.58%
Return on equity: 11.50%
Cash ($ mil.): 227
Current ratio: 104.04
Long-term debt ($ mil.): 8,936
No. of shares (mil.): 586
Dividends
Yield: —
Payout: 303.03%
Market value ($ mil.): 6,883

	STOCK PRICE ($) FY Close	P/E High	P/E Low	PER SHARE ($) Earnings	Dividends	Book Value
12/11	11.74	42	33	0.33	0.00	2.56
12/10	13.94	22	15	0.66	1.00	1.65
12/09	10.99	15	8	0.76	1.00	0.60
12/08	9.20	14	7	0.93	1.00	0.57
12/07	13.02	8	7	1.94	1.00	1.54
Annual Growth	(2.6%)	—	—	(35.8%)	—	13.5%

Wintrust Financial Corp. (IL)

Wintrust Financial is a holding company engaged in personal and commercial banking wealth management and specialty lending services primarily in the metropolitan Chicago and Milwaukee areas. With assets of more than $17 billion it operates about 15 subsidiary banks (most bear the name of the community they serve) with more than 100 branches in all. The banks offer traditional deposit services and emphasize business and commercial real estate lending which accounts for about half of the company's loan portfolio. Specifically Wintrust's banks target small business customers. Some of Wintrust's banks also provide niche lending for homeowners associations medical practices franchisees and municipalities.

Wintrust's nonbank subsidiaries include First Insurance Funding which provides financing for commercial insurance and life insurance premiums. In 2012 Wintrust expanded its premium funding business into Canada with the acquisition of Macquarie Premium Funding Inc which was a subsidiary of Macquarie Group. The deal marked Wintrust's first international venture.

Other Wintrust subsidiaries include Tricom Funding which offers financing and administrative services to the temporary staffing industry in the US and Wintrust Mortgage Corporation (formerly known as WestAmerica Mortgage Company) which deals in the origination and purchase of residential loans for sale. In 2011 Wintrust bought certain mortgage banking assets of Minnesota-based River City and Woodfield Planning Corporation in Chicago.

Wintrust's wealth management arm offers financial planning and brokerage services through a trio of companies bearing the Wayne Hummer name. The company built the business through the 2011 acquisition of institutional asset manager Great Lakes Advisors. The deal significantly increased Wintrust's assets under management to more than $13 billion.

On the banking side Wintrust has developed its community-based franchise through the formation of nine de novo (or new) banks new branch openings and acquisitions. Wintrust has also taken advantage of the rash of bank seizures in the Chicago area. Since 2010 the company has snapped up seven failed institutions in FDIC-assisted transactions adding some 20 branches. Acquisitions in 2011 included Community First Bank (now Rogers Park Community Bank) Bank of Commerce (now Wood Dale Bank & Trust) and First Chicago Bank & Trust.

Also in 2011 Wintrust bought Elgin State Bank in its first non-FDIC-assisted deal in several years. The purchase added three branches in Illinois. Also in a traditional transaction the company acquired HPK Financial the parent of Hyde Park Bank & Trust in late 2012. It will add two branches in the Hyde Park neighborhood of Chicago.

But Wintrust has not been unscathed by the economic crisis either. It has significant exposure to commercial real estate in the hard-hit Chicago area and in 2008 formed a new division to resolve problem loans usually through liquidation. The company remained profitable though its net income was down in 2010 as it dealt with an uptick in nonperforming loans and increased its allowance for loan losses. Wintrust has also formed a division to manage problem loans acquired from the failed banks.

By 2011 the economy and Wintrust's results improved. The company reported a more than 22% increase in net income. Assets deposits and loan amounts all increased that year as well. Wintrust's calculated growth strategy has helped it expand by reaching new customers and further deepening its relationship with current ones by offering new services.

EXECUTIVES

EVP Technology; President Wintrust Information Technology Services, Lloyd M. Bowden, age 58, $167,333 total compensation
SEVP COO Secretary and Treasurer; Regional Market Head Crystal Lake Bank State Bank of the Lakes and Town Bank, David A. Dykstra, age 51, $675,000 total compensation
President CEO and Director, Edward J. Wehmer, age 57, $900,000 total compensation
Chairman and CEO Libertyville Bank & Trust, J. Albert (Bert) Carstens
EVP, Frank J. Burke
EVP and Chief Credit Officer; Regional Market Head Hinsdale Bank, Richard B. Murphy, age 52, $413,750 total compensation
EVP; Regional Market Head Advantage Bank Barrington Bank and Village Bank, James H. Bishop, age 68
EVP and Chief Administration Officer, Leona A. Gleason
Chairman, Peter D. Crist, age 60
Chairman and CEO Northbrook Bank & Trust, Richard C. Rushkewicz
EVP and CFO, David L. Stoehr, age 52, $315,000 total compensation
EVP; Regional Market Head Lake Forest Bank Northbrook Bank Northshore Community Bank and Wintrust Information Technology Services, Timothy S. (Tim) Crane, age 50
Chairman and CEO Barrington Bank & Trust, W. Bradley Stetson
SVP Marketing, Matthew E. Doubleday
President and CEO Crystal Lake Bank & Trust, James N. (Jim) Thorpe
President Barrington Bank & Trust, Jon C. Stickney
President Northbrook Bank & Trust, David P. Masters
President Beverly Bank & Trust, Dennis C. O'Malley
President CEO and Director Town Bank, Jay C. Mack
CEO and Director Wheaton Bank & Trust, Stacey J. Huels
President CEO and Director State Bank of The Lakes, James B. Kinney
EVP Risk Management; Regional Market Head St. Charles Bank and Wintrust Mortgage Corp., John S. Fleshood, age 49, $292,750 total compensation
President and CEO Old Plank Trail Community Bank, Paul R. Slade
EVP and Market Head Wealth Management Services, Thomas P. (Tom) Zidar
EVP; Regional Market Head Libertyville Bank and Wheaton Bank, John A. Carstens, age 56
Vice Chairman North Shore Community Bank, Michael W. Kiss
President North Shore Community Bank, William (Bill) Lynch
President St. Charles Bank, Thomas W. (Tom) Hansen
President Wheaton Bank & Trust, Robert D. Hutchinson

CEO Beverly Bank & Brust, Michael (Mike) Johnstone
Chairman and CEO St. Charles Bank, Richard A. Davis
EVP and Senior Lender St. Charles Bank, Michael P. Trimarco
EVP St. Charles Bank, Roy F. Picciuca
Chief Credit Officer St. Charles Bank, John Czyzycki
President and COO Lake Forest Bank and Trust, David E. Lee
EVP General Counsel and Secretary, Lisa J. Pattis
President CEO and Director, Edward J. Wehmer, age 57
Director, Bruce K. Crowther, age 60
Director, Bert A. Getz Jr., age 44
Director, Christopher J. Perry, age 56
Director, Ingrid S. Stafford, age 58
Director, Thomas J. Neis, age 63
Director, Hollis W. Rademacher, age 76
Director, Scott K. Heitmann, age 63
Director, Joseph F. Damico, age 58
Director, Albin F. (Al) Moschner, age 59
Director, Charles H. (Chuck) James III, age 53
Director, H. Patrick Hackett Jr., age 60
Auditors: Ernst&YoungLLP

LOCATIONS

HQ: Wintrust Financial Corporation
727 N. Bank Ln., Lake Forest IL 60045
Phone: 847-615-4096 **Fax:** 847-615-4091
Web: www.wintrust.com

PRODUCTS/OPERATIONS

2011 Sales

	$ mil.	% of total
Interest		
Loans including fees	552	70
Securities	46	6
Other	6	1
Noninterest		
Mortgage banking	56	7
Wealth management	44	6
Gain on bargain purchases	38	5
Service charges on deposit accounts	15	2
Other	35	3
Total	**795**	**100**

Selected Subsidiaries and Affiliates

Banking
- Barrington Bank & Trust Company N.A.
- Beverly Bank & Trust Company N.A.
- Crystal Lake Bank & Trust Company N.A.
- Hinsdale Bank & Trust Company
- Lake Forest Bank & Trust Company
- Libertyville Bank & Trust Company
- North Shore Community Bank & Trust Company
- Northbrook Bank & Trust Company
- Old Plank Trail Community Bank N.A.
- Schaumburg Bank & Trust Company N.A.
- St. Charles Bank & Trust
- State Bank of The Lakes
- Town Bank
- Village Bank & Trust
- Wheaton Bank and Trust Company

Non-banking
- Chicago Trust Company N.A.
- First Insurance Funding Corporation
- Great Lakes Advisors LLC
- Tricom Inc. of Milwaukee
- Wayne Hummer Asset Management Company
- Wayne Hummer Investments LLC
- Wayne Hummer Trust Company N.A.
- Wintrust Information Technology Services Company
- Wintrust Mortgage Corporation (formerly WestAmerica Mortgage Company)

COMPETITORS

Associated Banc-Corp
MB Financial
Bank of America
Citigroup
Fifth Third
First Midwest Bancorp
Harris
JPMorgan Chase
Northern Trust
PrivateBancorp
RBS Citizens Financial Group
U.S. Bancorp

HISTORICAL FINANCIALS

Company Type: Public

Income Statement

FYE: December 31

	ASSETS ($ mil.)	NET INCOME ($ mil.)	INCOME AS % OF ASSETS	EMPLOYEES
12/11	15,893	77	0.5%	2,933
12/10	13,980	63	0.5%	2,588
12/09	12,215	73	0.6%	2,381
12/08	10,658	20	0.2%	2,326
12/07	9,368	55	0.6%	1,964
Annual Growth	14.1%	8.7%	—	10.5%

2011 Year-End Financials

Debt ratio: 9.07%
Return on equity: 5.03%
Cash ($ mil.): 897
Current ratio: —
Long-term debt ($ mil.): 1,442
No. of shares (mil.): 35
Dividends
Yield: —
Payout: 10.78%
Market value ($ mil.): 1,009

	STOCK PRICE ($) FY Close	P/E High/Low		PER SHARE ($) Earnings	Dividends	Book Value
12/11	28.05	18	12	1.67	0.00	42.90
12/10	33.03	41	26	1.02	0.18	41.20
12/09	30.79	15	4	2.18	0.27	47.04
12/08	20.57	50	22	0.76	0.36	44.90
12/07	33.13	22	14	2.24	0.32	31.56
Annual Growth	(4.1%)	—	—	(7.1%)	—	8.0%

Wisconsin Energy Corp.

While Wisconsin winters freeze Lake Superior Wisconsin Energy warms interiors. The company's utilities provide electricity to more than 1.1 million customers and natural gas to more than 1 million customers in eastern and northern Wisconsin and Michigan's Upper Peninsula. It also serves 460 steam customers in downtown Milwaukee. Wisconsin Energy has about 5970 MW of generating capacity primarily from coal-fired and nuclear-powered plants. The company's primary utility subsidiaries Wisconsin Gas and Wisconsin Electric operate together as We Energies. Other operations include real estate development and renewable energy technology.

The company's strategy is to invest in new gas coal and green energy plants and upgrade existing plants and its distribution system while selling non-core assets. Wisconsin Energy sold a number of assets in 2009 and 2010 in order to pay down debt and focus on its core businesses. It sold its water utility to the City of Mequon Wisconsin for $14.5 million and power utility to Edison Sault to Cloverland Electric Cooperative $61.5 million. It also sold its 25% stake in power plant Edgewater Generating Unit 5 to Wisconsin Power and Light Company.

To meet clean energy regulations Wisconsin Energy has been shifting the mix of its energy portfolio towards greener supply sources. In 2008 it completed the 145 MW Blue Sky Green Field wind project and announced plans to develop a 132 - 207 MW wind farm at Glacier Hills in Central Wisconsin (scheduled for completion in 2012). In 2009 it announced plans to build a biomass-fueled power plant at a Wisconsin paper mill site.

However in 2010 Wisconsin Energy's coal plants still accounted for 58% of generating capacity and the company faces significant costs in order to comply with environmental regulations and remediation compliance standards going forward even as its shifts to more efficient and greener power operations.

In 2011 the company completed the extensive emission-control system retrofitting and upgrade of its 615 MW coal-fired Oak Creek Power Plant Unit 2. (The upgrade of Unit 1 was completed in 2010).

Unusually warm summer weather in 2010 increased power demand helping to lift Wisconsin Energy's overall revenues and income.

EXECUTIVES

VP Environmental, Kristine M. Krause
VP Human Resources Wisconsin Energy and We Energies, Arthur A. (Art) Zintek
EVP and CFO WEC WE and WG, Frederick D. (Rick) Kuester, age 61, $657,000 total compensation
Chairman President and CEO WEC WE and WG, Gale E. Klappa, age 61, $1,129,008 total compensation
Assistant Treasurer Wisconsin Energy and We Energies, James A. Schubilske
VP Corporate Communications Wisconsin Energy and We Energies, Richard J. White
VP Controller Wisconsin Energy and We Energies, Stephen P. Dickson, age 51
VP; SVP State Public Affairs We Energies, Walter J. Kunicki
SVP and Chief Administrative Officer WEC WE and WG, Kristine A. Rappe, age 55, $393,708 total compensation
Assistant Corporate Secretary Wisconsin Energy and We Energies, Keith H. Ecke
EVP WEC WE and WG, Allen L. Leverett, age 45, $607,680 total compensation
VP Federal Policy Wisconsin Energy and We Energies, Darnell K. DeMasters
Assistant Treasurer; VP and Assistant Treasurer We Electric Power Co and We Electric Power Co, David L. Hughes
EVP General Counsel and Corporate Secretary, Susan H. Martin, age 59
Director and CIO IT Services We Energies, Steve Cartwright
EVP and CFO, J. Patrick Keyes, age 46
SVP External Affairs, Robert M. (Bert) Gavin
Director, Frederick P. Stratton Jr., age 72
Director, Robert A. Cornog, age 72
Director, Curt S. Culver, age 59
Director, John F. Bergstrom, age 65
Director, Ulice Payne Jr., age 56
Director, Barbara L. Bowles, age 64
Director, Thomas J. (Tom) Fischer, age 65
Director, Patricia W. Chadwick, age 63
Auditors: Deloitte&ToucheLLP

LOCATIONS

HQ: Wisconsin Energy Corporation
231 W. Michigan St., Milwaukee WI 53203
Phone: 414-221-2345 **Fax:** 414-221-2554
Web: www.wisconsinenergy.com

PRODUCTS/OPERATIONS

2011 Sales

	$ mil.	% of total
Utility	4,431	91
Non-utility	435	9
Corporate & other	0	
Adjustments	(381.1)	-
Total	**4,486**	**100**

Selected Subsidiaries

W.E. Power LLC (We Power regulated power plant construction)
Wisconsin Electric Power Company (operates as We Energies electric gas and steam utility)
Wisconsin Gas LLC (operates as We Energies gas and water utility)
Wispark LLC (real estate development)
Wisvest LLC (chilled water services for the Milwaukee Regional Medical Center)

COMPETITORS

AEP
ALLETE
Alliant Energy
CMS Energy
Dairyland Power
DTE
Integrys Energy Group
MGE Energy
Minnesota Power
SEMCO ENERGY
Wisconsin Power & Light
Xcel Energy

HISTORICAL FINANCIALS

Company Type: Public

Income Statement FYE: December 31

	REVENUE ($ mil.)	NET INCOME ($ mil.)	NET PROFIT MARGIN	EMPLOYEES
12/11	4,486	526	11.7%	4,595
12/10	4,202	456	10.9%	4,596
12/09	4,127	382	9.3%	4,692
12/08	4,431	359	8.1%	4,935
12/07	4,237	335	7.9%	4,985
Annual Growth	1.4%	11.9%	—	(2.0%)

2011 Year-End Financials

Debt ratio: 38.35%
Return on equity: 13.18%
Cash ($ mil.): 14
Current ratio: 104.52
Long-term debt ($ mil.): 4,614
No. of shares (mil.): 230
Dividends
Yield: —
Payout: 46.43%
Market value ($ mil.): 8,058

	STOCK PRICE ($) FY Close	P/E High/Low	PER SHARE ($) Earnings	Dividends	Book Value
12/11	34.96	27 12	2.24	0.00	17.33
12/10	58.86	31 24	1.93	0.80	16.39
12/09	49.83	31 22	1.62	0.68	15.39
12/08	41.98	32 25	1.52	0.54	14.40
12/07	48.71	35 29	1.42	0.50	13.38
Annual Growth	(8.0%)	— —	12.1%	—	6.7%

World Fuel Services Corp.

You can't fuel all the people all the time but World Fuel Services tries hard to do just that. World Fuel Services provides fuel and services to commercial and corporate aircraft petroleum distributors and ships at more than 6000 locations around the world 24 hours a day. Its aviation fueling business focuses on serving small to midsized air carriers cargo and charter carriers and private aircraft. World Fuel Services also markets fuel and related services to petroleum distributors operating in the land transportation market. All told it has almost 50 offices in more than 20 countries and does business in 200 countries and/or territories.

Operations

World Fuel Services maintains its competitive edge by offering a range of support services (such as fuel market analysis flight planning ground-handling services and weather reports) to its aviation and marine customers.

As part of its marine fueling services business World Fuel Services arranges fueling for ships on a brokered basis and extends credit to a global customer base which includes container lines cruise ships dry bulk carriers fishing fleets refrigerated vessels and tankers. The company also provides financial credit for aviation fuels.

Financial Analysis

High oil prices produced robust petroleum product prices in 2011 which (coupled with World Fuel Services' acquisitions) lifted the company's revenues that year by 81% and its net income by 32%.

Sales took a hit in 2009 because of the global recession low commodity prices and the slump in global transportation triggered by the weak economy. A rebounding economy and the impact of acquisitions saw the company's revenues jump sharply in 2010.

Strategy

World Fuel Services has increased its geographic coverage and the depth of its portfolio through acquisitions. In 2012 the company acquired CarterEnergy's wholesale motor fuel distribution business. Kansas-based CarterEnergy with an annual volume of more than of 500 million gallons distributes branded fuel to more than 700 retail operators and is a supplier to industrial commercial and government customers in more than a dozen states.

To improve its payment processing operations that year it also agreed to buy certain assets of Multi Service Corporation for $137 million.

Boosting its aviation fuel segment in 2011 (for an undisclosed amount) World Fuel Services acquired The Hiller Group an aviation fuel supplier to more than 600 fixed base operators. It also bought Ascent Aviation a national branded reseller of aviation fuel for ConocoPhillips and deicing fluid for Dow Chemical and which supplies more than 450 airports and fixed base operators and NATO aviation fuel and logistics supplier Nordic Camp Supply (for $68.5 million.)

In 2010 it beefed up its position in the branded onshore wholesale market to 1 billion gallons a year by acquiring Lakeside Oil Company based in Milwaukee. It also boosted its market position through the acquisition of leading independent petroleum marketing company Western Petroleum for $95 million.

HISTORY

Neighbors Ralph Weiser and Jerrold Blair founded International Oil Recovery an oil recycling company in Florida in 1984. The company moved into aviation fueling by acquiring Advance Petroleum in 1986. Two years later International Oil Recovery diversified further entering the hazardous waste market by buying Resource Recovery of America a soil remediation company. In 1989 the firm acquired JCo Energy Partners an aviation fuel company and subsequently renamed its aviation fueling division World Fuel Services. The company set up International Petroleum in 1993 to operate a Delaware used-oil and water-recycling plant.

The company changed its name to World Fuel Services Corporation in 1995 to reflect its expanded range of operations. Also that year it nearly doubled its revenue base with the purchase of Trans-Tec the world's #1 independent marine fuel services company. World Fuel also exited the environmental services business in 1995 to focus on its fuel services and oil recycling businesses.

The following year the company formed World Fuel International a subsidiary based in Costa Rica that serves World Fuel's aviation customers in South and Central America Canada and the Caribbean. In 1998 it acquired corporate jet fuel provider Baseops International which has offices in the UK and Texas.

In 1999 the company expanded its share of the marine fuel market with the acquisition of the Bunkerfuels group of companies one of the world's top marine fuel brokerages.

To focus on its marine and aviation fueling businesses World Fuel exited the oil recycling segment in 2000 when it sold its International Petroleum unit to waste services company EarthCare for about $33 million.

The company expanded into the United Arab Emirates with its 2001 acquisition of fuel services provider Marine Energy of Dubai. World Fuel acquired Rotterdam-based marine fuel reseller Oil Shipping Group in 2002.

In 2004 World Fuel Services acquired UK-based marine fuel reseller Tramp Holdings for $83 million.

The company diversified further in 2007 acquiring AVCARD a leading provider of contract fuel sales and charge card services to the aviation industry for $55 million.

In 2009 it bought wholesale motor fuel distributor TGS Petroleum. The company combined TGS with Texor to expand World Fuel Services' presence as the largest independent wholesale motor fuel distributor in Illinois.

Expanding its UK market share in 2009 the company acquired the Henty Oil Group of Companies a leading independent provider of marine and land fuels in the UK.

EXECUTIVES

President CEO and Director, Michael J. Kasbar, age 56, $575,000 total compensation
Chairman, Paul H. Stebbins, age 56, $575,000 total compensation
Chief Financial Officer; Executive Vice President; Interim Principal Accounting Officer, Ira M. Birns, age 50, $425,000 total compensation
President Aviation Segment, Michael S. Clementi, age 51, $500,000 total compensation
EVP and Chief Risk and Administration Officer, Francis X. (Frank) Shea, age 72, $325,000 total compensation
Vice Chairman, Ken Bakshi, age 62
SVP General Counsel and Corporate Secretary, R. Alexander (Alex) Lake
Global CIO Technology and Process, Massoud Sedigh, age 57
SVP and Chief Accounting Officer; SVP Finance Land Segment, Paul M. Nobel, age 44, $219,375 total compensation
Director, Richard A. Kassar, age 65
President CEO and Director, Michael J. Kasbar, age 56
Director, Myles Klein, age 73
Director, Ken Bakshi, age 63

Director, J. Thomas Presby, age 72
Director, Stephen K. Roddenberry, age 64
Director, John L. Manley, age 64
Independent Director, Abby Kohnstamm
Auditors: PricewaterhouseCoopersLLP

LOCATIONS

HQ: World Fuel Services Corporation
9800 NW 41st St. Ste. 400, Miami FL 33178
Phone: 305-428-8000 **Fax:** 305-392-5600
Web: www.wfscorp.com

2011 Sales

	$ mil.	% of total
Americas	19,965	58
Asia/Pacific	7,962	23
Europe & Middle East & Africa	6,695	19
Total	**34,622**	**100**

PRODUCTS/OPERATIONS

2011 Sales

	$ mil.	% of total
Marine	14,565	42
Aviation	12,866	37
Land	7,191	21
Total	**34,622**	**100**

Selected Subsidiaries

Ascent Aviation Group Inc.
Baseops Europe Ltd. (UK)
Baseops International Inc.
Casa Petro S.R.L. (Costa Rica)
Henty Oil Limited (UK)
Marine Energy Arabia Co. (L.L.C.) (United Arab Emirates)
Nordic Camp Supply ApS (Denmark)
PetroServicios de Costa Rica S.R.L.
TGS Petroleum
The Hiller Group Incorporated
Tramp Holdings Limited (UK)
Trans-Tec International S.R.L. (Costa Rica)
Western Petroleum Company
World Fuel International S.R.L. (Costa Rica)
World Fuel Services Inc.
World Fuel Services Ltd. (UK)
World Fuel Services (Singapore) Pte. Ltd.

COMPETITORS

BBA Aviation
BP Marine
Exxon Mobil
Fuchs Lubricants
Mercury Air Group
Shell Aviation
Sun Coast Resources

HISTORICAL FINANCIALS

Company Type: Public

Income Statement

FYE: December 31

	REVENUE ($ mil.)	NET INCOME ($ mil.)	NET PROFIT MARGIN	EMPLOYEES
12/11	34,622	194	0.6%	1,798
12/10	19,131	146	0.8%	1,499
12/09	11,295	117	1.0%	1,249
12/08	18,509	105	0.6%	1,164
12/07	13,729	64	0.5%	916
Annual Growth	26.0%	31.6%	—	18.4%

2011 Year-End Financials

Debt ratio: 7.77%
Return on equity: 14.56%
Cash ($ mil.): 205
Current ratio: 154.10
Long-term debt ($ mil.): 269
No. of shares (mil.): 71
Dividends
Yield: —
Payout: 5.54%
Market value ($ mil.): 2,987

	STOCK PRICE ($) FY Close	P/E High/Low		PER SHARE ($) Earnings	Dividends	Book Value
12/11	41.98	16	12	2.71	0.00	18.73
12/10	36.16	16	10	2.31	0.15	16.20
12/09	26.79	28	13	1.96	0.15	12.34
12/08	37.00	21	9	1.81	0.08	10.38
12/07	29.03	42	25	1.12	0.08	8.47
Annual Growth	9.7%	—	—	24.7%	—	21.9%

WSFS Financial Corp.

WSFS isn't a radio station but it is tuned into the banking needs of Delaware. WSFS Financial is the holding company for Wilmington Savings Fund Society (WSFS Bank) a thrift with about 40 branches in Delaware and southeastern Pennsylvania plus one each in Nevada and Virginia. Founded in 1832 WSFS Bank attracts deposits from individuals and local businesses by offering standard products like checking and savings accounts CDs and IRAs. The bank uses funds primarily to lend to businesses: Commercial loans and mortgages account for about 75% of its loan portfolio. Bank subsidiary Cypress Capital Management provides trust and investment advisory services to wealthy clients and institutional investors.

The company's Cash Connect division operates more than 325 ATMs for WSFS Bank which boasts the largest branded ATM network in Delaware. The division also manages some $340 million of vault cash in approximately 10000 ATMs nationwide and provides online reporting and ATM cash management predictive cash ordering armored carrier management and ATM processing and equipment sales.

Growing through acquisitions WSFS in 2010 bought Delaware-based Christiana Bank & Trust from National Penn Bancshares for $34.5 million. The deal added three branches in Delaware and one in Nevada and brought in more than $7 billion of assets under administration to augment the operations of Cypress Capital. WSFS acquired six bank branches in Delaware from Sun National Bank in 2008.

Another recent acquisition did not go as smoothly: Also in 2008 WSFS acquired a majority stake in nationwide reverse mortgage lender 1st Reverse Financial Services. However as a result of decreasing property values amid the financial crisis the unit lost money and WSFS which continues to write reverse mortgages for sale into the secondary market announced in 2009 that it would wind down the business of 1st Reverse Financial. Despite the setback WSFS as a whole remained profitable throughout the recession.

Peninsula Capital Advisors an investment firm of which WSFS director Ted Wechsler is a managing partner owns nearly 20% of WSFS Financial's stock.

EXECUTIVES

Vice Chairman, Charles G. Cheleden, age 68
President Cash Connect WSFS Bank, Thomas E. Stevenson
President CEO and Director WSFS Financial and WSFS Bank; President and CEO Wilmington Savings Fund Society, Mark A. Turner, age 48, $400,000 total compensation
SVP and Corporate Auditor WSFS Financial and WSFS Bank, Thomas W. Kearney
SVP and Division Manager Business Banking WSFS Bank, Douglas R. Quaintance
SVP and Director Retail Lending WSFS Bank, Deborah T. Roberts
SVP and Division Manager Commercial Real Estate WSFS Bank, Ann M. Rudolph
SVP and Controller WSFS Financial and WSFS Bank, Robert F. Mack
SVP and Treasurer WSFS Financial and WSFS Bank, Paul S. Greenplate
SVP Transaction Services WSFS Bank, Cheryl A. Hughes
EVP and Chief Administrative Officer WSFS Bank, Barbara J. Fischer, age 54
SVP Commercial Banking WSFS Bank, William M. (Bill) Byrne
SVP and Chief Credit Officer WSFS Bank, Glenn L. Kocher
EVP and Director of Retail Banking WSFS Bank, Richard M. (Rick) Wright, age 59, $225,000 total compensation
EVP and CFO WSFS Financial and WSFS Bank, Stephen A. Fowle, age 46, $207,833 total compensation
SVP and Team Leader, Ralph J. Cicalese
EVP and Director Commercial Banking WSFS Bank, Rodger Levenson, age 50, $235,000 total compensation
SVP and Team Leader Business Banking WSFS Bank, M. Scott Baylis
SVP Retail Administration WSFS Bank, Lisa M. Brubaker
SVP and Division Manager Middle Market WSFS Bank, Stephen P. Clark
SVP and Team Leader Business Banking Wilmington Savings Fund Society, Andrew N. Yatzus
SVP and Manager Private Banking Wilmington Savings Fund Society, Helen M. Zumsteg
Investor Relations, Beth Sellers
EVP Human Capital Management WSFS Bank, Peggy H. Eddens, age 56
EVP Wealth Management WSFS Bank, Richard J. (Rich) Immesberger, age 46
SVP and Director Trust Services, Deborah A. (Deb) Markwood
SVP and Manager Cash Management, Raymond C. Abbott
SVP and Regional Manager WSFS Bank, Syed A. Ahmed
SVP Small Business Banking WSFS Bank, Ralph A. Citino
SVP Cash Connect Client Opertations WSFS Bank, John D. Clatsworthy
SVP and Regional Manager WSFS Bank, Shari A. Kruzinski
SVP and Regional Manager WSFS Bank, Linda H. Ziegler
VP Marketing WSFS Bank, Stephanie Heist
VP and Chief Investment Officer WSFS Bank Wealth Strategies Group, John A. Molster Jr.
EVP and CTO, S. James Mazarakis
SVP Business Development Officer Trust and Wealth Management Division, Janis L. Julian
Director Community Relations, Michael D. Skipper
SVP and Team Leader, Dennis B. Mataranga
VP and Relationship Manager, Bruce W. Shively
Director, Calvert A. (Cal) Morgan Jr., age 63
President CEO and Director WSFS Financial and WSFS Bank; President and CEO Wilmington Savings Fund Society, Mark A. Turner, age 48

Director, R. Ted Weschler, age 50
Director, John F. Downey, age 74
Director, Thomas P. Preston, age 65
Director, Joseph R. Julian, age 74
Director, Linda C. Drake, age 63
Director, David E. Hollowell, age 64
Director, Claibourne D. Smith, age 73
Director, Anat Bird, age 61
Director, Donald W. Delson, age 61
Director, Dennis E. Klima, age 67
Director, Scott E. Reed, age 63
Director, Jennifer (J.J.) Davis, age 41
Director, Zissimos A. Frangopoulos
Auditors: KPMGLLP

LOCATIONS

HQ: WSFS Financial Corporation
500 Delaware Ave., Wilmington DE 19801-1490
Phone: 302-792-6000 Fax: 302-571-6842
Web: www.wsfsbank.com

2012 Branches

	No.
Delaware	42
Pennsylvania	7
Nevada	1
Virginia	1
Total	51

PRODUCTS/OPERATIONS

2011 Sales

	$ mil.	% of total
Interest		
Loans including fees	130	59
Mortgage-backed securities	27	12
Investment securities	0	-
Noninterest		
Credit/debit card & ATM income	21	10
Deposit service charges	16	8
Fiduciary & investment management income	11	5
Other	14	6
Total	222	100

2011 Sales

	$ mil.	% of total
WSFS Bank	184	83
Trust & wealth management	21	10
Cash Connect	15	7
Total	222	100

COMPETITORS

Bank of America
Fulton Financial
JPMorgan Chase
M&T Bank
PNC Financial
RBS Citizens Financial Group
Sovereign Bank
TD Bank USA
The Bancorp

HISTORICAL FINANCIALS

Company Type: Public

Income Statement FYE: December 31

	ASSETS ($ mil.)	NET INCOME ($ mil.)	INCOME AS % OF ASSETS	EMPLOYEES
12/11	4,289	22	0.5%	767
12/10	3,953	14	0.4%	695
12/09	3,748	0	0.0%	643
12/08	3,432	16	0.5%	633
12/07	3,200	29	0.9%	599
Annual Growth	7.6%	(6.5%)	—	6.4%

2011 Year-End Financials

Debt ratio: 14.12%
Return on equity: 5.78%
Cash ($ mil.): 468
Current ratio: —
Long-term debt ($ mil.): 605
No. of shares (mil.): 8
Dividends
Yield: —
Payout: 21.05%
Market value ($ mil.): 312

	STOCK PRICE ($) FY Close	P/E High	P/E Low	PER SHARE ($) Earnings	Dividends	Book Value
12/11	35.96	21	13	2.28	0.00	45.19
12/10	47.44	34	17	1.46	0.48	43.15
12/09	25.63	—	—	(0.30)	0.48	42.63
12/08	47.99	24	15	2.57	0.46	35.17
12/07	50.20	15	11	4.55	0.38	34.27
Annual Growth	(8.0%)	—	—	(15.9%)	—	7.2%

Wyndham Worldwide Corp

This chain promises lodgings wherever the winds may blow you. One of the world's largest hospitality firms Wyndham Worldwide includes a portfolio of some 7200 franchised hotels worldwide through its lodging segment which includes 15 familiar brands such as Days Inn Howard Johnson Ramada and Super 8. The company also operates a vacation exchange and rentals segment which has a relationship with some 4000 vacation exchange and rental properties in some 100 countries. In addition its Wyndham Vacation Ownership operates vacation ownership resorts in North America the Caribbean and the South Pacific. Revenues primarily come from franchise and hotel management fees membership dues and timeshare sales.

While the hospitality industry targets both business and leisure travelers most of Wyndham's customers come from the leisure market. The company's timeshare and vacation rentals businesses (which target the leisure market) generate more than 80% of the company's total revenue. Its lodging segment (which targets both business and leisure travelers) accounts for about 20%.

Nearly 30% of the company's revenues come from outside the US. A concentration of international business (some 12% of total revenues) comes from the UK and the Netherlands.

In 2011 Wyndham Worldwide posted increases in revenues (from $3.85 billion to $4.25 billion) and net income (from $379 million to $417 million). The company benefitted from growth in the hotel industry thanks to a recovering economy and increased consumer confidence. That year demand for rooms continued to increase as more vacations were booked.

Wyndham continues to expand its vacation holdings through acquisitions in this market. In 2012 it acquired Shell Vacations an independent vacation ownership club and property management group serving approximately 115000 members and 19 managed resorts in North America. The purchase price was some $102 million in cash plus the assumption of $153 million of debt.

In 2011 the company purchased The Resort Company (TRC) which operates about 30 mountain vacation resorts in Colorado (Beaver Creek Breckenridge Steamboat and Vail). The deal added approximately 1000 rental units to Wyndham Vacation Rentals part of its exchange and rentals business.

The TRC deal was a continuation of the previous year's expansion strategy. In 2010 Wyndham acquired ResortQuest a provider in full-service vacation rentals in the US. It paid some $56 million for the company which it added to its exchange and rentals segment. Later that year Wyndham acquired James Villa Holidays. The deal worth about $76 million added another 2300 villas and vacation rental properties in more than 50 destinations primarily in the Mediterranean.

A third purchase for the year was Hoseasons Holdings Ltd a UK-based vacation company. Wyndham made the acquisition for about $59 million in cash. Also in 2010 the company acquired the Tryp brand from Sol Melia for some $43 million. The deal added about 90 properties in Europe and South America to Wyndham's holdings.

EXECUTIVES

President and CEO Wyndham Vacation Ownership, Franz S. Hanning, age 58, $606,008 total compensation
Chairman and CEO, Stephen P. Holmes, age 55, $1,085,011 total compensation
EVP and CFO, Thomas G. (Tom) Conforti, age 53, $149,427 total compensation
Brand SVP Howard Johnson and Travelodge Wyndham Hotel Group, Rui Barros
Brand SVP Ramada Worldwide, Mark F. Young
EVP Marketing Wyndham Hotel Group, Flo M. Lugli
President Brand Operations The Americas Wyndham Hotel Group, Keith J. Pierce
President Super 8 Worldwide Wyndham Hotel Group, John Valletta
President and CEO Wyndham Exchange and Rentals, Geoffrey A. (Geoff) Ballotti, age 50, $550,004 total compensation
SVP Human Resources and Organizational Capability, Patricia A. Lee
Group President Microtel Inns & Suites Baymont Inn & Suites Wyndham Hotel Group, Roy E. Flora
President and Managing Director Asia Pacific Wyndham Hotel Group, Ken Greene
EVP and Chief Retention Officer Wyndham Hotel Group, Duane Elledge
President Wyndham Hotels and Resorts Wyndham Hotel Group, Jeffrey G. (Jeff) Wagoner
EVP Global Sales and Marketing Operations Wyndham Vacation Ownership, Geoff Richards
EVP and Chief Human Resources Officer, Mary R. Falvey, age 51
President North America Wyndham Exchange & Rentals, Gordon Gurnik
President and CEO Wyndham Hotel Group, Eric A. Danziger, age 57, $500,009 total compensation
EVP and CFO Wyndham Hotel Group, Robert Loewen
Brand SVP Knights Inn Wyndham Hotel Group, Rajiv Bhatia
EVP and General Counsel Wyndham Exchange & Rentals, Ilese Flamm
EVP Development Wyndham Hotel Group, Jim Alderman
EVP Development Wyndham Hotel Group, Gus Stamoutsos
EVP and General Counsel, Scott G. McLester, age 49
SVP and Chief Accounting Officer, Nicola Rossi, age 45
SVP Corporate Relations Wyndham Vacation Ownership, Adam Schwartz

EVP and Chief Real Estate Development Officer, Thomas F. Anderson, age 47, $418,200 total compensation
EVP and General Counsel Wyndham Hotel Group, Lynn A. Feldman
Brand SVP Baymont Inn & Suites Wyndham Hotel Group, Patrick Breen
SVP Enterprise Compliance and Employment Counsel, Kirsten Hotchkiss
SVP Investor Relations, Margo C. Happer
EVP and CFO Wyndham Exchange and Rentals, Gail Mandel
VP Mergers and Acquisitions, Roger Marinzoli
VP Talent Acquisition and Diversity Inclusion, Evelin Potts
SVP Compensation Benefits and Human Resources Technical Services, William Skrzat
VP Sustainability and Innovation, Faith Taylor
Director Media Relations, Alyson R. Johnson
Managing Director Pacific Wyndham Exchange & Rentals, Charisse Cox
CTO Wyndham Exchange & Rentals, Brad Dettmer
EVP and CFO Wyndham Exchange & Rentals, Tom Edwards
Managing Director Asia Wyndham Exchange & Rentals, Adrian Lee
SVP Revenue Management & Analytics Wyndham Exchange & Rentals, Sean Lowe
President Latin America Wyndham Exchange & Rentals, Ricardo Montaudon
EVP Global Human Resources Wyndham Exchange & Rentals, Faye Tylee
Brand SVP Wingate by Wyndham and Hawthorn Suites by Wyndham, Bill Hall
EVP Global Sales Wyndham Hotel Group, Ross Hosking
EVP and CFO Wyndham Vacation Ownership, Michael Hug
SVP Wyndham Consumer Finance, Mark Johnson
EVP International Development Wyndham Hotel Group, Tom Monahan
Director, Rt. Hon. Brian Mulroney, age 73
Director, James E. Buckman, age 67
Director, Myra J. Biblowit, age 63
Director, Pauline D.E. Richards, age 63
Director, George Herrera, age 55
Director, Michael H. (Mike) Wargotz, age 54
Auditors: Deloitte&ToucheLLP

LOCATIONS

HQ: Wyndham Worldwide Corporation
22 Sylvan Way, Parsippany NJ 07054
Phone: 973-753-6000 **Fax:** 973-753-7537
Web: www.wyndhamworldwide.com

2011 Sales

	$ mil.	% of total
US	3,037	71
UK	281	7
Netherlands	271	6
Other regions	665	16
Total	**4,254**	**100**

PRODUCTS/OPERATIONS

2011 Sales

	$ mil.	% of total
Vacation Ownership	2,077	49
Vacation Exchange & Rentals	1,444	34
Lodging	749	17
Adjustments	(16)	
Total	**4,254**	**100**

2011 Sales

$ mil % of total		
Service fees and membership	2,012	47
Vacation ownership interest sales	1,150	27
Franchise fees	522	12
Consumer financing	415	10
Other	155	4
Total	**4,254**	**100**

Selected Brands

Wyndham Vacation Ownership
- WorldMark by Wyndham
- Wyndham Vacation Resorts

Vacation Exchange & Rentals
- Canvas Holidays
- Cottages4you.com
- Cuendet
- Endless Vacation Rentals
- Landal GreenParks
- Novasol

Wyndham Hotel Group
- AmeriHost Inn
- Baymont Inn & Suites
- Days Inn
- Hawthorn Suites
- Howard Johnson
- Knights Inn
- Microtel Inns & Suites
- Ramada
- Super 8
- Travelodge
- Wingate by Windham
- Wyndham Hotels and Resorts

COMPETITORS

Accor North America
Best Western
Carlson Hotels
Disney Parks & Resorts
Fairmont Raffles
Four Seasons Hotels
Hilton Worldwide
Hyatt
InterContinental Hotels
Marriott
Starwood Hotels & Resorts

HISTORICAL FINANCIALS

Company Type: Public

Income Statement FYE: December 31

	REVENUE ($ mil.)	NET INCOME ($ mil.)	NET PROFIT MARGIN	EMPLOYEES
12/11	4,254	417	9.8%	27,800
12/10	3,851	379	9.8%	26,400
12/09	3,750	293	7.8%	24,600
12/08	4,281	(1,074)	—	27,000
12/07	4,360	403	9.2%	33,200
Annual Growth	(0.6%)	0.9%	—	(4.3%)

2011 Year-End Financials

Debt ratio: 44.50%
Return on equity: 18.68%
Cash ($ mil.): 142
Current ratio: 110.68
Long-term debt ($ mil.): 3,773
No. of shares (mil.): 147
Dividends
Yield: —
Payout: 23.90%
Market value ($ mil.): 5,563

	STOCK PRICE ($) FY Close	P/E High/Low		PER SHARE ($) Earnings	Dividends	Book Value
12/11	37.83	15	10	2.51	0.00	15.18
12/10	29.96	15	9	2.05	0.48	16.82
12/09	20.17	13	2	1.61	0.16	15.05
12/08	6.55	—	—	(6.05)	0.16	13.20
12/07	23.56	17	11	2.20	0.08	19.84
Annual Growth	12.6%	—	—	3.4%	—	(6.5%)

Wynn Resorts Ltd

What happens in Vegas no longer stays in Vegas. It also happens in China. Wynn Resorts the brainchild of gaming mogul and former Mirage Resorts chairman Steve Wynn operates luxury casino resorts in Las Vegas and South China's Macau the only place in China where gambling is legal. The company's Wynn Las Vegas is a $2.4 billion resort and casino built on the site of the former Desert Inn on the Strip. Wynn Resorts operates in China through Wynn Macau Limited. The company has expanded in both markets adding the Encore at Wynn Las Vegas next to the Wynn Las Vegas and the Encore at Wynn Macau adjacent to Wynn Macau.

Operations

The company's Las Vegas properties boast more than 4750 rooms 2430 slots and 240 table games 186000 square feet of casino gaming space some 20 restaurants a golf course two wedding chapels and a Ferrari and Maserati dealership. However Wynn Resorts actually makes more money in China where the economy is booming. Its Encore at Wynn Macau hotel and resort a development that cost some $650 million opened in 2010. The property includes more than 400 luxury suites and four villas as well as restaurants additional retail space and additional VIP gaming space.

Financial Analysis

In 2011 the company reported 26% jump in revenues attributable to a 14% increase in Las Vegas revenues due in part to a 3% increase in average table games win percentage and a 31% rise in Macau revenues thanks to an increase in both occupancy rate and room rates as well as the inclusion of a full year of the 414 additional suites added with the opening of Encore at Wynn Macau in 2010.

Net income surged by 283% in 2011 thanks to higher revenues a cut in depreciation expenses due to assets with a five-year life being fully depreciated in 2011 at Wynn Macau and assets with a five-year life being fully depreciated in 2010 at Wynn Las Vegas as well as a decrease in 2011 general and administrative expenses.

Strategy

While Las Vegas has been slower to recover from the economic downturn than other markets gaming companies with operations in Asia saw stronger growth in 2011. Strong performance in China benefitted the company's earnings that year when Wynn Resorts reported overall growth in revenues and net income.

The company previously raised some $1.6 billion in cash when it sold 25% of its Macau operations in the 2009 IPO of Wynn Macau Limited on the Hong Kong Stock Exchange. These proceeds are being used to fund the construction of new resorts as well as remodel older ones. The company has plans for a major new casino in Macau; the mega-resort could open in late 2014 or early 2015. Back in the US in 2011 the company completed a project to remodel rooms at Wynn Las Vegas. It spent some $61 million on the upgrade.

Ownership

In 2012 Steve Wynn and ex-wife Elaine Wynn each owned 10% of the company; Waddell & Reed Financial Inc. owned 18%. Director nominees and executive officers as a group owned 21%.

Company Background

Steve Wynn has a long history working in the Las Vegas gaming industry and is credited with building and/or refurbishing many of the properties on the Las Vegas Strip including the Golden Nugget The Mirage and Treasure Island. His Wynn Resorts opened its first property Wynn Las Vegas (formerly called Le Reve French for "The Dream") in 2005. It next opened the $1.1 billion Wynn Macau in late 2006.

EXECUTIVES

President Wynn Las Vegas, Marilyn W. Spiegel, age 60
CFO and Treasurer, Matt Maddox, age 36, $779,988 total compensation
SVP General Counsel and Secretary, Kim Sinatra, age 51, $535,582 total compensation
Chairman and CEO, Stephen A. Wynn, age 70, $2,953,125 total compensation
Vice Chairman, Kazuo Okada, age 69
COO and Board Member, Marc D. Schorr, age 64, $1,817,308 total compensation
EVP and Chief Administrative Officer, John Strzemp, age 60, $600,000 total compensation
EVP Architecture Wynn Design and Development, DeRuyter O. Butler
EVP Design Wynn Design and Development, Roger P. Thomas
Board Member; President Wynn International Marketing, Linda Chen, age 45, $951,701 total compensation
SVP; CFO Wynn Las Vegas, Scott Peterson, age 45
President Wynn Macau, Ian M. Coughlan, age 53
COO Wynn Las Vegas, Maurice Wooden
VP; CFO Wynn Resorts (Macau), Robert Alexander Gansmo, age 39
Board Member, Ray R. Irani, age 77
Board Member, Russell D. Goldsmith, age 62
Board Member, Alvin V. Shoemaker, age 73
Board Member, Robert J. Miller, age 66
Board Member, D. Boone Wayson, age 59
Director, Kazuo Okada, age 69
COO and Board Member, Marc D. Schorr, age 64
Board Member, Elaine P. Wynn, age 69
Board Member, Allan Zeman, age 64
Board Member, John A. Moran, age 80
Board Member; President Wynn International Marketing, Linda Chen, age 45
Auditors: Ernst&YoungLLP

LOCATIONS

HQ: Wynn Resorts Limited
3131 Las Vegas Blvd. South, Las Vegas NV 89109
Phone: 702-770-7555 **Fax:** 248-332-4168
Web: www.rdagroup.com

2011 Sales

	$ mil.	% of total
Macau	3,789	72
Las Vegas	1,480	28
Total	**5,269**	**100**

PRODUCTS/OPERATIONS

Properties
Las Vegas
Wynn Las Vegas
Encore at Wynn Las Vegas
Macau China
Wynn Macau
Encore at Wynn Macau

COMPETITORS

Boyd Gaming
Caesars Entertainment
Carnival plc
Emperor Entertainment Hotel
Golden Resorts
Hyatt
Las Vegas Sands
Marriott
Melco Crown Entertainment
MGM Resorts
priceline.com
Riviera Holdings
SJM
Starwood Hotels & Resorts
Station Casinos

HISTORICAL FINANCIALS

Company Type: Public

Income Statement FYE: December 31

	REVENUE ($ mil.)	NET INCOME ($ mil.)	NET PROFIT MARGIN	EMPLOYEES
12/11	5,269	613	11.6%	16,400
12/10	4,184	160	3.8%	16,405
12/09	3,045	20	0.7%	18,900
12/08	2,987	210	7.0%	20,600
12/07	2,687	258	9.6%	16,500
Annual Growth	18.3%	24.2%	—	(0.2%)

2011 Year-End Financials

Debt ratio: 48.34%
Return on equity: 29.36%
Cash ($ mil.): 1,262
Current ratio: 109.28
Long-term debt ($ mil.): 2,913
No. of shares (mil.): 125
Dividends
Yield: —
Payout: 133.20%
Market value ($ mil.): 13,820

	STOCK PRICE ($) FY Close	P/E High	P/E Low	PER SHARE ($) Earnings	Dividends	Book Value
12/11	110.49	33	21	4.88	0.00	16.70
12/10	103.84	90	45	1.29	8.50	17.96
12/09	58.23	431	91	0.17	4.00	24.61
12/08	42.26	62	16	1.92	0.00	14.22
12/07	112.13	71	36	2.34	6.00	17.03
Annual Growth	(0.4%)	—	—	20.2%	—	(0.5%)

Xcel Energy, Inc.

Xcel Energy has accelerated its energy engine in utility markets across the US. The utility holding company distributes electricity to 3.4 million customers and natural gas to 1.9 million in eight states through four regulated utilities; Colorado and Minnesota account for most of its customers. Its utilities –Northern States Power (NSP-Minnesota and NSP-Wisconsin) Public Service Company of Colorado and Southwestern Public Service (in New Mexico and Texas) –have the combined capacity of more than 17150 MW of electricity. Xcel owns transmission and distribution lines as well as natural gas assets. It is also the top wind power provider in the US with wind farms in Colorado Minnesota and Texas.

Geographic Reach The company serves customers in Colorado Michigan Minnesota New Mexico North Dakota South Dakota Texas and Wisconsin. Operations

Xcel operates power and gas utilities: Northern States Power Public Service Company of Colorado and Southwestern Public Service. The holding company has more than 80 generating plants more than 87750 miles of transmission lines and about 191840 miles of distribution lines. It also operates an interstate natural gas pipeline company and a joint venture to develop and lease natural gas pipelines storage and compression assets.

Financial Analysis

In 2011 Xcel reported a 3% jump in sales due to an increase in demand caused by a warmer-than-normal summer and a colder-than-normal winter. It was also assisted by a 3.7% increase in the electric segment due to cost recovery of the acquisition of the Rocky Mountain and Blue Spruce natural gas facilities by Public Service Company of Colorado and by natural gas retail rate increases in Minnesota.

Net income rose by 11% thanks to higher revenues and lower electric fuel and purchased power costs.

Higher rates and increased weather-related demand helped sales in 2010 to rise nearly 7% going from $9.6 billion to about $10.3 billion.

Strategy

Xcel is an energy company in transition with long-term plans to move from coal-fired plants to natural gas and on to alternative fuels such as wind solar and biomass to boost its green power capacity (88705 MWh by 2015).

In 2012 the company was seeking proposals for renewable resources other than wind or solar as part of its plan to diversify Southwestern Public Service Company renewable energy portfolio.

As the largest US utility wind energy provider Xcel controlled some 3500 MW of wind energy in its portfolio in 2011 and plans to have 7400 MW by 2020. In 2011 Xcel bought the 200 MW Limon Wind Energy Center which will have 125 turbines in Lincoln and Elbert counties on Colorado's Front Range east of Denver. The company is also the US's fifth-largest utility solar energy provider and owns the fourth-largest transmission system. In addition Xcel operates more than 25 hydroelectric power plants in Colorado Minnesota and Wisconsin.

The company believes its strategy of making environmentally sound investments is pivotal to its success. Among its 2010 projects were launching its 800-MW coal-fired unit in Colorado known as Comanche 3 after installing advanced emission-reduction equipment. It also began construction of its CapX2020 project a joint venture transmission expansion project with 10 other utilities scheduled for completion by 2020. The project includes a 240-mile transmission line from Minnesota to North Dakota. The company has filed to extend the licensing plants of its two nuclear plants on Prairie Island in Minnesota for 20 years which it expects to save customers more than $1 billion compared to alternative sources.

Xcel plans to construct one of the largest biomass generating plants in the Midwest. The facility proposed for the Bay Front Generating Station in Ashland Wisconsin will generate power from burning wood waste in all three operating units by 2014. In 2011 Xcel had 73 MW of biomass generating power in Minnesota and Wisconsin.

Xcel is also working to develop so-called "smart grid" technology which will provide customers with more reliability and control over their energy use. It has completed the nation's first fully integrated SmartGridCity in Boulder Colorado.

In 2010 Xcel acquired two gas-fired power plants from Calpine Corporation for $739 million. The two Denver-area plants have a generating capacity of more than 900 MW and were already providing power to Public Service Company of Colorado under a contract agreement. The company is planning to acquire 775 MW of new wind-power capacity for its Colorado system over the next several years.

HISTORY

The Minnesota Electric Light & Electric Motive Power Company was founded in 1881 and changed its name to Minnesota Brush Electric the next year. In the 1890s it provided street lighting and power for trolleys and became Minneapolis General Electric.

In 1909 Henry Byllesby formed rival firm Washington County Light and Power Co. (soon renamed Consumers Power Company) then created holding company Northern States Power Company of Delaware (NSPD). In 1910 he founded Standard Gas and Electric a holding company overseeing NSPD and many other US utilities.

NSPD bought Minneapolis General Electric in 1912 and Consumers Power was renamed the Northern States Power Company (NSP) in 1916. During the 1920s NSPD connected its subsidiaries via transmission lines. Byllesby died in 1924.

In 1931 NSP was placed under NSPD but the Public Utility Holding Company Act of 1935 dissolved Standard and NSPD. NSP became independent in the 1940s and spent $335 million on new facilities after WWII.

During the 1960s NSP moved into Michigan South Dakota and Wisconsin and brought its first nuclear power plant on line in 1964 (converted to natural gas in 1968). It began operating the Monticello and Prairie Island nukes in the early 1970s.

Company sales nearly doubled in the 1980s. In 1989 NSP created NRG Energy (incorporated 1992) to invest in independent power projects. The Federal Energy Policy Act allowed wholesale power competition in 1992 and NSP lost nine of its 19 municipal customers.

NSP acquired Viking Gas Transmission which owned an interstate pipeline in 1993. It also began developing affordable housing. In 1995 NSP and Wisconsin Electric planned to merge but dropped the deal amid antitrust concerns. NSP continued to diversify forming telecommunications provider Seren Innovations in 1996 and starting its cable-testing business in 1997. The next year NSP formed a power marketing unit.

NRG Energy began a shopping spree abroad in 1994 buying interests in plants in Germany and Australia. In 1996 it bought a 48% stake in Bolivia's COBEE (increased to 99% in 2001). Also that year it acquired PacifiCorp's Pacific Generating unit which owned stakes in a dozen geographically scattered plants.

In 1999 NRG Energy gained nearly 7600 MW of capacity through power plant acquisitions in California Connecticut Massachusetts and New York. The next year NRG Energy picked up another 1700 MW in Louisiana and it agreed to buy fossil-fueled plants (1875 MW) from Delaware's Conectiv for $800 million (half of the deal was completed in 2001 the other half was canceled the following year). NSP spun off part of NRG in 2000 in an IPO.

Meanwhile as the utility-merger trend gathered steam in 1999 NSP agreed to acquire Denver-based New Century Engines in a $4.9 billion deal. The acquisition was completed in 2000 and the expanded company changed its name to Xcel Energy.

The next year Xcel sold nearly all of its stake in UK-based Yorkshire Power Group which had been held by New Century Energies to Innogy (now RWE npower). It sold its remaining 5% stake in Yorkshire Power in 2002. NRG purchased several Latin American projects from Swedish utility Vattenfall in 2001. NRG also agreed to purchase four coal-fired plants (2500 MW) in Ohio from FirstEnergy for $1.5 billion; however the deal was later canceled.

In 2002 Xcel repurchased the 26% stake in NRG that it sold to the public in 2000-01.

Downturns in the wholesale energy industry (spurred by Enron's collapse and the ensuing financial scrutiny of other energy trading companies) led to serious financial difficulties for NRG in 2002. NRG entered into debt restructuring talks with its creditors and in 2003 the unit filed for Chapter 11 bankruptcy. Its reorganization plan which was completed that December included a settlement agreement in which Xcel Energy agreed to pay $752 million to NRG and its creditors and then divest its interest in NRG.

In 2003 the company sold pipeline company Viking Gas Transmission to Northern Border Partners (now ONEOK Partners) and its Arizona utility Black Mountain Gas (10000 gas and propane customers) to Las Vegas-based utility Southwest Gas. Xcel also sold its Utility Engineering Corp. to Zachry Construction in 2005.

The company sold off the assets of subsidiary Xcel Energy International (primarily Latin American power investments) in 2004 and its Seren Innovations business (cable TV phone and high-speed Internet access networks in California and Minnesota) in 2006.

Pushing green energy sources in 2008 Xcel announced that it would develop solar-generated power plants in Colorado as part of its green energy initiative. The company also spent more than $1 billion converting three coal-fired plants in Minnesota to natural gas units in 2008 and 2009. In the same time period it added gas-fired units to several of its other operations in Colorado and Minnesota.

EXECUTIVES

VP Corporate Services and Corporate Secretary, Cathy James Hart, age 62
SVP Operations, Kent T. Larson
Chairman President and CEO, Benjamin G. S. (Ben) Fowke III, age 54, $650,000 total compensation
SVP and Group President, David M. (Dave) Sparby, age 57, $386,667 total compensation
Managing Director Investor Relations and Assistant Treasurer, Paul A. Johnson
SVP and CFO, Teresa S. Madden, age 55
VP and Treasurer, George E. Tyson II, age 46
President and CEO Public Service Company of Colorado, David L. Eves, age 53
Director Media Relations, Steve Roalstad
Media Relations, Mary Sandok
SVP and Chief Nuclear Officer, Dennis L. Koehl
VP and CIO, David C. Harkness
SVP Strategy and Planning, Michael C. Connelly, age 50, $430,000 total compensation
Director Investor Relations, Jack E. Nielsen
Senior Analyst Investor Relations, Cindy A. Hoffman
Media Relations, Patti Nystuen
President and CEO Northern States Power Company Minnesota, Judy M. Poferl, age 51
SVP and Chief Administrative Officer, Marvin E. McDaniel Jr., age 51
VP Transmission, Teresa M. Mogensen
Assistant Corporate Secretary, Tara Heine
President and CEO Southwestern Public Service Company, C. Riley Hill, age 52
SVP and General Counsel, Scott M. Wilensky, age 55
Managing Director Business Systems and IT Operations and Strategy, Michael G. Lamb
SVP Public Policy and External Affairs, R. Roy Palmer
VP and Controller, Jeffrey S. (Jeff) Savage
President and CEO Northern States Power Wisconsin, Mark E. Stoering
Corporate Secretary Vice President Corporate Services, Cathy James
VP; Corporate Secretary; VP - Business Services Group of Xcel Energy Services Inc., Cathy Hart
Director, David A. Westerlund, age 62
Director, Timothy V. (Tim) Wolf, age 59
Director, Fredric W. (Fritz) Corrigan, age 70
Director, Albert F. Moreno, age 68
Director, Richard K. Davis, age 54
Director, A. Patricia Sampson, age 63
Director, Kim Williams, age 56
Director, James J. Sheppard
Director, Christopher J. Policinski, age 53
Independent Director, Gail Boudreaux
Auditors: Deloitte&ToucheLLP

LOCATIONS

HQ: Xcel Energy Inc.
414 Nicollet Mall, Minneapolis MN 55401-1993
Phone: 612-330-5500 **Fax:** 800-895-2895
Web: www.xcelenergy.com

PRODUCTS/OPERATIONS

2011 Sales

	$ mil.	% of total
Electric	8,766	82
Natural gas	1,811	17
Other	76	1
Total	**10,654**	**100**

COMPETITORS

AEP
ALLETE
Alliant Energy
Atmos Energy
Basin Electric Power
CenterPoint Energy
CMS Energy
DTE
Dynegy
Entergy
Integrys Energy Group
Minnesota Power
OGE Energy
Southern Company

HISTORICAL FINANCIALS

Company Type: Public

Income Statement FYE: December 31

	REVENUE ($ mil.)	NET INCOME ($ mil.)	NET PROFIT MARGIN	EMPLOYEES
12/11	10,654	841	7.9%	11,312
12/10	10,310	755	7.3%	11,290
12/09	9,644	680	7.1%	11,351
12/08	11,203	645	5.8%	11,223
12/07	10,034	577	5.8%	10,917
Annual Growth	1.5%	9.9%	—	0.9%

2011 Year-End Financials

Debt ratio: 34.33%
Return on equity: 9.92%
Cash ($ mil.): 60
Current ratio: 83.11
Long-term debt ($ mil.): 8,848
No. of shares (mil.): 486
Dividends
Yield: —
Payout: 60.03%
Market value ($ mil.): 13,447

	STOCK PRICE ($) FY Close	P/E High	P/E Low	PER SHARE ($) Earnings	Dividends	Book Value
12/11	27.64	16	13	1.72	0.00	17.44
12/10	23.55	15	12	1.62	1.00	16.98
12/09	21.22	15	11	1.48	0.97	16.15
12/08	18.55	15	11	1.46	0.94	15.58
12/07	22.57	18	14	1.35	0.91	14.94
Annual Growth	5.2%	—	—	6.2%	—	3.9%

Xerox Corp

You won't find many companies listed in the dictionary as a verb. Xerox once self-styled as "The Document Company" has grown from offering multifunction document machines to now also being an outsourcer of business processes (BPO) such as customer care and claims filing operations and IT functions such as infrastructure cloud computing and application services. Its document equipment is used not only in the office but also in mass-printing production settings. It serves customers in both the private and public sector. Major subsidiaries include office equipment and services provider Global Imaging Systems.

HISTORY

The Haloid Company was incorporated in 1906 to make and sell photographic paper. In 1935 it bought photocopier company Rectigraph which led Haloid to buy a license for a process called electrophotography (renamed xerography from the ancient Greek words for "dry" and "writing") from the Battelle Memorial Institute in 1947. Battelle backed inventor Chester Carlson who perfected a process for transferring electrostatic images from a photoconductive surface to paper.

Haloid commercialized xerography with the Model A copier in 1949 and the Xerox Copyflo in 1955 and by 1956 xerographic products represented 40% of sales. The company changed its name to Haloid Xerox in 1958 (Haloid was dropped from the name in 1961) and in 1959 it introduced the first simplified office copier. That machine took the world by storm beating out such competing technologies as mimeograph (A.B.Dick) thermal paper (3M) and damp copy (Kodak). Sales soared to nearly $270 million in 1965.

Xerox branched out in the 1960s by buying three publishing companies and a computer unit; all were later sold or disbanded. In the 1970s Xerox bought printer plotter and disk drive businesses as well as record carrier Western Union (1979; sold in 1982). In 1974 the FTC believing Xerox was dominating its market too much forced the company to license its technology.

In the 1980s Xerox bought companies specializing in optical character recognition scanning faxing and desktop publishing. It also diversified by buying insurance and investment banking firms among others. In 1986 Paul Allaire who had joined Xerox in 1966 was elected president. He was named CEO in 1990 and became chairman in 1991.

Eyeing future alliances Xerox agreed to supply computer print engines to Compaq (1992) and Apple (1993). In 1995 it introduced networked color laser printers and software for printing Web documents. Between 1996 and 1998 Xerox sold its struggling insurance units.

Xerox bought Rank's 20% stake in Rank Xerox the two companies' 41-year-old global marketing joint venture in 1997. That year Xerox launched a $500 PC printer copier and scanner –its first product specifically for home use –and Allaire hired IBM CFO Richard Thoman as president and COO to spearhead a push into network and digital products. In 1998 Xerox bought technology consultant XLConnect (renamed Xerox Connect) and parent company Intelligent Electronics.

In 1999 Xerox named Thoman CEO to replace Allaire who remained chairman. That year Xerox bought France's SET Electronique (high-speed digital printers). The company began selling its products online and reorganized its sales force by customer industry rather than geography. Layoffs also continued totaling 14000 for 1998 and 1999.

In an effort to stake a larger claim in the office color printing market Xerox bought Tektronix's ailing color printing and imaging division in 2000. The company also formed an Internet unit formed a joint venture with Fuji Photo Film (now FUJIFILM) and Sharp to make low-cost ink jet printers and spun off its digital rights management technology unit as ContentGuard. With profits shrinking and market value flagging Thoman resigned in 2000 amid pressure from the board. Allaire assumed the CEO post once again. Also that year the company sold its operations in China and Hong Kong to Fuji Xerox.

In 2001 the company laid off 4000 more employees. That year Xerox sold half of its 50% stake in Fuji Xerox to Fuji Photo Film and it discontinued its product lines aimed at consumer and small office users including its personal copiers and ink jet printers. Allaire stepped down as chief executive; COO Anne Mulcahy was named as his successor. Looking to reduce its massive debt Xerox transferred most of its US customer financing operations to GE Capital in a deal including $1 billion in cash financing from the lending giant (it later formed similar arrangements with GE Capital for many of its international operations). Xerox also began selling manufacturing operations to contract electronics manufacturer Flextronics International.

CEO Mulcahy replaced Allaire as chairman in 2002. Also that year Xerox agreed to pay a $10 million fine to settle a complaint brought by the SEC alleging financial reporting violations. After the settlement Xerox –which fired KPMG as its auditors the previous year and brought in PricewaterhouseCoopers –initiated an audit of its financial statements from 1997 through 2001; as a result of the audit in 2002 the company restated about $2 billion in revenues over the five-year period.

Also in 2002 Xerox made its celebrated Palo Alto Research Center (PARC) into a separate subsidiary. (Xerox was long criticized for failing to capitalize on numerous breakthrough PARC innovations –laser printer computer mouse Ethernet desktop icons.)

It sold its stake in IT systems integrator Integic in 2005 to Northrop Grumman for $96 million in cash. The following year Xerox reached a settlement with Palm in a patent infringement case it originally filed in 1997; Palm agreed to pay Xerox $22.5 million for a full license to three patents related to handwriting recognition and other technology.

Xerox acquired Amici a document management and search service company that primarily served the legal sector for $174 million in cash in 2006. Later that year it purchased XMPie a developer of software used to create customized marketing programs for $54 million in cash.

In 2007 Xerox acquired office equipment vendor Global Imaging Systems for approximately $1.5 billion. It also purchased Advectis a provider of electronic document collaboration software for the mortgage industry for $32 million that year. In 2008 Xerox acquired Veenman a Dutch office equipment reseller from Corporate Express for $68 million. The GIS and Veenman deals furthered a strategy to expand Xerox's presence in the small and midsized business segments in the US and Europe.

In an effort to promote the transformation of its business from a manufacturer of photocopiers to a full-line supplier of office products printing production equipment software and services Xerox unveiled a new corporate logo in 2008.

In 2009 Mulcahy was succeeded by president Ursula Burns as CEO; Mulcahy remained chairman of Xerox until her retirement in 2010 after eight years as head of the board. Burns was appointed as the new chairman.

The company invested heavily in its services business in 2010 buying Affiliated Computer Services for $6.4 billion. Xerox also made several smaller acquisitions that year to boost its services business including ExcellerateHRO (benefits administration and relocation services) TMS Health (outsourced customer service for the health care industry) and Spur Information Solutions (software for the transportation industry).

EXECUTIVES

VP; President United States Client Operations, Kevin M. Warren, age 49
SVP General Counsel and Corporate Secretary, Don H. Liu, age 51
EVP; President Corporate Operations, James A. (Jim) Firestone, age 57, $714,000 total compensation
EVP; President Xerox Services, Lynn R. Blodgett, age 58
Chairman and CEO, Ursula M. Burns, age 53, $900,000 total compensation
VP Chief Engineer and Graphic Communications Executive Liaison, Anthony M. Federico, age 64
VP Investor Relations, James H. Lesko, age 60
VP; President Global Technology and Delivery Group Global Imaging Systems and Xerox Canada, Russell M. Peacock, age 53
VP and CTO; President Xerox Innovation Group, Sophie V. Vandebroek, age 50
VP Finance and Controller, Leslie F. Varon, age 56
VP Global Imaging Support Operations, Richard F. Cerrone, age 63
EVP; President Xerox Technology, Armando Zagalo de Lima, age 53
VP and Chief Accounting Officer, Gary R. Kabureck, age 58
VP and Treasurer, Rhonda L. Seegal, age 61
Assistant Treasurer and Chief Investment Officer, Carol McFate
SVP; President Xerox Global Business and Services Group, Willem T. (Wim) Appelo, age 47
President Strategy Business Process Architecture and Change Management, John E. McDermott, age 58
VP; EVP ACS Major Accounts, John M. Kelly, age 47
VP; President Europe Client Operations, Shaun W. Pantling, age 59
VP; President Large Enterprise Operations, Michael Stephen Cronin, age 59
VP Worldwide Taxes, Kathleen S. Fanning, age 51
VP; SVP Global Accounts Operations, D. Cameron Hyde
VP Deputy General Counsel and Chief Ethics Officer, Ivy Thomas McKinney, age 56
Corporate VP and CIO, Carol J. Zierhoffer, age 52
VP; President Xerox Global Graphic Communications Operations, Jeffrey (Jeff) Jacobson, age 52
VP; President Graphic Communications Business Group, Eric Armour, age 53
EVP and CFO, Luca Maestri, age 48
VP; COO Europe Xerox Services, Tom Blodgett, age 59
VP; President North American Agent Operations, Jule E. Limoli, age 61
VP; President Developing Market Operations, Herve Tessler, age 49

VP; President Office and Solutions Business Group, Richard M. (Rick) Dastin, age 52
VP Global Public Relations, Carl Langsenkamp
VP; President Xerox Europe, Jacques Guers, age 57
Corporate Public Relations, Bill McKee
VP and Chief Strategy Officer, Uta Werner, age 53
VP and Chief Marketing Officer, Christa B. Carone, age 43
SVP and Chief Human Resources Officer, Tom Maddison, age 48
VP General Patent Counsel and Chief Strategy Counsel, Mark Costello, age 55
VP; CFO Xerox Services, Michael R. (Mike) Festa, age 52
VP; CFO Xerox Technology, Joseph H. (Joe) Mancini Jr., age 54
CEO Palo Alto Research Center, Steve Hoover
Chief Engineer Global Document Outsources, Eugene Shustef
Assistant Secretary, Douglas H. Marshall
Sales Manager, Ahmad Kasaby
Sales Manager, Khaled Antoun
VP; COO Information Technology Outsourcing Xerox Services, Kevin Kyser
Sales Manager, Hesham Deeb
VP; President Channel Partner Operations, Douraid Zaghouani
VP; COO State Government Xerox Services, David Bywater
VP; COO Transportation Central and Local Government Xerox Services, Dave Amoriell
VP; COO Commercial Services Xerox Services, Connie Harvey
VP; COO Enterprise Business Process Outsourcing Xerox Services, Ann Vezina
Director, Ann N. Reese, age 59
Director, Richard J. (Dick) Harrington, age 65
Director, Mary Agnes (Maggie) Wilderotter, age 57
Director, Charles O. (Chuck) Prince III, age 62
Director, Robert J. (Bob) Keegan, age 65
Director, Glenn A. Britt, age 63
Director, N. J. Nicholas Jr., age 72
Director, Robert A. (Bob) McDonald, age 59
Director, William C. Hunter, age 64
Director, Sara Tucker
Auditors: PricewaterhouseCoopersLLP

LOCATIONS

HQ: Xerox Corporation
45 Glover Ave., Norwalk CT 06850
Phone: 203-968-3000 **Fax:** 847-941-8200
Web: www.zenith.com

2012 Sales

	$ mil.	% of total
US	14,701	66
Europe	5,111	23
Other regions	2,578	11
Total	**22,390**	**100**

PRODUCTS/OPERATIONS

2012 Sales by Revenue Type

	$ mil.	% of total
Annuity		
Service outsourcing & rentals	15,215	68
Supplies paper & other	3,102	14
Financing	597	3
Equipment	3,476	16
Total	**22,390**	**100**

2012 Sales by Segment

	$ mil.	% of total
Services	11,528	52
Technology	9,462	42
Other	1,400	6
Total	**22,390**	**100**

Selected Products

Office (commercial government and education sectors)
- Copiers
- Displays
- Multifunction devices (copy fax print scan)
- Printers
- Projectors
- Scanners

Production (graphics communications industry and large corporations)
- Digital presses
- High-volume printers
- Software

Other
- Paper
- Services
- Wide-format printers

Service Types

Document Management
- Managed Print Services
- Communication and Marketing
- Enterprise Content Management
- Document and Data Management

IT Outsourcing
- IT Consulting
- Application Development
- IT Infrastructure
- IT Solutions
- Cloud Services

Business Processes
- Customer Care
- Finance & Accounting
- HR Services
- Application Services

COMPETITORS

Accenture
Agfa
Aon
Brother Industries
Canon
Capgemini
Computer Sciences Corp.
Convergys
Dell
Eastman Kodak
Epson
FUJIFILM
Fujitsu
Genpact
Heidelberger Druckmaschinen
Hewlett-Packard
Hitachi
IBM
Infosys
Konica Minolta
Kyocera Document Solutions
Lexmark
NEC
Oce
Oki Data
Olivetti
Panasonic Corp
Pitney Bowes
Ricoh Company
Sharp Corp.
Tata Consultancy
TeleTech
Toshiba
Unisys
Wipro

HISTORICAL FINANCIALS

Company Type: Public

Income Statement

FYE: December 31

	REVENUE ($ mil.)	NET INCOME ($ mil.)	NET PROFIT MARGIN	EMPLOYEES
12/11	22,626	1,295	5.7%	139,650
12/10	21,633	606	2.8%	136,500
12/09	15,179	485	3.2%	53,600
12/08	17,608	230	1.3%	57,100
12/07	17,228	1,135	6.6%	57,400
Annual Growth	7.1%	3.4%	—	24.9%

2011 Year-End Financials

Debt ratio: 28.67%
Return on equity: 10.59%
Cash ($ mil.): 902
Current ratio: 123.99
Long-term debt ($ mil.): 7,088
No. of shares (mil.): 1,337
Dividends
Yield: —
Payout: 18.89%
Market value ($ mil.): 10,645

	STOCK PRICE ($) FY Close	P/E High/Low		PER SHARE ($) Earnings	Dividends	Book Value
12/11	7.96	13	7	0.90	0.00	9.14
12/10	11.52	27	18	0.43	0.17	8.84
12/09	8.46	17	7	0.55	0.17	8.11
12/08	7.97	62	20	0.26	0.17	7.21
12/07	16.19	16	13	1.19	0.04	9.36
Annual Growth	(16.3%)	—	—	(6.7%)	—	(0.6%)

Yahoo! Inc.

Yahoo! wants to spread some cheer to Internet users around the world. Its network of websites offers news entertainment and shopping as well as search results powered by Microsoft's Bing. Yahoo! generates most of its revenue through providing search and display advertising to Web operations in three categories: Communications & Communities (including Yahoo! Mail Yahoo! Groups and Flickr) Search and Marketplaces (Yahoo! Search) and Media (Yahoo! Homepage Yahoo! Finance). Other revenues come from fee-based services such as premium e-mail; royalties licenses and mobile products; and broadband Internet access. Yahoo! publishes content in about 45 languages and in 60 countries regions and territories.

HISTORY

David Filo and Jerry Yang began developing the Yahoo! search engine and directory while students at Stanford in 1994. By the end of that year their website was attracting hundreds of thousands of visitors. The next year they incorporated the business and tapped former Motorola (now Motorola Solutions) executive Timothy Koogle as president. Revenue also began flowing in 1995 when Yahoo! started selling ad space on its website. The company went public the next year and share prices soared. Yahoo! teamed with SOFTBANK and its affiliates to form Yahoo! Japan and Yahoo! Europe in 1996.

In 1997 Yahoo! created Internet navigation service Netscape Guide by Yahoo! for Netscape Communications (now part of America Online). The company also acquired Internet directory specialist Four11 and launched Yahoo! Korea. The company's growth continued in 1998 with acquisitions of Viaweb (e-commerce software) WebCal (Internet scheduling products) and Yoyodyne (Internet direct marketing). With competition between Netscape and Yahoo! heating up the two companies agreed to pull the plug on the Netscape Guide by Yahoo! service.

Branching into audio the company launched its Yahoo! Radio broadcast Internet radio service in 1999. It also teamed with TIBCO Software to offer Corporate My Yahoo! the company's foray into corporate intranets. Yahoo's $3.7 billion acquisition of GeoCities and the more than $5 billion purchase of broadcast.com in 1999 stoked the Internet consolidation trend. Its purchase of software maker Encompass that year enhanced its Internet software holdings. Yahoo! also signed a deal with Sprint to provide information to Sprint's cell phone customers. Koogle was also named chairman in 1999.

Yahoo! waded into business-to-business waters in 2000 launching its Yahoo! B2B Marketplace. It later teamed with partners Inktomi Critical Path and TIBCO to develop enterprise information portals. The company also took a minority stake in Internet phone services firm Net2Phone and acquired e-mail communications firm eGroups for about $430 million. Streaming media application Yahoo! Player debuted in 2000 and Web broadcast channel FinanceVision was launched. Later that year Yahoo! dropped Inktomi as its search engine provider and switched to Google. The company also agreed to acquire Taiwanese portal Kimo in a deal valued at more than $150 million.

In the wake of a November 2000 French court order requiring Yahoo! to bar French users from accessing Nazi-related items for sale on its auction sites the company banned hate material from its auction websites in 2001. (It also stopped the sale of adult videos on its shopping sites that year.) To add a new source of revenue Yahoo! announced it would begin charging fees to list items; 90% of its users later abandoned the site. With advertising revenue declining and profits in danger Koogle said that year he would step down and the company announced that it would lay off about 400 staff members (later adding another 300 to that figure).

Former Warner Bros. executive Terry Semel was tapped as Koogle's replacement in 2001. That year Yahoo! became an affiliate of subscription music service pressplay (a joint venture between Universal Music Group and Sony Music Entertainment) which was rebranded in 2003 as the relaunched Napster. Yahoo! went even further into the digital music world by acquiring LAUNCH (now rebranded as Yahoo! Music). The company also added e-books to Yahoo! Shopping. In other efforts to diversify its revenue streams Yahoo! won an unsolicited takeover bid for HotJobs.com (which had already agreed to be acquired by TMP Worldwide now Monster Worldwide) late in 2001.

The next year Yahoo! unveiled a fee-based document search service provided by partner divine. In addition it completed its acquisition of HotJobs.com. Later in 2002 the company sold its small stake (less than 5%) in Net2Phone to a private investor and shut down its Yahoo! Radio service and its financial news programYahoo! FinanceVision. In addition the company unveiled a redesign of its home page with a less cluttered layout to allow for more ad space. In 2003 Yahoo! purchased Inktomi and Overture Services gaining additional search technology and paid inclusion services.

Following a boost in online advertising revenue and paid search performance in 2004 Yahoo! reported the most successful quarter in the company's history and approved a 2-for-1 stock split. The company also acquired online music service Musicmatch for about $160 million. Yahoo! paid $1 billion for a 40% stake in Alibaba.com a Chinese e-commerce company in 2005.

That year it bought Flickr a service for posting and sharing photos online as well as del.icio.us a service used to store and share Internet bookmarks. It also launched its own Web logging (blogging) service called Yahoo! 360 and picked up entertainment polling site Bix.com in 2006. The company continued to expand its music downloading services by introducing Web video service Yahoo! Video in 2006. Later that year Yahoo! rejected a buyout offer from Microsoft.

On the international front in 2006 Yahoo! formed a strategic partnership with Seven Network Limited an Australian media company to form Yahoo! 7 the result of a combination of Yahoo! Australia and Seven's online TV and magazine operations. Also that year Yahoo! combined its Spanish-language US website with Telemundo's site in order to target the growing Hispanic audience on the Web. Bowing to pressure from investors the company appointed Yang to replace Semel as CEO the following year.

In 2007 Yahoo! introduced Yahoo Smart Ads a product that includes tools to help marketers create custom online advertising aimed at specific groups of buyers. It also acquired online advertising exchange Right Media for $650 million shortly after Google purchased rival ad distribution network DoubleClick. In addition it launched a new search marketing system called Project Panama which included a new ranking model and personalization services designed to provide Yahoo! users with more relevant search results and Yahoo! advertisers with more valuable customer leads.

The company took to expand its service offerings to businesses with the acquisition of Zimbra in 2007. Zimbra provides Internet based e-mail and collaboration services targeting large organizations and businesses. Yahoo! paid about $350 million for the company. As part of its strategy to expand its ad reach Yahoo! purchased BlueLithium for some $300 million in 2007. BlueLithium operates a so-called online-advertising network whereby it buys graphical-display ad slots on sites owned by other Web publishers and resells the slots to advertisers.

Turnaround efforts in 2008 included job cuts a de-emphasis on certain areas of the business and a tight budget. Specifically in 2008 the company first cut 7% of its 14300-employee workforce equaling some 1000 jobs. Also that year Yahoo! sold British comparison shopping site Kelkoo for less than E100 million to UK private-equity firm Jamplant. (It had purchased the site in 2004 for approximately E475 million or some $579 million.) It additionally redesigned its home page with a simpler cleaner layout similar to those of Google and MSN and content and features from third-party services such as Amazon.com and Netflix. A troubled economy called for even more belt-tightening including a second round of layoffs (representing at least 10% of its work force) that occurred at the end of 2008.

Longtime advertising executive Roy Bostock was named chairman in early 2008. He had barely enough time to settle into his new office when Microsoft made another bid to buy the company; this time it offered nearly $45 billion. The offer increased the company's value more than 60% representing Microsoft's desire to expand its online offerings and more effectively compete with Google. Yahoo! rejected Microsoft on the grounds that the proposal significantly undervalued the company. In response Microsoft refused to raise its offer and the software giant eventually walked away from its pursuit of the company.

In 2009 outspoken Carol Bartz was brought on as CEO. The former executive at software firm Autodesk replaced co-founder Jerry Yang who left after a short and tumultuous tenure as CEO. (Yang had replaced Terry Semel for the top position in 2007; he remains a senior executive and board member). Charged with the considerable task of turning the business around Bartz promptly instituted a management overhaul and combined its technology and products groups. Also under her purview the company launched a newly redesigned home page with customizable links to third-party sites and applications such as Twitter and Facebook.

Also that year Microsoft announced plans to form a major search partnership with Yahoo! in lieu of an outright acquisition. (The 10-year search partnership with Microsoft was finalized in 2010.) It next sold Maven Networks which it had acquired in 2008 for some $160 million. (Maven managed premium online video content for more than 30 major media companies.) Also in 2009 the company discontinued live video streaming service Y!Live and online video editing tool Jumpcut.

On the international front in 2009 Yahoo! acquired Maktoob a leading online portal in the Middle East that operates sites for business finance games and blogging. Yahoo! made the purchase for $164 million in order to enter the emerging Middle East market. The region had previously been avoided by American Web companies due to its foreign cultural and political customs which include a ban on offensive content. Other international activity in 2009 included the sale of its direct investment in Chinese search firm Alibaba for $145 million.

After reporting three consecutive years of falling revenues in 2010 it worked to offset such declines by cutting costs including instituting layoffs and divesting assets. These efforts ultimately helped boost net income that year. It laid off employees some 600 employees in 2010. (The job cuts represent the fourth time in three years that Yahoo! has boosted earnings through massive layoffs.)

The company also in 2010 sold Yahoo! Hot Jobs to Monster Worldwide for some $225 million. (Yahoo! continues to provide online career services through a three-year licensing agreement with Monster in the US and Canada.) In addition the company sold e-mail technology unit Zimbra to virtualization technology firm VMware for $100 million. Later in 2010 it beefed up the content it offers across its sites when it acquired Associated Content an online publisher of articles videos audio and images from about 380000 contributors.

Bartz left the company in 2011 after failing to turn the business around and in early 2012 co-founder Jerry Yang resigned.

EXECUTIVES

Chairman, Alfred J. (Fred) Amoroso, age 62
Chairman, Roy J. Bostock, age 71
Co-Founder and Chief Yahoo!, David Filo, age 45
EVP Chief Strategy Officer and Head Yahoo! Labs, Prabhakar Raghavan, age 51
EVP and Chief Product Officer, Blake Irving, age 52
EVP Central Technology Organization, David E. Dibble, age 50
President and CEO Yahoo! Japan, Masahiro Inoue, age 55
EVP and Chief Human Resources Officer, David Windley
SVP Data and Analytics, Scott Burke
CEO and Director, Scott Thompson, age 54
Interim CEO and President, Ross B. Levinsohn, age 49
EVP Americas, Rich Riley, age 37
EVP General Counsel and Secretary, Michael J. (Mike) Callahan, age 43, $420,000 total compensation
President; Chief Executive Officer; Director, Marissa Mayer
CFO, Timothy R. (Tim) Morse, age 43, $251,923 total compensation
EVP and Chief Marketing Officer, Elisa Steele
Corporate Communications, Bahareh Ramin
Director, Daniel S. Loeb, age 49
SVP Advertising Sales North America, Wayne Powers
SVP and Managing Director Asia/Pacific, Rose Tsou, age 47
SVP Yahoo Media Network, Mickie Rosen
EVP Customer Advocacy, Jeff Russakow

Investor Relations, Cathy La Rocca
VP North Americas Ad Marketplaces, Joel Jones
Editor in Chief Yahoo! Media Network, Jai Singh
SVP Global Controller and Chief Accounting Officer, Aman S. Kothari, age 39
SVP and CTO, Raymie Stata
SVP Search and Marketplaces, Shashi Seth
VP Sports Games and Entertainment, Ken Fuchs
VP News and Finance, Robertson (Rob) Barrett
CFO, Ken Goldman
IR Contact, Joon Huh
Chief Marketing Officer, Kathy Savitt
Chief Financial Officer, Kenneth Goldman
General Counsel, Ron Bell
Director, Patti S. Hart, age 54
Director, Gary L. Wilson, age 72
Director, David W. Kenny, age 50
Director, Maynard G. Webb Jr., age 56
Director, Thomas E. McInerney, age 70
Director, Vyomesh (VJ) Joshi, age 57
Director, Arthur H. (Art) Kern, age 65
CEO and Director, Scott Thompson, age 54
Director, Peter Liguori, age 52
Director, Brad D. Smith, age 48
Director, Michael J. Wolf, age 50
President CEO and Director, Marissa Mayer
Director, Daniel S. Loeb, age 49
Director, Susan (Sue) James, age 66
Director, Harry J. Wilson, age 40
Independent Director, John D. Hayes, age 57
Auditors: PricewaterhouseCoopersLLP

LOCATIONS

HQ: Yahoo! Inc.
701 1st Ave., Sunnyvale CA 94089
Phone: 408-349-3300 **Fax:** 408-349-3301
Web: www.yahoo.com

2011 Sales

	$ mil.	% of total
Americas	3,303	66
Asia/Pacific	1,058	21
Europe Middle East & Africa	629	13
Total	**4,984**	**100**

Selected International Operations

Yahoo! 7 (Australia & New Zealand)
Yahoo! Argentina
Yahoo! Asia
Yahoo! Brasil
Yahoo! Canada
Yahoo! China
Yahoo! Danmark (Denmark)
Yahoo! En Espanol (US Hispanic)
Yahoo! Espa?a (Spain)
Yahoo! Europe
Yahoo! Deutschland (Germany)
Yahoo! France
Yahoo! UK
Yahoo! Hong Kong
Yahoo! India
Yahoo! Italia (Italy)
Yahoo! Japan (35%)
Yahoo! Korea
Yahoo! Mexico
Yahoo! Norge (Norway)
Yahoo! Singapore
Yahoo! Sverige (Sweden)

PRODUCTS/OPERATIONS

2011 Sales

	$ mil.	% of total
Display	2,160	43
Search	1,853	37
Other	970	20
Total	**4,984**	**100**

Selected Offerings

Communications & Communities
Yahoo! Mail
Yahoo! Messenger
Yahoo! Groups
Flickr
Media
Yahoo! Finance
Yahoo! Homepage
Yahoo! News
Yahoo! Screen
Yahoo! Sports
Search & Marketplace
Yahoo! Local
Yahoo! Search

COMPETITORS

24/7 Real Media
About.com
Amazon.com
AOL
Apple Inc.
Ask.com
Blucora
CBS Interactive
CityGrid Media
craigslist
Daum Communications
Disney Online
eBay
Facebook
Google
LookSmart
MSN
Myspace
RealNetworks
Twitter
Vertro

HISTORICAL FINANCIALS

Company Type: Public

Income Statement FYE: December 31

	REVENUE ($ mil.)	NET INCOME ($ mil.)	NET PROFIT MARGIN	EMPLOYEES
12/11	4,984	1,048	21.0%	14,100
12/10	6,324	1,231	19.5%	13,600
12/09	6,460	597	9.3%	13,900
12/08	7,208	424	5.9%	13,600
12/07	6,969	660	9.5%	14,300
Annual Growth	(8.0%)	12.3%	—	(0.4%)

2011 Year-End Financials

Debt ratio: 0.91%
Return on equity: 8.36%
Cash ($ mil.): 1,562
Current ratio: 285.96
Long-term debt ($ mil.): 134
No. of shares (mil.): 1,190
Dividends
Yield: —
Payout: —
Market value ($ mil.): 19,195

	STOCK PRICE ($) FY Close	P/E High/Low		PER SHARE ($) Earnings	Dividends	Book Value
12/11	16.13	23	14	0.82	0.00	10.54
12/10	16.63	21	14	0.90	0.00	9.60
12/09	16.78	41	26	0.42	0.00	8.89
12/08	12.20	97	29	0.29	0.00	8.09
12/07	23.26	69	46	0.47	0.00	7.16
Annual Growth	(8.7%)	—	—	14.9%	—	10.1%

YRC Worldwide Inc

YRC Worldwide stands for more than Your Regional Carrier. Operating through subsidiaries the holding company offers not only US regional transportation services but national and international services. Key subsidiaries include YRC Freight which specializes in transporting goods for manufacturing wholesale retail and government customers in the US Canada and certain international markets. YRC Regional Transportation provides of regional next-day ground services in the US Canada Mexico and Puerto Rico.

Geographic Reach

Most of YRC Worldwide's revenue comes from the US. However a small portion –less than 5% – is derived from international markets mainly Canada Mexico and Asia.

Operations

YRC Freight is the company's largest segment raking in about two-thirds of its parent's sales. With nearly 300 owned and leased facilities and a fleet of about 9500 tractors YRC Freight has one of the largest networks of less-than-truckload (LTL) service centers equipment and transportation staff in North America. YRC Freight subsidiary Reimer Express (also known as YRC Reimer) offers Canadian customers shipping options within the country throughout North America and around the world.

The YRC Regional Transportation business segment consists of New Penn USF Holland and USF Reddaway. Each provide next-day ground services in their respective regions.

YRC Worldwide formerly reported a Truckload segment which included the operations of USF Glen Moore a provider of US truckload services. Glen Moore concluded operations in December 2011 when some of its fleet was sold to a third-party and the rest was redeployed to YRC Freight and Regional Transportation companies. Truckload had accounted for only about 1% to 2% of sales in fiscal years 2011 2010 and 2009.

Financial Analysis

YRC Worldwide has had a rough go since fiscal 2009 when revenues slipped by half of 2008's total. Revenues fell from $8.3 billion in 2008 to about $4.9 billion in 2009 due to slumping demand for freight shipping and the company has yet to climb back up. Fiscal 2011 revenues stayed about flat at $4.9 billion. The company also has had recurring net losses though the loss decreased to $354.5 million in 2011 from $619.5 million in 2009.

While the company is working to improve its liquidity and pare down more than $1.3 billion in debt it also faces an uncertain future as factors like the rising cost of diesel a prime component of trucking fleet costs threaten it. YRC Worldwide like its competitors adjusts fuel surcharges in accordance with the cost of diesel.

Strategy

As a result of difficult market conditions arising from the global economic downturn YRC Worldwide like many of its competitors continues to reduce the size and scope of its operational networks staff and service offerings. A key part of the compnay's strategy today is sharpening its focus on North American LTL shipping one of the better performing parts of its business. It is trying to regain a position as a North American LTL market leader by simplifying its portfolio and divesting underperforming and noncore operations. In March 2012 it announced an agreement to sell its interest in its China-based joint venture Shanghai Jiayu Logistics Co. Ltd. to its JV partner.

HISTORY

In 1924 A. J. Harrell established a trucking company in conjunction with his Oklahoma City bus line and Yellow Cab franchise. Harrell's Yellow Transit trucking operation hauled less-than-truckload (LTL) shipments between Oklahoma City and Tulsa. By 1944 Yellow had more than 50 independent subsidiaries in Illinois Indiana Kansas Kentucky Missouri and Texas. That year the company was sold to an investment firm and renamed

Yellow Transit Freight Lines. But Yellow's policy of paying high dividends stunted its growth and by 1951 it faced bankruptcy.

George Powell Sr. took over in 1952 and turned Yellow around. His son George Powell Jr. became CEO in 1957 and the company went public two years later. George Jr. focused the company on long-haul interstate shipments and started buying up other trucking companies.

In 1965 Yellow expanded to the West Coast and the Southeast by purchasing Watson-Wilson Transportation System. Changing its name to Yellow Freight System (1968) the company acquired part of Norwalk Truck Lines and its routes in the Northeast (1970) and Adley Express (1972) providing new East Coast routes. Yellow extended routes into the Pacific Northwest by buying Republic Freight Systems in 1975. Its 1978 purchase of Braswell Motor Freight Lines consolidated its routes in California Texas and the Southeast. Yellow's only deviation from route acquisitions was its $4 million investment in oil firm Overland Energy in 1976 which it dissolved in the early 1980s.

The company was unprepared however when Congress deregulated trucking routes and shipping rates in 1980. Yellow upgraded its aging depots and terminals but profits still declined by 1983. In 1982 Yellow Freight formed a holding corporation (renamed Yellow Corporation in 1992). George Powell III took over from his father as CEO in 1990. Yellow purchased Preston Trucking an overnight freight hauler in 1992.

In 1994 Yellow Freight was hit by a 24-day Teamsters' strike that allowed nonunion carriers to gain a chunk of its market. The next year struggling during industry price wars it reported a $30 million loss. Yellow laid off about 250 employees mostly from Yellow Freight. George III resigned in 1996 and Maurice "Mr. Fix-it" Myers became CEO. Myers began moving the firm from a one-size-fits-all LTL trucker to a more flexible customer-responsive trucking and logistics firm.

Yellow Freight was restructured in 1997 into decentralized business units to improve customer service and hundreds of workers were laid off. The misfortunes of other companies also created good fortune for Yellow: UPS went on strike and rail traffic was still snarled from the 1996 Union Pacific-Southern Pacific merger.

To expand international operations Yellow created YCS International in 1998 (renamed Yellow Global in 2000). It also secured a five-year labor contract with its unions ending the danger of a strike. Loss-making Preston was sold to three company executives and Yellow acquired regional carriers Action Express (1998) and Jevic Transportation (1999).

Myers drove off into the sunset in 1999 to take over another troubled giant Waste Management and Yellow Freight president William Zollars became CEO of Yellow Corp. In 2000 Yellow and two venture capital firms set up online transportation marketplace transportation.com to provide freight-forwarding and multimodal brokerage services.

Yellow integrated Action Express and WestEx into Saia Motor Freight Line in 2001. The next year Yellow renamed its Yellow Freight subsidiary Yellow Transportation. The company created SCS Transportation to act as a holding company for its regional nonunion carriers Saia and Jevic. Also in 2002 Yellow combined transportation.com with its other logistics services to form Meridian IQ. That same year Yellow spun off SCS Transportation (later Saia Inc.). The next year Yellow and other leading LTL carriers negotiated a new contract with the Teamsters union.

Also in 2003 Yellow bought rival Roadway and became Yellow Roadway Corporation. The company expanded in 2005 with the acquisition of USF. The following year Yellow Roadway changed its name to YRC Worldwide and in 2007 it also changed the name of its Meridian IQ unit to YRC Logistics.

In order to reduce costs and improve its operating efficiency YRC Worldwide restructrued its operations and integrated its Roadway and Yellow Transportation units in March 2009. In mid-2011 the company appointed James Welch as its new CEO. Welch served at Yellow Transportation as CEO and later on as president and CEO of Dynamex. He succeeds William Zollars who retired as CEO of YRC.

EXECUTIVES

Chairman, James E. (Jim) Hoffman, age 58
President New Penn, Steven D. (Steve) Gast
EVP and Chief Sales Officer, John A. Garcia, age 58
CEO, James L. Welch, age 57
EVP and Chief Marketing Officer, Gregory A. (Greg) Reid, $237,500 total compensation
EVP Human Resources, James G. (Jim) Kissinger, age 55, $306,539 total compensation
President Reddaway, Thomas (TJ) O'Connor
Chief Strategy Officer, Richard M. Williamson, age 55
President Holland, Michael J. (Mike) Naatz
VP External Affairs and Chief Sustainability Officer, J. Mike Kelley
VP Taxation, Terry Gerrond
VP Pricing, Andy Slusher
President YRC Freight, Jeffrey A. (Jeff) Rogers
EVP General Counsel and Secretary, Michelle A. Russell
SVP and Treasurer, Christopher C. Wren
EVP and CFO, Jamie G. Pierson
Deputy General Counsel, Jeff P. Bennett
CFO YRC Freight, Tom Palmer
Chief Security Officer, Wayne Day
Director, James E. (Jim) Hoffman, age 59
Director, Douglas A. Carty, age 56
Director, Michael J. Kneeland, age 58
Director, Robert L. (Bob) Friedman, age 69
Director, James F. (Jim) Winestock, age 60
Director, Raymond J. Bromark, age 65
Director, Matthew Doheny, age 42
Director, Harry J. Wilson, age 40
Auditors: KPMGLLP

LOCATIONS

HQ: YRC Worldwide Inc.
10990 Roe Ave., Overland Park KS 66211
Phone: 913-696-6100 **Fax:** 312-263-4066
Web: www.ziegler.com

2011 Sales

	$ mil.	% of total
US	4,682	96
International	186	4
Total	**4,868**	**100**

PRODUCTS/OPERATIONS

2011 Sales

	$ mil.	% of total
YRC Freight	3,203	66
Regional Transportation	1,553	32
Truckload	86	2
Adjustments	25	-
Total	**4,868**	**100**

COMPETITORS

ABF Freight System
Arkansas Best
C.H. Robinson Worldwide
Central Freight Lines
Con-way Inc.
Estes Express
FedEx Freight
J.B. Hunt
Landstar System
Menlo Worldwide
Mullen Group
Old Dominion Freight
Saia
Schneider National
UPS Freight
UPS Supply Chain Solutions

HISTORICAL FINANCIALS

Company Type: Public

Income Statement FYE: December 31

	REVENUE ($ mil.)	NET INCOME ($ mil.)	NET PROFIT MARGIN	EMPLOYEES
12/11	4,868	(351)	—	32,000
12/10	4,334	(322)	—	32,000
12/09	5,282	(622)	—	36,000
12/08	8,940	(974)	—	55,000
12/07	9,621	(638)	—	63,000
Annual Growth	(15.7%)	—	—	(15.6%)

2011 Year-End Financials

Debt ratio: 54.50%
Return on equity: 987650001000000.00%
Cash ($ mil.): 200
Current ratio: 124.01
Long-term debt ($ mil.): 1,345
No. of shares (mil.): 6
Dividends
Yield: —
Payout: —
Market value ($ mil.): 68

	STOCK PRICE ($) FY Close	P/E High	P/E Low	PER SHARE ($) Earnings	Dividends	Book Value
12/11	9.97	—	—	(196.12)	0.00	(51.71)
12/10	3.72	—	—	(2,439.00)	0.00	(1,186.62)
12/09	0.84	—	—	(78,300.00)	0.00	13,055.90
12/08	2.87	—	—	(126,900.00)	0.00	59,964.86
12/07	17.09	—	—	(83,775.00)	0.00	213,222.60
Annual Growth	(12.6%)	—	—	—	—	—

Yum! Brands, Inc.

This company puts fast-food yummies in a whole lot of tummies. YUM! Brands is the largest fast-food operator in the world in terms of number of locations with more than 37000 outlets in about 120 countries. (It trails only hamburger giant McDonald's in sales.) The company's flagship chains include #1 chicken fryer KFC (with more than 17400 units) top pizza joint Pizza Hut (more than 13700) and quick-service Mexican leader Taco Bell (more than 5900). YUM! also operates the Long John Silver's seafood chain along with several hundred A&W root beer and burger stands. Franchisees affiliates and licensed operators run about 75% of the company's restaurants.

HISTORY

Yum! Brands took its original name TRICON from the three brand icons –KFC Pizza Hut and Taco Bell –it inherited from former parent PepsiCo. The soft drink company entered the fast-food business with its acquisition of Pizza Hut in 1977. The pizza chain had begun in 1958 when brothers Dan and Frank Carney borrowed $600 from their mother and opened the first Pizza Hut in Wichita Kansas with partner John Bender. Their first franchise opened the next year in Topeka Kansas. By 1971 the company had become the world's largest pizza chain with more than 1000 restaurants. Pizza Hut went public the following year. The chain had grown to 3000 locations by the time it was acquired.

In 1978 PepsiCo acquired Taco Bell. After trying other fast-food formats Glen Bell settled on the Mexican-style market. He bought and sold several chains before beginning Taco Bell in Downey California in 1962. The first franchise was sold two years later and by 1967 –the year after it went public –Taco Bell had more than 335 restaurants most of them franchised.

KFC was acquired in 1986. It had been founded by Harland Sanders –that's Colonel Sanders to you –who developed his secret 11-herbs-and-spices recipe and method of pressure-frying chicken during the 1930s. The Colonel began franchising the secret in 1952 and founded Kentucky Fried Chicken in 1955. More than 600 outlets in the US and Canada were open by 1963. It went public in 1969 and was operating some 6600 units in 55 countries when it was acquired by PepsiCo.

Through these acquisitions PepsiCo hoped to diversify and build sales channels for its beverages but the company had also incurred a huge debt load and fast-food competition had intensified. As same-store sales faltered shareholders clamored for PepsiCo to spin off the restaurants. Restaurant officials grumbled that PepsiCo put more effort into marketing blitzes than into building restaurants (its 1991 renaming of Kentucky Fried Chicken as KFC didn't fool many health-conscious consumers).

In 1997 PepsiCo created a new restaurant subsidiary which it spun off in the fall as TRICON Global Restaurants. To improve cash flow it stepped up efforts to close or franchise underperforming Pizza Huts and KFCs. TRICON also began opening "three-in-one" restaurants featuring all its brands under one roof. In 1998 it launched a Taco Bell advertising campaign featuring a bilingual Chihuahua; the sassy pooch quickly became a cultural icon.

The KFC Taco Bell and Pizza Hut cooperatives joined in 1999 to form Unified FoodService Purchasing the largest purchasing cooperative for fast-food restaurants in the US. Also that year TRICON spent some $2 billion on a massive "Star Wars: Episode I –The Phantom Menace" promotion that failed to increase traffic at its restaurants. Vice chairman David Novak took over as CEO in 2000. Additionally in 1999 the company joined Burger King in lending $150 million to its distributor AmeriServe (now McLane Foodservice) which had filed for bankruptcy. The following year TRICON began experimenting with debit and credit cards at Pizza Huts and KFCs. It also opened more than 300 multi-branded sites.

In 2002 TRICON acquired Yorkshire Global Restaurants for $320 million which brought Long John Silver's and A&W All-American Food Restaurants into the fold. Now a five-pack of well-known brands rather than a trio TRICON changed its name to YUM! Brands. Later that year it formed a joint venture with Favorite Restaurants Group (a leading franchisee of KFC and Pizza Hut in Indonesia and Hong Kong) to open a chain of Yan Can Asian restaurants based around popular international chef Martin Yan. (YUM! Brands dissolved its partnership in Yan Can and liquidated the business in 2004.)

Being market leaders did not save YUM!'s chains from the overall downturn in the economy however nor from the effects of changing eating habits as Americans sought healthier meal alternatives. KFC was hit particularly hard prompting the company to appoint veteran Gregg Dedrick the chain's new president in 2003. Both KFC and Pizza Hut saw same-store sales and the number of transactions decline in the US during 2003.

In 2004 KFC opened its 1000th restaurant in China where the chain had been operating since 1987. As YUM! Brands' China operations continued to grow it formed a separate division in 2005 to oversee its expansion. The company acquired the 50% stake it didn't already own in Pizza Hut (UK) from joint venture partner Whitbread in 2006 for almost $185 million plus the assumption of about $25 million in debt.

The following year YUM! was stung by an E. coli outbreak at some of its Taco Bell outlets. The source of the outbreak was traced to a lettuce supplier; the company announced new steps to test its food supply. YUM! also sold its 31% stake in KFC Japan to Mitsubishi that same year.

YUM! Brands sold its Long John Silver's chain and A&W All-American Food locations in 2011. The divestitures should impact the company's strategic focus more than its top or bottom line as the Long John Silver's and A&W units combined to account for only 1% of operating profit.

In 2012 the company upped its stake in Chinese restaurant operator Little Sheep Group to 93%.

EXECUTIVES

SVP General Counsel Chief Franchise Policy Officer and Secretary, Christian L. (Chris) Campbell, age 61, $509,231 total compensation
SVP and Chief Public Affairs Officer, Jonathan D. Blum, age 54
Chairman President and CEO, David C. Novak, age 59, $1,400,000 total compensation
Chief People Officer, Anne P. Byerlein, age 53
SVP Investor Relations, Timothy P. (Tim) Jerzyk
Vice Chairman; Chairman and CEO YUM! Brands China Division, Samuel (Sam) Jing-Shyh Su, age 60, $811,923 total compensation
CEO Taco Bell, Greg Creed, age 54, $647,692 total compensation
CEO Pizza Hut U.S. and Yum! Innovation Yum! Brands Inc., Scott O. Bergren, age 65
President YUM! Restaurants International, Graham D. Allan, age 56, $811,923 total compensation
CFO, Richard T. (Rick) Carucci, age 55, $711,923 total compensation
Corporate Counsel and Assistant Secretary, John P. Daly Sr., age 53
SVP Finance, Ted F. Knopf, age 60
COO, Roger Eaton, age 51
CEO Yum! Restaurants International, Micky Pant, age 58
President YRI India, Niren Chaudhary
VP and Corporate Controller, David Russell, age 42
VP and CIO Yum! International Restaurants, Jack Clare
CIO KFC Brand, Tom Romano
CIO Pizza Hut, Baron Concors
VP Global IT, Dickie Oliver
President KFC USA, John Cywinski
VP and Treasurer, Larry Gathof
Chief Planning and Control Officer, Patrick Grismer
Director, Jonathan S. (Jon) Linen, age 68
Director, Thomas M. (Tom) Ryan, age 59
Director, Robert D. (Bob) Walter, age 66
Director, Massimo Ferragamo, age 54
Director, David W. (Dave) Dorman, age 58
Director, Robert Holland Jr., age 72
Director, Kenneth G. (Ken) Langone, age 76
Director, J. David Grissom, age 73
Director, Bonnie G. Hill, age 70
Vice Chairman; Chairman and CEO YUM! Brands China Division, Samuel (Sam) Jing-Shyh Su, age 60
Director, Thomas C. Nelson, age 49
Auditors: KPMGLLP

LOCATIONS

HQ: YUM! Brands Inc.
1441 Gardiner Ln., Louisville KY 40213
Phone: 502-874-8300 **Fax:** 406-248-7440
Web: www.koakampgrounds.com

2011 Sales

	$ mil.	% of total
International		
Other countries	3,274	26
Total	**12,626**	**100**

PRODUCTS/OPERATIONS

2011 Sales

	$ mil.	% of total
Restaurants	10,893	86
Total	**12,626**	**100**

2011 Locations

Franchised & licensed	
Licensed	2,169
Company-owned	7,437

COMPETITORS

AFC Enterprises
Burger King
Chick-fil-A
Chipotle
Church' s Chicken
CKE Restaurants
Dairy Queen
Del Taco
Domino' s
Jack in the Box
Little Caesar' s
McDonald' s
Papa John' s
Quiznos
Subway
Wendy' s

HISTORICAL FINANCIALS

Company Type: Public

Income Statement FYE: December 31

	REVENUE ($ mil.)	NET INCOME ($ mil.)	NET PROFIT MARGIN	EMPLOYEES
12/11	12,626	1,319	10.4%	466,000
12/10	11,343	1,158	10.2%	378,000
12/09	10,836	1,071	9.9%	350,000
12/08	11,279	964	8.5%	336,000
12/07	10,416	909	8.7%	301,000
Annual Growth	4.9%	9.8%	—	11.5%

2011 Year-End Financials

Debt ratio: 37.55%
Return on equity: 72.35%
Cash ($ mil.): 1,198
Current ratio: 94.73
Long-term debt ($ mil.): 2,997
No. of shares (mil.): 460
Dividends
Yield: —
Payout: 37.77%
Market value ($ mil.): 27,145

	STOCK PRICE ($) FY Close	P/E High	P/E Low	PER SHARE ($) Earnings	PER SHARE ($) Dividends	PER SHARE ($) Book Value
12/11	59.01	21	17	2.74	0.00	3.96
12/10	49.66	21	13	2.38	0.00	3.36
12/09	35.38	16	10	2.22	0.00	2.19
12/08	30.28	20	11	1.96	0.00	(0.24)
12/07	38.54	40	17	1.68	0.00	2.28
Annual Growth	11.2%	—	—	13.0%	—	14.8%

ZEN-NOH GRAIN CORPORATION

LOCATIONS

HQ: ZEN-NOH GRAIN CORPORATION
1127 HWY 190 E SERVICE RD, COVINGTON, LA 704334929
Phone: 9858673500
Web: WWW.CGB.COM

HISTORICAL FINANCIALS

Company Type:

Income Statement FYE: May 31

	REVENUE ($ mil.)	NET INCOME ($ mil.)	NET PROFIT MARGIN	EMPLOYEES
05/11	6,217	66	1.1%	213
05/10	5,988	55	0.9%	0
05/09	5,454	37	0.7%	0
05/08	5,719	47	0.8%	0
Annual Growth	2.8%	12.3%	—	—

2011 Year-End Financials

Debt ratio: —
Return on equity: 1.10%
Cash ($ mil.): 35
Current ratio: 1.00
Long-term debt ($ mil.): —

Dividends
Yield: —
Payout: —
Market value ($ mil.): —

Zimmer Holdings, Inc.

Zimmer can put the spring back in your step or the zing back in your swing. The company designs and markets orthopedic products including reconstructive implants used in knee or hip replacement surgery shoulder implants that restore function in arthritic joints and bone and tissue grafting materials. It also makes dental implant systems spinal implants to fix aching or injured backs and trauma products (such as plates screws and pins) that help broken bones to heal. Additionally Zimmer makes surgical products used in orthopedic surgeries including tourniquets and devices for wound cleansing. Zimmer operates worldwide with direct operations in more than 25 countries.

Zimmer makes most of its money from sales of knee and hip replacement products (more than 70%). It sells its orthopedic products directly to health care providers (such as hospitals surgery centers and surgeons themselves) and to a lesser extent through distributors and health care dealers. Its dental products are sold directly to dental practices and laboratories. The Americas segment (largely consisting of US operations) accounts for more than half of Zimmer's annual revenues though sales in international markets (especially in the Asia/Pacific region) are rising. Zimmer's products are sold in more than 100 countries worldwide.

Some of Zimmer's lead products are the Alloclassic hip system Zimmer M/L taper hip prosthesis and NexGen knee product line. In its smaller segments top products include the Bigliani/Flatow line for shoulders the Tapered Screw-Vent dental implant system the PathFinder minimally invasive pedicle spine screw system the Zimmer locking plate systems for bone fractures and the Palacos and Hi-Fatigue bone cement surgical products. Outside of medical products manufacturing the company has an Accelero Health Partners unit that provides consulting to help surgeons design customized treatment programs.

Zimmer has kept its sales figures on the rise in most operating segments through new product development efforts. For instance revenues in the hip implant segment increased 7% in 2011 largely due to the introduction of the Continuum acetabular system and the next-generation Zimmer M/L taper stem with Kinectiv technology. The trauma segment's 16% gain was likewise helped along by the 2011 launch of the Zimmer natural nail system. In addition Zimmer boosts sales by introducing next-generation versions of existing best-sellers that add functionality or ease or use. For instance it launched the PathFinder NXT spinal pedicle screw system in 2010; however despite advances in the field pricing and US sales force challenges have caused sales to shrink in the spinal segment.

The firm also conducts substantial R&D work in the field of orthobiologics or the implantation of biological materials to help repair and regenerate damaged tissue. Zimmer markets biologic bone and tissue allografts for dental spinal and trauma procedures through a partnership with RTI Biologics. The company is also collaborating with ISTO Technologies to develop biologically-derived grafts for cartilage repair; the companies have thus far launched the DeNovo natural tissue graft for cartilage repair and the Chondrofix allograft for lesion (cartilage and bone) repair.

Acquisitions are also a means of expansion for Zimmer. In 2010 it acquired Beijing Montagne Medical Device to widen its hip operations in the Asia/Pacific region; it also purchased trauma products manufacturer Sodem Diffusion that year. Zimmer expanded in the fields of in minimally invasive surgeries and computer-aided surgery technologies through historical acquisitions including ORTHOsoft (computerized navigational systems) in 2007 and Abbott Spine (minimally invasive surgical devices) in 2008.

Along with increasing its sales through new product introductions acquisitions and international expansion efforts Zimmer expects overall industry trends to help keep its sales in the black. The aging US population chronic obesity and advances in surgical techniques are all expected to contribute to increased demand for Zimmer's products. While demand is set to surge the company could continue to see depressed prices in some segments until the economy fully recovers due to government measures meant to control health care costs and hospitals seeking to cut their budgets.

Zimmer has steadily increased its revenues throughout most of its operating history (with the exception of a slight drop in 2009) including a 6% increase to some $4.4 billion in 2011 due to increased and new product sales. However the company has had more trouble keeping a steady bottom line. It experienced a 15% drop in net income in 2009 and another 17% decrease in 2010 due to operational and restructuring expenses product litigation costs and value impairment charges related to the spine segment. As these expenses and charges faded Zimmer returned to profit growth in 2011 with a 27% increase to about $761 million.

To help reduce operational costs the company is undergoing restructuring initiatives that aim to streamline business functions and reduce management layers. The program was launched in 2009 and extends through 2012; savings will be reinvested in R&D and sales force expansion efforts.

Formerly part of Bristol Myers Squibb Zimmer Holdings was spun off into an independent operation in 2001.

EXECUTIVES

Chairman, John L. McGoldrick, age 71
President CEO and Director, David C. Dvorak, age 48, $787,067 total compensation
Chairman Europe Middle East and Africa, Bruno A. Melzi, age 64, $577,538 total compensation
President Zimmer Reconstructive, Jeffrey A. McCaulley, age 46, $500,000 total compensation
SVP and Chief Scientific Officer, Cheryl R. Blanchard, age 47, $400,618 total compensation
EVP Finance and CFO, James T. (Jim) Crines, age 52, $475,083 total compensation
Group President Global Businesses, Jeffrey B. Paulsen, age 51
President Asia/Pacific, Stephen H. L. Ooi, age 58, $387,427 total compensation
SVP Global Operations and Logistics, Richard C. (Rick) Stair
SVP General Counsel and Secretary, Chad F. Phipps, age 40
VP Finance Corporate Controller and Chief Accounting Officer, Derek M. Davis, age 42
SVP Global Human Resources, William P. (Bill) Fisher
VP Associate General Counsel and Chief Compliance Officer, Norman D. (Norm) Finch Jr.
President Europe Middle East and Africa (EMEA) Reconstructive, Katarzyna Mazur-Hofsaess
VP Investor Relations and Treasurer, Robert J. Marshall Jr.
Director, Arthur J. Higgins, age 56
President CEO and Director, David C. Dvorak, age 48
Director, Betsy J. Bernard, age 56
Director, Larry C. Glasscock, age 63
Director, Robert A. Hagemann, age 55
Director, Marc N. Casper, age 44
Director, Cecil B. Pickett, age 66
Auditors: PricewaterhouseCoopersLLP

LOCATIONS

HQ: Zimmer Holdings Inc.
345 E. Main St., Warsaw IN 46580
Phone: 574-267-6131 **Fax:** -5603
Web: www.inventec.com

2011 Sales

Americas	2,440	55
Asia/Pacific	796	18

PRODUCTS/OPERATIONS

2011 Sales

Reconstructive		
Hips	1,355	30
Extremities	163	4
Dental	248	6
Spine	225	5
Surgical & other	348	8
Total	**4,451**	**100**

Selected Products

Reconstructive implants
- Alloclassic hip system
- Anatomical shoulder implants
- Bigliani/Flatow shoulder implants
- MIS 2-Incision Total Hip Replacement

MIS Mini-Incision Total Knee Procedure
NexGen knee replacement
Trabecular Metal Primary Hip Prosthesis
VerSys Hip System
Zimmer Collagen Repair Patch (rotator cuff repair)

Trauma products
- I.T.S.T. Nail System (hip and proximal femur fractures)
- M/DN Intramedullary Fixation (for long bone fractures)
- NCB Locking Plate System (complex long bone fractures)
- Sirus Intramedullary Nail System (for long bone fractures)

Dental products
- AdVent dental implant system
- Tapered screw-vent implant system

Spine products
- CopiOs Bone Void Filler
- Dynesys Dynamic Stabilization System
- Optima ZD Spinal Fixation System
- Puros allografts
- ST360 Spinal Fixation System

Surgical products
- A.T.S. Tourniquet Systems
- Brasseler USA surgical power tools (for long bones)
- Pneumicro surgical power tools (for small bones)
- Pulsavac Plus (wound cleaning)
- Zimmer Ambulatory Pump (pain management)

COMPETITORS

B. Braun Melsungen
Biomet
Corin Group
DENTSPLY
DePuy
DJO Global
Exactech
Genzyme Biosurgery
JRI Orthopaedics
Lifecore Biomedical
MAKO Surgical
Medtronic
Nobel Biocare
NuVasive
Orthofix
ReGen Biologics
Smith & Nephew
Straumann
Stryker
Symmetry Medical
Synthes
Tornier
Wright Medical Group

HISTORICAL FINANCIALS

Company Type: Public

Income Statement FYE: December 31

	REVENUE ($ mil.)	NET INCOME ($ mil.)	NET PROFIT MARGIN	EMPLOYEES
12/11	4,451	760	17.1%	8,700
12/10	4,220	596	14.1%	8,800
12/09	4,095	717	17.5%	8,200
12/08	4,121	848	20.6%	8,500
12/07	3,897	773	19.8%	7,600
Annual Growth	3.4%	(0.4%)	—	3.4%

2011 Year-End Financials

Debt ratio: 20.19%
Return on equity: 13.81%
Cash ($ mil.): 768
Current ratio: 377.88
Long-term debt ($ mil.): 1,576
No. of shares (mil.): 178
Dividends
Yield: —
Payout: 4.22%
Market value ($ mil.): 9,509

	STOCK PRICE ($) FY Close	P/E High	P/E Low	PER SHARE ($) Earnings	Dividends	Book Value
12/11	53.42	17	12	4.03	0.00	30.94
12/10	53.68	21	16	2.97	0.00	29.51
12/09	59.11	18	10	3.32	0.00	27.61
12/08	40.42	21	9	3.72	0.00	25.27
12/07	66.15	28	19	3.26	0.00	23.40
Annual Growth	(5.2%)	—	—	5.4%	—	7.2%

Zions Bancorporation

Multibank holding company Zions Bancorporation operates eight bank subsidiaries with some 485 branches in 10 western and southwestern states. The banks operate under their own brands and leadership rather than sharing one corporate identity. They focus on commercial and retail banking as well as mortgage and construction lending. The banks' products and services include deposit accounts home mortgages and home equity lines of credit residential and commercial development loans credit cards and trust and wealth management services. Zions caters to small to medium-sized businesses by offering Small Business Administration (SBA) loans.

The company's eight subsidiaries keep their own names and branding in order to draw customers who are more comfortable banking at a local level. Its subsidiary banks include Zions First National Bank Nevada State Bank National Bank of Arizona and Vectra Bank Colorado. Additionally it owns The Commerce Bank of Washington California Bank & Trust The Commerce Bank of Oregon and Texas-based Amegy Corporation.

Zions also offers wealth management serivces through Contango Capital Advisors and Western National Trust Company. It provides online and traditional brokerage services via Zions Direct and Amegy Investments. In addition the company controls a handful of venture capital funds working with startups in the West.

Zions which built its empire on acquisitions managed to expand its reach during the economic downturn partly by helping the FDIC clean up failed banks. From 2008 through 2009 Zions took part in four FDIC-assisted transactions. It took over the assets of failed banks and gained about 40 new branches in Nevada and California. Zions continues to search for acquisition opportunties in order to grow.

Though Zions was largely shielded from problem loans in its FDIC-assisted transactions the company was hit by nonperforming loans in its own portfolio particularly in residential land acquisition development and construction lending in the Southwest. Its provision for loan losses for 2009 totaled more than $2 billion more than triple the amount that the company set aside the year before. To help raise capital Zions sold check processing subsidiary NetDeposit to BankServ in 2010.

In 2010 and 2011 Zions continued to focus on increasing its capital and reducing its risk. The company was able to substantially reduce its provision for loan losses thanks to improved credit quality. Asset quality improved in 2011 and there was a 42% decline in nonperforming loans and a 54% reduction in net charge-offs.

Zions returned to loan growth in 2011 after two years of low demand and the company's own efforts to reduce risk. Those factors helped the company turn a profit in 2011 reporting net income for the first time since 2007.

The company plans to focus future growth on organically building its wealth management and advisory services. Zions also looks forward to expanding residential and consumer lending following the recession which created dislocation and consolidation in those sectors.

HISTORY

Zions' history is entwined with that of the Mormon Church. Founded by the church in 1873 to take over the savings department of the Bank of Deseret when it obtained a national charter the new bank was headed by Brigham Young and other church leaders. The church kept control of the bank until 1960 when it sold its interest to a group of investors led by Roy Simmons who moved it into the holding company that became Zions Bancorporation. It went public in 1966.

The company fared well in Utah and when regulations changed in the mid-1980s to allow expansion into contiguous states it moved quickly into Arizona (1986). Zions was hit by the commercial real estate crash and a downturn in the copper industry. Nevertheless it remained healthy enough to pick up some Arizona bargain banks as they folded. In the 1990s it moved into California Colorado Idaho and New Mexico. Acquisitions in 1997 and 1998 included Colorado's Aspen Bancshares Tri-State Bank and Vectra Banking Corp.; California's GB Bancorporation; and Nevada's Sun State Bank. None of the new family members adopted the Zions name.

In 1998 the company bought Sumitomo Bank of California the state's #6 bank and merged it with Grossmont Bank to form California Bank & Trust. It also created a new subsidiary Digital Signature Trust Company to issue store and verify digital certificates used in electronic documents and transactions (Zions sold the company in 2004).

The firm increased its presence in 1999 in California and Nevada with the purchases of Regency Bancorp and Pioneer Bancorp respectively. Zions made plans to buy fellow Utah bank First Security in 2000 but the deal unraveled when the latter's share price plunged on news of low earnings. Had the sale been successful the bank would have dropped the Zions name to further distance itself from its connection with the Mormon Church. First Security later agreed to be bought by Wells Fargo. Failing to make an entrance into investment banking via First Security Zions in 2001 bought about a quarter of Los Angeles-based firm Roth Capital Partners.

In 2005 Zions bought Amegy Bancorporation giving it a presence in Dallas and Houston two of the more attractive banking markets in the US. Zions' wealth management unit Contango Capital Advisors acquired Phoenix-based BG Associates in 2006.

Zions bought Arizona-based Stockmen's Bancorp (and its 43 Stockmen's Bank branches) in 2007 merged it into National Bank of Arizona then sold 11 Stockmen's branches located in California later that year. Also in 2007 it acquired Texas-based Intercontinental Bank Shares and its three Intercon Bank branches in San Antonio which were rolled into Amegy Bank.

Zions made serveral acquisions of failed banks during the recession. It acquired some $800 million in deposits in 2008 from failed Nevada-based Silver State Bank whose 17 branches became either Nevada State Bank or National Bank of Arizona locations.

The following year Zions added another five branches to Nevada State Bank's network by picking up Great Basin Bank after the FDIC declared it insolvent. Also in 2009 California Bank & Trust added some 20 branches from the acquisitions of Alliance Bank and Vineyard Bank which had been seized by regulators as well.

EXECUTIVES

EVP Capital Markets and Investments; EVP Zions First National Bank, W. David Hemingway, age 64, $257,000 total compensation

Chairman National Bank of Arizona, John J. Gisi, $265,000 total compensation
EVP; President and CEO Zions First National Bank, Aldon (Scott) Anderson, age 65, $518,000 total compensation
Chairman President and CEO; Chairman Zions First National Bank, Harris H. Simmons, age 57, $875,000 total compensation
Chairman Amegy Bank, Walter E. Johnson, age 75
EVP; President and CEO Vectra Bank Colorado, Bruce K. Alexander, age 59
EVP; Chairman President and CEO Nevada State Bank, Dallas E. Haun, age 58
EVP; Chairman President and CEO The Commerce Bank of Washington, Stanley D. Savage, age 66, $312,000 total compensation
EVP; Chairman President and CEO California Bank & Trust, David E. Blackford, age 63, $497,000 total compensation
SVP Credit Examination, Ronald L. Johnson
VP, Melvin D. (Mel) Leibsla
VP, John A. Payne
Vice Chairman and CFO, Doyle L. Arnold, age 63, $542,000 total compensation
EVP Wealth Management; President and CEO Contango Capital Advisors, George M. Feiger, age 62, $460,000 total compensation
EVP Risk Management, Dean L. Marotta, age 59
EVP; CEO Amegy Bank of Texas, Scott J. McLean, age 55, $440,000 total compensation
President Zions Credit Corporation, Alan Ralphs
COO Zions Direct, James R. Cooper
EVP; President and CEO National Bank of Arizona, Keith D. Maio, age 54
VP, Jennifer R. Jolley
EVP and General Counsel, Thomas E. (Thom) Laursen, age 60
President and CEO The Commerce Bank of Oregon, Larry B. Ogg
EVP and Chief Human Resources Officer, Connie Spyropoulos-Linardakis, age 47
SVP Compliance, Norman W. Merritt
SVP Corporate Finance, H. Walter Young
SVP Corporate Development, Alvin Lee
SVP Internal Audit, Jennifer A. Smith
EVP; President Amegy Bank of Texas, Steve D. Stephens, age 53
EVP and Chief Credit Officer, Kenneth E. (Ken) Peterson, age 62
SVP Investor Relations and External Communications, James R. Abbott, age 38
SVP and Controller, Alexander J. Hume, age 38
VP and Manager Bankcard Sales, Maj. Brian McCaul
President Western National Trust, Kevin S. Mikan
SVP Internal Audit, Travis E. Finstad
Director, R. Don Cash, age 69
Director, Jerry C. Atkin, age 63
Director, Laurence E. Simmons, age 65
Director, Roger B. Porter, age 65
Director, J. David Heaney, age 63
Director, Shelley Thomas Williams, age 60
Vice Chairman and CFO, Doyle L. Arnold, age 63
Director, Stephen D. Quinn, age 57
Director, Patricia Frobes, age 65
Director, Steven C. Wheelwright, age 68
Auditors: Ernst&YoungLLP

LOCATIONS

HQ: Zions Bancorporation
1 S. Main St. 15th Fl., Salt Lake City UT 84133-1109
Phone: 801-524-4787 **Fax:** 713-462-2401
Web: www.hcch.com

PRODUCTS/OPERATIONS

2011 Sales

	$ mil.	% of total
Interest		
Loans including fees	2,066	76
Securities	124	5
Other	13	-
Noninterest		
Service charges and fees on deposit accounts	174	6
Other service charges commissions and fees	169	6
Dividends and other investment income	42	2
Capital markets and foreign exchange	31	1
Loan sales and servicing income	28.1	1
Trust and wealth management	26	1
Fixed income securities gains net	11	-
Other	36	2
Fair value and nonhedge derivative loss	(5.0)	-
Net impairment losses on investment securities	(33.7)	-
Total	**2,686**	**100**

Selected Subsidiaries

Amegy Corporation
California Bank & Trust
Great Western Financial Corporation
National Bank of Arizona
Nevada State Bank
The Commerce Bank of Oregon
The Commerce Bank of Washington
Vectra Bank Colorado
Zions First National Bank
Zions Insurance Agency Inc.
Zions Management Services Company

COMPETITORS

Bank of America
Bank of the West
BOK Financial
Capital One
Citigroup
Cullen/Frost Bankers
First National of Nebraska
Great Western Bancorporation
JPMorgan Chase
Prosperity Bancshares
U.S. Bancorp
UnionBanCal
Washington Federal
Wells Fargo

HISTORICAL FINANCIALS

Company Type: Public

Income Statement FYE: December 31

	ASSETS ($ mil.)	NET INCOME ($ mil.)	INCOME AS % OF ASSETS	EMPLOYEES
12/11	53,149	323	0.6%	10,606
12/10	51,034	(292)	—	10,524
12/09	51,123	(1,216)	—	10,529
12/08	55,092	(266)	—	11,011
12/07	52,947	493	0.9%	10,933
Annual Growth	0.1%	(10.0%)	—	(0.8%)

2011 Year-End Financials

Debt ratio: 3.68%
Return on equity: 4.64%
Cash ($ mil.): 8,245
Current ratio: —
Long-term debt ($ mil.): 1,954
No. of shares (mil.): 184
Dividends
Yield: —
Payout: 4.82%
Market value ($ mil.): 2,998

	STOCK PRICE ($) FY Close	P/E High	P/E Low	PER SHARE ($) Earnings	Dividends	Book Value
12/11	16.28	31	16	0.83	0.00	37.94
12/10	24.23	—	—	(2.48)	0.04	36.37
12/09	12.83	—	—	(9.92)	0.10	37.84
12/08	24.51	—	—	(2.66)	1.61	56.37
12/07	46.69	20	10	4.42	1.68	49.41
Annual Growth	(23.2%)	—	—	(34.2%)	—	(6.4%)

Hoover's Handbook of

American Business

The Indexes

Index by Headquarters

PA

QUEBEC

RI

SC

TN

TX

UT

VA

Index of Executives

A

B

C

D

E

F

G

H

I

J

K

L

M

N

O

P

Q

T

U

V